Sixth Canadian Edition

ABNORMAL
PSYCHOLOGY
AN INTEGRATIVE APPROACH

DAVID H. BARLOW
Boston University

V. MARK DURAND
University of South Florida–St. Petersburg

STEFAN G. HOFMANN
Boston University

MARTIN L. LALUMIÈRE
University of Ottawa

 CENGAGE

Australia • Brazil • Canada • Mexico • Singapore • United Kingdom • United States

Abnormal Psychology: An Integrative Approach,
Sixth Canadian Edition
David H. Barlow, V. Mark Durand,
Stefan G. Hofmann, and Martin L. Lalumière

VP, Product Solutions, K–20: Claudine O'Donnell

Director, Qualitative Publishing: Jackie Wood

Senior Publisher, Digital and Print Content: Lenore Taylor-Atkins

Product Marketing Manager: Sydney Pope

Content Manager: Christine Gilbert

Photo and Permissions Researcher: Carrie McGregor

Senior Production Project Manager: Natalia Denesiuk Harris

Production Service: SPi Global

Copy Editor: Dawn Hunter

Proofreader: SPi Global

Indexer: SPi Global

Design Director: Ken Phipps

Post-secondary Design PM: Pamela Johnston

Interior Design: Sharon Lucas

Cover Design: Pamela Johnston

Cover Image: Nick Fitzhardinge/Getty Images

Compositor: SPi Global

For product information and technology assistance, contact us at
Canada Support, canadasupport.cengage.com.

For permission to use material from this text or product, submit all requests online at **www.cengage.com/permissions.**

Library and Archives Canada Cataloguing in Publication:

Title: Abnormal psychology : an integrative approach/ David H. Barlow, V. Mark Durand, Stefan G. Hofmann, Martin L. Lalumière.

Names: Barlow, David H., author. | Durand, Vincent Mark, author. | Hofmann, Stefan G., author. | Lalumière, Martin L., author.

Description: Sixth Canadian edition. | Includes bibliographical references and indexes.

Identifiers: Canadiana (print) 20200165712 | Canadiana (ebook) 20200165755 | ISBN 9780176873219 (hardcover) | ISBN 9780176874810 (PDF)

Subjects: LCSH: Psychology, Pathological—Textbooks. | LCSH: Mental illness—Textbooks. | LCGFT: Textbooks.

Classification: LCC RC454 .B36 2020 | DDC 616.89—dc23

ISBN-13: 978-0-17-687321-9
ISBN-10: 0-17-687321-X

Cengage Canada
1120 Birchmount Road
Toronto, ON   M1K 5G4
Canada

Cengage is a leading provider of customized learning solutions with employees residing in nearly 40 different countries and sales in more than 125 countries around the world. Find your local representative at **www.cengage.com.**

To learn more about Cengage platforms and services, register or access your online learning solution, or purchase materials for your course, visit **www.cengage.ca.**

Printed in Canada
Print Number: 04   Print Year: 2022

ABOUT THE AUTHORS

DAVID H. BARLOW

Courtesy of David H. Barlow

David H. Barlow is an internationally recognized pioneer and leader in clinical psychology. Currently Professor Emeritus of Psychology and Psychiatry at Boston University, Dr. Barlow is Founder and Director Emeritus of the Center for Anxiety and Related Disorders, one of the largest research clinics of its kind in the world. From 1996 to 2004, he directed the clinical psychology programs at Boston University. From 1979 to 1996, he was distinguished professor at the University at Albany–State University of New York. From 1975 to 1979, he was professor of psychiatry and psychology at Brown University, where he also founded the clinical psychology internship program. From 1969 to 1975, he was professor of psychiatry at the University of Mississippi Medical Center, where he founded the psychology residency program. Dr. Barlow received his B.A. from the University of Notre Dame, his M.A. from Boston College, and his Ph.D. from the University of Vermont.

A fellow of every major psychological association, Dr. Barlow has received many awards in honour of his excellence in scholarship, including the National Institute of Mental Health Merit Award for his long-term contributions to the clinical research effort, the Distinguished Scientist Award for applications of psychology from the American Psychological Association, and the James McKeen Cattell Fellow Award from the Association for Psychological Science honouring individuals for their lifetime of significant intellectual achievements in applied psychological research. Other awards include the Distinguished Scientist Award from the Society of Clinical Psychology of the American Psychological Association and a certificate of appreciation from the APA section on the clinical psychology of women for "outstanding commitment to the advancement of women in psychology." He was awarded an Honorary Doctorate of Science from the University of Vermont, an Honorary Doctorate of Humane Letters from William James College, and the C. Charles Burlingame Award from the Institute of Living in Hartford Connecticut "for his outstanding leadership in research, education, and clinical care." In 2014, he was awarded a Presidential Citation from the American Psychological Association "for his lifelong dedication and passion for advancing psychology through science, education, training, and practice."

He also has received career/lifetime contribution awards from the Massachusetts, Connecticut, and California Psychological Associations, as well as the University of Mississippi Medical Center and the Association for Behavioral and Cognitive Therapies. In 2000, Dr. Barlow was named Honorary Visiting Professor at the Chinese People's Liberation Army General Hospital and Postgraduate Medical School in Beijing, China, and in 2015 was named Honorary President of the Canadian Psychological Association. In addition, the annual Grand Rounds in Clinical Psychology at Brown University was named in his honour. During the 1997–1998 academic year, he was Fritz Redlich Fellow at the Center for Advanced Study in the Behavioral Sciences in Palo Alto, California. His research has been continually funded by the National Institute of Mental Health for over 40 years.

Dr. Barlow has edited several journals, including *Clinical Psychology: Science and Practice*, and *Behavior Therapy*, has served on the editorial boards of more than 20 different journals, and is currently Editor in Chief of the "Treatments That Work" series for Oxford University Press. He has published more than 600 scholarly articles and written or edited more than 75 books and clinical manuals, including *Anxiety and Its Disorders*, Second Edition, Guilford Press; *Clinical Handbook of Psychological Disorders: A Step-by-Step Treatment Manual*, Fifth Edition, Guilford Press; *Single-Case Experimental Designs: Strategies for Studying Behaviour Change*, Third Edition, Allyn & Bacon (with Matthew Nock and Michael Hersen); *The Scientist-Practitioner: Research and Accountability in the Age of Managed Care*, Second Edition, Allyn & Bacon (with Steve Hayes and Rosemary Nelson-Gray); *Mastery of Your Anxiety and Panic*, Oxford University Press (with Michelle Craske); and more recently *The Unified Protocol for Transdiagnostic Treatment of Emotional Disorders* with the Unified Team at Boston University. The books and manuals have been translated into more than 20 languages, including Arabic, Chinese, and Russian.

Dr. Barlow was one of three psychologists on the task force that was responsible for reviewing the work of more than 1000 mental health professionals who participated in the creation of *DSM-IV*, and he continued on as an Advisor to the *DSM-5* Task Force. He also chaired the APA Task Force on Psychological Intervention Guidelines, which created a template for the development of clinical practice guidelines. His current research program focuses on the nature and treatment of anxiety and related emotional disorders.

At leisure he plays golf, skis, and retreats to his home on Nantucket Island, where he loves to write, walk on the beach, and visit with his island friends.

V. MARK DURAND

Courtesy of V. Mark Durand

V. Mark Durand is known worldwide as an authority in the area of autism spectrum disorder. He is a Professor of Psychology at the University of South Florida–St. Petersburg, where he was the founding Dean of Arts & Sciences and Vice Chancellor for Academic Affairs. Dr. Durand is a Fellow of the American Psychological Association. He has received more than $4 million in federal funding since the beginning of his career to study the nature, assessment, and treatment of behaviour problems in children with disabilities. Before moving to Florida, he served in a variety of leadership positions at the University at Albany, including Associate Director for Clinical Training for the doctoral psychology program from 1987 to 1990, Chair of the Psychology Department from 1995 to 1998, and Interim Dean of Arts and Sciences from 2001 to 2002. There he established the Center for Autism and Related Disabilities at the University at Albany, SUNY. He received his B.A., M.A., and Ph.D.—all in psychology—at the State University of New York–Stony Brook.

Dr. Durand was awarded the University Award for Excellence in Teaching at SUNY–Albany in 1991 and received the Chancellor's Award for Excellence in Research and Creative Scholarship at the University of South Florida–St. Petersburg in 2007. He was named a 2014 Princeton Lecture Series Fellow and received the 2015 Jacobson Award for Critical Thinking from the American Psychological Association for his body of work in the field of autism spectrum disorder. Dr. Durand is currently a member of the Professional Advisory Board for the Autism Society of America and was on the board of directors of the International Association of Positive Behavioural Support. He was co-editor of the *Journal of Positive Behavior Interventions*, serves on a number of editorial boards, and has written more than 125 publications on functional communication, educational programming, and behaviour therapy. His books include *Severe Behavior Problems: A Functional Communication Training Approach*; *Sleep Better! A Guide to Improving Sleep for Children with Special Needs*; *Helping Parents with Challenging Children: Positive Family Intervention*; the multiple national award-winning *Optimistic Parenting: Hope and Help for You and Your Challenging Child*; and most recently *Autism Spectrum Disorder: A Clinical Guide for General Practitioners*.

Dr. Durand developed a unique treatment for severe behaviour problems that is currently mandated by states across the United States and is used worldwide. He also developed an assessment tool that is used internationally and has been translated into more than 15 languages. Most recently, he developed an innovative approach to help families work with their challenging child (optimistic parenting), which was validated in a five-year clinical trial. He has been consulted by the departments of education in numerous states and by the U.S. Departments of Justice and Education. His current research program includes the study of prevention models and treatments for such serious problems as self-injurious behaviour.

In his leisure time, he enjoys long-distance running and has completed three marathons.

STEFAN G. HOFMANN

Courtesy of Stefan G. Hofmann

Stefan G. Hofmann is an international expert on psychotherapy for emotional disorders. He is a Professor of Psychology at Boston University, where he directs the Psychotherapy and Emotion Research Laboratory. He was born in a little town near Stuttgart in Germany, which may explain his thick German accent. He studied psychology at the University of Marburg, Germany, where he received his B.A., M.S., and Ph.D. A brief dissertation fellowship to spend some time at Stanford University turned into a longer research career in the United States. He eventually moved to the United States in 1994 to join Dr. Barlow's team at the University at Albany–State University of New York and has been living in Boston since 1996.

Dr. Hofmann has an actively funded research program studying various aspects of emotional disorders with a particular emphasis on anxiety disorders, cognitive-behavioural therapy, and neuroscience. More recently, he has been interested in mindfulness approaches, such as yoga and meditation practices, as treatment strategies of emotional disorders. Furthermore, he has been one of the leaders in translational research methods to enhance the efficacy of psychotherapy and to predict treatment outcome using neuroscience methods.

He has won many prestigious professional awards, including the Aaron T. Beck Award for Significant and Enduring Contributions to the Field of Cognitive Therapy by the Academy of Cognitive Therapy. He is a Fellow of the American Psychological Association and the Association for Psychological Science, and was president of various national and international professional societies, including the Association for Behavioural and Cognitive Therapies and the International Association for Cognitive Psychotherapy. He was an Advisor to the *DSM-5* Development Process and a member of the *DSM-5* Anxiety Disorder Sub-Work Group. As part of this, he participated in the discussions about the revisions of the *DSM-5* criteria for various anxiety disorders, especially social anxiety disorder, panic disorder, and agoraphobia. Dr. Hofmann is a Thomson Reuters Highly Cited Researcher.

Dr. Hofmann has been the Editor in Chief of *Cognitive Therapy and Research* and is also the incoming Associate Editor of *Clinical Psychological Science*. He published more than 300 peer-reviewed journal articles and 15 books, including *An Introduction to Modern CBT* (Wiley-Blackwell) and *Emotion in Therapy* (Guilford Press).

At leisure, he enjoys playing with his sons. He likes travelling to immerse himself into new cultures, make new friends, and reconnect with old ones. When time permits, he occasionally gets out his flute.

MARTIN L. LALUMIÈRE

Courtesy of Martin L. Lalumière

Martin L. Lalumière is recognized for his work in forensic psychology and sexology. He is a Professor of Clinical Psychology in the School of Psychology at the University of Ottawa and has taught courses in forensic psychology, psychopathology, evolutionary psychology, and clinical research. He obtained his B.Sc. (1989) and M.Ps. (1990) from the Université de Montréal and his Ph.D. (1995) from Queen's University at Kingston, where he won the Governor General's Academic Gold Medal for best graduating Ph.D. student.

Previously, Dr. Lalumière was on faculty in the Department of Psychology at the University of Lethbridge in Alberta (2004–2012) and a Research Psychologist in the Law and Mental Health Program at the Centre for Addiction and Mental Health (1997–2004), a psychiatric teaching hospital in Toronto. He was on faculty in the Department of Psychiatry and the Centre for Criminology at the University of Toronto (1997–2004) and a research psychologist at the maximum secure unit of the Mental Health Centre Penetanguishene (1996–1997)—a psychiatric hospital on Georgian Bay, Ontario (now called the Waypoint Mental Health Centre). He became a registered psychologist in Québec in 1991 and in Ontario in 1996.

Dr. Lalumière is currently on the editorial boards of the journals *Archives of Sexual Behavior*, *The Canadian Journal of Human Sexuality*, *Evolutionary Psychology*, and *Sexual Abuse*. He has published over 135 books, book chapters, and articles on sexual offending, the paraphilias, and psychopathy, among other topics. He has received over $2 million in research funds from the Social Sciences and Humanities Research Council, the Natural Sciences and Engineering Research Council, the Canadian Institutes of Health Research, and the Ontario Mental Health Foundation.

His current research at the University of Ottawa focuses on the assessment, treatment, and etiology of the paraphilias. He also conducts research on the measurement of sexual attraction and sexual arousal by using psychophysiological and cognitive methods with men and women. He has also started to think and write about the role of the placebo in psychotherapy.

He would like to thank Andrea Ashbaugh, Cary Kogan, Allison Ouimet, Rebecca Robillard, Michael Seto, and George Tasca for commenting on parts of the book; Gail Hepburn for her superb work locating and digesting Canadian statistics and other information; and Christine Gilbert, Natalia Denesiuk Harris, Dawn Hunter, and Lenore Taylor-Atkins at Nelson and Sangeetha Vijay at SPi Global for their support and competence in bringing this book to fruition. He would also like to thank undergraduate students who have taken his psychopathology course over the years at the University of Lethbridge and the University of Ottawa, for their feedback and stimulating discussions.

In his spare time, Dr. Lalumière enjoys fly-fishing, cycling, Tai Chi, reading, cooking, and watching hockey.

BRIEF CONTENTS

CONTENTS

3 | Clinical Assessment and Diagnosis

4 | Research Methods

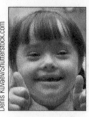

16 | Aging and Neurocognition

17 | Mental Health and the Law

PREFACE

Science is constantly evolving, but every now and then something groundbreaking occurs that alters our way of thinking. For example, evolutionary biologists, who long assumed that the process of evolution was gradual, suddenly had to adjust to evidence that says evolution happens in fits and starts in response to such cataclysmic environmental events as meteor impacts. Similarly, geology has been revolutionized by the discovery of plate tectonics.

Until recently, the science of psychological disorders (psychopathology) had been compartmentalized, with psychopathologists examining the separate effects of psychological, biological, and social influences. This approach is still reflected in popular media accounts that describe, for example, a newly discovered gene, a biological dysfunction (chemical imbalance), or early childhood experiences as a "cause" of a psychological disorder. This way of thinking still dominates discussions of causality and treatment in some psychology textbooks: "The psychoanalytic views of this disorder are . . . ," "the biological views are . . . ," and, often in a separate chapter, "psychoanalytic treatment approaches for this disorder are . . . ," "cognitive-behavioural treatment approaches are . . . ," or "biological treatment approaches are. . . ."

In the first edition of this text, we tried to do something very different. We thought the field had advanced to the point that it was ready for an integrative approach in which the intricate interactions of biological, psychological, and social factors are explicated in as clear and convincing a manner as possible. Recent advances in knowledge confirm this approach as the only viable way of understanding psychopathology. To take just two examples, Chapter 2 contains a description of a study demonstrating that stressful life events can lead to depression but that not everyone shows this response. Rather, stress is more likely to cause depression in individuals who already carry a particular gene that influences serotonin at the brain synapses. Similarly, Chapter 2 describes how the placebo effect involves changes in the brain. In addition, the entire section on genetics is revised with each new edition to highlight the new emphasis on gene–environment interaction, along with recent thinking from leading behavioural geneticists that the goal of basing the classification of psychological disorders on the firm foundation of genetics is fundamentally flawed. Descriptions of the emerging field of epigenetics, or the influence of the environment on gene expression, is also woven into the chapter, along with new studies on the seeming ability of extreme environments to largely override the effects of genetic contributions. Studies elucidating the mechanisms of epigenetics or specifically how environmental events influence gene expression are described.

These results confirm the integrative approach in this book: psychological disorders cannot be explained by genetic or environmental factors alone but rather arise from their interaction. We now understand that psychological and social factors directly affect neurotransmitter function and even genetic expression. Similarly, we cannot study behavioural, cognitive, or emotional processes without appreciating the contribution of biological and social factors to psychological expression. Instead of compartmentalizing psychopathology, we use a more accessible approach that accurately reflects the current state of our clinical science.

As colleagues, you are aware that we understand some disorders better than others. But we hope you will share our excitement in conveying to students both what we currently know about the causes and treatments of psychological disorders and how far we have yet to go in understanding these complex interactions.

INTEGRATIVE APPROACH

As noted earlier, the first edition of *Abnormal Psychology* pioneered a new generation of abnormal psychology textbooks, which offer an integrative and multidimensional perspective. (We acknowledge such one-dimensional approaches as biological, psychosocial, and supernatural as historic perspectives on our field, described in Chapter 1.) We include substantial current evidence of the reciprocal influences of biology and behaviour and of psychological and social influences on biology. Our examples hold the reader's attention; for example, we discuss genetic contributions to divorce, the effects of early social and behavioural experience on later brain function and structure, and new information on the relation of social networks to the common cold. We note that in the phenomenon of implicit memory and blind sight, which may have parallels in dissociative experiences, psychological science verifies the existence of the unconscious (although it does not much resemble the seething cauldron of conflicts envisioned by Freud). We present new evidence confirming the effects of psychological treatments on neurotransmitter flow and brain function. We acknowledge the often-neglected area of emotion theory for its rich contributions to psychopathology (e.g., the effects of anger on cardiovascular disease). We weave scientific findings from the study of emotions together with behavioural, biological, cognitive, and social discoveries to create an integrated tapestry of psychopathology.

LIFESPAN DEVELOPMENTAL INFLUENCES

No modern view of abnormal psychology can ignore the importance of lifespan developmental factors in the manifestation and treatment of psychopathology. Studies highlighting developmental windows for the influence of the environment on gene expression are explained. Accordingly, although we include a neurodevelopment chapter and an aging and neurocognition chapter, we consider the importance of development throughout the text; we discuss childhood and geriatric anxiety, for example, in the context of the anxiety chapter. This system of organization, which is for the most part consistent with the *DSM-5*, helps students appreciate the need to study each disorder from childhood through adulthood and old age. We note findings on developmental considerations in separate sections of each disorder chapter and, as appropriate, discuss how specific developmental factors affect causation and treatment.

SCIENTIST-PRACTITIONER APPROACH

We go to some lengths to explain why the scientist-practitioner approach to psychopathology is both practical and ideal. Like most of our colleagues, we view this as something more than simple awareness of how scientific findings apply to psychological disorders. We show how every clinician contributes to general scientific knowledge through astute and systematic clinical observations, functional analyses of individual cases, and systematic observations of series of cases in clinical settings. For example, we explain how information on dissociative phenomena provided by early psychoanalytic theorists remains relevant today. We also describe the formal methods used by scientist-practitioners, showing how complex research designs are actually implemented in research programs.

CLINICAL CASES OF REAL PEOPLE

We have enriched the book with authentic clinical histories to illustrate scientific findings on the causes and treatment of psychological disorders. We have run active clinics for years, so 95 percent of the cases are from our own files, and they provide a fascinating frame of reference for the findings we describe. The beginnings of most chapters include a case description, and most of the discussion of the latest theory and research is related to these very human cases.

DISORDERS IN DETAIL

We cover the major psychological disorders in 12 chapters, focusing on three broad categories: clinical description, causal factors, and treatment and outcomes. We pay considerable attention to case studies and *DSM-5* criteria, and we include statistical data, such as prevalence rates, sex ratio, age of onset, and the general course or pattern for the disorder. Throughout, we explore how biological, psychological, and social dimensions may interact to cause a particular disorder. Thus, by covering treatment and outcomes within the context of specific disorders, we provide a realistic sense of clinical practice.

TREATMENT

One of the best received innovations in the earlier Canadian and U.S. editions was our strategy of discussing treatments in the same chapter as the disorders themselves instead of in a separate chapter, an approach that is supported by the development of specific psychosocial and pharmacological treatment procedures for specific disorders. We have retained this integrative format and have improved upon it, and we include treatment procedures in the key terms and glossary.

LEGAL AND ETHICAL ISSUES

In our closing chapter, we integrate many of the approaches and themes that have been discussed throughout the text. We include case studies of people who have been involved directly with many legal and ethical issues and with the delivery of mental health services. We also provide a historical context for current perspectives so students will understand the effects of social and cultural influences on legal and ethical issues.

DIVERSITY

Issues of culture and gender are integral to the study of psychological disorders. Throughout the text, we describe current thinking about which aspects of the disorders are culturally specific and which are universal, and about the strong and sometimes puzzling effects of gender roles. For instance, we discuss the current information on such topics as the gender imbalance in depression, how panic disorders are expressed differently in various Asian cultures, ethnic differences in eating disorders, treatment of schizophrenia across cultures, and the diagnostic differences of attention-deficit/hyperactivity disorder (ADHD) in boys and girls. Clearly, our field will grow in depth and detail as these subjects and others become standard research topics. For example, why do some disorders overwhelmingly affect females and others appear predominantly in males? And why does this apportionment sometimes change from one culture to another? In answering questions like these, we adhere closely to science, emphasizing that gender and culture are each one dimension among several that constitute psychopathology.

NEW TO THE SIXTH CANADIAN EDITION

This exciting field moves at a rapid pace, and we take particular pride in how our book reflects the most recent developments. Therefore, once again, every chapter has been carefully revised to reflect the latest research studies on psychological disorders. In particular, new Canadian content has been added, such as statistics based on the most recent surveys, new information on mental health service delivery in Canada, and more information about Indigenous peoples in Canada. Some new headings have been added, and *DSM-5* criteria are included in their entirety as tables in the appropriate chapters. Additionally, to address reviewer feedback and in spite of these additions, non-essential material has been eliminated and the rest streamlined. We also revised the text to improve readability.

There are three major changes in this new edition. First, we reorganized some of the chapters so that each now refers to a major topic, and chapters describing specific disorders are organized in a more conceptually satisfying and clear manner. Thus, Chapter 5, Anxiety, is now about anxiety and the major and well-recognized anxiety disorders (generalized anxiety, panic/agoraphobia, phobias, and social anxiety). Chapter 6 is Preoccupation and Obsession and includes the somatic symptoms disorders and obsessive-compulsive and related disorders. Chapter 7 is Trauma and Dissociation (two phenomena that are often associated) and includes trauma- and stressor-related disorders, and dissociative disorders. Chapter 8, Mood, includes the depressive and bipolar disorders. Chapter 9 is Eating and Chapter 10 is Sleeping. Each describes disorders in these major life domains, along with their connection to disorders in other categories. Sex and Gender are covered in Chapter 11, and we make sure to mention that the three types of disorders discussed in this chapter (sexual dysfunctions, paraphilias, and gender dysphoria), although they fall under the topic of sex and gender, are quite independent from each other. We also provide a more nuanced discussion of gender dysphoria and the controversies associated with it. Other chapters describing disorders include Substance Use and Impulse Control (Chapter 12), Personality (Chapter 13), Psychosis (Chapter 14), Neurodevelopment (Chapter 15), and Aging and Neurocognition (Chapter 16). We think this organization will be more intuitive for students, allowing them to better digest and integrate the material. In addition, this change allowed us to reduce the length of some of the longer chapters; the chapters are now more even in length than they were before. We provide a thoroughly updated discussion of the important topic of suicide in the Mood chapter, but have also added relevant information about suicide in other chapters. In total, there are now 17 chapters, with one other chapter (Stress, Pain, and Health) in the supplementary material that can be found online at login.cengage.com.

The second major change has to do with Canadian statistics. Most of the statistics presented in the book have been updated and more clearly presented. We are now more specific about the people included in Canadian surveys, and also mention the people who are excluded. For example, the Canadian Community Health Survey is used widely by researchers, and we refer to it repeatedly in this text, but the survey excludes Indigenous people living on reserve, people living in remote regions, members of the Canadian Armed Forces, and people living in institutions (e.g., long-term-care homes, prisons). Clearly, then, this representative survey of Canadians is not quite about Canadians. Fortunately, improvements are being made and future surveys will more validly represent Canadians. One very useful feature of recent Canadian Community Health Surveys is that it asks Canadians about whether they are currently diagnosed with a psychological disorder, allowing us to match the responses to the disorders described in this book. Other surveys we relied on for this edition include the First Nations Regional Health Survey, the Survey on Living with Chronic Diseases in Canada, the Canadian Survey on Disability, the Canadian Health Measures Survey, and many others. We also accessed reports that are based on various health databases in Canada (e.g., the Hospital Mental Health Database out of the Canadian Institute for Health Information). Finally, we include more statistics about minority groups and about the fastest growing age group in Canada, older people.

The third major change is that we now include information about Indigenous people in Canada. Previous editions of this book had very limited information on Indigenous peoples and communities, despite the fact that Indigenous people represent 5 percent of the Canadian population. Fortunately, new surveys provide information about Indigenous peoples. Unfortunately, though, this information is incomplete: there is a focus in these surveys and studies on suicide and substance use, with information on mental disorders sadly lacking. In addition, Indigenous people in Canada are made up of hundreds of widely diverse communities, but most available information is for the wider group, hiding large variations. Finally, there is little information about Indigenous people living in urban areas, despite the fact that more than half of Indigenous people live in urban areas.

Nevertheless, the new information presented in the textbook provides a useful picture for this important group, or at least a starting point. In a recent review of mental health research about Indigenous people, University of Toronto researchers Sarah Nelson and Kathi Wilson (2017) wrote that "articles included in this study almost universally state that rates of mental health problems among Indigenous people are higher" (p. 101), and the statistics we present in this book concur. But Nelson and Wilson were also quick to point out that this general conclusion hides huge variations and many positive stories. For example, high rates of alcohol use are more frequently seen in First Nations women in Ontario, but high rates of alcohol abstinence are also observed in these same women. For another example, youth suicide is higher in general in some Indigenous communities, but some Indigenous communities have very low rates, lower than the Canadian average. For one last example, in a 2010 report on the prevalence of psychological distress and mental disorders in Canada by Montréal researchers Caron and Liu, Canadians identifying as Aboriginal (First Nations, Métis, or Inuit) who were living off-reserve had the highest rates of distress and disorders of all self-identified ethnic groups (i.e., white, black, Chinese, South Asian, Latin American, Others). However, when low socioeconomic status was considered, "non-low-income Aboriginal Canadians report a prevalence of high psychological distress quite similar to that for most of the other ethnic subgroups" (p. 87).

Canadian researchers agree that the history of colonialism in Canada, along with current policies, racism, health and employment inequalities, and trauma history (e.g., residential schools) are responsible for the difficulties experienced by some Indigenous communities. Carleton researchers Amy Bombay and Kim Matheson have proposed the concept of historical trauma: "the idea that the accumulation of collective stressors and trauma that began in the past may contribute to increased risk for negative health and social outcomes among contemporary Aboriginal peoples" (Bombay et al., 2014, p. 321). There is some evidence for this concept, and researchers are now investigating the possibility of epigenetic effects. We cover these ideas in this edition.

Other additions to this new edition include an update of the Canadian Code of Ethics for Psychologists (2017, Chapter 1), a discussion of difficulties in replicating gene–environment interaction results (Chapter 2), updated information on the forthcoming ICD-11, and more information on anti-stigma campaigns in Canada (Chapter 3). We now include a discussion of the current replication crisis in the field (Chapter 4), a description of virtual reality work at the Université du Québec en Outaouais (Chapter 5), culture-specific examples of somatic disorders, and an update on the interesting story of Howie Mandel and his struggles with obsessive-compulsive disorder (Chapter 6). There are better statistics on post-traumatic stress disorder (Chapter 7), the prevention of suicide in Inuit communities (Chapter 8), and information on a newly recognized and dangerous eating disorder in children, avoidant/restrictive food intake disorder (Chapter 9). There are new statistics about required amounts of sleep and bed sharing in Canada (Chapter 10) and new information on the neurological basis of pedophilia and the use of mindfulness meditation in the treatment of sexual dysfunctions (Chapter 11), as well as information about the legality of cannabis in Canada, the opioid crisis in Canada, and an Indigenous historical perspective on tobacco use and gambling (Chapter 12). We include a more streamlined description of antisocial personality disorder, introduce the interesting case of Christopher Knight, a man who lived in the woods by himself for 27 years (Chapter 13), and provide an update on the Genain quadruplets (Chapter 14). There is new information on accommodation for learning disabilities and access to postsecondary education, and the role of sleep in attention-deficit/hyperactivity disorder (Chapter 15), as well as much better statistics on dementia (Chapter 16), and new information about people who have been found not criminally responsible on account of a mental disorder (Chapter 17). These are only a few of the additions, but they give a flavour to our efforts to make the text stimulating, informative, and relevant.

PREVENTION

Looking to the future of abnormal psychology as a field, the prospect of helping the greatest number of people who display psychological disorders may lie in our ability to prevent these difficulties. Although this has long been a goal of many, we are now at the beginning of what appears to be a new age in prevention research. Numerous scientists from all over the globe are developing the methodologies and techniques that may finally provide us with the means to interrupt the debilitating toll of emotional distress caused by the disorders chronicled in this book. We therefore highlight these cutting-edge prevention efforts—such as preventing eating disorders, suicide, substance abuse, and health problems like HIV infection—in appropriate chapters as a means of celebrating these important events, as well as to encourage the field to continue this important work.

RETAINED FEATURES

STUDENT LEARNING OUTCOMES

Placed at the start of each chapter, Student Learning Outcomes assist instructors to accurately assess and map questions throughout the chapter. The outcomes are mapped to the core APA goals and are integrated throughout the instructor resources and testing program.

DSM CONTROVERSIES

DSM Controversies is a box that encourages critical thinking about issues related to updates to the *DSM-5*. Topics include binge-eating disorder, personality disorders, and attenuated psychosis, among others.

FROM THE INSIDE

The popularity of the case studies indicates that students appreciate the humanization of data that might otherwise appear dry and lifeless. To emphasize that psychological disorders affect real people who respond in a variety of ways, nearly all chapters on specific disorders include a compassionate review of a first-person memoir by someone who survived or is living with a challenging psychological condition. Many of these are first-person accounts by Canadian writers. These stories were chosen for the value of their deeply personal points of view; they complement the research-based text without pretending to be scientific.

INNOVATIVE APPROACHES

Most disorder chapters include a feature called Innovative Approaches that discusses forward-thinking treatments, such as dialectical behaviour therapy, the use of "vice vaccines" to manage addiction, and the development of designer drugs for attention-deficit/hyperactivity disorder and other conditions, based on a person's genetic profile.

VISUAL SUMMARIES

At the end of each chapter on disorders is a colourful two-page chart that succinctly summarizes the causes, development, symptoms, and treatment of each disorder covered in the chapter. Our integrative approach is instantly evident in these diagrams, which show the interaction of biological, psychological, and social factors in the etiology and treatment of disorders. The visual summaries will help the instructor wrap up discussions, and students will appreciate them as study aids.

PEDAGOGY

Each chapter contains several Concept Checks that let students verify their comprehension at regular intervals. Answers are at the end of each chapter, along with a detailed Summary; the Key Terms are listed in alphabetical order.

INSTRUCTOR RESOURCES

The following instructor resources have been created for *Abnormal Psychology*, Sixth Canadian Edition. Access these ultimate tools for customizing lectures and presentations at login.cengage.com.

TEST BANK

This resource was written by Jamie Prouse-Turner of Red Deer College. It includes over 1600 multiple-choice questions written according to guidelines for effective construction and development of higher-order questions. Also included are more than 150 essay questions.

The Test Bank is available in a new, cloud-based platform. **Cengage Testing Powered by Cognero®** is a secure online testing system that allows instructors to author, edit, and manage test bank content from anywhere Internet access is available. No special installations or downloads are needed, and the desktop-inspired interface, with its dropdown menus and familiar, intuitive tools, allows instructors to create and manage tests with ease. Multiple test versions can be created in an instant, and content can be imported or exported into other systems. Tests can be delivered from a learning management system, the classroom, or wherever an instructor chooses. Cengage Testing Powered by Cognero for *Abnormal Psychology* can be accessed through login.cengage.com.

POWERPOINT

Microsoft® PowerPoint® lecture slides for every chapter have been created by Barinder Bhavra. There is an average of 25 slides per chapter, many featuring key figures, tables, and photographs from *Abnormal Psychology*. principles of clear design and engaging content have been incorporated throughout, making it simple for instructors to customize the deck for their courses.

IMAGE LIBRARY

This resource consists of digital copies of figures, short tables, and photographs used in the book. Instructors may use these jpegs to customize the PowerPoint or create their own PowerPoint presentations. An Image Library Key describes the images and lists the codes under which the jpegs are saved.

MINDTAP

CENGAGE | MINDTAP

Offering personalized paths of dynamic assignments and applications, **MindTap** is a digital learning solution that turns cookie-cutter into cutting-edge, apathy into engagement, and memorizers into higher-level thinkers. MindTap enables students to analyze and apply chapter concepts within relevant assignments, and allows instructors to measure skills and promote better outcomes with ease. A fully online learning solution, MindTap combines all student learning tools—readings, multimedia, activities, and assessments—into a single Learning Path that guides the student through the curriculum. Instructors personalize the experience by customizing the presentation of these learning tools to their students, even seamlessly introducing their own content into the Learning Path.

VIDEOS

Instructors can enhance the classroom experience with the exciting and relevant videos provided to students through MindTap. These videos have been specifically selected to accompany *Abnormal Psychology*.

STUDENT ANCILLARIES

MINDTAP

CENGAGE | MINDTAP

Stay organized and efficient with **MindTap**—a single destination with all the course material and study aids you need to succeed. Built-in apps leverage social media and the latest learning technology. For example:

- ReadSpeaker will read the text to you.
- Flashcards are pre-populated to provide you with a jump start for review—or you can create your own.
- You can highlight text and make notes in your MindTap Reader. Your notes will flow into Evernote, the electronic notebook app that you can access anywhere when it's time to study for the exam.
- Self-quizzing allows you to assess your understanding.

Visit login.cengage.com to start using **MindTap**. Enter the Online Access Code from the card included with your text. If a code card is *not* provided, you can purchase instant access at Cengage.ca.

REVIEWERS

Creating this sixth Canadian edition would not have been possible without the superb feedback of the reviewers. To them we express our deepest gratitude. The reviewers read the fifth Canadian edition and provided extraordinarily perceptive critical comments, pointed to relevant information, and offered new insights. Readers who take the time to communicate their thoughts offer the greatest rewards to writers and scholars. For their assistance and their feedback, we would like to thank all of our reviewers, including Deborah Gural, Red River College; Naomi Koerner, Ryerson University; and Elaine Ply, Dalhousie University.

01 | Abnormal Behaviour in Historical Context

Jerry Cooke/Science Source

A clear and complete insight into the nature of madness, a correct and distinct conception of what constitutes the difference between the sane and the insane has, as far as I know, not been found.

—SCHOPENHAUER, The World as Will and Idea

Describe key concepts, principles, and overarching themes in psychology:	› Explain why psychology is a science with the primary objectives of describing, understanding, predicting, and controlling behaviour and mental processes (APA SLO 1.1b)
	› Use basic psychological terminology, concepts, and theories in psychology to explain behaviour and mental processes (APA SLO 1.1a)
Develop a working knowledge of the content domains of psychology:	› Summarize important aspects of history of psychology, including key figures, central concerns, methods used, and theoretical conflicts (APA SLO 1.2C)
	› Identify key characteristics of major content domains in psychology (e.g., cognition and learning, developmental, biological, and sociocultural) (APA SLO 1.2a)
Use scientific reasoning to interpret behaviour:	› See APA SLO 1.1b listed above
	› Incorporate several appropriate levels of complexity (e.g., cellular, individual, group/system, society/cultural) to explain behaviour (APA SLO 2.1C)

* Portions of this chapter cover learning outcomes suggested by the American Psychological Association (2013) in its guidelines for the undergraduate psychology major. Chapter coverage of these outcomes is identified above by APA Goal and APA Suggested Learning Outcome (SLO).

Today you may have gotten out of bed, had breakfast, gone to class, studied, and at the end of the day, enjoyed the company of your friends before falling asleep. It probably did not occur to you that many healthy people are unable to do some or any of these things. What they have in common is a **psychological disorder**, a psychological dysfunction within an individual that is associated with distress or impairment in functioning and a response that is not typical or culturally expected. Before examining exactly what this means, let's look at one individual's situation.

JODY | *The Boy Who Fainted at the Sight of Blood*

Jody, a 16-year-old boy, was referred to our anxiety disorders clinic after increasing episodes of fainting. Jody reported that he had always been somewhat queasy at the sight of blood. About two years before coming to our clinic, in his first biology class, the teacher showed a movie of a frog dissection to illustrate various points about anatomy. The film was particularly graphic, with vivid images of blood, tissue, and muscle. About halfway through, Jody felt a bit lightheaded and left the room, but the images did not leave him. He continued to be bothered by them and occasionally felt slightly queasy. He began to avoid situations in which he might see blood or an injury. He stopped looking at magazines that might have gory pictures. He found it difficult to look at raw meat, or even Band-Aids, because they brought the feared images to mind. Eventually, anything his friends or parents said that evoked an image of blood or injury caused Jody to feel lightheaded. It became so bad that if one of his friends exclaimed, "Cut it out!" he felt faint. Beginning about six months before his visit to the clinic, Jody actually fainted when he unavoidably encountered something bloody. His family physician could find nothing wrong with him, nor could several other physicians. By the time he was referred to our clinic, he was fainting five to ten times a week, often in class. Clearly, these episodes were problematic for him and disruptive in school; each time he fainted, the other students flocked around him, trying to help, and class was interrupted. Because no one could find anything wrong with Jody, the principal finally concluded that he was being manipulative and suspended him from school, even though he was an honour student.

Jody had what we now call blood-injury-injection phobia. His reaction was quite severe, thereby meeting the criteria for **phobia**, a psychological disorder characterized by marked and persistent fear of an object or a situation. But many people have similar reactions that are not as severe when they receive an injection or see someone who is injured, whether or not blood is visible. For people who react as severely as Jody, this phobia can be very disabling. They may avoid certain careers, such as medicine or nursing. If they are so afraid of needles and injections that they avoid them even when they are necessary, they put their health at risk.

WHAT IS A PSYCHOLOGICAL DISORDER?

Keeping in mind the real-life problems faced by Jody, let's look more closely at the definition of a psychological disorder, or abnormal behaviour: It is a *psychological dysfunction within an individual associated with distress or impairment in functioning and a response that is not typical or culturally expected.* On the surface, these three elements may seem obvious, but they were not easily arrived at, and it is worth exploring what they mean.

PSYCHOLOGICAL DYSFUNCTION

Psychological dysfunction refers to a breakdown in cognitive, emotional, or behavioural functioning. For example, if you are out on a date, it should be fun. If you experience severe fear all evening and just want to go home, even though you have nothing to be afraid of, and if the severe fear happens on every date, your emotions are not functioning properly. If all your friends agree that the person who asked you out is dangerous, however, then it would not be "dysfunctional" for you to be fearful and avoid the date.

A dysfunction was present for Jody—he fainted at the sight of blood. But many people experience a mild version of this reaction (feeling queasy at the sight of blood) without meeting the criteria for the disorder; knowing where to draw the line between normal and abnormal dysfunction is often difficult. For this reason, these problems are often considered to exist on a continuum or as a dimension, rather than as categories that are either present or absent. This is one reason that just having a dysfunction is not enough to meet the criteria for a psychological disorder.

PERSONAL DISTRESS OR IMPAIRMENT

That the disorder or behaviour must be associated with distress adds an important component and seems clear: The criterion is satisfied if the individual is extremely upset. We can certainly say that Jody was very distressed and even suffered with his phobia. But remember, by itself this criterion does not define abnormal behaviour. It is often quite normal to be distressed—for example, if someone close to you dies. The human condition is such that suffering and distress are very much part of life—and that is not likely to change. Furthermore, for some disorders, by definition, suffering and distress are absent. Consider the person who feels extremely elated and acts impulsively as part of a manic episode. As we see in Chapter 8, one major difficulty with this problem is that people enjoy the manic state so much they are reluctant to begin treatment or stay in treatment very long. Thus, defining psychological disorder by distress alone doesn't work, although the concept of distress contributes to a good definition. The concept of impairment is also useful, though it is not entirely satisfactory. For example, many people consider themselves shy or lazy, but this doesn't mean that they're abnormal. But if you are so shy that you find it impossible to date or even interact with people, and if you make every attempt to avoid interactions even though you would like to have friends, then your social functioning is impaired. Jody was clearly impaired by his phobia, but many people with similar, less severe reactions are not impaired. This difference again illustrates the important point that most psychological disorders are simply extreme expressions of otherwise normal emotions, behaviours, and cognitive processes.

▲ Distress and suffering are a natural part of life and do not in themselves constitute psychological disorder.

ATYPICAL OR NOT CULTURALLY EXPECTED

The criterion that the response be atypical or *not culturally expected* is important but also insufficient to determine abnormality. At times, something is considered abnormal because it occurs infrequently; it deviates from the average. The greater the deviation, the more abnormal it is. You might say that someone is abnormally short or abnormally tall, meaning that the person's height deviates substantially from average, but this obviously isn't a definition of a disorder. Many people are far from the average in their behaviour, but few would be considered disordered. We might call them talented or eccentric. Many artists, performers, and athletes fall into this category. For example, it's not normal to wear a dress made entirely out of meat, but when Lady Gaga wore one to an awards show it only enhanced her celebrity.

The late novelist J. D. Salinger, who wrote *The Catcher in the Rye*, retreated to a small town in New Hampshire and refused to see any outsiders for years, but he continued to write. Some rock singers wear outrageous costume on stage. These people are well paid and seem to enjoy their careers. In most cases, the more productive you are in the eyes of society, the more eccentricities society will tolerate. Therefore, "deviating from the average" doesn't work very well as a definition.

Another view is that your behaviour is abnormal if you are violating social norms in your culture. This view is very useful in considering important cultural differences in psychological disorders. For example, to enter a trance state and believe you are possessed would point to a psychological disorder in most Western cultures, but in many other societies the behaviour is accepted and expected.

▲ We accept extreme behaviours by entertainers, such as Lady Gaga, that would not be tolerated in other members of our society.

An informative example of this view is provided by prominent neuroscientist Robert Sapolsky (2002), who worked closely with the Masai tribe in East Africa. One day Sapolsky's Masai friend Rhoda asked him to bring his jeep as quickly as possible to the Masai village, where a woman had been acting very aggressively and had been hearing voices. The woman had actually killed a goat with her own hands. Sapolsky and several Masai were able to subdue her and transport her to a local health centre. Realizing that this was an opportunity to learn more of the Masai's view of psychological disorders, Sapolsky had the following discussion:

> "So Rhoda," I began laconically, "what do you suppose was wrong with that woman?"
> She looked at me as if I was mad.
> "She is crazy."

▲ Some religious behaviours may seem unusual to us but are culturally or individually appropriate.

> "But how can you tell?"
> "She's crazy. Can't you just see from how she acts?"
> "But how do you decide that she is crazy? What did she do?"
> "She killed that goat."
> "Oh," I said with anthropological detachment, "but Masai kill goats all the time."
> She looked at me as if I were an idiot. "Only the men kill goats," she said.
> "Well, how else do you know that she is crazy?"
> "She hears voices."
> Again, I made a pain of myself. "Oh, but the Masai hear voices sometimes." (At ceremonies before long cattle drives, the Masai trance-dance and claim to hear voices.) And in one sentence, Rhoda summed up half of what anyone needs to know about cross-cultural psychiatry. "But she hears voices at the wrong time." (2002, p. 138)

Social standards associated with what is *normal* have been misused. Consider, for example, the practice of committing political dissidents to mental institutions, which was common in the former Soviet Union before the fall of Communism. Although such dissident behaviour clearly violates social norms, it should not alone be cause for commitment.

In a very thoughtful analysis of the matter, Wakefield (1992, 1999) uses the shorthand definition "harmful dysfunction." According to Wakefield, a psychological disorder is caused by a failure of one or more mechanisms to perform their evolved function and the dysfunction produces harm or distress. The advantage of Wakefield's notion is that it provides a potentially objective or scientific view of dysfunction (it requires an objective analysis of the structure and function of the relevant psychological mechanisms, and how it is broken), along with allowing a subjective or culturally bound consideration of harm and distress (what is considered harmful in one culture may not be so in another). For example, to determine if Jody's condition of fainting when seeing or thinking about blood is a psychological disorder, psychologists would need to understand the functioning of the mechanisms designed to deal with reactions to sight of injury and blood in people in general, if such mechanisms exist. We could hypothesize that being exposed to blood and injuries signals danger and would trigger adaptive self-protective responses (e.g., getting away from danger, avoiding pathogens). The common reaction of feeling queasy at the sign of blood might motivate these protective responses. Fainting, however, might be an exaggerated reaction, and therefore can be considered dysfunctional if it led to poor outcomes in our ancestral environment, such as being more vulnerable to attackers or predators (in the terms of natural selection, if it led to poorer survival and reproduction compared with alternative, more typical responses in the environment in which we evolved). And with regard to the harm criterion, in our culture, fainting at the sign of blood and avoidance of any blood-related cues would be considered harmful in most situations.

A related concept that is also useful when considering the definition of psychological disorder is to determine whether the behaviour is beyond the individual's control (something he or she doesn't want to do or feel; Widiger & Sankis, 2000). Variants of these approaches are most often used in current diagnostic practice, as outlined in the fifth edition of the *Diagnostic and Statistical Manual of Mental Disorders* (*DSM-5*, American Psychiatric Association, 2013), which contains the current listing of criteria for psychological disorders. The *DSM-5* acknowledges that it is difficult to provide a clear and encompassing definition of psychological disorders, and offers a definition that is quite similar to the one we provided earlier. These approaches guide our thinking in this book.

AN ACCEPTED DEFINITION?

It is difficult to define "normal" and "abnormal" (Lilienfeld & Marino, 1995, 1999; Spitzer, 1999)—and the debate continues (Blashfield et al., 2014; McNally, 2011; Stein et al., 2010; Wakefield, 2003, 2009; Zachar & Kendler, 2014). The most widely accepted definition used in the *DSM-5* describes behavioural, psychological, or biological dysfunctions that are unexpected in their cultural context and associated with present distress and impairment in functioning, or increased risk of suffering, death, pain, or impairment. This definition can be useful across cultures and subcultures if we pay careful attention to what is functional or dysfunctional (or out of control) in a given society. But it is never easy to decide what represents dysfunction, and some scholars have argued persuasively that the health professions will never be able to satisfactorily define *disease* or *disorder* (e.g., Lilienfeld & Marino, 1995, 1999; Zachar & Kendler, 2014). Perhaps the best we can do is consider how the apparent disease or disorder matches a "typical" profile of a disorder—for example, major depression or schizophrenia—when most or all symptoms that experts agree are part of the disorder are present. We call this typical profile a *prototype*, and, as described in Chapter 3, the diagnostic criteria from *DSM-5* found throughout this book are all prototypes. This means that the patient may have only some features or symptoms of the disorder (a minimum number) and still meet the criteria for the disorder because his or her set of symptoms is close to the prototype. This concept is described more fully in Chapter 3, where the diagnosis of psychological disorder is discussed. Wakefield's notion of harmful dysfunction is likely to guide research on psychological disorders, but it is not clear when or how it will be applied in clinical practice.

Some controversial figures, such as Thomas Szasz and George Albee, are highly critical of medical diagnoses being used in the case of psychological disorders. In 1960, Szasz advanced his position that mental illness is a myth and that the practice of labelling mental illnesses should be abolished. For example, Szasz (1960) argued that a fundamental difference exists between the use of diagnoses for physical diseases and their use in mental illnesses. The former uses objective criteria (e.g., results of blood tests), but for mental illness, subjective judgments are required. Albee (1998, 2000) has argued that the biggest mistake made by the clinical psychology profession was uncritically accepting the concept of "mental disease" and using the medical model and associated diagnoses (e.g., the *DSM* system) in conceptualizing abnormal behaviour. Even among the many proponents of the *DSM* system, disagreement continues about how to define the concept of "disorder."

As a challenge, take the problem of defining abnormal behaviour a step further and consider this: What if Jody passed out repeatedly but regained consciousness so quickly that neither his classmates nor his teachers even noticed? Furthermore, what if Jody continued to get good grades? Would fainting all the time at the mere thought of blood be a disorder? Would it be impairing? Dysfunctional? Distressing? How would the notion of harmful dysfunction handle that situation? What do you think?

THE SCIENCE OF PSYCHOPATHOLOGY

Psychopathology is the scientific study of psychological disorders. Within this field are specially trained professionals, including clinical and counselling psychologists, psychiatrists, psychiatric social workers, psychiatric nurses, marriage and family therapists, sex therapists, and mental health counsellors. Clinical psychologists typically receive a Ph.D. (Doctor of Philosophy) following a course of graduate-level study that lasts six to seven years. This education prepares them to conduct research into the causes and treatment of psychological disorders and to assess, diagnose, and treat these disorders. Instead of a Ph.D., clinical psychologists sometimes receive a Psy.D. (Doctor of Psychology) degree for which the training is similar to the Ph.D. but with more emphasis on clinical practice and less on research training.

In Canada, regulation of the psychology profession is under the jurisdiction of the provinces and territories. Depending on the jurisdiction, a psychologist may have either a doctoral or a master's degree. For example, in Ontario, professional psychologists are regulated by the College of Psychologists of Ontario, as outlined in the Regulated Health Professions Act (1991). Largely to protect the public, but also in the interest of the profession, only those who are licensed or registered with their provincial or territorial board or college are permitted to call themselves psychologists (e.g., in advertising)—with the exception of university professors in psychology. The labels *psychotherapist* and *therapist* are not regulated in most provinces and territories. Thus, in Canada, the label of *psychologist* conveys information about the training and qualifications of the professional, whereas the label of *psychotherapist* does not always (as of 2015, Ontario has a new College of Registered Psychotherapists). In addition, the terms *therapist* and *psychotherapist* are not specific to a particular profession. For example, a social worker, a psychologist, a nurse, and a psychiatrist can all refer to themselves as psychotherapists if they provide therapy services to members of the public around psychological issues.

Psychologists with other specialty training, such as experimental and social psychologists, concentrate on investigating the basic determinants of behaviour but do not assess or treat psychological disorders. Although a great deal of overlap exists, *counselling psychologists* (who can receive a Ph.D., Psy.D., or Ed.D.—Doctor of Education, or a master's degree in education or counselling) tend to study and treat adjustment and vocational issues encountered by relatively healthy individuals, whereas clinical psychologists usually concentrate on more severe psychological disorders.

Psychiatrists first earn an M.D. in medical school and then specialize in psychiatry during a four-year residency training program. Psychiatrists also investigate the nature and causes of psychological disorders, often from a biological point of view, make diagnoses, and offer treatments. Many psychiatrists emphasize drugs or other biological treatments, although many use psychosocial treatments as well.

Psychiatric social workers typically earn a master's degree in social work as they develop expertise in collecting information relevant to the social and family situation of the individual with a psychological disorder. Social workers also treat disorders, often concentrating on family problems associated with them. *Psychiatric nurses* have advanced degrees, such as a master's or a Ph.D., and specialize in the care and treatment of patients with psychological disorders, usually in hospitals as part of a treatment team. Finally, *marriage and family therapists* and *mental health counsellors* typically spend one to two years earning a master's degree and provide clinical services in hospitals or clinics, usually under the supervision of a doctoral-level clinician. Sex therapists have specialized training, often in the context of a graduate degree. Table 1.1 shows the number of each major category of mental health professionals currently practising in Canada.

THE SCIENTIST-PRACTITIONER

The most important recent development in the history of psychopathology is the adoption of scientific methods to learn more about the nature of psychological disorders, their causes, and their treatment. Many mental health professionals take a scientific approach to their clinical work and are therefore referred to as **scientist-practitioners**. Mental health practitioners may function as scientist-practitioners at least one of three ways (see ■ Figure 1.1). First, they may keep up with the latest scientific developments in their field and therefore use the best empirically supported diagnostic and treatment procedures. In this sense, they are consumers of the science of psychopathology to the advantage of their patients. This approach is now often called *evidence-based practice* (Hunsley, 2007; Hunsley & Lee, 2007). Second, scientist-practitioners evaluate their own assessments or treatment procedures to see whether they work and to generate new knowledge, an approach called *practice-based evidence* (Wampold & Imel, 2015).

▲ University of Ottawa psychologist John Hunsley has written extensively on incorporating evidence into clinical practice.

They are accountable not only to their patients but also to the government agencies and insurance companies that pay for the treatments, so they must demonstrate clearly whether their treatments are effective or not. Third, scientist-practitioners might conduct research, often in clinics or hospitals, that produces new information about disorders or their treatment. This research helps suppress the fads that plague our field. For example, new "miracle cures" for psychological disorders that are reported several times a year in the popular media would not be used by a scientist-practitioner who did not have sound scientific data showing that they work. Such data flow from research that attempts three basic things: to describe psychological disorders, to determine their causes, and to treat them (see ■ Figure 1.2). These three categories compose an organizational structure that recurs throughout this book and is formally evident in the discussions of specific disorders beginning in Chapter 5. A general overview of the categories now will give you a clearer perspective on our efforts to understand abnormality.

TABLE 1.1 | Mental Health Professionals Practising in Canada, 2016

Profession	Number Currently Practising (per 100 000 in parentheses)
Psychiatrists	5 214 (14)
Psychologists	17 493 (49)
Psychiatric nurses (BC, AB, SK, MB, YT)	5 863 (52)
Social workers	52 283 (146)

Sources: Supply, Distribution and Migration of Physicians in Canada, 2016: Methodological Notes, by Institute of Health Information, 2017; *Canada's Health Care Providers: Provincial Profiles, 2007 to 2016—Data Tables,* by Canadian Institute of Health Information, 2017 (https://secure.cihi.ca/estore/productSeries .htm?pc=PCC314); *Health Workforce Database, 2016: Methodology Guide,* by Canadian Institute of Health Information, 2017.

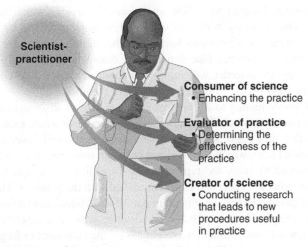

FIGURE 1.1 | Functioning as a scientist-practitioner.

Scientist-practitioner

Consumer of science
• Enhancing the practice

Evaluator of practice
• Determining the effectiveness of the practice

Creator of science
• Conducting research that leads to new procedures useful in practice

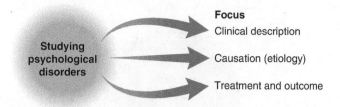

Focus
Clinical description

Causation (etiology)

Treatment and outcome

Studying psychological disorders

FIGURE 1.2 | Three major categories compose the study and discussion of psychological disorders.

CLINICAL DESCRIPTION

In hospitals and clinics we often say that a patient "presents" with a specific problem or set of problems, or we discuss the **presenting problem**. *Presents* is a traditional shorthand way of indicating why the person came to the clinic. Describing Jody's presenting problem is the first step in determining his **clinical description**, which represents the unique combination of behaviours, thoughts, and feelings that make up a specific disorder. The word *clinical* refers both to the types of problems or disorders you would find in a clinic or hospital and to the activities connected with assessment and treatment. Throughout this text are excerpts from many individual cases, most of them from our personal files.

Clearly, one important function of the clinical description is to specify what makes the disorder different from normal behaviour or from other disorders. Statistical data may also be relevant. For example, how many people in the population as a whole have the disorder? This figure is called the **prevalence** of the disorder. How many people in the population have ever had the disorder (**lifetime prevalence**)? Statistics on how many new cases occur during a given period, such as a year, represent the **incidence** of the disorder. Other statistics include the *sex ratio*—that is, what proportion of males and females have the disorder—and the typical *age of onset*, which often differs from one disorder to another.

In addition to having different symptoms, a different age of onset, and possibly a different sex ratio and prevalence, most disorders follow a somewhat individual pattern, or **course**. For example, some disorders, such as schizophrenia (Chapter 14), follow a *chronic course*, meaning that they tend to last a long time, sometimes a whole lifetime. Other disorders, like mood disorders (Chapter 8), follow an *episodic course* in which the individual is likely to recover within a few months, only to have a recurrence of the disorder later. Still other disorders may have a *time-limited course*, like some sleep disorders (Chapter 10), meaning the disorder will improve without treatment in a relatively short period with little or no risk of recurrence.

Closely related to differences in the course of disorders are differences in onset. Some disorders have an *acute onset*, meaning that they begin suddenly; others develop gradually over an extended time, which is sometimes called an *insidious onset*. It is important to know the typical course of a disorder so that we know what to expect and how best to deal with the problem. The anticipated course is an important part of the clinical description. For example, if someone has a mild disorder with acute onset that we know is time limited, we might advise the individual to forgo expensive treatment because the problem will resolve soon

bokan76/iStock

▲ Children experience panic and anxiety differently from adults, so their reactions may be mistaken for symptoms of physical illness.

enough, like a common cold. However, if the disorder is likely to last a long time (become chronic), the individual might want to seek treatment and take other appropriate steps. The anticipated course of a disorder is called the **prognosis**. So we might say, "the prognosis is good," meaning the individual will probably recover, or "the prognosis is guarded," meaning the probable outcome doesn't look good.

The patient's age may be a very important part of the clinical description. A specific psychological disorder occurring in childhood may present very differently from the same disorder in adulthood or old age. Children experiencing severe anxiety and panic often assume that they are physically ill because they have difficulty understanding there is nothing physically wrong. Because their thoughts and feelings are different from those experienced by adults with anxiety and panic, children are often misdiagnosed and treated for a medical disorder.

CAUSATION, TREATMENT, AND OUTCOMES

Etiology, or the study of origins, has to do with why a disorder begins (what causes it) and includes biological, psychological, and social dimensions. Because the etiology of psychological disorders is so important to this field, we devote an entire chapter to it (Chapter 2). Treatment is often important to the study of psychological disorders. If a new drug or psychosocial treatment is successful in treating a disorder, it may give us some hints about the nature of the disorder and its causes. For example, if a drug with a specific known effect within the nervous system alleviates a certain psychological disorder, we know that something in that part of the nervous system might be either causing the disorder or helping to maintain it. Similarly, if a psychosocial treatment designed to help clients regain a sense of control over their lives is effective with a certain disorder, a diminished sense of control may be an important psychological component of the disorder itself.

Concept Check 1.1

A clinical description includes the unique combination of behaviours, thoughts, and feelings that compose a given psychological disorder. Match the following words that are used in clinical descriptions with their corresponding examples: (a) presenting problem, (b) prevalence, (c) incidence, (d) prognosis, (e) course, and (f) etiology.

1. Maria should recover quickly with no intervention necessary. Without treatment, David will deteriorate rapidly. _____

2. Three new cases of bulimia have been reported in this county during the past month and only one in the next county. _____

3. Elizabeth visited the campus mental health centre because of her increasing feelings of guilt and anxiety. _____

4. Biological, psychological, and social influences all contribute to a variety of disorders. _____

5. The pattern a disorder follows can be chronic, time limited, or episodic. _____

6. How many people in the population as a whole have obsessive-compulsive disorder? _____

As we see in the next chapter, psychology is never that simple. This is because the effect does not necessarily imply the cause. To use a common example, you might take an Aspirin to relieve a tension headache that you developed during a gruelling day of taking exams. If you then feel better, it does not mean the headache was caused by a lack of Aspirin in the first place. Nevertheless, many people seek treatment for psychological disorders, and treatment can provide interesting hints about the nature of the disorder.

In the past, textbooks emphasized treatment approaches in a very general sense, with little attention to the disorder being treated. For example, a mental health professional might be thoroughly trained in a single theoretical approach, such as psychoanalysis or behaviour therapy (both described later in the chapter), and then use that approach on every disorder. More recently, as our science has advanced, we have developed specific effective treatments that do not always adhere neatly to one theoretical approach but that have grown out of a deeper understanding of the disorder in question. For this reason, this book does not have separate chapters on such types of treatment approaches as psychodynamic, cognitive behavioural, or humanistic. Rather, the latest and most effective drug and psychological treatments are described in the context of specific disorders, in keeping with our integrative multidimensional perspective and evidence-based approach.

We now survey many early attempts to *describe* and *treat* abnormal behaviour, and more still to comprehend its *causes*, which will give you a better perspective on current approaches. In Chapter 2, we examine contemporary views of causation and treatment. In Chapter 3, we discuss efforts to describe, or classify, abnormal behaviour. In Chapter 4, we review research methods—our systematic efforts to discover the truths underlying description, cause, and treatment that allow us to function as scientist-practitioners. In Chapters 5 through 16, we examine specific disorders; our discussion is organized in each case in the now familiar triad of description, cause, and treatment. Finally, in Chapter 17 we examine legal, professional, and ethical issues that are relevant to psychological disorders and their treatment in Canada today. The Online Chapter tackles issues related to stress, pain, and, health. But first, let us turn to the past.

For thousands of years, humans have tried to explain and control problematic behaviour. But our efforts always derive from the theories or models of behaviour that are popular at the time. The purpose of these models is to explain why someone is "acting like that." Three major models that have guided us date back to the beginnings of civilization.

Humans have always supposed that certain agents outside our bodies and environment influence our behaviour, thinking, and emotions. These agents, which might be divinities, demons, spirits, or other phenomena such as magnetic fields or the moon or the stars, are the driving forces behind the *supernatural model*. In addition, since ancient Greece, the mind has often been called the *soul* or the *psyche* and considered separate from the body. Although many have thought that the mind can influence the body and, in turn, the body can influence the mind, most philosophers looked for causes of abnormal behaviour in one or the other. This split gave rise to two traditions of thought about abnormal behaviour, summarized as the *biological model* and the *psychological model*.

These three models—the supernatural, the biological, and the psychological—are very old but still in use today.

THE SUPERNATURAL TRADITION

For much of our recorded history, deviant behaviour has been considered a reflection of the battle between good and evil. When confronted with unexplainable behaviour and by suffering and upheaval, people perceived evil.

DEMONS AND WITCHES

One strong current of opinion put the causes and treatment of psychological disorders squarely in the realm of the supernatural. During the last quarter of the 14th century, religious and lay authorities supported these popular superstitions, and society as a whole began to believe in the reality and power of demons and witches. The Catholic Church had split, and a second centre, complete with a pope, emerged in the south of France to compete with Rome.

DEA PICTURE LIBRARY/Getty Images

▲ During the Middle Ages, individuals with psychological disorders were sometimes thought to be possessed by evil spirits that had to be exorcised through rituals.

In reaction to this schism, the Roman church fought back against the evil in the world that must have been behind this heresy.

People turned increasingly to magic and sorcery to solve their problems. During these turbulent times, the bizarre behaviour of people afflicted with psychological disorders was seen as the work of the devil and witches. It followed that individuals possessed by evil spirits were probably responsible for any misfortune experienced by the townspeople, which inspired drastic action against the possessed. Treatments included *exorcism*, in which various religious rituals were performed to rid the victim of evil spirits. Other approaches included shaving the pattern of a cross in the victims' hair and securing them to a wall near the front of a church so that they might benefit from hearing mass.

The conviction that sorcery and witches were causes of madness and other evils continued into the 15th century. Evil continued to be blamed for unexplainable behaviour, even after the European founding of the New World, as evidenced by the Salem witch trials in the 17th century, which resulted in the hanging deaths of 20 women.

STRESS AND MELANCHOLY

An equally strong opinion, even during this period, reflected the enlightened view that insanity was a natural phenomenon, caused by mental or emotional stress, and that it was curable. Mental depression and anxiety were recognized as illnesses, although symptoms such as despair and lethargy were often identified by the church with the sin of *acedia*, or sloth. Common treatments were rest, sleep, and a healthy and happy environment. Other treatments included baths, ointments, and various potions. Indeed, during the 14th and 15th centuries, people with mental illnesses, along with people who had physical deformities or disabilities, were often moved from house to house in medieval villages, as neighbours took turns caring for them. We now know that this medieval practice of keeping people who have psychological disturbances in their own community is beneficial.

One of the chief advisers to the king of France Charles V, a bishop and philosopher named Nicholas Oresme, also suggested that the disease of melancholy (depression), rather than demons, was the source of some bizarre behaviour. Oresme pointed out that much of the evidence for the existence of sorcery and witchcraft, particularly among people with psychological disorders, was obtained from people who were tortured and who, quite understandably, would confess to anything.

These conflicting crosscurrents of natural and supernatural explanations for mental disorders are represented more or less strongly in various historical works, depending on the sources consulted by historians. Some assume that demonic influences were the predominant explanations of abnormal behaviour during the Middle Ages (e.g., Zilboorg & Henry, 1941); others believe the supernatural had little or no influence. As we see in the handling of the severe psychological disorder experienced by King Charles VI of France in the late 14th century, both influences were strong, sometimes alternating in the treatment of the same case.

CHARLES VI | *The Mad King*

In the summer of 1392, King Charles VI of France was under a great deal of stress, in part because of the division of the Catholic Church. As he rode with his army to the province of Brittany, a nearby aide dropped his lance with a loud clatter and the king, thinking he was under attack, turned on his own army, killing several prominent knights before being subdued from behind. The army immediately marched back to Paris. The king's lieutenants and advisers concluded that he was mad.

During the following years, at his worst the king hid in a corner of his castle, believing he was made of glass, or roamed the corridors howling like a wolf. At other times he couldn't remember who or what he was. He became fearful and enraged whenever he saw his own royal coat of arms and would try to destroy it if it were brought near him.

The people of Paris were devastated by their leader's apparent madness. Some thought it reflected God's anger, because the king had failed to take up arms to end the schism in the Catholic Church; others thought it was God's warning against taking up arms; still others thought it was

Mary Evans Picture Library

divine punishment for heavy taxes (a conclusion some people might make today). But most thought the king's madness was caused by sorcery, a belief strengthened by a great drought that dried up the ponds and rivers, causing cattle to die of thirst. Merchants claimed their worst losses in 20 years.

Naturally, the king was given the best care available. The most famous healer in the land was a 92-year-old physician whose treatment program included moving the king to one of his residences in the country where the air was thought to be the cleanest in the land. The physician prescribed rest, relaxation, and recreation. After some time, the king seemed to recover. The physician recommended that the king not be burdened with the responsibilities of running the kingdom, claiming that if he had few worries or irritations, his mind would gradually strengthen and further improve.

Unfortunately, the physician died and the insanity of King Charles VI returned more seriously than before. This time, however, he came under the influence of the conflicting crosscurrent of supernatural causation: "An unkempt evil-eyed charlatan and pseudo-mystic named Arnaut Guilhem was allowed to treat Charles on his claim of possessing a book given by God to Adam by means of which man could overcome all affliction resulting from original sin" (Tuchman, 1978, p. 514). Guilhem insisted that the king's malady was caused by sorcery, but his treatments failed to effect a cure.

A variety of remedies and rituals of all kinds were tried but none worked. High-ranking officials and doctors of the university called for the "sorcerers" to be discovered and punished: "On one occasion, two Augustinian friars, after getting no results from magic incantations and a liquid made from powdered pearls, proposed to cut incisions in the king's head. When this was not allowed by the king's council, the friars accused those who opposed their recommendation of sorcery" (Tuchman, 1978, p. 514). Even the king himself, during his lucid moments, came to believe the source of madness was evil and sorcery: "In the name of Jesus Christ," he cried weeping in his agony, "if there is any one of you who is an accomplice in this evil I suffer, I beg him to torture me no longer but let me die!" (Tuchman, 1978, p. 515).

TREATMENTS FOR POSSESSION

With a perceived connection between evil deeds and sin on the one hand, and psychological disorders on the other, it is logical to conclude that the person is largely responsible for his or her own disorder, which might well be a punishment for evil deeds. Does this sound familiar? The acquired immune deficiency syndrome (AIDS) epidemic reflects a very similar belief among some people. Because the human immunodeficiency virus (HIV) is, in Western societies, most prevalent among gay men, some people believe it is a divine punishment for what they consider abhorrent behaviour. This view is slowly dissipating as the AIDS virus spreads to other "less sinful" segments of the population, but it still persists. Possession, however, is not always connected with sin and may be seen as involuntary and the possessed individual as blameless. Furthermore, exorcisms at least have the virtue of being relatively painless. Interestingly, they are sometimes associated with relief, as are other forms of faith healing, for reasons we explore in subsequent chapters. But what if they did not? In the Middle Ages, if exorcism failed, some authorities thought that steps were necessary to make the body uninhabitable by evil spirits, and many people were subjected to confinement, beatings, and other forms of torture.

Somewhere along the way, a creative "therapist" decided that hanging people over a pit full of poisonous snakes might scare the evil spirits right out of their bodies (to say nothing of terrifying the people themselves). Strangely, this approach sometimes worked; that is, the most disturbed, oddly behaving individuals would suddenly come to their senses and experience relief from their symptoms, if only temporarily. Naturally, this was reinforcing to the therapist, and, so, snake pits were built in many institutions. Many other treatments based on the hypothesized therapeutic element of shock were developed, including dunking people in ice-cold water.

THE MOON AND THE STARS

Paracelsus, a Swiss physician who lived from 1493 to 1541, rejected notions of possession by the devil, suggesting instead that the movements of the moon and stars had profound effects on people's psychological functioning. This influential theory inspired the word *lunatic*, which is derived from the Latin word for moon, *luna*. You might hear some of your friends explain something crazy they did last night by saying, "It must have been the full moon." The belief that heavenly bodies affect human behaviour still exists, although no scientific evidence supports it. Despite much ridicule, millions of people around the world are convinced that their behaviour is influenced by the stages of the moon or the position of the stars. This belief is most noticeable today in followers of astrology, who hold that their behaviour and the major events in their lives can be predicted by their day-to-day relationship to the position of the planets. No serious evidence has ever confirmed such a connection, however.

COMMENTS

The supernatural tradition in psychopathology is alive and well, although it is relegated, for the most part, to some cultures outside North America and to small religious sects within North America. Members of organized religions in most parts of the world look to psychology and medical science for help with major psychological disorders; in fact, the Roman Catholic Church requires that all health-care resources be exhausted before spiritual solutions, such as exorcism, be considered. Nonetheless, miraculous cures are sometimes achieved by exorcism, magic potions, rituals, and other methods that seem to have little connection with modern science. It is fascinating to explore them when they do occur, and we return to this topic in subsequent chapters. But such

In hydrotherapy, patients were shocked back to their senses by being submerged in ice-cold water.

Universal History Archive/UIG via Getty Images

The Roman physician Galen (ca. 129–198 CE) later adopted the ideas of Hippocrates and his associates and developed them further, creating a powerful and influential school of thought within the biological tradition that extended well into the 19th century. One of the more interesting and influential legacies of the Hippocratic-Galenic approach is the *humoral theory* of disorders. Hippocrates assumed that normal brain functioning was related to four bodily fluids, or *humors*: blood, black bile, yellow bile, and phlegm. Blood came from the heart, black bile from the spleen, phlegm from the brain, and choler or yellow bile from the liver. Physicians believed that disease resulted from too much or too little of one of the humors; for example, too much black bile was thought to cause melancholia (depression). In fact, the term *melancholer*, which means black bile, is still used today in its derivative form *melancholy* to refer to aspects of depression. The humoral theory was, perhaps, the first example of associating psychological disorders with chemical imbalance, an approach that is widespread today.

Terms derived from the four humors are still sometimes applied to personality traits. For example, *sanguine* (red, like blood) describes someone who is ruddy in complexion—presumably from copious blood flowing through the body—and cheerful and optimistic, though insomnia and delirium were thought to be caused by excessive blood in the brain. *Melancholic*, of course, refers to a depressive personality (depression was thought to be caused by black bile flooding the brain). A *phlegmatic personality* (from the humor phlegm) indicates apathy and sluggishness but can also mean being calm under stress. A *choleric* person (from yellow bile or choler) is hot tempered.

Excesses of one or more humors were treated by regulating the environment to increase or decrease heat, dryness, moisture, or cold, depending on which humor was out of balance. One reason King Charles VI's physician moved him to the less stressful countryside was to restore the balance in his humors. In addition to rest, good nutrition, and exercise, two treatments were developed. In *bleeding* or *bloodletting*, a carefully measured amount of blood was removed from the body, often with leeches. In the other, vomiting was induced; indeed, in a well-known treatise on depression published in 1621, *Anatomy of Melancholy*, Burton recommended eating tobacco and a half-boiled cabbage to induce vomiting (Burton, 1621/1977). Three hundred years ago, under the influence of early biological traditions, Jody might have been diagnosed with an illness, a brain disorder, or some other physical problem and given the medical treatments of the day, including bed rest, a healthful diet, exercise, and other ministrations as indicated. The notion of a lack of balance in energy or other properties of the body as a cause of various symptoms is still quite alive today in alternative therapies, for example in traditional Chinese medicine and Ayurvedic medicine (Bausell, 2007).

Hippocrates also coined the word *hysteria* to describe a concept he learned from the Egyptians, who had identified what

cases are relatively rare, and almost no one would advocate supernatural treatment for severe psychological disorders except, perhaps, as a last resort.

THE BIOLOGICAL TRADITION

Physical causes of mental disorders have been sought since early in history. Important to the biological tradition are a man, Hippocrates; a disease, syphilis; and the early consequences of believing that psychological disorders are biologically caused.

HIPPOCRATES AND GALEN

The Greek physician Hippocrates (460–377 BCE) is considered the father of modern medicine. He and his associates left a body of work called the *Hippocratic Corpus*, written between 450 BCE and 350 BCE, in which they suggested that psychological disorders could be treated like any other disease. They did not limit their search for the causes of psychopathology to the general area of "disease," because they believed that psychological disorders might also be caused by brain pathology or head trauma and could be influenced by heredity (genetics). These were remarkably astute deductions for the time, and they have been supported in recent years. Hippocrates considered the brain to be the seat of wisdom, consciousness, intelligence, and emotion. Therefore, disorders involving these functions would logically be located in the brain. Hippocrates also recognized the importance of psychological and interpersonal contributions to psychopathology, such as the sometimes negative effects of family stress; on some occasions, he removed patients from their families.

▲ Bloodletting, the extraction of blood from patients, was intended to restore the balance of humors in the body.

The biological tradition waxed and waned during the centuries after Hippocrates and Galen, but was reinvigorated in the 19th century by two factors: the discovery of the nature and cause of syphilis, and strong support from the well-respected American psychiatrist John P. Grey.

Syphilis

Behavioural and cognitive symptoms of what we now know as advanced syphilis include believing that everyone is plotting against you (delusion of persecution) or that you are God (delusion of grandeur), as well as other bizarre behaviours. Although these symptoms are very similar to those of psychosis, researchers recognized that a subgroup of apparently psychotic patients deteriorated steadily, becoming paralyzed and dying within five years of onset. This course of events contrasted with that of most psychotic patients, who remained fairly stable. In 1825, the condition was designated a disease, *general paresis*, because it had consistent symptoms (presentation) and a consistent course that resulted in death. The relationship between general paresis and syphilis was only gradually established. Louis Pasteur's germ theory of disease, around 1870, facilitated the identification of the specific bacterial micro-organism that caused syphilis. Pasteur stated that all the symptoms of a disease were caused by a germ (bacterium) that had invaded the body.

Of equal importance was the discovery of a cure for general paresis. Physicians observed a surprising recovery in patients who had contracted malaria and deliberately injected others with blood from a soldier who was ill with malaria. Many recovered, because the high fever "burned out" the syphilis bacteria. Ultimately, clinical investigators discovered that penicillin cures syphilis, but the malaria cure convinced many for the first time that "madness" and associated behavioural and cognitive symptoms could be traced directly to a curable infection. Many mental

we now call the *somatic symptom disorders* (Chapter 6). In these disorders, the physical symptoms appear to be the result of a pathology for which no organic cause can be found, such as paralysis and some kinds of blindness. Because these disorders occurred primarily in women, the Egyptians (and Hippocrates) mistakenly assumed that they were restricted to women. They also presumed a cause: The empty uterus wandered to various parts of the body in search of conception (the Greek for "uterus" is *hysteron*). Numerous physical symptoms reflected the location of the wandering uterus. The prescribed cure might be marriage or, occasionally, fumigation of the vagina to lure the uterus back to its natural location (Alexander & Selesnick, 1966). Knowledge of physiology eventually disproved the wandering uterus theory; however, the tendency to stigmatize dramatic women as "hysterical" continued unabated well into the 1970s, when mental health professionals became sensitive to the prejudicial stereotype the term implied.

▲ In the 19th century, psychological disorders were attributed to mental or emotional stress, so patients were often treated sympathetically in a restful and hygienic environment.

health professionals then assumed that comparable causes and cures might be discovered for all psychological disorders.

John P. Grey

The champion of the biological tradition in North America was a very influential psychiatrist named John P. Grey, who was appointed superintendent of a large hospital in New York in 1854. Grey also became editor of the *American Journal of Insanity*, the precursor of the current *American Journal of Psychiatry*, and the flagship publication of the American Psychiatric Association. Grey's position was that insanity always has physical causes. Therefore, the mentally ill patient should be treated as physically ill. The emphasis was once again on rest, diet, and proper room temperature and ventilation, approaches used for centuries by previous therapists in the biological tradition. Grey even invented the rotary fan to ventilate his large hospital.

Under Grey's leadership, the conditions in hospitals greatly improved, and they became more humane, livable institutions. But in subsequent years they also became so large and impersonal that individual attention was not possible. In fact, leaders in psychiatry at the end of the 19th century were alarmed at the increasing size and impersonality of mental hospitals and recommended that they be downsized.

THE DEVELOPMENT OF BIOLOGICAL TREATMENTS

Renewed interest in the biological origin of psychological disorders led, ultimately, to an increased understanding of the biological contributions to psychopathology and to the development of new treatments. In the 1930s, the physical interventions of electric shock and brain surgery were often used. Their effects, and the effects of new drugs, were discovered quite by accident. For example, insulin was occasionally given to stimulate appetite in psychotic patients who were not eating, but it also seemed to calm them down. In 1927, a Viennese physician, Manfred Sakel, began using higher and higher dosages until, finally, patients convulsed and became temporarily comatose (Sakel, 1958). Some actually recovered their mental health, much to the surprise of everybody, and their recovery was attributed to the convulsions. The procedure became known as *insulin shock therapy*, but it was abandoned because it was too dangerous, often resulting in prolonged coma or even death. Other methods of producing convulsions were designed.

In the 1920s, Joseph von Meduna observed that schizophrenia was very rarely found in people suffering from epilepsy (which ultimately did not prove to be true). Some of his followers concluded that induced brain seizures might cure schizophrenia. Following suggestions on the possible benefits of applying electric shock directly to the brain—notably, by two Italian physicians, Cerletti and Bini, in 1938—a surgeon in London treated a depressed patient by sending six small shocks directly through his brain, producing convulsions. The patient recovered. Though greatly modified, shock treatment is still with us today. The controversial modern uses of *electroconvulsive therapy* (ECT) are described in Chapter 8. Even now we have very little knowledge of how ECT works.

During the 1950s, the first effective drugs for severe psychotic disorders were developed in a systematic way, and they were introduced to Canada by psychiatrist Heinz Lehman. Before that time, a number of medicinal substances, including opium (derived from poppies), had been used as sedatives, along with countless herbs and folk remedies. With the discovery of *Rauwolfia serpentina* (later renamed *reserpine*) and another class of drugs called neuroleptics (major tranquilizers), for the first time hallucinations and delusions could be diminished; these drugs also reduced agitation and aggressiveness. Other discoveries included *benzodiazepines* (minor tranquilizers), which seemed to reduce anxiety. By the 1970s, the benzodiazepines (known by such brand names as Valium and Librium) were among the most widely prescribed drugs in the world. As drawbacks and side effects of tranquilizers became apparent, along with their limited effectiveness, the number of prescriptions decreased somewhat.

Throughout the centuries, as Alexander and Selesnick (1966, p. 287) point out, "The general pattern of drug therapy for mental illness has been one of initial enthusiasm followed by disappointment." For example, bromides, a class of sedating drugs, were used at the end of the 19th and the beginning of the 20th centuries to treat anxiety and other psychological disorders. By the 1920s, they were reported as being effective for many serious psychological and emotional symptoms. By 1928, one of every five prescriptions in the United States was for bromides. When their side effects, including various undesirable physical symptoms, became widely known, and experience began to show that their overall effectiveness was relatively modest, bromides largely disappeared from the scene.

Neuroleptics were also used less when attention focused on their many side effects, such as chronic tremors and shaking. However, the positive effects of these drugs on some patients' psychotic symptoms of hallucinations, delusions, and agitation revitalized both the search for biological contributions to psychological disorders and the search for new and more powerful drugs, a search that has paid many dividends, as documented in later chapters.

CONSEQUENCES OF THE BIOLOGICAL TRADITION

In the late 19th century, John P. Grey and his colleagues, ironically, reduced or eliminated interest in treating patients with mental illnesses because they thought mental disorders were due to some as yet undiscovered brain pathology and were therefore incurable. The only available course of action was to hospitalize these patients. In fact, around the turn of the 20th century, some nurses documented clinical success in treating mental patients with psychological methods but were prevented from treating others for fear of raising hopes of a cure among family members. In place of treatment, interest centred on diagnosis, legal questions concerning the responsibility of patients for their actions during periods of insanity, and the study of brain pathology itself.

Emil Kraepelin (1856–1926) was the dominant figure during this period and one of the founding fathers of modern psychiatry. He was extremely influential in advocating the major ideas of the biological tradition, but he was little involved in treatment, reflecting the belief that disorders were due to brain pathology. His lasting contribution was in the area of diagnosis and classification, which we discuss in detail in Chapter 3. Kraepelin (1913) was one of the first to distinguish among various psychological disorders, seeing that each may have a different age of onset and course, with somewhat different clusters of presenting symptoms and probably a different cause. Many of his descriptions of schizophrenic disorders are still useful today.

By the end of the 19th century, a scientific approach to psychological disorders and their classification had begun with the search for biological causes. Furthermore, treatment was based on humane principles. There were many drawbacks, however, the most unfortunate being that active intervention and treatment were all but eliminated in some settings, despite the fact that some very effective approaches were available. It is to these that we now turn.

Concept Check 1.2

For thousands of years, humans have tried to understand and control abnormal behaviour. Check your understanding of these historical theories and match them to the treatments used to "cure" abnormal behaviour: (a) marriage, fumigation of the vagina; (b) hypnosis; (c) bloodletting; induced vomiting; (d) patient placed in socially facilitative environments; and (e) exorcism.

1. Supernatural causes; evil demons took over the victims' bodies and controlled their behaviours.

   _____

2. The humoral theory reflected the belief that normal functioning of the brain required a balance of four bodily fluids, or humors. _____

3. Maladaptive behaviour was caused by poor social and cultural influences within the environment.

   _____

THE PSYCHOLOGICAL TRADITION

It is a long leap from evil spirits to brain pathology as causes of psychological disorders. In the intervening centuries, where was the body of thought that put psychological development, both normal and abnormal, in an interpersonal and social context? In fact, this approach has a long and distinguished tradition. Plato, for example, thought that the two causes of maladaptive behaviour were the social and cultural influences in a person's life and the learning that took place in that environment. If something was wrong in the environment, such as abusive parents, a person's impulses and emotions would overcome reason. The best treatment was to re-educate the individual through rational discussion so that the power of reason would predominate. This approach was very much a precursor to modern **psychosocial** approaches, which focus not only on psychological factors but also on social and cultural ones. Other well-known early philosophers, including Aristotle, also emphasized the influence of the social environment and early learning on later psychopathology. These philosophers wrote about the importance of fantasies, dreams, and cognitions and thus anticipated, to some extent, later

developments in psychoanalytic thought and cognitive science. They also advocated humane and responsible care for people with psychological disturbances.

MORAL THERAPY

During the first half of the 18th century, a strong psychosocial approach to mental disorders called **moral therapy** became influential. The term *moral* really meant "emotional" or "psychological" rather than a code of conduct. Its basic tenets included treating institutionalized patients as normally as possible in a setting that encouraged and reinforced normal social interaction, thus providing them with many opportunities for appropriate social and interpersonal contact. Relationships were carefully nurtured. Individual attention clearly emphasized positive consequences for appropriate interactions and behaviour; the staff made a point of modelling this behaviour. Lectures on various interesting subjects were provided, and restraint and seclusion were eliminated.

Once again, these are old ideas. The principles of moral therapy date back to Plato and beyond. But moral therapy as a system originated with the well-known French psychiatrist Philippe Pinel (1745–1826). A former patient, Pussin, long since recovered, was working in the Parisian hospital La Bicêtre when Pinel took over. Pussin had already instituted remarkable reforms, remembering, perhaps, being shackled as a patient himself. Pussin persuaded Pinel to go along with the changes. Much to Pinel's credit, he did, first at La Bicêtre and then at the women's hospital Salpêtrière, where a humane, socially facilitative atmosphere produced "miraculous" results.

After William Tuke (1732–1822) followed Pinel's lead in England, Benjamin Rush (1745–1813), often considered the founder of North American psychiatry, introduced moral therapy to the New World. It then became the treatment of choice in the leading hospitals. Asylums had appeared in the 16th century in Europe, with the intent of providing places of refuge for the confinement and care of people with mental illnesses. These early asylums were more like prisons than hospitals, however. Many housed beggars as well as people with a variety of mental

▲ Patients with psychological disorders were freed from chains and shackles as a result of the influence of Philippe Pinel (1745–1826), a pioneer in making mental institutions more humane.

illnesses, conditions were often deplorable, and little was provided to patients in the way of treatment regimens. It was the rise of moral therapy in Europe and North America that made institutions habitable and even therapeutic.

Sussman (1998) provides a description of the history of the development of asylums in Canada in the 19th century. He notes that institutionalizing people with mental illnesses in Canada began with humane intentions, to relieve the suffering and neglect of these individuals who had previously been placed in jails or poorhouses, or left to care for themselves in the community. The provinces proceeded relatively independently to develop separate and more adequate provisions for people with mental illness in the form of mental hospitals or "asylums" (see Table 1.2 for a summary). Asylum development in most provinces was influenced to a great extent by systems and movements in Great Britain and to a lesser extent by those in the United States. The involvement of religious orders in the care of people with mental illnesses in Quebec was influenced by practices occurring in France. According to Sussman, the development of asylums through the moral therapy movement did bring some relief to many people with mental illnesses.

ASYLUM REFORM AND THE DECLINE OF MORAL THERAPY

Unfortunately, after the mid-19th century, humane treatment declined because of a convergence of factors. First, it was widely recognized that moral therapy worked best when the number of patients in an institution was 200 or fewer, allowing for a great deal of individual attention. However, patient loads in existing hospitals increased to 1000, 2000, and more with the enormous waves of immigrants arriving in North America at the time.

A second reason for the decline of moral therapy has an unlikely source. The great crusader Dorothea Dix (1802–1887) campaigned endlessly for reform in the treatment of the insane throughout Canada and the United States. A schoolteacher who had worked in various institutions, she had firsthand knowledge of the deplorable conditions imposed on people with mental disorders, and she made it her life's work to inform the public and their leaders of these abuses. Her work became known as the **mental hygiene movement**.

According to Hurd and colleagues (1916), Dix visited Canada in 1843 and 1844 and discovered appalling conditions involving the incarceration of "lunatics" at Beauport in Quebec and in the Toronto Jail. She was involved in the construction of the asylum in St. John's, Newfoundland and Labrador, in 1854. Probably most notable of her contributions to the mental hygiene movement in Canada was her appeal to the Nova Scotia Legislature in January 1850, when she described the deplorable conditions for people with mental illnesses at the time and argued for the development of an asylum in Nova Scotia:

▲ Dorothea Dix (1802–1887) began the mental hygiene movement and spent much of her life campaigning in the United States and Canada for reform in the treatment of people with mental illnesses.

In imagination, for a short time, place yourselves in their stead: enter the horrid, noisome cell, invest yourselves with the foul, tattered garments which scantily serve the purposes of decent protection; cast yourselves upon the loathsome pile of filthy straw; find companionship in your own cries and groans, or in the wailings and gibberings of wretches miserable like yourselves; call for help and release, for blessed words or soothing and kind offices of care, till the dull walls are weary in sending back the echo of your moans; then, if self-possession is not overwhelmed under the imaginary miseries of what are the actual distresses of the insane, return to the consciousness of your sound intellectual health, and answer if you will longer refuse or delay to make adequate appropriations for the establishment of a provincial hospital for those who are deprived of reason, and thereby of all that gladdens life or makes existence a blessing. (Hurd et al., 1916, p. 493)

TABLE 1.2 | Development of the First Asylums in Canada

Province	Date	Notes
Quebec	1845	Beauport, or the Quebec Lunatic Asylum, was opened.
New Brunswick	1847	The Provincial Lunatic Asylum was erected.
Ontario	1850	The Provincial Lunatic Asylum in Toronto admitted patients.
Newfoundland and Labrador	1854	An asylum was erected and admitted its first patients.
Nova Scotia	1857	The first patients were admitted to the Provincial Hospital for the Insane.
British Columbia	1872	A remodelled provincial general hospital (the Old Royal Hospital) was opened as the Asylum for the Insane in British Columbia.
Prince Edward Island	1877	The Prince Edward Island Hospital for the Insane was built.
Manitoba	1886	The Selkirk Lunatic Asylum admitted patients.
Saskatchewan	1911	The Saskatchewan Provincial Hospital admitted its first patients.
Alberta	1914	The Insane Asylum in Ponoka was opened.

Asylum Hospital, Hamilton, Ont.

Source: Republished with permission of SAGE Publications, from "The First Asylums in Canada: A Response to Neglectful Community Care and Current Trends," by S. Sussman, *Canadian Journal of Psychiatry* 1998 Vol. 43 (3) pp. 260–264; permission conveyed through Copyright Clearance Center, Inc.

In addition to improving the standards of care, Dix worked hard to make sure that everyone who needed care received it, including homeless people. Through her efforts, humane treatment became more widely available in North American institutions. As her career drew to a close, she was rightly acknowledged as a hero of the 19th century.

Unfortunately, an unforeseen consequence of Dix's heroic efforts was a substantial increase in the number of mental patients. This influx led to a rapid transition from moral therapy to custodial care because hospitals were inadequately staffed. Dix reformed asylums and single-handedly inspired the construction of numerous new institutions. But even her tireless efforts and advocacy could not ensure sufficient staffing to allow the individual attention necessary for effective moral therapy. Unfortunately, institutionalization in Canada eventually "became a synonym for an inhumane response to mentally ill people" (Sussman, 1998, p. 262), often because resources were insufficient to provide adequate care.

An important mental health reformer and crusader who followed Dix's example was Clarence Hincks, a University of Toronto medical school graduate who cofounded the Canadian Committee for Mental Hygiene in 1918. Early in his career, he toured mental institutions throughout Manitoba. In his unpublished autobiography and his report to the Manitoba government, Hincks documented continued appalling conditions for people with mental illnesses in these institutions (Griffin, 1989; Roland, 1990). Hincks often found that those working in institutions—including the superintendents—had no special psychiatric training. In one case only one doctor was in charge of 700 patients, and he also acted as the superintendent. In one institution in Portage La Prairie, Hincks encountered a woman who had been left in a closet for two years and had only been allowed out once—and then within the confines of a cage. Hincks noted that some of the institutions were not even meant for those with mental illness but had come to house them anyway, despite having no methods for caring for them. At another Manitoban institution, he discovered that mentally ill patients were locked into coffin-like boxes at night to sleep, and in another, "mentally defective" children were rolled in long strips of cotton at night, with their arms and legs bound, and then placed on shelves to sleep. Hincks had himself experienced and recovered from a bout of major depression while in university. His personal experience in recovering from depression led him to advocate for the idea that mental illness was treatable. Hincks's position stood in contrast to the prevailing view at the time that mental illness was incurable. In fact, one Manitoba institution that Hincks visited in 1918 in Portage La Prairie was named the "Home for Incurables."

A final blow to the practice of moral therapy, mentioned earlier, was the decision, in the middle of the 19th century, that mental illness was caused by brain pathology and, therefore, was incurable. The psychological tradition lay dormant for a time, only to re-emerge in several very different schools of thought in the 20th century.

The first major approach was **psychoanalysis**, based on Sigmund Freud's (1856–1939) elaborate theory of the structure of the mind and the role of unconscious processes in determining behaviour. The second was **behaviourism**, associated with John B. Watson, Ivan Pavlov, and B. F. Skinner, which focuses on how learning and adaptation affect the development of psychopathology.

PSYCHOANALYTIC THEORY

Have you ever felt as if someone had cast a spell on you? Have you ever been mesmerized by a look across a room from an attractive woman or man, or a stare from a rock musician as you sat in front at a concert? If so, you have something in common with the patients of Austrian physician Anton Mesmer (1734–1815) and with millions of people since his time who have been hypnotized. Mesmer suggested to his patients that their problem was due to an undetectable fluid found in all living organisms called "animal magnetism" that could become blocked. Mesmer had his patients sit in a dark room around a large vat of chemicals with rods extending from it and touching the patients. Dressed in flowing robes, he might then identify and tap various areas of their bodies where their animal magnetism was blocked while suggesting strongly that they were being cured. Because of his rather unusual techniques, Mesmer was considered an oddity and maybe a charlatan and was strongly opposed by the medical establishment.

Benjamin Franklin put animal magnetism to the test by conducting a brilliant experiment in which patients received either magnetized water or nonmagnetized water with strong suggestions that they would get better. Neither the patient nor the therapist knew which water was which, making it a double-blind experiment. When both groups got better, Franklin concluded that animal magnetism, or mesmerism, was nothing more than strong suggestion (McNally, 1999). Nevertheless, Mesmer is widely regarded as the father of hypnosis, a state in which suggestible subjects sometimes appear to be in a trance.

Many distinguished scientists and physicians were very interested in Mesmer's powerful methods of suggestion. One of the best known, Jean Charcot (1825–1893), was head of the Salpêtriére Hospital in Paris, where Philippe Pinel had introduced psychological treatments several generations earlier. A distinguished neurologist, Charcot demonstrated that some of the techniques of mesmerism were effective with several psychological disorders, and he did much to legitimize the fledgling practice of hypnosis while doing away with the flowing robes and chemicals. Significantly, in 1885 a young man named Sigmund Freud came from Vienna to study with Charcot.

After returning from France, Freud teamed up with Josef Breuer (1842–1925), who had experimented with a somewhat different hypnotic procedure. While his patients were in the highly suggestible state of hypnosis, Breuer asked them to describe their problems, conflicts, and fears in as much detail as

▲ Clarence Hincks (1885–1964) was an early crusader for the mental hygiene movement in Canada. He cofounded the Canadian National Committee for Mental Hygiene in 1918—a precursor to today's Canadian Mental Health Association.

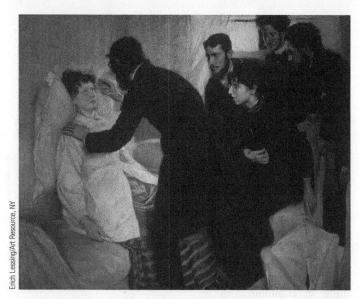

Anton Mesmer (1734–1815) and other early therapists used strong suggestions to cure their patients, who were often hypnotized.

they could. Breuer observed two extremely important phenomena during this process. First, patients often became extremely emotional as they talked and felt quite relieved and improved after emerging from the hypnotic state. Second, seldom would patients have gained an understanding of the relationship between their emotional problems and their psychological disorder. In fact, it was difficult or impossible for them to recall some of the details they had described under hypnosis. In other words, the material seemed to be beyond the awareness of the patient. With this observation, Breuer and Freud had "discovered" the **unconscious** mind and its apparent influence on the production of psychological disorders. This discovery is one of the most important developments in the history of psychology as a whole.

Josef Breuer (1842–1925) worked on the celebrated case of Anna O. and, with Freud, developed the theory of psychoanalysis.

A close second was their discovery that recalling and reliving emotional trauma that has been made unconscious and releasing the accompanying tension is therapeutic—a process that became known as **catharsis**. A fuller understanding of the relationship between current emotions and earlier events is called *insight*. As we see throughout this book, particularly in Chapters 5 and 6 on anxiety and somatic symptom disorders, the existence of unconscious memories and feelings and the importance of processing emotion-laden information have been verified and reaffirmed.

Freud and Breuer's theories were based on systematic case observations. An excellent example is Breuer's classic description of his treatment of "hysterical" symptoms in Anna O. in 1895 (Breuer & Freud, 1957). Anna O. was a young woman who was perfectly healthy until she turned 21. Shortly before her problems began, her father developed a serious chronic illness that led to his death. Throughout his illness, Anna O. had cared for him, spending hours at his bedside. Five months after her father became ill, Anna noticed that during the day her vision blurred and periodically she had difficulty moving her right arm and both legs. Soon, she began to experience some difficulty speaking, and her behaviour became very erratic. Shortly thereafter, she consulted Breuer.

In a series of treatment sessions, Breuer dealt with one symptom at a time through hypnosis and subsequent "talking through," tracing each symptom to its hypothetical causation in circumstances surrounding the death of Anna's father. One at a time her "hysterical" ailments disappeared, but only after treatment was administered to each respective behaviour. This process of treating one behaviour at a time fulfills a basic requirement for drawing scientific conclusions about the effects of treatment in an individual case study, as we see in Chapter 4.

Freud took these basic observations and expanded them into the **psychoanalytic model**, the most comprehensive theory yet constructed on the development and structure of our personalities. He also speculated on where this development could go wrong and produce psychological disorders.

Although most of it remains unproven, psychoanalytic theory has had a strong influence, and it is important to be familiar with its basic ideas; what follows is a brief outline of the theory. We focus on its three major facets: (1) *the structure of the mind* and the distinct functions of personality that sometimes clash

Jean Charcot (1825–1893) studied hypnosis and influenced Sigmund Freud to consider psychosocial approaches to psychological disorders.

▲ Bertha Pappenheim (1859–1936), famous as Anna O., was described as "hysterical" by Breuer.

. with one another; (2) *the defence mechanisms* with which the mind defends itself from these clashes or conflicts; and (3) *the stages of early psychosexual development* that provide grist for the mill of our inner conflicts.

The Structure of the Mind

The mind, according to Freud, has three major parts or functions: the id, ego, and superego (see ■ Figure 1.3). These terms, like many from psychoanalysis, have found their way into our common vocabulary, and although you may have heard them, you may not be fully aware of their meaning. The **id** is the source of our strong sexual and aggressive energies or our instinctual drives—the "animal" within us. The positive energy or drive within the id is the libido. Even today some people explain low sex drive as an absence of *libido*. A less important source of energy is the death instinct, or *thanatos*. Much like matter and antimatter, these two basic drives toward life and dominance and fulfillment on the one hand, and death and destruction on the other, are continually in opposition.

The id operates according to the *pleasure principle*, with an overriding goal of maximizing pleasure and eliminating any associated tension or conflicts. The goal of pleasure, which is particularly prominent in childhood, often conflicts with social rules and regulations. The id has its own characteristic way of processing information; referred to as primary process, this type of thinking is very emotional, irrational, illogical, led with fantasies, and preoccupied with sex, aggression, selfishness, and envy.

Fortunately for all of us, in Freud's view, the id's selfish and sometimes dangerous drives do not go unchecked. In fact, only a few months into life, we know we must adapt our basic demands to the real world; we must find ways to meet our basic

needs without offending everyone around us. The part of our mind that ensures we act realistically is called the **ego**, and it operates according to the *reality principle* instead of the pleasure principle. The cognitive operations or thinking styles of the ego, characterized by logic and reason, are referred to as the *secondary process*, as opposed to the illogical and irrational primary process of the id.

The third important structure within the mind, the **superego**, or what we might call the *conscience*, represents the *moral principles* instilled in us by our parents and our culture. It is the voice within us that nags at us when we know we're doing something wrong. Because the purpose of the superego is to counteract the aggressive and sexual drives of the id that are potentially dangerous, the basis for conflict is readily apparent.

The role of the ego is to mediate conflict between the id and the superego, juggling their demands with the realities of the world. The ego is often called the executive or manager of our minds. If it mediates successfully, we can go on to the higher intellectual and creative pursuits of life. If it is unsuccessful, and the id or the superego becomes too strong, conflict will overtake us and psychological disorders will develop. Because these conflicts are all within the mind, they are called **intrapsychic conflicts**. Lastly, Freud believed the id and the superego are almost entirely unconscious. We are fully aware only of the secondary processes of the ego, which is a relatively small part of the mind.

Defence Mechanisms

The ego fights a continual battle to stay on top of the warring id and superego. Occasionally, their conflicts produce anxiety that threatens to overwhelm the ego. The anxiety is a signal that alerts the ego to marshal **defence mechanisms**, unconscious protective processes that keep primitive emotions associated with conflicts in check so the ego can continue its coordinating function. Although Freud first conceptualized defence mechanisms, it was his daughter, Anna Freud, who developed the ideas more fully.

▲ Sigmund Freud (1856–1939) is considered the founder of psychoanalysis.

We all use defence mechanisms at times—sometimes they are adaptive and sometimes they are maladaptive. For example, have you ever done poorly on a test because the professor was unfair in the grading? And then when you got home, you yelled at your brother or perhaps at your dog? This is an example of the defence mechanism of displacement. The ego adaptively "decides" that expressing primitive anger at your professor might not be in your best interest. Because your brother and your dog don't have the authority to affect you in an adverse way, your anger is displaced to one of them. Here are some examples of defence mechanisms (adapted from an earlier

	Type of thinking	Driven by
Superego → Conscience	Conscience	Moral principles
Ego Mediator	Logical; rational	Reality principle
Id	Illogical; emotional; irrational	Pleasure principle

Intrapsychic conflicts

FIGURE 1.3 | Freud's structure of the mind.

version of the *DSM*, American Psychiatric Association, 2000a/© Cengage Learning):

- *Denial*: Refuses to acknowledge some aspect of objective reality or subjective experience that is apparent to others (e.g., a person not facing the fact that a romantic relationship is over)
- *Displacement*: Transfers a feeling about, or a response to, an object that causes discomfort onto another, usually less threatening, object or person (e.g., kicking the dog when actually angry with a teacher)
- *Projection*: Falsely attributes own unacceptable feelings, impulses, or thoughts to another individual or object (e.g., a man with sexual feelings toward a certain woman thinks that woman is coming on to him)
- *Rationalization*: Conceals the true motivations for actions, thoughts, or feelings through elaborate reassuring or self-serving but incorrect explanations (e.g., after not getting into a certain graduate school, an aspiring graduate student decides that school was not really where she wanted to study after all)
- *Reaction formation*: Substitutes behaviour, thoughts, or feelings that are the direct opposite of unacceptable ones (e.g., a man with sexual feelings toward children crusades against child pornography)
- *Repression*: Blocks disturbing wishes, thoughts, or experiences from conscious awareness (e.g., a person "forgets" about an embarrassing experience)
- *Sublimation*: Directs potentially maladaptive feelings or impulses into socially acceptable behaviour (e.g., redirecting energy from underlying conflict into artistic expression and achievement)

Defence mechanisms have been subjected to scientific study, and there is some evidence that they may be of potential import in the study of psychopathology (Vaillant, 1992, 2012). For example, Perry and Bond (2012, 2014) noted that reduction in unadaptive defence mechanisms, and strengthening of adaptive mechanisms such as humor and sublimation, correlated with psychological health. Thus, the concept of defence mechanisms—coping styles, in contemporary terminology—continues to be important to the study of psychopathology.

Psychosexual Stages of Development

Freud also theorized that during infancy and early childhood, we pass through several **psychosexual stages of development** that have a profound and lasting impact, thus providing the first developmental perspective on abnormal behaviour. The stages—oral, anal, phallic, latency, and genital—represent distinctive patterns of gratifying our basic needs and satisfying our drive for physical pleasure. For example, the oral stage, typically extending for approximately two years from birth, is characterized by a central focus on the need for food. In the act of sucking, necessary for feeding, the lips, tongue, and mouth become the focus of libidinal drives and, therefore, the principal source of pleasure. Freud hypothesized that, if we did not receive appropriate gratification during a specific stage or if a specific stage left a particularly strong impression (which he termed *fixation*), an individual's

personality would reflect the stage throughout adult life. For example, fixation at the oral stage might result in excessive thumb sucking and emphasis on oral stimulation through eating, chewing pencils, or biting fingernails. Adult personality characteristics theoretically associated with oral fixation include dependency and passivity or, in reaction to these tendencies, rebelliousness and cynicism.

One of the more controversial and frequently mentioned psychosexual conflicts occurs during the phallic stage (from age three to age five or six), which is characterized by early genital self-stimulation. This conflict is the subject of the Greek tragedy *Oedipus Rex*, in which Oedipus is fated to kill his father and, unknowingly, to marry his mother. Freud asserted that all young boys relive this fantasy when genital self-stimulation is accompanied by images of sexual interactions with their mothers. These fantasies, in turn, are accompanied by strong feelings of envy and perhaps anger toward their fathers, with whom they identify but whose place they want to take. Furthermore, strong fears develop that the father may punish that lust by removing the son's penis—thus, the phenomenon of castration anxiety. This fear helps the boy keep his lustful impulses toward his mother in check. The battle of the lustful impulses on the one hand and castration anxiety on the other creates a conflict that is internal, or intrapsychic, called the *Oedipus complex*. The phallic stage passes uneventfully only if several things happen. First, the child must resolve his ambivalent relationship with his parents and reconcile the simultaneous anger and love he has for his father. If this happens, he may go on to channel his libidinal impulses into heterosexual relationships while retaining harmless affection for his mother. Development of the superego is another consequence of successfully resolving this conflict.

The counterpart conflict in girls, called the *Electra complex*, is even more controversial. Freud viewed the young girl as wanting to replace her mother and possess her father. Central to this possession is the girl's desire for a penis so as to be more like her father and brothers—hence the term *penis envy*. According to Freud, the conflict is partially resolved when females develop healthy heterosexual relationships and look forward to having a baby, which he viewed as a healthy substitute for having a penis. It is the partial resolution of the Electra complex, resulting in a less highly developed superego, that makes females (in Freud's theory) less highly developed psychologically than are males. Needless to say, this particular theory has provoked marked consternation as being sexist and demeaning. It is important to remember that it is theory, not fact; no systematic research exists to support it.

In Freud's view, all nonpsychotic psychological disorders result from underlying unconscious conflicts, the anxiety that resulted from those conflicts, and the implementation of ego defence mechanisms. Freud called such disorders **neuroses**, or *neurotic disorders*, from an old term referring to disorders of the nervous system.

Later Developments in Psychoanalytic Thought

Freud's original psychoanalytic theories have been greatly modified and developed in many different directions, mostly by his students or followers.

▲ Anna Freud (1895–1982), here with her father, contributed the concept of defence mechanisms to the field of psychoanalysis.

Anna Freud (1895–1982), Freud's daughter, concentrated on the way in which the defensive reactions of the ego determine our behaviour. In so doing, she was the first proponent of the modern field of **ego psychology** or self-psychology. Her book *Ego and the Mechanisms of Defense* (1946) is still influential. According to Anna Freud, the individual slowly accumulates adaptational capacities, skill in reality testing, and defences. Abnormal behaviour develops when the ego is deficient in regulating such functions as delaying and controlling impulses, or in marshalling appropriate normal defences to strong internal conflicts.

Carl Jung (1875–1961) and Alfred Adler (1870–1937) were students of Freud who came to reject his ideas and form their own schools of thought. Unlike Freud, both Jung and Adler believed that the basic quality of human nature is positive and that people have a strong drive toward self-actualization. Jung and Adler believed by removing barriers to both internal and external growth, the individual would naturally improve and flourish.

Others took psychoanalytical theorizing in different directions, emphasizing development over the lifespan and the influence of culture and society on personality. Karen Horney (1885–1952), Erich Fromm (1900–1980), and Erik Erikson (1902–1994) are associated with these ideas. For example, Horney (1967) reanalyzed Freud's male-oriented views of women's psychological development and developed her own feminine psychology in which she recognized the influences of societal factors. Erikson's (1950) greatest contribution was his theory of development across the lifespan, in which he described in some detail the crises and conflicts that accompany eight specific psychosocial stages. For example, in the last of these stages, the *mature age*, beginning at about age 65, individuals review their lives and attempt to make sense of them, experiencing both the satisfaction of having completed some lifelong goals and despair at having failed at others. Scientific developments have borne out the wisdom of considering psychopathology from a developmental point of view.

Psychoanalytic Psychotherapy

Many techniques of psychoanalytic psychotherapy, or psychoanalysis, are designed to reveal the nature of unconscious mental processes and conflicts through catharsis and insight. Freud developed techniques of **free association**, in which patients are instructed to say whatever comes to mind without the usual socially mandated censoring. Free association is intended to reveal emotionally charged material that may be repressed because it is too painful or threatening to bring into consciousness. Freud's patients lay on a couch, and he sat behind them so they would not be distracted. This method is how the couch became the symbol of psychotherapy. Other techniques include **dream analysis** (still quite popular today), in which the content of dreams, supposedly reflecting the primary process thinking of the id, is systematically related to symbolic aspects of unconscious conflicts. The therapist interprets the patient's thoughts and feelings from free association and the content of dreams and relates them to various unconscious conflicts. This procedure is often difficult because the patient may resist the efforts of the therapist to uncover repressed and sensitive conflicts and may deny the interpretations. The goal of this stage of therapy is to help the patient gain insight into the nature of the conflicts.

The relationship between the therapist, called the **psychoanalyst**, and the patient is very important. In the context of this relationship as it evolves, the therapist may discover the nature of the patient's intrapsychic conflict: In a phenomenon called **transference**, patients come to relate to the therapist very much as they did toward important figures in their childhood, particularly their parents. Patients who resent the therapist but can verbalize no good reason for it may be re-enacting childhood resentment toward a parent. More often, the patient falls deeply in love with the therapist, which reflects strong positive feelings that existed earlier for a parent. In the phenomenon of *countertransference*, therapists project some of their own personal issues and feelings, often positive, onto the patient. Therapists are trained to deal with their own feelings as well as their patients', whatever the mode of therapy, and it is strictly against all ethical canons of the mental health professions to accept overtures from patients that might lead to relationships outside therapy. The Canadian Code of Ethics for Psychologists (2017), for example, exhorts therapists to "be acutely aware of the power relationship in therapy and, therefore, not encourage or engage in sexual intimacy with therapy clients, neither during therapy, nor for that period of time following therapy during which the power relationship reasonably could be expected to influence the client's decision making" (p. 22).

Classical psychoanalysis requires therapy four to five times a week for two to five years to analyze unconscious conflicts, resolve them, and restructure the personality to put the ego back in charge. A study by Norman Doidge at the Canadian Institute of Psychoanalysis in Toronto showed that the mean length of treatment for patients undergoing psychoanalysis in Canada is 4.8 years, 5.7 years in the United States, and 6.6 years in Australia (Doidge et al., 2002). In a meta-analysis of 14 studies on the effectiveness of psychoanalysis for complex problems, the range of number of therapy sessions was 234 to 971 (de Maat et al.,

2013). In psychoanalysis, reduction of symptoms (overt manifestations of psychological disorders) is seen as relatively inconsequential, because symptoms are only expressions of underlying intrapsychic conflicts that arise from psychosexual developmental stages. Thus, eliminating a phobia or depressive episode would be of little use unless the underlying conflict was dealt with adequately because another set of symptoms would almost certainly emerge (*symptom substitution*). Because of the extraordinary expense of psychoanalysis, and the lack of evidence that it is effective in alleviating psychological disorders, this approach is seldom used today.

Classical psychoanalysis is still practised, particularly in some large cities, but many psychotherapists employ a loosely related set of approaches referred to as **psychodynamic psychotherapy**. Although conflicts and unconscious processes are still emphasized, and efforts are made to identify trauma and active defence mechanisms, therapists use an eclectic mixture of tactics, with a social and interpersonal focus. It is significantly briefer than classical psychoanalysis—short-term psychodynamic psychotherapies involve around 20 sessions (Leichsenring et al., 2004). Also, psychodynamic therapists de-emphasize the goal of personality reconstruction, focusing instead on relieving the suffering associated with psychological disorders, addressing history of trauma, and dealing with issues of attachment, among other things. Some forms of psychodynamic psychotherapy have strong scientific evidence for their effectiveness, such as interpersonal therapy (IPT) in the treatment of depression, and group psychodynamic interpersonal psychotherapy for eating disorder.

Comments

Pure psychoanalysis is of historical more than current interest, and classical psychoanalysis as a treatment has been diminishing in popularity for years. In 1980, the term *neurosis*, which specifically implied a psychoanalytic view of the causes of psychological disorders, was dropped from the *DSM*, the official diagnostic system of the American Psychiatric Association.

A major criticism of psychoanalysis is that it is basically unscientific, relying on reports by the patient of events that happened years ago. These events have been filtered through the experience of the observer and then interpreted by the psychoanalyst in ways that certainly could be questioned and might differ from one analyst to the next. Finally, there has been no careful measurement of any of these psychological phenomena and no obvious way to prove or disprove the basic hypotheses of psychoanalysis. This fact is important, because measurement and the ability to prove or disprove a theory are the foundations of the scientific approach.

Nevertheless, psychoanalytic concepts and observations have been very valuable, not only to the study of psychopathology and psychodynamic psychotherapy but also to the history of ideas in Western civilization. Careful scientific studies of psychopathology have supported the observation of unconscious mental processes—that is, the notion that basic emotional responses are often triggered by hidden or symbolic cues and the understanding that memories of events in our lives can be repressed and otherwise avoided in a variety of ingenious ways. The relationship of the therapist and the patient, called the *therapeutic alliance*, is an important area of study across most therapeutic strategies. These concepts, along with the importance of various coping styles or defence mechanisms, appear repeatedly throughout this book.

Freud's revolutionary idea that pathological anxiety emerges in connection with some of our deepest and darkest instincts brought us a long way from witch trials and incurable brain pathology. Before Freud, the source of good and evil and of urges and prohibitions was conceived as external and spiritual, usually in the guise of demons confronting the forces of good. Since Freud, we ourselves have become the battleground for these forces, and we are inexorably caught up in the battle, sometimes for better and sometimes for worse.

HUMANISTIC THEORY

We have already seen that Jung and Adler broke sharply with Freud. Their fundamental disagreement concerned the very nature of humanity. Freud portrayed life as a battleground where we are continually in danger of being overwhelmed by our darkest forces. Jung and Adler, by contrast, emphasized the positive, optimistic side of human nature. Jung talked about setting goals, looking toward the future, and realizing our fullest potential. Adler believed that human nature reaches its fullest potential when we contribute to other individuals and to society as a whole. He believed we all strive to reach superior levels of intellectual and moral development. Nevertheless, both Jung and Adler retained many of the principles of psychodynamic thought. Their general philosophies were adopted in the middle of the 20th century by personality theorists and became known as *humanistic psychology*.

Self-actualizing was the watchword for this movement. The underlying assumption is that all of us can reach our highest potential, in all areas of functioning, if only we have the freedom to grow. Inevitably, a variety of conditions may block our actualization. Because every person is basically good and whole, most blocks originate outside the individual. Difficult living conditions or stressful life or interpersonal experiences may move you away from your true self. Abraham Maslow (1908–1970) was most systematic in describing the structure of personality. He postulated a *hierarchy of needs*, beginning with our most basic physical needs for food and sex and ranging upward to our needs for self-actualization, love, and self-esteem. Social needs, such as friendship, fall somewhere in between. Maslow hypothesized that we cannot progress up the hierarchy until we have satisfied the needs at lower levels.

Carl Rogers (1902–1987) is, from the point of view of therapy, the most influential humanist. Rogers originated client-centred therapy, later known as **person-centred therapy** (Rogers, 1961). In this approach, the therapist takes a passive role, making as few interpretations as possible. The point is to give the individual a chance to develop during the course of therapy, unfettered by threats to the self. Humanist theorists have great faith in the ability of human relations to foster this growth. **Unconditional positive regard**, the complete and almost unqualified acceptance of most of the client's feelings and actions, is critical to the humanistic approach. *Empathy* is the sympathetic understanding of the individual's particular view of the world. The hoped-for result of person-centred therapy is that clients will be more straightforward and honest with themselves and will access their innate tendencies toward growth.

Like psychoanalysis, the humanistic approach has had a substantial effect on theories of interpersonal relationships. For example, the human potential movements so popular in the 1960s and 1970s were a direct result of humanistic theorizing. This approach also emphasized the importance of the therapeutic relationship in a way quite different from Freud's. Rather than seeing the relationship as a means to an end (transference), humanistic therapists believed relationships, including the therapeutic relationship, were the single most positive influence in facilitating human growth. In fact, Rogers made substantial contributions to the scientific study of therapist–client relationships. Research by W. H. Coons and colleagues at the Ontario Hospital in Hamilton (Coons, 1957, 1967; Coons & Peacock, 1970) provided evidence for the importance of the humanistic concept of empathy or "the opportunity for interpersonal interaction in a consistently warm and accepting social environment" (Coons, 1957, p. 1) in explaining the success of psychotherapy. Proponents of the humanistic model stress the unique, nonquantifiable experiences of the individual, emphasizing that people are more different than alike. Thus, it does not come as a surprise that many humanistic model proponents have not been much interested in doing research that would discover or create new knowledge. A major exception is Carl Rogers himself, who conducted important work on understanding how psychotherapy works, an area known today as **psychotherapy process** research.

Frederich (Fritz) Perls developed a therapy known as Gestalt therapy that has humanistic elements (Levitsky & Perls, 1970; Perls, 1969). Like the person-centred therapy approach, Gestalt therapy focuses on people's positive and creative potentials. It helps clients develop an awareness of their desires and needs, and understand how they might be blocking themselves from reaching their potential. Unlike psychoanalytic therapy, Gestalt therapy does not involve delving into past experiences—instead, it is very focused on the present. Relative to person-centred therapy, which does not emphasize technique, Gestalt therapists are trained in the use of specific techniques. These include "I language," in which the therapist encourages the client to refer to "I" rather than to "it" to take more responsibility for emotions and behaviour, and the use of metaphor, in which the therapist uses stories or scenarios to illustrate and make a problem clearer to a client.

Where is the humanistic movement today? As Maslow noted, traditional person-centred therapy found its greatest application among individuals without psychological disorders. The application of person-centred therapy to more severe psychological disorders has decreased substantially over the decades, although certain variations have periodically arisen in some areas of psychopathology. For example, Leslie Greenberg and his colleagues at York University in Toronto have developed experiential and emotion-focused therapies that have their roots in both person-centred and Gestalt approaches (Goldman et al., 2006; Greenberg, 2004, 2010; Greenberg et al., 2003; Greenberg & Watson, 2005; Watson & Greenberg, 2017). These variations of traditional humanistic therapy are well researched and have demonstrated effectiveness in treating certain forms of psychopathology, such as certain mood and anxiety disorders.

THE BEHAVIOURAL MODEL

As psychoanalysis swept the world at the beginning of the 20th century, events in Russia and North America eventually provided an alternative psychological model that was just as powerful. The **behavioural model** brought the systematic development of a more scientific approach to psychological aspects of psychopathology. The behavioural model is more commonly referred to today as the cognitive-behavioural (e.g., Meichenbaum, 1995) or social learning model (e.g., Bandura, 1973, 1986), given the greater emphasis today on cognitive and social factors involved in learning. These more recent developments to the traditional behavioural model are described in Chapter 2.

Pavlov and Classical Conditioning

In his classic study of the salivation response in dogs, physiologist Ivan Petrovich Pavlov (1849–1936) of St. Petersburg, Russia, learned why dogs salivate before the presentation of food. This classic experiment initiated the study of **classical conditioning**, a type of learning in which a neutral stimulus is paired with a response until it elicits that response. The word *conditioning* (or *conditioned response*) resulted from an accident in translation from the original Russian. Pavlov was really talking about a response that occurred only on the "condition" of the presence of a particular event or situation (stimulus)—in this case, the footsteps of the laboratory assistant at feeding time. Thus, "conditional response" would have been more accurate. Conditioning is one way we acquire new information, particularly information that is somewhat emotional in nature. This process is not as simple as it first seems, and we continue to uncover many more facts about its complexity (Craske, Hermans, & Vansteenwegen, 2006; Lissek et al., 2014; Prenoveau et al., 2013; Rescorla, 1988). Let's look at a powerful contemporary example.

Psychologists working in oncology units have studied a phenomenon well known to many cancer patients, their nurses and physicians, and their families. Chemotherapy, a common treatment for some forms of cancer, has side effects that include severe nausea and vomiting. But as documented a long time ago in the research of Patricia Dobkin at McGill University, these patients often experience severe nausea and, occasionally, vomiting, when they merely see the medical personnel who administer the chemotherapy or any equipment associated with the treatment itself, even on days when their treatment is not delivered (Morrow & Dobkin, 1988; Kamen et al., 2014). For some patients, this reaction becomes associated with a wide variety of stimuli that evoke people or things present during chemotherapy—anybody in a nurse's uniform or even the sight of the hospital itself.

▲ Ivan Pavlov (1849–1936) identified the process of classical conditioning, which is important to many emotional disorders.

The strength of the response to similar objects or people is usually a function of how similar these objects or people are. This phenomenon is called *stimulus generalization* because the response generalizes to similar stimuli. In any case, this particular reaction, obviously, is very distressing and uncomfortable, particularly if it is associated with a wide variety of objects or situations. Psychologists have had to develop specific treatments to overcome this response.

Whether the stimulus is food, as in Pavlov's laboratory, or chemotherapy, the classical conditioning process begins with a stimulus that elicits a response in almost anyone and requires no learning; no conditions must be present for the response to occur. For these reasons, the food or chemotherapy is called the *unconditioned stimulus* (*UCS*). The natural or unlearned response to this stimulus—in these cases, salivation or nausea—is called the *unconditioned response* (*UCR*). Now the learning comes in. As we have already seen, a person or an object associated with the unconditioned stimulus (food or chemotherapy) acquire the power to elicit the same response, but now the response, because it was elicited by the conditional or *conditioned stimuli* (*CS*), is termed a *conditioned response* (*CR*). Thus, the nurse associated with the chemotherapy becomes a conditioned stimulus. The nausea, which is almost the same as that experienced during chemotherapy, becomes the conditioned response.

With unconditioned stimuli as powerful as chemotherapy, a conditioned response can be learned in one trial. However, most learning of this type requires repeated pairing of the unconditioned stimulus (e.g., chemotherapy) and the conditioned stimulus (e.g., nurses' uniforms or hospital equipment). When Pavlov began to investigate this phenomenon, he substituted a metronome for the footsteps of his laboratory assistants so he could quantify the stimulus more accurately and, therefore, study the approach more precisely. What he also learned is that presentation of the CS (e.g., the metronome) without the food for a long enough period would eventually eliminate the conditioned response to the food. In other words, the dog learned that the metronome no longer meant that a meal was on the way. This process was called **extinction**.

Because Pavlov was a physiologist, it was quite natural for him to study these processes in a laboratory and to be quite scientific about it. This method required precision in measuring and observing relationships and in ruling out alternative explanations. Although this approach is common in biology, it was not at all common in psychology at that time. For example, it was impossible for psychoanalysts to measure unconscious conflicts precisely or even to observe them. Early experimental psychologists such as Edward Titchener (1867–1927) emphasized the study of **introspection**. Subjects simply reported on their inner thoughts and feelings after experiencing certain stimuli, but the results were inconsistent and discouraging to many experimental psychologists.

Watson and the Rise of Behaviourism

An early American psychologist, John B. Watson (1878–1958), is considered the founder of behaviourism. Strongly influenced by the work of Pavlov, Watson decided that to base psychology on introspection was to head in the wrong direction, that psychology could be made as scientific as physiology, and that psychology no more needed introspection or other nonquantifiable methods than did chemistry and physics (Watson, 1913). This point of view is reflected in a famous quotation from a seminal article published by Watson in 1913: "Psychology, as the behaviorist views it, is a purely objective experimental branch of natural science. Its theoretical goal is the prediction and control of behavior. Introspection forms no essential part of its methods" (p. 158). This, then, was the beginning of behaviourism and, like most revolutionaries, Watson took his cause to extremes. For example, he wrote that "thinking," for purposes of science, could be equated with subvocal talking and that one need only measure movements around the larynx to study this process objectively.

Most of Watson's time was spent developing behavioural psychology as an empirical science, but he did dabble briefly in the study of psychopathology. In 1920, he and a student, Rosalie Rayner, presented an 11-month-old boy named Albert with a harmless fluffy white rat to play with. Albert was not afraid of the small animal and enjoyed playing with it. Every time Albert reached for the rat, however, the experimenters made a loud noise behind him. After only five trials, Albert showed the first signs of fear if the white rat came near. The experimenters then determined that Albert displayed mild fear of any similar white furry object, even a Santa Claus mask with a white fuzzy beard. You may not think this is surprising, but keep in mind that this was one of the first examples ever recorded in a laboratory of actually producing fear of an object not previously feared. Of course, this experiment would be considered unethical by today's standards. For example, Watson and Rayner's failure to remove Albert's fear before the end of the experiment, and their insufficient follow-up of the child's fears after the experiment, would be criticized on ethical grounds today.

Another student of Watson's, Mary Cover Jones, thought that if fear could be learned or classically conditioned in this way, perhaps it could also be unlearned or extinguished. She worked

▲ Mary Cover Jones (1896–1987) was one of the first psychologists to use behavioural techniques to free a patient from a phobia.

with a boy named Peter, who at two years, ten months old was already quite afraid of furry objects. Jones decided to bring a white rabbit into the room where Peter was playing for a short time each day. She also arranged for other children, whom she knew did not fear rabbits, to be in the same room. She noted that Peter's fear gradually diminished. Each time it diminished, she brought the rabbit closer. Eventually, Peter was touching and even playing with the rabbit (Jones, 1924a, 1924b), and years later the fear had not returned.

The Beginnings of Behaviour Therapy

The implications of Jones's research were largely ignored for two decades, given the fervour associated with more psychoanalytic conceptions of the development of fear. But in the late 1940s and early 1950s, Joseph Wolpe (1915–1997), a pioneering psychiatrist from South Africa, became dissatisfied with prevailing psychoanalytic interpretations of psychopathology and began looking for something else. He turned to the work of Pavlov and became familiar with the wider field of behavioural psychology. He developed a variety of behavioural procedures for treating his patients, many of whom had phobias. His best-known technique was termed **systematic desensitization**. In principle, it was really very similar to Jones's treatment of little Peter. Individuals were gradually introduced to the objects or situations they feared so their fear could extinguish; that is, they could test reality and see that nothing bad really happened in the presence of the phobic object or scene. Wolpe added another element by having his patients do something that was *incompatible with fear* while they were in the presence of the dreaded object or situation. Because he could not always reproduce the phobic object in his office, Wolpe had his patients carefully and systematically *imagine* the phobic scene, and the response he chose was relaxation, because it was convenient. For example, Wolpe treated a young man with a phobia of dogs by training him first to relax deeply and then imagine he was looking at a dog across the park. Gradually, he could imagine the dog across the park and remain relaxed, experiencing little or no fear, and Wolpe then had him imagine he was closer to the dog. Eventually, the young man imagined he was actually touching the dog while maintaining a very relaxed, almost trance-like state.

Wolpe (1958) reported success with systematic desensitization, one of the first wide-scale applications of the new science of behaviourism to psychopathology. Wolpe, working with fellow pioneers Hans Eysenck and Stanley J. Rachman in London, called this approach **behaviour therapy**. Wolpe eventually moved to the United States and Rachman to Canada, while Eysenck remained in the United Kingdom, which contributed to the dissemination of behaviour therapy knowledge and techniques throughout North America and Europe.

▲ Stanley J. Rachman, emeritus professor at the University of British Columbia, is one of the original founders of the behaviour therapy approach.

▲ B. F. Skinner (1904–1990) studied operant conditioning, a form of learning that is central to psychopathology.

B. F. Skinner and Operant Conditioning

Sigmund Freud's influence extended far beyond psychopathology into many aspects of our cultural and intellectual history. Only one other behavioural scientist has made a similar impact, Burrhus Frederic (B. F.) Skinner (1904–1990). In 1938, he published *The Behavior of Organisms*, in which he laid out, in a comprehensive manner, the principles of operant conditioning, a type of learning in which behaviour changes as a function of what follows the behaviour. Skinner observed early on that a large part of our behaviour is not automatically elicited by an unconditioned stimulus and we must account for this. In the ensuing years, Skinner did not confine his ideas to the laboratories of experimental psychology. He ranged broadly in his writings, describing, for example, the potential applications of a science of behaviour to our culture. Some of the best-known examples of his ideas are in the novel *Walden Two* (Skinner, 1948), which depicts a fictional society run on the principles of operant conditioning. In another well-known work, *Beyond Freedom and Dignity* (1971), Skinner lays out a broader statement of the problems facing our culture and suggests solutions based on his own view of a science of behaviour.

Skinner was strongly influenced by Watson's conviction that a science of human behaviour must be based on observable events and relationships among those events. The work of psychologist Edward L. Thorndike (1874–1949) also influenced Skinner. Thorndike is best known for the *law of effect*, which states that behaviour is either strengthened (likely to be repeated more frequently) or weakened (likely to occur less frequently) depending on the consequences of that behaviour. Skinner took the very simple notions that Thorndike had tested in the animal laboratories, using food as a reinforcer, and developed them in a variety of complex ways that apply to much of our behaviour. For example, if a five-year-old boy starts shouting at the top of his lungs in McDonald's, much to the annoyance of the people around him, it is unlikely his behaviour was automatically elicited by an unconditioned stimulus. Also, he will be less likely to do it in the future if his parents scold him, take him out to the car to sit for a bit, or consistently reinforce more appropriate behaviour. Then again, if the parents think his behaviour is cute and laugh, chances are he will do it again.

Skinner coined the term *operant conditioning* because behaviour operates on the environment and changes it in some way. For example, the boy's behaviour affects his parents' behaviour and probably the behaviour of other customers as well. Therefore, he changes his environment. Most things we do socially provide the context for other people to respond to us in one way or another, thereby providing consequences for our behaviour. The same is true of our physical environment, although the consequences may be long term (polluting the air eventually will poison us). Skinner preferred the term **reinforcement** to *reward* because it connotes the effect on the behaviour. Skinner once said that he found himself a bit embarrassed to be talking continually about reinforcement, much as Marxists used to see class struggle everywhere. But he pointed out that all our behaviour is governed to some degree by reinforcement, which can be arranged in an endless variety of ways, in schedules of reinforcement. Skinner wrote a book on different schedules of reinforcement (Ferster & Skinner, 1957). He also believed that using punishment as a consequence is relatively ineffective in the long run and that the primary way to develop new behaviour is to positively reinforce desired behaviour. Much like Watson, Skinner did not see the need to go beyond the observable and quantifiable to establish a satisfactory science of behaviour. He did not deny the existence of subjective states of emotion or cognition; he simply explained these phenomena as relatively inconsequential side effects of a particular history of reinforcement.

The subjects of Skinner's laboratory research were usually animals, mostly pigeons and rats. Using his new principles, Skinner and his disciples actually taught the animals a variety of tricks, including dancing, playing Ping-Pong, and playing a toy piano. To do this, he used a procedure called **shaping**, a process of reinforcing successive approximations to a final behaviour or set of behaviours. If you want a pigeon to play Ping-Pong, first you provide it with a pellet of food every time it moves its head slightly toward a Ping-Pong ball tossed in its direction. Gradually, you require the pigeon to move its head ever closer to the Ping-Pong ball until it touches it. Finally, receiving the food pellet is contingent on the pigeon's actually hitting the ball back with its head.

Pavlov, Watson, and Skinner contributed significantly to behaviour therapy, in which scientific principles of psychology are applied to clinical problems. Many psychologists and other mental health professionals quickly embraced behaviour therapy techniques and began applying them with their patients in the 1950s and 1960s. For example, in an early application of these principles at the Lakeshore Psychiatric Hospital in Toronto, Richard Steffy and his colleagues describe how they used operant conditioning techniques to modify the behaviour of a ward of severely aggressive female patients. These researchers documented how reinforcements could be used by staff to decrease these patients' violent activity and to improve their self-care and social responsiveness (Steffy et al., 1969). Similar results were reported by Teodoro Ayllon and Jack Michael (1959) from a study conducted at the Saskatchewan Hospital in Weyburn, showing that the use of reinforcements by nursing staff could produce substantial reductions in psychiatric patients' undesirable behaviour and increases in patients' desirable behaviour. The ideas of Pavlov, Watson, and Skinner have continued to contribute substantially to current psychological treatments, and so we refer to them repeatedly in this book.

Comments

The behavioural model has contributed greatly to the understanding and treatment of psychopathology, as will be apparent in the chapters that follow. Nevertheless, this model is incomplete in itself and inadequate to account for what we now know about psychopathology. In the past, behaviourism had little or no room for biology, because disorders were considered, for the most part, environmentally determined reactions. The model also fails to account for development of psychopathology across the lifespan. Recent advances in our knowledge of how information is processed, both consciously and subconsciously, have added a layer of complexity. We also now know that learning can occur indirectly or vicariously through observing others in social interactions (Bandura et al., 1974). Integrating all these dimensions requires a new model of psychopathology.

THE SCIENTIFIC METHOD AND AN INTEGRATIVE APPROACH

As Shakespeare wrote, "What's past is prologue." We have just reviewed three different traditions or ways of thinking about causes of psychopathology: the supernatural, the biological, and the psychological (further subdivided into two major historical components: psychoanalytic and behavioural).

Supernatural explanations of psychopathology are still with us. Superstitions prevail, including beliefs in the effects of the moon and the stars on our behaviour. However, this tradition has little influence on scientists and other professionals. Biological, psychoanalytic, and behavioural models, by contrast, continue to further our knowledge of psychopathology, as we see in the next chapter. Even with the many advances in our understanding of mental disorders, no blood test exists for mental illness, and no specific known cure either, as is often the case with other types of illnesses. This fact helps explain why there are many, sometimes competing, models for mental disorders today.

Despite the fact that the biological, psychoanalytic, and behavioural models continue to improve our understanding of the various forms of psychopathology, each tradition has failed in at least one important way. First, scientific methods were not often applied to the theories and treatments within a tradition, mostly because methods that would have produced the evidence necessary to confirm or disconfirm the theories and treatments had not been developed. Lacking such evidence, various fads and superstitions were widely accepted that ultimately proved untrue or useless. New fads often superseded truly useful theories and treatment procedures. This trend was at work in the so-called discovery of the drug reserpine, which, in fact, had been around for thousands of years. King Charles VI was subjected to a variety of procedures, some of which have since been proved useful and others that were mere fads or even harmful. How we use scientific methods to confirm or disconfirm findings in psychopathology is described in Chapter 4. Second, health professionals tend to look at psychological disorders very narrowly, from their own point of view alone. John Grey assumed psychological disorders are the result of brain disease and that other factors have no influence whatsoever. John Watson assumed that all behaviours, including disordered behaviour, are the result of psychological and social influences and that the contribution of biological factors is inconsequential.

In the 1990s, two developments came together as never before to shed light on the nature of psychopathology: (1) the increasing sophistication of scientific tools and methodology, and (2) the realization that no one influence—biological, behavioural, cognitive, emotional, or social—ever occurs in isolation. Every time we think, feel, or do something, the brain and the rest of the body are hard at work. Perhaps not as obvious, however, is the fact that our thoughts, feelings, and actions inevitably influence the function and even the structure of the brain, sometimes permanently. In other words, our behaviour, both normal and abnormal, is the product of the continual interaction of psychological, biological, and social influences.

The view that psychopathology is multiply determined had its early adherents. Perhaps the most notable was psychiatrist Adolf Meyer (1866–1950). Whereas most professionals during the first half of the 20th century held narrow views of the cause of psychopathology, Meyer steadfastly emphasized the equal contributions of biological, psychological, and sociocultural determinants. Although Meyer had some proponents, it was a century before the wisdom of his advice was fully recognized in the field.

By the turn of the 21st century, a veritable explosion of knowledge about psychopathology had occurred. The young fields of cognitive science and neuroscience began to grow exponentially as we learned more about the brain and about how we process, remember, and use information. At the same time, startling new findings from behavioural science revealed the importance of early experience in determining later development. It was clear that a new model was needed that would consider biological, psychological, and social influences on behaviour. This approach to psychopathology would combine findings from all areas with our rapidly growing understanding of how we experience life during different developmental periods, from infancy to old age. In 2010, the National Institute of Mental Health instituted a strategic plan to support research and development on the interrelationship of these factors with the aim of translating research findings to front-line treatment settings (Cuthbert, 2014; Insel, 2009; Sanislow et al., 2015). In the remainder of this book, we explore the reciprocal influences among neuroscience, cognitive science, behaviour science, and developmental science and demonstrate that the only currently valid model of psychopathology is multidimensional and integrative.

Concept Check   1.3

Match the treatment with the corresponding psychological theory of behaviour: (a) behavioural model, (b) moral therapy, (c) psychoanalytic theory, and (d) humanistic theory.

1. Treating institutionalized patients as normally as possible and encouraging social interaction and relationship development. _____ _____

2. Hypnosis, free association, and dream analysis, and balance of the id, ego, and superego. _____ _____

3. Person-centred therapy with unconditional positive regard. _____ _____

4. Classical conditioning, systematic desensitization, and operant conditioning. _____ _____

SUMMARY

What Is a Psychological Disorder?

- A psychological disorder is (1) a psychological dysfunction within an individual that is (2) associated with distress or impairment in functioning and (3) a response that is not typical or culturally expected. Although this definition is the most popular, no one description has yet been identified that defines the essence of abnormality.

The Science of Psychopathology

- The field of psychopathology is concerned with the scientific study of psychological disorders. Trained mental health professionals range from clinical and counselling psychologists to psychiatrists and psychiatric social workers and nurses. Each profession requires a specific type of training.
- Using scientific methods, mental health professionals can function as scientist-practitioners. They not only keep up with the latest findings but also use scientific data to evaluate their own work, and they often conduct research within their clinics or hospitals.

- Research about psychological disorders falls into three basic categories: description, causation, and treatment and outcomes.

The Supernatural, Biological, and Psychological Traditions

- Historically, three prominent approaches to abnormal behaviour have been used. In the supernatural tradition, abnormal behaviour is attributed to agents outside our bodies or social environment, such as demons or spirits, or the influence of the moon and stars; though still alive, this tradition has been largely replaced by biological and psychological perspectives. In the biological tradition, disorders are attributed to disease or biochemical imbalances; in the psychological tradition, abnormal behaviour is attributed to faulty psychological development and to social context.
- Each tradition has its own way of treating individuals who have psychological disorders. Supernatural treatments include exorcism to rid the body of the supernatural spirits. Biological treatments typically emphasize physical care and the search

for medical cures, especially drugs. Psychological approaches use psychosocial treatments, beginning with moral therapy and including modern psychotherapy.

- Sigmund Freud, the founder of psychoanalytic therapy, offered an elaborate conception of the unconscious mind, much of which is still conjecture. In therapy, Freud focused on tapping into the mysteries of the unconscious through such techniques as catharsis, free association, and dream analysis. Though Freud's followers veered from his path in many ways, Freud's influence can still be felt today.

- One outgrowth of Freudian therapy is humanistic psychology, which focuses more on human potential and self-actualizing than on psychological disorders. Therapy that has evolved from this approach is known as person-centred therapy; the therapist shows almost unconditional positive regard for the client's feelings and thoughts.

- The behavioural model moved psychology into the realm of science, with an emphasis on findings from the laboratories of psychology as applied to human behaviour. Therapeutic techniques derived from this model include systematic desensitization, reinforcement, and shaping.

The Scientific Method and the Integrative Approach

- With the increasing sophistication of our scientific tools and new knowledge from cognitive science, behavioural science, and neuroscience, we now realize that no contribution to psychological disorders ever occurs in isolation. Our behaviour, both normal and abnormal, is a product of a continual interaction of psychological, biological, and social influences.

KEY TERMS

behaviour therapy, 25
behavioural model, 23
behaviourism, 17
catharsis, 18
classical conditioning, 23
clinical description, 8
course, 8
defence mechanisms, 19
dream analysis, 21
ego, 19
ego psychology, 21
etiology, 8

extinction, 24
free association, 21
id, 19
incidence, 8
intrapsychic conflicts, 19
introspection, 24
lifetime prevalence, 8
mental hygiene movement, 16
moral therapy, 15
neurosis (neuroses *plural*), 20
person-centred therapy, 22
phobia, 3

presenting problem, 8
prevalence, 8
prognosis, 8
psychoanalysis, 17
psychoanalyst, 21
psychoanalytic model, 18
psychodynamic
   psychotherapy, 22
psychological disorder, 3
psychopathology, 6
psychosexual stages of
   development, 20

psychosocial, 15
psychotherapy process, 23
reinforcement, 26
scientist-practitioner, 7
self-actualizing, 22
shaping, 26
superego, 19
systematic desensitization, 25
transference, 21
unconditional positive
   regard, 22
unconscious, 18

ANSWERS TO CONCEPT CHECKS

1.1

1. d; **2.** c; **3.** a; **4.** f; **5.** e; **6.** b

1.2

1. e; **2.** c; **3.** d

1.3

1. b; **2.** c; **3.** d; **4.** a

MEDIA RESOURCES

CENGAGE | MINDTAP

Stay organized and efficient with MindTap—a single destination with all the course material and study aids you need to succeed. Built-in apps leverage social media and the latest learning technology. For example:

- ReadSpeaker will read the text to you.
- Flashcards are pre-populated to provide you with a jump start for review—or you can create your own.
- You can highlight text and make notes in your MindTap Reader. Your notes will flow into Evernote, the electronic notebook app that you can access anywhere when it's time to study for the exam.
- Self-quizzing allows you to assess your understanding.

Visit login.cengage.com to start using MindTap. Enter the Online Access Code from the card included with your text. If a code card is not provided, you can purchase instant access at Cengage.ca.

Timeline of Significant Events

400 BCE–1875

DEA PICTURE LIBRARY/Getty Images

National Library of Medicine

© North Wind Picture Archives/Alamy Stock Photo

400 BCE: Hippocrates suggests that psychological disorders have both biological and psychological causes.

1300s: Superstition runs rampant and mental disorders are blamed on demons and witches; exorcisms are performed to rid victims of evil spirits.

1400–1800: Bloodletting and leeches are used to rid the body of unhealthy fluids and restore chemical balance.

1793: Philippe Pinel introduces moral therapy and makes French mental institutions more humane.

400 BCE	1300s	1500s	1825–1875

200 BCE: Galen suggests that normal and abnormal behaviour are related to four bodily fluids, or humors.

1400s: Enlightened view that insanity is caused by mental or emotional stress gains momentum, and depression and anxiety are again regarded by some as disorders.

1500s: Paracelsus suggests that the moon and the stars affect people's psychological functioning, rather than possession by the devil.

1825–1875: Syphilis is differentiated from other types of psychosis in that it is caused by a specific bacterium; ultimately, penicillin is found to cure syphilis.

1930–1968

1930: Insulin shock therapy, electric shock treatments, and brain surgery begin to be used to treat psychopathology.

1950: The first effective drugs for severe psychotic disorders are developed. Humanistic psychology (based on ideas of Carl Jung, Alfred Adler, and Carl Rogers) gains some acceptance.

1958: Joseph Wolpe effectively treats patients with phobias using systematic desensitization based on principles of behavioural science.

1930	1940	1950	1970

1938: B. F. Skinner publishes *The Behavior of Organisms,* which describes the principles of operant conditioning.

1946: Anna Freud publishes *Ego and the Mechanisms of Defense.*

1952: The first edition of the *Diagnostic and Statistical Manual (DSM-I)* is published.

1968: *DSM-II* is published.

Bettmann/Getty Images

Imagno/Hulton Archive /Getty Images

1848–1920

1848: Dorothea Dix successfully campaigns for more humane treatment in American mental institutions.

1870: Louis Pasteur develops his germ theory of disease, which helps identify the bacterium that causes syphilis.

1900: Sigmund Freud publishes *The Interpretation of Dreams.*

1913: Emil Kraepelin classifies various psychological disorders from a biological point of view and publishes work on diagnosis.

1848 **1870** **1900** **1920**

1854: John P. Grey, head of New York's Utica Hospital, believes that insanity is the result of physical causes, thus de-emphasizing psychological treatments.

1895: Josef Breuer treats the "hysterical" Anna O., leading to Freud's development of psychoanalytic theory.

1904: Ivan Pavlov receives the Nobel Prize for his work on the physiology of digestion, which leads him to identify conditioned reflexes in dogs.

1920: John B. Watson experiments with conditioned fear in Little Albert using a white rat.

1980–2000

1990s: Increasingly sophisticated research methods are developed; no one influence—biological or environmental—is found to cause psychological disorders in isolation from the other.

1980: *DSM-III* is published.

2000: *DSM-IV-TR* is published.

1980 **1990s** **2000**

1987: *DSM-III-R* is published.

1994: *DSM-IV* is published.

2013: *DSM-5* is published.

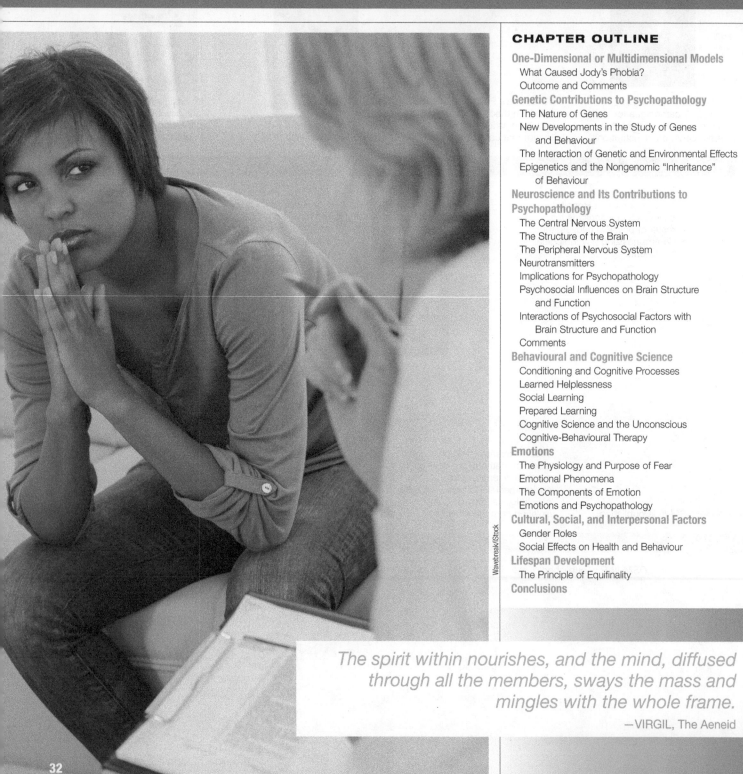

02 | An Integrative Approach to Psychopathology

Wavebreak/iStock

*The spirit within nourishes, and the mind, diffused
through all the members, sways the mass and
mingles with the whole frame.*

—VIRGIL, The Aeneid

Use scientific reasoning to interpret psychological phenomena; this outcome applies to APA SLO indicators 2.1a & 1.1C:	› Identify basic biological, psychological, and social components of behavioural explanations (e.g., inferences, observations, operational definitions, interpretation) (APA SLO 2.1a)
	› Incorporate several appropriate levels of complexity (e.g., cellular, individual, group/system, society/cultural) to explain behaviour (APA SLO 2.1C)
Develop a working knowledge of the content domains of psychology:	› Identify key characteristics of major content domains in psychology (e.g., cognition and learning, developmental, biological, and sociocultural) (APA SLO 1.2a)

* Portions of this chapter cover learning outcomes suggested by the American Psychological Association (2013) in its guidelines for the undergraduate psychology major. Chapter coverage of these outcomes is identified above by APA Goal and APA Suggested Learning Outcome (SLO).

Remember Jody from Chapter 1? We knew he had a blood-injury-injection phobia, but we did not know why. Here, we address the issue of causation. In this chapter, we examine the specific components of a **multidimensional integrative approach** to psychopathology (see ■ Figure 2.1). *Biological* dimensions include causal factors from the fields of genetics and neuroscience. *Psychological* dimensions include causal factors from behavioural and cognitive processes, including learned helplessness, social learning, prepared learning, and even unconscious processes (in a different guise from Freud's days). Emotional influences contribute in a variety of ways to psychopathology, as do social and *interpersonal* influences. Last, *developmental influences* figure in any discussion of causes of psychological disorders. You will become familiar with these areas as they relate to psychopathology and learn about some of the latest developments that are relevant to psychological disorders. But keep in mind what we confirmed in the previous chapter: no influence operates in isolation. Each dimension, biological or psychological, is strongly influenced by the others and by development, and they weave together in various complex and intricate ways to create a psychological disorder.

We explain briefly why we have adopted a multidimensional integrative model of psychopathology. Then we preview various causal influences and interactions, using Jody's case as background. After that, we look more deeply at specific causal influences in psychopathology, examining both the latest research and integrative ways of viewing what we know.

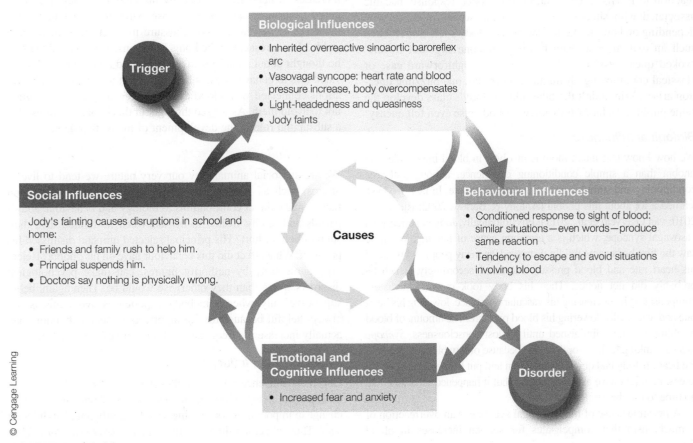

© Cengage Learning

FIGURE 2.1 | Jody's case.

ONE-DIMENSIONAL OR MULTIDIMENSIONAL MODELS

To say that psychopathology is caused by a physical abnormality or by conditioning is to accept a linear or one-dimensional model that attempts to trace the origins of behaviour to a single cause. A linear causal model might hold that schizophrenia or a phobia is caused by a chemical imbalance or by growing up surrounded by overwhelming conflicts among family members. In psychology and psychopathology, we still encounter this type of thinking occasionally, but most scientists and clinicians believe psychological problems result from multiple influences. A system, or feedback loop, may have independent inputs at many different points, but as each input becomes part of the whole, it can no longer be considered independent. This perspective on causality is systemic, which derives from the word system; it implies that any particular influence contributing to psychological health cannot be considered out of context. Context, in this case, is the biology and behaviour of the individual, as well as the cognitive, emotional, social, and cultural environment, because any one component of the system inevitably affects the other components. This is a multidimensional model.

WHAT CAUSED JODY'S PHOBIA?

From a multidimensional perspective, let's look at what might have caused Jody's phobia (see ■ Figure 2.1).

Behavioural Influences

The cause of Jody's phobia might at first seem obvious. He saw a movie with graphic scenes of blood and injury and had a bad reaction to it. His reaction, an unconditioned response, became associated with situations similar to the scenes in the movie, depending on how similar they were. But Jody's reaction reached such an extreme that even hearing someone say "cut it out!" evoked queasiness. Is Jody's phobia a straightforward case of classical conditioning? It might seem so, but one puzzling question arises: Why didn't the other kids in Jody's class develop the same phobia? As far as Jody knew, nobody else even felt queasy!

Biological Influences

We now know that much more is involved in blood-injury-injection phobia than a simple conditioning experience, although, clearly, conditioning and stimulus generalization contribute. In fact, we have learned a lot about this phobia (Antony & Barlow, 2002; Ritz et al., 2010; van Overveld et al., 2011). Physiologically, Jody experienced a vasovagal syncope, which is a common cause of fainting. When he saw the film he became mildly distressed, as many people would, and his heart rate and blood pressure increased accordingly, which he probably did not notice. Then his body took over, immediately compensating by decreasing his vascular resistance, lowering his heart rate and, eventually, lowering his blood pressure. The amount of blood reaching his brain diminished until he lost consciousness. *Syncope* means "sinking feeling" or "swoon" because of low blood pressure in the head. If Jody had quickly bent down and put his head between his knees, he might have avoided fainting, but it happened so fast he had no time to use this strategy.

A possible cause of the vasovagal syncope is an overreaction of a mechanism that compensates for sudden increases in blood pressure by lowering it. Interestingly, the tendency to overcompensate seems to be inherited, which may account for the high rate of blood-injury-injection phobia in families (Öst, 1992). Do you ever feel queasy at the sight of blood? If so, chances are your mother or father or someone else in your immediate family has the same reaction. But many people with rather severe syncope reaction tendencies do not develop phobias. They cope with their reaction in various ways, including tensing their muscles whenever they are confronted with blood. Tensing the muscles very quickly raises blood pressure and prevents the fainting response. Furthermore, some people with little or no syncope reaction develop the phobia anyway (Öst, 1992). Therefore, the cause of blood-injury-injection phobia is complicated. If we said that the phobia is caused by a biological dysfunction (an overactive vasovagal reaction) or a traumatic experience (seeing a gruesome film) and subsequent conditioning, we would be partly right on both counts, but in adopting a one-dimensional causal model, we would miss the most important point: to cause blood-injury-injection phobia, a complex *interaction* must occur between behavioural and biological factors. Inheriting a strong syncope reaction definitely puts a person at risk for developing this phobia, but other influences are at work as well.

Emotional Influences

Jody's case is a good example of biology influencing behaviour. But behaviour, thoughts, and feelings can also influence biology, sometimes dramatically. What role did Jody's fear and anxiety play in the development of his phobia, and where did they come from? Emotions can affect physiological responses such as blood pressure, heart rate, and respiration, particularly if we know rationally we have nothing to fear, as Jody did. In his case, rapid increases in heart rate, caused by his emotions, may have triggered a stronger and more intense baroreflex. The baroreflex increases or decreases blood pressure in an effort to maintain a stable blood pressure in the body. Emotions also changed the way he thought about situations involving blood and injury and motivated him to behave in ways he didn't want to—avoiding all situations connected with blood and injury, even if it was important not to avoid them. As we see throughout this book, emotions play a substantial role in the development of many disorders.

Social Influences

We are all social animals; by our very nature we tend to live in groups, such as families and communities. Social and cultural factors make direct contributions to biology and behaviour. Jody's friends and family rushed to his aid when he fainted. Did their support help or hurt? His principal rejected him and dismissed his problem. What effect did this behaviour have on his phobia? Rejection, particularly by authority figures, can make psychological disorders worse than they otherwise would be. Then again, being supportive only when somebody experiences symptoms is not always helpful because the strong effects of social attention may actually increase the frequency and intensity of the reaction.

Developmental Influences

One more influence affects us all—changes over the lifespan. As time passes, many things about ourselves and our environments change in important ways, causing us to react differently at different ages. Thus, at certain times we may enter a *developmental critical period* when we are more or less reactive to a given situation or influence than at other times. To go back to Jody, it is possible that he was previously exposed to other situations involving blood. Important questions to ask are these: Why did this problem develop when he was 16 years old and not before? Is it possible that his susceptibility to having a vasovagal reaction was highest in his teenage years? It may be that the timing of his physiological reaction, along with viewing the disturbing biology film, provided just the right (but unfortunate) combination to initiate his severe phobic response.

OUTCOME AND COMMENTS

Fortunately for Jody, he responded very well to brief but intensive treatment at one of our clinics, and he was back in school within seven days. Jody was gradually exposed, with his full cooperation, to words, images, and situations describing or depicting blood and injury while a sudden drop in blood pressure was prevented using applied muscle tension. Applied muscle tension is a simple behavioural technique that reduces vasovagal reactions by maintaining blood pressure. It has been used successfully in the treatment of people with blood and injury phobias, like Jody. Blaine Ditto and his colleagues at McGill University have successfully applied this technique in the context of blood donor clinics, where vasovagal reactions can significantly complicate the blood-collection process and discourage people from returning to donate blood again (Ditto et al., 2003). For Jody's exposure treatment, we began with something mild, such as the phrase "cut it out." By the end of the week, Jody was witnessing surgical procedures at the local hospital while practising applied muscle tension. Jody required close therapeutic supervision during this program. At one point, while driving home with his parents from an evening session, he had the bad luck to pass a car crash, and he saw a bleeding accident victim. That night, he dreamed about bloody accident victims coming through the walls of his bedroom. This experience made him call the clinic and request emergency intervention to reduce his distress, but it did not slow his progress.

As you can see, finding the causes of abnormal behaviour is a complex and fascinating process. Focusing on biological or behavioural factors would not have given us a full picture of the causes of Jody's disorder; we had to consider a variety of other influences and how they might interact. A discussion in more depth follows, examining the research underlying the many biological, psychological, and social influences that must be considered as causes of any psychological disorder.

GENETIC CONTRIBUTIONS TO PSYCHOPATHOLOGY

What causes you to look like one or both of your parents or, perhaps, your grandparents? Obviously, it is the genes that you inherit from your parents and from your ancestors before them. **Genes** are very long molecules of DNA (deoxyribonucleic acid) at various locations on chromosomes within the cell nucleus. Ever since Gregor Mendel's pioneering work in the 19th century, we have known that physical characteristics, such as hair colour and eye colour and, to a certain extent, height and weight, are determined—or at least strongly influenced—by our genetic endowment. Other factors in the environment influence our physical appearance as well, however. To some extent, our weight and even our height are affected by nutritional, social, and cultural factors. Consequently, our genes seldom determine our physical development in any absolute way. They do provide some boundaries to our development. Exactly where we go within these boundaries depends on environmental influences.

Except for identical twins, every person has a unique set of genes unlike those of anyone else in the world. Because there is plenty of room for the environment to influence our development within the constraints set by our genes, many reasons exist for the development of individual differences.

What about our behaviour and traits, our likes and dislikes? Do genes influence personality and, by extension, abnormal behaviour? This question of nature (genes) versus nurture (upbringing and other environmental influences) is age-old in psychology, and the answers that are emerging are fascinating.

THE NATURE OF GENES

We have known for a long time that each normal human cell has 46 chromosomes arranged in 23 pairs. In each pair, one chromosome comes from the father and one from the mother. We can actually see these chromosomes through a microscope, and we can sometimes tell when one is faulty and predict what problems it will cause.

The first 22 pairs of chromosomes provide programs for the development of the body and brain, and the last pair, called the *sex chromosomes*, determines an individual's sex. In females, both chromosomes in the 23rd pair are called X *chromosomes*. In males, the mother contributes an X *chromosome* but the father contributes a Y chromosome. This one difference is responsible for the variance in biological sex. Abnormalities in the sex chromosomal pair can cause ambiguous sexual characteristics.

The DNA molecules that contain genes have a certain structure, a double helix, discovered six decades ago. The shape of a helix is like a spiral staircase. A double helix is two spirals intertwined, turning in opposite directions. Located on this double spiral are simple pairs of molecules bound together and arranged in different orders. On the X chromosome are approximately 155 million base pairs. The ordering of these base pairs determines how the body develops and works.

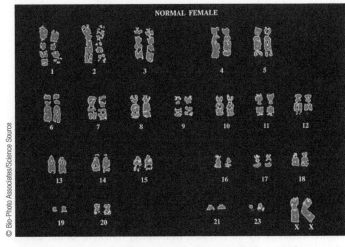

▲ A typical female has 23 pairs of chromosomes.

If something is wrong in the ordering of these molecules on the double helix, we have a defective gene, which may or may not lead to problems. If it is a single dominant gene, such as the type that controls hair or eye colour, the effect can be quite noticeable. A *dominant gene* is one of a pair of genes that determines a particular trait. A *recessive gene*, by contrast, must be paired with another recessive gene to influence a trait. Using Mendelian laws of genetics, we can predict fairly accurately how many offspring will develop a certain trait, characteristic, or disorder, depending on whether one or both of the parents carry the gene.

Most of the time, predictions are not so simple. Much of our development and, interestingly, most of our behaviour, our personality, and even our intelligence quotient (IQ) score are *polygenic*—that is, influenced by many genes, each contributing only a tiny effect, all of which, in turn, may be influenced by the environment. The same is true for psychiatric disorders (Geschwind & Flint, 2015). And because the human *genome*, or an individual's complete set of genes, comprises 20 000 to 25 000 genes, polygenic interactions can be quite complex. For this reason, most genetic scientists now use sophisticated procedures, such as quantitative genetics and molecular genetics, that allow them to look for patterns of influence across many genes (Kendler, 2011, 2013; Kendler et al., 2011; Plomin & Davis, 2009; Rutter et al., 2006). *Quantitative genetics* estimates the effects of genes in explaining individual differences (heritability), without necessarily telling us which genes are responsible for which effects. *Molecular genetics* focuses on examining the actual structure and functioning of genes with increasingly advanced technologies, such as *DNA microarrays*; these technologies allow scientists to analyze thousands of genes at once and identify broad networks of genes that may be contributing to a particular trait (Kendler, 2011; Plomin & Davis, 2009). Such studies have indicated that hundreds of genes can contribute to the heritability of a single trait (Hariri et al., 2002; Plomin et al., 1995; Rutter et al., 2006). There also continues to be research to identify specific genes that contribute to individual differences in traits or temperament, such as shyness or impulsivity (e.g., Gershon et al., 2001). For example, Joe Beitchman and his colleagues (2003) at the Centre for Addiction and Mental Health in Toronto have identified a serotonin transporter gene that is likely involved in attention deficit and hyperactivity in children.

It is very important to understand how genes work. Genes exert their influences on our bodies and our behaviour through a series of steps that produce proteins. Although all cells contain our entire genetic structure (except for red blood cells), only a small proportion of genes in any one cell are turned on or expressed. In this way, cells become specialized, with some influencing liver function and others affecting personality. What is interesting is that environmental factors, in the form of social and cultural influences, can determine whether genes are turned on (Cole, 2011). To take one example, in studies with rat pups, researchers have found that the absence of normal maternal behaviour of licking and grooming prevents the genetic expression of a glucocorticoid receptor that modulates stress hormones. This means rats with inadequate maternal care have greater sensitivity to stress (Meaney & Szyf, 2005). There is evidence that a similar model may be relevant in humans (Dickens et al., 2011; Hyman, 2009). We present more examples later in the chapter

when we discuss the interaction of genes and the environment. The study of gene expression and gene–environment interaction is the current frontier in the study of genetics (Kendler et al., 2011; Plomin & Davis, 2009; Rutter, 2006; Rutter et al., 2006; Thapar & McGuffin, 2009). In Chapter 4, we look at the methods that scientists use to study the influence of genes. Here, our interest is in what they are finding.

NEW DEVELOPMENTS IN THE STUDY OF GENES AND BEHAVIOUR

Scientists have now identified, in a preliminary way, the genetic contribution to psychological disorders and related behavioural patterns. The best estimates attribute about half of individual differences in personality traits and cognitive abilities to genetic influence (Rutter, 2006). For example, McClearn et al. (1997) compared 110 Swedish identical twin pairs, at least 80 years old, with 130 same-sex fraternal twin pairs of a similar age and found that heritability estimates for specific cognitive abilities, such as memory or ability to perceive spatial relations, ranged from 32 percent to 62 percent. This work built on earlier important twin studies with different age groups that showed similar results (e.g., Bouchard et al., 1990). Furthermore, a recently published important study of more than 1200 twins spanning 35 years confirmed that during adulthood (from early adulthood to late middle age) genetic factors determined stability in cognitive abilities, whereas environmental factors were responsible for any changes (Lyons et al., 2009). In other studies, the same heritability calculation for personality traits, such as shyness or activity levels, ranges between 30 and 50 percent (Bouchard et al., 1990; Kendler, 2001; Loehlin, 1992; Rutter, 2006; Saudino & Plomin, 1996; Saudino et al., 1996).

For psychological disorders, the evidence indicates that genetic factors make some contribution to all disorders but account for less than half of the variability. If one of a pair of identical twins has schizophrenia, for example, there is a little less than 50 percent likelihood that the other twin will also (Gottesman, 1991). Similar or lower rates exist for other psychological disorders (Kendler & Prescott, 2006; Rutter, 2006).

It has also become clear that adverse life events, such as a chaotic childhood, can overwhelm the influence of genes (Turkheimer et al., 2003). For example, one member of a set of twins in the Lyons et al. (2009) study showed marked variability or change in cognitive abilities if his or her environment changed dramatically from the other twin's because of some stressful event, such as the death of a loved one.

Behavioural geneticists have reached general conclusions in the past several years on the role of genes and psychological disorders relevant to this chapter's discussion of integrative approaches to psychopathology. First, specific genes or small groups of genes may ultimately be found to be associated with certain psychological disorders, as suggested in several important studies described later. But much of the current evidence suggests that contributions to psychological disorders come from many genes, each having a relatively small effect (Flint, 2009; Rutter, 2006). It is extremely important that we recognize this probability and continue to make every attempt to track the group of genes implicated in various disorders. Advances in gene mapping and

▲ Genetic contributions to behaviour are evident in twins who were raised apart. When these brothers were finally reunited, they were both firefighters, and they discovered many other shared characteristics and interests.

linkage studies help with this difficult research (e.g., Gershon et al., 2001; Hettema et al., 2005; see Chapter 4). Second, as noted earlier, it has become increasingly clear that genetic contributions cannot be studied in the absence of interactions with events in the environment that trigger genetic vulnerability or turn on specific genes (Kendler et al., 2011; Rutter, 2010). It is to this fascinating topic that we now turn.

THE INTERACTION OF GENETIC AND ENVIRONMENTAL EFFECTS

In 1983, Eric Kandel, a distinguished neuroscientist and Nobel Prize winner, speculated that the process of learning affects more than behaviour. He suggested that the very genetic structure of cells may actually change as a result of learning, if genes that were inactive or dormant interact with the environment in such a way that they become active. In other words, the environment may occasionally turn on certain genes. This type of mechanism may lead to changes in the number of receptors at the end of a neuron, which, in turn, would affect biochemical functioning in the brain.

Although Kandel was not the first to propose this idea, it had enormous effect. Most of us assume that the brain, like other parts of the body, may well be influenced by environmental changes during development. But we also assume that once maturity is reached, the structure and function of our internal organs and most of our physiology are set or, in the case of the brain, hardwired. The competing idea is that the brain and its functions are plastic, subject to continual change in response to the environment, even at the level of genetic structure. Now there is strong evidence supporting that view (Dick, 2011; Kendler et al., 2011; Kolb, Gibb, & Robinson, 2003; Landis & Insel, 2008; Robinson et al., 2008).

With these new findings in mind, we can now explore gene–environment interactions as they relate to psychopathology. Two models have received the most attention: the diathesis–stress model and the reciprocal gene–environment model (or gene–environment correlations).

The Diathesis–Stress Model

For years, scientists have assumed a specific method of interaction between genes and the environment. According to the **diathesis–stress model**, individuals inherit, from multiple genes, tendencies to express certain traits or behaviours, which may then be activated under conditions of stress (see ■ Figure 2.2). Each inherited tendency is a *diathesis*, which is a condition that makes a person susceptible to developing a disorder. When the right kind of life event, such as a certain type of stressor, comes along, the disorder develops. For example, according to the diathesis–stress model, Jody inherited a tendency to faint at the sight of blood. This tendency is the diathesis, or **vulnerability**. It would not become prominent until certain environmental events occurred, when he was in a situation in which escape, or at least closing his eyes, was not acceptable. The stress of seeing the dissection under these conditions activated his tendency to faint. Together, these factors led to him developing a disorder. If he had not taken biology, he might have gone through life without ever knowing he had the tendency, at least to such an extreme, although he might have felt queasy about minor cuts and bruises. You can see that the diathesis is genetically based and the stress is environmental, but they must combine to produce a disorder.

We might also take the case of someone who inherits a vulnerability to alcoholism, which would make that person substantially different from a close friend who does not have the same tendency. During university, both experience difficulties adjusting to the demands of university life; only the individual with the vulnerability genes begins the long downward spiral into alcoholism. The friend doesn't. Having a particular vulnerability doesn't mean you

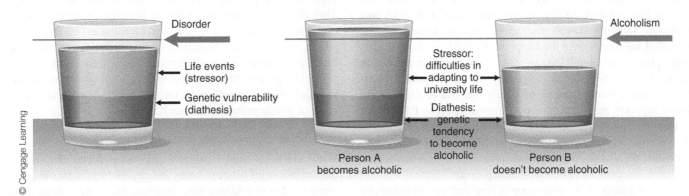

FIGURE 2.2 | In the diathesis–stress model, the greater the underlying vulnerability, the less stress is needed to trigger a disorder.

will develop the associated disorder. The smaller the vulnerability, the greater the life stress required to produce the disorder; conversely, with greater vulnerability, less life stress is required. This model of gene–environment interactions has been popular, although in view of the relationship of the environment to the structure and function of the brain, it is greatly oversimplified.

This relationship was elegantly demonstrated in a landmark study by Caspi et al. (2003). These investigators studied a group of 847 individuals in New Zealand who had undergone a variety of assessments for more than two decades, starting at the age of three. They noted whether the participants, at age 26, had been depressed during the past year. Overall, 17 percent of the study participants reported that they had experienced a major depressive episode during the prior year. The investigators also identified the genetic makeup of the individuals and, in particular, a gene that produces a substance called a *chemical transporter* that affects the transmission of serotonin in the brain. Serotonin, one of the neurotransmitters we will talk about later in the chapter, is particularly implicated in depression. But the gene that Caspi et al. were studying comes in two common versions or alleles: the long allele (L) and the short allele (S). They had reason to believe, from prior work with animals, that individuals with at least two copies of the long allele (LL) were able to cope better with stress than individuals with two copies of the short allele (SS). Since the investigators had been recording stressful life events for these individuals, they were able to test this relationship. In fact, in people with two S alleles, the risk for having a major depressive episode doubled if they had at least four stressful life events, compared with people experiencing four stressful events who had two L alleles.

Another interesting finding is observed when we look at the childhood experience of these individuals. In people with the SS alleles, severe and stressful maltreatment during childhood more than doubled their risk of depression in adulthood compared with those individuals carrying the SS alleles who were not maltreated or abused (63 percent versus 30 percent). For individuals carrying the LL alleles, however, stressful childhood experiences did not affect the incidence of depression in adulthood, since 30 percent of this group became depressed whether or not they had experienced stressful childhood maltreatment. This relationship is shown in ■ Figure 2.3. Therefore, unlike the SS group, depression in the LL allele group seems related to stress in their recent past rather than childhood experiences.

Other studies have replicated or supported these findings (Binder et al., 2008; Karg et al., 2011; Kilpatrick et al., 2007; Mercer et al., 2012; Rutter et al., 2006). For example, in the Kilpatrick et al. (2007) study on the development of post-traumatic stress disorder (PTSD), 589 adults who experienced the Florida hurricanes of 2004 were interviewed and their DNA was collected. Individuals with the same genetic makeup (SS) that signalled vulnerability in the Caspi et al. (2003) study were also more likely to develop PTSD after the hurricanes than those with the LL alleles. But another factor played a role as well. If individuals had a strong network of family and friends (i.e., strong social support), they were protected from developing PTSD even if they had the vulnerable genetic makeup and experienced a trauma (the hurricane). High-risk individuals (high hurricane exposure, SS alleles, and low social support) were at 4.5 times the risk of developing PTSD, as well as depression.

Also, in a study of the same group of New Zealand individuals by the investigators who carried out the study described earlier, Caspi et

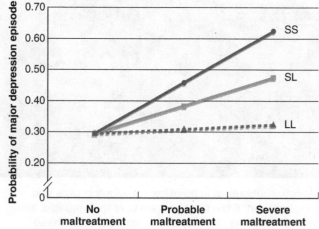

Key:
SS = Two short alleles
SL = One short allele, one long allele
LL = Two long alleles

FIGURE 2.3 | Interaction of genes and early environment in producing adult major depression.

Source: Republished with permission of the AMERICAN ASSOCIATION FOR THE ADVANCEMENT OF SCIENCE, from "Influence of Life Stress on Depression: Moderation by a Polymorphism in the 5-HTT Gene," by A. Caspi, K. Sugden, T.E. Moffitt, A. Taylor, I.W. Craig, H. Harrington et al., *Science* 18 July 2003, Vol. 301 no. 5631 pp. 386–389; permission conveyed through Copyright Clearance Center, Inc.

al. (2002) found that a different set of genes from those associated with depression seems to contribute to violent and antisocial behaviour in adults. But again, this genetic predisposition manifests itself only if the individuals were maltreated as children. That is, some children who were maltreated turned out to be violent and antisocial as adults, but they were four times more likely to commit their share of rape, robbery, and assault if they had a certain genetic makeup than were those who didn't have the genetic makeup. In fact, subsequent research suggests that it is not just any one genetic variation that makes people vulnerable (Goldman et al., 2010; Risch et al., 2009). A larger network of genes almost certainly plays a role in the development of depression and other disorders. These and subsequent studies, however, do provide powerful, if preliminary, support for the gene–environment interaction model that had only indirect support until this time (Uher, 2011).

The gene–environment interaction model, although very conceptually attractive, is not without its problems. Using enormous samples (up to near half a million people), researchers have been unable to replicate any polymorphism or gene effects on depression, or gene-by-environment interactions on depression. They did find, however, that stressful life events increased the risk of depression (Border et al., 2019). As a comment on this state of affairs, we note that researchers finding gene effects, and especially gene–environment interaction effects, may be more likely to publish positive than negative results, leading to a publication bias and later to replication problems. These issues occur in other areas of psychopathology research as well.

The Gene–Environment Correlation Model

With additional study, psychologists have found the web of interrelationships between genes and environment to be even more complex. Some evidence now indicates that genetic endowment may *increase the probability* that an individual will experience stressful life events (Kendler, 2006, 2011; Rutter, 2006, 2010; Saudino et al., 1997; Thapar & McGuffin, 2009). For example, people with a genetic vulnerability to develop a certain disorder, such as blood-injury-injection phobia, may also have a personality trait—let's say impulsiveness—that makes them more likely to be involved in minor accidents that would result in their seeing blood. In other words, they may be accident prone because they are continually rushing to complete things or to get to places without regard for their physical safety. These people, then, might have a genetically determined tendency to create the very environmental risk factors that trigger a genetic vulnerability to blood-injury-injection phobia.

This is the **gene–environment correlation model** or reciprocal gene–environment model (Jaffe, 2011; Kendler, 2011; Thapar & McGuffin, 2009) (see ■ Figure 2.4). Some evidence indicates that it applies to the development of depression because some people may tend to seek out difficult relationships or other circumstances that lead to depression (Eley, 2011). This did not seem to be the case, however, in the New Zealand study described earlier (Caspi et al., 2003), because stressful episodes during adulthood occurred with about the same frequency in the SS and the LL groups.

McGue and Lykken (1992) have even applied the gene–environment correlation model to some fascinating data on the influence of genes on the divorce rate. For example, if you and your spouse each have an identical twin, and both identical twins have been divorced, the chance that you will also divorce increases greatly. Furthermore, if your identical twin and your parents and your spouse's parents have been divorced, the chance that you will divorce is 78 percent. Conversely, if none of your family members on either side has been divorced, the probability that you will divorce is only 5 percent.

This is the extreme example, but McGue and Lykken (1992) demonstrated that the probability of your divorcing doubles over the probability in the population at large if your fraternal twin is also divorced and increases sixfold if your identical twin is divorced. Why would this happen? Obviously, no one gene causes divorce. To the extent it is genetically determined, the tendency to divorce is almost certainly related to various inherited traits, such as being high-strung, impulsive, or short-tempered, that make someone hard to get along with (Jockin et al., 1996). Another possibility is that an inherited trait makes it more likely you will choose an incompatible spouse. To take a simple example, if you are passive and unassertive, you may well choose a strong, dominant mate who turns out to be impossible to live with. You get

divorced but then find yourself attracted to another individual with the same personality traits, who is also impossible to live with. Some people would simply attribute this kind of pattern to poor judgment. Nevertheless, there's no doubt that social, interpersonal, psychological, and environmental factors play major roles in whether we stay married, and it's quite possible that our genes contribute to how we create our own environment.

EPIGENETICS AND THE NONGENOMIC "INHERITANCE" OF BEHAVIOUR

In a fascinating program of research with rodents (Cameron et al., 2005; Francis et al., 1999; Weaver et al., 2004), investigators studied stress reactivity and how it is passed through generations. Using a powerful experimental procedure called *cross-fostering*, in which a rat pup born to one mother is assigned to another mother for rearing, they first demonstrated, as had many other investigators, that maternal behaviour affected how the young rats tolerated stress. If the mothers were calm and supportive, their rat pups were less fearful and better able to tolerate stress. But we don't know if this effect results from genetic influences or from being raised by calm mothers. This is where cross-fostering comes in. Francis et al. (1999) took some newly born rat pups of fearful and easily stressed mothers and placed them for rearing with calm mothers. Other young rats remained with their easily stressed mothers. With this interesting scientific twist, Francis et al. demonstrated that calm and supportive behaviour by the mothers could be passed down through generations of rats *independent of genetic influences*, because rats born to easily stressed mothers but reared by calm mothers grew up more calm and supportive. The authors concluded that "these findings suggest that individual differences in the expression of genes in brain regions that regulate stress reactivity can be transmitted from one generation to the next through behaviour. . . . The results . . . suggest that the mechanism for this pattern of inheritance involves differences in maternal care" (p. 1158).

In subsequent studies from this group (Cameron et al., 2005), the investigators demonstrated that the maternal behaviour had lastingly altered the endocrine response to stress by affecting gene expression. But this effect occurred only if the rat mother was calm and nurturing during the rat pups' first week of life. After that—it didn't matter. This highlights the importance of early experience on behaviour.

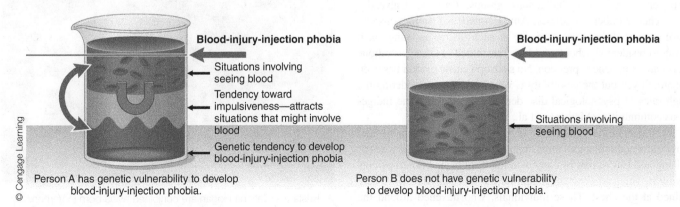

Person A has genetic vulnerability to develop blood-injury-injection phobia.

Person B does not have genetic vulnerability to develop blood-injury-injection phobia.

FIGURE 2.4 | Gene–environment correlation model.

Other scientists have reported similar results (Anisman et al., 1998; Harper, 2005). For example, Suomi (1999), working with rhesus monkeys and using the cross-fostering strategies just described, showed that if genetically reactive and emotional young monkeys are reared by calm mothers for the first six months of their lives, the animals behaved in later life as if they were not emotional and not reactive to stress at birth. In other words, the environmental effects of early parenting seem to override any genetic contribution to be anxious, emotional, or reactive to stress. Suomi also demonstrated that these emotionally reactive monkeys raised by calm, supportive parents were also calm and supportive when raising their own young, thereby influencing and even reversing the genetic contribution to the expression of personality traits or temperaments.

Strong effects of the environment have also been observed in humans. For example, Tienari et al. (1994) found that children of parents with schizophrenia who were adopted away as babies demonstrated a tendency to develop psychiatric disorders (including schizophrenia) themselves only if they were adopted into dysfunctional families. Those children adopted into functional families with high-quality parenting did not develop the disorders. Thus, it is probably too simplistic to say that genes contribute to a personality trait or to a psychological disorder; we can talk of a heritable (genetic) contribution only in the context of the individual's past and present environment (Dickens et al., 2011).

It seems that genes are turned on or off by cellular material that is located just outside of the genome (*epi*, as in the word **epigenetics**, means "on or around") and that stress, nutrition, or other factors can affect this epigenome, which is then immediately passed down to the next generation and maybe for several generations (Arai et al., 2009). The genome itself isn't changed, so if the stressful or inadequate environment disappears, eventually the epigenome will fade. These new conceptualizations of the role of genetic contributions in the context of environmental influences have implications for preventing psychological disorders. That is, it seems that environmental manipulations, particularly early in life, may do much to override the genetically influenced tendency to develop undesirable behavioural and emotional reactions. Although current research suggests that environmental influences, such as peer groups and schools, affect this genetic expression, the strongest evidence exists for the effects of early parenting influences and other early experiences (Cameron et al., 2005; Mill, 2011; Ouellet-Morin et al., 2008).

Epigenetics may be implicated in the intergenerational trauma experienced by some Indigenous groups. Carleton University researchers Kimberly Matheson, Amy Bombay, and Hymie Anisman have suggested that the experience of such trauma as being taken away to residential school could be transmitted to later generations via changes in gene expression. No such epigenetic marker has been identified yet, but the possibility is very intriguing, considering the high rates of psychological disorders and suicide in some Indigenous communities (Matheson et al., 2018).

Nowhere is the complexity of the interaction of genetic and environmental influences more apparent than in the famous cases of Chang and Eng, a pair of conjoined identical twins born to parents living in Thailand (known as Siam at the time) in 1810 who were joined at the chest. These individuals, who travelled around the world performing at exhibitions, were the source of the name "Siamese twins." These twins were very entrepreneurial and successful with their entertaining and exhibitions, and they amassed a small fortune. In 1839, they settled down with their wives, a pair of sisters. These two marital pairs produced 12 children each. These identical twins obviously shared identical genes as well as nearly identical environments throughout their lives. Thus, we would certainly expect them to behave in very similar ways when it comes to personality features, temperaments, and psychological disorders. Instead, everybody who knew these twins noted that they had very distinct personalities. Chang was prone to moodiness and depression, and finally started drinking heavily. Eng, on the other hand, was much more cheerful, quiet, and thoughtful (Moore, 2001). It is interesting to speculate about the similarities and differences in personality and susceptibility to specific psychological disorders that we might expect in Krista and Tatiana Hogan, conjoined twins born in Vernon, British Columbia, in October 2006 ("First Look," 2006). The twins are connected at the head and cannot be surgically separated. Their thalamuses are linked and evidence shows that they share sensory information, such as from sight and taste (Dominus, 2011; Pyke, 2014). In a recent and fascinating documentary, the twins demonstrate how they can see out of one another's eyes and move each other's limbs (Pyke, 2017).

In summary, a complex interaction between genes and the environment plays an important role in every psychological disorder (Kendler et al., 2011; Rutter, 2006, 2010; Turkheimer, 1998). Our genetic endowment does contribute to our behaviour, our emotions, and our cognitive processes and constrains the influence of environmental factors, such as upbringing, on our later behaviour, as is evident in the New Zealand study (Caspi et al., 2003) and its later replications. Environmental events, in turn, seem to affect our genes by determining whether certain genes are activated or not (Kendler 2011; Landis & Insel, 2008). Furthermore, strong environmental influences alone may be sufficient to override genetic diatheses. Thus, neither nature (genes) nor nurture (environmental events) alone, but rather a complex interaction of the two, influences the development of our behaviour and personalities.

▲ Krista and Tatiana Hogan are conjoined twins born in Vernon, British Columbia, in October 2006.

Determine whether these statements relating to the genetic contributions of psychopathology are true (T) or false (F).

1. _____ The first 20 pairs of chromosomes program the development of the body and brain.

2. _____ No individual genes have been identified that cause any major psychological disorders.

3. _____ According to the diathesis–stress model, people inherit a vulnerability to express certain traits or behaviours that may be activated under certain stress conditions.

4. _____ The idea that individuals may have a genetic endowment to increase the probability that they will experience stressful life events and therefore trigger a vulnerability is predicted by the diathesis–stress model.

5. _____ Environmental events alone influence the development of our behaviour and personalities.

NEUROSCIENCE AND ITS CONTRIBUTIONS TO PSYCHOPATHOLOGY

Knowing how the nervous system and, especially, the brain work is central to any understanding of our behaviour, emotions, and cognitive processes. This knowledge is the focus of **neuroscience**. To comprehend the newest research in this field, we first need an overview of how the brain and the nervous system function. The human nervous system includes the central nervous system, consisting of the brain and the spinal cord, and the peripheral nervous system, consisting of the somatic nervous system and the autonomic nervous system (see ■ Figure 2.5).

THE CENTRAL NERVOUS SYSTEM

The central nervous system (CNS) processes all information received from our sense organs and reacts as necessary. It sorts out what is relevant, such as a certain taste or a new sound, from what isn't, such as a familiar view or ticking clock; checks the memory banks to determine why the information is relevant; and implements the right reaction, whether it is to answer a

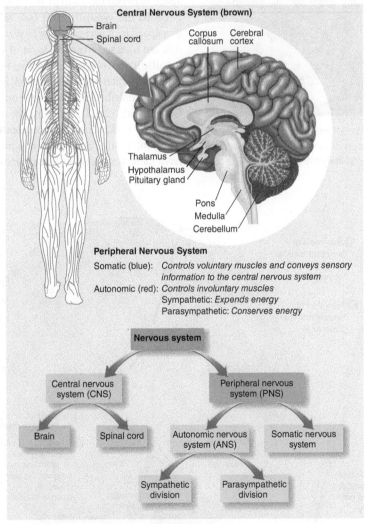

FIGURE 2.5 | Divisions of the nervous system.

Source: Reprinted, with permission, from Kalat, J. W. (2009). *Biological Psychology,* 10th edition, © 2009 Wadsworth.

▲ The central nervous system screens out information that is irrelevant to the current situation. From moment to moment we notice what moves or changes more than what remains the same.

question or to play a Chopin *étude*. The CNS performs a lot of complex work. The spinal cord is part of the central nervous system, but its primary function is to facilitate the sending of messages to and from the brain, which is the other major component of the CNS and the most complex organ in the body. The brain uses an average of 100 billion nerve cells, called *neurons*, that transmit information throughout the nervous system. Understanding how they work is important for our purposes because current research has confirmed that neurons are involved in psychological disorders.

The typical neuron contains a central cell body with two kinds of branches. One kind of branch is called a *dendrite*. Dendrites have numerous *receptors* that receive messages in the form of chemical impulses from other nerve cells, which are converted into electrical impulses. The other kind of branch, called an axon, transmits these impulses to other neurons. Any one nerve cell may have multiple connections to other neurons. The brain has billions of nerve cells, so you can see how complicated the system becomes, far more complicated than the most powerful computer that has ever been built (or will be for some time).

Nerve cells are not actually connected. There is a small space through which the impulse must pass to get to the next neuron. The space between the axon of one neuron and the dendrite of another is called the **synaptic cleft** (see ■ Figure 2.6). What happens in this space is of great interest to psychopathologists. The chemicals that are released from the axon of one nerve cell and transmit the impulse to the receptors of another nerve cell are called **neurotransmitters**, which were mentioned briefly when we described the genetic contribution to depression in the New Zealand study by Caspi et al. (2003). Only in the past several decades have we begun to understand the complexity of neurotransmitters. Now, using increasingly sensitive equipment and techniques, scientists have identified many different types of neurotransmitters.

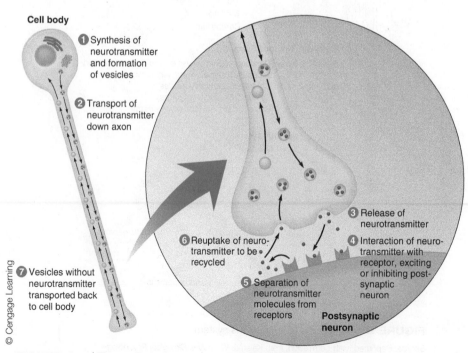

Cell body

❶ Synthesis of neurotransmitter and formation of vesicles

❷ Transport of neurotransmitter down axon

❼ Vesicles without neurotransmitter transported back to cell body

❻ Reuptake of neuro-transmitter to be recycled

❺ Separation of neurotransmitter molecules from receptors

❸ Release of neurotransmitter

❹ Interaction of neuro-transmitter with receptor, exciting or inhibiting post-synaptic neuron

Postsynaptic neuron

FIGURE 2.6 | The transmission of information from one neuron to another.

Major neurotransmitters relevant to psychopathology include *norepinephrine* (also known as noradrenaline), *serotonin*, *dopamine*, and *gamma aminobutyric acid* (GABA). You will see these terms many times in this book. Excesses or insufficiencies of some neurotransmitters are associated with different groups of psychological disorders. For example, reduced levels of GABA were initially thought to be associated with excessive anxiety (Costa, 1985). Early research (Snyder, 1976, 1981) linked increases in dopamine activity to schizophrenia. Other early research found correlations between depression and high levels of norepinephrine (Schildkraut, 1965) and low levels of serotonin (Siever et al., 1991). However, more recent research, described later in this chapter, indicates that these early interpretations were much too simplistic. Many types and subtypes of neurotransmitters are just being discovered, and they interact in very complex ways. In view of their importance, we will return to the subject of neurotransmitters shortly.

THE STRUCTURE OF THE BRAIN

Having an overview of the brain is useful because many of the structures described here are later mentioned in the context of specific disorders (see ■ Figures 2.7a to d). One way to view the brain is to see it in two parts—the *brain stem* and the *forebrain*. The brain stem is the lower and more ancient part of the brain. Found in most animals, this structure handles most of the essential automatic functions, such as breathing, sleeping, and moving around in a coordinated way. The forebrain is more advanced and has evolved more recently.

The lowest part of the brain stem, the *hindbrain*, contains the *medulla*, the *pons*, and the *cerebellum*. The hindbrain regulates many automatic activities, such as breathing, the pumping action of the heart (heartbeat), and digestion. The cerebellum controls motor coordination.

The *midbrain* coordinates movement with sensory input and contains parts of the *reticular activating system* (RAS), which

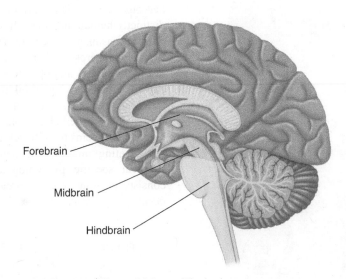

Forebrain

Midbrain

Hindbrain

FIGURE 2.7a | Three divisions of the brain.

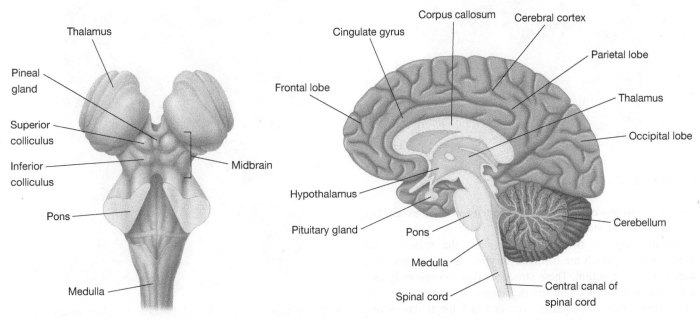

Thalamus

Pineal gland

Superior colliculus

Inferior colliculus

Midbrain

Pons

Medulla

Corpus callosum

Cerebral cortex

Cingulate gyrus

Frontal lobe

Parietal lobe

Thalamus

Occipital lobe

Hypothalamus

Pituitary gland

Pons

Medulla

Spinal cord

Cerebellum

Central canal of spinal cord

FIGURE 2.7b | Major structures of the brain.

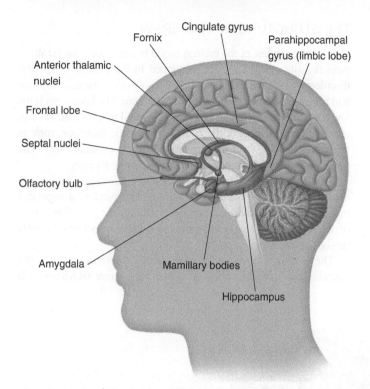

FIGURE 2.7c | The limbic system.

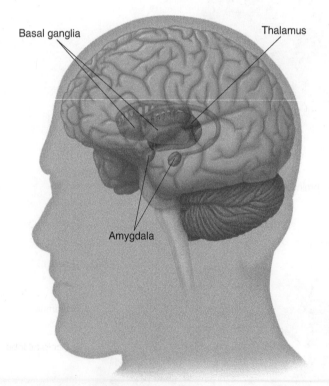

FIGURE 2.7d | The basal ganglia.

contributes to processes of arousal and tension, such as whether we are awake or asleep.

At the very top of the brain stem are the *thalamus* and *hypothalamus*, which are involved very broadly with regulating behaviour and emotion. These structures function primarily as a relay between the forebrain and the remaining lower areas of the brain stem. Some anatomists even consider the thalamus and hypothalamus parts of the forebrain.

At the base of the forebrain, just above the *thalamus* and *hypothalamus*, is the *limbic system*. *Limbic* means "border." The limbic system, which figures prominently in much of psychopathology, includes such structures as the *hippocampus* (sea horse), *cingulate gurus* (girdle), *septum* (partition), and *amygdala* (almond), all of which are named for their approximate shapes. This system helps regulate our emotional experiences and expressions and, to some extent, our ability to learn and to control our impulses. It is also involved with the basic drives of sex, aggression, hunger, and thirst.

The *basal ganglia*, also at the base of the forebrain, include the *caudate* (tailed) *nucleus*. Because damage to these structures may make us change our posture or twitch or shake, they are believed to control motor activity. Later in this chapter, we review some very interesting findings on the relationship of this area to obsessive-compulsive disorder.

The largest part of the forebrain is the *cerebral cortex*, which contains more than 80 percent of all the neurons in the central nervous system. This part of the brain provides us with our distinctly human qualities, allowing us to look to the future and plan, to reason, and to create. The cerebral cortex is divided into two hemispheres. Although the hemispheres look very much alike structurally and operate relatively independently (both are capable of perceiving, thinking, and remembering), each has different specialties. The left hemisphere seems to be chiefly responsible for verbal and other cognitive processes. The right hemisphere seems to be better at perceiving the world around us and creating images. The hemispheres may play differential roles in specific psychological disorders. Each hemisphere consists of four separate areas or lobes: *temporal*, *parietal*, *occipital*, and *frontal* (see ■ Figure 2.8). Each is associated with

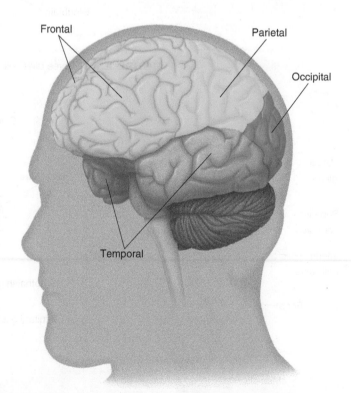

FIGURE 2.8 | Some major subdivisions of the human cerebral cortex and a few of their primary functions.

different processes: the temporal lobe with recognizing various sights and sounds and with long-term memory storage; the parietal lobe with recognizing various sensations of touch; the occipital lobe with integrating and making sense of various visual inputs. These three lobes, located toward the back (posterior) of the brain, work together to process sight, touch, hearing, and other signals from our senses.

The frontal lobe is the most interesting from the point of view of psychopathology. It carries most of the weight of our thinking and reasoning abilities, as well as our memory. It also enables us to relate to the world around us and to the people in it, to behave as social animals. When studying areas of the brain for clues to psychopathology, most researchers focus on the frontal lobe of the cerebral cortex, as well as on the limbic system and the basal ganglia.

Concept Check   2.2

Check your understanding of the structures of the brain by listing which is being described in the sentences here: (a) frontal lobe, (b) brain stem, (c) midbrain, or (d) cerebral cortex.

1. Movement, breathing, and sleeping depend on this ancient part of the brain, which is present in most animals. _____

2. This area contains parts of the reticular activating system and coordinates movement with sensory output.

   _____

3. More than 80 percent of the neurons in the human central nervous system are contained in this part of the brain, which gives us distinct qualities.

   _____

4. This area is responsible for most of our memory, thinking, and reasoning capabilities, and makes us social animals. _____

THE PERIPHERAL NERVOUS SYSTEM

The peripheral nervous system coordinates with the brain stem to make sure the body is working properly. Its two major components are the *somatic nervous system* and the *autonomic nervous system* (ANS). The somatic nervous system controls the muscles, so damage in this area might make it difficult for us to engage in any voluntary movement, including talking. The autonomic nervous system includes the *sympathetic nervous system* (SNS) and *parasympathetic nervous system* (PNS). The primary duties of the ANS are to regulate the cardiovascular system (e.g., the heart and blood vessels) and the endocrine system (e.g., the pituitary, adrenal, thyroid, and gonadal glands) and to perform various other functions, including aiding digestion and regulating body temperature.

The *endocrine system* works a bit differently from other systems in the body. Each endocrine gland produces its own chemical messenger, called a **hormone**, and releases it directly into the bloodstream. The adrenal glands produce epinephrine (also called *adrenaline*) in response to stress, as well as salt-regulating hormones; the thyroid gland produces thyroxine, which facilitates energy, metabolism, and growth; the pituitary is a master gland that produces a variety of regulatory hormones; and the gonadal glands produce sex hormones, such as estrogen and testosterone. The endocrine system is closely related to the immune system; it is also implicated in a variety of disorders, particularly the stress-related physical disorders discussed in the online supplementary chapter.

The sympathetic and parasympathetic divisions of the ANS often operate in a complementary fashion. The SNS is primarily responsible for mobilizing the body during times of stress or danger, by rapidly activating the organs and glands under its control. When the sympathetic division goes on alert, three things happen: The heart beats faster, thereby increasing the flow of blood to the muscles; respiration increases, allowing more oxygen to get into the blood and brain; and the adrenal glands are stimulated. These changes help mobilize us for action. If we are threatened by some immediate danger, such as a mugger coming at us on the street, we are able to run faster or defend ourselves with greater strength than if the sympathetic nervous system had not innervated our internal organs. When you read in the newspaper that a woman lifted a heavy object to free a trapped child, you can be sure her sympathetic nervous system was working overtime. This system mediates a substantial part of our emergency or alarm reaction, discussed later in this chapter and in Chapter 5.

One of the functions of the parasympathetic system is to balance the sympathetic system. In other words, because we cannot operate in a state of hyperarousal and preparedness forever, the PNS takes over after the SNS has been active for a while, normalizing our arousal and facilitating the storage of energy by helping the digestive process.

One brain connection that is implicated in some psychological disorders involves the hypothalamus and the endocrine system. The hypothalamus connects to the adjacent pituitary gland, which is the master or coordinator of the endocrine system. The pituitary gland, in turn, may stimulate the cortical part of the adrenal glands on top of the kidneys. As we noted previously, surges of epinephrine tend to energize us, arouse us, and get our bodies ready for threat or challenge. When athletes say their adrenaline was really flowing, they mean they were highly aroused and up for the competition. The cortical part of the adrenal glands also produces the stress hormone *cortisol*. This system is called the *hypothalamic-pituitary-adrenalcortical axis*, or *HPA axis* (see ■ Figure 2.9); it has been implicated in several psychological disorders.

This brief overview should give you a general sense of the structure and function of the brain and nervous system. New procedures for studying brain structure and function that involve photographing the working brain are discussed in Chapter 3. Here, we focus on what these studies reveal about the nature of psychopathology.

NEUROTRANSMITTERS

The biochemical neurotransmitters in the brain and nervous system that carry messages from one neuron to another continue to receive intense attention from psychopathologists (Bloom & Kupfer, 1995;

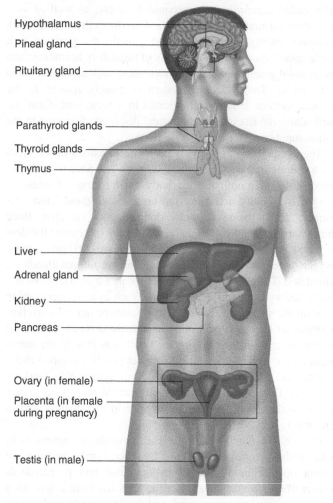

Hypothalamus

Pineal gland

Pituitary gland

Parathyroid glands

Thyroid glands

Thymus

Liver

Adrenal gland

Kidney

Pancreas

Ovary (in female)

Placenta (in female during pregnancy)

Testis (in male)

FIGURE 2.9 | Location of some of the major endocrine glands.

Source: Reprinted, with permission, from Kalat, J. W. (2009). *Biological Psychology*, 10th edition, © 2009 Wadsworth.

LeDoux, 2002; Iverson, 2006; Iversen & Iversen, 2007; Nestler et al., 2008). One good example is the role of the neurotransmitter serotonin in some studies of gene–environment interactions described earlier (e.g., Karg et al., 2011). These biochemicals were discovered only in recent decades, and only in the past few years have we developed the extraordinarily sophisticated procedures necessary to study them. One way to think of neurotransmitters is as narrow currents flowing through the ocean of the brain. Sometimes they run parallel with other currents, only to separate again. Often they seem to meander aimlessly, looping back on themselves before moving on. Neurons that are sensitive to one type of neurotransmitter cluster together and form paths from one part of the brain to another.

These paths may overlap with the paths of other neurotransmitters, but, as often as not, they end up going their separate ways (Bloom et al., 2001; Dean et al., 1993). There are thousands, perhaps tens of thousands, of these **brain circuits**, and we are just beginning to discover and map them (Arenkiel & Ehlers, 2009). Neuroscientists have identified several neural pathways that seem to play roles in various psychological disorders (Fineberg et al., 2010; LeDoux, 2002, 2015; Stahl, 2008; Tau & Peterson, 2010).

New neurotransmitters are frequently discovered, and existing neurotransmitter systems must be subdivided into separate classifications. Estimates suggest that more than 100 different neurotransmitters, each with multiple receptors, are functioning in various parts of the nervous system (Borodinsky et al., 2004; Kalat, 2013; Sharp, 2009). Also, scientists are increasingly discovering additional biochemicals and gases that have certain neurotransmitter properties. Because this dynamic field of research is in a state of considerable flux, the neuroscience of psychopathology is an exciting area of study that may lead to new drug treatments, among other advances. Research findings that seem to apply to psychopathology today may no longer be relevant tomorrow, however. Many years of study will be required before it is all sorted out.

You may still read reports that certain psychological disorders are "caused" by biochemical imbalances, excesses, or deficiencies in certain neurotransmitter systems. For example, abnormal activity of the neurotransmitter serotonin is often described as causing depression, and abnormalities in the neurotransmitter dopamine have been implicated in schizophrenia. Increasing evidence indicates that this is an enormous oversimplification. No neurochemical markers have been identified for depression or schizophrenia, for example. We are now learning that the effects of neurotransmitter activity are less specific. Changes in neurotransmitter activity may make people more or less likely to exhibit certain kinds of behaviour in certain situations without causing the behaviour directly. In addition, broad-based disturbances in our functioning are almost always associated with interactions of the various neurotransmitters rather than with alterations in the activity of any one system (Fineberg et al., 2010; LeDoux, 2002; Stahl, 2008; Xing et al., 2006). In other words, the currents intersect so often that changes in one neurotransmitter result in changes in the other, often in a way scientists have not yet been able to predict.

Research on neurotransmitter function focuses primarily on what happens when activity levels change. We can study this in several ways. We can introduce substances called **agonists** that effectively *increase* the activity of a neurotransmitter by mimicking its effects; substances called **antagonists** that *decrease*, or block, a neurotransmitter; or substances called **inverse agonists** that produce effects *opposite* to those produced by the neurotransmitter. By systematically manipulating the production of a neurotransmitter in different parts of the brain, scientists are able to learn more about its effects. Most drugs could be classified as either agonistic or antagonistic, although they may achieve these results in a variety of ways. That is, these drug therapies work by either increasing or decreasing the flow of specific neurotransmitters. Some drugs directly inhibit, or block, the production of a neurotransmitter. Other drugs increase the production of competing biochemical substances that may deactivate the neurotransmitter. Yet other drugs do not affect neurotransmitters directly but prevent the chemical from reaching the next neuron by closing down, or occupying, the receptors in that neuron. After a neurotransmitter is released, it is quickly drawn back from the synaptic cleft into the same neuron. This process is called **reuptake**. Some drugs work by blocking the reuptake process, thereby causing continued stimulation along the brain circuit.

Here, we will focus on several classic neurotransmitters most relevant to psychopathology. Two types of neurotransmitters, *monoamines* and *amino acids*, have been most studied in relation to psychopathology. These are considered the "classic" neurotransmitters because they are synthesized in the nerve. Neurotransmitters in the monoamine class include norepinephrine (also known as noradrenaline), serotonin, and dopamine. Amino acid neurotransmitters include GABA and glutamate.

Glutamate and GABA

Two major neurotransmitters are involved in much of what we do. Each of these substances is in the amino acid category of neurotransmitters. The first, **glutamate**, is an excitatory transmitter that turns on many different neurons, leading to action. A second type of amino acid transmitter is **gamma aminobutyric acid**, or **GABA** for short, which is an inhibitory neurotransmitter. Thus, the job of GABA is to inhibit (or regulate) the transmission of information and action potentials. Because these two neurotransmitters work in concert to balance functioning in the brain, they have been referred to as the "chemical brothers" (LeDoux, 2002). Glutamate and GABA operate relatively independently at a molecular level, but the relative balance of each in a cell will determine whether the neuron is activated (fires) or not.

Another characteristic of these "chemical brothers" is that they are fast acting, as they would have to be for the brain to keep up with the many environmental influences that require action or restraint. Overactivity of the glutamate system could literally burn out sections of the nervous system in a worst-case scenario. Some people who like Chinese food and who are sensitive to glutamate may have experienced a few adverse reactions from a common additive in Chinese food referred to as MSG. MSG stands for monosodium glutamate; it can increase the amount of glutamate in the body, causing headaches, ringing in the ears, or other physical symptoms in some people. We return to some exciting new findings involving glutamate-specific receptors when we discuss new treatments for anxiety disorders in Chapter 5.

As noted earlier, GABA reduces postsynaptic activity, which, in turn, inhibits a variety of behaviours and emotions. GABA was discovered before glutamate and has been studied for a longer period; its best-known effect is to reduce anxiety (Charney & Drevets, 2002; Davis, 2002; Griebel & Holmes, 2013; Sullivan & LeDoux, 2004). Scientists have discovered that a particular class of drugs, the *benzodiazepines*, or minor tranquilizers, makes it easier for GABA molecules to attach themselves to the receptors of specialized neurons. Thus, the higher the level of benzodiazepine, the more GABA becomes attached to neuron receptors and the calmer we become (to a point). Because benzodiazepines have certain addictive properties, clinical scientists are working to identify other substances that may also modulate levels of GABA; these include certain natural steroids in the brain (Eser et al., 2006; Gordon, 2002; Rupprecht et al., 2009).

As with other neurotransmitter systems, we now know that GABA's effect is not specific to anxiety but has a broader influence. The GABA system rides on many circuits distributed widely throughout the brain. GABA seems to reduce overall arousal somewhat and to temper our emotional responses. For example, in addition to reducing anxiety, minor tranquilizers have an anticonvulsant effect, relaxing muscle groups that may be subject to spasms. Drug compounds that increase GABA are also under evaluation as treatments for insomnia (Monti et al., 2010; Sullivan, 2012; Sullivan & Guilleminault, 2009; Walsh et al., 2008). Furthermore, the GABA system seems to reduce levels of anger, hostility, aggression, and perhaps even positive emotional states, such as eager anticipation and pleasure, making GABA a generalized inhibiting neurotransmitter, much as glutamate has a generalized excitatory function (Bond & Lader, 1979; Lader, 1975; Sharp, 2009). We are also learning that the GABA system is not just one system working in only one manner but is composed of a number of subsystems. Different types of GABA receptors seem to act in different ways, with perhaps only one of the subtypes having an affinity for the benzodiazepine component (D'Hulst et al., 2009; Gray, 1985; LeDoux, 2002; Sharp, 2009). Therefore, the conclusion that this system is responsible for anxiety seems just as out of date as concluding that the serotonin system is responsible for depression.

Serotonin

The technical name for **serotonin** is 5-hydroxytryptamine (5HT). It is in the monoamine category of neurotransmitters, along with norepinephrine and dopamine, discussed next. Approximately six major circuits of serotonin spread from the midbrain, looping around its various parts (Azmitia, 1978) (see ■ Figure 2.10). Because of the widespread nature of these circuits, many of them ending up in the cortex, serotonin is believed to influence a great deal of our behaviour, particularly the way we process information (Harmer, 2008; Merens et al., 2007; Spoont, 1992). It was genetically influenced dysregulation in this system that contributed to depression in the New Zealand study described earlier (Caspi et al., 2003).

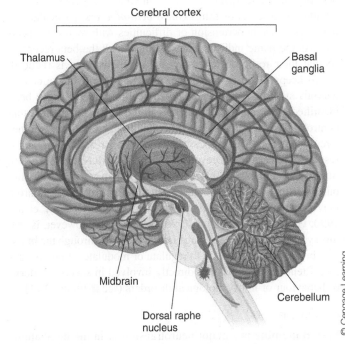

FIGURE 2.10 | Major serotonin pathways in the brain.

The serotonin system regulates our behaviour, moods, and thought processes. Extremely low activity levels of serotonin are associated with less inhibition and with instability, impulsivity, and the tendency to overreact to situations. Low serotonin activity has been associated with aggression, suicide, impulsive overeating, and excessive sexual behaviour (Berman et al., 2009). These behaviours do not *necessarily* happen if serotonin activity is low, however. Other currents in the brain, or other psychological or social influences, may well compensate for low serotonin activity. Therefore, low serotonin activity may make us more vulnerable to certain problematic behaviour without directly causing it (as mentioned earlier). On the other end, high levels of serotonin may interact with GABA to counteract glutamate (the same fact is emerging about other neurotransmitter systems).

To add to the complexity, serotonin has slightly different effects depending on the type or subtype of receptors involved, and we now know there are approximately 15 different receptors in the serotonin system (Olivier, 2015). Several classes of drugs primarily affect the serotonin system, including the tricyclic antidepressants, such as imipramine (known by its brand name, Tofranil). However, the class of drugs called selective-serotonin reuptake inhibitors (SSRIs), including fluoxetine (Prozac), affects serotonin more directly than other drugs, including the tricyclic antidepressants. SSRIs are used to treat a number of psychological disorders, particularly anxiety, mood, and eating disorders. The herbal medication St. John's wort, available in drug stores, is also believed to affect serotonin levels.

Norepinephrine

A third neurotransmitter system in the monoamine class important to psychopathology is **norepinephrine** (also known as **noradrenaline**). We have already seen that norepinephrine, like epinephrine (referred to as a catecholamine), is part of the endocrine system.

Norepinephrine seems to stimulate at least two groups (and probably several more) of receptors called *alpha-adrenergic* and *beta-adrenergic receptors*. Someone in your family may be taking a widely used class of drugs called *beta-blockers*, particularly if that person has hypertension or difficulties with regulating heart rate. As the name indicates, these drugs block the beta-receptors so that their response to a surge of norepinephrine is reduced, which keeps blood pressure and heart rate down. In the central nervous system, a number of norepinephrine circuits have been identified. One major circuit begins in the hindbrain, an area that controls basic bodily functions, such as respiration. Another circuit appears to influence the emergency reactions or alarm responses (Charney & Drevets, 2002; Gray & McNaughton, 1996; Sullivan & LeDoux, 2004) that occur when we suddenly find ourselves in a dangerous situation, suggesting that norepinephrine may bear some relationship to states of panic (Charney et al., 1990; Gray & McNaughton, 1996). More likely, however, is that this system, with all its varying circuits coursing through the brain, acts in a more general way to regulate or modulate certain behavioural tendencies and is not directly involved in specific patterns of behaviour or in psychological disorders (see ■ Figure 2.11).

Dopamine

Last, **dopamine** is a major neurotransmitter in the monoamine class, also termed a catecholamine because of the similarity of

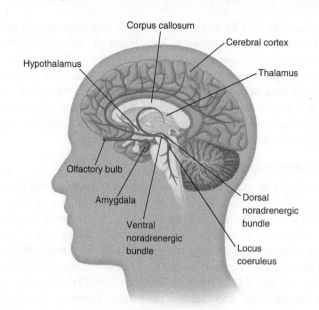

FIGURE 2.11 | Major norepinephrine pathways in the human brain.

its chemical structure to epinephrine and norepinephrine. Dopamine has been implicated in the pathophysiology of schizophrenia and disorders of addiction (LeFoll et al., 2009). Some research also indicates it may play a significant role in depression (Dunlop & Nemeroff, 2007) and attention deficit hyperactivity disorder (Volkow et al., 2009). Remember the wonder drug reserpine mentioned in Chapter 1 that reduced psychotic behaviours associated with schizophrenia? This drug and more modern antipsychotic treatments affect a number of neurotransmitter systems, but their greatest impact may be that they block specific dopamine receptors, thus lowering dopamine activity (e.g., Snyder et al., 1976). Thus, it was long thought possible that in schizophrenia, dopamine circuits may be too active. The recent development of second-generation antipsychotic drugs, such as clozapine, which has only weak effects on certain dopamine receptors, suggests this idea may need revising. We explore the dopamine hypothesis in some detail in Chapter 14.

In its various circuits throughout specific regions of the brain (see ■ Figure 2.12), dopamine also seems to have a more general effect, best described as a switch that turns on various brain circuits possibly associated with certain types of behaviour. Once the switch is turned on, other neurotransmitters may then inhibit or facilitate emotions or behaviour (Armbruster et al., 2009; Oades, 1985; Spoont, 1992; Stahl, 2008). Dopamine circuits merge and cross with serotonin circuits at many points and therefore influence many of the same behaviours. For example, dopamine activity is associated with exploratory, outgoing, pleasure-seeking behaviours (Elovainio et al., 2005), and serotonin is associated with inhibition and constraint; thus, in a sense they balance each other (Depue et al., 1994).

Again, we see that the effects of a neurotransmitter—in this case, dopamine—are more complex than we originally thought. Researchers have thus far discovered at least five different receptor sites that are selectively sensitive to dopamine (Beaulieu & Gainetdinov, 2011). One of a class of drugs that affects the dopamine circuits specifically is L-dopa, which is a dopamine

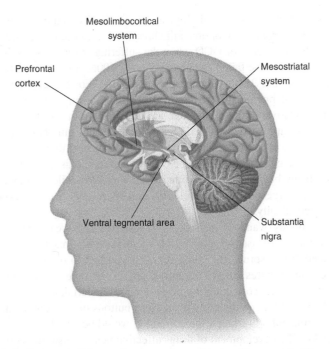

Mesolimbocortical system

Prefrontal cortex

Mesostriatal system

Ventral tegmental area

Substantia nigra

FIGURE 2.12 | Two major dopamine pathways: The mesolimbic system is apparently implicated in schizophrenia; the path to the basal ganglia contributes to problems in the locomotor system, such as tardive dyskinesia, which sometimes results from use of neuroleptic drugs.

agonist (it increases levels of dopamine). One of the systems that dopamine switches on is the locomotor system, which regulates ability to move in a coordinated way and, once turned on, is influenced by serotonin activity. Because of these connections, deficiencies in dopamine have been associated with disorders such as Parkinson's disease, in which a marked deterioration in motor behaviour includes tremors, rigidity of muscles, and difficulty with judgment. L-dopa has been successful in reducing some of these motor disabilities.

Concept Check 2.3

Check your understanding of the major functions of four important neurotransmitters by matching them to the descriptions provided: (a) GABA, (b) serotonin, (c) dopamine, and (d) norepinephrine.

1. Which neurotransmitter binds to neuron receptor sites, inhibiting postsynaptic activity and reducing overall arousal? _____

2. Which neurotransmitter is a switch that turns on various brain circuits? _____

3. Which neurotransmitter seems to be involved in your emergency reactions or alarm responses?

   _____

4. Which neurotransmitter is believed to influence the way we process information and to moderate or inhibit our behaviour? _____

IMPLICATIONS FOR PSYCHOPATHOLOGY

Psychological disorders typically mix emotional, behavioural, and cognitive symptoms, so identifiable lesions (or damage) localized in specific structures of the brain do not, for the most part, cause the disorders. Even widespread damage most often results in motor or sensory deficits, which are usually the province of the medical specialty of neurology; neurologists often work with neuropsychologists to identify specific lesions. Psychopathologists have been focusing lately on the more general role of brain function in the development of personality, with the goal of considering how different types of personalities might be more or less vulnerable to developing certain types of psychological disorders. For example, genetic contributions might lead to patterns of neurotransmitter activity that influence personality. Thus, some impulsive risk takers may have low serotonergic activity and high dopaminergic activity.

Procedures for studying images of the functioning brain have been applied to several disorders, including *obsessive-compulsive disorder* (OCD). Individuals with this severe anxiety-based disorder suffer from intrusive, frightening thoughts—for example, that they might have become contaminated with poison and will poison their loved ones if they touch them. To prevent this drastic consequence, they engage in compulsive rituals, such as frequent washing to try to scrub off the imagined poison. A number of investigators have found intriguing differences between the brains of patients with OCD and the brains of other people. Although the size and structure of the brain are the same, patients with OCD have increased activity in the part of the frontal lobe of the cerebral cortex called the *orbital surface* (Chamberlain et al., 2008; Harrison et al., 2013). Increased activity is also present in the cingulate gyrus and, to a lesser extent, in the caudate nucleus, a circuit that extends from the orbital section of the frontal area of the cortex to parts of the thalamus. Activity in these areas seems to be correlated; that is, if one area is active, the other areas are also. These areas contain several pathways of neurotransmitters, and one of the most concentrated is serotonin.

Remember that one of the roles of serotonin seems to be to moderate our reactions. Eating behaviour, sexual behaviour, and aggression are under better control with adequate levels of serotonin. Research, mostly on animals, demonstrates that lesions (damage) that interrupt serotonin circuits seem to impair the ability to ignore irrelevant external cues, making the organism overactive. Thus, if we were to experience damage or interruption in this brain circuit, we might find ourselves acting on every thought or impulse that enters our heads.

Thomas Insel (1992) described a case originally reported by Eslinger and Damasio (1985) of a man who had been successful as an accountant, a husband, and a father of two before undergoing surgery for a brain tumour. He made a good recovery from surgery and seemed to be fine, but in the following year his business failed and he separated from his family. Although his scores on IQ tests were as high as ever and all his mental functions were intact, he was unable to keep a job or even be on time for an appointment. What was causing all these problems? He was engaging in lengthy and uncontrollable compulsive rituals. Most of his days were consumed with washing, dressing, and rearranging things in the single room where he lived. In other words, he had classic obsessive-compulsive symptoms. The area of his brain damaged by removal of the tumour was a small area of his orbital frontal cortex.

This information seems to support a biological cause for psychological disorders—in this case, OCD. You might think there is no need to consider social or psychological influences here. But Insel and other neuroscientists interpret these findings cautiously. First, this case involves only one individual. Other individuals with the *same* lesion might react differently. Also, brain-imaging studies are often inconsistent with one another on many important details. Sometimes pinpointing the increased or decreased activity is difficult because brains differ in their structure, just as bodies and faces do. The orbital frontal cortex is also implicated in other anxiety disorders and maybe other emotional disorders (Gansler et al., 2009; Goodwin, 2009; Sullivan & LeDoux, 2004), so the damage in this area of the brain may just increase negative affect more generally rather than OCD specifically. Therefore, more work has to be done, and perhaps technology has to improve further, before we can be confident about the relation of the orbital frontal cortex to OCD. It is possible that activity in this area may simply be a result of the repetitive thinking and ritualistic behaviour that characterizes OCD, rather than a cause. To take a simple analogy, if you were late for class and began running, massive changes would occur throughout your body and brain. If someone who did not know that you had just sprinted to class then examined you with brain scans, your brain functions would look different from those of the brain of a person who had walked to class on time. The scientist might conclude, wrongly, that your unusual brain function caused your tardiness. It is also important to note that today, neuroscientists focus much more on the connectivity between certain brain areas (the brain circuitry) than the activity of any particular brain region that might be associated with a specific mental disorder (e.g., Whitfield-Gabrieli et al., 2016).

PSYCHOSOCIAL INFLUENCES ON BRAIN STRUCTURE AND FUNCTION

At the same time that psychopathologists are exploring the causes of psychological disorders, whether in the brain or in the environment, people are suffering and require the best treatments we have. Sometimes the effects of treatment tell us something about causes. For example, if a clinician thinks OCD is caused by a specific brain function or dysfunction or by learned anxiety to scary or repulsive thoughts, this view would determine the choice of treatment, as we noted in Chapter 1. Directing a treatment at one or the other of these theoretical causes of the disorder and then observing whether the patient gets better will test the accuracy of the theory. This common strategy has one overriding weakness. Successfully treating a patient's particular feverish state or toothache with Aspirin does not mean the fever or toothache was caused by an Aspirin deficiency, because an effect does not imply a cause. Nevertheless, this line of evidence gives us some hints about causes, particularly when it is combined with other, more direct experimental evidence.

If you knew that someone with OCD might have a somewhat faulty brain circuit, what treatment would you choose? Maybe you would recommend brain surgery, or neurosurgery. Neurosurgery

to correct severe psychological problems (sometimes called *psychosurgery*) is an option still chosen today on occasion, particularly in the case of OCD when the suffering is severe and other treatments have failed (Aouizerate et al., 2006; Bear et al., 2010; Denys et al., 2010; Greenberg et al., 2010). For the accountant described previously, the removal of his brain tumour seems to have inadvertently eliminated an inhibitory part of the brain circuit implicated in OCD. Precise surgical lesions might dampen the runaway activity that seems to occur in or near this particular area of the brain, triggering the OCD symptoms. This result would probably be welcome if all other treatments have failed, although psychosurgery is used seldom and has not been studied systematically.

Nobody wants to do surgery if less intrusive treatments are available. To use the analogy of a television set that has developed the "disorder" of going fuzzy, if you had to rearrange and reconnect wires on the circuit board every time the disorder occurred, the correction would be a major undertaking. Alternatively, if you could simply push some buttons on the remote and eliminate the fuzziness, the correction would be simpler and less risky. The development of drugs affecting neurotransmitter activity has given us one of those buttons. We now have drugs that, although not a cure or even an effective treatment in all cases, do seem to be beneficial in treating OCD. As you might suspect, most of them act by increasing serotonin activity in one way or another.

But is it possible to get at this brain circuit without either surgery or drugs? Could psychological treatment be powerful enough to affect the circuit directly? The answer seems to be yes. To take one of the first examples, Lewis R. Baxter and his colleagues (1992) used brain imaging on patients who had not been treated and then took an additional, important scientific step. They treated the patients with a cognitive-behavioural therapy known to be effective in OCD called *exposure and response prevention* and then repeated the brain imaging. In a remarkable finding, widely noted in the world of psychopathology, Baxter and his colleagues discovered that the brain circuit had been changed (normalized) by a psychological intervention. The same team of investigators then replicated the experiment with a different group of patients and found the same changes in brain function (Schwartz et al., 1996). In other examples, investigating teams noted changes in brain function after successful psychological treatment for depression, PTSD, obsessive-compulsive disorder, panic disorder, social anxiety disorder, specific phobias, and schizophrenia (Barsaglini et al., 2014). A review of the evidence suggests that, depending on the disorder, psychotherapy results in either a normalization of abnormal patterns of activity, the recruitment of additional areas, which did not show altered activation prior to treatment, or both. One study showed that as little as two hours of intense exposure-based therapy for specific phobia changed brain function dramatically, and these effects persisted six months later (Hauner et al., 2012).

The study of placebo effects offers another window on psychological factors directly affecting brain function. It is common for inactive placebo medications, which are just sugar pills, or other sham (inactive) treatments to result in behavioural and emotional changes in patients, presumably as a result of psychological factors, such as increasing hope and expectations or conditioning effects (Brody & Miller, 2011). The placebo effect was noticed a long time ago by self-described psychology professor Ferdinand Ueberwasser (1752–1812): "There are examples where bread crumbs, taken in the shape of pills have, by means of vivid imagination and expectations, yielded the same effects as the medication itself" (quoted in Schwarz & Pfister, 2016, p. 403).

Several recent studies have examined the conditions under which placebos are active. For example, one study administered medications for either pain or anxiety after surgery by means of an infusion pump that was either in plain view of the patients or was hidden behind a screen (Colloca et al., 2004). Even though the same dosage of medicine was administered, the effect was consistently greater when patients knew they were receiving the drug because they could see the pump working compared with when the pump was hidden behind a screen. No placebos were actually given in this study, but the difference in effects between knowing and not knowing whether the drug was given was considered a good estimate of the placebo effect. In another study, patients with irritable bowel syndrome received a sham treatment (acupuncture) that was not designed to be effective. The treatment was administered either impersonally or in the context of a warm therapeutic interpersonal relationship. The impersonal administration produced better results than no treatment (even though there was no active ingredient in the treatment), but the addition of a strong relationship added substantially to the therapeutic benefit (Kaptchuk et. al., 2008). But how and why do placebos work?

In an intriguing study, Leuchter, Cook, Witte, Morgan, and Abrams (2002) treated patients with major depressive disorder with either antidepressant medications or placebo medications. Measures of brain function showed that both antidepressant medications and placebos changed brain function but in somewhat different parts of the brain, suggesting different mechanisms of action for these two interventions—at least in the treatment of depression. Placebos alone are not usually as effective as active medication, but every time clinicians prescribe pills, they are also treating the patient psychologically by inducing positive expectation for change, and this intervention changes brain function.

Petrovic, Kalso, Petersson, and Ingvar (2002), in an important study, also examined how placebo pills (in other words, psychological factors) can change brain function in the context of treating pain. Participants were given (with their consent) a harmless but painful condition in which their left hand was subjected to intense heat. These participants were informed that two potent analgesics (pain-reducing medications) would be used in the experiment. In fact, one of these drugs was an opioid, and the other was a placebo. Opioid-based drugs are used routinely in medical settings to relieve severe pain. Each participant experienced the painful stimulus under three conditions: (1) under the influence of an opioid drug, (2) under the influence of a placebo pill that the patient assumed was an opioid-based drug, and (3) with no drug. All participants experienced each condition multiple times, while brain-imaging procedures monitored their brain functioning during administration of the painful stimulus. Whereas both the placebo drug and the opiate drug reduced pain to less than the level with no drug, the surprising results indicated that, unlike the study on depression just mentioned,

both treatments activated overlapping (although not identical) regions in the brain, primarily within the anterior cingulate cortex and the brain stem. These areas were not activated during the no drug condition. Thus, it appears that the anterior cingulate cortex is responsible for control of the pain response in the brain stem and that cognitive expectations of pain relief created by the placebo condition cause these brain circuits to be turned on. It would seem that psychological factors are another button on the remote with which we can directly change brain circuits.

An intriguing area of research, then, is exploring the specific ways in which drug and psychological treatments work in terms of changes in brain function. A group in Toronto treated individuals who had major depressive disorder with either a psychological treatment, cognitive-behavioural therapy (CBT), or the antidepressant drug venlafaxine (Kennedy et al., 2007). Although some brain changes were similar among the two treatment groups, complex differences were also noted, primarily in the way in which CBT facilitated changes in thinking patterns in the cortex that, in turn, affected the emotional brain. Sometimes this is called a *top-down* change because it originates in the cortex and works its way down into the lower brain. Drugs, on the other hand, often seem to work more in a *bottom-up* manner, reaching higher areas of the cortex (where thinking occurs) last. Many similar studies in this area are now in progress. Because we know that some people respond better to psychological treatments, and others respond better to drugs, this research provides hope that we will one day be able to choose the best treatments or better combine treatments based on an analysis of the individual's brain function.

INTERACTIONS OF PSYCHOSOCIAL FACTORS WITH BRAIN STRUCTURE AND FUNCTION

Several experiments illustrate the interaction of psychosocial factors and brain function as reflected in neurotransmitter activity. Some even indicate that psychosocial factors directly affect levels of neurotransmitters. In one classic experiment, Insel, Scanlan, Champoux, and Suomi (1988) raised two groups of rhesus monkeys identically except for their ability to control things in their cages. One group had free access to toys and food treats, but the second group got these toys and treats only when the first group did. In other words, the second group had the same number of toys and treats but they could not choose when they got them. Therefore, they had less control over their environment. In psychological experiments, we say the second group was *yoked* with the first group because their treatment depended entirely on what happened to the first group. The monkeys in the first group grew up with a sense of control over things in their lives and those in the second group didn't.

Later in their lives, all these monkeys were administered a benzodiazepine inverse agonist, a neurochemical that has the opposite effect of the neurotransmitter GABA; the effect is an extreme burst of anxiety. (The few times this neurochemical has been administered to people, usually scientists administering it to each other, the recipients have reported the experience—which lasts only a short time—to be one of the most horrible sensations they had ever endured.) When this substance was injected into the monkeys, the ones that had been raised with little control over their environment ran to a corner of their cage where they

▲ Rhesus monkeys injected with a specific neurotransmitter react with anger or fear, depending on their early psychological experiences.

crouched and displayed signs of severe anxiety and panic. But the monkeys that had a sense of control behaved quite differently. They did not seem anxious at all. Rather, they seemed angry and aggressive, even attacking other monkeys near them. Thus, the very same level of a neurochemical substance, acting as a neurotransmitter, had very different effects, depending on the psychological histories of the monkeys.

The Insel and colleagues (1988) experiment is an example of an interaction between neurotransmitters and psychosocial factors. Other experiments suggest that psychosocial influences directly affect the functioning and perhaps even the structure of the central nervous system. Scientists have observed that psychosocial factors routinely change the activity levels of many of our neurotransmitter systems (Barik et al., 2013; Cacioppo et al., 2007; Marinelli & McCutcheon, 2014; Sandi & Haller, 2015).

We are now beginning to learn how psychosocial factors affect brain function and structure (Kolb, Gibb, & Robinson, 2003; Kolb & Whishaw, 1998). For example, Greenough, Withers, and Wallace (1990), in a series of classic experiments, studied the cerebellum, which coordinates and controls motor behaviour. They discovered that the nervous systems of rats raised in a rich environment requiring a lot of learning and motor behaviour develop differently from the nervous systems of rats that were couch potatoes. The active rats had many more connections between nerve cells in the cerebellum and grew many more dendrites. In a follow-up study, Wallace, Kilman, Withers, and Greenough (1992) reported that these structural changes in the brain began in as little as four days in rats, suggesting enormous plasticity in brain structure as a result of experience. Similarly, stress during early development can lead to substantial changes in the functioning of the HPA axis (mentioned earlier in this chapter) that, in turn, make primates more or less susceptible to stress later in life (Barlow, 2002; Coplan et al., 1998; Gillespie & Nemeroff, 2007; Spinelli et al., 2009; Suomi, 1999). It may be something similar to this mechanism that was responsible for the effects of early stress on the later development of depression in genetically susceptible individuals in the New Zealand study described earlier (Caspi et al., 2003). So, we can conclude that early psychological experience affects the development of the nervous system and thus determines vulnerability to psychological

disorders later in life. It seems that the very structure of the nervous system is constantly changing as a result of learning and experience, even into old age, and that some of these changes become permanent (Kolb, Gibb, & Gorny, 2003; Suárez et al., 2009).

COMMENTS

The specific brain circuits involved in psychological disorders are very complex systems identified by pathways of neurotransmitters traversing the brain. The existence of these circuits suggests that the structure and function of the nervous system play major roles in psychological disorders. But other research suggests that the circuits are strongly influenced, perhaps even created, by psychological and social factors. Furthermore, both biological interventions, such as drugs, and psychological interventions or experience seem capable of altering the circuits. Therefore, we cannot consider the nature and cause of psychological disorders without examining both biological and psychological factors. We now turn to an examination of psychological factors.

▲ William Greenough and his associates raised rats in a complex environment that required significant learning and motor behaviour, which affected the structure of the rats' brains. This research supports the role of psychological factors on biological development.

BEHAVIOURAL AND COGNITIVE SCIENCE

Enormous progress has been made in understanding behavioural and cognitive influences in psychopathology. Some new information has come from the rapidly growing field of **cognitive science**, which is concerned with how we acquire and process information and how we store and ultimately retrieve it (one of the processes involved in memory). Scientists have also discovered that we are not necessarily aware of a great deal that goes on inside our heads. Because, technically, these cognitive processes are unconscious, some findings recall the unconscious mental processes that are so much a part of Freud's theory of psychoanalysis, although they do not look much like the ones he envisioned. A brief account of current thinking on what is happening during the process of classical conditioning will start us on our way.

CONDITIONING AND COGNITIVE PROCESSES

During the 1960s and 1970s, behavioural scientists in animal laboratories began to uncover the complexity of the basic processes of classical conditioning (Bouton et al., 2001; Meyers & Davis, 2002; Mineka & Zinbarg, 1996, 1998). Rescorla (1988) concluded that simply pairing two events closely in time (such as the food and the metronome in Pavlov's laboratories) is not really what's important in this type of learning; at the very least, it is a very simple summary. Rather, a variety of different judgments and cognitive processes combine to determine the final outcome of this learning, even in lower animals, such as rats.

To take just one simple example, Pavlov would have predicted that if the food and the metronome were paired, say, 50 times, then a certain amount of learning would take place. But Rescorla and others discovered that if one animal never saw the particular food at any time except for the 50 trials following the metronome sound, but the other animal saw the food many times *in between* the 50 times it was paired with the metronome, the two animals would learn very different things; that is, even though the metronome and the food were paired 50 times for each animal, the metronome *was much less meaningful* to the second animal (see ■ Figure 2.13). Put another way, the first animal learned that the sound of the metronome meant food came next; the second animal learned that the food sometimes came after the sound and sometimes without the sound. That two different conditions produce two different learning outcomes is really a commonsense notion, but it demonstrates, along with many far more complex scientific findings, that basic classical (and operant) conditioning paradigms really facilitate the learning of the *relationship* among events in the environment. This type of learning makes us able to develop working ideas about the world that allow us to make appropriate judgments. We can then respond in a way that will benefit or at least not hurt us. In other words, complex cognitive and emotional processing of information is involved when conditioning occurs, even in animals.

LEARNED HELPLESSNESS

Along similar lines, Martin Seligman, also working with animals, described the phenomenon of **learned helplessness**, which occurs when rats or other animals encounter conditions over which they have no control whatsoever. If rats are confronted with a situation in which they receive occasional foot shocks, they can function very well if they learn they can cope with these shocks by doing

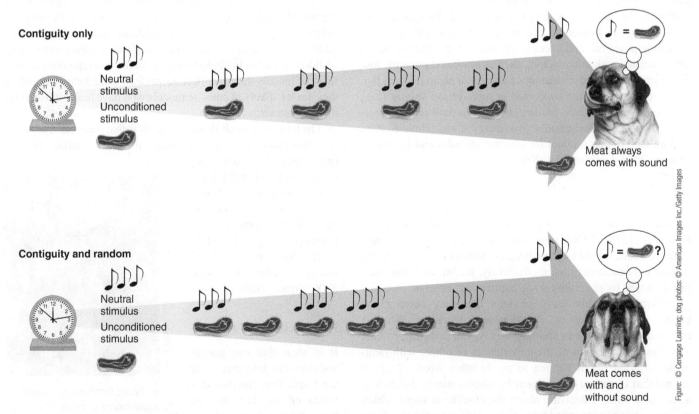

FIGURE 2.13 | Rescorla's experiment that showed contiguity—pairing a neutral stimulus (NS) and an unconditioned stimulus (UCS)—does not result in the same kind of learning. The dog in the contiguity-only group (top panel) experiences the usual conditioning procedure: Pairing a tone and meat causes the tone to take on properties of the meat. For the dog in the contiguity-and-random group, the fact that the meat appeared away from the tone as well as with it makes the tone much less meaningful.

something to avoid them (say, pressing a lever). But if the animals learn their behaviour has no effect whatsoever on their environment—sometimes they get shocked and sometimes they don't, no matter what they do—they become very "helpless"; in other words, they give up attempting to cope and seem to develop the animal equivalent of depression.

Seligman drew some important conclusions from these observations. He theorized that the same phenomenon may happen with people who are faced with uncontrollable stress in their lives. Subsequent work revealed this to be true under one important condition: people become depressed if they decide or think they can do little about the stress in their lives, even if it seems to others that they could do something. People make an attribution that they have no control, and they become depressed (Abramson et al., 1978; Miller & Norman, 1979). It illustrates, once again, the necessity of recognizing that different people process information about events in the environment in different ways. These cognitive differences are an important component of psychopathology.

More recently, Seligman has turned his attention to the positive side of learned helplessness, which he terms "learned optimism" (Seligman, 1998, 2002). If people faced with considerable stress and difficulty in their lives nevertheless display an optimistic, upbeat attitude, they are likely to function better psychologically and physically. In a study by Levy, Slade, Kunkel, and Kasl (2002), individuals between the ages of 50 and 94 who had positive views about themselves, and positive attitudes toward aging, lived 7.5 years longer than those without such positive, optimistic attitudes. This prediction was still true after the investigators controlled for age, sex, income, loneliness, and physical capability to engage in household and social activities. This effect is extremely powerful, and exceeds the one to four years of added life associated with other factors, such as low blood pressure, low cholesterol levels, and no history of obesity or cigarette smoking. These results have been supported in more recent studies (e.g., Steptoe & Wardle, 2012). Studies such as this have created interest in a new field called *positive psychology* in which investigators explore factors that account for positive attitudes and happiness (Diener, 2000; Lyubomirsky, 2001).

SOCIAL LEARNING

Another influential psychologist was Canadian Albert Bandura. Bandura (1973, 1986) observed that organisms, including lower animals, do not have to directly experience certain events in their environment to learn effectively. Rather, they can learn just as much by observing what happens to someone else in a given situation. This fairly obvious discovery came to be known as **modelling** or **observational learning**. What is important is that, even in animals, this type of learning requires a symbolic integration of the experiences of others with judgments of what might happen to us. In other words, even an animal that is not very intelligent by human standards, such as a rat, must make a decision about the conditions under which its own experiences would be very similar to those of the animal it is observing. Bandura expanded his observations into a network of ideas in which behaviour, cognitive factors, and environmental influences converged to produce the complexity

of behaviour that confronts us. He also specified in some detail the importance of the social context of our learning; that is, much of what we learn depends on our interactions with other people around us; thus, his approach became known as *social learning theory*.

In the 1960s, Bandura made notable contributions to the understanding of children's aggressive behaviours. He and his students conducted a series of experiments using models interacting with a plastic Bobo doll (e.g., Bandura et al., 1961, 1963). The results of these studies helped Bandura develop and refine his social learning theory. For example, Bandura and his colleagues (1963) conducted a study that was designed to examine the influence of consequences to the model on children's imitative learning of aggression. Nursery school children were randomly assigned to one of four groups. The first group observed a model who interacted aggressively with the Bobo doll and whose aggressive behaviour was rewarded. A second group of children observed a model who interacted aggressively with the Bobo doll but whose aggressive behaviour was punished. A third (control) group was exposed to highly expressive but nonaggressive models. A final additional control group had no exposure to models. All the children were then tested for the presence of aggressive responses. Children who had witnessed the aggressive model who was rewarded showed more aggression. In contrast, children who had witnessed the aggressive model who was punished failed to reproduce the model's behaviour. This important series of studies provided evidence consistent with Bandura's theory that the steps involved in vicarious learning are (1) noticing the model's behaviour (attention), (2) remembering the model's behaviour (retention), and (3) exhibiting the model's behaviour (reproduction). The findings also suggested an additional step in vicarious conditioning that involves motivation: Children are more likely to attend to, retain, and reproduce behaviours of models that have been rewarded for the behaviour, while they are less likely to emulate models who have been punished for their behaviour.

The basic idea in all Bandura's work is that a careful analysis of cognitive processes may well produce the most accurate scientific predictions of behaviour. Concepts of probability learning, information processing, and attention have become increasingly important in psychopathology (Bar-Haim et al., 2007; Barlow, 2002; Davey, 2006; Lovibond, 2006; Yiend, 2010).

Courtesy of Albert Bandura

PREPARED LEARNING

It is clear that our genetic endowments influence what we learn. This conclusion is based on the fact that we learn to fear some objects much more easily than others, as is demonstrated in the important experiments of

▲ Albert Bandura developed social learning theory. His work expanded on traditional learning perspectives by highlighting the importance of social and cognitive factors in learning.

Swedish psychologist Arne Öhman. In other words, we learn fears and phobias selectively (Morris et al., 1998; Öhman et al., 2000; Öhman & Mineka, 2001). Why might this be? According to the concept of **prepared learning**, we have become highly prepared for learning about certain types of objects or situations through evolution, because this knowledge contributed to the survival of our ancestors (Mineka, 1985; Seligman, 1971). Even without any contact, we are more likely to learn to fear snakes or spiders than rocks or flowers, even if we know rationally that the snake or spider is harmless (e.g., Fredrikson et al.,1997; Pury & Mineka, 1997). In the absence of experience, however, we are less likely to fear evolutionary novel objects like guns or electrical outlets, even though we know they are potentially much more deadly.

Why do we so readily learn to fear snakes or spiders? One possibility is that throughout evolution, people who avoided snakes and spiders eluded the deadly varieties and therefore survived in greater numbers to pass down their genes to us (de Silva et al., 1977). This idea is a theory, of course, but at present it seems a likely explanation. Something within us recognizes the connection between a certain signal and a threatening event. In other words, certain UCS (unconditioned stimuli) and CS (conditioned stimuli) "belong" to each other. If you've ever gotten sick on cheap wine or bad food, chances are you won't make the same mistake again. This very quick or *one-trial* learning also occurs in animals that eat something that tastes bad or contains poison. It is easy to see that survival is associated with quickly learning to avoid poisonous food. When animals are shocked instead of poisoned when eating certain foods, however, they do not learn this association nearly as quickly, probably because in nature shock is not a consequence of eating, whereas being poisoned can be (Cook et al., 1986; Garcia et al., 1972; Mallan et al., 2013).

COGNITIVE SCIENCE AND THE UNCONSCIOUS

Advances in cognitive science have revolutionized our conceptions of the unconscious. We are not aware of much of what goes on inside our heads, but our unconscious is not necessarily the seething cauldron of primitive emotional conflicts envisioned by Freud. Rather, we simply seem able to process and store information, and act on it, without having the slightest awareness of what the information is or why we are acting on it (Bargh & Chartrand, 1999). Is this fact surprising? Consider briefly these two examples.

Weiskrantz (1992) describes a phenomenon called *blind sight* or *unconscious vision*. He relates the case of a young man who, for medical reasons, had a small section of his visual cortex (the centre for the control of vision in the brain) surgically removed. Though the operation was considered a success, the young man became blind in both eyes. Later, during routine tests, a physician raised his hand to the left of the patient who, much to the shock of his doctors, reached out and touched it. Subsequently, scientists determined that he could not only reach accurately for objects but could also distinguish among objects and perform most of the functions usually associated with sight. Yet, when asked about his abilities, he would say, "I couldn't see anything, not a darn thing," and that all he was doing was guessing.

The phenomenon in this case, of course, is associated with real brain damage. Much more interesting, from the point of view of psychopathology, is that the same thing seems to occur in healthy individuals who have been hypnotized (Hilgard, 1992; Kihlstrom, 1992); that is, normal individuals, provided with hypnotic suggestions that they are blind, are able to function visually but have no awareness or memory of their visual abilities. This condition, which illustrates a process of dissociation between behaviour and consciousness, is the basis of the dissociative disorders discussed in Chapter 7.

A second example, more relevant to psychopathology, is called **implicit memory** (Bowers & Marsolek, 2003; Kihlstrom et al., 1992; McNally, 1999; Schacter et al., 1993). As has been described by cognitive psychologist Peter Graf and his colleagues at the University of British Columbia, implicit memory is apparent when someone clearly acts based on things that have happened in the past but can't remember the events (Graf et al., 1984). In contrast, a good memory for events is called *explicit memory*. Much research attests to the distinctiveness of implicit and explicit memory processes (see review by Ryan & Cohen, 2003), including evidence that they differ in their developmental patterns (e.g., Billingsley, Smith, & McAndrews, 2002), underlying brain structures (e.g., Billingsley, McAndrews, & Smith, 2002), and the degree to which they are affected by certain drugs (e.g., Stewart, Buffett-Jerrott, et al., 2006). Implicit memory can be very selective for only certain events or circumstances. Clinically, we have already seen in Chapter 1 an example of implicit memory at work in the story of Anna O., the classic case first described by Breuer and Freud (1895/1957) to demonstrate the existence of the unconscious. It was only after therapy that Anna O. remembered events surrounding her father's death and the connection of these events to her paralysis. Thus, Anna O.'s behaviour (occasional paralysis) was evidently connected to implicit memories of her father's death. Many scientists have concluded that Freud's speculations on the nature and structure of the unconscious went beyond the evidence, but the existence of unconscious processes has since been demonstrated, and we must take them into account as we study mental health.

What methods do we have for studying the unconscious? The black box refers to unobservable feelings and cognitions inferred by an individual's self-report. In recent decades, psychologists, confident in an established science of behaviour, have returned to the black box with new methods, attempting to reveal the unobservable. Such unobservable unconscious processes are often referred to as implicit cognitive processes or **implicit cognition**. Several methods for studying implicit cognition have been made possible by advances in technology. One of them is the Stroop colour-naming paradigm.

In the Stroop paradigm, subjects are shown a variety of words, each printed in a different colour. They are shown these words very quickly and asked to name the colours in which the words are printed while ignoring their meaning. Colour naming is delayed when the meaning of the word attracts the subject's attention, despite his or her efforts to concentrate on the colour; that is, the meaning of the word interferes with the subject's ability to process colour information (see Kolb & Whishaw, 2003). For example, experimenters have determined that people with certain

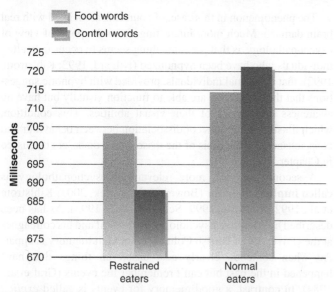

Food words
Control words

FIGURE 2.14 | Average colour-naming speeds (in milliseconds) for food and control words in restrained eaters and normal eaters. Only the restrained eaters show substantially slowed colour naming for words pertaining to food as compared with their colour naming speeds for words not pertaining to food.

Source: Adapted from "Dietary Restraint and the Selective Processing of Forbidden and Nonforbidden Food Words," by J. A. Francis, S. H. Stewart, and S. Hounsell, 1997, *Cognitive Therapy and Research, 21*(6), pp. 633–646.

psychological disorders are much slower at naming the colours of words associated with their problem than the colours of words that have no relation to the disorder. Jody, for instance, would be much slower at naming the colour of words like *blood*, *injury*, and *dissect* than the colours of words that have no relation to his phobia. Francis, Stewart, and Hounsell (1997) at Dalhousie University used the Stroop task in a study with women who were chronic dieters or "restrained eaters." On the Stroop, these researchers compared participants' colour-naming speeds for words pertaining to food (e.g., *icing, chips, cookie*) versus words unrelated to food (e.g., animal words like *snakes, insect, elephants*). Women who were restrained eaters, but not women who were normal eaters, showed substantially slowed colour naming for words pertaining to food (i.e., for words pertaining to their eating problem; see ■ Figure 2.14). A review by Keith Dobson at the University of Calgary and David Dozois at the University of Western Ontario came to similar conclusions. Across 29 studies that examined Stroop effects in eating-disordered samples, they found clear evidence of slowed colour-naming for food and body/weight words among those with bulimia, and of slowed colour-naming for body/weight words among those with anorexia (Dobson & Dozois, 2004). Thus, psychologists can now uncover particular patterns of emotional significance, even if the subject cannot verbalize them or is not even aware of them.

COGNITIVE-BEHAVIOURAL THERAPY

As scientists began to discover the important contributions of cognitive processes to behavioural development, psychologists began to integrate cognitive procedures and techniques directly

Concept Check 2.4

Check your understanding of behavioural and cognitive influences by identifying the descriptions. Choose your answers from (a) learned helplessness, (b) modelling, (c) prepared learning, and (d) implicit memory.

1. Karen noticed that every time Don behaved well at lunch, the teacher praised him. Karen decided to behave better to receive praise herself. _____

2. Jin stopped trying to please his father because he never knows whether his father will be proud or outraged. _____

3. Greg fell into a lake as a baby and almost drowned. Even though Greg has no recollection of the event, he hates to be around large bodies of water. _____

4. Céline was scared to death of the tarantula, even though she knew it wasn't likely to hurt her. _____

into therapy. Among the originators of **cognitive-behavioural therapy (CBT)** was Aaron T. Beck (1976), who developed methods for dealing with faulty attributions and attitudes associated with learned helplessness and depression. CBT is a strong and growing therapy approach in Canada today, spearheaded by a number of internationally renowned scientist-practitioners, including Martin Antony, Neil Rector, and Zindel Segal in Toronto; David Clark in Fredericton; Michel Dugas and David Zuroff in Montreal; and Keith and Deborah Dobson in Calgary. Another therapy approach that emphasizes cognitive procedures and techniques, called *rational-emotive therapy*, was developed by Albert Ellis (1962). This approach also focuses directly on the irrational beliefs Ellis thought were at the root of maladaptive feelings and behaviour. Clinical psychologist Donald Meichenbaum combined techniques from psychodynamic and behaviour therapies to develop a novel approach he called *self-instructional training*; in this approach, he worked on modifying what clients say to themselves about the consequences of their behaviour (Meichenbaum, 1977; Meichenbaum & Cameron, 1974). Meichenbaum and his colleagues applied this new cognitive-behavioural approach with success to a variety of populations, including patients with schizophrenia who had attentional control problems (Meichenbaum & Cameron, 1973) and impulsive, hyperactive children (Meichenbaum, 1971; Meichenbaum & Goodman, 1971).

Cognitive-behavioural approaches to treatment are described in some detail in later chapters, particularly in Chapter 5 on anxiety disorders, Chapter 8 on mood disorders, and Online Chapter, in which we describe stress-reduction procedures. In general, cognitive-behavioural therapists examine in some detail the ongoing thinking processes of individuals who are anxious, depressed, or stressed. This examination is often accomplished by having patients monitor their thoughts during periods of distress. For example, a straight-A student who experiences depression might assume before taking a particular course in university that she almost certainly will do very poorly; she is then likely to become more

▲ Donald Meichenbaum, a clinical psychologist who recently retired from the University of Waterloo, is a key figure in the development of cognitive-behavioural therapy. His work integrated aspects of psychodynamic and behavioural therapies, resulting in techniques like self-instructional training.

depressed. Such negative thoughts are clearly unrealistic and irrational. Similarly, individuals with severe anxiety might continually focus on dangers that could arise in normal situations. Anxious individuals are said to have an attentional bias—their attention is focused on information related to threat, at the expense of other types of information (Owens et al., 2004; Stewart, Conrod, et al., 1998; Teachman & Woody, 2004). Individuals with these types of depression or anxiety are often not aware that their thinking is inappropriate or negative, because it is automatic or unconscious. Automatic thoughts are believed to arise from an underlying maladaptive schema, which is a cognitive belief system about some aspect of life. For example, the depressed student in the example just mentioned might have the automatic thought, "I'm going to fail that course," because she has an underlying negative self-evaluation schema, believing she can never do anything correctly. Beck thought that such a schema could be formed by negative experiences when the individual was growing up.

The point of cognitive-behavioural therapy is to work with the patient to uncover these automatic thoughts and develop a different set of attitudes and attributions. This process is called *cognitive restructuring*, because the goal is to restructure the maladaptive schema. Patients are also assigned specific behavioural tasks, such as entering fearful situations, in which they can work on their emotional and cognitive reactions. Procedures such as relaxation or exercise that change arousal or activity levels may also be a component of therapy. Thus, the cognitive-behavioural approach continually targets both aspects of the problem: clarifying and modifying attributions and attitudes (cognitive), and avoiding situations that provoke unrealistic anxiety or depression, increasing activity, or improving social skills (behavioural). Such therapy is usually short term, requiring between 10 and 20 sessions. How cognitive-behavioural methods are used is described in more detail in the chapters on specific disorders.

EMOTIONS

Emotions play an enormous role in our day-to-day lives and can contribute in major ways to the development of psychological problems (Barrett, 2012; Gross, 2007; Kring & Sloan, 2010; Rottenberg & Johnson, 2007). Consider the emotion of fear. Have you ever found yourself in a really dangerous situation? Have you ever almost crashed your car and known for several seconds beforehand what was going to happen? Have you ever been swimming in the ocean and realized that you were out too far or caught in a current? Have you ever almost fallen from a height, such as from a ladder or a roof? In any of these instances, you would have felt an incredible surge of arousal. As the first great emotion theorist Charles Darwin (1872) pointed out a century and a half ago that this kind of reaction seems to be programmed in all animals, including humans, which suggests that it serves a useful function. The alarm reaction that activates during potentially life-threatening emergencies is called the **flight-or-fight response**. If you are caught in ocean currents, your almost instinctual tendency is to struggle toward shore. You might realize rationally that you're best off just floating until the current runs its course and then, more calmly, swimming in later. Yet somewhere, deep within, ancient instincts for survival won't let you relax, even though struggling against the ocean will only wear you out and increase your chance of drowning. Still, this same kind of reaction might momentarily give you the strength to lift a car off your trapped brother or fight off an attacker. The whole purpose of the physical rush of adrenaline that we feel in extreme danger is to mobilize us to escape the danger (flight) or to withstand it (fight).

THE PHYSIOLOGY AND PURPOSE OF FEAR

How do physical reactions prepare us to respond this way? The great physiologist Walter Cannon (1929) speculated on the reasons. Fear activates your cardiovascular system. Your blood vessels constrict, thereby raising arterial pressure and decreasing the blood flow to your extremities (fingers and toes). Excess blood is redirected to the skeletal muscles, where it is available to the vital organs that may be needed in an emergency. Often people seem "white with fear"; that is, they turn pale as a result of decreased blood flow to the skin. "Trembling with fear," with your hair standing on end, may be the result of shivering and piloerection (in which body hairs stand erect), reactions that conserve heat when your blood vessels are constricted.

These defensive adjustments can also produce the hot and cold spells that often occur during extreme fear. Breathing becomes faster and, usually, deeper to provide necessary oxygen to rapidly circulating blood. Increased blood circulation carries oxygen to the brain, stimulating cognitive processes and sensory functions, which makes you more alert and able to think more quickly during emergencies. An increased amount of glucose (sugar) is released from the liver into the

▲ Charles Darwin (1809–1882) drew this cat frightened by a dog to show the fight-or-flight reaction.

bloodstream, further energizing various crucial muscles and organs, including the brain. Pupils dilate, presumably to allow a better view of the situation. Hearing becomes more acute, and digestive activity is suspended, resulting in a reduced flow of saliva (the "dry mouth" of fear). In the short term, voiding the body of all waste material and eliminating digestive processes further prepare the organism for concentrated action and activity, so there is often pressure to urinate and defecate and, occasionally, to vomit.

It is easy to see why the flight-or-fight reaction is fundamentally important. Millennia ago, when our ancestors lived in very tenuous circumstances, those with strong emergency reactions were more likely to live through attacks and other dangers than those with weak emergency responses, and the survivors passed their genes down to us.

EMOTIONAL PHENOMENA

The **emotion** of fear is a subjective feeling of terror, a strong motivation for behaviour (escaping or fighting), and a complex physiological or arousal response. To define *emotion* is difficult, but most theorists agree that it is an action tendency (Lang, 1985, 1995; Lang et al., 1998)—that is, a tendency to behave in a certain way (e.g., escape), elicited by an external event (a threat) and a feeling state (terror), accompanied by a characteristic physiological response (Barrett, 2012; Gross, 2007; Izard, 1992; Lazarus, 1991, 1995). One purpose of a feeling state is to motivate us to carry out a behaviour: if we escape, our terror, which is unpleasant, will be decreased, so decreasing unpleasant feelings motivates us to escape (Campbell-Sills & Barlow, 2007; Gross, 2007; Hofmann, 2015; Öhman, 1996). As some have pointed out (Öhman, 1996; Öhman et al., 2000), the principal function of emotions can be understood as a clever means to get us to do the things that, on average, led to better chances of survival and reproduction throughout evolution. How do you think this works with anger or with love? What is the feeling state? What is the behaviour?

Emotions are usually short-lived, temporary states lasting from several minutes to several hours, occurring in response to an external event. **Mood** is a more persistent period of affect or emotionality. Thus, in Chapter 8 we describe enduring or recurring states of depression or excitement (mania) as mood disorders. But anxiety disorders, described in Chapter 5, are characterized by enduring or chronic anxiety and, therefore, could also be called mood disorders. Alternatively, both anxiety disorders and *mood disorders* could be called *emotional disorders*, a term not formally used in psychopathology. This is only one example of the occasional inconsistencies in the terminology of abnormal psychology. A related term you will see occasionally, particularly in Chapters 3 and 14, is **affect**, which usually refers to the momentary emotional tone that accompanies what we say or do. For example, if you just got an A+ on your test but you look sad, your friends might think your reaction strange because your affect is not appropriate to the event. The term *affect* can also be used more generally to summarize commonalities among emotional states that are characteristic of an individual. Thus, someone who tends to be fearful, anxious, and depressed is experiencing negative affect. Positive affect would subsume tendencies to be pleasant, joyful, excited, and so on.

THE COMPONENTS OF EMOTION

Emotion scientists now agree that emotion comprises three related components, *behaviour*, *physiology*, and *cognition*, but most emotion scientists tend to concentrate on one component or another (see ■ Figure 2.15). Those who concentrate on behaviour think that basic patterns of emotion differ from one another in fundamental ways; for example, anger may differ from sadness not only in how it feels but also in how it manifests behaviourally and physiologically. These scientists also emphasize that emotion is a way of communicating. One function of fear is to motivate immediate and decisive action, such as running away. But if you look scared, your facial expression will quickly communicate the possibility of danger to your friends, who may not be aware that a threat is imminent. Your facial communication increases their chance for survival because they can now respond more quickly to the threat when it occurs.

Other scientists have concentrated on the physiology of emotions, most notably W. B. Cannon (1929), in some pioneering work, who viewed emotion as primarily a brain function. Research in this tradition suggests that areas of the brain associated with emotional expression are generally more ancient and primitive than areas associated with higher cognitive processes, such as reasoning.

Other research demonstrates direct neurobiological connections between the emotional centres of the brain and parts of the eye (the retina) or ear that allow emotional activation without the influence of higher cognitive processes (LeDoux, 1996; Öhman et al., 2000; Zajonc, 1984, 1998); in other words, you may experience various emotions quickly and directly without necessarily thinking about them or being aware of why you feel the way you do.

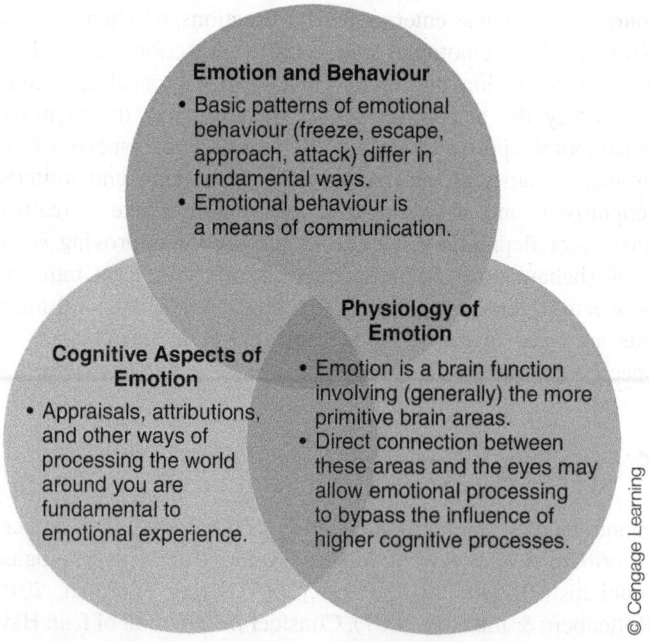

Emotion and Behaviour
- Basic patterns of emotional behaviour (freeze, escape, approach, attack) differ in fundamental ways.
- Emotional behaviour is a means of communication.

Cognitive Aspects of Emotion
- Appraisals, attributions, and other ways of processing the world around you are fundamental to emotional experience.

Physiology of Emotion
- Emotion is a brain function involving (generally) the more primitive brain areas.
- Direct connection between these areas and the eyes may allow emotional processing to bypass the influence of higher cognitive processes.

© Cengage Learning

FIGURE 2.15 | Emotion has three important and overlapping components: behaviour, cognition, and physiology.

Last, a number of prominent scientists concentrate on studying the cognitive aspects of emotion. Notable among these theorists is Richard S. Lazarus (e.g., 1968, 1991, 1995), who proposed that changes in a person's environment are appraised in terms of their potential impact on that person. The type of appraisal you make determines the emotion you experience. For example, if you see somebody holding a gun in a dark alley, you will probably appraise the situation as dangerous and experience fear. You would make a very different appraisal if you saw a tour guide displaying an antique gun in a museum. Lazarus would suggest that thinking and feeling cannot be separated, but other cognitive scientists are concluding otherwise, by suggesting that, although cognitive and emotional systems interact and overlap, they are fundamentally separate (Teasdale, 1993). In fact, all components of emotion—behaviour, physiology, and cognition—are important, and theorists are adopting more integrative approaches by studying their interaction (Barrett, 2009, 2012; Gendron & Barrett, 2009; Gross, 2015; Hoffman, 2015).

EMOTIONS AND PSYCHOPATHOLOGY

We now know that suppressing almost any kind of emotional response, such as anger or fear, increases sympathetic nervous system activity, which may contribute to psychological problems (Barlow et al., 2004; Campbell-Sills & Barlow, 2007; Fairholme et al., 2010). Other emotions seem to have a more direct effect. In Chapter 5, we study the phenomenon of *panic* and its relationship to anxiety disorders. One interesting possibility is that a panic attack is simply the normal emotion of fear occurring at the wrong time, when there is nothing to be afraid of (Barlow, 2002). Some patients with mood disorders become overly excited and joyful. They think they can do anything they want and spend as much money as they want because everything will turn out all right. Every little event is the most wonderful and exciting experience they have ever had. These individuals are experiencing *mania*, which is part of a serious mood disorder called *bipolar disorder*, discussed in Chapter 8. People with mania usually alternate periods of excitement with periods of extreme sadness and distress, when they feel that all is lost and the world is a gloomy and hopeless place. During extreme sadness, people are unable to experience any pleasure in life and often find it difficult even to get out of bed and move around. If hopelessness becomes acute, they are at risk for suicide. This emotional state is *depression*, a defining feature of many mood disorders. Thus, basic emotions of fear, anger, sadness or distress, and excitement may contribute to many psychological disorders and may even define them. Emotions and mood also affect our cognitive processes: if your mood is positive, then your associations, interpretations, and impressions also tend to be positive (Diener et al., 2003). Your impression of people you first meet and even your memories of past events are coloured to a great extent by your current mood. If you are consistently negative or depressed, then your memories of past events are likely to be unpleasant. The pessimist or depressed person sees the darker side of things. In contrast, the cheerful optimist is said to see the best in the world and the brighter side of things. This is a rich area of investigation for cognitive and emotion scientists (Eysenck, 1992; Rottenberg & Johnson, 2007; Teasdale, 1993),

particularly those interested in the close interconnection of cognitive and emotional processes. Leading psychopathologists are beginning to outline the nature of emotion disruption (or dysregulation) and to understand how these disruptions interfere with thinking and behaviour in various psychological disorders (Barlow et al., 2004; Campbell-Sills & Barlow, 2007; Gross, 2007; Kring & Sloan, 2010).

CULTURAL, SOCIAL, AND INTERPERSONAL FACTORS

Given the jumble of neurobiological and psychological variables impinging on our lives, is there any room for the influence of social, interpersonal, and cultural factors? Studies are beginning to demonstrate the substantial power and depth of such influences. In fact, researchers have now established that cultural and social influences can kill you. Consider the following example.

In many cultures around the world, individuals may experience fright disorders, exaggerated startle responses, and other observable fear reactions. One example is the Latin American *susto*, characterized by various anxiety-based symptoms, including insomnia, irritability, phobias, and the marked somatic symptoms of sweating and increased heart rate (tachycardia). But *susto* has only one cause: the individual believes that he or she has become the object of black magic, or witchcraft, and is suddenly badly frightened. In some cultures, the sinister influence is called the evil eye (Good & Kleinman, 1985; Tan, 1980), and the resulting fright disorder can be fatal. W. B. Cannon (1942), examining the Haitian phenomenon of voodoo death, suggested that the sentence of death by a medicine man may create an intolerable autonomic arousal in the subject, who has little ability to cope because absolutely no social support exists. Ultimately, the condition leads to damage to internal organs and death. Thus, from all accounts, an individual who, from a physical and psychological point of view, is functioning in a perfectly healthy and adaptive way suddenly dies because of marked changes in the social environment.

Fear and phobias are universal, occurring across all cultures. But what we fear is strongly influenced by our social environment and cultural context. As noted by cross-cultural psychologist John Berry of Queen's University at Kingston, although all human societies exhibit commonalities and share basic psychological processes, such underlying commonalities are expressed by various groups in vastly different ways from one time and place to another (Berry, 2003).

GENDER ROLES

Gender roles have a strong and sometimes puzzling effect on psychopathology (Kistner, 2009; Maeng & Milad, 2015; Rutter et al., 2006). For example, everyone experiences anxiety and fear, and phobias are found all over the world. But phobias have a peculiar characteristic: The likelihood of your having a particular phobia is powerfully influenced by your gender! Someone who complains of an insect or a small animal phobia severe enough to prohibit field trips or visits to friends in the country

▲ Our emotional reaction depends on context. Fire, for example, can be threatening or comforting.

is almost certain to be female, as are 90 percent of the people with this phobia. As another example, dramatic gender differences exist in rates of mood disorders: About two-thirds of those with major depression are women (Hasin et al., 2005)—a gender difference that has been found in ten countries worldwide, including Canada (Andrade et al., 2003).

It is possible that these substantial gender differences in rates of certain phobias and of depression have to do with cultural expectations of men and women or our gender roles. For example, with respect to animal phobias, an equal number of men and women may have an experience that could lead to an insect or a small animal phobia, such as being bitten by one, but in our society it isn't always acceptable for a man to show or even admit fear. So a man is more likely to hide or endure the fear until he gets over it. It is more acceptable for women to acknowledge fearfulness, and so a phobia develops. Similarly, gender roles may contribute to explaining why depression is more common in women. When experiencing a negative life event, women tend to ruminate about it and to blame themselves, whereas men are more likely to engage in activity to take their minds off the negative event—a behaviour that may make men less likely to experience depression in response to stress (Goldstein, 2006; Nolen-Hoeksema, 2000b).

Another important gender difference involves ways of coping with panic attacks. To avoid or survive a panic attack, an extreme experience of fear, some males drink alcohol instead of admitting they're afraid. In many cases, this attempt to cope may lead to alcoholism (Stewart et al., 1999), a disorder that affects many more males than females. One reason for this gender imbalance is that males are more likely than females to self-medicate their fear and panic with alcohol and in so doing start down the slippery slope to addiction.

It even seems that men and women may respond differently to the same standardized psychological treatment. In a study by Felmingham and Bryant (2012), after exposure therapy for post-traumatic stress disorder (see Chapter 5), both groups benefited, but women maintained their gains significantly better during a follow-up period. The authors suggest that the well-established ability of women to recall emotional memories somewhat better

than men may facilitate emotional processing and long-term treatment gains.

Bulimia nervosa, a severe eating disorder, occurs almost entirely in young females. Why? As we see in Chapter 9, a cultural emphasis on female thinness plagues our society and, increasingly, societies around the world. The pressures for males to be thin are less apparent, and of the few males who develop bulimia, a substantial percentage belong to a subculture where cultural imperatives to be thin are present (see Chapter 9).

Finally, in an exciting finding, Taylor (2002, 2006; Taylor et al., 2000) described a unique way in which females in many species respond to stress in their lives. This unique response to stress is called "tend and befriend" and refers to protecting themselves and their young through nurturing behaviour (tend) and forming alliances with larger social groups, particularly other females (befriend). Taylor et al. supposed that this response fits better with the way females respond to stress because it builds on the brain's attachment-caregiving system and leads to nurturing and affiliative behaviour. Furthermore, the response is characterized by identifiable neurobiological processes in the brain that are gender specific.

Gender doesn't cause psychopathology. But because gender role is a social and cultural factor that influences the form and content of a disorder, we attend closely to it in the chapters that follow.

SOCIAL EFFECTS ON HEALTH AND BEHAVIOUR

Several studies have demonstrated that the greater the number and frequency of social relationships and contacts, the longer you are likely to live (e.g., Miller, 2011). Conversely, the lower you score on a social index that measures the richness of your social life, the shorter your life expectancy. Studies documenting this finding have been reported in North America and in Sweden and Finland (Berkman & Syme, 1979; House et al., 1982; Schoenbach et al., 1986). The studies take into account existing physical health and other risk factors for dying young, such as high blood pressure, high cholesterol levels, and smoking habits, and still produce the same result. Studies also show that social relationships seem to protect individuals against many physical and psychological disorders, such as high blood pressure, depression, alcoholism, arthritis, the progression to AIDS, and low birth weight in newborns (Cobb, 1976; House et al., 1988; Leserman et al., 2000; Thurston & Kubzanksy, 2009). Similarly, the risk of depression for people who live alone is approximately 80 percent higher than for people who live with others, based on a count of new prescriptions for antidepressant medication (Pulkki-Raback et al., 2012). Also, social isolation increases the risk of death about as much as smoking cigarettes and more than physical inactivity or obesity (Holt-Lunstad et al., 2010). Interestingly, it is not just the absolute number of social contacts that is important—it is the actual perception of loneliness. Thus, some people can live alone with few ill effects; others might feel lonely despite frequent social contacts (Cacioppo et al., 2015).

Even whether or not we come down with a cold is strongly influenced by the quality and extent of our social network. Cohen and colleagues (Cohen et al., 1997) used nasal drops to expose 276 healthy volunteers to one of two different rhinoviruses (cold viruses), and then they quarantined the subjects for a week. The authors measured the extent of participation in 12 different types of social relationships (e.g., spouse, parent, friend, colleague), as well as other factors, such as smoking and poor sleep quality, that are likely to increase susceptibility to colds. The surprising results were that the greater the extent of social ties, the smaller the chance of catching a cold, even after all other factors were taken into consideration (controlled for). In fact, those with the fewest social ties were more than four times as likely to catch a cold as those with the greatest number of ties. This effect also extends to pets! Compared with people who do not have pets, people with pets evidenced lower resting heart rate and blood pressure, and responded with smaller increases in these variables during laboratory stressors (Allen et al., 2002). What could account for this? Once again, social and interpersonal factors seem to influence psychological and neurobiological variables—for example, the immune system—sometimes to a substantial degree (Cacioppo & Patrick, 2008). Thus, we cannot really study psychological and biological aspects of psychological disorders (or physical disorders, for that matter), without taking into account the social and cultural context of the disorder.

How do social relationships have such a profound impact on our physical and psychological characteristics? We don't know for sure, but we have some intriguing hints (Cacioppo & Patrick, 2008; Cacioppo et al., 2007). Some people think that interpersonal relationships give meaning to life and that people who have something to live for can overcome physical deficiencies and even delay death. You may have known an older person who far outlived his or her expected time in order to witness a significant family event such as a grandchild's graduation from university. Once the event has passed, the person dies. Another common observation is that if one spouse in a long-standing marital relationship dies, particularly a wife, the other often dies soon after, regardless of health status. It is also possible that social relationships facilitate health-promoting behaviours, such as exercising restraint in the use of alcohol and drugs, getting proper sleep, and seeking appropriate health care (House et al., 1988; Leserman et al., 2000).

Sometimes social upheaval is an opportunity for studying the impact of social networks on individual functioning. When Israeli settlements in the Sinai Peninsula were dismantled and the residents evacuated as part of peace negotiations with Egypt, Steinglass, Weisstub, and Kaplan De-Nour (1988) studied residents of an Israeli community threatened with dissolution. They found that believing that one is embedded firmly in a social context was just as important as actually having a social network. Poor long-term adjustment was best predicted in those who perceived that their social network was disintegrating, whether or not it actually did.

In another example, whether you live in a city or the country may be associated with your chances of developing schizophrenia, a very severe disorder. Lewis, David, Andreasson, and Allsbeck (1992) found that the incidence of schizophrenia was 38 percent greater in men who had been raised in cities than in those raised in rural areas. We have known for a long time that more schizophrenia exists in the city than in the country, but researchers thought that people with schizophrenia drifted to cities after developing schizophrenia or that other endemic urban factors, such as drug use or unstable family relationships, might be the real culprit. But Lewis and associates carefully controlled for such factors, and it now seems something about cities over and above those influences may contribute to the development of schizophrenia (Boydell & Allardyce, 2011; Pedersen & Mortensen, 2006; Vassos et al., 2012). We do not yet know what it is. This finding may be very important in view of the mass migration of individuals to overcrowded urban areas, particularly in less developed countries.

In summary, we cannot study psychopathology independently of social and interpersonal influences, and we still have much to learn. Many psychological disorders, such as social phobia and major depressive disorder, seem to occur in all cultures, but they may look different from one culture to another because individual symptoms are strongly influenced by social and interpersonal context (Cheung, 2012; Cheung et al., 2011). For example, as we see in Chapter 7, depression in Western culture is reflected in feelings of guilt and inadequacy and in developing countries with physical distress, such as fatigue or illness. Laurence Kirmayer, a cross-cultural psychiatrist from McGill University, has described how affective expressions of depression are often perceived as self-centred and threatening to the social structure in many Asian cultures, such as in Chinese society. This cultural context results in affective and cognitive dimensions of depression being less readily endorsed by Chinese patients (Kirmayer & Groleau, 2001). These types of cultural differences likely contribute to the consistent underuse of mainstream mental health services by Asian Canadians (Li & Browne, 2000; Whitley et al., 2006). In Canada, Asian immigrants (including those from the Middle East) represented 57 percent of all Canadian immigrants from 2006 to 2011 (Statistics Canada, 2013). Between 2011 and 2016, this majority increased to 62 percent (Statistics Canada, 2017).

As another clear example of social influences on mental health, consider the high rates of various psychological disorders and problems in some Indigenous communities. As we will discuss in more detail in the chapters to come, rates of suicide, substance abuse, and familial violence are elevated in many Indigenous groups (Bridges & Kunselman, 2005; Brownridge, 2003; Gotowiec & Beiser, 1993–1994). Poverty, an established risk factor for many psychological disorders (Richters, 1993), is higher among Indigenous Peoples (Lee, 2000), which very likely contributes substantially to their elevated rates of certain psychological disorders (Caron & Liu, 2010). However, the fact that more Indigenous individuals live in poverty is not the only reason for the elevated rates of these psychological and social problems. Their unique experiences of a history of oppression by the majority culture also need to be considered as a contributing factor, something that has been referred to as *historical trauma* (Bombay et al., 2014). These oppressive experiences include the maltreatment of Indigenous children in the residential school system from the late 19th century to as recently as the 1990s (Grant, 1996; Haig-Brown, 1988; Truth and Reconciliation Commission of Canada, 2015) and the continued discrimination against and reduced opportunities for Indigenous Peoples (Matheson et al., 2018; Shepard et al., 2006).

Social and Interpersonal Influences on Seniors

The effect of social and interpersonal factors on the expression of physical and psychological disorders may differ with age (Charles & Carstensen, 2010; Holland & Gallagher-Thompson, 2011). Grant, Patterson, and Yager (1988) studied 118 men and women 65 years old or older who lived independently. Those with fewer meaningful contacts and less social support from relatives had consistently higher levels of depression and more reports of unsatisfactory quality of life. If these individuals became physically ill, however, they had more substantial support from their families than those who were not physically ill. This finding raises the unfortunate possibility that it may be advantageous for seniors to become physically ill, because illness allows them to re-establish the social support that makes life worth living. Involving their families before they get ill might help maintain their physical health (and significantly reduce health-care costs).

The study of older adults is growing at a rapid pace, in line with the increase in the proportion of our population that is elderly. Frank Denton and his colleagues at McMaster University made projections of the age distribution of the Canadian population for the 45-years from 1996 to 2041. They concluded that substantial aging of the Canadian population as a whole is virtually certain (Denton et al., 1998). Statistics Canada (2017) concurs: in 2016, 16.9 percent of Canadians were 65 years of age and older. It predicts this number will increase to at least 23 percent by 2031 or that almost one in four Canadians will be 65 years of age or older. This was the first time that the proportion of seniors was larger than the proportion of children 14 years of age or younger (16.6 percent), and they anticipate that the proportion of these young Canadians will remain at a similar level in 2031. Some have suggested that with this growth will come a corresponding increase in the number of older adults with mental health problems, many of whom will not receive appropriate care (e.g., Gatz & Smyer, 1992). As you can see, understanding and treating the disorders experienced by older adults is necessary and important.

▲ A long and productive life usually includes strong social relationships and interpersonal relations.

Social Stigma

Other factors make the consideration of social and cultural issues imperative to the study of psychopathology. Psychological disorders continue to carry a substantial stigma in our society. To be anxious or depressed is to be weak and cowardly. To be schizophrenic is to be unpredictable and crazy. For physical injuries in times of war, we award medals. For psychological injuries, the unfortunate soldiers earn scorn and derision, as has been highlighted by Roméo Dallaire (2003a, 2003b), a high-ranking member of the Canadian military who led the peacekeeping mission in Rwanda. Often, someone with psychological disorders does not seek health care for fear a co-worker might learn about the problem. With far less social support than for physical illness, people have less chance of full recovery. We discuss some of the consequences of social attitudes toward psychological disorders in Chapter 17.

LIFESPAN DEVELOPMENT

Lifespan developmental psychopathologists (e.g., Galambos & Leadbeater, 2002) point out that we tend to look at psychological disorders from a snapshot perspective: We focus on a particular point in a person's life and assume it represents the whole person. The inadequacy of this way of looking at people should be clear. Think back on your own life over the past few years. The person you were, say, three years ago, is very different from the person you are now, and the person you will be three years from now will have changed in important ways (even though we tend to have a cognitive bias called "the end of history" illusion that makes us think that we will change very little in the years to come; Quoidbach et al., 2013). To understand psychopathology, we must appreciate how experiences during different periods of development may influence our vulnerability to other types of stress or to psychological disorders (Charles & Carstensen, 2010; Rutter, 2002).

Important developmental changes occur at all points in life. For example, adulthood, far from being a relatively stable period, is highly dynamic, with important changes occurring into old age. Erik Erikson suggested that we go through eight major crises during our lives (Erikson, 1982), each determined by our biological maturation and the social demands made at particular times. Unlike Freud, who envisioned no developmental stages beyond adolescence, Erikson believed that we grow and change beyond the age of 65. During older adulthood, for example, we look back and view our lives either as rewarding or as disappointing.

Although aspects of Erikson's theory of psychosocial development have been criticized as being too vague (Shaffer, 1993), it illustrates the comprehensive approach to human development advocated by lifespan developmentalists. Basic research is beginning to confirm the importance of this approach. In one experiment at the University of Lethbridge by Bryan Kolb and his colleagues (Kolb, Gibb, & Gorny, 2003), animals were placed in complex environments either as juveniles, as adults, or in very old age, when cognitive abilities were beginning to decline (senescence). The environment had different effects on the brains of these animals depending on their developmental stage. Basically, the complex and challenging environments increased the size and complexity of neurons in the motor and sensory cortical regions in the adult and aged animals, but unlike the older groups, decreased the spine density of neurons in very young animals. Nevertheless, this decrease was associated with enhanced motor and cognitive skills when the animals became adults. In fact, even prenatal experience seems to affect brain structure, since the offspring of an animal housed in a rich and complex environment during the term of her pregnancy have the advantage of more complex cortical brain circuits after birth (Kolb, Gibb, & Robinson, 2003). Thus, we can infer that the influence of developmental stage and prior experience has a substantial impact on the development and presentation of psychological disorders, an inference that is receiving confirmation from sophisticated lifespan developmental psychology research (e.g., Carstensen et al., 2003; Isaacowitz et al., 2003). For example, in depressive (mood) disorders, children and adolescents do not receive the same benefit from antidepressant drugs as do adults (Hazell et al., 1995; Santosh, 2009), and for many of them these drugs pose risks that are not present in adults (Santosh, 2009). Also, the gender distribution in depression is approximately equal until puberty, when it becomes more common in girls (Compas et al., 1997; Hankin et al., 2007).

THE PRINCIPLE OF EQUIFINALITY

When considering developmental influences on psychology, an important concept is the principle of **equifinality**. This principle is used in developmental psychopathology to indicate that we must consider many paths to a given outcome (Cicchetti, 1991). Like a fever, a particular behaviour or disorder may have several causes. Many examples of this equifinality principle exist; for example, a delusional syndrome may be an aspect of schizophrenia, but it can also arise from amphetamine abuse. Delirium, which involves difficulty focusing attention, often occurs in older adults after surgery, but it can also result from thiamine deficiency or renal (kidney) disease. Autism can sometimes occur in children whose mothers are exposed to rubella during pregnancy, but it can also occur in children whose mothers experience difficulties during labour.

Different paths can also result from the interaction of psychological and biological factors during various stages of development. How someone copes with impairment because of organic causes may have a profound effect on that person's overall functioning. For example, people with documented brain damage may have different levels of disorder. Those with healthy systems of social support, consisting of family and friends, as well as highly adaptive personality characteristics, such as marked confidence in their abilities to overcome challenges, may experience only mild behavioural and cognitive disturbance despite an organic pathology. Those without comparable support and personality may be incapacitated. This difference may be clearer if you think of people you know with physical disabilities. Some people paralyzed from the waist down by accident or disease (paraplegics) have become superb athletes or accomplished in business or the arts. Others with the same condition are depressed and feel hopeless; they have withdrawn from life or, even worse, ended their lives. Even the content of delusions and hallucinations that may accompany a disorder, and the degree to which they are frightening or difficult to cope with, is determined in part by psychological and social factors.

Researchers are exploring not only what makes people experience particular disorders but also what protects others from having the same difficulties. If you were interested in why someone would be depressed, for example, you would first look at people who display depression. But you could also study people in similar situations and from similar backgrounds who are not depressed. An excellent example of this approach is research on resilient children, which suggests that social factors may protect some children from being hurt by stressful experiences, such as one or both parents having a psychiatric disturbance (Becvar, 2013; Cooper et al., 2007; Garmezy & Rutter, 1983; Goldstein & Brooks, 2013). The presence of a caring adult friend or relative can offset the negative stresses of this environment, as can the child's own ability to understand and cope with unpleasant situations. People brought up in violent or otherwise dysfunctional families who have successfully gone on to attend a postsecondary school might want to look back for the factors that protected them. Perhaps if we can better understand why some people do not encounter the same problems as others in similar circumstances, we can better understand particular disorders, assist those who experience them, and even prevent some cases from occurring at all.

CONCLUSIONS

We have examined modern approaches to psychopathology and we have found the field to be complex indeed. In this brief overview (even though it may not seem brief), we have seen that we must take into account the contributions from the fields of behavioural genetics, neuroscience, and behavioural and cognitive science, as well as consider emotional, social and cultural influences, and lifespan developmental factors when we think about psychopathology. Even though our knowledge is incomplete, you can see why we could never resume the one-dimensional thinking typical of the various historical traditions described in Chapter 1.

And yet, books about psychological disorders and news reports in the popular press often describe the causes of these disorders in one-dimensional terms without considering other influences. For example, how many times have you heard that a psychological disorder such as depression, or perhaps schizophrenia, is caused by a chemical imbalance without considering other possible causes? When you read that a disorder is caused by a chemical imbalance, it sounds like nothing else really matters, and all you have to do is correct the imbalance in neurotransmitter activity to "cure" the problem. (Direct evidence for such imbalances is in fact still lacking.)

Based on research we will review when we talk about specific psychological disorders, there is no question whatsoever that psychological disorders are associated with neurotransmitter activity and other aspects of brain function. But we have learned in this chapter that neurotransmitter activity could, in turn, be caused by psychological or social factors, such as stress, strong emotional reactions, difficult family interactions, changes caused by aging, or, most likely, some interaction of all these factors.

Similarly, how many times have you heard that alcoholism or other addictive behaviours were caused by lack of willpower, implying that if these individuals simply developed the right attitude, they could overcome their addiction? People with severe addictions may well have faulty cognitive processes, as indicated by their rationalizing of their behaviour, their other faulty appraisals, or their attribution of their problems to stress in their lives or some other excuse. They may also misperceive the effects that alcohol has on them, and all these cognitions and attitudes contribute to someone developing an addiction. But considering only cognitive processes without considering other factors as causes of addictions would be as incorrect as saying that depression is caused by a chemical imbalance. In fact, our genes play a role in the development of addictive behaviours. Evidence also exists that brain function in people with addictions may well be different from brain function in individuals who, say, ingest similar amounts

of alcohol but do not develop addictive behaviour. Interpersonal, social, and cultural factors also contribute strongly to the development of addictive behaviours. To say, then, that addictive behaviours, such as alcoholism, are caused by lack of willpower or by certain faulty ways of thinking is highly simplistic.

If you learn one thing from this book, it should be that psychological disorders do not have just one cause. They have many causes—these causes all interact with one another—and we must understand this interaction to appreciate fully the origins of psychological disorders. To do this requires a multidimensional integrative approach. In chapters covering specific psychological disorders, we return to cases very much like Jody's and consider them from this multidimensional integrative perspective. But first we must explore the processes of assessment and diagnosis used to measure and classify psychopathology.

Concept Check   2.5

Fill in the blanks to complete these statements relating to the cultural, social, and developmental factors influencing psychopathology.

1. The likelihood of your having a particular phobia is powerfully influenced by your _____.

2. A large number of studies have demonstrated that the greater the number and frequency of _____ relationships, the longer you are likely to live.

3. The effect of social and interpersonal factors on the expression of physical and psychological disorders may differ with _____.

4. The principle of _____ is used in developmental psychopathology to indicate that we must consider a number of paths to a given outcome.

SUMMARY

One-Dimensional or Multidimensional Models

- The causes of abnormal behaviour are complex and fascinating. You can say that psychological disorders are caused by nature (biology) and by nurture (psychosocial factors), and you would be right on both counts—but also wrong on both counts.

- To identify the causes of various psychological disorders, we must consider the interaction of all relevant dimensions: genetic contributions, the role of the nervous system, behavioural and cognitive processes, emotional influences, social and interpersonal influences, and developmental factors. Thus, we have arrived at a multidimensional integrative approach to the causes of psychological disorders.

Genetic Contributions to Psychopathology

- The genetic influence on much of our development and most of our behaviour, personality, and even IQ is polygenic—that is, influenced by many genes, each contributing only a tiny effect. This is assumed to be the case in abnormal behaviour as well, although individual genes have yet to be identified that relate to the major psychological disorders.

- In studying causal relationships in psychopathology, researchers look at the interactions of genetic and environmental effects. In the diathesis–stress model, individuals are assumed to inherit certain vulnerabilities that make them susceptible to a disorder when the right kind of stressor comes along. In the gene–environment correlation model, the individual's genetic vulnerability toward a certain disorder may make it more likely that he or she will experience the stressor that, in turn, triggers the genetic vulnerability and thus the disorder. In epigenetics, the immediate effects of the environment (such as early stressful experiences) influence cells that turn certain genes on or off. This effect may be passed down through generations.

Neuroscience and Its Contributions to Psychopathology

■ The field of neuroscience promises much as we try to unravel the mysteries of psychopathology. Within the nervous system, levels of neurotransmitter and neuroendocrine activity interact in very complex ways to modulate and regulate emotions and behaviour and contribute to psychological disorders.

■ Critical to our understanding of psychopathology are the neurotransmitter currents called brain circuits. Of the neurotransmitters that may play a key role, we investigated five: glutamate, gamma aminobutyric acid (GABA), serotonin, norepinephrine, and dopamine.

Behavioural and Cognitive Science

■ The relatively new field of cognitive science provides a valuable perspective on how behavioural and cognitive influences affect the learning and adaptation each of us experiences throughout life. Clearly, such influences not only contribute to psychological disorders but also may directly modify brain functioning, brain structure, and even genetic expression.

We examined some of the research in this field by looking at learned helplessness, modelling, prepared learning, implicit memory, and cognitive-behavioural therapy.

Emotions

■ Emotions have a direct and dramatic impact on our functioning and play a central role in many disorders. Mood, a persistent period of emotionality, is often evident in psychological disorders.

Cultural, Social, and Interpersonal Factors

■ Social and interpersonal influences profoundly affect both psychological disorders and biology.

Lifespan Development

■ In considering a multidimensional integrative approach to psychopathology, it is important to remember the principle of equifinality, which reminds us that we must consider the various paths to a particular outcome, not just the result.

Conclusions

■ The field of psychopathology is complex, with contributions from behavioural genetics, neuroscience, and behavioural and cognitive science, and influences from emotional, social, cultural, and lifespan developmental factors. Psychological disorders do not have just one cause.

KEY TERMS

affect, 58
agonists, 46
antagonists, 46
brain circuits, 46
cognitive science, 52
cognitive-behavioural therapy (CBT), 56
diathesis–stress model, 37
dopamine, 48
emotion, 58

epigenetics, 40
equifinality, 63
flight-or-fight response, 57
gamma aminobutyric acid (GABA), 47
gene–environment correlation model, 39
genes, 35
glutamate, 47
hormone, 45

implicit cognition, 55
implicit memory, 55
inverse agonists, 46
learned helplessness, 53
modelling, 54
mood, 58
multidimensional integrative approach, 33
neuroscience, 41
neurotransmitters, 42

norepinephrine (also noradrenaline), 48
observational learning, 54
prepared learning, 55
reuptake, 46
serotonin, 47
synaptic cleft, 42
vulnerability, 37

ANSWERS TO CONCEPT CHECKS

2.1

1. F (first 22 pairs); 2. T; 3. T; 4. F (gene–environment correlation model); 5. F (complex interaction of both nature and nurture)

2.2

1. b; 2. c; 3. d; 4. a

2.3

1. a; 2. c; 3. d; 4. b

2.4

1. b; 2. a; 3. d; 4. c

2.5

1. gender; 2. social; 3. age; 4. equifinality

CENGAGE | MINDTAP

Stay organized and efficient with MindTap—a single destination with all the course material and study aids you need to succeed. Built-in apps leverage social media and the latest learning technology. For example:

- ReadSpeaker will read the text to you.

- Flashcards are pre-populated to provide you with a jump start for review—or you can create your own.

- You can highlight text and make notes in your MindTap Reader. Your notes will flow into Evernote, the electronic notebook app that you can access anywhere when it's time to study for the exam.

- Self-quizzing allows you to assess your understanding.

Visit login.cengage.com to start using MindTap. Enter the Online Access Code from the card included with your text. If a code card is not provided, you can purchase instant access at Cengage.ca.

03 | Clinical Assessment and Diagnosis

© SDI Productions/Getty

It is not the illness but the human being that needs help. As a doctor I am not concerned with the illness but with the human being.

—GEORG GRODDECK, The Meaning of Illness

Use scientific reasoning to interpret behaviour:	› Identify basic biological, psychological, and social components of behavioural explanations (e.g., inferences, observations, operational definitions, and interpretations) (APA SLO 2.1a)
Describe applications that employ discipline-based problem solving:	› Describe examples of relevant and practical applications of psychological principles to everyday life (APA SLO 4.1, 4.4)

*Portions of this chapter cover learning outcomes suggested by the American Psychological Association (2012) in their guidelines for the undergraduate psychology major. Chapter coverage of these outcomes is identified above by APA Goal and APA Suggested Learning Outcome (SLO).

The processes of clinical assessment and diagnosis are central to the study of psychopathology and, ultimately, to the treatment of psychological disorders. **Clinical assessment** is the systematic evaluation and measurement of psychological, biological, and social factors in an individual presenting with a possible psychological disorder. **Diagnosis** is the process of determining whether the particular problem afflicting the individual meets the criteria for a psychological disorder, as set forth in the *Diagnostic and Statistical Manual of Mental Disorders*, fifth edition, or *DSM-5* (American Psychiatric Association, 2013). In this chapter, after demonstrating assessment and diagnosis within the context of an actual case, we examine the development of the *DSM* into a widely used classification system for abnormal behaviour. Then we review the many assessment techniques available to the clinician. Finally, we turn to diagnostic issues and the related challenges of classification.

FRANK | *Young, Serious, and Anxious*

Frank, a 24-year-old mechanic, was referred to one of our clinics for evaluation and possible treatment of severe distress and anxiety centring on his marriage. He arrived neatly dressed in his work clothes. He reported that this was the first time he had ever seen a mental health professional. He wasn't sure that he really needed (or wanted) to be there, but he felt he was beginning to "come apart" because of his marital difficulties. What follows is a transcript of parts of this first interview.

THERAPIST: What sorts of problems have been troubling you during the past month?

FRANK: I'm beginning to have a lot of marital problems. I was married about nine months ago, but I've been really tense around the house and we've been having a lot of arguments.

THERAPIST: Is this something recent?

Therapist: Well, it wasn't too bad at first, but it's been worse lately. I've also been really uptight in my job, and I haven't been getting my work done.

We always begin by asking the patient to describe for us, in a relatively open-ended way, the major difficulties that have brought him or her to the office in the first place. When dealing with adults, or children old enough to tell us their story, this strategy tends to break the ice, and it reveals the central problems as seen through the patient's eyes.

After Frank described this major problem in some detail, the therapist then asked him about his marriage, his job, and other present life circumstances to get a better picture of his current situation. Frank seemed to be quite tense and anxious and would often look down at the floor while he talked, glancing up only occasionally to make eye contact. Sometimes his right leg would twitch. Although it was not easy to see at first because he was looking down, Frank was also closing his eyes very tightly for two to three seconds. It was during these periods when his eyes were closed that his right leg would twitch.

The interview proceeded for the next half hour, exploring marital and job issues. It became increasingly clear that Frank was feeling inadequate and anxious about handling situations in his life. By this time he was talking freely and looking up a little more at the therapist, but he was continuing to close his eyes and twitch his right leg slightly.

THERAPIST: Are you aware that once in a while you're closing your eyes while you're telling me this?

FRANK: I'm not aware all the time, but I know I do it.

THERAPIST: Do you know how long you've been doing that?

FRANK: Oh, I don't know, maybe a year or two.

THERAPIST: Are you thinking about anything when you close your eyes?

FRANK: Well, actually I'm trying not to think about something.

THERAPIST: What do you mean?

FRANK: Well, I have these really frightening and stupid thoughts, and . . . it's hard to even talk about it.

THERAPIST: The thoughts are frightening?

FRANK: Yes, I keep thinking I'm going to take a fit, and I'm just trying to get that out of my mind.

THERAPIST: Could you tell me more about this fit?

FRANK: Well, you know, it's those terrible things where people fall down and they froth at the mouth, and their tongues come out, and they shake all over. You know, seizures. I think they call it epilepsy.

THERAPIST: And you're trying to get these thoughts out of your mind?

FRANK: Oh, I do everything possible to get those thoughts out of my mind as quickly as I can.

THERAPIST: I've noticed you moving your leg when you close your eyes. Is that part of it?

Frank: Yes, I've noticed if I really jerk my leg and pray real hard for a little while, the thought will go away.

Source: Excerpt from "Behavioral Assessment: Basic Strategies and Initial Procedures," by R. O. Nelson and D. H. Barlow, in D. H. Barlow (Ed.), *Behavioral Assessment of Adult Disorders*, 1981, Guilford Press.

What's wrong with Frank? The interview reveals an insecure young man experiencing substantial stress as he questions whether he is capable of handling marriage and a job. He reports that he loves his wife very much and wants the marriage to work, and he is attempting to be as conscientious as possible on his job, a job from which he derives a lot of satisfaction and enjoyment. Also, for some reason, he is having troubling thoughts about seizures.

So, where do we go from here? How do we determine whether Frank has a psychological disorder or if he is simply one of many young men experiencing the normal stresses and strains of a new marriage who, perhaps, could benefit from some marital counselling? The purpose of this chapter is to illustrate how mental health clinicians address these types of questions in a systematic way, assessing patients to study the basic nature of psychological disorders and to make diagnoses and plan treatment.

ASSESSING PSYCHOLOGICAL DISORDERS

The process of clinical assessment in psychopathology has been likened to a funnel (Antony & Barlow, 2010; Hunsley & Mash, 2011; Urbina, 2014). The clinician begins by collecting a lot of information across a broad range of the individual's functioning to determine where the source of the problem may lie. After getting a preliminary sense of the overall functioning of the person, the clinician narrows the focus by ruling out problems in some areas and concentrating on areas that seem most relevant.

To understand the different ways clinicians assess psychological problems, we need to understand three basic concepts that help determine the value of our assessments: reliability, validity, and standardization (see ■ Figure 3.1). Assessment techniques are subject to a number of strict requirements, not the least of which is some evidence (research) that they actually do what they are designed to do. One of the more important requirements of these assessments is that they be reliable. **Reliability** is the degree to which a measurement is consistent (Asmundson et al., 2002). Imagine how irritated you would be if you had stomach pain and you went to four competent physicians and got four different diagnoses and four different treatments. The diagnoses would be said to be unreliable because the "raters" (the physicians)

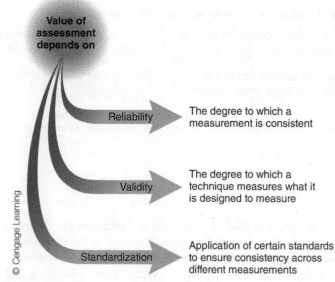

FIGURE 3.1 | Concepts that determine the value of clinical assessments.

did not agree on the conclusion. We expect, in general, that presenting the same symptoms to different physicians will result in similar diagnoses. One way psychologists improve their reliability is by carefully designing their assessment devices and then conducting research on them to ensure that two or more raters will get the same answers (called *interrater reliability*). They also determine whether these techniques are stable across time. In other words, if you go to a clinician in March and are told you have an IQ of 110, you should expect a similar result if you take the same test again in April. This is known as *test-retest reliability*. We return to the concept of reliability when we talk of diagnoses and classification.

Validity is whether something measures what it is designed to measure; in this case, whether a technique assesses what it is supposed to (Asmundson et al., 2002). Comparing the results of one assessment measure with the results of others that are better known allows you to begin to determine the validity of the first measure. This comparison is called *concurrent validity*. For example, if the results from a standard but very long IQ test were essentially the same as the results from a new brief version, you could conclude that the brief version had concurrent validity. *Predictive validity* is how well your assessment tells you what will happen in the future. For example, does it predict who will succeed in school and who will not (which is one goal of an IQ test)?

Standardization is the process by which a certain set of standards or norms is determined for a technique to make its use consistent. The standards might apply to the procedures of testing, scoring, and evaluating data. To illustrate, the assessment might be given to large numbers of people who differ on important factors, such as age, race, gender, socioeconomic status, and diagnosis; their scores would then be used as a standard, or norm, for comparison purposes. For example, if you are a recently immigrated male, 19 years old, and from a middle-class background, your score on a psychological test should be compared with the scores of others like you and not with the scores of very different people, such as a group of Canadian women of Asian descent in their 60s from working-class backgrounds. Reliability, validity, and standardization are important to all forms of psychological assessment.

Clinical assessment consists of strategies and procedures that help clinicians acquire the information they need to understand their patients and assist them. These procedures include a *clinical interview* and, within the context of the interview, a *mental status exam* that can be administered either formally or informally, often a thorough *physical examination, behavioural observation and assessment*, and *psychological tests* (if needed).

© FatCamera/Getty

▲ During the first meeting, the mental health professional focuses on the problem that brought the person to treatment.

THE CLINICAL INTERVIEW

The clinical interview, the core of most clinical work, is used by psychologists, psychiatrists, and other mental health professionals. The interview gathers information on current and past behaviour, attitudes, and emotions, as well as a detailed history of the individual's life in general and of the presenting problem. Clinicians determine when the specific problem first started and identify other events (e.g., life stress, trauma, physical illness) that might have occurred about the same time. In addition, most clinicians gather at least some information on the patient's current and past interpersonal and social history, including family makeup (e.g., marital status, number of children, student currently living with parents), and on the individual's upbringing. Information on sexual development, religious attitudes (current and past), relevant cultural concerns (such as stress induced by discrimination), and educational history are also routinely collected. To organize information obtained during an interview, many clinicians use a **mental status exam**.

The Mental Status Exam

In essence, the mental status exam involves the systematic observation of somebody's behaviour. In the mental status exam, clinicians organize their observations in a way that gives them sufficient information to determine whether a psychological disorder might be present. For the most part, the exams are performed relatively quickly by experienced clinicians in the course of interviewing or observing a patient.

The exam covers five categories: appearance and behaviour, thought processes, mood and affect, intellectual functioning, and sensorium.

1. *Appearance and behaviour*. The clinician notes any overt physical behaviours, such as Frank's leg twitch, as well as the individual's dress, general appearance, posture, and facial expression. For example, very slow and effortful motor behaviour is sometimes referred to as psychomotor retardation and may indicate severe depression.

2. *Thought processes*. When clinicians listen to a patient talk, they're getting a good idea of that person's thought processes. They might look for several things here. For example, does the person talk really fast or really slowly? Does the patient make sense when he or she talks or are ideas presented with no apparent connection? In some patients with schizophrenia, a disjointed speech pattern, referred to as "looseness of association," is quite noticeable. In addition to rate or flow and continuity of speech, what about the content? Is there any evidence of delusions (distorted views of reality)? A typical delusion involves *delusions of persecution*, where someone thinks people are after him and out to get him all the time. The individual might also have *ideas of reference*, where everything everyone else does somehow relates back to him. *Hallucinations* are things a person sees or hears but that really aren't there. For example, the clinician might ask, "Do you ever see things or maybe hear things when you know there is nothing there?"

3. *Mood and affect*. Mood is the predominant feeling state of the individual, as we noted in Chapter 2. Does the person appear to be down in the dumps or continually elated? Does she or he talk in a depressed or hopeless fashion? Are there times when the depression seems to go away? Affect, by contrast, refers to the feeling state that accompanies what we say at a given time. If a friend told you his or her mother has died and is laughing about it, or if your friend has just won the lottery and is sobbing, you would think it inconsistent. A mental health clinician would note that your friend's affect is "inappropriate."

4. *Intellectual functioning*. Clinicians make a rough estimate of others' intellectual functioning just by talking to them. Do they seem to have a reasonable vocabulary? Can they talk in abstractions and metaphors (as most of us do much of the time)? How is the person's memory? We usually make some gross or rough estimate of intelligence that is noticeable only

if it deviates from normal, such as concluding the person is above or below average intelligence.

5. *Sensorium*. Sensorium is our general awareness of our surroundings. Does the individual know what the date is, what time it is, where they are, who they are, and who you are? People with permanent brain damage or dysfunction—or temporary brain damage or dysfunction, often due to drugs or other toxic states—may not know the answer to these questions. If the patient knows who he or she is and who the clinician is and has a good idea of the time and place, the clinician would say that the patient's sensorium is "clear" and is "oriented times three" (to person, place, and time).

What can we conclude from these informal behavioural observations? Basically, they allow the clinician to make a preliminary determination of which areas of the patient's behaviour and condition should be assessed in more detail and perhaps more formally. If psychological disorders remain a possibility, the clinician may begin to hypothesize which disorders might be present. This process, in turn, provides more focus for the assessment and diagnostic activities to come.

Let's now return to Frank's case. What have we learned from his mental status exam (see ■ Figure 3.2)? Observing Frank's persistent motor behaviour in the form of a twitch led to the discovery of a functional relationship with some troublesome thoughts regarding seizures. Beyond this, his appearance was appropriate, and the flow and content of his speech were reasonable; his intelligence was well within normal limits, and he was oriented times three. He did display an anxious mood; however, his affect was appropriate to what he was saying. Observations during the mental status exam suggested that we direct the

remainder of the clinical interview and additional assessment and diagnostic activities to identifying the possible existence of a disorder characterized by intrusive, unwanted thoughts and the attempt to resist them—in other words, *obsessive-compulsive disorder*. Later we describe some of the specific assessment strategies, from among many choices, that we would use with Frank.

Patients usually have a good idea of their major concerns in a general sense ("I'm depressed"; "I'm phobic"); occasionally, the problem reported by the patient may not, after assessment, be the major issue in the eyes of the mental health clinician. The case of Frank illustrates this point well: He complained of distress relating to marital problems, but the clinician decided, on the basis of the initial interview, that the principal difficulties lay elsewhere. Frank wasn't attempting to hide anything from the clinician. He just didn't think his intrusive thoughts were the major problem.

These examples illustrate the importance of conducting the clinical interview in a way that elicits the patient's trust and empathy. Psychologists and other mental health professionals are trained extensively in methods that put patients at ease and facilitate communication, including using nonthreatening ways of seeking information and having appropriate listening skills. Information provided by patients to psychologists and psychiatrists is protected by confidentiality; that is, even if authorities want the information the therapist has received from the patient, they cannot have access to it without the express consent of the patient. The only exception to this rule occurs when the clinician judges that, because of the patient's condition, some harm or danger to either the patient or someone else is imminent. At the outset of the initial interview, the therapist should inform the patient of the confidential nature of their conversation and the (quite rare) conditions under which that confidence would not hold.

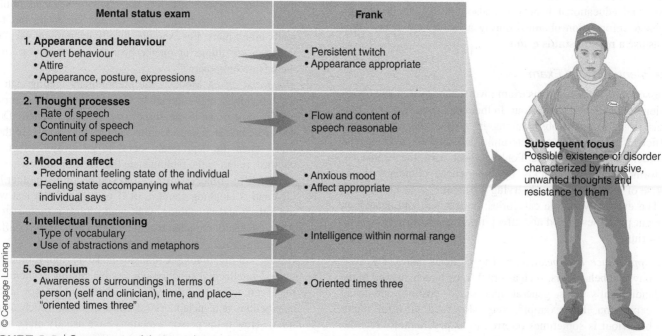

Mental status exam	Frank
1. Appearance and behaviour • Overt behaviour • Attire • Appearance, posture, expressions	• Persistent twitch • Appearance appropriate
2. Thought processes • Rate of speech • Continuity of speech • Content of speech	• Flow and content of speech reasonable
3. Mood and affect • Predominant feeling state of the individual • Feeling state accompanying what individual says	• Anxious mood • Affect appropriate
4. Intellectual functioning • Type of vocabulary • Use of abstractions and metaphors	• Intelligence within normal range
5. Sensorium • Awareness of surroundings in terms of person (self and clinician), time, and place—"oriented times three"	• Oriented times three

Subsequent focus
Possible existence of disorder characterized by intrusive, unwanted thoughts and resistance to them

FIGURE 3.2 | Components of the mental status exam.

Semistructured Clinical Interviews

Until relatively recently, most clinicians, after training, developed their own methods of collecting necessary information from patients. Different patients seeing different psychologists or other mental health professionals might encounter markedly different types and styles of interviews. *Unstructured interviews* follow no systematic format. *Semistructured interviews* are made up of questions that have been carefully phrased and tested to elicit useful information in a consistent manner, so clinicians can be sure they have inquired about the most important aspects of particular disorders. Clinicians may also depart from set questions to follow up on specific issues—thus the label "semistructured." Because the wording and sequencing of questions has been carefully worked out over many years, the clinician can feel confident that a semistructured interview will accomplish its purpose. The disadvantage, of course, is that it robs the interview of some of the spontaneous quality of two people talking about a problem. Also, if applied too rigidly, this type of interview may inhibit the patient from volunteering useful information that is not directly relevant to the questions being asked. For these reasons, fully structured interviews administered wholly by a computer have not caught on, although they are used in some settings.

An increasing number of mental health professionals routinely use semistructured interviews. Some are quite specialized. For example, Frank's clinician, in probing further into a possible obsessive-compulsive disorder, might use the *Anxiety and Related Disorders Interview Schedule for DSM-5* (*ADIS-5*) (Brown & Barlow, 2014)—developed specifically for diagnosing anxiety disorders—or the *Structured Clinical Interview for DSM-5* (*SCID-5*) (First, Williams, et al., 2015)—developed to assess a variety of the disorders discussed in the chapters of this text. These two structured interviews were designed for use in making diagnoses according to the criteria contained in the *Diagnostic and Statistical Manual of Mental Disorders*, fifth edition (*DSM-5*). According to the *ADIS-IV* interview schedule (Dinardo et al., 1994), the clinician first asks if the patient is bothered by thoughts, images, or impulses (obsessions) or currently feels driven to repeat some behaviour or thought over and over again (compulsions). Based on an eight-point rating scale that ranges from "never" to "occasionally" to "constantly," the clinician then asks the patient to rate each obsession on two measures: *persistence-distress* (how often it occurs and how much distress it causes) and *resistance* (types of attempts the patient makes to get rid of the obsession). For compulsions, the patient provides a rating of their *frequency*.

Concept Check   3.1

Identify which part of the mental status exam is being performed in each of the following situations:

1. Dr. Swan listened carefully to Joyce's speech pattern, noting its speed, content, and continuity. She noticed no looseness of association but did hear indications of delusional thoughts and visual hallucinations.

2. Anwar arrived at the clinic accompanied by police, who had found him dressed only in shorts although the temperature was −5˚C. He was reported to the police by someone who saw him walking very slowly down the street making strange faces and talking to himself. _____

3. When Lisa was brought to Dr. Miller's office, he asked if she knew the date and time, her identity, and where she was. _____

4. Dr. Jones viewed Tarik's laughter after discussing his near-fatal incident as inappropriate and noted that Tarik appeared to be elated. _____

5. Mark's vocabulary and memory seemed adequate, leading Dr. Epstein to estimate that Mark was of average intelligence.

PHYSICAL EXAMINATION

If the patient presenting with psychological problems has not had a physical exam in the past year, a clinician might recommend one, with particular attention to the medical conditions sometimes associated with the specific psychological problem. Many problems presenting as disorders of behaviour, cognition, or mood may, on careful physical examination, have a clear relationship to a temporary toxic state. This toxic state could be caused by bad food, the wrong amount or type of medicine, or the onset of a medical condition. For example, thyroid difficulties, particularly hyperthyroidism (overactive thyroid gland), may produce symptoms that mimic certain anxiety disorders, such as generalized anxiety disorder. Hypothyroidism (underactive thyroid gland) might produce symptoms consistent with depression. Certain psychotic symptoms, including delusions or hallucinations, might be associated with the development of a brain tumour. Withdrawal from cocaine often produces panic attacks, but many patients presenting with panic attacks are reluctant to volunteer information about their addiction, which may lead to an inappropriate diagnosis and improper treatment.

Usually, psychologists and other mental health professionals are well aware of the medical conditions and drug use and abuse that may contribute to the kinds of problems described by the patient. If a current medical condition or substance abuse situation exists, the clinician must ascertain whether it is merely co-existing or causal, usually by looking at the onset of the problem. If a patient has experienced severe bouts of depression for the past five years but within the past year also developed hypothyroid problems or began taking a sedative drug, then we would not conclude the depression was caused by the medical or drug condition. If the depression developed simultaneously with the initiation of sedative drugs and diminished considerably when the drugs were discontinued, we would be likely to conclude the depression was part of a substance-induced mood disorder.

BEHAVIOURAL ASSESSMENT

The mental status exam is one way to begin to sample how people think, feel, and behave and how these actions might contribute to or explain their problems. **Behavioural assessment** takes this process one step further by using direct observation to formally assess an individual's thoughts, feelings, and behaviour in specific situations or contexts; this information should explain why he or she is having difficulties at this time. Clinical interviews sometimes provide limited assessment information. Young children or individuals who are not verbal because of the nature of their disorder or because of cognitive deficits or impairments are not good candidates for clinical interviews. As we already mentioned, sometimes people deliberately withhold information because it is embarrassing or because they aren't aware that it is important. In addition to talking with a client in an office about a problem, some clinicians go to the person's home or workplace or even into the local community to observe the person and the reported problems directly. Others set up role-play simulations in a clinical setting to see how people might behave in similar situations in their daily lives. These techniques are all types of behavioural assessment.

Goldenkb/Dreamstime.com

▲ In behavioural observation, clinicians or researchers directly observe behaviour in real-world or simulated situations.

In behavioural assessment, *target behaviours* are identified and observed with the goal of determining the factors that seem to influence those behaviours. It may seem easy to identify what is bothering a particular person (i.e., the target behaviour), but even this aspect of assessment can be challenging. For example, when the mother of a seven-year-old child with a severe conduct disorder came to one of our clinics for assistance, she told the clinician, after much prodding, that her son "didn't listen to her" and he sometimes had an "attitude." The boy's schoolteacher, however, painted a very different picture. She spoke candidly of his verbal violence—of his threats toward other children and to her, threats she took very seriously. To get a clearer picture of the situation at home, the clinician visited one afternoon. Approximately 15 minutes after the visit began, the boy got up from the kitchen table without removing the drinking glass he was using. When his mother quite meekly asked him to put the glass in the sink, he picked it up and threw it across the room, sending broken glass throughout the kitchen. He giggled and went into his room to watch TV. "See," she said. "He doesn't listen to me!"

Obviously, this mother's description of her son's behaviour at home didn't give a good picture of what he was really like. It also didn't accurately portray her response to his violent outbursts. Without the home visit, the clinician's assessment of the problem and recommendations for treatment would have been very different. Clearly, this was more than simple disobedience. We developed strategies to teach the mother how to make requests of her son and how to follow up if he was violent.

Most clinicians assume that a complete picture of a person's problems requires direct observation in naturalistic environments.

But going into a person's home, workplace, or school isn't always possible or practical, so clinicians sometimes arrange analogue, or similar, settings. For example, one of us studies children with autism spectrum disorder, a disorder characterized by social withdrawal and communication problems. The reasons for self-hitting (called *self-injurious*) behaviour in this disorder are discovered by placing the children in simulated situations, such as sitting alone at home, playing with a sibling, or being asked to complete a difficult task (Durand et al., 2013). Observing how the children behave in these different situations

Photo by Victor Aziz, London, ON/Courtesy of David A. Wolfe

▲ Child clinical psychologist David Wolfe of the Centre for Addiction and Mental Health in Toronto uses analogue behavioural observation techniques in his study of the interactions of abused children with their parents.

helps us determine why they hit themselves, so we can design a successful treatment to eliminate the behaviour. David Wolfe (1991) used contrived situations to assess the emotional reactions of parents with a history of abuse toward their children. By asking parents to have their children put away favourite toys, which usually results in problem behaviour by the child, the therapist can see how the parents respond. These observations are later used to develop treatments.

The ABCs of Observation

Observational assessment is usually focused on the here and now. Therefore, the clinician's attention is usually directed to the immediate behaviour, its antecedents (or what happened just

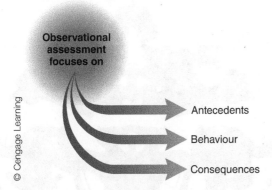

FIGURE 3.3 | The ABCs of observation.

before the behaviour), and its consequences (what happened afterward). To use the example of the young boy, an observer would note that the sequence of events was: (1) his mother asking him to put his glass in the sink (antecedent), (2) the boy throwing the glass (behaviour), and (3) his mother's lack of response (consequence). This sequence (the ABCs) might suggest that the boy was being reinforced for his violent outburst by not having to clean up his mess. And because there was no negative consequence for his behaviour (his mother didn't scold or reprimand him), he will probably act violently the next time he doesn't want to do something (see ■ Figure 3.3).

This is an example of a relatively *informal observation*. During the home visit, the clinician took rough notes about what occurred. Later, in his office, he elaborated on the notes. A problem with this type of observation is that it relies on the observer's recollection and on his or her interpretation of the events. *Formal observation* involves identifying specific behaviours that are *observable* and *measurable*. For example, it would be difficult for two people to agree on what "having an attitude" looks like. A formal observation, however, clarifies this behaviour by specifying that this is "any time the boy does not comply with his mother's reasonable requests." Once the target behaviour is selected and defined, an observer writes down each time it occurs, along with what happened just before (antecedent) and just after (consequence). The goal of collecting this information is to see whether there are any obvious patterns of behaviour and then to design a treatment based on these patterns.

Self-Monitoring

People can also observe their own behaviour to find patterns, a technique known as **self-monitoring** or *self-observation* (Haynes et al., 2011). People trying to quit smoking may write down the number of cigarettes they smoke and the times when and places where they smoke. This observation can tell them exactly how big their problem is (e.g., they smoke two packs a day) and what situations lead them to smoke more (e.g., talking on the phone). The use of smartphones is becoming common in these types of assessments (e.g., Faurholt-Jepsen et al., 2015; Swenderman et al., 2015). The goal here is to help clients monitor their behaviour more conveniently. When behaviours occur only in private (such as purging by people with bulimia nervosa), self-monitoring is essential. Because the people with the problem are in the best

position to observe their own behaviour throughout the day, clinicians often ask patients to self-monitor their behaviour to get more detailed information.

A more formal and structured way to observe behaviour is through checklists and *behaviour rating scales*, which are used as assessment tools before treatment and then periodically during treatment to assess changes in the person's behaviour (Maust et al., 2012). Of the many such instruments for assessing a variety of behaviours, the *Brief Psychiatric Rating Scale* (Clarkin et al., 2008), assesses 18 general areas of concern. Each symptom is rated on a seven-point scale from 0 (not present) to 6 (extremely severe). The rating scale screens for moderate to severe psychotic disorders and includes such items as somatic concern (preoccupation with physical health, fear of physical illness, hypochondriasis), guilt feelings (self-blame, shame, remorse for past behaviour), and grandiosity (exaggerated self-opinion, arrogance, conviction of unusual power or abilities; American Psychiatric Association, 2006).

A phenomenon known as *reactivity* can distort any observational data. Any time you observe how people behave, the mere fact of your presence may cause them to change their behaviour (Haynes et al., 2011). To test reactivity, you can tell a friend you are going to record every time she says the word *like*. Just before you reveal your intent, however, count the times your friend uses this word in a five-minute period. You will probably find that your friend uses the word less often when you are recording it. Your friend will react to the observation by changing the behaviour. The same phenomenon occurs if you observe your own behaviour, or self-monitor. Behaviours people want to increase, such as talking more in class, tend to increase, and behaviours people want to decrease, such as smoking, tend to decrease when they are self-monitored (Cohen et al., 2012). Clinicians sometimes rely on the reactivity of self-monitoring to increase the effectiveness of their treatments.

PSYCHOLOGICAL TESTING

We are confronted with so-called psychological tests in the popular press almost every week: "12 Questions to Test Your Relationship," "New Test to Help You Assess Your Lover's Passion," "Are You a Type Z Personality?" Although we may not want to admit it, many of us have probably taken one of these tests in a magazine or on Facebook. Many are no more than entertainment, designed to make you think about the topic (and to make you buy the magazine). They are typically made up for the purposes of the article and include questions that, on the surface, seem to make sense. We are interested in these tests because we want to understand better why we and our friends behave the way we do. In reality, the tests usually tell us little.

In contrast, the tests used to assess psychological disorders must meet the strict standards we have noted. They must be reliable—so two or more people administering the same test to the same person will come to the same conclusion about the problem—and they must be valid—so they measure what they say they are measuring.

Psychological tests include specific tests to determine cognitive, emotional, or behavioural responses that might be associated with a specific disorder and more general tests that assess long-standing personality features. Specialized areas include *intelligence* testing to determine the structure and patterns of cognition. Neuropsychological testing determines the possible contribution of brain damage or dysfunction to the patient's condition. *Neurobiological procedures* use imaging to assess brain structure and function.

Projective Testing

We saw in Chapter 1 how Freud brought to our attention the presence and influence of unconscious processes in psychological disorders. At this point we should ask, "If people aren't aware of these thoughts and feelings, how do we assess them?" To address this intriguing problem, psychoanalytic workers developed several assessment measures known as **projective tests**. They include a variety of methods in which ambiguous stimuli, such as pictures of people or things, are presented to a person who is asked to describe what he or she sees. The theory here is that people project their own personality and unconscious fears onto other people and things—in this case, the ambiguous stimuli—and, without realizing it, reveal their unconscious thoughts to the therapist.

Because these tests are based in psychoanalytic theory, they have been, and remain, controversial. Even so, the use of projective tests is quite common, with a majority of clinicians administering them at least occasionally and many doctoral programs providing training in their use (Durand et al., 1988); the number of programs offering training in projective testing may be declining, however (Piotrowski, 2015). Two of the more widely used projective tests are the Rorschach inkblot test and the Thematic Apperception Test.

More than 80 years ago, a Swiss psychiatrist named Hermann Rorschach developed a series of inkblots, initially to study perceptual processes and then to diagnose psychological disorders. The *Rorschach inkblot* test is one of the early projective tests. In its current form, the test includes 10 inkblot pictures that serve as the ambiguous stimuli (see ■ Figure 3.4). The examiner presents the inkblots one by one to the person being assessed, who responds by telling what he or she sees (Rorschach, 1951).

Much of the early use of the Rorschach is extremely controversial because of the lack of data on reliability or validity, among other things. Until relatively recently, therapists administered the test any way they saw fit, although one of the most important tenets of assessment is that the same test be given in the same way each time—that is, according to standardized procedures. If you encourage someone to give more detailed answers during one testing session but not during a second session, you may get different responses as the result of your administering the test differently on the two occasions—not because of problems with the test or with administration by another person (interrater reliability).

To respond to the concerns about reliability and validity, John Exner developed a standardized version of the Rorschach inkblot test, called the *Comprehensive System* (Exner, 2003). Exner's system of administering and scoring the Rorschach specifies how the cards should be presented, what the examiner should say, and how the responses should be recorded (Mihura et al., 2013). Vary-

FIGURE 3.4 | This inkblot resembles the ambiguous figures presented in the Rorschach test.

ing these steps can lead to varying responses by the patient. Despite the attempts to bring standardization to the Rorschach test, its use remains controversial. Critics of the Rorschach question whether research on the Comprehensive System supports its use as a valid assessment technique for people with psychological disorders (Hunsley & Mash, 2011; Mihura et al., 2013; Wood et al., 2015).

The *Thematic Apperception Test* (TAT) is perhaps the best-known projective test, after the Rorschach. It was developed in 1935 by Morgan and Murray (Bellak, 1975). The TAT consists of a series of 31 cards: 30 with pictures on them and 1 blank card, although only 20 cards are typically used during each administration (see ■ Figure 3.5). Unlike the Rorschach, which involves asking for a straightforward description of what the test taker sees, the instructions for the TAT ask the person to tell a dramatic story about the picture. The tester presents the pictures and tells the client, "This is a test of imagination, one form of intelligence." The person being assessed is asked to "let your imagination have its way, as in a myth, fairy story, or allegory" (Stein, 1978, p. 186). Again like the Rorschach, the TAT is based on the notion that people will reveal their unconscious mental processes in their stories about the pictures.

Several variations of the TAT have been developed for different groups, including a Children's Apperception Test and a Senior Apperception Test. In addition, modifications of the test have evolved for use with a variety of racial and ethnic groups. These modifications have included changes not only in the appearance of people in the pictures but also in the situations depicted.

FIGURE 3.5 | Example of a picture resembling those in the Thematic Apperception Test.

Unlike recent trends in the use of the Rorschach, the TAT, and its variants continue to be used inconsistently. How the stories people tell about these pictures are interpreted depends on the examiner's frame of reference and on what the patient may say. It is not surprising, therefore, that questions remain about its use in psychopathology (Hunsley & Mash, 2011).

Despite these problems, the TAT is still widely used, and some clinicians continue to report that they find it valuable in guiding their diagnostic and treatment decisions. Despite the popularity and increasing standardization of these tests, most clinicians who use projective tests have their own methods of administration and interpretation. When used as icebreakers, for getting people to open up and talk about how they feel about things going on in their lives, the ambiguous stimuli in these tests can be valuable tools. Their relative lack of reliability and validity, however, make them less useful as diagnostic tests. Concern over the inappropriate use of projective tests should remind you of the importance of the scientist–practitioner approach. Clinicians are not only responsible for knowing how to administer tests but also need to be aware of research that suggests the tests have limited usefulness as a means of diagnosing disorders.

Personality Inventories

Although many **personality inventories** are available, we look at the most widely used personality inventory in North America, the Minnesota Multiphasic Personality Inventory (MMPI; Hathaway & McKinley, 1943). In stark contrast to projective tests, which rely heavily on theory for an interpretation, the MMPI and similar inventories are based on an empirical approach, that is, the collection and evaluation of data. The administration of the MMPI is straightforward. The individual being assessed reads statements such as "I cry easily," or "I believe I am being followed," and answers either "true" or "false."

Obviously, clinicians have little room for interpretation of MMPI responses, unlike responses to projective tests such as the Rorschach and the TAT. A problem with administering the MMPI, however, is the time and tedium of responding to the 550 items on the original version and now the 567 items on the MMPI-2. A version of the MMPI is also now available that is appropriate for adolescents—MMPI-A (Nezami & Butcher, 2000). Individual responses on the MMPI are not examined; instead, the pattern of responses is reviewed to see if it resembles patterns from groups of people who have specific disorders (e.g., a pattern similar to a group with schizophrenia). Each group is represented on separate standard scales (Nichols, 2011; see Table 3.1).

Fortunately, clinicians can have these responses scored by computer; the program also includes an interpretation of the results, thereby reducing problems of reliability. Given the potential for some people to answer in ways that would downplay their problems—faking answers to MMPI items, such as "Someone has control over my mind"—the MMPI includes four scales that determine the validity of each administration. For example, on the Lie scale (L), one statement is "I have never had a bad night's sleep." Answering "true" to this is an indication that the person may be falsifying answers to look good. The other scales are the F, or Infrequency scale, which measures false claims about psychological problems or determines whether the person is answering randomly; the K, or Defensiveness scale, which assesses whether the person sees himself or herself in unrealistically positive ways; and the Cannot Say scale, which simply measures the number of items the test taker did not answer.

■ Figure 3.6 is an MMPI profile or summary of scores from an individual being clinically assessed; we'll call him James First, let's see what this 27-year-old man's MMPI profile tells us about him (note that these scores were obtained on the previous version of the MMPI). The first three data points represent scores on the L, F, and K scales; the high scores on the L and K scales were interpreted to mean that James made a naive attempt to look good for the evaluator and may have been trying to fake an appearance of having no problems. Another important part of his profile is the very high score on the Pd (psychopathic deviation) scale, which measures the tendency to behave in antisocial ways. The interpretation of this score is that James is "aggressive, unreliable, irresponsible; unable to learn from experience; may initially make a good impression but then psychopathic features will surface in longer interactions or under stress."

Why was James being evaluated? He is a young man with a criminal record that began in his childhood. He was evaluated as part of his trial for kidnapping, raping, and murdering a middle-aged woman. Throughout his trial, he made up several contradictory stories to make himself look innocent (remember his high scores on the L and K scales), including blaming his brother. There was overwhelming evidence of his guilt, however, and he was sentenced to life in a correctional institution. His answers on the MMPI resembled those of others who act in violent and antisocial ways.

TABLE 3.1 | Scales of the MMPI-2

Validity Scales	Characteristics of High Scorers
Cannot Say (reported as a raw score) (?CNS)	Reading difficulties, guardedness, confusion and distractibility, depression, rebellion, or obsessiveness
Variable Response Inconsistency (VRIN)	Responding to questions in a manner inconsistent with psychological disorder
True Response Inconsistency (TRIN)	Answering questions all true or all false
Infrequency (F)	Exhibit randomness of responses or psychotic psychopathology
Back F (Fb)	Changing the way the questions are answered at the end of the test
Infrequency—Psychopathology (Fr)	Claiming more psychiatric symptoms than expected
Symptom Validity (FBS)	Trying to appear to have more disabilities but not psychotic
Lie (L)	Dishonest, deceptive, and/or defended
Correction (K)	Person is very guarded and defensive
Superlative Self-Presentation (S)	Believes in human goodness and denies personal flaws
Clinical Scales	Characteristics of High Scorers
Hypochondriasis	Somatizers, possible medical problems
Depression	Dysphoric, possibly suicidal
Hysteria	Highly reactive to stress, anxious, and sad at times
Psychopathic deviate	Antisocial, dishonest, possible drug abusers
Masculinity–femininity	Exhibit lack of stereotypical masculine interests, aesthetic and artistic
Paranoia	Exhibit disturbed thinking, ideas of persecution, possibly psychotic
Psychasthenia	Exhibit psychological turmoil and discomfort, extreme anxiety
Schizophrenia	Confused, disorganized, possible hallucinations
Mania	Manic, emotionally labile, unrealistic self-appraisal
Social introversion	Very insecure and uncomfortable in social situations, timid

Source: Excerpted from the MMPI®-2 (Minnesota Multiphasic Personality Inventory®-2) Manual for Administration, Scoring, and Interpretation, revised edition. Copyright © 2001 by the Regents of the University of Minnesota. Used by permission of the University of Minnesota Press. All rights reserved. "MMPI-2" and "Minnesota Multiphasic Personality Inventory-2" are trademarks owned by the Regents of the University of Minnesota.

The MMPI is one of the most extensively researched assessment instruments in psychology (Cox et al., 2009; Friedman et al., 2014). (Vern Quinsey, emeritus professor of psychology at Queen's University at Kingston, once quipped that every man, woman, and child on the planet will eventually publish an MMPI study.) The original standardization sample—the people who first responded to the statements and set the standard for answers—included many people from Minnesota who had no psychological disorders and several groups of people who had particular disorders. The more recent versions of this test, including the MMPI-2 and the MMPI-A, eliminate problems with the original version, problems partly resulting from the original selective sample of people and partly resulting from the wording of questions (Ranson et al., 2009). For example, some questions were sexist. One item on the original version asks the respondent to say whether she has ever been sorry she is a girl (Worell & Remer, 1992). Another item reads, "Any man who is willing to

work hard has a good chance of succeeding" (Hathaway & McKinley, 1943). Other items were criticized as insensitive to cultural diversity. Items dealing with religion, for example, referred almost exclusively to Christianity (Butcher et al., 1990). The MMPI-2 has also been standardized with a sample that adequately reflects the composition of the general population, including black people and Aboriginal people for the first time. In addition, new items have been added that deal with contemporary issues, such as type A personality, low self-esteem, and family problems.

The reliability of the MMPI is excellent when it is interpreted according to standardized procedures, and thousands of studies on the original MMPI attest to its validity with a range of psychological problems (Butcher, 2009; Nichols, 2011). But a word of caution is necessary here. Some research suggests that the information provided by the MMPI—although informative—does not necessarily change how clients are treated and may not improve their outcomes (Lima et al., 2005).

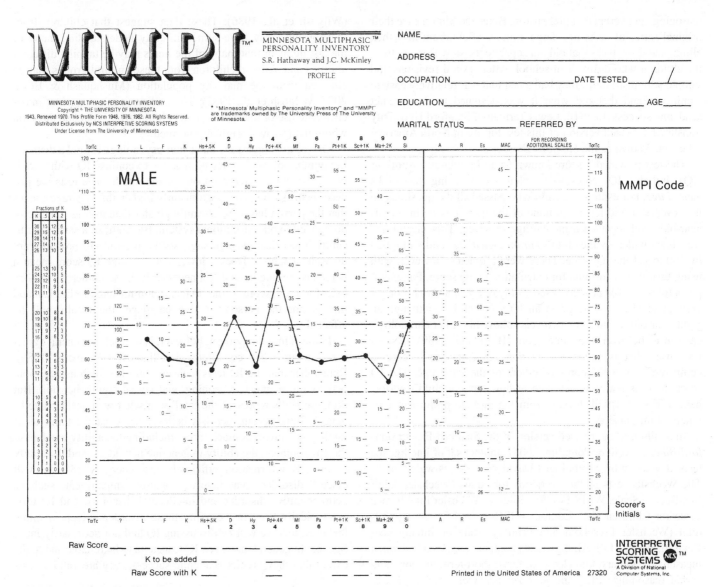

FIGURE 3.6 | An MMPI profile.

In addition to the MMPI, another example of an instrument used to assess an important aspect of personality functioning is the Revised Psychopathy Checklist (PCL-R). The MMPI profile of James discussed earlier illustrates a constellation of behaviours and characteristics that some refer to as psychopathy. Psychopathy can be assessed directly using the PCL-R, which was developed by forensic psychologist Robert Hare and his colleagues at the University of British Columbia (Hare, 1991, 1993; Hare et al., 2012). Since psychopaths are cunning and manipulative pathological liars, it is difficult to use self-report measures to assess psychopathy, especially in forensic settings (as a psychopath would likely lie and deny the existence of characteristics that would place him or her in a bad light). Hare developed the PCL-R as an instrument to assess the characteristics of psychopathy by using a semistructured interview with the client, along with material from institutional files (e.g., records from correctional institutions) or significant others. The PCL-R consists of a checklist of 20 characteristics, including pathological lying and superficial charm. Adelle Forth of Carleton University and her colleagues developed a youth version of the PCL-R (e.g., Kosson et al., 2013)

Intelligence Testing

"She must be very smart. I hear her IQ is 180!" What is IQ? What is intelligence? And how are they important in psychopathology? As many of you know from your introductory psychology course, intelligence tests were developed for one specific purpose: to predict who would do well in school. In 1904, a French psychologist, Alfred Binet, and his colleague, Théodore Simon, were commissioned by the government of France to develop a test that would identify "slow learners" who would benefit from remedial help. The two psychologists identified a series of tasks that presumably measured the skills children need to succeed in school, including tasks of attention, perception, memory, reasoning, and verbal comprehension. Binet and Simon gave their original series of tasks to a large number of children; they then eliminated those tasks that did not separate the slow learners from the children who did well in school. After several revisions and sample administrations, they had a test that was relatively easy to administer and that did what it was designed to do—predict academic success. In 1916, Lewis Terman of Stanford University translated a revised version of this test for use in North America; it became known as the *Stanford-Binet test*.

The test provided a score known as an **intelligence quotient (IQ)**. Initially, IQ scores were calculated by using the child's *mental age*. For example, a child who passed all the questions on the seven-year-old level and none of the questions on the eight-year-old level received a mental age of seven. This mental age was then divided by the child's *chronological age* and multiplied by 100 to get the IQ score. There were problems, however, with using this type of formula for calculating an IQ score. For example, a four-year-old needed to score only one year above his or her chronological age to be given an IQ score of 125, although an eight-year-old had to score two years above his or her chronological age to be given the same score (Bjorklund, 1989). Current tests use what is called a *deviation* IQ. A person's score is compared only with scores of others of the same age. The IQ score, then, is really an estimate of how much a child's performance in school will deviate from the average performance of others of the same age.

In addition to the revised version of the Stanford-Binet (*Stanford-Binet V*; Roid & Pomplun, 2005), another set of intelligence tests, developed by psychologist David Wechsler, is widely used. The Wechsler tests include versions for adults (Wechsler Adult Intelligence Scale, WAIS-IV), for children (Wechsler Intelligence Scale for Children-Fifth Edition, WISC-5), and for young children (Wechsler Preschool and Primary Scale of Intelligence-Revised, WPPSI-IV). All these tests contain *verbal scales* (which measure vocabulary, knowledge of facts, short-term memory, and verbal reasoning skills) and *performance scales* (which assess psychomotor abilities, nonverbal reasoning, and ability to learn new relationships).

In both American and Canadian samples, the adult version of this intelligence test—the WAIS-III—has been shown to tap four distinct intellectual abilities: verbal comprehension, perceptual organization, processing speed, and working memory (Saklofske et al., 2000; Wechsler, 1997). The fact that these same components have been supported in both Canadian and U.S. samples has been interpreted by some as evidence that the WAIS-III "is 'portable' across cultural boundaries" (Saklofske et al., 2000, p. 438). Others have been less optimistic about the portability of these intelligence tests to people from other countries and cultures, since these tests were developed and standardized largely with people from the majority culture in the United States. For example, several studies have documented lower than average scores on the verbal scales on the first two versions of the WISC in Canadian First Nations children (Beiser & Gotowiec, 2000; Seyfort et al., 1980; St. John et al., 1976; see also review by Mushquash & Bova, 2007) and a large majority of a sample of Canadian Inuit children scored in what was then called the "mentally retarded" range when their scores on the second version of the WISC were compared with the usual norms

(Wilgosh et al., 1986). These data suggest that children from these groups may have some difficulty understanding many of the test items or that many of the items may be tapping different abilities and skills in children from these cultural groups than in children from the majority population (Mushquash & Bova, 2007; Wilgosh et al., 1986). The findings caution against indiscriminate use of these tests with cultural groups outside those on whom the test was originally normed.

One of the biggest mistakes non-psychologists (and a distressing number of psychologists) make is to confuse IQ with intelligence. An IQ is a score on one of the intelligence tests we just described. An IQ score significantly higher than average means that the person has a significantly greater than average chance of doing well in our educational system. By contrast, a score significantly lower than average suggests the person will probably not do well in school. Does a lower than average IQ score mean a person is not intelligent? Not necessarily. First, numerous reasons exist for a low score. If the IQ test is administered in English and that is not the person's native language, the results will be affected.

Perhaps more important, however, is the lack of general agreement about what constitutes intelligence (Weinberg, 1989). Remember that the IQ tests measure abilities, such as attention, perception, memory, reasoning, and verbal comprehension. But do these skills represent the totality of what we consider intelligence? Some recent theorists believe that what we think of as intelligence involves much more, including the ability to adapt to the environment, the ability to generate new ideas, and the ability to process information efficiently (Sternberg, 1988). We will discuss disorders that involve cognitive impairment, such as neurocognitive disorder and intellectual disability, and IQ tests are typically used in assessing these disorders. Keep in mind, however, that we will be discussing IQ and not necessarily intelligence. In general, however, IQ tests tend to be reliable and to the extent that they predict academic success, they are valid assessment tools.

NEUROPSYCHOLOGICAL TESTING

Sophisticated tests have been developed that can pinpoint the location of brain dysfunction (Goldstein, 2000). Fortunately, these techniques are generally available and relatively inexpensive. **Neuropsychological testing** measures abilities in areas such as receptive and expressive language, attention and concentration, memory, motor skills, perceptual abilities, and learning and abstraction in such a way that the clinician can make educated guesses about the person's performance and the possible existence of brain impairment. In other words, this method of testing assesses brain dysfunction by observing its effects on the person's ability to perform certain tasks. Although you do not see damage, you can see its effects.

A simple neuropsychological test often used with children is the Bender Visual-Motor Gestalt Test (Canter, 1996). A child is given a series of cards on which are drawn various lines and shapes. The task is for the child to copy what is drawn on the card. The errors on the test are compared with test results of other children of the same age; if the number of errors exceeds a certain amount, then brain dysfunction is suspected. This test is less sophisticated than other neuropsychological tests because the nature or location of the problem cannot be determined with this test. The Bender Visual-Motor Gestalt Test can be useful for psychologists, however, because it provides a simple screening instrument that is easy to administer and can detect possible problems. Two of the most popular advanced tests of organic damage that allow more precise determinations of the location of the problem are the Luria-Nebraska Neuropsychological Battery (Golden et al., 1980) and the Halstead-Reitan Neuropsychological Battery (Reitan & Davison, 1974). These offer an elaborate battery of tests to assess a variety of skills. For example, the Halstead-Reitan Neuropsychological Battery includes the Rhythm Test (which asks the person to compare rhythmic beats, to test sound recognition, attention, and concentration), the Strength of Grip Test (which compares the grip of the right and left hands), and the Tactile Performance Test (which requires the test taker to place wooden blocks in a form board while blindfolded, to test learning and memory skills; McCaffrey et al., 2011).

Research on the validity of neuropsychological tests suggests they may be useful for detecting organic damage and cognitive disorders. Canadian researchers have played a very important role in this crucial area of scientific endeavour (see review by Hayman-Abello et al., 2003). More recent evidence suggests that performance on neuropsychological tests may even be useful in predicting the development of certain cognitive disorders. For example, one study by researchers at the University of Toronto found that a neuropsychological test battery was quite accurate in predicting the development of Alzheimer's disease in people who were part of the longitudinal Canadian Study of Health and Aging. Performance on tasks such as delayed verbal recall at the initial testing session with initially healthy participants accurately predicted whether or not the test taker developed Alzheimer's disease five or ten years later (Tierney et al., 2005). Most often, though, neuropsychological tests are used to help differentiate those who already have a given cognitive disorder from those people who do not. And neuropsychological tests are often quite accurate in doing so (e.g., Tierney et al., 1996). With this use of neuropsychological tests, however, we face the issue of **false positives** and **false negatives**. For any assessment strategy, the test will occasionally show a problem when none exists (false positive) and will not find a problem when indeed some difficulty is present (false negative). The possibility of false results is particularly troublesome for tests of brain dysfunction; a clinician who fails to find damage that exists might miss an important medical problem that needs to be treated. Fortunately, neuropsychological tests are used primarily as screening devices and are routinely paired with other assessments to improve the likelihood that real problems will be found.

▲ This child is concentrating on a standard psychological assessment test.

NEUROIMAGING: PICTURES OF THE BRAIN

For more than a century, we have known that many of the things that we do, think, and remember are partially controlled by specific areas of the brain. In recent years, we have developed the ability to look inside the brain and take increasingly accurate pictures of its structure and function by using a technique called **neuroimaging**. Neuroimaging can be divided into two categories. One category includes procedures that examine the structure of the brain, such as the size of various parts and whether they are damaged. In the second category are procedures that examine the actual *functioning* of the brain by mapping blood flow and other metabolic activity.

Images of Brain Structure

The first neuroimaging technique, developed in the early 1970s, uses multiple X-ray exposures of the brain from different angles; that is, X-rays are passed directly through the head. As with any X-ray, these are partially blocked or attenuated more by bone and less by brain tissue. The degree of blockage is picked up by detectors in the opposite side of the head. A computer then reconstructs pictures of various slices of the brain. This procedure, which takes about 15 minutes, is called a *computerized axial tomography (CAT) scan* or *CT scan*. It is relatively non-invasive and has proved useful in identifying and locating abnormalities in the structure or shape of the brain. CT scans are particularly useful in locating brain tumours, injuries, and other structural and anatomical abnormalities. One difficulty, however, is that these scans, like all X-rays, involve repeated X-radiation, which poses some risk of cell damage (Filippi, 2015).

Several more recently developed procedures give greater resolution (specificity and accuracy) than a CT scan without the inherent risks of X-ray tests. A now commonly used scanning technique is called nuclear *magnetic resonance imaging (MRI)*. The patient's head is placed in a high-strength magnetic field through which radio frequency signals are transmitted. These signals "excite" the brain tissue, altering the protons in the hydrogen atoms. The alteration is measured, along with the time it takes the protons to "relax" or return to normal. Where there are lesions or damage, the signal is lighter or darker. Technology now exists that allows the computer to view the brain in layers, which enables precise examination of the structure. Although an MRI is more expensive than a CT scan and originally took as long as 45 minutes, this is changing as technology improves. Newer versions of MRI procedures take as little as 10 minutes; the time and cost are decreasing yearly. Another disadvantage of MRI at present is that someone undergoing the procedure is totally enclosed inside a narrow tube with a magnetic coil surrounding the head. People who are somewhat claustrophobic often cannot tolerate an MRI, as demonstrated in a study by a team at the University of British Columbia (McIsaac et al., 1998).

Although neuroimaging procedures are useful for identifying damage to the brain, only recently have they been used to determine structural or anatomical abnormalities that might be associated with various psychological disorders. We review some tantalizing studies in subsequent chapters on specific disorders.

Images of Brain Functioning

Several widely used procedures are capable of measuring the actual functioning of the brain, as opposed to its structure. The first is called *positron emission tomography* (*PET*). Someone undergoing a PET scan is injected with an imaging tracer, a chemical attached to a radioactive isotope. The chemical component of a PET tracer is carefully selected to target a specific function in the body—for example, a metabolic process or neurotransmission. The PET scanner uses rings of detectors to measure the radioactive decay of the tracer, which accumulates at certain sites. Images representing the distribution of the tracer in the body are constructed. One tracer, for example, allows the measurement of the rate of cerebral glucose metabolism, in essence a way to assess brain function. To obtain clear images, the individual undergoing the procedure must remain motionless for the duration of the scan. Typical clinical brain PET scans take 30 minutes, while research imaging of processes like neurotransmitter function can take from 60 to 120 minutes. PET images can be superimposed on anatomical MRI images to show the precise location of the active areas. PET scans are also used to supplement MRI and CT scans in localizing the sites of trauma caused by head injury or stroke, as well as in localizing brain tumours.

More important, PET scans are used increasingly to look at varying patterns of glucose metabolism that might be associated with different disorders. Recent PET scans have demonstrated that many patients with early Alzheimer's-type dementia show reduced glucose metabolism in the parietal lobes. Other intriguing findings have been reported for obsessive-compulsive disorder

and bipolar disorder. For example, as we will learn in more detail in Chapter 8, excess activity in the dopamine neurotransmitter system has been implicated in manic states among patients with bipolar mood disorder. Researchers at the University of British Columbia Mood Disorders Clinical Research Unit used PET to identify the brain regions involved in dopamine overactivity among a group of patients with bipolar disorder who were tested during the manic state (Yatham et al., 2002). In this same study, the researchers also used PET to examine the effects of drug therapy on dopamine activity in bipolar disorder by testing patients twice: before and after drug treatment. Despite the exciting uses of PET for increasing understanding of many forms of abnormal behaviour, PET scanning is very expensive: in addition to the cost of setting up the facility (approximately $6 million), a cyclotron and chemistry facility must be onsite or close enough that the radioactive PET tracers can be transported quickly. Therefore, these facilities are available only in large medical centres.

A second procedure used to assess brain functioning is called *single photon emission computed tomography*. It works very much like PET, although a different tracer substance is used, and it is somewhat less accurate. It is also less expensive, however, and requires far less sophisticated equipment to pick up the signals. For this reason, it is used more frequently. The most exciting advances involve MRI procedures that have been developed to work much more quickly than the regular MRI (Filippi, 2015). Using sophisticated computer technology, these procedures take only milliseconds and, therefore, can actually take pictures of the brain at work, recording its changes from one second to the next (e.g., Stern et al., 2000). Because these procedures measure the functioning of the brain, they are called *functional MRI*, or *fMRI*. For example, fMRI was used by Kent Kiehl, Andra Smith, Robert Hare, and their colleagues at the University

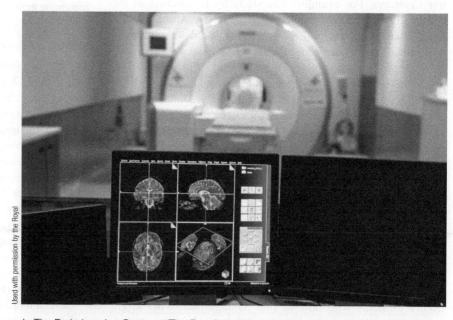

▲ The Brain Imaging Centre at The Royal's Institute of Mental Health Research, affiliated with the University of Ottawa, can perform brain imaging using PET, (f)MRI, and EMG and is used extensively for research on the etiology and treatment of psychological disorders. Copyright: The Royal's Institute of Mental Health Research, affiliated with the University of Ottawa.

Used with permission by the Royal

of British Columbia to explore how brain activity might be linked to the emotional responses of psychopaths (Kiehl et al., 2001). Their findings suggested that the emotional differences so often observed in psychopaths may be linked to a weakened input from limbic structures—the part of the brain responsible for regulating our emotional experiences. Today, fMRI has largely replaced PET scans in the leading brain-imaging centres (Cabeza & Nyberg, 2000), because it allows researchers to see the immediate response of the brain to a brief event, such as seeing a new face. This response is called an event-related fMRI.

Brain imagery procedures hold enormous potential for illuminating the contribution of neurobiological factors to psychological disorders. A review by Ruth Lanius and her colleagues in London, Ontario, has illuminated the contributions of various brain-imaging techniques to our understanding of post-traumatic stress disorder (PTSD; Lanius et al., 2006). For example, studies using fMRI have shown that PTSD participants who report primarily dissociative (numbing-type) responses to listening to scripts about their traumas showed very different patterns of brain activation than PTSD participants who experienced primarily hyperarousal patterns to trauma scripts. This finding suggests two distinct subtypes of patients with PTSD, with different neural mechanisms underlying their post-traumatic symptoms.

Neuroimaging research has not yet produced diagnostic tools or tests, however. Many researchers and clinicians are attempting to discover neurological (or biological) markers of specific psychological disorders or traits associated with them (e.g., suicidal tendencies).

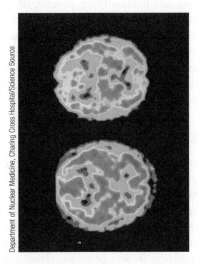

▲ PET scans display areas of high and low neurological activity, as in these scans of a brain affected by HIV.

PSYCHOPHYSIOLOGICAL ASSESSMENT

Yet another method for assessing brain structure and function specifically and nervous system activity more generally is called **psychophysiological assessment**. As the term implies, *psychophysiology* refers to measurable changes in the nervous system that reflect emotional or psychological events. The measurements may be taken either directly from the brain or peripherally from other parts of the body.

Frank feared that he might have seizures. If we had any reason to suspect he might really have periods of memory loss or exhibit bizarre, trance-like behaviour, even if only for a short time, it would be important for him to have an **electroencephalogram (EEG)**. Measuring electrical activity in the head related to the firing of a specific group of neurons reveals brain wave activity, the low-voltage electrical current ongoing in the brain, usually from the cortex. A person's brain waves can be assessed in both waking and sleeping states. In an EEG, electrodes are placed directly on various places on the scalp to record the different low-voltage currents.

We have learned much about EEG patterns in the past decades. Usually, we measure ongoing electrical activity in the brain. When brief periods of EEG patterns are recorded in response to specific events, such as hearing a psychologically meaningful stimulus, the response is called an *event-related potential* or *evoked potential*. EEG patterns are often affected by psychological or emotional factors and can be an index of these reactions. In a normal, healthy, relaxed adult, waking activities are characterized by a very regular pattern of changes in voltage termed *alpha waves*.

Many types of stress-reduction treatments attempt to *increase* the frequency of the alpha waves, often by relaxing the patients in some way. The alpha wave pattern is associated with relaxation and calmness. During sleep, we pass through several different stages of brain activity, at least partially identified by EEG patterns. During the deepest, most relaxed stage, typically occurring one to two hours after a person falls asleep, EEG recordings show a pattern of *delta* waves. These brain waves are slower and more irregular than the alpha waves, which is perfectly normal for this stage of sleep. We see in Chapter 5 that panic attacks occurring while a person is sound asleep come almost exclusively during the delta wave stage. If frequent delta wave activity occurred during the waking state, it might indicate dysfunction of localized areas of the brain.

Extremely rapid and irregular spikes on the EEG recordings of someone who is awake may reflect significant seizure disorders, depending on the pattern. The EEG recording is one of the primary diagnostic tools for identifying seizure disorders. Psychophysiological assessment of other bodily responses may also play a role in assessment. These responses include heart rate, respiration, and *electrodermal responding* (skin conductance), formerly called *galvanic skin response*, which is a measure of sweat gland activity controlled by the peripheral nervous system. Remember from Chapter 2 that the peripheral nervous system and, in particular, the sympathetic division of the automatic nervous system are very responsive to stress and emotional arousal.

Assessing psychophysiological responding to emotional stimuli is very important in many disorders, one being PTSD. Stimuli, such as sights and sounds, associated with the trauma evoke strong psychophysiological responding, even if the patient is not fully aware of the nature of the trauma because memories of it are inaccessible.

Psychophysiological assessment is also used with many sexual dysfunctions and disorders. For example, sexual arousal can be assessed through direct measurement of penile circumference in males or vaginal blood flow in females in response to erotic stimuli, usually movies or slides (see Chapter 11). As remarked by Queen's University at Kingston researcher Meredith Chivers and her colleagues, sometimes the individual might be unaware of specific patterns of sexual arousal (Chivers et al., 2010).

Physiological measures are also important in the assessment and treatment of conditions such as headaches and hypertension (Hazlett-Stevens & Bernstein, 2012); they form the basis for the treatment we call biofeedback. In biofeedback, levels of physiological responding, such as blood pressure readings, are fed back to the patient (provided on a continuous basis) by meters or gauges so the patient can try to regulate these responses.

Physiological assessment is not without its limits, for it requires a great deal of skill and some technical expertise. Even when administered properly, the measures sometimes produce inconsistent results because of procedural or technical difficulties or the nature of the response itself. For this reason, only clinicians specializing in certain disorders for which these measures are particularly important are likely to make extensive use of psychophysiological recording equipment, although more straightforward applications, such as monitoring heart rate during relaxation exercises, are more common. Psychophysiological assessment of genital responses (for the purpose of determining someone's sexual preferences), for example, requires much technical and clinical expertise (Lalumière & Harris, 1998). Sophisticated psychophysiological assessment is most often used in theoretical investigations of the nature of certain psychological disorders, particularly emotional disorders (Barlow, 2002; Heller et al., 1998).

DIAGNOSING PSYCHOLOGICAL DISORDERS

Thus far, we have looked at Frank's functioning on a very individual basis; that is, we have closely observed their behaviour, cognitive processes, and mood, and we have conducted semistructured interviewing, behavioural assessment, and psychological tests. These operations tell us what is unique about Frank, not what they may have in common with other individuals or even with each other.

Learning how Frank may resemble other people in terms of the problems each presents is also very important, for several reasons. If in the past people came in with similar problems or psychological profiles, we can go back and find a lot of information from their cases that might be applicable to Frank's case. We can see how the problems began for those other individuals, what factors seemed influential, and how long the problem or disorder lasted. Did the problem in the other cases just go away on its own? If not, what kept it going? Did it need treatment? Most important, what treatments seemed to relieve the problem for those other individuals? These general questions are very useful because they evoke a wealth of clinical and research information that enables the investigator to make certain inferences about what will happen next and what treatments may work. In other words, the clinician can establish a *prognosis*, a term we discussed in Chapter 1 that refers to the likely future course of a disorder under certain conditions.

Because classification is such an integral part of science and, indeed, of our human experience, we describe its various aspects (Blashfield et al., 2014; Millon, 1991; Widiger & Crego, 2013). The term **classification** itself is very broad, referring simply to

any effort to construct groups or categories and to assign objects or people to these categories on the basis of their shared attributes or relations—a nomothetic strategy. If the classification is in a scientific context, it is most often called **taxonomy**, which is the classification of entities for scientific purposes, such as insects or rocks or, if the subject is psychology, behaviours. If you apply a taxonomic system to psychological or medical phenomena or other clinical areas, you use the word **nosology**. The term **nomenclature** describes the names or labels of the disorders that make up the nosology (e.g., anxiety or mood disorders). Most mental health professionals in North America use the classification system contained in the *Diagnostic and Statistical Manual of Mental Disorders*, called the *DSM-5*, which includes definitions and conceptualizations of mental disorders to assist in diagnosis. It is not the only recognized system, however. Another system, the *International Classification of Diseases and Health Related Problems*, 10th edition (*ICD-10*; World Health Organization, 1992), is the most used worldwide. In addition to mental disorders, the *ICD-10* is also used to categorize health conditions. The *ICD-10* functions as a public health classification that ensures consistent definitions and conceptualization of diseases such that morbidity and mortality data are comparable throughout the world. Most countries, including Canada, have agreed to report health information to the World Health Organization about their population using this system. A specialist version of the *ICD-10* that was developed for mental health professionals is called the *ICD-10 Clinical Descriptions and Diagnostic Guidelines*, and its format resembles that of the *DSM-5*.

During the past several years, we have seen enormous changes in how we think about classifying psychopathology. Because these developments affect so much of what we do, we examine carefully the processes of classification and diagnosis as they are used in psychopathology. We look first at different approaches, examine the concepts of reliability and validity as they pertain to diagnosis, and then discuss our current system of classification in North America—the *DSM-5*.

CLASSIFICATION ISSUES

Classification is at the heart of any science, and much of what we have said about it is common sense. If we could not order and label objects or experiences, scientists could not communicate with one another and our knowledge would not advance. Everyone would have to develop a personal system, which, of course, would mean nothing to anyone else. In a biology or geology course, when studying insects or rocks, classification is fundamental. Knowing how one species of insects differs from another allows us to study its functioning and origins. When we are dealing with human behaviour or human behavioural disorders, however, the subject of classification becomes controversial. Some people have questioned whether it is proper or ethical to classify human behaviour. Even among those who recognize the necessity of classification, major controversies have arisen in several areas. Within psychopathology, for example, definitions of "normal" and "abnormal" are questioned and so is the assumption that a behaviour or cognition is part of one category or disorder and not another. Some would prefer to talk about behaviour and feelings on a continuum from happy to sad or fearful to nonfearful, rather than to create such categories as mania, depression, and phobia. Of course, for better or worse, classifying behaviour and people is something we all do. Few of us talk about our own emotions or those of our friends by using a number on a scale (where 0 is totally unhappy and 100 is totally happy), although this approach might be more accurate. ("How do you feel about that?" "About 65.") Rather, we talk about being happy, sad, angry, depressed, fearful, and so on.

Categorical, Dimensional, and Prototypical Approaches

The pure or **classical categorical approach** to classification originates in the work of Emil Kraepelin (1856–1926) and the biological tradition in the study of psychopathology. Here we assume that every diagnosis has a clear underlying pathophysiological cause, such as a bacterial infection or a malfunctioning endocrine system, and that each disorder is unique. When diagnoses are thought of in this way, the causes could be psychological or cultural, instead of pathophysiological, but each disorder has only one set of causative factors that do not overlap at all with other disorders. Because each disorder is fundamentally different from every other, we need only one set of defining criteria, which everybody in the category has to meet. If the criteria for a major depressive disorder are: (1) the presence of depressed mood, (2) significant weight gain or weight loss when not dieting, and (3) diminished ability to think or concentrate, and six additional specific symptoms, then, to be diagnosed with depression, an individual would have to meet all nine criteria. In that case, according to the classical categorical approach, the clinician would know the cause of the disorder.

Classical categorical approaches are quite useful in medicine. It is extremely important for a physician to make accurate diagnoses. If a patient has a fever accompanied by stomach pain, the doctor must determine quickly if the cause is food poisoning or an infected appendix. This distinction is not always easy to make, but physicians are trained to examine the signs and symptoms closely, and they usually reach the correct conclusion. To understand the cause of the symptoms (infected appendix) is to know what treatment will be effective (surgery). But if someone is depressed or anxious, is there a similar type of underlying cause? As we saw in Chapter 2, probably not. Most psychopathologists believe biological, psychological, and social factors interact in complex ways to produce a disorder. Therefore, despite the beliefs of Kraepelin and other early biological investigators, the mental health field has not adopted a classical categorical model of psychopathology.

A second strategy is a **dimensional approach**, in which we note the variety of cognitions, moods, and behaviours with which the patient presents and quantify them on a scale. For example, on a scale of 1 to 10, a patient might be rated as severely anxious (10), moderately depressed (5), and mildly manic (2) to create a profile of emotional functioning (10, 5, 2). Although dimensional approaches have been applied to psychopathology in the past—particularly to personality disorders (Blashfield et al., 2014; Helzer et al., 2008; Krueger et al., 2014; Widiger & Samuel, 2005), they have been relatively unsatisfactory (Brown & Barlow, 2009; Frances, 2009; Regier et al., 2009; Widiger & Edmundson, 2011). Most theorists can't agree on how many dimensions are required; some say one dimension is enough; others have identified as many as 33 (Millon, 1991, 2004).

▲ Emil Kraepelin (1856–1926) was one of the first psychiatrists to classify psychological disorders from a biological point of view.

A third strategy for organizing and classifying behavioural disorders has found increasing support in recent years as an alternative to classical categorical or dimensional approaches. It is a categorical approach but with the twist that it combines some of the features of each of the other approaches. Called a **prototypical approach**, this alternative identifies certain essential characteristics of an entity so you (and others) can classify it, but it also allows for certain non-essential variations that do not necessarily change the classification. For example, if someone were to ask you to describe a dog, you could very easily give a general description (the essential, categorical characteristics), but you might not exactly describe a specific dog. Dogs come in different colours, sizes, and breeds (the non-essential, dimensional variations), but they all share certain doggish characteristics that allow you to classify them separately from cats. Thus, requiring a certain number of prototypical criteria and only some of an additional number of criteria is adequate. Of course, this system is not perfect because greater blurring happens at the boundaries of categories, and some symptoms apply to more than one disorder. For this reason these categories are often called "fuzzy." It has the advantage, however, of fitting better with the current state of our knowledge of psychopathology, and it is relatively user friendly.

When this approach is used in classifying a psychological disorder, many of the different possible features or properties of the disorder are listed, and any candidate must meet enough (but not necessarily all) of them to fall into that category. Consider the types of *DSM-5* criteria defining a major depressive disorder (see DSM Table 8.1 in Chapter 8). Five or more specific symptoms must be present during the same two-week period and they must represent a change from the individual's previous functioning. At least one of the symptoms is either depressed mood or loss of interest or pleasure in most or all activities. The other symptoms can include considerable weight gain or loss without dieting, near-daily insomnia or hypersomnia, physical restlessness or extreme difficulty performing physical activities, near-daily fatigue, extreme feelings of worthlessness or needless guilt, the inability to concentrate or make decisions, and recurring thoughts of death (APA, 2013).

▲ Despite their wide physical variation, all dogs belong to the same class of animals.

As you can see, the criteria include many non-essential symptoms, but if you have either depressed mood or marked loss of interest or pleasure in most activities and at least four of the remaining eight symptoms, you come close enough to the prototype to meet the criteria for a major depressive disorder. One person might have depressed mood, significant weight loss, insomnia, psychomotor agitation, and loss of energy, whereas another person who also meets the criteria for major depressive disorder might have markedly diminished interest or pleasure in activities, fatigue, feelings of worthlessness, difficulty thinking or concentrating, and suicidal ideation. Although both have the requisite five symptoms that bring them close to the prototype, they look very different because they share only one symptom. This is a good example of a prototypical category. Other examples are the diagnosis of histrionic personality disorder (see DSM Table 13.7 in Chapter 13), in which individuals must meet five of eight criteria; and PTSD (see DSM Table 7.1 in Chapter 7), in which individuals must meet one of four exposure criteria, one of five intrusion symptom criteria, one of two avoidance criteria, two of seven alteration of mood criteria, and two of six alteration of arousal and reactivity criteria. The *DSM-5* is based on this prototypical approach.

Diagnosing forms of mental disorders is one very important activity engaged in by clinical psychologists and some other mental health professionals. The importance of establishing an accurate diagnosis cannot be stressed enough since errors in diagnosis can lead to inappropriate treatments being used with a given client. In part, accurate diagnoses are dependent on the strengths of the diagnostic system being used (e.g., *DSM-5*, *ICD-10*), but diagnostic accuracy is also dependent on the skills and training of the individual making the diagnosis. Therefore, only trained individuals are permitted to diagnose mental disorders, and the activity of diagnosis is often regulated to protect the public. For example, in Ontario, diagnosis by psychologists is one activity

that falls under the Regulated Health Professions Act (1991). The *DSM-5* criteria for major depressive episode, as just illustrated, highlight the importance of the adequate training of the individual making the diagnosis. At first glance, many university students would meet criteria for major depressive episode since many experience depressed mood, weight gain, insomnia, fatigue, and indecisiveness. However, a well-trained professional would recognize that the *DSM-5* also specifies that each of these symptoms must be present all day, every day, for two full weeks in the past month (American Psychiatric Association, 2000a), resulting in a much smaller proportion of students actually qualifying for the diagnosis.

Regardless of whether the classical categorical approach or the prototype approach to classification is used, diagnosis is involved. One limitation of the use of a medically derived concept such as diagnosis in psychology is that it relies on an acceptance of a disease model of mental illness drawn from medicine. Some continue to argue that this model is not suitable for the behavioural disorders for a variety of reasons (see reviews by Ausubel, 1971; Gorenstein, 1984; Horwitz, 2002). For example, some contend that psychiatric diagnoses play a very insignificant role in characterizing the kinds of difficulties faced by people seeking help for mental health issues (e.g., life problems such as social isolation, extramarital affairs, marital breakup, financial difficulties). On the other hand, some have argued that no inherent contradiction exists in viewing mental symptoms both as manifestations of illness and as expressions of problems in living (e.g., Ausubel, 1971). This debate has been ongoing for a very long time (Szasz, 1960).

Any classification system, whether it be a system involving the classical categorical approach, one involving the dimensional approach, or one involving the prototype approach, needs to be evaluated for two important characteristics: reliability and validity.

Reliability

A system of classification should describe specific subgroups of symptoms that are clearly evident and can be readily identified by experienced clinicians. If two clinicians interview the patient at separate times on the same day (and assuming the patient's condition does not change during the day), the two clinicians should see, and perhaps measure, the same set of behaviours and emotions. The psychological disorder can thus be identified reliably (Chmielewski et al., 2015; Kraemer, 2014). Obviously, if the disorder is not readily apparent to both clinicians, the resulting diagnoses might represent bias. For example, someone's clothes might provoke some comment. One of your friends might later say, "She looked kind of sloppy tonight." Another might comment, "No, that's just a real funky look; she's right in style." Perhaps a third friend would say, "Actually, I thought she was dressed kind of neatly." You might wonder if they had all seen the same person.

In any case, there would be no reliability to their observations. Getting your friends to agree about someone's appearance would require a careful set of definitions that you all accept.

One of the most unreliable categories in current classification is the area of personality disorders—chronic, trait-like sets of inappropriate behaviours and emotional reactions that characterize a person's way of interacting with the world. Although great progress has been made, particularly with certain personality disorders, determining the presence or absence of this type of disorder during one interview is still very difficult (Krueger et al., 2015). In a classic study, Morey and Ochoa (1989) asked 291 mental health professionals to describe an individual with a personality disorder they had recently seen, along with their diagnoses. They also collected from these clinicians detailed information on the actual signs and symptoms present in these patients. In this way, they were able to determine whether the actual diagnosis made by the clinicians matched the objective criteria for the diagnosis as determined by the symptoms. In other words, was the clinician's diagnosis accurate, based on the presence of symptoms that actually define the diagnosis?

Morey and Ochoa (1989) found substantial bias in making diagnoses. For example, clinicians who were either less experienced or were female diagnosed borderline personality disorder more frequently than the criteria indicated. More experienced clinicians and male clinicians diagnosed the condition less frequently than the criteria indicated. Patients who were white, female, or poor were diagnosed with borderline personality disorder more often than the criteria indicated. Although bias among clinicians is always a potential problem, the more reliable the nosology, or system of classification, the less likely it is to creep in during diagnosis.

Validity

In addition to being reliable, a system of nosology must be valid. Earlier we described validity as whether something measures what it is designed to measure. A valid diagnosis tells the clinician what is likely to happen with the prototypical patient; it may predict the course of the disorder and the likely effect of one treatment or another. This type of validity is often called *predictive validity* and sometimes *criterion validity*, when the outcome is the criterion by which we judge the usefulness of the category. *Content validity* simply means that if you create criteria for a diagnosis of, say, social phobia, it should reflect the way most experts in the field think of social phobia, as opposed to, say, depression. In other words, you need to get the label right.

DIAGNOSIS BEFORE 1980

The classification of psychopathology, as the old adage goes, has a long past but a very recent history. Observations of depressed, phobic, or psychotic features stretch back to the earliest recorded observations of human behaviour. Many of these observations were so detailed and complete that we could make a diagnosis today of the individuals they described. Nevertheless, only recently have we attempted the very difficult task of creating a formal nosology that would be useful for scientists and clinicians around the world. As late as 1959, at least nine different systems of varying usefulness were used for classifying psychological

disorders worldwide, but only three of the nine systems listed "phobic disorder" as a separate category (Marks, 1969). One reason for this confusion is that creating a useful nosology is easier said than done.

Early efforts to classify psychological disorders arose out of the biological tradition, particularly the work of Emil Kraepelin. Kraepelin first identified what we now know as the disorder of schizophrenia. His term for the disorder at the time was *dementia praecox*. Dementia praecox refers to deterioration of the brain that sometimes occurs with advancing age (dementia) and develops earlier than it is supposed to, or prematurely (praecox). This label (later changed to *schizophrenia*) reflected Kraepelin's belief that brain pathology is the cause of this particular disorder. Kraepelin's landmark 1913 book, *Textbook of Psychiatry*, described not only dementia praecox but also bipolar disorder, then called *manic depressive psychosis*. Kraepelin also described a variety of organic brain syndromes. Other well-known figures in their time, such as French psychiatrist Philippe Pinel, characterized psychological disorders, including depression (melancholia), as separate entities; but Kraepelin's theorizing that psychological disorders are basically biological disturbances had the greatest impact on the development of our nosology and led to an early emphasis on classical categorical strategies.

It was not until 1948 that the World Health Organization (WHO) added a section classifying mental disorders to the sixth edition of the *ICD*. This early system did not have much influence, however. Nor did the first *Diagnostic and Statistical Manual* (*DSM-I*) published in 1952 by the American Psychiatric Association. Only in the late 1960s did systems of nosology begin to have some real influence on mental health professionals. In 1968, the American Psychiatric Association published *DSM-II*, the second edition of its manual, in 1969, WHO published the eighth edition of the *ICD*, which was all but identical to *DSM-II*, since leaders in mental health began to realize the importance of at least trying to develop a uniform system of classification. Nevertheless, these systems lacked precision, often relying heavily on unproven theories of etiology not widely accepted by all mental health professionals. To make matters worse, the systems had very little reliability. Two mental health practitioners looking at the same patient often came to very different conclusions based on the nosology at that time. Even as late as the 1970s, many countries, such as France and Russia, had their own systems of nosology. In these countries, the same disorders would be labelled and interpreted very differently.

DSM-III AND DSM-III-R

The year 1980 brought a landmark in the history of nosology: *DSM-III*, the third edition of the American Psychiatric Association's manual. Under the leadership of Robert Spitzer, the *DSM-III* departed radically from its predecessors. Two changes stood out. First, the *DSM-III* attempted to take an atheoretical approach to diagnosis, relying on precise descriptions of the disorders as they presented to clinicians rather than on psychoanalytic or biological theories of etiology. With this focus, the *DSM-III* became a tool for clinicians with a variety of points of view. For example, rather than classifying phobia under the broad category "neurosis," defined by intrapsychic conflicts and defence mechanisms, it was assigned its own category within a new broader group, "anxiety disorders."

The second major change in the *DSM-III* was that the specificity and detail with which the criteria for identifying a disorder were listed made it possible to study their reliability and validity. Although not all categories in the *DSM-III* (and its 1987 revision, *DSM-III-R*) achieved perfect or even good reliability and validity, this system was a vast improvement over what was available before.

Despite numerous shortcomings, such as low reliability in identifying some disorders and arbitrary decisions on criteria for many disorders, the *DSM-III* and *DSM-III-R* had a substantial impact. Maser, Kaelber, and Weise (1991) surveyed the international usage of various diagnostic systems at that time and found that the *DSM-III* had become popular for a number of reasons. Primary among them were its precise descriptive format and its neutrality with regard to presuming a cause for diagnosis. The multiaxial format, which emphasizes a broad consideration of the whole individual rather than a narrow focus on the disorder alone, was also thought to be useful. Therefore, more clinicians around the world used the *DSM-III-R* at the beginning of the 1990s than the ICD system, which was designed to be applicable internationally (Maser et al., 1991).

DSM-IV AND DSM-IV-TR

By the late 1980s, clinicians and researchers realized once again the importance of a consistent, worldwide system of nosology. The *ICD-10* (WHO, 1992) was published in 1992. To make the *ICD-10* and the *DSM* as compatible as possible, work proceeded more or less as a collaboration between the developers of the *ICD-10* and the fourth edition of the *DSM* (*DSM-IV*) published in 1994. Although the final versions of both classifications share important similarities by virtue of the categories included and their definitions, there were important distinctions (First, 2009). The *DSM-IV* task force decided to rely as little as possible on a consensus of experts. Any changes in the diagnostic system were to be based on sound scientific data. The revisers attempted to review the voluminous literature in all areas pertaining to the diagnostic system (Widiger et al., 1996, 1998) and to identify large sets of data that might have been collected for other reasons but that, with reanalysis, would be useful to the *DSM-IV*. Finally, 12 independent studies or field trials examined the reliability and validity of alternative sets of definitions or criteria and, in some cases, the possibility of creating a new diagnosis.

Perhaps the most substantial change in the *DSM-IV* was that the distinction between organically based disorders and psychologically based disorders that was present in previous editions was eliminated. As you saw in Chapter 2, we now know that even disorders associated with known brain pathology are substantially affected by psychological and social influences. Similarly, disorders previously described as psychological in origin certainly have biological components and, most likely, identifiable brain circuits.

In 2000, a committee updated the text that describes the research literature accompanying the *DSM-IV* diagnostic category and made minor changes to some of the criteria themselves to improve consistency (American Psychiatric Association, 2000; First &

Pincus, 2002). This text revision (*DSM-IV-TR*) helped clarify many issues related to the diagnosis of psychological disorders.

DSM-5

In the more than 25 years since the publication of *DSM-IV*, our knowledge has advanced considerably and, after over a decade of concerted effort, the *DSM-5* was published in spring 2013. This massive undertaking was also carried out with considerable collaboration with international leaders working simultaneously on *ICD-11* such that each workgroup responsible for a set of disorders (e.g., anxiety disorders) had an international expert deeply involved in the work of the committee. Although working group members for the *ICD-11* were asked to consider the potential global applicability of the *DSM-5*, as was the case for *ICD-10*, the *ICD-11* will contain conceptual differences (e.g., the placement of some disorders) and structural differences (e.g., the ICD avoids the use of arbitrary symptom counts to establish a diagnosis) from *DSM-5* (First, Reed, et al., 2015). One motivation for these changes was to make the *ICD-11* as clinically useful as possible for clinicians working in vastly varied settings and circumstances, all over the world. The differences, in part, reflect the public health mandate of the ICD as a WHO document, although care was taken in the harmonization process with the *DSM-5* to avoid inadvertent differences (First, 2009). University of Ottawa professors Cary Kogan and Sabrina Paterniti have provided a useful analysis of the strengths and weaknesses of *DSM-5* and the *ICD-11* in the Canadian context (Kogan & Paterniti, 2017).

The general consensus is that the *DSM-5* is largely unchanged from the *DSM-IV*, although some new disorders are introduced and other disorders have been reclassified. There have also been some organizational and structural changes in the diagnostic manual itself. For example, the manual is divided into three main sections. The first section introduces the manual and describes how best to use it. The second section presents the disorders themselves, and the third section includes descriptions of disorders or conditions that need further research before they can qualify as official diagnoses.

The use of dimensional axes for rating severity, intensity, frequency, or duration of specific disorders in a relatively uniform manner across all disorders is also a feature of *DSM-5*. For example, for PTSD, LeBeau et al. (2014) developed the National Stressful Events Survey PTSD Short Scale (NSESSS–PTSD), which is a nine-item self-report scale based on data from a national study of U.S. adults (Kilpatrick et al., 2010). This scale was reviewed and approved by the *DSM-5* workgroup to assess the severity of PTSD symptoms over the past seven days.

In addition to dimensional assessments of severity or intensity for individual disorders, the *DSM-5* introduces cross-cutting dimensional symptom measures. These assessments are not specific to any particular disorder but rather evaluate, in a global sense, important symptoms that are often present across disorders, in almost all patients. Examples include anxiety, depression, and problems with sleep (Narrow et al., 2014). The idea is to monitor the symptoms, if present, across the course of treatment for the presenting disorder.

Thus one might diagnose bipolar disorder and provide a dimensional rating of the degree of anxiety also present because a greater degree of anxiety seems to predict a poorer response to treatment and thus may require additional treatment (Howland et al., 2009; Deckersbach et al., 2014). The suggested questions in the *DSM-5* are: "During the past two weeks how much (or how often) have you been bothered by (1) feeling nervous, anxious, frightened, worried, or on edge? (2) feeling panic or being frightened? or (3) avoiding situations that make you anxious?" (American Psychiatric Association, 2013, p. 738). The *DSM-5* uses a 0 to 4 scale where 0 = no anxiety and 4 = very severe anxiety.

Notice that this revision does not represent a change to the categories of disorders themselves; rather, these dimensions are added on to the categorical diagnoses to provide clinicians with additional information for assessment, treatment planning, and treatment monitoring. Specific changes to diagnostic categories and new diagnoses will be described in subsequent chapters.

DSM-5 *and Frank*

In Frank's case, initial observations indicate an obsessive-compulsive disorder diagnosis. He might also have long-standing personality traits that lead him to systematically avoid social contact. If so, there might also be a diagnosis of schizoid personality disorder. Job and marital difficulties might be indicated where clinicians note psychosocial or environmental problems that are not part of the disorder but might make it worse or affect treatment planning. Similarly, overall severity and impairment would be rated in a dimensional fashion periodically, as just described for PTSD, to monitor response to treatment by using a *DSM-5* scale devised for that purpose (LeBeau et al., 2013).

It is important to emphasize that impairment is a crucial determination in making any diagnosis. For example, if someone, such as Frank, has all the symptoms of obsessive-compulsive disorder but finds them only mildly annoying because the intrusive thoughts are not severe and don't occur that often, that person would not meet the criteria for a psychological disorder. It is essential that the various behaviours and cognitions composing the diagnosis interfere with functioning in some substantial manner. Thus, the criteria for disorders include the provision that the disorder must cause clinically significant distress or impairment in social, occupational, or other important areas of functioning. Individuals who have all the symptoms as noted earlier but do not cross this threshold of impairment could not be diagnosed with a disorder. As noted, one change in the *DSM-5* is to make this judgment of severity and impairment more systematic by using a dimensional scale. In one of our own clinics, we have been doing something similar to this for many years (Brown & Barlow, 2014). For instance, we have used a scale of 0 to 8, where 0 is no impairment and 8 is severely disturbing or disabling (usually housebound and barely functional). The disorder must be rated at least a 4 in severity (definitely disturbing or disabling) to meet the criteria for a psychological disorder. Many times, disorders such as obsessive-compulsive disorder would be rated a 2 or 3, meaning that all of the symptoms are there but in too mild a form to impair functioning; in this case, the disorder would be termed *subthreshold*. Using Frank as an example again, the severity of his obsessive-compulsive disorder would be rated 5.

Social and Cultural Considerations in the DSM-5

By emphasizing levels of stress in the environment, the *DSM-III* and *DSM-IV* facilitated a more complete picture of the individual. Furthermore, the *DSM-IV* corrected a previous omission by including a plan for integrating important social and cultural influences on diagnosis, a feature that remains in the *DSM-5*. "Culture" refers to the values, knowledge, and practices that individuals derive from membership in different ethnic groups, religious groups, or other social groups, as well as how membership in these groups may affect the individual's perspective on their experience with psychological disorders. The plan, referred to as "cultural formulation," allows the disorder to be described from the perspective of the patient's personal experience and in terms of the primary social and cultural group, such as Chinese or Indigenous Peoples. Answering suggested culture-related questions from the *DSM-5* Cultural Formulation Interview (American Psychiatric Association, 2013) will help accomplish these goals. The following are suggestions for accomplishing these goals (Mezzich et al., 1993, 1999):

1. What is the primary cultural reference group of the patient? For recent immigrants to the country and other ethnic minorities, how involved are they with their new culture versus their old culture? Have they mastered the language of their new country (e.g., English or French in Canada) or is language a continuing problem?

2. Does the patient use terms and descriptions from his or her old country or culture to describe the disorder? For example, as we will see in Chapter 5, *kayak-angst* in the Inuit culture is a type of anxiety disorder close to panic disorder with agoraphobia. Does the patient accept Western models of disease or disorder in which treatment is available in health-care systems, or does the patient also have an alternative health-care system in another culture (e.g., traditional herbal doctors in Chinese subcultures)?

3. What does it mean to have a disability? What kinds of disabilities are acceptable in a given culture, and which are not? For example, is it acceptable to be physically ill but not anxious or depressed? What are the typical family, social, and religious supports in the culture? Are they available to the patient? Does the clinician understand the first language of the patient and the cultural significance of the disorder?

These cultural considerations must not be overlooked in making diagnoses and planning treatment, and they are assumed throughout this book. But, as yet, there is no research supporting the use of these cultural formulation guidelines (Aggarwal et al., 2013). The consensus is that we have a lot more work to do in this area to make our nosology truly culturally sensitive.

Criticisms of the DSM-5

Because the collaboration among groups creating the *ICD-11* and *DSM-5* was largely successful, it is clear that the *DSM-5* and the closely related *ICD-11*'s section on mental disorders are the most advanced, scientifically based systems of nosology ever developed. Nevertheless, any nosological system should be considered a work in progress (Brown & Barlow, 2005; Frances & Widiger,

2012; Millon, 2004; Regier et al., 2009; Smith & Oltmanns, 2009), and the *DSM-5* has attempted to put operations in place allowing for interim revisions to categories as new information becomes available; for instance, updates are publishede online by the American Psychiatric Association (e.g., https://psychiatryon-line.org/pb-assets/dsm/update/DSM5Update_October2017.pdf).

For the time being, we still have fuzzy categories that blur at the edges, making diagnostic decisions difficult at times. As a consequence, individuals are often diagnosed with more than one psychological disorder at the same time, which is called **comorbidity**. How can we conclude anything definite about the course of a disorder, the response to treatment, or the likelihood of associated problems if we are dealing with combinations of disorders (Allen et al., 2010; Brown & Barlow, 2009; Krueger et al., 2014)? Is there a way to identify essential features of comorbid disorders and, perhaps, rate them dimensionally (Brown & Barlow, 2009; Rosellini et al., 2015)? Resolution of these tough problems simply awaits the long, slow process of science.

Criticisms of the *DSM-5* and the forthcoming *ICD-11* centre on two other aspects. First, the systems strongly emphasize reliability, sometimes at the expense of validity. This is understandable, because reliability is so difficult to achieve unless you are willing to sacrifice validity. If the sole criterion for establishing depression were to hear the patient say at some point during an interview, "I feel depressed," the clinician could theoretically achieve perfect reliability. But this achievement would be at the expense of validity because many people with differing psychological disorders, or none, occasionally say they are depressed. Thus, clinicians could agree that the statement occurred, but it would be of little use (Meehl, 1989). Second, as Carson (1996) pointed out, methods of constructing a nosology of mental disorders have a way of perpetuating definitions handed down to us from past decades, even if they might be fundamentally flawed (Lillienfield, 2014). Some (e.g., Markon, 2013) think that it might be better to start fresh once in a while and create a new system of disorders, or several new systems, based on emerging scientific knowledge and see which one turns out to be best rather than to simply fine-tune old definitions. But this is unlikely to happen because of the enormous effort and expense involved and the necessity of discarding the accumulated wisdom of previous versions.

In addition to the daunting complexity of categorizing psychological disorders, systems are subject to misuse, some of which can be dangerous and harmful. Diagnostic categories are just a convenient format for organizing observations that help professionals communicate, study, and plan. But if we reify a category, we literally make it a "thing," assuming it has a meaning that, in reality, may not exist. Categories may change occasionally with new knowledge, so none can be written in stone. If a case falls on the fuzzy borders between diagnostic categories, we should not expend all our energy attempting to force it into one category or another. It is a mistaken assumption that everything has to fit neatly somewhere.

A Caution about Labelling and Stigma

A related problem that occurs any time we categorize people is **labelling**. You may remember Kermit the Frog from *Sesame Street* sharing with us that "It's not easy being green." Some-

▲ The kinds of disabilities that are accepted in a given culture are socially determined.

thing in human nature causes us to use a label, even one as superficial as skin colour, to characterize the totality of an individual ("He's green . . . he's different from me"). We see the same phenomenon among psychological disorders ("He's a schizo"). Furthermore, if the disorder is associated with an impairment in cognitive or behavioural functioning, the label itself has negative connotations and contributes to **stigma**, which is a combination of stereotypic negative beliefs, prejudices, and attitudes resulting in reduced life opportunities for the devalued group in question, such as individuals with mental disorders (Hinshaw & Stier, 2008; Martinez et al., 2011; Parcesepe & Cabassa, 2013).

There have been many attempts over the years to categorize intellectual disability. Most of the categories were based on the severity of the impairment or highest level of developmental ability that the individual could reach. But we have had to change the labels for these categories of cognitive impairment periodically as the stigma associated with them builds up. One early categorization described levels of severity as *moron* (least severe), *imbecile*, and *idiot* (most severe). When these terms were introduced they were rather neutral, simply describing the severity of a person's cognitive and developmental impairment. But as they began to be used in common language, they picked up negative connotations and were used as insults. As these terms gradually became pejorative, it was necessary to eliminate them as categories and come up with a new set of classifying labels that were less derogatory. One recent development is to categorize intellectual disability functionally in terms of the levels of support needed by these individuals. In other words, a person's degree of intellectual disability is determined by how much assistance he or she requires (e.g., intermittent, limited, extensive, or pervasive) rather than by his or her IQ score (Lubinski, 2004; Luckasson et al., 1992). In the *DSM-5* the term "mental retardation" has been dropped in favour of the more accurate term "intellectual disability," which is further described as mild, moderate, severe, or profound (American Psychiatric Association, 2013). This is consistent with recent changes by other organizations (see Chapter 15).

In any case, once labelled, individuals with a disorder may identify with the negative connotations associated with the label (Hinshaw & Stier, 2008). This affects their self-esteem, although Ruscio (2004) indicated that the negative meanings associated with labelling are not a necessary consequence of making a diagnosis if it is relayed in a compassionate manner. Nevertheless, if you think of your own reactions to mental illness, you will probably recognize the tendency to generalize inappropriately from the label. We have to remember that terms in psychopathology do not describe people but identify patterns of behaviour that may or may not occur in certain circumstances. Thus, we must resist the temptation to identify the person with the disorder: Note the different implications of "John is a diabetic" and "John is a person who has diabetes."

Many efforts have been made in Canada to reduce the stigma associated with mental disorders. The Mental Health Commission of Canada has created anti-stigma programs, such as HEADSTRONG for schools, and initiatives, such as Mental Health First Aid for the workplace so that coworkers can become more informed about mental illness and better help people struggling with mental health issues (https://www.mentalhealthcommission.ca/English/what-we-do/stigma-and-discrimination). Other anti-stigma initiatives are more disorder specific, such as the Dementia Friendly Community project of the Alzheimer's Society of Ontario (https://alzheimer.ca/en/on/We-can-help/Dementia-Friendly-Communities-Ontario).

CREATING A DIAGNOSIS

During the extensive deliberations that led to the publication of both the *DSM-IV* and the *DSM-5*, several potentially new diagnostic categories were considered. Because one of us was a member of the *DSM-IV* task force, the final decision-making body overseeing the creation of the *DSM*, and an adviser to *DSM-5*, we can offer brief examples to illustrate how diagnostic categories are created. In one case, a potential new diagnosis was not included in the *DSM-5*; in a second case, a new diagnosis was indeed created. We now briefly describe each case.

Mixed Anxiety-Depression

Family physicians' offices, clinics, hospitals, and so on, are called *primary care settings* because they are where a person goes first with a problem. For years, people coming to these primary care

© PA Images/Alamy Stock Photo

▲ Would we label this man? The late Stephen Hawking, a famous physicist, had a severe disability caused by amyotrophic lateral sclerosis, a rare progressive degenerative disease of the spinal cord. Because he could not activate his voice box or move his lips, Hawking typed his words into an electronic voice synthesizer that "spoke" for him. He used his thumbprint to autograph his books. "I have been lucky," he said. "I don't have anything to be angry about."

clinics have complained of minor aches and pains that prove to have no obvious physical basis. They also complain of feeling uptight, down in the dumps, and anxious. Health-care professionals examining these individuals report that their symptoms of both anxiety and depression are classic but not frequent or severe enough to meet the criteria for an existing anxiety or mood disorder.

The *DSM-IV* task force was concerned about issues like this one for several reasons. First, because many individuals present with some minor symptoms of a given disorder, it is important to set thresholds high enough that only people who clearly experience some impairment qualify for the category. (Thresholds are the minimum number of criteria required to meet the definition of a disorder.) The primary reason for this concern is that substantial legal and policy implications are contingent on a diagnosis. That is, someone who presents with a psychological disorder that clearly qualifies for a diagnosis becomes part of the loosely organized medico-legal system and is eligible to ask the government or private insurance companies for financial reimbursement or disability payments.

In Canada, the services provided by a psychologist are covered by provincial health insurance only if the psychologist is employed by a publicly funded institution like a hospital, community health clinic, school, social agency, or correctional facility. In contrast, services provided by a psychologist in private practice are not covered by provincial or territorial health-care plans. These costs are either paid for by the patient or covered partially or in full by health benefits through private insurance plans offered by employers. The services of psychiatrists are covered through provincial health insurance plans regardless of where the psychiatrist is employed (Canadian Psychological Association, 2004). Disability payments are covered by the Canada Pension Plan based on contributions from workers and employers in Canada. The primary role of this plan is to replace a portion of income for contributors who cannot work because of a severe and prolonged disability, such as a severe mental health disorder (Social Development Canada, 2004).

Clearly, if the diagnostic system includes people who have only minor symptoms, who are not particularly impaired and just feel down periodically, or who don't like their job and want disability (an all-too-common request in mental health clinics), the health-care system would be even more strained and have fewer resources to treat the serious impairments. But if people are experiencing considerable problems and impairment in functioning, they should be covered in any health-care system. For these reasons, minor complaints of dysphoric mood, characterized by vague complaints of anxiety and depression, were not considered sufficiently severe to constitute a formal diagnosis.

In 1989, Klerman and Weissman, reporting on a large study by Wells et al. (1989), found that patients who claimed to be anxious and mildly depressed *were* impaired in a number of areas when compared with normal controls and with patients with chronic medical conditions. Substantial impairment was present in the areas of physical and social functioning, not only causing patients to miss work but also interfering with their functioning in the home; it was worse than the impairment of many patients with chronic medical conditions. The evidence also suggested that these individuals were already imposing an enormous burden on the health-care system by appearing in large numbers at community health clinics and the offices of family doctors.

Therefore, we concluded that it might be very valuable to identify these people and find out more about the etiology, course, and maintenance of the problem. The authors of the *ICD-10*, recognizing this phenomenon is prevalent throughout the world, had created a category of *mixed anxiety-depression*, but they had not defined it or created any criteria that would allow further examination of the potential disorder. Therefore, to explore the possibility of creating a new diagnostic category (Zinbarg & Barlow, 1996; Zinbarg et al., 1994, 1998), a study was undertaken that had three specific goals. First, if mental health professionals carefully administered semistructured interviews (the Anxiety Disorders Interview Schedule), would they find patients who fit the new category? Or would careful examination find the criteria for already existing disorders that had been overlooked by health professionals not well trained in identifying psychological disorders? Second, if mixed anxiety-depression did exist, was it really more prevalent in medical primary care settings than in outpatient mental health settings? Third, what set of criteria (e.g., types and number of symptoms) would best identify the disorder?

The study to answer these questions was conducted simultaneously in seven sites around the world (Zinbarg et al., 1994, 1998). Results indicated that people presenting with several symptoms of anxiety and depression, who did not meet the criteria for an existing anxiety or mood disorder (because they did not have the right mix or severity of anxious or depressed symptoms), were common in primary care settings. Furthermore, they were substantially impaired in their occupational and social functioning and experienced a great deal of distress. Additional analysis revealed that such people could be distinguished from people with existing anxiety or mood disorders on the basis of their symptoms with the very careful and detailed assessment procedures used. Because these people appeared both anxious and depressed, the potential new category possessed content validity.

This study also established some of the criteria important in determining *construct validity* for the new category of mixed anxiety-depression. Because the category is so new, however, we do not have information on additional criteria important in establishing construct validity, such as course, response to treatment, and the extent to which the disorder aggregates in families, and we cannot yet verify the reliability of the diagnosis or anything about predictive validity. Therefore, the decision of the *DSM-IV* task force was to place this mixed anxiety-depression diagnosis in the appendix, which is reserved for new diagnoses under study. After the publication of the *DSM-IV*, several studies re-examined this issue to see if mixed anxiety-depression should be included in the *DSM-5* (e.g., Weisberg et al., 2005). The general conclusion was that although people do present with these symptoms, it is relatively rare in the absence of a current or previous anxiety or mood disorder, the mixed anxiety-depressive symptoms do not last long, and it was very difficult to identify the condition in a reliable fashion. The findings eliminated further consideration of mixed anxiety-depression as a new and separate diagnosis; in fact, is was not even placed in Section 3 where disorders needing further study are found in *DSM-5*, and it is unlikely it will be considered in future *DSM* editions.

Premenstrual Dysphoric Disorder

Premenstrual dysphoric disorder (PMDD) evokes a very different issue that must be considered in the creation of any diagnostic category: bias and stigmatization. Evaluation of PMDD as a diagnostic category actually began well before the publication of *DSM-III-R* in 1987. Some clinicians had claimed to have identified a small group of women who presented with severe and sometimes incapacitating emotional reactions associated with the late luteal phase of their menstrual cycle (Rivera-Tovar et al., 1992). Subsequently, proposals were made to consider inclusion of this possible disorder in the *DSM-III-R*. In view of the difficulties and impairment associated with this condition, the proponents argued, women deserved the attention, care, and financial support that inclusion in a diagnostic category would provide. In addition, as with mixed anxiety-depression, proponents argued that the creation of this category would promote a substantial increase in research into the nature and treatment of the problem. Di Guilio and Reissing (2006) of the University of Ottawa, for example, argue that the accumulated research suggests that PMDD represents a distinct diagnostic entity that is separable from both normal premenstrual symptoms and major depression. They argue that recognition of this problem through formal diagnostic criteria would serve the important minority of women who suffer from this cyclical mood "disorder."

Nevertheless, arguments against the category were marshalled along several fronts. First, opponents noted that relatively little scientific information existed in either the clinical or research literature on this topic. The available information was insufficient to warrant the creation of a new diagnostic category. More important were substantial objections that what could be a normal endocrinological stage experienced by all or most women would be stigmatized as a psychiatric disorder. Some pointed to research showing that women who complain of premenstrual emotional symptoms are significantly more likely than other women to be in distressing life situations (e.g., being battered); thus, to label them as having a mental disorder may mask the real, external (societal) sources of their difficulties (see the review by Offman & Kleinplatz, 2004). In addition, the seeming similarities with the once widely accepted category of hysteria described in Chapter 1 were also noted. Questions were raised about whether the disorder would best be described as endocrinological or gynecological rather than psychological. Because premenstrual dysphoric disorder could occur only in women, should we include a comparable disorder associated with, for example, aggressiveness related to excessive male hormones?

The *DSM-III-R* task force decided to place this disorder in an appendix in the hope of promoting further study. The task force also wanted to clearly differentiate this syndrome from premenstrual syndrome (PMS), which has less severe and specific premenstrual symptoms. One way of accomplishing this was by naming the condition *late luteal phase dysphoric disorder* (LLPDD).

After the publication of the *DSM-III-R*, LLPDD attracted a great deal of research attention. By 1991, Judith Gold, a psychiatrist from Halifax, Nova Scotia, who chaired the *DSM-IV* work group on this issue, estimated that one research article per month on LLPDD was published (Gold et al., 1996). A variety of scientific findings began to accrue that supported the inclusion of this disorder in the *DSM-IV*. For example, although the rather vague and less severe symptoms of PMS occur in 20 percent to 40 percent of women (Severino & Moline, 1989), only a very small proportion of them—about 5 percent—experience the more severe and incapacitating symptoms associated with LLPDD (Rivera-Tovar & Frank, 1990). In addition, abnormalities in several biological systems appear to be associated with clinically significant premenstrual dysphoria (reviewed in Gold et al., 1996), and several different types of treatment showed promise of being effective with LLPDD (e.g., Stone et al., 1991). Hurt and colleagues, in a reanalysis of data from 670 women, recommended a set of criteria for this disorder that were not very different from those proposed in the *DSM-III-R* (Hurt et al., 1992).

Nevertheless, arguments continued against including this label in the diagnostic system. Most opponents cite the issue of stigmatization, warning that recognition might confirm the cultural belief that menstruation and resulting disability make women unfit for positions of responsibility. (There have been several cases where accusations of the less severe condition of PMS have been used against a mother in an attempt to win child custody for the father; see Gold et al., 1996.) Those arguing against the disorder also point out that some of the symptoms outlined in the criteria for LLPDD involve anger, which would not be viewed as inappropriate in a male. Only in a female does society presume that anger signifies something is wrong.

Interestingly, many women who have been given this label say they are quite comfortable with it. Some women presenting with other psychological disorders, such as depression, refuse to accept the suggestion that they have a psychiatric problem, insisting it is really premenstrual syndrome (Rapkin et al., 1989).

Early in 1994, the *DSM-IV* task force decided to retain the disorder in the appendix as needing further study. The committee wanted to see more epidemiological data using the new criteria and to examine more carefully the data on the relation of this problem to existing mood disorders, among other problems.

Several additional research findings indicated that the name late luteal phase dysphoric disorder was not entirely accurate, because the symptoms may not be exclusively related to the endocrine state of the late luteal phase. Therefore, the name has been changed to *premenstrual dysphoric disorder* (PMDD).

Since 1994, research has continued, and even accelerated, on the nature and treatment of PMDD, with thousands of papers published on this general topic (Bloch et al., 2014; Epperson et al., 2012; Hartlage et al., 2012; O'Brien et al., 2011; Pearlstein, 2010; Zachar & Kendler, 2014). Epidemiological studies from around the world supported the existence of disabling premenstrual symptoms in 2 to 5 percent of women, with another 14 to 18 percent experiencing moderate symptoms (Cunningham et al., 2009; Epperson et al., 2012; Gold, 1997a, 1997b; Ko et al., 1996; Pearlstein & Steiner, 2008). The American College of Obstetricians and Gynecologists (2002) has published systematic clinical practice guidelines recommending specific treatments, and new information on effective treatment is published frequently (Epperson et al., 2012; Freeman et al., 2009; Jang et al., 2014; Yonkers et al., 2014). One of the difficulties encountered has been distinguishing PMDD from premenstrual exacerbations of other disorders, such as binge eating disorder or mood disorders (Pearlstein et al., 2005). Hartlage et al. (2012) proposed a method that carefully considers the nature and timing of the symptoms to make a valid distinction between PMDD and premenstrual exacerbations of other disorders. For example, the symptoms of PMDD must be absent or present only mildly postmenstrually. To distinguish it from a mood disorder, at least some symptoms must be different from those associated with a mood disorder, such as certain physical symptoms or anxiety. The accumulating evidence thus far seems to suggest that PMDD is best considered a disorder of mood rather than, for example, an endocrine disorder and that it should continue to be considered a psychological disorder (Cunningham et al., 2009; Gold, 1999). Support for PMDD is now sufficient that it is now included as a distinct psychological disorder in the *DSM-5* in the chapter on mood disorders.

BEYOND *DSM-5*: DIMENSIONS AND SPECTRA

The process of changing the criteria for existing diagnoses and creating new ones will continue as science advances. New findings on brain circuits, cognitive processes, and cultural factors that affect our behaviour could date diagnostic criteria relatively quickly.

As mentioned earlier, although some new disorders have been added, and others relocated from one section to another, overall the *DSM-5* has not changed substantially from the *DSM-IV*. Nevertheless, it has been clear to most professionals involved in this process that an exclusive reliance on discrete diagnostic categories has not achieved its objective in achieving a satisfactory system of nosology (Blashfield et al., 2014; Frances & Widiger,

2012; Krueger, Watson, & Barlow, 2005; Lillienfeld, 2014). In addition to problems noted earlier with comorbidity and the fuzzy boundary between diagnostic categories, little evidence has emerged validating these categories, such as discovering specific underlying causes associated with each (Regier et al., 2009). In fact, not one biological marker, such as a laboratory test, that would clearly distinguish one disorder from another has been discovered (Frances, 2009; Widiger & Cregor, 2013; Widiger & Samuel, 2005). One exception might be narcolepsy, which seems to be associated with specific cerebrospinal biomarkers (e.g., Heier et al., 2014). It is also clear that the current categories lack treatment specificity. That is, certain treatments, such as cognitive-behavioural therapies or specific antidepressant drugs, are effective for a large number of diagnostic categories that are not supposed to be all that similar. Therefore, although some progress has been made, many are beginning to assume that the limitations of the current diagnostic system are substantial enough that continued research on these diagnostic categories may never be successful in uncovering their underlying causes or helping us develop new treatments.

It may be time for a new approach. A suggestion strongly supported by the last two directors of the U.S. National Institute of Mental Health (Hyman, 2010; Insel et al., 2010; Insel, 2014). Most people agree that this approach will incorporate a dimensional strategy to a much greater extent than in *DSM-5* (Krueger & Markon, 2014; Widiger & Cregor, 2013). The term "spectrum" is another way to describe groups of disorders that share certain basic biological or psychological qualities or dimensions. For example, in Chapter 15 you will read about one of the notable advances in the *DSM-5* where the term "Asperger's syndrome" (a mild form of autism) was integrated with autistic disorder into a new category of "autism spectrum disorder." But it is also clear at this point that research is not sufficiently advanced to attempt a wholesale switch to a dimensional or spectrum approach, so the categories in the *DSM-5* for the most part look very much like the categories in the *DSM-IV* with some updated language and increased precision and clarity. But sparked by research and conceptual advances during the process of creating the *DSM-5*, more conceptually substantial and consistent dimensional approaches are in development and may be ready for the 6th edition of the *DSM* in 10 to 20 years.

For example, most investigators have concluded that personality disorders are not qualitatively distinct from the personalities of normal-functioning individuals in community samples (Krueger et al., 2014; Trull et al., 2013). Instead, personality disorders simply represent maladaptive, and perhaps extreme, variants of common personality traits (Widiger & Edmundson, 2011; Widiger et al., 2009). Even the genetic structure of personality is not consistent with discrete categorical personality disorders. That is, personality dispositions more broadly defined, such as being shy and inhibited or outgoing, have a stronger genetic influence (higher genetic loading) than personality disorders as currently defined (First et al., 2002; Livesley & Jang, 2008; Livesley et al., 1998; Rutter et al., 2006; Widiger et al., 2009). For the anxiety and mood disorders, Brown and Barlow (2009) have proposed a new dimensional system of classification based on previous research (Brown et al., 1998) demonstrating that anxiety and depression have more in common than previously thought and may best be represented as points on a continuum of negative affect or a spectrum of emotional disorders (see Barlow, 2002; Brown & Barlow, 2005, 2009; Rosellini et al., 2015). Even for severe disorders with seemingly stronger genetic influences, such as schizophrenia, it appears that dimensional classification strategies or spectrum approaches might prove superior (Ahmed et al., 2013; Charney et al., 2002; Harvey & Bowie, 2013; Widiger & Edmundson, 2011).

At the same time, exciting new developments from the area of neuroscience relating to brain structure and function will provide enormously important information on the nature of psychological disorders. This information could then be integrated with more psychological, social, and cultural information into a diagnostic system. But even neuroscientists are abandoning the notion that groups of genes or brain circuits will be found that are specifically associated with *DSM-5* diagnostic categories, as noted in Chapter 2. Rather, it is now assumed that neurobiological processes will be discovered that are associated with specific cognitive, emotional, and behavioural patterns or traits (e.g., behavioural inhibition) that do not necessarily correspond closely with current diagnostic categories.

With this in mind, we can turn our attention to the current state of our knowledge about a variety of major psychological disorders. But first, we review the all-important area of research methods and strategies used to establish new knowledge of psychopathology.

Concept Check 3.2

Identify each of the following statements related to diagnosing psychological disorders as either true (T) or false (F).

1. _____ The classical categorical approach to classification assumes there is only one set of causative factors per disorder with no overlap between disorders, and the prototypical approach uses essential, defining features, as well as a range of other characteristics.

2. _____ As in earlier versions, the *DSM-IV* and *DSM-5* retain a distinction between organically and psychologically based disorders.

3. _____ The *DSM-IV* and *DSM-5* eradicated the problem of comorbidity, the identification of two or more disorders in an individual at one time, which was previously caused by imprecise categories.

4. _____ If two or more clinicians agree on a patient's classification, the assessments are said to be valid.

5. _____ A danger in psychological classification is that a diagnostic label might be used to characterize personally the total individual.

SUMMARY

Assessing Psychological Disorders

- Clinical assessment is the systematic evaluation and measurement of psychological, biological, and social factors in an individual with a possible psychological disorder; diagnosis is the process of determining that the individual meets all the criteria for a specific psychological disorder.
- Reliability, validity, and standardization are important components in determining the value of a psychological assessment.
- To assess various aspects of psychological disorders, clinicians may first interview and make an informal mental status exam of the patient. More systematic observations of behaviour are called behavioural assessment.
- A variety of psychological tests can be used during assessment, including projective tests, in which the patient responds to ambiguous stimuli by projecting unconscious thoughts; personality inventories, in which the patient takes a self-report questionnaire designed to assess personal traits; and intelligence testing that provides a score known as an intelligence quotient.
- Biological aspects of psychological disorders may be assessed through neuropsychological testing designed to identify possible

areas of brain dysfunction. Neuroimaging ca[...] directly to identify brain structure and function. Fin[...] physiological assessment refers to measurable chang[...] nervous system, reflecting emotional or psychological [...] that might be relevant to a psychological disorder.

Diagnosing Psychological Disorders

- The term *classification* refers to any effort to construct groups or categories and to assign objects or people to the categories on the basis of their shared attributes or relations. Methods of classification include classical categorical, dimensional, and prototypical approaches. Our current system of classification, the *Diagnostic and Statistical Manual*, fifth edition, is based on a prototypical approach, in which certain essential characteristics are identified but certain "non-essential" variations do not necessarily change the classification. The *DSM-5* categories are based, for the most part, on empirical findings to identify the criteria for each diagnosis. Although this system is the best to date in terms of scientific underpinnings, it is far from perfect, and research continues on the most useful way to classify psychological disorders.

KEY TERMS

behavioural assessment, 74
classical categorical
    approach, 85
classification, 84
clinical assessment, 69
comorbidity, 90
diagnosis, 69
dimensional approach, 85

electroencephalogram
    (EEG), 83
false negatives, 81
false positives, 81
intelligence quotient (IQ), 80
labelling, 90
mental status exam, 71
neuroimaging, 81

neuropsychological testing, 80
nomenclature, 84
nosology, 84
personality inventories, 77
projective tests, 76
prototypical approach, 85
psychophysiological
    assessment, 83

reliability, 70
self-monitoring, 75
standardization, 70
stigma, 90
taxonomy, 84
validity, 70

ANSWERS TO CONCEPT CHECKS

3.1

1. thought processes;
2. appearance and behaviour;
3. sensorium; 4. mood and affect; 5. intellectual functioning

3.2

1. T; 2. F; 3. F (still a problem); 4. F (reliable); 5. T

04 | Research Methods

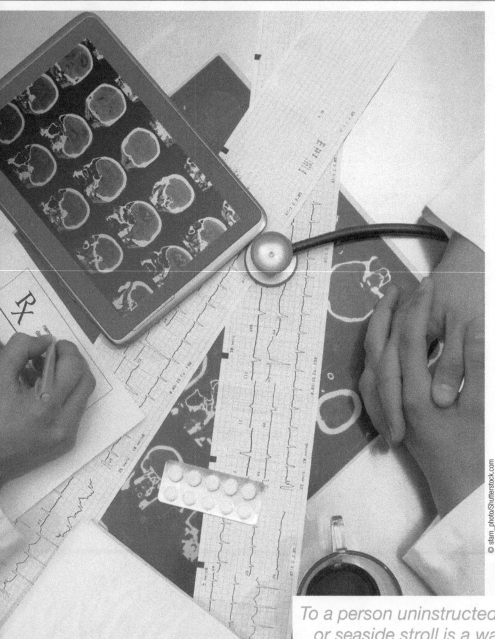

© stam_photo/Shutterstock.com

To a person uninstructed in natural history, his country or seaside stroll is a walk through a gallery filled with wonderful works of art, nine-tenths of which have their faces turned to the wall.

—THOMAS HENRY HUXLEY, On the Educational Value of the Natural History Sciences

Interpret, design, and conduct basic psychological research:	› Describe research methods used by psychologists including their respective advantages and disadvantages (APA SLO 2.4a)
	› Define and explain the purpose of key research concepts that characterize psychological research (e.g., hypothesis, operational definition) (APA SLO 2.4c)
Incorporate sociocultural factors in scientific inquiry:	› Recognize the systematic influences of sociocultural, theoretical, and personal biases on the research enterprise and evaluate the effectiveness with which researchers address those influences in psychological research (APA SLO 2.5a)
Apply ethical standards to psychological science and practice:	› Discuss relevant ethical issues that reflect principles in the APA Code of Ethics (APA SLO 3.1c)

*Portions of this chapter cover learning outcomes suggested by the American Psychological Association (2012) in their guidelines for the undergraduate psychology major. Chapter coverage of these outcomes is identified above by APA Goal and APA Suggested Learning Outcome (SLO).

Behavioural scientists explore human behaviour the same way other scientists study the path of a comet or the AIDS virus: They use the scientific method. As we've already seen, abnormal behaviour is a challenging subject because of the interaction of biological and psychological dimensions. Rarely are any simple answers available to such questions as "Why do some people have hallucinations?" or "How do you treat someone who is suicidal?"

In addition to the obvious complexity of human nature, another factor that makes an objective study of abnormal behaviour difficult is the inaccessibility of many important aspects of this phenomenon. The challenge is to get inside people's minds indirectly. Fortunately, some very creative individuals have accepted this challenge. Many ingenious methods have been developed for studying scientifically what behaviours constitute problems, why people develop behavioural disorders, and how to treat these problems. Some of you will ultimately contribute to this important field by applying the methods described in this chapter. Many critical questions regarding abnormal behaviour have yet to be answered, and we hope that some of you will be inspired to take them on. However, understanding research methods is extremely important for all of you. You or someone close to you may need the services of a psychologist, psychiatrist, or other mental health provider. You may have questions, such as these:

- Should childhood aggression be cause for concern, or is it just a phase my child will grow out of?
- The *Canada AM* show reported that increased exposure to sunlight alleviates depression. Instead of seeing a therapist, should I take a trip to Hawai'i?
- I read a story about the horrors of shock therapy. Should I advise my neighbour not to let her daughter have this treatment?
- My brother has been in therapy for three years but doesn't seem to be any better. Should I tell him to look elsewhere for help?
- My mother is still in her 50s but seems to be forgetting things. Friends tell me this is natural as you grow older. Should I be concerned?

To answer such questions, you need to be a good consumer of research. When you understand the correct ways of obtaining information—that is, research methodology—you will know when you are dealing with fact and not fiction. Knowing the difference between a fad and an established approach to a problem can be the difference between months of suffering and a quick resolution to a disturbing problem.

IMPORTANT CONCEPTS

As we said from the start, we examine several aspects of abnormal behaviour in this book. First, "What problems cause distress and impair functioning?" Second, "Why do people behave and feel like that?" And third, "How do we help them live in more adaptive ways?" The first question is about the nature of the problems people report; we explore research strategies that help us answer this question. The second question considers the causes, or *etiology*, of abnormal behaviour; we explore strategies for discovering why a disorder occurred. Lastly, because we want to help people who have disorders, we describe how researchers evaluate treatments. Before we discuss specific strategies, however, we must consider several general ways of evaluating research.

BASIC COMPONENTS OF A RESEARCH STUDY

The basic research process is very simple. You start with an educated guess, called a **hypothesis**, about what you expect to find. When you decide how you want to test this hypothesis, you have a **research design**. This includes the aspects you want to measure in the people you are studying (the **dependent variable**) and the influences on their behaviours (the **independent variable**). For example, a researcher interested in understanding the relationship between panic attacks and alcohol abuse might choose to study the effects of anxiety induction in the lab (the independent variable) on how much alcohol research participants choose to drink (the dependent variable). Finally, two forms of validity are specific to research studies: internal and external validity. **Internal validity** is the extent to which we can be confident that the independent variable is causing the dependent variable to change. **External validity** refers to how well the results relate to things outside your study, in other words, how well your findings describe similar individuals or processes outside the laboratory.

TABLE 4.1 | The Basic Components of a Research Study

Component	Description
Hypothesis	An educated guess or a statement to be tested by data
Research design	The plan for testing the hypothesis; affected by the question addressed, the hypothesis, and practical considerations
Dependent variable	Some aspect of the phenomenon that is measured and is expected to be changed or influenced by the independent variable
Independent variable	The aspect manipulated or thought to influence the change in the dependent variable
Internal validity	The extent to which the results of the study can be attributed to the independent variable
External validity	The extent to which the results of the study can be generalized or applied outside the immediate study

© Cengage Learning

Although we discuss a variety of research strategies, they all have these basic elements. Table 4.1 shows the essential components of a research study.

Hypothesis

Human beings look for order and purpose. We want to know why the world works as it does, and why people behave the way they do. Robert Kegan (cited in Lefrancois, 1990) describes us as "meaning-making" organisms, constantly striving to make sense of what is going on around us. In fact, fascinating research from social psychology tells us that we may have a heightened motivation to make sense of the world, especially if we experience situations that seem to threaten our sense of order and meaning (Heintzelman & King, 2014).

The familiar search for meaning and order also characterizes the field of abnormal behaviour. Almost by definition, abnormal behaviour defies the regularity and predictability we desire. It is this departure from the norm that makes the study of abnormal behaviour so intriguing. In an attempt to make sense of these phenomena, behavioural scientists construct hypotheses and then test them. Hypotheses are nothing more than educated guesses about the world, often informed from previous research. You may believe that watching violent television programs will cause children to be more aggressive. You may think that bulimia is influenced by media depictions of supposedly ideal female body types. You may suspect that someone abused as a child is likely to abuse his or her significant other or child. These concerns are all testable hypotheses.

Once a scientist decides what to study, the next step is to put it in words that are unambiguous and in a form that is testable. Consider a study of how self-esteem (how you feel about yourself) affects depression. Ulrich Orth from the University of California–Davis and his colleagues from around the world gathered information from more than 4000 people over several years (Orth et al., 2009). They knew from previous research that at least over a short period, having feelings of low self-esteem seems to put people at risk for later depression. The researchers posed the following hypothesis: Prior low self-esteem will be a predictor of later depression across all age groups of participants. The way the hypothesis is stated suggests the researchers already know the answer to their question. They won't know what they will find until the study is completed, but phrasing the hypothesis in this way makes it testable. If, for example, people with high self-esteem are at equal risk for later depression, then other influences must be studied. This concept of **testability** (the ability to confirm or refute the hypothesis) is important for science because it allows us to say that in this case, either (1) low self-esteem signals later depression, so maybe we can use this information for prevention efforts, or (2) there is no relationship between self-esteem and depression, so let's look for other early signs that might predict who will become depressed. The researchers did find a strong relationship between self-esteem and later depression for people in all age groups, which may prove useful for detecting people at risk for this debilitating disorder.

When they develop a hypothesis, researchers also specify the dependent and independent variables. A dependent variable is what is expected to change or be influenced by the study. Psychologists studying abnormal behaviour typically measure an aspect of the disorder, such as overt behaviours, thoughts, and feelings, or biological symptoms. In the study by Orth and colleagues (2009), the main dependent variable (level of depression) was measured using the person's responses on a questionnaire about his or her depression (Center for Epidemiologic Studies Depression Scale). Independent variables are those factors thought to affect the dependent variables. The independent variable in the study was measured using responses on a questionnaire on self-esteem (the Rosenberg Self-Esteem Scale). In other words, self-esteem was thought to influence later levels of depression. When possible, the independent variable is manipulated by the researcher, to provide a better test of its influence on the dependent variable. In the case of the Orth and colleagues' study, the independent variable was not manipulated but simply observed.

Internal and External Validity

The researchers in the study on self-esteem and depression used responses on the questionnaires collected from two very large studies conducted in the United States and Germany. Suppose they found that, unknown to them, most people who agree to participate in these types of studies have higher self-esteem than people who do not participate. This would have affected the data in a way that would limit what they could conclude about self-esteem and depression and would change the meaning of their results. This situation, which relates to internal validity, is called a **confound** (or **confounding variable**), defined as any factor occurring in a study that makes the results uninterpretable because a variable (in this instance, the type of population being studied) other than the independent variable (having high or low self-esteem) may also affect the dependent variable (depression).

Scientists use many strategies to ensure internal validity in their studies, three of which we discuss here: control groups, randomization, and analogue models. In a **control group**, people are similar to the experimental group in every way except that members of the experimental group are exposed to the independent variable and those in the control group are not. Because researchers can't prevent people from being exposed to many things around them that could affect the outcomes of the study, they try to compare people who receive the treatment with people who go through similar experiences except for the treatment (control group). Control groups help rule out alternative explanations for results, thereby strengthening internal validity.

Randomization is the process of assigning people to different research groups in such a way that each person has an equal chance of being placed in any group. Researchers can, for example, randomly place people in groups but still end up with more of certain people (e.g., people with more severe depression) in one group than another. Placing people in groups by flipping a coin or using a random number table helps improve internal validity by eliminating any systematic bias in assignment. You will see later that people sometimes put themselves in groups, and this self-selection can affect study results. Perhaps a researcher treating people with depression offers them the choice of being either in the treatment group, which requires coming into the clinic twice a week for two months, or in a wait-list control group, which means waiting until some later time to be treated. The most severely depressed individuals may not be motivated to come to frequent treatment sessions and so will choose the wait-list group. If members of the treated group are less depressed after several months, it could be because of the treatment or because group members were less depressed to begin with. Groups assembled randomly avoid these problems.

Analogue models create in the controlled conditions of the laboratory aspects that are comparable (analogous) to the phenomenon under study. Bulimia researchers could ask volunteers to binge eat in the laboratory, questioning them before they ate, while they were eating, and after they finished to learn whether eating in this way made them feel more or less anxious, guilty, and so on. Such "artificial" studies help improve internal validity.

In a research study, internal and external validity often seem to be in opposition. On the one hand, we want to be able to control as many things as possible to conclude that the independent variable (the aspect of the study we manipulated) was responsible for the changes in the dependent variables (the aspects of the study we expected to change). On the other hand, we want the results to apply to people other than the participants of the study and in other settings; this is **generalizability**, the extent to which results apply to everyone with a particular disorder. If we control all aspects of a study so that only the independent variable changes, the result may not be relevant to the real world. For example, if you reduce the influence of gender issues by studying only males, and if you reduce age variables by selecting only people from 25 to 30 years of age, and finally, if you limit your study to those with university degrees so that education level isn't an issue—then what you study (in this case, 25- to 30-year-old male university graduates) may not be relevant to many other populations. Internal and external validity are in this way often inversely related. Researchers constantly try to balance these two concerns and, as you will see later in this chapter, the best solution for achieving both internal and external validity is to conduct several different studies on the same research question.

STATISTICAL VERSUS CLINICAL SIGNIFICANCE

The introduction of statistics is part of psychology's evolution from a prescientific to a scientific discipline. Statisticians gather, analyze, and interpret data from research. As an example, consider a study evaluating whether a drug (naltrexone)—when added to a psychological intervention—helps those with alcohol addiction stay sober longer (Anton et al., 2006). The study found that the combination of medication and psychotherapy helped people stay abstinent 77 days on average and those receiving a placebo stayed abstinent 75 days on average. This difference was statistically significant. But is it an important difference? The difficulty is in the distinction between **statistical significance** (a mathematical calculation about the difference between groups) and **clinical significance** (whether or not the difference was meaningful for those affected) (Thirthalli & Rajkumar, 2009).

Closer examination of the results leads to concern about the size of the effect. Because this research studied a large group of people dependent on alcohol (1383 volunteers), even this small difference (75 versus 77 days) was statistically different. Few of us, however, would say staying sober for two extra days was worth taking medication and participating in extensive therapy—in other words, the difference may not be clinically significant.

Fortunately, concern for the clinical significance of results has led researchers to develop statistical methods that address not just that groups are different but also how large these differences are, or **effect size**. Calculating the actual statistical measures involves fairly sophisticated procedures that take into account how much each treated and untreated person in a research study improves or worsens. Some researchers have used more subjective ways of determining whether truly important change has resulted from treatment. The late behavioural scientist Montrose Wolf (1978) advocated the assessment of what he called *social validity*. This technique involves obtaining input from the person being treated, as well as from significant others, about the importance of the changes that have occurred. In the example here, we might ask the participants and family members if they thought the treatment led to truly important improvements in alcohol abstinence. If the effect of the treatment is large enough to impress those who are directly involved, the treatment effect is clinically significant. Statistical techniques of measuring effect size and assessing subjective judgments of change will let us better evaluate the results of our treatments.

THE AVERAGE CLIENT

Too often we look at results from studies and make generalizations about the group, ignoring individual differences. Kiesler (1966) labelled the tendency to see all participants as one homogeneous group the **patient uniformity myth**. Comparing groups according to their mean scores ("Group A improved by 50 percent over Group B") hides important differences in individual reactions to our interventions.

The patient uniformity myth leads researchers to make inaccurate generalizations about disorders and their treatments. To continue with our previous example, what if the researchers

Dynamics Graphics Group/Creatas/Alamy Stock Photo

▲ Studying people as part of a group sometimes masks individual differences.

STUDYING INDIVIDUAL CASES

Consider the following scenario: A psychologist thinks she has discovered a new disorder. She has observed several men who seem to have similar characteristics. All complain of a specific sleep disorder: falling asleep at work. Each man has obvious cognitive impairments that were evident during the initial interviews, and all are similar physically, each with significant hair loss and a pear-shaped physique. Finally, their personality styles are extremely egocentric, or self-centred. On the basis of these preliminary observations, the psychologist has come up with a tentative name, the Homer Simpson disorder, and she has decided to investigate this condition and possible treatments. But what is the best way to begin exploring a relatively unknown disorder? One method is to use the **case study method**, investigating intensively one or more individuals who display the behavioural and physical patterns.

studying the treatment of alcoholism concluded that the treatment was a good approach? And suppose we found that, although some participants improved with treatment, others worsened. Such differences would be averaged out in the analysis of the group as a whole, but for the person whose drinking increased with the treatment, it would make little difference that, on average, people improved. Because people differ in such ways as age, cognitive abilities, gender, and history of treatment, a simple group comparison may be misleading. Practitioners who deal with all types of disorders understand the heterogeneity of their clients and therefore do not know whether treatments that are statistically significant will be effective for a given individual. In our discussions of various disorders, we return to this issue.

One way to describe the case study method is by noting what it is not. It does not use the scientific method. Few efforts are made to ensure internal validity and, typically, many confounding variables are present that can interfere with conclusions. Instead, the case study method relies on a clinician's observations of differences among one person or one group with a disorder, people with other disorders, and people with no psychological disorders. The clinician usually collects as much information as possible to obtain a detailed description of the person. Interviewing the person under study yields a great deal of information on personal and family background, education, health, and work history, as well as the person's opinions about the nature and causes of the problems being studied.

Case studies are important in the history of psychology. Sigmund Freud developed psychoanalytic theory and the methods of psychoanalysis on the basis of his observations of dozens of cases. Freud and Josef Breuer's description of Anna O. (see Chapter 1) led to development of the clinical technique known as free association. Sexuality researchers Virginia Johnson and William Masters based their work on many case studies and helped shed light on numerous myths regarding sexual behaviour (Masters & Johnson, 1966). Joseph Wolpe, author of the landmark book *Psychotherapy by Reciprocal Inhibition* (1958), based his work with systematic desensitization on more than 200 cases. As our knowledge of psychological disorders has grown, psychological researchers' reliance on the case study method has gradually decreased.

One difficulty with depending heavily on individual cases is that sometimes coincidences occur that are irrelevant to the condition under study. Unfortunately, coincidences in people's lives often lead to mistaken conclusions about what causes certain conditions and what treatment appears to be effective. Because a case study does not have the controls of an experimental study, the results may be unique to a particular person without the researcher realizing it or may derive from a special combination of factors that are not obvious. Complicating our efforts to

---

Concept Check 4.1

In each of the statements provided, fill in the blanks with one of the following: hypothesis, dependent variable, independent variable, internal validity, external validity, or confound.

1. In a treatment study, the introduction of the treatment to the participants is referred to as the _____.

2. After the treatment study was completed, you found that many people in the control group received treatment outside of the study. This is called a _____.

3. A researcher's guess about what a study might find is labelled the _____.

4. Scores on a depression scale improved for a treatment group after therapy. The change in these scores would be referred to as a change in the _____.

5. A relative lack of confounds in a study would indicate good : _____, whereas good generalizability of the results would be called good _____.

understand abnormal behaviour is the portrayal of sensational cases in the media. For example, on April 16, 2007, a shooter on the campus of Virginia Tech University took the lives of 32 faculty members and students. Immediately after this horrific mass killing there was speculation about the shooter, including early bullying, descriptions of him being a "loner," and depictions of notes he wrote against "rich kids," "deceitful charlatans," and "debauchery" (Kellner, 2008). Attempts have been made to discover childhood experiences that could possibly explain this later behaviour. We must be careful, however, about concluding anything from such sensational portrayals, since many people are bullied as children, for example, but do not go on to kill dozens of innocent people.

As another illustration of both the limits and potential of the case study method, Canadian researcher Earls and Lalumière (2002) described the case of a man who showed a preference for sex with a horse over sex with humans (or any other species for that matter). The man in question had been convicted of animal cruelty, had received a diagnosis of antisocial personality disorder, and scored below average on a measure of IQ (80). The authors noted that the finding of low IQ was consistent with previous research and discussions linking low intelligence to acts of bestiality and to zoophilia (a sexual preference for animals). Later, the authors were contacted by a man who suggested that some high-functioning men also have a strong preference for animals, using himself as an example: "You published one case study and I am another one. Who determines which one is typical?" Earls and Lalumière (2009) later published a case report on this occupationally successful man: He had a long-standing sexual interest in horses (one that preceded his actual contact with horses), was a published medical doctor, and was married with children; he eventually left his wife to live on a farm alone with two horses, which he called his "mare-wives."

Researchers in cognitive psychology point out that the public and researchers themselves are often, unfortunately, more highly influenced by dramatic accounts than by scientific evidence (Nisbett & Ross, 1980). Remembering our tendency to ignore this fact, we highlight research findings in this book. To advance our understanding of the nature, causes, and treatment of abnormal behaviour, we must guard against premature and inaccurate conclusions.

RESEARCH BY CORRELATION

One of the fundamental questions posed by scientists is whether two variables are related to each other. A statistical relationship between two variables is called a **correlation**. For example, is schizophrenia related to the size of ventricles (spaces) in the brain? Are people with depression more likely to have negative attributions (negative explanations for their own and others' behaviour)? Is the frequency of hallucinations higher among older people? The answers depend on determining how one variable (e.g., number of hallucinations) is related to another (e.g., age). Unlike experimental designs, which involve manipulating or changing conditions, correlational designs are used to study phenomena just as they occur. The result of a correlational study—whether variables occur together—is important to the ongoing search for knowledge about abnormal behaviour.

One of the clichés of science is that correlation does not imply causation. In other words, two things occurring together does not necessarily mean that one caused the other. For example, the occurrence of marital problems in families is correlated with behaviour problems in children (e.g., Yoo & Huang, 2012). If you conduct a correlational study in this area, you will find that in families with marital problems you tend to see children with behaviour problems; in families with fewer marital problems, you are likely to find children with fewer behaviour problems. The most obvious conclusion is that having marital problems will cause children to misbehave. If only it were as simple as that! The nature of the relationship between marital discord and childhood behaviour problems can be explained in a number of ways. It may be that problems in a marriage cause disruptive behaviour in the children. Some evidence suggests, however, the opposite may be true as well: The disruptive behaviour of children may cause marital problems (Rutter & Giller, 1984). In addition, evidence suggests genetic influences may play a role in conduct disorders and in marital discord (D'Onofrio et al., 2006; Lynch et al., 2006), so parents who are genetically more inclined to argue pass on those genes to children who then have an increased tendency to misbehave.

This example points out the challenges in interpreting the results of a correlational study. We know that variable A (marital problems) is correlated with variable B (child behaviour problems). We do not know from these studies whether A causes B (marital problems cause child problems), whether B causes A (child problems cause marital problems), or whether some third variable, C, causes both (genes influence both marital and child problems).

The association between marital discord and child problems represents a **positive correlation**. This means that higher scores in one variable (a great deal of marital distress) is associated with higher scores in the other variable (more child disruptive behaviour). At the same time, lower scores in one variable (less marital distress) is associated with lower scores in the other (less disruptive behaviour). When there is a **negative correlation**, the relationship between the two variables is reversed. That is, higher scores in one variable are associated with lower scores in the other, and vice versa. The **correlation coefficient** can vary from −1.0 (a perfect negative correlation) to 0.0 (no correlation) to +1.0 (a perfect positive correlation). See ■ Figure 4.1 for an illustration of positive and negative correlations.

Marital problems in families and behaviour problems in children have a relatively strong positive correlation represented by a number around +0.50. Schizophrenia and height are not related, so the correlation is likely close to 0.00. We used an example of a negative correlation in Chapter 2, when we discussed social supports and illness. The more social supports that are present, the less likely it is that a person will become ill. The negative relationship between social supports and illness could be represented by a number such as −0.40.

EPIDEMIOLOGICAL RESEARCH

Scientists often think of themselves as detectives, searching for the truth by studying clues. One type of correlational research that is very much like the efforts of detectives is called **epidemiology**,

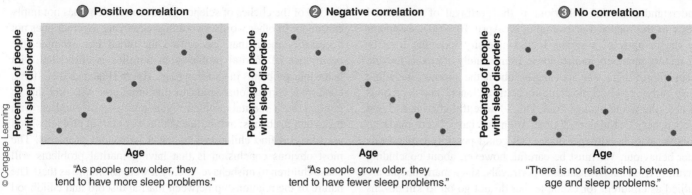

① **Positive correlation** ② **Negative correlation** ③ **No correlation**

Percentage of people with sleep disorders (y-axis)
Age (x-axis)

"As people grow older, they tend to have more sleep problems."

"As people grow older, they tend to have fewer sleep problems."

"There is no relationship between age and sleep problems."

FIGURE 4.1 | These three graphs represent hypothetical correlations between age and sleep problems.

the study of the incidence, distribution, and consequences of a particular problem or set of problems in a population. Epidemiologists expect that by tracking a disorder among many people, they will find important clues to why the disorder exists. One strategy is to determine the **incidence** of a disorder—the estimated number of new cases during a specific period. For example, as we see in Chapter 12, the incidence of new cases of cocaine use has been decreasing over the past decade among most age groups in Canada. A related strategy involves determining **prevalence**, the number of people with a disorder at any one time. For example, the prevalence of alcohol dependence among Canadian adults is about 3 percent (Statistics Canada, 2002a). Epidemiologists study the incidence and prevalence of disorders among different groups of people. For instance, data from epidemiological research conducted by Statistics Canada indicate that the prevalence of alcohol dependence among women is substantially lower than among men (Statistics Canada, 2002a).

Although the primary goal of epidemiology is to determine the extent of medical problems, it is also useful in the study of psychological disorders. In the early 20th century, many people displayed symptoms of a strange mental disorder. Its symptoms were similar to those of organic psychosis, which is often caused by mind-altering drugs or great quantities of alcohol. Many patients appeared catatonic (immobile for long periods) or exhibited symptoms similar to those of paranoid schizophrenia. Victims were likely to be poor, which led to speculation about class inferiority. Using the methods of epidemiological research, however, researcher Joseph Goldberger found correlations between the disorder and diet, and he identified the cause of the disorder as a deficiency of the B vitamin niacin among people with poor diets. The symptoms were successfully eliminated by niacin therapy and improved diets. A long-term, widespread benefit of Goldberger's findings was the introduction of vitamin-enriched bread in the 1940s (Colp, 2009).

Researchers have used epidemiological techniques to study the effects of stress on psychological disorders. For example, researchers have examined the psychological effects of the September 11, 2001, terrorist attacks on the U.S. World Trade Center and the American Pentagon. Following those events, Blanchard et al. (2004) examined rates of two anxiety disorders—acute stress disorder and post-traumatic stress disorder—in three samples of university students: those attending the University of Albany in New York state, those attending North Dakota State

▲ The more social supports people have, the less likely it is that they will become ill (a negative correlation).

University in North Dakota, and those attending Augusta State University in Georgia. They found significantly greater rates of both acute stress disorder (28 percent versus 10 percent versus 19 percent, respectively) and post-traumatic stress disorder (11 percent versus 3 percent versus 7 percent, respectively) in the New York students.

A similar study conducted in Saskatchewan by Gordon Asmundson and his colleagues showed rates of disorder comparable to those obtained by Blanchard and colleagues (2004) in the students from North Dakota and Georgia. More specifically, about 4 percent of the Canadian sample met the criteria for full or partial post-traumatic stress disorder following the events of September 11, 2001 (Asmundson et al., 2004).

Taken together, these findings suggest a relationship between geographical proximity and impact of the trauma, with those living closer to the site of the terrorist attacks showing the greatest levels of distress. The studies by Blanchard et al. (2004) and Asmundson et al. (2004) are correlational studies because the investigators did not manipulate the independent variable. Like other types of correlational research, epidemiological research can't tell us conclusively what causes a particular phenomenon. Knowledge about the prevalence and course of psychological disorders is extremely valuable to our understanding, however, because it points researchers in the right direction.

RESEARCH BY EXPERIMENT

An **experiment** involves the manipulation of an independent variable and the observation of its effects. We manipulate the independent variable to answer the question of causality. If we observe a correlation between social supports and psychological disorders, we can't conclude which of these factors influenced the other. We can, however, change the extent of social supports and see whether it triggers an accompanying change in the prevalence of psychological disorders—in other words, do an experiment.

What will this experiment tell us about the relationship between these two variables? If we increase the number of social supports and find no change in the frequency of psychological disorders, it may mean that the lack of such supports does not cause psychological problems. However, if we find that psychological disorders diminish with increased social support, we can be more confident that lack of support does contribute to disorders. However, because we are never 100 percent confident that our experiments are internally valid—that no other explanations are possible—we are cautious about interpreting our results. In the following section, we describe different ways researchers conduct experiments and consider how each one brings us closer to understanding abnormal behaviour.

EXPERIMENTAL DESIGNS

With correlational designs, researchers observe people to see how different variables are associated. In experimental designs, researchers are more active. They actually change an independent variable to see how the behaviour of the people is affected. Suppose researchers design an intervention to help reduce insomnia in older adults, who are particularly affected by the condition (Ancoli-Israel & Ayalon, 2009). They treat a number of individuals and follow them for 10 years to learn whether their sleep patterns improve. The treatment is the independent variable; that is, it would not have occurred naturally. They then assess the treated group to learn whether their behaviour changed as a function of what the researchers did. Introducing or withdrawing a variable in a way that would not have occurred naturally is called *manipulating a variable*.

Unfortunately, a decade later the researchers find that the older adults treated for sleep problems still, as a group, sleep less than eight hours per night. Is the treatment a failure? Maybe not. The question that can't be answered in this study is what would have happened to group members if they hadn't been treated. Perhaps their sleep patterns would have been worse. Fortunately, researchers have devised ingenious methods to help sort out these challenging questions.

A special type of experimental design is used more and more frequently in the treatment of psychological disorders and is referred to as a *clinical trial* (Durand & Wang, 2011; Pocock, 2013). A clinical trial is an experiment used to determine the effectiveness and safety of a treatment. The term *clinical trial* implies a level of formality with regard to how it is conducted. As a result, a clinical trial is not a design by itself but rather a method of evaluation that follows a number of generally accepted rules. For example, these rules cover how you should select the research participants, how many individuals should be included in

the study, how they should be assigned to groups, and how the data should be analyzed—and this represents only a partial list. Also, treatments are usually applied using formal protocols to ensure that everyone is treated the same.

The terms used to describe these experiments can be confusing. "Clinical trials" is the overarching term used to describe the general category of studies that follow the standards described previously. Within the "clinical trial" category are "randomized clinical trials," which are experiments that employ randomization of participants into each group. Another subset of clinical trials is "controlled clinical trials," which are used to describe experiments that rely on control conditions to be used for comparison purposes. Finally, the preferred method of conducting a clinical trial, which uses both randomization and one or more control conditions, is referred to as a "randomized controlled trial." We next describe the nature of control groups and randomization, and discuss their importance in **treatment outcome research**.

Control Groups

One answer to the what-if dilemma is to use a control group—people who are similar to the experimental group in every way except they are not exposed to the independent variable. In the previous study looking at sleep in older adults, suppose another group who didn't receive treatment was selected. Further suppose that the researchers also follow this group of people, assess them 10 years later, and look at their sleep patterns over this period. They probably observe that, without intervention, people tend to sleep fewer hours as they get older (Cho et al., 2008). Members of the control group, then, might sleep less than people in the treated group, who might themselves sleep somewhat less than they did 10 years earlier. Using a control group allows the researchers to see that their treatment did help the treated participants keep their sleep time from decreasing further.

Ideally, a control group is nearly identical to the treatment group in such factors as age, gender, socioeconomic backgrounds, and the problems they are reporting. Furthermore, a researcher would do the same assessments before and after the independent variable manipulation (e.g., a treatment) to people in both groups. Any later differences between the groups after the change would, therefore, be attributable only to what was changed.

People in a treatment group often expect to get better. When behaviour changes as a result of a person's expectation of change rather than as a result of any manipulation by an experimenter, the phenomenon is known as a **placebo effect** (from the Latin word *placebo*, which means "I shall please"). Conversely, people in the control group may be disappointed that they are not receiving treatment (analogously, we could label this a *frustro effect*, from the Latin word meaning "to disappoint"). Depending on the type of disorder they experience (e.g., depression), disappointment may make them worse. This phenomenon would also make the treatment group look better by comparison.

One way researchers address the expectation concern is through **placebo control groups**. The placebo is given to members of the control group to make them believe they are getting treatment. A placebo control in a medication study can be carried out with relative ease because people in the untreated group receive something that looks like the medication administered to the treatment group (e.g., a sugar pill). In psychological treatments, however, it is not always easy to devise something that people believe may help them but does not include the component the researcher believes is effective. Clients in these types of control groups are often given part of the actual therapy—for example, the same homework as the treated group—but not the portions the researchers believe are responsible for improvements.

Note that you can look at the placebo effect as one portion of any treatment. If someone you provide with a treatment improves, you may attribute the improvement to a combination of your treatment and the client's expectation of improving. Therapists want their clients to expect improvement; this helps strengthen the treatment. However, when researchers conduct an experiment to determine what portion of a particular treatment is responsible for the observed changes, the placebo effect is a confound that can dilute the validity of the research. Thus, researchers use a placebo control group to help distinguish the results of positive expectations from the results of the active treatment ingredients.

The **double-blind control** is a variant of the placebo control group procedure. As the name suggests, not only are the participants in the study "blind," or unaware of what group they are in or what treatment they are given (single blind), but so are the researchers or therapists providing treatment (double blind). This type of control eliminates the possibility that an investigator might bias the outcome. For example, a researcher comparing two treatments who expected one to be more effective than the other might try harder if the preferred treatment wasn't working as well as expected. On the other hand, if the treatment that wasn't expected to work seemed to be failing, the researcher might not push as hard to see it succeed. This reaction might not be deliberate, but it does happen. This phenomenon is referred to as an *allegiance effect* (Dragioti et al., 2015). If, however, both the participants and the researchers or therapists are blind, there is less chance that bias will affect the results.

A double-blind placebo control does not work perfectly in all cases. If medication is part of the treatment, participants and researchers may be able to tell whether or not they have received it by the presence or absence of physical reactions (side effects). Even with purely psychological interventions, participants often know whether or not they are receiving a powerful treatment, and they may alter their expectations for improvement accordingly.

As an alternative to using no-treatment control groups to help evaluate results, some researchers compare different treatments. In this design, the researcher gives different treatments to two or more comparable groups of people with a particular disorder and can then assess how or whether each treatment helped the people who received it. This is called **comparative treatment research**. In the sleep study we discussed, two groups of older adults could be selected, with one group given medication for insomnia, the other given a cognitive-behavioural intervention, and the results compared.

PROCESS AND OUTCOME OF TREATMENT

The *process* and *outcome* of treatment are two important issues to be considered when different approaches are studied. *Process research* focuses on the mechanisms responsible for behaviour change, or "why does it work?" In an old joke, someone goes to a physician for a new miracle cure for the common cold. The physician prescribes the new drug and tells the patient the cold will be gone in seven to ten days. As most of us know, colds typically improve in seven to ten days without treatment. The new drug probably does nothing to further the improvement of the patient's cold. The process aspect of testing medical interventions involves evaluating biological mechanisms responsible for change. Does the medication cause lower serotonin levels, for example, and does this account for the changes we observe? Similarly, in looking at psychological interventions, we determine what is "causing" the observed changes. This is important for several reasons. First, if we understand what the "active ingredients" of our treatment are, we can often eliminate aspects that are not important, thereby saving clients' time and money. For example, one study of insomnia found that adding a relaxation training component to a treatment package provided no additional benefit—allowing clinicians to reduce the amount of training and focus on only those aspects that really improve sleep (e.g., cognitive-behavioural therapy) (Harvey et al., 2002). In addition, knowing what is important about our interventions can help us create more powerful, newer versions that may be more effective.

Outcome research focuses on the positive and negative effects (results) of the treatment. In other words, does it work? Remember, treatment process involves finding out why or how your treatment works.

SINGLE-CASE EXPERIMENTAL DESIGNS

B. F. Skinner's innovations in scientific methodology were among his most important contributions to psychopathology. Skinner formalized the concept of **single-case experimental designs**. This method involves the systematic study of individuals under a variety of experimental conditions. Skinner thought it was much better to know a lot about the behaviour of one individual than to make only a few observations of a large group for the sake of presenting the "average" response. Psychopathology is concerned with the suffering of specific people, and this methodology has greatly helped us understand the factors involved in individual psychopathology (Barlow et al., 2009; Kazdin, 2011). Many applications throughout this book reflect Skinnerian methods.

Single-case experimental designs differ from case studies in their use of various strategies to improve internal validity, thereby reducing the number of confounding variables. As you will see, these strategies have strengths and weaknesses in comparison with traditional group designs. Although we use examples from treatment research to illustrate the single-case experimental designs, they, like other research strategies, can help explain why people engage in abnormal behaviour, as well as how to treat them.

REPEATED MEASUREMENTS

One of the more important strategies used in single-case experimental design is **repeated measurement**, in which a behaviour is measured several times instead of only once before you change the independent variable and once afterward. The researcher takes the same measurements repeatedly to learn how variable the behaviour is (how much does it change from day to day?) and whether it shows any obvious trends (is it getting better or worse?). Suppose a young woman, Wendy, comes into the office complaining about feelings of anxiety. When asked to rate the level of her anxiety, she gives it a nine (ten is the worst). After several weeks of treatment, Wendy rates her anxiety at six. Can we say that the treatment reduced her anxiety? Not necessarily.

Suppose we had measured Wendy's anxiety each day during the weeks before her visit to the office (repeated measurement) and observed that it differed greatly. On particularly good days, she rated her anxiety from five to seven. On bad days, it was up between eight and ten. Suppose further that, even after treatment, her daily ratings continued to range from five to ten. The rating of nine before treatment and six after treatment may only have been part of the daily variations she experienced normally. Wendy could just as easily have had a good day and reported a six before treatment and then had a bad day and reported a nine after treatment, which would imply that the treatment made her worse!

Repeated measurement is part of each single-subject experimental design. It helps identify how a person is doing before and after intervention and whether the treatment accounted for any changes. ■ Figure 4.2 summarizes Wendy's anxiety and the added information obtained by repeated measurements. The top graph shows Wendy's original before-and-after ratings of her anxiety. The middle graph shows that with daily ratings her reports are variable and that just by chance the previous measurement was probably misleading. She had good and bad days both before and after treatment and doesn't seem to have changed much.

The bottom graph shows a different possibility: Wendy's anxiety was on its way down before the treatment, which would also have been obscured with just before-and-after measurements. Maybe she was getting better on her own and the treatment didn't have much effect. Although the middle graph shows how the **variability** from day to day could be important in an interpretation of the effect of treatment, the bottom graph shows how the **trend** itself can also be important in determining the cause of any change. The three graphs illustrate important parts of repeated measurements: (1) the **level** or degree of behaviour change with different interventions (top), (2) the variability or degree of change over time (middle), and (3) the trend or direction of change (bottom). Again, before-and-after scores alone do not necessarily show what is responsible for behavioural changes.

WITHDRAWAL DESIGNS

One of the more common strategies used in single-subject research is a **withdrawal design**, in which a researcher tries to determine whether the independent variable is responsible for changes in behaviour. The effect of Wendy's treatment could be tested by stopping it for some time to see whether her anxiety increased. A simple withdrawal design has three parts. First, a person's condition is evaluated before treatment, to establish a **baseline**. Then comes the change in the independent variable—in Wendy's case, the beginning of treatment. Last, treatment is withdrawn ("return to baseline") and the researcher assesses whether Wendy's anxiety level changes again as a function of this last step. If with the treatment her anxiety lessens in comparison to baseline and then worsens after treatment is withdrawn, the researcher can conclude the treatment has reduced Wendy's anxiety.

How is this design different from a case study? An important difference is that the change in treatment is designed specifically

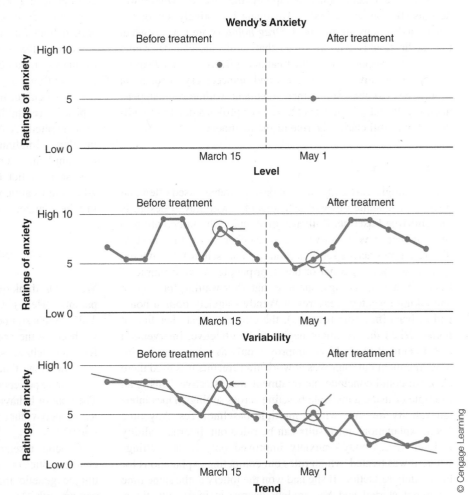

FIGURE 4.2 | The top graph seems to show Wendy's anxiety dropping significantly after treatment (measuring level). However, when you look at repeated measures before and after treatment, the middle graph reveals little change because her anxiety fluctuated a great deal (measuring variability). A different scenario is illustrated in the bottom graph (measuring trend), where her anxiety also varied. In general, there was a downward movement (improved anxiety) even before treatment, suggesting that she might have improved without help. Examining variability and trend can provide more information about the true nature of the change.

to show whether treatment caused the changes in behaviour. Although case studies often involve treatment, they don't include any effort to learn whether the person would have improved without the treatment. A withdrawal design gives researchers a better sense of whether or not the treatment itself caused a behaviour change.

Despite their advantages, withdrawal designs are not always appropriate. The researcher is required to remove what might be an effective treatment, a decision that is sometimes difficult to justify for ethical reasons. In Wendy's case, a researcher would have to decide there was a sufficient reason to risk making her anxious again. A withdrawal design is also unsuitable when the treatment can't be removed. Suppose Wendy's treatment involved visualizing herself on a beach on a tropical island. It would be difficult—if not impossible—to stop her from imagining something. Similarly, some treatments involve teaching people skills, which might be impossible to unlearn. If Wendy learned how to be less anxious in social situations, how could she revert to being socially apprehensive?

Several counterarguments support the use of withdrawal designs (Barlow et al., 2009). Treatment is routinely withdrawn when medications are involved. *Drug holidays* are periods when the medication is withdrawn so that clinicians can determine whether it is responsible for the treatment effects. Any medication can have negative side effects, and unnecessary medication should be avoided. Sometimes treatment withdrawal happens naturally. Withdrawal does not have to be prolonged; a brief withdrawal may still clarify the role of the treatment.

MULTIPLE BASELINES

Another single-case experimental design strategy used often that doesn't have some of the drawbacks of a withdrawal design is the **multiple baseline**. Rather than stopping the intervention to see whether it is effective, the researcher starts treatment at different times across settings (home versus school), behaviours (yelling at spouse/partner or boss), or people. As an example of treatment across settings, suppose that after waiting for a while and taking repeated measures of Wendy's anxiety both at home and at her office (the baseline), the clinician treats her first at home. When the treatment begins to be effective, intervention could begin at work. If she improves only at home after beginning treatment but improves at work after treatment is used there also, we could conclude the treatment was effective. This is an example of using a multiple baseline across settings. Does internal validity improve with a multiple baseline? Yes. Any time other explanations for results can be ruled out, internal validity is improved. Wendy's anxiety improved only in the settings where it was treated, which rules out competing explanations for her anxiety reduction. If she had won the lottery at the same time treatment started and her anxiety decreased in all situations, however, we couldn't conclude her condition was affected by treatment.

Suppose a researcher wanted to assess the effectiveness of a treatment for a child's problem behaviours. Treatment could focus first on the child's crying, and then on a second problem, such as fighting with siblings. If the treatment was first effective only in reducing crying, and effective for reducing fighting only

after the second intervention, the researcher could conclude that the treatment, not something else, accounted for the improvements. This is a multiple baseline conducted across behaviours.

Single-case experimental designs are sometimes criticized because they tend to involve only a small number of cases, leaving their external validity in doubt. In other words, we can't say the results we saw with a few people would be the same for everyone. However, although they are called *single-case* designs, researchers can and often do use them with several people at once, in part to address the issue of external validity. One of us studied the effectiveness of a treatment for the severe behaviour problems of children with autism (Durand, 1999) (see ■ Figure 4.3). We taught the children to communicate instead of misbehaving, using a procedure known as *functional communication training*. Using a multiple baseline, we introduced this treatment to a group of five children. Our dependent variables were the incidence of the children's behaviour problems and their newly acquired communication skills. As shows, only when we began treatment did each child's behaviour problems improve and communication begin. This multiple baseline design let us rule out coincidence or some other change in the children's lives as explanations for the improvements.

Among the advantages of the multiple baseline design in evaluating treatments is that it does not require withdrawal of treatment and, as you've seen, withdrawing treatment is sometimes difficult or impossible. Furthermore, the multiple baseline typically resembles the way treatment would naturally be implemented. A clinician can't help a client with numerous problems simultaneously but can take repeated measures of the relevant behaviours and observe when they change. A clinician who sees predictable and orderly changes related to where and when the treatment is used can conclude the treatment is causing the change.

STUDYING GENETICS

We tend to think of genetics in terms of what we inherit from our parents: "He's got his mother's eyes." "She's thin just like her dad." "She's stubborn like her mother." This simple view of how we become the people we are suggests that how we look, think, feel, and behave is predetermined. Yet, as you saw in Chapter 2, we now know that the interaction between our genetic makeup and our experiences is what determines how we will develop. The goal of behavioural geneticists (people who study the genetics of behaviour) is to tease out the role of genetics in these interactions.

Genetic researchers examine **phenotypes**, the observable characteristics or behaviour of the individual, and **genotypes**, the unique genetic makeup of individual people. For example, a person with Down syndrome typically has some level of intellectual disability and a variety of other physical characteristics, such as slanted eyes and a thick tongue. These characteristics are the phenotype. The genotype is the extra 21st chromosome that causes Down syndrome.

Our knowledge of the phenotypes of different psychological disorders exceeds our knowledge of the genotypes, but that may soon change. Ever since the discovery of the double helix in

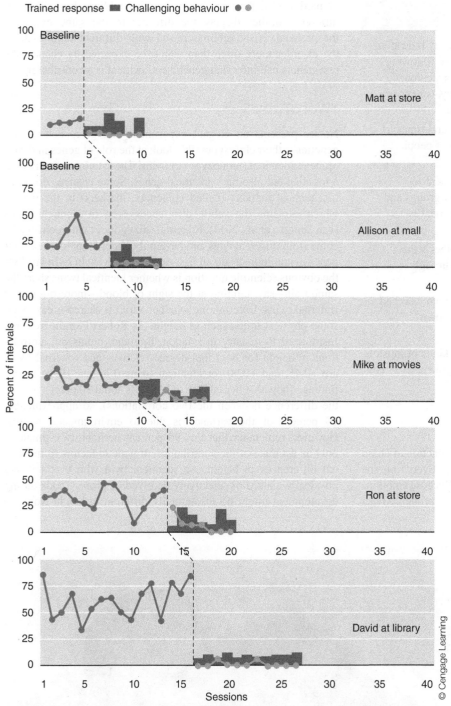

Trained response ■ Challenging behaviour ● ●

Percent of intervals

Baseline — Matt at store

Baseline — Allison at mall

Mike at movies

Ron at store

David at library

Sessions

© Cengage Learning

FIGURE 4.3 | This figure shows how a multiple baseline design was used to test that the treatment—functional communication training—was responsible for improvements in the children's behaviours. The circles represent how often each child exhibited behaviour problems (called challenging behaviour), and the blue-shaded areas show how often they communicated without help from the teacher (referred to as unprompted communication).

Source: From "Functional Communication Training Using Assistive Devices: Recruiting Natural Communities of Reinforcement," by V. Mark Durand, Fall 1999, *Journal of Applied Behavior Analysis, 32*(3), pp. 247–267. Reprinted by permission of the Society for the Experimental Analysis of Human Behavior.

organism"). Using the latest advances in molecular biology, scientists working on this project completed a rough draft of the mapping of the approximately 25 000 human genes. This work identified hundreds of genes that contribute to inherited diseases. These exciting findings represent truly astounding progress in deciphering the nature of genetic endowment and its role in psychological disorders.

With the rapid advance of the science of genes, a new concept is now the focus of intense study—**endophenotypes**. Endophenotypes are the genetic mechanisms that ultimately contribute to the underlying problems causing the symptoms and difficulties experienced by people with psychological disorders. In the case of schizophrenia, for example, researchers are not looking for a "schizophrenia gene"; instead, they are searching for the gene or genes responsible for the working memory problems characteristic of people with this disorder (endophenotype), as well as the genes responsible for other problems experienced by people with this disorder. What follows is a brief review of the research strategies that scientists use as they study the interaction between environment and genetics in psychological disorders.

FAMILY STUDIES

In **family studies**, scientists simply examine a behavioural pattern or emotional trait in the context of the family. The family member with the trait singled out for study is called the **proband**. If there is a genetic influence, presumably the trait should occur more often in first-degree relatives (parents, siblings, or offspring) than in second-degree or more distant relatives. The presence of the trait in distant relatives, in turn, should be somewhat greater than in the population as a whole. In Chapter 1 you met Jody, the adolescent with blood-injury-injection phobia who fainted at the sight of blood. The tendency of a trait to run in families, or familial aggregation, is as high as 60 percent for this disorder; that is, 60 percent of the first-degree relatives of someone with blood-injury-injection phobia have the same reaction to at least some degree. This is one of the highest rates of familial aggregation for any psychological disorder we have studied.

The complication with family studies is that family members tend to live together and there might be something in their shared environment that causes the high familial aggregation.

1953 by James Watson and Francis Crick, scientists have aimed to map the structure and location of every gene on all 46 chromosomes to fully understand our genetic endowment. Beginning in 1990, scientists around the world, in a coordinated effort, began the **human genome project** (*genome* means "all the genes of an

Check your understanding of research methods by indicating which would be most appropriate in each of the following situations. Choose from (a) case study, (b) correlation, (c) randomized clinical trials, (d) epidemiology, (e) experiment, and (f) single-case experimental design.

1. A researcher changes the level of noise several times to see how it affects concentration in a group of people.

   _____

2. A group of researchers uses chance assignment to include participants in one of two treatment groups and uses published protocols to make sure treatment is applied uniformly. _____

3. A researcher wants to investigate the hypothesis that children listen to louder music as they go through adolescence. _____

4. A researcher is interested in studying a woman who had no contact with civilization and created her own language._____

5. A researcher wants to know how different kinds of music will affect a five-year-old who has never spoken.

   _____

For example, Mom might have developed a bad reaction to blood as a young girl after witnessing a serious accident. Every time she sees blood she has a strong emotional response. Because emotions are contagious, the young children watching Mom probably react similarly. In adulthood, they pass it on, in turn, to their own children.

ADOPTION STUDIES

How do we separate environmental from genetic influences in families? One way is through **adoption studies**. Scientists identify adoptees who have a particular behavioural pattern or psychological disorder and attempt to locate first-degree relatives who were raised in different family settings. Suppose a young man has a disorder and scientists discover his brother was adopted as a baby and brought up in a different home. The researchers would then examine the brother to see whether he also displays signs of the disorder. If they can identify enough sibling pairs (and they usually do after a lot

of hard work), they can assess whether siblings brought up in different families display the disorder to the same extent as the proband. If the siblings raised with different families have the disorder more often than would be expected by chance, the researchers can infer that genetic endowment is a contributor.

TWIN STUDIES

Nature presents an elegant experiment that gives behavioural geneticists their closest possible look at the role of genes in development: identical (monozygotic) twins. These twins not only look a lot alike but also have identical genes. Some changes do occur in chemical markers (called epigenetic markers) in the womb, which explains the subtle differences even in identical twins (van Dongen et al., 2014). Fraternal (dizygotic) twins, conversely, come from different eggs and have only about 50 percent of their genes in common, as do all first-degree relatives. In **twin studies**, the obvious scientific question is whether identical twins share the same trait—say, fainting at the sight of blood—more often than fraternal twins. Determining whether a trait is shared is easy with some physical traits, such as height. As Robert Plomin from the Institute of Psychiatry in London, England, points out, correlations in height for both first-degree relatives and fraternal twins are +0.45, and +0.90 for identical twins (Plomin, 1990). These findings show that heritability of height is about 90 percent (twice the difference between the two correlations), so approximately 10 percent of the variance is due to environmental factors. However, remember that this 90 percent heritability estimate is only an estimate of the contribution of genetic factors to individual differences in height. An identical twin who was severely physically abused or selectively deprived of proper foods during development might be substantially different in height from the

▲ Scientists often study family members to examine the aggregation of a trait.

other twin, showing how environmental factors can have an impact on a given trait even for traits that have high heritability.

Behaviour genetics researchers Murray Stein, Kerry Jang, and John Livesley (2002) conducted a study on the heritability of social anxiety–related concerns. The variable of interest was *fear of negative evaluation*—a cognitive factor central to social phobia. The individuals in the study were 437 twin pairs in the University of British Columbia's twin database. The investigators found that monozygotic twins had a greater degree of resemblance for fear of negative evaluation than did dizygotic twins, suggesting a significant heritable component. However, this way of studying genetics isn't perfect. You can assume monozygotic twins have the same genetic makeup and dizygotic twins do not. A complicating concern, however, is whether monozygotic twins have the same experiences or environment as dizygotic twins. Some identical twins are dressed alike and are even given similar names. And the twins themselves influence each other's behaviour, and in some cases, monozygotic twins may affect each other more than dizygotic twins (Carey, 1992).

One way to address this problem is by combining the adoption study and twin study methods. If you can find identical twins, one or both of whom were adopted as an infant, you can better estimate the relative roles of genes and the environment in the development of individual differences in behavioural patterns.

GENETIC LINKAGE ANALYSIS AND ASSOCIATION STUDIES

The results of a series of family, twin, and adoption studies may suggest that a particular disorder has a genetic component, but they can't provide the location of the implicated gene or genes. To locate a gene, there are two general strategies: genetic linkage analysis and association studies (Fears et al., 2009; Zheng et al., 2012).

The basic principle of **genetic linkage analysis** is simple. When a family disorder is studied, other inherited characteristics are assessed at the same time. These other characteristics—called **genetic markers**—are selected because we know their exact location. If a match or link is discovered between the inheritance of the disorder and the inheritance of a genetic marker, the genes

for the disorder and the genetic marker are probably close together on the same chromosome. For example, bipolar disorder was studied in a large Amish family (Egeland et al., 1987). Researchers found that two markers on chromosome 11—genes for insulin and a known cancer gene—were linked to the presence of mood disorder in this family, suggesting that a gene for bipolar disorder might be on chromosome 11. Unfortunately, although this is a good example of a genetic linkage study, it also illustrates the danger of drawing premature conclusions from research. This linkage study and a second study that purported to find a linkage between bipolar disorder and the X chromosome (Baron et al., 1987) have yet to be replicated; that is, different researchers have not been able to show similar linkages in other families (Merikangas & Risch, 2014).

The inability to replicate findings in these studies is quite common (Fears et al., 2009; Zheng et al., 2012). This type of failure casts doubt on conclusions that only one gene is responsible for such complex disorders. Be mindful of such limitations the next time you read in a newspaper or hear on television that a gene has been identified as causing some disorder.

The second strategy for locating specific genes, **association studies**, also uses genetic markers. Association studies compare markers in a large group of people with a particular disorder to people without the disorder. If certain markers occur significantly more often in the people with the disorder, it is assumed the markers are close to the genes involved with the disorder. This type of comparison makes association studies better able to identify genes that may only be weakly associated with a disorder, but it is also plagued by failure to replicate, at least in our field. Nevertheless, both strategies for locating specific genes shed new light on the origins of specific disorders and may eventually inspire new approaches to treatment (Fears et al., 2009; Zheng et al., 2012).

STUDYING BEHAVIOUR OVER TIME

Sometimes we want to ask, "How will a disorder or behaviour pattern change (or remain the same) over time?" This question is important for several reasons. First, the answer helps us decide whether to treat a particular person. For example, should we begin an expensive and time-consuming program for a young adult who is depressed over the loss of a grandparent? You might not if you knew that with normal social support the depression is likely to diminish over the next few months without treatment. On the other hand, if you have reason to believe a problem isn't likely to go away on its own, you might decide to begin treatment. For example, as you will see later, aggression among young children often does not go away naturally and should be dealt with as early as possible.

It is also important to understand the developmental changes in abnormal behaviour because sometimes these can provide insight into how problems are created and how they become more serious. For example, some researchers identify newborns who are at risk for autism spectrum disorder because they are siblings of a child with the disorder and then follow them through infancy until some develop the disorder themselves. This type of study is showing us that the pattern of the onset of this disorder is actually much different than parents report after the fact—they tend to

▲ University of British Columbia behaviour geneticists Kerry Jang and John Livesley have used the twin method to determine the genetic versus environmental contributions to a variety of forms of abnormal behaviour, including traits related to personality disorders and anxiety disorders.

remember drastic changes in the child's behaviour when, in fact, the changes occur gradually (Zwaigenbaum et al., 2013). Prospective studies (which record changes over time as they occur) sometimes reveal dramatic differences in the development of psychological disorders or their treatment compared with the information discovered through retrospective studies (which ask people to remember what happened in the past).

PREVENTION RESEARCH

An additional reason for studying clinical problems over time is that we may be able to design interventions and services to prevent these problems. Clearly, preventing mental health difficulties would save countless families significant emotional distress, and the financial savings could be substantial. Prevention research has expanded over the years to include a broad range of approaches. These different methods can be viewed in four broad categories: positive development strategies (health promotion), universal prevention strategies, selective prevention strategies, and indicated prevention strategies (Kalra et al., 2012). *Health promotion or positive development strategies* involve efforts to blanket entire populations of people—even those who may not be at risk—to prevent later problems and promote protective behaviours. The intervention is not designed to fix existing problems but, instead, focuses on skill building, for example, to keep problems from developing. For example, the Seattle Social Development Program targets young children in public elementary schools in the Seattle school system that are in high-crime areas, providing intervention with teachers and parents to engage the children in learning and positive behaviours. Although this approach does not target one particular problem (e.g., drug use), long-term follow-up of these children suggests multiple positive effects in achievement, reductions in delinquency, and lower odds of contracting a sexually transmitted infection by age 30 (Bailey, 2009; Hill et al., 2014; Lonczak et al., 2002). *Universal prevention strategies* focus on entire populations and target certain risk factors (e.g., behaviour problems in inner-city class-rooms) without focusing on specific individuals. The third approach to prevention intervention—*selective prevention*—specifically targets whole groups at risk (e.g., children who have parents who have died) and designs specific interventions aimed at helping them avoid future problems. Finally, *indicated prevention* is a strategy for those individuals who are beginning to show signs of problems (e.g., depressive symptoms) but do not yet have a psychological disorder.

To evaluate the effectiveness of each of these approaches, the research strategies used in prevention research for examining psychopathology across time combine individual and group research methods, including both correlational and experimental designs. We look next at two of the most often used designs: cross-sectional and longitudinal.

CROSS-SECTIONAL DESIGNS

A variation of correlation research is to compare different people at different ages. For a **cross-sectional design**, researchers take a cross section of a population across the different age groups and compare them on some characteristic. For example, if they were trying to understand the development of alcohol abuse and dependence, they could take groups of adolescents at 12, 15, and 17 years of age and assess their beliefs about alcohol use. In an early comparison, Brown and Finn (1982) made some interesting discoveries. They found that 36 percent of the 12-year-olds thought the primary purpose of drinking was to get drunk. This percentage increased to 64 percent with 15-year-olds, but dropped again to 42 percent for the 17-year-old students. The researchers also found that 28 percent of the 12-year-olds reported drinking with their friends at least sometimes, a rate that increased to 80 percent for the 15-year-olds and to 88 percent for the 17-year-olds. Brown and Finn used this information to develop the hypothesis that the reason for excessive drinking among teens is a deliberate attempt to get drunk rather than a mistake in judgment once they are under the influence of alcohol. In other words, teenagers do not, as a group, appear to drink too much because once they've had a drink or two they show poor judgment and drink excessively. Instead, their attitudes before drinking seem to influence how much they drink later.

In cross-sectional designs, the participants in each age group are called **cohorts**; Brown and Finn studied three cohorts: 12-year-olds, 15-year-olds, and 17-year-olds. The members of each cohort are the same age at the same time and thus have all been exposed to similar experiences. Members of one cohort differ from members of other cohorts in age and in their exposure to cultural and historical experiences. You would expect a group of 12-year-olds in the early 1980s to have received a great deal of education about drug and alcohol use, whereas the 17-year-olds may not have. Differences among cohorts in their opinions about alcohol use may be related to their respective cognitive and emotional development at these different ages and to their dissimilar experiences. This **cohort effect**, the confounding of age and experience, is a limitation of the cross-sectional design.

Researchers prefer cross-sectional designs to study changes over time partly because they are easier to use than longitudinal designs (discussed next). In addition, some phenomena are less likely to be influenced by different cultural and historical experiences and therefore are less susceptible to cohort effects. For example, the prevalence of Alzheimer's disease among people at ages 60 and 70—assumed to be strongly influenced by biology—is not likely to be greatly affected by different experiences among the study participants.

One question not answered by cross-sectional designs is how problems develop in individuals. For example, do children who refuse to go to school grow up to have anxiety disorders? Researchers cannot answer this question simply by comparing adults with anxiety problems and children who refuse to go to school. They could ask the adults whether they were anxious about school when they were children, but this **retrospective information** (looking back) is usually less than accurate. To get a better picture of how individuals develop over the years, researchers use longitudinal designs.

LONGITUDINAL DESIGNS

Rather than looking at different groups of people of differing ages, researchers may follow one group over time and assess change in its members directly. The advantage of **longitudinal designs** is that they do not suffer from cohort effect problems and they allow the researchers to assess individual change. (■ Figure 4.4 illustrates both longitudinal and cross-sectional designs.)

Nagin and Tremblay (1999) conducted a longitudinal study on physical aggression in boys. They followed more than 1000 boys from low-socioeconomic neighbourhoods in Montréal from age 6 in kindergarten to age 15 in high school, examining their levels of physical aggression over this period. Using this method, Nagin and Tremblay were able to identify four distinct groups of boys based on their levels and stability of aggression over this period. The first group was a *chronic physical aggression* group comprising boys who displayed persistently high levels of aggression over the nine years of the study. The second group was a *high but declining* group comprising boys who displayed a high level of aggression in kindergarten but showed a decrease thereafter. A third group was a *moderate but declining* group whose members showed moderate levels of aggression in kindergarten but showed a decrease thereafter. The final group was a *low* group whose members rarely displayed aggression during the study.

In addition to measuring levels of physical aggression, the researchers also measured parental and early childhood variables that might help explain which boys would show persistently high aggression from childhood to adolescence. The researchers found that boys who displayed high hyperactivity or high oppositional behaviour in kindergarten were each about three times as likely as other boys to be a member of either the chronic physical aggression or the high but declining group. The researchers also found that boys with teenage mothers or the mothers with the least education were each about two times as likely as other boys to be a member of either the chronic or the high but declining group. The only characteristic that distinguished boys in the chronic physical aggression group from boys in the high but declining group was having a teenage mother or a mother with less education than other mothers (Nagin & Tremblay, 2001).

A more recent study with this same longitudinal sample of boys examined the longer-term impact of childhood aggression in terms of important outcomes in adolescence (Kokko et al., 2006). Aggression from ages 6 to 12 predicted physical violence and school dropout at age 17. In contrast to the researchers' expectations, however, childhood prosocial behaviour (e.g., helping, comforting, or displaying sympathetic behaviours) did not exert a protective effect against either physical violence or school dropout at age 17.

Imagine conducting a major longitudinal study. Not only must the researcher persevere over months and years but so must the people who participate in the study. They must remain willing to continue in the project, and the researcher must hope they will not move away, or worse, die! Longitudinal research is costly and time-consuming; it is also subject to the distinct possibility that the research question will have become irrelevant by the time the study is complete. Lastly, longitudinal designs can suffer from a phenomenon similar to the cohort effect on cross-sectional designs: The **cross-generational effect** involves trying to generalize the findings to groups whose experiences are very different from those of the study participants. For example, the drug use histories of people who were young adults in the 1960s and early 1970s are vastly different from those of people born in the 1990s.

Sometimes psychopathologists combine longitudinal and cross-sectional designs in a strategy called the **sequential design**, which involves repeated study of different cohorts over time. Marvin Krank of the University of British Columbia, Okanagan, in Kelowna and his colleagues studied the development of alcohol and drug use among British Columbia youth (e.g., Krank et al., 2011; Krank & Wall, 2006; Krank et al., 2005; Nealis et al., 2016). They used the sequential design to learn whether and how different forms of substance use and other risk behaviours changed over time among these youth. Their ambitious project, labelled the Project on Adolescent Trajectories and Health (PATH), involved collecting survey data from more than 1300 students in a large school district in Western Canada. Participants were recruited

▲ University of Montréal child psychologist Richard Tremblay and his colleagues at the Research Unit on Children's Psychosocial Maladjustment have used a longitudinal design to examine the factors accounting for childhood physical aggression in boys, as well as other childhood disruptive disorders.

Longitudinal design

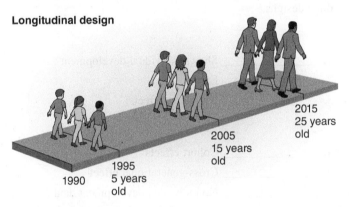

2015
25 years old

2005
15 years old

1995
5 years old

1990

Same people followed across time

Cross-sectional design

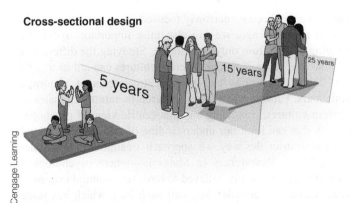

5 years

15 years

25 years

© Cengage Learning

People of different ages viewed at the same time

FIGURE 4.4 | Two research designs.

▲ Longitudinal studies can be complicated by the cross-generational effect; for example, young people in the 1960s shared experiences that were very different from those of young people today.

from all Grade 7 to 9 students in the school district. In the cross-sectional part of the study, the researchers looked at rates of use of various substances among students in different grades (cohorts): Grade 7, Grade 8, and Grade 9. Krank and his colleagues then retested the students for the longitudinal part of the study once a year for the next three academic years. Both parts of the sequential design produced similar findings. For example, regarding the development of drinking behaviour, adolescents' use of alcohol increased across grades. While only 30 percent of Grade 7 students had one or more drinks in the past year, this rate rose to nearly 70 percent by the second year of testing among Grade 10 students (Krank et al., 2005).

The longitudinal portion of the study allowed for an examination of predictors of substance use initiation and escalation. Interestingly, measures of substance-related "implicit cognition" (i.e., hypothetical cognitive processes about which people have no conscious awareness) at earlier waves predicted substance use at later testing waves. For example, implicit cognitions around alcohol were measured using two established tasks (Stacy, 1997). In the first, an ambiguous word task, the adolescents were asked to write down the first word that came to mind when they viewed

each of a set of words. The word set included homographs like "draft" and "mug" with two possible meanings, only one of which is alcohol-related. In the second task, a behavioural associates task, the adolescents were asked to write down the first activity that came to mind in response to a set of outcomes such as "having fun" or "feeling relaxed." For both tasks, coders summed the number of alcohol-related responses each student generated. Scores on these alcohol-related implicit measures in the first year predicted a variety of drinking indicators in the second year. The implicit alcohol measures in the first year even predicted initiation of drinking in the second year among those youth who did not drink in the first year (Krank et al., 2005).

In another study, Fulton, Krank, and Stewart (2012) found that a simple self-assessment of expectancies (what students thought would happen if they use alcohol or marijuana) was predictive of initiation and escalation for both alcohol and marijuana over a three-year period. The PATH study results suggest many potentially useful targets for alcohol and marijuana abuse prevention in youth.

Concept Check 4.3

The following are some advantages and limitations of methods used in research across time. Sort them out by marking CS for cross-sectional designs and L for longitudinal designs.

Benefits:

1. _____ Shows individual development
2. _____ Easier
3. _____ No cohort effects

Limitations:

4. _____ Cohort effects
5. _____ Cross-generational effect
6. _____ No individual development data

STUDYING BEHAVIOUR ACROSS CULTURES

Just as we can become narrowly focused when we study people only at a certain age, we can also miss important aspects by studying people from only one culture. Studying the differences in behaviour of people from different cultures can tell us a great deal about the origins and possible treatments of abnormal behaviours. Unfortunately, most research literature originates in Western cultures, producing an ethnocentric view of psychopathology that can limit our understanding of disorders in general and can restrict the way we approach treatment (Christopher et al., 2014). Researchers in Malaysia—where psychological disorders are commonly believed to have supernatural origins—have described a disorder they call *sakit gila*, which has some features of schizophrenia but differs in important ways (Csordas, 2015). Could we learn more about schizophrenia (and *sakit gila*)

▲ The same behaviours—for example, those of women in public— may be viewed very differently in different cultures.

by comparing the disorders themselves and the cultures in which they are found? Increasing awareness of the limited cultural scope of our research is creating a corresponding increase in cross-cultural research on psychopathology.

The designs we have described are adapted for studying abnormal behaviour across cultures. Some researchers view the effects of different cultures as though they were different treatments (López & Guarnaccia, 2012). In other words, the independent variable is the effect of different cultures on behaviour, rather than, say, the effect of cognitive therapy versus simple exposure for the treatment of fears. The difference between looking at culture as a treatment and our typical design, however, is important. In cross-cultural research, we can't randomly assign infants to different cultures and observe how they develop. People from varying cultures can differ in any number of important ways— their genetic backgrounds, for one—that could explain variations in their behaviour for reasons other than culture.

The characteristics of different cultures can also complicate research efforts. Symptoms, or descriptions of symptoms, can be dissimilar in different societies (Paniagua & Yamada, 2013). Nigerians who are depressed complain of heaviness or heat in the head, crawling sensations in the head or legs, burning sensations in the body, and a feeling that the belly is bloated with water

(James et al., 2012). In contrast, people in North America report feeling worthless, being unable to start or finish anything, losing interest in usual activities, and thinking of suicide. Natives of China, on the other hand, are less likely to report feeling depressed or losing interest in favourite things but may have thoughts of suicide or worthlessness (Yu et al., 2012). These few examples illustrate that applying a standard definition of depression across different cultures will result in vastly different outcomes (Corrigan et al., 2014).

An additional complicating factor is varying tolerances, or thresholds, for abnormal behaviour. If people in different cultures see the same behaviours very differently, researchers will have trouble comparing incidence and prevalence rates. For example, traditional Chinese customs include talking to deceased relatives and local deities—behaviours that might be characteristic of schizophrenia in other cultures (Fuji et al., 2014). Understanding cultural attitudes and customs is essential to such research (Paniagua & Yamada, 2013).

Finally, treatment research is also complicated by cross-cultural differences. Cultures develop treatment models that reflect their own values. In Japan, psychiatric hospitalization is organized in terms of a family model, with caregivers assuming parental roles. A family model was common in psychiatric institutions in 19th-century North America, until it was replaced with the medical model common today (Colp, 2009). In Saudi Arabia, women are veiled when outside the home, which prevents them from uncovering their faces in the presence of therapists; custom thus complicates efforts to establish a trusting and intimate therapeutic client–therapist relationship and may also prevent the therapist from gathering information about a patient's affective state from her facial expression (Ali et al., 2004; Mistry et al., 2009). Because in the Islamic perspective medicine and religion are inseparable, medical and religious treatments are combined (Tober & Budiani, 2014). As you can see, something as basic as comparing treatment outcomes is highly complex in a cross-cultural context.

THE POWER OF A PROGRAM OF RESEARCH

When we examine different research strategies independently, as we have done here, we often have the impression that some approaches are better than others. It is important to understand that this is not true. Depending on the type of question you are asking and the practical limitations inherent in the inquiry, any of the research techniques would be appropriate. Significant issues often are resolved not by one perfectly designed study but rather by a series of studies that examine different aspects of the problem—in a program of research. The research of one of this book's authors will be used to illustrate how complex research questions are answered with a variety of different research designs.

One of us studies why children with autism spectrum disorders display seemingly irrational behaviours, such as self-injury (hitting or biting oneself) or aggression. The expectation is that the more we understand why these behaviours occur, the better the chances of designing an effective treatment. In an early study we used a single-subject design (withdrawal design) to test the influence of adult attention and escaping from unpleasant educational tasks on these problem behaviours (Carr & Durand, 1985). We found that some children hit themselves more when people ignore them, and others will hit themselves to get out of school assignments that are too difficult, showing that these disturbing behaviours can be understood by looking at them as primitive forms of communication (e.g., "Please come here" or "This is too hard"). This led us to consider what would happen if we taught these children to communicate with us more appropriately (Durand, 1990). The next series of studies again used single-subject designs and demonstrated that teaching more acceptable ways of getting attention or help from others did significantly reduce these challenging behaviours (e.g., Durand & Carr, 1992). Several decades of research on this treatment (called functional communication training) demonstrates its value in significantly improving the lives of people with these once severe behaviour problems by reducing the severity of the misbehaviour through improving communication skills.

One of the questions that face researchers in this area is why some children develop severe forms of these behaviour problems, while others do not. To begin to answer this question, we conducted a three-year prospective longitudinal study on more than 100 children with autism to see what factors might cause more problems (Durand, 2001). We studied the children at age three and later at age six to determine what about the child or the family led to more severe problems. We found the following two factors to be the most important indicators of severe behaviour problems in the children: (1) the parents were pessimistic about their ability to help their child or (2) the parents were doubtful about their child's ability to change. These parents would give up and allow their child to dictate many of the routines around the house (e.g., eating dinner in the living room, or not going out to the movies because it would cause tantrums) (Durand, 2001).

This important finding then led to the next question: Could we make pessimistic parents more optimistic, and would this help prevent their children from developing severe behaviour problems? To answer this question, we next relied on a randomized clinical trial to see if adding a cognitive behaviour intervention would help make pessimistic parents more optimistic. We wanted to teach these parents to examine their own pessimistic thoughts (e.g., "I have no control of my child" or "My child won't improve because of his/her autism") and replace them with more hopeful views of their world (e.g., "I can help my child" or "My child can improve his/her behaviour"). We hypothesized that this cognitive intervention would help them carry out the parenting strategies we offer them and in turn improve the outcomes of our behavioural interventions. We randomly assigned groups of pessimistic parents who also had a child with very severe behaviour problems to either a group that taught them how to work with their child or a group that used the same techniques but also helped them explore their pessimistic thinking and helped them view themselves and their child in a better light. The treatments were applied very formally, using written protocols to make sure that each group received the treatment as designed (Durand & Hieneman, 2008). What we found was that addition of the cognitive-behavioural intervention had the expected effect—improving optimism and also improving child outcomes (Durand et al., 2009; Durand et al., 2013).

As this example indicates, research is conducted in stages, and a complete picture of any disorder and its treatment can be seen only after looking at it from many perspectives. An integrated program of research can help researchers explore various aspects of abnormal behaviour.

REPLICATION

Scientists in general, and behavioural scientists in particular, are never really convinced something is true. They are very skeptical when it comes to claims about causes or treatment outcomes. Replicating findings is what makes researchers confident that what they are observing isn't a coincidence. We noted when we described the case study method that if we look at a disorder in only one person, no matter how carefully we describe and document what we observe, we cannot draw strong conclusions.

The strength of a research program is in its ability to replicate findings in different ways to build confidence in the results. If you look back at the research strategies we have described, you will find that replication is one of the most important aspects of each. The more times a researcher repeats a process (and the behaviour he or she is studying changes as expected) the more sure he or she is about what caused the changes.

Many areas of science have experienced a *replication crisis*, in which findings were not duplicated when careful replication studies were conducted. Psychology is not exempt from this crisis (e.g., Open Science Collaboration, 2015), and we mentioned earlier the difficulties in replicating molecular genetic findings for mental disorders, for example. One recommendation we have for the consumer of science, and for you, the reader, is to be more impressed and influenced by findings that have been repeated by different scientific teams and to be a bit skeptical of findings that are based on single studies. Most of the information we present in this textbook is based on replicated findings.

RESEARCH ETHICS

An important final issue involves the ethics of doing research in abnormal psychology. For example, the appropriateness of a clinician's delaying treatment to people who need it, just to satisfy the requirements of an experimental design, is often questioned. One single-case experimental design, the withdrawal design, can involve removing treatment for some time. Treatment is also withheld when placebo control groups are used in group experimental designs. Researchers continue to discuss and caution others about just when it is appropriate to use placebo-controlled trials (Boot et al., 2013). The fundamental question is this: When does a scientist's interest in preserving the internal validity of a study outweigh a client's right to treatment?

One important aspect of this question involves **informed consent**—a research participant's formal agreement to cooperate in a study following full disclosure of the nature of the research and the participant's role in it. The concept of informed consent was derived from the war trials after World War II. Revelations that the Nazis had forced prisoners into so-called medical experiments helped establish the informed consent guidelines that are still used today. The ethical requirement of informed consent helps to prevent tragedies, such as the psychic driving experiments conducted by Dr. Ewan Cameron on vulnerable psychiatric patients (without their consent) at the Allan Memorial Institute in Montréal from 1957 to 1964 (see Chapter 17). Today, because of ethical requirements of informed consent, in studies using some form of treatment delay or withdrawal, the participant is told about why it will occur and the risks and benefits, and permission to proceed is then obtained. In placebo control studies, participants are told they may not receive an active treatment (all participants are blind to or unaware of which group they are placed in), but they are usually given the option of receiving treatment after the study ends.

True informed consent is at times elusive. The basic components are competence, voluntarism, full information, and comprehension on the part of the participant (Snyder, 2012). In other words, research participants must be capable of consenting to participation in the research, they must volunteer and not be coerced into participating, they must have all the information they need to make the decision, and they must understand what their participation will involve. In some circumstances, all these conditions are difficult to attain. Children, for example, often do not fully appreciate what will occur during research. Similarly, individuals with cognitive impairments, such as intellectual disability or schizophrenia, may not understand their role or their rights as participants. In institutional settings, participants should not feel coerced into taking part in research. And individuals from different cultures can have different perspectives about what is important in informed consent.

Certain general protections help ensure that these concerns are properly addressed. First, according to the Tri-Council Policy Statement for the Ethical Conduct for Research Involving Humans, research in Canadian university and medical settings must be approved by a research ethics board (REB; Government of Canada, 2014). These are committees made up of university faculty and nonacademic people from the community. Each committee is made up of five members (including both men and women): Two members must have expertise in the methods or areas of research covered by the particular REB, one member must be an expert in ethics, a fourth member should be an expert in relevant law (this type of member is required for a biomedical REB and suggested for other REBs), and the final member is a layperson from outside the institution. The purpose of the REB is to see that the rights of research participants are protected. The committee structure allows people other than the researcher to look at the research procedures to determine whether sufficient care is being taken to protect the welfare and dignity of the participants.

Psychological harm is difficult to define, but its definition remains the responsibility of the investigator. Researchers must hold in confidence all information obtained from participants, who have the right to conceal their identity on all data, either written or informal. Whenever deception is considered essential to research, the investigator must satisfy the REB that this judgment is correct. If deception is used, participants must be debriefed—that is, told in language they can understand the true purpose of the study and why it was necessary to deceive them.

The Society for Research in Child Development (2007) has endorsed ethical guidelines for research that address some issues unique to research on children. For example, these guidelines not only call for confidentiality, protection from harm, and debriefing but also require informed consent from children's caregivers and from the children themselves if they are age seven or older. These guidelines specify that the research must be explained to children in language they can understand so that they can decide whether they want to participate. Many other ethical issues extend beyond protection of the participants, including how researchers deal with errors in their research, fraud in science, and the proper way to give credit to others. Doing a study involves more than selecting the appropriate design. Researchers must be aware of numerous concerns that involve the rights of the people in the experiment, as well as their own conduct.

A final and important development in the field that will help to "keep the face" on psychological disorders is the involvement of consumers in important aspects of this research. The concern over not only how people are treated in research studies but also how the information is interpreted and used has resulted in many government agencies providing guidance on how the people who are the targets of the research (e.g., those with schizophrenia, depression, or anxiety disorders) should be involved in the process. The hope is that if people who experience these disorders are partners in selecting research questions, as well as designing, running, and interpreting this research, the relevance of the research, as well as the treatment of the participants in these studies, will be markedly improved.

Concept Check 4.4

Indicate whether the following statements are true (T) or false (F).

1. _____ After the nature of the experiment and their roles in it are disclosed to the participants, they must be allowed to refuse or agree to sign an informed consent form.

2. _____ If the participant is in the control group or taking a placebo, informed consent is not needed.

3. _____ Research ethics boards want to know whether or not the proposed participants lack the cognitive skills to provide informed consent.

4. _____ Participants have a right to conceal their identities on all data collected and reported.

5. _____ When deception is essential to the research, participants do not have to be debriefed regarding the true purpose of the study.

SUMMARY

- Research involves establishing a hypothesis that is then tested. In abnormal psychology, research focuses on hypotheses meant to explain the nature, the causes, or the treatment of a disorder.

- The individual case study is used to study one or more individuals in depth. Though case studies have an important role in the theoretical development of psychology, they are not subject to experimental control and must necessarily be suspect in terms of both internal and external validity.

- Research by correlation can tell us whether a relationship exists between two variables, but it does not tell us whether that relationship is a causal one. Epidemiological research is a type of correlational research that reveals the incidence, distribution, and consequences of a particular problem in one or more populations.

- Research by experiment can follow one of two designs: group or single case. In both designs, a variable (or variables) is manipulated and the effects are observed in order to determine the nature of a causal relationship.

- Genetic research focuses on the role of genes in behaviour. These research strategies include family studies, adoption studies, twin studies, genetic linkage analyses, and association studies.

- Research strategies that examine psychopathology across time include cross-sectional and longitudinal designs. Both focus on differences in behaviour or attitudes at different ages, but the former does so by looking at different individuals at different ages, while the latter looks at the same individuals at different ages.

- The clinical picture, causal factors, and treatment process and outcome can all be influenced by cultural factors.

- The more the findings of a research program are replicated, the more they gain in credibility.

- Ethics are important to the research process, and ethical guidelines are spelled out by many professional organizations and research funding bodies in an effort to ensure the well-being of research subjects.

KEY TERMS

adoption studies, 110	cross-sectional design, 112	independent variable, 99	research design, 99
analogue models, 101	dependent variable, 99	informed consent, 116	retrospective information, 112
association studies, 111	double-blind control, 106	internal validity, 99	sequential design, 113
baseline, 107	effect size, 101	level, 107	single-case experimental
case study method, 102	endophenotypes, 109	longitudinal designs, 112	designs, 106
clinical significance, 101	epidemiology, 103	multiple baseline, 108	statistical significance, 101
cohort effect, 112	experiment, 105	negative correlation, 103	testability, 100
cohorts, 112	external validity, 99	patient uniformity myth, 101	treatment outcome research, 105
comparative treatment	family studies, 109	phenotypes, 108	trend, 107
research, 106	generalizability, 101	placebo control groups, 105	twin studies, 110
confound (confounding	genetic linkage analysis, 111	placebo effect, 105	variability, 107
variable), 100	genetic markers, 111	positive correlation, 103	withdrawal design, 107
control group, 100	genotypes, 108	prevalence, 104	
correlation, 103	human genome project, 109	proband, 109	
correlation coefficient, 103	hypothesis, 99	randomization, 101	
cross-generational effect, 113	incidence, 104	repeated measurement, 106	

ANSWERS TO CONCEPT CHECKS

4.1

1. independent variable
2. confound
3. hypothesis
4. dependent variable
5. internal validity, external validity

4.2

1. e; 2. c; 3. b; 4. a; 5. f

4.3

1. L; 2. CS; 3. L; 4. CS; 5. L; 6. CS

4.4

1. T; 2. F; 3. T; 4. T; 5. F

MEDIA RESOURCES

CENGAGE | MINDTAP

Stay organized and efficient with MindTap—a single destination with all the course material and study aids you need to succeed. Built-in apps leverage social media and the latest learning technology. For example:

- ReadSpeaker will read the text to you.
- Flashcards are pre-populated to provide you with a jump start for review—or you can create your own.
- You can highlight text and make notes in your MindTap Reader. Your notes will flow into Evernote, the electronic notebook app that you can access anywhere when it's time to study for the exam.
- Self-quizzing allows you to assess your understanding.

Visit login.cengage.com to start using MindTap. Enter the Online Access Code from the card included with your text. If a code card is not provided, you can purchase instant access at Cengage.ca.

05 | Anxiety

© Goran Bogicevic/Alamy Stock Photo

One thing is certain, that the problem of anxiety is a nodal point, linking up all kinds of the most important questions; a riddle, of which the solution must cast a flood of light upon our whole mental life.

—SIGMUND FREUD, *Introductory Lectures on Psychoanalysis*

Use scientific reasoning to interpret behaviour:	› Identify basic biological, psychological, and social components of behavioural explanations (e.g., inferences, observations, operational definitions and interpretations) (APA SLO 2.1a)
Engage in innovative and integrative thinking and problem solving:	› Describe problems operationally to study them empirically (APA SLO 2.3A, 2.4b)
Describe applications of psychology:	› Correctly identify antecedents and consequences of behaviour and mental processes (APA SLO 1.3b)
	› Describe examples of relevant and practical applications of psychological principles to everyday life (APA SLO 1.3a)

*Portions of this chapter cover learning outcomes suggested by the American Psychological Association (2012) in their guidelines for the undergraduate psychology major. Chapter coverage of these outcomes is identified above by APA Goal and APA Suggested Learning Outcome (SLO).

THE COMPLEXITY OF ANXIETY DISORDERS

Anxiety is complex and mysterious, as Freud realized many years ago. In some ways, the more we learn about it, the more baffling it seems. "Anxiety" is a specific type of disorder, but it is much more than that. It is an emotion implicated so heavily across the full range of psychological disorders that our discussion first explores its general nature, both biological and psychological. Next, we consider fear, a somewhat different but clearly related emotion. We suggest that panic is fear that occurs at an inappropriate time. With these important ideas clearly in mind, we focus on specific anxiety and related disorders.

ANXIETY, FEAR, AND PANIC

Have you ever experienced anxiety? A silly question, you might say, because most of us feel some anxiety almost every day of our lives. Did you have a test in school today for which you weren't "perfectly" prepared? Did you have a date last weekend with somebody new? And how about that job interview coming up? Even thinking about that might make you nervous. But have you ever stopped to think about the nature of anxiety? What is it? What causes it?

Anxiety is a negative mood state characterized by physical tension and apprehension about the future (American Psychiatric Association, 2013; Barlow, 2002). Anxiety is very hard to study: It can be a subjective sense of unease, a set of behaviours (looking worried and anxious, fidgeting), or a physiological response originating in the brain and reflected in elevated heart rate and muscle tension. Because anxiety is also closely related to depression (Barlow, 2000, 2002; Brown & Barlow, 2005, 2009; Clark, 2005; Craske et al., 2009; Kessler, Petukhova et al., 2012), much of what we say here is relevant to Chapter 8.

Anxiety is not very pleasant, so why do we seem programmed to experience it almost every time we do something important? Surprisingly, anxiety is good for us, at least in moderate amounts. Psychologists have known for over a century that we perform better when we are a little anxious (Yerkes & Dodson, 1908). You would not have done as well on that test the other day if you had had no anxiety. You were a little more charming and lively on that date last weekend because you were a little anxious. And you will be better prepared for that upcoming job interview if you are anxious. In short, physical and intellectual performances are driven and enhanced by anxiety. Without it, very few of us would get much done.

But what happens when you have too much anxiety? You might actually fail the exam because you can't concentrate on the questions. All you can think about when you're too anxious is how terrible it will be if you fail. On that date with a new person, you might spend the evening with perspiration running off your face and a sick feeling in your stomach, unable to think of even one reasonably interesting thing to say. You might blow the interview for the same reason. Too much of a good thing can be harmful, and very few sensations are more harmful than severe anxiety that is out of control.

What makes the situation worse is that severe anxiety usually doesn't go away—that is, even if we "know" we really have nothing to be afraid of, we remain anxious. We constantly see examples of this kind of irrationality. Well-known singer and songwriter Alanis Morissette reportedly experiences severe anxiety. In one interview, she recounted an episode of anxiety that occurred shortly after she had moved to Los Angeles. Morissette was returning home to Canada for the holidays, and while writing cards on the plane, she suddenly began crying and shaking uncontrollably, and she felt as if she was going to faint. This experience scared her and she sought treatment ("The People's Courtney," 1995).

Morissette and countless other individuals who have anxiety-based disorders are well aware that they have little to fear in the situations they find so stressful. She should know, for example, that flying is the safest way to travel and that no objective danger existed in the situation when she experienced this anxiety attack. And yet Morissette, like others dealing with anxiety, cannot seem to shake her excessive fear. All the disorders discussed in this chapter are characterized by excessive anxiety, which takes many forms.

In Chapter 2, we saw that **fear** is an immediate alarm reaction to danger. Like anxiety, fear can be good for us. It protects us by activating a massive response from the autonomic nervous system (increased heart rate and blood pressure, for example), which, along with our subjective sense of terror, motivates us to escape or, possibly, to attack. As such, this emergency reaction is often called the flight-or-fight response.

Although not all emotion theorists agree, much evidence shows that fear and anxiety reactions differ psychologically and physiologically (Barlow, 2002; Bouton, 2005; Craske et al., 2010;

Even successful performers like Alanis Morissette can experience excessive anxiety.

accompanied by physical symptoms that usually include heart palpitations, chest pain, shortness of breath, and, possibly, dizziness (see DSM Table 5.1).

Two basic types of panic attacks are described in the *DSM-5*: expected and unexpected. If you know you are afraid of high places or of driving over long bridges, you might have a panic attack in such a situation but not anywhere else; this is an *expected (cued) panic attack*. By contrast, you might experience *unexpected (uncued) panic attacks* if you don't have a clue when or where the next attack will occur. We mention these types of attacks because they play a role in several anxiety disorders. Unexpected attacks are important in panic disorder. Expected attacks are more common in specific phobias or social anxiety disorder

Tovote et al., 2015; Waddell et al., 2006). As noted earlier, anxiety is a future-oriented mood state, characterized by apprehension because we cannot predict or control upcoming events. In contrast, fear is an immediate emotional reaction to current danger characterized by strong escapist action tendencies and, often, a surge in the sympathetic branch of the autonomic nervous system. Someone experiencing fear might say, "I've got to get out of here right now or I may not make it."

What happens if you experience the alarm response of fear when you have nothing to be afraid of? Alanis Morissette's episode of unexpected crying, shaking, and feeling faint on the airplane is a good example of this kind of false alarm. Consider also the case of Gretchen, who appeared at one of our clinics.

This sudden overwhelming reaction came to be known as **panic**, after the Greek god Pan who terrified travellers with blood-curdling screams. In psychopathology, a **panic attack** is defined as an abrupt experience of intense fear or acute discomfort,

GRETCHEN | *Attacked by Panic*

I was 25 when I had my first attack. It was a few weeks after I'd come home from the hospital. I had had my appendix out. The surgery had gone well, and I wasn't in any danger, which is why I don't understand what happened. But one night I went to sleep and I woke up a few hours later—I'm not sure how long—but I woke up with this vague feeling of apprehension. Mostly I remember how my heart started pounding. And my chest hurt; it felt like I was dying—that I was having a heart attack. And I felt kind of queer, as if I were detached from the experience. It seemed like my bedroom was covered with a haze. I ran to my sister's room, but I felt like I was a puppet or a robot who was under the control of somebody else while I was running. I think I scared her almost as much as I was frightened myself. She called an ambulance (Barlow, 2002).

ABNORMAL PSYCHOLOGY   VIDEO

Panic Disorder: Steve

"The first time it happened to me, I was driving down the highway, and I had a kind of a knot in my chest. I felt like I had swallowed something and it got stuck, and it lasted pretty much overnight. . . . I felt like I was having a heart attack. . . . I assumed that's what was happening. I felt very panicky. A flushed feeling came over my whole body. I felt as though I was going to pass out."

Visit login.cengage.com to start using MindTap. Enter the Online Access Code from the card included with your text. If a code card is not provided, you can purchase instant access at Cengage.ca.

(see ■ Figure 5.1). The famous painting by the Norwegian artist Edvard Munch is thought to be the artist's own depiction of a panic attack in progress.

Remember that fear is an intense emotional alarm accompanied by a surge of energy in the autonomic nervous system that motivates us to flee from danger. Does Gretchen's panic attack sound as if it could be the emotion of fear? A variety of evidence suggests it is (Barlow, 2002; Bouton, 2005; Craske & Barlow, 2014), including similarities in reports of the experience of fear and panic, similar behavioural tendencies to escape, and similar underlying neurobiological processes.

Over the years, we have recorded panic attacks during physiological assessments of our patients (e.g., Alpers, 2009; Hofmann & Barlow, 1996; Meuret et al., 2011). The physiological surge recorded in one patient is shown in ■ Figure 5.2. Notice the sudden dramatic increase in heart rate from minute 11 through minute 13, accompanied by increases in muscle tension (frontalis EMG) and finger temperature. This massive autonomic surge peaked and subsided within three minutes. The panic attack in the laboratory occurred quite unexpectedly from the patient's point of view and from ours. As the figure shows, fear and panic are experienced suddenly, which is necessary to mobilize us for instantaneous reaction to impending danger.

CAUSES OF ANXIETY

You learned in Chapters 1 and 2 that excessive emotional reactions have no simple one-dimensional cause but come from multiple sources. Next, we explore the biological, psychological, and social contributors and how they interact to produce anxiety disorders.

Biological Contributions

Increasing evidence shows that we inherit a tendency to be tense, uptight, and anxious, and some people more so than others (Barlow et al., 2014; Clark, 2005; Gray & McNaughton, 2003). The tendency to panic also seems to run in families and probably has a genetic component that differs somewhat from genetic contributions to anxiety (Craske & Barlow, 2014; Ollendick & Muris, 2015). As with almost all emotional traits and psychological disorders, no single gene seems to cause anxiety or panic or any other psychiatric disorder (Gratten et al., 2014). Instead, contributions from collections of genes in several areas on chromosomes make us vulnerable when certain psychological and social factors are in place.

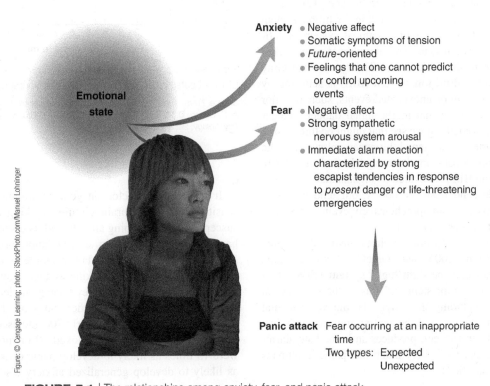

FIGURE 5.1 | The relationships among anxiety, fear, and panic attack.

Anxiety is also associated with specific brain circuits (Domschke & Dannlowski, 2010; Hermans et al., 2014; Tovote et al., 2015) and neurotransmitter systems (Durant et al., 2010). For example, depleted levels of gamma aminobutyric acid (GABA), part of the GABA–benzodiazepine system, are associated with increased anxiety, although the relationship is not quite so direct. The noradrenergic system has also been implicated in anxiety (Hermans et al., 2011), and evidence from animal studies, as well as studies of normal anxiety in humans, suggests the serotonergic neurotransmitter system is also involved (Canli & Lesch, 2007). But increasing attention in the last several years has focused on the role of the corticotropin-releasing factor (CRF) system as central to the expression of anxiety (and depression) and the groups of genes that increase the likelihood that this system will be turned on (Durant et al., 2010; Essex et al., 2010; Khan et al., 2009). This is because CRF activates the hypothalamic–pituitary–adrenocortical (HPA) axis, described in Chapter 2, which is part of the CRF system, and this CRF system has wide-ranging effects on areas of the brain implicated in anxiety, including the emotional brain (the limbic system), particularly the hippocampus and the amygdala; the locus coeruleus in the brain stem; the prefrontal cortex; and the dopaminergic neurotransmitter system. The CRF system is also directly related to the GABA–benzodiazepine system and the serotonergic and noradrenergic neurotransmitter systems.

The area of the brain most often associated with anxiety is the limbic system (Britton & Rauch, 2009; Hermans et al., 2011; LeDoux, 2002, 2015), which acts as a mediator between the brain stem and the cortex. The more primitive brain stem monitors and senses changes in bodily functions and relays these potential danger signals to higher cortical processes through the limbic system. The late Jeffrey Gray, a prominent British neuropsychologist, identified a brain circuit in the limbic system of animals that seems heavily involved in anxiety (Gray & McNaughton, 2013) and may be relevant to humans. This circuit leads from the septal and hippocampal area in the limbic system to the frontal cortex. (The septal–hippocampal system is activated by CRF and serotonergic- and noradrenergic-mediated pathways originating in the brain stem.) The system that Gray called the **behavioural inhibition system (BIS)** is activated by signals from the brain stem of unexpected events, such as major changes in body functioning that might signal danger. Danger signals in response to something we see that might be threatening descend from the cortex to the septal–hippocampal system. The BIS also receives a big boost from the amygdala (LeDoux, 1996, 2002, 2015). When the BIS is activated by signals that arise from the brain stem or descend from the cortex, our tendency is to freeze, experience anxiety, and apprehensively evaluate the situation to confirm that danger is present.

The BIS circuit is distinct from the circuit involved in panic. Gray and McNaughton (2003) and Graeff (2004) identified what Gray and others call the **fight/flight system (FFS)**. This circuit originates in the brain stem and travels through several midbrain structures, including the amygdala, the ventromedial nucleus of the hypothalamus, and the central grey matter. When stimulated in animals, this circuit produces an immediate alarm-and-escape response that looks very much like panic in humans (Gray & McNaughton, 2003).

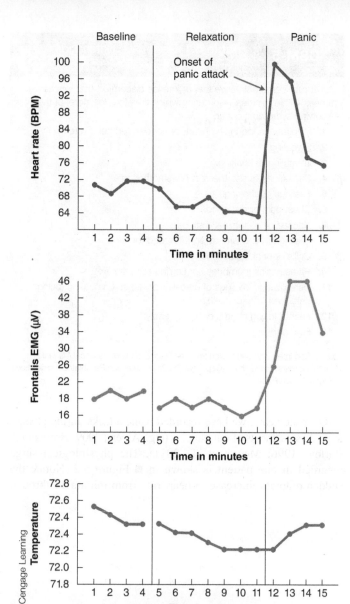

FIGURE 5.2 | Physiological measurements during a panic attack. BPM = beats per minute; EMG = electromyography.

Source: From "The Physiology of Relaxation-Associated Panic Attacks," by A. S. Cohen, D. H. Barlow, and E. B. Blanchard, February 1985, *Journal of Abnormal Psychology*, 94(1), pp. 96–101.

It is likely that factors in your environment can change the sensitivity of these brain circuits, making you more or less susceptible to developing anxiety and its disorders, a finding that has been demonstrated in several laboratories (Francis et al., 2002; Stein et al., 2007). For example, one important study suggested that cigarette smoking as a teenager is associated with greatly increased risk for developing anxiety disorders as an adult, particularly panic disorder and generalized anxiety disorder (Johnson et al., 2000). Nearly 700 adolescents were followed into adulthood. Teens who smoked 20 or more cigarettes daily were 15 times as likely to develop panic disorder and five times as likely to develop generalized anxiety disorder as teens who smoked less or didn't smoke. The complex interaction between smoking and anxiety disorders has been confirmed in more recent research (Leventhal & Zvolensky, 2015). The current thinking about the link between smoking and anxiety is that anxiety sensitivity (the general tendency to fear bodily sensations, which we will briefly discuss later), distress tolerance (how much distress a person can tolerate), and anhedonia (the inability to feel pleasure) all contribute to smoking, which could be one reason that so many people with anxiety find it very difficult to quit smoking.

Brain-imaging procedures are yielding more information about the neurobiology of anxiety and panic (Britton et al., 2015; Shin & Liberzon, 2010). For example, there is now general agreement that in people with anxiety disorders, the limbic system, including the amygdala, is overly responsive to stimulation or new information (abnormal bottom-up processing); at the same time, controlling functions of the cortex that would down-regulate the hyperexcitable amygdala are deficient (abnormal top-down processing), consistent with Gray's BIS model (Ellard, 2013; Britton & Rauch, 2009; Ochsner et al., 2009).

Psychological Contributions

Freud thought anxiety was a psychic reaction to danger surrounding the reactivation of an infantile fearful situation. Behavioural theorists thought anxiety was the product of early classical conditioning, modelling, or other forms of learning. But evidence is accumulating for an integrated model of anxiety involving a variety of psychological factors. In childhood, we may acquire an awareness that events are not always in our control. The continuum of this perception may range from total confidence in our control of all aspects of our lives to deep uncertainty about ourselves and our ability to deal with upcoming events. If you are anxious about schoolwork, for example, you may worry you will do poorly on the next exam, even though all your grades have been A's and B's. A general sense of uncontrollability may develop early as a function of upbringing and other disruptive or traumatic environmental factors.

The actions of parents in early childhood seem to do a lot to foster this sense of control or a sense of uncontrollability (Barlow et al., 2014). Generally, parents who interact in a positive and predictable way with their children by responding to their needs——particularly when the child communicates needs for attention, food, relief from pain, and so on—— perform an important function. These parents teach their children that they have control over their environment and that their behaviours have an effect on their parents and their environment. In addition, parents who provide a secure home base but allow their children to explore their world and develop the necessary skills to cope with unexpected occurrences enable their children to develop a healthy sense of control. In contrast, parents who are overprotective and overintrusive and who clear the way for their children, never letting them experience any adversity, create a situation in which children never learn how to cope with adversity when it comes along. Therefore, these children don't learn that they can control their environment. A variety of evidence has accumulated supporting these ideas (Barlow, 2002; Chorpita & Barlow, 1998; Dan et al., 2011;

Fulton et al., 2014; Gallagher et al. 2014; Gunnar & Fisher, 2006; White, Brown, et al., 2006). A sense of control (or lack of it) that develops from these early experiences is the psychological factor that makes us more or less vulnerable to anxiety in later life.

Another feature of some panic patients is the general tendency to respond fearfully to anxiety symptoms. This is known has *anxiety sensitivity*, which appears to be an important personality trait that determines who will and who will not experience problems with anxiety under certain stressful conditions.

Most psychological accounts of panic (as opposed to anxiety) invoke conditioning and cognitive explanations that are difficult to separate. Thus, a strong fear response initially occurs during extreme stress or perhaps as a result of a dangerous situation in the environment (a true alarm). This emotional response then becomes associated with a variety of external and internal cues. In other words, these cues, or conditioned stimuli, provoke the fear response and an assumption of danger, even if the danger is not actually present, so it is really a learned or false alarm. This is the conditioning process described in Chapter 2. External cues are places or situations similar to the one where the initial panic attack occurred. Internal cues are increases in heart rate or respiration that were associated with the initial panic attack, even if they are now the result of normal circumstances, such as exercise. Thus, when your heart is beating fast you are more likely to think of and, perhaps, experience a panic attack than when it is beating normally. Furthermore, you may not be aware of the cues or triggers of severe fear; as demonstrated in experimental work with animals, these cues or triggers may travel from the eyes directly to the amygdala in the emotional brain without going through the cortex, the source of awareness (Bouton et al., 2001; LeDoux, 2002, 2015).

Social Contributions

Stressful life events trigger our biological and psychological vulnerabilities to anxiety. Most are social and interpersonal in nature—marriage, divorce, difficulties at work, death of a loved one, pressures to excel in school, and so on. Some might be physical, such as an injury or illness.

The same stressors can trigger physical reactions, such as headaches or hypertension, and emotional reactions, such as panic attacks. The particular way we react to stress seems to run in families. If you get headaches when under stress, chances are other people in your family also get headaches. If you have panic attacks, other members of your family probably do also. This finding suggests a possible genetic contribution, at least to initial panic attacks.

An Integrated Model

Putting the factors together in an integrated way, we have described a theory of the development of anxiety called the *triple vulnerability theory* (Barlow et al., 2014; Brown & Naragon-Gainey, 2012). The first vulnerability (or diathesis) is a *generalized biological vulnerability*. We can see that a tendency to be uptight or high-strung might be inherited. But a generalized biological vulnerability to develop anxiety is not sufficient to produce anxiety itself. The second vulnerability is a *generalized psychological vulnerability*. That is, you might also grow up believing the world is dangerous and out of control and you might not be able to cope when things go wrong based on your early experiences. If this perception is strong, you have a generalized psychological vulnerability to anxiety. The third vulnerability is a *specific psychological vulnerability* in which you learn from early experience, such as being taught by your parents, that some situations or objects are fraught with danger (even if they really aren't). For example, if one of your parents is afraid of dogs or expresses anxiety about being evaluated negatively by others, you may well develop a fear of dogs or of social evaluation. These triple vulnerabilities are presented in ■ Figure 5.3 and revisited when we describe each anxiety disorder. If you are under a lot of pressure, particularly from interpersonal stressors, a given stressor could activate your biological tendencies to be anxious and your psychological tendencies to feel you might not be able to deal with the situation and control the stress. Once this cycle starts, it tends to feed on itself, so it might not stop even when the particular life stressor has long since passed. Anxiety can be general, evoked by many aspects of your life. But it is usually focused on one area, such as social evaluations or grades.

As noted earlier, panic is also a characteristic response to stress that runs in families and may have a genetic component that is separate from anxiety. Furthermore, anxiety and panic are closely related—anxiety increases the likelihood of panic. This relationship makes sense from an evolutionary point of view, because sensing a possible future threat or danger (anxiety) should prepare us to react instantaneously with an alarm response if the danger becomes imminent. Anxiety and panic need not occur together, but it makes sense that they often do.

COMORBIDITY

According to the 2016 Canadian Community Health Survey (CCHS), a survey conducted annually by Statistics Canada, 8.6 percent of Canadians ages 12 or older had a diagnosed anxiety disorder, with a greater proportion of women reporting this diagnosis than men (10.7 percent versus 6.4 percent; Statistics Canada, 2017). Because we refer to this survey often in this textbook, we mention here that since 2015 the CCHS has represented 97 percent of the Canadian population ages 12 or older living in every province and territory. However, the survey excludes persons living on reserves and other Indigenous settlements in the provinces, full-time members of the Canadian Forces, the institutionalized population, children ages 12 to 17 living in foster care, and persons living in the Québec health regions of Nunavik and Terres-Cries-de-la-Baie-James. Another survey helps to fill in these critical gaps. The First Nations Regional Health Survey (First Nations Information Governance Centre, 2018), a survey conducted in 2015–2016 among First Nations people living on reserves and in northern communities, documented similar proportions of adults (8.9 percent) and youth (8.2 percent) with a diagnosed anxiety disorder.

It is important to note that the different anxiety disorders often co-occur. As we described in Chapter 3, the co-occurrence of two or more disorders in a single individual is referred to as *comorbidity*. Rates of comorbidity among anxiety disorders and between anxiety and depression are high. For example, the 2014 Survey on Living with Chronic Diseases in Canada (SLCDC) revealed that among adult Canadians living with anxiety or mood disorders, almost one-third, 31 percent, report being diagnosed with both conditions (O'Donnell et al., 2016). The 2014 SLCDC covers the population of Canadians 18 years of age or older living with a diagnosed anxiety and/or mood disorders and represents 97 percent of this group while excluding similar groups to the 2016 CCHS described above.

The rates of comorbidity emphasize the fact that all anxiety disorders share the common features of anxiety and panic described here. They also share the same vulnerabilities—biological and psychological—for developing anxiety and panic. They differ only in the focus of anxiety (what they are anxious about) and, perhaps, the patterning of panic attacks. Of course, if each patient with an anxiety or a related disorder also had every other anxiety disorder, distinguishing among the specific disorders would make little sense. It would be enough to say, simply, that the patient had an anxiety disorder. But this

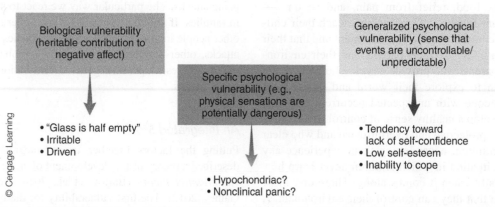

FIGURE 5.3 | The three vulnerabilities that contribute to the development of anxiety disorders. If individuals possess all three, the odds are greatly increased that they will develop an anxiety disorder after experiencing a stressful situation.

Source: From Anxiety and Its Disorders: The Nature and Treatment of Anxiety and Panic (2nd ed.), by D. H. Barlow, 2002, Guildford Press.

is not the case, and, although rates of comorbidity are high, they vary somewhat from disorder to disorder (Allen et al., 2010; Bruce et al., 2005; Tsao et al., 2002). A large-scale study completed at one of our centres examined the comorbidity of *Diagnostic and Statistical Manual of Mental Disorders*, fourth edition (*DSM-IV-TR*) anxiety and mood disorders (Brown & Barlow, 2002; Brown et al., 2001). Data were collected from 1127 patients carefully diagnosed using a semistructured interview. If we examine just rates of comorbidity at the time of assessment, the results indicate that 55 percent of the patients who received a principal diagnosis of an anxiety or a depressive disorder had at least one additional anxiety or depressive disorder at the time of the assessment. If we consider whether the patient met the criteria for an additional diagnosis at any time in his or her life, rather than just at the time of the assessment, the rate increases to 76 percent.

By far, the most common additional diagnosis for all anxiety disorders was major depression, which occurred in 50 percent of the cases over the course of the patient's life. This becomes important when we discuss the relationship of anxiety and depression later in this chapter. Also important is the finding that additional diagnoses of depression or alcohol or drug abuse makes it less likely that the person will recover from an anxiety disorder and more likely that there will be a relapse after recovery (Bruce et al., 2005; Ciraulo et al., 2013; Huppert, 2009).

COMORBIDITY WITH PHYSICAL DISORDERS

Anxiety disorders also co-occur with several physical conditions (Kariuki-Nyuthe & Stein, 2015). An important study indicated that the presence of any anxiety disorder was uniquely and significantly associated with thyroid disease, respiratory disease, gastrointestinal disease, arthritis, migraine headaches, and allergic conditions (Sareen et al., 2006). Thus, people with these physical conditions are more likely to have an anxiety disorder but are not any more likely to have another psychological disorder. Furthermore, the anxiety disorder most often begins before the physical disorder, suggesting (but not proving) that something about having an anxiety disorder might cause, or contribute to the cause of, the physical disorder. Finally, if someone has both an anxiety disorder and one of the physical disorders mentioned earlier, that person will suffer from greater disability and a poorer quality of life from both the physical problem and the anxiety problem than if that individual had just the physical disorder alone (Belik et al., 2009; Comer et al., 2011; Sareen et al., 2006). Other studies have also found the same relationship between anxiety disorders, particularly panic disorders, and cardiovascular (heart) disease (Gomez-Caminero et al., 2005). The *DSM-5* now makes it explicit that panic attacks often co-occur with certain medical conditions, particularly cardiovascular, respiratory, gastrointestinal, and vestibular (inner ear) disorders, even though the majority of these patients would not meet criteria for panic disorder (Kessler et al., 2006).

The 2014 SLCDC survey of adult Canadians living with a mood and/or anxiety disorder documented the prevalence of limitations and restrictions among those living with only an anxiety disorder (Loukine et al., 2016). Almost 30 percent reported a severe level of disability, 44 percent required accommodations at work to continue working, and almost one-quarter (24 percent) had stopped working altogether at some point. For those Canadians with both an anxiety and a mood disorder the proportions were higher: Half reported a severe level of disability, 66 percent required work accommodations, and 48 percent had experienced a stop in work.

SUICIDE

Based on epidemiological data, Weissman and colleagues found that 20 percent of patients with panic disorder had attempted suicide. They concluded that such attempts were associated with panic disorder. They also concluded that the risk of someone with panic disorder attempting suicide is comparable to that for individuals with major depression (Johnson et al., 1990; Weissman et al., 1989). This finding was alarming, because panic disorder is quite prevalent and clinicians had generally not been on the lookout for possible suicide attempts in such patients. The investigators also found that even patients with panic disorder who did not have accompanying depression were at risk for suicide.

The Weissman study suggests that having any anxiety disorder, not just panic disorder, uniquely increases the chances of having thoughts about suicide (suicidal ideation) or making suicidal attempts (Sareen et al., 2006) but the increase is strongest with panic disorder and post-traumatic stress disorder (Nepon et al., 2010; Sareen, 2011). Whereas earlier studies have suggested that panic disorder is not associated with suicidal behaviour in the absence of other risk factors (e.g., Warshaw et al., 2000), later epidemiological studies reported that all anxiety disorders are associated with an increased risk for suicide attempts and suicidal ideations after accounting for mood disorders, such as dysthymia, major depressive disorder, and bipolar disorder, as well as substance use disorders (Chartrand et al., 2012; Thibodeau et al., 2013). In these studies, people with generalized anxiety disorder and social anxiety disorder who engaged in deliberate self-harm were more likely to engage in this behaviour multiple times, and at least one of those times was a suicide attempt.

The relationship between generalized anxiety disorder and suicide ideation, even after accounting for the effects of other mental disorders (e.g., substance use disorder), was also established in a Canadian study using data from the 2012 Canadian Community Health Survey—Mental Health (CCHS-MH) (Gilmour, 2016). Gilmour further determined that having even subthreshold levels of generalized anxiety disorder (i.e., only meeting two of the three diagnostic criteria necessary for a diagnosis) was related to suicide ideation. The 2012 CCHS-MH was unique in its diagnostic measurement of several specific mental disorders. It covered Canadians 15 years of age or older living in the provinces, but it had exclusions similar to the 2016 CCHS described earlier (e.g., persons living on reserves, institutionalized population).

Clearly, many questions about the relationship between suicide anxiety disorders remain unanswered. We now turn to descriptions of the individual anxiety disorders. But keep in mind that approximately 50 percent of individuals with these disorders will present with one or more additional anxiety or depressive disorders and, perhaps, some other disorders, particularly substance abuse disorders, as described later.

GENERALIZED ANXIETY DISORDER

Disorders traditionally grouped together as anxiety disorders include generalized anxiety disorder, panic disorder and agoraphobia, specific phobia, and social anxiety disorder, as well as two new disorders, separation anxiety disorder and selective mutism. These specific anxiety disorders are complicated by panic attacks or other features that are the focus of the anxiety. But in generalized anxiety disorder, the focus is generalized to the events of everyday life. Therefore, we consider generalized anxiety disorder first.

Is somebody in your family a worrywart or a perfectionist? Perhaps it is you! Most of us worry to some extent. As we have said, worry can be very useful. It helps us plan for the future, make sure that we're prepared for that test, or double-check that we've thought of everything before we head home for the holidays. The worry process itself is not pleasant, but without it, nothing would go very smoothly. But what if you worry indiscriminately about everything? Furthermore, what if worrying is unproductive? What if no matter how much you worry, you can't seem to decide what to do about an upcoming problem or situation? And what if you can't stop worrying, even if you know it is doing you no good and probably making everyone else around you miserable? These features characterize **generalized anxiety disorder (GAD)**. Consider the case of Irene.

IRENE | Ruled by Worry

Irene was a 20-year-old university student with an engaging personality but not many friends. She came to the clinic complaining of excessive anxiety and general difficulties in controlling her life. Everything was a catastrophe for Irene. Although she carried a 3.7 grade-point average, she was convinced she would flunk every test she took. As a result, she repeatedly threatened to drop courses after only a few weeks of classes because she feared that she would not understand the material.

Irene worried excessively until she dropped out of the first university she attended after one month. She felt depressed for a while, and then decided to take a couple of courses at a local college, believing she could handle the work there better. After achieving straight A's at the college for two years, she enrolled once again in university as a third-year student. After a short time she began calling the clinic in a state of extreme agitation, saying she had to drop this or that course because she couldn't handle it. With great difficulty, her therapist and parents persuaded her to stay in the courses and to seek further help. In any course Irene completed, her grade was between an A and a B-minus, but she still worried about every test and every paper, afraid she would fall apart and be unable to understand and complete the work.

Irene did not worry only about school. She was also concerned about relationships with her friends, and whenever she was with her new boyfriend, she feared making a fool of herself and losing his interest. In fact, she reported that each date went extremely well, but she knew the next one would probably be a disaster. As the relationship progressed and some sexual contact seemed natural, Irene was worried sick that her inexperience would make her boyfriend consider her naive and stupid. Nevertheless, she reported enjoying the early sexual contact and admitted that he seemed to enjoy it also, but she was convinced the next time a catastrophe would happen.

Irene was also concerned about her health. She had minor hypertension, probably because she was somewhat overweight. She was also very worried about eating the wrong types or amounts of food. She became reluctant to have her blood pressure checked for fear it would be very high, or to weigh herself for fear she was not losing weight. She severely restricted her eating and as a result had an occasional episode of binge eating, although not often enough to warrant concern.

In addition, Irene worried about her religious faith and about her relationships with her family, particularly her mother and sister. Although Irene had an occasional panic attack, this was not a major issue to her. As soon as the panic subsided she focused on the next possible catastrophe. In addition to high blood pressure, Irene had tension headaches and a "nervous stomach," with a lot of gas, occasional diarrhea, and some abdominal pain. Irene's life was a series of impending catastrophes. Her mother reported that she dreaded a phone call from Irene, let alone a visit, because she knew she would have to see her daughter through a crisis. For the same reason, Irene had very few friends. Even so, when she temporarily gave up her anxiety she was really fun to be with.

CLINICAL DESCRIPTION

Irene suffered from GAD, which is, in many ways, the basic syndrome that characterizes every anxiety disorder considered in this chapter (Brown et al., 1994). The *DSM-5* criteria specify that at least six months of excessive anxiety and worry (apprehensive expectation) must be ongoing more days than not (see DSM Table 5.2). Furthermore, it must be difficult to turn off or control the worry process. This is what distinguishes pathological

DSM-5	**Table 5.2** Diagnostic Criteria for Generalized Anxiety Disorder

A. Excessive anxiety and worry (apprehensive expectation), occurring more days than not for at least 6 months, about a number of events or activities (such as work or school performance).

B. The individual finds it difficult to control the worry.

C. The anxiety and worry are associated with three (or more) of the following six symptoms (with at least some symptoms having been present for more days than not for the past 6 months):
Note: only one item is required in children.

 1. Restlessness or feeling keyed up or on edge.
 2. Being easily fatigued.
 3. Difficulty concentrating or mind going blank.
 4. Irritability.
 5. Muscle tension.
 6. Sleep disturbance (difficulty falling or staying asleep, or restless, unsatisfying sleep).

D. The anxiety, worry, or physical symptoms cause clinically significant distress or impairment in social, occupational, or other important areas of functioning.

E. The disturbance is not due to the direct physiological effects of a substance (e.g., a drug of abuse, a medication) or another medical condition (e.g., hyperthyroidism).

F. The disturbance is not better explained by another mental disorder (e.g., anxiety or worry about having panic attacks in panic disorder, negative evaluation in social anxiety disorder [social phobia], contamination or other obsessions in obsessive compulsive disorder, separation from attachment figures in separation anxiety disorder, reminders of traumatic events in post traumatic stress disorder, gaining weight in anorexia nervosa, physical complaints in somatic symptom disorder, perceived appearance flaws in body dysmorphic disorder, having a serious illness in illness anxiety disorder, or the content of delusional beliefs in schizophrenia or delusional disorder).

worrying from the normal kind we all experience occasionally as we prepare for an upcoming event or challenge. Most of us worry for a time but can set the problem aside and go on to another task. Even if the upcoming challenge is a big one, as soon as it is over, the worrying stops. For Irene, it never stopped. She turned to the next crisis as soon as the current one was over.

The physical symptoms associated with generalized anxiety and GAD differ somewhat from those associated with panic attacks and panic disorder (covered next). Whereas panic is associated with autonomic arousal, presumably as a result of a sympathetic nervous system surge (for instance, increased heart rate, palpitations, perspiration, and trembling), GAD is characterized by muscle tension, mental agitation (Brown et al., 1995), susceptibility to fatigue (probably the result of chronic excessive muscle tension), some irritability, and difficulty sleeping (Campbell-Sills & Brown, 2010). Focusing attention is difficult, as the mind quickly switches from crisis to crisis. For children, only one physical symptom is required for a diagnosis of GAD, and research validates this strategy (Tracey et al., 1997). People with GAD mostly worry about minor, everyday life events, a characteristic that distinguishes GAD from other anxiety disorders. When asked, "Do you worry excessively about minor things?" 100 percent of individuals with GAD respond "yes," compared with approximately 50 percent of individuals whose anxiety disorder falls within other categories (Barlow, 2002). Major events quickly become the focus of anxiety and worry, too. Adults typically focus on possible misfortune to their children, family health, job responsibilities, and more minor things, such as household chores or being on time for appointments. Children with GAD most often worry about competence in academic, athletic, or social performance, as well as family issues (Albano & Hack, 2004; Furr et al., 2009; Weems et al., 2000). Older adults tend to focus, understandably, on health (Wetherell et al., 2010; Beck & Averill, 2004); they also have difficulty sleeping, which seems to make the anxiety worse (Brenes et al., 2009).

STATISTICS

Although worry and physical tension are very common, the severe generalized anxiety experienced by Irene is quite rare. According to the 2012 CCHS-MH, 3 percent of Canadians met the criteria for GAD in 2012, with 9 percent meeting the criteria at some point during their lifetime (Pearson et al., 2013; Pelletier et al., 2017). An additional 2.3 percent of Canadians had subthreshold levels GAD in 2012 (Gilmour, 2016). Among those Canadians meeting the criteria for GAD, 50 percent also had symptoms of major depressive episode (Pelletier et al., 2017). Similar rates of GAD are reported from around the world, for example, in rural South Africa (Bhagwanjee et al., 1998) and the United States (Blazer, Hughes, et al., 1991; Kessler et al., 1994). Although GAD is one of the most common anxiety disorders, relatively few people with GAD come for treatment, compared with patients with panic disorder. Anxiety clinics report that only approximately 10 percent of their patients meet criteria for GAD, compared with 30 to 50 percent for panic disorder. This may be because most patients with GAD seek help from their primary care doctors, where they are found in large numbers (Roy-Byrne & Katon, 2000; Wittchen, 2002).

About two-thirds of individuals with GAD are female, in both clinical samples (Woodman et al., 1999; Yonkers et al., 1996) and epidemiological studies, which include people who do not necessarily seek treatment (Grant et al., 2005). The 2012 CCHS-MH data revealed that among Canadians 15 years of age or older, a greater proportion of women reported GAD than men (3.2 percent versus 2.0 percent; Gilmour, 2016; Pearson et al., 2013). But this sex ratio may be specific to developed countries. In the South African study mentioned here, GAD was more common in males. In the United States, the prevalence of the disorder is significantly lower among Asian, Hispanic, and black adults compared with whites (Grant et al., 2005).

▲ Many older adults suffer from generalized anxiety disorder.

Some people with GAD report onset in late adolescent and early adulthood, and others report an onset in older age. Stressful life events may play some role in the development of GAD. For example, Newman and Bland (1994) showed that a person with GAD is likely to have experienced an excess of life stressors compared with someone without this disorder. Nevertheless, most studies find that GAD is associated with an earlier and more gradual onset than most other anxiety disorders (Barlow, 2002; Beesdo et al., 2010; Brown et al., 1994). Like Irene, many people have felt anxious and tense all their lives. Once it develops, GAD most often is chronic. One study found only an 8 percent probability of becoming symptom-free after two years of follow-up (Yonkers et al., 1996). Another found that patients with GAD retained their symptoms more consistently over five years than patients with panic disorder (Woodman et al., 1999).

GAD is prevalent among seniors. In a large U.S. national comorbidity study and its replication, GAD was found to be most common in the group over 45 years of age, and least common in the youngest group, ages 15 to 24 (Byers et al., 2010; Wittchen et al., 1994). In Canada, however, those 65+ had the lowest past-year prevalence (1.2 percent; Gilmour, 2016). Nevertheless, the

use of minor tranquilizers in seniors is very high. For example, in 2008, 5 percent of adults in the United States used benzodiazepines, and the percentage increased with age (Olfson et al., 2015). The study showed that only 3 percent of the 18- to 35-year-olds, but 9 percent of the 65- to 80-year-olds filled at least one prescription for benzodiazepines during the year. It is not entirely clear why drugs are prescribed with such frequency for older adults. One possibility is that the drugs may not be entirely intended for anxiety. Prescribed drugs may be primarily for sleeping problems or other secondary effects of medical illnesses. In any case, benzodiazepines interfere with cognitive function (Buffett-Jerrott & Stewart, 2002) and put older adults at greater risk for falling down and breaking bones, particularly their hips (Barlow, 2002). Major difficulties that hamper the investigation of anxiety in seniors include the lack of good assessment instruments and treatment studies, largely because of insufficient research interest.

CAUSES

What causes GAD? We have learned a great deal in the past several years. As with most anxiety disorders, there may be a genetic contribution. This conclusion is based on studies showing that GAD tends to run in families (Noyes et al., 1987, 1992). Twin studies strengthen this suggestion. Kendler, Neale, Kessler, Heath, and Eaves (1992a) found that the risk of GAD was somewhat greater for monozygotic (identical) female twins when one twin already had GAD than in dizygotic female twins. But in a later, more broadly focused study, Kendler et al. (1995) confirmed that what seems to be inherited is the tendency to become anxious rather than GAD itself (see also Hettema et al., 2001). Heritability has been found for a particular trait, called *anxiety sensitivity*, which is the tendency to become distressed in response to arousal-related sensations, arising from beliefs that these anxiety-related sensations have harmful consequences (Davies et al., 2015).

For a long time, GAD has posed a real puzzle to investigators. Although the definition of the disorder is relatively new, originating in 1980 with the *DSM-III*, clinicians and psychopathologists were working with people with generalized anxiety long before diagnostic systems were developed. For years, clinicians thought that people who were generally anxious had simply not focused their anxiety on anything specific. Thus, such anxiety was described as free floating. But now scientists have looked more closely and have discovered some very interesting distinctions.

The first hints of difference between GAD and other anxiety disorders were found in the physiological responsivity of individuals with GAD. It is interesting that individuals with GAD do not respond as strongly as individuals with anxiety disorders in which panic is more prominent. In fact, several studies have found that individuals with GAD show less responsiveness on most physiological measures, such as heart rate, blood pressure, skin conductance, and respiration rate (Borkovec & Hu, 1990), than do individuals with other anxiety disorders.

When individuals with GAD are compared with nonanxious normal participants, the one physiological measure that consistently distinguishes the anxious group is muscle tension—people with GAD are chronically tense (Andrews et al., 2010; Marten et al., 1993). To understand this phenomenon of chronic muscle tension, we may have to know what's going on in the minds of people with GAD. With new methods from cognitive science, we are beginning to uncover the mental processes ongoing in GAD (Teachman et al., 2012).

Four distinct cognitive characteristics of people with GAD are outlined in a model developed by Québec researchers Michel Dugas and Robert Ladouceur and their colleagues (see Dugas et al., 1998): (1) intolerance of uncertainty, (2) positive beliefs about worry, (3) poor problem orientation, and (4) cognitive avoidance. Although unpredictable events are known to produce anxiety in humans and animals, people with GAD are less tolerant of situations involving uncertainty than people with other anxiety disorders or nonclinical controls (Ladouceur et al., 1999). People with GAD also hold stronger erroneous beliefs that worrying is effective in avoiding negative outcomes and promoting positive outcomes—beliefs that might maintain their worry. For example, they might believe that worrying about a family member's health is useful because if something should happen to the family member, then at least the worrier would not be taken by surprise. People with GAD also have a poor orientation toward problems. For example, they tend to view problems as threats to be avoided rather than as challenges to be met (Dugas et al., 1997).

The fourth cognitive characteristic of GAD in Ladouceur and Dugas's model pertains to the possibility that worry may serve an avoidance function. Borkovec and Inz (1990) have shown that people with GAD engage in frantic, intense thought processes or worry without accompanying images. This kind of worry may be exactly what causes these individuals to show less responsiveness on physiological measures. They are thinking so hard about upcoming problems, they don't have the attentional capacity left for the all-important process of creating images of the potential threat—images that would elicit more substantial negative affect and autonomic activity. In other words, they avoid all the negative affect associated with the threat. Although people with GAD may avoid much of the

▲ Robert Ladouceur, Michel Dugas, and their colleagues in Québec have theorized about the role of intolerance of uncertainty and other cognitive factors in the etiology and maintenance of generalized anxiety disorder. They have also developed an effective psychosocial treatment for GAD.

unpleasantness and pain associated with the negative affect and imagery, the avoidance means that they are never able to work through their problems and arrive at solutions. Therefore, they become chronic worriers, with accompanying autonomic inflexibility and quite severe muscle tension. Thus, intense worrying for an individual with GAD may serve the same maladaptive purpose as avoidance does for people with phobias. It prevents the person from facing the feared situation, and so adaptation never occurs.

Recent studies have tested various aspects of Ladouceur and Dugas's cognitive model of GAD. For example, University of Sherbrooke researcher Patrick Gosselin and his colleagues (Gosselin et al., 2007) showed that, consistent with model predictions, adolescents who are frequent worriers also hold more erroneous beliefs about worry and use more avoidance strategies. Another study by Dugas, Marchand, and Ladouceur (2005) showed that intolerance of uncertainty was related to GAD but not to panic disorder with agoraphobia, providing some support for the diagnostic specificity of this cognitive characteristic to GAD.

With new methods from cognitive science, we are beginning to uncover the sometimes unconscious mental processes ongoing in GAD. Evidence from this type of research indicates that individuals with GAD are highly sensitive to threat in general, particularly to a threat that has personal relevance. That is, they allocate their attention much more readily to sources of threat than do people who are not anxious (Bradley et al., 1999). Furthermore, this acute awareness of potential threat, particularly if it is personal, seems to be entirely automatic or unconscious (Mathews, 1997; Mogg et al., 1995).

In summary, some people inherit a tendency to be tense, and they develop a sense early on that important events in their lives may be uncontrollable and potentially dangerous. Significant stress makes them apprehensive and vigilant. These emotions set off intense worry, which helps the individual avoid anxious images and physiological arousal in the short term but eventually leads to the disorder of GAD. Cognitive factors, such as intolerance of uncertainty, positive beliefs about worry, and poor problem orientation, also seem to play contributing roles in causing and maintaining GAD. This model is very current, as it combines findings from cognitive science with biological data from both the central and peripheral nervous systems. Time will tell whether the model is correct, although there is much supporting data (Borkovec et al., 2004; Mineka & Zinbarg, 2006). In any case, it is consistent with our view of anxiety as a future-oriented mood state focused on potential danger or threat, as opposed to an emergency or alarm reaction to actual present danger. A model of the development of GAD is presented in ■ Figure 5.4.

TREATMENT

Available treatments for GAD, both drug and psychological, are reasonably effective. Benzodiazepines are most often prescribed for generalized anxiety, and the evidence indicates that they give some relief, at least in the short term. Few studies have looked at the effects of these drugs for a period longer than eight weeks (Mathew & Hoffman, 2009). The therapeutic effect is relatively modest. Furthermore, benzodiazepines carry some risks. First,

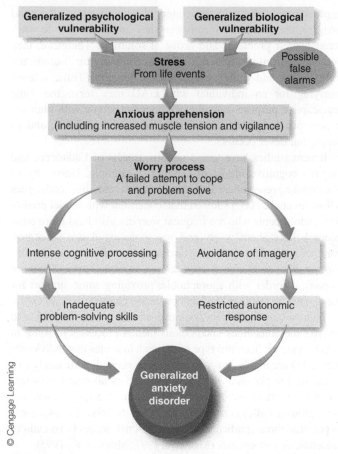

FIGURE 5.4 | An integrative model of generalized anxiety disorder.

© Cengage Learning

they seem to impair both cognitive and motor functioning (e.g., van Laar et al., 2001). Specifically, people don't seem to be as alert on the job or at school when they are taking benzodiazepines. The drugs may impair driving, and in older adults they seem to be associated with falls, resulting in hip fractures (Wang et al., 2001). More important, benzodiazepines seem to produce dependence, making it difficult for people to stop taking them (Mathew & Hoffman, 2009). There is reasonably wide agreement that the optimal use of benzodiazepines is for the short-term relief of anxiety associated with a temporary crisis or stressful event, such as a family problem. Under these circumstances, a physician may prescribe a benzodiazepine until the crisis is resolved but for no more than a week or two. There is stronger evidence for the usefulness of antidepressants in the treatment of GAD, such as paroxetine (also called Paxil) (Rickels et al., 2006) and venlafaxine (also called Effexor) (Schatzberg, 2000). These drugs may prove to be a better choice (Brawman-Mintzer, 2001; Mathew & Hoffman, 2009).

In the short term, psychological treatments seem to confer about the same benefit as drugs in the treatment of GAD, but psychological treatments are more effective in the long term (Barlow et al., 2007; Newman et al., 2011). Recent reports of innovations in brief psychological treatments are encouraging. Because we now know that individuals with GAD seem to avoid

feelings of anxiety and the negative affect associated with threatening images, clinicians have designed treatments to help patients with GAD process the threatening information on an emotional level, using images, so that they will feel anxious (rather than avoid the anxious feeling). These treatments have other components, such as teaching patients how to relax deeply to combat tension. Borkovec and his colleagues found such a treatment to be significantly better than a placebo psychological treatment, not only at post-treatment but also at a one-year follow-up (Borkovec & Costello, 1993). In the early 1990s, we developed a cognitive-behavioural treatment (CBT) for GAD in which patients evoke the worry process during therapy sessions and confront threatening images and thoughts head-on. The patient learns to use cognitive therapy and other coping techniques to counteract and control the worry process (Craske et al., 1992). In a major study, a brief adaptation of this treatment was also used successfully to decrease anxiety and improve quality of life in a primary care office (family doctors and nurses) where GAD is a frequent complaint (Rollman et al., 2005). Cuijpers and colleagues (Cuijpers et al., 2014) recently reviewed 41 studies with 2132 patients meeting criteria for GAD and found large treatment effects of psychotherapy, which primarily consisted of CBT, as compared with control conditions, which were primarily waitlist groups.

Ladouceur and his colleagues have also made important in-roads in the development of effective psychosocial interventions for GAD (see review by Dugas & Koerner, 2005). They developed and tested a GAD psychosocial treatment that targeted the four factors in their cognitive model of GAD described earlier (Ladouceur et al., 2000). For example, to combat positive beliefs about worry, the therapist used cognitive-behavioural strategies to help patients re-evaluate the actual usefulness of worry. Twenty-six GAD patients were randomly assigned to either a treatment condition or a delayed treatment control condition in which the patients received treatment after serving on the waiting list. Relative to those on the waiting list, those receiving the active treatment showed significant change in self-report, clinician, and significant-other ratings of GAD symptoms at post-treatment. Gains were maintained at 6-month and 12-month follow-ups. Moreover, 77 percent of the patients no longer met GAD diagnostic criteria following treatment. A subsequent study by this research team showed that this intervention is also effective when delivered in a group format, thereby increasing its cost-effectiveness (Dugas et al., 2003); they demonstrated that people continued to improve *following* treatment, suggesting that they used what they learned in therapy to continue to recover from their disorder. Dugas et al. (2010) also demonstrated that although their CBT package was equally effective as applied relaxation in the short term, only people who received CBT continued to improve up to two years after treatment.

Borkovec and Ruscio (2001) reviewed 13 controlled studies evaluating CBT treatments for GAD and found substantial gains compared with no treatment or alternative treatment, such as psychodynamic therapy. Moreover, a meta-analysis that focused specifically on the effects of CBT on excessive worry—the cardinal feature of GAD—demonstrated large overall effect sizes (Covin et al., 2008), suggesting that current CBT packages target the characteristic features of the disorder. Studies indicate that brief psychological treatments alter the sometimes unconscious cognitive biases associated with GAD (Mathews et al., 1995; Mogg et al., 1995). Recent studies also suggest that psychological interventions with GAD are effective to the extent that they focus on increasing the patient's ability to tolerate uncertainty (e.g., Ladouceur et al., 2000); in fact, according to Université du Québec en Outaouais professor Michael Dugas (2018), a focus on behavioural experiments dealing with intolerance of uncertainty might be all that is needed for treatment success.

A new psychological treatment for GAD has been developed that incorporates procedures focusing on acceptance of distressing thoughts and feelings in addition to cognitive therapy. Meditational and mindfulness-based approaches help teach the patient to be more tolerant of these feelings (Hofmann, Sawyer, et al., 2010; Khoury et al., 2013; Orsillo & Roemer, 2011). Results from a clinical trial reported some of the highest success rates yet to appear in the literature (Hayes-Skelton et al., 2013).

There is particularly encouraging evidence that psychological treatments are effective with children who suffer from generalized anxiety (Albano & Hack, 2004; Furr et al., 2009). In a major clinical trial with 488 children ages 7 to 17 years, CBT and the antidepressant drug sertraline (Zoloft) were equally effective immediately following treatment compared with taking placebo pills for children with GAD and other related disorders, but the combination of CBT and sertraline was even better, with 80 percent showing substantial improvement versus 24 percent on placebo (Walkup et al., 2008). Follow-up analyses showed that more severe and impairing anxiety, greater caregiver strain, and a principal diagnosis of social anxiety disorder were associated with less favourable outcomes (Compton et al., 2014). Mindfulness-based therapies for GAD are now also being adapted and tested with youth, with some indications of success (Semple & Burke, 2012). Similarly, progress is being made in adapting

psychological treatments for older adults, as important studies show (Stanley et al., 2003; Wetherell et al., 2005). One large clinical trial demonstrated very clearly the efficiency of this treatment for adults over 60 compared with the usual care they received (Stanley et al., 2009).

After trying several different drugs, Irene was treated with the CBT approach developed at our clinic and found herself much more able to cope with life. She completed college and graduate school, married, and is successful in her career as a counsellor in a nursing home. But even now, Irene finds it difficult to relax and stop worrying. She continues to experience mild to moderate anxiety, particularly when under stress; she takes minor tranquilizers on occasion to support her psychological coping skills.

PANIC DISORDER AND AGORAPHOBIA

Do you have a relative, maybe an eccentric great-aunt, for example, who never seems to leave the house? Family reunions or visits always have to be at her house. She never goes anywhere else. Most people attribute their old aunt's behaviour to her being a little odd or perhaps just not fond of travel. She is very warm and friendly when people come to visit, so she retains contact with the family.

In fact, your aunt may not be just odd or eccentric. She may have a very debilitating anxiety disorder called **panic disorder (PD)**, in which individuals experience severe unexpected panic attacks; they may think they're dying or otherwise losing control. In many cases, but not all, panic disorder is accompanied by a closely related disorder called **agoraphobia**, which is fear and avoidance of situations in which a person feels unsafe or unable to escape to get home or to a hospital in the event of developing panic symptoms or other physical symptoms, such as loss of

---

MRS. M. | *Self-Imprisoned*

Mrs. M. was 67 years old and lived in a second-floor walk-up apartment in a lower-middle-class section of the city. Her adult daughter, one of her few remaining contacts with the world, had requested an evaluation with Mrs. M.'s consent.

At her apartment building, I rang the front bell and entered a narrow hallway. Mrs. M. was nowhere in sight. Knowing that she lived on the second floor, I walked up the stairs and knocked on the door at the top. I opened the door when Mrs. M. asked me to come in. She was sitting in her living room, and I could quickly see the layout of the rest of the apartment. The living room was in the front; the kitchen was in the back, adjoining a porch. To the right of the stairs was the one bedroom, with a bathroom opening from it.

Mrs. M. was glad to see me and very friendly, offering me coffee and homemade cookies. I was the first person she had seen in three weeks. In fact, Mrs. M. had not left that

---

Concept Check 5.2

True (T) or false (F)?

1. _____ GAD is characterized by muscle tension, mental agitation, irritability, sleeping difficulties, and susceptibility to fatigue.

2. _____ Most studies show that in the majority of cases of GAD, onset is early in adulthood as an immediate response to a life stressor.

3. _____ GAD is prevalent in older adults and in females in our society.

4. _____ GAD has no genetic basis.

5. _____ Cognitive-behavioural treatment and other psychological treatments for GAD are probably better than drug therapies in the long run.

apartment in 20 years, and she had suffered from panic disorder with agoraphobia for more than 30 years.

As she told her story, Mrs. M. conveyed vivid images of a wasted life. And yet she continued to struggle in the face of adversity and to make the best she could of her limited existence. Even areas in her apartment signalled the potential for terrifying panic attacks. She had not answered the door herself for the past 15 years because she was afraid to look into the hallway. She could enter her kitchen and go into the areas containing the stove and refrigerator, but for the past ten years she had not been to the part of the room that overlooked the backyard or out onto the back porch. Thus, her life for the past decade had been confined to her bedroom, her living room, and the front half of her kitchen. She relied on her adult daughter to bring groceries and visit once a week. Her only other visitor was the parish priest, who came to deliver communion every two to three weeks when he could. Her only other contact with the outside world was through the television and the radio. Her husband, who had abused both alcohol and Mrs. M., had died ten years earlier of alcohol-related causes. Early in her very stressful marriage she had her first terrifying panic attack and had gradually withdrawn from the world. As long as she stayed in her apartment, she was relatively free of panic. For this reason, and because in her mind there were few reasons left near the end of her life to venture out, she declined treatment.

bladder control. People develop agoraphobia because they never know when these symptoms might occur. In severe cases, people with agoraphobia are totally unable to leave the house, sometimes for years on end, as in the example of Mrs. M.

CLINICAL DESCRIPTION

In the *DSM-IV*, panic disorder and agoraphobia were integrated into one disorder called panic disorder with agoraphobia, but investigators discovered that many people experienced panic disorder without developing agoraphobia and that some people develop agoraphobia in the absence of panic disorder (Wittchen et al., 2010). Often, however, they go together, so we discuss both disorders in this section.

At the beginning of the chapter, we talked about the related phenomena of anxiety and panic. In panic disorder, anxiety and panic are combined in an intricate relationship that can become as devastating as it was for Mrs. M. Many people who have panic attacks do not necessarily develop panic disorder.

To meet the criteria for panic disorder, a person must experience an unexpected panic attack and develop substantial anxiety over the possibility of having another attack or about the implications of the attack or its consequences (see DSM Table 5.3). If you are in a shopping mall or a crowded movie theatre or place of worship, not only is it difficult to leave but you are also probably going to embarrass yourself if you try. You may think you will

DSM-5	**Table 5.3** Diagnostic Criteria for Panic Disorder

A. Recurrent unexpected panic attacks. A panic attack is an abrupt surge of intense fear or intense discomfort that reaches a peak within minutes, and during which time four (or more) of the following symptoms occur:

Note: The abrupt surge can occur from a calm state or an anxious state.

1. Palpitations, pounding heart, or accelerated heart rate.
2. Sweating.
3. Trembling or shaking.
4. Sensations of shortness of breath or smothering.
5. Feelings of choking.
6. Chest pain or discomfort.
7. Nausea or abdominal distress.
8. Feeling dizzy, unsteady, light-headed, or faint.
9. Chills or heat sensations.
10. Paresthesias (numbness or tingling sensations).
11. Derealization (feelings of unreality) or depersonalization (being detached from oneself).
12. Fear of losing control or "going crazy."
13. Fear of dying.

Note: Culture-specific symptoms (e.g., tinnitus, neck soreness, headache, uncontrollable screaming or crying) may be seen. Such symptoms should not count as one of the four required symptoms.

B. At least one of the attacks has been followed by 1 month (or more) of one or both of the following:

1. Persistent concern or worry about additional panic attacks or their consequences (e.g., losing control, having a heart attack, "going crazy").
2. A significant maladaptive change in behavior related to the attacks (e.g., behaviors designed to avoid having panic attacks, such as avoidance of exercise or unfamiliar situations).

C. The disturbance is not attributable to the physiological effects of a substance (e.g., a drug of abuse, a medication) or another medical condition (e.g., hyperthyroidism, cardiopulmonary disorders).

D. The disturbance is not better explained by another mental disorder (e.g., the panic attacks do not occur only in response to feared social situations, as in social anxiety disorder); in response to circumscribed phobic objects or situations, as in specific phobia; in response to obsessions, as in obsessive-compulsive disorder; in response to reminders of traumatic events, as in post-traumatic stress disorder; or in response to separation from attachment figures, as in separation anxiety disorder.

Source: Reprinted with permission from the *Diagnostic and Statistical Manual of Mental Disorders*, Fifth Edition (Copyright © 2013). American Psychiatric Association. All Rights Reserved.

have to climb over everyone to get out, or get up in the middle of the movie and run out, or worse, faint in the movie theatre (in fact, individuals with agoraphobia seldom if ever do any of these things). For these reasons, when they do go to a place of worship or to the movies, people with agoraphobia always plan for rapid escape (e.g., by sitting very near the door). The *DSM-5* diagnostic criteria for agoraphobia are listed in DSM Table 5.4.

The Development of Agoraphobia

The term *agoraphobia* was coined in 1871 by Karl Westphal, a German physician, and, in the original Greek, refers to fear of the marketplace. This is a very appropriate term because the *agora*, the Greek marketplace, was a very busy, bustling area. One of the most stressful places for individuals with agoraphobia today is the shopping mall, the modern-day agora.

As noted by University of British Columbia professor Stanley J. Rachman, "the consequences of panic can constitute a more serious problem than the panic itself" (1988, p. 259). Most agoraphobic avoidance behaviour is simply a complication of severe, unexpected panic attacks. Simply put, if you have had unexpected panic attacks and are afraid you may have another one, you want to be in a safe place or at least with a safe person who knows what you are experiencing if another attack occurs, so you can quickly get to a hospital or at least go into your bedroom and lie down (the home is usually a safe place). We know that anxiety is diminished for individuals with agoraphobia if they think a location or person is safe, even if the person could do nothing effective if something bad did happen.

Even if agoraphobic behaviour is initially closely tied to the occasions of panic, it can become relatively independent of panic attacks (Craske & Barlow, 1988). In other words, an individual who has not had a panic attack for years may still have strong agoraphobic avoidance, like Mrs. M. agoraphobic avoidance seems to be determined by the extent to which you think or expect you might have another attack rather than by how many attacks you have actually had or how severe they have been. Thus, agoraphobic avoidance is simply one way of coping with unexpected panic attacks.

Other methods of coping with panic attacks include using (and sometimes abusing) alcohol or drugs. Indeed, a high comorbidity exists between panic disorder and alcohol abuse or dependence (Cox et al., 1990). An experimental study by MacDonald, Baker, Stewart, and Skinner (2000) at Dalhousie University showed that panic-prone individuals may be more susceptible than others to the anxiety-reducing effects of alcohol when they are experiencing panic-like bodily sensations. This may explain why these individuals are more likely to develop alcohol abuse and dependence. In fact, intervening with panic-prone individuals' fear of anxiety leads to reductions in their problematic drinking (Watt et al., 2006).

Some individuals do not actually avoid agoraphobic situations but endure them with intense dread. For example, people who simply must go to work each day or, perhaps, travel as part of the job will endure untold agonies of anxiety and panic simply to achieve their goals. Thus, the *DSM-5* notes that agoraphobia may be characterized either by avoiding the situations or by enduring them with intense fear and anxiety.

Canadian hockey player Shayne Corson, a forward who played 20 NHL seasons, won a Stanley Cup, and served as a member of Canada's 1998 Olympic hockey team, experienced crippling panic attacks. His panic attacks would come on suddenly and unexpectedly. He experienced uncomfortable sensations in his chest that he worried might be signs of a heart attack. Corson would try to distract himself, but he found these attacks extremely distressing. When out at a restaurant or nightclub, he reportedly wouldn't last more than four to five minutes before he would flee, fearful that he might experience a panic attack in public. Corson's panic attacks often occurred right on the Maple Leafs bench in front of unsuspecting teammates and fans. Corson was prescribed antianxiety medication and saw a psychiatrist for treatment of his panic attacks (Hornby, 2001; Kennedy, 2001). Unfortunately, his symptoms re-emerged and interfered so much with the effectiveness of his game that Corson decided to quit the Maple Leafs team during the 2003 playoffs (Hockey Hall of Fame and Museum, 2001). Corson eventually recovered sufficiently to return to his hockey career in 2004 (Foster, 2004).

Most patients with panic disorder and agoraphobic avoidance also display another cluster of avoidant behaviours that we call interoceptive avoidance or avoidance of internal physical sensations (Brown et al., 2005; Craske & Barlow, 2014). These behaviours involve removing oneself from situations or activities that might produce the physiological arousal that somehow resembles the beginnings of a panic attack. Some patients might avoid exercise because it produces increased cardiovascular activity or faster respiration, which reminds them of panic attacks. In fact, University of Regina researchers McWilliams and Asmundson (2001) showed that panic-prone university males reported engaging in exercise less frequently than other university males, consistent with the possibility that they might be avoiding exercise because of their fear of arousal sensations. Other patients might avoid sauna baths or any rooms in which they might perspire. Psychopathologists are beginning to recognize that this cluster of avoidance behaviours is every bit as important as more classical agoraphobic avoidance. A list of situations or activities typically avoided within the interoceptive cluster is found in Table 5.1.

STATISTICS

Panic disorder is fairly common. Approximately 3.5 percent of the U.S. population meet the criteria for panic disorder at some point during their lives, three-fourths of them women (Eaton et al., 1994), and another 5.3 percent meet the criteria for agoraphobia (Kessler et al., 1994). The rates of agoraphobia may be somewhat overestimated as a result of methodological difficulties, but most people with panic disorder do have agoraphobic avoidance. According to the 2002 CCHS—Mental Health and Wellbeing, 1.5 percent of Canadians 15 years of age or older had experienced panic disorder in the past 12 months, with 3.7 percent experiencing panic disorder in their lifetime (Ramage-Morin, 2004). The rates among Canadian women were higher than for men (4.6 percent versus 2.8 percent lifetime; 2.0 percent versus 1.0 percent in the past 12 months).

TABLE 5.1 | Interoceptive Daily Activities Typically Avoided by People with Agoraphobia

Running up flights of stairs	Getting involved in "heated" debates
Walking outside in intense heat	Hot, stuffy rooms
Having showers with the doors and windows closed	Hot, stuffy cars
Hot, stuffy stores or shopping malls	Having a sauna
Walking outside in very cold weather	Hiking
Aerobics	Sports
Lifting heavy objects	Drinking coffee or any caffeinated beverages
Dancing	Sexual relations
Eating chocolate	Watching horror movies
Standing quickly from a sitting position	Eating heavy meals
Watching exciting movies or sports events	Getting angry

© Cengage Learning

Source: From *Mastery of Your Anxiety and Panic II*, by D. H. Barlow and M. G. Craske, 1994, Graywind Publications.

Onset of panic disorder usually occurs in early adult life—from mid-teens through about 40 years of age. The mean age of onset is between 25 and 29 (Craske & Barlow, 2001). For example, analysis of the 2002 CCHS data showed that the average age of onset was 25 years of age and that three-quarters of the people with panic disorder had developed the disorder by 33 years of age (Ramage-Morin, 2004). Generally, panic disorder seems less pervasive among older adults, but our estimates are not yet firm (e.g., Beck & Stanley, 1997).

Most initial unexpected panic attacks begin at or after puberty. Furthermore, many prepubertal children who are seen by general medical practitioners have symptoms of hyperventilation that may well be panic attacks. These children do not report fear of dying or losing control, however, perhaps because they are not at a stage of their cognitive development where they can make these attributions (Nelles & Barlow, 1988).

As we have said, 75 percent or more of those who have agoraphobia are women. In fact, the higher the severity of agoraphobic avoidance, the greater the proportion of women. For example, in our clinic, in a group of patients with panic disorder with mild agoraphobia, 72 percent were women; but if the agoraphobia was moderate, however, the percentage was 81 percent. Similarly, if agoraphobia was severe, the percentage was 89 percent. For a long time, we didn't know why agoraphobia is more common in women, but now it seems the most logical explanation is cultural (Arrindell et al., 2003; Wolitzky-Taylor et al., 2010). It is more accepted for women to report fear and to avoid numerous situations. Men, however, are expected to be stronger and braver—to tough it out. Another possible reason pertains to gender differences in fear of anxiety. Research conducted at Dalhousie University and at the Royal Ottawa Hospital has shown that women are more fearful of anxiety symptoms than are men (Stewart et al., 1997), with women proving particularly fearful of the physical consequences of anxiety sensations (e.g., fearing an imminent heart attack; Foot & Koszycki, 2004). These gender differences are even observed in children (Walsh et al., 2004). Women with panic disorder have greater agoraphobia because they believe panic attacks are more likely and because they are more afraid of the potential negative consequences of a panic attack (Schmidt & Koselka, 2000).

What happens to men who have severe unexpected panic attacks? Is cultural disapproval of fear in men so strong that most of them simply endure panic? The answer seems to be "no." A large proportion of males with unexpected panic attacks cope in a culturally acceptable way: They consume large amounts of alcohol (see review by Cox et al., 1990). A study by clinical psychologist Brian Cox and his colleagues (Cox et al., 1993), conducted at the Centre for Addiction and Mental Health in Toronto, compared 74 men and 162 women with panic disorder. Although the women reported higher levels of agoraphobic avoidance, the men reported higher levels of weekly alcohol intake and greater beliefs in alcohol as an effective way to cope with anxiety. In fact, a study conducted by researchers at the University of Québec at Montréal showed that the lower agoraphobic avoidance of men with panic disorder was associated with their alcohol use (Turgeon et al., 1998). The problem is that these men with panic disorder can become dependent on alcohol, and many begin the long downward spiral into serious addiction.

Thus, males may end up with an even more severe problem than panic disorder with agoraphobia. Because these men are so impaired by alcohol abuse, clinicians may not realize they also have panic disorder and agoraphobia. And even if they are successfully treated for their addiction, the anxiety disorder still requires treatment (McHugh, 2015).

Cultural Influences

Panic disorder exists worldwide, although its expression may vary from place to place. Prevalence rates for panic disorder show some degree of cross-cultural variability with Asian and African countries usually showing the lowest rates. These findings mirror cross-ethnic comparisons within the United States, with Asian Americans showing the lowest, and white American showing the highest prevalence rates (Asnaani et al., 2009; Hofmann & Hinton, 2014; Lewis-Fernandez et al., 2010). Furthermore, rates of recovery from panic disorder are lower among African Americans as compared to non-Latino white individuals (Sibrava et al., 2013).

In addition to differences in prevalence rates and chronicity, cross-cultural studies have also identified interesting differences in the expression of the anxiety. In Chapter 2, we described a fright disorder that is called *susto* in Latin America and is characterized by sweating, increased heart rate, and insomnia but not by reports of anxiety or fear, even though a severe fright is the cause. An anxiety-related, culturally defined syndrome prominent among Hispanic people, particularly those from the Caribbean, is called *ataques de nervios* (Liebowitz et al., 1994). The symptoms of an *ataque* seem quite similar to those of panic attacks, although such manifestations as shouting uncontrollably or bursting into tears may be associated more frequently with an *ataque* than with panic. Another culture-bound syndrome that bears some relation to panic disorder occurs among the Inuit of northern Canada and western Greenland. This syndrome is called *kayak-angst* and involves episodes of intense fear, worries about drowning, physical arousal sensations (rapid heartbeat and trembling), and intense disorientation that occur when a seal hunter or fisher is alone at sea (Amering & Katschnig, 1990; Katschnig, 1999). Like the relation of panic disorder to agoraphobic avoidance, *kayak-angst* can cause the hunter or fisher to avoid travel in the kayak, which can obviously lead to significant impairments in his or her livelihood (Katschnig, 1999; Katschnig & Amering, 1990).

Nocturnal Panic

Think back to the case of Gretchen, whose panic attack was described earlier in this chapter. Is there anything unusual about her report? Yes—she was sound asleep when it happened! Approximately 60 percent of people with panic disorder have experienced such nocturnal attacks (Craske & Rowe, 1997). In fact, panic attacks occur more frequently between 1:30 a.m. and 3:30 a.m. than at any other time. In some cases, people are afraid to go to sleep at night. What is happening to them? Are they having nightmares? Research indicates they are not. Nocturnal

▲ This drawing depicts a victim of isolated sleep paralysis being "ridden by the witch."

attacks are studied in a sleep laboratory. Patients spend a few nights sleeping while attached to an electroencephalograph (EEG) that monitors their brain waves. We all go through various stages of sleep that are reflected by different patterns on the EEG. Nocturnal panic attacks occur during delta wave or slow-wave sleep, which typically occurs several hours after we fall asleep and is the deepest stage of sleep. People with panic disorder often begin to panic when they start sinking into delta sleep, and then they awaken in the midst of an attack. Because there is no obvious reason for them to be anxious or panicky when they are sound asleep, most of these individuals think they are dying (Craske & Barlow, 2014).

What causes nocturnal panic? Our best information at the current time is that the change in stages of sleep to slow-wave sleep produces physical sensations of "letting go" that are very frightening to an individual with panic disorder (Craske et al., 2002). This process is described more fully later when we discuss causes of panic disorder. Several other events also occur during sleep that resemble nocturnal panic and are mistakenly thought to be the cause of nocturnal panic by some. Initially, we thought it might be nightmares, but nightmares and other dream-like activity occur during a stage of sleep characterized by rapid eye movement (REM sleep). Therefore, people are not dreaming when they have nocturnal panics, a conclusion consistent with patient reports. Some therapists are not aware of the stage of sleep associated with nocturnal panic attacks and so assume that patients are repressing their dream material, perhaps because it might relate to an early trauma too painful to be admitted to consciousness. As we've seen, this explanation is unlikely to be true.

A fascinating condition that at first glance appears similar to nocturnal panic is called *isolated sleep paralysis*. Have you ever found yourself awake at night, unable to move, your heart pounding as you stare at aspects of the room—maybe the clock, maybe the window—feeling that a presence is in the room with you? If you were from Newfoundland and Labrador, you would refer to this experience as being visited by the "Old Hag" (Hufford, 1982); if you were from an African or Caribbean culture, this experience would be captured by the expression "the witch is riding you" (Bell et al., 1986); and if you were from China you would believe this experience is the result of being pressed down upon by a ghost (Yeung et al., 2005). Isolated sleep paralysis occurs during the transitional state between sleep and waking. During this period the individual is unable to move and experiences a surge of terror that resembles a panic attack; occasionally, the person also has vivid hallucinations. One possible explanation is that REM sleep is spilling over into the waking cycle. This seems likely because one feature of REM sleep is atonia, or lack of muscle strength. Another is vivid dreams, which could account for the experience of hallucination. The "Old Hag" is mentioned twice in E. Annie Proulx's novel *The Shipping News*, set in Newfoundland and Labrador.

CAUSES

It is not possible to understand panic disorder without referring to the triad of contributing factors mentioned throughout this book: biological, psychological, and social. Strong evidence indicates that agoraphobia often develops after a person has unexpected panic attacks (or panic-like sensations), but whether agoraphobia develops and how severe it becomes seem to be socially and culturally determined, as we noted earlier. Panic attacks and panic disorder, however, seem to be related most strongly to biological and psychological factors and their interaction.

As noted earlier, we all inherit—some more than others—a vulnerability to stress, which is a tendency to be generally neurobiologically overreactive to the events of daily life (generalized biological vulnerability). But some people are also more likely than others to have an emergency alarm reaction

(unexpected panic attack) when confronted with stress-producing events. These may include stress on the job or at school, death of a loved one, divorce, and positive events that are nevertheless stressful, such as graduating from school and starting a new career, getting married, or changing jobs. Other people might be more likely to have headaches or high blood pressure in response to the same kinds of stress. Particular situations quickly become associated in an individual's mind with external and internal cues that were present during the panic attack (Bouton et al., 2001). The next time the person's heart rate increases during exercise, she might assume she is having a panic attack (conditioning). Harmless exercise is an example of an internal cue or a conditioned stimulus for a panic attack. Being in a movie theatre when panic first occurred would be an external cue that might become a conditioned stimulus for future panics. Because these cues become associated with several different internal and external stimuli through a learning process, we call them *learned alarms*.

But none of this would make much difference without the next step. An individual must be susceptible to developing anxiety over the possibility of having another panic attack. That is, he or she thinks the physical sensations associated with the panic attack mean something terrible is about to happen, perhaps death. This is what creates panic disorder. This tendency to believe that unexpected bodily sensations are dangerous reflects a specific psychological vulnerability to develop panic and related disorders. This causal sequence is depicted in ■ Figure 5.5.

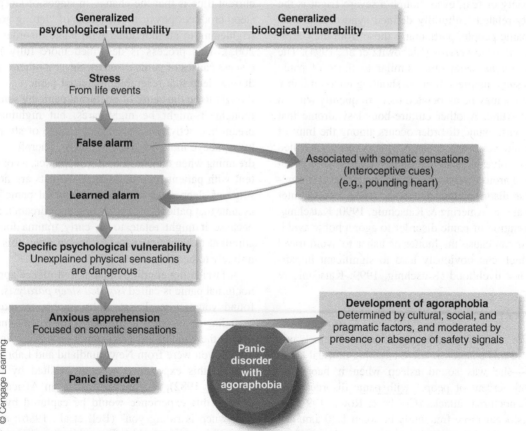

FIGURE 5.5 | A model of the causes of panic disorder with or without agoraphobia.

Source: Republished with permission of Guildford Publications, from White, K. S., & Barlow, D. H. (2002). "Panic disorder and agoraphobia," in D. H. Barlow, *Anxiety and its disorders: The nature and treatment of anxiety and panic,* 2nd ed.; permission conveyed through Copyright Clearance Center, Inc.

Approximately 8 to 12 percent of the population has an occasional unexpected panic attack, often during a period of intense stress over the previous year (Kessler et al., 2006; Mattis & Ollendick, 2002; Suárez et al., 2009; Telch et al., 1989). Most of these people do not develop anxiety (Telch et al., 1989). Only a few go on to develop anxiety over future panic attacks and thereby meet the criteria for panic disorder. What happens to those individuals who don't develop anxiety? They seem to attribute the attack to events of the moment, such as an argument with a friend, something they ate, or a bad day, and go on with their lives, perhaps experiencing an occasional panic attack when they are under stress again. This was illustrated recently by the experiences of professional golfer Charlie Beljan, known to his friends as a fun-loving, free-spirited guy. But in late 2012, on his way to winning his first Professional Golfers Association tournament, he experienced a panic attack that he thought was a heart attack. Determined to finish, and with paramedics following him in a golf cart, Beljan staggered from shot to shot, sometimes having to sit down on the fairway. Nevertheless, he had his best round of the year and, after finishing, took an ambulance to the hospital where he was diagnosed as having a panic attack (Crouse, 2013). Reacting to the news, Bubba Watson, the Masters champion in 2012, reported that panic attacks had put him in the hospital at least three times in his career.

The influential cognitive theories of David Clark (1986, 1996) explicate in more detail some cognitive processes that may be ongoing in panic disorder. Clark emphasizes the specific psychological vulnerability of people with this disorder to interpret normal physical sensations in a catastrophic way. In other words, although we all typically experience rapid heartbeat after exercise, if you have a psychological or cognitive vulnerability, you might interpret the response as dangerous and feel a surge of anxiety. This anxiety, in turn, produces more physical sensations because of the action of the sympathetic nervous system; you perceive these additional sensations as even more dangerous, and a vicious cycle begins that results in a panic attack. Thus, Clark emphasizes the cognitive process as most important in panic disorder.

Why would some people think something terrible is going to happen when they have an attack but others wouldn't? An important study prospectively followed young women at risk for developing anxiety disorders for several years. Those women who had a history of various physical disorders and were anxious about their health tended to develop panic disorder rather than another anxiety disorder such as social anxiety disorder (Rudaz et al., 2010). Thus, these women may have learned in childhood that unexpected bodily sensations may be dangerous—whereas other people experiencing panic attacks do not.

TREATMENT

As we noted in Chapter 1, research on the effectiveness of new treatments is important to psychopathology. Responses to certain treatments, whether drug or psychological, may indicate the causes of the disorder. We now discuss the benefits and some drawbacks of medication, psychological interventions, and a combination of these two treatments.

Medication

A large number of drugs affecting the noradrenergic, serotonergic, or GABA–benzodiazepine neurotransmitter systems or some combination seem effective in treating panic disorder, including high-potency benzodiazepines, the newer selective-serotonin reuptake inhibitors (SSRIs), such as Prozac and Paxil, and the closely related serotonin-norepinephrine reuptake inhibitors (SNRIs), such as venlafaxine (Barlow, 2002; Pollack, 2005; Pollack & Simon, 2009).

Each class of drugs has advantages and disadvantages. SSRIs are currently the indicated drug for panic disorder based on all available evidence, although sexual dysfunction seems to occur in 75 percent or more of people taking these medications (Lecrubier, Bakker, et al., 1997; Lecrubier, Judge, et al., 1997). On the other hand, high-potency benzodiazepines, such as alprazolam (Xanax), commonly used for panic disorder, work quickly but are hard to stop taking because of dependence. Therefore, they are not recommended as strongly as the SSRIs. All benzodiazepines also adversely affect cognitive and motor functions to some degree. Therefore, people taking them in high doses often find their ability to drive a car or study somewhat reduced. Nevertheless, benzodiazepines remain the most widely used class of drugs in practice (Blanco et al., 2004), and their use continues to increase (Comer, Mojtabai, & Olfson, 2011).

Approximately 60 percent of patients with panic disorder are free of panic as long as they stay on an effective drug (Lecrubier, Bakker, et al., 1997; Pollack & Simon, 2009), but 20 percent or more stop taking the drug before treatment is done (Otto et al., 2009), and relapse rates are high (approximately 50 percent) once the medication is stopped (Hollon et al., 2005). The relapse rate is closer to 90 percent for those who stop taking benzodiazepines (see, e.g., Fyer et al., 1987).

Psychological Intervention

Psychological treatments have proved quite effective for panic disorder. Originally, such treatments concentrated on reducing agoraphobic avoidance, using strategies based on exposure to feared situations. The strategy of exposure-based treatments is to arrange conditions in which the patient can gradually face the feared situations and learn there is nothing to fear. Most patients with phobias are well aware of this rationally, but they must be convinced on an emotional level as well by reality testing the situation and confirming that nothing dangerous happens. Sometimes the therapist accompanies the patients on their exposure exercises. At other times, the therapist simply helps patients structure their own exercises and provides them with a variety of psychological coping mechanisms to help them complete the exercises, which are typically arranged from least to most difficult. A sample of these is listed in Table 5.2.

Gradual exposure exercises, sometimes combined with anxiety-reducing coping mechanisms such as relaxation or breathing retraining, have proved effective in helping patients overcome agoraphobic behaviour whether associated with panic disorder or not (Craske & Barlow, 2014). As many as 70 percent of patients undergoing these treatments substantially improve as their anxiety and panic are reduced and their agoraphobic avoidance is greatly diminished. Few, however, are cured, because many still

TABLE 5.2 | Situation-Exposure Tasks (from Least to Most Difficult)

Shopping in a crowded supermarket for 30 minutes alone

Walking five blocks away from home alone

Driving on a busy highway for five miles [eight kilometres] with spouse and alone

Eating in a restaurant, seated in the middle

Watching a movie while seated in the middle of the row

Source: Mastery of Your Anxiety and Panic (4th ed., p. 133), by D. H. Barlow and M. G. Craske, 2007, Oxford University Press.

© Cengage Learning

experience some anxiety and panic attacks, although at a less severe level.

Effective psychological treatments have recently been developed that treat panic disorder directly even in the absence of agoraphobia (Barlow & Craske, 2007; Clark et al., 1994; Craske & Barlow, 2014). **Panic control treatment (PCT)** developed at one of our clinics concentrates on exposing patients with panic disorder to the cluster of interoceptive sensations that remind them of their panic attacks. The therapist attempts to create "mini" panic attacks in the office by having the patients exercise to elevate their heart rates or perhaps by spinning them in a chair to make them dizzy. A variety of exercises have been developed for this purpose. Patients also receive cognitive therapy. Basic attitudes and perceptions concerning the dangerousness of the feared but objectively harmless situations are identified and modified. As we learned earlier, many of these attitudes and perceptions are beyond the patient's awareness. Uncovering these unconscious cognitive processes requires a great deal of therapeutic skill. In addition to exposure to interoceptive sensations and cognitive therapy, patients are taught relaxation or breathing retraining to help them cope with increases in anxiety and to reduce excess arousal.

These psychological procedures are highly effective for panic disorder. Follow-up studies of patients who receive PCT indicate that most of them remain better after at least two years (Craske & Barlow, 2014; Craske et al., 1991). Remaining agoraphobic behaviour can then be treated with more standard exposure exercises.

Still, some people relapse over time, so our multisite collaborative team began investigating long-term strategies in the treatment of panic disorder, including the usefulness of providing booster sessions after therapy is complete to prevent relapse. In the initial phase, 256 patients with panic disorder with all levels of agoraphobia completed three months of initial treatment with cognitive-behavioural therapy (Aaronson et al., 2008). Those patients who responded very well to treatment were then randomized to nine months of monthly booster sessions ($n = 79$) or no booster sessions ($n = 78$) and then followed for an additional 12 months without treatment (White et al., 2013). Booster sessions produced lower relapse rates (5 percent) and reduced work and social impairment compared with no booster sessions (18 percent) at a 21-month follow-up. Thus, booster sessions aimed at reinforcing acute treatment gains to prevent relapse and offset disorder recurrence improved long-term outcome for panic

disorder and agoraphobia, even in those patients who responded well to treatment initially. Similar treatments have also been successfully used in children (In-Albon & Schneider, 2007) and older adults (Hendriks et al., 2014).

Researchers have also begun attempting to understand which aspects of PCT (i.e., exposure to interoceptive sensations, cognitive therapy, and relaxation and breathing retraining) are the most or least important components of the treatment. For example, as described by Hamilton researchers Martin Antony and Randi McCabe (2002), concerns have been raised about the breathing retraining component of PCT in that it does not seem to add to the effectiveness of PCT and may in fact lead to a poorer outcome for some patients by preventing them from learning that their catastrophic beliefs are unfounded. In a review of the literature, Steven Taylor (2001) recommends that therapists must exercise caution when using breathing retraining to ensure that it is not misused by panic patients as a means of escaping from or avoiding their feared bodily sensations.

Combined Psychological and Drug Treatments

Partly because primary care physicians are usually the first clinicians to treat those suffering from panic disorder, and psychological treatments are not available in those settings, when patients do get referred for psychological treatment, they are often already taking medications. So, important questions are as follows: How do these treatments compare with each other? And do they work together? One major study sponsored by the U.S. National Institute of Mental Health looked at the separate and combined effects of psychological and drug treatments (Barlow et al., 2000). In this double-blind study, patients were randomized into five treatment conditions: Psychological treatment alone (CBT); drug treatment alone (imipramine—IMI—a tricyclic antidepressant, was used because this study was begun before the SSRIs were available); a combined treatment condition (IMI + CBT); and two control conditions, one using placebo alone (PBO), and one using PBO + CBT (to determine the extent to which any advantage for combined treatment was caused by placebo contribution). The data indicate that all treatment groups responded significantly better than the placebo group, but approximately the same number of patients responded to both treatments. Combined treatment was no better than individual treatments. After six additional months of maintenance treatment (nine months after treatment was initiated), during which patients were seen once per month, the results looked much as they did after initial treatment, except there was a slight advantage for combined treatment at this point and the number of people responding to placebo had diminished. A later follow-up, six months after treatment was discontinued (15 months after it was initiated), revealed that patients on medication, whether combined with CBT or not, had deteriorated somewhat, and those receiving CBT without the drug had retained most of their gains (Barlow et al., 2000).

Some studies show that drugs, particularly benzodiazepines, may interfere with the effects of psychological treatments (Craske & Barlow, 2014). Furthermore, benzodiazepines taken over a long period are associated with cognitive impairment (Deckersbach et al., 2011). Because of this, our multisite collaborative team asked whether a sequential strategy in which one treatment was delayed until later and only given to those patients who didn't do as well as hoped would work better than giving both treatments at the same time. In this study, which was the second part of our long-term strategies research described earlier, Payne et al. (2016) studied 58 of the original 256 patients treated with CBT who did not respond adequately to the initial treatment and randomized these patients to a study where they either received continued CBT or the SSRI drug paroxetine. Paroxetine was administered for up to 12 months, whereas the CBT was delivered for three months. At the end of three months, patients receiving paroxetine responded better than those receiving continued CBT, but these differences had disappeared by the one-year follow-up. Specifically, 53 percent of the inadequate responders receiving paroxetine became responders, compared with 33 percent receiving continued CBT, but at 12 months the results were 56 percent and 53 percent, respectively. So clinicians must judge whether the more rapid response among some patients is worth trying drug treatment, given that subsequent improvement will be about the same at a later date. For some patients, the more rapid response will be very important. Others may be less enthusiastic about taking a drug and enduring the potential side effects, knowing that they are likely to improve over time without the drug.

What about those patients already taking drugs? In the primary care setting, adding CBT to the treatment of patients already on medications resulted in significant further improvement compared with those patients on medication who did not have CBT added (Craske et al., 2005). Both of the studies we just discussed indicate that a stepped care approach in which the clinician begins with one treatment and then adds another if needed may be superior to combining treatments from the beginning.

Concept Check	5.3

True (T) or false (F)?

1. _____ Panic disorder without agoraphobia is a disorder in which an individual experiences anxiety and panic with phobic avoidance of what that person considers an unsafe situation.

2. _____ About 40 percent of the population meets the criteria for panic disorder at some point in their lives.

3. _____ Some individuals with panic disorder are suicidal, have nocturnal panic, and/or are agoraphobic.

4. _____ Psychological treatments like PCT or CBT are effective for treating panic disorder.

General conclusions from these studies suggest no advantage to combining drugs and CBT initially for panic disorder and agoraphobia. Furthermore, the psychological treatments seemed to perform better in the long run (six months after treatment had stopped). This suggests the psychological treatment should be offered initially, followed by drug treatment for those patients who do not respond adequately or for whom psychological treatment is not available.

SPECIFIC PHOBIA

Remember Jody in Chapter 1? When he saw a film of the frog being dissected, Jody began feeling queasy. Eventually, he reached the point of fainting if someone simply said "cut it out." Consider next the case of Bob, who has difficulties with flying. Jody and Bob have in common what we call a *specific phobia*.

BOB | *Too Scared to Fly*

Bob was a 29-year-old Caucasian man who worked as a translator. His main complaint was a fear of flying. Although his work as a translator did not necessitate air travel, the places he could travel for vacations were severely limited by his flying phobia. Bob had always been very interested in art and history and he had long dreamed of travelling in Europe. However, his intense fear of flying had prevented him from making the trip.

Bob had tried psychoanalytically oriented psychotherapy mainly to help with his phobia. However, despite being in therapy for six years, he reported that it had not been particularly helpful. Although his overall level of general anxiety was somewhat reduced, his flying phobia remained. He had ended this therapy a year earlier. He was not taking any medications for his anxiety.

Three years earlier, in an attempt to overcome his avoidance behaviour, he had purchased an airline ticket for a round trip from Québec to Paris. He purchased the ticket well in advance of his planned travel dates. However, Bob became increasingly anxious as the day of the trip approached. Eventually, he became so overwhelmed by his anxiety about the flight that he cancelled his trip and returned the ticket to the travel agent. He was even willing to pay a hefty financial penalty for his late cancellation— anything to avoid having to fly!

The therapist learned that Bob had never flown in his lifetime. This provided evidence that his fear of flying was not due to a direct traumatic experience during some previous flight (i.e., his phobia was not acquired through classical conditioning). Instead, it appeared that he had developed his flying phobia from various vicarious sources (e.g., seeing dangerous flights depicted in films or airplane crashes described in the news).

Source: Republished with permission of SAGE Publications, from "In vivo cognitive desensitization of flight phobia: A case study," by R. Ladouceur, *Psychological Reports*, 50, 459–462; permission conveyed through Copyright Clearance Centre, Inc.

CLINICAL DESCRIPTION

A **specific phobia** is an irrational fear of a specific object or situation that markedly interferes with an individual's ability to function. In earlier versions of the *DSM*, this category was called "simple" phobia to distinguish it from the more complex agoraphobia condition, but we now recognize there is nothing simple about it. Many of you might be afraid of something that is not dangerous, such as going to the dentist, or have a greatly exaggerated fear of something that is only mildly dangerous, such as driving a car or flying. For this reason, most people can identify to some extent with a phobia. Surveys indicate that specific fears of a variety of objects or situations occur in a majority of the population (Myers et al., 1984). But the very commonness of fears, even severe fears, often causes people to trivialize the more serious psychological disorder known as a specific phobia. These phobias can be extremely disabling, as we saw with Jody (see DSM Table 5.5).

In contrast to the devastating effects of phobias for some people, for others like Bob, phobias are simply a nuisance—sometimes an extremely inconvenient nuisance, but they can adapt to life with a phobia by simply working around it somehow. Where we live and work, some people are afraid to drive in the snow. We have had people come to our clinics who have been so severely phobic that during the winter they were ready to uproot, change their jobs and their lives, and move to a warmer climate. That is one way of dealing with a phobia. We discuss some other ways at the end of this chapter.

The major characteristic held in common by Jody and Bob, of course, is the *DSM-5* criterion of marked fear and anxiety about a specific object or situation. Both also recognized that their fear and anxiety were out of proportion to any actual danger. Finally, both went to considerable lengths to avoid situations where their phobic response might occur.

The similarities end there. In fact, there are as many phobias as there are objects and situations. The variety of Greek and Latin names contrived to describe phobias stuns the imagination. Table 5.3 gives only the phobias beginning with the letter A from a long list compiled from medical dictionaries and other diverse sources. Of course, this sort of list has little value for people studying psychopathology, but it does show the extent of the named phobias.

Before the publication of *DSM-IV* in 1994, no meaningful classification of specific phobias existed. We have now learned, however, that the cases of Jody and of Bob represent types of specific phobia that differ in major ways. Four major subtypes of specific phobia have been identified: (1) animal type, (2) natural environment type (e.g., heights, storms, and water), (3) blood-injury-injection type, and (4) situational type (such as planes, elevators, or enclosed places). A fifth category, "other," includes phobias that do not fit any of the four major subtypes (e.g., situations that may lead to choking, vomiting, or contracting an illness; or, in children, avoidance of loud sounds or costumed characters). Although this subtyping strategy is useful, we also know that most people who suffer from phobia tend to have multiple phobias of several types (Hofmann et al., 1997; LeBeau et al., 2010).

Blood-Injury-Injection Phobia

How do phobia subtypes differ from each other? We have already seen one major difference in the case of Jody. Rather than the usual surge of activity in the sympathetic nervous system and increased heart rate and blood pressure, Jody experienced a marked drop in heart rate and blood pressure and fainted as a consequence. Many people who have phobias and experience panic attacks in their feared situations report that they feel like they are going to faint but they never do, because their heart rate and blood pressure are actually increasing. Therefore, those with **blood-injury-injection phobias** almost always differ in their physiological reaction from people with other types of phobia (Barlow & Liebowitz, 1995; Hofmann et al., 2009; Öst, 1992). We also noted in Chapter 2 that blood-injury-injection phobia runs in families more strongly than any phobic disorder we know. This is probably because people with this phobia inherit a strong vasovagal response to blood, injury, or the possibility of an injection, all of which cause a drop in blood pressure and a tendency to faint (Grassick, 1990). The phobia develops over the possibility of having this response. The average age of onset for this phobia is approximately nine years (LeBeau et al., 2010).

DSM-5	**Table 5.5** Diagnostic Criteria for Specific Phobia

A. Marked fear or anxiety about a specific object or situation (e.g., flying, heights, animals, receiving an injection, seeing blood).

   Note: In children, the fear or anxiety may be expressed by crying, tantrums, freezing, or clinging.

B. The phobic object or situation almost always provokes immediate fear or anxiety.

C. The phobic object or situation is actively avoided or endured with intense fear or anxiety.

D. The fear or anxiety is out of proportion to the actual danger posed by the specific object or situation and to the sociocultural context.

E. The fear, anxiety, or avoidance is persistent, typically lasting for 6 months or more.

F. The fear, anxiety, or avoidance causes clinically significant distress or impairment in social, occupational, or other important areas of functioning.

G. The disturbance is not better explained by the symptoms of another mental disorder, including fear, anxiety, and avoidance of situations associated with panic-like symptoms or other incapacitating symptoms (as in agoraphobia); objects or situations related to obsessions (as in obsessive-compulsive disorder); reminders of traumatic events (as in post-traumatic stress disorder); separation from home or attachment figures (as in separation anxiety disorder); or social situations (as in social anxiety disorder).

Specify if:

   Animal (e.g., spiders, insects, dogs).

   Natural environment (e.g., heights, storms, water).

   Blood-injection-injury (e.g., needles, invasive medical procedures).

   Situational (e.g., airplanes, elevators, enclosed places).

   Other (e.g., situations that may lead to choking or vomiting; in children, e.g., loud sounds or costumed characters).

TABLE 5.3 | Phobias Beginning with "A"

Term	Fear of
Ablutophobia	Washing, bathing
Achievemephobia	Success
Achluophobia	Darkness, night
Acousticophobia	Sounds; noise
Acrophobia	Heights
Aerophobia	Flying
Agoraphobia	Open or crowded spaces
Agyiophobia	Crossing the street
Aichmophobia	Needles sharp pointed objects; knives
Ailurophobia	Cats
Algophobia	Pain
Amaxophobia	Riding in a car
Ancraophobia	Wind
Androphobia	Men
Anginophobia	Angina pectoris (brief attacks of chest pain); choking or narrowness
Anatidaephobia	Ducks
Anthropophobia	People or society
Anthrophobia	Flowers
Aphephobia	Physical contact, being touched
Apiphobia	Bees, bee stings
Aphenphosmphobia	Intimacy
Arachnophobia	Spiders
Astraphobia	Thunder, lightning
Atelophobia	Imperfection
Athaazagoraphobia	Being forgotten, ignored, forgetting
Atychiphobia	Failure
Automysophobia	Being dirty
Aviophobia	Flying

Sources: *The Phobias List* (http://phobialist.com); *Phobia List—The Ultimate List of Phobias and Fears* (https://www.fearof.net/); *List of Phobias, Common and Unique Fears Explained*, Healthline (http://healthline.com/health/list-of-phobias).

Situational Phobia

Phobias characterized by fear of public transportation or enclosed places are called **situational phobias**. Claustrophobia, a fear of small, enclosed places (see Radomsky et al., 2001), is situational, as is a phobia of planes (Ladouceur, 1982). Situational phobia, as with panic disorder and agoraphobia, tends to emerge around age 20 to 25 and has been shown to run in families (Craske et al., 2006; Curtis et al., 1990; LeBeau et al., 2010). The main difference between situational phobia and panic disorder with agoraphobia is that people with situational phobia never experience panic attacks outside the context of their phobic object or situation (Antony et al., 1997a, 1997b). Therefore, they can relax when they don't have to confront their phobic situation.

Natural Environment Phobia

Sometimes very young people develop fears of situations or events occurring in nature. These fears are called **natural environment phobias**. The major examples are heights, storms, and water. These fears also seem to cluster together (Antony & Barlow, 2002; Hofmann et al., 1997): If you fear one situation or event, such as deep water, you are likely to fear another, such as storms. Many of these situations have some danger associated with them and, therefore, mild to moderate fear can be very adaptive. For example, we should be careful in a high place or in deep water. It is entirely possible that we are somewhat prepared to be afraid of these situations; as we discussed in Chapter 2, something in our genetic makeup makes us very sensitive to these situations if any sign of danger is present. In any case, these phobias have a peak age of onset of about seven years. They are not phobias if they are only passing fears. They have to be persistent (lasting at least six months) and interfere substantially with the person's functioning, leading to avoidance of boat trips or summer vacations in the mountains where there might be a storm.

Animal Phobia

Fears of animals and insects are called **animal phobias**. Once again, these fears are common but become phobic only if severe interference with functioning occurs. For example, we have seen cases in our clinic where people with snake or mice phobias are unable to read magazines for fear of unexpectedly coming across a picture of one of these animals. There are many places that these people are unable to go, even if they want to very much, such as to the country to visit someone. The fear experienced by people with animal phobias is very different from an ordinary mild revulsion. The age of onset for these phobias, like that of natural environment phobias, peaks at around seven years (Antony et al., 1997a; LeBeau et al., 2010).

Other Phobias

Several additional types of phobias appear in considerable numbers and can cause substantial problems. For example, if you are afraid of contracting a disease and go to excessive and irrational lengths to avoid exposure to that disease, you may have an *illness phobia*. In these cases, the individuals do not believe they have the disease but are afraid they might acquire it in any number of ways (Barlow & Liebowitz, 1995; Craske et al., 1996). When this fear occurs in severe form it can be very incapacitating, because individuals with illness phobia may avoid all contact with people or places where they might catch something (Asmundson & Taylor, 2005; Taylor & Asmundson, 2004). Illness phobia likely became more prevalent during the SARS

▲ People who develop a natural environment phobia intensely fear such places as heights and such events as lightning.

TABLE 5.4 | Prevalence of Intense Fears and Phobias

Intense Fear	Prevalence per 1000 Population	Sex Distribution (% F)
Snakes	253	76
Heights	120	54
Flying	109	67
Enclosures	50	66
Illness	33	53
Death	33	31
Injury	23	48
Storms	31	84
Dentists	24	54
Journeys alone	16	100
Being alone	10	72

Phobia	Prevalence per 1000 Population*	Sex Distribution (% F)
Illness/Injury	31 (42%)	64
Storms	13 (18%)	100
Animals	11 (14%)	75
Agoraphobia	6 (8%)	46
Death	5 (7%)	60
Crowds	4 (5%)	75
Heights	4 (5%)	0

*Percentage total of those with phobias are in parentheses.

Source: Adapted, with permission, from Agras, W. S., Sylvester, D., & Oliveau, D. (1969). The epidemiology of common fears and phobias. *Comprehensive Psychiatry*, 10, 151–156, © 1969 Elsevier.

epidemic, just as it became more prevalent during the AIDS epidemic (McCabe, 2003). During the SARS epidemic, some people who had no reason to believe they would contract SARS avoided public gatherings, restaurants, and any contact whatsoever with strangers who displayed signs of a cold (or people who had recently travelled to China or Toronto) for fear of contracting the disease (Cheng & Tang, 2004; Lee-Baggley et al., 2004; McCabe, 2003). Illness phobia can also resemble other disorders, such as obsessive-compulsive disorder or illness anxiety disorder, but is sufficiently different to be classified as a type of specific phobia. We return to this issue when we discuss these two disorders.

STATISTICS

Specific fears occur in a majority of people. The ones most commonly found in the population at large are presented in Table 5.4. Not surprisingly, fears of snakes and heights rank near the top. Notice also that the sex ratio among common fears is overwhelmingly female with a couple of exceptions. Among these exceptions is fear of heights, for which the sex ratio is approximately equal. Very few people who report specific fears

qualify as having a phobia, but for approximately 6.4 percent of the Canadian population, their fears are at some point severe enough to be classified as disorders and earn the label "phobia" (Offord et al., 1996). As with common fears, the sex ratio for specific phobias is overwhelmingly female. In the Offord et al. survey of Ontarians ages 15 to 64, the lifetime prevalence rate was about twice as high in women as in men (i.e., 8.9 percent for women and 4.1 percent for men). Once a phobia develops, it tends to run a chronic course (i.e., last a lifetime; Antony et al., 1997; McCabe & Antony, 2002; Rowa et al., 2006).

As noted by leading anxiety investigator Martin Antony of Ryerson University, specific phobias represent an interesting paradox (Antony & Barlow, 2002). Despite the fact that specific phobia is a common, treatable, and well-understood condition, people with this condition present for treatment only rarely. For example, Antony and Barlow (2002) report that of a sample of

522 patients with anxiety disorders referred to a Canadian anxiety disorders clinic, only 6 percent received a principal diagnosis of specific phobia. Diagnoses of panic disorder, social anxiety disorder, and obsessive-compulsive disorder were much more common as primary diagnoses.

Thus, even though phobias may interfere with an individual's functioning, only the most severe cases actually come for treatment, because affected people tend to work around their phobias. For example, someone with a fear of heights arranges her life so she never has to be in a tall building or other high places, just as Bob arranged his life so that he never had to fly. People with situational phobias of such things as driving or small, enclosed places most frequently come for treatment. However, we have reason to believe that blood-injury-injection phobias are quite prevalent in the population (Agras et al., 1969; Myers et al., 1984); people with this phobia might seek help if they knew good treatments were available.

Although most anxiety disorders look much the same in adults and children, clinicians must be very aware of the types of normal fears and anxieties experienced throughout childhood so they can distinguish them from specific phobias (Albano et al., 1996; King, 1993; Silverman & Rabian, 1993). Infants, for example, show marked fear of loud noises and strangers. At one to two years of age, children quite normally are very anxious about separating from parents, and fears of animals and the dark also develop and may persist into the fourth or fifth year of life. Fear of various monsters and other imaginary creatures may begin at about age three and last for several years. At age ten, children may fear evaluation by others and feel anxiety over their physical appearance. Generally, reports of fear decline with age, although performance-related fears of such activities as taking a test or talking in front of a large group may increase with age. Specific phobias seem to decline with old age (Ayers et al., 2009; Blazer, George, et al., 1991; Sheikh, 1992).

The prevalence of specific phobias varies from one culture to another. A variant of phobia in Chinese cultures is called *Pa-leng*, sometimes *frigo* phobia or "fear of the cold." *Pa-leng* can be understood only in the context of traditional ideas—in this case the Chinese concept of yin and yang (Tan, 1980). Chinese medicine holds that there must be a balance of yin and yang forces in the body for health to be maintained. Yin represents the cold, dark, windy, energy-sapping aspects of life; yang refers to the warm, bright, energy-producing aspects of life. Individuals with *Pa-leng* have a morbid fear of the cold. They ruminate over loss of body heat and may wear several layers of clothing even on a hot day. They may complain of belching and flatulence, which indicate the presence of wind and therefore of too much yin in the body.

CAUSES

For a long time we thought that most specific phobias began with an unusual traumatic event. For example, if you were bitten by a dog, you developed a phobia of dogs. We now know this is not necessarily the case (Barlow, 2002; Craske et al., 2006). This is not to say that traumatic conditioning experiences do not result in subsequent phobic behaviour. Almost every person with a choking phobia has had some kind of a choking experience.

An individual with claustrophobia who recently came to our clinic reported being trapped in an elevator for an extraordinarily long time. These are examples of phobias acquired by direct experience, where real danger or pain results in an alarm response (a true alarm). As noted by Rachman (1977), such direct conditioning is merely one way of developing a phobia. He notes that there are at least two other pathways: observing someone else experience severe fear (vicarious experience) or, under the right conditions, being told about danger. In fact, vicarious and informational transmission of fears can take place in the absence of any direct contact with the phobic object or situation.

People develop phobias in at least one other way: by experiencing a false alarm (panic attack) in a specific situation. Remember our earlier discussion of unexpected panic attacks? Studies show that many people with phobias do not necessarily experience a true alarm resulting from real danger at the onset of their phobia. Many initially have an unexpected panic attack in a specific situation, related, perhaps, to current life stress. A phobia of that situation may then develop. This was evident in a study with driving phobia (Ehlers et al., 1994). Although only a minority (14 percent) met criteria for panic disorder, the majority (81 percent) of people with excessive fear of driving an automobile reported having had panic attacks. When asked about the primary reason for their phobia, only 15 percent attributed it to an accident, whereas 53 percent attributed it to the possibility of having panic attacks. These people were also more concerned about anxiety symptoms while driving than phobic patients who gave other, non-accident-related reasons for their driving phobia.

We also learn fears vicariously. Seeing someone else have a traumatic experience or endure intense fear may be enough to instill a phobia in the watcher. Emotions are very contagious. If someone you are with is either happy or fearful, you will probably feel a tinge of happiness or fear also. This has been illustrated in a study with 8- to 11-year-old children who watched a short, 80s animated film clip of a person trying to score in basketball as part of a try out for a basketball team while being evaluated by judges (Askew et al., 2015). In one of the films the outcome was neutral; the animated person threw the ball into the basket with positive thoughts appearing in a thought cloud and a neutral expression as if it was a routine practice. In the other film clip, the person missed the basket, slipped, and fell while negative thoughts appeared in a thought cloud. After watching these clips, the children filled out a questionnaire asking them how fearful they thought they would feel in similar performance situations. Results showed that, compared with children who watched the neutral film clip, those who watched the negative film clip with the negative outcome expected that they would feel more fearful. They also showed a greater attention bias toward social threat, which was measured with an emotion Stroop task in which children were asked to name the colour of threating words, such as "audience" or "criticize" (rather than naming the word). This suggests that fear can be acquired through vicarious learning even after watching a brief film clip. Sometimes just being warned repeatedly about a potential danger is sufficient for someone to develop a phobia (Muris & Field, 2010). We call this mode of developing a phobia *information transmission*.

A true phobia also requires anxiety over the possibility of another extremely traumatic event or false alarm. Remember, when we are anxious, we persistently anticipate something terrible, and we are likely to avoid situations where that terrible thing might occur. If we don't develop anxiety, our reaction would presumably be in the category of normal fears experienced by more than half the population. Normal fear can cause mild distress, but it is usually ignored and forgotten. A diagram of the etiology of specific phobia is presented in ■ Figure 5.6.

In summary, several things have to occur for a person to develop a phobia. First, a traumatic conditioning experience often plays a role (even hearing about a frightening event is sufficient for some individuals). Second, fear is more likely to develop if we are "prepared"; that is, we seem to carry an inherited tendency to fear situations that have been dangerous to humans over evolutionary time, such as being threatened by wild animals or trapped in small places. Third, we also have to be susceptible to developing anxiety by focusing on the possibility that the event will happen again.

Finally, social and cultural factors are very strong determinants of who ultimately develops and reports a specific phobia. In most societies around the world, it is almost unacceptable for males to express fears and phobias. Thus, the overwhelming majority of reported specific phobias occur in women. What happens to the males? Very possibly they work hard to overcome their fears by repeatedly exposing themselves to their feared situations. Another more likely possibility is that they simply endure their fears

without telling anyone about them and without seeking any treatment (Antony & Barlow, 2002). Pierce and Kirkpatrick (1992) asked male and female college students to report their fears on two occasions before watching a videotape of something frightening. Before the second evaluation, subjects were told their heart rate would be monitored to assess the "truthfulness" of their report. Reports from women were the same on both occasions, but men reported substantially more fear when it was important to be truthful.

TREATMENT

Although the development of phobias is relatively complex, the treatment is fairly straightforward. Almost everyone agrees that specific phobias require structured and consistent exposure-based exercises. This approach was used successfully by Ladouceur (1982) in the treatment of Bob's flying phobia (described earlier). At a follow-up 14 months after his treatment had ended, Bob had made two overseas trips without any incapacitating anxiety. Nevertheless, most patients who expose themselves gradually to what they fear must be under therapeutic supervision. As was illustrated in Bob's case, individuals who attempt to carry out the exercises alone often attempt to do too much too soon and end up escaping the situation, which may strengthen the phobia. In addition, if a patient fears having another unexpected panic attack in this situation, it is helpful to direct therapy at panic attacks in the manner described for panic disorder

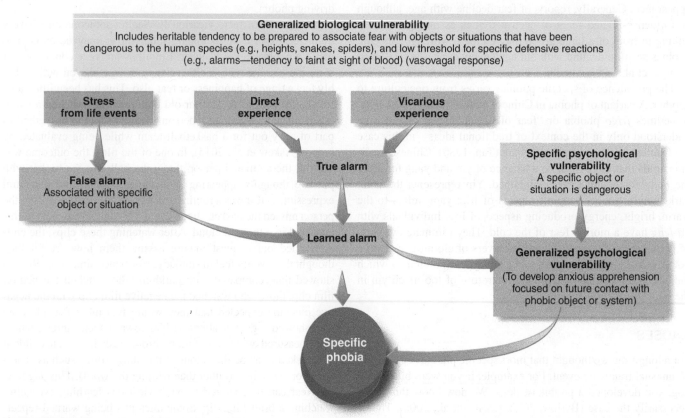

FIGURE 5.6 | A model of the various ways a specific phobia may develop.

Source: Republished with permission of Guilford Publications, from *Anxiety and Its Disorders: The Nature and Treatment of Anxiety and Panic* by Barlow, David H. © 2019; permission conveyed through Copyright Clearance Center, Inc.

(Antony et al., 2006; Craske et al., 2006). In cases of blood-injury-injection phobia, where fainting is a real possibility, graduated exposure-based exercises must be done in specific ways. Individuals must tense various muscle groups during exposure exercises to keep their blood pressure sufficiently high to complete the practice (Ayala et al., 2009; Öst & Sterner, 1987).

New developments make it possible to treat many specific phobias, including blood phobia, in a single session taking anywhere from approximately two to six hours (e.g., Antony et al., 2006; Craske et al., 2006; Hauner et al., 2012; Oar et al., 2015; Öst et al., 2001). Basically, the therapist spends most of the session with the individual, working through exposure exercises with the phobia object or situation. The patient then practises approaching the phobic situation at home, checking in occasionally with the therapist. It is interesting that in these cases not only does the phobia disappear, but in blood phobia the tendency to experience the vasovagal response at the sight of blood also lessens considerably. It is now clear based on brain-imaging work that these treatments change brain functioning in an enduring way by modifying neural circuitry in such areas as the amygdala, insula, and cingulate cortex (Hauner et al., 2012). After treatment, responsiveness is diminished in this fear-sensitive network but increased in prefrontal cortical areas, suggesting that more rational appraisals were inhibiting emotional appraisals of danger. Thus, these treatments "rewire" the brain (Paquette et al., 2003).

A new approach to the treatment of phobias is virtual reality exposure therapy. Virtual reality technology has recently gained interest as an effective medium for administering exposure therapy by putting phobic patients into an environment that simulates their real-world feared situation (Robillard et al., 2003; Rothbaum et al., 1997). The Cyberpsychology Lab at the University du Québec en Outaouais is an interdisciplinary laboratory involved in some of the most innovative virtual reality phobia treatment research in the world. Several studies have shown this new form of exposure therapy to be effective in the treatment of phobias of heights, spiders, flying, and small spaces (reviewed in Wald & Taylor, 2000). In vivo exposure therapy has some risks and limitations in the treatment of driving phobia (e.g., real-world driving situations are unpredictable and hard to control, presenting difficulties in allowing for graduated exposure to increasingly more anxiety-provoking driving situations). These risks and limitations make virtual reality a promising alternative modality for treating driving phobias.

Separation Anxiety Disorder

All the anxiety disorders described in this chapter may occur during childhood, and one additional anxiety disorder is unique to children. **Separation anxiety disorder** is characterized by a child's unrealistic and persistent worry that something will happen to his or her parents or other important people in the child's life, or that something will happen to the child himself or herself that will separate him or her from his or her parents (e.g., the child will be lost or hurt in an accident). The child often refuses to go to school or to leave home, not because the child is afraid of school but because he or she is afraid of separating from loved ones. These fears can result in nightmares involving possible separation and by physical symptoms, distress, and anxiety (Barlow et al., 2003).

Of course, all young children experience separation anxiety to some extent; this fear usually decreases as the child grows older. Therefore, a clinician must judge whether the separation anxiety is greater than would be expected at that particular age (Barlow et al., 2003; Ollendick & Huntzinger, 1990). It is also important to differentiate separation anxiety from school phobia.

© Sasiistock/iStock

▲ A child with separation anxiety disorder persistently worries that parting with an important person drastically endangers either the loved one or the child.

In school phobia, the fear is clearly focused on something specific to the school situation; the child can leave the parents or other attachment figures to go somewhere other than school. In separation anxiety, the act of separating from the parent or attachment figure provokes anxiety and fear. There is now evidence that separation anxiety, if untreated, can extend into adulthood in approximately 35 percent of cases (Shear et al., 2006). Furthermore, very recent evidence suggests that we have overlooked this disorder in adults and that it occurs in approximately 7 percent of the adult population over the lifetime (Shear et al., 2006). In some cases, the onset is in adulthood rather than carrying over from childhood. The focus of anxiety in adults is the same: That harm may befall loved ones during separation (Manicavasagar et al., 2010; Silove et al., 2010).

For the treatment of separation anxiety, parents are often included to help structure the exercises and also to address parental reaction to childhood anxiety (Choate et al., 2005). More recently, an intensive one-week program for girls ages 8 to 11 developed at one of our clinics in which the girls end up having a sleepover at the clinic has proved highly successful (Pincus et al., 2008; Santucci et al., 2009).

SOCIAL ANXIETY DISORDER (SOCIAL PHOBIA)

STEVE AND CHUCK | *Star Players?*

In the second inning of an All-Star game, Los Angeles Dodger second baseman Steve Sax fielded an easy grounder, straightened up for the lob to first, and bounced the ball past first baseman Al Oliver, who was less than 12 metres away. It was a startling error, especially in an All-Star game. But hard-core baseball fans knew it was one more manifestation of a leading mystery of the 1983 season: Sax, 23, the National League Rookie of the Year, could not seem to make routine throws to first base. (Of his first 27 errors that season, 22 were bad throws.)

Chuck Knoblauch won the Golden Glove Award in 1997 but led the league in errors in 1999 with 26, most of them throwing errors. Announcers and reporters observed that his throws would be hard and on target to first base if he made a difficult play and had to quickly turn and throw the ball "without thinking about it." But if he fielded a routine ground ball and had time to think about the accuracy of his throw, he would throw awkwardly and slowly—and often off target. The announcers and reporters concluded that, because his arm seemed fine on the difficult plays, his problem must be "mental." For the 2001 season, he was moved to left field to avoid having to make that throw and by 2003 was out of baseball.

Are you shy? If so, you have something in common with 20 to 50 percent of university students, depending on which survey you read. In fact, the vast majority of university students experience symptoms of anxiety in social situations from time to time (Purdon et al., 2001). A much smaller number of people, who suffer severely around others, have **social anxiety disorder (SAD)**, also called social phobia. Consider the case of Billy, a 13-year-old boy.

BILLY | *Too Shy*

Billy was the model boy at home. He did his homework, stayed out of trouble, obeyed his parents, and was generally so quiet and reserved he didn't attract much attention. However, when he got to junior high school, something his parents had noticed earlier became painfully evident. Billy had no friends. He was unwilling to attend social or sporting activities connected with school, even though most of the other kids in his class went to these events. When his parents decided to check with the guidance counsellor, they found that she had been about to call them. She reported that Billy did not socialize or speak up in class and was sick to his stomach all day if he knew he was going to be called on. His teachers had difficulty getting anything more than a yes or no answer from him. More troublesome was that he had been found hiding in a stall in the boys' washroom during lunch, which he said he had been doing for several months instead of eating. After Billy was referred to our clinic, we diagnosed a severe case of SAD, an irrational and extreme fear of social situations. Billy's disorder took the form of extreme shyness. He was afraid of being embarrassed or humiliated in the presence of almost everyone except his parents.

CLINICAL DESCRIPTION

SAD is more than exaggerated shyness (Morrison & Heimberg, 2013). The cases described here are typical of many that appear occasionally in the press over the years. Whereas Knoblauch continued to struggle, Sax overcame his problems. Many other athletes are not so fortunate. This problem is not limited to athletes but is also experienced by well-known lecturers and performers. Actress Scarlett Johansson avoided doing Broadway for many years because of intolerable performance anxiety, in this case also called "stage fright." The inability of a skilled athlete to throw a baseball to first base or a seasoned performer to appear on stage certainly does not match the concept of "shyness" with which we are all familiar. Many of these performers may well be among our more gregarious citizens. And what if when you're with other people you continually worry about a physical reaction you have that is very noticeable to others, but difficult to control? What if you blush to the extent that you're so embarrassed that you can't socialize? Or if your palms sweat so much that you're reluctant to shake hands?

What holds these seemingly different conditions together within the category of SAD? Billy, Knoblauch, Sax, and Johansson (and anyone who worries about blushing or sweating excessively) all experienced marked fear or anxiety focused on one or more social or performance situations. In Billy's case, these situations were any in which he might have to interact with people. For Knoblauch and Johansson, they were specific to performing some special behaviour in public. Individuals with just performance anxiety, which is a subtype of SAD, usually have no difficulty with social interaction, but when they must do something specific in front of people, anxiety takes over and they focus on the possibility that they will embarrass themselves. The most common type of performance anxiety, to which most people can relate, is public speaking. Other situations that commonly provoke performance anxiety are eating in a restaurant or signing a paper or cheque in front of a person or people who are watching. Anxiety-provoking physical reactions include blushing, sweating, trembling, or, for males when urinating in a public restroom, "bashful bladder" or paruresis. Males with this problem must wait until a stall is available, a difficult task at times. What these examples have in common is that the individual is very anxious only while others are present and maybe watching and, to some extent, evaluating their behaviour. This is truly SAD because the people have no difficulty eating, writing, or urinating in private. Only when others are watching does the behaviour deteriorate. DSM Table 5.6 outlines the criteria for SAD.

STATISTICS

According to the National Comorbidity Survey in the United States, as many as 13.3 percent of the general population experience SAD at some point in their lives (Kessler et al., 1994). This makes SAD the most prevalent psychological disorder in the United States. Similarly, high rates of SAD were revealed in a Canadian community survey by Stein, Torgrud, and Walker (2000). They interviewed about 2000 people in Winnipeg, Calgary, Edmonton, and rural Alberta and found a one-year prevalence of 7.2 percent for SAD. According to the 2002 CCHS—Mental Health and Wellness, 8.1 percent of Canadians reported SAD at one point in their lifetime, with 3 percent indicating they had experienced SAD during the past year (Shields, 2004). The sex ratio favours females only somewhat (1.4:1.0), unlike other anxiety disorders where females predominate more drastically (Magee et al., 1996; see also Somers et al., 2006). This distribution differs a bit from the sex ratio of people with SAD who appear at clinics, which is nearly 50–50 (Hofmann & Barlow, 2002; Marks, 1985), suggesting that males may seek help more frequently, perhaps because of career-related issues.

SAD usually begins during adolescence, with a peak age of onset at about 15 years. SAD also tends to be more prevalent in people who are young (18 to 29 years), undereducated, single, and of low socioeconomic class. Many of these findings were demonstrated with the 2002 CCHS data (Shields, 2004). Prevalence declines slightly among seniors (Magee et al., 1996; Sheikh, 1992). Considering their difficulty meeting people, it is not surprising that a greater percentage of individuals with

DSM-5	**Table 5.6** Diagnostic Criteria for Social Anxiety Disorder (Social Phobia)

A. Marked fear or anxiety about one or more social situations in which the person is exposed to possible scrutiny by others. Examples include social interactions (e.g., having a conversation; meeting unfamiliar people), being observed (e.g., eating or drinking), or performing in front of others (e.g., giving a speech).

Note: In children, the anxiety must occur in peer settings and not just during interactions with adults.

B. The individual fears that he or she will act in a way or show anxiety symptoms that will be negatively evaluated (i.e., will be humiliating, embarrassing, will lead to rejection or offend others).

C. The social situations almost always provoke fear or anxiety.

Note: In children, the fear or anxiety may be expressed by crying, tantrums, freezing, clinging, shrinking, or failing to speak in social situations.

D. The social situations are avoided or endured with intense fear or anxiety.

E. The fear or anxiety is out of proportion to the actual threat posed by the social situation and to the sociocultural context.

F. The fear, anxiety, or avoidance is persistent, typically lasting for 6 months or more.

G. The fear, anxiety, or avoidance causes clinically significant distress or impairment in social, occupational, or other important areas of functioning.

H. The fear, anxiety, or avoidance is not attributable to the physiological effects of a substance (e.g., a drug of abuse, a medication) or another medical condition.

I. The fear, anxiety, or avoidance is not better explained by the symptoms of another mental disorder, such as panic disorder, body dysmorphic disorder, or autism spectrum disorder.

J. If another medical condition (e.g., Parkinson's disease, obesity, disfigurement from burns or injury) is present, the fear, anxiety, or avoidance is clearly unrelated or is excessive.

Specify if:

Performance only: If the fear is restricted to speaking or performing in public.

SAD are single than in the population at large. The Ontario Mental Health Survey further suggests that individuals with this disorder are more likely to drop out of school (Stein & Kean, 2000).

SAD distributes relatively equally among different ethnic groups (Magee et al., 1996). In a cross-national study of the rates of SAD in Canada, the United States, Puerto Rico, and Korea, the authors found that the lifetime prevalence of the disorder was quite similar across the four countries surveyed. They did find, however, some different expressions of SAD cross-culturally (Weissman et al., 1996). In the United States, white Americans are typically more likely to be diagnosed with SAD (as well as GAD and panic disorder) than African Americans, Hispanic Americans, and Asian Americans (Asnaani et al., 2010). Cross-national data suggest that Asian cultures show the lowest rates of SAD, whereas Russian and U.S. samples show the highest rates

(Hofmann, Asnaani, & Hinton, 2010). In Japan, the clinical presentation of anxiety disorders is best summarized under the label *shinkeishitsu*. One of the most common subcategories is referred to as *taijin kyōfushō*, which resembles SAD in some of its forms (Dinnel et al., 2002). Japanese people with this form of SAD strongly fear embarrassing others, because they believe some aspect of their personal presentation (blushing, stuttering, body odour, etc.) will appear reprehensible. Thus, the focus of anxiety in this disorder is on offending or embarrassing others rather than embarrassing themselves, as in SAD. Japanese males with this disorder outnumber females by a three-to-two ratio (Takahasi, 1989). More recently, it has been established that this syndrome is found in many cultures around the world but predominantly in Asian cultures (Vriends et al., 2013). Nevertheless, one manifestation of this set of symptoms called "olfactory reference syndrome" has even been reported in North America (Feusner et al., 2010). The key feature once again is preoccupation with a belief that one is embarrassing oneself and offending others with a foul body odour. As such, it seems to resemble obsessive-compulsive disorder (discussed shortly) more than SAD, and seems to respond to psychological treatments used to treat obsessive-compulsive disorder (Martin-Pichora & Antony, 2011).

Although it makes intuitive sense that cross-cultural differences in social norms may relate to differences in the extent of social anxiety, cultural factors are rarely investigated in research on SAD. Heinrichs and her colleagues (2006) conducted a cross-cultural study that showed that collectivistic countries (e.g., Japan, Spain, and Korea) were more accepting toward socially reticent and withdrawn behaviours than were individualistic countries (e.g., Canada, Australia, the Netherlands, Germany, and the United States). Collectivistic countries also reported more social anxiety and greater fear of blushing. The more that attention-avoiding behaviours were accepted in a given culture, the greater were the levels of social anxiety. These fascinating results suggest that variations in SAD rates across countries may be related to differences in cultural norms (Heinrichs et al., 2006).

CAUSES

We have noted that we seem to be prepared to fear certain wild animals and dangerous situations in the natural environment. Similarly, it seems we are also prepared to fear angry, critical, or rejecting people (Blair et al., 2008; Mineka & Zinbarg, 2006; Mogg et al., 2004). In a series of studies, Öhman and colleagues (e.g., Dimberg & Öhman, 1983; Öhman & Dimberg, 1978) noted that we learn more quickly to fear angry expressions than other facial expressions, and this fear diminishes much more slowly than other types of learning. Lundh and Öst (1996) demonstrated that people with SAD who saw a number of pictures of faces were likely to remember critical expressions. Mogg and colleagues (2004) showed that socially anxious individuals more quickly recognized angry faces than nonanxious individuals, who themselves remembered the accepting expressions. Other studies show that individuals with SAD react to angry faces with greater activation of the amygdala and less cortical control or regulation than

nonanxious individuals (Goldin et al., 2009; Stein, Goldin, et al., 2002). Fox and Damjanovic (2006) demonstrated that the eye region specifically is the threatening area of the face.

Why should we inherit a tendency to fear angry faces? Our ancestors probably avoided hostile, angry, domineering people who might attack or kill them. In fact, in all species, dominant, aggressive individuals high in the social hierarchy tend to be avoided. Possibly, individuals who avoided people with angry faces were more likely to survive and pass their genes down to us.

Jerome Kagan and his colleagues (see, for example, Kagan, 2014a, 2014b) have demonstrated that some infants are born with a temperamental profile or trait of inhibition or shyness that is evident as early as four months of age. Four-month-old infants with this trait become more agitated and cry more frequently when presented with toys or other age-appropriate stimuli than infants without the trait. There is now evidence that individuals with excessive behavioural inhibition are at increased risk for developing phobic behaviour (Essex et al., 2010).

A model of the etiology of SAD would look somewhat like models of panic disorder and specific phobia. Three pathways to SAD are possible, as depicted in ■ Figure 5.7. First, someone could inherit a generalized biological vulnerability to develop anxiety, a biological tendency to be socially inhibited, or both. The existence of a generalized psychological vulnerability—such as the belief that events, particularly stressful events, are potentially uncontrollable—would increase an individual's vulnerability. When under stress, a person could have anxiety and self-focused attention could increase to the point of disrupting performance, even in the absence of a false alarm (panic attack). Second, when under stress, someone might have an unexpected panic attack in a social situation that would become associated (conditioned) to social cues. The individual would then become anxious about having additional panic attacks in the same or similar social situations. Third, someone might experience a real social trauma resulting in a true alarm. Anxiety would then develop (be conditioned) in the same or similar social situations. Traumatic social experiences may also extend back to difficult periods in childhood. Early adolescence—usually ages 12 through 15—is when children may be brutally taunted by peers who are attempting to assert their own dominance. This experience may produce anxiety and panic that are reproduced in future social situations. For example, McMaster University researchers McCabe, Anthony, Summerfeldt, Liss, and Swinson (2003) noted that 92 percent of adults with SAD in their sample experienced severe teasing and bullying in childhood, compared with only 35 to 50 percent among people with other anxiety disorders. Such developmental experiences may produce anxiety

▲ University of British Columbia psychologist Lynn Alden has conducted important work on the interpersonal aspects of SAD.

Courtesy of Lynn E. Alden

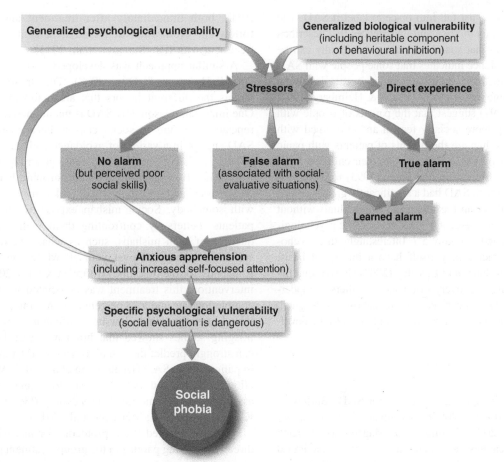

FIGURE 5.7 | A model of the various ways social anxiety disorder may develop.

Source: Republished with permission of Guilford Publications, from *Anxiety and Its Disorders: The Nature and Treatment of Anxiety and Panic* by Barlow, David H. © 2019; permission conveyed through Copyright Clearance Center, Inc.

and panic that are reproduced in future social situations and might also lead them to develop biased perceptions about the likelihood that others will treat them similarly in the future (Alden, 2001; Taylor & Alden, 2005).

University of British Columbia researcher Lynn Alden is a leading expert in interpersonal processes that contribute to SAD. She has outlined an interpersonal transaction cycle whereby individuals' interactions with people in their social environment contribute to and maintain social anxiety. More specifically, people with SAD have biased social perceptions and expectations that lead them to behave in certain maladaptive ways in social situations. The social behaviour of the socially anxious person in turn elicits negative reactions from others, which confirms the biased perceptions (see Alden & Taylor, 2004, for a review).

Alden and others have conducted considerable research on the various aspects of this hypothesized interpersonal cycle. For example, in some situations, people with SAD incorrectly interpret others' behaviour as cold or unfriendly (Alden & Wallace, 1995) and they selectively attend to negative social information (Asmundson & Stein, 1994) and to anxiety-related symptoms that are noticeable to others, such as blushing (Specto et al., 2003). People with SAD also make more "upward

comparisons" (i.e., assessments that someone else is superior to them) and fewer "downward comparisons" than others, and that the upward comparisons that people with SAD make cause them more anxiety and distress (Antony et al., 2005). Although people with SAD do not always show maladaptive social behaviour, in certain situations they do. For example, when they are faced with a critical, controlling person, people who have SAD avert their eyes, talk less, and engage in less personal disclosure (Alden et al., 1995; Meleshko & Alden, 1993). In turn, this behaviour evokes distinct negative reactions from other people: Socially anxious individuals are rated more negatively by others on a variety of measures (Ashbaugh et al., 2005), including being rated as less intelligent by peers during social interactions (Paulhus & Morgan, 1997), and other people are less likely to desire future interactions with a socially anxious person after a first encounter (Meleshko & Alden, 1993; Papsdorf & Alden, 1998). Even when socially anxious individuals are not rated more negatively by others, they are perceived less accurately—thus, they are more difficult to get to know (Aiken et al., 2014). These reactions from other people likely loop back to reinforce the biased social perceptions of people with social anxiety. And so the cycle continues.

But one more factor must fall into place to label it SAD. The individual with the vulnerabilities and experiences just described must also have learned that social evaluation specifically can be dangerous. In fact, evidence indicates that some people with SAD are predisposed to focusing their anxiety on events involving social evaluation. Some investigators (Bruch & Heimberg, 1994; Rapee & Melville, 1997) suggest that the parents of people with SAD are significantly more socially fearful and concerned with the opinions of others than are the parents of patients with panic disorder and that they pass this concern on to their children. Fyer, Mannuzza, Chapman, Liebowitz, and Klein (1993) reported that the relatives of people with SAD had a significantly greater risk of developing the disorder than the relatives of individuals without SAD (16 percent versus 5 percent)—thus, the specific psychological vulnerability depicted in Figure 5.7. Interestingly, this psychological vulnerability factor may itself have a biological basis. A twin study by Stein, Jang, and Livesley (2002) showed that the tendency to fear being negatively evaluated by others is moderately heritable. Thus, as you can see, a combination of biological, psychological, and interpersonal events seem to lead to the development of SAD.

TREATMENT

Effective treatments have been developed for SAD (Barlow & Lehman, 1996; Hofmann, 2007b; Hofmann & Otto, 2008; Hofmann & Smits, 2008; Heimberg & Magee, 2014). Rick Heimberg and colleagues developed a cognitive-behavioural group therapy program in which groups of patients rehearse or role-play their socially phobic situations in front of one another (Heimberg et al., 1990; Turk et al., 2008). The group members participate in the role-playing, for example, acting as an audience for someone who has extreme difficulty giving a speech. At the same time, the therapist conducts rather intensive cognitive therapy aimed at uncovering and changing the automatic or unconscious perceptions of danger that the socially phobic client assumes to exist. These treatments have proven to be more effective than comparison treatments involving education about anxiety and social phobia and social support for stressful life events. More important, a follow-up after five years indicates that the therapeutic gains are maintained (Heimberg et al., 1993). Virtual reality technology, such as the one used at the Université du Québec en Outaouais, can also be used with socially anxious individuals, and this approach may be even more efficient and cost-effective than treatment involving in vivo exposure (Bouchard et al., 2017).

Clark and colleagues (2006) evaluated a new and improved cognitive therapy program that emphasized more real-life experiences during therapy to disprove automatic perceptions of danger. This program substantially benefited 84 percent of individuals receiving treatment, and these results were maintained at a one-year follow-up. This outcome is the best yet for this difficult condition and significantly better than previous approaches to which it has been compared. Subsequent studies indicated that this treatment was clearly superior to a second very credible treatment, interpersonal psychotherapy

(IPT), both immediately after treatment and at a one-year follow-up, even when delivered in a centre specializing in treatment with IPT (Stangier et al., 2011).

A similar approach was developed at our centre (Hofmann, 2007b; Hofmann & Otto, 2008). This treatment specifically targets the different factors that are maintaining the disorder. One important reason why SAD is maintained in the presence of repeated exposure to social cues is because individuals with SAD engage in a variety of avoidance and safety behaviours to reduce the risk of rejection and, more generally, prevent patients from critically evaluating their catastrophic beliefs about how embarrassed and foolish they will look if they attempt to interact with somebody. Social mishap exposures directly target the patients' beliefs by confronting them with the actual consequences of such mishaps, such as what would happen if you spilled something all over yourself while you were talking to somebody for the first time (Hofmann & Otto, 2008). As a group intervention, this treatment was associated with an 82 percent completion rate and a 73 percent response rate, which was maintained at six-month follow-up (Hofmann et al., 2013). Brain-imaging studies showed that brain measures before treatment can strongly predict the extent to which CBT reduces symptoms in patients with SAD (Doehrmann et al., 2013; Whitfield-Gabrieli et al., 2016) and that CBT leads to changes in brain activity associated with emotional processing (Goldin et al., 2013; Klumpp et al., 2013; Månsson et al., 2013).

We have adapted these protocols for use with adolescents, directly involving parents in the group treatment process. Results of numerous studies suggest that severely socially anxious adolescents can attain relatively normal functioning in school and other social settings after receiving CBT (Albano & Barlow, 1996; Garcia-Lopez et al., 2006; Masia-Warner et al., 2005; Scharfstein et al., 2011). Several clinical trials have now compared individual and family-based treatment approaches for youth with social anxiety; while both treatment approaches appear to be equally efficacious (Barmish & Kendall 2005), family-based treatment appears to outperform individual treatment when the child's parents also have an anxiety disorder (Kendall et al., 2008). A more recent long-term follow-up study indicates that youth who receive a parent component as part of anxiety treatment are significantly more likely to be diagnosis-free three years following treatment (Cobham et al., 2010); and a family-based intervention can even prevent the onset of anxiety disorders in the children of anxious parents (Ginsburg et al., 2015). Once the child develops an anxiety disorder, early treatment with CBT can be successful to treat the symptoms or prevent future problems with anxiety (Benjamin et al., 2013; Ginsburg et al., 2014), with a slight advantage of family-based CBT over child-based CBT (Schneider et al., 2013).

Effective drug treatments have been discovered as well (Van Ameringen et al., 2009). For a time, clinicians assumed that beta-blockers (drugs that lower heart rate and blood pressure, such as Inderal) would work, particularly for performance anxiety, but the evidence did not seem to support that contention (Liebowitz et al., 1992; Turner et al., 1994). Since 1999, the SSRIs Paxil, Zoloft, and Effexor have received approval for treatment of SAD—based on studies showing effectiveness compared with placebo (see, e.g., Stein et al., 1998).

Several major studies have compared psychological and drug treatments. One impressive study compared Clark's cognitive therapy described earlier with the SSRI drug Prozac, along with instructions to the patients with SAD to attempt to engage in more social situations (self-exposure). Another group received placebo plus instructions to attempt to engage in more social activities. Assessments were conducted before the 16-week treatment, at the midpoint of treatment, post-treatment, and then after three months of booster sessions. Lastly, researchers followed up with patients in the two treatment groups 12 months later (Clark et al., 2003). Results are presented in ■ Figure 5.8. Both treatments did well, but the psychological treatment was substantially better at all times, with most patients improving with few remaining symptoms. Gains made during cognitive therapy were maintained when assessed after five years (Mörtberg et al., 2011).

The evidence is mixed on the usefulness of combining SSRIs or related drugs with psychological treatments. Davidson, Foa, and Huppert (2004) found that a CBT and an SSRI were comparable in efficacy but that the combination was no better than the two individual treatments.

Selective Mutism

Now grouped with the anxiety disorders in the *DSM-5*, selective mutism is a rare childhood disorder characterized by a lack of speech in one or more settings in which speaking is socially expected. As such, it seems clearly driven by social anxiety, since the failure to speak is not because of a lack of knowledge

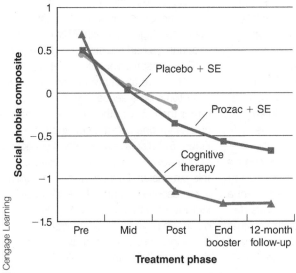

FIGURE 5.8 | Results from a comparison of Prozac and instructions to attempt more social interactions or "self-exposure" (Prozac + SE), placebo and the same instruction (placebo + SE), and cognitive therapy (CT) in the treatment of patients with social anxiety disorder.

Source: Reprinted from "Cognitive Therapy versus Fluoxetine in Generalized Social Phobia: A Randomized Placebo-Controlled Trial," by D. M. Clark, A. Ehlers, F. McManus, A. Hackmann, M. Fennell, H. Campbell, T. Flower, C. Davenport, and B. Louis, 2003, *Journal of Consulting and Clinical Psychology, 71*, pp. 1058–1067. © 2003. American Psychological Association.

of speech or any physical difficulties, nor is it due to another disorder in which speaking is rare or can be impaired such as autism spectrum disorder. In fact, speech in SM commonly occurs in some settings, such as home, but not others, such as school—hence, the term "selective." To meet diagnostic criteria for SM, the lack of speech must occur for more than one month and cannot be limited to the first month of school. Further evidence that this disorder is strongly related to social anxiety is found in the high rates of comorbidity of SM and anxiety disorders, particularly SAD (Bögels et al., 2010). In fact, in one study nearly 100 percent of a series of 50 children with SM also met the criteria for SAD (Dummit et al., 1997). Another recent study found substantially more social anxiety in children with SM than a matched control group without SM (Buzzella et al., 2011). Estimates of the prevalence of SM average about 0.5 percent of children, with girls more affected than boys (Kumpulainen, 2002; Viana et al., 2009).

Why does lack of speech in certain situations emerge as the specific symptom in SM instead of other socially anxious behaviours? It is not entirely clear yet, but there is some evidence that well-meaning parents enable this behaviour by being more readily able to intervene and "do their talking for them" (Buzzella et al., 2011).

Treatment employs many of the same cognitive-behavioural principles used successfully to treat social anxiety in children but with a greater emphasis on speech (Carpenter et al., 2014).

Concept Check 5.4

Identify the following specific phobias: (a) blood-injury-injection, (b) acrophobia, (c) animal, (d) social, (e) natural environment, and (f) other. The same phobia may apply to more than one statement.

1. Mark had no friends at school and hid in the boys' bathroom during both lunch and recess.

   _____

2. Dennis fears and strenuously avoids storms. Not surprisingly, on his first ocean-going cruise, he found that deep water terrified him, too. _____

3. Rita was comfortable at the zoo until the old terror gripped her at the insect display. _____

4. Armando would love to eat fish with his fishing buddies, but he experiences an inordinate fear of choking on a bone. _____

5. John had to give up his dream of becoming a surgeon because he faints at the sight of blood.

   _____

6. Rachel turned down several lucrative job offers that involved public speaking and took a low-paying desk job instead. _____

7. Farrah can't visit her rural friends because of her fear of snakes. _____

For example, in one of our clinics we run a specialized program called the Boston University Brave Buddies Camp. This is a week-long intensive group treatment program for children ages four to eight who have been diagnosed with SM or have difficulty speaking in social or school situations with familiar or unfamiliar peers and adults. The BU Brave Buddies Camp provides guided opportunities for children to interact with a number of new children and adults, participate in classroom-like activities (e.g., morning meeting, circle time, show and tell, group creative projects), engage in field trips (e.g., to the library, the park), and play socializing games that promote verbal participation ("brave talking") and spontaneous speaking. This approach uses behavioural interventions such as modelling, stimulus fading, and shaping that allow for gradual exposure to the speaking situation; these techniques are combined with a behavioural reward system for participation in treatment (Furr et al., 2012; Sacks et al., 2011). Results from this program have been very encouraging: 80 percent of 15 children who participated in this camp were successfully initiating speech and maintaining speech productivity at a two-year follow-up. Unfortunately, these highly specialized programs are not readily available yet.

DSM CONTROVERSIES

DSM Controversies in Classifying Anxiety and Related Disorders

Anxiety disorders are now divided into three separate groupings or classes of disorders in *DSM-5*, and ten disorders have been added to these groupings either by splitting existing disorders, relocating disorders from other diagnostic sections, such as the somatoform disorders, or introducing new disorders appearing for the first time in the *DSM*. In Chapter 3, we introduced the idea that emerging conceptions of psychopathology move us away from an emphasis on categorical (individual) diagnoses to a consideration of larger dimensions, or spectra, in which similar and related diagnoses might be grouped. One such spectrum consists of what some call emotional disorders, including anxiety and depression. But how would this dimensional approach to psychopathology change the way we make diagnoses? Recently, we speculated on how a future diagnostic system using dimensional approaches for emotional disorders might work (Brown & Barlow, 2009), and emerging theoretical development and empirical evidence should be more satisfactory than having to consider a very large number of individual categorical diagnoses as represented in this chapter, as well as in subsequent chapters. To illustrate this approach, let's consider a case from our clinic.

Mr. S. was a high school teacher in his mid-50s who had been in a very serious car accident several months before coming in and was suffering from symptoms related to that accident. These included intrusive memories of the crash, "flashbacks" of the accident itself that were very intense emotionally, and images of the cuts and bruises on his wife's face. He also had a very strong startle reaction to any cues that reminded him of the accident, and avoided driving in certain locations that were somewhat similar to where he had his accident. These symptoms intermingled with a similar set of symptoms emerging from a series of traumatic experiences that had occurred during his service in the Vietnam War. In addition to these trauma symptoms, he also spent a lot of his day worrying about various life events, including his own health and that of his family. He also worried about his performance at work and whether he would be evaluated poorly by other staff members, despite his having received consistently high evaluations for his teaching.

After considering everything he said and evaluating him clinically, therapists found that he clearly met the criteria for PTSD. He also met the criteria for GAD, given his substantial worry that was occurring every day about life events unrelated to the trauma. In addition he had some mild depression, perhaps in part because of all the anxiety he was experiencing. In summary, the patient could be diagnosed with PTSD, although he had substantial features of GAD and depression. But what would it look like if we attempted to describe his symptoms on a series of dimensions rather than on whether they meet the criteria for one category or another? Figure 5.9 displays a simplified version of one possible dimensional system. In this dimensional scheme, "anxiety" (AN) is represented on the left because all individuals with anxiety or depressive disorders have some level of anxiety. Many individuals, but not all, are also depressed (DEP) (as was Mr. S.).

Mr. S. would score fairly high on anxiety and somewhat lower on depression. Looking to the far right of the figure, Mr. S. displayed a lot of behavioural avoidance, as well as avoidance of physical sensations (interoceptive avoidance) (AV-BI). Mostly he was having difficulty driving and would avoid cues connected with his earlier trauma by refusing if at all possible to engage in activities or conversations associated with the war. Another related type of avoidance is when you avoid experiencing intense emotions or thoughts about emotional experiences. We call this cognitive and emotional avoidance (AV-CE) and Mr. S. also scored relatively high on this aspect of avoidance.

But what was the focus of Mr. S.'s anxiety? Here we look at five characteristics that currently categorize anxiety and related disorder diagnoses. Looking first at trauma (TRM) focus, obviously, this earned the highest score on Mr. S.'s profile. He also was suffering from frequent flashbacks to his traumatic experiences, which as you may remember, are very similar to panic attacks and consist of strong autonomic surges, such as rapidly increasing heart rate. Thus, he scored high on panic and related autonomic surges (PAS). Other kinds of intrusive obsessive thoughts were not present and he scored low on this dimension (IC). His worry about his health and the health of his family caused him to score moderately high on somatic anxiety (SOM), but social anxiety (SOC) was not particularly high.

As you can see, this dimensional profile provides a more complete picture of

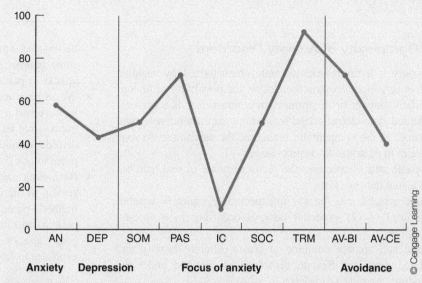

FIGURE 5.9 | Proposed *DSM-5* (or 6) Dimensional Diagnosis of a Patient with PTSD. *AN*, anxiety; *DEP*, unipolar depression; *SOM*, somatic anxiety; *PAS*, panic and related autonomic surges; *IC*, intrusive cognitions; *SOC*, social evaluation; *TRM*, past trauma; *AV-BI*, behavioural and interoceptive avoidance; *AV-CE*, cognitive and emotional avoidance. Higher scores on the *y*-axis (0–100) indicate higher levels of the *x*-axis dimension, but otherwise the *y*-axis metric is arbitrary and is used for illustrative purposes.

Source: "A Proposal for a Dimensional Classification System Based on the Shared Features of the DSM-IV Anxiety and Mood Disorders: Implications for Assessment and Treatment," by T. A. Brown and D. H. Barlow, September 2009, *Psychological Assessment, 21*(3), pp. 256–271. Copyright © 2009 by the American Psychological Association.

Mr. S.'s clinical presentation than simply noting that he met the criteria for PTSD. This is because the profile captures the relative severity of a number of key features of anxiety and mood disorders that are often present together in patients who might meet the criteria for only a single diagnosis in the current categorical system. This profile also captures the fact that Mr. S. had some depression that was below the severity threshold to meet the criteria for mood disorder. Knowing

all of this by glancing at Mr. S.'s profile in Figure 5.9 should help clinicians match therapy more closely to his presenting problems.

This is just one possible example, but it does provide some idea of what a diagnostic system might look like in the future. Although this system was not ready for the *DSM-5* because much more research is needed on how best to make it work, a system like this might be ready for the *DSM-6*.

SUMMARY

The Complexity of Anxiety Disorders

- Anxiety is a future-oriented state characterized by negative affect in which a person focuses on the possibility of uncontrollable danger or misfortune; in contrast, fear is a present-oriented state characterized by strong escapist tendencies and a surge in the sympathetic branch of the autonomic nervous system in response to current danger.
- A panic attack represents the alarm response of real fear, but no actual danger exists.
- Panic attacks may be (1) unexpected (completely without warning) or (2) expected (always occurring in a specific situation).
- Panic and anxiety combine to create different anxiety and related disorders. Several disorders are grouped under the heading "Anxiety Disorders."

Generalized Anxiety Disorder

- In generalized anxiety disorder (GAD), anxiety focuses on minor everyday events, and not on one major worry or concern.
- Both genetic and psychological vulnerabilities seem to contribute to the development of GAD.
- Although drug and psychological treatments may be effective in the short term, drug treatments are no more effective in the long term than placebo treatments. Successful treatment may help individuals with GAD focus on what is really threatening to them in their lives.

Panic Disorder and Agoraphobia

- In panic disorder, which may or may not be accompanied by agoraphobia (a fear and avoidance of situations considered to be unsafe), anxiety is focused on the next panic attack. For some people, agoraphobia develops in the absence of panic attacks or panic-like symptoms.
- We all have some genetic vulnerability to stress, and many of us have had a neurobiological overreaction to some stressful event—that is, a panic attack. Individuals who develop panic disorder develop anxiety over the possibility of having another panic attack.
- Both drug and psychological treatments have proven successful in the treatment of panic disorder. One psychological method, panic control treatment, concentrates on exposing patients to clusters of sensations that remind them of their panic attacks. For agoraphobia, therapeutically supervised exposure to feared situations is most effective.

Specific Phobia

- In phobic disorders, the individual avoids situations that produce severe anxiety or panic. In specific phobia, the fear is focused on a particular object or situation.
- Phobias can be acquired by experiencing some traumatic event; they can also be learned vicariously or even taught.
- Treatment of phobias is rather straightforward, with a focus on structured and consistent exposure-based exercises.

Social Anxiety Disorder (Social Phobia)

- Social anxiety disorder is a fear of being around others, particularly in situations that call for some kind of "performance" in front of other people.
- Although the causes of social anxiety disorder are similar to those of specific phobias, treatment has a different focus that includes rehearsing or role-playing socially phobic situations. In addition, drug treatments have been effective.

KEY TERMS

agoraphobia, 133
animal phobias, 143
anxiety, 121
behavioural inhibition system (BIS), 124

blood-injury-injection phobias, 142
fear, 121
fight/flight system (FFS), 124
generalized anxiety disorder (GAD), 128

natural environment phobias, 143
panic, 122
panic attack, 122
panic control treatment (PCT), 140

panic disorder (PD), 133
separation anxiety disorder, 147
situational phobias, 143
social anxiety disorder, 148
specific phobia, 141

ANSWERS TO CONCEPT CHECKS

5.1

1. b; **2.** c; **3.** e, d; **4.** a; **5.** f

5.2

1. T; **2.** F (more gradual); **3.** T; **4.** F; **5.** T

5.3

1. F; **2.** F (3.5%); **3.** T; **4.** T

5.4

1. d; **2.** e; **3.** c; **4.** f; **5.** a; **6.** d; **7.** c

MEDIA RESOURCES

⁂ CENGAGE | MINDTAP

Stay organized and efficient with MindTap—a single destination with all the course material and study aids you need to succeed. Built-in apps leverage social media and the latest learning technology. For example:

- ReadSpeaker will read the text to you.
- Flashcards are pre-populated to provide you with a jump start for review—or you can create your own.
- You can highlight text and make notes in your MindTap Reader. Your notes will flow into Evernote, the electronic notebook app that you can access anywhere when it's time to study for the exam.
- Self-quizzing allows you to assess your understanding.

Visit login.cengage.com to start using MindTap. Enter the Online Access Code from the card included with your text. If a code card is not provided, you can purchase instant access at Cengage.ca.

Exploring Anxiety Disorders

People with anxiety disorders:

❯ Feel overwhelming tension, apprehension, or fear when there is no actual danger

❯ May take extreme action to avoid the source of their anxiety

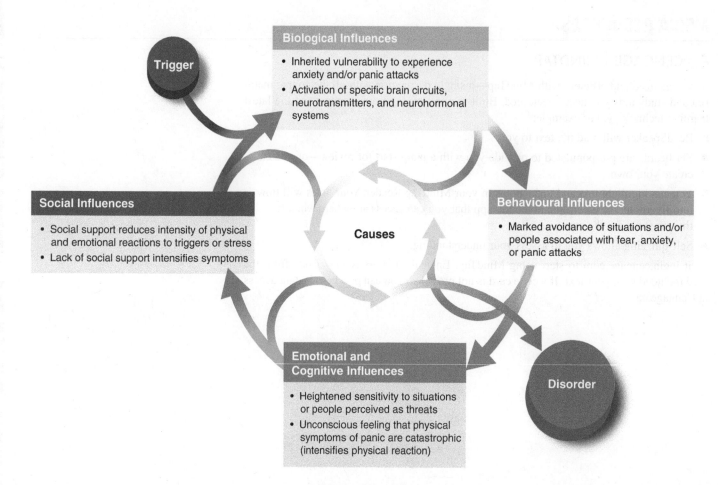

Trigger

Biological Influences

- Inherited vulnerability to experience anxiety and/or panic attacks
- Activation of specific brain circuits, neurotransmitters, and neurohormonal systems

Social Influences

- Social support reduces intensity of physical and emotional reactions to triggers or stress
- Lack of social support intensifies symptoms

Causes

Behavioural Influences

- Marked avoidance of situations and/or people associated with fear, anxiety, or panic attacks

Emotional and Cognitive Influences

- Heightened sensitivity to situations or people perceived as threats
- Unconscious feeling that physical symptoms of panic are catastrophic (intensifies physical reaction)

Disorder

TREATMENT FOR ANXIETY DISORDERS

Cognitive-Behavioural Therapy

- Systematic exposure to anxiety-provoking situations or thoughts
- Learning to substitute positive behaviours and thoughts for negative ones
- Learning new coping skills: relaxation exercises, controlled breathing, etc.

Drug Treatment

- Reduces the symptoms of anxiety disorders by influencing brain chemistry
  - antidepressants (Tofranil, Paxil, Effexor)
  - benzodiazepines (Xanax, Klonopin)

Other Treatments

- Managing stress through a healthy lifestyle: rest, exercise, nutrition, social support, and moderate alcohol or other drug intake

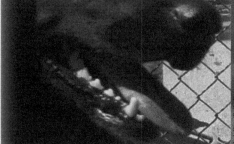

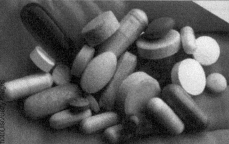

TYPES OF ANXIETY DISORDERS

Panic

People with panic disorders have had one or more panic attacks and are anxious and fearful about having future attacks.

PhotoDisc/Getty Images

What is a panic attack?
A person having a panic attack feels:
- Apprehension leading to intense fear
- Sensation of "going crazy" or of losing control
- Physical signs of distress: racing heartbeat, rapid breathing, dizziness, nausea, or sensation of heart attack or imminent death

When/why do panic attacks occur?
Panic attacks can be:
- Expected: Always occurring in a specific situation
- Unexpected: Occurring without warning

Phobias

People with phobias avoid situations that produce severe anxiety and/or panic. There are three main types:

Eyewire/Getty Images

Agoraphobia
- Fear and avoidance of situations, people, or places where it would be unsafe to have a panic attack: malls, grocery stores, buses, planes, tunnels, etc.
- In the extreme, inability to leave the house or even a specific room
- Begins after a panic attack but can continue for years even if no other attacks occur

Specific Phobia
- Fear of specific object or situation that triggers attack: heights, closed spaces, insects, snakes, or flying
- Develops from personal or vicarious experience of traumatic event with the triggering object or situation or from misinformation

Social Anxiety Disorder
- Fear of being called for some kind of "performance" that may be judged: speaking in public, using a public restroom (for males), or generally interacting with people

Generalized Anxiety

- Uncontrollable unproductive worrying about everyday events
- Feeling impending catastrophe even after successes
- Inability to stop the worry–anxiety cycle: e.g., Irene's fear of failure about school relationships and health even though everything seemed fine
- Physical symptoms of muscle tension

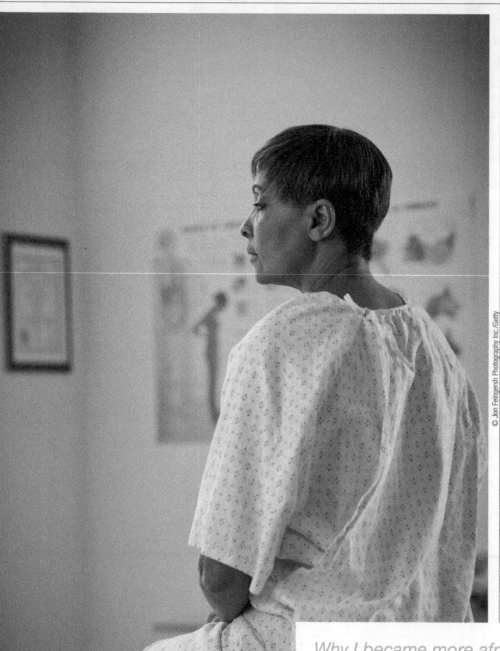

© Jon Feingersh Photography Inc./Getty

*Why I became more afraid of living and of dying than
others will forever remain an enigma.*
—CARLA CANTOR, Phantom Illness: Shattering the Myth of Hypochondria

Engage in innovative and integrative thinking and problem solving:	› Describe problems operationally to study them empirically (APA SLO 2.3A)
Describe applications that employ discipline-based problem solving:	› Correctly identify antecedents and consequences of behaviour and mental processes (APA SLO 1.3b)
	› Describe examples of relevant and practical applications of psychological principles to everyday life (APA SLO 1.3a)

*Portions of this chapter cover learning outcomes suggested by the American Psychological Association (2012) in their guidelines for the undergraduate psychology major. Chapter coverage of these outcomes is identified above by APA Goal and APA Suggested Learning Outcome (SLO).

Many people continually run to the doctor even though nothing is wrong with them. This is usually a harmless tendency that may even be worth some good-natured jokes. But for a few individuals, the preoccupation with their health becomes so great that it dominates their lives. The popular image of this condition, now called **illness anxiety disorder** in the fifth edition of the *Diagnostic and Statistical Manual of Mental Disorders* (*DSM-5*; American Psychiatric Association, 2013), is of someone who exaggerates the slightest physical symptom. These problems fall under the general heading of **somatic symptom disorders**. *Soma* means "body," and the problems preoccupying these people seem, initially, to be physical disorders. In some cases, the medical cause of the presenting physical symptoms is known, but the emotional distress, the extreme preoccupations, or level of impairment in response to this symptom is maladaptive and may even make the condition worse.

Another new class of disorders in *DSM-5* brings together several disorders that share a number of characteristics, such as driven repetitive behaviours and some other symptoms, as well as a similar course and treatment response (Abramowitz & Jacoby, 2015). Previously, these disorders had been scattered in other areas of the *DSM-IV*. In addition to obsessive-compulsive disorder, which had been classified as an anxiety disorder before the *DSM-5*, this grouping now includes a separate diagnostic category for hoarding disorder, body dysmorphic disorder (which was previously located with the somatoform disorders), and trichotillomania (which was previously grouped with the impulse control disorders). Another new disorder in this group is excoriation (skin picking) disorder.

Thus, this chapter covers two classes of disorders, many of which feature extreme preoccupations, obsessive thinking, rituals and checking, and repetitive and compulsive behaviours. Most involve significant amounts of anxiety and worry, which is why many of these disorders were thought of (and still are by many researchers and clinicians) as anxiety disorders.

SOMATIC SYMPTOM DISORDER AND RELATED DISORDERS

The *DSM-5* lists five basic somatic symptom and related disorders: somatic symptom disorder, illness anxiety disorder, psychological factors affecting medical condition, conversion disorder, and factitious disorder. In each, individuals are pathologically preoccupied and concerned with the appearance or functioning of their bodies. The first three disorders covered in this section—somatic symptom disorder, illness anxiety disorder, and psychological factors affecting medical condition—overlap considerably, since each focuses on a specific somatic symptom, or set of symptoms, about which the patient is so excessively anxious or distressed that it interferes with his or her functioning, or the anxiety or distress is focused on just the possibility of developing an illness as in illness anxiety disorder.

SOMATIC SYMPTOM DISORDER

Clinical Description

In 1859, Pierre Briquet, a French physician, described patients who came to see him with seemingly endless lists of somatic complaints for which he could find no medical basis. Despite his negative findings, patients returned shortly with either the same complaints or new lists containing slight variations. For more than a century this disorder was called *Briquet's syndrome*, but now it would be known as somatic symptom disorder. Consider the case of Linda.

LINDA | *Full-Time Patient*

Linda, an intelligent woman in her 30s, came to our clinic looking distressed and pained. As she sat down she noted that coming into the office was very difficult for her, as she had trouble breathing and considerable swelling in the joints of her legs and arms. She was also in some pain from chronic urinary tract infections and might have to leave at any moment to go to the washroom, but she was extremely happy she had kept the appointment. At least she was seeing someone who could help alleviate her considerable suffering. She said she knew we would have to go through a detailed initial interview, but she had something that might save time. At this point she pulled out several sheets of paper and handed them over. One section, some five pages long, described her contacts with the health-care system for major difficulties only. Times, dates, potential diagnoses, and days hospitalized were noted. The second section, one-and-a-half single-spaced pages, consisted of a list of all the medications she had taken for various complaints.

(Continued)

Linda felt she had any one of a number of chronic infections that nobody could properly diagnose. She had begun to have these problems in her teenage years. She often discussed her symptoms and fears with doctors and clergy. Drawn to hospitals and medical clinics, she had entered nursing school after high school. However, during hospital training, she noticed her physical condition deteriorating rapidly: She seemed to pick up the diseases she was learning about. A series of stressful emotional events resulted in her leaving nursing school.

After developing unexplained paralysis in her legs, Linda was admitted to a psychiatric hospital, and after a year she regained her ability to walk. On discharge she obtained disability status, which freed her from having to work full-time, and she volunteered at the local hospital. With her chronic but fluctuating incapacitation, on some days she could go in and on some days she could not. She was seeing a family practitioner and six specialists, who monitored various aspects of her physical condition. She was also seeing two ministers for pastoral counselling.

Linda easily met and exceeded all the *DSM-5* diagnostic criteria for somatic symptom disorder (see DSM Table 6.1). Linda was concerned with the symptoms themselves, not with what they might mean. People with somatic symptom disorder do not always feel the urgency to take action but continually feel weak and ill, and they avoid exercising, thinking it will make them worse (Rief et al., 1998). Furthermore, Linda's entire life revolved around her symptoms; she once said her symptoms were her identity: Without them she would not know who she was. By this she meant that she would not know how to relate to people except in the context of discussing her symptoms, much as other people might talk about their day at the office or their kids' accomplishments at school. Her few friends who were not health-care professionals had the patience to relate to her sympathetically, through the veil of her symptoms, and she thought of them as friends because they "understood" her suffering.

Another common example of a somatic symptom disorder is the experience of severe pain in which psychological factors play a major role in maintaining or exacerbating the pain, whether or not the pain has a clear physical reason. Consider the case of the medical student.

THE MEDICAL STUDENT | *Temporary Pain*

During her first clinical rotation, a 25-year-old third-year medical student in excellent health was seen at her student health service for intermittent abdominal pain of several weeks' duration. The student claimed no past history of similar pain. Physical examination revealed no physical problems, but she told the physician that she had recently separated from her husband. The student was referred to the health service psychiatrist. No other psychiatric problems were found. She was taught relaxation techniques and given supportive therapy to help her cope with her current stressful situation. The student's pain subsequently disappeared, and she successfully completed medical school.

DSM-5	**Table 6.1** Diagnostic Criteria for Somatic Symptom Disorder

A. One or more somatic symptoms that are distressing or result in significant disruption of daily life.

B. Excessive thoughts, feelings, and behaviours related to the somatic symptoms or associated health concerns as manifested by at least one of the following:

  1. Disproportionate and persistent thoughts about the seriousness of one's symptoms.
  2. Persistently high level of anxiety about health or symptoms.
  3. Excessive time and energy devoted to these symptoms or health concerns.

C. Although any one somatic symptom may not be continuously present, the state of being symptomatic is persistent (typically more than 6 months).

Specify if:

With predominant pain (previously pain disorder): This specifier is for individuals whose somatic complaints predominantly involve pain.

Specify if:

Persistent: A persistent course is characterized by severe symptoms, marked impairment, and long duration (more than 6 months).

Specify current severity:

Mild: Only one of the symptoms specified in Criterion B is fulfilled.

Moderate: Two or more of the symptoms specified in Criterion B are fulfilled.

Severe: Two or more of the symptoms specified in Criterion B are fulfilled, plus there are multiple somatic complaints (or one very severe somatic symptom).

Once again, the important factor in this condition is not whether the physical symptom, in this case pain, has a clear medical cause but rather that psychological or behavioural factors, particularly anxiety and distress, are compounding the severity and impairment associated with the physical symptoms. The new emphasis in the *DSM-5* on the psychological symptoms in these disorders is useful to clinicians, because it highlights the psychological experiences of anxiety and distress focused on the somatic symptoms as the most important target for treatment (Tomenson et al., 2012; Voigt et al., 2012). But an important feature of these physical symptoms, such as pain, is that they are real and they hurt, whether or not there are clear physical reasons for the pain (Asmundson & Carleton, 2009; Dersh et al., 2002).

ILLNESS ANXIETY DISORDER

Illness anxiety disorder was formerly known as *hypochondriasis*, which is still the term widely used among the public. In illness anxiety disorder as we know it today, physical symptoms are either not experienced at the present time or are very mild, but severe anxiety is focused on the possibility of having or developing a serious disease. If one or more physical symptoms are relatively severe and are associated with anxiety and distress, then the diagnosis would be somatic symptom disorder. Using *DSM-5* criteria, only about 20 percent of patients who used to meet the diagnostic criteria for *DSM-IV* hypochondriasis now meet the criteria for illness anxiety disorder, in part because they do not complain about having any somatic symptoms despite experiencing serious anxiety about contracting an illness (Rief & Martin, 2014). This justified the creation of the illness anxiety disorder category, to cover that 20 percent segment who do not report symptoms. Once again, in illness anxiety disorder. the concern is primarily with the *idea* of being sick instead of the physical symptom itself. And the threat seems so real that reassurance from physicians does not seem to help. See DSM Table 6.2. Consider the case of Gail.

DSM-5	**Table 6.2** Diagnostic Criteria for Illness Anxiety Disorder

A. Preoccupation with having or acquiring a serious illness.

B. Somatic symptoms are not present or, if present, are only mild in intensity. If another medical condition is present or there is a high risk for developing a medical condition (e.g., strong family history is present), the preoccupation is clearly excessive or disproportionate.

C. There is a high level of anxiety about health, and the individual is easily alarmed about personal health status.

D. The individual performs excessive health-related behaviours (e.g., repeatedly checks his or her body for signs of illness) or exhibits maladaptive avoidance (e.g., avoids doctors' appointments and hospitals).

E. Illness preoccupation has been present for at least 6 months, but the specific illness that is feared may change over that period of time.

F. The illness-related preoccupation is not better explained by another mental disorder, such as somatic symptom disorder, panic disorder, generalized anxiety disorder, body dysmorphic disorder, or obsessive-compulsive disorder, or delusional disorder, somatic type.

Specify whether:

Care-seeking type: Medical care, including physician visits or undergoing tests and procedures, is frequently used.

Care-avoidant type: Medical care is rarely used.

Source: Reprinted with permission from the *Diagnostic and Statistical Manual of Mental Disorders*, Fifth Edition (Copyright © 2013). American Psychiatric Association. All Rights Reserved.

GAIL | *Invisibly Ill*

Gail was married at 21 and looked forward to a new life. As one of many children in a lower-middle-class household, she felt weak and somewhat neglected and suffered from low self-esteem. An older stepbrother berated and belittled her when he was drunk. Her mother and stepfather refused to listen to her or believe her complaints. But she believed that marriage would solve everything; she was finally someone special. Unfortunately, it didn't work out that way. She soon discovered her husband was continuing an affair with an old girlfriend.

Three years after her wedding, Gail came to our clinic complaining of anxiety and stress. She was working part-time as a server and found her job extremely stressful.

Although to the best of her knowledge her husband had stopped seeing his former girlfriend, she had trouble getting the affair out of her mind.

Although Gail complained initially of anxiety and stress, it soon became clear that her major concerns were about her health. Any time she experienced a minor physical symptom, such as breathlessness or a headache, she was afraid she had a serious illness. A headache indicated a brain tumour. Breathlessness was an impending heart attack. Other sensations were quickly elaborated into the possibility of AIDS or cancer. Gail was afraid to go to sleep at night for fear that she would stop breathing. She avoided exercise, drinking, and even laughing because the resulting sensations upset her. Public restrooms and, on occasion, public telephones were feared as sources of infection.

The major trigger of uncontrollable anxiety and fear was the news in the newspaper and on television. Each time an article or show appeared on the "disease of the month," Gail found herself irresistibly drawn into it, intently noting symptoms that were part of the disease. For days afterward she was vigilant, looking for the symptoms in herself and others and often noticing some physical sensations that she would interpret as the beginnings of the disease. She even watched her dog closely to see whether he was coming down with the dreaded disease. Only with great effort could she dismiss these thoughts after several days. Real illness in a friend or relative would incapacitate her for days at a time.

Gail's fears developed during the first year of her marriage, around the time she learned of her husband's affair. At first, she spent a great deal of time and more money than they could afford going to doctors. Over the years, she heard the same thing during each visit: "There's nothing wrong with you; you're perfectly healthy." Finally, she stopped going because she became convinced her concerns were excessive, but her fears did not go away and she was chronically miserable.

Clinical Description

Do you notice any differences between Linda, who presented with somatic symptom disorder, and Gail, who presented with illness anxiety disorder? There is certainly a lot of overlap between the two disorders (Creed & Barsky, 2004; Leibbrand et al., 2000), but Gail was somewhat less concerned with any specific physical symptom and more worried about the idea that she was either ill or developing an illness. Gail's problems are fairly typical of illness anxiety disorder.

Illness anxiety disorder and somatic symptom disorder share many features with the anxiety and mood disorders, particularly panic disorder (Craske et al., 1996; Creed & Barsky, 2004), including similar age of onset, personality characteristics, and patterns of familial aggregation (running in families). Indeed, anxiety and mood disorders are often comorbid with somatic symptom disorders; that is, if individuals with somatic symptom disorders have additional diagnoses, these most likely are anxiety or mood disorders (Creed & Barsky, 2004; Simon et al., 2001; Wollburg et al., 2013).

As noted above, illness anxiety disorder is characterized by anxiety or fear that one has a serious disease. Therefore, the essential problem is anxiety, but its expression is different from that of the other anxiety disorders. In illness anxiety disorders, the individual is preoccupied with bodily symptoms, misinterpreting them as indicative of illness or disease. Almost any physical sensation may become the basis for concern. Some may focus on normal bodily functions, such as heart rate or perspiration, others on minor physical abnormalities, such as a cough. Some individuals complain of vague symptoms, such as aches or fatigue. Because a key feature of this disorder is preoccupation with physical symptoms, individuals with these disorders almost always go initially to family physicians. They come to the attention of mental health professionals only after family physicians have ruled out realistic medical conditions as a cause of the patient's symptoms.

Another important feature of this disorder is that reassurances from numerous doctors that all is well and the individual is healthy have, at best, only a short-term effect. It isn't long before patients like Gail or Linda are back in the office of another doctor on the assumption that the previous doctors have missed something. This is because many of these individuals mistakenly believe they have a disease; this difficult-to-shake belief is sometimes referred to as "disease conviction." Therefore, along with anxiety focused on the possibility of disease or illness, disease conviction is a core feature of the disorder (Fergus & Valentiner, 2010; Woolfolk & Allen, 2011).

If you have just read Chapter 5, you may think that patients with panic disorder resemble patients with both disorders, particularly patients with illness anxiety disorder. Patients with panic disorder also misinterpret physical symptoms as the beginning of the next panic attack, which they believe may kill them. Craske and colleagues (1996) and Hiller, Leibbrand, Rief, and Fichter (2005) suggested several differences between panic disorder and the somatic symptom disorders. Although all disorders include characteristic concern with physical symptoms, patients with panic disorder typically fear immediate symptom-related catastrophes that may occur during the few minutes they are having a panic attack, and these concerns lessen between attacks. Individuals with somatic symptom disorders, on the other hand, focus on a long-term process of illness and disease (e.g., cancer or AIDS). Patients with these disorders also continue to seek the opinions of additional doctors in an attempt to rule out (or perhaps confirm) disease and are more likely to demand unnecessary medical treatments. Despite numerous assurances that they are healthy, they remain unconvinced and unreassured. In contrast, patients with panic attacks continue to believe their panic attacks might kill them, but most learn rather quickly to stop going to doctors and emergency rooms, where they are told repeatedly that nothing is physically wrong with them. Lastly, the anxieties of individuals with panic disorder tend to focus on the specific set of 10 or 15 sympathetic nervous system symptoms associated with a panic attack. Concerns range much wider in somatic symptom disorders. Nevertheless, there are probably more similarities than differences between these groups.

▲ In illness anxiety disorder, normal experiences and sensations are often transformed into life-threatening illnesses.

Statistics for Somatic Symptom and Illness Anxiety Disorder

We can only estimate prevalence of somatic symptom disorders in the general population, mostly from studies of similar *DSM-IV* disorders that were defined a bit differently than the current *DSM-5* disorders. For example, the lifetime prevalence of *DSM-IV* hypochondriasis, which would encompass illness anxiety disorder and part of somatic symptom disorder, has been estimated to be from 1 to 5 percent (American Psychiatric Association, 2000). In primary care settings the median prevalence rate for hypochondriasis is 7 percent, but it is as high as 17 percent for distressing somatic symptoms, which should closely approximate the prevalence of somatic symptom disorder and illness anxiety disorder combined in these settings (Creed & Barsky, 2004). Severe illness anxiety has a late age of onset, possibly because more physical health problems occur with aging (El-Gabalawy et al., 2013).

Linda's disorder developed during adolescence. Several studies have demonstrated that individuals with what would now be diagnosed as somatic symptom disorder tend to be women, unmarried, and from lower socioeconomic groups (e.g., Creed & Barsky, 2004; Lieb et al., 2002). In addition to a variety of somatic complaints, individuals may also have psychological complaints, usually anxiety or mood disorders (Simms et al., 2012; Lieb et al., 2002).

A culture-specific disorder, prevalent in India, is an anxious concern about losing semen, something that obviously occurs during sexual activity. The disorder, called *dhat*, is associated with a vague mix of physical symptoms, including dizziness, weakness, and fatigue. These low-grade depressive or anxious symptoms are simply attributed to a physical factor: semen loss (Ranjith & Mohan, 2004). Other specific culture-bound somatic symptoms include hot sensations in the head or a sensation of something crawling in the head, specific to African patients (Ebigno, 1986), and a sensation of burning in the hands and feet in Pakistani or Indian patients (Kirmayer & Weiss, 1993).

Causes of Somatic Symptom and Illness Anxiety Disorder

Investigators with otherwise differing points of view agree on psychopathological processes ongoing in somatic symptom disorders. Faulty interpretation of physical signs and sensations as evidence of physical illness is central, so almost everyone agrees that these disorders are basically disorders of cognition or perception with strong emotional contributions (olde Hartman et al., 2009; Taylor & Asmundson, 2004, 2009; Witthöft & Hiller, 2010).

Individuals with somatic symptom disorders experience physical sensations common to all of us, but they quickly focus their attention on these sensations. Remember that the very act of focusing on yourself increases arousal and makes the physical sensations seem more intense than they are (see Chapter 5). If you also tend to misinterpret these as symptoms of illness, your anxiety will increase further. Increased anxiety produces additional physical symptoms, which creates a vicious cycle (see ■ Figure 6.1, which was developed to apply to the *DSM-IV*'s hypochondriasis but also applies to the *DSM-5*'s somatic symptom disorder and illness anxiety disorder; Salkovskis et al., 2003; Warwick & Salkovskis, 1990; Witthöft & Hiller, 2010).

Using procedures from cognitive science such as the Stroop test (see Chapter 2), a number of investigators (Hitchcock & Mathews,

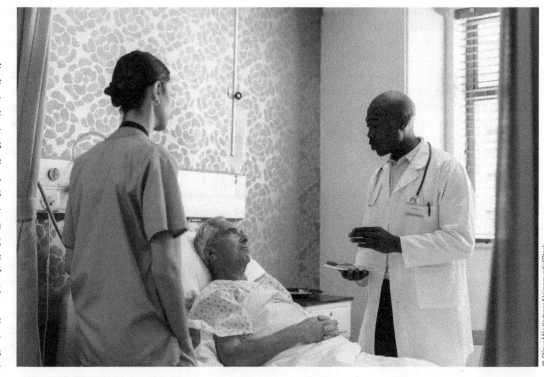

▲ In somatic symptom disorder, primary relationships are often with medical caregivers; a person's symptoms are that person's identity.

1992; Pauli & Alpers, 2002) have confirmed that participants with these disorders show enhanced perceptual sensitivity to illness cues. They also tend to interpret ambiguous stimuli as threatening (Haenen et al., 2000). Thus, they quickly become aware (and frightened) of any sign of possible illness or disease. A minor headache, for example, might be interpreted as a sure sign of a brain tumour. Smeets, de Jong, and Mayer (2000) demonstrated that individuals with these disorders, compared with others, take a better-safe-than-sorry approach to dealing with even minor physical symptoms by getting them checked out as soon as possible. More fundamentally, they have a restrictive concept of health as being symptom-free (Rief et al., 1998).

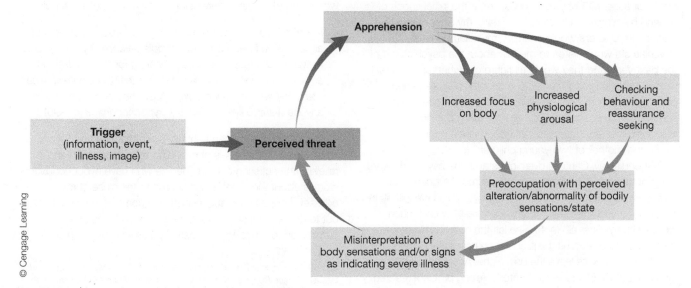

FIGURE 6.1 | Integrative model of causes of hypochondriasis.

Source: Based on "Hypochondriasis," by H. M. Warwick and P. M. Salkovskis, 1990, *Behavior Research Therapy, 28*, pp. 105–117.

What causes individuals to develop this pattern of somatic sensitivity and distorted beliefs? Although it is not certain, the cause is unlikely to be found in isolated biological or psychological factors. For some patients, the fundamental causes of these disorders are similar to those implicated in the anxiety disorders (Barlow, 2002). For example, evidence shows that somatic symptom disorders run in families (Bell, 1994; Guze et al., 1986; Katon, 1993) and that there is a modest genetic contribution (Taylor et al., 2006). But this contribution may be nonspecific, such as a tendency to overrespond to stress, and thus may be indistinguishable from the nonspecific genetic

contribution to anxiety disorders. Hyperresponsivity might combine with a tendency to view negative life events as unpredictable and uncontrollable and, therefore, to be guarded against at all times (Noyes et al., 2004). As we noted in Chapter 5, these factors would constitute biological and psychological vulnerabilities to anxiety.

Why does this anxiety focus on physical sensations and illness? We know that children with these concerns often report the same kinds of symptoms that other family members may have reported at one time (Kellner, 1985; Kirmayer, Looper, & Taillefer, 2003). It is therefore quite possible, as in panic disorder, that

---

FROM THE INSIDE — Phantom Illness: Shattering the Myth of Hypochondria
by Carla Cantor with Brian A. Fallon, M.D.

One warm June evening I found myself imprisoned, a patient on a psychiatric ward of a hospital a few miles from my New Jersey home. It was not at all what I had intended. I had come to the emergency room earlier that day in desperation: I had to talk to someone about the undiagnosed pain in my wrist, my thinning hair, and the unrelenting fear that I was morbidly ill. (p. 1)

Carla Cantor opens *Phantom Illness* with the story of a hospital stay that turned out to be the beginning of her road to recovery from lifelong hypochondria. Though not entirely a memoir, the book begins and ends with episodes and personal insights from Cantor's life as a hypochondriac. In between are straightforward chapters outlining current medical and psychiatric thinking on different types of somatic symptom disorders, possible causes, and steps toward treatment. Throughout the book, Cantor weaves in strands of her personal experiences, as well as revealing stories and insightful quotes from many people with somatic symptom disorders.

The hospital misadventure begins when an emergency-room physician misdiagnoses her condition as clinical depression. Cantor's reaction demonstrates the depths of her preoccupation with physical illness. "After the initial shock of hearing his words, I felt relief. . . . Finally, my illness would be diagnosed! Doctors would examine my inflamed wrist, psychiatrists would listen to me talk about the psychic pain of the past year, and they would all figure out whether I was really sick or just plain crazy" (p. 4). The hospital stay also seemed to promise relief from her stressful life. "Being in a hospital also seemed like a reasonable excuse for leaving behind the responsibilities and stresses that go with being a freelance writer and mother of two young children" (p. 4).

To her dismay, Cantor's overnight stay in the psychiatric ward was not the restful respite she had expected. "Suddenly, my undiagnosed illness didn't seem so terrible. I could live with it. In fact, maybe, just maybe, I thought, there really wasn't much wrong with me after all" (p. 5). She left the next morning, determined to overcome the problem on her own. "Perhaps the best thing to do was leave the pain alone. Accept the symptoms, ignore them" (p. 6). However, Cantor's lifelong problem resisted solution. "My existence was peppered with episodes of illness.

When the going got tough, I'd get sick. Or just the opposite: when things seemed to be going well, I'd come down with a symptom, or at least what I interpreted as one" (p. 10). In addition, Cantor experienced the shame that is common to hypochondriacs. As one of the people she interviewed put it, "Unless you have it yourself, it's looked upon as a character flaw. . . . Hypochondria is not something you can admit to anyone. It's so embarrassing" (p. 51). She continued to suffer.

Help came to her by chance. Although Cantor had never before read anything about hypochondria, the moment she saw a newspaper article about the disorder, "suddenly something clicked for me. The myriad tests, the files of medical bills, the dozens of maladies for which doctors could never find a cause. There was something wrong with me, but not a deadly disease, which in my more rational moments, I believe I had always known" (p. 6). For Cantor, the realization that she was not alone was the catalyst to seek help.

After consulting with Brian Fallon, Cantor received treatment, including fluoxetine (Prozac), which helped her tremendously. She contacted Fallon with the idea of writing a book about hypochondria. Her rationale was that the book would spread information and hope to other hypochondriacs, whom she views as experiencing intense psychological pain:

If you're lucky, as I was, you finally wake up, not just intellectually but deep in your soul, to a simple paradox: if you are going to live out the rest of your life preparing for the day the tumor arrives, when you get the report of that terrible blood test, when you collapse in crushing pain, what's the point? Why would anyone want to live to 120 as a hypochondriac? (p. 290)

In the end, Cantor can rightfully claim that she and Fallon have achieved their goals of providing solid information and relieving the suffering of many people who have hypochondriacal worries about their health. "As I come to the close of my odyssey, I hope I have succeeded in accomplishing what I set out to do: erase a stigma, debunk some myths, lend some illumination to a puzzling, perpetually elusive malady" (p. 219).

some individuals who develop somatic symptom disorder or illness anxiety disorder have *learned* from family members to focus their anxiety on specific physical conditions and illness.

Three other factors may contribute to this etiological process (Côté et al., 1996; Kellner, 1985). First, these disorders seem to develop in the context of a stressful life event, as do many disorders, including anxiety disorders. Such events often involve death or illness (Noyes et al., 2004; Sandin et al., 2004). (Gail's traumatic first year of marriage seemed to coincide with the beginning of her disorder.) Second, people who develop these disorders tend to have had a disproportionate incidence of disease in their family when they were children. Thus, even if they did not develop somatic symptom disorders until adulthood, they carry strong memories of illness that could easily become the focus of anxiety. Third, an important social and interpersonal influence may be involved (Noyes et al., 2003). Some people who come from families where illness is a major issue seem to have learned that an ill person often gets a lot of attention. The "benefits" of being sick might contribute to the development of the disorder in some people. A person who receives increased attention for being ill and is able to avoid work or other responsibilities is described as adopting a "sick role."

Treatment of Somatic Symptom and Illness Anxiety Disorder

Unfortunately, relatively little is known about treating these disorders. It used to be common clinical practice in the past to uncover unconscious conflicts through psychodynamic psychotherapy. Results on the effectiveness of this kind of treatment have seldom been reported, however.

There is scientific support for cognitive-behavioural treatments for health anxiety (e.g., Bouman, 2014; Taylor & Asmundson, 2009) and also somatic symptom disorder (e.g., Kleinstäuber et al., 2011; Sharma & Manjula, 2013; Witthöft & Hiller, 2010; Woolfolk & Allen, 2011). Surprisingly, clinical reports indicate that reassurance and education can be effective in some cases with health anxiety (Haenen et al., 2000; Kellner, 1992)—surprisingly, because, by definition, patients with these disorders are not supposed to benefit from reassurance about their health. Reassurance is usually given only briefly, however, by family doctors who have little time to provide the ongoing support and reassurance that might be necessary. Mental health professionals may well be able to offer reassurance in a more effective and sensitive manner, devote sufficient time to all concerns the patient may have, and attend to the meaning of the symptoms (e.g., their relation to the patient's life stress).

Fava, Grandi, Rafanelli, Fabbri, and Cazzaro (2000) tested this idea by assigning 20 patients who met diagnostic criteria for *DSM-IV* hypochondriasis to two groups. One received explanatory therapy in which the clinician went over the source and origins of their symptoms in some detail. These patients were assessed immediately after the therapy and again at a six-month follow-up. The other group was a wait-list control group that did not receive the explanatory therapy until after their six months of waiting. All patients received usual medical care from their physicians. In both groups, taking the time to explain in some detail the nature of the patient's disorder in an educational framework was associated with a significant reduction in fears and beliefs about somatic symptoms and a decrease in health-care usage, and these

gains were maintained at the follow-up. For the wait-list group, treatment gains did not occur until they received explanatory therapy, suggesting this treatment is effective. This is a small study and follow-ups occurred for only six months, but the results are promising (although explanatory therapy most likely only benefits those with more mild forms of the disorders; Taylor et al., 2005). Participation in support groups may also give these people the reassurance they need.

Evaluations of more robust treatments are now available (for a review, see Bouman, 2014). For example, in one strong study, Barsky and Ahern (2005) randomized 187 patients with *DSM-IV* hypochondriasis to receive either six sessions of cognitive-behavioural treatment (CBT) from trained therapists or treatment as usual from primary care physicians. CBT focused on identifying and challenging illness-related misinterpretations of physical sensations and on showing patients how to create "symptoms" by focusing attention on certain body areas. Bringing on their own symptoms persuaded many patients that such events were under their control. Patients were also coached to seek less reassurance regarding their concerns. CBT was more effective after treatment and at each follow-up point for both symptoms of hypochondriasis and overall changes in functioning and quality of life. But results were still modest, and many eligible patients refused to enter treatment because they were convinced their problems were medical rather than psychological. In another strong study, Allen et al. (2006) found that 40 percent of patients with more severe somatic symptom disorder treated with CBT (versus 7 percent of a group receiving standard medical care) evidenced clinical improvement, and these gains lasted at least a year. Escobar et al. (2007) reported similar results.

One recent trial suggests that cognitive interventions do not seem to be necessary for treating hypochondriasis (Weck et al., 2015). This study randomly assigned patients with hypochondriasis to receive cognitive therapy alone, exposure therapy without explicit cognitive interventions, or a wait-list control group. Compared with the control group, both treatments resulted in large-sized effects for improving symptoms of hypochondriasis. Although the study found a significant reduction in depressive symptoms and bodily complaints for both treatments in comparison with the wait-list, anxiety symptoms were only significantly reduced by the exposure treatment. The exposure procedures consisted of repeatedly confronting the patient with stimuli that are relevant for health anxieties (e.g., documentaries about diseases) without using any avoidance and safety behaviours (e.g., reassurance by doctors, checking the abdomen for cancer).

In our clinics, we concentrate on providing reassurance, reducing stress, and, in particular, reducing the frequency of help-seeking behaviours. One of the most common patterns is the person's tendency to visit numerous medical specialists according to the symptom of the week. An extensive medical and physical workup occurs with every visit to a new physician (or to one who has not been seen for a while). In treatment, to limit these visits, a gatekeeper physician is assigned to each patient to screen all physical complaints. Subsequent visits to specialists must be specifically authorized by this gatekeeper. In the context of a positive therapeutic relationship, most patients are amenable to this arrangement.

Additional therapeutic attention is directed at reducing the supportive consequences of relating to significant others on the basis of physical symptoms alone. More appropriate methods of interacting with others are encouraged. Because Linda, like many patients with this disorder, had managed to become eligible for disability payments, additional goals involved encouraging at least part-time employment, with the ultimate goal of discontinuing disability.

PSYCHOLOGICAL FACTORS AFFECTING MEDICAL CONDITION

A related somatic symptom disorder is called **psychological factors affecting medical condition**. The essential feature of this disorder is the presence of a diagnosed medical condition, such as asthma, diabetes, or severe pain, clearly caused by a known medical condition, such as cancer, that is adversely affected (increased in frequency or severity) by one or more psychological or behavioural factors. These behavioural or psychological factors would have a direct influence on the course or perhaps the treatment of the medical condition. One example would be anxiety severe enough to clearly worsen asthma. Another example would be a patient with diabetes who is in denial about the need to regularly check insulin levels and intervene when necessary. In this case, the pattern would have to be consistent in the neglect of appropriate monitoring and intervention, but the neglect is clearly a behavioural or psychological factor that is adversely affecting the medical condition. This diagnosis would need to be distinguished from the development of stress or anxiety in response to having a severe medical condition that would more appropriately be diagnosed as an adjustment disorder (see Chapter 7). In the Online Chapter, we discuss health psychology and the contribution of psychological factors to physical disorders, including cardiovascular disease, cancer, AIDS, and chronic pain.

CONVERSION DISORDER (FUNCTIONAL NEUROLOGICAL SYMPTOM DISORDER)

The term *conversion* has been used off and on since the Middle Ages (Mace, 1992) but was popularized by Freud, who believed the anxiety resulting from unconscious conflicts somehow was converted into physical symptoms to find expression. This conversion allowed the individual to discharge some anxiety without actually experiencing it. As in phobic disorders, the anxiety resulting from unconscious conflicts might be "displaced" onto another object. In the *DSM-5*, "functional neurological symptom disorder" is a subtitle to conversion disorder, because the term is more often used by neurologists who see the majority of patients receiving a conversion disorder diagnosis and because the term is more acceptable to patients. "Functional" refers to a symptom without an organic cause (Stone et al., 2010). It is likely that the old term "conversion" will be dropped in future editions of the *DSM*.

Clinical Description

Conversion disorders generally have to do with physical malfunctioning, such as paralysis, blindness, or difficulty speaking (aphonia), without any physical or organic pathology to account for the malfunction (see DSM Table 6.3). Most conversion symptoms suggest that some kind of neurological disease is affecting sensory-motor systems, although conversion symptoms can mimic the full range of physical malfunctioning. This disorder has been associated with dissociative symptoms, but we discuss it in this chapter because *DSM-5* lists is as part of the somatic symptom disorders.

DSM-5 | **Table 6.3** Diagnostic Criteria for Conversion Disorder (Functional Neurological Symptom Disorder)

A. One or more symptoms of altered voluntary motor or sensory function.

B. Clinical findings provide evidence of incompatibility between the symptom and recognized neurological or medical conditions.

C. The symptom or deficit is not better explained by another medical or mental disorder.

D. The symptom or deficit causes clinically significant distress or impairment in social, occupational, or other important areas of functioning or warrants medical evaluation.

Specify if:

Acute episode: Symptoms present for less than 6 months

Persistent: Symptoms occurring for 6 months or more

Specify if:

With psychological stressor (specify stressor)

Without psychological stressor

Source: Reprinted with permission from the *Diagnostic and Statistical Manual of Mental Disorders*, Fifth Edition (Copyright © 2013). American Psychiatric Association. All Rights Reserved.

Conversion disorders provide us with some of the most intriguing, sometimes astounding, examples of psychological disorders. What could possibly account for somebody going blind when all visual processes are perfectly normal, or experiencing paralysis of the arms or legs when there is no neurological damage? Consider the case of Eloise.

ELOISE | *Unlearning Walking*

Eloise sat on a chair with her legs under her, refusing to put her feet on the floor. Her mother sat close by, ready to assist her if she needed to move or get up. Her mother had made the appointment and, with the help of a friend, had all but carried Eloise into the office. Eloise was a 20-year-old of borderline intelligence who was friendly and personable during the initial interview and who readily answered all questions with a big smile. She obviously enjoyed the social interaction.

Eloise's difficulty walking developed over five years. Her right leg had given way and she began falling. Gradually, the condition worsened to the point that six months before her admission to the hospital, Eloise could move around only by crawling on the floor.

Physical examinations revealed no physical problems. Eloise presented with a classic case of conversion disorder. Although she was not paralyzed, her specific symptoms included weakness in her legs and difficulty keeping her balance, with the result that she fell frequently. This particular type of conversion symptom is called *astasia-abasia*.

Eloise lived with her mother, who ran a gift shop in the front of her house in a very small rural town. Eloise had been schooled through exceptional education programs until she was about 15; after this, no further programs were available. When Eloise began staying home, her walking began to deteriorate.

In addition to blindness (see Fraser, 1994) and paralysis or weakness in the limbs, conversion symptoms may include the loss of the sense of touch. Some people have seizures, which may be psychological in origin, because no significant EEG changes can be documented. These "seizures" are usually called psychogenic nonepileptic seizures. Another relatively common symptom is *globus hystericus*, the sensation of a lump in the throat that makes it difficult to swallow, eat, or sometimes talk. Conversion symptoms can also include aphonia or even total mutism.

Closely Related Disorders

Distinguishing among conversion reactions, medically explained symptoms, and outright **malingering** (faking) is sometimes difficult. Several factors can help.

First, conversion reactions often have the same quality of indifference to the symptoms that is present in some people with severe somatic symptom disorder. This attitude, called *la belle indifférence*, is considered a hallmark of conversion reactions but, unfortunately, it is not a foolproof sign. A blasé attitude toward illness is sometimes displayed by people with actual physical disorders, and some people with conversion symptoms do become quite distressed.

Second, conversion symptoms are often precipitated by marked stress. Often this stress takes the form of a physical injury. In one large survey, 324 out of 869 patients (37 percent) reported prior physical injury (Stone et al., 2009a). But the occurrence of some identifiable stressor has not been a reliable sign of conversion disorder, since many other disorders are associated with stressful events and stressful events often occur in the lives of people without any disorders. For this reason, the diagnostic criterion that conversion disorder is associated with preceding stress does not appear in the *DSM-5*. Although people with conversion symptoms can usually function normally, they seem truly unaware either of this ability or of sensory input. For example, individuals with the conversion symptom of blindness can usually avoid objects in their visual field, but they will tell you they can't see the objects. Similarly, individuals with conversion symptoms of paralysis of the legs might suddenly get up and run in an emergency and then be astounded they were able to do this. It is possible that at least some people who experience miraculous cures during religious ceremonies may have been dealing with conversion reactions. These factors may help in distinguishing between conversion and organically based physical disorders, but clinicians sometimes make mistakes, although it is not common with modern diagnostic techniques. For example, Moene and colleagues (2000) carefully reassessed 85 patients diagnosed with conversion disorder and found 10 (11.8 percent) had developed some evidence of a neurological disorder approximately 2.5 years after the first exam. Stone and colleagues (2005), summarizing a number of studies, estimate the rate of misdiagnosis of conversion disorders that are really physical problems is approximately 4 percent, having improved considerably from earlier decades. In any case, ruling out medical causes for the symptoms is crucial to making a diagnosis of conversion and, given advances in medical screening procedures, this is the principal diagnostic criterion in the *DSM-5* (American Psychiatric Association, 2013; Stone et al., 2010).

It can be very difficult to distinguish between individuals who are truly experiencing conversion symptoms in a seemingly involuntary way and malingerers who are very good at faking symptoms. Once malingerers are exposed, their motivation is clear: They are either trying to get out of something, such as work or legal difficulties, or they are attempting to gain something, such as a financial settlement. Malingerers are fully aware of what they are doing and are clearly attempting to manipulate others to gain a desired end.

More puzzling is a set of conditions called **factitious disorders**, which fall somewhere between malingering and conversion disorders. The symptoms are under voluntary control, as with malingering, but the person has no obvious reason for voluntarily producing the symptoms except, possibly, to assume the sick role and receive increased attention. Tragically, this disorder may extend to producing symptoms in other members of the family. An adult, almost always a mother, may purposely make her child sick, evidently for the attention and pity then given to the mother who is causing the symptoms—a condition called *factitious disorder imposed on another*. It was known previously as *Munchausen syndrome by proxy* (Check, 1998). DSM Table 6.4 shows the diagnostic criteria for factitious disorders.

The offending parent may resort to extreme tactics to create the appearance of illness in the child. For example, one mother stirred her child's urine specimen with a vaginal tampon obtained during menstruation. Another mother mixed feces into her child's vomit (Check, 1998). Because the mother typically establishes a positive relationship with a medical staff, the true nature of the illness is most often unsuspected and the staff perceives the parent as remarkably caring and very involved in providing for her child's well-being. For this reason the mother is often very successful at eluding suspicion. Helpful procedures to assess the possibility of factitious disorder imposed on another by proxy include a trial separation of the mother and the child or video surveillance of the child while in the hospital. An important study has appeared validating the utility of surveillance in hospital rooms of children with suspected factitious disorder imposed on another. In this study, video surveillance was the method used to

DSM-5	**Table 6.4** Diagnostic Criteria for Factitious Disorder

A. Falsification of physical or psychological signs or symptoms, or induction of injury or disease, associated with identified deception.

B. The individual presents himself or herself to others as ill, impaired or injured.

C. The deceptive behavior is evident even in the absence of obvious external rewards.

D. The behavior is not better accounted for by another mental disorder, such as delusional disorder or another psychotic disorder.

Specify:

Single episode

Recurrent episodes (two or more events of falsification of illness and/or induction of injury)

Source: Reprinted with permission from the *Diagnostic and Statistical Manual of Mental Disorders*, Fifth Edition (Copyright © 2013). American Psychiatric Association. All Rights Reserved.

establish the diagnosis in many cases. In one case a child was suffering from recurring *Escherichia coli infections*, and cameras caught the mother injecting her own urine into the child's intravenous line (Hall et al., 2000).

Unconscious Mental Processes

Unconscious cognitive processes seem to play a role in much of psychopathology (although not necessarily as Freud envisioned them), but nowhere is this phenomenon more readily and dramatically apparent than when we attempt to distinguish between conversion disorders and related conditions. New information (reviewed in Chapter 2) on unconscious cognitive processes becomes important. We are all capable of receiving and processing information in a number of sensory channels (such as vision and hearing) without being aware of it. Remember the phenomenon of blind sight or unconscious vision? Weiskrantz (1980) and others discovered that people with small, localized damage to certain parts of their brains could identify objects in their field of vision, but they had no awareness whatsoever that they could see. Could this happen to people without brain damage? Consider the case of Celia.

CELIA | *Seeing through Blindness*

A 15-year-old girl named Celia was suddenly unable to see. Shortly thereafter she regained some of her sight, but her vision was so severely blurred that she could not read. When she was brought to a clinic for testing, psychologists arranged a series of sophisticated vision tests that did not require her to report when she could or could not see. One of the tasks required her to examine three triangles displayed on three separate screens and to press a button under the screen containing an upright triangle. Celia performed perfectly on this test without being aware that she could see anything (Grosz & Zimmerman, 1970). Was Celia faking? Evidently not, or she would have purposely made a mistake.

Sackeim, Nordlie, and Gur (1979) evaluated the potential difference between real unconscious process and faking by hypnotizing two subjects and giving each a suggestion of total blindness. One subject was also told it was extremely important that she appears to everyone to be blind. The second subject was not given further instructions. The first subject, evidently following instructions to appear blind at all costs, performed far below chance on a visual discrimination task similar to the upright triangle task. On almost every trial she chose the wrong answer. The second subject, with the hypnotic suggestion of blindness but no instructions to appear blind at all costs, performed perfectly on the visual discrimination tasks—although she reported she could not see anything.

How is this relevant to identifying malingering? In an earlier case, Grosz and Zimmerman (1965) evaluated a male who seemed to have conversion symptoms of blindness. They discovered that he performed much more poorly than chance on a visual discrimination task. Subsequent information from other sources confirmed that he was almost certainly malingering. To review these distinctions, someone who is truly blind would perform at a chance level on visual discrimination tasks. People with conversion symptoms, conversely, can see objects in their visual field and, therefore, would perform well on these tasks, but this experience is dissociated from their awareness of sight. Malingerers and, perhaps, individuals with factitious disorders simply do everything possible to pretend they can't see.

Statistics

We have already seen that conversion disorder may occur in conjunction with other disorders, particularly somatic symptom disorder, as in the case of Linda. Linda's paralysis passed after several months and did not return, although on occasion she would report feeling as if it were returning. Conversion disorders are relatively rare in mental health settings, but remember that people who seek help for this condition are more likely to consult neurologists or other specialists. The prevalence estimate in neurological settings is high, averaging about 30 percent (Rowe, 2010; Stone et al., 2009). One study estimated that 30 percent of all patients referred to epilepsy centres have psychogenic nonepileptic seizures (Benbadis & Allen-Hauser, 2000; Schoenberg et al., 2012).

Like severe somatic symptom disorder, conversion disorders are found primarily in women (Brown & Lewis-Fernandez, 2011; Deveci et al., 2007) and typically develop during adolescence or slightly thereafter. Conversion reactions have also been reported in soldiers exposed to severe combat, mainly during World War I and II (Mucha & Reinhardt, 1970; Perez-Sales, 1990). The symptoms often disappear after a time, only to return later in the same or similar form when a new stressor occurs. A three-year longitudinal study of 88 patients by University of Toronto researchers suggests that, in the case of conversion disorders involving movement disturbances (like those seen in the case of Eloise), long-term prognosis is quite poor (Feinstein et al., 2001). The conversion disorder (i.e., the movement disturbance) had remitted or resolved in only 5 percent of the participants at the follow-up.

In some cultures, conversion symptoms are very common aspects of religious or healing rituals. Seizures, paralysis, and trances are common in some fundamentalist religious groups in North America (Griffith et al., 1980), and they are often seen as evidence of contact with God. Individuals who exhibit such symptoms are thus held in high esteem by their peers. These symptoms do not meet the criteria for a disorder unless they persist and interfere with an individual's functioning.

Causes

Freud described four basic processes in the development of conversion disorder. First, the individual experiences a traumatic event—in Freud's view, an unacceptable, unconscious conflict. Second, because the conflict and the resulting anxiety are unacceptable, the person represses the conflict, making it unconscious. Third, the anxiety continues to increase and threatens to emerge into consciousness, and the person converts it into physical symptoms, thereby relieving the pressure of having to deal directly with the conflict. This reduction of anxiety is considered to be the primary gain or reinforcing event that maintains the conversion symptom. Fourth, the individual receives greatly increased attention and sympathy from loved ones and may also be allowed to avoid a difficult situation or task. Freud considered such attention or avoidance to be the *secondary gain* or the secondarily reinforcing set of events.

We believe Freud was basically correct on at least three counts and possibly a fourth, although firm evidence supporting any of these ideas is sparse and Freud's views were far more complex than represented here. What seems to happen is that individuals with conversion disorder have experienced a traumatic event or events that must be escaped at all costs (Brown & Lewis-Fernandez, 2011; Stone et al., 2009a). This might be combat, where death is imminent, or being exposed to an accident or a homicide. Because simply running away is unacceptable in most cases, the socially acceptable alternative of getting sick is substituted; but getting sick on purpose is also unacceptable, so this motivation is detached from the person's consciousness. Finally, because the escape behaviour (the conversion symptoms) is successful to an extent in obliterating the traumatic situation, the behaviour continues until the underlying problem is resolved.

One study confirms these hypotheses, at least partially (Wyllie et al., 1999). In this study, 34 child and adolescent patients, 25 of them girls, were evaluated after receiving a diagnosis of psychologically based pseudoseizures (psychogenic nonepileptic seizures). Many of these children and adolescents presented with additional psychological disorders, including 32 percent with mood disorders and 24 percent with separation anxiety and school refusal. Other anxiety disorders were present in some additional patients.

When the extent of psychological stress in the lives of these children was examined, it was found that most of the patients had substantial stress, including a history of sexual abuse, recent parental divorce or death of a close family member, and physical abuse. The authors conclude that major mood disorders and severe traumatic stress, especially sexual abuse, are common among children and adolescents with the conversion disorder of pseudoseizures, as other studies have similarly indicated (Roelofs et al., 2002).

The one step in Freud's progression of events about which some questions remain is the issue of primary gain. The notion of primary gain accounts for the feature of *la belle indifférence* (cited previously), where individuals seem not the least bit distressed about their symptoms. In other words, Freud thought that because symptoms reflected an unconscious attempt to resolve a conflict, the patient would not be upset by them. But patients with conversion disorder are in fact often quite distressed by their symptoms. Formal tests of this feature of indifference also provide little support for Freud's claim. For example, Lader and Sartorius (1968) compared patients with conversion disorder with control groups of anxious patients without conversion symptoms. The patients with conversion disorder showed equal or greater anxiety and physiological arousal than the control group. The impression of indifference may be more in the mind of the therapist than true of the patient.

Social and cultural influences also contribute to conversion disorder, which, like somatic symptom disorder, tends to occur in less educated, lower socioeconomic groups, in which knowledge about disease and medical illness is not well developed (Brown & Lewis-Fernandez, 2011; Kirmayer et al., 2003). For

▲ The seizures and trances that may be symptomatic of conversion disorder are also common in some fundamentalist religious groups in North America.

example, Binzer, Andersen, and Kullgren (1997) noted that 13 percent of their 30 patients with motor disabilities due to conversion disorder had attended high school, compared with 67 percent in a control group with motor symptoms due to a physical cause.

Prior experience with real physical problems, usually among other family members, tends to influence the later choice of specific conversion symptoms; that is, patients tend to adopt symptoms with which they are familiar (e.g., Brady & Lind, 1961). Furthermore, the incidence of these disorders has decreased over the decades (Kirmayer et al., 2003). The most likely explanation is that increased knowledge of the real causes of physical problems by both patients and loved ones eliminates much of the possibility of secondary gain so important in these disorders.

Finally, many conversion symptoms seem to be part of a larger constellation of psychopathology. In some cases, individuals may have a marked biological vulnerability to develop the disorder when under stress, with biological processes like those discussed in the context of somatic symptom disorder. In other cases, exposure to traumatic events may play a large contributing role. For countless other cases, however, biological contributory factors seem to be less important than the overriding influence of interpersonal factors, such as the actions of Eloise's mother, as we will see. We talk about Eloise's treatments in the next section. There you will see that the extent of these patients' suffering and the successful resolution of their symptoms point primarily to a psychological and social etiology.

Treatment

Although few systematic controlled studies have evaluated the effectiveness of treatment for conversion disorders, we often treat these conditions in our clinics, as do others (e.g., Campo & Negrini, 2000; Moene et al., 2002, 2003), and our methods closely follow our thinking on etiology. Because conversion disorder has much in common with somatic symptom disorder, many of the treatment principles are similar.

Some conversion symptoms involve movements, such as tremors, that are perceived as involuntary. But what makes a movement either voluntary or involuntary? In one recent study, neuroscientists attempted to find out (Voon et al., 2010). These investigators assessed eight patients who presented with motor tremors without any neurological basis (conversion tremors). In a clever experiment, they used functional magnetic resonance imaging (fMRI) to compare brain activity during the conversion tremor but also during a voluntary mimicked tremor in which patients were instructed to produce the tremor on purpose. The investigators found that the conversion tremor, as compared with the voluntary tremor, was associated with lower activity in the right inferior parietal cortex. This is an area of the brain that functions to compare internal predictions with actual events. In other words, if an individual wants to move his or her arm and then decides to go ahead and move it, this area of the brain determines if the desired action has occurred. Because we think about making a movement before we do it, the brain concludes (correctly in most cases) that we caused the movement to occur. But if this area of the brain is not functioning properly, then the brain might conclude that the movement is involuntary.

Of course, it is not clear whether this brain activity is a cause or a result of conversion symptoms, but these sophisticated brain-imaging technologies may eventually bring us closer to understanding at least one part of the puzzle of conversion symptoms in some people.

A principal strategy in treating conversion disorder is to identify and attend to the traumatic or stressful life event, if it is still present (either in real life or in memory). As in the case of Anna O., therapeutic assistance in re-experiencing or "reliving" the event (catharsis) is a reasonable first step. The therapist must also work very hard to reduce any reinforcing or supportive consequences of the conversion symptoms (secondary gain). For example, in the case of Eloise, it was quite clear that her mother found it convenient if Eloise stayed pretty much in one place most of the day while her mother attended to the store in the front of the house. Eloise's immobility was thus strongly reinforced by motherly attention and concern. Any unnecessary mobility was punished. The therapist must collaborate with both the patient and the family to eliminate such self-defeating behaviours.

Many times, removing the secondary gain is easier said than done. Eloise was successfully treated in the clinic. Through intensive daily work with the staff, she was able to walk again. To accomplish this, she had to practise walking every day with considerable support, attention, and praise from the staff. When her mother visited, the staff noticed that she verbalized her pleasure with Eloise's progress, but her facial expressions, or affect, conveyed a different message. The mother lived a good distance from the clinic, so she could not attend sessions, but she promised to carry out the program at home after Eloise was discharged. She didn't, however. A follow-up contact six months after Eloise was discharged revealed that she had totally relapsed and was once again spending almost all her time in a room in the back of the house while her mother attended to business out front.

Cognitive-behavioural programs appear to hold promise in the treatment of conversion disorder. In one study, 65 percent of a group of 45 patients with mostly motor behaviour conversions (e.g., difficulty walking) responded well to such treatment. Hypnosis, which was administered to approximately half of the patients, did not confer any additional benefit to the CBT (Moene et al., 2002).

Concept Check 6.1

Diagnose the somatic symptom and related disorders described here by choosing one of the following: (a) illness anxiety disorder, (b) somatic symptom disorder, and (c) conversion disorder.

1. Emily constantly worries about her health. She has been to numerous doctors for her concerns about cancer and other serious diseases—even though she doesn't report current notable physical symptoms—only to be reassured of her well-being. Emily's anxiousness is exacerbated by each small ailment (e.g., mild headaches or stomach pains) that she considers to be indications of a major illness. _____

2. D. J. arrived at Dr. Blake's office with a folder crammed full of medical records, symptom documentation, and lists of prescribed treatments and drugs. Several doctors are monitoring him for his complaints, ranging from marked chest pain to difficulty swallowing. D. J. recently lost his job for using too many sick days.

_____

3. Sixteen-year-old Chad suddenly lost the use of his arms, with no medical cause. The complete paralysis slowly improved to the point that he could slightly raise them. However, Chad cannot drive, pick up objects, or perform most tasks necessary for day-to-day life.

OBSESSIVE-COMPULSIVE AND RELATED DISORDERS

The disorders described in this section involve preoccupations, rituals, and compulsions that are excessive and maladaptive. We begin with the most prominent disorder in this group—obsessive-compulsive disorder.

Obsessive-compulsive disorder (OCD) is the devastating culmination of the anxiety and related disorders. It is not uncommon for someone with OCD to experience severe generalized anxiety, recurrent panic attacks, debilitating avoidance, and major depression, all occurring simultaneously in conjunction with obsessive-compulsive symptoms. With OCD, establishing even a foothold of control and predictability over the dangerous events in life seems so utterly hopeless that victims resort to magic and rituals.

RICHARD | *Enslaved by Ritual*

Richard, a 19-year-old first-year university student majoring in philosophy, withdrew from school because of incapacitating ritualistic behaviour. He abandoned personal hygiene because the compulsive rituals that he had to carry out during washing or cleaning were so time-consuming that he could do nothing else. Almost continual showering gave way to no showering. He stopped cutting and washing his hair and beard, brushing his teeth, and changing his clothes. He left his room infrequently and, to avoid rituals associated with the toilet, defecated on paper towels, urinated in paper cups, and stored the waste in the closet. He ate only at night when his family was asleep. To be able to eat he had to exhale completely, making a lot of hissing noises, coughs, and hacks, and then fill his mouth with as much food as he could while no air was in his lungs. He would eat only a mixture of peanut butter, sugar, cocoa, milk, and mayonnaise. All other foods he considered contaminants. When he walked he took very small steps on his toes while continually looking back, checking and rechecking. On occasion he ran quickly in place. He withdrew his left arm completely from his shirtsleeve as if he were injured and his shirt was a sling.

Clinical Description

In other anxiety disorders the danger is usually in an external object or situation, or at least the memory of one. In OCD the dangerous event is a thought, an image, or an impulse that the client attempts to avoid as completely as someone with a snake phobia avoids snakes (Clark & O'Connor, 2005). For example, has anyone ever told you not to think of pink elephants? If you really concentrate on not thinking of pink elephants, using every mental means possible, you will realize how difficult it is to suppress a suggested thought or image. Individuals with OCD fight this battle all day, every day, sometimes for most of their lives, and they usually fail miserably. In Chapter 3, we discussed the case of Frank, who experienced involuntary thoughts of epilepsy or seizures and prayed or shook his leg to try to distract himself. **Obsessions** are intrusive and mostly nonsensical thoughts, images, or urges that the individual tries to resist or eliminate. **Compulsions** are the thoughts or actions used to suppress the obsessions and provide relief. Frank had both obsessions and compulsions but his disorder was mild compared with the case of Richard.

Like everyone with OCD, Richard experienced intrusive and persistent thoughts and impulses; in his case, they were about sex, aggression, and religion. His various behaviours were efforts to suppress sexual and aggressive thoughts or to ward off the disastrous consequences he thought would ensue if he did not perform his rituals. Richard performed most of the repetitive behaviours and mental acts mentioned in the *DSM* (see DSM Table 6.5).

DSM-5	**Table 6.5** Diagnostic Criteria for Obsessive-Compulsive Disorder

A. Presence of obsessions, compulsions or both:

Obsessions are defined by (1) and (2):

1. Recurrent and persistent thoughts, urges, or images that are experienced, at some time during the disturbance, as intrusive and inappropriate and that in most individuals cause marked anxiety or distress.

2. The individual attempts to ignore or suppress such thoughts, impulses, or images, or to neutralize them with some other thought or action (i.e., by performing a compulsion). Compulsions are defined by (1) and (2):

    1. Repetitive behaviors (e.g., handwashing, ordering, checking) or mental acts (e.g., praying, counting, repeating words silently) that the individual feels driven to perform in response to an obsession or according to rules that must be applied rigidly.

    2. The behaviors or mental acts are aimed at preventing or reducing distress, or preventing some dreaded event or situation; however, these behaviors or mental acts either are not connected in a realistic way with what they are designed to neutralize or prevent, or are clearly excessive.

    Note: Young children may not be able to articulate the aims of these behaviours or mental acts.

B. The obsessions or compulsions are time-consuming (e.g., take more than 1 hour per day) or cause clinically significant distress or impairment in social, occupational, or other important areas of functioning.

C. The obsessive-compulsive symptoms are not attributable to the physiological effects of a substance (e.g., a drug of abuse, a medication) or another medical condition.

D. The disturbance is not better explained by the symptoms of another mental disorder (e.g., excessive worries, as in generalized anxiety disorder; preoccupation with appearance, as in body dysmorphic disorder; difficulty discarding or parting with possessions, as in hoarding disorder; hair pulling, as in trichotillomania [hair-pulling disorder]; skin picking, as in excoriation [skin-picking disorder]; stereotypies, as in stereotypic movement disorder; ritualized eating behavior, as in eating disorders; preoccupation with substances or gambling, as in substance-related and addictive disorders; preoccupation with having an illness, as in illness anxiety disorder; sexual urges or fantasies, as in paraphilic disorders; impulses, as in disruptive, impulse-control and conduct disorders; guilty ruminations, as in major depressive disorder; thought insertion or delusional preoccupations, as in schizophrenia spectrum and other psychotic disorders; or repetitive patterns of behavior, as in autism spectrum disorder).

Specify if:

With good or fair insight: The individual recognizes that obsessive-compulsive disorder beliefs are definitely or probably not true or that they may or may not be true.

With poor insight: The individual thinks obsessive-compulsive disorder beliefs are probably true.

With absent insight/delusional beliefs: The individual is completely convinced that obsessive-compulsive disorder beliefs are true.

Specify if:

Tic-related: The individual has a current or past history of a tic disorder.

Compulsions can be either behavioural (handwashing, checking) or mental (thinking about certain words in a specific order, counting, praying, and so on; Foa et al., 1996; Purdon, 2009; Steketee & Barlow, 2002). The important thing is that they are believed to reduce stress or prevent a dreaded event. Compulsions are often "magical" in that they frequently bear no logical relation to the obsession.

Types of Obsessions and Compulsions

Based on statistically associated groupings, there are four major types of obsessions (Bloch et al., 2008; Mathews, 2009) and each is associated with a pattern of compulsive behaviour (see Table 6.1). Symmetry obsessions account for most obsessions (27 percent), followed by "forbidden thoughts or actions" (21 percent), cleaning and contamination (16 percent), and hoarding (15 percent) (Bloch et al., 2008). Symmetry refers to keeping things in perfect order or doing something in a specific way. As a child, were you careful not to step on cracks in the sidewalk? You and your friends might have kept this up for a few minutes before tiring of it. But what if you had to spend your whole life avoiding cracks, on foot or in a car, to prevent something bad from happening? You wouldn't have much fun. People with aggressive (forbidden) obsessive impulses may feel they are about to yell out a swear word in a place of worship. One patient of ours, a young and moral woman, was afraid to ride the bus for fear that if a man sat down beside her she would grab his crotch! In reality, this would be the last thing she would do, but the aggressive urge was so horrifying that she made every attempt possible to suppress it and to avoid riding the bus or similar situations where the impulse might occur.

Certain kinds of obsessions are strongly associated with certain kinds of rituals (Bloch et al., 2008; Calamari et al., 2004; Leckman et al., 1997a). For example, forbidden thoughts or actions, as indicated in Table 6.2, seem to lead to checking rituals. Checking rituals serve to prevent an imagined disaster or catastrophe. Many are logical, such as repeatedly checking the stove to see whether you turned it off, but severe cases can be illogical. For example, Richard thought that if he did not eat in a certain way he might become possessed. If he didn't take small

steps and look back, some disaster might happen to his family. A mental act, such as counting, can also be a compulsion. Obsessions with symmetry lead to ordering and arranging or repeating rituals; obsessions with contamination lead to washing rituals that may restore a sense of safety and control (Rachman, 2006). Like Richard, many patients have several kinds of obsessions and compulsions.

On rare occasions, patients, particularly children, will present with compulsions, but few or no identifiable obsessions. We saw an eight-year-old child who felt compelled to undress, put on his pyjamas, and turn down the covers in a time-consuming fashion each night; he always repeated the ritual three times. He could give no particular reason for his behaviour; he simply had to do it.

Canadian comedian Howie Mandel has OCD. He is a member of the Bell Let's Talk team and speaks very openly about it (Bell Canada, 2019). Like the majority of people with OCD, his obsessions centre on themes of contamination. He is concerned he will be infected by germs from other people around him. Thus, Mandel carefully avoids shaking hands with other people, unless he is wearing latex gloves. Mandel has reported that his OCD symptoms cause him disruption when he stays in hotels. He reportedly orders two-dozen towels when he arrives at a hotel, and makes paths with them so that he does not have to step on the hotel carpets. He also avoids being around people if they have any sign of illness, like a cold. When his OCD symptoms are at their worst, his compulsions include retreating to a second "sterile" house he had built on his property where he isolates himself from the world. He even retreats there to avoid family members if he suspects any of them have something contagious, like the flu (CBS News, 1999).

In a recent interview (Hedegaard, 2019), Mandel said he was doing okay but also admitted to significant struggles: "Yeah, I don't touch shoelaces," he says, almost bristling with disgust. "I just won't." Then he brightens and says, "I'm not as bad as I was [with these things]. I have OCD, I have ADHD, I have anxiety, I have depression, I go see somebody, I'm heavily medicated, and I'm constantly in fear and constantly uncomfortable and constantly fighting. But it's gotten to where I'm really comfortable with discomfort. I've learned that's who I am, and that's what makes me feel alive."

TABLE 6.1 | Types of Obsessions and Associated Compulsions

Symptom Subtype	Obsession	Compulsion
Symmetry/exactness/"just right"	Needing things to be symmetrical/aligned just so Urges to do things over and over until they feel "just right"	Putting things in a certain order Repeating rituals
Forbidden thoughts or actions (aggressive/sexual/religious)	Fears, urges to harm self or others Fears of offending God	Checking Avoidance Repeated requests for reassurance
Cleaning/contamination	Germs Fears of germs or contaminants	Repetitive or excessive washing Using gloves, masks to do daily tasks
Hoarding	Fears of throwing anything away	Collecting/saving objects with little or no actual or sentimental value, such as food wrappings

Source: Adapted from Mathews (2009) and Bloch et al. (2008).

© Cengage Learning

Obsessive-Compulsive Disorder: Chuck

"I'm a little bit obsessive-compulsive. . . . It's a little difficult to deal with. The obsessive part—I'll get a thought in my head, and I can't put it out. It's just there all the time. I think about it when I go to bed, I think about it when I get up. . . . I'm a 'checker'—I have to check things. . . . I don't cook, but I have to check the stove every morning . . . not always really rational."

Visit login.cengage.com to start using MindTap. Enter the Online Access Code from the card included with your text. If a code card is not provided, you can purchase instant access at Cengage.ca.

Tic Disorder and OCD

It is common for tic disorder, characterized by involuntary movement (sudden jerking of limbs, for example), to co-occur in patients with OCD (particularly children) or in their families (Browne et al., 2015; Grados et al., 2001; Leckman et al., 2010; Mataix- Cols et al., 2013). More complex tics with involuntary vocalizations are referred to as Tourette's disorder (Leckman et al., 2010). In some cases, these movements are not tics but may be compulsions, as they were in the case of Frank in Chapter 3 who kept jerking his leg if thoughts of seizures entered his head. Approximately 10 to 40 percent of children and adolescents with OCD also have had tic disorder at some point (Leckman et al., 2010). The obsessions in tic-related OCD are almost always related to symmetry. CBT has been found to be quite effective for treating tic disorders (McGuire et al., 2015).

Observations among one small group of children presenting with OCD and tics suggest that these problems occurred after a bout of strep throat. This syndrome has been referred to as pediatric autoimmune disorder associated with streptococcal infection, or "Pandas" (Leckman et al., 2010; Radomsky & Taylor, 2005). Presentation of OCD in these cases differs somewhat from OCD without a history of Pandas in several ways. The Pandas group is more likely to be male, experience dramatic onset of symptoms, often associated with fever or sore throat, have full remissions between episodes, show remission of symptoms during antibiotic therapy, have evidence of past streptococcal infections, and present with noticeable clumsiness (Murphy et al., 2012). Recently, this syndrome has been revised and broadened under the umbrella term pediatric autoimmune neuropsychiatric syndrome (PANS) (Sweo et al., 2012). The prevalence of this condition has yet to be determined.

Statistics

Estimates of the lifetime prevalence of OCD range from 1.6 to 2.3 percent (Calamari et al., 2012; Kessler, Berglund, et al., 2005), and in a given one-year period, the prevalence is about 1 percent (Calamari et al., 2012; Kessler, Chiu, et al., 2006). Not all cases meeting criteria for OCD are as severe as Richard's. Obsessions and compulsions can be arranged along a continuum,

like most clinical features of most disorders. Intrusive and distressing thoughts are common in nonclinical ("normal") individuals (Boyer & Liénard, 2008; Clark & Rhyno, 2005; Fullana et al., 2009). Spinella (2005) found that 13 percent of a "normal" community sample of people had moderate levels of obsessions or compulsions that were not severe enough to meet diagnostic criteria for OCD. Between 10 and 15 percent of university students engaged in checking behaviour substantial enough to score within the range of patients with OCD (Frost et al., 1986).

It would also be unusual not to have an occasional intrusive or strange thought. Many people have bizarre, sexual, or aggressive thoughts, particularly if they are bored—for

▲ Comedian Howie Mandel, host of the television game show *Deal or No Deal* and judge on *America's Got Talent*, has OCD characterized by obsessions of becoming contaminated by germs.

example, when sitting in class. Some of these thoughts are listed in Table 6.2.

Have you had any of these thoughts? Most people do, but they let these thoughts drift into their mind and out of it again. Certain individuals, however, are horrified by such thoughts, considering them signs of an alien, intrusive, evil force. OCD has a female-to-male ratio that is nearly 1:1. However, there is some evidence in children that there are more males than females (Hanna, 1995). This seems to be because boys tend to develop OCD earlier.

TABLE 6.2 | Obsessions and Intrusive Thoughts Reported by Nonclinical Samples*

Harming

Impulse to jump out of high window

Idea of jumping in front of a car

Impulse to push someone in front of train

Wishing a person would die

While holding a baby, having a sudden urge to kick it

Thoughts of dropping a baby

The thought that if I forget to say goodbye to someone, they might die

Thought that thinking about horrible things happening to a child will cause it

Contamination or Disease

Thought of catching a disease from public pools or other public places

Thoughts I may have caught a disease from touching toilet seat

Idea that dirt is always on my hand

Inappropriate or Unacceptable Behaviour

Idea of swearing or yelling at my boss

Thought of doing something embarrassing in public, like forgetting to wear a top

Hoping someone doesn't succeed

Thought of blurting out something in church

Thought of "unnatural" sexual acts

Doubts about Safety, Memory, and So On

Thought that I haven't locked the house up properly

Idea of leaving my curling iron on the carpet and forgetting to pull out the plug

Thought that I've left the heater and stove on

Idea that I've left the car unlocked when I know I've locked it

Idea that objects are not arranged perfectly

*Examples were obtained from Rachman (1978) and from unpublished research by Dana Thordarson, Ph.D., and Michael Kyrios, Ph.D. (personal communication), at the University of British Columbia.

Source: Republished with permission of Guilford Publications, from *Anxiety and Its Disorders: The Nature and Treatment of Anxiety and Panic* by Barlow, David H. © 2019; permission conveyed through Copyright Clearance Center, Inc.

By mid-adolescence, the sex ratio is approximately equal (Albano et al., 1996). The average age of onset ranges from early adolescence to the mid-20s but peaks earlier in males (at 13 to 15) than in females (at 20 to 24; Rasmussen & Eisen, 1990). Once OCD develops, it tends to become chronic (Calamari et al., 2012; Steketee & Barlow, 2002).

In Arabic countries, OCD is easily recognizable, although, as always, cultural beliefs and concerns influence the content of the obsessions and the nature of the compulsions. In Saudi Arabia and Egypt, obsessions are primarily related to religious practices, specifically the Muslim emphasis on cleanliness. Contamination themes are also highly prevalent in India. Nevertheless, OCD looks remarkably similar across cultures. Studies from England, Hong Kong, India, Egypt, Japan, and Norway have found essentially similar types and proportions of obsessions and compulsions, as did studies from Canada, Finland, Taiwan, Africa, Puerto Rico, Korea, and New Zealand (Horwath & Weissman, 2000; Weissman et al., 1994).

Causes

Many of us sometimes have intrusive, even horrific thoughts (Rachman, 2003; Rachman & deSilva, 1978) and occasionally engage in ritualistic behaviour, especially when we are under stress (Parkinson & Rachman, 1981a, 1981b; Rachman & deSilva, 2004). But very few of us develop OCD. Once again, as with panic disorder and post-traumatic stress disorder, one must develop anxiety focused on the possibility of having additional intrusive thoughts.

The repetitive, intrusive, unacceptable thoughts of OCD may well be regulated by the brain circuit described in Chapter 2. However, the tendency to develop anxiety over having additional compulsive thoughts may have the same generalized biological and psychological precursors as anxiety in general (Barlow et al., 2013; Suárez et al., 2009).

Why would people with OCD focus their anxiety on the occasional intrusive thought rather than on the possibility of a panic attack or some other external situation? One hypothesis is that early experiences taught them that some thoughts are dangerous and unacceptable because the terrible things they are thinking might actually happen and they would be responsible. The experiences would result in a specific psychological vulnerability to develop OCD. They learn this through the same process of misinformation that convinced the person with snake phobia that snakes were dangerous and could be everywhere. Clients with OCD equate thoughts with the specific actions or activity represented by the thoughts. Rachman and his colleagues call this "thought-action fusion" (Rachman, 1998; Rachman & Shafran, 1998; Shafran et al., 1996). Thought-action fusion may, in turn, be caused by attitudes of excessive responsibility and resulting guilt developed during childhood where even a bad thought is associated with evil intent (Clark & O'Connor, 2005; Steketee & Barlow, 2002; Taylor et al., 2012). One patient believed thinking about abortion was the moral equivalent of having an abortion.

Richard finally admitted to having strong homosexual impulses that were unacceptable to him and to his minister father, and he believed the impulses were as sinful as actual acts. Many people with OCD who believe in the tenets of fundamental religions, whether Christian, Jewish, or Islamic, present with similar attitudes of inflated responsibility and thought-action fusion. One study showed that the strength of religious belief, but not the type of belief, was associated with severity of OCD (Steketee et al., 1991). Of course, the vast majority of people with fundamental beliefs do not develop OCD.

But what if the most frightening thing in your life was not a snake, or speaking in public, but a terrible thought that happened to pop into your head? You can't avoid it as you would a snake, so you resist this thought by attempting to suppress it or neutralize it using mental or behavioural strategies such as distraction, praying, or checking. These strategies become compulsions, but they are doomed to fail in the long term because these strategies backfire and actually increase the frequency of the thought (Franklin & Foa, 2014; Wegner, 1989). Christine Purdon at the University of Waterloo and David Clark at the University of New Brunswick have conducted a large body of research in this area. On the basis of their work and reviews of the literature, they conclude that there is indeed an association between attempted thought suppression and obsessional thinking (Clark & Purdon, 1995; Purdon, 1999, 2004; Purdon & Clark, 2000). Moreover, if someone appraises a given negative thought as unacceptable, that person will be motivated to try to suppress the thought (Purdon, 2004). Once again, generalized biological and psychological vulnerabilities must be present for OCD to develop. Believing some thoughts are unacceptable and therefore must be suppressed (a specific psychological vulnerability) may put people at greater risk of OCD (Parkinson & Rachman, 1981b; Salkovskis & Campbell, 1994). A model of the etiology of OCD that is somewhat similar to other models of anxiety disorders is presented in ■ Figure 6.2.

Treatment

The effects of drugs on OCD have been evaluated extensively (Dougherty et al., 2012; Steketee & Barlow, 2002; Stewart et al., 2009). The most effective seem to be those that specifically inhibit the reuptake of serotonin, such as clomipramine or the SSRIs, which benefit up to 60 percent of patients with OCD, with no particular advantage to one drug over another. However, relapse frequently occurs when the drug is discontinued (Dougherty et al., 2012; Lydiard et al., 1996).

Highly structured psychological treatments work somewhat better than drugs, but they are not readily available. The most effective approach is exposure and ritual prevention (ERP), a process whereby the rituals are actively prevented and the patient is systematically and gradually exposed to the feared thoughts or situations (Abramowitz et al., 2012; Franklin & Foa, 2014). Richard would be systematically exposed to harmless objects or situations that he thought were contaminated, including certain foods and household chemicals, and his washing and checking rituals would be prevented. Usually, this can be done by simply working closely with patients to see that they do not wash or check. In severe cases, patients may be hospitalized and the faucets removed from the bathroom sink for a time to discourage repeated washing. No matter how the rituals are prevented, the procedures seem to facilitate "reality testing," because the client soon learns, at an emotional level, that no harm will result whether he carries out the rituals or not. More recent innovations to evidence-based psychological treatments for OCD have examined the efficacy of cognitive treatments with a focus on the overestimation of threat, the

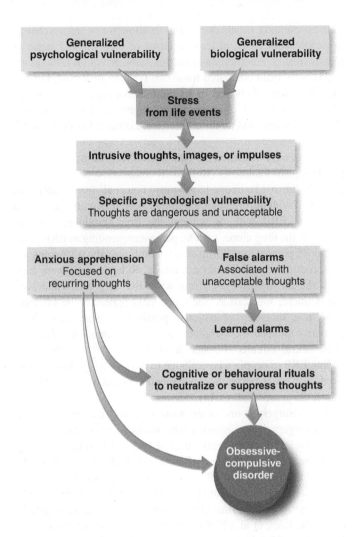

FIGURE 6.2 | A model of the causes of obsessive-compulsive disorder.

Source: Republished with permission of Guilford Publications, from *Anxiety and Its Disorders: The Nature and Treatment of Anxiety and Panic* by Barlow, David H. © 2019; permission conveyed through Copyright Clearance Center, Inc.

importance and control of intrusive thoughts, the sense of inflated responsibility present in patients with OCD who think they alone may be responsible for preventing a catastrophe, and the need for perfectionism and certainty present in these patients (Whittal & Robichaud, 2012). Initial results indicate that these strategies are effective, perhaps as effective as ERP.

A treatment study led by Peter McLean at the University of British Columbia compared ERP to a CBT that targeted the dysfunctional cognitions characteristic of OCD, such as thought-action fusion and inflated responsibility (McLean et al., 2001). Patients were randomized to either the ERP or CBT conditions and half in each group received their treatment immediately, while the other half served as a waiting list control (and received their assigned treatment later). Both treatments were delivered in a group context. Both types of treatment were better than the wait list control in terms of reducing symptoms of OCD. The ERP treatment was slightly more effective than CBT both immediately post-treatment and at a three-month follow-up. Inflated responsibility beliefs decreased with treatment improvement, but contrary to hypothesis, it decreased in both the CBT and the ERP conditions.

Thus, preventing rituals does seem to allow for cognitive change in people with OCD, at least in terms of their inflated sense of responsibility. Another study by this same group (Whittal et al., 2005) once again compared these two types of treatment, but this time they were delivered in an individual (one-on-one) format. ERP and CBT were once again both highly effective in treating OCD symptoms, and no differences were obtained in their overall efficacy.

Studies have evaluated the combined effects of medication and psychological treatments (Romanelli et al., 2014; Simpson et al., 2013; Tolin, 2012). In one large study (Foa et al., 2005), ERP was compared with the drug clomipramine, as well as with a combined condition. ERP, with or without the drug, produced superior results to the drug alone, with 86 percent responding to ERP alone versus 48 percent to the drug alone. Combining the treatments did not produce any additional advantage. Relapse rates were high from the medication-only group when the drug was withdrawn. Furthermore, medication, such as SSRIs appear to be effective only in a subgroup of patients, possibly because these drugs primarily dampen the symptoms but do not correct the dysregulated neural circuits (Ressler & Rothbaum, 2013). Therefore, adding ERP to people who continue to have OCD symptoms after starting an SSRI can be more beneficial than adding another medication (Simpson et al., 2014).

Psychosurgery is one of the more radical treatments for OCD. Psychosurgery is a misnomer that refers to neurosurgery for a psychological disorder. Jenike et al. (1991) reviewed the records of 33 patients with OCD, most of them extremely severe cases who had failed to respond at all to either drug or psychological treatment. After a very specific surgical lesion to the cingulate bundle (cingulotomy), approximately 30 percent benefited substantially. Similarly, Rück et al. (2008) performed a related surgery (capsulotomy) on 25 patients who had not responded to five years of previous treatment; 35 percent (9 patients) benefited substantially, but six of those nine patients suffered from serious adverse side effects of the surgery. These results seem typical from the surgical procedures (Greenberg et al., 2010), and are similar to results from a procedure called deep brain stimulation in which electrodes are placed through small holes drilled in the skull and are connected to a pacemaker-like device in the brain. The advantage of deep brain stimulation over more traditional surgery is that it is reversible (McLaughlin & Greenberg, 2012). Considering that these patients seemed to have no hope whatsoever from other treatments, surgery deserves consideration as a last resort.

Concept Check 6.2

Fill in the blanks to form facts about OCD.

1. _____ are intrusive and nonsensical thoughts, images, or urges an individual tries to eliminate or suppress.

2. The practices of washing, counting, and hoarding to suppress obsessions and provide relief are called _____.

3. _____ is most likely the most effective treatment for OCD.

BODY DYSMORPHIC DISORDER

Did you ever wish you could change part of your appearance? Maybe the size of your nose or the way your ears stick out? Most people fantasize about improving something, but some relatively normal-looking people think they are so ugly they refuse to interact with others or otherwise function normally for fear that people will laugh at their ugliness. This curious affliction is called **body dysmorphic disorder (BDD)**, and at its centre is a preoccupation with some imagined defect in appearance by someone who actually looks reasonably normal (Fang & Wilhelm, 2015). The disorder has been referred to as "imagined ugliness" (Phillips, 1991). Consider the case of Jim.

JIM | Ashamed to Be Seen

In his mid-20s, Jim was diagnosed with social anxiety disorder; he was referred to our clinic by another professional. Jim had just finished rabbinical school and had been offered a position at a synagogue in a nearby city. He found himself unable to accept, however, because of marked social difficulties. Lately he had given up leaving his small apartment for fear of running into people he knew and being forced to stop and interact with them.

Jim was a good-looking young man of about average height, with dark hair and eyes. Although he was somewhat depressed, a mental status exam and a brief interview focusing on current functioning and past history did not reveal any remarkable problems. There was no sign of a psychotic process (he was not out of touch with reality). We then focused on Jim's social difficulties. We expected the usual kinds of anxiety about interacting with people or "doing something" (performing) in front of them. But this was not Jim's concern. Rather, he was convinced that everyone, even his good friends, was staring at a part of his body that he found grotesque. He reported that strangers would never mention his deformity and his friends felt too sorry for him to mention it. Jim thought his head was square! Like the Beast in *Beauty and the Beast* who could not imagine people reacting to him with anything less than revulsion, Jim could not imagine people getting past his square head. To hide his condition as well as he could, Jim wore soft floppy hats and was most comfortable in winter, when he could all but completely cover his head with a large stocking cap. To us, Jim looked normal.

For many years, BDD was considered a somatoform disorder because its central feature is a psychological preoccupation with somatic (physical) issues. But increasing evidence indicated it was more closely related to OCD, accounting for its relocation to the obsessive-compulsive and related disorders section in the *DSM-5*. For example, OCD often co-occurs with BDD and is found among family members of BDD patients (Chosak et al., 2008; Gustad & Phillips, 2003; Phillips & Stout, 2006; Phillips et al., 2010). There are other similarities. People with BDD complain of persistent, intrusive, and horrible thoughts about their appearance, and they engage in such compulsive behaviours as repeatedly looking in mirrors to check their physical features. BDD and OCD also have approximately the same age of onset and run the same course. One brain-imaging study demonstrated similar abnormal brain functioning between patients with BDD and patients with OCD (Rauch et al., 2003).

Clinical Description

To give you a better idea of the types of concerns people with BDD present to health professionals, the locations of imagined defects in 200 patients are shown in Table 6.3. The average number of body areas of concern to these individuals was five to seven (Phillips et al., 2005). In another group of 23 adolescents with BDD, 61 percent focused on their skin and 55 percent on their hair (Albertini & Phillips, 1999). A variety of checking or compensating rituals are common in people with BDD in attempts to alleviate their concerns. For example, excessive tanning is common, with 25 percent of one group of 200 patients tanning themselves in an attempt to hide skin defects (Phillips et al., 2005). Excessive grooming and skin picking are also common. Many people with this disorder become fixated on mirrors (Veale & Riley, 2001). They often check their presumed ugly feature to see whether any change has taken place. Others avoid mirrors to an almost phobic extent. Quite understandably, suicidal ideation, suicide attempts, and suicide itself are typical consequences of this disorder (Phillips et al., 2005). People with BDD also have "ideas of reference," which means they think everything that goes on in their world somehow is related to them—in this case, to their imagined defect. This disorder can cause considerable disruption in the patient's life. Many patients with severe cases become housebound for fear of showing themselves to other people.

TABLE 6.3 | Location of Imagined Defects in 200 Patients with Body Dysmorphic Disorder

Location	%	Location	%
Skin	80	Overall appearance of face	19
Hair	58	Small body build	18
Nose	39	Legs	18
Stomach	32	Face size or shape	16
Teeth	30	Chin	15
Weight	29	Lips	14.5
Breasts	26	Arms or wrists	14
Buttocks	22	Hips	13
Eyes	22	Cheeks	11
Thighs	20	Ears	11
Eyebrows	20		

Source: Adapted from "Demographic Characteristics, Phenomenology, Comorbidity, and Family History in 200 Individuals with Body Dysmorphic Disorder," by K. A. Phillips, B. A. Menard, C. Fay, and R. Weisberg, 2005, *Psychosomatics, 46*(4), pp. 317–325.

© Cengage Learning

DSM-5 | **Table 6.6** Diagnostic Criteria for Body Dysmorphic Disorder

A. Preoccupation with one or more defects or flaws in physical appearance that are not observable or appear slight to others.

B. At some point during the course of the disorder, the individual has performed repetitive behaviors (e.g., mirror checking, excessive grooming, skin picking, reassurance seeking) or mental acts (e.g., comparing his or her appearance with that of others) in response to the appearance concerns.

C. The preoccupation causes clinically significant distress or impairment in social, occupational, or other important areas of functioning.

D. The appearance preoccupation is not better explained by concerns with body fat or weight in an individual whose symptoms meet diagnostic criteria for an eating disorder.

Specify if:

With muscle dysmorphia: The individual is preoccupied with the idea that his or her body build is too small or insufficiently muscular. This specifier is used even if the individual is preoccupied with other body areas, which is often the case.

Specify if:

Indicate degree of insight regarding body dysmorphic disorder beliefs (e.g., "I look ugly" or "I look deformed").

With good or fair insight: The individual recognizes that the body dysmorphic disorder beliefs are definitely or probably not true or that they may or may not be true.

With poor insight: The individual thinks that the body dysmorphic disorder beliefs are probably true.

With absent insight/delusional beliefs: The individual is completely convinced that the body dysmorphic disorder beliefs are true.

Source: Reprinted with permission from the *Diagnostic and Statistical Manual of Mental Disorders*, Fifth Edition (Copyright © 2013). American Psychiatric Association. All Rights Reserved.

If this disorder seems strange to you, you are not alone. For decades, this condition, previously known as *dysmorphophobia* (literally, fear of ugliness), was thought to represent a psychotic delusional state because the affected individuals were unable to realize, even for a fleeting moment, that their ideas were irrational. For example, in 200 cases examined by Phillips, Menard, Fay, and Weisberg (2005) and in 50 cases reported by Veale, Boocock, and colleagues (1996), between 33 and 50 percent of participants were convinced their imagined bodily defect was real and a reasonable source of concern. Even though this lack of insight is also present in approximately 10 percent of patients with OCD, it is much higher in BDD based on direct comparisons of individuals with these two disorders (Phillips et al., 2012). Is this delusional? Phillips, Menard, Pagano, Fay, and Stout (2006) looked closely at differences that may exist between delusional and nondelusional types and found nothing significant, beyond the fact that the delusional type was more severe and found in less educated patients. Other studies have supported this lack of meaningful differences between these two groups (Mancuso et al., 2010; Phillips et al., 2010). It is also the case that these two groups both respond equally well to treatments for BDD and that the "delusional" group does not respond to drug treatments for psychotic disorders (Phillips et al., 2010). Thus, in the *DSM-5*, patients receive a BDD diagnosis whether they are "delusional" or not. DSM Table 6.6 outlines the diagnostic criteria for BDD.

Body Dysmorphic Disorder: Doug

"I didn't want to talk to anybody. . . . I was afraid because what I saw on my face . . . they saw . . . If I could see it, they could see it. And I thought there was like an arrow pointing at it. And I was very self-conscious. And I felt like the only time I felt comfortable was at night, because it was dark time."

Visit login.cengage.com to start using MindTap. Enter the Online Access Code from the card included with your text. If a code card is not provided, you can purchase instant access at Cengage.ca.

Statistics

The prevalence of BDD is hard to estimate because by its very nature it tends to be kept secret. The best estimates, however, are that it is far more common than we had previously thought. Without some sort of treatment, it tends to run a lifelong course (Phillips, 1991; Veale, Boocock, et al., 1996). One of the patients with BDD reported by Phillips and colleagues (1993) had suffered from her condition for 71 years, since the age of nine. If you think a college friend seems to have at least a mild version of BDD, you're probably correct. Studies suggest that as many as 70 percent of college students report at least some dissatisfaction with their bodies, with 4 to 28 percent of these appearing to meet all the criteria for the disorder (Fitts et al., 1989; Phillips, 2005). This study was done by questionnaire, however, and may well have reflected the large percentage of students who are concerned simply with weight. Another study investigated the prevalence of BDD, specifically in an ethnically diverse sample of 566 adolescents between the ages of 14 and 19. The overall prevalence of BDD in this group was 2.2 percent, with adolescent girls more dissatisfied with their bodies than boys and black adolescents of both genders more satisfied with their bodies than Caucasians, Asians, and Hispanics (Mayville et al., 1999; Roberts et al., 2006). Overall, about 1 to 2 percent of individuals in community samples and from 2 to 13 percent of student samples meet criteria for BDD (Koran et al., 2008; Phillips et al., 2005; Woolfolk & Allen, 2011). A somewhat higher proportion of individuals with BDD are interested in art or design compared with individuals without BDD, reflecting, perhaps, a strong interest in aesthetics or appearance (Veale et al., 2002).

In mental health clinics, the disorder is also uncommon because most people with BDD seek other types of health professionals, such as plastic surgeons and dermatologists. BDD is seen equally in men and women. In the larger series of 200 individuals reported by Phillips, Menard, Fay, and Weisberg (2005), 68 percent were female, but 62 percent of a large number of individuals with BDD in Japan were males. Generally, there are more similarities than differences between men and women with BDD, but some differences have been noted (Phillips, Menard, & Fay, 2006). Men tend to focus on body build, genitals, and thinning hair, and tend to have more severe BDD. A focus on muscle defects and body building is nearly unique to men with the disorder (Pope et al., 2005). Women focus on more varied body areas andare more likely to also have an eating disorder.

Age of onset ranges from early adolescence through the 20s, peaking at the age of 16–17 (Phillips et al., 2005; Veale, Boocock, et al., 1996; Zimmerman & Mattia, 1998). Individuals are somewhat reluctant to seek treatment. In many cases, a relative will force the issue, demanding the individual get help; this insistence may reflect the disruptiveness of the disorder for family members. Severity is also reflected in the high percentage (24 percent) of past suicide attempts among the 50 cases described by Veale, Boocock, and colleagues (1996); 28 percent of the 200 cases described by Phillips, Menard, Fay, and Weisberg (2005); and 21 percent of a group of 33 adolescents (Albertini & Phillips, 1999).

One study of 62 consecutive outpatients with BDD found that the degree of psychological stress, quality of life, and impairment were generally worse than comparable indices in patients with depression, diabetes, or a recent myocardial infarction (heart attack) on several questionnaire measures (Phillips et al., 2000). Similar results were reported on a larger sample of 176 patients (Phillips et al., 2005). Thus, BDD is among the more serious of psychological disorders, and depression and substance abuse are common consequences of BDD (Gustad & Phillips, 2003; Phillips et al., 2010). As you might suspect, few people with this disorder get married. Further reflecting the intense suffering that accompanies this disorder, Veale (2000) collected information on 25 patients with BDD who had sought cosmetic surgery in the past. Of these, nine patients who could not afford surgery or were turned down for other reasons had attempted by their own hand to alter their appearance dramatically, often with tragic results. One example was a man preoccupied by his skin, who believed it was too "loose." He used a staple gun on both sides of his face to try to keep his skin taut. The staples fell out after ten minutes and he narrowly missed damaging his facial nerve. In a second example, a woman was preoccupied by her skin and the shape of her face. She filed down her teeth to alter the appearance of her jawline. Yet another woman who was preoccupied by what she perceived as the ugliness of multiple areas of her body and desired liposuction, but could not afford it, used a knife to cut her thighs and attempted to squeeze out the fat. BDD is also stubbornly chronic. In a prospective study of 183 patients, only 21 percent were somewhat improved over a year, and 15 percent of that group relapsed during that year (Phillips, Pagano, et al., 2006).

▲ In various cultures, a child's head or face is manipulated to produce desirable features, as in the addition of rings to lengthen the necks of these Burmese girls.

What can we learn about BDD from such practices of mutilation around the world? The behaviour of individuals with BDD seems remarkably strange because they go *against* current cultural practices that put less emphasis on altering facial features. In other words, people who simply conform to the expectations of their culture do not have a disorder. Nevertheless, aesthetic plastic surgery, particularly for the nose and lips, is still widely accepted and, because it is most often undertaken by the wealthy, carries an aura of elevated status. In this light, BDD may not be so strange. As with most psychopathology, its characteristic attitudes and behaviour may simply be an exaggeration of normal culturally sanctioned behaviour.

Causes and Treatment

We know little about the etiology of BDD specifically. There is almost no information on whether it runs in families, so we can't investigate a specific genetic contribution. Similarly, there is no meaningful information on biological or psychological predisposing factors or vulnerabilities. Psychoanalytic speculations are numerous, but most centre on the defensive mechanism of displacement—that is, an underlying unconscious conflict would be too anxiety-provoking to admit into consciousness, so the person displaces it onto a body part.

What little evidence we do have on etiology comes from the pattern of comorbidity of BDD with OCD described earlier. The marked similarities to OCD suggest, perhaps, somewhat similar patterns of etiology. Approximately 15 percent of a series of 100 patients with eating disorders suffered from comorbid BDD, with their body dysmorphic concerns unrelated to weight and shape (Kollei, Schieber, de Zwaan, Svitak, & Martin, 2013).

Perhaps more significantly, there are two, and only two, treatments for BDD with any evidence of effectiveness, and these treatments are the same found effective in OCD. First, drugs that block the reuptake of serotonin, such as clomipramine (Anafranil)

and fluvoxamine (Luvox), provide relief to at least some people (Hadley et al., 2006). One controlled study of the effects of drugs on BDD demonstrated that clomipramine was significantly more effective than desipramine, a drug that does not specifically block reuptake of serotonin, for the treatment of BDD, even BDD of the delusional type (Hollander et al., 1999). A second controlled study reported similar findings for fluoxetine (Prozac), with 53 percent showing a good response compared with 18 percent on placebo after three months (Phillips et al., 2002). Intriguingly, these are the same drugs that have the strongest effect in OCD. Second, exposure and response prevention, the type of cognitive-behavioural therapy effective with OCD, has also been successful with BDD (McKay et al., 1997; Rosen et al., 1995; Veale, Gournay, et al., 1996; Wilhelm et al., 1999). In the Rosen and colleagues study, 82 percent of patients treated with this approach responded, although these patients may have been somewhat less severely affected by the disorder than in other studies (Wilhelm et al., 1999; Williams et al., 2006). Furthermore, patients with BDD and OCD have similar rates of response to these treatments (Saxena et al., 2001; Williams et al., 2006). As with OCD, cognitive-behavioural therapy tends to produce better and longer lasting outcomes compared with medication alone (Buhlmann et al., 2008). But CBT is not as readily available as drugs.

Another interesting lead on causes of BDD comes from cross-cultural explorations of similar disorders. You may remember the Japanese variant of social anxiety disorder, *taijin kyofusho*, in which individuals may believe they have horrendous bad breath or body odour and thus avoid social interaction. But people with *taijin kyofusho* also have all the other characteristics of social anxiety disorder. Patients who would be diagnosed with BDD in our culture might simply be considered to have severe social anxiety in Japan and Korea. Possibly, then, social anxiety is fundamentally related to BDD, a connection that would give us further hints on the nature of the disorder. Indeed, a recent study of BDD in Western countries indicates that concerns relating to perceived negative evaluation of their appearance by others is

▲ Michael Jackson as a child and as an adult. Many people alter their features through surgery. However, people with body dysmorphic disorder are seldom satisfied with the results.

every bit as important as self-evaluation of the imagined defects in appearance (Anson et al., 2012). Studies of comorbidity indicate that social anxiety disorder, along with OCD, is also commonly found in people with BDD (Fang & Hofmann, 2010; Phillips & Stout, 2006).

Plastic Surgery and Other Medical Treatments

Patients with BDD believe they are physically deformed in some way and go to medical doctors to attempt to correct their deficits (Woolfolk & Allen, 2011). Phillips, Grant, Siniscalchi, and Albertini (2001) studied the treatments sought by 289 patients with BDD, including 39 children or adolescents, and found that fully 76 percent had sought this type of treatment and 66 percent were receiving it. Dermatology (skin) treatment was the most often received (45 percent), followed by plastic surgery (23 percent). Looking at it another way, in one study of 268 patients seeking care from a dermatologist, 12 percent met criteria for BDD (Phillips et al., 2000).

Because the concerns of people with BDD involve mostly the face or head, it is not surprising that the disorder is big business for the plastic surgery profession—but it is bad business. These patients do not benefit from surgery and may return for additional surgery or, on occasion, file malpractice lawsuits. Investigators estimate that as many as 8 to 25 percent of all patients who request plastic surgery may have BDD (Barnard, 2000; Crerand et al., 2004). The most common procedures are rhinoplasties (nose jobs), facelifts, eyebrow elevations, liposuction, breast augmentation, and surgery to alter the jawline. Between 2000 and 2012, according to the American Society of Plastic Surgeons (2012), the total number of cosmetic procedures increased by 98 percent. The problem is that surgery for individuals with BDD seldom produces the desired results. These individuals return for additional surgery on the same defect or concentrate on some new defect. Phillips, Menard, Fay, and Pagano (2005) reported that 81 percent of 50 individuals seeking surgery or similar medical consults were dissatisfied with the result. In 88 percent of a large group of people with BDD seeking medical rather than psychological treatment, the severity of the disorder and accompanying distress either did not change or *increased* after surgery. Similar discouraging or negative results are evident from other forms of medical treatment, such as skin treatments (Phillips et al., 2001). It is important that plastic surgeons screen out these patients; many do so by collaborating with medically trained psychologists (Pruzinsky, 1988).

HOARDING DISORDER

Several years ago, a group of patients came to the attention of specialty clinics because they compulsively hoard things, fearing that if they throw something away, even a ten-year-old newspaper, they then might urgently need it. At first, the specialty clinics assumed that this was just a strange variant of OCD, but it soon became apparent that it was a major problem unto itself, as is obvious to anyone who has seen the recent spate of television programs showing individuals with this disorder in their almost unlivable homes. Estimates of prevalence range between 2 and 5 percent of the population, which is twice as high as the prevalence of OCD, with nearly equal numbers of men and women, and is found worldwide (Frost et al., 2012). The three major characteristics of this problem are excessive acquisition of things, difficulty discarding anything, and living with excessive clutter under conditions best characterized as gross disorganization (Frost & Rasmussen, 2012; Grisham & Barlow, 2005; Steketee & Frost, 2007a, 2007b). It is not uncommon for some patients' houses and yards to come to the attention of public health authorities (Tolin, 2011). One patient's house and yard was condemned because junk was piled so high it was both unsightly and a fire hazard. Among her hoard was a 20-year collection of used sanitary napkins! Although only a tiny percentage of fires in residences occur in the homes of individuals who hoard, these fires account for 24 percent of all fire-related fatalities (Frost et al., 2012).

These individuals usually begin acquiring things during their teenage years and often experience great pleasure, even euphoria, from shopping or otherwise collecting various items. Shopping or collecting things may be a response to feeling down or depressed and is sometimes called, facetiously, "retail therapy." But unlike most people who like to shop or collect, these individuals then experience strong anxiety and distress about throwing anything away because everything has either some potential use or sentimental value in their minds, or simply becomes an extension of their own identity. Their homes or apartments may become almost impossible to live in. Most of these individuals don't consider that they have a problem until family members or authorities insist that they seek help. As with OCD, the extent of insight that the patients have about the problematic status of their hoarding problem is specified when making the diagnosis. The average age when these people come for treatment is approximately 50, after many years of hoarding (Grisham et al., 2006, 2012). Often they live alone (Frost & Rasmussen, 2012; Mataix-Cols et al., 2010). Careful analysis of what we know about hoarding suggests it has similarities and differences with both OCD and impulse control disorders. Therefore, it is best considered a separate disorder and now appears as such in the *DSM-5*.

For example, OCD tends to wax and wane, whereas hoarding behaviour can begin early in life and get worse with each passing decade (Ayers et al., 2010). Cognitive and emotional abnormalities associated with hoarding alluded to earlier include extraordinarily strong emotional attachment to possessions, an exaggerated desire for control over possessions, and marked deficits in deciding when a possession is worth keeping or not (all possessions are believed to be equally valuable). One study examined the neural mechanisms of decision making about whether to keep or discard possessions among individuals with hoarding disorder compared with individuals with OCD without hoarding. The study found specific differences in areas of the brain related to problems identifying the emotional significance of an object and generating the appropriate emotional response (Tolin et al., 2012).

People who hoard animals compose a special group that is now being investigated more closely. Occasionally, articles appear in newspapers describing homes occupied by one owner, usually a middle-aged or older woman, and 30 or more animals—often cats. Sometimes, some of them will be dead, either lying on the floor out in the open or stored in the freezer. In addition to owning an unusually large number of animals, animal hoarders are characterized by the failure or inability to care for the animals or provide suitable living quarters, which results in threats to health and safety because of unsanitary conditions associated with accumulated animal waste (Frost et al., 2011). One study compared individuals who met criteria for animal hoarding with a small group of nonhoarding controls who owned a large number of animals (Steketee et al., 2011). Individuals in both groups were mostly middle-aged white women. While both groups expressed strong caretaking roles and a particularly intense love for and attachment to animals, the hoarding group was characterized by attribution of human characteristics to their animals, the presence of more dysfunctional current relationships (with other people), and significantly greater mental health concerns. Much like other individuals with hoarding, animal hoarders typically have little or no realization that they have a problem, despite often living in unsanitary conditions with dead and sick animals.

CBT is a promising treatment for hoarding disorder (Tolin et al., 2015). These treatments for hoarding developed at our clinic teach people to assign different values to objects and to reduce anxiety about throwing away items that are somewhat less valued (Grisham et al., 2012; Steketee & Frost, 2007a). Preliminary results are promising, but results are more modest than those achieved with OCD. Also, more information on long-term effects of these treatments is needed. Little or nothing is known about effective interventions for individuals who hoard animals.

TRICHOTILLOMANIA AND EXCORIATION DISORDER

The urge to pull out one's own hair from anywhere on the body, including the scalp, eyebrows, and arms, is referred to as **trichotillomania**. This behaviour results in noticeable hair loss, distress, and significant social impairments. This disorder can often have severe social consequences, and, as a result, those affected can go to great lengths to conceal their behaviour (Grant et al., 2012; Lochner et al., 2012). Compulsive hair pulling is more common than once believed and is observed in between 1 and 5 percent of college students, with females reporting the problem more than males (Scott et al., 2003). There may be some genetic influence on trichotillomania, with one study finding a unique genetic mutation in a small number of people (Zuchner et al., 2006).

Excoriation (skin-picking disorder) is characterized, as the label implies, by repetitive and compulsive picking of the skin, leading to tissue damage (Grant et al., 2012). Many people pick their skin on occasion without any serious damage to their skin or any distress or impairment, but for somewhere between 1 and 5 percent of the population, noticeable damage to skin occurs, sometimes requiring medical attention. There can be significant embarrassment, distress, and impairment in terms of social and work functioning. In one case, a young woman spent two to three hours a day picking her skin, resulting in numerous scabs, scars, and open wounds on her face. As a result, she would often be late for work or unable to work if the open wounds were too bad. She had not socialized with friends for over a year (Grant et al., 2012). Excoriation is also largely a female disorder.

Before the *DSM-5*, both disorders were classified under impulse-control disorders, but it has been established that these disorders often co-occur with OCD and BDD, as well as with each other (Grant et al., 2012; Odlaug & Grant, 2012). For this reason, all of these disorders, which share repetitive and compulsive behaviours, are now grouped together under obsessive-compulsive and related disorders in the *DSM-5*. Nevertheless, significant differences exist. For example, individuals with BDD may pick at their skin occasionally to improve their appearance, which is not the case for individuals with skin-picking disorder.

Until recently, it was assumed that the repetitive behaviours of hair pulling and skin picking function to relieve stress or tension. While this seems to be the case for many patients, a substantial number of individuals do not engage in this behaviour to relieve tension and do not show evidence of tension relief. For this reason, diagnostic criteria referring to tension relief, present in the *DSM-IV*, have been removed in the *DSM-5* (Nock et al., 2011).

Psychological treatments, particularly an approach called "habit reversal training," has the most evidence for success with these two disorders. In this treatment, patients are carefully taught to be more aware of their repetitive behaviour, particularly as it is just about to begin, and to then substitute a different behaviour, such as chewing gum, applying a soothing lotion to the skin, or some other reasonably pleasurable but harmless behaviour. Results may be evident in as little as four sessions, but the procedure requires teamwork between the patient and therapist and close monitoring of the behaviour throughout the day (Nock et al., 2011). Drug treatments, mostly serotonin-specific reuptake inhibitors, hold some promise, particularly for trichotillomania (Chamberlain et al., 2007), but the results have been mixed with excoriation (Grant et al., 2012).

SUMMARY

Somatic Symptom Disorders and Related Disorders

- Individuals with somatic symptom and related disorders are pathologically preoccupied and concerned with the functioning of their bodies and bring these concerns to the attention of health professionals, who usually find no identifiable medical basis for the physical complaints.

- Somatic symptom disorder is characterized by a focus on one or more physical symptoms accompanied by marked distress focused on the symptom that is disproportionate to the nature or severity of the physical symptoms. This condition may dominate the individual's life and interpersonal relationships. Illness anxiety disorder is a condition in which individuals believe they are seriously ill and become anxious over this possibility, even though they are not experiencing any notable physical symptoms at the time. In conversion disorder, there is physical malfunctioning, such as paralysis, without any apparent physical problems. Distinguishing among conversion reactions, real physical disorders, and outright malingering (faking) is sometimes difficult. Even more puzzling can be factitious disorder, in which the person's symptoms are feigned and under voluntary control, as with malingering, but for no apparent reason.

- The causes of somatic symptom disorder are not well understood. Patients with this disorder are often preoccupied with physical symptoms, causing significant distress or interference with their lives. In the case of illness anxiety disorder (formerly known as hypochondriasis), the person experiences significant anxiety about having or developing a serious medical disease. The latter diagnosis is similar to an anxiety disorder.

- Treatment of somatic symptom disorders ranges from basic techniques of reassurance and social support to interventions meant to reduce stress and remove any secondary gain for the behaviour. Recently, specifically tailored cognitive-behavioural therapy has proved successful with these conditions.

Obsessive-Compulsive and Related Disorders

- Obsessive-compulsive disorder (OCD) focuses on avoiding frightening or repulsive intrusive thoughts (obsessions) or neutralizing these thoughts through the use of ritualistic behaviour (compulsions).

- Biological and psychological vulnerabilities seem to be involved in the development of OCD.

- Drug treatment seems to be only modestly successful in treating OCD. The most effective treatment approach is exposure and response prevention.

- In body dysmorphic disorder (BDD), a person who looks normal is obsessively preoccupied with some imagined defect in appearance. These patients typically have more insight into their problem and may seek out plastic surgery as a remedy. Psychological treatment approaches are also similar to those for OCD and are approximately equally successful.

- Hoarding disorder is characterized by excessive acquisition of things, difficulty discarding anything, and living with excessive clutter under conditions best characterized as gross disorganization. Treatment approaches are similar to those for OCD but are less successful.

- Repetitive and compulsive hair pulling resulting in significant noticeable loss of hair or repetitive and compulsive picking of the skin leading to tissue damage characterize trichotillomania and excoriation disorders, respectively.

KEY TERMS

ANSWERS TO CONCEPT CHECKS

6.1

1. a; **2.** b; **3.** C

6.2

1. obsessions; **2.** compulsions; **3.** ERP

⁙ CENGAGE | MINDTAP

Stay organized and efficient with MindTap—a single destination with all the course material and study aids you need to succeed. Built-in apps leverage social media and the latest learning technology. For example:

- ReadSpeaker will read the text to you.

- Flashcards are pre-populated to provide you with a jump start for review—or you can create your own.

- You can highlight text and make notes in your MindTap Reader. Your notes will flow into Evernote, the electronic notebook app that you can access anywhere when it's time to study for the exam.

- Self-quizzing allows you to assess your understanding.

Visit login.cengage.com to start using MindTap. Enter the Online Access Code from the card included with your text. If a code card is not provided, you can purchase instant access at Cengage.ca.

Exploring Somatic Disorders

Characterized by a pathological concern with physical functioning or appearance

SOMATIC SYMPTOM AND RELATED DISORDERS

Illness Anxiety Disorder

Additional physical symptoms → Faulty interpretation of physical sensations

Causes

Increased anxiety → Intensified focus on symptoms

Characteristics

- Severe anxiety over physical problems that are medically undetectable
- Affects women and men equally
- May emerge at any age
- Evident in diverse cultures

Treatment

- Psychotherapy to challenge illness perceptions
- Counselling and/or support groups to provide reassurance

Somatic Symptom Disorder

Eventual social isolation → Continual development of new symptoms

Causes

Immediate sympathy and attention

Characteristics

- Reports of multiple physical symptoms
- Runs in families; probably heritable basis
- Rare—most prevalent among unmarried women in low socioeconomic groups
- Onset usually in adolescence; often persists into old age

Treatment

- Hard to treat
- Cognitive-behavioural therapy (CBT) to provide reassurance, reduce stress, and minimize help-seeking behaviours
- Therapy to broaden basis for relating to others

Conversion Disorder

Social influences (symptoms learned from observing real illness or injury) → Life stresses or psychological conflict

Causes

Reduced by incapacitating symptoms

Characteristics

- Severe physical dysfunctioning (e.g., paralysis and blindness) without corresponding physical pathology
- Affected people are genuinely unaware that they can function normally
- May coincide with other problems, especially somatization disorder
- Most prevalent in low socioeconomic groups, women, and men under extreme stress (e.g., soldiers)

Treatment

- Same as for somatization disorder, with emphasis on resolving life stress or conflict and reducing help-seeking behaviours

Exploring Obsessive-Compulsive and Related Disorders

Characterized by preoccupations, rituals, and compulsions that are excessive and maladaptive

OBSESSIVE-COMPULSIVE AND RELATED DISORDERS

Obsessive-Compulsive Disorder	Characteristics	Treatment
	• Fear of unwanted and intrusive thoughts (obsessions) • Repeated ritualistic actions or thoughts (compulsions) designed to neutralize the unwanted thoughts: e.g., Richard's attempts to suppress "dangerous" thoughts about sex, aggression, and religion with compulsive washing and cleaning rituals	• Exposure and response prevention are most effective • Drug treatment is only moderately successful

Body Dysmorphic Disorder	Characteristics	Treatment
	• Preoccupation with some imagined defect in appearance by someone who looks normal • Compulsive behaviours, such as repeatedly looking in mirrors to check their physical features	• Drugs that block the reuptake of serotonin successful with some people • Exposure and response prevention, a type of cognitive-behavioural therapy, somewhat successful

Hoarding Disorder	Characteristics	Treatment
	• Fear of throwing anything away • Collecting/saving objects with little or no actual or sentimental value, such as food wrappings • Those who hoard animals compose a special group	• CBT is promising • Almost nothing known about effective interventions for individuals who hoard animals

Trichotillomania and Excoriation Disorder	Characteristics	Treatment
	• Repetitive and compulsive hair pulling, including from the scalp, eyebrows, and arms • Compulsive picking of the skin that leads to tissue damage	• Habit reversal training (being aware of repetitive behaviour and substituting a harmless and pleasurable one) is most successful • Drug treatments, mostly SSRIs, have some promise for trichotillomania, less so for excoriation

07 | Trauma and Dissociation

Istefiana/Getty

For anyone who wonders what it's like to have a tragedy shatter your existence, this is what I would tell them: it's like going through the motions of everyday life in a zombified state. It's having outbursts of anger for what seems like no apparent reason, for even the smallest of offenses. It's forgetting how to be your once cheerful, perky self, and having to relearn basic social skills when mingling with new people.

—SARABETH CAPLIN, Someone You Already Know

Engage in innovative and integrative thinking and problem solving:	› Describe problems operationally to study them empirically (APA SLO 2.3A)
Describe applications that employ discipline-based problem solving:	› Correctly identify antecedents and consequences of behaviour and mental processes (APA SLO 1.3b)
	› Describe examples of relevant and practical applications of psychological principles to everyday life (APA SLO 1.3a)

*Portions of this chapter cover learning outcomes suggested by the American Psychological Association (2012) in their guidelines for the undergraduate psychology major. Chapter coverage of these outcomes is identified above by APA Goal and APA Suggested Learning Outcome (SLO).

This chapter deals with trauma and its aftermaths. Not everyone who experiences a traumatic event suffers from it in the long term—in fact, people can be quite resilient—nevertheless trauma can be associated with significant difficulties afterward. In this chapter, we cover two related classes of disorders: trauma- and stressor-related disorders, in which the experience of trauma or a significant stressor is part of the diagnostic definition of each disorder, and dissociative disorders, which are frequently observed after the experience of a traumatic event. The experiences of dissociation (disruptions or disconnection in awareness, self, memory, or perception of the environment) are sometimes part of the phenomenology of post-traumatic stress disorder, meaning that these two classes of disorder are closely related. The *DSM-5* made sure to show the link between these two classes of disorders by placing them next to each other.

TRAUMA- AND STRESSOR-RELATED DISORDERS

New to the *DSM-5* is a group of formerly disparate disorders that all develop after a relatively stressful life event, often an extremely stressful or traumatic life event. This set of disorders—trauma- and stressor-related disorders—include attachment disorders in childhood following inadequate or abusive child-rearing practices, adjustment disorders characterized by persistent anxiety and depression following a stressful life event, and reactions to trauma, such as post-traumatic stress disorder and acute stress disorder. Investigators working in this area concluded that these disorders did not fit as neatly with other classes of disorders, such as the anxiety disorders as previously assumed. This is because trauma- and stressor-related disorders all share a proximal instigating stressful event followed by intense emotional responses. Also, a wider range of emotions—such as rage, horror, guilt and shame, in addition to fear and anxiety—may be implicated in the onset, particularly for post-traumatic stress disorder (Friedman et al., 2011; Keane et al., 2011; Miller et al., 2015). We begin with a description of post-traumatic stress disorder.

POST-TRAUMATIC STRESS DISORDER

Recently, we have heard a great deal about the severe and long-lasting emotional reactions that can occur after a variety of traumatic events. Perhaps the most impressive traumatic event is war, but severe emotional reactions also occur after physical assault (particularly rape), car accidents, natural catastrophes, or the sudden death of a loved one. The emotional disorder that follows a trauma is known as **post-traumatic stress disorder (PTSD)**.

Clinical Description

The *DSM-5* describes the setting event for PTSD as exposure to a traumatic event during which an individual experiences or witnesses death or threatened death, actual or threatened serious injury, or actual or threatened sexual violation. Learning that the traumatic event occurred to a close family member or friend, or enduring repeated exposure to details of a traumatic event as in first responders to a terrorist attack dealing with human remains are also setting events. Afterward, some survivors re-experience the event through memories and nightmares. When memories occur very suddenly and the survivors find themselves reliving the event, they are having a *flashback*.

Survivors often avoid anything that reminds them of the trauma. They often report feeling numb or having a restricted range of emotions, which may be very disruptive to interpersonal relationships. They are sometimes unable to remember certain aspects of the event. Some survivors attempt to avoid experiencing certain emotions or sensations, like people with panic disorder, because they might bring back memories of the trauma, They sometimes report changes in the way they think about themselves, other people and the world, maybe feeling like the world is no longer safe or that other people can't be trusted. Lastly, survivors typically are chronically overaroused, easily startled, and quick to anger. They may also engage in reckless or self-destructive behaviour. A subgroup of individuals with PTSD may also experience dissociative symptoms (Wolf, Lunney, et al., 2012; Wolf, Miller, et al., 2012). Individuals with PTSD seem to respond somewhat differently to treatment if they meet the criteria for a dissociative subtype (Lanius et al., 2012).

PTSD was first named in 1980 in the *DSM-III* (American Psychiatric Association, 1980), but it has a long history. In 1666, the British diarist Samuel Pepys witnessed the Great Fire of London, which caused substantial loss of life and property and threw the city into chaos for a time. He captured the events in an account that is still read today. But Pepys did not escape the effects of the horrific event. Six months later, he wrote, "It is strange to think how to this very day I cannot sleep a night without great terrors of fire; and this very night could not sleep to

▲ Exposure to a traumatic event may create profound fear and helplessness. People who have post-traumatic stress disorder may re-experience such feelings in flashbacks, involuntarily reliving the horrifying event, such as these volunteers helping after the Swissair Flight 111 disaster in Nova Scotia.

TABLE 7.1 | Percentage of Swissair Disaster Volunteers Endorsing PTSD Symptom on a Self-Report Scale

Symptom Domain Item	Percentage Endorsing (%)
Cognitive Re-experiencing	
Intrusive thoughts	69
Nightmares	39
Flashbacks	46
Emotional reactivity	77
Physiological reactivity	31
Avoidance	
Avoid thoughts of trauma	46
Avoid trauma reminders	39
Inability to recall trauma	31
Emotional Numbing	
Loss of interest	39
Detachment	53
Restricted affect	15
Foreshortened future	23
Somatic Hyperarousal	
Sleep disturbance	31
Increased irritability	23
Difficulty concentrating	46
Hypervigilance	46
Excessive startle	31

Source: Mitchell, T.L., et al. "We will never forget" The Swissair Flight 111 disaster and its impact on volunteers and communities. *Journal of Health Psychology*, 9(2), pp. 245–262. Copyright © 2004 by SAGE Publications. Reprinted by permission of SAGE Publications, Ltd.

almost 2 in the morning through thoughts of fire" (Daly, 1983, p. 66). The *DSM-5* criteria show that difficulty sleeping and recurring intrusive dreams of the event are prominent features of PTSD. Pepys described his guilt at saving himself and his property while others died. He also experienced a sense of detachment and a numbing of his emotions concerning the fire, common experiences in PTSD (Keane & Miller, 2012).

One recent Canadian study on PTSD deals with the psychological impact of an airline disaster on volunteers in a rural community (Mitchell et al., 2004, 2006; Weerasinghe et al., 2016). Swissair Flight 111 crashed off the coast of Peggy's Cove in Nova Scotia on September 2, 1998. When local residents heard the crash, many went out in their boats and attempted to rescue survivors. Unfortunately, none of the 229 passengers and crew survived the crash, and these community volunteers unexpectedly were confronted with airplane debris, passengers' personal effects, and gruesome human remains. In some cases, they were faced with dismembered body parts, and the skin of crash victims had often separated from the rest of their bodies, a phenomenon called "degloving." Many volunteers continued assisting with the recovery work (e.g., volunteering for ground search and rescue) over the ensuing weeks and were continually exposed to these sights and smells. Well after their exposure to the disaster had ended, many volunteers reported psychological symptoms attributable to their trauma exposure. Many reported having intrusive memories of the horrors they had encountered in their volunteer work, avoiding reminders of the disaster, experiencing emotional numbing, and having difficulties sleeping. These are all common symptoms in PTSD. The percentage of volunteers reporting PTSD symptoms is illustrated in Table 7.1.

Consider next the case of the Joneses from one of our clinics. Not only did Marcie develop PTSD, but so did her eight-year-old brother. In addition, Cathy, four, and Susan, two, although quite young, also showed symptoms of the disorder, as did their mother. Jeff evidenced classic survivor guilt symptoms, reporting that he should have saved Marcie or at least put himself between Marcie and the dog. Both Jeff and Marcie regressed

THE JONESES | *One Target, Many Traumas*

Mrs. Betty Jones and her four children arrived at a farm to visit a friend. (Mr. Jones was at work.) Jeff, the oldest child, was eight years old. Marcie, Cathy, and Susan were six, four, and two years of age. Mrs. Jones parked the car in the driveway, and they all started across the yard to the front door. Suddenly, Jeff heard growling somewhere near the house. Before he could warn the others, a large German shepherd charged and leapt at Marcie, the six-year-old, knocking her to the ground and tearing viciously at her face. The family, too stunned to move, watched the attack helplessly. After what seemed like an eternity, Jeff lunged at the dog and it moved away. The owner, in a state of panic, ran to a nearby house to get help. Mrs. Jones immediately put pressure on Marcie's facial wounds in an attempt to stop the bleeding. The owner had neglected to retrieve the dog, and it stood a short distance away, growling and barking at the frightened family. Eventually, the dog was restrained and Marcie was rushed to the hospital. Marcie, who was hysterical, had to be restrained on a padded board so emergency room physicians could stitch her wounds.

developmentally, wetting the bed (nocturnal enuresis) and experiencing nightmares and separation fears. In addition, Marcie, having been strapped down and given local anaesthetic and stitches, became very frightened of any medical procedures and even of such routine daily events as having her nails trimmed or taking a bath. Furthermore, she refused to be tucked into bed, something she had enjoyed all her life, probably because it reminded her of the hospital board. Jeff started sucking his fingers, which he had not done for years. These behaviours, along with intense separation anxiety, are common, particularly in younger children (Silverman & La Greca, 2002). Cathy, the four-year-old, evidenced considerable fear and avoidance when tested but denied having any problem when she was interviewed by a child psychologist. Susan, the two-year-old, also had some symptoms but was too young to talk about them. However, for several months following the trauma she repeatedly said, without provocation, "Doggy bit sister."

Children's memories of traumatic events can become embellished over the years. For example, some children incorporate a superhero coming to the rescue. These intense memories are very malleable and subject to distortion (Garry & Wade, 2005; Porter, Spencer, & Birt, 2003; Porter, Yuille, & Lehman, 1999).

Since many individuals experience strong reactions to stressful events that typically disappear within a month, the diagnosis of PTSD cannot be made until at least one month after the occurrence of the traumatic event. When PTSD continues longer than three months, it is considered chronic. Chronic PTSD is usually associated with more prominent avoidance behaviours, as well as with the more frequent co-occurrence of additional diagnoses such as social phobia. In delayed-onset PTSD, individuals show few if any symptoms immediately or for months after a trauma, but at least six months later, and perhaps years afterward develop full-blown PTSD (O'Donnell et al., 2013). Why onset is delayed in some individuals is not yet clear. The diagnostic criteria for PTSD are outlined in DSM Table 7.1.

As we noted, PTSD cannot be diagnosed until a month after the trauma. In *DSM-IV* a disorder called **acute stress disorder** was introduced. This is similar to PTSD, occurring within the first month after the trauma, but the different name emphasizes the severe reaction that some people have immediately (Cardeña & Carlson, 2011). According to a recent survey, approximately 50 percent of individuals with acute stress disorder go on to develop PTSD (Bryant, 2010; Bryant et al., 2011). But these surveys also found that as many as 52 percent of a sample of trauma survivors who go on to develop PTSD did not meet criteria for acute stress disorder in the month following the trauma (Bryant et al., 2011). Acute stress disorder was included in the *DSM-IV* because many people with very severe early reactions to trauma could not otherwise be diagnosed and, therefore, could not receive insurance coverage for immediate treatment. The surveys just described confirm that people with early severe reactions to traumatic stress are severely affected and can benefit from treatment. But these early reactions are not particularly good predictors of who will go on to develop PTSD.

DSM-5	**Table 7.1** Diagnostic Criteria for Post-Traumatic Stress Disorder

A. Exposure to actual or threatened death, serious injury, or sexual violence in one (or more) of the following ways:

1. Directly experiencing the traumatic event(s).

2. Witnessing, in person, the event(s) as they occurred to others.

3. Learning that the traumatic event(s) occurred to a close family member or close friend. In cases of actual or threatened death of a family member or friend, the event(s) must have been violent or accidental.

4. Experiencing repeated or extreme exposure to aversive details of the traumatic event(s) (e.g., first responders collecting human remains; police officers repeatedly exposed to details of child abuse).

   Note: Criterion A4 does not apply to exposure through electronic media, television, movies, or pictures, unless this exposure is work related.

B. Presence of one (or more) of the following intrusion symptoms associated with the traumatic event(s), beginning after the traumatic event(s) occurred:

1. Recurrent, involuntary and intrusive distressing memories of the traumatic event(s).

   Note: In children older than 6 years, repetitive play may occur in which themes or aspects of the traumatic event(s) are expressed.

2. Recurrent distressing dreams in which the content and/or affect of the dream are related to the traumatic event(s).

   Note: In children, there may be frightening dreams without recognizable content.

3. Dissociative reactions (e.g., flashbacks) in which the individual feels or acts as if the traumatic event(s) were recurring. (Such reactions occur on a continuum, with the most extreme expression being a complete loss of awareness of present surroundings).

   Note: In young children, trauma-specific re-enactment may occur in play.

4. Intense or prolonged psychological distress at exposure to internal or external cues that symbolize or resemble an aspect of the traumatic event(s).

5. Marked physiological reactions to internal or external cues that symbolize or resemble an aspect of the traumatic event(s).

C. Persistent avoidance of stimuli associated with the traumatic event(s), beginning after the traumatic event(s) occurred, as evidenced by one or both of the following:

1. Avoidance of or efforts to avoid distressing memories, thoughts, or feelings about or closely associated with the traumatic event(s).

2. Avoidance of or efforts to avoid external reminders (people, places, conversations, activities, objects, situations) that arouse distressing memories, thoughts, or feelings about or closely associated with the traumatic event(s).

D. Negative alterations in cognitions and mood associated with the traumatic event(s), beginning or worsening after the traumatic event(s) occurred, as evidenced by two (or more) of the following:

1. Inability to remember an important aspect of the traumatic event(s) (typically due to dissociative amnesia and not to other factors such as head injury, alcohol, or drugs).

2. Persistent and exaggerated negative beliefs or expectations about oneself, others, or the world (e.g., "I am bad," "No one can be trusted," "The world is completely dangerous," "My whole nervous system is permanently ruined").

3. Persistent distorted cognitions about the cause or consequences of the traumatic event(s) that lead the individual to blame himself/herself or others.

4. Persistent negative emotional state (e.g., fear, horror, anger, guilt, or shame).

5. Markedly diminished interest or participation in significant activities.

6. Feelings of detachment or estrangement from others.

7. Persistent inability to experience positive emotions (e.g., inability to experience happiness, satisfaction, or loving feelings).

E. Marked alterations in arousal and reactivity associated with the traumatic event(s), beginning or worsening after the traumatic event(s) occurred, as evidenced by two or more of the following:

1. Irritable behaviour and angry outbursts (with little or no provocation) typically expressed as verbal or physical aggression toward people or objects.

2. Reckless or self-destructive behavior.

3. Hypervigilance.

4. Exaggerated startle response.

5. Problems with concentration.

6. Sleep disturbance (e.g., difficulty falling or staying asleep or restless sleep).

F. Duration of the disturbance (Criteria B, C, D, and E) is more than 1 month.

G. The disturbance causes clinically significant distress or impairment in social, occupational, or other important areas of functioning.

H. The disturbance is not attributable to the physiological effects of a substance (e.g., medication, alcohol) or another medical condition.

Specify whether:

With dissociative symptoms: The individual's symptoms meet the criteria for post-traumatic stress disorder, and in addition, in response to the stressor, the individual experiences persistent or recurrent symptoms of either of the following:

1. **Depersonalization:** Persistent or recurrent experiences of feeling detached from, and as if one were an outside observer of, one's mental processes of body (e.g., feeling as though one were in a dream; feeling a sense of unreality of self or body or of time moving slowly).

2. **Derealization:** Persistent or recurrent experiences of unreality of surroundings (e.g., the world around the individual is experienced as unreal, dreamlike, distant or distorted).

Note: To use this subtype, the dissociative symptoms must not be attributable to the physiological effects of a substance (e.g., blackouts, behavior during alcohol intoxication) or another medical condition (e.g., complex partial seizures).

Specify if:

With delayed expression: If the full diagnostic criteria are not met until at least 6 months after the event (although the onset and expression of some symptoms may be immediate).

Statistics

Determining the prevalence rates for PTSD seems relatively straightforward: Simply observe survivors of a trauma and see how many develop PTSD. But several studies have demonstrated the remarkably low prevalence of PTSD in populations of trauma survivors. Rachman (1978) studied the British citizenry who endured numerous life-threatening air raids during World War II. He concluded that "a great majority of people endured the air raids extraordinarily well, contrary to the universal expectation of mass panic. Exposure to repeated bombings did not produce a significant increase in psychiatric disorders. Although short-lived fear reactions were common, surprisingly few persistent phobic reactions emerged" (Rachman, 1991, p. 162). Similar results have been observed after disastrous fires, earthquakes, and floods (Green et al., 1983).

However, some studies have found a very high incidence of PTSD after trauma. Kilpatrick et al. (1985) sampled more than 2000 adult women who had personally experienced such trauma as rape, sexual molestation, robbery, and aggravated assault. They were asked whether they had thought about suicide after the trauma, attempted suicide, or had a *nervous breakdown* (a lay term that is commonly used to refer to a severe psychological upset). Rape had the most significant emotional impact. Compared with 2 percent of nonvictims, 19 percent of rape survivors had attempted suicide, and 44 percent reported suicidal ideation at sometime following the rape. Similarly, Resnick, Kilpatrick, Dansky, Saunders, and Best (1993) found that 32 percent of rape survivors met the criteria for PTSD at some point in their lives. Looking at all types of trauma (e.g., physical assault, accidents) in a large sample of U.S. adult women, Resnick et al. found that 18 percent experienced PTSD. Taylor and Koch (1995) found that 15 to 20 percent of Canadian adults experiencing severe auto accidents developed PTSD. Eleven percent of members of the Canadian Armed Forces reported experiencing PTSD during their lifetime, with higher rates among members who had been deployed to Afghanistan compared with those who had not been deployed (Pearson et al., 2014). Furthermore, Brunet and Monson (2014) suggest that PTSD among members is related to suicidality. One US National survey reported that, 8 percent of the population had experienced PTSD in their lifetime (Kessler et al., 1995), with combat and sexual assault being the most common traumas. In fact, a diagnosis of PTSD predicts suicide attempts independently of any other problem, such as alcohol abuse (Wilcox et al., 2009).

What accounts for the discrepancies between the low rate of PTSD in citizens who endured bombing and shelling in London, England, and the relatively high rate in survivors of assaultive violence? Investigators have now concluded that during air raids many people may not have directly experienced the horrors of dying, death, and direct attack. Close exposure to the trauma seems to be necessary to developing this disorder (Friedman, 2009; Keane & Barlow, 2002; King et al., 1996). This is also evident among Vietnam War veterans, where 19 percent developed PTSD, with prevalence rates directly related to their amount of combat exposure (Dohrenwend et al., 2006). Surveys of 76 survivors of Hurricane Katrina in 2005 also report a doubling of severe mental illness based on extent of direct exposure to danger (Kessler, Galea, et al., 2006). The connection between proximity to the traumatic event and the development of PTSD was starkly evident following the terrorist attacks on the United States on September 11, 2001. Galea and colleagues (2002) contacted a representative sample of adults living south of 110th Street in Manhattan and found that 8 percent reported symptoms consistent with a diagnosis of acute stress disorder or PTSD. But among respondents who lived close to the World Trade Center (south of Canal Street), the prevalence of the disorders was 20 percent. Again, those who experienced the disaster most personally and directly seemed to be the ones most affected.

In addition, tens of thousands of public school children in New York City who lived close to the disaster experienced chronic nightmares, fear of public places, and other symptoms of PTSD. After the attack, a large study conducted with the help of U.S. government agencies estimated that 75 000 schoolchildren in New York City in Grades 4 through 12, or 10.5 percent of children in those grades, suffered PTSD after September 11 (Goodnough, 2002). In addition, 155 suffered from agoraphobia, a fear of leaving a safe place such as home. Many of these children feared riding public transportation. Two-thirds of the children sampled lived near the World Trade Center or in other neighbourhoods directly affected by the tragedy, such as Staten Island, home to many who were killed, or Brooklyn, where smoke drifted over its neighbourhoods for days. Since a diagnosis of PTSD predicts suicide attempts independently of any other problem, such as alcohol abuse, every case should be taken very seriously (Wilcox et al., 2009).

But is this the whole story? It seems not. Some people experience the most horrifying traumas imaginable and emerge psychologically healthy. For others, even relatively mild stressful events are sufficient to produce a full-blown disorder. Moreover, PTSD symptoms change over time more for some people than for others, which may be due to individual differences in resiliency, coping skills, levels of trauma exposure, early adversities, ongoing stress, and even the presence of mild traumatic brain injuries (Berntsen et al., 2012; Bonnano, 2004; Bryant et al., 2013; Marmar et al., 2015; Nash et al., 2014).

Looking at data from the Canadian Community Health Survey, 1.7 percent of the Canadian population 15 years or older had a current diagnosis of PTSD in 2012 (Statistics Canada, 2012).

Causes

PTSD is the one disorder for which we are sure of the etiology: Someone experiences a trauma and develops a disorder. Clearly, however, since only a small proportion of people who experience a trauma go on to develop PTSD, other factors must contribute to an individual's chance of developing the disorder. Whether or not someone develops PTSD is a surprisingly complex issue involving biological, psychological, and social factors. We know that intensity of exposure to assaultive violence contributes to the etiology of PTSD (Dohrenwend et al., 2012; Friedman, 2009) but does not account for all of it. To take a particularly dramatic example, approximately 67 percent of prisoners of war in Vietnam developed PTSD (Foy et al., 1987). This means that 33 percent of the prisoners who endured long-term deprivation and torture did not develop the disorder. Similarly, Resnick

et al. (1993) demonstrated that the percentage of female crime victims who developed PTSD increased as a function of the severity of the trauma (see ■ Figure 7.1). In addition, children experiencing severe burns are likely to develop PTSD in proportion to the severity of the burns and the pain associated with them (Saxe et al., 2005). At lower levels of trauma, some people develop PTSD, but most do not. In the sample of the Swissair recovery volunteers discussed earlier, the longer the individual was involved in recovery work (presumably reflecting more severe exposure), the more severe and frequent were the PTSD symptoms; yet not all volunteers developed PTSD, despite exposure to such an awful event (Mitchell et al., 2004). What accounts for these differences?

As with other disorders, we bring our own generalized biological and psychological vulnerabilities with us. The greater the vulnerability, the more likely we are to develop PTSD. If certain characteristics run in your family, you have a much greater chance of developing the disorder (Foy et al., 1987). A family history of anxiety suggests a generalized biological vulnerability for PTSD. True et al. (1993) reported that, given the same amount of combat exposure and one twin with PTSD, a monozygotic (identical) twin was more likely to develop PTSD than a dizygotic twin. This suggests some genetic influence in the development of PTSD. A twin study by Stein, Jang, Taylor, Vernon, and Livesley (2002) showed that PTSD symptoms after noncombat trauma are also moderately heritable. Interestingly, they further found that exposure to certain types of traumas (i.e., assaultive trauma like robbery but not nonassaultive trauma like car accidents) was also affected by genetics. In other words, genetic factors seem to influence the risk of being exposed to certain kinds of trauma,

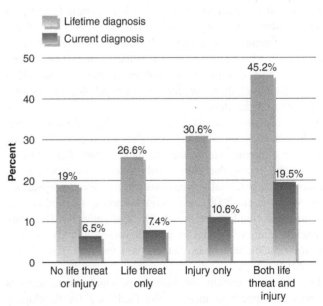

FIGURE 7.1 | Prevalence of lifetime and current post-traumatic stress disorder associated with assault characteristics.

Source: Resnick, Heidi S.; Kilpatrick, Dean G.; Dansky, Bonnie S.; Saunders, Benjamin E.; Best, Connie L., "Prevalence of civilian trauma and posttraumatic stress disorder in a representative national sample of women," *Journal of Consulting and Clinical Psychology*, Vol 61(6), Dec 1993, 984–991. Copyright © 1993 by the American Psychological Association.

perhaps through inherited personality characteristics that affect what kinds of environments (e.g., risky versus safe) a person will choose. Nevertheless, as with other disorders, there is little or no evidence that genes directly cause PTSD (Norrholm & Ressler, 2009). Rather, the stress-diathesis model described in Chapter 2 comes into play again whereby genetic factors predispose individuals to be easily stressed and anxious, which then may make it more likely that a traumatic experience will result in PTSD (Uddin et al., 2012). This was demonstrated recently in a study of female undergraduates who witnessed a tragic shooting on the campus of Northern Illinois University in 2008. While all endured the same traumatic experience, specific characteristics of what is referred to as the serotonin transporter gene involving two short alleles (SS), described in Chapter 2 as increasing the probability of becoming depressed (Caspi et al., 2003), also increased the probability of experiencing symptoms of acute stress after the shooting, even though other factors, such as amount of exposure to the shooting, were equalized (Mercer et al., 2012). Wang et al. (2011) identified the same genetic risk factors in combat veterans.

Breslau, Davis, and Andreski (1995; Breslau, 2012) demonstrated among a random sample of 1200 individuals that characteristics such as a tendency to be anxious, as well as factors such as minimal education, predict exposure to traumatic events in the first place and therefore an increased risk for PTSD. Breslau, Lucia, and Alvarado (2006) elaborated on this finding by showing that six-year-old children with externalizing (acting out) problems were more likely to encounter trauma (such as assaults), probably because of their acting out, and later develop PTSD. Higher intelligence was associated with decreased exposure to these types of traumatic events. That is, personality and other characteristics, some of them at least partially heritable, may predispose people to the experience of trauma by making it likely that they will be in (risky) situations where trauma is likely to occur (Norrholm & Ressler, 2009). This is reminiscent of the studies on gene-environment correlations we described in Chapter 2, in which existing vulnerabilities, some of them heritable, may help determine the kind of environment in which someone lives and, therefore, the type of psychological disorder that person may develop.

There seems to be a generalized psychological vulnerability described in the context of other disorders based on early experiences with unpredictable or uncontrollable events. Family instability is one factor that may instill a sense the world is an uncontrollable, potentially dangerous place (Chorpita & Barlow, 1998; Suárez et al., 2009), so it is not surprising that individuals from unstable families are at risk for developing PTSD if they experience trauma. This factor was relevant in a study of more than 1600 male and female Vietnam War veterans (King et al., 1996, 2012).

In addition, certain biological personal characteristics (biomarkers) appear to increase the likelihood for developing PTSD. In one such study, Telch and colleagues (Telch et al., 2012) asked 158 soldiers before their deployment to Iraq to inhale air that was enriched with 35 percent carbon dioxide. Inhaling such gas mixture typically leads to strong physiological symptoms (shortness of breath, tingling, sweating, etc.) and anxiety in some people. Telch and colleagues found that those who reported more emotional reactivity to the gas mixture also experienced the war zone as much more stressful after they came back from Iraq. These soldiers were at greater risk for developing PTSD symptoms and other anxiety and stress symptoms later. This example illustrates how certain vulnerabilities can lead to a disorder when the person is exposed to stressors.

Another psychological vulnerability factor is anxiety sensitivity, which we discussed previously in the context of panic disorder. A study by Fedoroff, Taylor, Asmundson, and Koch (2000) examined levels of anxiety sensitivity in 81 survivors of car accidents who were receiving treatment for PTSD in Vancouver or Regina. Greater levels of anxiety sensitivity at pretreatment baseline predicted greater severity of PTSD. Moreover, the more a patient reduced his or her level of anxiety sensitivity during treatment, the better the outcome in terms of his or her PTSD symptoms. In the study of the Swissair disaster volunteers, a greater fear of anxiety (specifically those who were most fearful of losing control when anxious) predicted greater levels of PTSD

▲ Lieutenant-General (Retired) Roméo Dallaire, who is an activist promoting recognition of stress reactions in Canadian military personnel, has PTSD related to his experiences on a peacekeeping mission in Rwanda.

symptoms following exposure to the disaster work (Mitchell et al., 2004). These findings suggest that anxiety sensitivity is an important psychological vulnerability for PTSD.

Finally, social and cultural factors play a major role in the development of PTSD (King et al., 2012; Ruzek, 2012). The results from several studies are very consistent in showing that, if you have a strong and supportive group of people around you, it is much less likely you will develop PTSD after a trauma. In a particularly interesting study, Vernberg, LaGreca, Silverman, and Prinstein (1996) studied 568 elementary-school children three months after Hurricane Andrew hit the coast of south Florida. More than 55 percent of these children reported moderate to very severe levels of PTSD symptoms. When the authors examined factors contributing to who developed PTSD symptoms and who didn't, social support from parents, close friends, classmates, and teachers was a very important protective factor. Similarly, positive coping strategies involving active problem solving seemed to be protective, whereas becoming angry and placing blame on others were associated with higher levels of PTSD. Longer follow-up of children at 9 and 21 months after Hurricane Charley hit Florida in 2004 confirmed that strong social support systems reduced the persistence of PTSD symptoms over time (La Greca et al., 2010).

Why is this? We are all social animals and something about having a loving, caring group of people around us directly affects our biological and psychological responses to stress. In fact, several studies show that support from loved ones reduces cortisol secretion and HPA axis activity in children during stress (e.g., Tarullo & Gunnar, 2006). It is likely that one reason for the very high prevalence of PTSD in Vietnam War veterans is the tragic absence of social support when they returned from the war.

It seems clear that PTSD involves a number of neurobiological systems, particularly elevated or restricted corticotropin-releasing factor (CRF), which indicates heightened activity in the HPA axis (Amat et al., 2005; Gunnar & Fisher, 2006; Shin et al., 2004; Shin et al., 2009; Yehuda et al., 2012). Chronic arousal associated with HPA axis activity and some other symptoms of PTSD may be directly related to changes in brain function and structure (Bremner, 1999; McEwen & Magarinos, 2004) and in turn influence treatment response (Rauch et al., 2014). For example, evidence of damage to the hippocampus has appeared in groups of patients with war-related PTSD (Gurvits et al., 1996; Wang et al., 2010), adult survivors of childhood sexual abuse (Bremner et al., 1995), and firefighters exposed to extreme trauma (Shin et al., 2004).

The hippocampus is a part of the brain that plays an important role in regulating the HPA axis and in learning and memory. Thus, if there is damage to the hippocampus, we might expect persistent and chronic arousal, as well as some disruptions in learning and memory. These memory deficits are evident in veterans of the Gulf War (Vasterling et al., 1998) and Holocaust survivors with PTSD, as compared with Holocaust survivors without PTSD or healthy Jewish adults (Golier et al., 2002).

In Chapter 5, we described a panic attack as an adaptive fear response occurring at an inappropriate time. We have speculated that the "alarm reaction" that is a panic attack is similar in both panic disorder and PTSD but that in panic disorder the alarm is false. In PTSD, the initial alarm is true in that real danger is pres-

ent (Jones & Barlow, 1990; Keane & Barlow, 2002). If the alarm is severe enough, we may develop a conditioned or learned alarm reaction to stimuli that remind us of the trauma (e.g., being tucked into bed may have reminded Marcie of the emergency room board) (Lissek & Grillon, 2012). We may also develop anxiety about the possibility of additional uncontrollable emotional experiences (such as flashbacks, which are common in PTSD). Whether or not we develop anxiety partly depends on our vulnerabilities. This model of the etiology of PTSD is presented in ■ Figure 7.2.

Treatment

From a psychological point of view, most clinicians agree that individuals with PTSD should face the original trauma to develop effective coping procedures and thus overcome the debilitating effects of the disorder (Beck & Sloan, 2012; Monson et al., 2014; Najavits, 2007). The trick, of course, is in arranging the re-exposure so it will be therapeutic rather than traumatic once again. Unlike the object of a specific phobia, a traumatic event is difficult to recreate, and very few therapists want to try. Therefore, *imaginal exposure*, in which the content of the trauma and the emotions associated with it are worked through systematically, has been used for decades under a variety of names. At present,

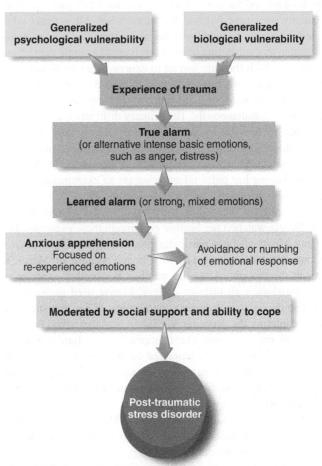

FIGURE 7.2 | A model of the causes of PTSD.

Source: Republished with permission of Guilford Publications, from *Anxiety and Its Disorders: The Nature and Treatment of Anxiety and Panic* by Barlow, David H. © 2019; permission conveyed through Copyright Clearance Center, Inc.

the most common strategy to achieve this purpose with adolescents or adults is to work with the victim to develop a narrative of the traumatic experience and to expose the patients for an extended period of time to the image (*prolonged exposure therapy*) that is then reviewed extensively in treatment (Eftekhari et al., 2013; Foa, Gillihan, & Bryant, 2013; Foa, McLean, et al., 2013). Recently, some authors have suggested that the effects of the exposure practices may be strengthened by strategically timing the exposure treatment with sleep and ask patients to take a nap soon after an exposure, because extinction learning appears to take place during slow-wave sleep and because sleep quality reduces anxiety (Pace-Schott et al., 2015).

Cognitive therapy to correct negative assumptions about the trauma, such as blaming oneself in some way, feeling guilty, or both, is often part of treatment (Monson et al., 2014; Najavits, 2007).

Evidence is now accumulating that early, structured interventions delivered as soon after the trauma as possible *to those who require help* are useful in preventing PTSD (Bryant et al., 2003; Ehlers et al., 2003; Kearns et al., 2012), and these preventive psychological approaches seem more effective than medications (Shalev et al., 2012). For example, in the study by Ehlers and colleagues of patients who had experienced a frightening car accident and were clearly at risk for developing PTSD, only 11 percent developed PTSD after 12 sessions of cognitive therapy, compared with 61 percent of those receiving a detailed self-help booklet, or 55 percent of those who were just assessed repeatedly over time but had no intervention. All patients who needed it were then treated with cognitive therapy. Of note, there is evidence that subjecting trauma survivors to a single debriefing session, in which they are forced to express whether or not they are feeling distressed, can be harmful (Ehlers & Clark, 2003).

Both Marcie, the young girl bitten by the dog, and her brother were treated simultaneously. The primary difficulty was Marcie's reluctance to be seen by a doctor or to undergo any physical examinations, so a series of experiences was arranged from least to most intense. Mildly anxiety-provoking procedures for Marcie included having her pulse taken, lying on an examination table, and taking a bath after accidentally cutting herself. The most intense challenge was being strapped on a restraining board. First, Marcie watched her brother go through these exercises. He was not afraid of these particular procedures, although he was anxious about being strapped to a board because of Marcie's terror at the thought. After she watched her brother experience these situations with little or no fear, Marcie tried each one in turn. The therapist took instant photographs of her that she kept after completing the procedures. Marcie was also asked to draw pictures of the situations. The therapist and her family warmly congratulated her as she completed each exercise. Because of Marcie's age, she was not adept at imaginatively re-creating memories of the traumatic medical procedures. Therefore, her treatment offered experiences designed to alter her current perceptions of the situations. Marcie's PTSD was successfully treated, and her brother's guilt was greatly reduced as a function of helping in her treatment.

A modification to traditional imaginal exposure therapy is Donald Meichenbaum's CBT treatment for PTSD. Meichenbaum (1994, 2006) uses a *constructivist-narrative* approach for treating individuals who have been traumatized. In this approach, the therapist assists the client in reconstructing his or her "story" about the traumatic event—changing the meaning that the client has attached to the traumatic event and helping the client develop adaptive coping strategies and a sense of survivorship.

A popular psychological treatment for PTSD is known as *eye-movement desensitization and reprocessing* (EMDR; Shapiro, 1995, 1999). While in therapy and thinking about their traumatic experience, the client is asked to follow the therapist's moving fingers with his or her eyes, all the while keeping the image of the trauma in mind. This unusual technique is said by proponents to facilitate rapid reprocessing of the traumatic event (Shapiro, 1999). A group of researchers at the University of British Columbia compared the efficacy of this newer approach with imaginal exposure and with relaxation training (S. Taylor et al., 2003). Sixty patients with PTSD were randomly assigned to one of the three treatment modalities. Treatments did not differ in their effects on PTSD symptoms of emotional numbing or physiological arousal. However, exposure therapy was superior to the other two treatments in that it led to larger reductions in avoidance and cognitive re-experiencing, achieved reductions in avoidance more quickly, and led to more patients who were PTSD-free after treatment. EMDR did not differ on any outcomes from relaxation training.

Drugs can also be effective for symptoms of PTSD (Dent & Bremner, 2009). Some of the drugs, such as SSRIs (e.g., Prozac and Paxil), that are effective for anxiety disorders in general have been shown to be helpful for PTSD, perhaps because they relieve the severe anxiety and panic attacks so prominent in this disorder.

OTHER TRAUMA- AND STRESSOR-RELATED DISORDERS

Adjustment disorders describe anxious or depressive reactions to life stress that are generally milder than one would see in acute stress disorder or PTSD but are nevertheless impairing in terms of interfering with work or school performance, interpersonal relationships, or other areas of living (Friedman et al., 2011; Strain & Friedman, 2011). Sometimes, particularly in adolescence, the life stress may provoke some conduct problems. The stressful events themselves would not be considered traumatic, but it is clear that the individual is nevertheless unable to cope with the demands of the situation and some intervention is typically required. If the symptoms persist for more than six months after the removal of the stress or its consequences, the adjustment disorder would be considered chronic. In the past, adjustment disorder has often been used as a residual diagnostic category for people with significant anxiety or depression associated with an identifiable life stress that does not meet criteria for another anxiety or mood disorder. Partly for this reason, there has been very little research on these reactions. Presumably it describes individuals with the biological and psychological vulnerabilities that are described throughout this chapter and that are associated with trait anxiety that flares up when confronting stressful events, although not to the extent that it would meet the criteria for another more serious disorder.

Attachment disorders refer to disturbed and developmentally inappropriate behaviours in children, emerging before five years of age, in which the child is unable or unwilling to form normal attachment relationships with caregiving adults. These seriously maladaptive patterns are due to inadequate or abusive child-rearing practices. In many cases, these inadequate child-rearing practices might be caused by frequent changes in the primary caregiver because of multiple foster care placements, or possibly just neglect in the home. In either case, the result is a failure to meet the child's basic emotional needs for affection and comfort or even providing for the basic necessities of daily living. As such, these disorders are considered to be pathological reactions to early extreme stress (Kay & Green, 2013). In previous editions of the *DSM*, two kinds of presentations were included under the heading "reactive attachment disorder." In the *DSM-5*, two separate disorders are described—the first an emotionally withdrawn inhibited type, and the second an indiscriminately social disinhibited type (Gleason et al., 2011; Zeanah & Gleason, 2010).

In **reactive attachment disorder** the child will very seldom seek out a caregiver for protection, support, and nurturance and will seldom respond to offers from caregivers to provide this kind of care. Generally, they would evidence lack of responsiveness, limited positive affect, and additional heightened emotionality, such as fearfulness and intense sadness. In **disinhibited social engagement disorder**, a similar set of child-rearing circumstances— perhaps including early persistent harsh punishment—would

Concept Check 7.1

Match the correct preliminary diagnosis with the cases below: (a) post-traumatic stress disorder, (b) acute stress disorder, and (c) delayed-onset post-traumatic stress disorder.

1. Judy witnessed a horrific tornado level her farm three weeks ago. Since then, she's had many flashbacks of the incident, trouble sleeping, and a fear of going outside in storms. _____

2. Jack was involved in a car accident six weeks ago in which the driver of the other car was killed. Since then, Jack has been unable to get into a car because it brings back the horrible scene he witnessed. Nightmares of the incident haunt him and interfere with his sleep. He is irritable and has lost interest in his work and hobbies.

   _____

3. Patricia was raped 30 years ago, when she was 17. Just recently, she has been having flashbacks of the event, difficulty sleeping, and fear of sexual contact with her husband. _____

result in a pattern of behaviour in which the child shows no inhibitions whatsoever to approaching adults. Such a child might engage in inappropriately intimate behaviour by showing a willingness to immediately accompany an unfamiliar adult figure somewhere without first checking back with a caregiver. These patterns of behaviour were combined into one disorder in the *DSM-IV* but have been separated into two different disorders in the *DSM-5*, partly because of the markedly different presentations of inadequate detachment behaviour (Gleason et al., 2011).

DISSOCIATIVE DISORDERS

Have you ever felt detached from yourself or your surroundings? "This isn't really me," or "That doesn't really look like my hand," or "There's something unreal about this place." During these experiences some people feel as if they are dreaming. These mild sensations that most people experience periodically are slight alterations, or detachments, in consciousness or identity called dissociative experiences, but they are perfectly normal. For a few people, these experiences are so intense and extreme that they lose their identity entirely and assume a new one, or they lose their memory or sense of reality and are unable to function. We discuss several types of **dissociative disorders** in this section. Morton Prince, founder of the prestigious *Journal of Abnormal Psychology*, noted more than a century ago that many people experience something like dissociation occasionally (Prince, 1906–1907). It is most likely to happen after an extremely stressful or traumatic event, such as an accident. It might also happen when you're very tired or under physical or mental pressure from, say, staying up all night cramming for an exam (Giesbrecht et al., 2007). If you have had an experience of dissociation, it may not have bothered you much, perhaps because you knew the cause (Barlow, 2002; Dixon, 1963). On the other hand, it may have been extremely frightening.

These kinds of experiences can be divided into two types. During an episode of **depersonalization**, your perception alters so that you temporarily lose the sense of your own reality. During an episode of **derealization**, your sense of the reality of the external world is lost. Things may seem to change shape or size; people may seem dead or mechanical. Symptoms of unreality are characteristic of the dissociative disorders because depersonalization is, in a sense, a psychological mechanism whereby one dissociates from reality. Depersonalization is often part of a serious set of conditions where reality, experience, and even our own identity seem to disintegrate. As we go about our daily lives, we ordinarily have an excellent sense of who we are and a general knowledge of the identity of other people. We are also aware of events around us, of where we are, and of why we are there. Except for occasional small lapses, our memories remain intact so that events leading up to the current moment are clear in our minds.

But what happens if we can't remember why we are in a certain place or even who we are? What happens if we lose our sense that our surroundings are real? Or what happens if we not only forget who we are but also begin to think we are somebody else—somebody who has a different personality, different memories, and even different physical reactions, such as allergies, that

we never had? These are examples of disintegrated experience. In each case, there are alterations in our relationship to the self, to the world, or to our memory processes.

Although we have much to learn about these disorders, we briefly describe two of them—depersonalization-derealization disorder and dissociative amnesia—before examining the fascinating condition of dissociative identity disorder. As you will see, the influence of social and cultural factors is strong in dissociative disorders. Even in severe cases, the expression of the pathology does not stray far from socially and culturally sanctioned forms (Giesbrecht et al., 2008; Kihlstrom, 2005a).

DEPERSONALIZATION-DEREALIZATION DISORDER

When feelings of unreality are so severe and frightening that they dominate an individual's life and prevent normal functioning, clinicians may diagnose the very rare **depersonalization-derealization disorder**. In this disorder, the individual has repeated experiences of feeling detached from his or her own thoughts or body. The person may feel as if he or she is an outside observer of his or her own body or thoughts—for example, feeling as if he or she is dreaming. But unlike someone experiencing psychosis, the person experiencing episodes of depersonalization-derealization remains in good contact with reality—the person knows, for example, that he or she is not really an outside observer of his or her own body. Trying to describe the uncomfortable feeling of depersonalization-derealization can be very difficult to convey in words.

A 40-year-old woman with periods of depersonalization-derealization treated by Ottawa psychiatrist George Fraser described the experience as follows:

> Very often, I feel that I can't make contact with people, as if we are existing in different dimensions. I think they hear me speaking, but are puzzled about what I'm saying and, as I talk, I feel a gap between my intentions and my voice, as if my thoughts were a high *slow*-moving gear and way out the top of my consciousness is a little tiny gear going at top speed, which is my voice and I can't feel the connection. Sometimes I feel like I don't overlap with people (Fraser, 1994, p. 142).

Consider next the case of Bonnie.

BONNIE | *Dancing Away from Herself*

Bonnie, a dance teacher in her late 20s, was accompanied by her husband when she first visited the clinic and complained of "flipping out." When asked what she meant, she said,

> It's the most scary thing in the world. It often happens when I'm teaching my modern dance class. I'll be up in front and I will feel focused on. Then, as I'm demonstrating the steps, I just feel like it's not really me and that I don't really have control of my legs. Sometimes I feel like I'm standing in back of myself just watching. Also I get tunnel vision.

It seems like I can only see in a narrow space right in front of me and I just get totally separated from what's going on around me. Then I begin to panic and perspire and shake.

It turns out that Bonnie's problems began after she smoked marijuana for the first time about ten years before. She had the same feeling then and found it very scary, but with the help of friends she got through it. Lately the feeling recurred more frequently and more severely, particularly when she was teaching dance class.

You may remember from Chapter 5 that during an intense panic attack many people (approximately 50 percent) experience feelings of unreality. People undergoing intense stress or experiencing a traumatic event may also experience these symptoms, which, in fact, characterize the newly defined acute stress disorder. Feelings of depersonalization-derealization are part of several different disorders (Boon & Draijer, 1991). But when severe depersonalization-derealization is the primary problem, the individual meets the criteria for depersonalization-derealization disorder (Steinberg, 1991; see DSM Table 7.2).

Montreal researchers Jean Charbonneau and Kieron O'Connor (1999) interviewed 20 individuals who were self-referred from the general population as experiencing depersonalization-derealization. They found that in the majority of cases, onset occurred following a traumatic life event, after sexual abuse, or after giving birth. Simeon et al. (1997) described 30 cases of depersonalization-derealization disorder, 19 women and 11 men.

Mean age of onset was 16.1 years and the course tended to be chronic, lasting an average of 15.7 years so far in those cases. All the patients were substantially impaired. Although none had any additional dissociative disorders, more than 50 percent had additional mood and anxiety disorders.

Guralnick, Schmeidler, and Simeon (2000) compared 15 patients with depersonalization-derealization disorder to 15 matched comparison subjects without the disorder on a comprehensive neuropsychological test battery that assessed cognitive function. Although both groups were of equal intelligence, the subjects with depersonalization-derealization disorder showed a distinct cognitive profile, reflecting some specific cognitive deficits on measures of attention, short-term memory, and spatial reasoning. Basically, these patients were easily distracted and had some trouble perceiving three-dimensional objects because they tended to flatten these objects into two dimensions. It is not clear how these cognitive and perceptual deficits develop, but they seem to correspond with reports of tunnel vision (perceptual distortions) and mind emptiness (difficulty absorbing new information) that characterize these patients.

Specific aspects of brain functioning are also associated with depersonalization-derealization (e.g., Sierra & Berrios, 1998; Simeon, 2009; Simeon et al., 2000). Sierra and colleagues (2002) compared skin conductance responding, a psychophysiological measure of emotional responding, among 15 patients with depersonalization-derealization disorder, 11 patients with anxiety disorders, and 15 participants without any disorder. Patients with depersonalization-derealization disorder showed greatly reduced emotional responding compared with other groups, reflecting a tendency to selectively inhibit emotional expression. Brain-imaging studies now confirm deficits in perception (Simeon, 2009; Simeon et al., 2000) and emotion regulation (Phillips et al., 2001). Other studies note dysregulation in the hypothalamic–pituitary–adrenocortical (HPA) axis among these patients, compared with normal controls (Simeon et al., 2001; Spiegel et al., 2013), suggesting, again, deficits in emotional responding. Psychological treatments have not been systematically studied. One evaluation of the drug Prozac did not show any treatment effect compared with placebo (Simeon et al., 2004).

DISSOCIATIVE AMNESIA

Perhaps the easiest to understand of the severe dissociative disorders is one called **dissociative amnesia**, which includes several different patterns (see DSM Table 7.3). People who are unable to remember anything, including who they are, are said to have **generalized amnesia**. Generalized amnesia may be lifelong or may extend from a period in the more recent past, such as six months or a year previously.

Far more common than general amnesia is **localized amnesia** or **selective amnesia**, a failure to recall specific events, usually traumatic, that occur during a specific period (Fraser, 1994). In fact, dissociative amnesia is very common during war (Cardena & Gleaves, 2003; Spiegel et al., 2013). An interesting case concerns a woman whose father deserted her and who then was forced to have an abortion at age 14. Years later, she came for treatment for frequent headaches. In therapy she reported early events (e.g., the

DSM-5	**Table 7.2** Diagnostic Criteria for Depersonalization-Derealization Disorder

A. The presence of persistent or recurrent experiences of depersonalization, derealization, or both:

  1. Depersonalization: Experiences of unreality, detachment, or being an outside observer with respect to one's thoughts, feelings, sensations, body or actions (e.g., perceptual alterations, distorted sense of time, unreal or absent self, emotional and/or physical numbing).

  2. Derealization: Experiences of unreality or detachment with respect to surroundings (e.g., individuals or objects are experienced as unreal, dreamlike, foggy, lifeless, or visually distorted).

B. During the depersonalization or derealization experience, reality testing remains intact.

C. The symptoms cause clinically significant distress or impairment in social, occupational, or other important areas of functioning.

D. The disturbance is not attributable to the physiological effects of a substance (e.g., a drug of abuse, medication) or another medical condition (e.g., seizures).

E. The disturbance is not better explained by another mental disorder, such as schizophrenia, panic disorder, major depressive disorder, acute stress disorder, post-traumatic stress disorder, or another dissociative disorder.

Source: Reprinted with permission from the *Diagnostic and Statistical Manual of Mental Disorders*, Fifth Edition (Copyright © 2013). American Psychiatric Association. All Rights Reserved.

A. An inability to recall important autobiographical information, usually of a traumatic or stressful nature, that is inconsistent with ordinary forgetting.

Note: Dissociative amnesia most often consists of localized or selective amnesia for a specific event or events; or generalized amnesia for identity and life history.

B. The symptoms cause clinically significant distress or impairment in social, occupational, or other important areas of functioning.

C. The disturbance is not attributable to the physiological effects of a substance (e.g., alcohol or other drug of abuse, a medication) or a neurological or other medical condition (e.g., partial complex seizures, transient global amnesia, sequelae of a closed head injury/traumatic brain injury, or other neurological condition).

D. The disturbance is not better explained by dissociative identity disorder, post-traumatic stress disorder, acute stress disorder, somatic symptom disorder, or major or mild neurocognitive disorder.

Specify if:

With dissociative fugue: Apparently purposeful travel or bewildered wandering that is associated with amnesia for identity or for other important autobiographical information.

▲ Famous British mystery writer Agatha Christie once disappeared from her home for 11 days. Her memory loss and flight from home were reportedly triggered by the stresses of the recent death of her mother and knowledge of her husband's extramarital affair.

In the 1920s, renowned British author Agatha Christie disappeared from her home one evening after she was to have gone out for a drive. Her car was found abandoned the next day. Christie returned home several days later. Memory loss caused by the stresses of her mother's recent death and her husband's extramarital affair were said to have been the causes of her 11-day disappearance (Phillip, 2003).

During these trips a person sometimes assumes a new identity or at least becomes confused about the old identity. Like Agatha Christie, Alderwoman Darlene (Dar) Heatherington from Lethbridge, Alberta, vanished while on business in Great Falls, Montana, in May 2003. She went missing after renting a bicycle for a ride in the park, and Great Falls launched a large-scale search for her. Three days later she was found disoriented in a Las Vegas hotel parking lot ("Alderwoman to Seek Therapy," 2003). Although the circumstances surrounding Dar Heatherington's trip to Las Vegas remain unclear, her story bears some striking similarities to the disappearance of Agatha Christie (Philip, 2003). For example, before her disappearance, Heatherington was also stressed because of overwork and reportedly being stalked through letters and email and by a prowler in her backyard ("Husband of 'missing' Alderwoman," 2003; Harrington, 2003). She was mandated to receive psychotherapy by the Montana court. Might Agatha Christie or Dar Heatherington have experienced a dissociative fugue?

Later evidence emerged in the Heatherington case that made the possibility of a dissociative fugue appear unlikely. Specifically, although Heatherington initially claimed that she had been drugged, kidnapped, and sexually assaulted in explaining her sudden disappearance to Las Vegas, she later admitted to having made up this story. Taken together, these facts suggest that Dar Heatherington likely did not experience a dissociative fugue, although Agatha Christie may have. Consider next the clinical case of the misbehaving sheriff.

abortion) rather matter-of-factly; but under hypnosis she would relive, with intense emotion, the early abortion and remember the fact that subsequently she was raped by the abortionist. She also had images of her father attending a funeral for her aunt, one of the few times she ever saw him. On awakening from the hypnotic state, she had no memory whatsoever of emotionally re-experiencing these events, and she wondered why she had been crying. In this case the woman did not have amnesia for the events themselves but rather for her intense emotional reactions to the events. In most cases of dissociative amnesia, the forgetting is very selective for traumatic events or memories rather than generalized.

A possible case of dissociative amnesia in Canada was the first-degree murder trial of Kenneth Mackay in Saskatoon ("Possible Mackay Forgets," 2003). Mackay was charged with killing Crystal Paskemin in 2000. Although Mackay admitted to having run over the victim with his truck, which he claimed was an accident, he could not explain why the victim's body was found burned. His defence lawyer claimed that Mackay had forgotten about burning the victim's body because of the trauma of the accident. In fact, a memory expert testified in court that Mackay may have had dissociative amnesia. Despite the expert witness testimony, the jury rejected his defence, and Mackay was sentenced to life in prison with no possibility of parole for 25 years (O'Hara, 2004).

A subtype of dissociative amnesia is referred to as **dissociative fugue** (Ross, 2009); *fugue* literally means "flight" (*fugitive* is from the same root). In these curious cases, memory loss revolves around a specific incident—an unexpected trip (or trips). Mostly, individuals simply leave and later find themselves in a new place, unable to remember why or how they got there. Usually, they have left behind an intolerable situation.

The Misbehaving Sheriff

Aktar and Brenner (1979) described a 46-year-old sheriff who reported at least three episodes of dissociative fugue. On each occasion he found himself as far as 320 kilometres from his home. When he came to, he immediately called his wife, but he was never able to completely recall what he did while he was away, sometimes for several days. During treatment the sheriff remembered who he was during these trips.

Despite his occupation, he became the outlaw type he had always secretly admired. He adopted an alias, drank heavily, mingled with a rough crowd, and went to brothels and wild parties.

Dissociative amnesia seldom appears before adolescence and usually occurs in adulthood. It is rare for dissociative amnesia to appear for the first time after an individual reaches the age of 50 (Sackeim & Devanand, 1991). Once dissociative disorders do appear, however, they may continue well into old age. Estimates of prevalence range anywhere from 1.8 to 7.3 percent, suggesting that dissociative amnesia is the most prevalent of all the dissociative disorders (Spiegel et al., 2011).

Fugue states usually end rather abruptly, like those of the misbehaving sheriff, and the individual returns home recalling most, if not all, of what happened. In this disorder, the disintegrated experience is more than memory loss, involving at least some disintegration of identity, if not the complete adoption of a new one.

An apparently distinct dissociative state not found in Western cultures is called *amok* (as in "running amok"). Most people with this disorder are males. Amok has attracted attention because individuals in this trance-like state often brutally assault and sometimes kill people or animals. If the person is not killed himself, he probably will not remember the episode. Running amok is only one of several "running" syndromes in which an individual enters a trance-like state and suddenly, imbued with a mysterious source of energy, runs or flees for a long time. Except for amok, the prevalence of running disorders is somewhat greater in women, as with most dissociative disorders. Among the Inuit, running disorder is termed *pivloktoq*. Among the Navajo tribe, it is called *frenzy witchcraft*. Despite their different culturally determined expression, running disorders seem to resemble dissociative fugue, with the possible exception of amok.

Trance and possession are a common part of some traditional religious and cultural practices and are not considered abnormal in that context. Dissociative trances commonly occur in India, Nigeria (where they are called *vinvusa*), Thailand (*phiipob*), and other Asian and African countries (Mezzich et al., 1992; Saxena & Prasad, 1989). In North America, culturally accepted dissociation commonly occurs during African-American prayer meetings (Griffith et al., 1980), First Nations sweat lodge ceremonies (Jilek, 1982), and Puerto Rican spiritist sessions (Comas-Diaz, 1981). Among Bahamians and blacks from the southern United States, trance syndromes are often referred to colloquially as "falling out."

Only when the state is undesirable and considered pathological by members of the culture would the individual be diagnosed with **dissociative trance disorder (DTD)** as a subtype of dissociative identity disorder (American Psychiatric Association, 2010; Spiegel, 2013).

DISSOCIATIVE IDENTITY DISORDER

People with **dissociative identity disorder (DID)** may adopt as many as 100 new identities, all simultaneously co-existing inside one body and mind. In some cases, the identities are complete, each with its own behaviour, tone of voice, and physical gestures. In other cases, only a few characteristics are distinct, because the identities are only partially independent, so it is not true that there are "multiple" complete personalities. Consider the case of Jonah, originally reported by Ludwig, Brandsma, Wilbur, Bendfeldt, and Jameson (1972).

JONAH | Bewildering Blackouts

Jonah, a 27-year-old black man, experienced severe headaches that were unbearably painful and lasted for increasingly longer periods. Furthermore, he couldn't remember things that happened while he had a headache, except that sometimes a great deal of time passed. Finally, after a particularly bad night, when he could stand it no longer, he arranged for admission to the local hospital. What really prompted Jonah to come to the hospital, however, was that other people told him what he did during his severe headaches. For example, he was told that the night before he had a violent fight with another man and attempted to stab him. He fled the scene and was shot at during a high-speed chase by the police. His wife told him that during a previous headache he chased her and his three-year-old daughter out of the house, threatening them with a butcher knife. During his headaches, and while he was violent, he called himself "Usoffa Abdulla, son of Omega." Once he attempted to drown a man in a river. The man survived and Jonah escaped by swimming half a kilometre upstream. He woke up the next morning in his own bed, soaking wet, with no memory of the incident.

Clinical Description

During Jonah's hospitalization, the staff was able to observe his behaviour directly, both when he had headaches and during other periods that he did not remember. He claimed other names at these times, acted differently, and generally seemed to be another person entirely. The staff distinguished three separate identities, or **alters**, in addition to Jonah. (Alters is the shorthand term for the different identities or personalities in DID.) The first alter was named Sammy. Sammy seemed rational, calm, and in control. The second alter, King Young, seemed to be in charge of all sexual activity and was particularly interested in having as many heterosexual interactions as possible. The third alter was the violent and dangerous Usoffa Abdulla. Characteristically, Jonah knew nothing of the three alters. Sammy was most aware of the other personalities. King Young and Usoffa Abdulla knew a little bit about the others but only indirectly.

In the hospital, psychologists determined that Sammy first appeared when Jonah was about six, immediately after Jonah saw his mother stab his father. Jonah's mother sometimes dressed him as a girl in private. On one of these occasions, shortly after Sammy emerged, King Young appeared. When Jonah was nine or ten, he was brutally attacked by a group of white youths. At this point Usoffa Abdulla emerged, announcing that his sole reason for existence was to protect Jonah.

DSM-5 criteria for dissociative identity disorder (see DSM Table 7.4) include amnesia, as in dissociative amnesia. In DID, however, identity is also fragmented. How many identities are displayed is relatively unimportant, whether there are three, four, or even 100 of them. Rather, the defining feature of this disorder is that certain aspects of the person's identity are dissociated (Spiegel et al., 2013).

DSM-5	Table 7.4 Diagnostic Criteria for Dissociative Identity Disorder

A. Disruption of identity characterized by two or more distinct personality states, which may be described in some cultures as an experience of possession. The disruption of marked discontinuity in sense of self and sense of agency, accompanied by related alterations in affect, behavior, consciousness, memory, perception, cognition, and/or sensory-motor functioning. These signs and symptoms may be observed by others or reported by the individual.

B. Recurrent gaps in the recall of everyday events, important personal information, and/or traumatic events that are inconsistent with ordinary forgetting.

C. The symptoms cause clinically significant distress or impairment in social, occupational, or other important areas of functioning.

D. The disturbance is not a normal part of a broadly accepted cultural or religious practice.

Note: In children, the symptoms are not attributable to imaginary playmates or other fantasy play.

E. The symptoms are not attributable to the physiological effects of a substance (e.g., blackouts or chaotic behaviour during alcohol intoxication) or another medical condition (e.g., complex partial seizures).

Source: Reprinted with permission from the *Diagnostic and Statistical Manual of Mental Disorders*, Fifth Edition (Copyright © 2013). American Psychiatric Association. All Rights Reserved.

Characteristics

The identity who becomes the patient and asks for treatment is usually a *host* identity. The first identity to seek treatment is seldom the original identity of the person. Usually, the host personality develops later (Putnam, 1992). Many patients have at least one impulsive alter who handles sexuality and generates income, sometimes by acting as a prostitute. In other cases, all alters may abstain from sex. Cross-gendered alters are not uncommon. For example, a small agile woman might have a strong powerful male alter who serves as a protector.

The transition from one personality to another is called a *switch* (Putnam, 1994). Usually, the switch is instantaneous (although in movies and television it is often drawn out for dramatic effect). Physical transformations may occur during switches. Posture, facial expressions, patterns of facial wrinkling, and even physical disabilities may emerge. In one study, changes in handedness occurred in 37 percent of the cases (Putnam et al., 1986).

Can DID Be Faked?

The question of faking is relevant for all dissociative disorders but tends to be raised more often for dissociative identity disorder. Are the fragmented identities "real," or is the person faking them

to avoid responsibility or stress? As with conversion disorders, it is very difficult to answer this question for several reasons (Kluft, 1999). First, evidence indicates that individuals with DID are very suggestible (Bliss, 1984; Giesbrecht et al., 2008; Kihlstrom, 2005a). It is possible that alters are created in response to leading questions from therapists, either during psychotherapy or while the person is in a hypnotic state.

KENNETH | *The Hillside Strangler*

During the late 1970s, Kenneth Bianchi brutally raped and murdered ten young women in the Los Angeles area and left their bodies naked and in full view on the sides of various hills. Despite overwhelming evidence that Bianchi was the "Hillside Strangler," he continued to assert his innocence, prompting some professionals to think he might have DID. His lawyer brought in a clinical psychologist, who hypnotized Bianchi and asked whether there was another part of Bianchi with whom he could speak. Guess what? Somebody called "Steve" answered and said that he had done all the killing. Steve also said that Ken knew nothing about the murders. With this evidence, the lawyer entered a plea of not guilty by reason of insanity.

The prosecution called on Martin Orne, then one of the world's leading experts on hypnosis and dissociative disorders (Orne et al., 1984). Orne used procedures similar to those we described in the context of conversion blindness to determine whether Bianchi was simulating DID or had a true psychological disorder. For example, Orne suggested during an in-depth interview with Bianchi that a true dissociative identity disorder included at least three personalities. Bianchi soon produced a third personality. By interviewing Bianchi's friends and relatives, Orne established that there was no independent corroboration of different personalities before Bianchi's arrest. Psychological tests also failed to show significant differences among the personalities; true fragmented identities often score differently on personality tests. Several textbooks on psychopathology were found in Bianchi's room; therefore, he presumably had studied the subject. Orne concluded that Bianchi responded like someone simulating hypnosis, not someone deeply hypnotized. Based on Orne's testimony, Bianchi was found guilty and sentenced to life in prison.

Some investigators have studied the ability of individuals to fake dissociative experiences. Carleton University psychologist Nicholas Spanos conducted important work on this issue. Spanos, Weeks, and Bertrand (1985) demonstrated in an experiment that a university student could simulate an alter if it was suggested that faking was plausible, as in the interview with Bianchi. All the students in the group were told to play the role of an accused murderer claiming his innocence. The subjects received exactly

▲ Nicholas Spanos (now deceased), a psychologist at Carleton University, was a leading expert worldwide on hypnosis, dissociative disorders, and false memories.

the same interview as Bianchi, word for word. More than 80 percent simulated an alternate personality to avoid conviction. Groups that were given more vague instructions, and no direct suggestion that an alternate personality might exist, were much less likely to use one in their defence.

These findings on faking and the effect of hypnosis led Spanos (1994, 1996) to suggest that the symptoms of DID could, for the most part, be accounted for by therapists who inadvertently suggested the existence of alters to suggestible individuals, a model known as the *sociocognitive model* because the possibility of identity fragments and early trauma is socially reinforced by a therapist (Kihlstrom, 2005a; Lilienfeld et al., 1999). A survey of American psychiatrists showed little consensus on the scientific validity of DID, with only one-third in the sample believing the diagnosis should be included without reservation in the *DSM* (Pope et al., 1999). A similar study of Canadian psychiatrists showed that fewer than one-third had no reservations about including DID in the *DSM* (Lalonde et al., 2001). Canadian psychiatrists were significantly more skeptical about the legitimacy of the DID diagnosis than were the American psychiatrists.

The diagnosis of captured the fascination of the public after popular books, movies, and TV series appeared on this topic. Chris Costner Sizemore was the real-life subject of a popular book and movie *The Three Faces of Eve*. Sizemore, who used the pseudonym Evelyn Lancaster in her book, was played by Joanne Woodward, who later received the Academy Award for Best Actress for her role in the movie. Woodward later also played the psychiatrist who treated another patient with DID in the 1976 TV miniseries *Sybil*. The patient in Sybil was played by Sally Fields who won an Emmy Award for her role in the film. Although these two cases of DID became very popular, critics soon questioned the patients' reports and the accuracy of the diagnosis.

Objective tests suggest, however, that many people with fragmented identities are not consciously and voluntarily simulating (Kluft, 1991, 1999). For example, a study by University of British Columbia psychologist Eric Eich and his colleagues (Eich et al., 1997a) compared the performance of real DID patients and simulators on objective memory tests. They found that "interpersonality amnesia" (i.e., in which events experienced by a particular personality state or identity are retrievable by the same identity but not by a different one; Eich et al., 1997b) could not be explained by deliberate simulating. In another study, Condon, Ogston, and Pacoe (1969) examined Sizemore and determined that one of the personalities (Eve Black) showed *a transient micro-strabismus* (divergence in conjugant lateral eye movements) that was not observed in the other personalities. These optical differences have been confirmed by Miller (1989), who demonstrated that DID subjects had 4.5 times the average

number of changes in optical functioning in their alter identities that control subjects had who simulated alter personalities. Miller concludes that optical changes, including measures of visual acuity, manifest refraction, and eye muscle balance, would be difficult to fake. Ludwig et al. (1972) found that Jonah's various identities had different physiological responses—including galvanic skin response (GSR), a measure of otherwise imperceptible sweat gland activity, and electroencephalogram (EEG) brain waves—to emotionally laden words. Using up-to-date functional magnetic resonance imaging (fMRI) procedures, changes in brain function were observed in one patient while switching from one personality to another. Specifically, this patient showed changes in hippocampal and medial temporal activity after the switch (Tsai et al., 1999). A number of subsequent studies confirmed that various alters have unique psychophysiological profiles (Putnam, 1997). Kluft (1999) suggested several additional clinical strategies to distinguish malingerers from patients with DID, including the observations that malingerers are usually eager to demonstrate their symptoms and do so in a very fluid fashion. Patients with DID, conversely, are more likely to attempt to hide symptoms.

The notion of multiple identities living inside someone's body and competing with each other for access to the outside world is based on the old idea that there is a self that lives *inside* each of us (and on the modern notion that that self can be fragmented). This idea is often portrayed in popular movies like *The Change-Up*, in which two friends trade bodies but maintain their personalities. There is indeed a self, but that self is not dissociable from the body. There is no doubt that some people feel *as if* there are multiple persons or personalities living inside them, but that feeling need not be taken literally. The neurological and physiological differences observed for different alters may simply reveal the fact that the different identities are often associated with very specific emotional states (e.g., calm and collected versus impulsive and angry), as in the case of Jonah.

▲ Chris Sizemore's history of dissociative identity disorder was dramatized in *The Three Faces of Eve*.

Diagnose the dissociative disorders described here by choosing one of the following: (a) dissociative fugue, (b) depersonalization-derealization disorder, (c) generalized amnesia, (d) dissociative identity disorder, and (e) localized amnesia.

1. Ann was found wandering the streets, unable to recall any important personal information. After searching her purse and finding an address, doctors were able to contact her mother. They learned that Ann had just been in a terrible accident and was the only survivor. Ann could not remember her mother nor any details of the accident. She was distressed. _____

2. Karl was brought to a clinic by his mother. She was concerned because at times his behaviour was strange. His speech and his way of relating to people and situations would change dramatically, almost as if he were a different person. What bothered her and Karl most was that he could not recall anything he did during these periods. _____

3. Terry complained about feeling out of control. She said she felt sometimes as if she were floating under the ceiling and just watching things happen to her. She also experienced tunnel vision and felt uninvolved in the things that went on in the room around her. This always caused her to panic and perspire. _____

4. Henry is 64 and recently arrived in town. He does not know where he is from or how he got here. His driver's licence proves his name, but he is unconvinced it is his. He is in good health and not taking any medication. _____

5. Rosita cannot remember what happened last weekend. On Monday she was admitted to a hospital, suffering from cuts, bruises, and contusions. It also appeared that she had been sexually assaulted. _____

Statistics

Jonah had four identities, but the average number of alter personalities is reported by clinicians as closer to 15 (Ross, 1997; Sackeim & Devanand, 1991). Of people with DID, the ratio of females to males is as high as nine to one, although these data are based on accumulated case studies rather than survey research (Maldonado et al., 1998). The onset is almost always in childhood, often as young as four years of age, although it is usually approximately seven years after the appearance of symptoms before the disorder is identified (Maldonado et al., 1998; Putnam et al., 1986). Once established, the disorder tends to last a lifetime in the absence of treatment. The form it takes does not seem to vary substantially over the person's lifespan, although some evidence indicates that the frequency of switching decreases with age (Sackheim & Devanand, 1991). Different personalities may emerge in response to new life situations, as was the case with Jonah.

We don't have many good epidemiological studies on the prevalence of the disorder in the population at large, although investigators now think it is more common than previously estimated (Kluft, 1991; Ross, 1997). Some have argued that, in the past, dissociative disorders may have been overlooked or misdiagnosed by mental health professionals (Ross et al., 1989). Semistructured interviews of large numbers of inpatients with severe disturbances found prevalence rates of DID of between 3 and 6 percent in Canada and the United States (Horen et al., 1995; Ross, 1997; Ross et al., 1991; Saxe et al., 1993), and approximately 2 percent in Holland (Friedl & Draijer, 2000). Additional studies in nonclinical samples, conducted in Winnipeg (Ross, 1991, 1997), suggest that between 0.5 and 1 percent of these large samples (more than 400 people in each) have DID.

A very large percentage of DID patients have simultaneous psychological disorders that may include substance abuse, depression, somatization disorder, borderline personality disorder, panic attacks, and eating disorders (Kluft, 1999; Ross et al., 1990). In one sample of over 100 patients, more than seven additional diagnoses were noted on the average (Ellason & Ross, 1997). Another study of 42 patients documented a pattern of severe comorbid personality disorders, including severe borderline pathology (Dell, 1998). It seems likely that different personalities will present with differing patterns of comorbidity, but the research has not yet been done. In some cases this high rate of comorbidity may reflect the fact that certain disorders, such as borderline personality disorder, share many features with DID—for example, self-destructive, sometimes suicidal behaviour, and emotional instability. Some investigators believe that most of DID symptoms can be best accounted for by characteristics of borderline personality disorder (Lilienfeld & Lynn, 2003).

For the most part, however, the high frequency of additional disorders accompanying DID simply reflects an intensely severe reaction to what seems to be in almost all cases horrible child abuse. Because auditory hallucinations are very common, DID is often misdiagnosed as a psychotic disorder. But the voices in DID are reported by patients as coming from inside their heads, not outside as in psychotic disorders. Because patients with DID are usually aware the voices are hallucinations, they don't report them and instead try to suppress them. These voices often encourage doing something against the person's will, so some individuals, particularly in other cultures, appear to be possessed by demons (Putnam, 1997). Although systematic studies are lacking, DID seems to occur in a variety of cultures throughout the world, particularly in terms of experiencing possession, which is one manifestation of DID (Boon & Draijer, 1993; Coons et al., 1991; Ross, 1997). Coons et al. (1991) found reports of DID in 21 different countries.

Causes

It is informative to examine current evidence on causes for all dissociative disorders, but our emphasis here is on the etiology of DID. Life circumstances that encourage the development of DID seem quite clear in at least one respect. Almost all patients presenting with this disorder report to their mental health professional that they were horribly, often unspeakably, abused as a child.

SYBIL

You may have seen the movie *Sybil*, which was based on the biography of the same name (Schreiber, 1973). Sybil's mother had schizophrenia and her father refused or was unable to intervene in the mother's brutality. Day after day throughout her childhood, Sybil was sexually tortured and occasionally nearly murdered. Before she was one year old, her mother began tying her up in various ways and, on occasion, suspending her from the ceiling. Many mornings her mother placed Sybil on the kitchen table and forcefully inserted various objects into her daughter's vagina. Sybil's mother reasoned, psychotically, that she was preparing her daughter for adult sex. In fact, she so brutally tore the child's vaginal canal that scars were evident during adult gynecological exams. Sybil was also given very strong laxatives but prohibited from using the bathroom. Because of her father's detachment and the normal appearance of the family, the abuse continued without interruption throughout Sybil's childhood.

Imagine you are a child in a situation like Sybil's. What can you do? You're too young to run away. You're too young to call the authorities. Although the pain may be unbearable, you have no way of knowing it is unusual or wrong. But you can do one thing! You can escape into a fantasy world; you can be somebody else. If the escape blunts the physical and emotional pain just for a minute or makes the next hour bearable, chances are you'll escape again. Your mind learns there is no limit to the identities that can be created as needed. Fifteen? Twenty-five? A hundred? Such numbers have been recorded in some cases. You do whatever it takes to get through life.

As mentioned, most surveys report a very high rate of childhood trauma in cases of DID (Gleaves, 1996; Ross, 1997). Putnam et al. (1986) examined 100 cases and found that 97 percent of the patients had experienced significant trauma, usually sexual or physical abuse. Sixty-eight percent reported incest. A four-site study by Colin Ross and colleagues (1990) was conducted on identified cases of DID from Winnipeg, Utah, California, and Ottawa. They reported that, of 102 cases, 95 percent reported physical or sexual abuse, and the prevalence of abuse histories was found to be similar across sites. Some children reported being buried alive. Some were tortured with matches, steam irons, razor blades, or glass. Investigators have corroborated the existence of at least some early sexual abuse in 12 patients with DID, by examining early records, interviewing relatives and acquaintances, and so on (Lewis, Yeager, et al., 1997). However, Harold Merskey, a retired psychiatrist from the University of Western Ontario, exhaustively analyzed several studies claiming to corroborate abuse reports among DID patients (Piper & Merskey, 2004). Merskey noted several methodological deficiencies in the research in this area, causing him to question whether we yet have corroborative evidence of childhood abuse in DID. Similarly, Kluft (1995, 1999) cautions that some reports of childhood abuse by DID patients are not true and have been confabulated (made up).

In cases where childhood trauma does contribute to DID development, it is important to note that not all the trauma is caused by abuse. Putnam (1992) describes a young girl in a war zone who saw both her parents blown to bits in a minefield. In a heart-rending response, she tried to piece the bodies back together, bit by bit.

Such observations have led to wide-ranging agreement that DID is rooted in a natural tendency to escape or dissociate from the unremitting negative affect associated with severe childhood trauma (Kluft, 1984, 1991). A lack of social support during or after the trauma also seems to be implicated. A study of 428 adolescent twins by Waller and Ross (1997) demonstrated that a surprisingly high percentage (33 to 50 percent) of the variance in dissociative experience could be attributed to a chaotic, nonsupportive family environment. The remainder of the variance was associated with individual experience and personality factors.

The behaviour and emotions that make up disorders seem to be related to otherwise normal tendencies present in all of us to some extent. It is quite common for otherwise normal individuals to escape in some way from emotional or physical pain (Spiegel et al., 2013). Noyes and Kletti (1977) surveyed more than 100 survivors of various life-threatening situations and found that most had experienced some type of dissociation, such as feelings of unreality, a blunting of emotional and physical pain, and even separation from their bodies. Dissociative amnesia and fugue states are clearly reactions to severe life stress. But the life stress or trauma is in the present rather than the past, as in the case of the overwrought mother who had dissociative amnesia. Many patients are escaping from legal difficulties or severe stress at home or on the job (Sackheim & Devanand, 1991). But sophisticated statistical analyses indicate that ordinary dissociative reactions differ substantially from the pathological experiences we've described (Waller et al., 1996; Waller & Ross, 1997), and that at least some people do not develop severe pathological dissociative experiences no matter how extreme the stress. These findings are consistent with the diathesis-stress model, in that only with the appropriate vulnerabilities (the diathesis) will a person react to stress with pathological dissociation.

You may have noticed that DID seems very similar in its etiology to post-traumatic stress disorder (PTSD). Both conditions feature strong emotional reactions to experiencing a severe trauma (Butler et al., 1996). But remember that not everyone goes on to experience PTSD after severe trauma. Only people who are biologically and psychologically vulnerable to anxiety are at risk for developing PTSD in response to moderate levels of trauma. As the severity of the trauma increases, however, a greater percentage of people develop PTSD as a consequence, some with the dissociative subtype of PTSD. But some people do not become victims of the disorder even after the most severe traumas, suggesting that individual psychological and biological factors interact with the trauma to produce PTSD.

There is a growing opinion that DID is an extreme subtype of PTSD, with a much greater emphasis on the process of dissociation than on symptoms of anxiety, although both are present in each disorder (Butler et al., 1996). Some evidence also shows that the developmental window of vulnerability to the abuse that leads to DID closes at approximately nine years of age (Putnam, 1997). After that, DID is unlikely to develop, although severe PTSD might.

If true, this is a particularly good example of the role of development in the etiology of psychopathology.

We also must remember that we know relatively little about DID. Our conclusions are based on retrospective case studies or correlations rather than on the prospective examination of people who may have undergone the severe trauma that seems to lead to DID (Kihlstrom et al., 1994). Therefore, it is hard to say what psychological or biological factors might contribute, but there are hints concerning individual differences that might play a role.

Suggestibility. Suggestibility is a personality trait distributed normally across the population, much like weight and height. Some people are much more suggestible than others; some are relatively immune to suggestibility; and the majority fall in the mid-range.

Did you ever have an imaginary childhood playmate? Many people did, and it is one sign of the ability to lead a rich fantasy life, which can be very helpful and adaptive. However, according to a literature review by Lise McLewin and Robert Muller (2006) at York University in Toronto, having had an imaginary childhood playmate is much more common among those with DID than among people in the general population. Having had an imaginary playmate in childhood also seems to correlate with being suggestible or easily hypnotized (some people equate the terms *suggestibility* and *hypnotizability*). A hypnotic trance is also very similar to dissociation (Spiegel et al., 2013). People in a trance tend to be totally focused on one aspect of their world, and they become very vulnerable to suggestions by the hypnotist. There is also the phenomenon of self-hypnosis, in which individuals can dissociate from most of the world around them and "suggest" to themselves that, for example, they won't feel pain in one of their hands.

According to the *autohypnotic model*, people who are suggestible may be able to use dissociation as a defence against extreme trauma (Putnam, 1991). According to the work of Colin Ross and his colleagues, as many as 50 percent of DID patients clearly remember imaginary playmates in childhood (Ross et al., 1990); whether they were created before or after the trauma is not entirely clear. When the trauma becomes unbearable, the person's very identity splits into multiple dissociated identities. Children's ability to distinguish clearly between reality and fantasy as they grow older may be what closes the developmental window for developing DID at approximately age nine. People who are less suggestible may develop a severe post-traumatic stress reaction but not a dissociative reaction. Once again, these explanations are all very speculative (Giesbrecht et al., 2008; Kihlstrom, 2005b).

Biological Contributions. As in post-traumatic stress disorder, where the evidence is more solid, there is almost certainly a biological vulnerability to DID, but it is difficult to pinpoint.

For example, in the large twin study mentioned earlier (Waller & Ross, 1997), none of the variance or identifiable causal factors were attributable to heredity: They were all environmental. In contrast, another twin study by University of British Columbia professors Kerry Jang and John Livesley found evidence for a strong genetic contribution to dissociative disorder symptoms. About half the variance in dissociative symptoms was attributable to genetic factors (Jang et al., 1998). Given these inconsistent findings, more research is clearly needed on the role of genetic factors.

Interesting observations may provide some hints about brain activity during dissociation. Individuals with certain neurological disorders, particularly seizure disorders, experience many dissociative symptoms (Bob, 2003; Bowman & Coons, 2000). Especially temporal lobe epileptic seizure can be associated with dissociative symptoms (Bob, 2003). Patients with dissociative experiences who have seizure disorders are clearly different from those who do not (Ross, 1997). The patients with seizures develop dissociative symptoms in adulthood that are not associated with trauma, in clear contrast to DID patients without seizure disorders. This is an area for future study (Hara et al., 2015).

Head injury and resulting brain damage may induce amnesia or other types of dissociative experience. But these conditions are usually easily diagnosed because they are generalized, irreversible, and associated with an identifiable head trauma (Butler et al., 1996). Lastly, strong evidence exists that sleep deprivation produces dissociative symptoms, such as marked hallucinatory activity (Giesbrecht et al., 2007; van der Kloet et al., 2012). In fact, the symptoms of individuals with DID seem to worsen when they feel tired. Simeon and Abugal (2006) report that patients with DID "often liken it to bad jet lag and feel much worse when they travel across time zones" (p. 210).

▲ A person in a hypnotic trance is very suggestible and may become very absorbed in a particular experience.

Real and False Memories. Again, retrospective case studies suggest that individuals presenting with dissociation, and particularly DID, may have experienced severe trauma, such as sexual abuse, early in their lives but that they have dissociated themselves from this experience and repressed the memory. But some clinical scientists suggest that many such memories are simply the result of strong suggestions by careless therapists who assume people with this condition have been abused. One of the most controversial issues in the field of abnormal psychology today concerns the extent to which memories of early trauma, particularly sexual abuse, are accurate or not. This issue is not specific to any particular mental disorder. Rather, whenever clinical decisions are based on a person's memory, it is important to consider the fact that memories are not always very accurate or even true, even if they *feel* true. Sometimes, we can't remember important things that did happen and other times, we seem to remember things that actually never happened. But this controversy often arises in the context of studying traumatic memories, particularly as identified in DID, so we discuss the research, both pro and con, bearing on this important topic. The stakes in this controversy are enormous, with considerable opportunity for harm to innocent people on each side of the controversy, as has been noted by Clare MacMartin and A. Daniel Yarmey (1999) at the University of Guelph.

On the one hand, if early sexual abuse did occur but was not remembered because of dissociative amnesia, it is crucially important to re-experience aspects of the trauma under the direction of a skilled therapist to relieve current suffering. Without therapy the patient is likely to experience PTSD or a dissociative disorder indefinitely. It is also important that perpetrators are held accountable for their actions, perhaps through the legal system, because abuse of this type is a crime, and prevention is an important goal. Connie Kristiansen and her colleagues at Carleton University have expressed concern that because the validity of recovered memories has been questioned, this may discourage those who have been abused from speaking out about their abuse, decreasing the chance that perpetrators of abuse will be punished for their crimes (Kristiansen et al., 1999).

On the other hand, if memories of early trauma are inadvertently created in response to suggestions by a careless therapist but seem real to the patient, false accusations against loved ones could lead to irreversible family breakup and, perhaps, unjust prison sentences for those falsely accused as perpetrators. In recent years, allegedly inaccurate accusations based on false memories have led to substantial lawsuits against therapists, resulting in awards of millions of dollars in damages. As with most issues that reach this level of contention and disagreement, it is clear that the final answer will not involve an all-or-none resolution. There is irrefutable evidence that false memories *can* be created by reasonably well-understood psychological processes (Bernstein & Loftus, 2009; Ceci, 2003; Frenda et al., 2011; Geraerts et al., 2009; Lilienfeld et al., 1999; Loftus & Davis, 2006; McNally, 2003, 2012; Shaw & Porter, 2015; Toth et al., 2011; Wilson et al., 2015). Some authors content that early traumatic experiences can cause selective dissociative amnesia, with substantial implications for psychological functioning (Dahlenberg et al., 2012; Gleaves et al., 2004; Kluft, 1999; Spiegel et al., 2013). In contrast, others question the assumption that people can encode traumatic experiences without being able to recall them (e.g., Lynn et al., 2014).

In an official position statement on recovered memories, the Canadian Psychiatric Association warned that childhood memories later recovered in adulthood were of questionable reliability and should never be accepted without corroboration (Blackshaw et al., 1996). Similarly, in 1998, the Canadian Psychological Association recommended to the federal justice minister that a full judicial inquiry should be undertaken in all convictions in Canada that stemmed from evidence involving recovered memories. Although the federal government rejected this recommendation, it illustrates the attempts of professional bodies to ensure that recovered memory evidence cannot be used to convict people innocent of the crime in question (see the review by Porter, Campbell, et al., 2003).

Evidence supporting the existence of distorted or illusory memories comes from lab-based experiments conducted by cognitive psychologists. For example, Loftus, Coan, and Pickrell (1996) successfully convinced several individuals that they had been lost for an extended time when they were approximately five years old, which was not true. A trusted companion was recruited to plant the memory. In one case, a 14-year-old boy was told by his older brother that he had been lost in a nearby shopping mall when he was five years old, rescued by an older man, and ultimately reunited with his mother and brother. Several days after receiving this suggestion, the boy reported remembering the event and even that he felt very frightened when he was lost. As time went by, the boy remembered increasingly more details of the event, beyond those described in the plant, including an exact description of the older man. When he was finally told the incident never happened, the boy was very surprised, and he continued to describe details of the event as if they were true.

Another study by Stephen Porter at Dalhousie University and John Yuille and Darrin Lehman at the University of British Columbia (1999) further tested whether it is possible to "remember" a highly emotional event that never actually occurred. These researchers first contacted participants' parents to learn about which of a variety of stressful events (e.g., being seriously attacked by an animal) each participant had actually been exposed to as a child. Then, participants were brought into the laboratory and were encouraged by interviewers to "recover" a memory for a false event using guided imagery and repeated attempts to retrieve the memory. The false events were presented to the participants as actually having happened to them, according to their parents' reports. A shockingly large number of participants "recovered" a full (26 percent) or partial (another 30 percent) memory for the false experience.

But we also have plenty of evidence that therapists need to be very sensitive to signs of trauma that may not be fully remembered in patients presenting with symptoms of dissociative or post-traumatic stress disorders. Even if patients are unable to report or remember early trauma, it can sometimes be confirmed through corroborating evidence (Coons, 1991). In a compelling study, Williams (1994) interviewed 129 women with previously documented histories, such as hospital records, of having been sexually abused as children. Thirty-eight percent did not recall the incidents that had been reported to authorities at least 17 years earlier, even with extensive probing. Dissociative amnesia was more extensive if the victim had been very young and knew the abuser. As noted earlier, Lewis et al. (1997) provided similar documentation of severe early abuse.

In one study, Elliot (1997) surveyed 364 individuals out of a larger group who had experienced substantial trauma, such as a natural disaster, car accident, or physical abuse. Fully 32 percent reported delayed recall of the event, which suggested at least temporary dissociative amnesia. This phenomenon was most prevalent among combat veterans, people who had witnessed the murder or suicide of a family member, and those who had suffered sexual abuse. The severity of the trauma predicted the extent of the amnesia, and the most common trigger for recalling the trauma was a media presentation, such as a movie.

How will this controversy be resolved? Because false memories can be created through strong repeated suggestions by an authority figure, therapists must be fully aware of the conditions under which this is likely to occur, particularly when dealing with young children. This situation requires an extensive knowledge of the workings of memory and other aspects of psychological functioning and illustrates, once again, the dangers of dealing with inexperienced or inadequately trained psychotherapists. Elaborate tales of satanic abuse of children under the care of women in daycare centres are most likely cases of memories implanted by aggressive and careless therapists or law enforcement officials (Lilienfeld et al., 1999). An extreme example is the case of Victoria, British Columbia, native Michelle Smith, who was treated by psychiatrist Dr. Lawrence Pazder in the late 1970s. During her therapy sessions, Smith came to "remember" instances of childhood satanic ritual abuse by her parents and other adults in Victoria. Although she originally sought therapy for depression related to a miscarriage, she was eventually diagnosed with DID by Dr. Pazder. With the help of her therapist, Smith wrote a book about her alleged childhood experiences that was entitled *Michelle Remembers* (Smith & Pazder, 1980). The book was later revealed as a fraud. It contains sections that strongly suggest that Smith's "memories" emerged as a consequence of hypnosis and therapist suggestion. The controversy around this book contributed to the recovered memory debate that began around that time and continues to this day (Allen & Midwinter, 1990).

Advocates on both sides of this issue agree that clinical science must proceed as quickly as possible to specify the processes under which the implantation of false memories is likely and to define the presenting features that indicate a real but dissociated traumatic experience (Frenda et al., 2011; Goodman et al., 2010; Kihlstrom, 1997; Lilienfeld et al., 1999; Pope, 1996, 1997). Until then, mental health professionals must be extremely careful not to prolong unnecessary suffering, among both victims of actual abuse and people falsely accused as abusers (e.g., Lynn et al., 2012).

Treatment

Individuals who experience dissociative amnesia or a fugue state usually get better on their own and remember what they have forgotten. The episodes are so clearly related to current life stress

that prevention of future episodes usually involves therapeutic resolution of the distressing situations and increasing the strength of personal coping mechanisms. When necessary, therapy focuses on recalling what happened during the amnesic or fugue states, often with the help of friends or family who know what happened, so patients can confront the information and integrate it into their conscious experience.

For DID, however, the process is not so easy. With the person's very identity shattered into many different elements, reintegrating the personality might seem hopeless. Fortunately, this is not always the case. Although no controlled research has been reported on the effects of treatment, many documented successes exist of attempts to reintegrate identities through long-term psychotherapy (Brand et al., 2009; Ellason & Ross, 1997; Kluft, 2009). Nevertheless, the prognosis for most people remains guarded. Coon (1986) found that only 5 out of 20 patients achieved a full integration of their identities. Ellason and Ross (1997) reported that 12 out of 54 (22 percent) patients in Canada and the United States had achieved integration two years after presenting for treatment, which in most cases had been continual. Russell Powell and his colleague have pointed out that these results could be attributed to factors other than therapy, because no experimental comparison was present (Powell & Howell, 1998).

The strategies that therapists use today in treating DID are based on accumulated clinical wisdom, as well as on procedures that have been successful for PTSD (Gold & Seibel, 2009; Keane et al., 2011; Maldonado et al., 1998). The fundamental goal is to identify cues or triggers that provoke memories of trauma or dissociation and to neutralize them. More importantly, the patient must confront and relive the early trauma and gain control over the horrible events, at least as they recur in the patient's mind (Kluft, 2009; Ross, 1997). To instill this sense of control, the therapist must skilfully, and very slowly, help the patient visualize and relive aspects of the trauma until it is simply a terrible memory instead of a current event. Because the memory is unconscious, aspects of the experience are often not known to either the patient or the therapist until they emerge during treatment. Hypnosis is often used to access unconscious memories and bring various alters into awareness. Because the process of dissociation may be very similar to the process of hypnosis, the latter may be a particularly efficient way to access traumatic memories (Maldonado et al., 1998). (As yet no evidence supports that hypnosis is a necessary part of treatment.) We know that DID seems to run a chronic course and very seldom improves spontaneously, which suggests that current treatments, primitive as they are, have some effectiveness.

It is possible that re-emerging memories of trauma may trigger further dissociation. The therapist must be on guard against this happening. Trust is important to any therapeutic relationship, but it is absolutely essential in the treatment of DID. Occasionally, medication is combined with therapy, but there is little indication that it helps much. What little clinical evidence there is indicates that antidepressant drugs might be appropriate in some cases (Kluft, 1996; Putnam & Loewenstein, 1993).

SUMMARY

Trauma- and Stressor-Related Disorders

- Post-traumatic stress disorder (PTSD) focuses on avoiding thoughts or images of past traumatic experiences.
- The underlying cause of PTSD is obvious—a traumatic experience. But mere exposure is not enough. The intensity of the experience seems to be a factor in whether an individual develops PTSD; biological vulnerabilities, as well as social and cultural factors, appear to play a role as well.
- Treatment involves re-exposing the survivor of the trauma in order to overcome the debilitating effects of PTSD.

Dissociative Disorders

- Dissociative disorders are characterized by alterations in perceptions: a sense of detachment from one's own self, from the world, or from memories.
- Dissociative disorders include depersonalization-derealization disorder, in which the individual's sense of personal reality is temporarily lost (depersonalization), as is the reality of the external world (derealization). In dissociative amnesia, the individual may be unable to remember important personal information. In generalized amnesia, the individual is unable to remember anything; more commonly, the individual is unable to recall specific events that occur during a specific period (localized or selective amnesia). In dissociative fugue, a subtype of dissociative amnesia, memory loss is combined with an unexpected trip (or trips). In the extreme, new identities, or alters, may be formed, as in dissociative identity disorder (DID). The causes of dissociative disorders are not well understood but often seem related to the tendency to escape psychologically from stress or memories of traumatic events.
- Treatment of dissociative disorders involves helping the patient re-experience the traumatic events in a controlled therapeutic manner to develop better coping skills. In the case of DID, therapy is often long term. Particularly essential with this disorder is a sense of trust between therapist and patient.

KEY TERMS

acute stress disorder, 191
adjustment disorders, 196
alters, 201
attachment disorders, 196
depersonalization, 198
depersonalization-derealization disorder, 198

derealization, 198
disinhibited social engagement disorder, 197
dissociative amnesia, 199
dissociative disorders, 198
dissociative fugue, 200

dissociative identity disorder (DID), 201
dissociative trance disorder (DTD), 201
generalized amnesia, 199
localized amnesia, 199

post-traumatic stress disorder (PTSD), 189
reactive attachment disorder, 197
selective amnesia, 199

ANSWERS TO CONCEPT CHECKS

7.1

1. b; **2.** a; **3.** c

7.2

1. c; **2.** d; **3.** b; **4.** a; **5.** e

MEDIA RESOURCES

⁎ CENGAGE | MINDTAP

Stay organized and efficient with MindTap—a single destination with all the course material and study aids you need to succeed. Built-in apps leverage social media and the latest learning technology. For example:

- ReadSpeaker will read the text to you.
- Flashcards are pre-populated to provide you with a jump start for review—or you can create your own.
- You can highlight text and make notes in your MindTap Reader. Your notes will flow into Evernote, the electronic notebook app that you can access anywhere when it's time to study for the exam.
- Self-quizzing allows you to assess your understanding.

Visit login.cengage.com to start using MindTap. Enter the Online Access Code from the card included with your text. If a code card is not provided, you can purchase instant access at Cengage.ca.

Exploring Trauma- and Stressor-Related Disorders

A proximal instigating stressful event is followed by intense emotional responses.

Disorder	Characteristics	Treatment
Post-traumatic stress disorder	• Fear of re-experiencing a traumatic event: rape, war, life-threatening situation, etc. • Nightmares or flashbacks (of the traumatic event) • Avoidance of the intense feelings of the event through emotional numbing	• Imaginal exposure used for decades, especially prolonged exposure therapy; can reduce avoidance and cognitive re-experiencing • Cognitive therapy can help correct negative assumptions about the trauma • Subjecting trauma survivors to one debriefing session and forcing them to express themselves can be harmful • Eye-movement desensitization and reprocessing is popular but results similar to relaxation training • Drugs can be effective for symptoms
Adjustment disorders	• Anxious or depressive reactions to life stress but milder than PTSD	• Very little research on the treatment of these disorders
Attachment disorders	• Disturbed and developmentally inappropriate behaviours in children • Unable or unwilling to form normal attachment relationships with caregiving adults • Two types: in reactive attachment disorder, child will very seldom seek out a caregiver; in disinhibited social engagement disorder, child shows no inhibitions whatsoever to approaching adults	

Exploring Dissociative Disorders

Characterized by detachment from the self (depersonalization) and objective reality (derealization)

Similar etiology
to post-traumatic
stress disorder

Severe abuse during childhood
• Fantasy life is the only "escape"
• Practice becomes automatic
and then involuntary

Causes

Biological
vulnerability
likely

High suggestibility
a possible trait

Hristo Shindov/Getty Images

Controversy

The scientific community is divided over the question of whether multiple identities are a genuine experience or faked. Studies have shown that "false memories" can be created ("implanted") by therapists. Other tests confirm that various alters are physiologically distinct.

Disorder	Characteristics	Treatment
Dissociative identity disorder (DID)	• Affected person adopts new identities, or alters, that co-exist simultaneously; the alters may be complete and distinct personalities or only partly independent • Average number of alters is 15 • Childhood onset; affects more women than men • Patients often suffer from other psychological disorders simultaneously • Rare outside of Western cultures	• Long-term psychotherapy may reintegrate separate personalities in 25 percent of patients • Treatment of associated trauma similar to post-traumatic stress disorder; lifelong condition without treatment
Depersonalization-derealization disorder	• Severe and frightening feelings of detachment dominate the person's life • Affected person feels like an outside observer of his or her own mental or body processes • Causes significant distress or impairment in functioning, especially emotional expression and deficits in perception • Some symptoms are similar to those of panic disorder • Rare; onset usually in adolescence	• Psychological treatments similar to those for panic disorder may be helpful • Stresses associated with onset of disorder should be addressed • Tends to be lifelong
Dissociative amnesia	• Generalized: Inability to remember anything, including identity; comparatively rare • Localized: Inability to remember specific events (usually traumatic); frequently occurs in war • More common than general amnesia • Usually adult onset for both types	• Usually self-correcting when current life stress is resolved • If needed, therapy focuses on retrieving lost information
Dissociative trance	• Sudden changes in personality accompany a trance or believed possession • Causes significant distress and/or impairment in functioning • Often associated with stress or trauma • Prevalent worldwide, usually in a religious context; rarely seen in Western cultures • More common in women than in men	• Little is known

PhotoDisc/Getty Images

08 | Mood

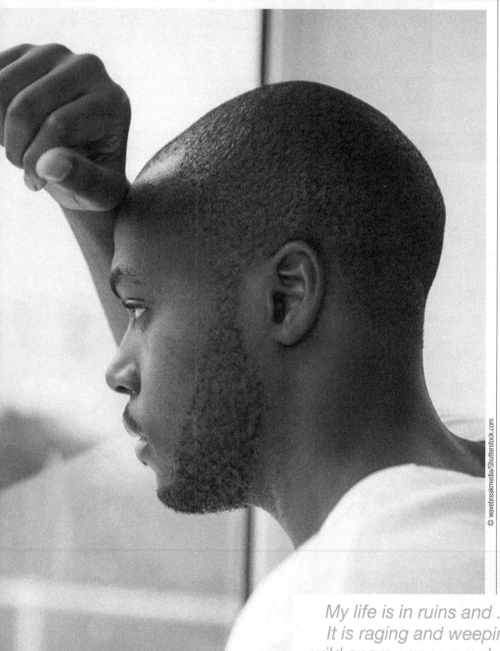

© wavebreakmedia/Shutterstock.com

*My life is in ruins and . . . my body is uninhabitable.
It is raging and weeping and full of destruction and
wild energy gone amok. In the mirror I see a creature
I don't know but must live and share my mind with.*

—KAY REDFIELD JAMISON, An Unquiet Mind

Use scientific reasoning to interpret behaviour:	› Identify basic biological, psychological, and social components of behavioural explanations (e.g., inferences, observations, operational definitions, and interpretations) (APA SLO 2.1a)
Describe key concepts, principles, and overarching themes in psychology:	› Analyze the variability and continuity of behaviour and mental processes within and across animal species (APA SLO 1.2d2)
Engage in innovative and integrative thinking and problem solving:	› Describe problems operationally to study them empirically (APA SLO 2.3A)
Develop a working knowledge of the content domains of psychology:	› Recognize major historical events, theoretical perspectives, and figures in psychology and their link to trends in contemporary research (APA SLO 1.2c)
Describe applications that employ discipline-based problem solving:	› Correctly identify antecedents and consequences of behaviour and mental processes (APA SLO 1.3c)
	› Describe examples of relevant and practical applications of psychological principles to everyday life (APA SLO 1.3a)

*Portions of this chapter cover learning outcomes suggested by the American Psychological Association (2013) in its guidelines for the undergraduate psychology major. Chapter coverage of these outcomes is identified above by APA Goal and APA Suggested Learning Outcome (SLO).

Think back over the last month of your life. It may seem normal in most respects: you studied during the week, socialized on the weekend, and thought about the future occasionally. Perhaps you were anticipating with some pleasure the next school break or seeing an old friend. But maybe sometime during the past month you also felt kind of down, maybe because you broke up with your boyfriend or girlfriend or, worse yet, somebody close to you died. Think about your feelings during this period. Were you sad? Perhaps you remember crying. Maybe you felt listless and you couldn't seem to get up the energy to go out with your friends. It may be that you feel this way occasionally for no good reason you can think of, and your friends think you're moody.

If you are like most people, you know such a mood will pass. You will be back to your old self in a day or two. In fact, if you never felt down and always saw only what was good in a situation, it might be more remarkable than if you were depressed occasionally. Feelings of depression (and joy) are universal, which makes it all the more difficult to understand disorders of mood, disorders possibly so incapacitating that suicide may seem by far a better option than living. Consider the case of Katie.

KATIE | *Weathering Depression*

Katie was an attractive but very shy 16-year-old who came to our clinic with her parents. For several years, Katie had seldom interacted with anybody outside her family because of her considerable social anxiety. Going to school was very difficult, and as her social contacts decreased, her days became empty and dull. By the time she was 16, a deep, all-encompassing depression blocked the sun from her life. Here is how she described it later.

> The experience of depression is like falling into a deep, dark hole that you cannot climb out of. You scream as you fall, but it seems like no one hears you. Some days you float upward without even trying; on other days, you wish that you would hit bottom so that you would never fall again. Depression affects the way you interpret events. It influences the way you see yourself and the way you see other people. I remember looking in the mirror and thinking that I was the ugliest creature in the world. Later in life, when some of these ideas

would come back, I learned to remind myself that I did not have those thoughts yesterday and chances were that I would not have them tomorrow or the next day. It is a little like waiting for a change in the weather.

But at 16, in the depths of her despair, Katie had no such perspective. She often cried for hours at the end of the day. She had begun drinking alcohol the year before, with the blessing of her parents, strangely enough, since the pills prescribed by her family doctor did no good. A glass of wine at dinner had a temporary soothing effect on Katie, and both she and her parents, in their desperation, were willing to try anything that might make her a more functional person. But one glass was not enough. She drank more and more often. She began drinking herself to sleep. It was a means of escaping what she felt: "I had very little hope of positive change. I do not think that anyone close to me was hopeful, either. I was angry, cynical, and in a great deal of emotional pain." Katie's life continued to spiral downward.

For several years, Katie had thought about suicide as a solution to her unhappiness. At 13, in the presence of her parents, she reported these thoughts to a psychologist. Her parents wept, and the sight of their tears deeply affected Katie. From that point on she never expressed her suicidal thoughts again, but they remained with her. By the time she was 16, her preoccupation with her own death had increased.

> I think this was just exhaustion. I was tired of dealing with the anxiety and depression day in and day out. Soon I found myself trying to sever the few interpersonal connections that I did have, with my closest friends, with my mother, and my oldest brother. I was almost impossible to talk to. I was angry and frustrated all the time. One day I went over the edge. My mother and I had a disagreement about some unimportant little thing. I went to my bedroom where I kept a bottle of whiskey or vodka or whatever I was drinking at the time. I drank as much as I could until I could pinch myself as hard as I could and feel nothing. Then I got out a very sharp knife that I had been saving and slashed my wrist deeply. I did not feel anything but the warmth of the blood running from my wrist.

The blood poured out onto the floor next to the bed that I was lying on. The sudden thought hit me that I had failed, that this was not enough to cause my death. I got up from the bed and began to laugh. I tried to stop the bleeding with some tissues. I stayed calm and frighteningly pleasant. I walked to the kitchen and called my mother. I cannot imagine how she felt when she saw my shirt and pants covered in blood. She was amazingly calm. She asked to see the cut and said that it was not going to stop bleeding on its own and that I needed to go to the doctor immediately. I remember as the doctor shot Novocain into the cut he remarked that I must have used an anesthetic before cutting myself. I never felt the shot or the stitches.

After that, thoughts of suicide became more frequent and much more real. My father asked me to promise that I would never do it again and I said I would not, but that promise meant nothing to me. I knew it was to ease his pains and fears and not mine, and my preoccupation with death continued.

Think for a moment about your own experience of depression. What are the major differentiating factors between your feelings and Katie's? Clearly, Katie's depression was outside the boundaries of normal experience by virtue of its intensity and duration. In addition, her severe or clinical depression interfered substantially with her ability to function. Finally, she experienced several of the associated psychological and physical symptoms that accompany clinical depression.

Sometimes, mood disorders lead to tragic consequences. So developing a full understanding is key. In the following sections, we describe how various emotional experiences and symptoms interrelate to produce specific mood disorders. We offer detailed descriptions of different mood disorders and examine the many criteria that define them. We discuss the relationship between anxiety and depression, and the causes and treatment of mood disorders. We conclude with a discussion of suicide.

AN OVERVIEW OF DEPRESSION AND MANIA

The disorders described in this chapter used to be categorized under several different general labels, such as "depressive disorders," "affective disorders," or even "depressive neuroses." Traditionally, these problems have been grouped under the heading **mood disorders** because they are characterized by severe deviations in mood. In *DSM-5*, these various mood disorders are grouped in two adjacent chapters: depressive disorders, and bipolar and related disorders.

The fundamental experiences of depression and mania contribute, either singly or together, to all the mood disorders. We describe each state and discuss its contributions to the various mood disorders. Then we briefly describe the additional defining criteria, features, or symptoms that define the specific disorders.

The most commonly diagnosed and most severe depression is called a **major depressive episode**. *DSM-5* criteria, items A to C listed under major depressive disorder (see DSM Table 8.1),

describe it as an extremely depressed mood state that lasts at least two weeks and includes cognitive symptoms (such as feelings of worthlessness and indecisiveness) and disturbed physical functions (such as altered sleeping patterns, significant changes in appetite and weight, or a very notable loss of energy) to the

DSM-5 | **Table 8.1** Diagnostic Criteria for Major Depressive Disorder

A. Five (or more) of the following symptoms have been present during the same 2-week·period and represent a change from previous functioning; at least one of the symptoms is either (1) depressed mood or (2) loss of interest or pleasure.

Note: Do not include symptoms that are clearly attributable to another medical condition.

1. Depressed mood most of the day, nearly every day, as indicated by either subjective report (e.g., feels sad, or empty, or hopeless) or observation made by others (e.g., appears tearful).

   (**Note:** In children and adolescents, can be irritable mood.)

2. Markedly diminished interest or pleasure in all, or almost all, activities most of the day, nearly every day (as indicated by either subjective account or observation).

3. Significant weight loss when not dieting or weight gain (e.g., a change of more than 5 percent of body weight in a month), or decrease or increase in appetite nearly every day. (Note: In children, consider failure to make expected weight gains.)

4. Insomnia or hypersomnia nearly every day.

5. Psychomotor agitation or retardation nearly every day (observable by others, not merely subjective feelings of restlessness or being slowed down).

6. Fatigue or loss of energy nearly every day.

7. Feelings of worthlessness or excessive or inappropriate guilt (which may be delusional) nearly every day (not merely self-reproach or guilt about being sick).

8. Diminished ability to think or concentrate, or indecisiveness, nearly every day (either by subjective account or as observed by others).

9. Recurrent thoughts of death (not just fear of dying), recurrent suicidal ideation without a specific plan, or a suicide attempt or a specific plan for committing suicide.

B. The symptoms cause clinically significant distress or impairment in social, occupational, or other important areas of functioning.

C. The episode is not attributable to the physiological effects of a substance or to another medical condition.

Note: Criteria A–C represent a major depressive episode.

Note: Responses to a significant loss (e.g., bereavement, financial ruin, losses from a natural disaster, a serious medical illness or disability) may include the feelings of intense sadness, rumination about the loss, insomnia, poor appetite, and weight loss noted in Criterion A, which may resemble a depressive episode. Although such symptoms may be understandable or considered appropriate to the loss, the presence of a major depressive episode in addition to the normal response to a significant loss should also be carefully considered. This decision inevitably requires the exercise of clinical judgment based on the individual's history and the cultural norms for the expression of distress in the context of loss.

D. The occurrence of the major depressive episode is not better explained by schizoaffective disorder, schizophrenia, schizophreniform disorder, delusional disorder, or other specified and unspecified schizophrenia spectrum and other psychotic disorders.

E. There has never been a manic episode or a hypomanic episode.

Note: This exclusion does not apply if all of the manic-like or hypomanic-like episodes are substance-induced or are attributable to the physiological effects of another medical condition.

In recording the name of a diagnosis, terms should be listed in the following order: major depressive disorder, single or recurrent episode, severity/psychotic/remission specifiers, followed by as many of the following specifiers without codes that apply to the current episode.

Specify:

With anxious distress

With mixed features

With melancholic features

With atypical features

With mood-congruent psychotic features

With mood-incongruent psychotic features

With catatonia

With peripartum onset

With seasonal pattern (recurrent episode only)

point that even the slightest activity or movement requires an overwhelming effort. The episode is typically accompanied by a marked general loss of interest and of the ability to experience any pleasure from life, including interactions with family or friends and accomplishments at work or at school. (The inability to experience pleasure is termed *anhedonia*.) Although all symptoms are important, evidence suggests that the most central indicators of a full major depressive episode are the physical changes (sometimes called somatic or vegetative symptoms) (Bech, 2009; Buchwald & Rudick-Davis, 1993; Keller et al., 1995; Kessler & Wang, 2009), along with the behavioural and emotional shutdown, as reflected by low behavioural activation (Dimidjian et al., 2011). The average duration of such an episode if untreated is approximately nine months (Eaton et al., 1997; Tollefson, 1993).

The second fundamental state in mood disorders is abnormally exaggerated elation, joy, or euphoria. In **mania**, individuals find

DSM-5 — Table 8.2 Diagnostic Criteria for Manic Episode

A. A distinct period of abnormally and persistently elevated, expansive, or irritable mood and abnormally and persistently increased goal-directed activity or energy, lasting at least 1 week and present most of the day, nearly every day (or any duration if hospitalization is necessary).

B. During the period of mood disturbance and increased energy or activity, three (or more) of the following symptoms (four if the mood is only irritable) are present to a significant degree and represent a noticeable change from usual behavior:

1. Inflated self-esteem or grandiosity.
2. Decreased need for sleep (e.g., feels rested after only 3 hours of sleep).
3. More talkative than usual or pressure to keep talking.
4. Flight of ideas or subjective experience that thoughts are racing.
5. Distractibility (i.e., attention too easily drawn to unimportant or irrelevant external stimuli), as reported or observed.
6. Increase in goal-directed activity (either socially, at work or school, or sexually) or psychomotor agitation (e.g., purposeless non-goal-directed activity).
7. Excessive involvement in activities that have a high potential for painful consequences (e.g., engaging in unrestrained buying sprees, sexual indiscretions, or foolish business investments).

C. The mood disturbance is sufficiently severe to cause marked impairment in social or occupational functioning or to necessitate hospitalization to prevent harm to self or others, or there are psychotic features.

D. The episode is not attributable to the physiological effects of a substance (e.g., a drug of abuse, a medication, other treatment) or to another general medical condition.

Note: A full manic episode that emerges during antidepressant treatment (e.g., medication, electroconvulsive therapy) but persists at a fully syndromal level beyond the physiological effect of that treatment is sufficient evidence of a manic episode and, therefore, a bipolar I diagnosis.

extreme pleasure in every activity; in fact, some patients compare their daily experience of mania with a continuous orgasm. They become extraordinarily active (hyperactive), requiring very little sleep, and may develop grandiose plans, believing they can accomplish anything they desire. The *DSM-5* highlights this feature by adding "persistently increased goal-directed activity or energy" to the "A" criterion (see DSM Table 8.2; American Psychiatric Association, 2013). Speech is typically very rapid and may become incoherent, because the individual is attempting to express so many exciting ideas at once; this feature is typically referred to as *flight of ideas*.

The *DSM-5* criteria for a manic episode require a duration of only one week, less if the episode is severe

ABNORMAL PSYCHOLOGY | VIDEO

Major Depressive Disorder: Barbara

"I've been sad, depressed most of my life. . . . I had a headache in high school for a year and a half. . . . There have been different periods in my life when I wanted to end it all. . . . I hate me, I really hate me. I hate the way I look, I hate the way I feel. I hate the way I talk to people. . . . I do everything wrong. . . . I feel really hopeless."

Visit login.cengage.com to start using MindTap. Enter the Online Access Code from the card included with your text. If a code card is not provided, you can purchase instant access at Cengage.ca.

© Cengage Learning

enough to require hospitalization. Hospitalization could occur, for example, if the individual was engaging in a self-destructive buying spree, charging thousands of dollars in the expectation of making a million dollars the next day. Irritability is often part of a manic episode, usually near the end. Paradoxically, being anxious or depressed is also commonly part of mania, as described later. The average duration of an untreated manic episode is two to six months (Angst, 2009; Solomon et al., 2010).

The *DSM-5* also defines a **hypomanic episode**, a less severe version of a manic episode that does not cause marked impairment in social or occupational functioning and need last only four days rather than a full week. (*Hypo* means "below"; thus, the episode is below the level of a manic episode.) A hypomanic episode is not in itself necessarily problematic, but it does contribute to the definition of several mood disorders.

THE STRUCTURE OF MOOD DISORDERS

Individuals who experience either depression or mania are said to have a *unipolar mood disorder*, because their mood remains at one "pole" of the depression-mania continuum. Mania by itself (unipolar mania) probably does occur but seems to be rare, because most people with a unipolar mood disorder eventually develop depression. Manic episodes alone may be somewhat more frequent in adolescents, however. Someone who alternates between depression and mania is said to have a *bipolar mood disorder*, travelling from one pole of the depression–elation continuum to the other and back again. This label is somewhat misleading, however, because depression and elation may not exactly be at opposite ends of the same mood state; in fact, though related, they are often relatively independent. An individual can experience manic symptoms but feel somewhat depressed or anxious at the same time or be depressed with a few symptoms of mania. This episode is characterized as having **mixed features**. Manic episodes are characterized by dysphoric (anxious or depressive) features more commonly than was thought, and dysphoria can be severe (Cassidy et al., 2008; Swann et al., 2013). In one study, 30 percent of 1090 patients hospitalized for acute mania had mixed episodes (Hantouche et al., 2006). In another carefully constructed study of more than 4000 patients, as many as two-thirds of patients with bipolar depressed episodes also had manic symptoms, most often racing thoughts (flight of ideas), distractibility, and agitation. These patients were also more severely impaired than those without concurrent depression and manic symptoms (Goldberg et al., 2009; Swann et al., 2013). The rare individual who suffers from manic episodes alone can be expected to become depressed later. In general, newer models view bipolar disorder as an evolving condition, proceeding through different at-risk stages with mild symptoms early in the disease progressing to a later chronic disorder (Frank et al., 2015; Kupfer et al., 2015). In the *DSM-5*, the term "mixed features" requires specifying whether a predominantly manic or predominantly depressive episode is present, and then noting if enough symptoms of the opposite polarity are present to meet the mixed features criteria.

It is important to determine the course or temporal patterning of the depressive or manic episodes. For example, do they tend to recur? If they do, does the patient recover fully for at least two months between episodes (termed "full remission") or only partially recover retaining some symptoms ("partial remission")? Do the depressive episodes alternate with manic or hypomanic episodes or not? All these patterns for mood disorders are important to note, since they contribute to decisions on which diagnosis is appropriate.

The importance of temporal course (patterns of recurrence and remittance) makes the goals of treating mood disorders somewhat different from those for other psychological disorders. Clinicians want to do everything possible to relieve people like Katie of their current depressive episode, but an equally important goal is to prevent future episodes—in other words, to help people like Katie stay well for a longer period.

DEPRESSIVE DISORDERS

CLINICAL DESCRIPTION

The most easily recognized mood disorder is **major depressive disorder**, defined by the presence of depression and the absence of manic, or hypomanic, episodes before or during the episode (see DSM Table 8.1). We now know that an occurrence of just one isolated depressive episode in a lifetime is rare (Angst, 2009; Eaton et al., 2008; Kessler & Wang, 2009).

If two or more major depressive episodes occurred and were separated by at least two months during which the individual was not depressed, the major depressive disorder is noted as being recurrent. Recurrence is very important in predicting the future course of the disorder and in choosing appropriate treatments. Individuals with recurrent major depression usually have a family history of depression, unlike people who experience single episodes. As many as 85 percent of single-episode cases later experience a second episode (Angst, 2009; Eaton et al., 2008; Judd, 2000; Souery et al., 2012), based on follow-ups as long as 23 years (Eaton et al., 2008). In the first year following an episode, the risk of recurrence is 20 percent, but it rises as high as 40 percent in the second year (Boland & Keller, 2009). Because of this finding and others reviewed later, clinical scientists have recently concluded that unipolar depression is often a chronic condition that waxes and wanes over time but seldom disappears (Judd, 2012). The median lifetime number of major depressive episodes is four to seven; in one large sample, 25 percent experienced six or more episodes (Angst, 2009; Kessler & Wang, 2009). The median duration of recurrent major depressive episodes is four to five months (Boland & Keller, 2009; Kessler et al., 2003), somewhat shorter than the average length of the first episode.

On the basis of these criteria, how would you diagnose Katie? Katie experienced severely depressed mood, feelings of worthlessness, difficulty concentrating, recurrent thoughts of death, sleep difficulties, and loss of energy. She clearly met the criteria for major depressive disorder, recurrent. Katie's depressive episodes were quite severe when they occurred, but she tended to cycle in and out of them.

Persistent depressive disorder (dysthymia) shares many of the symptoms of major depressive disorder but differs in its course. There may be fewer symptoms (as few as two; see

▲ Canadian singer and songwriter Sarah McLachlan has reportedly had bouts of depression. Her music provides her fans a window into her emotional pain. She has said of her early work that "it was almost as if I needed to be depressed to be creative" (Waliszewski & Smithouser, 1997).

independent of whether the symptom presentation meets criteria for a major depressive disorder (as just noted), because these two groups (chronic and nonchronic) seem different not only in course over time but also in family history and cognitive style. About 20 percent of patients with a major depressive episode report chronicity of this episode for at least two years, thereby meeting criteria for persistent depressive disorder (Klein, 2010).

DSM-5	**Table 8.3** Diagnostic Criteria for Persistent Depressive Disorder (Dysthymia)

A. Depressed mood for most of the day, for more days than not, as indicated by either subjective account or observation by others, for at least 2 years. *Note:* In children and adolescents, mood can be irritable and duration must be at least 1 year.

B. Presence, while depressed, of two (or more) of the following:

    1. Poor appetite or overeating.

    2. Insomnia or hypersomnia.

    3. Low energy or fatigue.

    4. Low self-esteem.

    5. Poor concentration or difficulty making decisions.

    6. Feelings of hopelessness.

C. During the 2-year period (1 year for children or adolescents) of the disturbance, the person has never been without the symptoms in criteria A and B for more than 2 months at a time.

D. Criteria for major depressive disorder may be continuously present for 2 years.

E. There has never been a manic episode or a hypomanic episode, and criteria have never been met for cyclothymic disorder.

F. The disturbance is not better explained by a persistent schizoaffective disorder, schizophrenia, delusional disorder, or other specified or unspecified schizophrenia spectrum and other psychotic disorder.

G. The symptoms are not attributable to the physiological effects of a substance (e.g., a drug of abuse, a medication) or another medical condition (e.g., hypothyroidism).

H. The symptoms cause clinically significant distress or impairment in social, occupational, or other important areas of functioning.

Specify if:

    With anxious distress

    With mixed features

    With melancholic features

    With atypical features

    With mood-congruent psychotic features

    With mood-incongruent psychotic features

    With peripartum onset

Specify if:

    In partial remission

    In full remission

Specify if:

    Early onset: If onset is before age 21 years.

    Late onset: If onset is at age 21 years or older.

Specify if (for most recent 2 years of persistent depressive disorder):

    With pure dysthymic syndrome: Full criteria for a major depressive episode have not been met in at least the preceding 2 years.

    With persistent major depressive episode: Full criteria for a major depressive episode have been met throughout the preceding 2-year period.

DSM Table 8.3) but depression remains relatively unchanged over long periods, sometimes 20 or 30 years or more (Angst, 2009; Cristancho et al., 2012; Klein, 2008; Klein et al., 2000, 2006; Murphy & Byrne, 2012).

Persistent depressive disorder is defined as depressed mood that continues at least two years, during which the patient cannot be symptom free for more than two months at a time even though they may not experience all of the symptoms of a major depressive episode. It identifies patients who were formerly diagnosed with dysthymic disorder and other depressive disorders (Rhebergen & Graham, 2014). Persistent depressive disorder differs from a major depressive disorder in the number of symptoms required, but mostly in the chronicity. It is considered more severe, since patients with persistent depression present with higher rates of comorbidity with other mental disorders, are less responsive to treatment, and show a slower rate of improvement over time. In a 10-year prospective follow-up study, Klein and colleagues (2006) suggest that chronicity (versus nonchronicity) is the most important distinction in diagnosing depression

Also, 22 percent of people suffering from persistent depression with fewer symptoms (specified as "with pure dysthymic syndrome") eventually experienced a major depressive episode (Klein et al., 2006). These individuals, who suffer from both major depression episodes and persistent depression with fewer symptoms, are said to have **double depression**. Typically, a few depressive symptoms develop first, perhaps at an early age, and then one or more major depressive episodes occur later, only to revert to the underlying pattern of depression once the major depressive episode has run its course (Boland & Keller, 2009; Klein et al., 2006; Rubio et al., 2011). Identifying this particular pattern is important because it is associated with higher severity and a problematic future course (Boland & Keller, 2009; Klein et al., 2006). For example, Klein et al. (2006) found that the relapse rate of depression among people meeting criteria for *DSM-IV* dysthymia was 71 percent. Consider the case of Jack.

JACK | *A Life Kept Down*

Jack was a 49-year-old divorced white man who lived at his mother's home with his ten-year-old son. He complained of chronic depression, saying he finally realized he needed help. Jack reported that he had been a pessimist and a worrier for much of his adult life. He consistently felt kind of down and depressed and did not have much fun. He had difficulty making decisions, was generally pessimistic about the future, and thought very little of himself. During the past 20 years, the longest period he could remember in which his mood was "normal" or less depressed lasted only four or five days.

Despite his difficulties, Jack had managed to finish college and obtain a master's degree in public administration. People told him his future was bright and he would be highly valued in state government. Jack did not think so. He took a job as a low-level clerk in a state agency, thinking he could always work his way up. He never did, remaining at the same desk for years.

Jack's wife, fed up with his continued pessimism, lack of self-confidence, and relative inability to enjoy day-to-day events, became discouraged and divorced him. Jack moved in with his mother so she could help care for his son and share expenses.

About five years before coming to the clinic, Jack had experienced a bout of depression worse than anything he had previously known. His self-esteem went from low to nonexistent. From indecisiveness, he became totally unable to decide anything. He was exhausted all the time and felt as if lead had filled his arms and legs, making it difficult even to move. He became unable to complete projects or to meet deadlines. Seeing no hope, he began to consider suicide. After tolerating a listless performance for years from someone they had expected to rise through the ranks, Jack's employers finally fired him.

After about six months, the major depressive episode resolved and Jack returned to his chronic but milder state of depression. He could get out of bed and accomplish some things, although he still doubted his own abilities. He was unable to obtain another job, however. After several years of waiting for something to turn up, he realized he was totally unable to solve his own problems and that without help his depression would certainly continue. After a thorough assessment, we determined that Jack had a classic case of double depression.

Persistent depressive disorder is further specified depending on whether or not a major depressive episode is part of the picture. Thus, one might meet criteria for the disorder "with pure dysthymic syndrome," meaning one has not met criteria for a major depressive episode in at least the preceding two years, "with persistent major depressive episode," indicating the presence of a major depressive episode over at least a two-year period, or "with intermittent major depressive episodes," which is the double depression that Jack suffered from. In these cases, it is important to note whether or not the patient is currently in a major depressive episode. For both major depressive disorder and persistent depressive disorder, a depiction of the various course configurations of depression can be seen in ■ Figure 8.1.

Additional Defining Criteria for Depressive Disorders

Look again at DSM Table 8.1 on the diagnostic criteria for major depressive disorder; notice the section at the bottom that asks the clinician to specify the features of the latest depressive episode. These instructions are here because these symptoms, or *specifiers*, may or may not accompany a depressive disorder; when they do, they are often helpful in determining the most effective treatment or likely course.

In addition to rating the severity of the episode as mild, moderate, or severe, clinicians use eight basic specifiers to describe depressive disorders. These are (1) with psychotic features (mood-congruent or mood-incongruent), (2) with anxious distress (mild to severe), (3) with mixed features, (4) with melancholic features, (5) with atypical features, (6) with catatonic features, (7) with

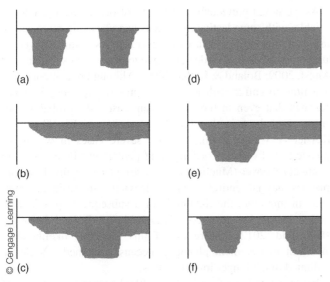

FIGURE 8.1 | Pictorial representation of various course configurations of non-bipolar depression. The horizontal axis represents time and the vertical axis represents mood, with the horizontal black line representing euthymic, or normal, mood, and the magnitude of downward deflection (the blue area) reflecting severity of depressive symptoms. Panel (a) is nonchronic major depressive disorder (in this case, recurrent, as two depressive episodes are depicted). Panel (b) is persistent depressive disorder. Panel (c) is double depression (major depressive episode superimposed on antecedent persistent depressive disorder). Panel (d) is chronic major depressive episode. Panel (e) is major depressive episode in partial remission. Panel (f) is recurrent major depression without full inter-episode recovery.

Source: From "Chronic Depression: Diagnosis and Classification," by D. N. Klein, 2010, *Current Directions in Psychological Science, 19*(2), pp. 96–100.

peripartum onset, and (8) with seasonal pattern. Some of these specifiers apply only to major depressive disorder. Others apply to both major depressive disorder and persistent depressive disorder. Three are described briefly below.

Psychotic features specifiers. Some individuals in the midst of a major depressive (or manic) episode may experience psychotic symptoms, specifically hallucinations (seeing or hearing things that aren't there) and delusions (strongly held but inaccurate beliefs) (Rothschild, 2013). Patients may also have *somatic (physical) delusions*, believing, for example, that their bodies are rotting internally and deteriorating into nothingness. Some may hear voices telling them how evil and sinful they are (*auditory hallucinations*). Such hallucinations and delusions are called *mood congruent*, because they seem directly related to the depression. On rare occasions, depressed individuals might have other types of hallucinations or delusions such as *delusions of grandeur* (believing, for example, they are supernatural or supremely gifted) that do not seem consistent with the depressed mood. This is a *mood-incongruent* hallucination or delusion. Although quite rare, this condition signifies a serious type of depressive episode that may progress to schizophrenia (or may be a symptom of schizophrenia to begin with). Delusions of grandeur accompanying a manic episode are mood congruent. Conditions in which psychotic symptoms accompany depressive episodes are relatively rare, occurring in 5 to 20 percent of identified cases of depression (Flores & Schatzberg, 2006; Ohayon & Schatzberg, 2002). Psychotic features in general are associated with a poor response to treatment, greater impairment, and fewer weeks with minimal symptoms, compared with nonpsychotic depressed patients over a 10-year period (Busatto, 2013; Flint et al., 2006).

Peripartum onset specifier. Peri means "surrounding"—in this case, the period of time just before and just after giving birth. This specifier can apply to both major depressive and manic episodes. Between 13 and 19 percent of all women giving birth (one in eight) meet criteria for a diagnosis of depression, referred to as peripartum depression. In one study, 7 percent met criteria for a full major depressive episode (Gavin et al., 2005). Typically, a somewhat higher incidence of depression is found postpartum (after the birth) than during pregnancy itself (Viguera et al., 2011). In another recent important study, 14 percent of 10 000 women who gave birth screened positively for depression and fully 19 percent of those depressed new mothers had serious thoughts of harming themselves (Wisner et al., 2013). During the peripartum period (pregnancy and the six-month period immediately following childbirth), early recognition of possible psychotic depressive (or manic) episodes is important, because in a few tragic cases a mother in the midst of an episode has killed her newborn child (Purdy & Frank, 1993; Sit et al., 2006). Fathers don't entirely escape the emotional consequences of birth. Ramchandani and colleagues (2005) followed 11 833 mothers and 8431 fathers for eight weeks after the birth of their child. Of the mothers, 10 percent showed a marked increase in depressive symptoms on a rating scale, but so did 4 percent of the fathers. If you extend the period from the first trimester to one year after birth, the rate of depression is approximately 10 percent for fathers and as high as 40 percent for mothers. And depression in fathers was associated with adverse emotional and behavioural outcomes in children 3.5 years later (Paulson & Bazemore, 2010).

More minor reactions in adjustment to childbirth—called the "baby blues"—typically last a few days and occur in 40 to 80 percent of women between one and five days after delivery. During this period, new mothers may be tearful and have some temporary mood swings, but these are normal responses to the stresses of childbirth and disappear quickly; the peripartum onset specifier does not apply to them (O'Hara & McCabe, 2013; Wisner et al., 2010). However, in peripartum depression, most people, including the new mother herself, have difficulty understanding why she is depressed, because they assume this is a joyous time. Many people forget that extreme stress can be brought on by physical exhaustion, new schedules, adjustment to nursing, sleep deprivation, and other changes that follow the birth. There is also some evidence that women with a history of peripartum depression meeting full criteria for an episode of major depression may be affected differently by the rapid decline in reproductive hormones that occurs after delivery (Wisner et al., 2002; Workman et al., 2012) or may have elevated corticotrophin-releasing hormone in the placenta (Meltzer-Brody et al., 2011; Yim et al., 2009) and that these factors may contribute to peripartum depression. But these findings need replication, because all women experience very substantial shifts in hormone levels after delivery, but only some develop a depressive disorder. Nor is there strong evidence that hormonal levels are significantly different in peripartum depressed and nondepressed women (Workman et al., 2012). A close examination of women with peripartum depression revealed no essential differences between the characteristics of this mood disorder and others (O'Hara & McCabe, 2013; Wisner et al., 2002). Therefore, peripartum depression did not require a separate category in the *DSM-5* and is simply a specifier for a depressive disorder. (Approaches to treatment for peripartum depression do not differ from those for non-peripartum depression.)

Seasonal pattern specifier. This temporal specifier applies to recurrent major depressive disorder (and also to bipolar disorders). It accompanies episodes that occur during certain seasons (e.g., winter depression). The most usual pattern is a depressive episode that begins in the late fall and ends with the beginning of spring. (In bipolar disorder, individuals may become depressed during the winter and manic during the summer.) These episodes must have occurred for at least two years with no evidence of nonseasonal major depressive episodes occurring during that period of time. This condition is called **seasonal affective disorder (SAD)**.

Although some studies have reported seasonal cycling of manic episodes, the overwhelming majority of seasonal mood disorders involve winter depression, which has been estimated to affect as many as 3 percent of North Americans (Lam et al., 2006; Levitt & Boyle, 2002). But fully 15 to 25 percent of the population might have some vulnerability to seasonal cycling of mood that does not reach criteria for a disorder (Kessler & Wang, 2009; Sohn & Lam, 2005). Unlike more severe melancholic types of depression, people with winter depressions tend toward excessive sleep (rather than decreased sleep) and increased appetite and weight gain (rather than decreased appetite and weight loss), symptoms shared with atypical depressive episodes. Although SAD seems a bit different from other major depressive episodes, family studies have not yet revealed any significant differences that would suggest winter depressions are a separate type (Lam & Lavitan, 2000).

ONSET AND DURATION

The mean age of onset for major depressive disorder is 25 years in community samples who are not in treatment (Burke et al., 1990) and 29 years for patients who are in treatment (Judd et al., 1998a), but the average age of onset seems to be decreasing (Kessler et al., 2003; Weissman et al., 1991). In fact, the prevalence of major depression increases dramatically during the adolescent years (e.g., Offord et al., 1987), particularly in adolescent girls (Georgiades et al., 2006; see also review in Santor & Kusumakar, 2001). In 1989, a survey of people in five different American cities (Klerman & Weissman, 1989; Wickramaratne et al., 1989) revealed a greatly increased risk of developing depression in younger people. Among those born before 1905, only 1 percent had developed depression by age 75; of those born since 1955, 6 percent had become depressed by age 24. A later study based on very similar surveys conducted in Canada, Puerto Rico, Italy, Germany, France, Taiwan, Lebanon, and New Zealand suggests that this trend toward developing depression at increasingly earlier ages is occurring worldwide (Cross-National Collaborative Group, 1992).

As we noted previously, the length of depressive episodes is variable, with some lasting as little as two weeks; in more severe cases, an episode might last for several years, with the average duration of the first episode being two to nine months if untreated (Angst, 2009; Boland & Keller, 2009). Although nine months is a long time to suffer with a severe depressive episode, evidence indicates that even in the most severe cases, the probability of remission of the episode within one year approaches 90 percent (Kessler & Wang, 2009). In those severe cases in which the episode lasts five years or longer, 38 percent can be expected to eventually recover (Mueller et al., 1996). Occasionally, however, episodes may not entirely clear up, leaving some residual symptoms. In this case, the likelihood of a subsequent episode with another incomplete recovery is much higher (Boland & Keller, 2009; Judd, 2012). Awareness of this increased likelihood is important to treatment planning, because treatment should be continued much longer in these cases.

Investigators have found a lower (0.07 percent) prevalence of persistent mild depressive symptoms in children compared with adults (3 to 6 percent) (Klein et al., 2000), but symptoms tend to be stable throughout childhood (Garber, Gallerani, & Frankel, 2009). Kovacs, Akiskal, Gatsonis, and Parrone (1994) found that 76 percent of a sample of children with persistent mild depressive symptoms later developed major depressive disorder.

Persistent depressive disorder may last 20 to 30 years or more, although a preliminary study reported a median duration of approximately five years in adults (Klein et al., 2006) and four years in children (Kovacs et al., 1994). Klein and colleagues (2006) conducted a 10-year follow-up of 97 adults with *DSM-IV* dysthymia and found that 74 percent had recovered at some point, but 71 percent of those had relapsed. The whole sample of 97 patients spent approximately 60 percent of the 10-year follow-up period meeting full criteria for a mood disorder. This compares with 21 percent of a group of patients with major depressive disorder also followed for 10 years. Even worse, patients with persistent depressive disorder with less severe depressive symptoms (dysthymia) were more likely to attempt suicide than a comparison group with (nonpersistent) episodes of major depressive disorder during a five-year period.

FROM GRIEF TO DEPRESSION

At the beginning of the chapter, we asked if you had ever felt down or depressed. Almost everyone has. But if someone you love has died—particularly if the death was unexpected and the person was a member of your immediate family—you may, after your initial reaction to the trauma, have experienced a number of depressive symptoms, as well as anxiety, emotional numbness, and denial (Kendler et al., 2008; Shear, 2012; Shear et al., 2011; Simon, 2012). Sometimes individuals experience very severe symptoms requiring immediate treatment such as a full major depressive episode, perhaps with psychotic features, suicidal ideation, or severe weight loss and so little energy that the individual cannot function (Maciejewski et al., 2007). We must confront death and process it emotionally. All religions and cultures have rituals, such as funerals and burial ceremonies, to help us work through our losses with the support and love of our relatives and friends (Bonanno & Kaltman, 2001; Gupta &

Bonanno, 2011; Shear, 2012). Usually, the natural grieving process resolves within the first several months, although some people grieve for a year or longer (Currier et al., 2008; Maciejewski et al., 2007). The acute grief most of us feel eventually evolves into what is called **integrated grief**, in which the finality of death and its consequences are acknowledged and the individual adjusts to the loss. New, bittersweet, but mostly positive memories of the deceased person that are no longer dominating or interfering with functioning are then incorporated into memory (Shear et al., 2011).

Integrated grief often recurs at significant anniversaries, such as the birthday of the loved one, holidays, and other meaningful occasions, including the anniversary of the death. This is all a very normal and positive reaction. In fact, mental health professionals are concerned when someone does *not* grieve after a death, because grieving is our natural way of confronting and handling loss.

When grief lasts beyond the typical time, mental health professionals become concerned (Neimeyer & Currier, 2009). After six months to a year or so, the chance of recovering from severe grief without treatment is considerably reduced and, for approximately 7 percent of bereaved individuals (Kersting et al., 2011; Shear et al., 2011), a normal process becomes a disorder. At this stage, suicidal thoughts increase substantially and focus mostly on joining the beloved deceased (Stroebe et al., 2005).

▲ Queen Victoria remained in such deep mourning for her husband, Prince Albert, that she was unable to perform as monarch for several years after his death.

The ability to imagine events in the future is generally impaired, because it is difficult to think of a future without the deceased (MacCallum & Bryant, 2011; Robinaugh & McNally, 2013). Individuals also have difficulty regulating their own emotions, which tend to become rigid and inflexible (Gupta & Bonanno, 2011). Many of the psychological and social factors related to mood disorders in general, including a history of past depressive episodes, also predict the development of what is called the syndrome of **complicated grief**, although this reaction can develop without a preexisting depressed state (Bonanno et al., 2004).

A longitudinal study by a group including researchers at the University of British Columbia (Bonanno et al., 2002) showed that pre-loss dependency was predictive of a pathological grief reaction following the loss of a spouse. Particularly prominent symptoms of a pathological grief reaction include intrusive memories and distressingly strong yearnings for the loved one and avoiding people or places that are reminders of the loved one. In cases of complicated grief, the rituals intended to help us face and accept death were ineffective. As with victims who have post-traumatic stress, one therapeutic approach is to help grieving individuals re-experience the trauma under close supervision (Shear, 2010). Usually the grieving person is encouraged to talk about the loved one, the death, and the meaning of the loss while experiencing all the associated emotions, until he or she can come to terms with reality. This would include finding some meaning in the traumatic loss, incorporating positive emotions associated with memories of the relationship into the intense negative emotions connected with the loss, and arriving at the position that the person can cope with the pain and life will go on, thereby achieving a state of integrated grief (Bonanno & Kaltman, 1999).

Some researchers have cautioned against treating pathological grief reaction and depression in the same manner. For example, at the University of British Columbia, John Ogrodniczuk and his colleagues (2003) showed that dimensions of pathological grief could be distinguished from dimensions of depression among close to 400 psychiatric outpatients who had experienced one or more significant losses. And it was the grief dimensions that showed the most improvement in group therapy specifically designed to treat pathological grief reaction.

OTHER DEPRESSIVE DISORDERS

Premenstrual dysphoric disorder (PMDD) and **disruptive mood dysregulation disorder**, both depressive disorders, were added to the *DSM-5*.

Premenstrual Dysphoric Disorder (PMDD)

The history of the development of PMDD over the last several decades as a diagnosis was described in some detail in Chapter 3. Clinicians identified a small group of women, from 2 to 5 percent, who experienced severe and sometimes incapacitating emotional reactions during the premenstrual time (Epperson et al., 2012). But strong objections to making this condition an official diagnosis were based on concerns that women who were experiencing a very normal monthly physiological cycle, as part of being female, would now be classified as having a disorder, which would be very stigmatizing. It has now been clearly established that this small group of women differs in a number of ways from the 20 to 40 percent of women who experience uncomfortable premenstrual symptoms (PMS) that, nevertheless, are not associated with impairment of functioning. Criteria defining PMDD are presented in DSM Table 8.4. As you can see, a combination of physical symptoms, severe mood swings, and anxiety is associated with incapacitation during this

time (Hartlage et al., 2012). All the evidence indicates that PMDD is best considered a disorder of mood as opposed to a physical disorder (such as an endocrine disorder), and, as pointed out in Chapter 3, the creation of this diagnostic category should greatly help the thousands of women coping with this disorder receive the treatment they need to relieve their suffering and improve their functioning.

Disruptive Mood Dysregulation Disorder

Children and adolescents have been diagnosed with bipolar disorder at greatly increasing rates over the last several years. In fact, from 1995 to 2005 the diagnosis of bipolar disorder in children increased 40-fold overall and has quadrupled in U.S. community hospitals (up to 40 percent) (Leibenluft & Rich, 2008; Moreno et al., 2007). Why the increase? Many clinicians are now using much broader diagnostic criteria that would not correspond to current definitions of bipolar I or bipolar II disorder but rather fall under the relatively vague category of bipolar disorder not otherwise specified, and include children with chronic irritability, anger, aggression, hyperarousal, and frequent temper tantrums that are not limited to an occasional episode (as might be the case if the child were cycling into a manic episode since irritability sometimes accompanies discrete manic episodes).

But the most important observation is that these children show no evidence of periods of elevated mood (mania), which has been a requirement for a diagnosis of bipolar disorder (Leibenluft, 2011). Additional research demonstrated that these children with chronic and severe irritability and difficulty regulating their emotions resulting in frequent temper tantrums are at increased risk for additional depressive and anxiety disorders rather than manic episodes, and that there is no evidence of excessive rates of bipolar disorder in their families, which would expect if this condition were truly bipolar disorder. It was also recognized that this severe irritability is more common than bipolar disorder but has not been well studied (Brotman et al., 2006). This irritability is associated with substantial suffering in the children themselves, reflecting as it does chronically high rates of negative affect and marked disruption of family life. Although these broader definitions of symptoms do display some similarities with more classic bipolar disorder symptoms (Biederman et al., 2000, 2005), the danger is that these children are being misdiagnosed when they might better meet criteria for more classic diagnostic categories, such as attention-deficit/hyperactivity disorder (ADHD) or conduct disorder (see Chapter 15). In that case, the very potent drug treatments for bipolar disorder with substantial side effects would pose more risks for these children than they would benefits. But these cases also differ from more typical conduct or ADHD conditions as well, since it is the intense negative affect that seems to be driving the irritability and marked inability to regulate mood. In view of the distinctive features of this condition reviewed above, it seemed very important to better describe these children up to 12 years of age as suffering from a diagnosis termed disruptive mood dysregulation disorder rather than have them continue to be mistakenly diagnosed with bipolar disorder or perhaps conduct disorder (Roy et al., 2014). Criteria for this new disorder are presented in DSM Table 8.5.

| DSM-5 | **Table 8.4** Diagnostic Criteria for Premenstrual Dysphoric Disorder |

A. In the majority of menstrual cycles, at least five symptoms must be present in the final week before the onset of menses, start to *improve* within a few days after the onset of menses, and become *minimal* or absent in the week post-menses.

B. One (or more) of the following symptoms must be present:
  1. Marked affective lability (e.g., mood swings; feeling suddenly sad or tearful, or increased sensitivity to rejection).
  2. Marked irritability or anger or increased interpersonal conflicts.
  3. Marked depressed mood, feelings of hopelessness, or self-deprecating thoughts.
  4. Marked anxiety, tension, and/or feelings of being keyed up or on edge.

C. One (or more) of the following symptoms must additionally be present, to reach a total of *five* symptoms when combined with symptoms from Criterion B above.
  1. Decreased interest in usual activities (e.g., work, school, friends, hobbies).
  2. Subjective difficulty in concentration.
  3. Lethargy, easy fatigability, or marked lack of energy.
  4. Marked change in appetite; overeating; or specific food cravings.
  5. Hypersomnia or insomnia.
  6. A sense of being overwhelmed or out of control.
  7. Physical symptoms such as breast tenderness or swelling, joint or muscle pain, a sensation of "bloating," or weight gain.
  Note: The symptoms in Criteria A to C must have been met for most menstrual cycles that occurred in the preceding year.

D. The symptoms are associated with clinically significant distress or interference with work, school, usual social activities, or relationships with others (e.g., avoidance of social activities; decreased productivity and efficiency at work, school, or home).

E. The disturbance is not merely an exacerbation of the symptoms of another disorder, such as major depressive disorder, panic disorder, persistent depressive disorder (dysthymia), or a personality disorder (although it may co-occur with any of these disorders).

F. Criterion A should be confirmed by prospective daily ratings during at least two symptomatic cycles. (*Note*: The diagnosis may be made provisionally prior to this confirmation).

G. The symptoms are not attributable to the physiological effects of a substance (e.g., a drug of abuse, a medication) or another medical condition (e.g., hypothyroidism).

A. Severe recurrent temper outburst manifested verbally (e.g., verbal rages) and/or behaviorally (e.g., physical aggression toward people or property) that are grossly out of proportion in intensity or duration to the situation or provocation.

B. The temper outbursts are inconsistent with developmental level.

C. The temper outbursts occur, on average, three or more times per week.

D. The mood between temper outbursts is persistently irritable or angry most of the day, nearly every day, and is observable by others (e.g., parents, teachers, peers).

E. Criteria A to D have been present for 12 or more months. Throughout that time, the individual has not had a period lasting 3 or more consecutive months without all of the symptoms in Criteria A to D.

F. Criteria A and D are present in at least two of three settings (i.e., at home, at school, with peers) and are severe in at least one of these.

G. The diagnosis should not be made for the first time before age 6 years or after age 18 years.

H. By history or observation, the age at onset of Criteria A to E is before 10 years.

I. There has never been a distinct period lasting more than one day during which the full symptom criteria, except duration, for a manic or hypomanic episode have been met.

Note: Developmentally appropriate mood elevation, such as occurs in the context of a highly positive event or its anticipation, should not be considered as a symptom of mania or hypomania.

J. The behaviors do not occur exclusively during an episode of major depressive disorder and are not better explained by another mental disorder (e.g., autism spectrum disorder, post-traumatic stress disorder, separation anxiety disorder, persistent depressive disorder [dysthymia]).

K. The symptoms are not attributable to the physiological effects of a substance or to another medical or neurological condition.

In one case seen at our clinic, a nine-year-old girl we will call Betsy was brought in by her father for evaluation for severe anxiety. The father described a situation in which Betsy, a very bright child from an upper middle class family who had done well in school, was continually irritable and increasingly unable to get along at home, engaging in intense arguments, particularly with her mother, at the slightest provocation. Her mood would then deteriorate into a full-blown aggressive temper tantrum, and she would run to her room and on occasion begin throwing things. She began refusing to eat meals with the family, since bitter arguments would often arise, and it just became easier to allow her to eat in her room. Since nothing else seemed to work to calm her down, her father resorted to something he used to do when she was a baby—take her for a long ride in the family car. After a while Betsy would begin to relax, but during one long ride she turned to her father and said, "Daddy, please help me feel better because if I keep feeling like this I just want to die."

Adults with a history of disruptive mood dysregulation disorder are at increased risk for developing mood and anxiety disorders,

as well as many other adverse health outcomes (Copeland et al., 2014). Therefore, a very important objective for the immediate future will be developing and evaluating both psychological and drug treatments for this difficult condition. For example, it is very possible that new psychological treatments under development for severe emotional dysregulation in children may be useful with this condition (Ehrenreich et al., 2009).

BIPOLAR DISORDERS

CLINICAL DESCRIPTION

The key identifying feature of bipolar disorders is the tendency of manic episodes to alternate with major depressive episodes in an unending roller coaster ride from the peaks of elation to the depths of despair. Beyond that, bipolar disorders are parallel in many ways to depressive disorders. For example, a manic

JANE | *Funny, Smart, and Desperate*

Jane was the wife of a well-known surgeon and the loving mother of three children. The family lived in an old country house on the edge of town with plenty of room for family members and pets. Jane was nearly 50; the older children had moved out; the youngest son, 16-year-old Mike, was having substantial academic difficulties in school and seemed very anxious. Jane brought Mike to the clinic to find out why he was having problems.

As they entered the office, I observed that Jane was well dressed, neat, vivacious, and personable; she had a bounce to her step. She began talking about her wonderful and successful family before she and Mike even reached their seats. Mike, by contrast, was very quiet and reserved. He seemed resigned and perhaps relieved that he would have to say very little during the session. By the time Jane sat down, she had mentioned the personal virtues and material achievement of her husband, and the brilliance and beauty of one of her older children, and she was proceeding to describe the second child. But before she finished, she noticed a book on anxiety disorders and, having read voraciously on the subject, began a litany of various anxiety-related problems that might be troubling Mike.

In the meantime, Mike sat in the corner with a small smile on his lips that seemed to be masking considerable distress and uncertainty over what his mother might do next. It became clear as the interview progressed that Mike had obsessive-compulsive disorder, which disturbed his concentration both in and out of school. He was failing all his courses.

It also became clear that Jane herself was in the midst of a *hypomanic* episode, evident in her unbridled enthusiasm, grandiose perceptions, uninterruptible speech, and report that she needed very little sleep these days. She was also easily distracted, as when she quickly switched from describing her children to the book on the table. When asked about her own psychological state, Jane readily admitted that she was a "manic depressive" (the old name for *bipolar disorder*) and that she alternated rather rapidly between feeling on top of the world and feeling very depressed; she was taking medication for her condition. I immediately wondered if Mike's obsessions had anything to do with his mother's condition.

Mike was treated intensively for his obsessions and compulsions, but he made little progress. He said that life at home was very difficult when his mother was depressed. She sometimes went to bed and stayed there for three weeks. During this time, she seemed to be in a depressive stupor, essentially unable to move for days. It was up to the children to care for themselves and their mother, whom they fed by hand. Because the older children had now left home, much of the burden had fallen on Mike. Jane's profound depressive episodes would remit after about three weeks, and she would immediately enter a hypomanic episode that might last several months or more. During hypomania, Jane was, for the most part, funny and entertaining and a delight to be with—if you could get a word in edgewise. Consultation with her therapist, an expert in the area, revealed that he had prescribed a number of medications but was so far unable to bring her mood swings under control.

episode might occur only once or repeatedly. Consider the case of Jane.

Jane had **bipolar II disorder**, in which major depressive episodes alternate with hypomanic episodes rather than full manic episodes (see DSM Table 8.6). As we noted earlier, hypomanic episodes are less severe. Although she was noticeably "up," Jane functioned pretty well while in this mood state. The criteria for **bipolar I disorder** are the same, except the individual experiences a full manic episode. As in the criteria set for major depressive disorder, for the manic episodes to be considered separate, they must have a symptom-free period of at least two months between them. Otherwise, one episode is seen as a continuation of the last.

BILLY | *The World's Best at Everything*

Before Billy reached the ward, you could hear him laughing and carrying on in a deep voice; it sounded as if he was having a wonderful time. As the nurse brought Billy down the hall to introduce him to the staff, he spied the Ping-Pong table. Loudly, he exclaimed, "Ping-Pong! I love Ping-Pong! I have only played twice but that is what I am going to do while I am here; I am going to become the world's greatest Ping-Pong player! And that table is gorgeous! I am going to start work on that table immediately and make it the finest Ping-Pong table in the world. I am going to sand it down, take it apart, and rebuild it until it gleams and every angle is perfect!" Billy soon went on to something else that totally absorbed his attention.

The previous week, Billy had emptied his bank account, taken his credit cards and those of his elderly parents with whom he was living, and bought every piece of fancy stereo equipment he could find. He thought that he would set up the best sound studio in the city and make millions of dollars by renting it to people who would come from far and wide. This episode had precipitated his admission to the hospital.

The case of Billy illustrates a full manic episode. This individual was first encountered when he was admitted to a hospital.

During manic or hypomanic phases, patients often deny they have a problem, which was characteristic of Billy. Even after spending inordinate amounts of money or making foolish business decisions, these individuals, particularly if they are in the

DSM-5	**Table 8.6** Diagnostic Criteria for Bipolar II Disorder

A. Criteria have been met for at least one hypomanic episode *and* at least one major depressive episode. Criteria for a hypomanic episode are identical to those for a manic episode (see DSM Table 7.2), with the following distinctions: (1) Minimum duration is four days; (2) Although the episode represents a definite change in functioning, it is not severe enough to cause marked social or occupational impairment or hospitalization; (3) There are no psychotic features.

B. There has never been a manic episode.

C. The occurrence of the hypomanic episode(s) and major depressive episode(s) is not better explained by schizoaffective disorder, schizophrenia, schizophreniform disorder, delusional disorder, or other specified or unspecified schizophrenia spectrum and other psychotic disorder.

D. The symptoms of depression or the unpredictability caused by frequent alternation between periods of depression and hypomania causes clinically significant distress or impairment in social, occupational, or other important areas of functioning.

Specify current or most recent episode:
   Hypomanic
   Depressed

Specify if:
   With anxious distress
   With mixed features
   With rapid cycling
   With mood-congruent psychotic features
   With mood-incongruent psychotic features
   With catatonia
   With peripartum onset
   With seasonal pattern

Specify course if full criteria for a mood episode are not currently met:
   In partial remission
   In full remission

Specify severity if full criteria for a mood episode are currently met:
   Mild
   Moderate
   Severe

Source: Reprinted with permission from the *Diagnostic and Statistical Manual of Mental Disorders*, Fifth Edition (Copyright © 2013). American Psychiatric Association. All Rights Reserved.

▲ Margaret Trudeau, Canadian author, social advocate, and mother of the current prime minister of Canada, recently revealed that she has struggled with bipolar disorder throughout her adult life. She was treated as an inpatient at the Royal Ottawa Hospital in 2001 and has gone public with her story in hopes of helping reduce the stigma associated with this mental health disorder (Berthiaume, 2006).

midst of a full manic episode, are so wrapped up in their enthusiasm and expansiveness that their behaviour seems perfectly reasonable to them. The high during a manic state is so pleasurable, people may stop taking their medication during periods of distress or discouragement in an attempt to bring on a manic state once again; this is a serious challenge to professionals.

Returning to Jane, we continued to treat her son Mike for several months. We had made very little progress before the school year ended. Because Mike was doing so poorly, the school administrators informed his parents that he would not be accepted back the next year. Mike and his parents wisely decided it might be a good idea if he got away from the house and did something different for a while, and he began working and living at a ski and tennis resort. Several months later, his father called to tell us that Mike's obsessions and compulsions had completely lifted since he'd been away from home. The father thought Mike should continue living at the resort, where he had entered school and was doing better academically. He now agreed with our previous assessment that Mike's condition might be related to his relationship with his mother. Several years later, we heard that Jane, in a depressive stupor, had killed herself, an all-too-tragic outcome in bipolar disorder.

A milder but more chronic version of bipolar disorder is called **cyclothymic disorder** (Akiskal, 2009; Parker et al., 2012). Cyclothymic disorder is a chronic alternation of mood elevation and depression that does not reach the severity of manic or major depressive episodes (see DSM Table 8.7). Individuals with cyclothymic disorder tend to be in one mood state or the other for many years with relatively few periods of neutral (or euthymic) mood. This pattern must last for at least two years (one year for children and adolescents) to meet criteria for the disorder. Individuals with cyclothymic disorder alternate between the kinds of mild depressive symptoms Jack experienced during his dysthymic states and the sorts of hypomanic episodes Jane experienced. In neither

▲ Actress Catherine Zeta-Jones has announced that she struggles with bipolar II disorder.

DSM-5	**Table 8.7** Diagnostic Criteria for Cyclothymic Disorder

A. For at least 2 years (at least 1 year in children and adolescents) there have been numerous periods with hypomanic symptoms that do not meet criteria for a hypomanic episode and numerous periods with depressive symptoms that do not meet criteria for a major depressive episode.

B. During the above 2-year period (1 year in children and adolescents), the hypomanic and depressive periods have been present for at least half the time and the individual has not been without the symptoms for more than 2 months at a time.

C. Criteria for a major depressive, manic, or hypomanic episode have never been met.

D. The symptoms in Criterion A are not better explained by schizoaffective disorder, schizophrenia, schizophreniform disorder, delusional disorder, or other specified or unspecified schizophrenia spectrum and other psychotic disorder.

E. The symptoms are not attributable to the physiological effects of a substance (e.g., a drug of abuse, a medication) or another medical condition (e.g., hyperthyroidism).

F. The symptoms cause clinically significant distress or impairment in social, occupational, or other important areas of functioning.

Specify if:

With anxious distress

case was the behaviour severe enough to require hospitalization or immediate intervention. Much of the time, such individuals are just considered moody. However, the chronically fluctuating mood states are, by definition, substantial enough to interfere with functioning. Furthermore, people with cyclothymia should be treated because of their increased risk of developing the more severe bipolar I or bipolar II disorder (Akiskal, 2009; Goodwin & Jamison, 2007; Otto & Applebaum, 2011; Parker et al., 2012).

Additional Defining Criteria for Bipolar Disorders

For depressive disorders, we discussed additional defining criteria that may or may not accompany a mood disorder and noted that it was important to identify these specifiers or symptoms to plan the most effective treatment. All these specifiers apply to bipolar disorders (see DSM Table 8.4). Specifically, the catatonic features specifier applies mostly to major depressive episodes although rarely may apply to a manic episode. The psychotic features specifier may apply to manic episodes, during which it is common to have delusions of grandeur. The anxious distress specifier is also present in bipolar disorders, as it is in depressive disorders. New to the *DSM-5* is the "mixed features" specifier, which, as in depressive disorders, is meant to describe the major depressive or manic episode that has some symptoms from the opposite polarity; for example, a depressive episode with some manic symptoms. The seasonal pattern specifier may also apply to bipolar disorders. In the usual presentation, individuals may become depressed during the winter and manic during the summer. Finally, manic episodes may occur surrounding, but mostly after, childbirth in the peripartum period.

ABNORMAL PSYCHOLOGY VIDEO

Bipolar Disorder: Mary

"Whoo, whoo, whoo—on top of the world! . . . It's going to be one great day! . . . I'm incognito for the Lord God Almighty. I'm working for him. I have been for years. I'm a spy. My mission is to fight for the American way . . . the Statue of Liberty. . . . I can bring up the wind, I can bring the rain, I can bring the sunshine, I can do lots of things. . . . I love the outdoors. . . ."

Visit login.cengage.com to start using MindTap. Enter the Online Access Code from the card included with your text. If a code card is not provided, you can purchase instant access at Cengage.ca.

Just as for depression, it is important to determine whether a patient suffering from a manic episode has had episodes of major depression or mania in the past, as well as whether the individual has fully recovered between past episodes. Just as it is important to determine if persistent depressive disorder preceded a major depressive episode, it is also important to determine whether cyclothymia preceded the onset of bipolar disorder. This is because the presence of cyclothymia predicts a decreased chance for a full inter-episode recovery (Akiskal, 2009).

Rapid-Cycling Specifier

One specifier is unique to bipolar I and II disorders: rapid-cycling specifier. Some people move quickly in and out of depressive or manic episodes. An individual with bipolar disorder who experiences at least four manic or depressive episodes within a year is considered to have a rapid-cycling pattern, which appears to be a severe variety of bipolar disorder that does not respond well to standard treatments (Angst, 2009; Kupka et al., 2005; Schneck et al., 2004, 2008). Coryell and colleagues (2003) demonstrated a higher probability of suicide attempts and more severe episodes of depression in 89 patients with a rapid-cycling pattern compared with a non-rapid-cycling group. Kupka and colleagues (2005) and Nierenberg and colleagues (2010) also found these patients' symptoms were more severe on a number of measures. Some evidence indicates that alternative drug treatment, such as anticonvulsants and mood stabilizers, rather than antidepressants, may be more effective with this group of patients (Kilzieh & Akiskal, 1999).

Approximately 20 to 50 percent of bipolar patients experience rapid cycling. From 60 to 90 percent are female, a higher rate than in other variations of bipolar disorder (e.g., Altshuler et al., 2010; Coryell et al., 2003; Kupka et al., 2005; Schneck et al., 2004), and this finding is consistent across 10 studies (Kilzieh & Akiskal, 1999). In most cases, rapid cycling tends to increase in frequency over time and can reach severe states in which patients cycle between mania and depression without any break. When this direct transition from one mood state to another happens, it is referred to as *rapid switching* or *rapid mood switching* and is a particularly treatment-resistant form of the disorder (MacKinnon et al., 2003; Maj et al., 2002). Interestingly, one precipitant of rapid cycling may

be taking antidepressant medication, which is prescribed for some individuals with bipolar disorder, because the frequency of rapid cycling is considerably higher among those taking antidepressants compared with those who are not taking them (Schneck et al., 2008). Fortunately, rapid cycling does not seem to be permanent, because only 3 to 5 percent of patients continue with rapid cycling across a five-year period (Coryell et al., 1992; Schneck et al., 2008), with 80 percent returning to a non–rapid-cycling pattern within two years (Coryell et al., 2003). There are also cases of *ultra-rapid* cycle lengths that only last for days to weeks and *ultra-ultra-rapid cycling* in cases where cycle lengths are less than 24 hours (Wilk & Hegerl, 2010). In ultra-ultra-rapid cycling, switches into depression occurred at night and switches into mania occurred at daytime, suggesting a link to circadian aspects.

ONSET AND DURATION

The average age of onset for bipolar I disorder is 18, and for bipolar II disorder it is 22, although cases of both can begin in childhood (Angst, 2009; Judd et al., 2003; Merikangas & Pato, 2009). This is somewhat younger than the average age of onset for major depressive disorder, and bipolar disorders begin more acutely; that is, they develop more suddenly (Angst & Sellaro, 2000; Johnson, Turkheimer, et al., 2009). About one-third of the cases of bipolar disorder begin in adolescence (Taylor & Abrams, 1981), and the onset is often preceded by minor oscillations in mood or mild cyclothymic mood swings (Goodwin & Jamison, 2007; Merikangas et al., 2007). Only 10 to 13 percent of bipolar II disorder cases progress to full bipolar I syndrome (Coryell et al., 1995; Depression Guideline Panel, 1993). The distinction between unipolar and bipolar mood disorder also seems well defined because only 5 percent of a large group of 381 patients with unipolar depression experienced a manic episode during a 10-year follow-up period (Coryell et al., 1995), although Angst and Sellaro (2000), in reviewing some older studies, estimated the rate of individuals with depression later experiencing mania at closer to 25 percent. In any case, if these disorders were more closely related, we would expect to see more individuals moving from one to the other.

It is relatively rare for someone to develop bipolar disorder after the age of 40. Once it does appear, the course is chronic; that is, mania and depression alternate indefinitely. Therapy usually involves managing the disorder with ongoing drug regimens that prevent recurrence of episodes. Suicide is an all-too-common consequence of bipolar disorder, usually occurring during depressive episodes, as it did in the case of Jane (Angst, 2009; Valtonen et al., 2007). A large Swedish study showed that, on average, people with bipolar disorder died eight to nine years earlier of various medical diseases and suicide than did the general population (Crump et al., 2013). When patients receive treatment early, however, the mortality rate was comparable to that of the general population. Bipolar disorder is associated with a high risk of suicide attempts and suicide death, the latter being associated with male sex and having a first-degree relative who committed suicide (Schaffer et al., 2015). The risk of suicide is not limited to Western countries but occurs in countries around the world (Merikangas et al., 2011).

In typical cases, cyclothymia is chronic and lifelong. In about one-third to one-half of patients, cyclothymic mood swings develop into full-blown bipolar disorder (Kochman et al., 2005; Parker et al., 2012). In one sample of cyclothymic patients, 60 percent were female, and the age of onset was often during the teenage years or before, with some data suggesting the most common age of onset to be 12 to 14 years (Goodwin & Jamison, 2007). The disorder is often not recognized, and sufferers are thought to be high-strung, explosive, moody, or hyperactive (Akiskal, 2009; Goodwin & Jamison, 2007). One subtype of cyclothymia is based on the predominance of mild depressive symptoms, one on the predominance of hypomanic symptoms, and another on an equal distribution of both.

Concept Check 8.1

Match each description or case by choosing its corresponding disorder: (a) mania, (b) double depression (C) dysthymic disorder, (d) major depressive episode, and (e) bipolar I disorder.

1. Last week, as he does about every three months, Ryan went out with his friends, buying rounds of drinks, socializing until early morning, and feeling on top of the world. Today Ryan will not even get out of bed to go to work, see his friends, or even turn on the lights. _____

2. Feeling certain he would win the lottery, Charles went on an all-night shopping spree, maxing out all his credit cards without a worry. We know he's done this several times, feeling abnormally extreme elation, joy, and euphoria. _____

3. Ayana has had some mood disorder problems in the past, although some days she's better than others. Many days it seems like she has fallen into a rut. Although she manages to get by, she has trouble making decisions because she doesn't trust herself. _____

4. For the past few weeks, Jennifer has been sleeping a lot. She feels worthless, can't get up the energy to leave the house, and has lost a lot of weight. Her problem is the most common and extreme mood disorder.

   _____

5. Eusebio is always down and a bit blue, but occasionally he becomes so depressed that nothing pleases him.

   _____

PREVALENCE OF MOOD DISORDERS

In the 2017 Canadian Community Health Survey (CCHS), about 2.6 million Canadians, 8.6 percent of the population 12 years of age or older, reported that they have a mood disorder, such as depression, bipolar disorder, mania, or dysthymia (Statistics Canada, 2018). Half of this group reported that they also have been diagnosed with an anxiety disorder.

With regard to depression specifically, the best estimates of the worldwide prevalence suggest that approximately 16 percent of the population experience major depressive disorder over a lifetime, and approximately 6 percent have experienced a major depressive disorder in the last year (Hasin et al., 2005; Kessler et al., 2003; Kessler, Chiu, et al., 2005). Two community studies conducted in large urban centres, one in Toronto by De Marco (2000) and a second in Calgary by Patten (2000), show similar one-year prevalence rates for major depression, 10.4 and 11 percent, respectively. However, estimates of the Canadian population based on two cycles of the CCHS (2002 and 2012) were lower, documenting annual prevalence for major depression to be 4.7 and 4.8 percent and estimating the lifetime prevalence at 12.2 and 11.3 percent (Patten et al., 2016; Pearson et al., 2013).

As Roger Bland, a leading psychiatric epidemiologist from the University of Alberta, has pointed out, different research methods may account for the differing rates of prevalence (Bland, 1997). Scott Patten at the University of Calgary concurred (Patten, 2000) but also provided another explanation for different prevalence rates: prevalence rates for depression in Canada appear to be decreasing, suggesting progress in public health efforts toward combating depression in our country (Patten, 2002). Patten's more recent work with the 2002 and 2012 CCHS found support for an increase in the proportion of Canadians receiving treatment for major depression—however, the evidence did not support a reduction in the annual prevalence rate of major depression as it remained essentially the same, about 5 percent, over the 10-year period (Patten, 2016).

Women are about twice as likely to have mood disorders as men. For example, in the 2012 CCHS, the annual prevalence of major depressive episode for women was 5.8 percent and for men was 3.6 percent (Pearson et al., 2012; see ■ Figure 8.2). In fact, women were more likely to have a major depressive episode than men in all age groups except those 65 years and older. Bipolar disorders are distributed approximately equally across gender (Merikangas & Pato, 2009).

LIFESPAN DEVELOPMENTAL INFLUENCES ON MOOD DISORDERS

The prevalence of mood disorders varies with age, and age and development also affect many of the characteristics of mood disorders. We review and highlight these developmental characteristics—first for children and adolescents, and then for older adults.

IN CHILDREN AND ADOLESCENTS

You might assume that depression requires some experience with life, that an accumulation of negative events or disappointments might create pessimism, which then leads to depression. Like many reasonable assumptions in psychopathology, this one is not uniformly correct. There is some evidence that three-month-old babies can show signs of depression. Infants of depressed mothers display marked depressive behaviours (sad faces, slow movement, lack of responsiveness), even when interacting with a nondepressed adult (Garber et al., 2009; Guedeney, 2007). Whether this behaviour or temperament is caused by a genetic tendency inherited from the mother, the result of early interaction patterns with a depressed mother or primary caregiver, or a combination is not yet clear.

Most investigators agree that mood disorders are fundamentally similar in children and in adults (Brent & Birmaher, 2009; Garber et al., 2009; Weiss & Garber, 2003). Therefore, no "childhood" mood disorders in the *DSM-5* are specific to a developmental stage, with the exception of disruptive mood dysregulation disorder, which can be diagnosed only up to 12 years of age. This is unlike the anxiety disorders in which a number of conditions occur only early in development. It seems clear, however, that the look of depression changes with age. For example, children under three years of age might manifest depression by their facial expressions, as well as by their eating and sleeping. In the extreme, this could develop into disruptive mood dysregulation disorder. In children between the ages of 9 and 12, many of these features would not occur. Psychologist Ian Gotlib, formerly of the University of Western Ontario, has shown that adolescents who are forced to limit their activities because of illness or injury are at high risk for depression (Lewinsohn et al., 1997).

Estimates on the prevalence of mood disorders in children and adolescents vary widely, although more sophisticated studies are beginning to appear. The general conclusion is that depressive disorders occur less frequently in children than in adults but rise dramatically in adolescence, when, if anything, depression is more frequent than in adults (Kashani et al., 1987; Kessler et al., 2012; Petersen et al., 1993; Rohde et al., 2013). In their study of

major depressive disorder, Patten and his colleagues found evidence of a decline in annual prevalence rates from adolescence to adulthood. The 2002 and the 2012 cycles of the CCHS targeted Canadians 15 years of age or older and Patten and his colleagues (2006, 2015) found the highest annual prevalence rates occurred in the youngest age group and that there was a tendency for the rates to decline with age. The 2012 CCHS data have also been used to document this decline for annual rates of major depressive episode (Pearson et al., 2013; see ■ Figure 8.2).

Furthermore, some evidence indicates that, in young children, dysthymia is more prevalent than major depressive disorder, but this ratio reverses in adolescence. Like adults, adolescents experience major depressive disorder more frequently than dysthymia (Kashani et al., 1983; Kashani et al., 1987). Major depressive disorder in adolescents is also largely a female disorder (Santor & Kusumakar, 2001), as it is in adults, although this is not true for more mild depression. Only among the adolescents referred to treatment does the gender imbalance exist (Compas et al., 1997), though why more girls reach a more severe state requiring referral to treatment is not clear.

As far as mania is concerned, children under the age of nine seem to present with more irritability and emotional swings as compared with classic manic states, and they are often mistaken as being hyperactive. In addition, their symptoms are more chronic in that they are always present rather than episodic as in adults (Biederman et al., 2000). This presentation seems to continue through adolescence (Faraone et al., 1997), although

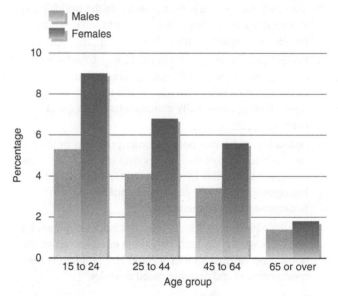

FIGURE 8.2 | Rates of depression,[1] 12-month, by age and sex, Canada, household population 15 and older, 2012.

Notes: Use with caution (these data have a coefficient of variation from 16.6 to 33.3 percent).

[1] Respondents were classified with depression if they met the criteria for this condition in the 12 months before the survey.

Source: Statistics Canada, https://www150.statcan.gc.ca/n1/pub/82-624-x/2013001/article/c-g/11855-c-g-01-eng.htm, Canadian Community Health Survey - Mental Health, 2012. 82-624-X, Chart 1, Rates of depression, 12-month, by age and sex, Canada, household population 15 and older, 2012. By Caryn Pearson, Teresa Janz, and Jennifer Ali. Mental and substance use disorders in Canada: Health at a glance.

▲ Among adolescents, severe major depressive disorder occurs mostly in girls.

© gawrav/iStock

adolescents may appear more typically manic. Bipolar disorder seems to be rare in childhood, although case studies of children as young as four years of age displaying bipolar symptoms have been reported (Poznanski et al., 1984), and the diagnosis may be mistaken for conduct disorder or ADHD. However, the prevalence of bipolar disorder rises substantially in adolescence, which is not surprising in that many adults with bipolar disorder report a first onset during the teen years (Keller & Wunder, 1990). "Emotional swing," or oscillating manic states that are less distinct than in adults, may also be characteristic of children, as are brief or rapid-cycling manic episodes lasting only part of a day (Youngstrom, 2009).

One developmental difference between children and adolescents compared with adults concerns patterns of comorbidity. For example, childhood depression (and mania) is often associated with and sometimes misdiagnosed as ADHD or, more often, conduct disorder in which aggression and even destructive behaviour are common (Fields & Fristad, 2009; Garber et al., 2009). Conduct disorder and depression often co-occur in bipolar disorder. But, once again, many of these children might now meet the criteria for disruptive mood dysregulation disorder, which would better account for this comorbidity. In any case, successful treatment of the underlying depression (or spontaneous recovery) may resolve the associated ADHD or conduct disorder in these patients. Adolescents with bipolar disorder may also become aggressive, impulsive, sexually provocative, and accident prone (Carlson, 1990; Keller & Wunder, 1990).

Whatever the presentation, mood disorders in children and adolescents are very serious because of their likely consequences. In an important prospective study, conducted as part of the Ontario Child Health Study, Fleming, Boyle, and Offord (1993) followed 652 adolescents with either a major depressive disorder or a conduct disorder for four years. These adolescents largely continued to experience serious problems and markedly impaired functioning. Lewinsohn, Rhode, Seeley, Klein, and Gotlib (2000) also followed 274 adolescents with major depressive disorder into adulthood and identified several risk factors for additional depressive episodes as adults. Prominent among these were conflicts with parents, being female, and a higher proportion of family members experiencing depressive episodes. Their more recent longitudinal work shows that young adults who had experienced an episode of major depressive disorder in adolescence exhibited a very pervasive pattern of psychosocial impairments in areas such as interpersonal functioning, quality of life, and occupational performance. Reduced life satisfaction in young adulthood was uniquely associated with a history of major depressive disorder, rather than with a history of other mental disorders, in adolescence. These findings underline the seriousness of adolescent depression, in terms of negative consequences continuing into adulthood.

IN OLDER ADULTS

Only recently have we seriously considered the problem of depression in older adults (Wittchen, 2012). A Canadian study by Dalhousie University researcher Kenneth Rockwood and colleagues estimated that 18 to 20 percent of nursing home residents may experience major depressive episodes (Rockwood et al., 1991; see also Katz et al., 1989), which are likely to be chronic if they appear first after the age of 60 (Rapp et al., 1991). Late-onset depressions are associated with marked sleep difficulties, illness anxiety disorders, and agitation. It can be difficult to diagnose depression in seniors because the presentation of mood disorders is often complicated by the presence of medical illnesses or symptoms of dementia (e.g., Blazer, 1989; Small, 1991). That is, seniors who become physically ill or begin to show signs of dementia might become depressed about it, but the signs of depression would be attributed to the illness or dementia and thus missed. Nevertheless, the overall prevalence of major depressive disorder is the same or slightly lower in the older adults as in the general population (Patten et al., 2006; Weissman et al., 1991), perhaps because stressful life events that trigger major depressive episodes decrease with age. But, as noted by Ian Gotlib, milder symptoms that do not meet the criteria for major depressive disorder may be more common among seniors (Gotlib & Nolan, 2000), perhaps because of illness and infirmity (Roberts et al., 1997).

Anxiety disorders frequently accompany depression in seniors (in about a third of cases), particularly generalized anxiety disorder and panic disorder (Lenze et al., 2000), and when they do, patients are more severely depressed. In the *DSM-5*, as described earlier, clinicians now must specify the presence and severity of anxiety when diagnosing a mood disorder because of the implications for severity and course of the mood disorder, as well as for treatment. Depression can also contribute to physical disease in seniors (Whooley & Wong, 2013). In fact, being depressed doubles the risk of death in older adults who have suffered a heart attack or stroke (Schulz et al., 2002).

The earlier gender imbalance in depression disappears after the age of 65. In early childhood, boys are more likely to be depressed than girls, but an overwhelming surge of depression in adolescent girls produces an imbalance in the sex ratio (Santor & Kusumakar, 2001) that is maintained until old age, when just as

▲ Depression among seniors is a serious problem that can be difficult to diagnose because the symptoms are often similar to those of physical illness or dementia.

many women are depressed, but increasing numbers of men are also affected (Wallace & O'Hara, 1992). From the perspective of the lifespan, this is the first time since early childhood that the sex ratio for depression is balanced.

ACROSS CULTURES

We noted the strong tendency of anxiety to take very physical or somatic forms in some cultures; instead of talking about fear, panic, or general anxiety, many people describe stomachaches, chest pains or heart distress, and headaches. Much the same tendency exists across cultures for mood disorders (Kim & Lopez, 2014), which is not surprising, given the close relationship of anxiety and depression (Kessler & Bromet, 2013). Feelings of weakness or tiredness particularly characterize depression that is accompanied by mental or physical slowing or retardation.

Although somatic symptoms that characterize mood disorders seem roughly equivalent across cultures, it is difficult to compare subjective feelings. The way people think of depression may be influenced by the cultural view of the individual and the role of the individual in society (Kleinman, 2004; Ryder et al., 2008). For example, in societies that focus on the *individual* instead of the *group*, it is common to hear statements such as "I feel blue," or "I am depressed." In cultures where the individual is tightly integrated into the larger group, however, someone might say, "Our life has lost its meaning," referring to the group in which the individual resides (Manson & Good, 1993). Despite these influences, it is generally agreed that to study the nature and prevalence of mood disorders (or any other psychological disorder) in other cultures is first to determine their prevalence by using standardized criteria (Neighbors et al., 1989). The *DSM* criteria are increasingly used, along with semistructured interviews in which the same questions are asked, with some allowances for different words that might be specific to a culture or subculture.

One such study is the International Consortium of Psychiatric Epidemiology study, which used the same structured interview and diagnostic criteria in ten countries, including Canada (Andrade et al., 2003). The Canadian data were collected by a team led by David Offord of the Chedoke-McMaster Hospital in Hamilton, Ontario. As shown in ■ Figure 8.3, the highest rates of major depressive episode were observed in the U.S. sample (17 percent prevalence), and the lowest in the Japanese sample (3 percent prevalence). Compared with the prevalence rates in the other countries, the rates in the Canadian sample were moderate (8 percent prevalence).

As noted by Laurence Kirmayer (Kirmayer et al., 2000; Kirmayer, Simpson, & Cargo, 2003), the appalling social and economic conditions faced by many groups of Indigenous Peoples in North America, as well as their long history of cultural oppression and marginalization, fulfill all the requirements for chronic major life stress, which is strongly related to the onset of mood disorders, particularly major depressive disorder. Kinzie, Leung, Boehnlein, and Matsunaga (1992) used a structured interview to determine the percentage of adult members of a First Nations reserve who met the criteria for mood disorders. The lifetime prevalence for any mood disorder was 19 percent in men, 37 percent in women, and 28 percent overall, approximately four times as high as in the general population. Examined by disorder, almost all the increase is accounted for by greatly elevated rates of major depression. A study of mental health services use among the Cree of James Bay, Québec, indicated that depression was the most common psychiatric illness, occurring in 16 percent of the 242 Cree people who were receiving treatment by nursing or other medical professionals in the region (Lavallee et al., 1991). Similar findings emerged in a study conducted in a Canadian Arctic Inuit community of about 1100 people (Haggarty et al., 2000): This study revealed an estimated rate of past-week depression of 26 percent—a rate that is much higher than that seen in the general population.

More recently, and using data from the CCHS, Statistics Canada (2016a) documented the four-year prevalence rates (2011–2014) of mood disorders (i.e., depression, bipolar disorder, mania, or dysthymia) by Aboriginal identity among Canadians 12 years of age or older. The estimates were higher among the First Nations population living off-reserve (12 percent) and Métis (12.6 percent) than among the non-Aboriginal identity population (7.2 percent). In all groups, the rates for women were higher than for men. It is important to remember that the CCHS excludes persons living on reserves and other settlements in the provinces. The First Nations Regional Health Survey provided estimates for mood disorders among First Nations living on reserve (First Nations Information Governance Centre, 2018a, 2018b). Estimates based on data collected during 2015–2016 were that 7.8 percent of adults and 6.6 percent of First Nations youth had been diagnosed with a mood disorder during this period, lower rates than those found in the First Nations off-reserve population from the CCHS.

AMONG THE CREATIVE

Is there truth in the enduring belief that "genius is allied with madness"? Several researchers have attempted to find out. The results are surprising. Handel wrote *The Messiah* in only three weeks, apparently during a manic episode, and Rossini composed *The Barber of Seville* in only 13 days during a likely period of hypomania (Endler, 1990). Table 8.1 lists a group of famous poets, many of whom won the coveted Pulitzer Prize. All almost certainly had bipolar disorder. Many committed suicide. These eight poets are among the 36 born in the 20th century who are represented in *The New Oxford Book of American Verse*, a collection reserved for the most distinguished poets. It is certainly striking that about 20 percent of these 36 poets exhibited bipolar disorders, given the population prevalence of slightly less than 1 percent.

Many composers, artists, and writers, whether suspected of mood disorders or not, speak of periods of inspiration when thought processes quicken, moods lift, and new associations are generated. Perhaps something inherent in manic states fosters creativity, and recent studies confirm that creativity is specifically associated with manic episodes and not depressive states

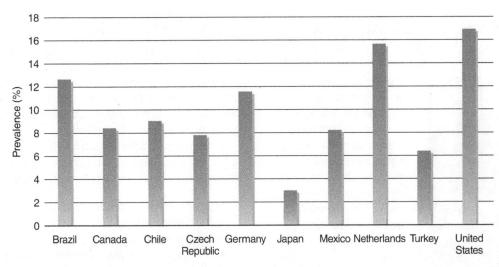

FIGURE 8.3 | Lifetime international rate per 100 people for major depressive episode.

Source: Adapted from Andrade et al. (2003).

(Soeiro-de-Souza et al., 2011). But, as noted by the late Norman Endler (1990), "It is one thing to have the high degree of energy that exists in a manic state; it is another thing to channel it in a direction that creates new works and accomplishes effective tasks" (p. 19). It is also possible that the genetic vulnerability to mood disorders is independently accompanied by a predisposition to creativity. In other words, the genetic patterns associated with bipolar disorder may also carry the spark of creativity. Yet another possibility is suggested by the work of Ghadirian, Gregoire, and Kosmidis (2001), Montréal researchers who conducted a scientific study into the relationship of bipolar disorder to creativity. They compared a group of 20 patients with

bipolar disorder to a group of 24 patients with other mental health disorders on measures of creativity. While the bipolar patients were not any more creative than the patients with other disorders, the researchers did find that moderately ill patients were significantly more creative than severely ill patients. These findings suggest that creativity may peak at a stage of the illness where symptoms are moderate but that creativity may actually decline as symptoms become progressively worse. These various possibilities are little more than speculations at present, but the study of creativity and leadership, so highly valued in all cultures, may well be enhanced by a deeper understanding of psychological disorders.

TABLE 8.1 | Partial Listing of Major 20th-Century Poets, Born between 1895 and 1935, with Documented Histories of Manic-Depressive Illness (Bipolar Disorder)

Poet	Pulitzer Prize in Poetry	Treated for Major Depressive Illness	Treated for Mania	Committed Suicide
Hart Crane (1899–1932)		X	X	X
Theodore Roethke (1908–1963)	X	X	X	
Delmore Schwartz (1913–1966)		X	X	
John Berryman (1914–1972)	X	X	X	X
Randall Jerrell (1914–1965)		X	X	X
Robert Lowell (1917–1977)	X	X	X	
Anne Sexton (1928–1974)	X	X	X	X
Sylvia Plath* (1932–1963)	X	X		X

*Plath, although not treated for mania, probably had bipolar II disorder.

Source: Manic Depressive Illness, by F. K. Goodwin and K. R. Jamison, 1990, Oxford University Press.

© Cengage Learning

Holiday of Darkness
by Norman Endler

Reprinted with permission of Wall & Emerson Inc.

The late Norman Endler was an eminent clinical psychologist from York University. He not only conducted research on the nature and causes of emotional disorders, but he also experienced first-hand the terrifying turmoil of bipolar disorder. He provided a compelling account of his experiences with episodes of depression and mania in a book he entitled *Holiday of Darkness: A Psychologist's Personal Journey Out of His Depression* (Endler, 1990).

Endler was a high achiever. He had an international reputation for his interactional model of anxiety and was chairman of the psychology department at York University when he experienced his first episode of depression. He attributes the triggering event to the professional humiliation he experienced when one spring he learned that his research grant that he had held for more than 12 years was not going to be renewed. Later that same month, Endler reports that he began

> *having difficulty sleeping, my sex drive was completely gone, and my appetite was beginning to go. For the first time in my life, I felt overwhelmed by my job and remarked to a number of people how difficult it was being chairman. . . . At work I was sullen and rarely spoke to or listened to anyone. . . . I wandered in and out of my office—almost in a fog. I went home in the middle of the day. (p. 7)*

By the end of May, he noted that "every little thing was becoming a monumental task. Everything was becoming a test of my personal competence" (p. 8). But he was too proud to seek help until his symptoms were so severe that he could no longer concentrate on giving lectures in summer school. Then he consulted with his family doctor, admitting he was experiencing a depressive episode.

In retrospect, Endler realized that he had experienced an episode of hypomania before plummeting into his first depression. Here is how he described that period:

> *Most of the time I was busy, busy, busy; taping records, playing tennis, skiing, writing manuscripts, talking to Ann, reading, going to movies, staying up late at night, waking up early in the morning, always on the go—busy, busy, busy. Furthermore, I was boasting about all the energy I had that enabled me to keep up this fast pace. . . . [My wife] asked me to slow down and take it easy. . . . Instead of occasionally "idling" in neutral I was always in "overdrive." (pp. 5–6)*

Endler's personal experiences convinced him of the importance of biological treatments for depression but also made him aware of their side effects. For example, he was administered monoamine oxidase inhibitors to treat his depression and suffered a severe hypertensive (i.e., high blood pressure) reaction. When he was correctly diagnosed with bipolar illness, lithium and electroconvulsive therapy (ECT) were both extremely helpful treatments for him. His book contains a section in which he attempts to dispel some myths about ECT. He also speaks about the continuing stigma attached to emotional disorders. Clearly, it would take a great deal of courage for a mental health professional to speak out about his own experiences with a mood disorder. In fact, many colleagues warned him that writing this book might be perceived as poor judgment on his part.

Norman Endler's dual role as both expert and patient provides a unique perspective on the disorder that has no doubt been extremely helpful to many individuals with bipolar illness.

Source: From *Holiday of Darkness: A Psychologist's Personal Journey Out of His Depression* by Norman Endler, 1982.

CAUSES OF MOOD DISORDERS

In Chapter 2, we described *equifinality* as the same end product resulting from possibly different causes. Just as a fever may have many causes, depression may also have a number of causes. For example, a depressive disorder that arises in winter has a different precipitant than a severe depression following a death, even though the episodes might look quite similar. Nevertheless, psychopathologists are identifying biological, psychological, and social factors that seem strongly implicated in the etiology of mood disorders, whatever the precipitating factor. An integrative theory of the etiology of mood disorders considers the interaction of biological, psychological, and social dimensions and also notes the very strong relationship between anxiety and depression.

Before describing this, we review evidence pertaining to each contributing factor.

BIOLOGICAL DIMENSIONS

Familial and Genetic Influences

In family studies, we look at the prevalence of a given disorder in the first-degree relatives of an individual known to have the disorder (the proband). We have found that, despite wide variability, the rate in relatives of probands with mood disorders is consistently about two to three times that in relatives of people who don't have mood disorders (Klein et al., 2002; Lau & Eley, 2010; Levinson, 2009). Increasing severity, recurrence of major depression, and earlier age of onset in the proband is associated with the highest rates of depression in relatives (Kendler et al., 2007; Klein et al., 2002; Weissman et al., 2005).

The best evidence that genes have something to do with mood disorders comes from *twin studies*, in which we examine the frequency with which identical twins (with identical genes) have the disorder, compared with fraternal twins, who share only 50 percent of their genes (as do all first-degree relatives). If a genetic contribution exists, the disorder should be present in identical twins to a much greater extent than in fraternal twins. Several twin studies, including those by Randy Katz and colleagues, suggest that the mood disorders are heritable (e.g., Hodgson & McGuffin, 2013; McGuffin et al., 2003). In a large meta-analysis of twin studies, Sullivan et al. (2000) estimated the heritability of depression to be 37 percent. Shared environmental factors have little influence, whereas 63 percent of the variance in depression can be attributed to nonshared environmental factors.

Two reports have appeared suggesting sex differences in genetic vulnerability to depression. Bierut et al. (1999) studied 2662 twin pairs in the Australian twin registry and found the characteristically higher rate of depressive disorders in women. Estimates of heritability in women ranged from 36 to 44 percent, consistent with other studies. But estimates for men were lower and ranged from 18 to 24 percent. These results agree for the most part with an important study of men in North America by Lyons et al. (1998). The authors conclude that environmental events play a larger role in causing depression in men than in women.

Note that bipolar disorder confers an increased risk of developing *some* mood disorder but not necessarily bipolar disorder. This conclusion supports the notion that bipolar disorder may simply be a more severe variant of mood disorders rather than a fundamentally different disorder. Then again, of identical twins concordant for a mood disorder, 80 percent are also concordant for polarity. This finding suggests that these disorders may be inherited separately and may therefore be separate disorders after all (Nurnberger, 2012; Nurnberger & Gershon, 1992). A twin study drew similar conclusions and noted that most of the genetic variance in vulnerability to bipolar disorder is specific to the bipolar syndrome (McGuffin et al., 2003).

McGuffin and colleagues (2003) concluded that both points are partially correct. They found that the genetic contributions to depression in both disorders are the same or similar but that the genetics of mania are distinct from depression. Thus, individuals with bipolar disorder are genetically susceptible to depression and independently genetically susceptible to mania. This hypothesis still requires further confirmation.

Although research continues to raise questions about the relative contributions of psychosocial and genetic factors to mood disorders, overwhelming evidence suggests that such disorders are familial and almost certainly reflect at least a small underlying genetic vulnerability, particularly for women. As with other psychological disorders, it seems unlikely that we will find any single dominant gene that is responsible, although occasional reports appear to that effect.

In conclusion, the best estimates of genetic contributions to depression fall in the range of approximately 40 percent for women, but seem to be significantly less for men. Genetic contributions to bipolar disorder seem to be somewhat higher. Behavioural geneticists break down environmental factors into events shared by twins (experiencing the same upbringing in the same house, and perhaps, experiencing the same stressful events) and events that are not shared. What part of our experience causes depression? Wide agreement exists that it is the unique nonshared events, rather than what is shared, that interact with biological vulnerability to cause depression (Bierut et al., 1999; Plomin et al., 1997).

Joint Heritability of Anxiety and Depression

Although most studies have looked at specific disorders in isolation, a growing trend is to examine the heritability of related groups of disorders. Evidence supports the supposition of a close relationship among depression, anxiety, and panic. For example, data from family studies indicate that the more signs and symptoms of anxiety and depression a given patient has, the greater the rate of anxiety or depression or both in first-degree relatives and children (e.g., Hammen et al., 1990). In several important reports from a major set of data on more than 2000 female twins, Kendler and his colleagues (Kendler et al., 1987, 1992b, 1995) also found that the same genetic factors contribute to both anxiety and depression. Social and psychological explanations seemed to account for the factors that differentiate anxiety from depression. These findings suggest, once again, that the biological vulnerability for mood disorders may not be specific to that disorder but may reflect a more general predisposition to anxiety or mood disorders, or, more likely to a basic temperament underlying all emotional disorders, such as neuroticism. The specific form of the disorder would be determined by unique psychological, social, or additional biological factors (Kilpatrick et al., 2007; Rutter, 2010; Slavich & Irwin, 2014).

Neurotransmitter Systems

Mood disorders have been the subject of more intense neurobiological study than almost any other area of psychopathology, with the possible exception of schizophrenia. New findings describing the relationship of specific neurotransmitters to mood disorders appear almost monthly and are punctuated by occasional reports of so-called breakthroughs. In this difficult area, most breakthroughs prove to be illusory, but false starts provide us with an ever-deeper understanding of the enormous complexity of the neurobiological underpinnings of mood disorders.

In Chapter 2, we observed that we now know that neurotransmitter systems have many subtypes and interact in many complex ways, with one another and with neuromodulators (products of the endocrine system). Research implicates low levels of serotonin in the etiology of mood disorders (Berney et al., 2006; Rosa-Neto et al., 2004; Sokolov & Kutcher, 2001) but only in relation to other neurotransmitters, including norepinephrine and dopamine (e.g., Goodwin & Jamison, 1990; Spoont, 1992). Remember that the apparent primary function of serotonin is to regulate our emotional reactions. For example, we are more impulsive, and our moods swing more widely, when our levels of serotonin are low, possibly because one of the functions of serotonin is to regulate systems involving norepinephrine and dopamine (Mandell & Knapp, 1979). According to the permissive hypothesis, when serotonin levels are low, other neurotransmitters are permitted to range more widely, become dysregulated, and contribute to mood irregularities, including depression. Current thinking is that the balance of the various neurotransmitters and their subtypes is more important than the absolute level of any one neurotransmitter (Carver et al., 2009; Whisman et al., 2011; Yatham et al., 2012).

In the context of this delicate balance, there is continued interest in the role of dopamine, particularly in relationship to manic episodes, atypical depression, or depression with psychotic features (Dunlop & Nemeroff, 2007; Garlow & Nemeroff, 2003; Thase, 2009). For example, the dopamine agonist L-dopa seems to produce hypomania in bipolar patients (see, for instance, Van Praag & Korf, 1975), along with other dopamine agonists (Silverstone, 1985). Chronic stress also reduces dopamine levels and produces depressive-like behaviour (Thase, 2009). But, as with other research in this area, it is quite difficult to pin down any relationships with certainty.

The Endocrine System

Investigators became interested in the endocrine system when they noticed that patients with diseases affecting this system sometimes became depressed. For example, hypothyroidism, or Cushing's disease, affects the adrenal cortex. This disease leads to excessive secretion of cortisol and, often, to depression (and anxiety).

In Chapter 2, and again in Chapter 5 on anxiety disorders, we discussed the brain circuit called the HPA axis. This axis begins in the hypothalamus and runs through the pituitary gland, which coordinates the endocrine system (see Figure 2.9). One of the glands influenced by the pituitary is the cortical section of the adrenal gland. The adrenal gland produces the stress hormone cortisol, which is called a stress hormone because it is elevated during stressful life events. For now, it is enough to know that cortisol levels are elevated in depressed patients, a finding that makes sense considering the relationship between depression and severe life stress (Bradley et al., 2008; Thase, 2009).

This connection led to the development of what was thought to be a biological test for depression, the dexamethasone suppression test. Dexamethasone suppresses cortisol secretion in normal subjects. However, when dexamethasone was given to depressed patients, much less suppression was noticed, and what did occur didn't last very long (Carroll et al., 1968; Carroll et al., 1980). Approximately 50 percent of depressed patients show this reduced suppression, particularly if their depression is severe (Rush et al., 1997). The thinking was that in depressed patients, the adrenal cortex secreted too much cortisol. This oversecretion of cortisol was thought to overwhelm the suppressive effects of dexamethasone in depressed people. This theory was heralded as very important, because it promised the first biological laboratory test for a psychological disorder. However, later research demonstrated that individuals with other disorders, particularly anxiety disorders, also demonstrate this nonsuppression effect (Feinberg & Carroll, 1984; Goodwin & Jamison, 2007). This finding obviously casts doubt on the usefulness of a test to diagnose depression. Thus, as with early theories about single neurotransmitters, our understanding of the role of cortisol in producing depression has proven overly simplistic.

Researchers nevertheless remain very interested in the relationship of cortisol to depression. Recent research in this area has taken some exciting new turns. Investigators have discovered that neurotransmitter activity in the hypothalamus regulates the release of hormones that affect the HPA axis. **Neurohormones** are an increasingly important focus of study in psychopathology (e.g., Hammen & Keenan-Miller, 2013; Ladd et al., 1996). We have literally thousands of neurohormones. Determining their effects on the central nervous system and sorting out their relationship to the various neurotransmitter systems is likely to be a very complex task indeed.

Sleep and Circadian Rhythms

We have known for several years that sleep disturbances are a hallmark of most mood disorders. Most important, in people who are depressed, there is a significantly shorter period after falling asleep before *rapid eye movement (REM) sleep* begins. As you may remember from your introductory psychology or biology course, there are two major stages of sleep: REM sleep and non-REM sleep (see Chapter 10). When we first fall asleep, we go through several substages of progressively deeper sleep during which we achieve most of our rest. After about 90 minutes, we begin to experience REM sleep, when the brain arouses, and we begin to dream. Our eyes move rapidly back and forth under our eyelids, hence the name *rapid eye movement* sleep. As the night goes on, we have increasing amounts of REM sleep. In addition to entering REM sleep more quickly, depressed patients experience REM activity that is more intense, and the stages of deepest sleep, called *slow wave sleep*, don't occur until later, if at all (Jindal et al., 2002; Kupfer, 1995; Thase, 2009). It seems that some sleep characteristics occur only while we are depressed and not at other times (Riemann et al., 2001; Rush et al., 1986). But other evidence suggests that, at least in more severe cases with recurrent depression, disturbances in sleep continuity, as well as reduction of deep sleep, may be present even when the individual is not depressed (Kupfer, 1995; Thase, 2009). In addition, unusually short and long sleep durations were associated with an increased risk for depression in adults (Zhai et al., 2015).

There are indications that the nature of sleep and circadian disturbances linked to depression differs across the lifespan, illustrating once again the importance of developmental stage. The increase in REM and reduction in slow wave sleep seem to be less pronounced in depressed children than in adults, perhaps because children are very deep sleepers (Brent & Birmaher, 2009; Garber et al., 2009). Depression is more often accompanied by prominent delays in the sleep-wake cycle in younger individuals, while the sleep-wake cycle of older individuals with depression seems to have a lower amplitude, suggestive of a weaker circadian signal (Robillard et al., 2014). Insomnia, frequently experienced by older adults, is a risk factor for both the onset and persistence of depression (Fiske et al., 2009; Perlis et al., 2006; Talbot et al., 2012). In an interesting study, researchers found that treating insomnia directly in those patients who have both insomnia and depression may enhance the effects of treatment for depression (Manber et al., 2008).

Sleep disturbances also occur in bipolar patients, where they are particularly severe and are characterized not only by decreased REM latency but also by severe insomnia and hypersomnia (excessive sleep) (Goodwin & Jamison, 2007; Harvey, 2008; Harvey et al., 2009). Talbot and colleagues (2012) studied the

▲ Canadian sleep researcher Rebecca Robillard, at the Institute of Mental Health Research in Ottawa, has made important connections between sleep and mental health.

Used with permission of Dr. Rebecca Robillard

relationship between sleep and mood in patients with bipolar disorder who were not currently in a depressed or manic state (inter-episode), compared with a group of patients experiencing insomnia. Both the bipolar and insomnia patients had greater sleep disturbance compared with a healthy control group. But the investigators discovered that the relationship between sleep and mood was bidirectional in both groups. That is, negative mood predicted sleep disruptions and sleep disruptions subsequently resulted in negative mood. Treating the insomnia of patients with bipolar I between episodes with CBT has been shown to reduce the risk of relapse and improve sleep, mood, and functioning (Harvey et al., 2015). .

Increasing evidence suggests that some of the sleep disturbances previously reported in depression studies may not be specific to depression, highlighting considerable overlaps across multiple psychological disorders (Baglioni et al., 2016; Benca et al., 1992; Robillard et al., 2015). While these sleep disturbances may cut across different diagnoses, perhaps the most important thing is that treating sleep disruptions directly might positively affect mood not only in people insomnia but also in people with depression and other psychological disorders.

Another interesting finding is that depriving depressed patients of sleep, particularly during the second half of the night, causes temporary improvement in their condition (Giedke & Schwarzler, 2002; Thase, 2009), particularly for patients with bipolar disorder in a depressive state (Harvey, 2008; Johnson et al., 2009), although the depression returns when the patients start sleeping normally again. In any case, because sleep patterns reflect a biological rhythm, there may be a relationship among SAD, sleep disturbances in depressed patients, and a more general disturbance in biological rhythms (Soreca et al., 2009). This would not be surprising if it were true, because most mammals are exquisitely sensitive to day length at the latitudes at which they live, and this internal clock controls eating, sleeping, and weight changes. Thus, substantial disruption in circadian rhythm might be particularly problematic for some vulnerable individuals (Moore, 1999; Sohn & Lam, 2005; Soreca et al., 2009). For instance, mood disorders have been linked with significant abnormalities in circadian rhythms, such as delays in the timing of the soporific hormone melatonin (Crasson et al., 2004; Nair et al., 1984; Robillard et al., 2013). Considerable subgroups of people with depression show major temporal disorganization of circadian rhythms, a factor linked to worse depression severity (Emens et al., 2009; Hasler et al., 2010; Robillard et al., 2018). As such, similar to sleep disruptions, abnormalities in biological rhythms are thought to contribute to the pathophysiology of depression (Germain & Kupfer, 2008; Zaki et al., 2018). These types of circadian disruptions linked to mood disorders are well amenable to chronotherapies, or treatments directly targeting the realignment of the biological clock (Benedetti, 2012; Hickie et al., 2013; Robillard et al., 2018).

Finally, abnormal sleep profiles and, specifically, disturbances in REM sleep and poor sleep quality predict a somewhat poorer response to psychological treatment (Buysse et al., 1999; Thase, 2009; Thase et al., 1996), further supporting the potential usefulness of treating disrupted sleep directly.

ADDITIONAL STUDIES OF BRAIN STRUCTURE AND FUNCTION

Measuring electrical activity in the brain with electroencephalogram (EEG) was described in Chapter 3, where we also described a type of brain wave activity, alpha waves, that indicate calm, positive feelings. In the 1990s, Davidson (1993) and Heller and Nitschke (1997) demonstrated that depressed individuals exhibit greater right-sided anterior activation of their brains, particularly in the prefrontal cortex (and less left-sided activation and, correspondingly, less alpha wave activity) than nondepressed individuals (Davidson et al., 2002). Furthermore, right-sided anterior activation was also found in patients who are no longer depressed (Gotlib et al., 1998; Tomarken & Keener, 1998), suggesting this brain function might also exist *before* the individual becomes depressed and represent a vulnerability to depression. Follow-up studies showed that adolescent offspring of depressed mothers tend to show this pattern, compared with offspring of nondepressed mothers (Tomarken et al., 2004), also suggesting that this type of brain functioning could become an indicator of a biological vulnerability to depression (Gotlib & Abramson, 1999). In contrast, one recent study suggests that bipolar spectrum patients (individuals with subthreshold swings in mood) show elevated rather than diminished relative left-frontal EEG activity and that this brain activity predicts the onset of a full bipolar I disorder (Nusslock et al., 2012). In addition to studying the prefrontal cortex and hippocampus, neuroscientists are also studying the anterior cingulate cortex and the amygdala for clues to understanding brain function in depression and finding that some areas are less active, and other areas more active, in people with depression than in normal subjects, confirming the EEG studies just mentioned (Davidson et al., 2009). These areas of the brain are all interconnected and seem to be associated with increased inhibition and with deficits in pursuing desired goals, which happen to be characteristics of depression. Scientists hope that further study of these brain circuits will lead to a deeper understanding of the origins of differences in depressed individuals, and whether these differences precede depression and may contribute to causing depression, as some studies suggest, or are simply a consequence of being depressed.

PSYCHOLOGICAL DIMENSIONS

Stressful Life Events

In reviewing the genetic contribution to the causes of depression, we noted that fully 60 to 80 percent of the causes of depression could be attributed to psychological experiences. Furthermore, most of those experiences are unique to the individual. Stress and trauma are among the most striking unique contributions to the etiology of all psychological disorders. This is reflected throughout psychopathology and is evident in the wide adoption of the diathesis–stress model of psychopathology presented in Chapter 2 (and referred to throughout this book), which describes possible genetic and psychological vulnerabilities. But in seeking what activates this vulnerability (diathesis), we usually look for a stressful or traumatic life event.

You would think it would be sufficient to ask people whether anything major had happened in their lives before they developed depression or some other psychological disorder. Most people do report losing a job, getting divorced, having a child, or graduating from school and starting a career. But, as with most issues in the study of psychopathology, the significance of a major event is not easily discovered (Carter & Garber, 2011; Hammen, 2005; Hammen & Keenan-Miller, 2013), so most investigators have stopped simply asking patients whether something bad (or good) happened, and they have begun to look at the context of the event and the *meaning* it has for the individual.

For example, losing a job is stressful for most people, but it is far more difficult for some than others. A few people might even see it as a blessing. If you were laid off as a manager in a large corporation because of a restructuring, but your partner is the president of another corporation and makes more than enough money to support the family, it might not be so bad. Furthermore, if you are an aspiring writer or artist who has not had time to pursue your art, becoming jobless might be the opportunity you have been waiting for, particularly if your partner has been telling you for years to devote yourself to your creative pursuits.

Now consider losing your job if you are a single mother of two young children living from day to day and, because of a recent dentist's bill, you have to choose between paying the electric bill or buying enough food. The stressful life event is the same, but the context is very different and transforms the significance of the event substantially. To complicate the scenario further, think for a minute about how such a woman might react to losing her job. One woman might well decide she is a total failure and thus becomes unable to carry on and provide for her children. Another woman might realize the job loss was not her fault at all and take advantage of a job-training program while scraping by somehow.

Thus, both the context of the life event and its meaning are important.

It is difficult to study life events, and psychologists are actively developing new methods to do so (e.g., Hammen, 2005; Monroe & Roberts, 1990; Monroe et al., 2009). One crucial issue is the bias inherent in remembering events. If you ask people who are currently depressed what happened when they first became depressed more than five years ago, you will probably get answers different from answers they would give if they were not currently depressed. Because current moods distort memories, many investigators have concluded that the only useful way to study stressful life events is to follow people prospectively, to determine more accurately the precise nature of events and their relation to subsequent problems.

In any case, in summarizing a large amount of research, it is clear that stressful life events are strongly related to the onset of mood disorders (Grant et al., 2004; Hammen, 2005; Kendler & Gardner, 2010; Monroe & Reid, 2009; Monroe et al., 2009). Measuring the context of events and their impact in a random sample of the population, several studies have found a marked relationship between severe and, in some cases, traumatic life events and the onset of depression (Brown, 1989; Brown et al., 1994; Kendler et al., 1999a; Mazure, 1998). Severe events precede nearly all types of depression (Brown et al., 1994). Major life stress is a somewhat stronger predictor for initial episodes of depression compared with recurrent episodes (e.g., Lewinsohn et al., 1999). In addition, for people with recurrent depression, the clear occurrence of a severe life stress before or early in the latest episode predicts a much poorer response to treatment and a longer time before remission (Monroe et al., 1992, 2009), as well as a greater likelihood of recurrence (Monroe et al., 1996, 2009). Again, the context and meaning are probably more important than the exact nature of the event itself. The work of Canadian researchers Williams, Connolly, and Segal (2001) similarly suggests that romantic relationships play a key role in vulnerability to depression in adolescent girls.

Despite this strong relationship, scientists are discovering that the link between stressful events and depression is not straightforward. Remember in Chapter 2 where we noted that our genetic endowment might actually increase the probability that we will experience stressful life events? We referred to this as the *gene–environment correlation model* (Kendler, 2011; Kendler et al., 2011). One example would be people who tend to seek out difficult relationships because of genetically based personality characteristics that then lead to depression. Another example would be people who display problematic social behaviours, such as complaining too often about personal difficulties to others, which may result in interpersonal rejection. Rejection in turn serves as a trigger for a depressive episode (Vaerum & McCabe, 2001; Wiebe & McCabe, 2002). Kendler et al. (1999a) reported that about one-third of the association between stressful life events and depression is not the usual arrangement of stress triggering depression, but rather individuals vulnerable to depression who are placing themselves in high-risk stressful environments.

The relationship of stressful events to the onset of episodes in bipolar disorder is also strong (Goodwin & Jamison, 1990; Johnson & Roberts, 1995). Several issues may be particularly relevant to the etiology of bipolar disorders, however

(Goodwin & Ghaemi, 1998). First, stressful life events seem to trigger early mania (Alloy et al., 2012) and depression, but as the disorder progresses these episodes seem to develop lives of their own. In other words, once the cycle begins, a process takes over and ensures the disorder will continue (e.g., Post, 1992; Post et al., 1989). Second, some of the precipitants of manic episodes seem to be related to loss of sleep, as in the postpartum period (Goodwin & Jamison, 1990), or as a result of jet lag, that is, disturbed circadian rhythms (Alloy et al., 2015). In most cases of bipolar disorder, nevertheless, stressful life events are implicated not only in provoking relapse but also in preventing recovery (Johnson & Miller, 1997).

Finally, although almost everyone who becomes depressed has experienced a significant stressful event, most people who experience such events do not become depressed. Although the data are not yet as precise as we would like, somewhere between 20 and 50 percent of individuals who experience severe events become depressed. Thus, between 50 and 80 percent of individuals do not develop depression or, presumably, any other psychological disorder. Once again, data strongly support the interaction of stressful life events with some kind of vulnerability, either genetic, psychological, or, more likely, a combination of the two influences (Haeffel & Hames, 2014).

Given a genetic vulnerability (diathesis) and a severe life event (stress), what happens then? Research has isolated a number of psychological and biological processes. To illustrate one, let's return to Katie. Her life event was attending a new school.

KATIE | *No Easy Transition*

I was a serious and sensitive 11-year-old at the edge of puberty and at the edge of an adventure that many teens and preteens embark on—the transition from elementary to junior high school. A new school, new people, new responsibilities, new pressures. Academically, I was a good student up to this point but I didn't feel good about myself and generally lacked self-confidence.

Katie began to experience severe anxiety reactions. Then she became quite ill with the flu. After recovering and attempting to return to school, Katie discovered that her anxieties were worse than ever. More important, she began to feel she was losing control.

As I look back I can identify events that precipitated my anxieties and fears, but then everything seemed to happen suddenly and without cause. I was reacting emotionally and physically in a way that I didn't understand. I felt out of control of my emotions and body. Day after day I wished, as a child does, that whatever was happening to me would magically end. I wished that I would awaken one day to find that I was the person I was several months before.

Katie's feeling of loss of control leads to another important psychological factor in depression: learned helplessness.

Learned Helplessness

As discussed in Chapter 2, Martin E. P. Seligman discovered that dogs and rats have an emotional reaction to events over which they have no control. If rats receive occasional shocks, they can function reasonably well, if they can cope with the shocks by doing something to avoid them, such as pressing a lever. But if they learn that nothing they do helps them avoid the shocks, they eventually become very helpless, give up, and manifest an animal equivalent of depression (Seligman, 1975).

Do humans react the same way? Seligman suggests we seem to, but only under one important condition: People become anxious and depressed when they make an attribution that they have no control over the stress in their lives (Abramson et al., 1978; Miller & Norman, 1979). These findings evolved into an important model called the **learned helplessness theory of depression**. Often overlooked is Seligman's point that anxiety is the first response to a stressful situation. Depression may follow marked hopelessness about coping with the difficult life events. The depressive attributional style is (1) *internal*, in that the individual attributes negative events to personal failings ("It is all my fault"), (2) *stable*, in that, even after a particular negative event passes, the attribution that "additional bad things will always be my fault" remains, and (3) *global*, in that the attributions extend across a wide variety of issues. Research continues on this interesting concept, but you can see how it applies to Katie. Early in her difficulties with attending school, she began to believe events were totally out of her control and that she was unable even to begin to cope. More important, in her eyes the bad situation was all her fault: "I blamed myself for my lack of control." A downward spiral into a major depressive episode followed.

But a major question remains: Is learned helplessness a cause of depression or a correlated side effect of becoming depressed? If it were a cause, learned helplessness would have to exist before the depressive episode. Results from a classic five-year longitudinal study in children may shed some light on this issue. Nolen-Hoeksema, Girgus, and Seligman (1992) reported that negative attributional style did not predict later symptoms of depression in *young* children; rather, stressful life events seemed to be the major precipitant of symptoms. As children under stress grew older, however, they tended to develop more negative cognitive styles, which *did* tend to predict symptoms of depression in reaction to additional negative events. Nolen-Hoeksema and colleagues speculate that meaningful negative events early in childhood may give rise to negative attributional styles in a developmental fashion, making these children more vulnerable to future depressive episodes when stressful events occur.

This thinking recalls the types of psychological vulnerabilities theorized to contribute to the development of anxiety disorders. That is, in a person who has a nonspecific genetic vulnerability to either anxiety or depression, stressful life events activate a psychological sense that life events are uncontrollable (Barlow, 2002; Chorpita & Barlow, 1998). Evidence suggests that negative attributional styles are not specific to depression but characterize anxiety patients as well (Barlow, 2002; Heimberg et al., 1989). This overlap may indicate that a psychological (cognitive) vulnerability is no more specific for mood disorders than is genetic vulnerability. Both types of vulnerabilities may underlie numerous disorders.

Abramson, Metalsky, and Alloy (1989) revised the learned helplessness theory to de-emphasize specific attributions and highlight the development of a *sense of hopelessness* as a crucial cause of many forms of depression. Attributions are important only to the extent that they contribute to a sense of hopelessness. This fits well with recent thinking on crucial differences between anxiety and depression. Both anxious and depressed individuals feel helpless and believe they lack control, but only in depression do they give up and become hopeless about ever regaining control (Alloy & Abramson, 2006).

Evidence from the work of Ian Gotlib and his colleagues indicates that a pessimistic style of attributing negative events to our own character flaws results in hopelessness (Gotlib & Abramson, 1999). This style may predate and therefore, in a sense, contribute to anxious or depressive episodes that follow negative or stressful events. In fact, a longitudinal study by McGill University psychologist John Abela and psychology student Sabina Sarin (2002) followed children in Grade 7 for 10 weeks, obtaining information on their initial attributional styles, negative life events, and later symptoms of depression. This study obtained results supporting the hopelessness theory of depression, as has more recent work by this same research group (e.g., Abela et al., 2006).

Negative Cognitive Styles

In 1967, Aaron T. Beck (1967, 1976) suggested that depression may result from a tendency to interpret everyday events in a negative way. According to Beck, people with depression make the worst of everything; for them, the smallest setbacks are major catastrophes. In his extensive clinical work, Beck observed that all his depressed patients thought this way, and he began classifying the types of cognitive errors that characterized this style. From the long list he compiled, two representative examples are arbitrary inference and overgeneralization. Arbitrary inference is evident when a depressed individual emphasizes the negative rather than the positive aspects of a situation. A teacher may assume he is a terrible instructor because two students in his class fell asleep. He fails to consider other reasons they might be sleeping (up all night partying) and infers that his teaching style is at fault. As an example of overgeneralization, when your professor makes one critical remark on your paper, you then assume you will fail the class, despite a long string of very positive comments and good grades on other papers. You are overgeneralizing from one small remark. According to Beck, people who are depressed think like this all the time. They make cognitive errors in thinking negatively *about themselves*, their *immediate world*, and their *future*, three areas that together are called the **cognitive triad** (see ■ Figure 8.4).

In addition, Beck theorized, after a series of negative events in childhood, individuals may develop a deep-seated negative schema, an enduring negative cognitive belief system about some aspect of life (Dozois et al., 2006; Young et al., 2014). In a self-blame schema, individuals feel personally responsible for every bad thing that happens. With a negative self-evaluation schema, they believe they can never do anything correctly. In Beck's view, these cognitive errors and schemas are automatic—that is, not

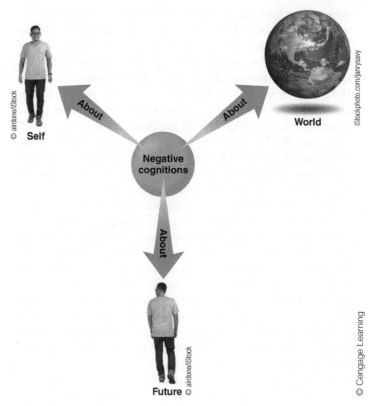

FIGURE 8.4 | Beck's cognitive triad for depression.

necessarily conscious. Indeed, an individual might not even be aware of thinking negatively and illogically. Thus, very minor negative events can lead to a major depressive episode.

A variety of evidence supports a cognitive theory of emotional disorders in general and depression in particular (Gotlib et al., 2014; Hammen & Keenan-Miller, 2013; Ingram et al., 2006; Mazure et al., 2000), and Canadian researchers have been at the forefront of developments in testing Beck's cognitive theory of depression (Rector et al., 1998). The thinking of depressed individuals is consistently more negative than that of nondepressed individuals (Dobson & Shaw, 1987; Gotlib & Abramson, 1999; Gotlib et al., 2014; Zuroff et al., 1999) in each dimension of the cognitive triad—the self, the world, and the future (e.g., Bradley & Mathews, 1988; Gotlib et al., 2014; Segal et al., 1988).

Research by Nicholas Kuiper and his colleagues at the University of Western Ontario has focused on the self-component of Beck's cognitive triad. For example, Derry and Kuiper (1981) asked depressed and nondepressed individuals to complete a "self-referent encoding task" in which they rated a series of traits as to whether or not each

▲ Aaron T. Beck

described them. The depressed group viewed traits with depressive content (e.g., stupid, boring) as being significantly more applicable to themselves than did nondepressed participants. Conversely, the depressed group viewed traits with nondepressive content (e.g., nice, attractive) as being significantly less applicable to themselves. Keith Dobson and Brian Shaw (1987) replicated this finding and took it a step further by showing that when depressed patients were in remission (i.e., no longer actively depressed), their self-descriptiveness ratings of depressive content traits were no different from those made by a nondepressed comparison group. Brinker, Harris, Guyitt, and Dozois (2006) took this research yet another step further by having participants complete the self-referent encoding task and subsequently asking them to indicate how important it was for them to possess or fail to exhibit each trait. They found that the greater the importance of positive traits that an individual believed he or she lacks, the higher the person's level of depression. For example, if a person believed it was very important to be nice but also felt that she was not a nice person, then she was at higher risk for depressed mood. Conversely, the more important the negative traits a person believed he or she is free of, the lower the person's level of depression. For example, if a person believed it was very important not to be boring and also felt that he was not a boring person, then he was at lower risk for depressed mood.

Much of the recent work in this area has focused on whether these cognitive biases are stable features of the individual or whether they instead shift with a depressed person's mood state. Some interesting work by David Dozois at the University of Western Ontario and Keith Dobson at the University of Calgary demonstrates that the answer to this question is complex. These authors followed 45 depressed patients over six months. Participants completed tests of information processing (e.g., the self-referent encoding task described earlier) and tests of cognitive organization, which allowed the researchers to determine how closely related certain topics were to one another in a given person. Each test was completed twice, once when all participants were depressed and again six months later, when half of the participants had recovered from their depression. Only those who had recovered from their depression showed less negative cognitive biases on the two information-processing tasks at the six-month follow-up than they had when they were actively depressed. In contrast, these same individuals showed a high level of interconnectedness of negative material at both testing times on the tests of cognitive organization. These results are consistent with Beck's theoretical predictions that underlying negative schemas are stable in individuals prone to depression and that these schemas become activated by negative events, in turn triggering negative information-processing biases (Dozois & Dobson, 2001). Dozois and Dobson have continued to use these tests of cognitive organization with clinically depressed research participants. Their more recent work has shown that higher levels of interconnectedness of negative material and lower levels of interconnectedness of positive material are associated with recurrent depression (Dozois & Dobson, 2003).

The implications of Beck's theory are very important. By recognizing cognitive errors and the underlying schemas, we can correct them and potentially alleviate depression and related emotional disorders. In developing ways to do this, Beck became the father of cognitive therapy, one of the most important developments in psychotherapy in the past 50 years.

Cognitive Vulnerability for Depression: An Integration

Seligman and Abramson, on the one hand, and Beck, on the other, developed their theories independently, and good evidence indicates their models are independent, in that some people may have a negative outlook (dysfunctional attitudes), whereas others may explain things negatively (hopeless attributes). Nevertheless, the basic premises overlap a great deal and considerable evidence suggests that depression is always associated with pessimistic explanatory style and negative cognitions. Evidence also exists that cognitive vulnerabilities predispose some people to view events in a very negative way, putting them at risk for depression (e.g., Abela et al., 2011; Alloy et al., 2012; Ingram et al., 2006; Reilly-Harrington et al., 1999).

SOCIAL AND CULTURAL DIMENSIONS

Marital Relations

Depression and bipolar disorder are strongly influenced by interpersonal stress (Sheets & Craighead, 2014; Vrshek-Schallhorn et al., 2015), and especially marital dissatisfaction, as disruptions in relationships often lead to depression (Davila et al., 2009). Bruce and Kim (1992) collected data on 695 women and 530 men and then interviewed them again up to one year later. During this period some participants separated from or divorced their spouses, though the majority reported stable marriages. Approximately 21 percent of the women who reported a marital split during the study experienced severe depression, a rate three times that for women who remained married. Nearly 17 percent of the men who reported a marital split developed severe depression, a rate nine times that for men who remained married. When the researchers considered only those participants with no history of severe depression, however, 14 percent of the men who separated or divorced during the period experienced severe depression, as did approximately 5 percent of the women. In other words, *only the men* faced a heightened risk of developing a mood disorder for the first time immediately following a marital split.

Another finding with considerable support is that depression, particularly if it continues, may lead to substantial deterioration in marital relationships (Beach et al., 1990, 2009; Davila et al., 2009; Uebelacker & Whisman, 2006). It is not hard to figure out why. Being around someone who is continually negative, ill tempered, and pessimistic becomes tiring after a while. Because emotions are contagious, the spouse probably begins to feel bad also. These kinds of interactions precipitate arguments or, worse, make the nondepressed spouse want to leave (Joiner & Timmons, 2009; Whisman et al., 2006).

But conflict within a marriage seems to have different effects on men and women. Depression seems to cause men to withdraw or otherwise disrupt the relationship. For women, in contrast, it is problems in the relationship that most often cause depression. Thus, for both men and women, depression and problems in marital relations are associated, but the causal direction is different (Fincham et al., 1997), a result also found by Spangler, Simons, Monroe, and Thase (1996). Given these factors, Beach, Jones, and Franklin (2009) suggest that therapists treat disturbed marital relationships at the same time as the mood disorder to ensure the highest level of success for the patient and the best chance of preventing future relapses. Individuals with bipolar disorder are less likely to be married at all and more likely to get divorced if they do marry, although those who stay married have a somewhat better prognosis, perhaps because their spouses are helpful in regulating their treatments and keeping them on medications (Davila et al., 2009).

Mood Disorders in Women

There is a fairly dramatic gender imbalance in mood disorders (Bland, 1997). Although bipolar disorder is evenly divided between men and women, almost 70 percent of the individuals with major depressive disorder and persistent depressive disorder are women (Nolen-Hoeksema, 1987; Kessler, 2006; Kessler & Bromet, 2013). What is particularly striking is that, even though overall rates of disorder may vary from country to country, this gender imbalance is constant around the world (Andrade et al., 2003; Kessler & Bromet, 2013; Seedat et al., 2009; Weissman & Olfson, 1995). For example, according to the 2017 CCHS, 6.4 percent of Canadian men and 10.7 percent of Canadian women 12 years of age or older report they are currently diagnosed with a mood disorder such as depression, bipolar disorder, mania, or dysthymia (Statistics Canada, 2018). Often overlooked is the similar ratio for most anxiety disorders, particularly panic disorder and generalized anxiety disorder. Women represent an even greater proportion of specific phobias, as we noted in Chapter 2. What could account for this?

It may be that gender differences in the development of emotional disorders are strongly influenced by perceptions of uncontrollability. If you feel a sense of mastery over your life and the difficult events we all encounter, you might experience occasional stress, but you will not feel the helplessness central to anxiety and mood disorders. The source of these differences is cultural, in the sex roles assigned to men and women in our society. Boys and men are strongly encouraged to be independent, masterful, and assertive; girls and women, by contrast, are expected to be more passive, to be sensitive to other people, and, perhaps, to rely on others more than males do. Although these stereotypes are slowly changing, they still describe current sex roles, to a large extent. But this culturally induced dependence and passivity may well put women at severe risk for emotional disorders by increasing their feelings of uncontrollability and helplessness. Evidence has accumulated that parenting styles encouraging stereotypic gender roles are implicated in the development of early psychological vulnerability to later depression or anxiety (Chorpita & Barlow, 1998; Suárez et al., 2009), specifically, a smothering overprotective style that prevents the child from developing initiative.

The value women place on intimate relationships may also put them at risk. Disruptions in such relationships, combined with an inability to cope with the disruptions, may be far more damaging to women than to men (Kendler & Gardner, 2014; Nolen-Hoeksema & Hilt, 2009). Cyranowski and associates (2000) note that the tendency for adolescent girls to express aggression by rejecting other girls, combined with a greater sensitivity to rejection, may precipitate more depressive episodes in these adolescent girls compared with boys. Kendler, Myers, and Prescott

(2005) also observed that women tend to have larger and more intimate social networks than men and that emotionally supportive groups of friends protect against depression.

Another potentially important gender difference is that women tend to ruminate more than men about their situation and blame themselves for being depressed (Nolen-Hoeksema, 1990, 2000b; Nolan-Hoeksema et al., 2008). This response style predicted the later development of depression when under stress (Abela & Hankin, 2011). Men tend to ignore their feelings, perhaps engaging in activity to take their minds off them (Addis, 2008). This male behaviour may be therapeutic because activating people (getting them busy doing something) is a common element of successful therapy for depression (Dimidjian et al., 2014; Jacobson et al., 2001).

Another issue to consider is that the majority of the people living in poverty in North America are women and children. Women, particularly single mothers, have a difficult time entering the workplace. Therefore, the meaning of conflict in a relationship is greater for women than for men, who are likely to respond more to problems at work. Data from the Canadian National Population Health Survey indicate that rates of depression are 2.5 times as high in single women with a child under five years old as among married mothers (Cairney et al., 1999; see also Bulloch et al., 2009). In fact, married women employed full-time outside the home report levels of depression no greater than those of employed married men. Single, divorced, and widowed women experience significantly more depression than men in the same categories (Weissman & Klerman, 1977). These results do not necessarily mean that people should get a job to avoid becoming depressed. Indeed, for a man or woman, feeling mastery, control, and value in the strongly socially supported role of homemaker and parent should be associated with low rates of depression. Moreover, findings from the Canadian National Population Health Survey show that work stress can be associated with depression in both men and women. It is just that gender may alter the type of work stress that is most strongly associated with depression (i.e., psychological demands predict depression in men whereas physical demands do so in women; Wang & Patten, 2001). In another study with the same survey, job insecurity was associated with depression in men but not in women (Wang et al., 2002).

A further possible contributing factor to the higher rates of depression in women pertains to a particular type of stressor—specifically, abuse histories. A study by Robert Levitan and his colleagues at the University of Toronto indicated that a history of abuse in childhood was a risk factor for depression (Levitan et al., 1998). A later study by this same research group noted a particularly strong association between early sexual abuse and comorbid depression and anxiety (Levitan et al., 2003). Another Toronto study by Sahay, Piran, and Maddocks (2000) examined the prevalence of sexual victimization in 60 female patients with depression. An alarming 65 percent reported sexual violation in childhood, adolescence, or adulthood. These studies are certainly suggestive of the possibility that the higher rates of abuse experiences may help explain women's greater susceptibility to depression.

Finally, other disorders may reflect gender role stereotypes but in the opposite direction. Disorders associated with aggressiveness,

Aurora Photos/Alamy Stock Photo

▲ Of the impoverished people in North America, the majority are women and children.

from postpartum depression. Johnson, Winett, Meyer, Greenhouse, and Miller (1999) examined the effects of social support in speeding recovery from both manic and depressive episodes in patients with bipolar disorder, and they came up with a surprising finding: A socially supportive network of friends and family helped speed recovery from depressive episodes but not from manic episodes. This finding highlights the uniquely different quality of manic episodes. These and related findings on the importance of social support have led to an exciting new psychosocial therapeutic approach for emotional disorders called interpersonal psychotherapy, which we discuss later in this chapter.

overactivity, and substance abuse occur far more frequently in men than in women (Barlow, 2002). Identifying the reasons for gender imbalances across the full range of psychopathological disorders may prove important in discovering causes of disorders.

Social Support

In Chapter 2, we examined the powerful effect of social influences on our psychological and biological functioning. We cited several examples of how social influences seem to contribute to early death, such as the evil eye or lack of social support in old age. It is not surprising, then, that social factors influence whether we become depressed (Beach et al., 2009).

To take one example, the risk of depression for people who live alone is almost 80 percent higher than for people who live with others (Pulkki-Råback et al., 2012). In an early landmark study, Brown and Harris (1978) first suggested the important role of social support in the onset of depression. In a study of a large number of women who had experienced a serious life stress, they discovered that only 10 percent of the women who had a friend in whom they could confide became depressed, compared with 37 percent of the women who did not have a close supportive relationship. Later prospective studies have also confirmed the importance of social support (or lack of it) in predicting the onset of depressive symptoms at a later time (Cutrona, 1984; Joiner, 1997). Other studies have established the importance of social support in speeding recovery from depressive episodes (Johnson et al., 2008, 2009; Keitner et al., 1995; Sherbourne et al., 1995).

A Canadian randomized control study by Misri, Kostaras, Fox, and Kostaras (2000) examined the effects of partner support on the treatment of women with postpartum depression. Relative to other treated patients, women who received the treatment involving partner support showed a significant decrease in their symptoms of depression, attesting to the importance of social support in recovery

AN INTEGRATIVE THEORY

How do we put all this together? Depression and anxiety may often share a common, genetically determined biological vulnerability (Barlow, 2002) that can be described as an overactive neurobiological response to stressful life events. One genetic pattern implicated in this vulnerability is in the serotonin transporter gene-linked polymorphic region, which was described in Chapter 2. Once again, this vulnerability is simply a general tendency to develop depression (or anxiety) rather than a specific vulnerability for depression or anxiety itself. This biological vulnerability to develop depression seems stronger for women than for men (Bierut et al., 1999). To understand the causes of depression, we must look at psychological vulnerabilities as well as life experiences that interact with genetic vulnerabilities.

People who develop mood disorders also possess a psychological vulnerability experienced as feelings of inadequacy for coping with the difficulties confronting them. As with anxiety, we may develop this sense of control in childhood (Barlow, 2002; Chorpita & Barlow, 1998). It may range on a continuum from total confidence to a complete inability to cope. When vulnerabilities are triggered, the giving-up process seems crucial to the development of depression (Alloy et al., 2000; Alloy & Abramson, 2006). A variety of evidence indicates that these attitudes and attributions correlate rather strongly with such biochemical markers of stress and depression as by-products of norepinephrine (Samson et al., 1992) and hemispheric lateral asymmetry (Davidson 1993; Heller & Nitschke, 1997).

The causes of this psychological vulnerability can be traced to adverse experiences in childhood or exposure to caregivers with psychopathology perhaps years before the onset of mood disorders. For example, Taylor and Ingram (1999) demonstrated that children of depressed mothers possess a less positive self-concept and more negative information processing if one probes for this vulnerability. This enduring psychological vulnerability intensifies the biochemical and cognitive response to stress later in life (Nolen-Hoeksema, 2000a).

Good evidence suggests that stressful life events trigger the onset of depression in most cases, particularly initial episodes (Jenness et al., 2011). How do these factors interact? The best current thinking is that stressful life events in vulnerable individuals activate stress hormones, which, in turn, have wide-ranging effects on neurotransmitter systems, particularly those involving serotonin, norepinephrine, and the corticotropin-releasing factor system. Evidence also indicates that activation of stress hormones over the long term may actually turn on certain genes, producing long-term structural and chemical changes in the brain. For example, processes triggered by long-term stress may lead to atrophy of neurons in the hippocampus that help regulate emotions. Such structural change might permanently affect the

regulation of neurotransmitter activity. The extended effects of stress may also disrupt the circadian rhythms in certain individuals, who then become susceptible to the recurrent episodic cycling that seems so uniquely characteristic of the mood disorders (Moore, 1999; Post, 1992).

As noted earlier, triggering stressful life events also activate a dormant psychological vulnerability characterized by negative thinking and a sense of helplessness and hopelessness. What we have so far is a possible mechanism for the diathesis–stress model. Finally, it seems clear that such factors as interpersonal relationships or our gender may protect us from the effects of stress and therefore from developing mood disorders. Alternatively, these factors may at least determine whether we quickly recover from these disorders.

In summary, biological, psychological, and social factors all influence the development of mood disorders, as depicted in ■ Figure 8.5. This model does not account for the varied

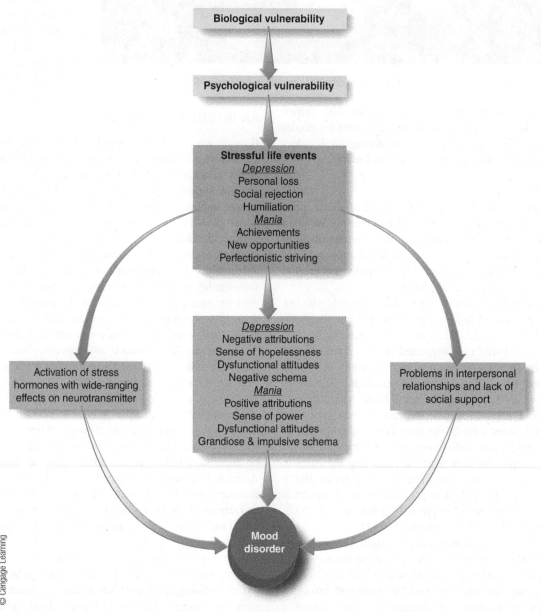

© Cengage Learning

FIGURE 8.5 | An integrative model of mood disorders.

presentation of mood disorders—unipolar, bipolar, and so on. In other words, why would someone with an underlying genetic vulnerability who experiences a stressful life event develop a bipolar disorder rather than a unipolar disorder or, for that matter, an anxiety disorder? As with the anxiety disorders and other stress disorders, specific psychosocial circumstances, such as early learning experiences, may interact with specific genetic vulnerabilities and personality characteristics to produce the rich variety of emotional disorders. Only time will tell.

TREATMENT

We have learned a great deal about the neurobiology of mood disorders during the past several years. Findings on the complex interplay of neurochemicals are beginning to shed light on the nature of mood disorders. As we have noted, the principal effect of medications is to alter levels of these neurotransmitters and other related neurochemicals. Other biological treatments, such as electroconvulsive therapy (ECT), dramatically affect brain chemistry. A more interesting development, however, alluded to throughout this book, is that powerful psychological treatments also alter brain chemistry. Despite these advances, most cases of depression go untreated because neither health-care professionals nor patients recognize and correctly identify or diagnose depression. Similarly, many professionals and patients are unaware of the existence of successful treatments (Delano-Wood & Abeles, 2005; Hirschfeld et al., 1997). For this reason, it is important to learn about treatments for depression.

MEDICATIONS

Three basic types of **antidepressant** medications are used to treat depressive disorders: tricyclic antidepressants, monoamine oxidase (MAO) inhibitors, and the newer selective-serotonin reuptake inhibitors (SSRIs).

Tricyclic antidepressants are widely used treatments for depression. The best-known variants are probably imipramine (Tofranil) and amitriptyline (Elavil). It is not yet clear how these drugs work, but initially, at least, they block the reuptake of certain neurotransmitters, allowing them to pool in the synapse and, as the theory goes, desensitize or down regulate the transmission of that particular neurotransmitter (so less of the neurochemical is transmitted). Tricyclic antidepressants seem to have their greatest effect by down regulating norepinephrine, although other neurotransmitter systems, particularly serotonin, are also affected. This process then has a complex effect on both presynaptic and postsynaptic regulation of neurotransmitters activity. This process takes a while to work, often between two and eight weeks. During this time, many patients feel a bit worse and develop side effects such as blurred vision, dry mouth, constipation, difficulty urinating, drowsiness, weight gain (at least six kilograms), and, sometimes, sexual dysfunction. For this reason, as many as 40 percent of these patients stop taking the drug, thinking that the cure is worse than the disease. Nevertheless, with careful management, many side effects disappear. Tricyclics alleviate depression in approximately 50 percent of patients, compared with approximately 25 to 30 percent of patients taking placebo pills, based on a summary analysis of more than 100 studies (American Psychiatric Association, 2000a; Depression Guideline Panel, 1993). If dropouts are excluded and only those who complete treatment are counted, success rates increase to between 60 and 70 percent (American Psychiatric Association 2010), but one thorough meta-analysis indicated that antidepressants were relatively ineffective for mild to moderate depression compared with placebo. Only in severely depressed patients is there a clear advantage for taking an antidepressant compared with placebo (Fournier et al., 2010). Another issue clinicians must consider is the potential cardiac side effect of the tricyclic antidepressants (Tingelstad, 1991). In fact, tricyclics are *lethal* if taken in excessive doses; therefore, they must be prescribed with great caution to patients with suicidal tendencies.

MAO inhibitors work very differently; as their name suggests, they block the enzyme monoamine oxidase that breaks down such neurotransmitters as norepinephrine and serotonin. The result is roughly equivalent to the effect of the tricyclics. Because they are not broken down, the neurotransmitters pool in the synapse, ultimately leading to a down regulation or desensitization. The MAO inhibitors seem to be as effective as the tricyclics (American Psychiatric Association, 2010), with somewhat fewer side effects. But MAO inhibitors are used far less often because of two potentially serious consequences: Consuming foods and beverages containing tyramine, such as cheese, red wine, or beer, can lead to severe hypertensive episodes and, occasionally, death. In addition, many other drugs that people take daily, such as cold medications, are dangerous and even fatal in interaction with an MAO inhibitor. For this reason, MAO inhibitors are usually prescribed only when tricyclics are not effective.

The class of drugs currently considered the first choice in drug treatment for depression seems to have a specific effect on the serotonin neurotransmitter system (although such drugs affect other systems to some extent). These *SSRIs* specifically block the presynaptic reuptake of serotonin. This temporarily increases levels of serotonin at the receptor site, but again the precise long-term mechanism of action is unknown (Gitlin, 2009; Thase & Denko, 2008). Perhaps the best-known drug in this class is *fluoxetine* (Prozac). Like many other medications, Prozac was initially hailed as a breakthrough drug; it even made the cover of *Newsweek* (March 26, 1990). Then reports began to appear that it might lead to suicidal preoccupation, paranoid reactions, and, occasionally, violence (e.g., Mandalos & Szarek, 1990; Teicher et al., 1990). Prozac went from being a wonder drug in the eyes of the press to a potential menace to modern society. Of course, neither conclusion was true. More recent findings indicate that the risks of suicide with this drug are no greater than with any other antidepressant, and the effectiveness is about the same (Fava & Rosenbaum, 1991). However, Prozac has its own set of side effects, the most prominent of which are physical agitation, sexual dysfunction or low desire (which is very prevalent, occurring in 50 to 75 percent of cases), insomnia, and gastrointestinal upset. But these side effects, on the whole, seem to bother most patients less than the side effects associated with tricyclic antidepressants, with the possible exception of the sexual dysfunction. Studies suggest similar effectiveness of SSRIs and tricyclics with dysthymia (Lapierre, 1994).

Two newer antidepressants seem to have somewhat different mechanisms of neurobiological action. Venlafaxine is related to tricyclic antidepressants but acts in a slightly different manner, reducing some of the associated side effects and the risk of damage to the cardiovascular system. Other typical side effects remain, including nausea and sexual dysfunction. Nefazodone is closely related to the SSRIs but seems to improve sleep efficiency instead of disrupting sleep. Both drugs are roughly comparable in effectiveness to older antidepressants (American Psychiatric Association, 2000b; Preskorn, 1995; Thase & Kupfer, 1996).

Finally, there has been a great deal of interest in the antidepressant properties of the natural herb St. John's wort (*Hypericum*). St. John's wort is very popular in Europe, and it began catching on in Canada and the United States around 1995 (Canterbury Farms, 1997). While uncontrolled trials suggest benefits for those who complete treatment (e.g., Simeon et al., 2005), a large North American study showed no specific effectiveness for the herb compared with placebo treatments or other medications (Hypericum Depression Trial Study Group, 2002). The latter controlled trial has been criticized because it included only severely depressed patients, and St. John's wort might work better with people who are only mildly depressed. Furthermore, it is significant that even the active antidepressant drug did no better than placebo in this study, although this finding is not uncommon, since many studies on the effects of drugs on depression do not show differences between drug and placebo. In any case, St. John's wort is available at many health food stores and nutritional supplement stores, but there is no guarantee that any given brand of St. John's wort contains the appropriate ingredients, since this herb is not regulated by any government agency. Moreover, Health Canada issued a letter to Canadian physicians, pharmacists, and alternative medicine practitioners warning them about the possibility of negative drug interactions with St. John's wort (e.g., with drug treatments for HIV, immunosuppressant drugs taken by transplant patients, antidepressants, and oral contraceptives; Health Canada, 2000a). For example, there have been case reports of grogginess, weakness, and lethargy resulting from the combination of St. John's wort and prescribed antidepressants, such as paroxetine (Vermani et al., 2005).

Current studies indicate that drug treatments effective with adults are not necessarily effective with children (American Psychiatric Association, 2010b). Sudden deaths of children under 14 who were taking tricyclic antidepressants have been reported, particularly during exercise, as in routine school athletic competition (Tingelstad, 1991). Cardiac side effects have been implicated in these deaths. Traditional antidepressant drug treatments are usually effective with seniors, but administering them takes considerable skill because older people may experience a variety of side effects not experienced by younger adults, including memory impairment and physical agitation (Deptula & Pomara, 1990; Marcopulos & Graves, 1990).

Clinicians and researchers have concluded that recovery from depression, although important, may not be the most important therapeutic outcome (Frank et al., 1990; Prien & Kupfer, 1986). The large majority of people eventually recover from a major depressive episode, some rather quickly. A more important goal is often to delay the next depressive episode or even prevent it entirely (Thase, 1990; Thase & Kupfer, 1996). This prevention is particularly important for patients who retain some symptoms of depression or have a past history of chronic depression or multiple depressive episodes (Forand & DeRubeis, 2013; Hammen & Keenan-Miller, 2013). Because all these factors put people at risk for relapse, it is recommended that drug treatment go well beyond the termination of a depressive episode, continuing perhaps 6 to 12 months after the episode is over, or even longer (American Psychiatric Association, 2010). The drug is then gradually withdrawn over a period of weeks or months.

Antidepressant medications have relieved severe depression and undoubtedly prevented suicide in many patients around the world, particularly in cases of more severe depression. Although these medications are readily available, many people refuse or are not eligible to take them. Some are wary of long-term side effects. Women of childbearing age must protect themselves against the possibility of conceiving while taking antidepressants, because they can damage the fetus. In one recent study of all births over a 10-year period in Denmark, infants of mothers who were taking SSRIs during pregnancy, but not other antidepressants, had an almost twofold increased risk of having a low Apgar score—a measure of infant health immediately after birth that predicts IQ scores, performance in school, and neurological disability, including cerebral palsy, epilepsy, and cognitive impairment lasting for many years after birth (Jensen et al., 2013). In addition, 40 to 50 percent of patients do not respond to these drugs, and a substantial number of the remainder are left with residual symptoms. A review of the literature by Michael Bagby and his colleagues at the University of Toronto indicates that response to antidepressant medications appears to be better in those with high social support and worse in those with co-occurring anxiety disorders (Bagby, Ryder, & Cristi, 2002).

▲ Of the synthetic drugs for depression, fluoxetine (Prozac, left) is the most widely used; the common groundcover *Hypericum* (St. John's wort, right) is popular as a natural treatment in Europe and in North America.

Lithium

Another type of antidepressant drug, *lithium carbonate*, is a common salt widely available in the natural environment (Alda, 2015). It is found in our drinking water in amounts too small to have any effect. The side effects of therapeutic doses of lithium, however, are potentially more serious than the side effects of other antidepressants. Dosage has to be very carefully regulated to prevent toxicity (poisoning) and lowered thyroid functioning, which might intensify the lack of energy associated with depression. Substantial weight gain is also common. Lithium, however, has one major advantage that distinguishes it from other antidepressants: It is often effective in preventing and treating manic episodes. For this reason it is most often referred to as a mood-stabilizing drug. Because tricyclic antidepressants can induce manic episodes, even in individuals without preexisting bipolar disorder (Goodwin & Ghaemi, 1998; Goodwin & Jamison, 2007), lithium is a treatment of choice for bipolar disorder, as outlined in the Canadian Network for Mood and Anxiety Treatment guidelines (Yatham et al., 2013). Other pharmacological treatments for acute bipolar depression include antidepressants, anticonvulsants, and antipsychotics (Vazques et al., 2015).

We are not sure how lithium works (Alda, 2015; Nivoli et al., 2010). It may limit the availability of dopamine and norepinephrine, but it may have more important effects on some of the neurohormones in the endocrine system, particularly those that influence the production and availability of sodium and potassium, electrolytes found in body fluids (Goodwin & Jamison, 1990). Results indicate that 50 percent of bipolar patients respond well to lithium initially, with at least a 50 percent reduction in manic symptoms (Goodwin & Jamison, 2007). Thus, although effective, lithium provides many people with inadequate therapeutic benefit. Patients who don't respond to lithium can take other drugs with antimanic properties, including anticonvulsants, such as carbamazepine and valproate (Divalproex), as well as calcium channel blockers such as verapamil (Keck & McElroy, 2002; Sachs & Rush, 2003; Thase & Denko, 2008). Valproate has recently overtaken lithium as the most commonly prescribed mood stabilizer for bipolar disorder (Thase & Denko, 2008) and is equally effective, even for patients with rapid-cycling symptoms (Calabrese et al., 2005). But newer studies show that these drugs have one distinct disadvantage: They are less effective than lithium in preventing suicide (Thase & Denko, 2008; Tondo et al., 1997). Goodwin and colleagues (2003) reviewed records of more than 20 000 patients taking either lithium or valproate and found the rate of completed suicides was 2.7 times as high in people taking valproate as in people taking lithium. Thus, lithium remains the preferred drug for bipolar disorder, although other mood-stabilizing drugs are often combined with therapeutic doses of lithium (Dunlop et al., 2013; Goodwin & Jamison, 2007; Nierenberg et al., 2013). This finding on the importance of mood-stabilizing drugs was confirmed in a large trial that demonstrated no advantage to adding a traditional antidepressant drug, such as an SSRI, to a mood stabilizer, such as lithium (Sachs et al., 2007).

For those patients who *do* respond to lithium, studies following patients for up to five years report that approximately 70 percent relapse, even if they continue to take lithium (Frank et al., 1999; Hammen & Keenan-Miller, 2013). Nevertheless, for almost anyone with recurrent manic episodes, maintenance on lithium or a related drug is recommended to prevent relapse (Yatham et al., 2013).

Another problem with drug treatment of bipolar disorder is that people usually like the euphoric or high feeling that mania produces and they often stop taking lithium to maintain or regain the state; that is, they do not comply with the medication regimen. Because the evidence now clearly indicates that individuals who stop their medication are at considerable risk for relapse, other treatment methods, usually psychological in nature, are used to increase compliance.

ELECTROCONVULSIVE THERAPY AND TRANSCRANIAL MAGNETIC STIMULATION

When someone does not respond to medication (or in an extremely severe case), clinicians may consider a more dramatic treatment, **electroconvulsive therapy (ECT)**, the most controversial treatment for psychological disorders after psychosurgery. In Chapter 1, we described how ECT was used in the early 20th century. Despite many unfortunate abuses along the way, ECT is considerably changed today. It is now a safe and reasonably effective treatment for those cases of severe depression that do not improve with other treatments (American Psychiatric Association, 2010; Gitlin, 2009; Kellner et al., 2012; National Institute of Mental Health, 2003).

In current administrations, patients are anaesthetized to reduce discomfort and given muscle-relaxing drugs to prevent bone breakage from convulsions during seizures. Electric shock is administered directly through the brain for less than a second, producing a seizure and a series of brief convulsions that usually lasts for several minutes. In current practice, treatments are administered once every other day for a total of six to ten treatments (fewer if the patient's mood returns to normal). Side effects are generally limited to short-term memory loss and confusion that disappear after a week or two, although some patients may have long-term memory problems. For severely depressed inpatients with psychotic features, controlled studies indicate that approximately 50 percent of those *not responding* to medication will benefit. Continued treatment with medication or psychotherapy is then necessary because the relapse rate approaches 60 percent (American Psychiatric Association, 2010a; Gitlin, 2009). For example, Sackeim and colleagues (2001) treated 84 patients with ECT and then randomly assigned them to follow-up placebo or one of several antidepressant drug treatments. All patients assigned to placebo relapsed within six months compared to 40 to 60 percent on medication. Thus, follow-up treatment with antidepressant drugs or psychological treatments is necessary, but relapse is still high. Nevertheless, it may not be in the best interest of psychotically depressed and acutely suicidal inpatients to wait three to six weeks to determine whether a drug or psychological treatment is working; in these cases, immediate ECT may be appropriate.

We do not really know why ECT works. Repeated seizures induce massive functional and perhaps structural changes in the brain, which seems to be therapeutic. There is some evidence that ECT increases levels of serotonin, blocks stress hormones, and promotes neurogenesis in the hippocampus. Because of the controversial nature of this treatment, its use declined considerably during the 1970s and 1980s (American Psychiatric Association, 2001; De Raedt et al., 2015).

Recently, another method for altering electrical activity in the brain by setting up a strong magnetic field has been introduced. This procedure is called *transcranial magnetic stimulation (TMS)*, and it works by placing a magnetic coil over the individual's head to generate a precisely localized electromagnetic pulse. Anaesthesia is not required, and side effects are usually limited to headaches. Initial reports, as with most new procedures, showed promise in treating depression (George et al., 2013), and recent observations and reviews have confirmed that TMS can be effective (De Raedt et al., 2015; Mantovani et al., 2012; Schutter, 2009). But results from several important clinical trials with severe or treatment-resistant psychotic depression reported ECT to be clearly more effective than TMS (Eranti et al., 2007). It may be that TMS is more comparable to antidepressant medication than to ECT, and one study reported a slight advantage for combining TMS and medication compared to using either treatment alone (Brunoni et al., 2013; Gitlin, 2009).

Several other nondrug approaches for treatment-resistant depression are in development. Vagus nerve stimulation involves implanting a pacemaker-like device that generates pulses to the vagus nerve in the neck, which, in turn, is thought to influence neurotransmitter production in the brain stem and limbic system (Gitlin, 2009; Marangell et al., 2002). Sufficient evidence has accumulated, but results are generally weak and it has been little used. Deep brain stimulation has been used with a few severely depressed patients. In this procedure, electrodes are surgically implanted in the limbic system (the emotional brain). These electrodes are also connected to a pacemaker-like device (Mayberg et al., 2005). Initial results show some promise in treatment-resistant patients, but time will tell if this is a useful treatment (Kennedy et al., 2011; Lozano et al., 2012).

PSYCHOSOCIAL TREATMENTS

Of the effective psychosocial treatments now available for depressive disorders, two major approaches are most effective. The first is cognitive behavioural; Aaron T. Beck, the founder of cognitive therapy, is most closely associated with this approach. The second approach, interpersonal psychotherapy, was developed by Myrna Weissman and Gerald Klerman.

Cognitive Therapy

Beck's **cognitive therapy** grew directly out of his observations of the role of deep-seated negative thinking in generating depression (Beck, 1967, 1976; Clark et al., 1999; Young et al., 2014). University of New Brunswick Emeritus Professor David A. Clark described the approach as follows. First, clients are taught to examine carefully their thought processes while they are depressed and to recognize "depressive" errors in thinking. This task is not always easy, because many thoughts are automatic and beyond clients' awareness. Negative thinking seems natural to them. Clients are taught that errors in thinking can directly cause depression. Treatment involves correcting cognitive errors and substituting less depressing and (perhaps) more realistic thoughts and appraisals. Later in therapy, underlying negative cognitive

schemas (characteristic ways of viewing the world) that trigger specific cognitive errors are targeted, not only in the clinic but also as part of the client's daily life. The therapist purposefully takes a Socratic approach, making it clear that therapist and client are working as a team to uncover faulty thinking patterns and the underlying schemas from which they are generated. Therapists must be skillful and highly trained (see Clark et al., 1999). What follows is an example of an actual interaction between Beck and a client named Irene.

BECK AND IRENE | *A Dialogue*

Because an intake interview had already been completed by another therapist, Beck did not spend time reviewing Irene's symptoms in detail or taking a history. Irene began by describing her "sad states." Beck almost immediately started to elicit her automatic thoughts during these periods.

THERAPIST: What kind of thoughts were you having during these four days when you said your thoughts kept coming over and over again?

PATIENT: Well, they were just—mostly, "Why is this happening again"—because, you know, this isn't the first time he's been out of work. You know, "What am I going to do"—like I have all different thoughts. They are all in different things like being mad at him, being mad at myself for being in this position all the time. Like I want to leave him or if I could do anything to make him straighten out and not depend so much on him. There's a lot of thoughts in there.

THERAPIST: Now can we go back a little bit to the sad states that you have? Do you still have that sad state?

PATIENT: Yeah.

THERAPIST: You have it right now?

PATIENT: Yeah, sort of. They were sad thoughts about—I don't know—I get bad thoughts, like a lot of what I'm thinking is bad things. Like not—there is like, ah, it isn't going to get any better, it will stay that way. I don't know. Lots of things go wrong, you know, that's how I think.

THERAPIST: So one of the thoughts is that it's not going to get any better?

PATIENT: Yeah.

THERAPIST: And sometimes you believe that completely?

PATIENT: Yeah, I believe it, sometimes.

THERAPIST: Right now do you believe it?

PATIENT: I believe—yeah, yeah.

THERAPIST: Right now you believe that things are not going to get better?

PATIENT: Well, there is a glimmer of hope but it's mostly. . . .

THERAPIST: What do you kind of look forward to in terms of your own life from here on?

PATIENT: Well, what I look forward to—I can tell you but I

don't want to tell you. (Giggles). Um, I don't see too much.

THERAPIST: You don't want to tell me?

PATIENT: No, I'll tell you but it's not sweet and great what I think. I just see me continuing on the way I am, the way I don't want to be, like not doing anything, just being there, like sort of with no use, that like my husband will still be there and he will, you know, he'll go in and out of drugs or whatever he is going to do, and I'll just still be there, just in the same place.

By inquiring about Irene's automatic thoughts, the therapist began to understand her perspective—that she would go on forever, trapped, with her husband in and out of drug centres. This hopelessness about the future is characteristic of most depressed patients. A second advantage to this line of inquiry is that the therapist introduced Irene to the idea of looking at her own thoughts, which is central to cognitive therapy.

Source: Republished with permission of Guildford Publications, from *Clinical handbook of psychological disorders: a step-by-step treatment manual* by Barlow, David H. © 2008; permission conveyed through Copyright Clearance Center, Inc.

Between sessions, clients are instructed to *monitor* and *log* their thought processes carefully, particularly during situations in which they might feel depressed. They also attempt to change their behaviour by carrying out specific activities assigned as homework, such as tasks in which clients can test their faulty thinking. For example, a client who has to participate in an upcoming meeting might think, "If I go to that meeting, I'll just make a fool of myself and all my colleagues will think I'm stupid." The therapist might instruct the client to go to the meeting, predict ahead of time the reaction of her colleagues, and then see what really happens. This part of treatment is called a *behavioural experiment* because the client makes a hypothesis about what's going to happen (usually a depressing outcome) and then, most often, discovers it is incorrect ("My colleagues congratulated me on my presentation"). The therapist typically schedules other activities to reactivate depressed patients who have given up most activities.

Interpersonal Psychotherapy

We have seen that major disruptions in our interpersonal relationships are an important category of stresses that can trigger mood disorders (Joiner & Timmons, 2009; Kendler et al., 2003). In addition, people with few, if any, important social relationships seem at risk for developing and sustaining mood disorders (Beach et al., 2009). **Interpersonal psychotherapy (IPT)** focuses on resolving problems in existing relationships and learning to form important new interpersonal relationships (Bleiberg & Markowitz, 2014; Gillies, 2001; Klerman et al., 1984; Weissman, 1995).

Therapist Laurie Gillies of the Ontario Institute for Studies in Education and the University of Toronto has described the approach as follows. Like cognitive-behavioural approaches, IPT is highly structured and seldom takes longer than 15 to 20 sessions, usually scheduled once a week (Cuijpers et al., 2011). After identifying life stressors that seem to precipitate the depression, the therapist and patient work collaboratively on the patient's current interpersonal problems. Typically, these include one or more of four interpersonal issues: (1) dealing with interpersonal role disputes, such as marital conflict; (2) adjusting to the loss of a relationship, such as grief over the death of a loved one; (3) acquiring new relationships, such as getting married or establishing professional relationships; and (4) identifying and correcting deficits in social skills that prevent the person from initiating or maintaining important relationships (Gillies, 2001).

To take a common example, the therapist's first job is to identify and define an interpersonal dispute (Bleiberg & Markowitz, 2014; Weissman, 1995), perhaps with someone who expects her spouse to support her but has had to take an outside job to help pay bills. The spouse might expect her to share equally in generating income. If this dispute seems to be associated with the onset of depressive symptoms and to result in a continuing series of arguments and disagreements without resolution, it would become the focus for IPT.

After helping identify the dispute, the next step is to bring it to a resolution. First, the therapist helps the patient determine the stage of the dispute.

1. *Negotiation stage*: Both partners are aware it is a dispute, and they are trying to renegotiate it.
2. *Impasse stage*: The dispute smoulders beneath the surface and results in low-level resentment, but no attempts are made to resolve it.
3. *Resolution stage*: The partners are taking some action, such as divorce or separation.

The therapist works with the patient to define the dispute clearly for both parties and develop specific strategies for resolving it.

Studies comparing the results of cognitive therapy and IPT with those of tricyclic antidepressants and other control conditions have found that psychosocial approaches and medication are equally effective, and all treatments are more effective than placebo conditions, brief psychodynamic treatments, or other appropriate control conditions for both major depressive disorder and persistent depressive disorder (Hollon, 2011; Hollon & Dimidjian, 2009; Miller, Norman, & Keitner, 1989; Paykel & Scott, 2009; Schulberg et al., 1996). Depending on how success is defined, approximately 50 to 70 percent or more of people benefit from treatment to a significant extent, compared with approximately 30 percent in placebo or control conditions.

Research by Darcy Santor and Vivek Kusumakar at Dalhousie University evaluated the effectiveness of IPT in depressed adolescents. Twenty-five adolescents (mean age of 16 years) received 12 weeks of IPT. The majority of teens improved substantially on both self-ratings and clinician ratings of depression symptoms. Depending on the criteria used, 80 to 84 percent of the teens were no longer showing meaningful levels of depressive symptoms by therapy completion. The study suggests that IPT may be effective for treating moderate to severe depression in adolescents, although this needs to be demonstrated in a randomized control study before we can be sure that the changes were actually due to the therapy (Santor & Kusumakar, 2001).

In view of the seriousness of mood disorders in children and adolescents, work has begun on preventing these disorders in these age groups (Muñoz et al., 2010, 2012). Most researchers focus on instilling in children social and problem-solving skills that are adequate to prevent the kinds of social stress so often associated with depression. In fact, Sanders and colleagues (1992) and Dadds, Sanders, Morrison, and Rebgetz (1992) determined that disordered communication and problem-solving skills, particularly within the family, are characteristic of depressed children and a natural target for treatment. Beardslee et al. (1997) have observed sustained effects from a preventive program directed at families with children between the ages of 8 and 15 in which one parent had experienced a recent episode of depression. Eighteen months after participating in six to ten family sessions, these families were doing substantially better on most measures than the control families.

In another preventive effort, Gilham, Reivich, Jaycox, and Seligman (1995) taught cognitive and social problem-solving techniques to 69 children in Grades 5 and 6 who were at risk for depression. Compared with children in a matched no-treatment control group, the prevention group reported fewer depressive symptoms during the two years they were followed. More importantly, moderate to severe symptoms were reduced by half and the positive effects of this program increased during the period of follow-up. In a replication, Seligman, Schulman, DeRubeis, and Hollon (1999) conducted a similar course for university students who were at risk for depression based on a pessimistic cognitive style. After three years, students taking the eight-session program experienced less anxiety and depression than a control group receiving the assessments only. This suggests that it might be possible to psychologically "immunize" children and adolescents against depression by teaching appropriate cognitive and social skills before they enter puberty.

COMBINED TREATMENTS

A few studies have tested the very important question of whether combining psychosocial treatments with medication is effective in treating depression (e.g., Beck et al., 1985; Blackburn & Moore, 1997; Hollon et al., 1992; Miller, Norman, Keitner, Bishop, & Down, 1989). With one exception, the results thus far do not strongly suggest any immediate advantage of combined treatment over separate drug or psychosocial treatment. The exception to this finding is a very large study reported by Keller et al. (2000) on the treatment of chronic major depression that was conducted at 12 different clinics. In this, the largest study ever conducted on the treatment of depression, 681 patients were assigned to receive either antidepressant medication (nefazodone), a cognitive-behavioural therapy constructed specifically for chronically depressed patients, or the combination of the two treatments.

Forty-eight percent of patients receiving each of the individual treatments either were remitted or responded in a clinically satisfactory way, compared with 73 percent of the patients receiving combined treatment. Because this study was conducted with only a subset of depressed patients, those with chronic

depression, the findings would need to be replicated before we could say combined treatment was useful for depression generally. In addition, because the study did not include a condition in which the cognitive-behavioural treatment was combined with placebo, we cannot rule out the fact that the enhanced effectiveness of the combined treatment was due to placebo factors. A review by Zindel Segal and his colleagues at the Centre for Addiction and Mental Health in Toronto suggests that combined treatment is generally just as effective as separate drug or psychosocial therapies in the treatment of depression. However, when the depression is severe, combined drug and psychosocial treatments appear to have some additional benefits over either treatment administered separately (Segal, Vincent, & Levitt, 2002).

Drugs and CBT seem to operate in different ways, but it remains uncertain which is more effective. It might just be that the most effective treatment depends on the individual, but we know little about these patient characteristics that could be used to personalize therapies. Until we develop such methods, studies continue to compare groups of individuals who share the same diagnosis. Moreover, it is possible that medication, when it works, does so more quickly than psychological treatments for the most part, which in turn have the advantage of increasing the patient's long-range social functioning (particularly in the case of IPT) and protecting against relapse or recurrence (particularly cognitive-behavioural therapy). Combining treatments, therefore, might take advantage of the drugs' rapid action and the psychosocial protection against recurrence or relapse, thereby allowing eventual discontinuation of the medications.

PREVENTING RELAPSE

Given the high rate of recurrence in depression, it is not surprising that well over 50 percent of patients on antidepressant medication relapse if their medication is stopped within four months after their last depressive episode (Thase, 1990). Therefore, one important question has to do with **maintenance treatment** to *prevent* relapse or recurrence over the long term.

In several studies, cognitive therapy reduced rates of subsequent relapse in depressed patients by more than 50 percent over groups treated with antidepressant medication (see, e.g., Hollon et al., 2005, 2006; Teasdale et al., 2000). Jarrett and colleagues (2013) compared CBT, an SSRI (fluoxetine), and a pill placebo as a relapse prevention strategy for people with recurrent major depressive disorder. The study first treated everybody with CBT and then randomized people to receive either continued CBT, the SSRI, or the placebo for eight months. Then, treatment was stopped and patients were followed up for two years to examine relapse rates. The study showed that, overall, both CBT and the SSRI prevented relapse equally well and more so than the placebo. Relapse rates after having received CBT and fluoxetine did not differ.

Zindel Segal and his colleagues collaborated with researchers in the United Kingdom on a variant of traditional cognitive therapy that is specifically designed to prevent depressive relapse. This new therapy is called mindfulness-based cognitive therapy (Segal, Williams, & Teasdale, 2002). It is a group therapy designed to teach recovered depressed patients to disengage from

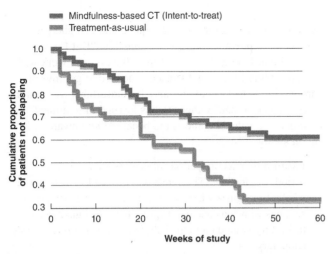

FIGURE 8.6 | Survival (nonrelapse/nonrecurrence) curves comparing relapse/recurrence to major depression for treatment as usual and Segal's mindfulness-based cognitive therapy in patients with three or more previous episodes of major depression.

Note: CT = cognitive therapy.

Source: From "Prevention of Relapse/Recurrence in Major Depression by Mindfulness-Based Cognitive Therapy," by J. D. Teasdale, Z. V. Segal, J. M. Williams, V. A. Ridgeway, J. M. Soulsby, and M. A. Lau, 2000, *Journal of Consulting and Clinical Psychology*, 4, pp. 615–623. Copyright © 2000 by the American Psychological Association.

the kinds of negative thinking that can precipitate a relapse to depression. More specifically, they are trained in mindfulness meditation to help them become more aware of their thoughts and feelings and to view their thoughts as mental events rather than as accurate reflections of reality. In a recent randomized control study, 145 patients recovered from depression were assigned to receive either mindfulness-based cognitive therapy or treatment as usual, and relapse of major depression was assessed over a 60-week period. For patients with a history of recurrent depression, the mindfulness treatment significantly reduced their risk of another relapse (Teasdale et al., 2000). The proportion of patients not relapsing in both groups is presented in ■ Figure 8.6. Subsequent work by this research team has shown that mindfulness-based cognitive therapy works in preventing depressive relapse by changing patients' relationships to their negative thoughts (e.g., by allowing them to distance themselves from their thoughts and feelings; Teasdale et al., 2002).

▲ Zindel Segal is a professor of psychology in mood disorders at the University of Toronto Scarborough and a senior scientist in the Campbell Family Research Institute at the Centre for Addiction and Mental Health. He has been involved in the development of a new variant of cognitive therapy called mindfulness-based cognitive therapy that is designed to prevent relapses to depression in people with recurrent major depression.

PSYCHOSOCIAL TREATMENTS FOR BIPOLAR DISORDER

Although medication, particularly lithium, is the preferred treatment for bipolar disorder, most clinicians emphasize the need for psychosocial intervention to manage interpersonal and practical problems, such as marital and job difficulties, that result from the disorder (Clarkin et al., 1988). Until recently, the principal objective of psychosocial intervention was to increase compliance with medication regimens, such as lithium (Cochran, 1984). We noted before that the "pleasures" of a manic state make refusal to take lithium a major therapeutic obstacle. Giving up drugs between episodes or skipping dosages during an episode significantly undermines treatment. Therefore, a careful integration of psychosocial and lithium treatments is very important (Goodwin & Jamison, 2007). For example, Clarkin, Carpenter, Hull, Wilner, and Glick (1998) evaluated the advantages of adding a psychological treatment to medication in inpatients and found it improved adherence to medication for all patients and resulted in better overall outcomes for the most severe patients compared with medication alone.

More recently, psychological treatments have also been directed at psychosocial aspects of bipolar disorder. Ellen Frank and her colleagues developed a psychological treatment that regulates circadian rhythms by helping patients regulate their eating and sleep cycles and other daily schedules and cope more effectively with stressful life events, particularly interpersonal issues (Frank et al., 1997, 1999, 2005). In an evaluation of this approach, called interpersonal and social rhythm therapy (IPSRT), patients receiving IPSRT lasted longer without a new manic or depressive episode compared with patients undergoing standard, intensive clinical management. Initial results with adolescents are also promising (Hlastala et al., 2010).

David Miklowitz and his colleagues found that family tension is associated with relapse in bipolar disorder. Preliminary studies indicate that treatments directed at helping families understand symptoms and develop new coping skills and communication styles do change communication styles (Simoneau et al., 1999) and prevent relapse (Miklowitz, 2014). Miklowitz, George, Richards, Simoneau, and Suddath (2003) demonstrated that their family-focused treatment combined with medication results in significantly less relapse one year following initiation of treatment than occurs in patients receiving crisis management and medication over the same period. Specifically, only 35 percent of patients receiving family therapy plus medication relapsed, compared with 54 percent in the comparison group. Similarly, family therapy patients averaged over a year and a half (73.5 weeks) before relapsing, significantly longer than the comparison group.

Rea, Tompson, and Miklowitz (2003) compared this approach to an individualized psychotherapy in which patients received the same number of sessions over the same period and continued to find an advantage for the family therapy after two years. Reilly-Harrington et al. (2007) found some evidence that CBT is effective for bipolar patients with rapid cycling. In view of the relative ineffectiveness of antidepressant medication for the depressive stage of bipolar disorder reviewed above, Miklowitz et al. (2007) reported an important study showing that up to 30 sessions of an intensive psychological treatment was significantly more effective than the customary best treatment in promoting recovery from bipolar depression and remaining well. A more recent trial compared the effects after one year of four months of family-focused therapy and an educational control condition on preventing mood symptoms in youths who are at high risk for developing bipolar disorder based on their family history and environment (Miklowitz et al., 2013). The study showed that participants who received the family-focused therapy had a more rapid recovery from their initial mood symptoms and were more often in remission one year following treatment than those in the education control condition. The specificity of this effect on bipolar depression, which is the most common stage of bipolar disorder, combined with the lack of effectiveness of antidepressants, suggest that these procedures will provide an important contribution to the comprehensive treatment of bipolar disorder.

Let us now return to Katie who, you will remember, had made a serious suicide attempt in the midst of a major depressive episode.

KATIE | *The Triumph of the Self*

Like the overwhelming majority of people with serious psychological disorders, Katie had never received an adequate course of treatment, although she was evaluated periodically by various mental health professionals. She lived in a rural area where competent professional help was not readily available. Her life ebbed and flowed with her struggle to subdue anxiety and depression. When she could manage her emotions sufficiently, she took an occasional course in the high school independent study program. Katie discovered that she was fascinated by learning. She enrolled in a local community college at the age of 19 and did extremely well, despite the fact that she had not progressed beyond Grade 9 in school. At the college she earned a high school equivalency diploma. She went to work in a local factory. But she continued to drink heavily and to take Valium; on occasion, anxiety and depression would return and disrupt her life.

Finally, Katie left home, attended college full-time, and fell in love. But the romance was one-sided, and she was rejected.

> One night after a phone conversation with him, I nearly drank myself to death. I lived in a single room alone in the dorm. I drank as much vodka as quickly as I could. I fell asleep. When I awoke, I was covered in vomit and couldn't recall falling asleep or being sick. I was drunk for much of the next day. When I awoke the following morning, I realized I could have killed myself by choking on my own vomit. More importantly, I wasn't sure if I fully wanted to die. That was the last of my drinking.

Katie decided to make some changes. Taking advantage of what she had learned in the little treatment she had received, she began looking at life and herself differently.

Instead of dwelling on how inadequate and evil she was, she began to pay attention to her strengths. "But I now realized that I needed to accept myself as is, and work with any stumbling blocks that I faced. I needed to get myself through the world as happily and as comfortably as I could. I had a right to that." Other lessons learned in treatment now became valuable, and Katie became more aware of her mood swings:

> I learned to objectify periods of depression as [simply] periods of "feeling." They are a part of who I am, but not the whole. I recognize when I feel that way, and I check my perceptions with someone that I trust when I feel uncertain of them. I try to hold on to the belief that these periods are only temporary.

Katie developed other strategies for coping successfully with life:

> I try to stay focused on my goals and what is important to me. I have learned that if one strategy to achieve some goal doesn't work there are other strategies that probably will. My endurance is one of my blessings. Patience, dedication, and discipline are also important. None of the changes that I have been through occurred instantly or automatically. Most of what I have achieved has required time, effort, and persistence.

Katie dreamed that if she worked hard enough she could help other people who had problems similar to her own. Katie pursued that dream and earned her Ph.D. in psychology.

Concept Check 8.2

Indicate which type of treatment for mood disorders is being described in each statement.

1. The controversial but somewhat successful treatment involving the production of seizures through electrical current to the brain. _____

2. This teaches clients to carefully examine their thought process and recognize depressive styles in thinking. _____

3. These come in three main types (tricyclics, MAO inhibitors, and SSRIs) and are often prescribed but have numerous side effects. _____

4. This antidepressant must be carefully regulated to avoid illness but has the advantage of affecting manic episodes. _____

5. This therapy focuses on resolving problems in existing relationships and learning to form new interpersonal relationships. _____

6. This is an effort to prevent relapse or recurrence over the long run. _____

SUICIDE

STATISTICS

Most days we are confronted with news about the war on cancer or the frantic race to find a cure for AIDS. We also hear never-ending admonitions to improve our diet and to exercise more to prevent heart disease. But another cause of death is as frightening and dangerous as these medical conditions—the decision to kill oneself, made by about 800 000 people per year worldwide (World Health Organization, 2014). Suicide mortality rates are given per 100 000 people, and in 2016 the World Health Organization (2019) estimated the global suicide rate to be 10.5 per 100 000 people. The global rate has declined since 2000, but not in all regions or countries; some have seen dramatic increases in their suicide mortality rate (World Health Organization [WHO], 2014). Canada is one of the fortunate countries witnessing a decline; the suicide rate dropped from 14.4 per 100 00 people in 1979 to 10.4 per 100 000 in 2012 (Skinner et al., 2016). However, it is important to recognize that most epidemiologists agree that the actual number of suicides is higher than official statistics suggest. Many of these unreported suicides occur when people purposefully drive off a bridge or a cliff (Blumenthal, 1990).

Regardless of age, in every country around the world except China, men are more likely to commit suicide than women. Although it was previously thought that men were at least three times as likely to commit suicide as women, recent work by the WHO (2014) demonstrated that this is likely a phenomenon specific to high-income countries. In high-income countries, the ratio of male-to-female suicides was 3.5, compared to a ratio of 1.6 in middle- and low-income countries. The Public Health Agency of Canada (PHAC, 2018), in a high-income country, estimated that Canadian men committed suicide at rates 3.3 times that of Canadian women. ■ Figure 8.7 displays the suicide rates for Canadian men and women across time. It clearly illustrates this gender difference as well as the general decline in suicide rates over time, although it appears that the rates continue to decline for men but not women (Skinner et al., 2016)

This gender difference seems to be related in part to the types of suicide attempts made by men and women. Men generally choose far more violent methods, such as guns and hanging; women tend to rely on less violent options, such as drug overdose (Buda & Tsuang, 1990; Callanan & Davis, 2012; Nock et al., 2011). A Canadian study provides further support for gender differences in method of suicide (Skinner et al., 2016). Although suffocation accounted for the majority of suicide deaths for both men and women (48 and 44 percent, respectively), it was estimated that in 2012 firearms accounted for 18 percent of suicide deaths for men but only 2 percent of women, whereas poisoning accounted for 40 percent of suicide deaths for women but only 18 percent of men. In China, and uniquely in China, more women commit suicide than do men, particularly in rural settings (Nock et al., 2008; Sun, 2011; Wu, 2009). What accounts for this reversal? Chinese scientists agree that China's suicide rates are due to an absence of stigma. In fact, suicide, particularly among women, is often portrayed in classical Chinese literature as a reasonable solution to problems. A rural Chinese woman's family is her entire world, and suicide is an honourable solution if the family collapses.

Globally, the suicide mortality rate is lowest among young people 15 years of age or younger and highest among those 70 years of age and older. However, as with gender differences, age differences are affected by a country's income (WHO, 2014). For example, young adults and older women have higher suicide mortality rates in lower- and middle-income countries than in

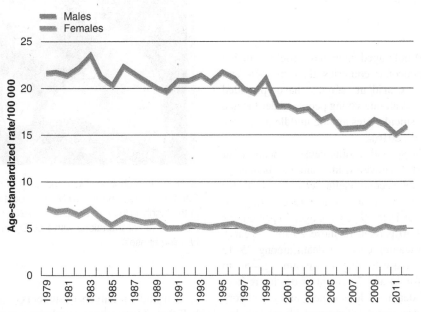

FIGURE 8.7 | Age-standardized suicide rates/100 000, by year and sex, Canada 1979 to 2012.

Note: APC = annual percent change.

© CP PHOTO/Aaron Harris

▲ James Bartleman, former lieutenant governor of Ontario (2002–2007), is a member of the Mnjikaning First Nation. His early years were marked by discrimination and poverty. Despite his many successes, Bartleman struggles with depression. He is determined to decrease the high rates of suicide among young people in many Canadian Indigenous communities, and he is an active advocate for reducing the stigma associated with mental illness.

high-income countries. Middle-aged men have higher suicide mortality rates in higher-income countries than in low- and middle-income countries. Canadian studies have provided evidence for low suicide rates among young people under the age of 15, as well as a peak in suicide rates among middle-aged men (PHAC, 2018; Skinner et al., 2016).

In Canada, suicide is the second-leading cause of death, after accidents (Navaneelan, 2012). However, this ranking changes as Canadians age. Suicide is the second-leading cause of death for Canadians between 15 and 34 years of age (accounting for 28 percent of deaths for those 15 to 19 years of age, 23 percent for those 20 to 24 years, and 20 percent of those 25 to 34 years). Suicide drops to the third-leading cause of death among 35- to 44-year-olds and to the fourth-leading cause among 45- to 54-year-olds (accounting for 14 and 7 percent of deaths, respectively) as other causes of death, such as cancer and circulatory problems, become more prominent (Skinner et al., 2016). For teenagers in the United States, suicide is the third-leading cause of death, behind motor vehicle accidents and homicide (Centers for Disease Control and Prevention [CDC], 2010b). Suicide rates

are also a concern among seniors, often connected to the growing incidence of medical illness in our oldest citizens and to their increasing loss of social support. As we have noted, a strong relationship exists between illness or infirmity and hopelessness or depression (Brown et al., 2000). Suicide is not attempted only by adolescents and adults: Rosenthal and Rosenthal (1984) described 16 children aged two to five years who had attempted suicide at least once, many injuring themselves severely.

In addition to completed suicides, two other important indices of suicidal behaviour are **suicidal attempts** (the person survives) and **suicidal ideation** (thinking seriously about suicide). Although males *commit* suicide more often than females in most of the world (e.g., CDC, 2013), females *attempt* suicide more often (Berman & Jobes, 1991). The high incidence of suicidal attempts among women may reflect the fact that more women than men are depressed and that depression is strongly related to suicide attempts (Frances et al., 1986). Some estimates place the ratio of attempted to completed suicides at 50 or more to one (Garfield & Zigler, 1993). In addition, results from another study (Kovacs et al., 1993) suggest that among adolescents, the ratio of thoughts about suicide to attempts is between three to one and six to one. In other words, between 16 and 30 percent of adolescents in this study who had thought about killing themselves actually attempted it. "Thoughts" in this context does not refer to a fleeting philosophical type of consideration but rather to a serious contemplation of the act. The first step down the dangerous road to suicide is seriously thinking about it (Mishara, 1999).

Gijsbert Hanekroot/Contributor/Redferns/Getty Images

▲ Men often choose violent methods of committing suicide. Canadian musician Richard Manuel, best known for his membership in the highly influential 1960s and 1970s rock group The Band and for his musical collaborations with Bob Dylan, committed suicide by hanging himself.

In a study of university students (whose rate of suicide is about half that of the general population), approximately 12 percent had thoughts about suicide during the past 12 months (Wilcox et al., 2010). Only a minority of these students with thoughts of suicide (perhaps around 10 percent) attempt to kill themselves, and only a few succeed (Schwartz, 2011). Nevertheless, given the enormity of the problem, suicidal thoughts are taken very seriously by mental health professionals.

In Canada, the suicide rate and the rate of suicidal attempts vary widely across the provinces and territories (Skinner et al., 2016). For example, the highest rates of suicide occurred in the territories (Nunavut at 64 per 100 000 people, Yukon at 18.7 per 100 000, and the Northwest Territories at 18.4 per 100 000), and Newfoundland and Labrador and Ontario having two of the lowest rates (7.8 per 100 000 and 8.5 per 100 000, respectively). The alarmingly high suicide rates in Nunavut highlight concerns about suicide among Canadian Inuit. While recognizing that previous research has found that suicide rates can vary dramatically across First Nations and Inuit communities (e.g., Chandler & Lalonde, 1998), PHAC (2018) documented that areas with high concentrations of Indigenous Peoples had suicide rates several times as high as areas with low concentrations of Indigenous Peoples. This difference in rates was much higher in areas where Inuit were the predominant group. The rate was 6.5 times as high for areas with a high concentration of Inuit compared to only 3.7 and 2.7 as high for areas with high concentrations of First Nations and Métis, respectively. Men in all groups had higher suicide rates than women—the suicide rate among male Inuit was five times that of female Inuit (118.2 per 100 000 compared to 24.5 per 100 000).

Boothroyd, Kirmayer, Spreng, Malus, and Hodgins (2001) studied cases of completed suicides in Nunavik from 1982 to 1996 to identify risk factors. Most cases were young males, ages 15 to 24, who usually committed suicide by hanging or gunshot. Psychiatric problems, such as depression, personality disorder, and drug abuse, were very common in these cases. A study of all suicides by Inuit that occurred between 2003 and 2006 found differences between these individuals and community-matched comparison persons who did not commit suicide (Chachamovich et al., 2015). Similar to findings in the previous study, Inuit who committed suicide were more likely to have been affected by depression or a personality disorder and be dependent on alcohol or cannabis. They also were more likely to have experienced abuse during childhood and to have family histories that included depression and suicide. As we describe in a later section, these factors are typically related to suicide in studies of the general population. The authors also noted a high prevalence of mental health problems among the community-comparison persons who did not commit suicide and called for improved access to mental health services for Inuit.

A study of suicidal ideation (thinking seriously about suicide) found similar patterns of results when comparing the population of non-Indigenous adults living in the Canadian provinces with adult Indigenous Peoples (Statistic Canada, 2016b). Data from the 2012 Canadian Community Health Survey-Mental Health Survey (CCHS-MH) and the 2012 Aboriginal Peoples Survey demonstrated that a greater proportion of off-reserve First Nations (21 percent), Métis (18 percent), and Inuit (22 percent) had seriously thought about suicide in their lifetime compared to the non-Indigenous Canadian population (12 percent). These surveys do not cover First Nations living on reserve, but a separate study indicated 16 percent of adult First Nations living on reserve had considered suicide in

their lifetime (First Nations Information Governance Centre [FNIGC], 2018b). In keeping with the findings discussed earlier regarding suicide attempts, for all groups in these studies, a greater proportion of women than men had seriously considered suicide in their lifetime.

The impact of residential schools on suicide ideation was examined for First Nations living on reserve (FNIGC, 2018a). The study examined four groups: First Nations not affected by residential schools, those who had at least one grandparent who attended, those with at least one parent who attended, and survivors (15 percent of First Nations had personally attended residential school). The proportion of adults who had seriously considered suicide in their lifetime varied considerably across the groups. Among adults, the proportion considering suicide in their lifetime was lowest among those not affected by residential schools (8.7 percent) and highest among those with at least one parent who had attended (21.6 percent). Survivors (16.6 percent) and those with at least one grandparent who attended (18.7 percent) also had higher proportions of those who seriously considered suicide compared with those not affected by residential schools.

CAUSES

Past Conceptions

The great sociologist Émile Durkheim (1951) defined several suicide types, based on the social or cultural conditions in which they occurred. One type is "formalized" suicides that were approved of, such as the ancient custom of *hara-kiri* in Japan, in which an individual who brought dishonour to himself or his family was expected to impale himself on a sword. Durkheim referred to this as *altruistic suicide*. Durkheim also recognized the loss of social supports as an important provocation for suicide; he called this *egoistic suicide*. (Seniors who kill themselves after losing touch with their friends or family fit into this category.) Magne-Ingvar, Ojehagen, and Traskman-Bendz (1992) found that only 13 percent of 75 individuals who had seriously attempted suicide had an adequate social network of friends and relationships. Similarly, a recent study found that suicide attempters perceived themselves to have lower social support than did those who did not attempt suicide (Riihimaki et al., 2013). *Anomic suicides* are the result of marked disruptions, such as the sudden loss of a high-prestige job. (*Anomie* is feeling lost and confused.) Finally, *fatalistic suicides* result from a loss of control over our own destiny. The mass suicide of 39 Heaven's Gate cult members is an example of this type, because the lives of those people were largely in the hands of Marshall Applewhite, a supreme and charismatic leader.

Durkheim's work was important in alerting us to the social contribution to suicide. Freud (1917, 1957) believed that suicide (and depression, to some extent) indicated unconscious hostility directed inward to the self rather than outward to the person or situation causing the anger. Indeed, suicide victims often seem to be psychologically punishing others who may have rejected them or caused some other personal hurt. Current thinking considers social and psychological factors but also highlights the potential importance of biological contributions.

RISK FACTORS

Edward Shneidman pioneered the study of risk factors for suicide (Shneidman, 1989; Shneidman et al., 1970). Among the methods he and others have used to study those conditions and events that make a person vulnerable is **psychological autopsy**. The psychological profile of the person who committed suicide is reconstructed through extensive interviews with friends and family members who are likely to know what the individual was thinking and doing in the period before death. This and other methods have allowed researchers to identify a number of risk factors for suicide.

Family History

If a family member committed suicide, the risk increases that someone else in the family will also (Brent et al., 2014; Mann et al., 2005). In fact, among depressed patients, the strongest predictor of suicidal behaviour was having a family history of suicide (Hantouche et al., 2010). This may not be surprising, because so many people who kill themselves are depressed, and depression runs in families. Nevertheless, the question remains: Are people who kill themselves simply adopting a familiar solution or does an inherited trait, such as impulsivity, account for increased suicidal behaviour in families? The possibility that something is inherited is supported by several adoption studies. One found an increased rate of suicide in the biological relatives of adopted individuals who had committed suicide, compared with a group of adoptees who had not committed suicide (Nock et al., 2011). Also, reviewing studies of adopted children and their biological and adopted families, Brent and Mann (2005) found that adopted individuals' suicidal behaviour was predicted only by suicidal behaviour in their biological relatives. In a small study of people whose twins had committed suicide, 10 out of 26 surviving monozygotic co-twins, and none of nine surviving dizygotic co-twins had themselves attempted suicide (Roy et al., 1995). This finding suggests some biological (genetic) contribution to suicide, even if it is relatively small.

Neurobiology

A variety of evidence suggests that low levels of serotonin may be associated with suicide and with violent suicide attempts (Cremniter et al., 1999; Pompili et al., 2010; Winchel et al., 1990). As we have noted, extremely low levels of serotonin are associated with impulsivity, instability, and the tendency to overreact to situations (Spoont, 1992). It is very possible then that low levels of serotonin may contribute to creating a vulnerability to act impulsively. This impulsiveness may include suicide, which is sometimes a very impulsive act. Studies by Brent and colleagues (2002) and Mann and colleagues (2005) suggest that transmission of vulnerabilities for a mood disorder, including the trait of impulsivity, may mediate family transmission of suicide attempts.

Existing Psychological Disorders

More than 90 percent of people who kill themselves have a psychological disorder (Conwell et al., 1996; Orbach, 1997). Suicide is often associated with mood disorders and for good reason. As many as 60 percent of suicides (75 percent of adolescent suicides) are associated with an existing mood disorder (Brent & Kolko, 1990; Frances et al., 1986). Lewinsohn, Rohde, and Seeley (1993) concluded that, in adolescents, suicidal behaviour is in large part an expression of severe depression. But many people with mood disorders do not attempt suicide. Analyses of the 2012 CCHS-MH revealed that only 6.6 percent of those Canadians 15 years of age or older with major depressive disorder attempted suicide in the past year compared to less than 1 percent of those without major depressive disorder (Patten et al., 2015). Conversely, some people who attempt suicide do not have mood disorders. Looking more closely at the relationship of mood disorder and suicide, some investigators have isolated hopelessness, a specific component of depression, as strongly predictive of suicide (Beck, 1986; Kazdin, 1983). Hopelessness also predicts suicide among individuals whose primary mental health problem is not depression (David Klonsky et al., 2012; Simpson et al., 2011).

Alcohol use and abuse are associated with approximately 25 to 50 percent of suicides and are particularly evident in suicide among college students (Lamis et al., 2010) and adolescents (Berman, 2009; Hawton et al., 2003; Pompili et al., 2012). Brent and colleagues (1988) found that about one-third of adolescents who commit suicide were intoxicated when they died and that many more might have been under the influence of drugs. Combinations of disorders, such as substance abuse and mood disorders in adults or mood disorders and conduct disorder in children and adolescents, seem to create a stronger vulnerability than any one disorder alone (Conwell et al., 1996; Nock, Hwang, et al., 2010; Woods et al., 1997). Woods and colleagues found that substance abuse combined with other risk-taking behaviours, such as getting into fights, carrying a gun, or smoking, were predictive of teenage suicide, possibly reflecting impulsivity in these troubled adolescents. A closely related trait termed *sensation-seeking* predicts teenage suicidal behaviour as well—beyond its relationship with depression and substance use (Ortin et al., 2012). Past suicide attempts are another strong risk factor and must be taken seriously (Berman, 2009). Cooper and colleagues (2005) followed for up to four years almost 8000 individuals who were treated in the emergency room for deliberate self-harm. Sixty of these people later killed themselves, which equates to 30 times the rate for the general population.

A disorder characterized more by impulsivity than depression is borderline personality disorder (see Chapter 13). Frances and Blumenthal (1989) suggest that these individuals, known for making manipulative and impulsive suicidal gestures without necessarily wanting to destroy themselves, sometimes kill themselves by mistake in as many as 10 percent of the cases. The combination of borderline personality disorder and depression is particularly deadly (Soloff et al., 2000).

Stressful Life Events

Perhaps the most important risk factor for suicide is a severe, stressful event experienced as shameful or humiliating, such as a failure (real or imagined) in school or at work, an unexpected arrest, or rejection by a loved one (Conwell et al., 2002; Joiner & Rudd, 2000). Physical and sexual abuse are also important sources of stress (Kirmayer et al., 1996; Wagner, 1997). New evidence now confirms that the stress and disruption of natural disasters increase the likelihood of suicide (Krug et al., 1998),

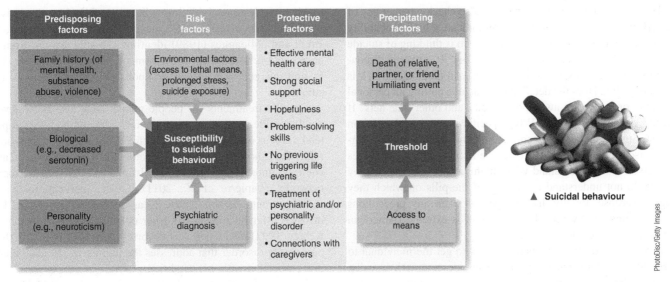

Predisposing factors	Risk factors	Protective factors	Precipitating factors

Family history (of mental health, substance abuse, violence)

Environmental factors (access to lethal means, prolonged stress, suicide exposure)

• Effective mental health care

• Strong social support

• Hopefulness

• Problem-solving skills

• No previous triggering life events

• Treatment of psychiatric and/or personality disorder

• Connections with caregivers

Death of relative, partner, or friend Humiliating event

Biological (e.g., decreased serotonin)

Susceptibility to suicidal behaviour

Threshold

Personality (e.g., neuroticism)

Psychiatric diagnosis

Access to means

▲ Suicidal behaviour

PhotoDisc/Getty Images

FIGURE 8.8 | Threshold model for suicidal behaviour.

particularly in the case of extreme catastrophes, like massive earthquakes (Matsubayashi et al., 2012). Based on data from 337 countries experiencing natural disasters in the 1980s, Krug and colleagues (1998) concluded that the rates of suicide increased 14 percent in the four years after severe floods, 31 percent in the two years after hurricanes, and 63 percent in the first year after an earthquake. Given preexisting vulnerabilities—including psychological disorders, traits of impulsiveness, and lack of social support—a stressful event can often put a person over the edge. An integrated model of the causes of suicidal behaviour is presented in ■ Figure 8.8.

IS SUICIDE CONTAGIOUS?

We hear all too often of the suicide of a teenager or celebrity. Most people react with sadness and curiosity. Some people react by attempting suicide themselves, often by the same method they have just heard about. Gould (1990) reported an increase in suicides during the nine days after widespread publicity about a suicide, and a recent review found a positive relationship between suicidal behaviour and exposure to media coverage related to suicide (Sisask & Varnik, 2012). Clusters of suicides (several people copying one person) seem to predominate among teenagers, with as many as 5 percent of all teenage suicides reflecting an imitation (Gould, 1990; Gould et al., 2003).

Why would anyone want to copy a suicide? First, suicides are often romanticized in the media: An attractive young person under unbearable pressure commits suicide and becomes a martyr to friends and peers by getting even with the (adult) world for creating such a difficult situation. Media accounts often describe in detail the methods used in the suicide, thereby providing a guide to potential victims. Little is reported about the paralysis, brain damage, and other tragic consequences of the incomplete or failed suicide or about the fact that suicide is almost always associated with a severe psychological disorder. More important, even less is said about the futility of this method

of solving problems (Gould, 1990; O'Carroll, 1990). To prevent these tragedies, the media should not inadvertently glorify suicides in any way, and mental health professionals must intervene immediately in schools and other locations with people who might be depressed or otherwise vulnerable to the contagion of suicide (Boyce, 2011). But it isn't clear that suicide is really contagious in the infectious disease sense. Rather, the stress of a friend's suicide or some other major stress may affect several individuals who are vulnerable because of existing psychological disorders (Blasco-Fontecilla, 2012; Joiner, 1999). Nevertheless, effective intervention is essential.

TREATMENT

Despite the identification of important risk factors, predicting suicide is still an uncertain art. Individuals with very few precipitating factors unexpectedly kill themselves, and many who live with seemingly insurmountable stress and illness and have little social support or guidance somehow survive and overcome their difficulties.

Mental health professionals are very thoroughly trained in assessing for possible suicidal ideation (Fowler, 2012; Joiner et al., 2007). Others might be reluctant to ask leading questions for fear of putting the idea in someone's head. We know, however, that it is far more important to check for these ideas than to do nothing, because the risk of inspiring suicidal thoughts is very small and the risk of leaving them undiscovered is enormous (Berman, 2009). Gould and colleagues (2005) found that more than 1000 high school students who were asked about suicidal thoughts or behaviours during a screening program showed no risk of increased suicidal thoughts compared with a second group of 1000 students who had the screening program without the questions about suicide. Therefore, if there is any indication whatsoever that someone is suicidal, the mental health professional will inquire, "Has there been any time recently when you've had some thoughts about hurting yourself or possibly killing yourself?"

The mental health professional will also check whether any of the risk factors are present that might indicate a high probability of suicide. For example, does a person who is thinking of suicide have a detailed plan or just a vague fantasy? If a plan is discovered that includes a specific time, place, and method, the risk is obviously high. Does the detailed plan include putting all personal affairs in order, giving away possessions, and other final acts? If so, the risk is higher still. What specific method is the person considering? Generally, the more violent the method (guns, hanging, poison, and so on), the greater the risk it will be used. Does the person really understand what might actually happen? Many people do not understand the effects of the pills on which they might overdose. Finally, has the person taken any precautions against being discovered? If so, the risk is extreme (American Psychiatric Association, 2003).

If a risk is present, clinicians attempt to get the individual to agree to or perhaps even sign a "no-suicide contract." Usually, this includes a promise not to do anything remotely connected with suicide without contacting the mental health professional first. Although signing a contract will not prevent a suicide attempt in someone who is determined, if the person at risk refuses a contract (or the clinician has serious doubts about the patient's sincerity) and the suicidal risk is judged to be high, immediate hospitalization is indicated, even against the will of the patient. Whether the person is hospitalized or not, treatment aimed at resolving underlying life stressors and treating existing psychological disorders should be initiated immediately.

In view of the public health consequences of suicide, many programs have been implemented to reduce the rates of suicide both in Canada and in other parts of the world. They include curriculum-based programs in which teams of professionals go into schools or other organizations to educate people about suicide and provide information on handling life stress. The United Kingdom targeted reducing suicide rates by 15 percent, and policymakers and mental health professionals are determining the best methods for achieving this goal (Lewis, Hawton, & Jones, 1997). More than 200 suicide prevention and crisis centres across Canada provide 24-hour phone service to people in crisis, including those considering suicide (Dyck & White, 1998). Some findings are encouraging, such as a study showing that suicide rates declined in the years following the establishment of suicide prevention centres in several cities (Lester, 1991). Unfortunately, however, most research indicates that such educational and crisis phone line programs are not effective (Garfield & Zigler, 1993; Shaffer et al., 1991). As Garfield and Zigler point out, hotline volunteers must be backed up by competent mental health professionals who can identify potentially serious risks.

More helpful are programs targeted to at-risk individuals, including adolescents in schools where a student has committed suicide. The Institute of Medicine (2002) recommends making services available immediately to friends and relatives of victims. In a study following a suicide in a high school, Brent and colleagues (1989) identified 16 students as strongly at risk and referred them for treatment. Another important step is limiting access to lethal weapons for anyone at risk for suicide.

Specific treatments for people at risk have also been developed. Suicide prevention programs for older adults, for example, tend to focus on decreasing risk factors (e.g., treating depression) rather than shoring up protective factors like familial support, and could be improved by greater involvement of individuals' social networks (Lapierre et al., 2011). Other interventions target specific mental health problems associated with suicide. For instance, Marsha Linehan and her colleagues (e.g., Linehan & Kehrer, 1993) developed a noteworthy treatment for borderline personality disorder that addresses the impulsive suicidal behaviour associated with this condition.

Emphasizing protective factors, such as culture and community, is likely critical to the success of programs developed for Indigenous Peoples in Canada. One study documented that among First Nations adults living on reserve and in northern communities, those who had never made a suicidal attempt reported higher levels of community wellness than those who had made a suicidal attempt (FNIGC, 2018b). First Nations emphasize the interconnections between mental wellness and factors such as language, land, family, and environment, and have embedded them in the First Nations Mental Wellness Continuum, a model to support First Nations mental health initiatives (Assembly of First Nations & Health Canada, 2015). Concerns about suicide rates among Inuit youth prompted the development of an intervention program for youth that was based on Inuit and community perspectives on health (Healey et al., 2016). The resulting camp program emphasized Inuit identity and cultural skill building, and early evaluations have documented its success in promoting wellness among the participants.

Empirical research indicates that cognitive-behavioural interventions can help decrease suicide risk. For example, in an important study, David Rudd and colleagues developed a brief psychological treatment targeting young adults who were at risk for suicide due to the presence of suicidal ideation accompanied by previous suicidal attempts or mood or substance use disorders (Rudd et al., 1996). Patients were assessed up to two years following treatment, and results indicated reductions in suicidal ideation and behaviour, as well as marked improvement in problem-solving ability. This program has now been expanded into the first psychological treatment for suicidal behaviour with empirical support for its efficacy (Rudd et al., 2001). The quest will go on to determine more effective and efficient ways of preventing one of the most serious consequences of any psychological disorder.

Before the *DSM-5*, if you met criteria for a major depressive episode in the two months following the loss of a loved one, you would not receive a diagnosis of major depressive disorder, even if you otherwise met the criteria for it (unless you had very severe symptoms, such as strong suicidal ideation or psychotic features). This was called the "bereavement exclusion." This exclusion was dropped in the *DSM-5* for several reasons (Zisook et al., 2012). For example, it was noted that major depressive episodes are often triggered by stressful events other than the loss of a loved one in vulnerable individuals, and, if all the criteria are otherwise met for a major depressive episode, there seemed no reason to exclude people simply because the precipitating event was the death of a loved one. Furthermore, data from a number of sources suggest no differences between depressive episodes triggered by loss or not triggered by loss, and the biological, psychological, and social factors that make one vulnerable to developing major depression are the same whether or not the trigger is the loss of a loved one (Shear et al., 2011; Zisook et al., 2012).

Lastly, the data indicated that eliminating the two months bereavement exclusion would not greatly increase the numbers of people requiring treatment for major depression (Gilman et al., 2012; Zisook et al., 2012).

Nevertheless, this change was controversial, since some concluded that the *DSM-5* would be making the natural grieving process a disorder resulting in, among other things, frequent prescriptions of antidepressant medication to those who might be undergoing a normal process of grieving (Fox & Jones, 2013; Maj, 2008). This is one part of the larger criticism levied at the *DSM-5* that the major purpose of the *DSM* is to increase business for mental health professionals and make sure that large drug companies remain profitable. Advocates for dropping the bereavement exclusion point out that the diagnosis of major depressive disorder or post-traumatic stress disorder in response to other major life stressors is not controversial, nor should be the development of major depressive disorder in some people in response to the loss of a loved one. Furthermore, the advocates continue, there are differences between a major depressive episode and grief. Individuals undergoing grief experience feelings of emptiness and loss, and these feelings come in waves sometimes referred to as the "pangs of grief," always triggered by thoughts of the loss of the loved one. Grieving individuals are usually able to experience some positive emotions, and even humour and self-esteem are generally intact. In a major depressive episode, feelings of depression are persistent and seldom accompanied by any positive emotions. Thought processes are typically very generally pessimistic and self-critical, accompanied by very low self-esteem and a sense of worthlessness (American Psychiatric Association, 2013).

In response, some mental health professionals propose that all intense sadness or stress—or even depression that is proportionate to the loss, the trauma, or the stress—should not be considered a disorder, since it is a natural experience of being human (Wakefield et al., 2007). Time will tell if removing the bereavement exclusion from the diagnosis of major depressive disorder is a positive or negative development.

SUMMARY

An Overview of Depression and Mania

- Mood disorders are among the most common psychological disorders, and the risk of developing them is increasing worldwide, particularly in younger people.
- Two fundamental experiences can contribute either singly or in combination to all the specific mood disorders: a major depressive episode and mania. A less severe episode of mania that does not cause impairment in social or occupational functioning is known as a *hypomanic episode*. An episode of mania coupled with anxiety or depression at the same time is known as a *mixed episode* or *mixed state*.

The Structure of Mood Disorders

- An individual who has episodes of depression is said to have a *unipolar disorder*. An individual who alternates between depression and mania has a *bipolar disorder*.

Depressive Disorders

- Major depressive disorder may be a single episode or recurrent, but it is always time limited; in another form of depression, persistent depressive disorder (dysthymia), the symptoms are often somewhat milder but remain relatively unchanged over long periods. In some cases, fewer symptoms are observed than in a major depressive episode, but they persist for at least two years (persistent depressive disorder); in other cases a major depressive episode will last at least two years (chronic major depressive episode). In cases of *double depression*, an individual experiences both major depressive episodes and persistent depressive disorder.
- Approximately 20 percent of bereaved individuals may experience pathological grief reaction, in which the normal grief response develops into a full-blown mood disorder.

Bipolar Disorders

- The key identifying feature of bipolar disorders is an alternation of manic episodes and major depressive episodes. *Cyclothymic disorder* is a milder but more chronic version of bipolar disorder.
- Patterns of additional features that sometimes accompany mood disorders, called specifiers, may predict the course or patient response to treatment, as does the temporal patterning or course of mood disorders. One pattern, seasonal affective disorder, often occurs in winter.

Prevalence of Mood Disorders

- Worldwide, approximately 16 percent of people experience major depressive disorder over their lifetime, and approximately 6 percent have experienced a major depressive disorder in the last year. The variability in prevalence rates may be accounted for by different research methods or perhaps decreasing rates reflect progress in the treatment of depression.
- Women are twice as likely as men to have mood disorders.

Lifespan Developmental Influences on Mood Disorders

- Mood disorders in children are fundamentally similar to mood disorders in adults.
- Symptoms of depression are increasing dramatically in older adults.
- The experience of depression across cultures varies, and it can be difficult to make comparisons, especially, for example, when we attempt to compare subjective feelings of depression.

Causes of Mood Disorders

- The causes of mood disorders lie in a complex interaction of biological, psychological, and social factors. From a biological perspective, researchers are particularly interested in the role of neurohormones. Psychological theories of depression focus on learned helplessness and depressive cognitive schemas as well as interpersonal disruptions.

Treatment

- A variety of treatments, both biological and psychological, have proven effective for mood disorders, at least in the short term. For those individuals who do not respond to antidepressant drugs or psychosocial treatments, a more dramatic physical treatment, *electroconvulsive therapy* (*ECT*), is sometimes used. Two psychological treatments—*cognitive therapy* and *interpersonal psychotherapy* (*IPT*)—seem to be effective in treating depressive disorders.
- Relapse and recurrence of mood disorders are common in the long term, and treatment efforts must focus as well on maintenance treatment, that is, on preventing relapse or recurrence.

Suicide

- Suicide is often associated with mood disorders but can occur in their absence or in the presence of other disorders. In adolescents it is the second-leading cause of death in Canada.
- In understanding suicidal behaviour, two indices are important: *suicidal attempts* (that are not successful) and *suicidal ideation* (serious thoughts about committing suicide). Important, too, in learning about risk factors for suicides is the psychological autopsy, in which the *psychological profile* of an individual who has committed suicide is reconstructed and examined for clues.
- Suicide is a significant problem in some Indigenous communities, and culture-specific prevention program appear to have promise.

KEY TERMS

antidepressant, 243
bipolar I disorder, 224
bipolar II disorder, 224
cognitive therapy, 246
cognitive triad, 238
complicated grief, 221
cyclothymic disorder, 225
disruptive mood dysregulation disorder, 221

double depression, 218
electroconvulsive therapy (ECT), 245
hypomanic episode, 216
integrated grief, 221
interpersonal psychotherapy (IPT), 247
learned helplessness theory of depression, 237

maintenance treatment, 248
major depressive disorder, 216
major depressive episode, 214
mania, 215
mixed features, 216
mood disorders, 214
neurohormones, 234
persistent depressive disorder (dysthymia), 216

premenstrual dysphoric disorder (PMDD), 221
psychological autopsy, 254
seasonal affective disorder (SAD), 220
suicidal attempts, 252
suicidal ideation, 252

ANSWERS TO CONCEPT CHECKS

8.1

1. e; **2.** a; **3.** c; **4.** d; **5.** b

8.2

1. electroconvulsive therapy; **2.** cognitive therapy; **3.** antidepressants; **4.** lithium; **5.** interpersonal psychotherapy; **6.** maintenance treatment

MEDIA RESOURCES

CENGAGE | MINDTAP

Stay organized and efficient with MindTap—a single destination with all the course material and study aids you need to succeed. Built-in apps leverage social media and the latest learning technology. For example:

- ReadSpeaker will read the text to you.
- Flashcards are pre-populated to provide you with a jump start for review—or you can create your own.
- You can highlight text and make notes in your MindTap Reader. Your notes will flow into Evernote, the electronic notebook app that you can access anywhere when it's time to study for the exam.
- Self-quizzing allows you to assess your understanding.

Visit login.cengage.com to start using MindTap. Enter the Online Access Code from the card included with your text. If a code card is not provided, you can purchase instant access at Cengage.ca.

Exploring Mood Disorders

> **Mania:** A frantic "high" with extreme overconfidence and energy, often leading to reckless behaviour
> **Depression:** A devastating "low" with extreme lack of energy, interest, confidence, and enjoyment of life

- Negative or positive life changes (death of a loved one, promotion, etc.)
- Physical illness

Trigger

© Prostock-studio/Shutterstock

Biological Influences

- Inherited vulnerability
- Altered neurotransmitters and neuro-hormonal systems
- Sleep deprivation
- Circadian rhythm disturbances

Social Influences

- Women and minorities—social inequality and oppression and a diminished sense of control
- Social support can reduce symptoms
- Lack of social support can aggravate symptoms

Causes

Behavioural Influences

Depression
- General slowing down
- Neglect of responsibilities and appearance
- Irritability; complaints about matters that used to be taken in stride

Mania
- Hyperactivity
- Reckless or otherwise unusual behaviour

PhotoDisc/Getty Images

Disorder

Emotional and Cognitive Influences

Depression
- Emotional flatness or emptiness
- Inability to feel pleasure
- Poor memory
- Inability to concentrate
- Hopelessness and/or learned helplessness
- Loss of sexual desire
- Loss of warm feelings for family and friends
- Exaggerated self-blame or guilt
- Overgeneralization
- Loss of self-esteem
- Suicidal thoughts or actions

Mania
- Exaggerated feelings of euphoria and excitement

© Nopphon_1987/Shutterstock

© Cengage Learning

TYPES OF MOOD DISORDERS

Depressive

Major Depressive Disorder

Symptoms of major depressive disorder:
- Begin suddenly, often triggered by a crisis, change, or loss
- Are extremely severe, interfering with normal functioning
- Can be long term, lasting months or years if untreated

Some people have only one episode, but the pattern usually involves repeated episodes or lasting symptoms.

Persistent Depressive Disorder

Long-term unchanging symptoms of mild depression, sometimes lasting 20 to 30 years if untreated. Daily functioning not as severely affected, but over time impairment is cumulative.

Double Depression

Periods of major depression and persistent depressive disorder

© gawrav/iStock

Bipolar

People who have a bipolar disorder live on an unending emotional roller coaster.

Types of Bipolar Disorders
- **Bipolar I**: major depression and full mania
- **Bipolar II**: major depression and hypomania
- **Cyclothymia**: milder depression with hypomania, chronic and long term

During the **depressive phase**, the person may:
- Lose all interest in pleasurable activities and friends
- Feel worthless, helpless, and hopeless
- Have trouble concentrating
- Lose or gain weight without trying
- Have trouble sleeping or sleep more than usual
- Feel tired all the time
- Feel physical aches and pains that have no medical cause
- Think about death or attempt suicide

During the **manic phase**, the person may:
- Feel extreme pleasure and joy from every activity
- Be extraordinarily active, planning excessive daily activities
- Sleep little without getting tired
- Develop grandiose plans leading to reckless behaviour: unrestrained buying sprees, sexual indiscretions, foolish business investments, etc.
- Have "racing thoughts" and talk on and on
- Be easily irritated and distracted

TREATMENT OF MOOD DISORDERS

Treatment for mood disorders is most effective and easiest when it's started early. Most people are treated with a combination of these methods.

Treatment

Medication

- Tricyclics (Tofranil, Elavil)
- Monamine oxidase inhibitors (MAOIs): (Nardil, Parnate); MAOIs can have severe side effects, especially when combined with certain foods or over-the-counter medications
- Selective-serotonin reuptake inhibitors or SSRIs (Prozac, Zoloft) are newer and cause fewer side effects than tricyclics or MAOIs
- Lithium is the preferred drug for bipolar disorder; side effects can be serious; and dosage must be carefully regulated

PhotoDisc/Getty Images

Cognitive-Behavioural Therapy

- Learn to replace negative depressive thoughts and attributions with more positive ones
- Develop more effective coping behaviours and skills

Interpersonal Psychotherapy

- Focus on the social and interpersonal triggers for their depression (such as the loss of a loved one)
- Develop skills to resolve interpersonal conflicts and build new relationships

© George Rudy/Shutterstock

Electroconvulsive Therapy (ECT)

- For severe depression, ECT is used when other treatments have been ineffective. It usually has temporary side effects, such as memory loss and lethargy. In some patients, certain intellectual and/or memory functions may be permanently lost.

Light Therapy

- For seasonal affective disorder

© Cengage Learning

09 | Eating

© Burger/Phanie/Science Source

I saw that I needed to work from the "inside out," from my feelings, my dreams, my angers, rather than from the "outside in," which began with my body.

—GENEEN ROTH, Feeding the Hungry Heart: The Experience of Compulsive Eating

STUDENT LEARNING OUTCOMES*

Use scientific reasoning to interpret behaviour:	› Identify basic biological, psychological, and social components of behavioural explanations (e.g., inferences, observations, operational definitions, and interpretations) (APA SLO 2.1A)
Engage in innovative and integrative thinking and problem solving:	› Describe problems operationally to study them empirically (APA SLO 2.3A)
Describe applications that employ discipline-based problem solving:	› Correctly identify antecedents and consequences of behaviour and mental processes (APA SLO 1.3b). Describe examples of relevant and practical applications of psychological principles to everyday life (APA SLO 1.3a)

*Portions of this chapter cover learning outcomes suggested by the American Psychological Association (2013) in its guidelines for the undergraduate psychology major. Chapter coverage of these outcomes is identified above by APA Goal and APA Suggested Learning Outcome (SLO).

Most of us take our bodies for granted. We wake up in the morning assuming we will be alert enough to handle our required daily activities; we eat two or three meals a day and perhaps some snacks in between; we may engage in some vigorous exercise, and, on some days, in sexual activity. We don't focus on our functioning to any great degree unless it is disrupted by illness or disease. And yet, psychological and social factors can significantly disrupt these important activities. In this chapter and the next chapter, we talk about psychological disruptions of two of our relatively automatic behaviours, eating and sleeping, which have substantial impact on the rest of our behaviour, including our psychological health.

OVERVIEW OF EATING DISORDERS

Although some of the disorders we discuss in this chapter can be deadly, many of us are not aware they are widespread. They began to increase during the 1950s or early 1960s and have spread insidiously over the ensuing decades. In **bulimia nervosa**, out-of-control eating episodes, or **binges**, are followed by self-induced vomiting, excessive use of laxatives, or other attempts to purge (get rid of) the food. In **anorexia nervosa**, the person eats only minimal amounts of food or exercises vigorously to offset food intake, so body weight sometimes drops dangerously. The chief characteristic of these related disorders is an overwhelming, all-encompassing drive to be thin.

Of the people with anorexia nervosa who are followed over an extended time, up to 20 percent die as a result of their disorder, with slightly more than 5 percent dying within ten years (e.g., Franko et al., 2013; Millar et al., 2005; Papadopoulos et al., 2009). In fact, anorexia nervosa has the highest mortality rate of any psychological disorder reviewed in this book, including depression (Papadopoulos et al., 2009; Park, 2007). From 20 to 30 percent of anorexia-related deaths are suicides, which is 50 times as high as the risk of death from suicide in the general population (Agras, 2001; Arcelus et al., 2011; Chavez & Insel, 2007; Thompson & Kinder, 2003). Suicide attempts are very common in people with eating disorders, occurring in from 30 to 40 percent of patients at least once during their lifetime (Bulik et al., 2008; Pisetsky et al., 2013).

Studies in different countries indicate that eating disorders are widespread and that they increased dramatically in Western countries from about 1960 to 1995, before seeming to level off somewhat according to the most recent data (Hoek, 2002; Russell, 2009; Steiger et al., 2013). In Switzerland, from 1956 to 1958, the number of new cases of anorexia nervosa under treatment among females between the ages of 12 and 25 was 4 per 100 000. There were 17 new cases per 100 000 from 1973 to 1975, a fourfold increase (Willi & Grossman, 1983). Similar results were found in Scotland by Eagles, Johnston, Hunter, Lobban, and Millar (1995) between 1965 and 1991; by Lucas, Beard, O'Fallon, and Kurlan (1991) in North America over a 50-year period; and by Moller-Madsen and Nystrup (1992) in Denmark between 1970 and 1989.

Most dramatic are the data for bulimia nervosa (Russell, 2009). Garner and Fairburn (1988) reviewed rates of referral to a major eating disorder centre in Toronto. Between 1975 and 1986, the referral rates for anorexia rose slowly, but the rates for bulimia rose dramatically—from virtually none to more than 140 per year. Similar findings have been reported from other parts of the world (Hay & Hall, 1991; Lacey, 1992). The reason for this increase is not known. Toronto researchers Paul Garfinkel and Barbara Dorian (2001) have suggested that it may relate to the increased prevalence of dieting and preoccupation with the body among young women who are simultaneously being exposed to social pressures toward consumption and incredible food availability.

Although reports of cases of eating disorders are documented throughout history, eating problems were not recognized as psychological disorders until relatively recently. In 1872, Sir William Withey Gull, a British physician, was the first to use the term *anorexia nervosa*. According to Canadian psychiatrists Sidney Kennedy and David Goldbloom (1996), the first Canadian description of anorexia nervosa appeared in the *Maritime Medical Journal* in 1895. The recognition of bulimia nervosa as a separate entity did not occur until much later, when the condition was described in the 1970s (e.g., Russell, 1979). Eating disorders were included for the first time as a separate group of disorders in the *DSM-IV*; before then, they had been classified as one of the disorders usually first diagnosed in infancy, childhood, or adolescence because of their typical onset in adolescence.

What makes this increase in eating disorders even more intriguing is that the increase tends to be culturally specific. Until recently, eating disorders, particularly bulimia, were not found in developing countries, where access to sufficient food is so often a daily struggle; only in the West, where food is generally plentiful, have they been rampant. Now this has changed; evidence suggests that eating disorders are going global. For example, the prevalence

▲ The Princess of Wales (now deceased) spoke candidly about her battle against bulimia.

in China and Japan is approaching those in Canada, the United States, and other Western countries (Chen & Jackson, 2008; Chisuwa & O'Dea, 2010; Jackson & Chen, 2011; Steiger et al., 2013). Not everyone in the world is at risk. Eating disorders tend to occur in a relatively small segment of the population. More than 90 percent of the severe cases are young females who live in a socially competitive environment. Perhaps the most visible example is the late Diana, Princess of Wales, who recounted her seven-year battle with bulimia (Morton, 1992). She reported bingeing and vomiting four or more times a day during her honeymoon. Canadian singer/songwriter Alanis Morissette has also revealed that she struggled with an eating disorder during her teenage years (McQueen, 2005).

The specificity of these disorders in terms of sex and age is unparalleled and makes the search for causes even more intriguing. In these disorders, unlike almost any other, the strongest contributions to etiology seem to be sociocultural rather than psychological or biological factors. We look in some detail at bulimia nervosa and anorexia nervosa. We then briefly consider binge-eating disorder.

BULIMIA NERVOSA

You may be familiar with bulimia nervosa from your own experience or a friend's. It is one of the most common psychological disorders on university campuses. Consider the case of Phoebe.

PHOEBE | *Apparently Perfect*

Phoebe was a popular, attractive, intelligent, and talented teenager. By the time she was finishing high school, she had accomplished a great deal. She was on the student council throughout her high school years, and she dated the captain of the football team. Phoebe had many talents, among them a beautiful singing voice and marked ability in ballet. Each year at Christmastime, her ballet company performed the *Nutcracker Suite*, and Phoebe attracted much attention with her poised performance in a lead role. She played on several of the school athletic teams. Phoebe maintained an A-minus average, was considered a model student, and was headed for a top-ranked university.

But Phoebe had a secret: She was haunted by her belief that she was fat and ugly. Every single bite of food that she put in her mouth was, in her mind, another step down the inexorable path that led to the end of her success and popularity. Phoebe had been concerned about her weight since she was 11. Ever the perfectionist, she began regulating her eating in junior high school. She would skip breakfast (over the protestations of her mother), eat a small bowl of pretzels at noon, and allow herself one-half of whatever she was served for dinner.

This behaviour continued into high school, as Phoebe struggled to restrict her eating to occasional binges on junk food. Sometimes she stuck her fingers down her throat after a binge (she even tried a toothbrush once), but this tactic was unsuccessful. In Grade 10, Phoebe reached her full adult height of 1.57 metres and weighed 50 kilograms; she continued to fluctuate between 48 and 50 kilograms throughout high school. By the time she was in Grade 12, Phoebe was obsessed with what she would eat and when. She used every bit of her willpower to restrict her eating, but occasionally she failed.

One day during the fall of Grade 12, she came home after school, and alone in front of the TV, she ate two big boxes of candy. Depressed, guilty, and desperate, she went to the bathroom and stuck her fingers farther down her throat than she had ever before dared. She vomited. And she kept vomiting. Although so physically exhausted that she had to lie down for half an hour, Phoebe had never in her life felt such an overwhelming sense of relief from the anxiety, guilt, and tension that always accompanied her binges. She realized that she had actually gotten to eat all that candy and now her stomach was empty. It was the perfect solution to her problems.

Phoebe learned very quickly what foods she could easily vomit. And she always drank lots of water. She began to restrict her eating even more and her bingeing increased.

This routine went on for about six months, until April of that same academic year. By this time, Phoebe had lost much of her energy, and her schoolwork was deteriorating. Her teachers noticed this and saw that she looked ill. She was continually tired, her skin was broken out, and her face puffed up, particularly around her mouth. Her teachers and mother suspected that she might have an eating problem. When they confronted her, she was relieved her problem was finally out in the open and stopped bingeing for a while. Mortally afraid of gaining weight and losing her popularity, however, Phoebe resumed her pattern, but she was now much better at hiding it. For six months, Phoebe binged and purged approximately 15 times a week.

When Phoebe went away to university that fall, things became more difficult. Now she had a roommate in residence to contend with, and she was more determined than ever to keep her problem a secret. Although the student health service offered workshops and seminars on eating disorders for first-year university students, Phoebe knew that she could not break her cycle without the risk of gaining weight. To avoid the communal bathroom in the residence, she went to a deserted place behind a nearby building to vomit.

She kept her secret until the beginning of her second year in university, when her world fell apart. One night, after drinking a lot of beer and eating fried chicken at a party, Phoebe attempted to cope with her guilt, anxiety, and tension in the usual manner, but when she tried to vomit, her gag reflex seemed to be gone. Breaking into hysterics, she called her boyfriend and told him she was ready to kill herself. Her loud sobbing and crying attracted the attention of her friends in her residence, who attempted to comfort her. She confessed her problem to them. She also called her parents. At this point, Phoebe realized that her life was totally out of control and that she needed professional help.

Clinical Description

The hallmark of bulimia nervosa is eating a large amount of food—typically, junk food rather than fruits and vegetables—and more than most people would eat under similar circumstances (Fairburn & Cooper, 2014; Wilson & Pike, 2001). Patients with bulimia readily identify with this description, even though the actual caloric intake for binges varies significantly from person to person (Franko et al., 2004). Just as important as the *amount* of food eaten is the fact that the eating is experienced as *out of control* (Fairburn & Cooper, 2014), a criterion that is an integral part of the definition of binge eating. Both criteria characterized Phoebe.

Another important criterion is that the individual attempts to *compensate* for the binge eating and potential weight gain, usually by **purging techniques**. Techniques include self-induced vomiting immediately after eating, as in the case of Phoebe, and using laxatives (drugs that relieve constipation) and diuretics (drugs that result in loss of fluids through greatly increased frequency of urination). While some use laxatives and diuretics, others attempt to compensate in other ways. Some fast for long periods between binges. Others exercise excessively. However, rigorous exercising is usually more characteristic of anorexia nervosa. Caroline Davis and colleagues at York University (Davis et al., 1997) found that 81 percent of a group of patients with anorexia nervosa exercised excessively, compared with 57 percent of a group of patients with bulimia nervosa. Activity levels increase at least a year before the development of full-blown anorexia nervosa, suggesting that excessive exercise may be an early warning sign for anorexia nervosa development (Davis et al., 2005).

Bulimia nervosa was subtyped in the *DSM-IV-TR* into purging type and nonpurging type (exercise or fasting). But the nonpurging type has turned out to be rare, accounting for only 6 to 8 percent of patients with bulimia (Hay & Fairburn, 1998; Striegal-Moore et al., 2001). A study by Paul Garfinkel and colleagues in Toronto compared purging versus nonpurging bulimics (Garfinkel et al., 1996). In comparison with nonpurging bulimics, those who purged developed their eating disorder at a younger age and had higher rates of comorbid depression, anxiety disorders, and alcohol abuse, as well as higher rates of earlier sexual abuse. However, other studies have found little evidence of any differences between purging and nonpurging types of bulimia, leading some to question whether this manner of subtyping is useful (e.g., Franko et al., 2004). As a result, this distinction was dropped in the *DSM-5*.

Purging is not a particularly efficient method of reducing caloric intake (Fairburn, 2013). Vomiting reduces approximately 50 percent of the calories that were just consumed, less if it is delayed at all (Kaye et al., 1993); laxatives and related procedures have very little effect, acting, as they do, so long after the binge (Fairburn, 2013).

One of the more important additions to the *DSM-IV-TR* that was maintained in the *DSM-5* is the specification of a psychological characteristic clearly present in Phoebe (see DSM Table 9.1). Despite her accomplishments and success, she felt her continuing popularity and self-esteem would be determined largely by the weight and shape of her body. Paul Garfinkel (1992) noted that, of 107 women seeking treatment for bulimia nervosa, only 3 percent did not share this attitude. Recent investigations confirm the construct validity of the diagnostic category of bulimia nervosa, suggesting that the major features of the disorder (bingeing, purging, overconcern with body shape, etc.) cluster together in someone with this problem (Bulik et al., 2000; Fairburn & Cooper, 2014; Franko et al., 2004).

Medical Consequences

Chronic bulimia with purging has a number of medical consequences (Russell, 2009). One is salivary gland enlargement caused by repeated vomiting, which gives the face a chubby

DSM-5	**Table 9.1** Diagnostic Criteria for Bulimia Nervosa

A. Recurrent episodes of binge eating. An episode of binge eating is characterized by both of the following:

   1. Eating, in a discrete period of time (e.g., within any 2-hour period), an amount of food that is definitely larger than most people would eat during a similar period of time and under similar circumstances.

   2. A sense of lack of control over eating during the episode (e.g., a feeling that one cannot stop eating or control what or how much one is eating).

B. Recurrent inappropriate compensatory behaviors in order to prevent weight gain, such as self-induced vomiting; misuse of laxatives, diuretics or other medications; fasting; or excessive exercise.

C. The binge eating and inappropriate compensatory behaviors both occur, on average, at least once a week for 3 months.

D. Self-evaluation is unduly influenced by body shape and weight.

E. The disturbance does not occur exclusively during episodes of anorexia nervosa.

Source: Reprinted with permission from the *Diagnostic and Statistical Manual of Mental Disorders*, Fifth Edition (Copyright © 2013). American Psychiatric Association. All Rights Reserved.

appearance. This was very noticeable with Phoebe. Repeated vomiting also may erode the dental enamel on the inner surface of the front teeth. More important, continued vomiting may upset the chemical balance of bodily fluids, including sodium and potassium levels. This condition, called an *electrolyte imbalance*, can result in serious medical complications if unattended, including cardiac arrhythmia (disrupted heartbeat) and renal (kidney) failure, both of which can be fatal. Surprisingly, young women with bulimia also develop more body fat than age- and weight-matched healthy controls (Ludescher et al., 2009), the very effect they are trying to avoid. Normalization of eating habits will quickly reverse the imbalance. Intestinal problems resulting from laxative abuse are also potentially serious; they can include severe constipation or permanent colon damage. Finally, some individuals with bulimia have marked calluses on their fingers or the backs of their hands caused by the friction of contact with the teeth and throat when repeatedly using their fingers to stimulate the gag reflex.

Associated Psychological Disorders

A community study of households across Ontario demonstrated links between eating disorders and both mood and anxiety disorders (Garfinkel et al. 1995; Woodside et al., 2001). Overall, both men and women with bulimia usually present with additional psychological disorders, particularly anxiety and mood disorders (O'Brien & Vincent, 2003; Woodside et al., 2001). In the 2002 Canadian Community Health Survey (CCHS), about half of people who met the criteria for eating problems (which include bulimia) had an anxiety or mood disorder as well (Meng & D'Arcy, 2015). We compared 20 patients with bulimia nervosa to 20 individuals with panic disorder and another 20 with social phobia (Schwalberg et al., 1992). The most striking finding was that 75 percent of the patients with bulimia also presented with an anxiety disorder, such as social phobia or generalized anxiety disorder; patients with anxiety disorders, in contrast, did not necessarily have an elevated rate of eating dis-orders. Mood disorders, particularly depression, also commonly co-occur with eating disorders (e.g., Dunkley & Grillo, 2007). For several years, one prominent theory suggested that eating disorders are simply a way of expressing depression. But almost all evidence indicates that depression follows bulimia and may be a reaction to it (Steiger et al., 2013).

Some research suggests a high prevalence of borderline personality disorder in patients with bulimia (e.g., Cassin & von Ranson, 2005). Researchers at Simon Fraser University noted an association between eating disorder symptoms and non-suicidal self-injury in their online survey (Turner et al., 2015). Last, substance abuse commonly accompanies bulimia nervosa and vice versa (Stewart & Brown, 2007). For example, Stewart, Brown, Theakston, Devoulyte, and Larsen (2003) studied 58 women receiving treatment for alcoholism through Addiction Prevention and Treatment Services in the Capital District Health Authority in Nova Scotia. Seventy-one percent of the women reported binge eating, with 91 percent of those displaying binge-eating patterns that clinicians would consider severe. In a study by Kristin von Ranson at the University of Calgary and colleagues, eating disorders were associated with nicotine dependence in adolescent girls and with alcohol abuse in adult women

(von Ranson et al., 2002). Toronto psychiatrists Allan Kaplan and Blake Woodside have examined smoking across the eating disorders and have shown that those with binge-purge types of eating disorders smoke the most and that smoking is related to impulsive personality traits (Anzengruber et al., 2006). Research by Elliot Goldner and colleagues in Vancouver suggests that bulimia may also be related to other behaviours suggesting poor impulse control, such as compulsive shoplifting (Goldner et al., 2000). In sum, bulimia seems related to anxiety disorders, mood disorders, substance use disorders, borderline personality, and impulsivity.

ANOREXIA NERVOSA

Like Phoebe, the overwhelming majority of individuals with bulimia are within 10 percent of their normal weight (Fairburn & Cooper, 2014; Hsu, 1990). In contrast, individuals with anorexia nervosa (which literally means a "nervous loss of appetite," an incorrect name because appetite often remains healthy) differ in one important way from individuals with bulimia. They are so successful at losing weight that they put their lives in considerable danger. Both anorexia and bulimia are characterized by a morbid fear of gaining weight and losing control over eating. The major difference seems to be whether the individual is successful at losing weight. People with anorexia are proud of both their diets and their extraordinary control, and they usually do not see themselves as having an illness. People with bulimia are ashamed of both the problem itself and their lack of control, and they tend to be secretive about their bulimic symptoms. The denial of illness in anorexia and the shame and secrecy in bulimia mean that people with eating disorders do not seek treatment as early as they should. Consider the case of Julie.

JULIE | *The Thinner the Better*

Julie was 17 years old when she first came for help. If you looked hard enough past her sunken eyes and pasty skin, you could see that she had once been attractive. But at present, she looked emaciated and unwell. Eighteen months earlier she had been overweight, weighing almost 65 kilograms at 1.55 metres. Her mother, a well-meaning but overbearing and demanding woman, nagged Julie incessantly about her appearance. Her friends were kinder but no less relentless. Julie, who had never had a date, was told by a friend she was cute and would have no trouble at all getting dates if she lost some weight. So she did. After many previous unsuccessful attempts, she was determined to succeed this time.

After several weeks on a strict diet, Julie noticed she was losing weight. She felt a control and mastery that she had never known before. It wasn't long before she received positive comments, not only from her friends but also from her mother. Julie began to feel good about herself. The difficulty was that she was losing weight too fast. She stopped menstruating. But now nothing could stop her from dieting. By the time she reached our clinic, she weighed 35 kilograms, but she thought she looked fine and, perhaps, could even stand to lose a bit more weight. Her parents had just begun to worry about her. In fact, Julie did not initially seek treatment for her eating behaviour. Rather, she had developed a numbness in her left lower leg and a left foot drop that a neurologist determined was caused by peritoneal nerve paralysis believed to be related to inadequate nutrition. The neurologist referred her to our clinic.

Like most people with anorexia, Julie said she probably should put on a little weight, but she didn't mean it. She thought she looked fine but she had "lost all taste for food," a report that may not have been true, because most people with anorexia crave food at least some of the time but control their cravings. Nevertheless, she was participating in most of her usual activities and continued to do extremely well in school and in her extracurricular pursuits. Her parents were happy to buy her most of the workout videotapes available, and she began doing one every day, and then two. When her parents suggested she was really exercising enough, perhaps too much, she worked out when no one was around. After every meal, she exercised with a workout tape until, in her mind, she had burned up all the calories she had just taken in.

Responses to the current physical fitness and exercise craze can become extreme for female athletes (Davis & Strachan, 2001). Perhaps the best-known example was world-class gymnast Christy Henrich, who died of kidney failure at the age of 22. Christy weighed approximately 43 kilograms at the peak of her career. Later, during repeated hospitalizations for anorexia, Christy had to be physically restrained to prevent excessive exercise; like Julie, she exercised to the point of exhaustion if given half a chance. When she died in 1994, Christy weighed only 30 kilograms. Elaine Tanner, who represented Canada in swimming at the Commonwealth Games, the Pan-Am Games, and the Olympics in the 1960s (winning 15 medals and setting new records), also developed anorexia after competing in the Olympics at age 17 (Bornath, 2002). She was finally able to overcome her disorder, but it took 19 years. The tragic consequences of anorexia among young performers and athletes and within the modelling world have also been well publicized in the media. In November 2006, 21-year-old Brazilian model Ana Carolina Reston died, weighing just 40 kilograms.

Clinical Description

Bulimia nervosa is more common than anorexia, but they have a great deal of overlap. For example, many individuals with bulimia have a history of anorexia; that is, they once used fasting to reduce their body weight below desirable levels (Fairburn & Cooper, 2014; Fairburn et al., 1997; Mitchell & Pyle, 1988).

Although decreased body weight is the most notable feature of anorexia nervosa, it is not the core of the disorder. Many people lose weight because of a medical condition, but people with anorexia have an intense fear of obesity and relentlessly pursue thinness (Bruch, 1986; Fairburn & Cooper, 2014; Russell, 2009). As with Julie, the disorder most commonly begins in an adolescent who is actually overweight or who perceives herself to be. She then starts a diet that escalates into an obsessive preoccupation with being thin. She continues to see herself as overweight despite her weight loss. In fact, a study by Randi McCabe at McMaster University showed that patients with anorexia nervosa have a tendency to overestimate their body weight (McCabe et al., 2001). Dramatic weight loss is achieved through severe caloric restriction or by combining caloric restriction and purging.

The *DSM-5* specifies two subtypes of anorexia nervosa (see DSM Table 9.2). In the *restricting type*, individuals diet to limit calorie intake; in the *binge-eating/purging type*, they rely on purging. Unlike individuals with bulimia, individuals with binge-eating/purging binge on relatively small amounts of food and purge more consistently, in some cases each time they eat. Approximately half the individuals who meet the criteria for anorexia engage in binge eating and purging (Fairburn & Cooper, 2014; Garfinkel et al., 1979). Prospective data collected over eight years on 136 individuals with anorexia reveal few differences between these two subtypes on severity of symptoms or personality (Eddy et al., 2002). At that time, 62 percent of the restricting subtype had begun bingeing or purging. Another study showed few differences between these subtypes and comorbidity with anxiety disorders (Kaye et al., 2014).

DSM-5	**Table 9.2** Diagnostic Criteria for Anorexia Nervosa

A. Restriction of energy intake relative to requirements, leading to a significantly low body weight in the context of age, sex, developmental trajectory, and physical health. *Significantly low weight* is defined as a weight that is less than minimally normal or, for children and adolescents, less than that minimally expected.

B. Intense fear of gaining weight or of becoming fat, or persistent behavior that interferes with weight gain, even though at a significantly low weight.

C. Disturbance in the way in which one's body weight or shape is experienced, undue influence of body weight or shape on self-evaluation, or persistent lack of recognition of the seriousness of the current low body weight.

Specify whether:

Restricting type: During the last 3 months, the individual has not engaged in recurrent episodes of binge eating or purging behavior (i.e., self-induced vomiting or the misuse of laxatives, diuretics, or enemas). This subtype describes presentations in which weight loss is accomplished primarily through dieting, fasting, and/or excessive exercise.

Binge-eating/purging type: During the last 3 months, the individual has engaged in recurrent episodes of binge eating or purging behavior (i.e., self-induced vomiting or the misuse of laxatives, diuretics, or enemas).

Thus, subtyping may not be useful in predicting the future course of the disorder but rather may reflect a certain phase or stage of anorexia, a finding confirmed in a more recent study (Eddy et al., 2008). For this reason, *DSM-5* criteria specify that subtyping refers only to the last three months (Peat et al., 2009).

An individual with anorexia is never satisfied with his or her weight loss. Staying the same weight from one day to the next or gaining any weight is likely to cause intense panic, anxiety, and depression. Only continued weight loss every day for weeks on end is satisfactory. Although *DSM-5* criteria specify only "significantly low weight," one study suggests that body mass index (BMI) averages close to 16 by the time treatment is sought (Berner et al., 2013). Another key criterion of anorexia is a marked disturbance in body image—the way a person sees and feels about her body. When Julie looked at herself in the mirror, she saw something very different from what others saw. Others saw an emaciated, sickly, frail girl in the throes of semistarvation. Julie saw a girl who needed to lose at least a few kilograms from some parts of her body. For Julie, her face and buttocks were the problems. Other girls might focus on other parts, such as the arms or legs or stomach.

After seeing numerous doctors, people like Julie become good at saying what others expect to hear. They may agree they are underweight and need to gain a few kilograms—but they don't really believe it themselves. Question them further and they will tell you that the person in the mirror is fat. For this reason, individuals with anorexia seldom seek treatment on their own. Usually, pressure from somebody in the family leads to the initial visit, as in Julie's case. Some anorexic individuals show increased interest in cooking and food. Some have become expert chefs, preparing all the food for the family. Others hoard food in their rooms, looking at it periodically.

Medical Consequences

One common medical complication of anorexia nervosa is cessation of menstruation (amenorrhea), which also occurs relatively often in bulimia (Crow et al., 2002). This feature can be an objective physical index of the degree of food restriction but is inconsistent because it does not occur in all cases (Franko et al., 2004). Because of this inconsistency, amenorrhea was dropped as a diagnostic criterion in the *DSM-5*. Other medical signs and symptoms of anorexia include dry skin, brittle hair or nails, and sensitivity to or intolerance of cold temperatures. Also, it is relatively common to see *lanugo*, downy hair on the limbs and cheeks. Cardiovascular problems, such as chronically low blood pressure and heart rate, can also result. If vomiting is part of the anorexia, electrolyte imbalance and resulting cardiac and kidney problems can result, as in bulimia (Mehler et al., 2010).

Associated Psychological Disorders

As with bulimia nervosa, anxiety disorders and mood disorders are often present in individuals with anorexia (Agras, 2001; Garfinkel et al., 1996; O'Brien & Vincent, 2003; Russell, 2009). One that seems to co-occur frequently is obsessive-compulsive disorder (OCD; Cederlöf et al., 2015; Kaye et al., 2014; Keel

▲ Many women with anorexia develop an obsessive preoccupation with being thin.

▲ These women are at different stages of anorexia.

et al., 2004). In anorexia nervosa, unpleasant thoughts are focused on gaining weight and the individual engages in a variety of behaviours, some of them ritualistic, to rid herself of such thoughts. Future research will determine whether anorexia and OCD are truly similar or simply resemble each other. Substance abuse is also common in individuals with anorexia nervosa (Keel et al., 2003; Root et al., 2010; Stewart & Brown, 2007; Swanson et al., 2011) and, in conjunction with anorexia, is a strong predictor of mortality, particularly by suicide.

BINGE-EATING DISORDER

Recent research has focused on a group of individuals who experience marked distress from binge eating but do not engage in extreme compensatory behaviours and therefore cannot be diagnosed with bulimia. These individuals have **binge-eating disorder (BED)**. After classification in the *DSM-IV* as a disorder needing further study, BED is now included as a full-fledged disorder in the *DSM-5* (see DSM Table 9.3). Evidence that supports its elevation to disorder status includes somewhat different patterns of heritability compared with other eating disorders (Bulik et al., 2000), as well as a greater likelihood of occurring in males and a later age of onset. There is also a greater likelihood of remission and a better response to treatment of BED compared with other eating disorders (Striegel-Moore & Franko, 2008; Wonderlich et al., 2009).

Individuals who meet preliminary criteria for BED are often found in weight-control programs. For example, Brody, Walsh, and Devlin (1994) studied mildly obese participants in a weight-control program and identified 19 percent who met the criteria for BED. In other programs, with participants ranging in degree of obesity, close to 30 percent met the criteria (Spitzer et al., 1993). But Hudson and colleagues (2006) concluded that BED is a disorder caused by a separate set of factors from obesity without BED and is associated with more severe obesity. The general consensus is that about 20 percent of obese individuals in weight-loss programs engage in binge eating, with the number rising to approximately 50 percent among candidates for bariatric surgery (stomach surgery to correct severe or morbid obesity). Fairburn, Cooper, Doll, Norman, and O'Connor (2000) identified 48 individuals with BED and were able to prospectively follow 40 of them for five years. The prognosis was relatively good for this group, with only 18 percent retaining the full diagnostic criteria for BED. The percentage of this group who were obese, however, increased from 21 to 39 percent at the five-year mark. Crossing over to bulimia is very common among individuals with BED (Allen et al., 2013; Stice et al., 2013).

About half of individuals with BED try dieting before bingeing, and half start with bingeing and then attempt to diet (Abbott et al., 1998); those who begin bingeing first become more severely affected by BED and are more likely to have additional disorders (Brewerton et al., 2014; Spurrell et al., 1997). It's also increasingly clear that individuals with BED have some of the same concerns about shape and weight as people with anorexia and bulimia, which distinguishes them from individuals who are obese without BED (Fairburn & Cooper, 2014; Goldschmidt et al., 2010; Grilo et al., 2010; Steiger et al., 2013). It seems that approximately 33 percent of those with BED binge to alleviate "bad moods" or negative affect (Grilo et al., 2001; Steiger et al., 2013; Stice et al., 2000). These individuals are more psychologically disturbed than the 67 percent who do not use bingeing to regulate mood (Grilo et al., 2001).

DSM-5	**Table 9.3** Diagnostic Criteria for Binge-Eating Disorder

A. Recurrent episodes of binge eating. An episode of binge eating is characterized by both of the following:

1. Eating, in a discrete period of time (e.g., within any 2-hour period), an amount of food that is definitely larger than what most people would eat in a similar period of time under similar circumstances.

2. A sense of lack of control over eating during the episode (e.g., a feeling that one cannot stop eating or control what or how much one is eating).

B. The binge-eating episodes are associated with three (or more) of the following:

1. Eating much more rapidly than normal.

2. Eating until feeling uncomfortably full.

3. Eating large amounts of food when not feeling physically hungry.

4. Eating alone because of feeling embarrassed by how much one is eating.

5. Feeling disgusted with oneself, depressed, or very guilty afterward.

C. Marked distress regarding binge eating is present.

D. The binge eating occurs, on average, at least once a week for 3 months.

E. The binge eating is not associated with the recurrent use of inappropriate compensatory behavior as in bulimia nervosa and does not occur exclusively during the course of bulimia nervosa or anorexia nervosa.

Source: Reprinted with permission from the *Diagnostic and Statistical Manual of Mental Disorders*, Fifth Edition (Copyright © 2013). American Psychiatric Association. All Rights Reserved.

Concept Check 9.1

Check your understanding of eating disorders by identifying the proper disorder in the following scenarios: (a) bulimia nervosa, (b) anorexia nervosa, and (c) binge-eating disorder.

1. Manny has been having episodes lately when he eats prodigious amounts of food. He's been putting on a lot of weight because of it. _____

2. I noticed Elena eating a whole pie, a cake, and two bags of potato chips the other day when she didn't know I was there. She ran to the bathroom when she finished and it sounded like she was vomiting. _____

3. Joo-Yeon eats large quantities of food in a short time. She then takes laxatives and exercises for long periods to prevent weight gain. She has been doing this almost daily for several months and feels she will become worthless and ugly if she gains even the slightest weight. _____

4. Kirsten has lost several kilograms and now weighs less than 40 kilograms. She eats only a small portion of the food her mother serves her and fears that intake above her current 500 calories daily will make her fat. Since losing the weight, Kirsten has stopped having periods. She sees a fat person in the mirror. _____

Clear cases of bulimia have been described for thousands of years (Parry-Jones & Parry-Jones, 2002), but bulimia nervosa was recognized as a distinct psychological disorder only in the 1970s (Boskind-Lodahl, 1976; Russell, 1979). Therefore, information on prevalence has been acquired relatively recently.

We have already noted that the overwhelming majority (90 to 95 percent) of individuals with bulimia are women. The 5 to 10 percent of cases who are male have a slightly later age of onset, and a large minority are predominantly males of minority sexual orientation (Matthews-Ewald, 2014; Rothblum, 2002). Research by D. Blake Woodside and colleagues in Toronto indicates that men with eating disorders are similar in most respects to women with eating disorders (Woodside et al., 2001). One place that men and women with eating disorders may differ, however, is in personality risk factors, such as perfectionism (Woodside et al., 2004). In addition to men with a gay or bisexual orientation, male athletes in sports that require weight regulation, such as wrestling, are another group of males with eating disorders. More recent studies suggest that the incidence among males is increasing (Dominé et al., 2009; Field et al., 2014). Interestingly, the gender imbalance in bulimia was not always present. Historians of psychopathology note that for hundreds of years, the vast majority of (unsystematically) recorded cases were male (Parry-Jones & Parry-Jones, 1994, 2002). Because women with bulimia are overwhelmingly preponderant today, most of our examples are of women.

Age of onset for bulimia is typically 16 to 19 years (Fairburn et al., 1997; Garfinkel et al., 1995), although signs of impending bulimic behaviour can occur much earlier, as in Phoebe's case. Among women, adolescent girls are most at risk. A prospective eight-year survey of 496 adolescent girls reported that more than 13 percent experienced some form of eating disorder by the time they were 20 (Stice et al., 2009, 2013). In another elegant prospective study, the eating-related problems of 1498 freshmen women at a large university were studied over the four-year college experience. Only 28 to 34 percent had no eating-related concerns. But 29 to 34 percent consistently attempted to limit their food intake because of weight/shape concerns; 14 to 18 percent engaged in overeating and binge eating; another 14 to 17 percent combined attempts to limit intake with binge eating; and 6 to 7 percent had pervasive bulimic-like concerns. These tendencies were stable for the most part throughout their four years of college (Cain et al., 2010).

A somewhat different view of the prevalence of bulimia comes from studies of the population as a whole rather than of specific groups of adolescents. In one comprehensive study, sampling more than 8000 individuals between the ages of 15 and 64 in Ontario, the lifetime prevalence was 1.46 percent for women and 0.13 percent for men (Woodside et al., 2001). Another 1.70 percent of women and 0.95 percent of men showed partial syndromes in which they displayed some of the symptoms of bulimia nervosa, but not enough to meet the full *DSM-5* diagnostic criteria (Woodside et al., 2001). In a study in New Zealand (Bushnell et al., 1990), the lifetime prevalence of bulimia nervosa among women ages 18 to 44 years was 1.6 percent. However, the rate was substantially higher among younger women. For instance, among women ages 18 to 24, the prevalence was 4.5 percent. Among women ages 25 to 44, the prevalence was 2 percent, but it was only 0.4 percent among women ages 45 to 64. Numbers seem to be highest in urban areas (Hoek et al., 1995).

In an important prevalence study by Kendler and colleagues (1991), 2163 twins (more than 1000 sets of twins) were interviewed, and the lifetime prevalence of bulimia nervosa was found to be 2.8 percent, increasing to 5.3 percent when marked bulimic symptoms that did not meet full criteria for the disorder were included. Once again, the prevalence was greatest in younger women. As is evident in ■ Figure 9.1, the risk was much higher for females born after 1960 than for females born before 1960. Nevertheless, as pointed out by Fairburn and colleagues (Fairburn & Beglin, 1990; Fairburn et al., 1993), estimates are probably low because many individuals with eating disorders refuse to participate in studies. Therefore, the percentages represent only those individuals who consented to participate in the survey.

After bulimia develops, it tends to be chronic if untreated (Fairburn et al., 2003); one study by Todd Heatherton and colleagues shows the drive for thinness and accompanying symptoms were still present in a group of women ten years after diagnosis (Joiner et al., 1997). In an important study of the course of bulimia, referred to earlier, Fairburn and colleagues identified a group of 102 females with bulimia nervosa and followed 92 of them prospectively for five years. About one-third improved to the point where they no longer met diagnostic criteria each year, but another third who had improved previously had then relapsed.

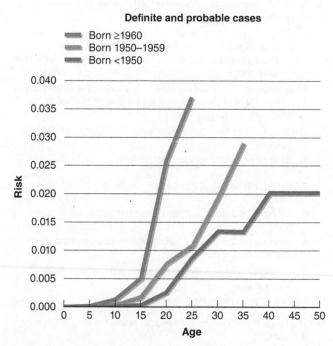

FIGURE 9.1 | Lifetime cumulative risk for bulimia among female twins.

Source: From K.S. Kendler, C. MacLean, M. Neale, R. Kessler, A. Heath, and L. Eaves, "The genetic epidemiology of bulimia nervosa," *American Journal of Psychiatry*, vol. 148(12), December 1991, pp. 1627–1637. Reprinted with permission from the American Journal of Psychiatry (Copyright © 1991). American Psychiatric Association. All Rights Reserved.

Between 50 and 67 percent evidenced serious eating disorder symptoms at the end of each year of the five-year study, indicating that this disorder has a relatively poor prognosis. In a follow-up study, Fairburn et al. (2003) reported that the strongest predictors of persistence were a history of childhood obesity and a continuing overemphasis on the importance of being thin. In addition, individuals tend to retain their bulimic symptoms instead of shifting to other eating disorder symptomatology (Keel et al., 2000).

The same high percentage (90 to 95 percent) of individuals with anorexia are female, with onset also in adolescence, usually around the age of 15 (Fairburn, Cooper, et al., 1999; Herzog, 1988). Studies cited in the beginning of this chapter noted the increase in rates of anorexia, particularly in the 1960s and 1970s. Walters and Kendler (1995) have analyzed data from the same 2163 twins mentioned earlier to determine the prevalence of anorexia nervosa. The results indicate that 1.6 percent met criteria for lifetime prevalence and this figure increased to 3.7 percent with the inclusion of marked anorexic symptoms that did not meet full criteria for the disorder. The comprehensive study of households in the province of Ontario (Woodside et al., 2001) reported lifetime prevalence of 0.66 percent for women and 0.16 percent for men, with an additional 1.15 percent of women and 0.76 percent of men having partial syndromes (i.e., most but not all symptoms required for a diagnosis). Once anorexia develops, its course seems chronic—although not so chronic as bulimia, based on data from Hudson and colleagues (2007), particularly if it is identified early and treated. But individuals with anorexia tend to maintain a low BMI over a long period, along with distorted perceptions of shape and weight, indicating that even if they no longer meet criteria for anorexia they continue to restrict their eating (Fairburn & Cooper, 2014). Perhaps for this reason, anorexia is thought to be more resistant to treatment than bulimia, based on clinical studies (Vitiello & Lederhendler, 2000). In one seven-year study following individuals who had received treatment, 33 percent of those with anorexia versus 66 percent of those with bulimia reached full remission at some point during the follow-up (Eddy et al., 2008).

There is more information about the prevalence of all eating disorders taken together. About one million Canadians have an eating disorder according to Canada's National Institute for Eating Disorders (NIED, 2019). In the 2012 CCHS—Mental Health, 0.4 percent of Canadians over 15 years of age reported that they have a diagnosed eating disorder (Statistics Canada, 2019). The Canadian Institute for Health Information (CIHI, 2019) tracks discharges from hospitals for a number of health conditions and report rates out of 100 000 people. For the years 2017–2018, CIHI estimates that 5.77 in every 100 000 Canadians were discharged from hospital with a primary diagnosis of an eating disorder, and this rate is 10 times as high in women than in men.

Cross-Cultural Considerations

We have already discussed the very culturally specific nature of anorexia and bulimia. A particularly striking finding is that these disorders develop in immigrants who have recently moved to Western countries (Anderson-Fye, 2009; Nasser, 1988). One of the more interesting classic studies is Nasser's survey of 50 Egyptian women in London universities and 60 Egyptian women in Cairo universities. None of the women studied in Cairo had eating disorders, but 12 percent of the Egyptian women in England had developed eating disorders. Mumford, Whitehouse, and Platts (1991) found the same result with Asian women living in North America. The prevalence of eating disorders varies somewhat among most North American minority populations. Earlier surveys revealed that black adolescent girls have less body dissatisfaction, fewer weight concerns, and a more positive self-image, and perceive themselves to be thinner than they actually are, compared with Caucasian adolescent girls (Celio et al., 2002). Major risk factors for eating disorders in all groups include being overweight, being in a higher social class, and acculturating to the Western majority (Crago et al., 1997; Raich et al., 1992; Smith & Krejci, 1991; Wilfley & Rodin, 1995).

One culturally determined difference in criteria for eating disorders has been reported by Lee, Leung, Wing, Chiu, and Chen (1991). In traditional Chinese cultures, it has been widely assumed that being slightly plump is highly valued, with ideals of beauty focused on the face rather than the body. Therefore, in this group, acne was more often reported as a precipitant for anorexia nervosa than was a fear of being fat, and body image disturbance was rare (Lee et al., 1992). Patients said they refused to eat because of feelings of fullness or pain, although it is possible they related food intake to their skin conditions. Beyond that, they met all criteria for anorexia. More recent studies, however, call into question these affirmations (Kawamura, 2002). Leung, Lam, and Sze (2001) analyzed data from the Miss Hong Kong Beauty Pageant from 1975 to 1999 and found that winners were taller and thinner than the average Chinese woman, with a curvaceous narrow-waist-and-full-hip body shape. They note that this ideal matches depictions of beauty in classical Chinese literature, and it challenges the notion that plumpness is valued, at least in Hong Kong.

In Japan, the prevalence of anorexia nervosa among teenage girls is still lower than the rate in North America but, as mentioned previously, it seems to be increasing. The need to be thin or the fear of becoming overweight has not been as important in Japanese culture as it is in North America, although this may be changing as cultures around the world become more Westernized (Kawamura, 2002). Body image distortion and denial that a problem exists are clearly present in Japanese patients who have the disorder (Ritenbaugh et al., 1993).

An interesting study by Madhulika Gupta and colleagues at the University of Western Ontario compared weight-related body image concerns in young women ages 18 to 24 years in Canada and in India (Gupta et al., 2001). This cross-cultural study found that women's overall levels of the core eating disorder features of drive for thinness and body dissatisfaction did not differ between the two cultures. However, body image concerns presented slightly differently in the two samples. In the Canadian women, body dissatisfaction was related to concerns about the weight of the abdomen, hips, thighs, and legs. In the Indian women, in contrast, body dissatisfaction was related to concerns about the weight of the face, neck, shoulders, and chest (i.e., upper torso).

▲ Anorexia seldom occurs among North American black women.

In conclusion, anorexia and bulimia are relatively homogeneous, and both—particularly bulimia—were overwhelmingly associated with Western cultures until recently. In addition, the frequency and pattern of occurrence among minority Western cultures differed somewhat in the past, but those differences seem to be diminishing (Marques et al., 2011; Pike et al., 2014).

Developmental Considerations

Because the overwhelming majority of cases begin in adolescence, it is very clear that anorexia and bulimia are strongly related to development (McVey et al., 2002; Polivy et al., 2003; Steiger et al., 2013). As pointed out in classic studies by Striegal-Moore, Silberstein, and Rodin (1986) and Attie and Brooks-Gunn (1995), differential patterns of physical development in girls and boys interact with cultural influences to create eating disorders. After puberty, girls gain weight primarily in fat tissue, whereas boys develop muscle and lean tissue. As the ideal look in Western countries is muscular for men and thin for women, physical development brings boys closer to the ideal and takes girls farther away.

Eating disorders, particularly anorexia nervosa, occasionally occur in children under the age of 11 (Walsh, 2010). In those rare cases of young children developing anorexia, they are likely to restrict fluid intake, as well as food intake, perhaps not understanding the difference (Gislason, 1988; Walsh, 2010). This is particularly dangerous. Concerns about weight are somewhat less common in young children. Nevertheless, negative attitude toward being overweight emerges as early as three years of age, and more than half of girls ages six to eight would like to be thinner (Striegel-Moore & Franko, 2002). By nine years of age, 20 percent of girls reported trying to lose weight, and by age 14, 40 percent were trying to lose weight (Field et al., 1999). Another study followed girls and boys for 10 years starting around age 12 and found that about 55 percent of the girls at age 12 were dieting and about 59 percent were dieting at age 22. Further, they found that extreme weight-control behaviours increased over time in this group with a particular increase between adolescence and young adulthood (Neumark-Sztainer et al., 2011).

Both bulimia and anorexia can occur in later years, particularly after the age of 55. Hsu and Zimmer (1988) reported that most of these individuals had had an eating disorder for decades with little change in their behaviour. In a few cases, however, onset did not occur until later years, and it is not yet clear what factors were involved. Generally, concerns about body image decrease with age (Peat et al., 2008; Tiggemann & Lynch, 2001; Whitbourne & Skultety, 2002).

A new eating disorder listed in *DSM-5* does not involve concerns about appearance: **avoidant/restrictive food intake disorder (ARFID)**. It involves a lack of interest in eating food, oversensitivity to certain aspects of food (e.g., smell, taste, colour), or concerns about consequences of eating (e.g., choking). It is usually detected in infants and children and may persist in adulthood. This is a dangerous condition because children may experience weight loss and nutritional deficiencies, leading to growth delay and problems with learning. This disorder can also lead to other eating disorders later in life (Katzman et al., 2016).

Debra Katzman, at the Hospital for Sick Children in Toronto, conducted important research on restrictive eating in children, even before this disorder appeared in *DSM-5*. Using the Canadian Paediatric Surveillance Program survey, she and her colleagues reported that restrictive eating (which would include a diagnosis of anorexia) was seen by pediatricians in 2.6 cases per 100 000 people, six times more often in girls than in boys. About half of children showed growth delay, and many required hospital admission (Pinhas et al., 2011). Many of these children appeared to have typical anorexia (62 percent), but the researchers noted that some of these children did not have concerns about their body image and would likely meet a diagnosis of ARFID after the *DSM-5* was in use. More recently, Katzman and colleagues (2018) used the Surveillance Program specifically to study ARFID. Almost 40 percent of the patients identified were male—a proportion much higher than is usually found among those with eating disorders.

CAUSES OF EATING DISORDERS

As with all the disorders discussed in this book, biological, psychological, and social factors contribute to the development of these serious eating disorders, but the evidence is increasingly clear that the most dramatic factors are social and cultural. Here we focus on bulimia, anorexia, and binge eating disorders.

SOCIAL DIMENSIONS

Remember that anorexia and particularly bulimia are the most culturally specific psychological disorders yet diagnosed. What drives so many young people into a punishing and life-threatening routine of semistarvation or purging? For many young women, looking good is more important than being healthy. In fact, for young females in competitive environments, self-worth, happiness, and success are determined to a large extent by body measurements and percentage of body fat, factors that have little or no correlation with personal happiness and success in the long run. The cultural imperative for thinness directly results in dieting, the first dangerous step down the slippery slope to anorexia and bulimia.

What makes the modern emphasis on thinness in women even more puzzling is that standards of desirable body sizes change much like fashion styles in clothes, if not as quickly (Cash & Pruzinsky, 2002). Several groups of investigators have documented this phenomenon in some interesting ways. Garner, Garfinkel, Schwartz, and Thompson (1980) collected data from *Playboy* magazine centrefolds and from contestants in major beauty pageants from 1959 to 1978. During this period, both *Playboy* centrefolds and the beauty pageant contestants became significantly thinner. Bust and hip measurements became smaller, although waists became somewhat larger, suggesting a change in what is considered desirable in the shape of the body in addition to weight. The preferred shape during the 1960s and 1970s was thinner and more tubular than before (Agras & Kirkley, 1986). Wiseman, Gray, Mosimann, and Ahrens (1992) updated the research, collecting data from 1979 to 1988, and reported that 69 percent of the *Playboy* centrefolds and 60 percent of the beauty pageant contestants weighed 15 percent or more below normal for their age and height, actually meeting one of the criteria for anorexia. Data from both studies are presented in ■ Figure 9.2. More recently, Rubinstein and Caballero (2000) compiled data on weight and height from beauty pageant winners from 1922 through 1999 and found that most of these winners since the 1970s would be considered undernourished.

Levine and Smolak (1996) referred over 20 years ago to "the glorification of slenderness" in magazines and on television,

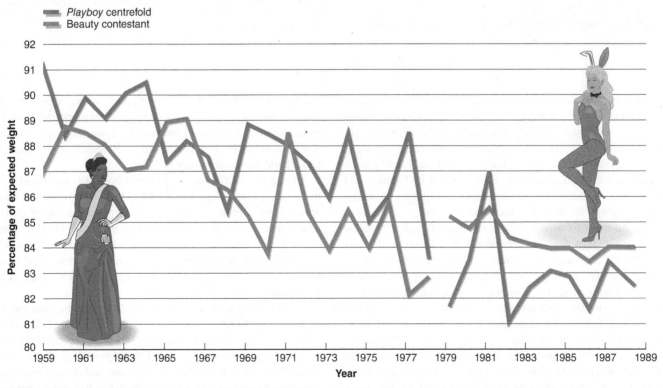

FIGURE 9.2 | Average percentage of expected weight of Playboy centrefolds and contestants in a major North American beauty pageant, 1959–1988.

Source: From "Cultural Expectations of Thinness in Women: An Update" by C. V. Wiseman and J. J. Gray, J. E. Mosimann and A. H. Ahrens, 1992, *International Journal of Eating Disorders, 11*(1), 85–89. © 1992 by John Wiley & Sons, Inc.

Wasted: A Memoir of Anorexia and Bulimia
by Marya Hornbacher

Marya Hornbacher begins her memoir, "It was a landmark event: We were having lunch. We were playing normal."

Those who believe that eating lunch is "playing normal" will recognize Marya's story. At age five, contrary to all appearances, she believed that she was fat. At age nine, she was bingeing and purging while watching *Brady Bunch* reruns. Hornbacher recounts in (sometimes grisly) detail the journey from self-conscious little girl to full-grown woman bent on self-inflicted starvation. At her all-time low, she weighs 24 kilograms and is still not sure that she's thin enough.

How does she get to that point? Hornbacher traces the influence her parents had on her self-image. She also recognizes the pressures of her peers and of society, and the limitations of her own personality. She points out that "junior high is an unpleasant experience for many people" (p. 65)— and certainly most people can relate to that. In fact, many young women can probably relate to some of the feelings of self-loathing in this memoir. But most do not hate their bodies with such ferocity that they willingly commit to starve themselves. When a schoolmate tells the school counsellor that Hornbacher is throwing up, "As mad as I said I was at the time, I had never been so grateful for anything in my life. . . . I was worth giving a shit about" (p. 81).

She describes in wrenching detail the cult-like, lonely world of eating disorders in which nearly every waking thought centres on food, exercise, and weight loss. She views the prospect of attending boarding schools with questions like, "How will I throw up without offending? How will I do my callisthenics at night while reading a book?" (p. 101).

For Hornbacher, the underlying issue is one of self-control; she wants to limit her needs. "I distinctly did not want to be seen as bulimic. I wanted to be an anorectic. . . . a person whose passions were ascetic rather than hedonistic" (p. 107). She believes that the issue of self-control resonates most with women: "We claim a loss of appetite, a most-sacred aphysicality" (p. 118) and "we turn skeletons into goddesses and look to them as if they might teach us how to not-need" (p. 119).

Hornbacher is very intelligent and has done a lot of research on anorexia and bulimia. Her narrative is peppered with facts about eating disorders and the people who experience them. She knows, for example, the telltale signs of bulimia. She has included a comprehensive bibliography at the end of her book. Yet she still has an eating disorder herself. In the final pages, to bring the reader up to speed on her present-day struggles, she tells of running on the treadmill for an hour and a half, "until my bad knee feels like it's exploding with every step, but I have lost weight!" (p. 288). Although she doesn't give us the happy ending we're hoping for, she does provide a realistic glimpse into the struggle with food that she still faces every day.

Source: Text excerpts from *Wasted: a memoir of anorexia and bulimia* by Marya Hornbacher, published by HarperCollins Publishers Inc. Copyright © 1998 by Marya Hornbacher-Beard.

---

where the vast majority of females are thinner than the average North American woman. Because overweight men are two to five times more common as television characters than overweight women, the message from the media to be thin is clearly aimed at women; the message got through loud and clear and is still getting through. Grabe, Ward, and Hyde (2008) reviewed 77 studies and demonstrated a strong relationship between exposure to media images depicting the thin-ideal body and body image concerns in women. An analysis of prime-time situation comedies revealed that 12 percent of female characters were dieting and many were making disparaging comments about their body image (Tiggemann, 2002). Interestingly, a recent analysis of images of women in *Ebony* magazine, which has a wide African-American readership, generally does not show this thin-ideal body image, seemingly reflecting the somewhat lower prevalence of body image disturbances in African-American women (Thompson-Brenner et al., 2011). Stice, Schupak-Neuberg, Shaw, and Stein (1994) established a strong relationship between amount of media exposure and eating disorder symptomatology in university women. In another study, girls who watched eight or more hours of TV per week reported significantly greater body dissatisfaction than girls who watched less TV (Gonzalez-Lavin & Smolak, 1995; Levine & Smolak, 1996). Finally, Thompson and Stice

(2001) found that risk for developing eating disorders was directly related to the extent to which women internalize or buy in to media messages and images glorifying thinness, a finding also confirmed by Cafri, Yamamiya, Brannick, and Thompson (2005) and Keel and Forney (2013).

During the 1920s, the ideal female body was similar in shape to the ideal today (Agras & Kirkley, 1986); however, this shape was achieved through fashion (e.g., through the use of girdles) rather than dieting. In fact, no diet articles appeared in the magazines of the period that were sampled, whereas today we see what Brownell and Rodin (1994) have called "the dieting maelstrom," in which health professionals, the media, and a powerful diet and food industry all have stakes.

The problem with today's standards is that they are increasingly difficult to achieve, because the size and weight of the average woman has increased over the years with improved nutrition; size has also generally increased throughout history (Brownell, 1991; Brownell & Rodin, 1994). Whatever the cause, the collision between our culture and our physiology has had some very negative effects, one of which is that women are no longer satisfied with their bodies.

A second clear effect is the dramatic increase, especially among women, in dieting and exercise to achieve what may, in fact, be an impossible goal. Look at the increase in dieting since the 1950s. Dwyer, Feldman, Seltzer, and Mayer reported in 1969 that more than 80 percent of female high school students in Grade 12 wanted to lose weight and that 30 percent were dieting. Among their male counterparts, fewer than 20 percent wanted to lose weight and only 6 percent were dieting. Hunicutt and Newman (1993) surveyed a sample of 3632 students in Grades 8 and 10 and found that 61 percent of females and 28 percent of males were dieting. Although these studies are not directly comparable, younger girls typically diet less than older girls, suggesting that the increase in dieting is even more dramatic.

In a classic case study, Fallon and Rozin (1985) studied male and female undergraduates and found that men rated their current size, their ideal size, and the size they figured would be most attractive to the opposite sex as approximately equal; indeed, they rated their ideal body weight as *heavier* than the weight females thought most attractive in men (see ■ Figure 9.3). Women, however, rated their current figures as much heavier than the most attractive, which, in turn, was rated as heavier than the ideal.

A study by Forestell, Humphrey, and Stewart (2004) at Dalhousie University using figures similar to those displayed in Figure 9.3 showed that undergraduate women are particularly

critical of women's hip size when making evaluations of physical attractiveness. An additional interesting finding from the Fallon and Rozin (1985) study was that women's judgment of ideal female body weight was less than the weight that men thought was most attractive. This conflict between reality and fashion seems most closely related to the current epidemic of eating disorders. In fact, the efforts of some people to maintain thin, athletic shapes are almost superhuman. Contestants in major beauty pageants work out an average of 14 hours per week, with some exercising 35 hours per week (Trebbe, 1979).

We have information on how these attitudes about body image are socially transmitted in adolescent girls. Paxton, Schutz, Wertheim, and Muir (1999) explored the influence of close friendship groups on attitudes concerning body image, dietary restraint, and extreme weight-loss behaviours. In a very clever study, the authors identified 79 different friendship cliques in a group of 523 adolescent girls. They found that these friendship cliques tended to share the same attitudes toward body image, dietary restraint, and the importance of attempts to lose weight. In other words, if your friends tend to use extreme dieting or other weight-loss techniques, there is a greater chance that you will, too (Hutchinson & Rapee, 2007). A recent, more definitive study concludes that while young girls do tend to share body image concerns, these friendship cliques do not necessarily cause these attitudes or the disordered eating that follows. Rather, adolescent girls simply tend to choose friends who already share these attitudes (Rayner et al., 2012). Nevertheless, any attempts to treat eating disorders must take into account the influence of

▲ Changing concepts of ideal weight are evident in a 17th-century painting by Peter Paul Rubens and in a recent photograph of fashion models.

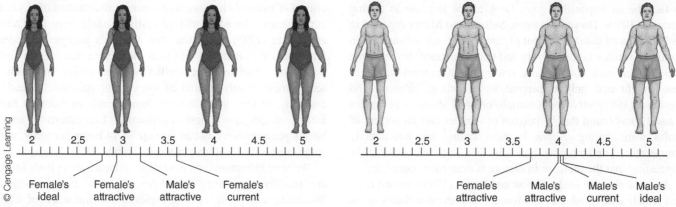

FIGURE 9.3 | Male and female ratings of body size.

Source: Based on Stunkard, Sorensen, and Schulsinger, 1980.

the social network in maintaining these attitudes.

Most people who diet don't develop eating disorders, but Patton, Johnson-Sabine, Wood, Mann, and Wakeling (1990) determined in a prospective study that adolescent girls who dieted were eight times as likely to develop an eating disorder one year later as those who weren't dieting. Telch and Agras (1993) noted marked increases in bingeing during and after rigorous dieting in 201 obese women. Stice, Cameron, Killen, Hayward, and Taylor (1999) demonstrated that one of the reasons that attempts to lose weight may lead to eating disorders is that weight reduction efforts in adolescent girls are more likely to result in weight gain than weight loss. To establish this finding, 692 girls, initially the same weight, were followed for four years. Girls who

ABNORMAL PSYCHOLOGY   VIDEO

Anorexia Nervosa: Susan

"Basically . . . I don't want to eat because it seems like, as soon as I eat, I just gain weight, get fat. . . . There are some times when I can't stop it, I just have to, and then, once I eat, there is a strong urge to either purge or take a laxative. . . . It never stops. . . . It becomes very obsessive, where you're getting on the scales ten times a day. . . . I weigh 96 pounds [43 kilograms] now."

Visit login.cengage.com to start using MindTap. Enter the Online Access Code from the card included with your text. If a code card is not provided, you can purchase instant access at Cengage.ca.

attempted dieting faced a more than 300 percent greater risk of obesity than those who did not diet. Results are presented in ■ Figure 9.4.

Why does dieting cause weight gain? Cottone and colleagues (2009) began feeding rats junk food, which the rats came to love, instead of a boring diet of pellets. They then withdrew the junk food but not the pellets. Based on observations of brain function compared with rats that never had junk food, it was clear that these rats became extremely stressed and anxious. Furthermore, the junk food rats began eating more of the pellets than the control group, and this behaviour then seemed to relieve the stress. Thus, repeated cycles of "dieting" seem to produce stress-related withdrawal symptoms in the brain, much like other addictive substances, resulting in more eating than would have occurred without dieting.

It is not yet entirely clear why dieting leads to bingeing in some people but not all. A daily diary study by Howard Steiger and colleagues at the Douglas Hospital Eating Disorders Unit in Montréal showed that patients' attempts to limit and control their dietary intake contributed to binge cravings but were not direct antecedents to binge-eating episodes (Engelberg et al., 2005). The researchers concluded that dietary restraint sets the stage for binge eating (Urbszat et al., 2002) but does not necessarily trigger its occurrence. Instead, factors like negative affect may operate to

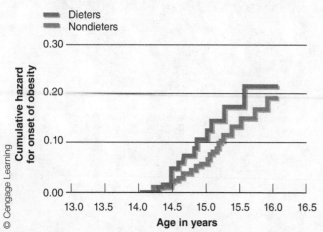

FIGURE 9.4 | Cumulative hazard curves for the onset of obesity for self-labelled dieters versus self-labelled nondieters.

Source: From Stice et al., 1999.

trigger individual binge-eating episodes (as discussed earlier) among those who are currently restricting their dietary intake.

The work of Janet Polivy and C. Peter Herman at the University of Toronto has contributed much to our understanding of the negative consequences of chronic dieting. Their early lab-based work showed how a broken diet can readily lead to a binge in women who chronically restrict their diets (Polivy & Herman, 1985). Their more recent work focuses on the more general negative psychological impacts of dieting, such as low self-esteem, food preoccupation, and negative mood—a phenomenon they have labelled the "false hope syndrome" (Polivy, 2001; Polivy & Herman, 2002; Trottier et al., 2005). In brief, this perspective asserts that people's false hopes about self-change attempts are initially strongly reinforced. Recall the praise that Julie received from her friends and her mother when she first started to lose weight. Unfortunately, the positive feelings and sense of control that people feel with their initial successes at self-change lead them to continue to pursue unrealistic or even impossible goals for weight loss that ultimately result in extreme disappointment and a decline in self-esteem (see also Polivy & Heatherton, 2015).

The conflict over body image would be bad enough if size were infinitely malleable, but it is not. Increasing evidence indicates a strong genetic contribution to body size (e.g., Livesley et al., 2005; Rutherford et al., 1993); that is, some of us are born to be heavier than others, and we are all shaped differently. Although most of us can be physically fit, very few can achieve the levels of fitness and shape so highly valued today. It is biologically nearly impossible (Brownell, 1991; Brownell & Fairburn, 2002). Nevertheless, many young people in our society fight biology to the point of starvation. In adolescence, cultural standards are often experienced as peer pressure and are much more influential than reason and fact. The high number of gay men among the relatively small numbers of males with eating disorders has also been attributed to pressures in the gay culture to be physically trim (Carlat et al., 1997; Feldman & Meyer, 2007). Conversely, pressure to appear more fit and muscular are also very apparent for a substantial proportion of men (Pope et al., 2000).

If cultural pressures to be thin are as important as they seem to be in triggering eating disorders, then such disorders would be expected to occur where these pressures are particularly severe, which is the case with ballet dancers, who are under extraordinary pressures to be thin. In an important study, Garner, Garfinkel, Rockert, and Olmsted (1987) followed a group of 11- to 14-year-old female students in an internationally acclaimed ballet school in Toronto. Their conservative estimate was that at least 25 percent of these girls developed eating disorders during the two years of the study. In another study, Szmukler, Eisler, Gillis, and Haywood (1985) examined 100 adolescent female ballet students in London, England. Seven percent were diagnosed with anorexia nervosa, and an additional 3 percent were borderline cases. Another 20 percent had lost a significant amount of weight, and 30 percent were clearly afraid of becoming fat, although they were actually below normal weight (Garner & Garfinkel, 1985). All these figures are much higher than in the population as a whole.

Similar results are apparent among athletes, particularly females, such as gymnasts, figure skaters, and tennis players (Davis & Strachan, 2001). For example, in a study of 41 female Canadian competitive figure skaters, Gail Taylor and Diane Ste-Marie of the University of Ottawa found that all the figure skaters had used weight-control measures at some point in their lives. About 93 percent reported that they perceived weight-loss pressures to be associated with the sport of figure skating (Taylor & Ste-Marie, 2001). And in a study of female gymnasts, Gretchen Kerr and colleagues at the University of Toronto found that disordered eating patterns were particularly common among those gymnasts who had received negative comments about their weight (Kerr et al., 2006).

The case of Canadian tennis player Carling Bassett illustrates how weight-loss pressures in competitive athletics can serve as triggers for an eating disorder. Bassett was Canada's leading female tennis player in the 1980s and was inducted into Canada's Sports Hall of Fame. She experienced a three-year bout of bulimia, which she developed as a teenager while she was competing professionally. "At fifteen, I wasn't heavy by any means" she told a reporter, "but I gained a lot of weight; I went from 111 to 126 [pounds; 51 to 57 kilograms]. At fourteen, fifteen, sixteen . . . you want to look good all the time. You start feeling pressure" (Neill & Sider, 1992). Bassett was introduced to self-induced vomiting as a weight-control strategy at age 16 by an older female tennis player. She said about purging: "It's so easy to get into and so hard to get out of. I hated myself that I couldn't stop." Her mother recalls the negative impact the eating disorder had on Bassett and her family: "She became skeletal. You'd try to force food on her, and she'd just throw up. We screamed and yelled." Bassett kept her eating disorder hidden from other tennis players, even from her husband, tennis star Robert Seguso, until her symptoms became so disruptive that she attempted recovery with Seguso's help (Neill & Sider, 1992).

Courtesy of Janet Polivy

▲ Janet Polivy is a clinical psychologist at the University of Toronto. Her work with C. Peter Herman has contributed significantly to the understanding of why chronic dieting is so closely linked with binge eating and eating disorders.

PHOEBE | Dancing to Destruction

Phoebe remembered very clearly that during her early years in ballet, the older girls talked incessantly about their weight. Phoebe performed very well and looked forward to the rare compliment. In fact, the ballet mistress seemed to comment more on weight than on dance technique, often remarking, "You'd dance better if you lost weight." If one little girl managed to lose a kilogram through heroic dieting, the instructor always pointed it out: "You've done well working on your weight; the rest of you had better follow this example." One day, without warning, the instructor said to Phoebe, "You need to lose three kilograms before the next class." At that time Phoebe was 1.57 metres and weighed 44 kilograms. The next class was in two days. After one of these admonitions and several days of restrictive eating, Phoebe experienced her first uncontrollable binge.

Early in high school, Phoebe gave up the rigours of ballet to pursue a variety of other interests. She did not forget the glory of her starring roles as a young dancer or how to perform the steps. She still danced by herself sometimes and retained the grace that serious dancers effortlessly display. But in university, as she stuck her head in the toilet bowl, vomiting for perhaps the third time that day, she realized that she had learned one lesson in ballet class more deeply and thoroughly than any other—the life-or-death importance of being thin at all costs.

Family matters too. Several clinicians and investigators in decades past (Attie & Brooks-Gunn, 1995; Bruch, 1985; Humphrey, 1989; Minuchin et al., 1978) observed that the "typical" anorexic's family is successful, hard driving, concerned about external appearances, and eager to maintain harmony. To accomplish these goals, family members often deny or ignore conflicts or negative feelings and tend to attribute their problems to other people at the expense of frank communication among themselves (Fairburn, Shafran, & Cooper, 1999).

Pike and Rodin (1991) confirmed some differences in interactions within the families of girls with disordered eating in comparison with other families. Mothers of girls with disordered eating seemed to act as "society's messengers" in wanting their daughters to be thin, at least initially (Steinberg & Phares, 2001). They were very likely to be dieting themselves and, generally, were more perfectionistic than other mothers in that they were less satisfied with their families and family cohesion (Fairburn et al., 1997, 1999).

A study by D. Blake Woodside and colleagues reported similar findings from data collected in the international Price Foundation family study of eating disorders. Participants were recruited from London, Los Angeles, Munich, New York, Philadelphia, Pittsburgh, and Toronto. Mothers of those girls with eating disorders showed elevated levels of perfectionism and more concerns about weight and shape than did other mothers (Woodside et al., 2002). Other family studies by Howard Steiger and colleagues demonstrated that a link exists between the abnormal eating attitudes of daughters and their mothers (Steiger et al., 1996) and that family preoccupation with appearance had a direct influence on body dissatisfaction and eating disorder symptoms (Leung et al., 1996). Caroline Davis and colleagues in Toronto and Hamilton have shown that family preoccupation with appearance exerts its greatest negative effects in influencing weight preoccupation in more anxiety-prone young women (Davis et al., 2004).

Lynn Carpenter is the mother of the late Sheena Carpenter—a young woman who died of starvation in Toronto at age 22. Lynn has spoken about the role of parents' attitudes toward weight and shape in inadvertently triggering eating disorder behaviours in their children. Sheena had wanted to be a model or an actor. When she died, she weighed only 23 kilograms. In a candid interview, Lynn Carpenter talked about the role she believes she had in initiating her daughter's illness: "Sheena didn't stand a chance. I always had body issues, so she grew up with me always griping about my cellulite. Always negative." These messages about the importance of being thin reportedly had an effect on Sheena quite early in life. Lynn recalled an event that took place when Sheena was only six years old. On a hot summer day, Lynn found Sheena dressed in a snowsuit and doing jumping jacks. "Look, Mom," Sheena said, "This way I won't put on any weight." But Lynn Carpenter was not the sole messenger in relaying society's message about the importance of low body weight to her daughter. Apparently, when Sheena was 14 years old, a modelling agency told her a thinner face would make her more photogenic. Sheena Carpenter's tragic story led to her mother establishing a refuge in Toronto called Sheena's Place, which offers support programs and group sessions to women with eating disorders (sheenasplace.org).

Whatever the pre-existing relationships, after the onset of an eating disorder, particularly anorexia, family relationships can deteriorate quickly. Nothing is more frustrating than watching your daughter starve herself at a dinner table where food is plentiful.

© Hero Images/Getty

▲ Ballet dancers and female athletes face extreme pressures to be thin and appear to be at high risk for the development of eating disorders.

Educated and knowledgeable parents, including psychologists and psychiatrists with full understanding of the disorder, have reported resorting to physical violence (e.g., hitting or slapping) in moments of extreme frustration, in a vain attempt to get their daughters to put some food, however little, in their mouths. The parents' guilt and anguish, very evident in the interview with Lynn Carpenter (Strobel, 2002), often exceed the levels of anxiety and depression present in the children with the disorder and is associated with poorer outcomes of the eating disorder (Ducios et al., 2012).

BIOLOGICAL DIMENSIONS

Like most psychological disorders, eating disorders seem to have a genetic component (Trace et al., 2013). Relatives of patients with eating disorders are four to five times as likely as the general population to develop eating disorders themselves, with the risks for female relatives of patients with anorexia higher (Strober et al., 2000).

In important twin studies of bulimia by Kendler and colleagues (1991) and of anorexia by Walters and Kendler (1995), researchers used structured interviews to ascertain the prevalence of the disorders among 2163 female twins. In 23 percent of identical twin pairs, both twins had bulimia, as compared with 9 percent of fraternal twins. Because no adoption studies have yet been reported, strong sociocultural influences cannot be ruled out, and other studies have produced inconsistent results (Fairburn, Cowen, & Harrison, 1999). For anorexia, numbers were too small for precise estimates, but the disorder in one twin did seem to confer a significant risk for both anorexia and bulimia in the co-twin. In a large twin study, Bulik and colleagues (2006) estimated heritability at 0.56. However, once again, no clear agreement exists on just what (if anything) is inherited (Steiger et al., 2013; Trace et al., 2013). Hsu (1990) and Steiger and colleagues (2013) speculated that nonspecific personality traits, such as emotional instability and, perhaps, poor impulse control, might be inherited. In other words, a person might inherit a tendency to be emotionally responsive to stressful life events and, as one consequence, might eat impulsively in an attempt to relieve stress and anxiety (Pearson et al., 2015). Klump, Kaye, and Strober (2001) mentioned perfectionist traits with negative affect. This biological vulnerability might then interact with social and psychological factors to produce an eating disorder.

A twin study by Vancouver-based researchers Livesley and colleagues (2005) suggests that some symptoms of eating disorders may themselves have a partially genetic basis. In a community-recruited sample of 221 twin pairs, they estimated that heritability for BMI is 0.57, 0.42 for purging, and 0.20 for concern for overeating. The rest of the variance in these eating disorder domains is attributable to environmental influences.

Obviously, biological processes are quite active in the regulation of eating and thus of eating disorders, and substantial evidence points to the hypothalamus as playing an important role. Investigators have studied the hypothalamus and the major neurotransmitter systems—including norepinephrine, dopamine, and, particularly, serotonin—that pass through it to determine whether something is malfunctioning when eating disorders occur (Vitiello & Lederhendler, 2000). Low levels of serotonergic activity, the system most often associated with eating disorders (Russell, 2009; Steiger et al., 2011), are associated with impulsivity in general and binge eating specifically. Thus, most drugs currently under study as treatments for eating dis-orders target the serotonin system (e.g., Grilo et al., 2012; Kaye, 2008).

Biological investigators are also interested in the influence of hormones on eating behaviour, particularly binge eating, which is an important component of bulimia. In an impressive program of research, Kelly Klump and colleagues (2014) found strong associations between ovarian hormones and dysregulated or impulsive eating in women prone to binge-eating episodes. Furthermore, emotional eating behaviour (eating to relieve stress or anxiety) and binge-eating frequencies peaked in the postovulatory phases of the menstrual cycle for all women whether they binged or not during other phases of their cycle. High levels of hormones at least partially accounted for these peaks.

Some interesting research also points to the role of exercise in causing or maintaining anorexia nervosa. Recall the case of Julie who also reported having "lost all taste for food." According to the work of John Pinel and colleagues at the University of British Columbia, Julie and other individuals with anorexia differ from most people who are starving because food lacks "positive incentive value" for them in terms of their desire to actually eat it (Pinel et al., 2000). Julie's reported loss of positive incentive to eat can be explained by the fact that she was exercising excessively—completing a workout videotape after every meal—phenomenon called "activity anorexia" where excessive physical activity can paradoxically cause a loss of appetite (Belke et al., 2006; Epling & Pierce, 1992; Pierce & Epling, 1996) for reasons that are not yet well understood.

If investigators do find a strong association between neurobiological functions and eating disorders, the question of cause or effect remains. At present, the consensus is that some neurobiological abnormalities do exist in people with eating disorders (e.g., Mainz et al., 2012) but that they may be a result of semistarvation or a binge-purge cycle rather than a cause, although they may well contribute to the maintenance of the disorder once it is established.

PSYCHOLOGICAL DIMENSIONS

Clinical observations over the years have indicated that many young women with eating disorders have a diminished sense of personal control and confidence in their own abilities and talents (Bruch, 1973, 1985; Striegal-Moore et al., 1993; Walters & Kendler, 1995). They also display more perfectionistic attitudes learned, perhaps, from their families, which may reflect attempts to exert control over important events in their lives (Boone et al., 2012; Bulik et al., 2003; Halmi et al., 2012; Martinez & Craighead, 2015). However, perfectionism alone is only weakly associated with the development of an eating disorder, because individuals must first consider themselves overweight and also manifest low self-esteem before the trait of perfectionism makes a contribution, as indicated by the work of Kathleen Vohs at the University of British Columbia (Abramson et al., 2006;

Vohs et al., 1999, 2001). Similarly, a study by McGee, Hewitt, Sherry, Parkin, and Flett (2005) showed that perfectionism predicted eating disorder symptoms, but only among women who were dissatisfied with their bodies.

Specific distortions in perception of body shape change frequently, depending on day-to-day experience. McKenzie, Williamson, and Cubic (1993) found that bulimic women judged their body size to be larger than, and their ideal weight to be less than, same-size comparison women did. Indeed, women with bulimia judged that their bodies were larger after they ate a chocolate bar and soft drink, whereas the judgments of other women were unaffected by snacks. Thus, rather minor events related to eating may activate fear of gaining weight, further distortions in body image, and corrective schemes, such as purging.

Another important observation is that at least a subgroup of these patients has difficulty tolerating any negative emotion (mood intolerance) and may binge or engage in other behaviours, such as self-induced vomiting or intense exercise, in an attempt to regulate their mood (reduce their anxiety or distress by doing something they think will help them avoid being fat) (Haynos & Fruzzetti, 2011; Paul et al., 2002). This seemed to be true for Phoebe. For example, Mauler, Hamm, Weike, and Tuschen-Caffier (2006) investigated reaction to food cues in women with bulimia and other women who had been food deprived. They discovered that women with bulimia, when hungry, had more intense negative emotional reactions (distress, anxiety, and depression) when viewing pictures of food and subsequently ate more at a buffet, presumably to decrease their anxiety and distress and make themselves feel better, even though this overeating would cause problems in the long run. These individuals, understandably, then evidenced even more intense negative affect after overeating and seemed threatened by food cues, which could lead to the extreme food restriction or intense exercise noted above. Fairburn and Cooper (2014) also noted the importance in treatment of countering the tendency to overly restrict food intake and the associated negative attitudes about body image that lead to bingeing and purging. What all of these studies have in common is the role of intense emotions triggered by food cues and fear of becoming fat, and faulty attempts to regulate these emotions as factors driving eating disorders.

AN INTEGRATIVE MODEL

Although the three major eating disorders are identifiable based on their unique characteristics, and the specific diagnoses have some validity, it is becoming increasingly clear that all eating disorders have much in common in terms of causal factors (Fairburn et al., 2007; Fairburn & Cooper, 2014). Thus, we have integrated a discussion of the causes of eating disorders.

In putting together what we know about eating disorders, it is important to remember, once again, that no one factor seems sufficient to cause them (see ■ Figure 9.5). Individuals with eating disorders may have some of the same biological vulnerabilities (such as being highly responsive to stressful life events) as individuals with anxiety disorders (Kendler et al., 1995; Klump et al., 2014; Rojo et al., 2006). Anxiety and mood disorders are also common in the families of individuals with eating disorders (Steiger et al., 2013), and negative emotions and "mood

intolerance" seem to trigger binge eating in many patients (Davis et al., 1988; Polivy & Herman, 1993). In addition, as we will see, drug and psychosocial treatments with proven effectiveness for anxiety disorders are also the treatments of choice for eating disorders. Indeed, we could conceptualize eating disorders as anxiety disorders focused exclusively on becoming overweight.

In any case, it is clear that social and cultural pressures to be thin motivate significant restriction of eating, usually through severe dieting. Many people go on strict diets, however, including adolescent females, but only a minority develops eating disorders, so dieting alone does not explain eating disorders. An emphasis on looks and achievement, and perfectionistic tendencies, in higher-achieving families may also help establish very strong attitudes about the overriding importance of physical appearance to popularity and success, attitudes reinforced in peer groups. These attitudes result in an exaggerated focus on body shape and weight. Lastly, there is the question of why a minority of individuals with eating disorders can successfully control their intake through dietary restraint, resulting in alarming weight loss, whereas the majority are unsuccessful at losing weight and compensate in a cycle of bingeing and purging (bulimia). These differences may be determined by biology or physiology, such as a genetically determined disposition to be somewhat thinner to begin with. Then again, perhaps pre-existing personality characteristics, such as a tendency to be overcontrolling or a tendency to act impulsively, are important determinants of which disorder a girl develops—anorexia nervosa or bulimia nervosa, respectively (Goldner et al., 1999; Polivy & Herman, 2002). In any case, most individuals with anorexia do go on to bingeing and purging at some point.

TREATMENT OF EATING DISORDERS

Only since the 1980s have there been treatments for bulimia; treatments for anorexia had been around much longer but were not initially well developed. Rapidly accumulating evidence indicates that at least one, possibly two, psychological treatments are effective, particularly for bulimia nervosa. Certain drugs may also help, although the evidence is not strong.

DRUG TREATMENTS

At present, drug treatments have generally not been found to be effective in the treatment of anorexia nervosa (Crow et al., 2009; Garner & Needleman, 1996; Hsu, 1990; Kruger & Kennedy, 2000). For example, one definitive study reported that fluoxetine (Prozac) had no benefit in preventing relapse in patients with anorexia after weight has been restored (Walsh et al., 2006).

There is some evidence that drugs may be useful for some people with bulimia, particularly during the bingeing and purging cycle. The drugs generally considered the most effective for bulimia (e.g., Prozac) are the same antidepressant medications used for mood disorders and anxiety disorders (Broft et al., 2010; Shapiro et al., 2007; Wilson & Fairburn, 2007). Effectiveness is usually measured by reductions in the frequency of binge eating as well as by the percentage of patients who stop binge eating and purging (Flament et al., 2005). In two studies, one using tricyclic

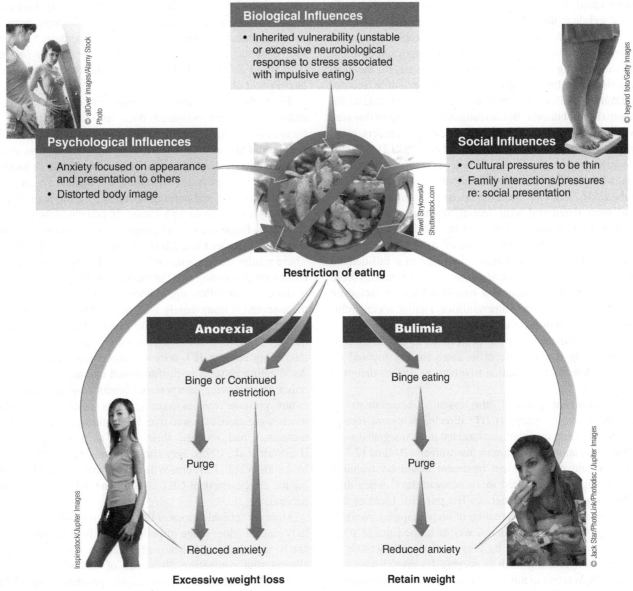

FIGURE 9.5 | An integrative causal model of eating disorders.

Figure: © Cengage Learning

Biological Influences
- Inherited vulnerability (unstable or excessive neurobiological response to stress associated with impulsive eating)

Psychological Influences
- Anxiety focused on appearance and presentation to others
- Distorted body image

Social Influences
- Cultural pressures to be thin
- Family interactions/pressures re: social presentation

Restriction of eating

Anorexia

Binge or Continued restriction

Purge

Reduced anxiety

Excessive weight loss

Bulimia

Binge eating

Purge

Reduced anxiety

Retain weight

antidepressant drugs and the other using fluoxetine (Prozac), researchers found the average reduction in binge eating and purging was, respectively, 47 percent and 65 percent (Walsh, 1991; Walsh et al., 1991). A more recent review (meta-analysis) suggested that selective serotonin reuptake inhibitors are helpful in the treatment of bulimia (Tortorella et al., 2014). However, although antidepressants are more effective than placebo in the short term, and they may enhance the effects of psychological treatment somewhat (Whittal et al., 1999; Wilson et al., 1999), the available evidence suggests that antidepressant drugs alone do not have substantial long-lasting effects on bulimia nervosa and current expert opinions suggest that medications are likely most useful in conjunction with psychological treatments (Reas & Grilo, 2014; Walsh, 1995; Wilson & Fairburn, 2007), as suggested in the work by Maureen Whittal and colleagues at the University of British Columbia (Whittal et al., 1999).

PSYCHOSOCIAL TREATMENTS

Until recently, psychosocial treatments were directed at the patient's low self-esteem and difficulties in developing an individual identity. Disordered patterns of family interaction and communication were also targeted for treatment. These treatments alone, however, have not had the effectiveness that clinicians had hoped they might (Minuchin et al., 1978; Russell et al., 1987). Short-term cognitive-behavioural treatments target problem eating behaviour and associated attitudes about the overriding importance and significance of body weight and shape, and these strategies became the treatment of choice for bulimia (Fairburn & Cooper, 2014; Sysko & Wilson, 2011).

More recently, this approach has been updated and improved in two major ways based on more than a decade of experience. First, a variety of new procedures intended to improve outcome have been added. Second, noting the common concern with body shape and weight at the core of all eating disorders, the treatment has become *transdiagnostic* in that it is applicable with minor alterations to all eating disorders. This is an important development because eating disorders in the *DSM-IV* were, for the most part, considered to be mutually exclusive. For example, according to *DSM-IV* guidelines, a person could not meet criteria for both anorexia and bulimia. But investigators working in this area discovered that features of the various eating disorders overlapped considerably (Fairburn, 2008; Keel et al., 2012). Furthermore, a large portion of patients, perhaps as many as 50 percent or more, who met the criteria for a clinically severe eating disorder in the *DSM-IV* did not meet the criteria for anorexia or bulimia and were diagnosed with "eating disorder not otherwise specified" (eating disorder NOS) (Fairburn & Bohn, 2005). As described earlier in the chapter, some of these patients would now meet criteria for BED, which is included as a full-fledged diagnostic category in the *DSM-5*. As we have noted, these eating disorders have very similar causal influences, including similar inherited biological vulnerabilities, similar social influences (primarily cultural influences glorifying thinness), and a strong family influence toward perfectionism in all things. Finally, all eating disorders seem to share anxiety focused on one's appearance and presentation to others, as well as distorted body image.

In this treatment protocol, the essential components of cognitive-behavioural therapy (CBT) directed at causal factors common to all eating disorders are targeted in an integrated way. Individuals with anorexia and a very low weight—BMI of 17.5 or less—who would need inpatient treatment would be excluded until their weight was restored to an adequate level when they could then benefit from the program. The principal focus of this protocol is on the distorted evaluation of body shape and weight, and maladaptive attempts to control weight in the form of strict dieting, possibly accompanied by binge eating, and methods to compensate for overeating, such as purging, laxative misuse, and so forth. Fairburn refers to this treatment as cognitive-behavioural therapy-enhanced (CBT-E; Fairburn & Cooper, 2014). Nevertheless, since there are some differences in outcome across the eating disorders, we will review treatment of each separately.

Bulimia Nervosa

In the CBT-E approach pioneered by British psychologist Christopher Fairburn (2008), the first stage is teaching the patient the physical consequences of binge eating and purging, as well as the ineffectiveness of vomiting and laxative abuse for weight control. The adverse effects of dieting are also described. Patients are scheduled to eat small, manageable amounts of food five or six times per day with no more than a three-hour interval between any planned meals and snacks, which eliminates the alternating periods of overeating and dietary restriction that are hallmarks of bulimia. In later stages of treatment, CBT-E focuses on altering dysfunctional thoughts and attitudes about body shape, weight, and eating. Coping strategies for resisting the impulse to binge and/or purge are also developed, including arranging activities so the individual will not spend time alone after eating during the early stages of treatment (Fairburn & Cooper, 2014). Evaluations

of the earlier versions of short-term (approximately three months) cognitive-behavioural treatments for bulimia have been good, showing a mean reduction in purging of 79 percent; 57 percent of the patients eliminated bingeing and purging altogether (Craighead & Agras, 1991). Furthermore, these results seem to last (Pike et al., 2003).

In a thorough, carefully conducted study, Fairburn and colleagues (1993) evaluated three different treatments. CBT focused on changing eating habits and changing attitudes about weight and shape; behaviour therapy focused only on changing eating habits; and interpersonal psychotherapy (IPT) focused on improving interpersonal functioning. For patients receiving CBT, both binge eating and purging declined by more than 90 percent at a one-year follow-up. In addition, 36 percent of the patients had ceased all binge eating and purging; the others had occasional episodes. Attitudes toward body shape and weight also improved. These results were significantly better than the results from BT. Even more interesting was the finding that IPT did as well as CBT at the one-year follow-up, although CBT was more effective at the assessment immediately after treatment was completed. This result indicates that IPT caught up with CBT in terms of effectiveness by the end of the one-year follow-up. This is particularly interesting because IPT does not concentrate directly on disordered eating patterns or dysfunctional attitudes about eating but rather on improving interpersonal functioning, a focus that may, in turn, promote changes in eating habits and attitudes. Both treatments were more effective than BT. Patients in the two effective treatments had retained their gains at a six-year follow-up (Fairburn et al., 1995). Very similar results were found in a study by Agras, Walsh, Fairburn, Wilson, and Kraemer (2000), comparing the effectiveness of CBT and IPT in the treatment of bulimia nervosa.

More recent evaluations of CBT-E are very promising, particularly since a wider range of patients with bulimia-like symptoms can be included (e.g. Fairburn et al., 2009). Results from a major clinical trial comparing 20 weeks of CBT-E with two years of weekly long-term psychoanalytic psychotherapy (PPT) in 70 patients with bulimia revealed that patients in each group were comfortable with their treatment, but at five months (when the CBT-E treatment concluded), 42 percent of CBT-E patients were recovered compared with 6 percent of PPT patients. After two years (when the PPT treatment concluded), the comparable figures were 44 percent and 15 percent (Poulsen et al., 2014). Thus, CBT-E was more efficient in terms of the number of sessions required and more effective at each time point assessed, with evidence for the durability in improvement among those who responded to CBT-E. Now, results from a major clinical trial similar to the Agras at al. (2000) study described above, but comparing the transdiagnostic version of CBT (CBT-E) with interpersonal psychotherapy (IPT) in 130 patients with any form of eating disorder have been reported (Fairburn et al., 2015). Just after treatment 66 percent of the CBT-E participants met criteria for remission compared with 33 percent of the IPT participants. One year later, the figures were 69 percent for CBT-E compared with 49 percent for IPT, with IPT catching up somewhat but still less effective. Therefore, currently, CBT-E would seem to be the treatment of choice for adults based on these studies.

There is also good evidence that family therapy directed at the painful conflicts present in families with an adolescent who has an eating disorder can be helpful (le Grange et al., 2007). Integrating family and interpersonal strategies into CBT is a promising new direction (Sysko & Wilson, 2011). Clearly, we need to understand more about how to improve such treatments to deal more successfully with the growing number of patients with eating disorders. One of the problems with the best treatment, CBT-E, is that access to the treatment is limited because trained therapists are not always available. Guided self-help programs that use CBT principles also seem to be effective, at least for less severe cases (Schmidt et al., 2007; Wagner et al., 2013).

PHOEBE | *Taking Control*

During her second year in university, Phoebe entered a short-term cognitive-behaviour therapy program. She made good progress during the first several months and worked carefully to eat regularly and gain control over her eating. She also made sure that she was with somebody during her high-risk times and planned alternative activities that would reduce her temptation to purge if she felt she had eaten too much at a restaurant or drunk too much beer at a party. During the first two months, Phoebe had three slips; she and her therapist discussed what led to her temporary lapses. Much to Phoebe's surprise, she did not gain weight on this program, even though she did not have time to increase her exercise. Nevertheless, she still was preoccupied with food, was concerned about her weight and appearance, and had strong urges to vomit if she thought she had overeaten the slightest amount.

During the nine months following treatment, Phoebe reported that her urges seemed to decrease somewhat, although she had one major slip after eating a big pizza and drinking a lot of beer. She reported that she was thoroughly disgusted with herself for purging and was quite careful to return to her program after this episode. Two years after finishing treatment, Phoebe reported that her urges to vomit had disappeared, a report confirmed by her parents. All that remained of her problem were some very bad but increasingly distant memories.

Another variant of CBT, developed by Ron Davis of Lakehead University and his colleagues in Toronto, is brief group psychoeducation for bulimia nervosa. The main goal of psychoeducation is to help bulimic individuals normalize their eating and reduce their body image disturbance. This goal is achieved through providing them with information relevant to bulimia nervosa and with useful strategies, such as meal planning, problem solving, and self-monitoring. The main differences from CBT are that psychoeducation is briefer, is delivered in a lecture-type format, and is not tailored to the unique needs of individual patients (Davis & Olmsted, 1992). Research has shown this approach to be better than a wait list control in helping bulimic individuals reduce their symptoms (Davis et al., 1990). The intervention is particularly effective for those with less severe bulimia (Davis et al., 1992). Nonetheless, improvements in bulimia are even better when the psychoeducation approach is followed by 16 weeks of CBT than when patients receive the psychoeducation approach alone (Davis et al., 1999).

Binge-Eating Disorder

Early studies adapting CBT treatments for bulimia to obese binge eaters were quite successful (Smith et al., 1992). To take one example, Agras, Telch, Arnow, Eldredge, and Marnell (1997) followed 93 obese individuals with BED for one year and found that immediately after treatment 41 percent of the participants abstained from bingeing and 72 percent binged less frequently. After one year, binge eating was reduced by 64 percent, and 33 percent of the group remained abstinent. Importantly, those who had stopped binge eating during CBT maintained a weight loss of approximately four kilograms over the follow-up period; those who continued to binge gained almost three kilograms. Thus, stopping binge eating is critical to sustaining weight loss in obese patients, a finding consistent with other studies of weight-loss procedures (Marcus et al., 1990). Widely available behavioural weight-loss programs for obese patients with BED, such as Weight Watchers, do have some positive effect on bingeing but not nearly so much as CBT (Grilo et al., 2011).

Self-help procedures may be useful in the treatment of BED (Carter & Fairburn, 1998; Wilson & Zandberg, 2012). For example, CBT delivered as guided self-help was demonstrated to be more effective than a standard behavioural weight-loss program for BED both after treatment and at a two-year follow-up (Wilson, Wilfley, et al., 2010), and this same program is effective when delivered out of a doctor's office in a primary care setting (Striegel-Moore et al., 2010). In view of these results, it would seem a self-help approach should probably be the first treatment offered for BED before engaging in more expensive and time-consuming therapist-led treatments. Much as with bulimia, however, more severe cases may need the more intensive treatment delivered by a therapist, particularly when people have multiple (comorbid) disorders in addition to BED, as well as low self-esteem (Wilson et al., 2010). A recent report following up the Wilson et al. (2010) study indicated that rapid response (at least 70 percent reduction in binge eating by week 4) was a specific positive indicator of greater rates of remission compared with nonrapid responders up to two years later in the CBT guided self-help treatment but not in the IPT or the behavioural weight-loss group (Hilbert, Hildebrandt, Agras, Wilfley, and Wilson, 2015). The authors suggest that since IPT was effective for both rapid and nonrapid responders that participants who do not show a rapid response to CBT might be switched over to IPT. Matching treatment to individuals based on their personal characteristics or patterns of responding (personalized medicine) is regarded by many as the next important step for improving success rates of our treatments. It is also important to emphasize again that if an obese person is bingeing, standard weight-loss procedures will be ineffective without treatment directed at bingeing.

Anorexia Nervosa

In anorexia, of course, the most important initial goal is to restore the patient's weight to a point that is at least within the low-normal range. If body weight is below 85 percent of the average healthy body weight for a given individual or if weight has been lost rapidly and the individual continues to refuse food, inpatient treatment is recommended (American Psychiatric Association, 2010b; Russell, 2009) because severe medical complications, particularly acute cardiac failure, could occur if weight is not restored immediately. If the weight loss has been more gradual and seems to have stabilized, weight restoration can be accomplished on an outpatient basis.

Restoring weight, although often a difficult task, is probably the easiest part of treatment. Clinicians who treat patients in different settings, as reported in a variety of studies, find that at least 85 percent will be able to gain weight. The gain is often as much as one-quarter to a half a kilogram a day until weight is within the normal range. In fact, knowing they cannot leave the hospital until their weight gain is adequate is often sufficient to motivate adolescents with anorexia. Julie gained about eight kilograms during her five-week hospital stay. Weight gain is very important, since starvation induces loss of grey matter and hormonal dysregulation in the brain (Mainz et al., 2012), changes that are reversible when normal weight is restored.

Then the more difficult stage begins. As Hsu (1988) and others have demonstrated, initial weight gain is a poor predictor of long-term outcome in anorexia. Without attention to the patient's underlying dysfunctional attitudes about body shape, she will almost always relapse. For restricting anorexics, the focus of treatment must shift to their marked anxiety over becoming obese and losing control of eating, as well as to their undue emphasis on thinness as a determinant of self-worth, happiness, and success. In this regard, effective treatments for restricting anorexics are similar to those for patients with bulimia nervosa, particularly in the transdiagnostic approach (CBT-E) described earlier (Fairburn & Cooper, 2014). In one earlier study (Pike et al., 2003), extended (one-year) outpatient CBT was found to be significantly better than continued nutritional counselling in preventing relapse after weight restoration, with only 22 percent failing (relapsing or dropping out) with CBT versus 73 percent failing with nutritional counselling. Carter and colleagues (2009) reported similar findings and both studies demonstrate the ineffectiveness of nutritional counselling alone. More recently, results from 99 adults with anorexia treated with CBT-E suggest the efficiency of this transdiagnostic treatment (only "suggest" because there was no control or comparison group). In the 64 percent who completed treatment after 40 sessions, weight increased substantially and eating disorder features improved markedly. This improvement was stable at a 60-week follow-up (Fairburn et al., 2013).

Other research highlights the importance of assessing clients with eating disorders' readiness for change, since patients with anorexia nervosa are often difficult to treat (Goldner, 1989). Interventions derived from those used in the treatment of substance abuse disorders are being developed that focus on enhancing the patient's motivation to change (Kaplan & Garfinkel, 1999). For example, a study by Joanne Gusella and colleagues at the IWK Health Centre in Halifax administered a motivational measure to 34 adolescents with eating disorders before the commencement of an eating disorder group. Those girls who reported being more ready to change at treatment outset showed greater improvements in their eating disorder symptoms over the course of the group. The group also assisted the girls in earlier stages to be more ready to change by the end of the group (Gusella et al., 2003). A similar study by Josie Geller at the St. Paul's Hospital Eating Disorders Program in Vancouver examined motivation to change in 56 adult women with anorexia. Like the findings in Gusella's study, Geller (2002) found that patients who were at a more advanced stage of readiness to change were more likely to complete assigned behavioural recovery activities (e.g., increasing caloric intake) and to accept intensive treatment for their anorexia. Given the clear importance of motivation to change in recovery from anorexia, new treatments that target motivational enhancement are promising innovations in eating disorder treatment (Dunn et al., 2006; Kaplan & Garfinkel, 1999).

In addition, every effort is made to include the family to accomplish two goals. First, the negative and dysfunctional communication regarding food and eating must be eliminated and meals made more structured and reinforcing. Second, attitudes toward body shape and image distortion are discussed at some length in family sessions. Unless the therapist attends to these attitudes, individuals with anorexia are likely to face a lifetime preoccupation with weight and body shape, struggle to maintain marginal weight and social adjustment, and be subject to repeated hospitalization. Family therapy seems effective, particularly with young girls with a short history of the disorder (Eisler et al., 2000). Recent research by a team at the Hospital for Sick Children in Toronto showed that a substantially less costly family group psychoeducation approach was just as effective as a more traditional family therapy approach in assisting hospitalized adolescents with anorexia and their families, at least in the short term (Geist et al., 2000).

Until recently, the long-term results of treatment for anorexia have been less encouraging than for bulimia, with substantially lower rates of full recovery than for bulimia over a 7.5-year period (Eddy et al., 2008; Herzog et al., 1999). But this may be changing. In a recent important clinical trial, 121 adolescents with anorexia received 24 sessions of either family-based treatment (FBT) in which the parents became intimately involved in the treatment program with a focus on facilitating weight gain, or individual psychotherapy. At treatment conclusion, 42 percent met criteria for remission in the FBT condition and 49 percent at a one-year follow-up, compared with 23 percent at both points in time in the individual psychotherapy condition (Lock et al., 2010). A subsequent study demonstrated that FBT was at least as effective as and was less costly than other forms of family therapy addressing general family processes (Agras et al., 2014). As in some studies with bulimia, a positive early response (gaining at least two kilograms or five pounds in the first four weeks) predicts a better outcome in the long run (Lock et al. 2015). At present FBT has the most support from clinical trials for treating adolescents with anorexia (Lock et al., 2015), but there is some support for its efficacy in treating bulimia (Le Grange et al., 2015). Promising results have also recently been reported with CBT-E for adolescents with anorexia (Dalle Grave et al., 2013).

University of Ottawa psychologist George Tasca, his Ph.D. student Renee Grenon, and their colleagues recently conducted meta-analyses on the efficacy of psychological treatments for eating disorders. Meta-analyses involve analyzing the results of many studies to arrive at a general conclusion. The general conclusion from his work is that people with eating disorders who undergo psychological treatment experience much improvement in their symptoms, compared with people with eating disorders who are on a waitlist. Interestingly, the type of treatment is not related to the size of the improvement: treatment based on CBT principles, treatments not based on CBT principles (e.g., short-term psychodynamic treatment), individual treatments, and group treatments produce similar outcomes (Grenon et al., 2016, 2018).

Probably one of the most talked-about stories of the treatment of anorexia nervosa in Canadian history involves the Montreux Clinic—an expensive and exclusive private clinic for women and adolescents with anorexia nervosa in Victoria, British Columbia. Montreux was directed by Peggy Claude-Pierre—a mother who had helped her own two teenage daughters overcome eating disorders. Claude-Pierre received a good deal of media attention, including interviews by Oprah Winfrey and Pamela Wallin, given her claims of a striking 90 percent recovery rate for clinic patients and the message of hope contained in her reported treatment philosophy of unconditional love. The clinic came under investigation when a former employee made allegations that the staff was inadequately trained and the clients not properly screened. More serious allegations were made that clients were being force-fed and held against their will. Although, as mentioned earlier, it is essential for very emaciated patients with anorexia to be hospitalized to prevent potentially severe medical complications, these clients were admitted to Montreux with no medical supervision. In fact, the director Claude-Pierre did not have a graduate degree in psychology or any medical training. In spite of strong protests from her supporters, the residential clinic was eventually closed in December 1999 on the order of the local health officer (Dineen, 2002; McLintock, 2002).

PREVENTING EATING DISORDERS

Attempts are being made to prevent the development of eating disorders. If successful methods are confirmed, they will be very important, because many cases of eating disorders are resistant to treatment and most individuals who do not receive treatment suffer for many years, in some cases all their lives (Eddy et al., 2008; Killen, 1996). The development of eating disorders during adolescence is a risk factor for a variety of additional problems and disorders during adulthood, including cardiovascular symptoms, chronic fatigue and infectious diseases, binge drinking and drug use, and anxiety and mood disorders (Field et al., 2012; Johnson et al., 2002). Before implementing a prevention program, however, it is necessary to target specific behaviours to change.

Stice, Shaw, and Marti (2007) concluded after a review of prevention programs that selecting girls age 15 or over, focusing on eliminating an exaggerated focus on body shape or weight, and encouraging acceptance of one's body stood the best chance of success in preventing eating disorders. This finding is similar to results from prevention efforts for depression, where a selective approach of targeting high-risk individuals was more successful rather than a universal approach targeting everyone in a certain age range (Stice & Shaw, 2004). Using this selective approach, a program developed by Stice, Rohde, Shaw, and colleagues (2012) called Healthy Weight was compared with just handing out educational material in 398 college women at risk for developing eating disorders because of weight and shape concerns. During four weekly hour-long group sessions, the women were educated about food and eating habits (and motivated to alter these habits using motivational enhancement procedures). Eating disorder risk factors and symptoms were substantially reduced in the Healthy Weight group compared with the comparison group, particularly for the most severely at risk women, and the effect was durable at a six-month follow-up.

In Canada, Gail McVey and Ron Davis have examined the effectiveness of a program aimed at girls in Grade 6 that is designed to promote a healthy body image and ultimately prevent the development of eating disorders. The program was tested on 258 girls, who were assigned to either the intervention or to a control group. The intervention focused on countering the effects of the media portrayals of the desirability of being thin as well as training the girls in self-esteem enhancement, stress management, and peer relationship skills. Relative to the control group, the six-session intervention was successful in improving body image satisfaction and self-esteem and in reducing dieting attitudes immediately following the intervention. Unfortunately, these benefits were not maintained one year following the intervention (McVey et al., 2004).

Niva Piran of the Ontario Institute for Studies in Education ran a prevention program for young women that emphasized changes in the school culture at a well-known ballet school in Toronto (Piran, 1998). In focus groups, students explored their experiences of body image dissatisfaction at the school and outside school. They each formed an action plan to implement changes in the school culture (Piran, 2001). Specific changes included moving away from a focus on a body shape and toward an increased focus on body conditioning and physical stamina, and not permitting teachers to make comments about students' body shape (recall the impact of Phoebe's experiences with her ballet instructor's comments about her body weight and shape). This prevention program has been very successful: dysfunctional eating attitudes have decreased among girls in the school, as have rates of bingeing, vomiting, and laxative abuse (Piran, 1999). In view of the severity and chronicity of eating disorders, preventing these disorders through widespread educational and intervention efforts would be clearly preferable to waiting until the disorders develop (Piran, 1997, 2004).

Mark the following statements about the causes and treatment of eating disorders as either true (T) or false (F).

1. _____ Many young women with eating disorders have a diminished sense of personal control and confidence in their own abilities and talents, are perfectionists, and/or are intensely preoccupied with how they appear to others.

2. _____ Biological factors, as well as the societal pressure to use diet and exercise to achieve nearly impossible weight goals, contribute to the high numbers of people with anorexia nervosa and bulimia nervosa.

3. _____ One study showed that males consider a smaller female body size to be more attractive than women do.

4. _____ Antidepressants help individuals overcome anorexia nervosa but have no effect on bulimia nervosa.

5. _____ Cognitive-behavioural treatment (CBT) and interpersonal psychotherapy (IPT) are both successful treatments for bulimia nervosa, although CBT is the preferred method.

6. _____ Attention must be focused on dysfunctional attitudes about body shape in anorexia, or relapse will most likely occur after treatment.

DSM-5 CONTROVERSIES | Binge-Eating Disorder

BED is a new diagnosis in the *DSM-5*, but, as with most new disorders, some controversy has surrounded its inclusion. Alan J. Frances, the psychiatrist who chaired the task force that created the *DSM-IV*, has criticized BED as he has many of the new disorders introduced into the *DSM-5*. He notes that the history of our system of nosology in mental health has been littered with fad diagnoses that in retrospect have done more harm than good (Frances, 2012). In his view, BED may be one of those fads. He notes that eating excessively at least 12 times over a period of three months (part of the criteria for BED; see DSM Table 9.3) could really be considered just a manifestation of modern-day gluttony caused by the easy availability of really great-tasting food (Frances, 2012). How many of us have "overeaten" approximately once a week over the past month? If you continued that for three months, then you might be eligible for this diagnosis.

But look again at the description of BED. Notice that only a small minority of individuals who are obese and have joined commercial weight-control programs to deal with their problem also evidence binge eating. Notice, also, that the percentage of obese individuals who binge rises considerably in groups who are so severely obese that they would be candidates for bariatric surgery. Note that these individuals, but not those who are obese without bingeing, share the same concerns about shape and weight as people with anorexia and bulimia, and their bingeing is often driven by attempts to alleviate bad moods. The tendency of binge eating to run in families, to have a heritable component, its responsiveness to the same types of treatments effective for other eating disorders (something that is not the case for individuals who are obese without bingeing), and other factors were sufficient to convince the eating disorders workgroup and the *DSM-5* task force that this condition should be a diagnosis. With this designation, this condition will now achieve greater recognition, and its treatment can be reimbursed by health insurance, thereby increasing the likelihood that individuals suffering from this disorder will receive appropriate care.

SUMMARY

Overview of Eating Disorders

- The prevalence of eating disorders has increased rapidly over the last half century. As a result, they were included for the first time as a separate group of disorders in the *DSM-IV*.

- There are three prevalent eating disorders. In bulimia nervosa, dieting results in out-of-control binge-eating episodes that are often followed by purging the food through vomiting or other means. Anorexia nervosa, in which food intake is cut down dramatically, results in substantial weight loss and sometimes dangerously low body weight. In binge-eating disorder, a pattern of binge eating is *not* followed by purging.

- Bulimia nervosa and anorexia nervosa are largely confined to young women in developed countries who are pursuing a thin body shape that is culturally mandated and biologically inappropriate, making it extremely difficult to achieve.

- Without treatment, eating disorders become chronic and can result in death.

Causes of Eating Disorders

- In addition to sociocultural pressures, causal factors include possible biological and genetic vulnerabilities (the disorders tend to run in families), psychological factors (low self-esteem), social anxiety (fears of rejection), and distorted body image (relatively normal-weight individuals view themselves as fat and ugly).

Treatment of Eating Disorders

■ Several psychosocial treatments are effective, including cognitive-behavioural approaches combined with family therapy and interpersonal psychotherapy. Drug treatments are less effective at the current time.

KEY TERMS

anorexia nervosa, 263
avoidant/restrictive food intake disorder (ARFID), 272

binge-eating disorder (BED), 269

binges, 263
bulimia nervosa, 263

purging techniques, 265

ANSWERS TO CONCEPT CHECKS

9.1

1. c; **2.** a; **3.** a; **4.** b

9.2

1. T; **2.** T; **3.** F (females find a smaller size more attractive than men do); **4.** F (they help with bulimia nervosa, not anorexia); **5.** T; **6.** T

MEDIA RESOURCES

⁎ CENGAGE | MINDTAP

Stay organized and efficient with MindTap—a single destination with all the course material and study aids you need to succeed. Built-in apps leverage social media and the latest learning technology. For example:

■ ReadSpeaker will read the text to you.

■ Flashcards are pre-populated to provide you with a jump start for review—or you can create your own.

■ You can highlight text and make notes in your MindTap Reader. Your notes will flow into Evernote, the electronic notebook app that you can access anywhere when it's time to study for the exam.

■ Self-quizzing allows you to assess your understanding.

Visit login.cengage.com to start using MindTap. Enter the Online Access Code from the card included with your text. If a code card is not provided, you can purchase instant access at Cengage.ca.

Exploring Eating Disorders

Individuals with eating disorders:

> Feel a relentless, all-encompassing drive to be thin
> Are overwhelmingly young females from middle- to upper-class families, who live in socially competitive environments
> Lived only in Western countries until recently

Psychological—Diminished sense of personal control and self-confidence, causing low self-esteem; distorted body image

Social—Cultural and social emphasis on slender ideal, leading to body dissatisfaction and pre-occupation with food and eating

Causes

Biological—Possible genetic tendency to poor impulse control, emotional instability, and perfectionistic traits

EATING DISORDERS

Disorder	Characteristics	Treatment
Bulimia Nervosa	• Out-of-control consumption of excessive amounts of mostly non-nutritious food within a short time • Elimination of food through self-induced vomiting and/or abuse of laxatives or diuretics • To compensate for binges, some bulimics exercise excessively or fast between binges • Vomiting may enlarge salivary glands (causing a chubby face), erode dental enamel, and cause electrolyte imbalance resulting in cardiac failure or kidney problems • Weight usually within 10 percent of normal • Age of onset is typically 16 to 19 years of age	• Drug treatment, such as antidepressants • Short-term cognitive-behavioural therapy (CBT) to address behaviour and attitudes on eating and body shape • Interpersonal psychotherapy (IPT) to improve interpersonal functioning • Tends to be chronic if left untreated
Anorexia Nervosa	• Intense fear of obesity and persistent pursuit of thinness; perpetual dissatisfaction with weight loss • Severe caloric restriction, often with excessive exercise and sometimes with purging, to the point of semistarvation • Severely limiting caloric intake may cause cessation of menstruation, downy hair on limbs and cheeks, dry skin, brittle hair or nails, sensitivity to cold, and danger of acute cardiac or kidney failure • Weight at least 15 percent below normal • Average age of onset is about 13 years of age	• Hospitalization (at 70 percent below normal weight) • Outpatient treatment to restore weight and correct dysfunctional attitudes on eating and body shape • Family therapy • Tends to be chronic if left untreated; more resistant to treatment than bulimia
Binge Eating	• Similar to bulimia with out-of-control food binges, but no attempt to purge the food (vomiting, laxatives, diuretics) or compensate for excessive intake • Marked physical and emotional stress; some sufferers binge to alleviate bad moods • Binge eaters share some concerns about weight and body shape as individuals with anorexia and bulimia • Tends to affect more older people than either bulimia or anorexia	• Short-term CBT to address behaviour and attitudes on eating and body shape • IPT to improve interpersonal functioning • Drug treatments that reduce feelings of hunger • Self-help approaches

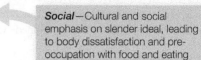

PhotoDisc/Getty Images

10 | Sleeping

© LjupcoiStock

Insomnia is a vertiginous lucidity that can convert paradise itself into a place of torture. . . .

—EMIL CIORAN

Use scientific reasoning to interpret behaviour:	› Identify basic biological, psychological, and social components of behavioural explanations (e.g., inferences, observations, operational definitions and interpretations) (APA SLO 2.1A)
Engage in innovative and integrative thinking and problem solving:	› Describe problems operationally to study them empirically (APA SLO 2.3A)
Describe applications that employ discipline-based problem solving:	› Correctly identify antecedents and consequences of behaviour and mental processes (APA SLO 1.3b). Describe examples of relevant and practical applications of psychological principles to everyday life (APA SLO 1.3a)

*Portions of this chapter cover learning outcomes suggested by the American Psychological Association (2013) in its guidelines for the undergraduate psychology major. Chapter coverage of these outcomes is identified above by APA Goal and APA Suggested Learning Outcome (SLO).

We spend about one-third of our lives asleep. That means most of us sleep nearly 3000 hours per year. ■ Figure 10.1 contains the recommended number of hours of sleep per night across the lifespan (Hirshkowitz et al., 2015). How do Canadians measure up? Using data from the Canadian Health Measures Survey (CHMS), estimates have been calculated for Canadians between the ages of 6 and 79 years. Almost 80 percent of school-age children meet the requirements, but only 68 percent of teenagers meet them (Michaud & Chaput, 2016). The downward trend in number of people meeting the recommended number of hours of sleep continues, with 65 percent of young adults and adults meeting the requirements and only 54 percent of older adults meeting them (Chaput et al., 2017). Those not meeting the required number of hours of sleep were more likely to be short on hours of sleep—long sleepers tended to be rare. Similar to the Canadian Community Health Survey (CCHS) referred to in earlier chapters, the CHMS excludes approximately 4 percent of the population (i.e.,

persons living in the territories or on reserves or other settlements, full-time members of the Canadian Forces, the institutionalized population, and residents of some remote regions).

For many of us, sleep is energizing, both mentally and physically. However, you or someone you know may have a problem with sleep. Most of us know what it's like to have a bad night's sleep. The next day we're a little groggy, and as the day wears on we may become irritable. Imagine, if you can, that it has been years since you've had a good night's sleep. Your relationships suffer, it is difficult to do your schoolwork, and your efficiency and productivity at work are diminished. Lack of sleep might also affect you physically. As noted by sleep researcher Charles Morin at Laval University, people who do not get enough sleep report more health problems and are more often hospitalized than people who sleep normally (Morin, 1993). According to the research of Harvey Moldofsky, director of the University of Toronto Centre for Sleep and Chronobiology, and his colleagues,

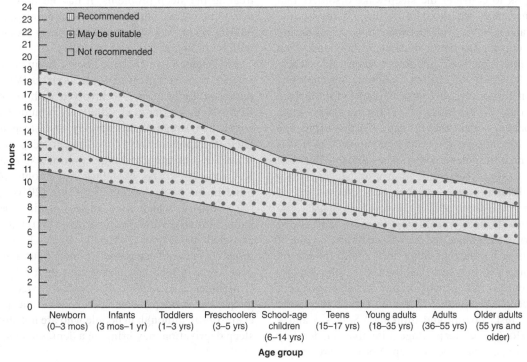

FIGURE 10.1 | Sleep duration recommendations across the lifespan.

Source: Republished with permission of Elsevier, from "National Sleep Foundation's updated sleep duration recommendations: final report," by Hirshkowitz, M. et al., *Sleep Health,* 1, 2015, 233–243; permission conveyed through Copyright Clearance Center, Inc.

▲ Charles Morin is the director of the Centre on Sleep Disorders at Laval University in Québec and is a past president of the Canadian Sleep Society. His research has contributed substantially to the understanding of the relationships between sleep and cognitive and immunological functions, and he has made important contributions in developing empirically validated treatments for insomnia.

some chronic physical health problems are linked to insomnia: circulatory problems, digestive and respiratory disease, migraines, allergies, and rheumatic disorders (Sutton et al., 2001). Why are health problems linked to sleep problems? Perhaps because immune system functioning is reduced with the loss of even a few hours of sleep (Irwin et al., 1994; Jaffe, 2000; Savard et al., 2003). Sleep problems are a costly health problem resulting in substantial annual expenditures because of lost worker productivity, absenteeism, and related outcomes (Chilcott & Shapiro, 1996; Morin, Rodrigue, & Ivers, 2003; Walsh & Ustun, 1999).

You might ask yourself how sleep-wake disorders fit into a textbook on abnormal psychology. Different variations of disturbed sleep clearly have physiological bases and therefore could be considered purely medical concerns. Like other physical disorders, however, sleep problems interact in important ways with psychological factors.

AN OVERVIEW OF SLEEP-WAKE DISORDERS

Before moving on to consider the sleep-wake disorders that people can experience, we should first discuss the normal stages of sleep and how we cycle between these stages during a typical sleep episode, to better understand how and when this cycle is interrupted in abnormal sleep. As clearly described by University of British Columbia psychologist Stanley Coren in his popular book *Sleep Thieves* (1996), sleep can be divided into two broad states: (1) the slow-wave state in which the person sleeps deeply, and (2) the **rapid eye movement (REM)** state in which the brain appears as if it is awake and in which the sleeper experiences dreams. Between these two broad states are some transition stages. Sleep researchers traditionally refer to four numbered stages of sleep that differ in the depth of sleep involved. In Stage 1, the person transitions through wakefulness into drowsiness and then sleep. During this stage, the person drifts in and out of awareness of his or her surroundings. In Stage 2, the person is truly sleeping, yet the sleep is light (i.e., the sleeper can easily be aroused). When awoken from this stage of sleep, 70 percent of people report that they didn't think they were asleep but were just "dozing and thinking." Stages 3 and 4 make up deep, slow-wave sleep. Stage 3 involves moderately deep sleep and Stage 4 very deep sleep. Not only are people hard to awaken when in Stage 4 sleep, but when awoken, they may appear disoriented for a few minutes.

Throughout the night, we show a 90-minute cycle of sleep, progressing from light sleep to deeper sleep, then back to light sleep, and ending with REM sleep and dreaming. When we awaken in the morning, we typically awaken out of REM sleep during a dream. Normal sleepers spend about 20 percent of their sleep time in deep sleep, 30 percent dreaming, and 50 percent in light sleep (Coren, 1996).

Several disorders covered in this book are frequently associated with sleep complaints, including schizophrenia, major depression, bipolar disorder, and anxiety-related disorders. Individuals with a wide range of developmental disorders are also at greater risk for having sleep disorders (Durand, 1998). For example, Penny Corkum of Dalhousie University and her colleagues note that reports of sleep problems in children with attention-deficit/hyperactivity disorder (ADHD) are prevalent, although the exact nature of sleep problems in children with ADHD remains to be determined (Corkum et al., 1998; see also Weiss et al., 2006). You may think at first that a sleep problem is the result of a psychological disorder. For example, how often have you been anxious about a future event (an upcoming exam, perhaps) and not been able to fall asleep? However, the relationship between sleep disturbances and mental health is more complex (Pires et al., 2015; McEwen & Karatsoreos, 2015). Sleep problems may cause the difficulties people experience in everyday life (Kreutzmann et al., 2015; Almklov et al., 2015; McKenna & Eyler, 2012; Talbot et al., 2012; van der Kloet et al., 2012), or they may result from some disturbance common to a psychological disorder. For example, Mullane and Corkum (2006) examined the possibility that sleep problems contribute to ADHD symptoms in children. In a series of three cases, they implemented a behavioural treatment for children with sleep problems and ADHD. While the behavioural treatment was effective in treating the sleep problems, it had no impact on the ADHD symptoms. This study provides preliminary evidence that ADHD is not simply secondary to sleep problems in children with both disorders.

In Chapter 5, we explained how a brain circuit in the limbic system may be involved with anxiety. We know that this region of the brain is also involved with our dream sleep, or REM sleep (Verrier et al., 2000). This mutual neurobiological connection suggests that anxiety and sleep may be interrelated in important ways. Insufficient sleep, for example, can stimulate overeating and may contribute to obesity (Hanlon & Knutson, 2014). As explained by Toronto physician Jason Fund in his book *The Obesity Code* (2016), poor sleep can raise cortisol, which itself raises insulin, leading to weight gain. Similarly, REM sleep seems to be related to depression, as noted in Chapter 7 (Emslie et al., 1994). In one study, researchers found that cognitive-behavioural therapy improved depression in men and normalized their REM sleep patterns (Nofzinger et al., 1994). Furthermore, sleep deprivation has temporary antidepressant effects on some people (Hillman et al., 1990), although in people who are not already depressed, sleep deprivation may bring on a depressed mood (Voderhozer et al., 2014).

In yet another example of the relation of sleep problems to psychological disorders, sleep difficulties are commonly reported by people with schizophrenia in the prodromal phase (i.e., just before the onset of the psychotic episode; see Herz, 1985). For example, in a study conducted at four sites in Canada and the United States, Miller and colleagues (2002) found that sleep disturbances were experienced by 37 percent of the patients with schizophrenia just before the onset of their psychotic episode. We do not fully understand how psychological disorders are related to sleep, yet accumulating research points to the importance of understanding sleep if we are to complete the broader picture of abnormal behaviour.

Sleep-wake disorders are divided into two major categories: **dyssomnias** and **parasomnias**. Dyssomnias involve difficulties getting enough sleep—not being able to fall asleep until 2 a.m. when you have a 9 a.m. class—and complaints about the quality of sleep, such as not feeling refreshed even though you have slept the whole night. The parasomnias are characterized by abnormal events that occur during sleep, such as nightmares and sleepwalking.

The clearest and most comprehensive picture of your sleep habits can be determined only by a **polysomnographic (PSG) evaluation** (Mindell & Owens, 2015). The patient spends one or more nights sleeping in a sleep laboratory, being monitored on measures that include respiration; leg movements; brain wave activity, measured by an *electroencephalograph* (EEG); eye movements, measured by an *electrooculograph* (EOG); muscle movements, measured by an *electromyograph* (EMG); and heart activity, measured by an *electrocardiogram* (ECG). Daytime behaviour and typical sleep patterns are also noted, for example, whether the person uses drugs or alcohol, is anxious about work or interpersonal problems, takes afternoon naps, or has a psychological disorder. A less time-consuming and less costly alternative to the comprehensive assessment of sleep involves using a wristwatch-size device called an *actigraph*, which records the number of arm movements. The data can be downloaded onto a computer to determine the length and quality of sleep (Monk et al., 1999). Actigraphs are useful aids in monitoring sleep in insomnia treatment outcome studies (Vallières & Morin, 2003).

In addition, clinicians and researchers find it helpful to know the average number of hours the individual sleeps each day, taking into account **sleep efficiency**, the percentage of time actually spent asleep, not just lying in bed trying to sleep. sleep efficiency is calculated by dividing the amount of time sleeping by the amount of time in bed (Milner et al., 2006). A sleep efficiency of 100 percent would mean you fall asleep as soon as your head hits the pillow and do not wake up at all during the night. In contrast, a sleep efficiency of 50 percent would mean half your time in bed is spent trying to fall asleep. Such measurements help the clinician determine objectively how well you sleep.

One way to determine whether a person has a problem with sleep is to observe his or her *daytime sequelae*, or behaviour while awake. For example, if it takes you 90 minutes to fall asleep at night, but this doesn't bother you and you feel rested during the day, then you do not have a problem. A friend who also takes 90 minutes to fall asleep but finds this delay anxiety provoking and is fatigued the next day might be considered to have a sleep problem.

INSOMNIA DISORDER

Insomnia is one of the most common sleep-wake disorders. You may picture someone with insomnia as being awake all the time. It isn't possible to go completely without sleep, however. For example, after being awake for about one or two nights, a person begins having **microsleeps** that last several seconds or longer (Roehrs et al., 2000). In the very rare occurrences of *fatal familial insomnia* (a degenerative brain disorder), total lack of sleep eventually leads to death (Parchi et al., 2012). Despite the common use of the term *insomnia* to mean "not sleeping," it actually applies to a number of complaints (Savard et al., 2003). People are considered to have insomnia if they have trouble falling asleep at night (difficulty initiating sleep), if they wake up frequently or too early and can't go back to sleep (difficulty maintaining sleep), or even if they sleep a reasonable number of hours but are still not rested the next day (nonrestorative sleep). Consider the case of Kathryn.

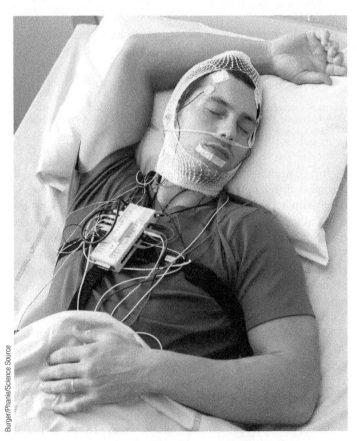

Burger/Phanie/Science Source

▲ This person is participating in a polysomnograph, an overnight electronic evaluation of sleep patterns.

KATHRYN | *Tossing and Turning*

Kathryn, who was 73, reported having serious sleep problems ever since her husband died 19 years earlier. She could not fall asleep until she had lain in bed for several hours, and she awakened a number of times each night. She had an average of four to five hours of broken sleep per night. It is not surprising she was chronically tired throughout the day and complained that fatigue interfered with her friendships. She no longer enjoyed going out with her friends because she fell asleep in public, which was very embarrassing to her.

Kathryn used nonprescription sleeping pills on and off over the years, and sometimes she just lay in bed listening to the radio and nodding off occasionally. When her sleep problems started, Kathryn recognized that her distress over her husband's death was probably to blame. As the years passed, she assumed poor sleep was normal for a person her age and her fatigue was also part of the aging process. However, during the past months, she began to realize she wasn't playing with her grandchildren or leaving her house because she was too tired. On the advice of a friend, she decided to get some help.

Clinical Description

Kathryn's symptoms meet the *DSM-5* criteria for **insomnia disorder** (also referred to as primary insomnia) because her sleep problems were not related to other medical or psychiatric problems (see DSM Table 10.1). Kathryn's is a typical case of insomnia disorder. She had trouble both initiating and maintaining sleep. Other people sleep all night but still feel as if they've been awake for hours. Although most people can carry out necessary daily activities, their inability to concentrate can have serious consequences, such as debilitating accidents when they attempt to drive long distances (like truck drivers do). Kathryn wouldn't drive her car on the highway because she feared falling asleep at the wheel. Students with insomnia may do poorly in school because of difficulty concentrating.

Statistics

According to data from the 2014–2015 cycle of the CHMS, almost a quarter of Canadians (24 percent) between the ages of 6 and 79 have experienced nighttime insomnia symptoms that have lasted at least one year (Chaput et al., 2018). This was an increase over the 17 percent in the 2007–2009 cycle of the survey. Women report insomnia symptoms more often than men. Thirty percent of women reported experiencing nighttime insomnia symptoms for at least one year, compared to 21 percent of men.

For many individuals, sleep difficulties are a lifetime affliction (Lind et al., 2015). In one study, 31 percent of the people who expressed concern about sleep continued to experience difficulties a year later (Ford & Kamerow, 1989), a result showing that sleep problems may become chronic (Lind et al., 2015). Approximately 15 percent of older adults report excessive daytime sleepiness, and this contributes to increased risk for falling in older women (Hayley et al., 2015).

DSM-5 | **Table 10.1** Diagnostic Criteria for Insomnia Disorder

A. A predominant complaint of dissatisfaction with sleep quantity or quality associated with one or more of the following symptoms:
  1. Difficulty initiating sleep. (In children, this may manifest as difficulty initiating sleep without caregiver intervention.)
  2. Difficulty maintaining sleep, characterized by frequent awakenings or problems returning to sleep after awakenings. (In children, this may manifest as difficulty returning to sleep without caregiver intervention.)
  3. Early-morning awakening with inability to return to sleep.

B. The sleep disturbance causes clinically significant distress in social, occupational, educational, academic, behavioral, or other important areas of functioning.

C. The sleep difficulty occurs at least 3 nights per week.

D. The sleep difficulty is present for at least 3 months.

E. The sleep difficulty occurs despite adequate opportunity for sleep.

F. The insomnia is not better explained by and does not occur exclusively during the course of another sleep-wake disorder (e.g., narcolepsy, breathing-related sleep disorder, a circadian rhythm sleep-wake disorder, a parasomnia).

G. The insomnia is not attributable to the physiological effects of a substance (e.g., a drug of abuse, a medication).

H. Co-existing mental disorders and medical conditions do not adequately explain the predominant complaint of insomnia.

Specify if:
  With non-sleep disorder mental comorbidity, including substance use disorders
  With other medical comorbidity
  With other sleep disorder

Specify if:
  Episodic: Symptoms last at least 1 month but less than 3 months.
  Persistent: Symptoms last 3 months or longer.
  Recurrent: Two (or more) episodes within the space of 1 year.

Source: Reprinted with permission from the *Diagnostic and Statistical Manual of Mental Disorders*, Fifth Edition (Copyright © 2013). American Psychiatric Association. All Rights Reserved.

Just as normal sleep needs change over time, complaints of insomnia differ in frequency among people of different ages. Approximately one in five young children experiences insomnia (Calhoun et al., 2014). As children move into adolescence, their biologically determined sleep schedules shift toward a later bedtime (Skeldon et al., 2015). At least in North America, however, children are still expected to rise early for school, causing sleep deprivation. As people age, the percentage who complain of sleep problems rises to more than 25 percent for people over the age of 65 (Mellinger et al., 1985). This change across age groups was apparent in the 2014–2015 cycle of the CHMS (Chaput et al., 2018). The percentage of Canadians experiencing nighttime insomnia symptoms for at least a year increased with age: it was lowest at 9 percent among young Canadian children (ages 6 to 13), rose to 15 percent among those 14 to 17 years of age, and hit highs of 25 percent among adults (ages 18 to 64) and 22 percent for seniors (ages 65 to 79).

Several psychological disorders are associated with insomnia (Benca et al., 1992). Total sleep time often decreases with depression, substance use disorders, anxiety disorders, and dementia of the Alzheimer's type. The interrelationship between alcohol use and sleep disorders can be particularly troubling. Alcohol is often used to initiate sleep (Morin et al., 2012). In small amounts it may work, but it also interrupts ongoing sleep. Interrupted sleep causes anxiety, which often leads to repeated alcohol use and an obviously vicious cycle (Stewart, 1996).

Causes

Insomnia accompanies many medical and psychological disorders, including pain and physical discomfort, physical inactivity during the day, and respiratory problems. Sometimes insomnia is related to problems with the biological clock and its control of temperature. Light exposure causes an acute increase in human body temperature, which normally falls during the night (Song & Rusak, 2000). People who can't fall asleep at night may have a delayed temperature rhythm: Their body temperature doesn't drop and they don't become drowsy until later at night (Morris et al., 1990). As a group, people with insomnia seem to have higher body temperatures than good sleepers, and their body temperatures seem to vary less; this lack of fluctuation may interfere with sleep (Taylor et al., 2014).

Among the other factors that can interfere with sleeping are drug use and a variety of environmental influences, such as changes in light, noise, or temperature. People admitted to hospitals often have difficulty sleeping because the noises and routines differ from those at home. Other sleep disorders, such as *sleep apnea* (a disorder that involves pauses in nighttime breathing that are sometimes caused by obstruction) or *periodic limb movement disorder* (excessive jerky leg movements), can cause interrupted sleep and may seem similar to insomnia.

Finally, various psychological stresses can also disrupt your sleep (Morin, 1993). Poll your friends around the time of final exams to see how many of them are having trouble falling asleep or are not sleeping through the night. The stress you experience during such times may interfere with your sleep, at least temporarily. A survey study by Sutton and colleagues (2001) found that having a very stressful life was one of the three strongest predictors of insomnia among Canadians. A study by Morin and colleagues (2003) compared 40 individuals with insomnia to 27 good sleepers. They found that those with insomnia reported a greater impact of daily minor stressors and a greater intensity of major negative life events than the good sleepers. Not only did the insomniac people perceive their lives to be more stressful, they also reported greater levels of arousal before sleep than did the good sleepers.

Many studies illuminate the role of cognition in insomnia, suggesting that our thoughts alone may disrupt our sleep. Indeed, people with insomnia may have unrealistic expectations about how much sleep they need ("I need a full eight hours") and about how disruptive disturbed sleep will be ("I won't be able to think or do my job if I sleep for only five hours") (Morin, Stone, et al., 1993). Ryerson University psychologist Colleen Carney and her colleagues have found that unhelpful sleep-related beliefs and ruminations about sleep are present even during the daytime in people with insomnia (Palagini et al., 2015).

Is poor sleeping a learned behaviour? It is generally accepted that some people associate the bedroom and bed with the frustration and anxiety that go with insomnia. Eventually, the arrival of bedtime itself may cause anxiety (Morin & Benca, 2012). Interactions associated with sleep may contribute to children's sleep problems. For example, one study found that a parent's depression and negative thoughts about child sleep negatively influenced infant night waking (Teti & Crosby, 2012). Researchers think that some children learn to fall asleep only with a parent present; if they wake up at night, they are frightened at finding themselves alone and their sleep is

▲ In many cultures, all family members share the same bed.

▲ Colleen Carney is a Ryerson University professor and expert on insomnia.

disrupted. It is unlikely that learning alone accounts for children's sleep difficulties, however. Instead, biological and psychological factors are likely reciprocally related. For example, Adair and colleagues (1991) noted that a child's temperament (or personality) may play a role in explaining the relation between parental presence when a child is going to sleep and sleep problems in the child. The children with sleep problems had comparatively more difficult temperaments, and their parents were presumably present to attend to sleep initiation difficulties. In other words, personality characteristics, sleep difficulties, and parental reaction interact in a reciprocal manner to produce and maintain sleep problems.

Cultural factors may also play a role. Cross-cultural sleep research has focused primarily on children. In the predominant culture in North America, infants are expected to sleep on their own, in a separate bed, and, if possible, in a separate room. However, in many other cultures as diverse as rural Guatemala and Korea and urban Japan, the child spends the first few years of life in the same room and sometimes the same bed as the mother (Burnham & Gaylor, 2011). In many cultures, mothers report that they do not ignore the cries of their children (Giannotti & Cortesi, 2009), in stark contrast to North America, where most pediatricians recommend that parents ignore the cries of their infants at night (Moore, 2012). Recent data from Canada suggest that bed-sharing is more common than we thought: about one-third of Canadian mothers says they very frequently sleep with their infant in their first year, to assist breastfeeding but also to make sleeping easier for them or their infants (Gilmour et al., 2019).

People may be biologically vulnerable to disturbed sleep. This vulnerability differs from person to person and can range from mild to more severe disturbances. For example, a person may be a light sleeper (easily aroused at night) or have a family history of insomnia, narcolepsy, or obstructed breathing. All these factors can lead to eventual sleeping problems. Such influences have been referred to as predisposing conditions (Spielman & Glovinsky, 1991); they may not, by themselves, always cause problems, but they may combine with other factors to interfere with sleep (see ■ Figure 10.2).

An Integrative Model

Biological vulnerability may in turn interact with sleep stress (Durand, 2008), which includes a number of events that can negatively affect sleep. For example, poor bedtime habits (such as having too much alcohol or caffeine) can interfere with falling asleep (Morin et al., 2012). Note that biological vulnerability and sleep stress influence each other (see the double arrows in the integrative model of sleep disturbance in Figure 10.2). Although we may intuitively assume that biological factors come first, extrinsic influences such as poor sleep hygiene (the daily activities that affect how we sleep) can affect the physiological activity of sleep. One of the most striking examples of this phenomenon is jet lag, in which people's sleep patterns are disrupted, sometimes seriously, when they fly across several time zones. Whether disturbances continue or become more severe may depend on how they are managed. For example,

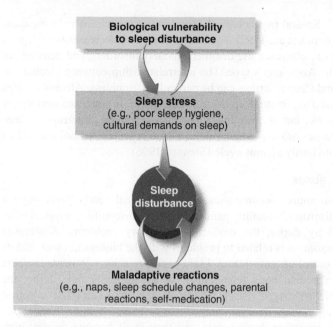

FIGURE 10.2 | An integrative multidimensional model of sleep disturbance.

© Cengage Learning

many people react to disrupted sleep by taking over-the-counter sleeping pills. Unfortunately, most people are not aware that **rebound insomnia** may occur when the medication is withdrawn. This rebound leads people to think they still have a sleep problem, re-administer the medicine, and go through the cycle repeatedly. In other words, taking sleep aids can perpetuate sleep problems (Westra & Stewart, 2002).

Other ways of reacting to poor sleep can also prolong problems. It seems reasonable that a person who hasn't had enough sleep can make up for this loss by napping during the day. Unfortunately, naps that alleviate fatigue during the day can also disrupt sleep that night. Anxiety can also extend the problem. Lying in bed worrying about school, family problems, or even about not being able to sleep will interfere with your sleep (O'Kearney & Pech, 2014).

HYPERSOMNOLENCE DISORDERS

Insomnia disorder involves not getting enough sleep (the prefix *in* means "lacking" or "without"), and **hypersomnolence disorders** involve sleeping too much (*hyper* means "in great amount" or "abnormal excess"). Many people who sleep all night find themselves falling asleep several times the next day. Consider the case of Ann.

ANN | *Sleeping in Public*

Ann, a college student, came to my office to discuss her progress in class. We talked about several questions that she had gotten wrong on the last exam, and as she was about to leave she said that she never fell asleep during my class. This seemed like faint praise, but I thanked her for the feedback. "No," she said, "you don't understand. I usually fall asleep in all of my classes, but not in yours." Again, I didn't quite understand what she was trying to tell me and joked that she must pick her professors more carefully. She laughed. "That's probably true. But I also have this problem with sleeping too much."

As we talked more seriously, Ann told me that excessive sleeping had been a problem since her teenage years. In situations that were monotonous or boring, or when she couldn't be active, she fell asleep. This could happen several times a day, depending on what she was doing. Recently, large lecture classes had become a problem unless the lecturer was particularly interesting or animated. Watching television and driving long distances were also problematic.

Ann reported that her father had a similar problem. He had recently been diagnosed with *narcolepsy* (which we discuss next) and was now getting help at a clinic. Both she and her brother had been diagnosed with hypersomnolence disorder. Ann had been prescribed Ritalin (a stimulant medication) about four years ago and said that it was only somewhat effective in keeping her awake during the day. She said the drug helped reduce the sleep attacks but did not eliminate them altogether.

The *DSM-5* diagnostic criteria for hypersomnolence include not only the excessive sleepiness that Ann described but also the subjective impression of this problem (American Psychiatric Association, 2013; see DSM Table 10.2). Remember that whether insomnia disorder is a problem depends on how it affects each person individually. Ann found her disorder very disruptive because it interfered with her driving and paying attention in class. Hypersomnolence caused her to be less successful academically and also upset her personally, both of which are defining features of this disorder. She slept approximately eight hours each night, so her daytime sleepiness couldn't be attributed to insufficient sleep.

Several factors that can cause excessive sleepiness would not be considered hypersomnolence. For example, people with insomnia disorder (who get inadequate amounts of sleep) often report being tired during the day. In contrast, people with hypersomnolence sleep through the night and appear rested on awakening but still complain of being excessively tired throughout the day. Another sleep problem that can cause a similar excessive sleepiness is a breathing-related sleep disorder called **sleep apnea**. People with this problem have difficulty breathing at night. They often snore loudly, pause between breaths, and wake in the morning with a dry mouth and headache. In identifying hypersomnolence, you need to rule out insomnia, sleep apnea, or other reasons for sleepiness during the day (American Psychiatric Association, 2013).

We are just beginning to understand the nature of hypersomnolence, so relatively little research has been done on its causes. Genetic influences seem to be involved in a portion of cases

DSM-5	**Table 10.2** Diagnostic Criteria for Hypersomnolence Disorder

A. Self-reported excessive sleepiness (hypersomnolence) despite a main sleep period lasting at least 7 hours, with at least one of the following symptoms:

  1. Recurrent periods of sleep or lapses into sleep within the same day.

  2. A prolonged main sleep episode of more than 9 hours per day that is nonrestorative (i.e., unrefreshing).

  3. Difficulty being fully awake after abrupt awakening.

B. The hypersomnolence occurs at least three times per week, for at least 3 months.

C. The hypersomnolence is accompanied by significant distress or impairment in cognitive, social, occupational, or other important areas of functioning.

D. The hypersomnolence is not better explained by and does not occur exclusively during the course of another sleep disorder (e.g., narcolepsy, breathing-related sleep disorder, circadian rhythm sleep-wake disorder, or a parasomnia).

E. The hypersomnolence is not attributable to the physiological effects of a substance (e.g., a drug of abuse, a medication).

F. Co-existing mental and medical disorders do not adequately explain the predominant complaint of hypersomnolence.

Specify if:

  With mental disorder, including substance use disorders

  With medical condition

  With another sleep disorder

Specify if:

  Acute: Duration of less than 1 month.

  Subacute: Duration of 1–3 months.

  Persistent: Duration of more than 3 months.

Specify current severity:

  Specify severity based on degree of difficulty maintaining daytime alertness as manifested by the occurrence of multiple attacks of irresistible sleepiness within any given day occurring, for example, while sedentary, driving, visiting with friends, or working.

  Mild: Difficulty maintaining daytime alertness 1–2 days/week

  Moderate: Difficulty maintaining daytime alertness 3–4 days/week

  Severe: Difficulty maintaining daytime alertness 5–7 days/week

Source: Reprinted with permission from the *Diagnostic and Statistical Manual of Mental Disorders,* Fifth Edition (Copyright © 2013). American Psychiatric Association. All Rights Reserved.

(Buysse et al., 2008). A significant subgroup of people diagnosed with hypersomnolence disorder previously were exposed to a viral infection, such as mononucleosis, hepatitis, and viral pneumonia, which suggests there may be more than one cause (Hirshkowitz et al., 2009).

NARCOLEPSY

Ann described her father as having **narcolepsy**, a different form of the sleeping problem she and her brother shared (Goodrick, 2014). In addition to daytime sleepiness, some people with narcolepsy experience *cataplexy*, a sudden loss of muscle tone (see DSM Table 10.3). Cataplexy occurs while the person is awake, and it can range from slight weakness in the facial muscles to complete physical collapse. Cataplexy

DSM-5	**Table 10.3** Diagnostic Criteria for Narcolepsy

A. Recurrent periods of irrepressible need to sleep, lapsing into sleep, or napping occurring within the same day. These must have been occurring at least three times per week over the past 3 months.

B. The presence of at least one of the following:

1. Episodes of cataplexy defined as either (a) or (b), occurring at least a few times per month:

   (a) In individuals with long-standing disease, brief (seconds to minutes) episodes of sudden bilateral loss of muscle tone with maintained consciousness, precipitated by laughter or joking.

   (b) In children or in individuals within 6 months of onset, spontaneous grimaces or jaw-opening episodes with tongue thrusting or a global hypotonia, without any obvious emotional triggers.

2. Hypocretin deficiency, as measured using cerebrospinal fluid (CSF) hypocretin-1 immunoreactivity values (less than or equal to one-third of values obtained in healthy subjects tested using the same assay, or less than or equal to 110 pg/ml). Low CSF levels of hypocretin-1 must not be observed in the context of acute brain injury, inflammation, or infection.

3. Nocturnal sleep polysomnography showing rapid eye movement (REM) sleep latency less than or equal to 15 minutes, or a multiple sleep latency test showing a mean sleep latency less than or equal to 8 minutes and two or more sleep onset REM periods.

Specify current severity:

Mild: Infrequent cataplexy (less than once per week), need for naps only once or twice per day, and less disturbed nocturnal sleep

Moderate: Cataplexy once daily or every few days, disturbed nocturnal sleep, and need for multiple naps daily

Severe: Drug-resistant cataplexy with multiple attacks daily, nearly constant sleepiness, and disturbed nocturnal sleep (i.e., movements, insomnia, and vivid dreaming)

Source: Reprinted with permission from the *Diagnostic and Statistical Manual of Mental Disorders*, Fifth Edition (Copyright © 2013). American Psychiatric Association. All Rights Reserved.

lasts from several seconds to several minutes; it is usually preceded by strong emotion, such as anger or happiness. Imagine that while cheering for your favourite team, you suddenly fall asleep, or while arguing with a friend, you collapse to the floor in a sound sleep!

Cataplexy appears to result from a sudden onset of REM sleep. Instead of falling asleep normally and going through the four nonrapid eye movement (NREM) sleep stages (i.e., Stages 1 to 4, discussed previously) that typically precede REM sleep, people with narcolepsy periodically progress right to this dream sleep stage almost directly from the state of being awake. One outcome of REM sleep is the inhibition of input to the muscles, and this seems to be the process that leads to cataplexy.

Two other characteristics distinguish people who have narcolepsy (Ahmed & Thorpy, 2012), both of which were discussed in Chapter 5 in the context of Newfoundlanders' experience of the "Old Hag" and African and Caribbean people's experience of being "ridden by the witch." Specifically, people with narcolepsy commonly report *sleep paralysis* and *hypnagogic hallucinations*. Sleep paralysis refers to a brief period after awakening when the person can't move or speak that is often frightening to those who go through it. Hypnagogic hallucinations are vivid experiences that begin at the start of sleep and are said to be unbelievably realistic because they include not only visual aspects but also touch, hearing, and even the sensation of body movement. Examples of hypnagogic hallucinations, which, like sleep paralysis, can be quite terrifying, include the vivid illusion of being caught in a fire or flying through the air. Narcolepsy is relatively rare, occurring in 0.03 to 0.16 percent of the population, with the numbers approximately equal among males and females. The problems associated with narcolepsy usually are first seen during the teenage years. Fortunately, the cataplexy, hypnagogic hallucinations, and sleep paralysis often decrease in frequency over time, although sleepiness during the day does not seem to diminish with age.

Sleep paralysis and hypnagogic hallucinations may serve a role in explaining a most unusual phenomenon—UFO or alien abduction experiences (Sharpless & Doghramji, 2015). Each year numerous people report seeing unidentified flying objects—UFOs—and some even tell of visiting with inhabitants of other planets (Sheaffer, 1986). A group of scientists led by the late Nicholas Spanos, whose research was first discussed in Chapter 6, examined people who had had such experiences, separating them into those who had nonintense experiences (seeing only lights and shapes in the sky) and those with intense experiences (seeing and communicating with aliens; Spanos, et al., 1993). They found that a majority of the reported UFO incidents occurred at night, and that 60 percent of the intense UFO stories were associated with sleep episodes. Specifically, the reports of these intense accounts were often described in ways that resembled accounts of people experiencing a frightening episode of sleep paralysis and hypnagogic hallucination, as illustrated by the following account:

> I was lying in bed facing the wall, and suddenly my heart started to race. I could feel the presence of three entities standing beside me. I was unable to move my body but could move my eyes. One of the entities, a male, was laughing at me, not verbally but with his mind. He made me feel stupid. He told me telepathically, "Don't you know by now that you can't do anything unless we let you?" (Spanos et al., 1993, p. 627)

Specific genetic models of narcolepsy are now being developed (Peall & Robertson, 2014). Previous research with Doberman pinschers and Labrador retrievers, who also inherit this disorder, suggests that narcolepsy is associated with a cluster of genes on chromosome 6, and it may be an autosomal recessive trait. Advances in understanding the etiology and treatment of such disorders can be credited to the help of man's best friend.

BREATHING-RELATED SLEEP DISORDERS

For some people, sleepiness during the day or disrupted sleep at night has a physical origin, namely, problems with breathing while asleep. In the *DSM-5*, these problems are diagnosed as **breathing-related sleep disorders**. People whose breathing is

▲ Excessive sleepiness can be very disruptive.

interrupted during their sleep often experience numerous brief arousals throughout the night and do not feel rested even after eight or nine hours asleep (Overeem & Reading, 2010). For all of us, the muscles in the upper airway relax during sleep, constricting the passageway somewhat and making breathing a little more difficult. For some, unfortunately, breathing is constricted a great deal and may be very laboured (*hypoventilation*) or, in the extreme, there may be short periods (10 to 30 seconds) when they stop breathing altogether, called *sleep apnea*. Just over 6 percent of Canadians report having been diagnosed with sleep apnea; the diagnosis twice as likely among men than women, and three times more likely among older adults compared to those under 60 years of age (Edjoc & Gal, 2018). Often the affected person is only minimally aware of breathing difficulties and doesn't attribute the sleep problems to the breathing. A bed partner usually notices loud snoring (which is one sign of this problem), however, or will have noticed frightening episodes of interrupted breathing. Other signs that a person has breathing difficulties are heavy sweating during the night, morning headaches, and episodes of falling asleep during the day (*sleep attacks*) with no resulting feeling of being rested (Hauri, 1982). As noted by Charles George at the University of Western Ontario and his colleagues, sleep apnea is associated with an increased number of motor vehicle accidents (Hartenbaum et al., 2006), likely because of these associated sleep attacks.

There are three types of apnea, each with different causes, daytime complaints, and treatment: obstructive, central, and mixed sleep apnea. *Obstructive sleep apnea hypopnea syndrome* occurs when airflow stops despite continued activity by the respiratory system (Mbata & Chukwuka, 2012). In some people, the airway is too narrow; in others, some abnormality or damage interferes with the ongoing effort to breathe. Everyone in a group of people with obstructive sleep apnea hypopnea syndrome reported snoring at night (Goel et al., 2015). Obesity is sometimes associated with this problem, as is increasing age. Some work now suggests that the use of MDMA (ecstasy) can lead to obstructive apnea hypop-

nea syndrome even in young and otherwise healthy adults (McCann et al., 2009). Obstructive sleep apnea is most common in males and is thought to occur in approximately 20 percent of the population (Franklin & Lindberg, 2015). The second type of apnea, *central sleep apnea*, involves the complete cessation of respiratory activity for brief periods and is often associated with certain central nervous system disorders, such as cerebral vascular disease, head trauma, and degenerative disorders (Badr, 2012). Unlike people with obstructive sleep apnea hypopnea syndrome, those with central sleep apnea wake up frequently during the night but they tend not to report excessive daytime sleepiness and often are not aware of having a serious breathing problem. Because of the lack of daytime symptoms, people tend not to seek treatment, so we know relatively little about this disorder's prevalence or course. The third breathing disorder, *sleep-related hypoventilation*, is a decrease in airflow without a complete pause in breathing. This tends to cause an increase in carbon dioxide (CO_2) levels, because insufficient air is exchanged with the environment. All these breathing difficulties interrupt sleep and result in symptoms similar to those of insomnia.

CIRCADIAN RHYTHM SLEEP-WAKE DISORDERS

"Spring forward; fall back": Many Canadians use this mnemonic device to remind themselves to turn the clocks ahead one hour in the spring and back again one hour in the fall. Most of us consider the shift to daylight savings time a minor inconvenience and are thus surprised to see how disruptive this time change can be. For at least a day or two, we may be sleepy during the day and have difficulty falling asleep at night, almost as if we had jet lag. The difficulty has to do with how our internal clocks adjust to this change in time. Convention says to go to sleep at this new time while our brains are saying something different. If the struggle continues, you may have what is called a **circadian rhythm sleep-wake disorder**. This disorder is characterized by disturbed sleep (either insomnia or excessive sleepiness during the day) brought on by the brain's inability to synchronize its sleep patterns with the current patterns of day and night.

In the 1960s, German and French scientists identified several bodily rhythms that seem to persist without cues from the environment—rhythms that are self-regulated (Aschoff & Wever, 1962; Siffre, 1964). Because these rhythms don't exactly match our 24-hour day, they are called "circadian" (from *circa* meaning "about" and *dian* meaning "day"). If our circadian rhythms don't match the 24-hour day, why isn't our sleep completely disrupted over time?

Fortunately, our brains have a mechanism that keeps us in sync with the outside world. As noted by Michael Antle at the University of Calgary, our internal clock is in the *suprachiasmatic nucleus* in the hypothalamus (Antle & Silver, 2005). Connected to the suprachiasmatic nucleus is a pathway that comes from our eyes. The light we see in the morning and the decreasing light at night signal the brain to reset the internal clock each day (see also

Coren, 1996). Unfortunately, some people have trouble sleeping when they want to because of problems with their circadian rhythms, since sleep onset is closely related to circadian rhythms (Mistlberger & Rusak, 2005). The causes may be outside the person (e.g., crossing several time zones in a short amount of time) or internal.

Not being synchronized with the normal sleep-wake cycles causes people to be interrupted when they do try to sleep, and to be tired during the day. There are several different types of circadian rhythm sleep disorders. *Jet lag type* is, as its name implies, caused by rapidly crossing multiple time zones (Abba et al., 2014). People with jet lag usually report difficulty going to sleep at the proper time and feeling fatigued during the day. Travelling more than two time zones westward usually affects people the most. Travelling eastward and/or less than three time zones is usually tolerated better (Kolla et al., 2012). Research with mice suggests that the effects of jet lag can be quite serious—at least among older adults. When older mice were exposed to repeated artificial jet lag, a significant number of them lived shorter lives (Davidson et al., 2006), and artificial jet lag has also been shown to increase cancer risk in mice (van Dycke et al., 2015). *Shift-work-type* sleep problems are associated with work schedules (Abba et al., 2012). Many people, such as hospital employees, police, or emergency personnel, work at night or must work irregular hours; as a result, they may have problems sleeping or experience excessive sleepiness during waking hours. Unfortunately, the problems of working (and thus staying awake) at unusual times can go beyond sleep and may contribute to cardiovascular disease, ulcers, and breast cancer in women (Truong et al., 2014). Working rotating shifts is consistently predictive of poor sleep (Linton et al., 2015).

In contrast with jet lag and shift-work sleep-related problems, which have external causes such as long-distance travel and job selection, several circadian rhythm sleep problems seem to arise from within the person experiencing the problems. Extreme night owls, people who stay up late and sleep late, may have a problem known as *delayed sleep phase type*. Sleep is delayed or later than normal bedtime. At the other end of the extreme, people with an advanced sleep phase type of circadian rhythm disorder are "early to bed and early to rise." Here, sleep is advanced or earlier than normal bedtime. Finally, two other types, *irregular sleep-wake type* (people who experience highly varied sleep cycles) and *non-24-hour sleep-wake type* (e.g., sleeping on a 25- or 26-hour cycle with later and later bedtimes ultimately going throughout the day), illustrate the diversity of circadian rhythm sleep-wake problems some people experience.

Research on why our sleep rhythms are disrupted is advancing quickly, and we are now beginning to understand the circadian rhythm process. Scientists believe the hormone *melatonin* contributes to the setting of our internal clocks that tell us when to sleep. This hormone is produced by the pineal gland, in the centre of the brain. Melatonin has been nicknamed the "Dracula hormone" because its production is stimulated by darkness and ceases in daylight. When our eyes see it is nighttime, this information is passed on to the pineal gland, which, in turn, begins producing melatonin. Researchers believe that both light and melatonin help set the internal clock (Stevens & Zhu, 2015). Thus, this hormone

may help us treat some of the sleep problems people experience. For example, melatonin may be used as a treatment for people who experience severe jet lag and other sleep problems associated with circadian rhythm disruption (Sack & Lewy, 1993).

Concept Check   10.1

Match the following descriptions of sleeping problems with the correct term: (a) cataplexy, (b) hypersomnolence disorder, (c) insomnia disorder, (d) sleep apnea, (e) sleep paralysis, (f) narcolepsy, (g) circadian rhythm sleep disorder, and (h) breathing-related sleep disorder.

1. Sonia has problems staying awake throughout the day. Even while talking on the phone or riding the bus, she unexpectedly loses muscle tone and falls asleep for a while. This is _____.

2. Jaime sometimes awakens and cannot move or speak. This is a particularly frightening experience known as

   _____.

3. Brett has started a new job that requires him to change shifts monthly. He sometimes has day shifts and at other times has night shifts. Since then he has considerable trouble sleeping. _____

4. Rama is extremely overweight. His wife suspects he may be suffering from _____ because he snores every night and often wakes up exhausted as though he never slept.

5. Melinda sleeps all night and still finds herself falling asleep throughout the next day. This happens even when she goes to bed early and gets up as late as possible.

   _____

TREATMENT OF SLEEP-WAKE DISORDERS

When we can't fall asleep or when we awaken frequently, or when sleep does not restore our energy and vitality, we need help. Several biological and psychological interventions have been designed and evaluated to help people regain the benefits of normal sleep.

MEDICAL TREATMENTS

Perhaps the most common treatments for insomnia are medical. According to a Statistics Canada report, based on the 2002 CCHS, among those people with insomnia symptoms, 29 percent use sleep medications: 23 percent use prescribed sleep medications and 6 percent use over-the-counter sleep aids. Thus, an estimated 4 percent of Canadians in the general population use medications for insomnia (Tjepkema, 2005). This estimate was higher in a recent study of 2000 Canadian adults wherein 10 percent had used prescribed medications to help them sleep, 9 percent used natural products, 6 percent used over-the-counter medications, and 5 percent used alcohol to help them sleep (Morin et al., 2011).

People who complain of insomnia to a medical professional are likely prescribed one of several benzodiazepine medications, which include short-acting drugs, such as triazolam (Halcion) and long-acting drugs such as flurazepam (Dalmane). Short-acting drugs (those that cause only brief drowsiness) are preferred because the long-acting drugs sometimes do not stop working by morning, and people report more daytime sleepiness. The long-acting benzodiazepines are sometimes preferred when negative effects, such as daytime anxiety, are observed in people taking the short-acting drugs (Neubauer, 2009). Newer medications, such as those that work directly with the melatonin system (e.g., ramelteon [Rozerem]), are also being developed to help people fall and stay asleep. People over the age of 65 are most likely to use medication to help them sleep. A study by Keith Brownlee and his colleagues at Lakehead University showed that older patients were significantly more likely than younger patients to be prescribed benzodiazepines for insomnia (Brownlee et al., 2003). Benzodiazepine prescriptions for insomnia are a particularly important problem among seniors in nursing homes (Voyer et al., 2006).

Medical treatments for insomnia have several drawbacks. First, benzodiazepine medications can cause excessive sleepiness. Second, people can easily become dependent on them and rather easily misuse them, deliberately or not. Third, these medications are meant for short-term treatment and are not recommended for use longer than four weeks. Longer use can cause dependence and rebound insomnia. A newer concern for some medications (e.g., Ambien) is that they may increase the likelihood of sleepwalking-related problems, such as sleep-related eating disorder (Nzwalo et al., 2013). Therefore, although medications may be helpful for sleep problems that will correct themselves in a short period (e.g., insomnia because of anxiety related to hospitalization), they are not intended for long-term chronic problems.

To help people with hypersomnolence or narcolepsy, physicians usually prescribe a stimulant, such as methylphenidate (Ritalin, the medication Ann was taking) or modafinil (Nevsimalova, 2009). Cataplexy, or loss of muscle tone, can be treated with antidepressant medication, not because people with narcolepsy are depressed but because antidepressants suppress REM (or dream) sleep. Sodium oxybate is also recommended to treat cataplexy (Bogan et al., 2014).

Treatment of breathing-related sleep disorders focuses on helping the person breathe better during sleep. For some, this means recommending weight loss—in some people who are obese, the neck's soft tissue compresses the airways. Unfortunately, this treatment has not proven to be very successful for breathing-related sleep disorders (Guilleminault & Dement, 1988). For mild or moderate cases of obstructive sleep apnea, treatment can involve medications, including those that help stimulate respiration (e.g., medroxyprogesterone) or the tricyclic antidepressants, which are thought to act on the locus coeruleus, which affects REM sleep such that the respiratory muscles do not relax as much (Kryger, 2000).

The gold standard for the treatment of obstructive sleep apnea involves the use of a mechanical device—called the continuous positive air pressure (CPAP) machine—that improves breathing (Patel et al., 2003). Patients wear a mask that provides slightly pressurized air during sleep and it helps them breathe more normally throughout the night. Unfortunately, many people have difficulty using the device because of issues of comfort and some even experience a form of claustrophobia. To assist these individuals, a variety of strategies are tried, including the use of psychological interventions, such as desensitization for claustrophobia, patient and partner education, and motivational interviewing (a counselling technique used to help patients match their goals with their behaviours) (Olsen et al., 2012). Severe breathing problems may require surgery to help remove blockages in parts of the airways.

ENVIRONMENTAL TREATMENTS

Because medication as a primary treatment isn't usually recommended (Doghramji, 2000; Roehrs & Roth, 2000), other ways of getting people back in step with their sleep rhythms are usually tried. One general principle for treating circadian rhythm disorders is that *phase delays* (moving the bedtime later) are easier than *phase advances* (moving bedtime earlier). Scheduling shift changes in a clockwise direction (going from day to evening schedule) seems to help workers adjust better. People can best readjust their sleep patterns by going to bed several hours later each night, until bedtime is at the desired hour (Sack et al., 2007). A drawback of this approach is that it requires the person to sleep during the day for several days, which is obviously difficult for people with regularly scheduled responsibilities.

Another recent effort to help people with sleep problems involves using *bright light* to trick the brain into readjusting the internal clock. Very bright light may help people with circadian rhythm problems readjust their sleep patterns (Burkhalter et al., 2015). People typically sit in front of a bank of fluorescent lamps that generate light greater than 2500 lux, an amount significantly different from normal indoor light (250 lux). Several hours of exposure to this bright light have successfully reset the circadian

▲ Bright light therapy can help people with circadian rhythm sleep disorders readjust their sleep patterns.

rhythms of a number of individuals (Czeisler & Allan, 1989). Although this type of treatment is still new, it provides some hope for people with sleep problems.

PSYCHOLOGICAL TREATMENTS

As you can imagine, the limitations of using drugs to help people sleep better has led to the development of psychological treatments. Table 10.1 lists and briefly describes some of the psychological approaches to insomnia.

Given the links of anxiety to insomnia, Viens, De Koninck, Mercier, St-Onge, and Lorrain (2003) from the University of Ottawa compared progressive relaxation with a treatment they referred to as anxiety management training (which basically combined progressive relaxation with cognitive relaxation techniques). Both groups were able to get to sleep more quickly following therapy. Furthermore, lab-based sleep evaluations showed that participants in both groups increased in slow-wave sleep and sleep satisfaction. Both groups also showed decreases in anxiety and depression. The two treatments were equally effective.

Other research shows that some psychological treatments for insomnia may be more effective than others. For adult sleep problems, stimulus control may be recommended. People are instructed to use the bedroom only for sleeping and for sex and not for work or other anxiety-provoking activities (e.g., watching the news on television).

Kathryn's sleep problems were addressed with several techniques. She was instructed to limit her time in bed to about four hours of sleep time (sleep restriction), about the amount of time she actually slept each night. The period was lengthened when she began to sleep through the night. Kathryn was also asked not to listen to the radio while in bed and to get out of bed if she couldn't fall asleep (stimulus control). Finally, therapy involved confronting her unrealistic expectations about how much sleep was enough for a person of her age (cognitive therapy; see Bélanger et al., 2006). Within about three weeks of treatment, Kathryn was sleeping longer (six to seven hours per night as opposed to four to five hours previously) and had fewer interruptions in her sleep. She felt more refreshed in the morning and had more energy during the day.

Kathryn's results mirror those of studies by Charles Morin and his colleagues that find combined treatments to be effective in older adults with insomnia (e.g., Morin, Kowatch, et al., 1993). One such study, using a randomized placebo-control design, found that both medical and psychological approaches were effective in improving the sleep of older adults (Morin et al., 1999). Over the long term, however, the psychological treatment was better able to maintain its effectiveness with this group (see also review by Morin & Wooten, 1996). Morin has examined the effectiveness of sequential (CBT and medication) treatments for insomnia. Participants received either (1) medication and then combined medication and CBT; (2) combined treatment and then CBT alone; or (3) CBT alone. For the first treatment group, significant improvements only appeared after the introduction of CBT, while in the other two groups improvement appeared near the beginning of treatment. The study also showed that the treatment involving combined treatment followed by CBT alone led to the best outcomes. These findings show that sleep improvement seems to be affected by the way in which medication and CBT are combined.

For young children, some of the cognitive treatments may not be possible. Instead, treatment often includes setting up bedtime routines, such as a bath, followed by a parent reading a story, to help children go to sleep at night. Graduated extinction (described in Table 10.1) has been used with some success for bedtime problems as well as for waking up at night (Hill, 2011). Integrating both medical and behavioural treatments seems especially important for insomnia. Research suggests that short-term use of medication in combination with other types of interventions may prove to be a quick and lasting treatment for insomnia (Milby et al., 1993; Morin & Azrin, 1988).

TABLE 10.1 | Some Psychological Treatments for Insomnia

Sleep Treatment	Description
Cognitive	This approach focuses on changing the sleepers' unrealistic expectations and beliefs about sleep ("I must have eight hours of sleep each night"; "If I get less than eight hours of sleep it will make me ill"). The therapist attempts to alter beliefs and attitudes about sleeping by providing information on topics such as normal amounts of sleep and a person's ability to compensate for lost sleep.
Cognitive relaxation	Because some people become anxious when they have difficulty sleeping, this approach uses meditation or imagery to help with relaxation at bedtime or after a night of waking.
Graduated extinction	Used for children who have tantrums at bedtime or wake up crying at night, this treatment instructs the parent to check on the child after progressively longer periods, until the child falls asleep on his or her own.
Paradoxical intention	This technique involves instructing individuals in the opposite behaviour from the desired outcome. Telling poor sleepers to lie in bed and try to stay awake as long as they can is used to try to relieve the performance anxiety surrounding efforts to try to fall asleep.
Progressive relaxation	This technique involves relaxing the muscles of the body in an effort to introduce drowsiness.

Importantly, researchers are now examining the treatment of both sleep problems and psychological disorders (e.g., depression) together, because the link appears to be strong, and treating one type of problem alone may not be enough (e.g., Carney et al., 2017). Colleen Carney, for example, mentions that insomnia may remain during the treatment of depression, it may interfere with the treatment of depression, and it makes it more likely that depression will return (https://psychlabs.ryerson.ca/carney/).

PREVENTING SLEEP DISORDERS

Sleep professionals generally agree that a significant portion of the sleep problems people experience daily can be prevented by following a few steps during the day. Referred to as *sleep hygiene*, these changes in lifestyle can be relatively simple to follow and can help avoid problems such as insomnia for some people (Goodman & Scott, 2012). Some sleep hygiene recommendations rely on allowing the brain's normal drive for sleep to take over, replacing the restrictions we place on our activities that interfere with sleep. For example, setting a regular time to go to sleep and awaken each day can help make falling asleep at night easier. Avoiding the use of caffeine and nicotine—which are both stimulants—can also help prevent problems such as nighttime awakening. Table 10.2 illustrates a number of the sleep hygiene steps recommended for preventing sleep

TABLE 10.2 | Good Sleep Habits

Establish a set bedtime routine.
Develop a regular bedtime and a regular time to awaken.
Eliminate all foods and drinks that contain caffeine six hours before bedtime.
Limit any use of alcohol or tobacco.
Try drinking milk before bedtime.
Eat a balanced diet.
Go to bed only when sleepy and get out of bed if you are unable to fall asleep or back to sleep after 15 minutes.
Do not exercise or participate in vigorous activities in the hours before bedtime.
Do include a weekly program of exercise during the day.
Restrict activities in bed to those that help induce sleep.
Reduce noise and light in the bedroom.
Increase exposure to natural and bright light during the day.
Avoid extreme temperature changes in the bedroom (that is, too hot or too cold).

© Cengage Learning

Source: Adapted, with permission, from *Sleep Better: A Guide to Improving Sleep for Children with Special Needs* (revised ed., p. 60), by V. M. Durand, 2014, Paul H. Brookes.

problems. Although there is little controlled prospective research on preventing sleep disorders, practising good sleep hygiene appears to be among the most promising techniques available.

A few studies have investigated the value of educating parents about the sleep of their young children in an effort to prevent later difficulties. Adachi and colleagues (2009), for example, provided ten minutes of group guidance and a simple educational booklet to the parents of four-month-old children. They followed up on these children three months later and found that, compared with a randomly selected control group of children, the ones whose parents received education about sleep experienced fewer sleep problems. Because so many children display disruptive sleep problems, this type of preventive effort could significantly improve the lives of many families.

PARASOMNIAS AND THEIR TREATMENT

Have you ever been told that you walk in your sleep? Talk in your sleep? Have you ever had troublesome nightmares? Do you grind your teeth in your sleep? If you answered yes to one or more of these questions (and it's likely you did), you have experienced sleep problems in the category of *parasomnia*. Parasomnias are not problems with sleep itself but abnormal events that occur either during sleep or during that twilight time between sleeping and waking. Some of the events associated with parasomnia are not unusual if they happen while you are awake (walking to the kitchen to look into the refrigerator) but can be distressing if they take place while you are sleeping.

The *DSM-5* identifies a number of different parasomnias (American Psychiatric Association, 2013). As you might have guessed, **nightmares** (or nightmare disorder) occur during REM or dream sleep (Augedal et al., 2013). The prevalence of nightmare disorder is unknown, but we do know that between 10 and 50 percent of children aged three to five years have nightmares that are severe enough to concern their parents. About 9 to 30 percent of adults experience them regularly (Schredl, 2010). The research of Tore Nielsen, Philippe Stenstrom, and Ross Levin (2006) in Montréal indicates that women experience more frequent nightmares than men do. To qualify as a *DSM-5* nightmare disorder, these nightmares must be so distressful that they impair a person's ability to carry on normal activities (see DSM Table 10.4). Some researchers distinguish nightmares from *bad dreams* by whether or not you wake up as a result. Nightmares are defined as very disturbing dreams that awaken the sleeper; bad dreams are those that do not awaken the person experiencing them. According to Montréal researchers Antonio Zadra and Don Donderi (2000), university students report an average of 30 bad dreams and 10 nightmares per year.

Nightmares are thought to be influenced by genes (Barclay & Gregory, 2013), trauma, and medication use and are associated with some psychological disorders (e.g., substance abuse, anxiety, borderline personality disorder, and schizophrenia spectrum disorders; Augedal et al., 2013). Research on the treatment

▲ A nightmare is distressing for both child and parent.

DSM-5	Table 10.4 Diagnostic Criteria for Nightmare Disorder

A. Repeated occurrences of extended, extremely dysphoric, and well-remembered dreams that usually involve efforts to avoid threats to survival, security or physical integrity and that generally occur during the second half of the major sleep episode.

B. On awakening from the dysphoric dreams, the person rapidly becomes oriented and alert.

C. The sleep disturbance causes clinically significant distress or impairment in social, occupational, or other important areas of functioning.

D. The nightmare symptoms are not attributable to the physiological effects of a substance (e.g., a drug of abuse, a medication).

E. Co-existing mental and medical disorders do not adequately explain the predominant complaint of dysphoric dreams.

Specify current severity:

Severity can be rated by the frequency with which the nightmares occur:

Mild: Less than one episode per week on average.

Moderate: One or more episodes per week but less than nightly.

Severe: Episodes nightly.

of nightmares suggests that both psychological intervention (e.g., cognitive behaviour therapy) and pharmacological treatment (i.e., prazosin) can help reduce these unpleasant sleep events (Augedal et al., 2013; Aurora et al., 2010).

Disorder of arousal includes a number of motor movements and behaviours during NREM sleep, such as sleepwalking, sleep terrors, and incomplete awakening. **Sleep terrors**, which most commonly afflict children, usually begin with a piercing scream. The child is extremely upset, often sweating, and frequently has a rapid heartbeat. On the surface, sleep terrors appear to resemble nightmares—the child cries and appears frightened—but they occur during NREM sleep and therefore are not caused by frightening dreams. During sleep terrors, children cannot be easily awakened and comforted, as they can during a nightmare. Children do not remember sleep terrors, despite their often dramatic effect on the observer (Durand, 2008). As many as one-third of 18-month-old children may experience sleep terrors, but this number drops to 13 percent by age 5 and just 5 percent by age 13 (Petit et al., 2015). We know relatively little about sleep terrors, although several theories have been proposed, including the possibility of a genetic component because the disorder tends to cluster in families (Durand, 2008).

Treatment for sleep terrors usually begins with a recommendation to wait and see if they disappear on their own. If the problem is frequent or continues for a long time, sometimes antidepressants (imipramine) or benzodiazepines are recommended, although their effectiveness has not yet been clearly demonstrated (Mindell, 1993). In an approach called *scheduled awakenings*, parents of children experiencing chronic sleep terrors are instructed to awaken their child briefly approximately 30 minutes before a typical episode. In a controlled study, this simple technique was shown to be successful in almost completely eliminating these disturbing events (Durand & Mindell, 1999).

It might surprise you to learn that **sleepwalking** (also called *somnambulism*) occurs during NREM sleep (Perrault et al., 2014). Thus, when people walk in their sleep they are probably not acting out a dream. This parasomnia typically occurs during the first few hours while a person is in the deep stages of sleep. The *DSM-5* criteria for sleepwalking require that the person leave the bed. Because sleepwalking occurs during the deepest stages of sleep, waking someone during an episode is difficult; if the person is wakened, he or she typically will not remember what has happened. It is not true, however, that waking a sleepwalker is somehow dangerous.

Sleepwalking is primarily a problem during childhood, affecting more than 10 percent of school-age children (Petit et al., 2015), but a small proportion of adults are affected. For the most part, the course of sleepwalking is short, and few people over the age of 15 continue to exhibit this parasomnia. When sleepwalking occurs among adults, it is often associated with other psychological disorders (Kales et al., 1980).

We do not yet clearly understand why some people sleepwalk, although factors such as extreme fatigue, previous sleep deprivation, the use of sedative or hypnotic drugs, and stress have been implicated (Shatkin & Ivanenko, 2009). On occasion, sleepwalking episodes have been associated with violent behaviour, including homicide and suicide (Cartwright, 2006). In one case in Toronto, a 23-year-old man, Kenneth Parks, drove to his in-laws' house, killed his mother-in-law, and attempted to kill his father-in-law. He was acquitted of the charges of murder and attempted murder, using sleepwalking as his legal defence (Broughton et al., 1994). Such cases are controversial, although there is evidence for the legitimacy of some violent behaviour coinciding with sleepwalking episodes. There also seems to be a genetic component to sleepwalking, with a higher incidence observed within families (Petit et al., 2015).

In a related disorder, *nocturnal eating syndrome*, individuals rise from their beds and eat while they are still asleep (Yamada, 2015). This problem may be more frequent than previously thought; it was found in almost 6 percent of individuals in one study who were referred because of insomnia complaints (Manni et al., 1997; Winkelman, 2006). Another uncommon parasomnia is *sexsomnia*; acting out sexual behaviours, such as masturbation and sexual intercourse, with no memory of the event (Béjot et al., 2010). This rare problem can cause relationship problems and, in extreme cases, legal problems when cases occur without consent or with minors (Howell, 2012; Schenck et al., 2007). An Ottawa man was found not criminally responsible for the sexual assault of his daughter on the basis of testimony by psychiatrists that he suffered from sexsomnia ("Sexsomnia Case," 2019).

The *DSM-5* also includes a disorder that occurs during REM sleep. In the case of REM sleep behaviour disorder, the individual talks or moves while sleeping, sometimes acting out a dream. In contrast to NREM disorders, when awakened, the person is not confused or anxious.

There is an increasing awareness that sleep is important for both our mental and our physical well-being. Sleep problems are also comorbid with many other disorders and therefore can compound the difficulties of people with significant psychological difficulties. Researchers are coming closer to understanding the basic nature of sleep and its disorders, and we anticipate significant treatment advances in the years to come.

Part A

Diagnose the sleep problems of the cases here using one of the following: (a) nocturnal eating syndrome, (b) sleep terrors, and (c) nightmares.

1. Jaclyn's dad is sometimes awakened by his daughter's screams. He runs to Jaclyn's room to comfort her and is eventually able to calm her down. Jaclyn usually explains that she was being chased by a big, one-eyed, purple monster. The events typically happen after watching scary movies with friends. _____

2. Sho-jen's parents hear her piercing screams on many nights and rush to comfort her, but she does not respond. During these episodes, her heart rate is elevated, and her pyjamas are soaked in sweat. When she gets up the next day, however, she has no memory of the experience.

   _____

3. Jack has made a serious commitment to his diet for more than a month but continues to gain weight. He has no memory of eating but noticed that food is always missing from the refrigerator. _____

Part B

Fill in the blanks.

1. Karen wakes up screaming every night, disregarding her parents' efforts to comfort her. Her heart rate is elevated in these episodes, and her pyjamas are soaked in sweat. The next day, she has no memory of the experience. To help reduce these night terrors, Karen's pediatrician used

   _____.

2. After George's wife died at the age of 68, he could not sleep. To help him through the hardest first week, Dr. Brown prescribed _____ for his insomnia.

3. Carl's doctor suggested some relatively simple lifestyle changes otherwise known as good _____ when he expressed concern about developing a sleep disorder.

SUMMARY

An Overview of Sleep-Wake Disorders

- Sleep-wake disorders are highly prevalent in the general population and are of two types: dyssomnias (disturbances of sleep) and parasomnias (abnormal events such as nightmares and sleepwalking that occur during sleep).

- Of the dyssomnias, insomnia disorder is the most common disorder. It involves the inability to initiate sleep, problems maintaining sleep, or failure to feel refreshed after a full night's sleep. Other dyssomnias include hypersomnolence (excessive sleep), narcolepsy (sudden and irresistible sleep attacks), circadian rhythm sleep disorders (sleepiness or insomnia caused by the body's inability to synchronize its sleep patterns with day and night), and breathing-related sleep disorders (disruptions that have a physical origin, such as sleep apnea, that leads to excessive sleepiness or insomnia).

- The formal assessment of sleep disorders, a polysomnographic (PSG) evaluation, is typically done by monitoring the heart, muscles, respiration, brain waves, and other functions of a sleeping client in the lab. In addition to such monitoring, it is helpful to determine the individual's sleep efficiency (SE), a percentage based on the time the individual *actually* sleeps as opposed to time spent in bed trying to sleep.

Treatment of Sleep-Wake Disorders

- Benzodiazepine medications have been helpful for short-term treatment of many of the dyssomnias, but they must be used carefully, or they might cause rebound insomnia, a withdrawal experience that can cause worse sleep problems after the medication is stopped. Any long-term treatment of sleep problems should include psychological interventions, such as stimulus control and sleep hygiene.

- Parasomnias, such as nightmares, occur during REM (or dream) sleep, and sleep terrors and sleepwalking occur during NREM sleep.

KEY TERMS

breathing-related sleep disorders, 298

circadian rhythm sleep-wake disorders, 299

dyssomnias, 293

hypersomnolence disorders, 296

insomnia disorder, 294

microsleeps, 293

narcolepsy, 297

nightmares, 303

parasomnias, 293

polysomnographic (PSG) evaluation, 293

rapid eye movement (REM), 292

rebound insomnia, 296

sleep apnea, 297

sleep efficiency, 293

sleep terrors, 304

sleepwalking, 304

ANSWERS TO CONCEPT CHECKS

10.1

1. f; **2.** e; **3.** g; **4.** d; **5.** b

10.2

1. c; **2.** b; **3.** a; **4.** scheduled awakenings; **5.** benzodiazepines; **6.** sleep hygiene

MEDIA RESOURCES

CENGAGE | MINDTAP

Stay organized and efficient with MindTap—a single destination with all the course material and study aids you need to succeed. Built-in apps leverage social media and the latest learning technology. For example:

- ReadSpeaker will read the text to you.

- Flashcards are pre-populated to provide you with a jump start for review—or you can create your own.

- You can highlight text and make notes in your MindTap Reader. Your notes will flow into Evernote, the electronic notebook app that you can access anywhere when it's time to study for the exam.

- Self-quizzing allows you to assess your understanding.

Visit login.cengage.com to start using MindTap. Enter the Online Access Code from the card included with your text. If a code card is not provided, you can purchase instant access at Cengage.ca.

Exploring Sleep Disorders

Characterized by extreme disruption in the everyday lives of affected individuals, and are an important factor in many psychological disorders.

SLEEP DISORDERS

Diagnosing Sleep Disorders

A polysomnographic (PSG) evaluation assesses an individual's sleep habits with various electronic tests to measure airflow, brain activity, eye movements, muscle movements, and heart activity. Results are weighed with a measure of sleep efficiency (SE), the percentage of time spent asleep.

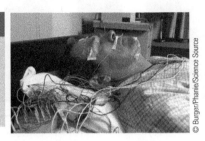

Dyssomnias

Disturbances in the timing, amount, or quality of sleep.

Disorder	Characteristics	Causes	Treatment
Insomnia Disorder	• Characteristics include difficulty initiating sleep, difficulty maintaining sleep, or nonrestorative sleep.	• Causes include pain, insufficient exercise, drug use, environmental influences, anxiety, respiratory problems, and biological vulnerability.	• Treatment may be medical (benzodiazepines) or psychological (anxiety reduction, improved sleep hygiene); combined approach is usually most effective.
Narcolepsy	• Characteristics include sudden daytime onset of REM sleep combined with cataplexy, a rapid loss of muscle tone that can be quite mild or result in complete collapse. Often accompanied by sleep paralysis and/or hypnagogic hallucinations.	• Causes are likely to be genetic.	• Treatment is medical (stimulant drugs).
Hypersomnolence Disorder	• Characteristics include abnormally excessive sleep and sleepiness, and involuntary daytime sleeping. Classified as a disorder only when it's subjectively perceived as disruptive.	• Causes may involve genetic link and/or excess serotonin.	• Treatment is usually medical (stimulant drugs).
Breathing-Related Sleep Disorder	• Characteristics include disturbed sleep and daytime fatigue resulting from hypoventilation (laboured breathing) or sleep apnea (suspended breathing).	• Causes may include narrow or obstructed airway, obesity, and increasing age.	• Treatments to improve breathing are medical or mechanical.
Circadian Rhythm Sleep Disorder	• Characteristics include sleepiness or insomnia.	• Caused by inability to synchronize sleep patterns with current pattern of day and night due to jet lag, shift work, delayed sleep, or advanced sleep (going to bed earlier than normal bedtime).	• Treatment includes phase delays to adjust bedtime and bright light to readjust internal clock.

Parasomnias

Abnormal behaviours that occur during sleep.

Nightmares	Sleep Terrors	Sleepwalking
• Frightening REM dreams that awaken the sleeper. Nightmares qualify as nightmare disorder when they are stressful enough to impair normal functioning. Causes are unknown, but they tend to decrease with age.	• Occur during non-REM (nondreaming) sleep and most commonly afflict children. Sleeping child screams, cries, sweats, sometimes walks, has rapid heartbeat, and cannot easily be awakened or comforted. More common in boys than girls, and possible genetic link since it tends to run in families. May subside with time.	• Occurs at least once during non-REM sleep in 15 to 30 percent of children under age 15. Causes may include extreme fatigue, sleep deprivation, sedative or hypnotic drugs, and stress. Adult sleepwalking is usually associated with other psychological disorders. May have a genetic link.

11 | Sex and Gender

© fstop123/iStock

> *Man, dominated by drives, has no power over himself. . . . We are in bondage in proportion as we are dominated by drives.*
> —BENEDICT DE SPINOZA

Use scientific reasoning to interpret behaviour:	› Identify basic biological, psychological, and social components of behavioural explanations (e.g., inferences, observations, operational definitions and interpretations) (APA SLO 2.1a)
Engage in innovative and integrative thinking and problem solving:	› Describe problems operationally to study them empirically (APA SLO 2.3a)
Describe applications that employ discipline-based problem solving:	› Correctly identify antecedents and consequences of behaviour and mental processes (APA SLO 1.3c)
	› Describe examples of relevant and practical applications of psychological principles to everyday life (APA SLO 1.3a)

*Portions of this chapter cover learning outcomes suggested by the American Psychological Association (2013) in their guidelines for the undergraduate psychology major. Chapter coverage of these outcomes is identified above by APA Goal and APA Suggested Learning Outcome (SLO).

What is normal sexual behaviour? As we will see, it depends. When does sexual behaviour that is somewhat different from the norm become a disorder? Again, it depends. Current views tend to be quite tolerant of a variety of sexual expressions, even if they are unusual, unless the behaviour is associated with a substantial impairment in functioning. Two kinds of sexual behaviour meet this definition. Individuals with sexual dysfunction find it difficult to function adequately while having sex. For example, they may not become aroused or achieve orgasm. In paraphilic disorders, sexual arousal occurs primarily in the context of unusual objects or individuals. *Philia* means a strong attraction or liking, and *para* indicates that the attraction is abnormal or atypical. Paraphilic arousal patterns tend to be focused rather narrowly, often precluding mutually consenting adult patterns, even if they are desired. Paraphilic disorders have little to do with sexual dysfunctions except for the fact that they both involve sexual behaviour. For this reason, paraphilic disorders now compose a separate category of disorders in the *DSM-5*. Another condition that has been separated from sexual disorders altogether is *gender dysphoria*. In gender dysphoria, there is dissatisfaction with the gender assigned at birth, causing clinically significant distress and impairment. All three categories of disorders and very controversial, especially gender dysphoria, and their inclusion in *DSM-5* has been much debated.

AN OVERVIEW OF SEXUAL DYSFUNCTIONS

Before describing **sexual dysfunctions**, note that the problems that arise in the context of sexual interactions may occur in all types of sexual relationships. Inability to become aroused or reach orgasm seems to be as common in same-sex as in other-sex relationships, for example. The three stages of the sexual response cycle—desire, arousal, and orgasm (see ■ Figure 11.1)—are each associated with specific sexual dysfunctions. In addition, pain can become associated with sexual functioning in women, which leads to an additional dysfunction.

An overview of the *DSM-5* categories of the sexual dysfunctions we examine is in Table 11.1. As you can see, both males and females can experience parallel versions of most disorders, which take on specific forms determined by anatomy and other gender-specific characteristics. However, two disorders are sex specific: premature (early) ejaculation obviously occurs only in males, and genito-pelvic pain/penetration disorder—which

includes difficulties with penetration during intercourse—appears only in females. Sexual dysfunctions can be either *life-long* or *acquired*. "Lifelong" refers to a chronic condition that is present during a person's entire sexual life; "acquired" refers to a disorder that begins after sexual activity has been relatively normal. In addition, disorders can either be generalized, occurring every time the individual attempts sex, or they can be situational, occurring only with some partners or at certain times, but not with other partners or at other times.

We have learned much about the prevalence of the various sexual dysfunctions around the world from a large survey called the *Global Study of Sexual Attitudes and Behaviors, 2001–2002* (Nicolosi et al., 2006). This survey focused on adults aged 40 to 80 years. The surprising estimates of prevalence of sexual dysfunctions are presented and discussed in the context of each disorder. But taken together, fully 28 percent of all Canadian women and 18 percent of all Canadian men experience sexual dysfunction, making this class of disorder one of the most prevalent of all psychological or physical disorders.

SEXUAL DESIRE DISORDERS

Three disorders reflect problems with the desire or arousal phase of the sexual response cycle. Two of these disorders are characterized by little or no interest in sex that is causing significant distress in the individual or couple. In males, this disorder is called **male hypoactive sexual desire disorder**. In females, low sexual interest is almost always accompanied by a diminished ability to become excited or aroused by erotic cues or sexual activity. Thus, deficits in interest or the ability to become aroused in women is combined in a disorder called **female sexual interest/arousal disorder** (Basson et al., 2010; Brotto, 2010a; Brotto & Luria, 2014). For males, there is a specific disorder of arousal, erectile dysfunction.

Male Hypoactive Sexual Desire Disorder and Female Sexual Interest/Arousal Disorder

Males with hypoactive sexual desire disorder and females with sexual interest/arousal disorder have little or no interest in any type of sexual activity (see DSM Table 11.1 and DSM Table 11.2). It is difficult to assess low sexual desire, and a great deal of clinical judgment is required (Leiblum, 2010; Segraves & Woodard, 2006; Wincze, 2009; Wincze et al., 2008; Wincze & Weisberg, 2015). You might gauge it by frequency of sexual activity—say, less than twice a month for

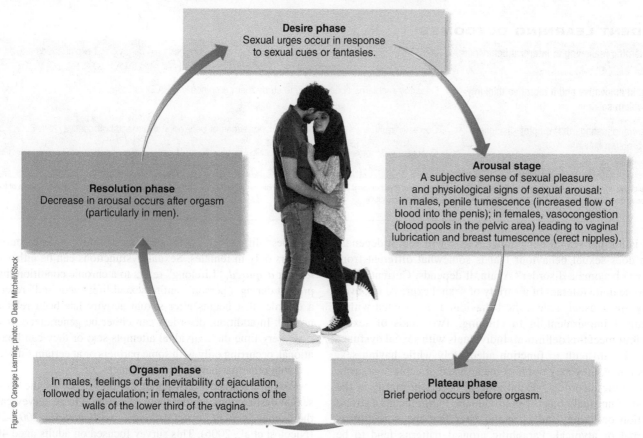

FIGURE 11.1 | The human sexual response cycle.

Sources: Based on *Disorders of Sexual Desire*, by H. S. Kaplan, 1979, Brunner/Mazel; *Human Sexual Response*, by W. H. Masters and V. E. Johnson, 1966, Little, Brown.

TABLE 11.1 | Categories of Sexual Dysfunction among Men and Women

Type of Disorder	Men	Women
Desire	Male hypoactive sexual desire disorder (little or no desire to have sex)	Female sexual interest/arousal disorder (little or no desire to have sex)
Arousal	Erectile disorder (difficulty attaining or maintaining erections)	Female sexual interest/arousal disorder (little or no desire to have sex)
Orgasm	Delayed ejaculation; premature (early) ejaculation	Female orgasmic disorder
Pain		Genito-pelvic pain/penetration disorder (pain, anxiety, and tension associated with sexual activity; vaginismus, i.e., muscle spasms in the vagina that interfere with penetration)

Sources: Wincze and Carey, 1991; American Psychiatric Association, 2003.

a married couple. Or you might determine whether someone ever thinks about sex or has sexual fantasies. Then there is the person who has sex twice a week but really doesn't want to and thinks about it only because his wife wants to have sex more often. This individual might, in fact, have no desire whatsoever, despite having frequent sex. Consider the case of Mr. and Mrs. C.

MR. AND MRS. C | *Getting Started*

Mrs. C, a 31-year-old very successful businesswoman, was married to a 32-year-old lawyer. They had two children, ages two and five, and had been married eight years when they entered therapy. The presenting problem was Mrs. C's lack of sexual desire. Mr. and Mrs. C were interviewed separately during the initial assessment and both professed attraction to and love for their partner. Mrs. C reported that she could enjoy sex once she got involved and usually was orgasmic. The problem was her total lack of desire to get involved in the first place. She avoided her husband's sexual advances and looked on his affection and romanticism with great skepticism and, usually, anger and tears. Mrs. C was raised in an upper-middle-class family that was supportive and loving. From age 6 to 12, however, she had been repeatedly pressured into sexual activity by a male cousin who was five years her senior. This sexual activity was always initiated by the cousin, always against her will. She did not tell her parents because she felt guilty, as the boy did not use physical force to make her comply. It appeared that romantic advances by Mr. C triggered memories of abuse by her cousin.

A. Persistently or recurrently deficient (or absent) sexual/erotic thoughts or fantasies and desire for sexual activity. The judgment of deficiency is made by the clinician, taking into account factors that affect sexual functioning, such as age and general and socio-cultural contexts of the individual's life.

B. The symptoms in Criterion A have persisted for a minimum duration of approximately 6 months.

C. The symptoms in Criterion A cause clinically significant distress in the individual.

D. The sexual dysfunction is not better explained by a nonsexual mental disorder or as a consequence of severe relationship distress or other significant stressors and is not attributable to the effects of a substance/medication or another medical condition.

Specify whether:

Lifelong: The disturbance has been present since the individual became sexually active.

Acquired: The disturbance began after a period of relatively normal sexual function.

Specify whether:

Generalized: Not limited to certain types of stimulation, situations, or partners.

Situational: Only occurs with certain types of stimulation, situations, or partners.

Specify current severity:

Mild: Evidence of mild distress over the symptoms in Criterion A.

Moderate: Evidence of moderate distress over the symptoms in Criterion A.

Severe: Evidence of severe or extreme distress over the symptoms in Criterion A.

Source: Reprinted with permission from the *Diagnostic and Statistical Manual of Mental Disorders*, Fifth Edition (Copyright © 2013). American Psychiatric Association. All Rights Reserved.

A. Lack of, or significantly reduced, sexual interest/arousal, as manifested by at least three of the following:

1. Absent/reduced interest in sexual activity.

2. Absent/reduced sexual/erotic thoughts or fantasies.

3. No/reduced initiation of sexual activity, and typically unreceptive to a partner's attempts to initiate.

4. Absent/reduced sexual excitement/pleasure during sexual activity in almost all or all (approximately 75%–100%) sexual encounters (in identified situational contexts or, if generalized, in all contexts).

5. Absent/reduced sexual interest/arousal in response to any internal or external sexual/erotic cues (e.g., written, verbal, visual).

6. Absent/reduced genital or nongenital sensations during sexual activity in almost all or all (approximately 75%–100%) sexual encounters (in identified situational contexts or, if generalized, in all contexts).

B. The symptoms in Criterion A have persisted for a minimum duration of approximately 6 months.

C. The symptoms in Criterion A cause clinically significant distress in the individual.

D. The sexual dysfunction is not better explained by a nonsexual mental disorder or as a consequence of severe relationship distress or other significant stressors and is not attributable to the effects of a substance/medication or another medical condition.

Specify whether:

Lifelong: The disturbance has been present since the individual became sexually active.

Acquired: The disturbance began after a period of relatively normal sexual function.

Specify whether:

Generalized: Not limited to certain types of stimulation, situations, or partners.

Situational: Only occurs with certain types of stimulation, situations, or partners.

Specify current severity:

Mild: Evidence of mild distress over the symptoms in Criterion A.

Moderate: Evidence of moderate distress over the symptoms in Criterion A.

Severe: Evidence of severe or extreme distress over the symptoms in Criterion A.

Source: Reprinted with permission from the *Diagnostic and Statistical Manual of Mental Disorders*, Fifth Edition (Copyright © 2013). American Psychiatric Association. All Rights Reserved.

Problems of sexual interest or desire used to be considered as marital rather than sexual difficulties. Since the recognition in the late 1980s of low sexual desire as a distinct disorder, however, more and more couples present to sex therapy clinics with one of the partners reporting this problem (Kleinplatz et al., 2013; Leiblum, 2010; Pridal & LoPiccolo, 2000). Best estimates suggest that more than 50 percent of patients who come to sexuality clinics for help complain of low sexual arousal or interest (Leiblum 2010; Pridal & LoPiccolo, 2000). In many clinics it is the most frequent presenting complaint of women; men present more often with erectile dysfunction (Hawton, 1995). Earlier studies (e.g., Frank et al., 1978) suggested that approximately 25 percent of individuals might have low sexual interest. The global survey mentioned earlier suggests that 11 percent of Canadian women and 5 percent of Canadian men report a sexual dysfunction involving a lack of interest in sex (Nicolosi et al., 2006). For men the prevalence increases with age; for women, it decreases with age (DeLamater & Sill, 2005; Fileborn et al., 2015; Laumann et al., 1999). Schreiner-Engel and Schiavi (1986) noted that patients with this disorder rarely have sexual fantasies, seldom masturbate (in their sample, 35 percent of the women and 52 percent of the men never masturbated and most of the rest masturbated no more than once a month), and attempt intercourse once a month or less.

SEXUAL AROUSAL DISORDERS

Erectile disorder is a specific disorder of arousal (see DSM Table 11.3). The problem here is not desire. Many males with erectile disorder have frequent sexual urges and fantasies and a strong desire to have sex. Their problem is in becoming aroused. For females who are also likely to have low interest, deficits in arousal are reflected in an inability to achieve or maintain adequate lubrication (Basson, 2007; Rosen, 2007; Wincze, 2009; Wincze et al., 2008; Wincze & Weisberg, 2015). Consider the case of Bill.

A. At least one of the three following symptoms must be experienced on almost all or all (approximately 75%–100%) occasions of sexual activity (in identified situational contexts or, if generalized, in all contexts):

   1. Marked difficulty in obtaining an erection during sexual activity.

   2. Marked difficulty in maintaining an erection until the completion of sexual activity.

   3. Marked decrease in erectile rigidity.

B. The symptoms in Criterion A have persisted for a minimum duration of approximately 6 months.

C. The symptoms in Criterion A cause clinically significant distress in the individual.

D. The sexual dysfunction is not better explained by a nonsexual mental disorder or as a consequence of severe relationship distress or other significant stressors and is not attributable to the effects of a substance/medication or another medical condition.

Specify whether:

   Lifelong: The disturbance has been present since the individual became sexually active.

   Acquired: The disturbance began after a period of relatively normal sexual function.

Specify whether:

   Generalized: Not limited to certain types of stimulation, situations, or partners.

   Situational: Only occurs with certain types of stimulation, situations, or partners.

Specify current severity:

   Mild: Evidence of mild distress over the symptoms in Criterion A.

   Moderate: Evidence of moderate distress over the symptoms in Criterion A.

   Severe: Evidence of severe or extreme distress over the symptoms in Criterion A.

Source: Reprinted with permission from the *Diagnostic and Statistical Manual of Mental Disorders*, Fifth Edition (Copyright © 2013). American Psychiatric Association. All Rights Reserved.

BILL | *Long Marriage, New Problem*

Bill, a 58-year-old white man, was referred to our clinic by his urologist. He was a retired accountant who had been married for 29 years to his 57-year-old wife, a retired nutritionist. They had no children. For the past several years, Bill had had difficulties obtaining and maintaining an erection. He reported a rather rigid routine he and his wife had developed to deal with the problem. They scheduled sex for Sunday mornings. Bill had to do chores first, however, including letting the dog out, washing the dishes, and shaving. The couple's current behaviour consisted of mutual hand stimulation. Bill was "not allowed" to attempt insertion until after his wife had climaxed. Bill's wife was adamant that she was not going to change her sexual behaviour and "become a whore," as she put it. This included refusing to try K-Y jelly as a lubricant appropriate to her postmenopausal decrease in lubrication. She described their behaviour as "lesbian sex."

Bill and his wife agreed that despite marital problems over the years, they had always maintained a good sexual relationship until the onset of the current problem and that sex had kept them together during their earlier difficulties. Useful information was obtained in separate interviews. Bill masturbated on Saturday night in an attempt to control his erection the following morning; his wife was unaware of this. In addition, he quickly and easily achieved a full erection when viewing erotica in the privacy of the sexuality clinic laboratory (surprising the assessor). Bill's wife privately acknowledged being very angry with her husband for an affair that he had had 20 years earlier.

At the final session, three specific recommendations were made: for Bill to cease masturbating the evening before sex, for the couple to use a lubricant, and for them to delay the morning routine until after they had had sexual relations. The couple called back one month later to report that their sexual activity was much improved.

The old and somewhat pejorative terms for male erectile disorder and female interest arousal difficulties are *impotence* and *frigidity*, but these are imprecise labels that do not identify the specific phase of the sexual response in which the problems are localized. The man typically feels more impaired by his problem than the woman does by hers. Inability to achieve and maintain an erection makes intercourse difficult or impossible. Women who are unable to achieve vaginal lubrication, however, may be able to compensate by using a commercial lubricant (Leiblum 2010; Wincze, 2009). In women, arousal and lubrication may decrease at any time but, as in men, such problems tend to accompany aging (Bartlik & Goldberg, 2000; Basson, 2007; DeLamater & Sill, 2005; Rosen, 2000; Shamloul & Ghanem, 2013). In addition, until relatively recently, some women were not as concerned as men about experiencing intense pleasure during sex as long as they could consummate the act; this is generally no longer the case. It is unusual for a man to be unable to achieve an erection. More typical is a situation like Bill's, where full erections are possible during masturbation and partial erections during attempted intercourse but with insufficient rigidity to allow penetration.

Before we describe the prevalence of arousal disorders and other sexual dysfunctions, we need to note an important study in which 100 well-educated, happily married couples who were not seeking treatment were carefully interviewed (Frank et al., 1978). More than 80 percent of these couples reported that their marital and sexual relations were happy and satisfying. Surprisingly, 40 percent of the men reported occasional erectile and ejaculatory difficulties, and 63 percent of the women reported occasional dysfunctions of arousal or orgasm. But the crucial finding was that these dysfunctions did not detract from the respondents' overall sexual satisfaction. In another study, only 45 percent of women having trouble with orgasm reported the issue as problematic (Fugl-Meyer & Sjogren Fugl-Meyer, 1999). These studies indicate that sexual satisfaction and occasional sexual dysfunction are not mutually exclusive categories (Bradford & Meston, 2011; Graham, 2010). In the context of a healthy relationship, occasional or partial sexual dysfunctions are easily accommodated.

But this does raise problems for diagnosing sexual dysfunctions. Should a sexual problem be identified as a diagnosis when dysfunction is clearly present but the person is not distressed about it? This is one debate that has occurred during discussions about possible revisions for the *DSM-5* (Balon et al., 2007; Zucker, 2010). In the *DSM-5*, the symptoms must clearly cause clinically significant distress in the individual.

The prevalence of erectile disorder is startlingly high and increases with age. Data from the global survey mentioned earlier indicate that 7 percent of Canadian men report sexual dysfunctions involving erection difficulties (Nicolosi et al., 2006). But this figure most certainly underestimates the prevalence because erectile disorder increases rapidly in men after age 60. Data from another study suggest that at least some impairment is present in approximately 40 percent of men in their 40s and 70 percent of men in their 70s (Feldman et al., 1994; Kim & Lipshultz, 1997). Male erectile disorder is easily the most common problem for which men seek help, accounting for 50 percent or more of the men referred to specialists for sexual problems (Hawton, 1995). The prevalence of female arousal disorders is somewhat more difficult to estimate because many women still do not consider absence of arousal to be a problem, let alone a disorder.

The Nicolosi et al. (2006) survey reported a prevalence of 12 percent of Canadian women experiencing a sexual dysfunction involving lubrication difficulties. Because disorders of desire, arousal, and orgasm often overlap, it is difficult to estimate precisely how many women with specific arousal disorders present to sex clinics (Segraves & Althof, 1998; Wincze & Carey, 2001). And some researchers, including Rosemary Basson and Lori Brotto in Vancouver, argued that the current definition of female arousal disorder focuses too much on "genital events" (e.g., lubrication difficulties) and instead should focus on women's feelings of arousal. This is because studies have shown that women with arousal disorder often show normal vaginal responding to erotic movies while reporting low subjective excitement (reviewed in Basson et al., 2004; Lalumière et al., 2019).

ORGASM DISORDERS

Inhibited Orgasm

An inability to achieve an orgasm despite adequate sexual desire and arousal is commonly seen in women and less commonly seen in men. Males who achieve orgasm only with great difficulty or not at all meet criteria for a condition called **delayed ejaculation**. In women, the condition is referred to as **female orgasmic disorder**. Consider the case of Greta and Will.

GRETA AND WILL | *Loving Disunion*

Greta, a teacher, and Will, an engineer, were a very attractive couple who came together to the first interview and entered the office clearly showing affection for each other. They had been married for five years and were in their late 20s. When asked about the problems that had brought them to the office, Greta quickly reported that she didn't think that she had ever had an orgasm—"didn't think" because she wasn't really sure what an orgasm was! She loved Will very much and on occasion would initiate lovemaking, although with decreased frequency over the past several years.

Will certainly didn't think Greta was reaching orgasm. In any case, he reported, they were clearly going in "different directions" sexually, in that Greta was less and less interested. She had progressed from initiating sex occasionally early in their marriage to almost never doing so, except for an occasional spurt every six months or so, when she would initiate two or three times in a week. But Greta noted that it was the physical closeness she wanted most during these times rather than sexual pleasure. Further inquiry revealed that she did, in fact, become sexually aroused on occasion but had never in her life reached orgasm, even during several attempts at masturbation mostly before her marriage. Both Greta and Will reported that the sexual problem was a concern to them because everything else about their marriage was very positive.

Greta had been brought up in a strict but loving and supportive Catholic family that more or less ignored sexuality. The parents were always very careful not to display their affections in front of Greta, and when her mother caught Greta touching her own genital area, she was cautioned rather severely to avoid that kind of activity.

An inability to reach orgasm is the most common complaint among women who seek therapy for sexual problems (see DSM Table 11.4). One study suggests that approximately 25 percent of women report significant difficulty reaching orgasm (Heiman, 2000). The problem is equally present in different age groups, and unmarried women were 1.5 times more likely than married women to experience orgasmic disorder. In the global survey mentioned earlier, 11 percent of Canadian women reported a sexual dysfunction involving an inability to achieve orgasm (Nicolosi et al., 2006). In diagnosing this problem, it is necessary to determine whether the women "never or almost never" reach orgasm (Wincze & Weisberg, 2015). This distinction is important because only approximately 50 percent of all women experience reasonably regular orgasms during sexual intercourse (LoPiccolo & Stock, 1987). Therefore, approximately 50 percent do not achieve orgasm with every sexual encounter, unlike most men, who tend to experience orgasm more consistently. Thus, the "never or almost never" inquiry is important, along with establishing the extent of the woman's distress, in diagnosing orgasmic dysfunction.

In the global survey, approximately 5 percent of Canadian men report a sexual dysfunction involving inability to achieve orgasm (Nicolosi et al., 2006). Men seldom seek treatment for this condition. It is quite possible that in many cases some men reach climax through alternative forms of stimulation than sexual intercourse and that **male orgasmic disorder** is accommodated by the couple (Apfelbaum, 2000).

Some men who are unable to ejaculate with their partners can obtain an erection and ejaculate during masturbation. In the most usual pattern, ejaculation is delayed; this is called *retarded ejaculation*. Occasionally men experience *retrograde ejaculation*, in which ejaculatory fluids travel backward into the bladder. This phenomenon is usually due to the effects of certain drugs or a co-existing medical condition and should not be confused with male orgasmic disorder.

A far more common male orgasmic disorder is **premature ejaculation** (see DSM Table 11.5), ejaculation that occurs well before the man and his partner want it to (Althof, 2006; Polonsky, 2000; Wincze, 2009; Wincze & Weisberg, 2015), defined as approximately one minute after penetration in the *DSM-5*. Consider the rather typical case of Gary.

The frequency of premature ejaculation seems to be quite high. In the Nicolosi et al. (2006) survey, 9 percent of all Canadian men reported a sexual dysfunction involving premature ejaculation, making it the most frequent male sexual dysfunction. A high rate was also reported in a survey conducted by Guy Grenier and Sandra Byers at the University of New Brunswick: 23 percent of a sample of male university alumni

self-identified with premature ejaculation (Grenier & Byers, 2001). This difficulty is also a presenting complaint in as many as 60 percent of men who seek treatment (Malatesta & Adams, 1984; Polonsky, 2000). (Many men also present with erectile disorder as the major problem.) In one clinic, premature ejaculation was the principal complaint of 16 percent of men seeking treatment (Hawton, 1995).

GARY | *Running Scared*

Gary, a 31-year-old sales representative, engaged in sexual activity with his wife three or four times a month. He noted that he would like to have sex more often, but his very busy schedule kept him working about 80 hours a week. His primary difficulty was an inability to control the timing of his ejaculation. Approximately 70 to 80 percent of the time he ejaculated within seconds of penetration. This pattern had been constant since he met his wife approximately

13 years earlier. Previous experience with other women, although limited, was not characterized by premature ejaculation. In an attempt to delay his ejaculation, Gary distracted himself by thinking of nonsexual things (scores of ball games or work-related issues) and sometimes attempted sex soon after a previous attempt because he seemed not to climax as quickly under these circumstances. Gary reported masturbating very seldom (three or four times a year at most). When he did masturbate, he usually attempted to reach orgasm quickly, a habit he acquired during his teens to avoid being caught by a family member.

One of his greatest concerns was that he was not pleasing his wife, and under no circumstances did he want her told that he was seeking treatment. Further inquiry revealed that he made many extravagant purchases at his wife's request, even though it strained their finances, because he wanted to please her. He felt that if they had only met recently, his wife probably would not even have accepted a date with him because he had lost much of his hair and she had lost weight and was more attractive than she used to be.

Although the *DSM-5* specifies a duration of less than approximately one minute, it is very difficult to define "premature." An adequate length of time before ejaculation varies from individual to individual. Some surveys indicate that men who complain of premature ejaculation typically climax no more than one or two minutes after penetration, compared with seven to ten minutes in individuals without this complaint (Strassberg et al., 1987). A perception of lack of control over orgasm, however, may be the more important psychological determinant of this complaint (Wincze et al., 2008). The work of Grenier and Byers (2001) suggests that self-identifying with premature ejaculation had three components: a behavioural component (i.e., the regularity of their rapid ejaculation experiences), an emotional component (i.e., worry or concern about ejaculating too early), and an efficiency component (i.e., perceiving that they have little control over the timing of their ejaculation).

Although occasional early ejaculation is perfectly normal, serious and consistent premature ejaculation appears to occur primarily in inexperienced men with less education (Laumann et al., 1999). Grenier and Byers (2001) found the only predictor of premature ejaculation in their sample was a lower frequency of intercourse. The contrast in ages between men with erectile disorder and those complaining of premature ejaculation is striking. Although premature ejaculation is typically seen in young men (American Psychiatric Association, 2000a), the majority of men consulting physicians about erectile disorder are between 40 and 64 years of age (IMS Health Canada, 2004a).

SEXUAL PAIN DISORDERS

A sexual dysfunction specific to women refers to difficulties with penetration during attempted intercourse or significant pain during intercourse. This disorder is called **genito-pelvic pain/penetration disorder** (see DSM Table 11.6). For some women,

DSM-5	**Table 11.6** Criteria for Genito-Pelvic Pain/Penetration Disorder

A. Persistent or recurrent difficulties with one (or more) of the following:

1. Vaginal penetration during intercourse.

2. Marked vulvovaginal or pelvic pain during vaginal intercourse or penetration attempts.

3. Marked fear or anxiety about vulvovaginal or pelvic pain in anticipation of, during, or as a result of vaginal penetration.

4. Marked tensing or tightening of the pelvic floor muscles during attempted vaginal penetration.

B. The symptoms in Criterion A have persisted for a minimum duration of approximately 6 months.

C. The symptoms in Criterion A cause clinically significant distress in the individual.

D. The sexual dysfunction is not better explained by a nonsexual mental disorder or as a consequence of severe relationship distress (e.g., partner violence) or other significant stressors and is not attributable to the effects of a substance/medication or another medical condition.

Specify whether:

Lifelong: The disturbance has been present since the individual became sexually active.

Acquired: The disturbance began after a period of relatively normal sexual function.

Specify current severity:

Mild: Evidence of mild distress over the symptoms in Criterion A.

Moderate: Evidence of moderate distress over the symptoms in Criterion A.

Severe: Evidence of severe or extreme distress over the symptoms in Criterion A.

Source: Reprinted with permission from the *Diagnostic and Statistical Manual of Mental Disorders*, Fifth Edition (Copyright © 2013). American Psychiatric Association. All Rights Reserved.

sexual desire is present, and arousal and orgasm are easily attained, but the pain during attempted intercourse is so severe that sexual behaviour is disrupted. In other cases, severe anxiety or even panic attacks may occur in anticipation of possible pain during intercourse.

The most usual presentation of this disorder is referred to as **vaginismus**: the pelvic muscles in the outer third of the vagina undergo involuntary spasms when intercourse is attempted (Binik et al., 2007; Kleinplatz et al., 2013). The spasm reaction of vaginismus may occur during any attempted penetration, including a gynecological exam or insertion of a tampon (Beck, 1993; Bradford & Meston, 2011). Many women report sensations of "ripping, burning, or tearing during attempted intercourse" (Beck, 1993, p. 384). Consider the case of Jill.

Although there are no data on the prevalence of vaginismus in community samples, best estimates are that it affects 6 percent of women (Bradford & Meston, 2011). Twenty-five percent of women who report suffering from some sexual dysfunction experience vaginismus, according to Crowley, Richardson, and Goldmeir (2006). Because vaginismus and the experience of pain during intercourse overlap quite a bit in women, the conditions have been combined in the *DSM-5* into genito-pelvic/penetration disorder (Binik, 2010; Bradford & Meston, 2011; Payne et al., 2005). Results from one North

American survey indicate that approximately 7 percent of women have one or the other types of sexual pain disorder, with higher proportions of younger and less educated women reporting this problem (Laumann et al., 1999). Somewhat higher estimates of 15 percent of women in North America reporting recurring pain during intercourse have been reported in the *DSM-5* (American Psychiatric Association, 2013).

JILL | *Sex and Spasms*

Jill was referred to our clinic by another therapist because she had not consummated her marriage of one year. At 23 years of age, she was an attractive and loving wife who managed a motel while her husband worked as an accountant. Despite numerous attempts in a variety of positions to engage in intercourse, Jill's severe vaginal spasms prevented penetration of any kind. Jill was also unable to use tampons. With great reluctance, she submitted to gynecological exams at infrequent intervals. Sexual behaviour with her husband consisted of mutual masturbation or, on occasion, Jill had him rub his penis against her breasts to the point of ejaculation. She refused to engage in oral sex. Jill, a very anxious young woman, came from a family in which sexual matters were seldom discussed and sexual contact between the parents had ceased some years before. Although she enjoyed petting, Jill's general attitude was that intercourse was disgusting. Furthermore, she expressed some fears of becoming pregnant despite taking adequate contraceptive measures. She also thought that she would perform poorly when she did engage in intercourse, therefore embarrassing herself with her new husband.

ASSESSING SEXUAL BEHAVIOUR

There are three major aspects to the assessment of sexual behaviour (Wiegel et al., 2002):

1. *Interviews*, usually supported by numerous questionnaires because patients may provide more information on paper than in a verbal interview.
2. A *thorough medical evaluation*, to rule out the variety of medical conditions that can contribute to sexual problems.
3. *Psychophysiological assessment*, to measure directly the physiological aspects of sexual arousal.

INTERVIEWS

All clinicians who conduct interviews for sexual problems should be aware of several useful assumptions (Wiegel et al., 2002; Wincze, 2009). For example, they must demonstrate to the patient through their actions and interviewing style that they are comfortable talking about these issues. Because many patients do not know the various clinical terms professionals use to describe the sexual response cycle and various aspects of sexual behaviour, clinicians must always be prepared to use the vernacular (language) of the patient, realizing also that terms vary from person to person.

The following are examples of the questions asked in semistructured interviews in our sexuality clinic:

- How would you describe your current interest in sex?
- Do you avoid engaging in sexual behaviour with a partner?
- Do you have sexual fantasies?
- How often do you masturbate?
- How often do you engage in sexual intercourse?
- How often do you engage in mutual caressing or cuddling without intercourse?
- Have you ever been sexually abused or raped or had a negative experience associated with sex?
- Do you have problems attaining an erection? [or] Do you have problems achieving or maintaining vaginal lubrication?
- Do you ever have problems reaching orgasm?
- Do you ever experience pain associated with sexual activity?

A clinician must be careful to ask these questions in a manner that puts the patient at ease. During an interview lasting approximately two hours, the clinician also covers nonsexual relationship issues and physical health and screens for the presence of additional psychological disorders. When possible, the partner is interviewed concurrently.

Patients may volunteer in writing some information they are not ready to talk about, so they are usually given a variety of questionnaires that help reveal sexual activity and attitudes toward sexuality.

MEDICAL EXAMINATION

Human sexuality clinicians routinely inquire about medical conditions that affect sexual functioning. A variety of drugs, including some commonly prescribed for hypertension, anxiety, and depression, often disrupt sexual arousal and functioning. Recent surgery or concurrent medical conditions must be evaluated for their impact on sexual functioning; often the surgeon or treating physician may not have described possible side effects, or the patient may not have told the physician that a medical procedure or drug has affected sexual functioning. Some males with specific sexual dysfunctions, such as erectile disorder, have already visited a urologist—a physician specializing in disorders of the genitals, bladder, and associated structures—before coming to a sexuality clinic, and many females already have visited a gynecologist. These specialists may check levels of sexual hormones necessary for adequate sexual functioning and, in the case of males, evaluate vascular functioning necessary for an erectile response.

PSYCHOPHYSIOLOGICAL ASSESSMENT

Many clinicians assess the ability of individuals to become sexually aroused under a variety of conditions by taking psychophysiological measurements while the patient is either awake or asleep. In men, penile erection is measured directly, using, for example, a *penile strain gauge*. As the penis expands, the strain gauge picks up the changes, which are then recorded by a computer program. Note that patients are often not aware of these more objective measures of their arousal; their awareness differs as a function of the type of problem they have. Measuring penile rigidity is also important in cases of erectile disorder, because large erections with insufficient rigidity will not be adequate for intercourse (Wiegel et al., 2002).

The comparable device for women is a *vaginal photoplethysmograph*. This device, which is about the size of a tampon, is inserted by the woman into her vagina. A light source at the tip of the instrument and light-sensitive photoreceptors on the sides of the instrument measure the amount of light reflected back from the vaginal walls. Because blood flows to the vaginal walls during arousal, the amount of light passing through them decreases with increasing arousal. Meredith Chivers, at Queen's University in Kingston, Ontario, has used the penile strain gauge and the photoplethysmograph to uncover interesting gender differences in patterns of sexual arousal.

Typically, in the clinic of one of the authors of this textbook, individuals undergoing physiological assessment view an erotic videotape for two to five minutes or, on occasion, listen to an erotic audiotape. The patient's sexual responsivity during this time is assessed psychophysiologically. Patients also report subjectively on the amount of sexual arousal they experience. This assessment allows the clinician to observe carefully the conditions under which arousal is possible for the patient. For example, many individuals with psychologically based sexual dysfunctions may achieve strong arousal in a laboratory but be unable to become aroused with a partner.

Because erections most often occur during REM sleep in physically healthy men, psychophysiological measurement of

Greg Black

▲ Meredith Chivers of Queen's University (Kingston, Ontario) has conducted research on gender differences in patterns of sexual arousal.

nocturnal penile tumescence was in the past used frequently to determine a man's ability to obtain erectile responses. If he could attain erections while he was asleep, the reasoning went, then the causes of his dysfunction were psychological. An inexpensive way to monitor nocturnal erections is for the clinician to provide a simple "snap gauge" that the patient fastens around his penis each night before he goes to sleep. If the snap gauge has come undone, he has probably had a nocturnal erection. But this is a crude and often inaccurate screening device that should not supplant medical and psychological

© Cengage Learning

Erectile Disorder: Clark

"In the process of becoming aroused, all of a sudden it would be over. And I didn't understand that at all. So then everything is coupled with a bunch of depressing thoughts, like fear of failure. And so I begin to say, is this happening to me because I'm afraid I'm going to fail, and I don't want to be embarrassed by that? It's really very difficult to deal with emotionally. . . . The worse I feel about myself, the slower I am sexually, and sometimes I describe it as the fear of losing masculinity."

Visit login.cengage.com to start using MindTap. Enter the Online Access Code from the card included with your text. If a code card is not provided, you can purchase instant access at Cengage.ca.

evaluation. We now know that lack of nocturnal penile tumescence could also be due to psychological problems, such as depression, or to a variety of medical difficulties that have nothing to do with physiological problems preventing erections (Rosen, 2000; Wiegel et al., 2001).

CAUSES OF SEXUAL DYSFUNCTION

Individual sexual dysfunctions seldom present in isolation. Usually a patient referred to a sexuality clinic complains of a wide assortment of sexual problems, although one may be of most concern (Rosen, 2007; Wincze, 2009). A 45-year-old man referred to one of the authors' clinics had been free of problems until ten years earlier, when he was under a great deal of pressure at work and was preparing to take a major career-related licensing examination. He began experiencing erectile disorder about 50 percent of the time, a condition that had now progressed to approximately 80 percent of the time. In addition, he reported that he had no control over ejaculation, often ejaculating before penetration with only a semi-erect penis. Over the past five years, he had lost most interest in sex and was coming to treatment only at his wife's insistence. Thus, this man simultaneously experienced erectile disorder, premature ejaculation, and low sexual desire. Because of the frequency of such combinations, we discuss the causes of various sexual dysfunctions together, reviewing briefly the biological, psychological, and social contributions and specifying causal factors thought to be associated exclusively and specifically with one or another dysfunction.

BIOLOGICAL CONTRIBUTIONS

Many physical and medical conditions contribute to sexual dysfunction (Basson, 2007; Bradford & Meston, 2011; Rosen, 2007; Wincze et al., 2008; Wincze & Weisburg. 2015). Although this is not surprising, most patients and even many health professionals are, unfortunately, unaware of the connection. Neurological diseases and other conditions that affect the nervous system, such as diabetes and kidney disease, may directly interfere with sexual functioning by reducing sensitivity in the genital area, and they are a common cause of erectile disorder in males (Rosen, 2007; Wincze, 2009). Feldman et al. (1994) reported that 28 percent of men with diabetes experienced complete erectile failure and other studies have replicated these high prevalence rates (Phe & Roupret, 2012). Vascular disease is a major cause of erectile difficulties. The two relevant vascular problems are arterial insufficiency (constricted arteries), which makes it difficult for blood to reach the penis, and venous leakage (blood flows out too quickly for an erection to be maintained; Wincze & Weisburg, 2015).

Chronic illness can also indirectly affect sexual functioning. For example, it is not uncommon for individuals who have had heart attacks to be wary of the physical exercise involved in sexual activity to the point of preoccupation. They often become unable to achieve arousal despite being assured by their physicians that sexual activity is safe for them. Also, coronary artery disease and sexual dysfunction commonly co-exist, and it is now recommended that men presenting with erectile disorder should be screened for cardiovascular disease (Gandaglia et al., 2014; Jackson et al., 2006).

A major physical cause of sexual dysfunction is prescription medication. Antihypertensive medications, in the class known as beta-blockers, including propranolol, may contribute to sexual dysfunction. Androgen deprivation therapy, used in the treatment of prostate cancer, has massive effects on sexual functioning (Elliott et al., 2010). Selective-serotonin reuptake inhibitor (SSRI) antidepressant medications and other antidepressant and antianxiety drugs may also interfere with sexual desire and arousal in both men and women (Balon, 2006; Kleinplatz et al., 2013). A number of these drugs, particularly the psychoactive drugs, may dampen sexual desire and arousal by altering levels of serotonin in the brain. Sexual dysfunction—specifically low sexual desire and arousal difficulties—is the most widespread side effect of the antidepressant SSRIs, such as Prozac, and as many as 80 percent of individuals who take these medications may experience some degree of sexual dysfunction, although estimates closer to 50 percent seem more reliable (Balon, 2006; Clayton et al., 2014).

Some people are aware that alcohol suppresses sexual arousal, but they may not know that most *other drugs of abuse*, such as cocaine and heroin, also produce widespread sexual dysfunction in frequent users and abusers, both male and female. More than 60 percent of a large number of cocaine users had a sexual dysfunction in some studies (Cocores et al., 1988; Macdonald et al., 1988).

There is also the misconception that alcohol facilitates sexual arousal and behaviour. As explained in a review article by Toronto-based researcher Alexander McKay (2005), what actually happens is that alcohol at low and moderate levels reduces social inhibitions so people feel more like having sex (and perhaps are more willing to seek it; Wiegel et al., 2001). In fact, people's expectation that arousal will increase when they drink alcohol may have more effect than any disinhibition that does occur because of the effects of the alcohol itself, at least at low doses (Roehrich & Kinder,

1991; Wilson, 1977). Physically, alcohol is a central nervous system *suppressant*, and for men to achieve erection and women to achieve lubrication is much more difficult when the central nervous system is suppressed. Chronic alcohol abuse may cause permanent neurological damage and may virtually eliminate the sexual response cycle. Such abuse may lead to liver and testicular damage, resulting in decreased testosterone levels and concomitant decreases in sexual desire and arousal. This dual effect of alcohol (social disinhibition and physical suppression) has been recognized since the time of Shakespeare:

> It provokes the desire, but it takes away the performance; therefore much drink may be said to be an equivocator with lechery: it makes him and it mars him; it sets him on and it takes him off; it persuades him and disheartens him; makes him stand to and not stand to; in conclusion, equivocates him in a sleep, and giving him the lie, leaves him. (Macbeth, II, iii, 29)

Chronic alcoholism can also cause sexual problems in both men and women. Fahrner (1987) examined the prevalence of sexual dysfunction among male alcoholics and found that 75 percent had erectile disorder, low sexual desire, and premature or delayed ejaculation.

Many people report that cocaine or marijuana enhances sexual pleasure. Although little is known about the effects of marijuana across the wide range of use, it is unlikely that chemical effects increase pleasure. Rather, in those individuals who report some enhancement of sexual pleasure (and many don't), the effect may be psychological in that their attention is focused more completely and fully on sensory stimulation (Buffum, 1982), a factor that seems to be an important part of healthy sexual functioning. If so, imagery and attentional focus can be enhanced with nondrug procedures, such as meditation, in which a person practises concentrating on something with as few distractions as possible.

Nicotine is similarly associated with impaired sexual performance. One report from Mannino, Klevens, and Flanders (1994), studying more than 4000 male army veterans, found that cigarette smoking alone was associated with increased erectile dysfunction after controlling for other factors, such as alcohol and vascular disease. Similarly, a more recent study found that nicotine used before viewing an erotic film was associated with reduced erectile response to the film for men (Harte & Meston, 2008a). A parallel study also found decreased arousal in women who used nicotine before viewing the film (Harte & Meston, 2008b).

PSYCHOLOGICAL CONTRIBUTIONS

The work of Rosemary Basson of the Vancouver Hospital Centre for Sexuality, Gender Identity, and Reproductive Health has contributed much to our understanding of psychological contributions to low sexual desire in women (e.g., Basson, 2001, 2006; Basson et al., 2005). For example, Basson studied 47 women referred to her clinic for low sexual desire and identified several contributing factors. As shown in Table 11.2, psychological factors that decreased arousability were the most common contributing variable, being relevant in 85 percent of the cases. Environmental factors (e.g., insufficient sexual context), depression, and perceptions that emotional intimacy was lacking in the relationship were each relevant in approximately half the cases.

TABLE 11.2 | Contributing Factors to Low Sexual Desire in a Clinic-Referred Sample of Women (*n* = 47)

Contributing Factor	Percentage of Cases Where Relevant
Psychological factors decreasing arousability	85
Minimal sexual stimuli or context	53
Emotional intimacy lacking	50
Depression	43
Androgen deficiency	25

Source: From "Using a different model for a female sexual response to address women's problematic low sexual desire" by R. Basson, *Journal of Sex and Marital Therapy*, 27(5), 395–403. © 2001. Reproduced by permission of the publisher, Taylor & Francis Ltd, http://www.tandfonline.com on behalf of the Society for the Scientific Study of Sexuality (SSSS).

The one biological factor investigated—androgen deficiency as suggested by the referring doctor—was the contributing factor least commonly involved. It proved relevant in only one-quarter of the cases in this study.

But psychological contributing factors obviously compose a broad category of influences. How do we account for sexual dysfunction from a psychological perspective? One important psychological concept is that of performance anxiety, which can be further broken into several components. One component is arousal, another is cognitive processes, and third is negative affect (Wincze & Weisburg, 2015).

When confronted with the possibility of having sexual relations, individuals who are dysfunctional tend to expect the worst and find the situation to be relatively negative and unpleasant (Wincze & Weisburg, 2015). As far as possible, they avoid becoming aware of any sexual cues (and therefore are not aware of how aroused they are). They also may distract themselves with negative thoughts, such as "I'm going to make a fool of myself; I'll never be able to get aroused; she [or he] will think I'm stupid" (Renaud & Byers, 2001). We know that as arousal increases, a person's attention focuses more intently and consistently. But the person who is focusing on negative thoughts will find it difficult to become sexually aroused. A recent study by Marta Meana's group has shown that there may be gender differences in the types of negative thoughts that distract attention away from sexual enjoyment. Specifically, women were shown to be more susceptible to "appearance-based" negative thoughts (e.g., "If the lights are on during sexual activity, I worry too much about how appealing my body is to my partner"), whereas men were more susceptible to "performance-based" negative thoughts (e.g., "During sexual activity, I think too much about whether my partner is happy with the way I am touching his/her body") (Meana & Nunnink, 2005).

People with good sexual functioning react to a sexual situation very positively. They focus their attention on the erotic cues and do not become distracted. When they become aroused, they focus even more strongly on the sexual and erotic cues, allowing themselves to become increasingly sexually aroused. The model presented in ■ Figure 11.2 illustrates both functional and dysfunctional sexual arousal (Barlow, 1986; Barlow et al., 1996; Sbrocco & Barlow, 1996). Experiments demonstrate that sexual arousal is strongly determined by psychological factors, particularly cognitive and emotional factors, that are powerful enough to determine whether blood flows to the appropriate areas of the body, such as the genitals, confirming once again the strong interaction of psychological and biological factors in most of our functioning.

We know little about the psychological (or biological) factors associated with premature ejaculation (Althof, 2007; Bradford & Meston, 2011; Malavige & Jayawickrema, 2015). We do know that the condition is most prevalent in young men and that excessive physiological arousal in the sympathetic nervous system may lead to rapid ejaculation. These observations suggest some men may have a naturally lower threshold for ejaculation; that is, they require less stimulation and arousal to ejaculate. Unfortunately, the psychological factor of anxiety also increases sympathetic arousal. Thus, when a man becomes anxiously aroused about ejaculating too quickly, his concern only makes the problem worse. We return to the role of anxiety in sexual dysfunctions later.

SOCIAL AND CULTURAL CONTRIBUTIONS

The model of sexual dysfunction displayed in Figure 11.2 helps explain why some individuals may be dysfunctional now, but not how they *became* that way in the first place. Although we do not know for sure why some people develop problems, many people learn early that sexuality can be negative and somewhat threatening, and the responses they develop reflect this belief. This negative cognitive set has been termed *erotophobia*, which is presumably learned early in childhood from families, religious authorities, or others. Erotophobia seems to predict sexual difficulties later in life (Byrne & Schulte, 1990). Thus, for some individuals, sexual cues become associated early with negative affect. In other cases, both men and women may experience specific negative or traumatic events after a period of relatively well-adjusted sexuality. These negative events might include sudden failure to become aroused or actual sexual trauma, such as rape. Meston and her colleagues have shown that childhood sexual abuse may exert its negative effects on adult sexual functioning by way of its impact on the meanings that women attribute to many sexuality-relevant concepts (Meston & Heiman, 2000). For example, a woman who was sexually abused as a child may think of concepts pertaining to sex as bad or dirty, which in turn would have a negative impact on her ability to function sexually.

Laumann et al. (1999) found a substantial impact of early traumatic sexual events on later sexual functioning. For example, if women experienced sexual victimization through adult sexual contact before puberty, or were forced to have sexual contact of some kind, they were approximately twice as likely to have orgasmic dysfunction as women who had not been touched before puberty or not forced to have sex at any time. For male victims of adult–child contact, the probability of experiencing erectile disorder is more than three times greater than if they had not had the contact. Thus, traumatic sexual acts of all kinds have long-lasting effects on subsequent sexual

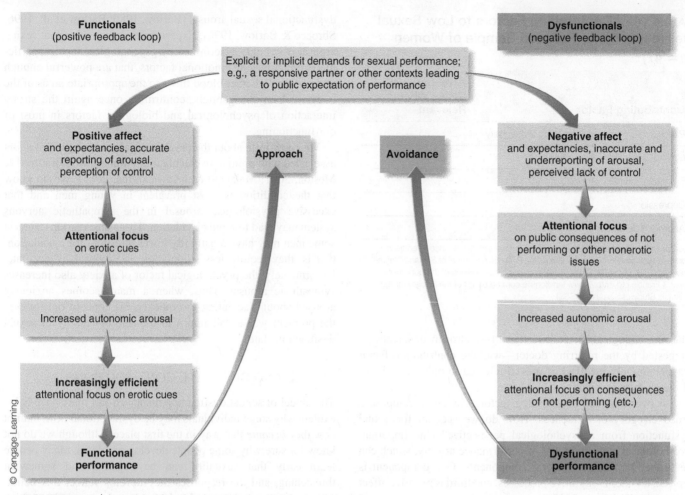

FIGURE 11.2 | A model of functional and dysfunctional sexual arousal.

Source: Adapted from "Causes of Sexual Dysfunction: The Role of Anxiety and Cognitive Interference," by D. H. Barlow, 1986, *Journal of Consulting and Clinical Psychology*, *54*, pp. 140–148.

functioning, in both men and women, sometimes lasting decades beyond the original event. Such stressful events may initiate negative affect, in which individuals experience a loss of control over their sexual response cycle, throwing them into the kind of dysfunctional pattern depicted in Figure 11.2. It is common for people who experience erectile failure during a particularly stressful time to continue sexual dysfunction long after the stressful situation has ended.

In addition to generally negative attitudes or experiences associated with sexual interactions, several other factors may contribute to sexual dysfunction. Among these, the most common is a marked deterioration in close interpersonal relationships (Burri et al., 2013; Jiann et al., 2009; Wincze & Weisberg, 2015). It is difficult to have a satisfactory sexual relationship in the context of growing dislike for a partner. Occasionally, the partner may no longer seem physically attractive. Kelly, Strassberg, and Kircher (1990) found that anorgasmic women, in addition to displaying more negative attitudes toward masturbation, greater sex guilt, and greater endorsement of sex myths, reported discomfort in telling their partners what sexual activities might increase their arousal or lead to orgasm, such as direct clitoral stimulation.

Thus, social and cultural factors seem to affect later sexual functioning. Researchers studying this phenomenon have constructed an important concept called script theory of sexual functioning. According to this theory, we all operate according to "scripts" that reflect social and cultural expectations and guide our behaviour (Gagnon, 1990; Laumann et al., 1994). Discovering these scripts, both in individuals and across cultures, will tell us much about sexual functioning. For example, a person who learns that sexuality is potentially dangerous, dirty, or forbidden is more vulnerable to developing sexual dysfunction later in life. This pattern is most evident in cultures with very restrictive attitudes toward sex (McGoldrick et al., 2007; Meston et al., 1998). For example, vaginismus is relatively rare in North America but is the most common cause of unconsummated marriages in Ireland, Turkey, and Iran (Doğan, 2009; Farnam et al., 2014; McGoldrick et al., 2007).

Cultural scripts may also contribute to the type of sexual dysfunction reported. In India, for example, Verma, Khaitan, and Singh (1998) reported that 77 percent of a large number of male patients in a sexuality clinic in India reported difficulties with premature ejaculation. In addition, 71 percent of male patients complained of being extremely concerned about nocturnal emissions associated with erotic dreams. The authors note that this focus on problems with ejaculation is most likely due to a strongly culturally held belief in India that loss of semen causes depletion of physical and mental energy. It is also interesting that out of 1000 patients presenting to this clinic, only 36 were women, most likely reflecting the devaluation of sexual experiences for women for religious and social reasons in some parts of India.

Cultural factors may also play a role in sexual attitudes, which in turn may contribute to sexual dysfunctions. A study by Lori Brotto and her colleagues, conducted with students at the University of British Columbia, compared Euro-Canadian women's sexual attitudes and functioning to those of Asian women (Brotto et al., 2005). They found that Euro-Canadian women had significantly more sexual knowledge and experiences, more liberal attitudes, and higher rates of desire, arousal, sexual receptivity, and sexual pleasure than the Asian women. Anxiety from anticipated sexual activity was significantly higher in Asian women. Beyond these significant ethnic group comparisons, the degree of acculturation to Western culture was significantly related to sexual attitudes, even after accounting for how long the women had lived in Canada. The authors suggest that assessing the level of acculturation may be important in the treatment of Asian women's sexual dysfunctions.

Even in Canadian culture, certain socially communicated expectations and attitudes may stay with us despite our relatively enlightened and permissive attitude toward sex. Cyranowski and colleagues (1999) have demonstrated that a negative sexual self-schema (being emotional and self-conscious about sex) may later lead to sexual difficulties under stressful situations. Zilbergeld (1992) has elaborated a number of myths about sex believed by many men, and Heiman and LoPiccolo (1988) have done the same for women. They found that men with dysfunctions showed significantly greater belief in the myths (e.g., "Good sex requires orgasm") than did men who were sexually functional. We explore such myths further in our discussion of treatment.

THE INTERACTION OF PSYCHOLOGICAL AND PHYSICAL FACTORS

Having reviewed the various causes, we must now say that seldom is any sexual dysfunction associated exclusively with either psychological or physical factors (Rosen, 2007; Wiegel et al., 2006; Wincze & Weisburg, 2015). More often it's a subtle combination of factors. To take a typical example, a young man, vulnerable to developing anxiety and holding to a certain number of sexual myths (the social contribution), may experience erectile failure unexpectedly after using drugs or alcohol, as many men do (the biological contribution). He will anticipate the next sexual encounter with anxiety, wondering whether the failure might happen again. This combination of experience and apprehension activates the psychological sequence depicted in Figure 11.2, regardless of whether he's had a few drinks.

In summary, socially transmitted negative attitudes about sex may interact with a person's relationship difficulties and predispositions to develop performance anxiety and, ultimately, lead to sexual dysfunction. From a psychological point of view, we don't know why some individuals develop one dysfunction and not another, although it is common for several dysfunctions to occur in the same patient. Very possibly, an individual's specific biological predispositions interact with psychological factors to produce a specific sexual dysfunction.

TREATMENT OF SEXUAL DYSFUNCTION

Unlike most other disorders discussed in this book, one surprisingly simple treatment is effective for a large number of individuals who experience sexual dysfunction: education. Ignorance of the most basic aspects of the sexual response cycle and intercourse often leads to long-lasting dysfunctions (Bach et al., 2001; Wincze et al., 2008; Wincze & Weisberg, 2015). Consider the case of Carl, who recently came to our sexuality clinic.

CARL | *Never Too Late*

Carl, a 55-year-old white man, was referred to our clinic by his urologist because Carl had difficulty maintaining an erection. Although he had never been married, he was at present involved in an intimate relationship with a 50-year-old woman. This was only his second sexual relationship. He was reluctant to ask his partner to come to the clinic because of his embarrassment in discussing sexual issues. A careful interview revealed that Carl engaged in sex twice a week, but requests by the clinician for a step-by-step description of his sexual activities revealed a very unusual pattern: Carl skipped foreplay and immediately proceeded to intercourse! Unfortunately, because his partner was not aroused and lubricated, he was unable to penetrate her. His valiant efforts sometimes resulted in painful abrasions for both of them. Two sessions of extensive sex education, including very specific instructions for carrying out foreplay, provided Carl with a whole new outlook on sex. For the first time in his life, he had successful, satisfying intercourse, much to his and his partner's delight.

In the case of hypoactive sexual desire disorder, one common presentation is a marked difference within a couple that leads to one partner being labelled as having low desire. For example, if one partner is quite happy with sexual relations once a week but the other partner desires sex every day, the latter partner may blame the former of having low desire and, unfortunately, the former partner might agree. Facilitating better conditions often resolves these misunderstandings. Fortunately, for people with this and more complex sexual dysfunctions, treatments are now available, both psychosocial and biological (medical). We look first at psychosocial treatments; then we examine the latest medical procedures.

PSYCHOSOCIAL TREATMENTS

Among the many advances in our knowledge of sexual behaviour, none was more dramatic than the publication in 1970 of *Human Sexual Inadequacy* by Masters and Johnson. The procedures outlined in this book literally revolutionized sex therapy by providing a brief, direct, and reasonably successful therapeutic program for sexual dysfunctions. Underscoring once again the common basis of most sexual dysfunctions, a very similar approach to therapy is taken with all patients, male and female, with slight variations depending on the specific sexual problem (e.g., premature ejaculation, orgasmic disorder). This intensive program involves a male and a female therapist to facilitate communication between the dysfunctional partners. (Masters and Johnson were the original male and female therapists.) Therapy is conducted daily for two weeks.

In addition to providing basic education about sexual functioning, altering deep-seated myths, and increasing communication, the clinicians' primary goal is to eliminate psychologically based performance anxiety. To accomplish this, Masters and Johnson introduced *sensate focus* and *nondemand pleasuring*. In this exercise, couples are instructed to refrain from intercourse or genital caressing and simply to explore and enjoy each other's body through touching, kissing, hugging, massaging, or similar kinds of behaviour. In the first phase, nongenital pleasuring, breasts and genitals are excluded from the exercises. After successfully accomplishing this phase, the couple moves to genital pleasuring but with a ban on orgasm and intercourse and clear instructions to the man that achieving an erection is not the goal.

At this point, arousal should be re-established and the couple should be ready to attempt intercourse. So as not to proceed too quickly, this stage is also broken down into parts. For example, a couple might be instructed to attempt the beginnings of penetration; that is, the depth of penetration and the time it lasts are only very gradually built up, and both genital and nongenital pleasuring continue. Eventually, full intercourse and thrusting are accomplished. After this two-week intensive program, recovery was reported by Masters and Johnson for the vast majority of more than 790 sexually dysfunctional patients, with some differences in the rate of recovery depending on the disorder. Close to 100 percent of individuals with premature ejaculation recovered, whereas the rate for more difficult cases of lifelong generalized erectile disorder was closer to 60 percent.

After the results were published, specialty sexuality clinics based on the pioneering work of Masters and Johnson were established to administer these new treatment techniques. Subsequent research revealed that many of the structural aspects of the program did not seem necessary. For example, one therapist seems to be as effective as two (LoPiccolo et al., 1985), and seeing patients once a week seems to be as effective as seeing them every day (Heiman & LoPiccolo, 1983a, 1983b). It has also become clear in the succeeding decades that the results achieved by Masters and Johnson were much better than those achieved in clinics around the world using similar procedures. Reasons for this difference are not entirely clear. One possibility is that patients were highly motivated because they had to take at least two weeks off and fly to St. Louis to meet with Masters and Johnson.

Sex therapists have expanded on and modified these procedures over the years to take advantage of recent advances in knowledge (e.g., Bach et al., 2001; Bradford & Meston, 2011; Leiblum & Rosen, 2000;

Weiner & Avery-Clark, 2014; Wincze, 2009; Wincze et al., 2008). Results with sex therapy for erectile disorder indicate that as many as 60 to 70 percent of the cases show a positive treatment outcome for at least several years, although there may be some slipping after that (Fruhauf et al., 2013; Rosen, 2007; Segraves & Althof, 1998). For better treatment of *specific* sexual dysfunctions, sex therapists integrate specific procedures into the context of general sex therapy. For example, to treat premature ejaculation, most sex therapists use a procedure developed by Semans (1956), sometimes called the *squeeze* technique, in which the penis is stimulated, usually by the partner, to nearly full erection. At this point the partner firmly squeezes the penis near the top where the head of the penis joins the shaft, which quickly reduces arousal. These steps are repeated until (for heterosexual partners) eventually the penis is briefly inserted in the vagina without thrusting. If arousal occurs too quickly, the penis is withdrawn and the squeeze technique is employed again. In this way the man develops a sense of control over arousal and ejaculation. Reports of success with this approach over the past 20 years suggest that 60 to 90 percent of men benefit, but the success rates drop to about 25 percent after three years or more of follow-up (Althof, 2007; Malavige & Jayawickrema, 2015; Polonsky, 2000; Segraves & Althof, 1998). Gary, the 31-year-old sales representative, was treated with this method, and his wife was very cooperative during the procedures. Brief marital therapy also persuaded Gary that his insecurity over his perception that his wife no longer found him attractive was unfounded. After treatment, he reduced his work hours somewhat, and the couple's marital and sexual relations improved.

Lifelong female orgasmic disorder may be treated with explicit training in masturbatory procedures (Bradford & Meston, 2011). For example, Greta was still unable to achieve orgasm with manual stimulation by her husband, even after proceeding through the basic steps of sex therapy. At this point, following certain standardized treatment programs for this problem (e.g., Heiman, 2000; Heiman & LoPiccolo, 1988), Greta and Will purchased a

▲ A therapist usually treats a sexual dysfunction in one partner by seeing the couple together.

Romilly Lockyer/Brand X Pictures/PictureQuest/Jupiter Images vibrator and Greta was taught to let go of her inhibitions by talking out loud about how she felt during sexual arousal, even shouting or screaming if she wanted to. In the context of appropriate genital pleasuring and disinhibition exercises, the vibrator brought on Greta's first orgasm. With practice and good communication, the couple eventually learned how to bring on Greta's orgasm without the vibrator. Although Will and Greta were both delighted with her progress, Will was concerned that Greta's screams during orgasm would attract the attention of the neighbours. Summaries of results from several studies, including work by Meston and her colleagues, suggests 70 to 90 percent of women benefit from treatment, and these gains are stable and even improve over time (Fruhauf et al., 2013; Heiman, 2007; Heiman & Meston, 1997; Segraves & Althof, 1998).

To treat vaginismus and pain related to penetration in genito-pelvic pain/penetration disorder, the woman and, eventually, the partner gradually insert larger and larger dilators at the woman's own pace (see Basson et al., 2004). After the woman (and then the partner) can insert the largest dilator, in a heterosexual couple the woman gradually inserts the man's penis. These exercises are carried out in the context of genital and nongenital pleasuring so as to retain arousal. Of course, close attention must be accorded to any increased fear and anxiety that may be associated with the process, which may trigger memories of early sexual abuse that may have contributed to the onset of the condition. These procedures are highly successful, with a large majority of women (80 to 100 percent) overcoming vaginismus in a relatively short time (Binik et al., 2007; Leiblum & Rosen, 2000; ter Kuile et al., 2007; ter Kuile et al., 2013). However, Elke Reissing, Irv Binik, and Samir Khalife (1999) in Montréal have been critical of this literature's focus on the achievement of penile–vaginal intercourse as the indicator of therapy "success." These researchers argue that additional relevant outcomes that should be (but rarely are) assessed are (1) whether the vaginal muscle spasm has in fact been resolved, (2) whether interference with intercourse has been decreased, (3) whether intercourse is less painful or more pleasurable, and (4) whether the couple is experiencing greater sexual satisfaction (Reissing et al., 1999). These authors have also suggested that there may be two subtypes of vaginismus requiring two different types of treatment. First, there may be a subtype involving a phobia of penetration for which cognitive-behavioural techniques developed for fear reduction would be most appropriate. Second, there may be a separate subtype involving genital pain for which psychosocial techniques developed for the treatment of chronic pain would be most appropriate.

A variety of treatment procedures have also been developed for low sexual desire (Basson et al., 2004; Pridal & LoPiccolo, 2000; Wincze, 2009; Wincze & Weisberg, 2015). At the heart of these treatments are the standard education and communication phases of traditional sex therapy with, possibly, the addition of masturbatory training and exposure to erotic material. Of course, each case may require individual strategies. Remember Mrs. C., who was sexually abused by her cousin? Therapy involved helping the couple understand the impact of the repeated, unwanted sexual experiences in Mrs. C.'s past and to approach sex so that Mrs. C. was much more comfortable with foreplay. She gradually lost the idea that once sex was started she had no control. She and her husband worked on starting and stopping sexual encounters. Cognitive restructuring was used to help Mrs. C. interpret her husband's amorousness in a positive rather than a skeptical light. In general, the clinical literature suggests that approximately 50 to 70 percent of individuals with low sexual desire benefit from sex therapy, at least initially (Basson, 2007; Brotto, 2006).

Vancouver-based psychologist and sex researcher Lori Brotto and her colleagues have done extensive work developing and evaluating a mindfulness intervention for women struggling with low sexual desire and genital pain. Mindfulness interventions typically involve learning to be in the present moment and to observe your own thoughts and feelings without judgment. That work was recently summarized in a book for a general audience, *Better Sex Through Mindfullness* (Brotto, 2018). Results so far indicate that women are very receptive to this type of intervention and seem to benefit from it. It is not year clear, however, if this particular treatment is more effective than other types of treatment. In one study, mindfulness-based cognitive therapy was more effective than cognitive therapy for reducing pain intensity during penetrative sex (Brotto et al., 2019).

Used with permission of Dr. Lori Brotto

▲ Canada Research Chair in Women's Sexual Health, Lori Brotto, conducts research on the treatment of sexual dysfunctions.

MEDICAL TREATMENTS

A variety of pharmacological and surgical techniques have been developed in recent years to treat sexual dysfunction, almost all focusing on male erectile disorder. But the drug Viagra, which was introduced in Canada in March 1999, and similar drugs, such as Levitra and Cialis, introduced subsequently, are the best known. We look at the four most popular procedures: oral medication, injection of vasoactive substances directly into the penis, surgery, and vacuum device therapy. It is often important to combine any medical treatment with a comprehensive educational and sex therapy program to ensure maximum benefit.

Photo by Guy L'Heureux/McGill University

▲ Yitzchak (Irv) Binik is a clinical psychologist at McGill University and the Sex and Couple Therapy Service of the Royal Victoria Hospital. His research has contributed substantially to the understanding and effective treatment of a variety of sexual dysfunctions, including vaginismus.

Several so-called wonder drugs for various disorders have been introduced with a flourish, including Prozac for depression and Redux for obesity. As noted in Chapter 2, the usual course is initial overwhelming enthusiasm that the drug is a cure-all, followed by a period of profound disappointment as people realize the drug is not what it was promised to be and may even be harmful in some cases. Finally, rationality sets in and the drug, if it has been proven effective in a number of studies, usually is found to be of moderate benefit to some people and becomes a useful part of a treatment plan. The wonder drug of 1999 was sildenafil (brand name Viagra) for erectile disorder. Guy Lafleur, a famous hockey player from the Montréal Canadiens, was the spokesperson in the initial marketing campaign for Viagra in Canada. Results from several clinical trials suggest that between 50 and 80 percent of men benefit from this treatment (Conti et al., 1999; Goldstein et al., 1998) in that erections become sufficient for intercourse, compared to approximately 30 percent who benefit from placebo. Results are similar with Cialis and Levitra (Carrier et al., 2005). However, as many as 30 percent may experience severe headaches as a side effect, particularly at higher doses (Rosen, 2000, 2007; Virag, 1999), and reports of sexual satisfaction are not optimal. For example, Virag (1999) evaluated a large number of men and defined success as both ability to engage in intercourse and the patient's rating of sexual satisfaction on a scale of 0 to 10. By these criteria, 32 percent of the men were successful if success was defined as an erection sufficient to engage in intercourse, and satisfaction of at least 7 on the 0 to 10 scale. Results were categorized as fair for the 29 percent who reported adequate erection but satisfaction from 4 to 6, and unsatisfactory for 39 percent with inadequate erection and satisfaction rated as 0 to 3. Thus, erections were sufficiently firm for intercourse in 61 percent of the men, consistent with other studies, but only 32 percent rated the results as at least good, suggesting the need for, perhaps, additional drug or psychological treatment.

For some time, testosterone (Schiavi et al., 1997) has been used to treat erectile disorder. But although it is safe and have relatively few side effects, it has only negligible effects on erectile disorder (Forti et al., 2012; Mann et al., 1996). A group of researchers at the University of Western Ontario has reported preliminary evidence that testosterone may alleviate hypoactive sexual desire in women (Van Anders et al., 2005). Cindy Meston and her colleagues have produced results suggesting that yohimbine—when combined with another drug, l-arginine glutamate—is superior to placebo in increasing vaginal responses to erotic stimuli among women with sexual arousal disorder (Meston & Worcel, 2002); future research needs to establish the utility of this drug combination in treating symptoms of the disorder outside the laboratory.

Some urologists teach patients to inject vasodilating drugs, such as *papaverine* or *prostaglandin*, directly into the penis when they want to have sexual intercourse. These drugs dilate the blood vessels, allowing blood to flow to the penis and thereby producing an erection within 15 minutes that can last from one to four hours (Rosen, 2000; Segraves & Althof, 1998). Because this procedure is a bit painful (although not as much as you might think), a substantial number of men, usually 50 to 60 percent, stop using it after a short time. In one study, 50 of 100 patients discontinued papaverine for various reasons (Lakin et al., 1990; Segraves & Althof, 1998). Side effects include bruising and, with repeated injections, the development of fibrous nodules in the penis (Gregoire, 1992; Rosen, 2000). Although some patients have found papaverine very helpful, it needs more study, and scientists are attempting to develop more palatable ways to deliver the drug. A soft capsule that contains the drug, called MUSE (medical urethral system for erections), can be inserted directly into the urethra; this is somewhat painful, but it is less effective than injections and remains awkward and artificial enough to most likely preclude wide acceptance (Delizonna et al., 2001).

Insertion of *penile prostheses* or implants has been a surgical option for almost 100 years; only recently have they become good enough to approximate normal sexual functioning. One procedure involves implanting a semirigid silicone rod that can be bent by the male into correct position for intercourse and manoeuvred out of the way at other times. In a more popular procedure, the male squeezes a small pump that is surgically implanted into the scrotum, forcing fluid into an inflatable cylinder and thus producing an erection. The newest model of penile prosthetic device is an inflatable rod that contains the pumping device, which is more convenient than having the pump outside the rod. However, surgical implants fall short of restoring presurgical sexual functioning or ensuring satisfaction in most patients (Gregoire, 1992; Kim & Lipshultz, 1997) and are now generally used only if other approaches don't work. On the other hand, this procedure has proved useful for men who must have a cancerous prostate removed, because this surgery often causes erectile disorder, although newer "nerve-sparing" surgeries lessen the effect to some extent (Ramsawh et al., 2005).

Another approach is *vacuum device therapy*, which works by creating a vacuum in a cylinder placed over the penis. The vacuum draws blood into the penis, which is then trapped by a specially designed ring placed around the base of the penis. Although using the vacuum device is rather awkward, between 70 and 100 percent of users report being able to achieve an erection with this device, particularly if psychosocial sex therapy is ineffective (Segraves & Althof, 1998; Witherington, 1988). The procedure is also less intrusive than surgery or injections, but remains awkward and artificial enough to, most likely, preclude wide acceptance (Delizonna et al., 2001). In recent years this therapy has gained traction as a first line therapy for men who have been treated for prostate cancer (Pahlajani et al., 2012).

SUMMARY

Treatment programs, both psychosocial and medical, offer hope to most people who have sexual dysfunctions. Unfortunately, such programs are not readily available in many locations because few health and mental health professionals are trained to apply them (although the availability of Viagra for male erectile disorder is widespread). Psychosocial treatment of sexual arousal disorders requires improvement, and treatments for low sexual desire are largely untested. New medical developments appear yearly, but most are still intrusive and clumsy. Drugs such as Viagra, Cialis, and Levitra appear promising, and many more Viagra-like drugs are in development (Rosen, 2000). Flibanserin, a drug that failed as a treatment for depression, was proposed as a treatment of low sexual desire in women. It came to the US and Canadian markets under much controversy: its very modest effect on sexual desire demonstrated in a very specific group of women was accompanied by worrisome side effects (Brotto, 2015).

Unfortunately, most health professionals tend to ignore the issue of sexuality in aging. Along with the usual emphasis on communication, education, and sensate focus, appropriate lubricants for women and a discussion of methods to maximize the erectile response in men should be a part of any sexual counselling for older couples. More important, even with reduced physical capabilities, continued sexual relations, not necessarily including intercourse, should be a very enjoyable and important part of an aging couple's relationship. Further research and development in the treatment of sexual dysfunction must address all these issues. Nevertheless, the overwhelming consensus is that a combination of psychological and drug treatment, when indicated, will continue to be the treatment strategy of choice.

Concept Check   11.1

Determine whether the following statements are true (T) or false (F) for the causes and treatments of sexual dysfunctions.

1. _____ Many physical and medical conditions and their treatments (for example, prescription medications) contribute to sexual dysfunction; however, many doctors are unaware of the connection.

2. _____ Anxiety always decreases or even eradicates sexual arousal.

3. _____ Sexual dysfunctions can result from a growing dislike for a partner, traumatic sexual events, or childhood lessons about the negative consequences of sexual behaviour.

4. _____ A simple, effective treatment for many disorders is education.

5. _____ All sexual dysfunctions are treated with the same psychosocial technique.

6. _____ Most surgical and pharmacological treatments of recent years have focused on erectile disorder.

AN OVERVIEW OF PARAPHILIC DISORDERS

If you are like most people, your sexual interest is directed to other physically mature adults (or late adolescents), all of whom are capable of freely offering or withholding their consent. But what if you are sexually attracted to something or somebody other than another adult? What if you are attracted to high-heeled shoes? Or what if your only means of obtaining sexual satisfaction is to hurt a stranger? Such patterns of sexual attraction and arousal and countless others exist in a large number of individuals, sometimes causing human suffering both for them and, if their behaviour involves nonconsenting others, for their victims. As noted in the beginning of the chapter, these disorders of sexual attraction and arousal—if they cause distress or impairment to the

individual, or cause personal harm, or cause the risk of harm to others—are called **paraphilic disorders**. It is important to note that the *DSM-5* does not consider a paraphilia a disorder unless it is associated with distress and impairment or harm or the threat of harm to others. Thus, unusual patterns of sexual attraction are not considered to be sufficient to meet criteria for a disorder.

The distinction between a passing interest in some unusual sexual activity, a long-standing interest, and a disorder is important to keep in mind. University of Lethbridge researchers have provided useful definitions of key terms: "A *paraphilic interest* is generally defined as a sexual interest in an atypical target (e.g., articles of clothing, children) or activity (e.g., hurting a partner, looking at an unsuspecting person); when this interest becomes long-standing, persistent, and necessary for sexual enjoyment, it is considered a *paraphilia* (e.g., fetishism, pedophilia, sadism, voyeurism). When the paraphilia results in significant distress or impairment of functioning, it is considered a *paraphilic disorder*" (italics in original; Dawson et al., 2016, p. 21). In this chapter we are concerned with paraphilic disorders.

Over the years, we have assessed and treated a large number of individuals with paraphilic disorders, ranging from the slightly eccentric case to some of the most dangerous killers. We begin by describing briefly the major types of paraphilic disorders, using in all instances cases from our own files. It is common for an individual to have more than one paraphilic disorders. Many of our cases may present with two, three, or more, although one is sometimes dominant. Furthermore, it is not uncommon for individuals with paraphilic disorder to also have comorbid mood, anxiety, and substance abuse disorders, as recently demonstrated in a large study of about 1000 patients seen as a specialized clinic in Ottawa, Ontario (Renaud, 2019).

Although paraphilic disorders are not widely prevalent and estimates of their frequency are hard to come by, some disorders, such as transvestic disorder, seem relatively common (Bancroft, 1989; Mason, 1997). You may have been the victim of **frotteuristic disorder** in a large city, typically on a crowded subway or bus. (We mean really crowded, with people packed in like sardines.) In this situation people have been known to experience more than the usual jostling and pushing from behind. What they discover, much to their horror, is a (usually) male with a frotteuristic arousal pattern rubbing against them until he is stimulated to the point of ejaculation (see DSM Table 11.7). Because the victims cannot escape easily, the frotteuristic act is usually successful (Lussier & Piché, 2008).

DSM-5	Table 11.7 Criteria for Frotteuristic Disorder

A. Over a period of at least 6 months, recurrent and intense sexual arousal from touching or rubbing against a nonconsenting person, as manifested by fantasies, urges, or behaviors.

B. The individual has acted on these sexual urges with a nonconsenting person, or the sexual urges or fantasies cause clinically significant distress or impairment in social, occupational, or other important areas of functioning.

FETISHISTIC DISORDER

In **fetishistic disorder**, a person is sexually attracted to nonliving objects (see DSM Table 11.8). There are almost as many different types of fetishes as there are objects, although women's undergarments and shoes are very popular. Fetishistic arousal is associated with two different classes of objects or activities: (1) an inanimate object or (2) a source of specific tactile stimulation, such as rubber, particularly clothing made out of rubber. Shiny black plastic is also used (Bancroft, 1989; Junginger, 1997). Most, if not all, of the person's sexual fantasies, urges, and desires focus on this object. A third source of attraction (sometimes called *partialism*) is a part of the body, such as the foot, buttocks, or hair.

In one city for several months, bras hung out on women's backyard clotheslines disappeared. The women in the neighbourhood soon began talking to each other and discovered that bras were missing from every clothesline for blocks around. A police stakeout caught the perpetrator, who turned out to have a strong fetish for brassieres. As another example of fetishistic behaviour related to tactile stimulation, it is relatively common for a urologist to be called to the emergency room to remove surgically a long thin object, such as a pencil or the arm of an eyeglass frame, from a man's urethra. Men who insert such objects think that partially blocking the urethra in this way can increase the intensity of ejaculation during masturbation. However, if the entire object slips into the penis, major medical intervention is required.

VOYEURISTIC AND EXHIBITIONISTIC DISORDERS

Voyeuristic disorder is the practice of observing an unsuspecting individual undressing or naked in order to become aroused. **Exhibitionistic disorder**, by contrast, is achieving sexual

DSM-5	**Table 11.8** Criteria for Fetishistic Disorder

A. Over a period of at least 6 months, recurrent and intense sexual arousal from the use of nonliving objects or a highly specific focus on nongenital body part(s), as manifested by fantasies, urges, or behaviors.

B. The fantasies, sexual urges, or behaviors cause clinically significant distress or impairment in social, occupational, or other important areas of functioning.

C. The fetish objects are not limited to articles of clothing used in cross-dressing (as in transvestic disorder) or devices specifically designed for the purpose of tactile genital stimulation (e.g., a vibrator).

Source: Reprinted with permission from the *Diagnostic and Statistical Manual of Mental Disorders*, Fifth Edition (Copyright © 2013). American Psychiatric Association. All Rights Reserved.

arousal and gratification by exposing one's genitals to unsuspecting strangers. Contrary to popular ideas, therefore, individuals with voyeuristic and exhibitionistic disorders would not have satisfying sexual interactions. See DSM Table 11.9 for the criteria for both disorders. Consider the case of Robert.

ROBERT | *Outside the Curtains*

Robert, a 31-year-old married blue-collar worker, reported that he first started "peeping" into windows when he was 14. He rode around the neighbourhood on his bike at night, and when he spotted a female through a window he stopped and watched. During one of these episodes, he felt the first

▲ A crowded bus or subway car is a typical setting for frotteuristic activity, in which a person takes advantage of physical contact with strangers to become aroused.

pangs of sexual arousal. Eventually, he began masturbating while watching, thereby exposing his genitals, although out of sight. When he was older, he drove around until he spotted some prepubescent girls. He parked his car near them, unzipped his fly, called them over, and attempted to carry on a nonsexual conversation. Later he was sometimes able to talk a girl into mutual masturbation and fellatio. He was arrested several times, and the threat of arrest increased his arousal (Barlow & Wincze, 1980).

Source: Barlow & Wincze (1980).

DSM-5	**Table 11.9** Criteria for Voyeuristic and Exhibitionistic Disorders

Voyeuristic Disorder

A. Over a period of at least 6 months, recurrent and intense sexual arousal from observing an unsuspecting person who is naked, in the process of disrobing or engaging in sexual activity, as manifested by fantasies, urges, or behaviors.

B. The individual has acted on these sexual urges with a nonconsenting person, or the sexual urges or fantasies cause clinically significant distress or impairment in social, occupational, or other important areas of functioning.

C. The individual experiencing the arousal and/or acting on the urges is at least 18 years of age.

Exhibitionistic Disorder

D. Over a period of at least 6 months, recurrent and intense sexual arousal from the exposure of one's genitals to an unsuspecting person, as manifested by fantasies, urges, or behaviors.

E. The individual has acted on these sexual urges with a nonconsenting person, or the sexual urges or fantasies cause clinically significant distress or impairment in social, occupational, or other important areas of functioning.

Source: Reprinted with permission from the *Diagnostic and Statistical Manual of Mental Disorders*, Fifth Edition (Copyright © 2013). American Psychiatric Association. All Rights Reserved.

Although prevalence is unknown, in a random sample of 2450 adults in Sweden, 3 percent reported at least one incident of being sexually aroused by exposing their genitals to a stranger and 8 percent reported at least one incident of being sexually aroused by spying on others having sex (Långström & Seto, 2006). To meet the diagnosis for exhibitionistic disorder, however, the behaviour must occur repeatedly and be compulsive or out of control.

TRANSVESTIC DISORDER

In **transvestic disorder**, sexual arousal is strongly associated with the act of (or fantasies of) dressing in clothes of the other sex, or cross-dressing (see DSM Table 11.10). Consider the case of Mr. M.

MR. M. | *Strong Man in a Dress*

Mr. M., a 31-year-old married police officer, came to our clinic seeking treatment for uncontrollable urges to dress in women's clothing and appear in public. He had been doing this for 16 years and had been discharged from the Armed Forces for cross-dressing. Since then, he had risked public disclosure on several occasions. Mr. M.'s wife had threatened to divorce him because of the cross-dressing, and yet she frequently purchased women's clothing for him and was "compassionate" while he wore them.

Note that Mr. M. was in the Armed Forces before he joined the police force. It is not unusual for males who are strongly inclined to dress in female clothes to compensate by associating with so-called macho organizations. Some of our cross-dressing patients have been associated with various paramilitary organizations. Nevertheless, most individuals with this disorder do not seem to display any compensatory behaviours. The same survey in Sweden mentioned earlier found 3 percent of men and 0.4 percent of women reported at least one episode of transvestistic disorder (Långström & Zucker, 2005). The 3 percent prevalence rate in males, while a rough estimate, is generally accepted (American Psychiatric Association, 2013).

The wives of many men who cross-dress have accepted their husbands' behaviour and can be supportive if it is a private matter between them. Docter and Prince (1997) reported that 60 percent of more than 1000 cases of transvestistic disorder were married at the time of the survey. Some people, both married and single, join cross-dressing clubs that meet periodically or subscribe to newsletters devoted to the topic. If sexual arousal is primarily focused on the clothing itself, the diagnostic criteria require a specification "with fetishism." Research by the late Kurt Freund and his colleagues at the Centre for Addiction and Mental Health in Toronto suggests that transvestism of this type is indistinguishable from other fetishes in most respects (Freund et al., 1996). Another specifier for transvestism describes a pattern of sexual arousal associated not with clothing itself but rather with thoughts or images of oneself as a female. This specifier is called "autogynephilia." Consider the case of Ron, who was recently seen in our clinic.

RON AND RHONDA | *Sexual Confusion*

Ron was a 47-year-old divorced male with a six-year-old son. For the past several years Ron had been living with his girlfriend and his girlfriend's seven-year-old daughter, mother, and sister. He was large and muscular with a short but full beard. His initial complaint was severe social anxiety, which he felt had interfered with his ability to make friends and advance in his job since he sought out positions that required only limited social interaction. He reported that he loved his girlfriend and wanted to get married and was particularly concerned about being the best father he could be for his six-year-old son. He was assigned to group treatment for social anxiety, but showed up for the first session much to our surprise dressed in a jean miniskirt, knee-high black leather boots, and a blouse.

During the session, he expressed considerable confusion about his sexuality and we decided his needs would be better met in individual treatment.

At that point he requested to be called Rhonda and began volunteering a previous history of cross-dressing and frequenting gay nightclubs from time to time. He reported that his first marriage had ended after his wife discovered photos of him wearing her wedding dress. Presently, the most sexually arousing scenario for him was the image of himself as a woman, such as imagining himself performing domestic chores or activities, such as cooking for a male partner while wearing an apron. But he was clear that it was not the clothes that were arousing so much as the image in his own mind of himself as a woman. He also reported engaging in risky sexual behaviours, such as unprotected sex, meeting up with strangers to engage in sexual behaviours in parking lots, texting naked/provocative photos of himself to potential partners, and engaging in sexual acts in public places, such as the gym shower, all of which would begin with him dressed in his female clothes and assuming the role of a woman. He had kept this behaviour from his girlfriend mostly by hiding his clothes in the trunk of his car and in a back closet at work. In spite of this behaviour, he maintained a strong and frequent sexual relationship with his girlfriend and was terrified of contracting AIDS and infecting her. Nor could he imagine giving up the strong relationship with his son.

Treatment focused on eliminating risky sexual behaviour and clarifying with him the most important values in his life. He chose his girlfriend and his son and, after a course of treatment and occasional follow-up sessions, reported himself to be at peace with his decision and had given up his risky infidelities with no reports of slips or relapses.

DSM-5	Table 11.10 Criteria for Transvestic Disorder

A. Over a period of at least 6 months, recurrent and intense sexual arousal from cross-dressing, as manifested by fantasies, urges, or behaviors.

B. The fantasies, sexual urges, or behaviors cause clinically significant distress or impairment in social, occupational, or other important areas of functioning.

Specify if:

   With fetishism: If sexually aroused by fabrics, materials, or garments.

   With autogynephilia: If sexually aroused by thoughts or images of self as female.

Source: Reprinted with permission from the *Diagnostic and Statistical Manual of Mental Disorders*, Fifth Edition (Copyright © 2013). American Psychiatric Association. All Rights Reserved.

This specifier is very controversial because the "sexual confusion" experienced by Ron overlaps to some degree with gender dysphoria (described shortly), and some think this confusion is better captured by the concept of gender dysphoria. Indeed, there is a somewhat greater risk that individuals with this paraphilic disorder will develop gender dysphoria and request transition through gender reassignment surgery (Blanchard, 2010; Lawrence, 2013). But as we can see in the case of Ron/Rhonda, gender dysphoria was not a major component of his presentation and he did not once consider surgical gender reassignment. Rather, he was very strongly sexually aroused by thoughts and images of himself as a woman.

Concept Check	11.2

People have a wide range of sexual preferences. Check your understanding of some sexual paraphilic disorders by matching the scenarios with the correct label:
(a) exhibitionistic disorder, (b) voyeuristic disorder,
(c) fetishistic disorder, or (d) transvestic disorder. This is a story about Tom.

1. Tom loves to look through Susie's bedroom window and watch her undress. He gets extremely excited as she slowly exposes her body. _____.

2. What Tom does not realize is that Susie is aroused by undressing in front of her window while unsuspecting people are walking by. _____.

3. Tom also loves to look at Susie's shoes while she is undressing, especially her ultra-high black stilettos. _____.

4. What Tom would be shocked to find out is that Susie is really not "Susie"; she is actually Scott, who can become aroused only if he wears feminine clothing. _____.

SEXUAL SADISM AND SEXUAL MASOCHISM DISORDERS

Both **sexual sadism disorder** and **sexual masochism disorder** are associated with either inflicting pain or humiliation (sadism) or suffering pain or humiliation (masochism; see DSM Table 11.11), and becoming sexually aroused is specifically associated with violence and injury in these conditions (Seto et al., 2012). Although Mr. M. was extremely concerned about his cross-dressing, he was also disturbed by another problem. To maximize his sexual pleasure during intercourse with his wife, he had her wear a collar and leash, tied her to the bed, and handcuffed her. He sometimes tied himself with ropes, chains, handcuffs, and wires, all while he was cross-dressed. Mr. M. was concerned he might injure himself seriously. As a member of the police force, he had heard of cases—and even investigated one himself—in which an individual was found dead, very tightly and completely bound up in harnesses, handcuffs, and ropes. In many such cases, something goes wrong and the individual accidentally hangs himself or herself, an event that should be distinguished from the closely related condition called *autoerotic asphyxia*, which involves self-strangulation to reduce the flow of oxygen to the brain and enhance the sensation of orgasm (Hucker, 2011).

▲ Belts, chains, and handcuffs may increase sexual arousal in individuals with sadistic or masochistic tendencies.

PEDOPHILIC DISORDER

Perhaps the most tragic paraphilia is sexual attraction to children (or very young adolescents generally aged 13 years or younger), called **pedophilic disorder** (see DSM Table 11.12). Individuals with this pattern of arousal may be attracted to male children, female children, or both. It is important to distinguish between *sexually offending against a child* and having a *pedophilic disorder*. An offender may or may not have the disorder, and an individual with pedophilic disorder may or may not have offended against a child (many men caught with child pornography material, for example, have been found to have the disorder but have not ever attempted to engage in sexual activities with a child; Seto, 2013).

DSM-5	**Table 11.11** Criteria for Sexual Sadism Disorder and Sexual Masochism Disorder

Sexual Sadism Disorder

A. Over a period of at least 6 months, recurrent and intense sexual arousal from the psychological or physical suffering of another person, as manifested by fantasies, urges, or behaviors.

B. The individual has acted on these sexual urges with a nonconsenting person, or the sexual urges or fantasies cause clinically significant distress or impairment in social, occupational, or other important areas of functioning.

Sexual Masochism Disorder

C. Over a period of at least 6 months, recurrent and intense sexual arousal from the act of being humiliated, beaten, bound, or otherwise made to suffer, as manifested by fantasies, urges, or behaviors.

D. The fantasies, sexual urges, or behaviors cause clinically significant distress or impairment in social, occupational, or other important areas of functioning.

Source: Reprinted with permission from the *Diagnostic and Statistical Manual of Mental Disorders*, Fifth Edition (Copyright © 2013). American Psychiatric Association. All Rights Reserved.

DSM-5	**Table 11.12** Criteria for Pedophilic Disorders

A. Over a period of at least 6 months, recurrent, intense sexually arousing fantasies, sexual urges, or behaviors involving sexual activity with a prepubescent child or children (generally age 13 years or younger).

B. The individual has acted on these sexual urges, or the sexual urges or fantasies cause marked distress or interpersonal difficulty.

C. The individual is at least age 16 years and at least 5 years older than the child or children in Criterion A.

Note: Do not include an individual in late adolescence involved in an ongoing sexual relationship with a 12- or 13-year-old.

Specify whether:
Exclusive type (attracted only to children)
Nonexclusive type

Specify if:
Sexually attracted to males
Sexually attracted to females
Sexually attracted to both

Specify if:
Limited to incest

Source: Reprinted with permission from the *Diagnostic and Statistical Manual of Mental Disorders*, Fifth Edition (Copyright © 2013). American Psychiatric Association. All Rights Reserved.

It may seem paradoxical that some people have to either inflict or receive pain to become sexually aroused, but these types of cases are not uncommon. On many occasions, the behaviours themselves are quite mild and harmless (Krueger, 2010a, 2010b), but they can become dangerous and costly. It was not unusual that Mr. M. presented with three different patterns of atypical arousal—in his case, sexual masochism, sexual sadism, and transvestism.

Penile plethysmography can be used to diagnose many paraphilic disorders, including pedophilic disorder. In our research using clinical files at a sexual behaviour clinic in Toronto, we found that offenders against children are more likely to be pedophilic (to show significant penile responses to children) when they

▲ Ontario-based forensic psychologist Michael C. Seto has conducted extensive research on pedophilia and child pornography offenders.

have multiple victims, when they have a boy victim, when they offend against a child outside the family, when they offend against a very young child, and when they have possessed child pornography (e.g., Seto et al., 2017). An incest offender against a young teenage daughter, therefore, is much less likely to be diagnosed with pedophilia than an offender against two very young boys he met on vacation.

Although it is rare, some pedophilic men can be quite violent. An example is the case of 36-year-old Michael Brière. The Montréal native pled guilty to the murder of 10-year-old Holly Jones in Toronto. Jones was abducted while walking home from a friend's house in May 2003. Her dismembered body was found a day later. Brière was arrested a month later and charged with her murder. A statement of facts filed with the court revealed that Brière had abducted Jones off the street. He sexually assaulted the little girl, strangled her, and then dismembered her body to dispose of it. Brière pled guilty and was sentenced to life in prison in June 2004 ("Brière Pleads Guilty," 2004; "Holly Jones," 2003; "Killer of Holly Jones," 2004; "Police Lay Murder Charge," 2003).

PARAPHILIC DISORDERS IN WOMEN

Paraphilic disorders are seldom seen in women and were thought to be totally absent in women for many years, with the possible exception of sadomasochistic practices. But in recent years, several reports have appeared describing individual cases or small series of cases (Davis, 2014; Seto, 2009). Now estimates suggest that approximately 5 to 10 percent of all sexual offenders are women (Logan, 2009; Wiegel, 2008), although not all of these offenders would receive a paraphilic disorder diagnosis. J. Paul Fedoroff and his colleagues at the forensic service of the Centre for Addiction and Mental Health in Toronto have reported what seems to be the largest series of cases of women with paraphilic disorder—12 cases seen in their clinic (Fedoroff et al., 1999). Although some women had more than one paraphilic disorder, five of them presented with pedophilia, four with exhibitionism, and three with sadomasochistic tendencies. Female sexual offenders are often treated similarly to male sexual offenders; however, recent work

suggests that more attention is needed to understand the differences between these offenders and the best ways to treat them (Cortoni & Gannon, 2016).

To take several examples, one heterosexual woman had been convicted of sexually molesting an unrelated nine-year-old boy while she was babysitting. It seems she had touched the boy's penis and asked him to masturbate in front of her while she watched religious programs on television. It is not unusual for individuals with paraphilic disorder to rationalize their behaviour by engaging in some other practices that they consider to be morally correct or uplifting at the same time, a practice sometimes referred to as "moral cleansing." Another woman came to treatment because of her "uncontrollable" rituals of masturbating and undressing in front of her apartment window approximately five times a month. In addition she would, on occasion, drive her truck through the neighbourhood, where she would attempt to befriend cats and dogs by offering them food. She would then place honey or other food substances on her genital area so the animals would lick her. As with most women with paraphilic disorders, she was horrified by this activity and was seeking treatment to eliminate it, although she found it highly sexually arousing.

Nevertheless, paraphilic disorders are principally a male phenomenon. Toronto researchers provided an extreme demonstration of the male bias in paraphilic disorders when they investigated death scene characteristics of individuals who died from autoerotic asphyxia or asphyxia suicide in Ontario and Alberta between 1974 and 1987 (Hucker & Blanchard, 1992). They conducted the study because coroners and medical examiners sometimes struggle with determining the difference between the two types of death. They found that 117 out of the 118 autoerotic asphyxiation deceased were men (in comparison, 84 out of the 118 matched suicide case were males). Although this study is old, it remains informative today.

▲ Many boys were molested by the Christian Brothers at the Mount Cashel Orphanage in Newfoundland in the 1970s. The adverse psychological consequences that many victims suffered from these molestation experiences lasted into adulthood.

CAUSES OF PARAPHILIC DISORDERS

Although no substitute for scientific inquiry, case histories often provide hypotheses that can then be tested by controlled scientific observations. Let's consider the cases of Robert and Tony to see if their histories contain any clues.

These cases remind us that paraphilic patterns of sexual arousal often occur in the context of other sexual and social problems. Undesired kinds of arousal may be associated with deficiencies in levels of "desired" arousal with consensual adults; this was certainly true for both Tony and Robert, whose sexual relationships with adults were incomplete. As some researchers have pointed out, in many cases, an inability to develop adequate social relations with the appropriate people for sexual relationships seems to be associated with developing inappropriate sexual outlets (Marshall, 1997), but remember that it is sometimes difficult to establish what is the cause and what is the effect. Theories of the causes of paraphilic disorders often include the presence of disordered relationships during childhood and adolescence, with resulting deficits in healthy sexual development (Marshall & Barbaree, 1990; Ward & Beech, 2008). Many people with deficient sexual and social skills, however, do not develop paraphilic patterns of arousal.

Accidental early experience may have an impact. Tony's early sexual experiences just happened to be of the type he later found sexually arousing. Robert's first erotic experience occurred while he was peeping. But many of us do not find our early experiences reflected in our sexual patterns. Adolescent and adult males who have committed sexual offences are much more likely (perhaps five times more likely) than adolescent and adult males who have committed other types of offences to report having been the victim of sexual abuse when they were children (Jespersen et al., 2009; Seto & Lalumière, 2010). The causal status of early sexual abuse is unclear, however, because most sexual abuse survivors do not develop paraphilic interests or commit sexual crimes. Furthermore, females are more likely to be sexually abused as children, but males are much more likely to be sexual offenders.

Another factor may be the nature of the person's early sexual fantasies. For example, in a famous study, Stanley J. Rachman demonstrated that sexual arousal could become associated with a neutral object—a boot, for example—if the boot was repeatedly presented while the individual was sexually aroused (Rachman & Hodgson, 1968; see also Bancroft, 1989). One of the most powerful engines for the development of unwanted arousal may be early sexual fantasies that are repeatedly reinforced through the very strong sexual pleasure associated with masturbation. Before an individual with a pedophilic or sadism disorder ever acts on his behaviour, he may fantasize about it hundreds of times while masturbating. Expressed as a clinical or an operant conditioning paradigm, this is another example of a learning process in which a behaviour (sexual arousal to a specific object or activity) is repeatedly reinforced through association with a pleasurable consequence (orgasm). This mechanism may explain why paraphilic disorders are almost exclusively male disorders. The basic differences in frequency of masturbation and reliability of orgasms between men and women that exist across cultures may contribute to the differential development of paraphilic disorders.

The conditioning of sexual arousal to previously neutral stimuli is difficult to demonstrate in the laboratory, however (e.g., Lalumière & Quinsey, 1998).

ROBERT | *Revenge on Repression*

Robert (who sought help for voyeurism) was raised by a very stern authoritarian father and a passive mother in a small town in British Columbia. His father, who was a firm believer in Fundamentalist Christian religion, often preached the evils of sexual intercourse to his family. Robert learned little about sex from his father except that it was bad, so he suppressed any emerging heterosexual urges and fantasies, and as an adolescent, he felt very uneasy around girls his own age. By accident, he discovered a private source of sexual gratification: staring at attractive and unsuspecting females through a window. This led to his first masturbatory experience.

Robert reported in retrospect that being arrested was not so bad because it disgraced his father, which was his only way of getting back at him. In fact, the courts treated him lightly (which is not unusual for this offence), and his father was publicly humiliated, forcing the family to move away from their small town.

Source: Barlow & Wincze (1980).

TONY | *Trained Too Young*

Tony, who sought help because of an incestuous relationship with his daughter, reported an early sexual history that contained a number of events. Although he was brought up in a reasonably loving and outwardly normal Catholic family, he had an uncle who did not fit the family pattern. When he was nine or ten, Tony was encouraged by his uncle to observe a game of strip poker that the uncle was playing with a neighbour's wife. During this period, he also observed his uncle fondling a waitress at a drive-in restaurant and shortly thereafter was instructed by his uncle to fondle his young female cousin. Thus, he had an early model for mutual fondling and masturbation and obtained some pleasure from interacting in this way with young girls. Although the uncle never touched Tony, his behaviour was clearly abusive.

When Tony was about 13, he engaged in mutual masturbation with a sister and her girlfriend, which he remembers as pleasurable. Later, when Tony was 18, a brother-in-law took him to a prostitute and he first experienced sexual intercourse. He remembered this visit as unsatisfactory because, on that and subsequent visits to prostitutes, he ejaculated prematurely—a sharp contrast to his early experience with young girls. Other experiences with adult women were also unsatisfactory. When he joined the Armed Forces and was sent overseas, he sought out prostitutes who were often as young as 12.

Therapists and sex researchers who work with individuals with paraphilic disorders have observed what seems to be an incredibly strong sex drive. It is not uncommon for some individuals to masturbate three or four times a day. In one case seen in our clinic, a sadistic rapist masturbated approximately every half hour all day long, just as often as it was physiologically possible. We have speculated elsewhere that activity this consuming may be related to the obsessional processes of obsessive-compulsive disorder (Barlow, 2002). In both instances, the very act of trying to suppress unwanted emotionally charged thoughts and fantasies seems to have the paradoxical effect of increasing their frequency and intensity. This process is also ongoing in eating disorders and addictions, when attempts to restrict strong addictive cravings lead to uncontrollable increases in the undesired behaviours. (Recall Janet Polivy and Peter Herman's work on the causal role of dietary restraint in explaining binge eating, discussed in Chapter 9.) Psychopathologists are becoming interested in the phenomenon of weak inhibitory control across these disorders, which may indicate a weak biologically based behavioural inhibition system (BIS) in the brain that might repress serotonergic functioning. (You may remember from Chapter 5 that the BIS is a brain circuit associated with anxiety and inhibition.) In a study of a community sample, men on average reported more interest in a variety of paraphilic activities than women did, but the gender difference disappeared when individual differences in sex drive were statistically controlled (Dawson et al., 2016).

The model shown in ■ Figure 11.3 incorporates the factors thought to contribute to the development of paraphilic disorders. Nevertheless, all speculations, including the hypotheses we have described, have little scientific support at this time. For example, this model does not include the biological dimension. Paraphilic disorders could be neurologically based. In fact, there is now good evidence of a neurobiological basis for pedophilia, thanks to research by Toronto-based psychologist James Cantor and his colleagues. Pedophilia is associated with lower IQ, higher rates of left-handedness (left-handedness is thought to be a marker for prenatal perturbations), less dense white matter in some areas of the brain as determined by neuroimaging, poorer memory on neuropsychological tests, and traumatic head injuries before age 13 (reviewed in Dyshniku et al., 2015). More research on the other paraphilias is needed.

ASSESSING AND TREATING PARAPHILIC DISORDERS

ASSESSMENT

In recent years, we have developed sophisticated methods for assessing specific patterns of sexual arousal (Lalumière & Harris, 1998; Ponseti et al., 2012; Wincze, 2009; Wincze & Weisberg, 2015). This is important in studying paraphilic disorder because sometimes even the individual presenting with the problem is not fully aware of what caused the arousal. An individual once came in to our clinic complaining of uncontrollable arousal to open-toed white sandals worn by women. He noted that he was irresistibly

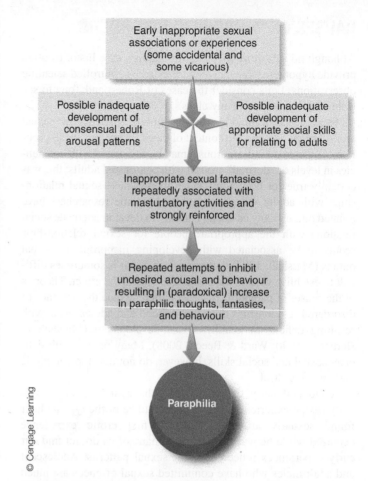

FIGURE 11.3 | A model of the development of paraphilia.

drawn to any woman wearing open-toed white sandals and would follow her for long distances. These urges occupied much of his summer. Subsequent assessment revealed that the sandal itself had no erotic value for this individual; rather, he had a strong sexual attraction to women's feet, particularly moving in a certain way. He had no reason to hide this fact; it was just that he did not realize it himself.

Using the model of paraphilic disorders described previously, we assess each patient not only for the presence of paraphilic arousal but also for levels of desired arousal to adults, for social skills, and for the ability to form relationships. Tony had no problems with social skills: he was 52 years old, reasonably happily married, and generally compatible with his second wife. His major difficulty was his continuing strong incestuous attraction to his daughter. Nevertheless, he loved his daughter very much and wanted strongly to interact in a normal fatherly way with her.

PSYCHOSOCIAL TREATMENT

Several treatment procedures are available for decreasing unwanted arousal. Most are behaviour therapy procedures directed at changing the associations and context from arousing and pleasurable to neutral. One procedure, carried out entirely in the imagination of the patient, called **covert sensitization**, was first described by Cautela (1967; see also Barlow, 2004). Sexually arousing images are associated with the very consequences of the behaviour that bring the patient to treatment in the first place. The notion here is that the patient's arousal patterns are undesirable because of their long-term consequences, but the immediate pleasure they provide, and thus the strong reinforcement, more than overcomes any thoughts of possible harm or danger that might arise in the future. This model also applies to much unwanted addictive behaviour, as we will discuss in Chapter 12.

In imagination, harmful or dangerous consequences can be associated quite directly with the unwanted behaviour and arousal in a very powerful and emotionally meaningful way. One of the most powerful negative aspects of Tony's behaviour was his embarrassment over the thought of being discovered by his current wife, other family members, or, most important, the family priest. Therefore, he was guided through the fantasy described here.

TONY | *Imagining the Worst*

You are alone with your daughter in your trailer. You realize that you want to caress her breasts. So you put your arm around her, slip your hand inside her blouse, and begin to caress her breasts. Unexpectedly, the door to the trailer opens and in walks your wife with Father X (the family priest). Your daughter immediately jumps up and runs out the door. Your wife follows her. You are left alone with Father X. He is looking at you as if waiting for an explanation of what he has just seen. Seconds pass, but they seem like hours. You know what Father X must be thinking as he stands there staring at you. You are very embarrassed and want to say something, but you can't seem to find the right words. You realize that Father X can no longer respect you as he once did. Father X finally says, "I don't understand this; this is not like you." You both begin to cry. You realize that you may have lost the love and respect of both Father X and your wife, who are very important to you. Father X asks, "Do you realize what this has done to your daughter?" You think about this and you hear your daughter crying; she is hysterical. You want to run, but you can't. You are miserable and disgusted with yourself. You don't know if you will ever regain the love and respect of your wife and Father X.

Source: Republished with permission of SAGE, from Harbert, T. L., Barlow, D. H., Hersen, M., Austin, J. B. Measurement and Modification of Incestuous Behavior: A Case Study. *Psychological Reports* Vol. 34 pp. 79–86, © 1974; permission conveyed through Copyright Clearance Center, Inc.

During six or eight sessions, the therapist narrates such scenes dramatically, and the patient is then instructed to imagine them every day until all arousal disappears. The results of Tony's

treatment are presented in ■ Figure 11.4. "Card-sort scores" are a measure of how much Tony wanted sexual interactions with his daughter in comparison with his desire for nonsexual fatherly interactions. His incestuous arousal was largely eliminated after three to four weeks, but the treatment did not affect his desire to interact with his daughter in a healthier manner. These results were confirmed by psychophysiological measurement of his arousal response. A return of some arousal at a three-month follow-up prompted us to ask Tony whether anything unusual was happening in his life. He confessed that his marriage had taken a turn for the worse and sexual relations with his wife had all but ceased. A period of marital therapy restored the therapeutic gains (see Figure 11.4). Several years later, after his daughter's therapist decided she was ready, she and Tony resumed a nonsexual relationship, which they both wanted.

Two major areas in Tony's life needed treatment: deviant sexual arousal and marital problems. As noted by Howard Barbaree and Michael Seto at the Centre for Addiction and Mental Health in Toronto, most individuals with paraphilic arousal patterns need a great deal of attention to family functioning or other interpersonal systems in which they operate (Barbaree & Seto, 1997). In addition, many require intervention to help strengthen desired patterns of arousal. In **orgasmic reconditioning**, patients are instructed to masturbate to their usual fantasies but to substitute more appropriate ones just before ejaculation. With repeated practice, subjects should be able to begin the desired fantasy earlier in the masturbatory process and still retain their arousal. This technique, first described by Davison (1968), has been used with some success in a variety of different settings (Brownell et al., 1977; Maletzky, 1998). Lastly, as with most strongly pleasurable but undesirable behaviours (including addiction), care must be taken to provide the patient with coping skills to prevent slips or relapses (see Chapter 12). **Relapse**

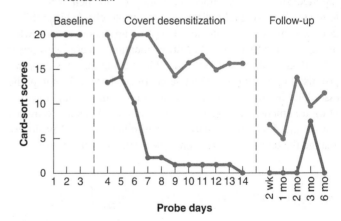

FIGURE 11.4 | Ratings of Tony's incestuous urges (deviant) and desire for normal interactions with his daughter (nondeviant) during covert desensitization treatment.

Source: Republished with permission of SAGE, from Harbert, T. L., Barlow, D. H., Hersen, M., Austin, J. B. Measurement and Modification of Incestuous Behavior: A Case Study. *Psychological Reports* Vol. 34 pp. 79–86, © 1974; permission conveyed through Copyright Clearance Center, Inc.

prevention treatment created for addictions (Laws & O'Donohue, 1997) does just that. Patients are taught to recognize the early signs of temptation and to institute a variety of self-control procedures before their urges become too strong.

Although some researchers have reported encouraging results, it has been difficult to demonstrate the success of this treatment in reducing paraphilic arousal or in reducing recidivism in treatment outcome studies. Maletzky (1998) examined factors associated with failure. Among the strongest predictors were a history of unstable social relationships, an unstable employment history, strong denial that the problem exists, a history of multiple victims, and a situation in which the offender continues to live with a victim (as might be typical in cases of incest). Moreover, it remains clear that we must continue to incorporate effective treatments into our correctional system and to develop improved treatments that specifically focus on relapse prevention, given the high rates of relapse for some sexual offenders (e.g., pedophiles with male victims). Newer treatments tend to incorporate successful practices seen in the field of correctional psychology for other types of offenders (e.g., skill-based treatments focusing on reducing risk factors and increasing protective factors; Hanson et al., 2008).

DRUG TREATMENTS

The most popular drug used to treat individuals with paraphilic disorders is an antiandrogen called *cyproterone acetate*. This "chemical castration" drug eliminates sexual desire and fantasy by reducing testosterone levels dramatically, but fantasies and arousal return as soon as the drug is removed. A second drug is *medroxy-progesterone* (Depo-Provera is the injectable form), a hormonal agent that reduces testosterone. These drugs may be useful for dangerous sexual offenders who do not respond to alternative treatments or for temporarily suppressing the sexual arousal of patients who require it, but they are not always successful. Rösler and Witztum (1998) of Hadassah University Hospital in Jerusalem reported successful chemical castration of 30 men with severe long-standing paraphilic disorder using triptorelin, which inhibits gonadotropin secretion in men. This drug appears to be somewhat more effective than the other drugs mentioned here, with fewer side effects. Rösler and Witztum (2000) argue that this drug has promise in providing an effective pharmacotherapy for paraphilic disorders, but this conclusion is based on a single study thus far. Drug treatments have effects on the strength of sexual desire but not on the direction of that desire; in other words, they do not change the target of arousal, only the intensity of the arousal.

AN OVERVIEW OF GENDER DYSPHORIA

Now we move to a very different topic, one that is both fascinating and controversial. What is it that makes you think you are a man? Or a woman? Is it something more than your sexual arousal patterns or your anatomy? Is it something more than the reactions and experiences of your family and society? Is there an essence of your masculinity or femininity that is a deep-seated personal sense of something we generally call gender identity? These are difficult questions scientists and philosophers continue to grapple with. According to *DSM-5* **gender dysphoria** is present if people experience an "incongruence between one's experienced or expressed gender and one's assigned gender" (p. 451). While gender dysphoria can occur on a continuum (American Psychological Association [APA] Task Force of Gender Identity and Gender Variance, 2008; Cohen-Kettenis & Pfäfflin, 2010), at the extreme end of the continuum are individuals who reject their natal sex altogether and want to change it. People with this condition often report feeling trapped in a body of the wrong sex. Consider the case of Josée.

JOSÉE | *Trapped in the Wrong Body*

Josée is a 17-year-old who was considered male at birth (and given the name Joe). She is the last of five children. Although her mother had wanted a girl, Josée became her favourite child. Her father worked long hours and had little contact with Josée. For as long as Josée could remember, she had thought of herself as a girl. She began dressing in girls' clothes of her own accord before she was five years old and continued cross-dressing into junior high school. She developed interests in cooking, knitting, crocheting, and embroidering, skills she acquired by reading an encyclopedia. Her older brother often scorned her for her distaste of such "masculine" activities as hunting.

Josée associated mostly with girls during this period, although she remembered being strongly attached to a boy in Grade 1. In her sexual fantasies, which developed around 12 years of age, she pictured herself as a female having intercourse with a male. Her extremely effeminate behaviour made her the object of scorn and ridicule when she entered high school at age 15. Usually passive and unassertive, she ran away from home and attempted suicide. Unable to continue in high school, she attended secretarial school, where she was the only "boy" in her class. During her first interview with a therapist, she reported, "I am a woman trapped in a man's body and I would like to have surgery to become a woman."

If the natal sex is female but the experienced gender (gender identity) is strongly male, the individual is typically referred to as a trans man, and a natal male whose experienced gender is female would be a trans woman (see DSM Table 11.13). Some also prefer not to be referred to as a specific gender at all. For example, one person coming into our clinic recently preferred to be referred to as *hen* (a Swedish gender-neutral pronoun, used in place of *him* or *her*); others prefer the pronoun *they*.

Although *DSM-5* specifies that the disorder of gender dysphoria is about the dysphoria, not the identity, many think that gender identity has nothing to do with psychiatric problems and that the dysphoria is mainly caused by lack of acceptance. Cross-cultural research by University of Lethbridge professor Paul Vasey supports this position (e.g., Vasey & Bartlett, 2007). Others worry that removing gender dysphoria from *DSM-5* will result in lack of medical coverage for gender transitions (many insurance companies require a diagnosed disorder to cover particular procedures).

Gender dysphoria must be distinguished from transvestic disorder, a paraphilic disorder (discussed earlier) in which individuals, usually males, are sexually aroused by wearing articles of clothing associated with the other sex. There is an occasional preference on the part of the male with transvestite patterns of sexual arousal for the female role, but the primary purpose of cross-dressing is sexual gratification. In the case of gender dysphoria, the primary goal is the desire to live life openly in a manner consistent with that of the desired gender.

Gender dysphoria can also occur among individuals with *disorders of sex development* (DSD), formerly known as *intersexuality* or *hermaphroditism*, who are born with ambiguous genitalia associated with documented hormonal or other physical abnormalities. Depending on their particular mix of characteristics, individuals with DSDs are usually "assigned" to a specific sex at birth, sometimes undergoing surgery, as well as hormonal treatments, to alter their sexual anatomy. If gender dysphoria occurs in the context of a DSD, this should be specified when making a diagnosis. But most individuals with gender dysphoria have not demonstrated physical abnormalities.

Gender dysphoria resulting in a rejection of natal sex is relatively rare. The estimated prevalence in natal males is between 5 and 14 per 1000 and for natal females between 2 and 3 per 1000 (APA, 2013; Judge et al., 2014). Many countries now require a series of legal steps to change gender. In Germany, between 2.1 and 2.4 per 100 000 in the population took at least the first legal step of changing their first names in the 1990s; in that country, the male:female ratio of people with gender dysphoria is 2.3:1 (Weitze & Osburg, 1996). Since 2006, in New York City people have been able to alter the natal sex listed on their birth certificates following surgery.

Enza Anderson is a well-known trans woman in Canada. She gained international attention when she ran for mayor of Toronto in November 2000. She also ran for a city council seat in the 2003 and 2010 Toronto municipal election. Enza has always felt she was female and started dressing as a girl secretly as a teen, borrowing clothes from her mother. She was raised in a very traditional Italian Catholic family. Enza trained and worked as a civil engineer but is not working in the engineering field because she cannot as easily dress as a woman and be herself. She is a columnist and a strong activist within the gay-lesbian-bisexual-transgender community in Toronto (see YouTube video at https://www.youtube.com/watch?v=UzALALhZRi4)

In some cultures, individuals with a different gender experience are often accorded the status of *shaman* or *seer* and treated

---

DSM-5 **Table 11.13** Criteria for Gender Dysphoria

In Children:

A. A marked incongruence between one's experienced/expressed gender and assigned gender, of at least 6 months' duration, as manifested by at least six of the following (one of which must be Criterion A1):

1. A strong desire to be of the other gender or an insistence that one is the other gender (or some alternative gender different from one's assigned gender).

2. In boys (assigned gender), a strong preference for cross-dressing or simulating female attire; or in girls (assigned gender), a strong preference for wearing only typical masculine clothing and a strong resistance to the wearing of typical feminine clothing.

3. A strong preference for cross-gender roles in make-believe play or fantasy play.

4. A strong preference for the toys, games, or activities stereotypically used or engaged in by the other gender.

5. A strong preference for playmates of the other gender.

6. In boys (assigned gender), a strong rejection of typically masculine toys, games, and activities and a strong avoidance of rough-and-tumble play; or in girls (assigned gender), a strong rejection of typically feminine toys, games, and activities.

7. A strong dislike of one's sexual anatomy.

8. A strong desire for the primary and/or secondary sex characteristics that match one's experienced gender.

B. The condition is associated with clinically significant distress or impairment in social, school, or other important areas of functioning.

In Adolescents and Adults:

A. A marked incongruence between one's experienced/expressed gender and assigned gender, of at least 6 months' duration, as manifested by at least two of the following:

1. A marked incongruence between one's experienced/expressed gender and primary and/or secondary sex characteristics (or in young adolescents, the anticipated secondary sex characteristics).

2. A strong desire to be rid of one's primary and/or secondary sex characteristics because of a marked incongruence with one's experienced/expressed gender (or in young adolescents, a desire to prevent the development of the anticipated secondary sex characteristics).

3. A strong desire for the primary and/or secondary sex characteristics of the other gender.

4. A strong desire to be of the other gender (or some alternative gender different from one's assigned gender).

5. A strong desire to be treated as the other gender (or some alternative gender different from one's assigned gender).

6. A strong conviction that one has the typical feelings and reactions of the other gender (or some alternative gender different from one's assigned gender).

B. The condition is associated with clinically significant distress or impairment in social, occupational, or other important areas of functioning.

as wisdom figures. A shaman is almost always a male adopting a female role (e.g., Coleman et al., 1992). Stoller (1976) reported on two contemporary feminized Indigenous men who were not only accepted but also esteemed by their tribes for their expertise in healing rituals. Contrary to the respect accorded these individuals in some cultures, social tolerance for them remains relatively low in Western cultures, although that is changing as individuals such as Chaz Bono and Caitlyn Jenner forthrightly and openly discuss gender dysphoria.

CAUSES

Research has yet to uncover any specific biological contributions to gender dysphoria or alternative gender experience for that matter, although it seems likely that a biological predisposition will be discovered. Coolidge, Thede, and Young (2002) estimated that genetics contributed about 62 percent to creating a vulnerability to experience gender dysphoria in their twin sample. Thirty-eight percent of the vulnerability came from nonshared (unique) environmental events. A study from the Netherlands twin registry suggested that 70 percent of the susceptibility for cross-gender behaviour (behaving in a manner consistent with the opposite natal sex) was genetic as opposed to environmental, but this behaviour is not the same as gender identity, which was not measured (van Beijsterveldt et al., 2006). Gomez-Gil et al. (2010) found a somewhat higher prevalence of gender dysphoria than would be expected by chance in nontwin siblings of a larger group (995) of individuals with gender dysphoria. Segal (2006), on the other hand, found two monozygotic (identical) female twin pairs in which one twin had gender dysphoria and the other did not; no unusual medical or life history factors were identified to account for this difference. Nevertheless, genetic contributions are clearly part of the picture (Heylens et al., 2012).

Early research suggested that slightly higher levels of testosterone or estrogen at certain critical periods of development might masculinize a female fetus or feminize a male fetus (e.g., Keefe, 2002). Variations in hormonal levels could occur naturally or because of medication that a pregnant mother is taking. Scientists have studied girls ages 5 to 12 with an intersex condition known as congenital adrenal hyperplasia (CAH). In CAH, the brains of these chromosomal females are flooded with male hormones (androgens), which, among other results, produce mostly masculine external genitalia, although internal organs (ovaries and so on) remain female. Meyer-Bahlburg and colleagues (2004) studied 15 girls with CAH, who had been identified as female at birth and raised as girls, and looked at their development. Compared with groups of girls and boys without CAH, the girls with CAH were masculine in their behaviour, but there were no differences in gender identity. Thus, scientists have yet to establish a link between prenatal hormonal influence and later gender identity, although it is still possible that one exists. Structural differences in the area of the brain that controls male sex hormones have also been observed in individuals with natal male with gender dysphoria (Hannema, et al., 2014; Zhou et al.,

1995), with the result that the brains are comparatively more feminine. But it isn't clear whether this is a cause or an effect.

At least some evidence suggests that gender identity firms up between 18 months and three years of age (Ehrhardt & Meyer-Bahlburg, 1981; Money & Ehrhardt, 1972) and is relatively fixed after that. But newer studies suggest that possible pre-existing biological factors have already had their impact. One interesting case illustrating this phenomenon was originally reported by Green and Money (1969), who described the sequence of events that occurred in the case of David/Brenda. There are other case studies of children whose gender was reassigned at birth who adapted successfully (see, for example, Gearhart, 1989), but it certainly seems that biology expressed itself in David's case.

Richard Green, a pioneering researcher in this area, has studied boys who behave in feminine ways and girls who behave in masculine ways, investigating some of the factors involved and following what happens to them (Green, 1987). This set of behaviours and attitudes is referred to as **gender nonconformity** (see,

▲ Enza Anderson is a columnist and transgender activist living in Toronto. She gained international attention when she ran for mayor of Toronto in 2000.

e.g., Skidmore et al., 2006). Green discovered that when most young boys spontaneously display "feminine" interests and behaviours, they are typically discouraged by most families and these behaviours usually cease. Boys who consistently display these behaviours are not discouraged, however, and are sometimes encouraged.

DAVID/BRENDA | *Gender and Biology*

A set of male identical twins was born into a well-adjusted family in Winnipeg, Manitoba. Several months later, an unfortunate accident occurred. Although circumcision went routinely for one of the boys, the physician's hand slipped so that the electric current in the device burned off the penis of the second baby. After working through their hostility toward the physician, the parents consulted specialists in children with intersexual problems and were faced with a choice. The specialists pointed out that the easiest solution would be to reassign their son David as a girl, and the parents agreed. At the age of several months, David became "Brenda." The parents purchased a new wardrobe and treated the child in every way possible as a girl. These twins were followed through childhood and, on reaching puberty, the young girl was given hormonal replacement therapy. After six years, the doctors lost track of the case but assumed the child had adjusted well. However, Brenda endured almost intolerable inner turmoil. We know this because two clinical scientists found this individual and reported a long-term follow-up (Diamond & Sigmundson, 1997). Brenda never adjusted to her assigned gender. As a child, she preferred rough-and-tumble play and resisted wearing girls' clothes. In public bathrooms, she often insisted on urinating while standing up, which usually made a mess. By early adolescence, Brenda was pretty sure she was a boy, but her doctors pressed her to act more feminine. When she was 14, she confronted her parents, telling them she was so miserable she was considering suicide. At that point, they told her the true story and the muddy waters of her mind began to clear. Shortly thereafter, Brenda had additional surgery, changing her back to David. He later married and became the father of three adopted children. But the turmoil of his early life never fully resolved. Perhaps because of this turmoil, perhaps because his twin brother had recently died and he had lost his job and was divorcing, or perhaps because of a combination of these factors, David Reimer (his real name) committed suicide at age 38 in 2004. His mother is reportedly of the opinion that her son's suicide was directly related to the emotional hardship he suffered as a consequence of the gender experiment (Canadian Press, 2004). David Reimer's story is told in the book *As Nature Made Him* (Colapinto, 2001).

Other factors, such as excessive attention and physical contact on the part of the mother, may also play some role, as may a lack of male playmates during the early years of socialization. These are just some factors identified by Green as characteristic of gender-nonconforming boys. Remember that as-yet-undiscovered biological factors may also contribute to the spontaneous display of cross-gender behaviours and interests. For example, one recent study found that exposure to higher levels of fetal testosterone was associated with more masculine play behaviour in both boys and girls during childhood (Auyeng et al., 2009). In following up with these boys, however, Green discovered that few seem to develop gender incongruence. The most likely outcome is the development of same-sex preferences, but even this particular sexual arousal pattern seems to occur exclusively in only approximately 40 percent of the gender-nonconforming boys. Another 32 percent show some degree of bisexuality. These results were replicated in subsequent prospective studies of boys in Toronto (Zucker, 2005).

Girls with gender-nonconforming behaviour are seldom studied, because their behaviour attracts much less attention in Western societies. But one recent study in Toronto followed 25 girls prospectively, beginning at approximately nine years of age, whose behaviour was extreme enough that they were referred to a gender identity clinic. Most of these girls met criteria for childhood gender dysphoria disorder or came very close to it. At a follow-up, when these girls (now women) averaged 25 years of age, only three met criteria for gender dysphoria. Another six reported bisexual/homosexual behaviour; eight more would have homosexual fantasies but not behaviour. The remaining eight women were heterosexual (Drummond et al., 2008).

This finding of a relationship between gender-nonconforming behaviour and later sexual orientation is not unique to North American culture. For example, similar relationships between early gender-nonconforming behaviour and later sexual orientation exist among the *Fa'afafine*, a group of natal males attracted to masculine men in the Pacific Islands country of Samoa (Bartlett & Vasey, 2006). The *Fa'afafine* represent a third gender in Samoa and are perceived as a normal part of the culture. They experience very few (if any) signs of dysphoria associated with their gender.

TREATMENT

Treatment is available for gender dysphoria in specialty clinics around the world, although much controversy surrounds treatment (Carroll, 2007; Meyer-Bahlberg, 2010), especially treatment of children (see the recent controversy surrounding the closing of a gender identity clinic for children at the Centre for Addiction and Mental Health in Toronto; Singal, 2016). For adults requesting full sex transition treatment, guidelines from both the American Psychiatric Association (Byne et al., 2012) and the American Psychological Association (APA Task Force on Gender Identity and Gender Variance, 2008) have now been published. The treatment guidelines published by the American Psychological Association highlight the diversity of problems facing gender-nonconforming individuals and encourage therapists to take a holistic view of these patients (i.e., helping to build resilience, working within existing family structures, and collaborating with other care providers). For adults with gender dysphoria, the American Psychiatric Association guidelines recommend beginning with the least intrusive step of full psychological evaluation and education before proceeding to partially reversible steps, such as the administration of gonadal hormones to bring about desired secondary sex characteristics. The final nonreversible step is to alter anatomy physically to be consistent with gender identity through **gender reassignment surgery**.

Gender Reassignment Surgery

This procedure is also called sex reassignment surgery and gender confirming surgery. To qualify for surgery at a reputable clinic, individuals must live in the desired gender for one to two years so that they can be sure they want to change gender. They also must be stable psychologically, financially, and socially (Blanchard & Steiner, 1990). In trans women, hormones are administered to promote *gynecomastia* (the growth of breasts) and the development of other secondary sex characteristics. Facial hair is typically removed through electrolysis. If the individual is satisfied with the events of the trial period, the genitals are removed and a vagina is constructed.

For trans men, an artificial penis is typically constructed through plastic surgery, using sections of skin and muscle from elsewhere in the body, such as the thigh. Breasts are surgically removed. Genital surgery is more difficult and complex in natal females. Estimates of satisfaction with surgery indicate predominantly successful adjustment (between 75 and 100 percent are generally satisfied) among those who could be reached for follow-ups, with trans men generally adjusting better than trans women (Blanchard & Steiner, 1992; Bodlund & Kullgren, 1996; Byne et al., 2012; Carroll, 2007; Costantino et al., 2013; Johansson et al., 2010). Many people were not available for follow-up, however. Approximately 1 to 7 percent of individuals who have had gender reassignment surgery and were reached for follow-up later regret having the surgery to some extent (Bancroft, 1989; Byne et al., 2012; Dhejne et al., 2014; Johansson et al., 2010; Lundstrom et al., 1984). This is unfortunate, because the surgery is irreversible. As many as 2 percent attempt suicide after surgery, a rate much higher than the rate for the general population. One problem may be incorrect diagnosis and assessment. For example, one study of 186 Dutch psychiatrists reporting on 584 patients presenting with gender dysphoria revealed little consensus on diagnostic features or the minimum age at which gender reassignment surgery is safe. Rather, the decision seemed to rest on the personal preferences of the psychiatrist (Campo et al., 2003). These assessments are complex and should always be done at highly specialized gender clinics. Predictors of regret in addition to misdiagnosis include the presence of comorbid diagnoses, such as alcohol use

and psychosis, and poor family support (Byne et al., 2012). Nevertheless, surgery has made life much better for many people who suffered the effects of existing in what they felt to be the wrong body, with rates of satisfaction in recent years averaging about 90 percent (Johansson et al., 2010).

A controversial issue in Canada has been whether gender reassignment surgery should be a publicly funded medical procedure. The treatment of this issue varies by province and territory. Several jurisdictions (e.g., Alberta, British Columbia, Ontario, Saskatchewan) fund gender reassignment surgery, whereas others do not. The procedure was funded in Ontario from 1969 until 1998. In the almost 30 years that the procedure was publicly funded in Ontario, statistics show that there were, on average, six people approved for the surgery each year at an average cost of $28 000. The cost of the procedure, and efforts to cut costs in healthcare spending, led the Ontario government to delist this surgery as eligible for medicare coverage. However, advocacy groups, such as Egale Canada, argued that it is a human rights issue and that transgender people's dignity was being harmed by the change in access to this surgery. In fact, four transgender individuals took the Ontario government to task in September 2003, in an important human rights hearing (Egale Canada, 2003). In November 2005, the Human Rights Tribunal ruled that the province should pay for gender reassignment surgery for three of the four complainants. However, the tribunal stopped short of requiring the Ontario government to relist this procedure as an eligible expense under the province's public health insurance plan (CUPE, 2005). Coverage was reinstated in 2008.

Treatment of Gender Dysphoria in Children

Even more controversial is the treatment of gender dysphoria and gender nonconformity in children (e.g., Cantor, 2017). Some segments of society are becoming more open to gender variations in both children and adults. In some schools, children are being allowed and even encouraged to dress and appear in gender-nonconforming ways on the assumption that this gives freer rein to who they "really are" (Brown, 2006). Although many people report being gender nonconforming as children, many became more conforming as they reached adulthood, perhaps because of persistent social pressure from their family and peers. Interventions exist to build resilience in children who exhibit gender-nonconforming behaviour by strengthening their relationships with peers and caregivers, increasing their sense of self-control, and increasing their sense of belonging within a community or culture (Allan & Unger, 2014).

Thus, society is faced with a dilemma that requires more research. Should the free expression of gender nonconformity be encouraged? Current research suggests that a wait and see approach is preferred, considering that the majority of gender nonconforming children do not persist. A careful clinical assessment is required to determine the causes of gender nonconformity and dysphoria. Sometimes children are nonconforming for reasons other than feelings about gender per se; for example, a boy may be bullied at school or at home, and wants to be girl because he thinks girls are not bullied so much. An even more difficult question is gender transition at puberty, when sex hormones have wide and large effects on the body; failure to intervene can have negative impacts on a child who is persistent in his or her desire to transition and, similarly, interventions for a child who was going to desist can be damaging as well. Strong negative feelings about one's anatomy is one of the best predictors of persistence among children.

Gender roles are determined by the society we live in. The greater openness that some societies are experiencing regarding gender might open more and new avenues for gender expression, which will likely have an impact on how psychiatry and psychology deal with gender.

Treatment of Disorders of Sex Development (Intersexuality)

As we noted, surgery and hormonal replacement therapy have been standard treatment for many individuals with DSDs who may be born with physical characteristics of both sexes in order to make their sexual anatomy match as closely to their assigned gender as possible. These procedures usually take place soon after birth. But in later years gender dysphoria may also develop in these individuals and, if it does, a similar sequence of treatment steps beginning with the least intrusive would be initiated (Byne et al., 2012). Of course, treatment for gender dysphoria in any form has always been controversial and particularly so when a DSD is present. Fausto-Sterling (2000a, 2000b) estimated, based on the best evidence available, that for every 1000 children born, 17, or 1.7 percent, may have a DSD in some form. Fausto-Sterling (2000b) and others have noted that individuals in this group are often dissatisfied with surgery, much as David was in the case we described. There have been instances in which doctors, on observing anatomical sexual ambiguity after birth, treat it as an emergency and immediately perform surgery.

An increasing number of pediatric endocrinologists, urologists, and psychologists are examining the wisdom of early genital surgery that results in an irreversible gender assignment. Instead, health professionals may want to examine closely the precise nature of the DSD and consider surgery only as a last resort. Otherwise, psychological treatments to help individuals adapt to their sexual anatomy, or their emerging gender experience, might be more appropriate. There is a strong movement to allow people to make their own choices.

SUMMARY

Sexual Dysfunctions

- Sexual dysfunction includes a variety of disorders in which people find it difficult to function adequately during sexual relations.
- Specific sexual dysfunctions include disorders of sexual desire (hypoactive sexual desire disorder in males and female sexual interest/arousal disorder) in which interest in sexual relations is extremely low or nonexistent, disorders of sexual arousal (erectile disorder and female sexual interest/arousal disorder) in which achieving or maintaining adequate penile erection or sexual excitement and vaginal lubrication is problematic; and orgasmic disorders (female orgasmic disorder and delayed or premature ejaculation in males) in which orgasm occurs too quickly or not at all. The most common disorder in this category is premature ejaculation, which occurs in males; inhibited orgasm is more commonly seen in females.
- Sexual pain disorder, specifically genito-pelvic pain/penetration disorder in women, in which unbearable pain is associated with sexual relations, includes vaginismus in which the pelvic muscles in the outer third of the vagina undergo involuntary spasms when intercourse is attempted.
- Sexual dysfunctions are associated with socially transmitted negative attitudes about sex, current relationship difficulties, and anxiety focused on sexual activity.
- Psychosocial treatment of sexual dysfunctions is generally successful but not readily available. In recent years, various medical approaches have become available, including Viagra and similar drugs. These treatments focus mostly on erectile disorder and are effective and satisfying for about one-third of patients who try them.

Paraphilic Disorders

- Paraphilia is a sexual attraction to inappropriate people, such as children, or to inappropriate objects, such as articles of clothing. Paraphilia becomes a paraphilic disorder when the sexual attraction causes significant distress or impairment to the individual or causes harm or the risk of harm to others.

- The paraphilic disorders include fetishistic disorder, in which sexual arousal occurs almost exclusively in the context of inappropriate objects or individuals; exhibitionistic disorder, in which sexual gratification is attained by exposing one's genitals to unsuspecting strangers; voyeuristic disorder, in which sexual arousal is derived from observing unsuspecting individuals undressing or naked; transvestic disorder, in which individuals are sexually aroused by wearing clothing of the other sex; sexual sadism disorder, in which sexual arousal is associated with inflicting pain or humiliation; sexual masochism disorder, in which sexual arousal is associated with experiencing pain or humiliation; and pedophilic disorder, in which there is a strong sexual attraction toward children.

- The development of paraphilic disorders may be associated with deficiencies in consensual adult sexual arousal, deficiencies in consensual adult social skills, deviant sexual fantasies that may develop before or during puberty, and attempts by the individual to suppress thoughts associated with these arousal patterns. Neurodevelopmental factors have been associated with pedophilia.

- Psychological and medical treatments have shown promise in reducing paraphilic arousal and criminal recidivism in some studies, but scientifically good studies of treatment outcome are lacking.

Gender Dysphoria

- Gender dysphoria is a dissatisfaction with one's assigned gender and the sense that one is really the opposite gender. A person develops a sense of gender or gender identity between 18 months and 3 years of age, and it seems that both congruent gender identity and incongruent gender identity have biological roots influenced by learning.

- Treatment for adults with marked gender incongruence may include gender reassignment surgery integrated with psychological approaches.

KEY TERMS

covert sensitization, 333
delayed ejaculation, 313
erectile disorder, 311
exhibitionistic disorder, 326
female orgasmic disorder, 313
female sexual interest/arousal
   disorder, 309

fetishistic disorder, 326
frotteuristic disorder, 325
gender dysphoria, 334
gender nonconformity, 336
gender reassignment surgery, 338
genito-pelvic pain/penetration
   disorder, 315

male hypoactive sexual desire
   disorder, 309
male orgasmic disorder, 313
orgasmic reconditioning, 333
paraphilic disorders, 329
pedophilic disorder, 329
premature ejaculation, 314

relapse prevention, 334
sexual dysfunctions, 310
sexual masochism disorder, 328
sexual sadism disorder, 328
transvestic disorder, 327
vaginismus, 315
voyeuristic disorder, 326

ANSWERS TO CONCEPT CHECKS

11.1
1. T; 2. F; 3. T; 4. T; 5. F; 6. T

11.2
1. b; 2. a; 3. c; 4. d

MEDIA RESOURCES

⁘ CENGAGE | MINDTAP

Stay organized and efficient with MindTap—a single destination with all the course material and study aids you need to succeed. Built-in apps leverage social media and the latest learning technology. For example:

- ReadSpeaker will read the text to you.
- Flashcards are pre-populated to provide you with a jump start for review—or you can create your own.
- You can highlight text and make notes in your MindTap Reader. Your notes will flow into Evernote, the electronic notebook app that you can access anywhere when it's time to study for the exam.
- Self-quizzing allows you to assess your understanding.

Visit login.cengage.com to start using MindTap. Enter the Online Access Code from the card included with your text. If a code card is not provided, you can purchase instant access at Cengage.ca.

Exploring Sexual Dysfunctions, Paraphilias, and Gender Dysphoria

SEXUAL DYSFUNCTIONS

Sexual dysfunctions can be
- Lifelong: Present during entire sexual history
- Acquired: Interrupts normal sexual pattern
- Generalized: Present in every encounter
- Situational: Present only with certain partners or at certain times

The Human Sexual Response Cycle
A dysfunction is an impairment in one of the sexual response stages.

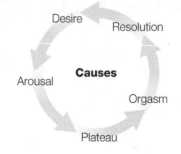

Desire → Resolution → Orgasm → Plateau → Arousal → Desire

Causes

Types of Sexual Dysfunctions

Sexual Desire Disorders
- *Male hypoactive sexual desire disorder:* Apparent lack of interest in sexual activity or fantasy

Sexual Arousal Disorders
- *Erectile disorder:* Recurring inability to achieve or maintain adequate erection
- *Female sexual interest/arousal disorder:* Recurring inability to achieve or maintain adequate lubrication

Orgasm Disorders
- *Female orgasmic disorder:* Inability to achieve orgasm despite adequate desire and arousal
- *Premature ejaculation:* Ejaculation before it is desired, with minimal stimulation

Sexual Pain Disorders
- *Genito-pelvic pain/penetration disorder:* Marked pain, anxiety, and tension associated with intercourse for which there is no medical cause; vaginismus (i.e., involuntary muscle spasms in the front of the vagina that prevent or interfere with intercourse); occurs in females

Psychological Contributions
- Distraction
- Underestimates of arousal
- Negative thought processes

Psychological and Physical Interactions
- A combination of influences is almost always present
  - Specific biological predisposition and psychological factors may produce a particular disorder

Causes

Socio-cultural Contributions
- Erotophobia, caused by formative experiences of sexual cues as alarming
- Negative experiences, such as rape
- Deterioration of relationship

Biological Contributions
- Neurological or other nervous system problems
- Vascular disease
- Chronic illness
- Prescription medication
- Drugs of abuse, including alcohol

Treatment

- *Psychosocial*: Therapeutic program to facilitate communication, improve sexual education, and eliminate anxiety. Both partners participate fully.
- *Medical*: Almost all interventions focus on male erectile disorder, including drugs, prostheses, and surgery. Medical treatment is combined with sexual education and therapy to achieve maximum benefit.

Jupiter Images

PARAPHILIC DISORDERS

Sexual arousal occurs almost exclusively in the context of inappropriate objects, partners, or activities.

Types

- **Fetishistic disorder:** Sexual attraction to nonliving objects
- **Voyeuristic disorder:** Sexual arousal achieved by viewing unsuspecting person undressing or naked
- **Exhibitionistic disorder:** Sexual gratification from exposing one's genitals to unsuspecting strangers
- **Transvestic disorder:** Sexual arousal from wearing opposite-sex clothing (cross-dressing)
- **Sexual sadism disorder:** Sexual arousal associated with inflicting pain or humiliation
- **Sexual masochism disorder:** Sexual arousal associated with experiencing pain or humiliation
- **Pedophilic disorder:** Strong sexual attraction to children
- **Frotteurism disorder:** Sexual attraction to touching or rubbing against unsuspecting strangers

Causes

- Pre-existing deficiencies in levels of arousal with consensual adults
- Pre-existing deficiencies in consensual adult social skills
- Negative sexual interactions with adults during childhood
- Early sexual fantasies reinforced by masturbation
- Attempts to suppress undesirable sexual attractions which increases sexual attraction and drive
- Neurodevelopment
- Causes not yet confirmed

Treatment

- Covert sensitization: Repeated mental reviewing of aversive consequences to establish negative associations with behaviour
- Relapse prevention: Therapeutic preparation for coping with future situations
- Orgasmic reconditioning: Pairing appropriate stimuli with masturbation to create positive arousal patterns
- Medical: Drugs that reduce testosterone to suppress sexual desire; fantasies and arousal return when drugs are stopped

GENDER DYSPHORIA

People experience a distressing incongruence between their assigned gender at birth and their experienced or expressed gender.

Causes

Biological Influences

- Not yet confirmed, although likely to involve prenatal exposure to hormones
  - Hormonal variations may be natural or result from medication

Psychological Influences

- Gender identity develops between 1½ and 3 years of age
  - "Masculine" behaviours in girls and "feminine" behaviours in boys evoke different responses in different families

Treatment

- Sex reassignment surgery: removal of breasts or penis; genital reconstruction
  - Requires rigorous psychological preparation and financial and social stability
- Psychosocial intervention to change gender identity
  - Usually unsuccessful except as temporary relief until surgery

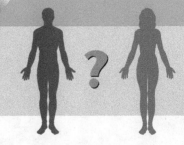

12 | Substance Use and Impulse Control

MediaImages/PhotoDisc/Getty Images

I've seen the needle and the damage done. A little part of it in everyone. But every junkie's like a settin' sun.

—NEIL YOUNG, "Needle and the Damage Done" (1972)

Use scientific reasoning to interpret behaviour:	❯ Identify basic biological, psychological, and social components of behavioural explanations (e.g., inferences, observations, operational definitions, and interpretations) (APA SLO 2.1a)
Engage in innovative and integrative thinking and problem solving:	❯ Describe problems operationally to study them empirically (APA SLO 2.3a)
Describe applications that employ discipline-based problem solving:	❯ Correctly identify antecedents and consequences of behaviour and mental processes (APA SLO 5.3c). Describe examples of relevant and practical applications of psychological principles to everyday life (APA SLO 1.3c)

*Portions of this chapter cover learning outcomes suggested by the American Psychological Association (2013) in its guidelines for the undergraduate psychology major. Chapter coverage of these outcomes is identified above by APA Goal and APA Suggested Learning Outcome (SLO).

According to the 2012 Canadian Community Health Survey—Mental Health (CCHS), 3.8 percent of Canadians had a substance use disorder in the previous year, with another 1.2 percent having both a substance use disorder and a mood or anxiety disorder (Khan, 2017). Some groups are more affected than others. For example, using Census and hospital discharge data, Statistics Canada estimates that First Nations people living on and off reserve have, respectively, seven and four times the acute care hospitalization rates for substance-related disorders than Canadians of non-Aboriginal identity (Carrière et al., 2018). In this chapter, we explore the **substance-related and addictive disorders**, which are associated with the problematic use of drugs and other substances that people take to alter the way they think, feel, and behave. In addition, the newly added disorder to this category in the *DSM-5*—gambling disorder—will be discussed. These disorders have cursed us for millennia and continue to affect how we live, work, and play.

Equally disruptive to the people affected, **impulse-control disorders** represent a number of related problems that involve the inability to resist acting on a drive or temptation. Included in this group are those who cannot resist aggressive impulses or the impulse to steal, for example, or to set fires. Controversy surrounds substance-related, addictive, and impulse-control disorders because our society sometimes believes that these problems result simply from a lack of willpower. If you wanted to stop drinking, gambling, or stealing well, you would just stop. It's just not that simple.

PERSPECTIVES ON SUBSTANCE-RELATED AND ADDICTIVE DISORDERS

The cost in lives, money, and emotional turmoil has made the issue of alcohol and drug misuse a major concern worldwide. In 1992, the Roman Catholic Church issued a new universal catechism, officially declaring that drug abuse and drunk driving are sins (Riding, 1992). Yet from the well-known heavy drug use of musician Neil Young in his early career and the death of two of his close friends from drug overdoses (McDonough, 2002) to the boozing and drug involvement of singer and songwriter Leonard Cohen (Walsh, 2001), illicit drug use and heavy drinking occupy the lives of many. At only 31 years of age, Canadian actor Cory Monteith died in a Vancouver hotel room of an accidental overdose of alcohol and heroin. Monteith was at the height of his fame, playing quarterback Finn Hudson on the hit television show *Glee* ("Cory Monteith's Overdose," 2013). Consider also the public controversies surrounding former Alberta premier Ralph Klein's intoxicated behaviour while visiting a homeless shelter in 2001, former British Columbia premier Gordon Campbell's embarrassing driving-while-intoxicated charge in Hawaii in 2003, and former Toronto mayor Rob Ford's admission of using crack cocaine in 2013. Klein and Campbell eventually quit drinking (O'Malley & Missio, 2003), and Ford continued to struggle with substances (Church & Friesen, 2013). Stories such as these are not only about the rich and famous but are also retold in every corner of our society.

Consider the case of Danny, who has the disturbing but common habit of **polysubstance use**, using multiple substances.

DANNY | *Comorbid Substance Use Disorders*

At the age of 35, Danny was in jail, awaiting trial on charges that he broke into a gas station and stole money. Danny's story illustrates the lifelong pattern that characterizes the behaviour of many people who are affected by substance-related disorders.

Danny grew up in the suburbs. He was well liked in school and an average student. Like many of his friends, he smoked cigarettes in his early teens and drank beer with his friends at night behind his high school. Unlike most of his friends, however, Danny almost always drank until he was obviously drunk; he also experimented with many other drugs, including cocaine, heroin, speed (amphetamines), and downers (barbiturates).

After high school, Danny attended a local community college for one semester, but he dropped out after failing most of his courses. His dismal performance seemed to be related to his missing most classes. He had difficulty getting up for classes after partying most of the night. His moods were highly variable, and he was often unpleasant. Danny's family knew he occasionally drank too much, but they didn't know (or didn't want to know) about his other drug use. He had for years forbidden anyone from going into his room, after his mother found little packets of white powder (probably cocaine) in his sock drawer. He said he was keeping them for a friend and that he would return them immediately. Money was sometimes missing from the house, and once some stereo equipment disappeared, but if anyone in his family suspected Danny, they never admitted it.

After he dropped out of college, Danny held a series of low-paying jobs, and when he was working, his family reassured themselves that he was back on track and things would be fine. Unfortunately, he rarely held a job for more than a few months. He was usually fired for poor job attendance and performance. Because he continued to live at home, Danny could survive despite frequent periods of unemployment. When he was in his late 20s, Danny announced that he needed help and planned to check into an alcohol rehabilitation centre; he still would not admit to using other drugs. His family's joy and relief were overwhelming, and no one questioned his request for several thousand dollars to help pay for the private program he said he wanted to attend. Danny disappeared for several weeks, presumably because he was in the rehabilitation program. However, a call from the local police station put an end to this fantasy: Danny had been found quite high, living in an abandoned building. Danny had spent his family's money on drugs and had had a three-week binge with some friends.

Danny's deceptiveness and financial irresponsibility greatly strained his relationship with his family. He was allowed to continue living at home, but his parents and siblings excluded him from their emotional lives. Danny seemed to straighten out, and he held a job at a gas station for almost two years. He became friendly with the station owner and his son. However, without any obvious warning, Danny resumed drinking and using drugs and was arrested for robbing the very place that had kept him employed for many months.

Why did Danny's drug use become so problematic when many of his friends' and siblings' did not? Why did he steal from his family and friends? What ultimately became of him? We return to Danny's frustrating story later when we look at the causes and treatment of substance-related disorders.

Although each drug described in this chapter has unique effects, they have similarities in the ways they are used and how people who abuse them are treated. First, we present some concepts that apply to substance-related disorders in general, noting important terminology and addressing several diagnostic issues.

Can you use drugs without meeting criteria for a disorder? Can you use drugs and not become addicted to or dependent on them? To answer these important questions, we first need to clarify what we mean by *substance* and then outline potential levels of involvement with substances: *substance use*, *substance intoxication*, and *substance use disorder*. The *DSM-5* includes substance use disorders and substance-induced disorders under the umbrella term *substance-related disorders*. Substance use disorder refers to problematic use of a substance (for example, the person continues to use despite experiencing severe consequences of use). Substance-induced disorders refer to specific conditions resulting from use (for example, intoxication, withdrawal). In this chapter, we focus on substance use disorders, but we also touch on substance-induced disorders as well.

The term *substance* refers to chemical compounds that are ingested to alter mood or behaviour. **Psychoactive substances** alter mood, behaviour, or both. Although you might first think of drugs such as cocaine and heroin, this definition also includes more commonplace legal drugs, such as alcohol, the nicotine found in tobacco, and the caffeine in coffee and tea. As we will see, these so-called safe drugs also affect mood and behaviour, they can be addictive, and they account for more health problems and mortality than all the illegal drugs combined. You could make a good argument for directing drug prevention efforts toward cigarette smoking (nicotine use) because of its addictive properties and negative health consequences.

LEVELS OF INVOLVEMENT

Use

Substance use is the ingestion of psychoactive substances in moderate amounts that do not significantly interfere with social, educational, or occupational functioning. Most of you reading this chapter probably use some sort of psychoactive substance on occasion. Drinking a cup of coffee in the morning to wake up or smoking a cigarette and having a drink with a friend to relax are examples of substance use, as is the occasional ingestion of illegal drugs, such as amphetamines and cocaine. Until 2018, cannabis use in Canada was illegal as well, and it still is in many countries.

Intoxication

Our physiological reaction to ingested substances—drunkenness or getting high—is **substance intoxication**. For a person to become intoxicated, many variables interact, including the type of drug taken, the amount ingested, and the person's individual

▲ Substance use

biological reaction. For many of the substances we discuss here, intoxication is experienced as impaired judgment, mood changes, and lowered motor ability (e.g., problems walking or talking).

Substance Use Disorder

Defining **substance use disorder** by how much of a substance is ingested is problematic. For example, is drinking two glasses of wine in an hour abuse? Three glasses? Six? Is taking one injection of heroin considered abuse? The *DSM-5* (American Psychiatric Association, 2013) defines substance use disorder in terms of how significantly the use interferes with the user's life. If substances disrupt your education, job, or relationships with others, and put you in physically dangerous situations (e.g., while driving), you would be considered to have a disorder.

Danny seems to fit this definition of a disorder. His inability to complete a semester of community college was a direct result of drug use. Danny often drove while drunk or under the influence of other drugs, and he had already been arrested twice. In fact, Danny's use of multiple substances was so relentless and pervasive that he would probably be diagnosed with a severe form of the disorder.

Substance use disorder is usually described as addiction. Although we use the term *addiction* routinely when we describe people who seem to be under the control of drugs, there is some disagreement about how to define addiction (Rehm et al., 2013; G. Edwards, 2012). To meet the criteria for a disorder, a person must meet criteria for at least two symptoms in the last year that interfered with his or her life or bothered the person a great deal. When a person has four or five symptoms, he or she is considered to fall in the moderate range. A severe substance use disorder would be someone like Danny who has six or more symptoms. Symptoms for substance use disorders can include a **physiological dependence** on the drug or drugs, meaning the use of increasingly

greater amounts of the drug to experience the same effect (**tolerance**), and a negative physical response when the substance is no longer ingested (**withdrawal**) (Higgins et al., 2014).

Tolerance and withdrawal are physiological reactions to the chemicals being ingested. Have you ever experienced a headache when you didn't have your morning coffee? You were probably going through caffeine withdrawal. In a more extreme example, withdrawal from alcohol can cause *alcohol withdrawal delirium* (or *delirium tremens*—the DTs), in which a person can experience frightening hallucinations and body tremors. Withdrawal from many substances can bring on chills, fever, diarrhea, nausea and vomiting, and aches and pains. Not all substances are physiologically addicting, however. For example, you do not go through severe physical withdrawal when you stop taking LSD. Cocaine withdrawal has a pattern that includes anxiety, sleep changes, lack of motivation, and boredom, and withdrawal from cannabis includes such symptoms as irritability, nervousness, appetite change, and sleep disturbance. We return to the ways drugs act on our bodies when we examine the causes of problematic drug use.

Other symptoms that make up a substance use disorder include drug-seeking behaviours. The repeated use of a drug, a desperate need to ingest more of the substance (stealing money to buy drugs, standing outside in the cold to smoke), and the likelihood that use will resume after a period of abstinence are behaviours that define the extent of substance use disorders. Such behavioural reactions are different from the physiological responses to drugs we described before and are sometimes referred to in terms of *psychological dependence*. The previous version of the *DSM* considered substance abuse and substance dependence as separate diagnoses. The *DSM-5* combines the two into the general definition of substance use disorders based on research that suggests the two co-occur (American Psychiatric Association, 2013; Dawson, Goldstein, & Grant, 2012; O'Brien, 2011).

Let's return to the questions we started with: Can you use drugs and not misuse them? Can you use drugs and not become addicted to them? The answer to the first question is yes. Obviously, some people drink wine or beer regularly without drinking to excess. And contrary to popular belief, some people use drugs, such as heroin, cocaine, or crack (a form of cocaine), on an occasional basis (for instance, several times a year) without problems (Ray, 2012). What is disturbing is that we do not know ahead of time who is likely to become dependent with even a passing use of a substance.

© Gabor Geissler/Getty

▲ Intoxication

▲ Substance dependence

It may seem counterintuitive, but dependence can be present without misuse. For example, cancer patients who take morphine for pain may become dependent on the drug—build up a tolerance and go through withdrawal if it is stopped (Flemming, 2010; Portenoy, & Mathur, 2009). Later in this chapter, we discuss biological and psychosocial theories of the causes of substance use disorders and why we have individualized reactions to these substances.

DIAGNOSTIC ISSUES

In early editions of the *DSM*, alcoholism and drug abuse weren't treated as disorders in and of themselves. Instead, they were categorized as *sociopathic personality disturbances* (a forerunner of the current *antisocial personality disorder*, which we discuss in Chapter 13), because substance use was seen as a symptom of other problems. It was considered a sign of moral weakness, and the influence of genetics and biology was hardly acknowledged. A separate category was created in the *DSM-III* in 1980, and since then we have acknowledged the complex biological and psychological nature of the problem.

The *DSM-5* term *substance use disorders* includes 11 symptoms that range from relatively mild (e.g., substance use results in a failure to fulfill major role obligations) to more severe (e.g., occupational or recreational activities are given up or reduced because of substance use). The *DSM-5* removed the previous symptom that related to substance-related legal problems and added a symptom that indicates the presence of craving or a strong desire to use the substance (Dawson et al., 2012). These distinctions help clarify the problem and focus treatment on the appropriate aspect of the disorder. Danny would be considered to have a cocaine use disorder in the severe range because of the tolerance he showed for the drug, his use of larger amounts than he intended, his unsuccessful attempts to stop using it, and the activities he gave up to buy it.

Symptoms of other disorders can complicate the picture significantly. For example, do some people drink to excess because they are depressed, or do drinking and its consequences (e.g., loss of friends, job) create depression? Some researchers have estimated that more than half the people with alcohol disorders have an additional psychiatric disorder, such as major depression, antisocial personality disorder, or bipolar disorder

(Compton et al., 2003; Conrod & Stewart, 2005; Lieb, 2015; McGovern et al., 2006). For example, in an epidemiological study of six countries, including Canada, alcohol disorders were found to be highly comorbid with mood and anxiety disorders (Merikangas et al., 1998). As another example, in reviews of the literature by Canadian researchers (Crockford & el-Guebaly, 1998; Stewart & Kushner, 2003), alcohol disorders were shown to be highly comorbid with pathological gambling.

Substance use disorder might occur concurrently with other disorders for several reasons (Grant & Dawson, 1999; Stewart, 1996; Strain, 2009). First, substance use disorders and anxiety and mood disorders are highly prevalent in our society and may occur together frequently just by chance. Second, drug intoxication and withdrawal can cause symptoms of anxiety, depression, and psychosis, and can increase risk taking. A laboratory-based study by Ellery, Stewart, and Loba (2005) showed that ingestion of alcohol led to increased risk taking among regular gamblers when they were using a video lottery terminal relative to gamblers ingesting a nonalcoholic control beverage. This finding suggests that alcohol's effects in increasing risk taking may contribute to the high co-occurrence of alcohol and gambling disorders. A third explanation for the high comorbidity of substance use disorders with other mental health problems is that the mental health disorders cause the substance use disorder. For example, people with anxiety disorders like post-traumatic stress disorder or social phobia may self-medicate with substances for their anxiety symptoms (Stewart, 1996; Stewart, Morris, et al., 2006).

The *DSM-5* tries to define when a symptom is a result of substance use and when it is not. For example, if symptoms seen in schizophrenia or in extreme states of anxiety appear during intoxication or within six weeks after withdrawal from drugs, they are not considered signs of a separate psychiatric disorder. And individuals who show signs of severe depression just after they have stopped taking heavy doses of stimulants would not be diagnosed with a major mood disorder. However, individuals who were severely depressed before they used stimulants and those whose symptoms persist for more than six weeks after they stop might have a separate disorder (Sheperis et al., 2015).

Concept Check   12.1

To check your understanding of substance-related definitions, read the following case summaries and then state whether they describe (a) use, (b) intoxication, or (c) dependence.

1. Jonas is a member of the high school football team and is out celebrating a big win. Jonas doesn't drink alcohol but doesn't mind taking a puff of cannabis every now and then. Because Jonas had such a good game, he decides to smoke cannabis to celebrate. Despite his great performance in the game, Jonas is easily irritated, laughing one minute, and yelling the next. During a game of darts, at which he usually excels, Jonas barely hits the target. And the more Jonas boasts about his stats, the more difficult it is to understand him. _____

2. Jill routinely drinks diet cola. Instead of having coffee in the morning, she heads straight for the fridge. Another habit of Jill's is having a cigarette immediately after dinner. If Jill is unable to have her diet cola in the morning or her cigarette in the evening, she is not dependent on them and can still function normally. Jill also smokes cannabis with her friends every few weeks to escape the real world. _____

3. Steve is a 23-year-old university student who started drinking heavily when he was 16. Instead of getting drunk at weekend parties, Steve drinks a moderate amount every night. In high school, Steve would become drunk after about six beers; now his tolerance has more than doubled. Steve claims alcohol relieves the pressures of university life. He once attempted to quit drinking, but he had chills, fever, diarrhea, nausea and vomiting, and body aches and pains. At one point, he even experienced scary hallucinations and tremors. _____

We now turn to the individual substances themselves, their effects on our brains and bodies, and how they are used in our society. We have grouped the substances into five general categories:

1. **Depressants:** These substances result in behavioural sedation and can induce relaxation. They include alcohol (ethyl alcohol) and the sedative and hypnotic drugs in the families of barbiturates (e.g., Seconal) and benzodiazepines (e.g., Valium, Halcion, Xanax).

2. **Stimulants:** These substances cause us to be more active and alert and can elevate mood. Included in this group are amphetamines, cocaine, nicotine, and caffeine.

3. **Opioids:** The major effect of these substances is to produce analgesia temporarily (reduce pain) and euphoria. Heroin, opium, codeine, morphine, and oxycodone are included in this group.

4. **Hallucinogens:** These substances alter sensory perception and can produce delusions, paranoia, and hallucinations. Cannabis and LSD are included in this category.

5. **Other drugs:** Other substances that are misused but do not fit neatly into one of the categories here include inhalants (e.g., airplane glue), anabolic steroids, and other over-the-counter and prescription medications (e.g., nitrous oxide). These substances produce a variety of psychoactive effects that are characteristic of the substances described in the previous categories.

DEPRESSANTS

Depressants primarily decrease central nervous system activity. Their principal effect is to reduce our levels of physiological arousal and help us relax. Included in this group are alcohol and the sedative, hypnotic, and anxiolytic drugs, such as those prescribed for insomnia. These substances are among those most likely to produce symptoms of tolerance and withdrawal. We first look at the most commonly used of these substances—alcohol—and the **alcohol-related disorders** that can result; see DSM Table 12.1.

DSM-5	**Table 12.1** Diagnostic Criteria for Alcohol Use Disorder

A. A problematic pattern of alcohol use leading to clinically significant impairment or distress, as manifested by at least two of the following, occurring within a 12-month period:

1. Alcohol is often taken in larger amounts or over a longer period than was intended.
2. There is a persistent desire or unsuccessful efforts to cut down or control alcohol use.
3. A great deal of time is spent in activities necessary to obtain alcohol, use alcohol, or recover from its effects.
4. Craving, or a strong desire or urge to use alcohol.
5. Recurrent alcohol use resulting in a failure to fulfill major role obligations at work, school, or home.
6. Continued alcohol use despite having persistent or recurrent social or interpersonal problems caused or exacerbated by the effects of alcohol.
7. Important social, occupational, or recreational activities are given up or reduced because of alcohol use.
8. Recurrent alcohol use in situations in which it is physically hazardous.
9. Alcohol use is continued despite knowledge of having a persistent or recurrent physical or psychological problem that is likely to have been caused or exacerbated by alcohol.
10. Tolerance, as defined by either or both of the following:
    a. A need for markedly increased amounts of alcohol to achieve intoxication or desired effect.
    b. A markedly diminished effect with continued use of the same amount of alcohol.
11. Withdrawal, as manifested by either of the following:
    a. The characteristic withdrawal syndrome for alcohol.
    b. Alcohol (or a closely related substance such as benzodiazepine) is taken to relieve or avoid withdrawal symptoms.

Specify current severity:

Mild: Presence of 2–3 symptoms.

Moderate: Presence of 4–5 symptoms.

Severe: Presence of 6 or more symptoms.

Source: Reprinted with permission from the *Diagnostic and Statistical Manual of Mental Disorders*, Fifth Edition (Copyright © 2013). American Psychiatric Association. All Rights Reserved.

ALCOHOL-RELATED DISORDERS

Danny's substance abuse began when he drank beer with friends, a rite of passage for many teenagers. Alcohol has been widely used throughout history. For example, scientists have found evidence of wine or beer in pottery jars at the site of a Sumerian trading post in western Iran and in the country of Georgia that date back 7000 years (McGovern, 2007). For hundreds of years, Europeans drank large amounts of beer, wine, and hard liquor. When they came to North America in the early 1600s, they brought their considerable thirst for alcohol with them. Alcohol was not a problem for Indigenous peoples until the French introduced brandy and the British introduced rum (Smart, 1985; Stewart, 2002).

Reports of the early missionaries contain many descriptions of intoxication among Indigenous peoples and early settlers (e.g., Dailey, 1968); government controlled activities and antidrinking movements quickly followed. For example, the Temperance Movement allowed for the benefits of moderate drinking while morally condemning the heavy use of spirits. The Women's Christian Temperance Union tried to have alcohol education courses introduced into schools and was successful in several Canadian provinces. The work of Temperance Movement proponents paved the way for the American Prohibition (1919–1933). Although prohibition did reduce overall levels of use in the United States, it had some unintended side effects, such as increases in organized crime and bootlegging, some of which originated in Canada. These problems led to the repeal of prohibition near the beginning of the Depression era.

Clinical Description

Apparent stimulation is the initial effect of alcohol, although it is a depressant. We generally experience a feeling of well-being, our inhibitions are reduced, and we become more outgoing. These reactions occur partly because the inhibitory centres in the brain are initially depressed, or slowed. With continued drinking, however, alcohol depresses more areas of the brain, which impedes the ability to function properly. Motor coordination is impaired (staggering, slurred speech), reaction time is slowed, we become confused, our ability to make judgments is reduced, and even vision and hearing can be negatively affected, all of which help to explain why driving while intoxicated is very dangerous.

Effects

Alcohol affects many parts of the body (see ■ Figure 12.1). After it is ingested, it passes through the esophagus (1) and into the stomach (2), where small amounts are absorbed. From there, most of it travels to the small intestine (3), where it is easily absorbed into the bloodstream. The circulatory system distributes the alcohol throughout the body, where it contacts every major organ, including the heart (4). Some of the alcohol goes to the lungs, where it vaporizes and is exhaled, a phenomenon that is the basis for the breath analyzer test that measures levels of intoxication. As alcohol passes through the liver (5), it is broken down or metabolized into carbon dioxide and water by enzymes (Maher, 1997). An average-size person is able to metabolize about 7 to 10 grams of alcohol per hour, an amount comparable

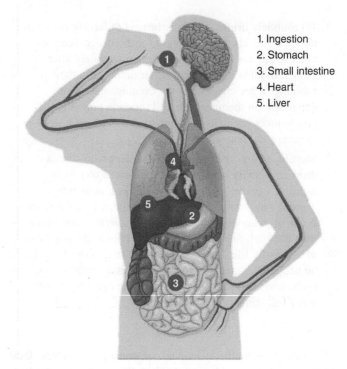

1. Ingestion
2. Stomach
3. Small intestine
4. Heart
5. Liver

FIGURE 12.1 | The path travelled by alcohol throughout the body (see text for complete description).

to about one glass of beer or 30 millilitres (one ounce) of 90-proof spirits (Moak & Anton, 1999).

Most of the substances we describe in this chapter, including cannabis, the opioids, and tranquilizers, interact with specific receptors in the brain cells. The effects of alcohol, however, are much more complex. Alcohol influences several neuroreceptor systems, which makes it difficult to study (Ray, 2012). For example, the **gamma aminobutyric acid (GABA) system**, which we discussed in Chapter 2 and Chapter 5, seems to be particularly sensitive to alcohol. GABA, as you will recall, is an inhibitory neurotransmitter. Its major role is to interfere with the firing of the neuron it attaches to. Because the GABA system seems to affect anxiety, alcohol's antianxiety properties may result from its interaction with the GABA system. Also, when GABA attaches to its receptor, chloride ions enter the cell and make it less sensitive to the effects of other neurotransmitters. Alcohol seems to reinforce the movement of these chloride ions; as a result, the neurons have difficulty firing. In other words, although alcohol seems to loosen our tongues and makes us more sociable, it makes it difficult for neurons to communicate with each other (Joslyn et al., 2010). There is some evidence from genetic research (further discussed below) that the genes responsible for communication between neurons may also be responsible for individual differences in response to alcohol.

Blackouts, the loss of memory for what happens during intoxication, may result from the interaction of alcohol with the *glutamate system*. The *serotonin system* also appears to be sensitive to alcohol. This neurotransmitter system affects mood, sleep, and eating behaviour and is thought to be responsible for alcoholic cravings (Sari et al., 2011). Alcohol also exerts effects on the dopamine reward system, and these effects may be responsible for the pleasurable feelings people experience when drinking alcohol (Conrod et al., 1997). Finally, as noted by Christina Gianoulakis of McGill University, at certain doses, alcohol also results in release of endogenous opioids—our bodies' naturally occurring analgesics—which may explain why alcohol has pain-numbing effects (Gianoulakis, 2001; Peterson et al., 1996). Because alcohol affects so many neurotransmitter systems, we should not be surprised that it has such widespread and complex effects.

The long-term effects of heavy drinking are often severe. Withdrawal from chronic alcohol use typically includes hand tremors and, within several hours, nausea or vomiting, anxiety, transient hallucinations, agitation, insomnia, and, at its most extreme, **withdrawal delirium** (or **delirium tremens**—the **DTs**), a condition that can produce frightening hallucinations and body tremors. The devastating experience of DTs can be reduced with adequate medical treatment (Schuckit, 2014).

Whether alcohol will cause organic damage depends on genetic vulnerability, frequency of use, the length of drinking binges, the blood alcohol levels attained during the drinking periods, and whether the body is given time to recover between binges (Mack et al., 2003). Consequences of long-term excessive drinking include liver disease, pancreatitis, cardiovascular disorders, and brain damage (see ■ Figure 12.2 and ■ Figure 12.3).

Part of the folklore concerning alcohol is that it permanently kills brain cells (neurons). As you will see later, this may not be true. Some evidence for brain damage comes from the experiences of people who are alcohol dependent and experience blackouts, seizures, and hallucinations. Memory and the ability to perform certain tasks may also be impaired. Two types of organic brain syndromes may result from long-term heavy alcohol use: dementia and Wernicke-Korsakoff syndrome. *Dementia*,

which we discuss more fully in Chapter 16, involves the general loss of intellectual abilities and can be a direct result of neurotoxicity or poisoning of the brain by excessive amounts of alcohol (Ridley et al., 2013). *Wernicke-Korsakoff syndrome* results in confusion, loss of muscle coordination, and unintelligible speech (Isenberg-Grzeda et al., 2012); it is believed to be caused by a deficiency of thiamine, a vitamin metabolized poorly by heavy drinkers. The dementia caused by this disease does not go away once the brain is damaged. It is important to note that mild to moderate intake of alcohol (especially wine) may actually serve a protective role in cognitive decline as we age (Panza et al., 2012).

The effects of alcohol abuse extend beyond the health and well-being of the drinker. Although alcohol was suspected for years to negatively affect prenatal development, this connection has been studied in earnest only since the 1960s (Jones & Smith, 1973; Lemoine, Harousseau, Borteyru, & Menuet, 1968). **Fetal alcohol syndrome (FAS)** is now generally recognized as a combination of problems that can occur in a child whose mother drank while she was pregnant. These problems include fetal growth retardation, cognitive deficits, behaviour problems, and learning difficulties (Barr & Streissguth, 2001; Douzgou et al., 2012; Hamilton et al., 2003; Kerns et al., 1997). In addition, children with FAS often have characteristic facial features (Caprara et al., 2007).

Statistics on Use and Abuse

Alcohol use in Canada is similar to that in other countries, as shown in ■ Figure 12.4. Because alcohol consumption is legal in North America, we know more about it than most of the other psychoactive substances that we discuss in this chapter (with the possible exceptions of nicotine and caffeine). Despite a national history of heavy alcohol use, most adults in Canada drink in moderation. For example, in a Canadian Addiction Survey (CAS), about 23 percent of Canadians were found to exceed low-risk guidelines for alcohol consumption, and about 17 percent were classified as high-risk drinkers (Canadian Centre for Substance Abuse [CCSA], 2004). Men are more likely than women to drink alcohol and are also more likely to drink heavily (Statistics Canada, 2003). Heavy drinking was studied in the 2018 Canadian

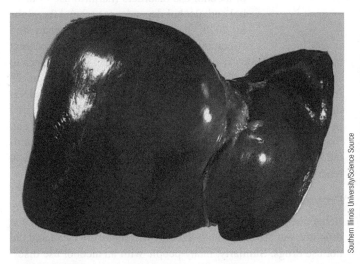
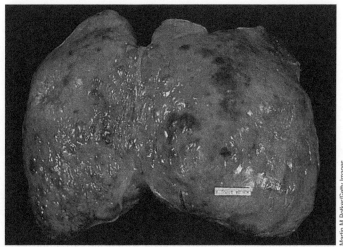

FIGURE 12.2 | A healthy liver (left) and a cirrhotic liver scarred by years of alcohol abuse (right).

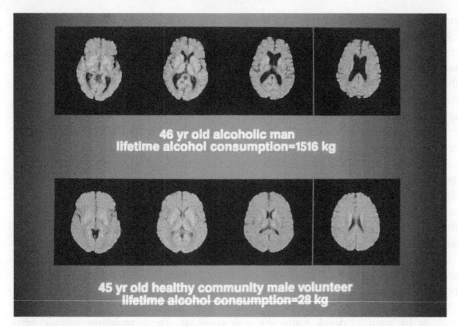

46 yr old alcoholic man
lifetime alcohol consumption=1516 kg

45 yr old healthy community male volunteer
lifetime alcohol consumption=28 kg

FIGURE 12.3 | The dark areas in the top brain images show the extensive loss of brain tissue that result from heavy alcohol use.

Source: Dr. Adolf Pfefferbaum, Stanford University, with the support from the National Institute on Alcohol Abuse and Alcoholism and the Department of Veteran Affairs

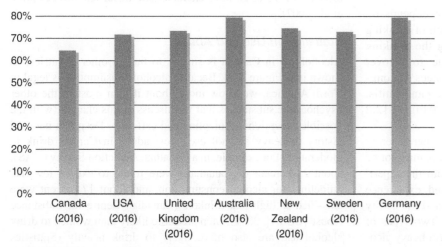

FIGURE 12.4 | Prevalence of self-reported past year alcohol use among the general population, age 15+, by country.

Source: World Health Organization, Global Health Observatory Data Repository, 2018.

Community Health Survey. Heavy drinking in the past year was defined as five or more drinks on one occasion for men, four or more drinks for women, at least once a month for the past year. Nineteen percent of Canadians met the criteria: 24 percent of men and 15 percent of women (McDiarmid, 2019). Alcohol binge consumption (episodic heavy drinking) is frequent among students: in a 2013 survey of over 34 000 Canadian college students, 37 percent of male drinkers and 22 percent of female drinkers reported consuming seven or more drinks the last time they partied (American College Health Association, 2014).

Drinking practices also vary across societies, even in Westernized countries. For example, a comparison of the results from the 1998 Canadian Campus Survey conducted with the undergraduates at 16 universities across Canada with results from the 1999 College Alcohol Study of 119 colleges and universities in the United States revealed that a higher proportion of Canadian than U.S. students drink alcohol, but that a higher proportion of U.S. students are binge drinkers (Kuo et al., 2002, 2003).

A study of health inequalities in Canada revealed that, compared to non-Indigenous peoples, heavy drinking was more prevalent among Inuit, Métis, and First Nations people living both on and off reserve (Public Health Agency of Canada [PHAC], 2018). These results are discussed in light of the challenges faced by many Indigenous communities (e.g., unemployment, inadequate health services, language barriers), the legacy of colonization, and the evidence suggesting that abstaining from drinking alcohol is *more* prevalent among First Nations people living on and off reserve and among Inuit than in the Canadian general population.

We know that not everyone who drinks develops an alcohol-related disorder. About 9 percent of Canadian drinkers experience some level of problem with alcohol (CCSA, 2004), however, with about 3 percent of Canadian adults thought to be alcohol dependent in any given year (Statistics Canada, 2002a). For example, in the 2004 CAS, 5 percent of current drinkers admitted to experiencing physical health problems as a consequence of their drinking, 3 percent reported financial problems related to their alcohol use, and 3 percent reported problems in their social life or friendships caused by their drinking (CCSA, 2004). Among the general population, young (18–29), single males are most likely to be heavy drinkers and to have alcohol use problems (Statistics Canada, 2002a).

The rates of alcohol use problems vary widely around the world. The World Health Organization (2018) estimated the prevalence of alcohol use disorders (harmful use of alcohol and alcohol dependence) around the globe in 2016. It was highest in European and Americas regions, affecting 8.8 and 8.2 percent of these populations over the age of 15 years. With respect to specific countries within these regions, the highest rates in the European region were found in Hungary and the Russian Federation (both at 21 percent). The United States had the highest rate in the Americas at 14 percent; Canada had a rate of 8 percent. Such cultural differences can be accounted for by different attitudes toward drinking, the availability of alcohol, physiological reactions, and family norms and patterns.

Progression

Remember that Danny went through periods of heavy alcohol and drug use, but also had times when he was relatively clean and did not use drugs. Similarly, many people with an alcohol use disorder fluctuate between drinking heavily, drinking socially without negative effects, and being abstinent, not drinking at all (McCrady, 2014; Vaillant, 1983). It seems that about 20 percent of people with severe alcohol dependence have a spontaneous remission and do not re-experience problems with drinking (Ludwig, 1985; Vaillant, 1983).

Alcohol researchers Linda and Mark Sobell, who worked at the Addiction Research Foundation in Toronto in the 1980s and 1990s, noted that it was previously thought that once problems arose with drinking, they would become steadily worse, following a predictable downward pattern as long as the person kept drinking (Sobell & Sobell, 1993). In other words, like a disease that isn't treated properly, alcoholism will get progressively worse if left unchecked. First championed by Jellinek more than 75 years ago, this view continues to influence the way people view and treat the disorder (Jellinek, 1946, 1952, 1960). Unfortunately, Jellinek based his model of the progression of alcohol use on a now famous but faulty study (Jellinek, 1946).

It appears instead that the course of a severe alcohol use disorder may be progressive for most people. For example, early use of alcohol may predict later abuse. A study of almost 6000 lifetime drinkers by David DeWit and his colleagues at the Centre for Addiction and Mental Health found that drinking at an early age—from age 11 to 14—was predictive of later alcohol-related disorders (DeWit et al., 2000). Similarly, a study tracking alcohol use onset and later use found that those who started drinking at age 11 or earlier were at higher risk for chronic and severe alcohol use disorders (Guttmannova et al., 2011). A third study followed 636 male inpatients in an alcohol rehabilitation centre (Schuckit et al., 1993). Among these chronically alcohol-dependent men, a general progression of alcohol-related life problems did emerge, although not in the specific pattern proposed by Jellinek. Three-quarters of the men reported moderate consequences of their drinking in their 20s, such as demotions at work. During their 30s, the men had more serious problems, such as regular blackouts and signs of alcohol withdrawal. By their late 30s and early 40s, these men demonstrated long-term serious consequences of their drinking, which included hallucinations, withdrawal convulsions, and hepatitis or pancreatitis. This study suggests a common pattern among people with chronic alcohol abuse and dependence, one with increasingly severe consequences. This progressive pattern is not inevitable for everyone who abuses alcohol, although we do not yet understand what distinguishes those who are and those who are not susceptible (Krenek & Maisto, 2013).

Research on the mechanism responsible for the differences in early alcohol use suggests that a person's response to the sedative effects of the substance affects later use. In other words, those individuals who tend not to develop the slurred speech, staggering, and other sedative effects of alcohol use are more likely to abuse it in the future (Chung & Martin, 2009; Schuckit, 2014). This is of particular concern, given the trend to mix highly caffeinated energy drinks with alcohol (McKetin et al., 2015). This combination of drinks can reduce the sedative effect of alcohol, which may increase the likelihood of later abuse.

▲ Physical characteristics of FAS include skin folds at the corners of the eyes, a low nasal bridge, a short nose, a groove between nose and upper lip, small head circumference, small eye openings, a small midface, and a thin upper lip.

▲ Males ages 18 to 29 are most vulnerable to drinking problems.

Finally, statistics frequently link alcohol with violent behaviour (Boden et al., 2012; Bye, 2007). A review of numerous studies conducted by Robert Pihl and his colleagues established that many people who commit such violent acts as murder, rape, and assault are often intoxicated at the time of the crime (Rossow & Bye, 2012). We hope you are skeptical of this type of correlation. Just because drunkenness and violence overlap does not mean that alcohol will necessarily make you violent. Laboratory studies show that alcohol may increase participants' aggression (Bushman, 1993; see also review by Hoaken & Stewart, 2003). Whether a person behaves aggressively outside the laboratory, however, probably involves several interrelated factors, such as the quantity and timing of alcohol consumed, the person's history of violence, his or her expectations about drinking, and what happens to the individual while intoxicated. Alcohol may reduce the fear associated with being punished, and it may impair the ability to consider the consequences of acting impulsively (Nestor, 2002; Pihl et al., 1993). Robert Pihl suggested that people with poorer executive cognitive function (planning, organizing abilities) are more likely than others to behave aggressively when intoxicated (Hoaken et al., 2003; Pihl et al., 2003). Toronto-based researchers Christine Wekerle and Anne-Marie Wall (2002) have further

Photo by Owen Egan/McGill University

▲ Robert Pihl, a clinical psychologist at McGill University, has made many notable contributions to the understanding and treatment of alcohol abuse and dependence. In particular, his work has focused on understanding the relation between alcohol and aggression, and on identifying factors that mediate familial-genetic risk for alcoholism.

noted that alcohol intoxication can also increase the risk of being the victim of violence. Finally, in an impressive longitudinal study of couples who soon were going to be parents, Victoria researchers found that harmful alcohol use in men was predictive of intimate partner violence (Woodin et al., 2014).

SEDATIVE-, HYPNOTIC-, AND ANXIOLYTIC-RELATED DISORDERS

The general group of depressants also includes sedative (calming), *hypnotic* (sleep-inducing), and anxiolytic (anxiety-reducing) drugs (Bond & Lader, 2012). These drugs include the barbiturates and the benzodiazepines. **Barbiturates** (which include Amytal, Seconal, and Nembutal) are a family of sedative drugs first synthesized in Germany in 1882 (McKim, 1991). They were prescribed to help people sleep and replaced such drugs as alcohol and opium. Barbiturates were widely prescribed by physicians during the 1930s and 1940s, before their addictive properties were fully understood. By the 1950s, they were among the drugs most abused by adults in North America (Franklin & Frances, 1999).

The **benzodiazepines** (which today include Valium, Xanax, and Ativan) have been used since the 1960s, primarily to reduce anxiety. These drugs were originally touted as a miracle cure for the anxieties of living in our highly pressured technological society. Although it has been known since the 1980s that they are not appropriate for reducing the tension and anxiety resulting from everyday stresses and strains (Cooperstock & Hill, 1982), billions of doses of benzodiazepines are consumed by North Americans each year (Olfson et al., 2015). Sixteen million prescriptions of benzodiazepines were made to Canadians in 2000 alone (Gadsby, 2001). According to the Canadian Institute for Health Information (CIHI, 2018), 12 248 daily doses per 1000 people were prescribed in Canada in 2017 (the highest rate was in New Brunswick, and the lowest, in Ontario; the territories were not included in the study). In general, benzodiazepines are considered safer than barbiturates, with less risk of abuse and dependence (Warneke, 1991). Nonetheless, as noted by clinical psychologist Henny Westra of York University, the potential for developing dependence on benzodiazepines for those using them in the treatment of anxiety or sleep disorders should not be minimized (Westra & Stewart, 1998). The potential for benzodiazepine dependence was recognized as early as the 1970s, as is illustrated in the case study of Susan, published in the *Canadian Psychiatric Association Journal* in 1978.

sdecoret/Shutterstock.com

▲ Intoxication is often involved in cases of domestic violence.

SUSAN | *Taking a Harmless Muscle Relaxant or an Addictive Drug?*

Susan was a 30-year-old Caucasian woman with a small child. She had recently separated from her husband. Susan had originally been prescribed a low dose of Diazepam by her general practitioner as a muscle relaxant for a backache. Over three months, Susan increased her dose until she reached a level 12 times greater than the dose prescribed by her physician.

On her initial psychiatric evaluation, Susan stated that Diazepam helped her to be "fully awake," "to get energy," and "to get motivated." She would take a dose immediately upon awakening, and thereafter every two to three hours. Susan reported that when she failed to take the drug, she would experience dizziness, vomiting, headaches, and drowsiness.

Following her visit to a psychiatrist, she was admitted to hospital, where she displayed extreme restlessness, anxiety, trembling, irritability, and suspiciousness. She was put on a gradual dose reduction to withdraw her from the medication. During this process, Susan was administered other (nonaddictive) medications to minimize her experience of anxiety and agitation, and to prevent seizures, which can occur during benzodiazepine withdrawal.

Susan cooperated fully with the gradual tapering of her Diazepam for five days. Despite her intense craving for the medication, she was willing to remain at the lower dose. However, on the fifth day, Susan refused to go through gradual withdrawal any longer and demanded abrupt cessation of the medication. At this point her withdrawal symptoms became quite severe: insomnia, trembling, agitation, emotional lability, photophobia (aversion to light), blurred vision, pain behind the eyes, headaches, nausea, and muscle and stomach cramps. She became very paranoid, hostile, irritable, and tearful. Susan developed visual hallucinations (e.g., seeing insects) and illusions (e.g., seeing the sink faucet moving). These symptoms subsided over two weeks.

On a follow-up visit to her psychiatrist a week after her discharge, Susan reported that she had been free of all the withdrawal symptoms she experienced while in hospital. Her sleep had also returned to normal.

Source: Adapted from Agrawal (1978).

Susan's case illustrates the features of benzodiazepine dependence. High tolerance developed in that Susan escalated her dose over time to achieve the original effect, to the point that she was able to take very large doses without drowsiness. She experienced a very severe set of benzodiazepine withdrawal symptoms during her hospitalization—some of which she had experienced previously in milder form when she missed a dose of her medication at home. The author of this case study published this report to warn other doctors about the potential for addiction to this type of medication and to argue against its indiscriminate prescription by physicians (Agrawal, 1978).

In addition to the potential for dependence with anxiolytics, reports on the misuse of Rohypnol show how dangerous some benzodiazepine drugs can be. Rohypnol (otherwise known as "roofies") gained a following among teenagers in the 1990s because it has the same effect as alcohol without the telltale odour. However, disturbing reports have emerged of men giving the drug to women without their knowledge, making it easier for them to engage in sexual coercion; this led to Rohypnol being nicknamed the "date rape drug" (Ramsey, 2003; Smith & Wesson, 1999).

Clinical Description

At low doses, barbiturates relax the muscles and can produce a mild feeling of well-being. Larger doses can have results similar to those of heavy drinking: slurred speech and problems walking, concentrating, and working. At extremely high doses the diaphragm muscles can relax so much as to cause death by suffocation. In fact, overdosing on barbiturates is a common means of suicide.

Like the barbiturates, benzodiazepines are used to calm an individual and induce sleep. In addition, drugs in this class are prescribed as muscle relaxants and anticonvulsants (antiseizure medications; Bond & Lader, 2012). People who use them for nonmedical reasons report first feeling a pleasant high and a reduction of inhibition, similar to the effects of drinking alcohol. With continued use, however, tolerance and dependence can develop. Users who try to stop taking the drug experience symptoms like those of alcohol withdrawal (anxiety, insomnia, tremors, and delirium; Westra & Stewart, 1998).

The *DSM-5* criteria for sedative-, hypnotic-, and anxiolytic-related drug use disorders do not differ substantially from those for alcohol disorders (see DSM Table 12.2). Both include maladaptive behavioural changes, such as inappropriate sexual or aggressive behaviour, variable moods, impaired judgment, impaired social or occupational functioning, slurred speech, motor coordination problems, and unsteady gait.

Sedative, hypnotic, and anxiolytic drugs affect the brain by acting on the GABA neurotransmitter system (Bond & Lader, 2012), although by mechanisms slightly different from those involving alcohol. As a result, when people combine alcohol with any of these drugs, there can be synergistic effects (Fils-Aime, 1993). In other words, if you drink alcohol after taking a benzodiazepine or barbiturate, the total effects can reach dangerous levels. One theory about actor Marilyn Monroe's death in 1962 is that she combined alcohol with too many barbiturates and unintentionally killed herself. Actor Heath Ledger's death in 2008 was attributed to the combined effects of oxycodone and a variety of barbiturates and benzodiazepines.

Statistics

Data out of the Canadian Institute for Health Information (CIHI, 2018) suggest that the amount of benzodiazepines (and related drugs) dispensed in Canada dropped by almost 6 percent between 2016 and 2017. In the 2017 Canadian Tobacco, Alcohol and Drugs Survey (CTADS; Health Canada, 2019), 12 percent of Canadians reported using sedatives in the past year, 9 percent of men and 14 percent of women. Similar to other national surveys, the CTADS covers Canadians 15 years of age or older and excludes residents in Yukon, the Northwest Territories, and Nunavut, as well as those living in institutions.

A. A problematic pattern of sedative, hypnotic, or anxiolytic use leading to clinically significant impairment or distress, as manifested by at least two of the following, occurring within a 12-month period:

1. Sedatives, hypnotics, or anxiolytics are often taken in larger amounts or over a longer period than was intended.

2. There is a persistent desire or unsuccessful efforts to cut down or control sedative, hypnotic, or anxiolytic use.

3. A great deal of time is spent in activities necessary to obtain the sedative, hypnotic, or anxiolytic; use the sedative, hypnotic, or anxiolytic; or recover from its effects.

4. Craving, or a strong desire to use the sedative, hypnotic, or anxiolytic.

5. Recurrent sedative, hypnotic, or anxiolytic use resulting in a failure to fulfill major role obligations at work, school, or home (e.g., repeated absences from work or poor work performance related to sedative, hypnotic, or anxiolytic use; sedative-, hypnotic-, or anxiolytic-related absences, suspensions, or expulsions from school; neglect of children or household).

6. Continued sedative, hypnotic, or anxiolytic use despite having persistent or recurrent social or interpersonal problems caused or exacerbated by the effects of sedatives, hypnotics, or anxiolytics (e.g., arguments with a spouse about consequences of intoxication; physical fights).

7. Important social, occupational, or recreational activities are given up or reduced because of sedative, hypnotic, or anxiolytic use.

8. Recurrent sedative, hypnotic, or anxiolytic use in situations in which it is physically hazardous (e.g., driving an automobile or operating a machine when impaired by sedative, hypnotic, or anxiolytic use).

9. Sedative, hypnotic, or anxiolytic use is continued despite knowledge of having a persistent or recurrent physical or psychological problem that is likely to have been caused or exacerbated by the sedative, hypnotic, or anxiolytic.

10. Tolerance, as defined by either of the following:

    a. A need for markedly increased amounts of sedative, hypnotic, or anxiolytic to achieve intoxication or desired effect.

    b. A markedly diminished effect with continued use of the same amount of sedative, hypnotic, or anxiolytic.

    Note: This criterion is not considered to be met for individuals taking sedatives, hypnotics, or anxiolytics under medical supervision.

11. Withdrawal, as manifested by either of the following:

    a. The characteristic withdrawal syndrome for sedatives, hypnotics, or anxiolytics.

    b. Sedatives, hypnotics, or anxiolytics (or closely related substance, such as alcohol) are taken to relieve or avoid withdrawal symptoms.

    Note: This criterion is not considered to be met for individuals taking sedatives, hypnotics, or anxiolytics under medical supervision.

Specify current severity:

Mild: Presence of 2–3 symptoms.

Moderate: Presence of 4–5 symptoms.

Severe: Presence of 6 or more symptoms.

STIMULANTS

Of all the psychoactive drugs used in Canada, the most commonly consumed are the stimulants. Included in this group are caffeine (in coffee, chocolate, and many soft drinks and energy drinks), nicotine (in tobacco products such as cigarettes), amphetamines, and cocaine. You probably used caffeine when you got up this morning. In contrast to the depressant drugs, stimulants—as their name suggests—make you more alert and energetic. They have a long history of use. Chinese physicians, for example, have used an amphetamine compound called Ma-huang for more than 5000 years (King & Ellinwood, 1997). Ma-huang (or ephedra) was marketed in North America in health food stores as a dietary supplement and weight-loss aid. Ma-huang made the news when its manufacture and sale was banned, given its links to serious health problems (e.g., it can cause a serious rise in blood pressure) and even deaths (Canadian Press, 2003). The case of Ma-huang provides an important illustration of how natural compounds can be just as dangerous as manufactured drugs. We describe several stimulants and their effects on behaviour, mood, and cognition. DSM Table 12.3 displays the diagnostic criteria for stimulant use disorder.

STIMULANT-RELATED DISORDERS

Amphetamines

At low doses, amphetamines can induce feelings of elation and vigour, and can reduce fatigue. You feel "up." After a period of elevation, however, you come back down and crash, feeling depressed or tired. Amphetamines are manufactured in laboratories; they were first synthesized in 1887 and later used as a treatment for asthma and as a nasal decongestant (Carvalho et al., 2012). Because amphetamines also reduce appetite, some people take them to lose weight. Long-haul truck drivers, pilots, and some university students trying to pull all-nighters use amphetamines to get an extra energy boost and stay awake. In fact, the use of amphetamines by two U.S. pilots to stay awake was implicated in the friendly fire death of four Canadian soldiers in Afghanistan in 2002. The case increased awareness of how common amphetamine use is among pilots and has raised consciousness of possible negative consequences of this practice such as impaired judgment (Campbell, 2003). Amphetamines are prescribed for people with narcolepsy, a sleep disorder characterized by excessive sleepiness (see Chapter 10). Some of these drugs (Ritalin) are even given to children with attention-deficit/hyperactivity disorder (discussed in Chapter 15). Amphetamines too are being misused for their psychostimulant effects (Barrett et al., 2006a).

The *DSM-5* diagnostic criteria for intoxication in *amphetamine use disorders* include significant behavioural symptoms, such as euphoria or affective blunting, changes in sociability, interpersonal sensitivity, anxiety, tension, anger, stereotyped behaviours, impaired judgment, and impaired social or occupational functioning. In addition, physiological symptoms occur during or shortly after amphetamine or related substances are ingested, including heart rate or blood pressure changes, perspiration or chills, nausea or vomiting, weight loss, muscular weakness, respiratory depression, chest pain, seizures, or coma. The

▲ Designer drugs, especially ecstasy, are popular among young people.

© Peter Dazeley/Getty

danger in using amphetamines and the other stimulants is their negative effects, like those experienced by the pilots involved in the friendly fire incident in Afghanistan. Severe intoxication or overdose can cause hallucinations, panic, agitation, and paranoid delusions (Mack et al., 2003; Carvalho et al., 2012). Amphetamine tolerance builds quickly, making it doubly dangerous. Withdrawal often results in apathy, prolonged periods of sleep, irritability, and depression.

Periodically, certain "designer drugs" appear in local mini-epidemics. An amphetamine called methylenedioxymethamphetamine (MDMA), first synthesized in 1912 in Germany, was used as an appetite suppressant (McCann & Ricaurte, 2009). Recreational use of this drug, now commonly called ecstasy, rose sharply in the late 1980s. Among Toronto students surveyed in 1999, past-year use of ecstasy was 7 percent, the highest rate observed in a gradual upward trend since 1991 (Bernstein et al., 2002). In the 2017 CTADS, 1 percent reported using ecstasy (Health Canada, 2019). Rates may be much higher in certain subcultures. For example, a study by Dalhousie clinical psychologist Sean Barrett and his colleagues examined drug use among rave attendees in Montréal. They found that 65 percent of rave-goers had used ecstasy (Gross et al., 2002). The effects of this drug are best described by a user: "just like speed but without the comedown, and you feel warm and trippy like acid, but without the possibility of a major freak-out" (O'Hagan, 1992, p. 10). A purified crystallized form of amphetamine, called *ice*, is ingested through smoking. This drug causes marked aggressive tendencies and stays in the system longer than cocaine, making it particularly dangerous (Stein & Ellinwood, 1993). However enjoyable these new amphetamines may be in the short term, the potential for users to become dependent on them is extremely high, with great risk for long-term difficulties. Some research shows that repeated use of MDMA can cause lasting memory problems (Wagner, Becker, et al., 2013). Moreover, death can result: in 1999, there were nine MDMA-related deaths in Ontario (Bernstein et al., 2002). In August 2019, in British Columbia, 14-year-old Carson Crimeni died after taking ecstasy for the first time; he was trying to fit in. Tragically, his so-called friends posted videos of his intoxication on social media, making fun of him, two hours before he died (McDonald, 2019). The Canadian Centre on Substance Use and Addiction (2017) has also highlighted that while people may expect ecstasy to contain only MDMA, substitutions are often made, some of which have deadly consequences. For example, one study documented 27 deaths in Alberta and British Columbia between June 2011 and April 2012 that were due to paramethoxymethamphetamine or PMMA (Nicol et al., 2015).

Amphetamines stimulate the central nervous system by enhancing the activity of norepinephrine and dopamine. Specifically, amphetamines help the release of these neurotransmitters and block their reuptake, thereby making more of them available throughout the system (Carvalho et al., 2012). Too much amphetamine—and therefore too much dopamine and norepinephrine—can lead to hallucinations and delusions. As we see in Chapter 14, this effect has stimulated theories on the causes of schizophrenia, which can also include hallucinations and delusions.

Cocaine

The use and misuse of drugs wax and wane according to societal fashion, moods, and sanctions (Uddo et al., 1993). Cocaine replaced amphetamines as the stimulant of choice in the 1970s (Jaffe et al., 2005). Cocaine is derived from the leaves of the coca plant, a flowering bush indigenous to South America.

Latin Americans have chewed coca leaves for centuries to get relief from hunger and fatigue (Daamen et al., 2012). Cocaine was introduced into North America in the late 19th century and was widely used from then until the 1920s. In 1885, Parke, Davis & Co. manufactured coca and cocaine in 15 different forms, including coca-leaf cigarettes and cigars, inhalants, and crystals. For people who couldn't afford these products, a cheaper alternative was in Coca-Cola, which up until 1903 contained 60 milligrams of cocaine per 240 millilitre serving (Daamen et al., 2012).

Clinical Description

Like amphetamines, in small amounts cocaine increases alertness, produces euphoria, increases blood pressure and pulse, and causes insomnia and loss of appetite. Remember that Danny snorted (inhaled) cocaine when he partied through the night with his friends. He later said the drug made him feel powerful and invincible—the only way he really felt self-confident. The effects of cocaine are short lived; for Danny they lasted less than an hour, and he had to snort repeatedly to keep himself up. During these binges he often became paranoid, experiencing exaggerated fears that he would be caught or that someone would steal his cocaine. Such paranoia is common among cocaine abusers, occurring in two-thirds or more (Daamen et al., 2012; Mack et al., 2003). Cocaine also makes the heart beat more rapidly and irregularly, and it can have fatal consequences, depending on a person's physical condition and the amount of the drug ingested.

We saw that alcohol can damage the developing fetus. It has also been suspected that the use of cocaine by pregnant women may adversely affect their babies. Susan Potter of Acadia University, Philip Zelazo of McGill University, and their colleagues (Potter et al., 2000) conducted a study of the cognitive effects of cocaine exposure on the developing fetus. They found subtle deficits in auditory information processing in the cocaine-exposed infants that may help explain the growing evidence that fetal cocaine exposure is associated with subsequent language deficits among children exposed to this drug while still developing in the mother's uterus.

Statistics

Surveys indicate low levels of past-year cocaine use in the general population in Canada. For example, a 1998–1999 Toronto survey found that about 1 percent of adults and about 6 percent of students used cocaine in the past year (Bernstein et al., 2002). The 2017 CTADS reported that 2 percent of Canadians used cocaine, an increase from the 1 percent reported in the 2015 and 2013 cycles of the survey (Health Canada, 2019). Cocaine is most often snorted through the nose, but it may also be injected. Crack cocaine is a crystallized form of cocaine that is smoked rather than snorted or injected (Closser, 1992). In Toronto, use of crack cocaine is reported in surveys by less than 1 percent of adults and by about 2 percent of students (Bernstein et al., 2002).

Cocaine is in the same group of stimulants as amphetamines because it has similar effects on the brain. The "up" seems to come primarily from the effect of cocaine on the dopamine system. Cocaine enters the bloodstream and is carried to the brain.

▲ For centuries, Latin Americans have chewed coca leaves to get relief from hunger and fatigue.

There, the cocaine molecules block the reuptake of dopamine. As you know, neurotransmitters released at the synapse stimulate the next neuron and then are recycled back to the original neuron. Cocaine seems to bind to places where dopamine neurotransmitters re-enter their home neuron, blocking their reuptake by the neuron. The dopamine that cannot be taken in by the neuron remains in the synapse, causing repeated stimulation of the next neuron. This stimulation of the dopamine neurons in the "pleasure pathway" (the site in the brain that seems to be involved in the experience of pleasure) causes the high associated with cocaine use.

As late as the 1980s, many felt cocaine was a wonder drug that produced feelings of euphoria without being addictive (Weiss & Iannucci, 2009). Such a conservative source as the *Comprehensive Textbook of Psychiatry* in 1980 indicated that "taken no more than two or three times per week, cocaine creates no serious problems" (Grinspoon & Bakalar, 1980). Just imagine—a drug that gives you extra energy, helps you think clearly and more creatively, and lets you accomplish more throughout the day, all without any negative side effects! In our highly competitive and complex technological society, this would be a dream come true. But, as you probably realize, such temporary benefits have a high cost. Cocaine fooled us. Addiction does not resemble that of many other drugs early on, and typically people only find that they have a growing inability to resist taking more (Weiss & Iannucci, 2009). Few negative effects are noted at first; however, with continued use, sleep is disrupted, increased tolerance causes a need for higher doses, paranoia and other negative symptoms set in, and the cocaine user gradually becomes socially isolated. Chronic use may result in premature aging of the brain (Ersche et al., 2012).

Again, Danny's case illustrates this pattern. He was a social user for a number of years, using cocaine only with friends and only occasionally. Eventually he had more frequent episodes of excessive use or binges, and he found himself increasingly craving the drug between binges. After the binges, Danny would crash and sleep. Cocaine withdrawal isn't like that of alcohol. Instead of rapid heartbeat, tremors, or nausea, withdrawal from cocaine produces pronounced feelings of apathy and boredom. Think for

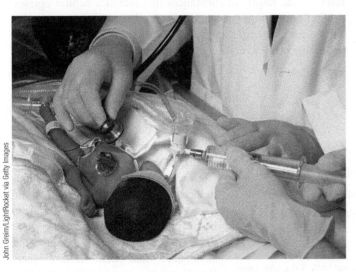

▲ This little girl's mother used cocaine during her pregnancy. Research continues into the effects of the drug on children of dependent mothers.

John Greim/LightRocket via Getty Images

a minute about how dangerous this type of withdrawal is. First, you're bored with everything and find little pleasure in the everyday activities of work or relationships. The one thing that can bring you back to life is cocaine. As you can imagine, a particularly vicious cycle develops: cocaine is abused, withdrawal causes apathy, cocaine abuse resumes. The atypical withdrawal pattern misled people into believing that cocaine was not addictive. We now know that cocaine abusers go through patterns of tolerance and withdrawal comparable to those experienced by abusers of other psychoactive drugs (Daamen et al., 2012).

TOBACCO-RELATED DISORDERS

When you think of people addicted to drugs, what image comes to mind? Do you see dirty and dishevelled people huddled on an old mattress in an abandoned building, waiting for the next fix? Do you picture businesspeople huddled outside a city building on a rainy afternoon furtively smoking cigarettes? Both these images are accurate because the nicotine in tobacco is a psychoactive substance that produces patterns of dependence, tolerance, and withdrawal—**tobacco-related disorders**—comparable to the other drugs we have discussed so far (Litvin et al., 2012). In 1942, Scottish physician Lennox Johnson shot up nicotine extract and found after 80 injections that he liked it more than cigarettes and felt deprived without it (Kanigel, 1988). This colourless, oily liquid is what gives smoking its pleasurable qualities.

The tobacco plant is native to North America. Various Indigenous peoples cultivated and used the leaves starting centuries ago and continuing today as part of ceremony, prayer, and medicinal practice. Little evidence suggests that Indigenous peoples used tobacco recreationally before contact with Europeans. In traditional usage, tobacco can be inhaled through a pipe but also placed on a fire, in water, or on the ground, and is often given as a gift (Rafertti & Mann, 2014).

According to the 2017 CTADS, only 15 percent of Canadians 15 years of age and older smoke, down from the 50 percent who smoked in 1965 (Health Canada, 2019; Physicians for a Smoke-Free Canada, 2012). A study of health inequalities in Canada determined that smoking prevalence increases as socioeconomic status decreases and that prevalence is higher among men than women, and higher among Indigenous than non-Indigenous people (PHAC, 2018).

The *DSM-5* does not describe an intoxication pattern for tobacco-related disorders. Rather, it lists withdrawal symptoms, which include depressed mood, insomnia, irritability, anxiety, difficulty concentrating, restlessness, and increased appetite and weight gain. Once smokers are dependent on nicotine, going without it causes these withdrawal symptoms (Slade, 1999). Nicotine is inhaled into the lungs, where it enters the bloodstream. Only 7 to 19 seconds after a person inhales the smoke, the nicotine reaches the brain (Benowitz, 1996). Nicotine in small doses stimulates the central nervous system; it can also relieve stress and improve mood. But it can also cause high blood pressure and increase the risk of heart disease and cancer (Litvin et al., 2012). High doses can blur vision, cause confusion, lead to convulsions, and sometimes even cause death. Nicotine appears to stimulate specific receptors—nicotinic acetylcholine receptors—in the midbrain reticular formation and the limbic system, the site of the "pleasure pathway" mentioned earlier (McGehee et al., 1995). Smokers dose themselves throughout the day in an effort to keep nicotine at a steady level in the bloodstream (10 to 50 nanograms per millilitre; Dalack et al., 1993). Some evidence also points to how maternal smoking can predict later substance-related disorders in children, but this appears to be an environmental (e.g., home environment) rather than a biological influence (D'Onofrio et al., 2012).

Research may help explain why cigarette smoking and alcohol drinking are so commonly paired. A lab-based study showed that nicotine administration (as delivered through tobacco smoke) leads to increases in alcohol consumption among a significant majority of smokers (Barrett et al., 2006b). The authors suggest that one potential explanation for the finding that nicotine increases alcohol responding is that simultaneous smoking may make drinking alcohol more rewarding in terms of effects on the dopamine reward system.

Severe depression is found to occur significantly more often among people with nicotine dependence. Does this mean that smoking causes depression or depression causes smoking? There is a complex and bi-directional relationship between cigarette smoking and negative affect (Litvin et al., 2012). In other words, being depressed increases your risk of becoming dependent on nicotine, and at the same time, being dependent on nicotine will increase your risk of becoming depressed. Genetic studies suggest that a genetic vulnerability and certain life stresses may combine to make you vulnerable to both a nicotine use disorder and depression (e.g., A. C. Edwards & Kendler, 2012).

CAFFEINE-RELATED DISORDERS

Caffeine is the most common of the psychoactive substances, used regularly by about 90 percent of all North Americans (Mitchell et al., 2014). Called the *gentle stimulant* because it is thought to be the least harmful of all the addictive drugs, caffeine can still lead to problems similar to problems with other drugs (e.g., interfering with social and work obligations; Meredith et al., 2013). This drug is found in tea, coffee, many soft drinks, and cocoa products. High levels of caffeine are added to the energy drinks that are widely consumed in North America today but are banned in some European countries (including France, Denmark,

and Norway) because of health concerns (Price et al., 2010; Thorlton et al., 2014).

As most of you have experienced firsthand, caffeine in small doses can elevate your mood and decrease fatigue. In larger doses, it can make you feel jittery and can cause insomnia. Because caffeine takes a relatively long time to leave our bodies (it has a blood half-life of about six hours), sleep can be disturbed if the caffeine is ingested close to bedtime. This effect is especially pronounced among those already suffering from insomnia (Byrne et al., 2012). As with the other psychoactive drugs, people react differently to caffeine; some are very sensitive to it and others can consume relatively large amounts with little effect. Research suggests that moderate use of caffeine (a cup of coffee per day) by pregnant women does not harm the developing fetus (Loomans et al., 2012).

The *DSM-5* includes **caffeine use disorder**, defined as problematic caffeine use that causes significant impairment and distress, as a condition for further study, not as a formal disorder (American Psychiatric Association, 2013). As with other stimulants, regular caffeine use can result in tolerance and dependence on the drug, and also intoxication and withdrawal (part of the substance-induced disorders). Those of you who have experienced headaches, drowsiness, and a generally unpleasant mood when denied your morning coffee have had the withdrawal symptoms characteristic of this drug (Meredith et al., 2013). Caffeine's effect on the brain seems to involve the neuromodulator *adenosine* and, to a lesser extent, the neurotransmitter *dopamine* (Juliano et al., 2015). Adenosine plays an important role in the release of dopamine and glutamate in the striatum, which may explain the elation and increased energy that come with caffeine use (Juliano et al., 2015).

OPIOIDS

The word **opiate** refers to the natural chemicals in the opium poppy that have a narcotic effect (they relieve pain and induce sleep; see DSM Table 12.4). In some circumstances, they can cause **opioid-related disorders**. The broader term **opioids** refers to the family of substances that includes natural opiates, synthetic variations (methadone, pethidine), and the comparable substances that occur naturally in the brain (enkephalins, beta-endorphins, and dynorphins; Borg et al., 2015). In *The Wizard of Oz*, the Wicked Witch of the West puts Dorothy, Toto, and the Cowardly Lion to sleep by poisoning poppies in a field that is on the way to Oz, an allusion to the opium poppies used to produce morphine, codeine, and heroin.

Just as the poppies lull Dorothy, the Cowardly Lion, and Toto, opioids induce euphoria, drowsiness, and slowed breathing. High doses can lead to death if respiration is completely depressed. Opioids are also *analgesics*, substances that help relieve pain. People are sometimes given morphine before and after surgery to calm them and help block pain.

In the early 2000s, a newer prescription opioid drug used in the treatment of pain, oxycodone (OxyContin), raised concerns because of its potential for abuse and for lethal overdose. Oxycodone was featured prominently in the news on the Canadian east coast, particularly in Cape Breton, Nova Scotia, where it had become a popular street drug. Along with other prescription narcotics, oxycodone was linked to the death of 12 residents in 2003–2004. The Nova Scotia College of Physicians and Surgeons sent out a letter to its members, providing practice guidelines to minimize inappropriate prescribing of oxycodone and thus minimize its abuse potential (Moulton, 2004). The manufacturers of oxycodone were fined $635 million for misleading the public about the addictive properties of the drug (Lindsey, 2007).

Today, Canada is in the grip of an opioid crisis, one powered by the use of both prescription and illegal opioids (Belzak & Halverson, 2018). According to a national report on opioid-related deaths, 11 500 Canadians died from overdose between January 2016 and December 2018 (Special Advisory Committee on the Epidemic of Opioid Overdoses, 2019). Most of the deaths in 2018, 94 percent, were deemed accidental. Fentanyl and related substances were a major focus of analysis, with almost three-quarters of the accidental opioid-related deaths in 2018 attributed to them. The rate of hospitalizations for opioid poisoning increased between 2007 and 2017, with the highest rates occurring among some of our most vulnerable citizens: Canadians over the age of 65 (O'Connor et al., 2018). Concerns are also being raised about high rates of opioid-related hospitalizations and deaths among First Nations people (as cited in Belzak & Halverson, 2018, pp. 228–229). The Canadian Institute for Health Information (CIHI, 2018) reported that 21.3 million prescriptions for opioids were dispensed in 2017 in Canada, a small drop from 21.7 million in 2016. The 2015/2016 First Nations Regional Health Survey reported that one-quarter of First Nations adults living on-reserve, and 10 percent of youth (12 to 17 years of age), had used prescription opioids in the past year (First Nations Information Governance Centre, 2018). In 2017, the CTADS estimated 3.5 million Canadians (12 percent) used opioid pain relievers (Health Canada, 2019).

Withdrawal from opioids can be so unpleasant that people continue to use these drugs despite a sincere desire to stop. People who cease or reduce their opioid intake begin to experience symptoms within 6 to 12 hours; these include excessive yawning, nausea and vomiting, chills, muscle aches, diarrhea, and insomnia—temporarily disrupting work, school, and social relationships. The symptoms can persist for one to three days, and the process is completed in about a week.

People who use opioids face risks beyond addiction and the threat of overdose. Because some of these drugs are usually injected intravenously, users are at increased risk for HIV infection and therefore AIDS. In fact, a survey conducted in the late 1990s (Strathdee et al., 1997) showed that HIV incidence among injection drug users in Vancouver was the highest ever documented among injection drug users in the developed world (Wood & Kerr, 2006). According to the Canadian AIDS Treatment Information Exchange (CATIE), a recognized source of knowledge for HIV that is sponsored by the Public Health Agency of Canada, injection drug users in Canada are 59 times more likely to contract HIV than those who do not inject drugs

(Challacombe, 2018). CATIE estimates that in 2014, 89 855 Canadians injected drugs, about 0.3 percent of Canada's population, and that in 2016, 14 percent of new HIV infections were likely related to injection drug use.

The life of someone addicted to an opioid is bleak. Mortality rates in this population range from 6 to 20 times that of the general population. Those individuals who live face much hardship when recovering from addiction, with stable abstinence rates as low as 30 percent and most individuals undergoing many relapses. Even those who discontinue opioids often use alcohol and other drugs in their place (Hser et al., 2015). Results from a 33-year follow-up study of more than 80 opioid users in an English town highlight this pessimistic view (Rathod et al., 2005).

DSM-5	**Table 12.4** Diagnostic Criteria for Opioid Use Disorder

A. A problematic pattern of opioid use leading to clinically significant impairment or distress, as manifested by at least two of the following, occurring within a 12-month period:

1. Opioids are often taken in larger amounts or over a longer period than was intended.
2. There is a persistent desire or unsuccessful efforts to cut down or control opioid use.
3. A great deal of time is spent in activities necessary to obtain the opioid, use the opioid, or recover from its effects.
4. Craving, or a strong desire or urge to use opioids.
5. Recurrent opioid use resulting in a failure to fulfill major role obligations at work, school, or home.
6. Continued opioid use despite having persistent or recurrent social or interpersonal problems caused or exacerbated by the effects of opioids.
7. Important social, occupational, or recreational activities are given up or reduced because of opioid use.
8. Recurrent opioid use in situations in which it is physically hazardous.
9. Continued opioid use despite knowledge of having a persistent or recurrent physical or psychological problem that is likely to have been caused or exacerbated by the substance.
10. Tolerance, as defined by either of the following:
    a. A need for markedly increased amounts of opioids to achieve intoxication or desired effect.
    b. A markedly diminished effect with continued use of the same amount of an opioid.
    Note: This criterion is not considered to be met for those taking opioids solely under appropriate medical supervision.
11. Withdrawal, as manifested by either of the following:
    a. The characteristic opioid withdrawal syndrome.
    b. Opioids (or a closely related substance) are taken to relieve or avoid withdrawal symptoms.
    Note: This criterion is not considered to be met for those taking opioids solely under appropriate medical supervision.

Specify current severity:

Mild: Presence of 2–3 symptoms.

Moderate: Presence of 4–5 symptoms.

Severe: Presence of 6 or more symptoms.

Source: Reprinted with permission from the *Diagnostic and Statistical Manual of Mental Disorders*, Fifth Edition (Copyright © 2013). American Psychiatric Association. All Rights Reserved.

▲ Opium poppies

At the follow-up, 22 percent of opioid users had died, about twice the national rate of about 12 percent for the general population. More than half the deaths were the result of drug overdose, and several people took their own lives. The good news from this study was that of those who survived, 80 percent were no longer using opioids and the remaining 20 percent were being treated with methadone. Persistent opioid use may be related to comorbid mental disorders and sexual or physical abuse. Long-term recovery has been shown to be associated with family and social support, employment, and opioid abstinence of at least five years (Hser et al., 2015).

The high or rush experienced by users comes from activation of the body's natural opioid system. In other words, the brain already has its own opioids—called enkephalins and endorphins—that provide narcotic effects (Simon, 1997). Heroin, opium, morphine, and other opioids activate this system (just as does alcohol at certain doses; Gianoulakis, 2001; Peterson et al., 1996). The discovery of the natural opioid system has allowed us to study the effects of addictive drugs on the brain and has led to important discoveries that may help us treat people dependent on these drugs.

HALLUCINOGENS

On a Monday afternoon in April 1943, Albert Hoffmann, a scientist at a large Swiss chemical company, prepared to test a newly synthesized compound. He had been studying derivatives of ergot, a fungus that grows on diseased kernels of grain, and sensed that he had missed something important in the 25th compound of the lysergic acid series. Ingesting what he thought was an infinitesimally small amount of this drug, which he referred to in his notes as LSD-25, he waited to see what subtle changes might come over him as a result. Thirty minutes later he reported no change; but some 40 minutes after taking the drug he began to feel dizzy and had a noticeable desire to laugh. Riding his bicycle home, he hallucinated that the buildings he passed were moving and melting. By the time he arrived home, he was terrified that he was losing his mind. Albert Hoffmann was experiencing the first recorded "trip" on LSD (Stevens, 1987).

LSD (d-lysergic acid diethylamide), sometimes referred to as acid, is a common hallucinogenic drug. It is produced synthetically in laboratories, although naturally occurring derivatives of this grain fungus (ergot) have been found historically. In Europe during the Middle Ages, an outbreak of illnesses occurred after people ate grain that was infected with the fungus. One version of this illness—later called *ergotism*—constricted the flow of blood to the arms or legs and eventually resulted in gangrene and the loss of limbs. Another type of illness resulted in convulsions, delirium, and hallucinations. Years later, scientists connected ergot with the illnesses and began studying versions of this fungus for possible benefits. This is the type of work Albert Hoffmann was engaged in when he discovered LSD's hallucinogenic properties.

LSD largely remained in the laboratory until the 1960s, when it was first produced illegally for recreational use. The U.S. Central Intelligence Agency did, however, test LSD as a "truth serum" during interrogations though the agency abandoned their efforts after several serious incidents and no evidence of truth (Lee & Shlain, 1992). The mind-altering effects of the drug suited the social effort to reject established culture and enhanced the search for enlightenment that characterized the mood and behaviour of many people during the decade (Parrott, 2012). The late Timothy Leary, at the time a Harvard research professor, first used LSD in 1961 and immediately began a movement to have every child and adult try the drug and "turn on, tune in, and drop out."

During this time, LSD was also being experimented with in the context of therapy. For example, based on the spirituality theory of sobriety (i.e., that spirituality can induce sobriety from alcohol among those with alcohol disorders), some reasoned that therapists could exploit the spiritual aspect of the LSD trip to assist in recovery from alcoholism. In the 1950s, Dr. Humphrey Osmond performed an experiment to test this theory on a sample of 1000 patients with a history of severe alcoholism receiving treatment at the Weyburn Hospital in Saskatchewan. Participants were administered a single high dose of LSD. Osmond reported that 50 percent did not drink alcohol again, leading him to argue strongly for the efficacy of this approach (Lee & Shlain, 1985). In fact, William (Bill) Wilson, co-founder of Alcoholics Anonymous (AA), is known to have experimented with and advocated this controversial approach to the treatment of alcoholism (Roberts & Hruby, 1984).

A number of other hallucinogens exist, some occurring naturally in a variety of plants: *psilocybin* (found in certain species of mushrooms), *lysergic acid amide* (found in the seeds of the morning glory plant), *dimethyltryptamine* (DMT; found in the bark of the Virola tree, which grows in South and Central America), and *mescaline* (found in the peyote cactus plant); and some produced synthetically *phencyclidine* (PCP). Phencyclidine is snorted, smoked, or injected intravenously, and it causes impulsivity and aggression.

The *DSM-5* diagnostic criteria include perceptual changes, such as the subjective intensification of perceptions, depersonalization, and hallucinations. Physical symptoms include pupillary dilation, rapid heartbeat, sweating, and blurred vision (American Psychiatric Association, 2013). Many users have written about hallucinogens, and they describe a variety of experiences. The kinds of sensory distortions reported by Hoffmann are characteristic reactions. People tell of watching intently as a friend's ear grows and bends in beautiful spirals or of looking at the bark of a tree and seeing little civilizations living there. These people will tell you that they usually know what they are seeing isn't real but that it looks as real as anything they have ever seen. But many also recount experiences that are more intense than hallucinations, with an emotional content that sometimes takes on religious proportions.

Tolerance develops quickly to many of the hallucinogens, including LSD, psilocybin, and mescaline (hallucinogen use disorders) (Passie & Halpern, 2015). If taken repeatedly over several days, these drugs completely lose their effectiveness. Sensitivity returns after about a week of abstinence, however. For most hallucinogens, no withdrawal symptoms are reported. Even so, a number of concerns have been expressed about their use. One is the possibility of psychotic reactions. Stories in the press about people jumping out of windows because they believed they could fly or stepping into moving traffic with the mistaken idea that they couldn't be hurt make for sensational reading, but little evidence suggests that using hallucinogens produces a greater risk than being drunk or under the influence of any other drug. People do report having "bad trips"; these are the sort of frightening episodes in which clouds turn into threatening monsters or deep feelings of paranoia take over. Usually, someone on a bad trip can be talked down by supportive people who provide constant reassurance that the experience is the temporary effect of the drug and it will wear off in a few hours (Parrott, 2012).

Hallucinogens seem to affect the brain in diverse and non-specific ways, meaning by affecting multiple receptors at one time in opposing ways. It is thought that this broad impact on brain receptors may lead to consciousness expanding experienced by some (Passie & Halpern, 2015). Most of these drugs bear some resemblance to neurotransmitters; LSD, psilocybin, lysergic acid amide, and DMT are chemically similar to serotonin; mescaline resembles norepinephrine; and several other hallucinogens we have not discussed are similar to acetylcholine. However, the mechanisms responsible for the hallucinations and other perceptual changes that users experience remain unknown.

CANNABIS

We classify cannabis as a hallucinogen in this book, but cannabis can have effects that fall in three categories: depressant, stimulant, and hallucinogenic. Marijuana is the name given to the dried parts of the cannabis or hemp plant (its full scientific name is *Cannabis sativa*).

Cannabis (marijuana) was the drug of choice in the 1960s and early 1970s and continues to be in favour today. According to the 2017 Canadian Tobacco, Alcohol and Drug Survey,

▲ The psychedelic art of the 1960s reflects the visual distortions that result from taking hallucinogens.

15 percent of Canadians had used cannabis in the previous year (Health Canada, 2019). This is an estimated increase of 60 percent since 2004, when it was only 9 percent of Canadians (Rotermann, 2019). Over this period, previous-year use remained stable or declined among Canadians 15 to 24 years of age and increased among Canadians 25 to 64 years of age. On October 17, 2018, Canada legalized the use of nonmedical cannabis by adults (Department of Justice, 2018). During the first three months of 2019, 18 percent of Canadians reported using cannabis (Rotermann, 2019), an increase attributed to men between the ages of 45 and 64.

People who smoke marijuana often experience altered perceptions of the world. Reactions to cannabis usually include mood swings. Otherwise normal experiences seem extremely funny, or the person might enter a dreamlike state where time seems to stand still. Users often report heightened sensory experiences, seeing vivid colours, or appreciating the subtleties of music. Perhaps more than any other drug, however, cannabis can produce very different reactions in people. It is not uncommon for someone to report having no reaction to the first use of the drug; it also appears that people can "turn off" the high if they are sufficiently motivated (Jager, 2012). The feelings of well-being produced by small doses can change to paranoia, hallucinations, and dizziness when larger doses are taken. Research on frequent cannabis users suggests that impairments of memory, concentration, motivation, self-esteem, relationships with others, and employment are common negative outcomes of long-term use (possibly leading to cannabis use disorder), although some researchers suggest that some psychological problems precede usage—increasing the likelihood that someone will use cannabis (Heron et al., 2013; Macleod et al., 2004). The introduction of synthetic marijuana (referred to by several names, such as fake weed, K2, and Spice and marketed as "herbal incense") has caused alarm—in many places, it can be purchased legally and the reaction to its use can be extremely harmful (e.g., hallucinations, seizures, heart rhythm problems; Palamar & Barratt, 2016; Wells & Ott, 2011). The diagnostic criteria for cannabis use disorder are presented in DSM Table 12.5.

The evidence for cannabis tolerance is contradictory. Chronic and heavy users report tolerance, especially to the euphoric high (Mennes et al., 2009); they are unable to reach the levels of

pleasure they experienced earlier. However, evidence also indicates "reverse tolerance," when regular users experience more pleasure from the drug after repeated use. Major signs of withdrawal do not usually occur with cannabis. Chronic users who stop taking the drug report a period of irritability, restlessness, appetite loss, nausea, and difficulty sleeping (Johnson, 1991); but no evidence suggests they go through the craving and psychological dependence characteristic of other substances (Grinspoon & Bakalar, 1997).

The use of cannabis for medicinal purposes is controversial. However, there appears to be increasing evidence documenting the successful use of cannabis and its by-products for the symptoms of certain diseases. Many cannabis products are available for medical use, including an herbal cannabis extract (Sativex—delivered in a nasal spray), dronabinol (Marinol), nabilone (Cesamet), and the herbal form of cannabis that is typically smoked (Borgelt et al., 2013; Wang et al., 2008). These cannabis-derived products are prescribed for chemotherapy-induced nausea and vomiting, HIV-associated anorexia, neuropathic pain in multiple sclerosis, and cancer pain. Unfortunately, cannabis smoke may contain as many carcinogens as tobacco smoke, although one long-term study that followed more than 5000 men and women over 20 years suggested that occasional use does not appear to have a negative effect on

DSM-5	**Table 12.5** Diagnostic Criteria for Cannabis Use Disorder

A. A problematic pattern of cannabis use leading to clinically significant impairment or distress, as manifested by at least two of the following, occurring within a 12-month period:

1. Cannabis is often taken in larger amounts or over a longer period than was intended.
2. There is a persistent desire or unsuccessful efforts to cut down or control cannabis use.
3. A great deal of time is spent in activities necessary to obtain cannabis, use cannabis, or recover from its effects.
4. Craving, or a strong desire or urge to use cannabis.
5. Recurrent cannabis use resulting in a failure to fulfill major role obligations at work, school, or home.
6. Continued cannabis use despite having persistent or recurrent social or interpersonal problems caused or exacerbated by the effects of cannabis.
7. Important social, occupational, or recreational activities are given up or reduced because of cannabis use.
8. Recurrent cannabis use in situations in which it is physically hazardous.
9. Cannabis use is continued despite knowledge of having a persistent or recurrent physical or psychological problem that is likely to have been caused or exacerbated by cannabis.
10. Tolerance, as defined by either of the following:
    a. A need for markedly increased amounts of cannabis to achieve intoxication or desired effect.
    b. Markedly diminished effect with continued use of the same amount of cannabis.
11. Withdrawal, as manifested by either of the following:
    a. The characteristic withdrawal syndrome for cannabis.
    b. Cannabis (or a closely related substance) is taken to relieve or avoid withdrawal symptoms.

Specify current severity:

Mild: Presence of 2–3 symptoms.

Moderate: Presence of 4–5 symptoms.

Severe: Presence of 6 or more symptoms.

Source: Reprinted with permission from the *Diagnostic and Statistical Manual of Mental Disorders*, Fifth Edition (Copyright © 2013). American Psychiatric Association. All Rights Reserved.

▲ Marijuana

lung function (Pletcher et al., 2012). The 2017 Canadian Tobacco, Alcohol and Drug Survey estimated that 37 percent of the Canadians who used cannabis in the previous year, used it for medical purposes. This represents about 1.6 million Canadians and is an increase from the estimated 831 000 Canadians in 2015 (Health Canada, 2019).

Decriminalization of the use and possession of small amounts of cannabis is happening in many places. In the past, people gained a criminal record if they were found guilty of possession of even a small amount of cannabis. Cannabis was first banned in Canada in 1923 under the Opium and Drug Act. In 2013, more than 58 000 Canadians were arrested for simple possession (Canadian Centre on Substance Abuse, 2015). Canadians with previous records for possession may now apply through the Parole Board of Canada to have their record suspended (Government of Canada, 2019).

Most cannabis users inhale the drug by smoking the dried leaves in marijuana cigarettes; others use preparations, such as hashish, which is the dried form of the resin in the leaves of the female plant. Marijuana contains more than 80 varieties of the

▲ Canadian Olympic snowboarding champion Ross Rebagliati was stripped of his gold medal in 1998 after testing positive for marijuana. He later had his medal reinstated, as there was no policy in place for the sport stating that marijuana is a banned substance. Neither is marijuana considered performance-enhancing (Kingsley, 1998).

chemicals called *cannabinoids*, which are believed to alter mood and behaviour. The most common of these chemicals includes the *tetrahydrocannabinols* (THC). An exciting finding in the area of cannabis research was that the brain makes its own version of THC, a neurochemical called anandamide after the Sanskrit word *ananda*, which means "bliss" (Sedlak & Kaplin, 2009; Volkow et al., 2014).

OTHER DRUGS

Other substances are used by individuals to alter sensory experiences. These drugs do not fit neatly into the classes of substances we just described but are nonetheless of great concern because they can be physically damaging to those who ingest them. We briefly describe *inhalants*, *steroids*, and a group of drugs commonly referred to as *designer drugs*.

Inhalants include a variety of substances found in volatile solvents—making them available to breathe into the lungs directly. Among the more common inhalants are spray paint, hair spray, paint thinner, gasoline, amyl nitrate, nitrous oxide ("laughing gas"), nail polish remover, felt-tipped markers, airplane glue, contact cement, dry-cleaning fluid, and spot remover (Ridenour & Howard, 2012). Inhalant use is highest during early adolescence, ages 13 to 14, especially in those in correctional or psychiatric institutions. Higher rates of inhalant use are found among Caucasians and Indigenous peoples, as well as those who live in rural or small towns, come from disadvantaged backgrounds, have higher levels of anxiety and depression, and show more impulsive and fearless temperaments (Garland et al., 2011; Halliburton & Bray, 2016). In Canada, inhalant use among Indigenous groups is often reported in the media, but a recent study reported that 99.2 percent of First-Nation youth say they have never used inhalants (First Nations Information Governance Centre, 2018). These drugs are rapidly absorbed into the bloodstream through the lungs when inhaled from containers or on a cloth held up to the mouth and nose. The high associated with the use of inhalants resembles that of alcohol intoxication and usually includes dizziness, slurred speech, poor coordination, euphoria, and lethargy. Users build up a tolerance to the drugs, and withdrawal—which involves sleep disturbance, tremors, irritability, and nausea—can last from two to five days. Use can also increase aggressive and antisocial behaviour, and long-term use can damage bone marrow, kidneys, liver, lungs, nervous system, and the brain (Sakai & Crowley, 2009). For example, cognitive impairment can occur for the user and for infants born to mothers who use while pregnant (Ford et al., 2014). If users are startled, this can cause a cardiac event that can lead to death (called "sudden sniffing death"; Ridenour & Howard, 2012).

Anabolic-androgenic steroids (more commonly referred to as steroids or *roids*) are derived from or are a synthesized form of the hormone testosterone (Pope & Kanayama, 2012). The legitimate medical uses of these drugs focus on people with asthma, anemia, and breast cancer, and males with sexual development issues. However, the anabolic action of these drugs (that can produce increased body mass) has resulted in their illicit use by those wanting to improve their physical abilities or looks by increasing muscle bulk. Some estimates suggest that approximately 2 to 6 percent of males use the drug illegally at some point in their lives (Pandina & Hendren, 1999; Pope & Kanayama, 2012). Users sometimes administer the drug on a schedule of several weeks or months followed by a break from its use—called *cycling*—or combine several types of steroids—called *stacking*. Steroid use differs from other drug use because the substance does not produce a desirable high but instead is used to enhance performance and body size. One well-known Canadian example involves sprinter Ben Johnson who won the 100-metre dash at the 1988 Seoul Olympic Games. He was later stripped of his gold medal after officials found he had taken anabolic steroids to enhance his performance ("Johnson Stripped," 2004). Research on the long-term effects of steroid use suggests that mood disturbances are common (e.g., depression, anxiety, and panic attacks; Pope & Kanayama, 2012), and there is a concern that more serious physical consequences may result from its regular use.

The term *designer drugs* is applied to a growing group of drugs developed by pharmaceutical companies to target specific diseases and disorders. It was only a matter of time before some would use the developing technology to design recreational drugs. We have already described one of the more common illicit designer drugs—methylenedioxymethamphetamine (MDMA, or ecstasy)—in our discussion on stimulants. This amphetamine is one of a small but growing list of related substances that includes 3,4-methelenedioxyeth amphetamine (MDEA or Eve) and 2-(4-Bromo-2,5-dimethoxyphenyl)ethylamine (BDMPEA or Nexus). Their ability to heighten a person's auditory and visual perception, as well as the senses of taste and touch, have been incorporated into the activities of those who attend nightclubs, all-night dance music parties, or other large social gatherings. Another drug associated with the "drug club" scene is ketamine (street names include K, Special K, and Cat Valium), a dissociative anaesthetic that produces a sense of detachment along with a reduced awareness of pain (McDowell, 1999; Wolff, 2012). Gamma hydroxybutyrate (GHB, or liquid ecstasy) is a central nervous system depressant that was marketed in health food stores in the 1980s as a means of stimulating muscle growth. Users report that, at low doses, it can produce a state of relaxation and increased tendency to verbalize, but at higher doses or in combination with alcohol or other drugs, it can result in seizures, severe respiratory depression, and coma. These drugs taken at high doses may be especially dangerous for the developing teenager brain because their high toxicity may cause irreversible memory loss and other cognitive problems (Domino & Miller, 2015). Use of all these drugs can result in tolerance and dependence, and their increasing popularity among adolescents and young adults raises significant public health concerns.

Concept Check 12.2

Identify the terms relating to substance abuse from the following descriptions.

1. These drugs influence perception, distorting feelings, sights, sounds, and smells. _____
2. Greater and greater amounts of a substance are required to achieve the same effect. _____
3. These substances affect behaviour, cognition, and mood. Many accepted, commonly used substances are in this category. _____
4. An unpleasant physical response occurs when a dependent user stops taking a substance. _____
5. Substances that include alcohol, reduce arousal, and cause relaxation. _____

CAUSES

People continue to use psychoactive drugs for their effects on mood, perception, and behaviour despite the obvious negative consequences of abuse and dependence. We saw that despite his clear potential as an individual, Danny continued to use drugs to his detriment. Various factors help explain why people like Danny persist in using drugs. Drug abuse and dependence, once thought to be the result of moral weakness, are now believed to be influenced by a combination of biological and psychosocial factors.

Why do some people use psychoactive drugs without abusing or becoming dependent on them? Why do some people stop using these drugs or use them in moderate amounts after being dependent on them, and others continue a lifelong pattern of dependence despite their efforts to stop? These questions continue to occupy the time and attention of researchers throughout the world.

BIOLOGICAL DIMENSIONS

Familial and Genetic Influences

In 2007, American model and television personality Anna Nicole Smith died from an apparently accidental overdose of at least nine prescription medications—including methadone, Valium, and the sedative chloral hydrate. The tragedy was compounded by the fact that, just months before, her only son Daniel had died, also from an apparent drug overdose. Did the son inherit a vulnerability to addiction from his mother? Did he pick up Anna Nicole's habits from living with her over the years? Is it just a coincidence that both mother and son were so involved with drugs?

As you have seen throughout this book, many of the psychological disorders are influenced in important ways by genetics. Mounting evidence indicates that problematic drug use generally, and problematic alcohol use specifically, follows this pattern. Research in twin, family, adoption, and other genetic studies indicates that certain people may be genetically vulnerable to drug abuse (Strain, 2009; Volkow & Warren, 2015). Twin studies of smoking, for example, find a moderate genetic influence (Hardie et al., 2006; Seglem et al., 2015). Most genetic data on substance abuse come from research on alcoholism, which is widely studied because alcohol use has been legal for a long time and a great many people are struggle with it (Gordis, 2000b; Lerman et al., 1999). Among men, both twin and adoption studies suggest genetic factors play a role in alcoholism (McGue, 1999). The research on women, however, is sometimes contradictory. Several studies suggest that genetics has relatively little influence on alcoholism in women (e.g., McGue et al., 1992), and others suggest the disorder may be inherited in some form (e.g., Pickens et al., 1991).

A group of researchers—the Collaborative Study on the Genetics of Alcoholism (COGA)—have worked together to search for the genes that may influence alcoholism. Two studies have pointed to genes that may influence alcoholism on chromosomes 1, 2, 7, and 11, and a gene on chromosome 4 that may serve to protect people from becoming dependent (Long et al., 1998; Reich et al., 1998). As the search for the genes responsible for alcoholism continues, the next obvious question is how these genes work to influence addiction—a field of research called functional genomics.

One genetic factor that appears to be involved in alcoholism involves the body's ability to metabolize alcohol. The liver produces an enzyme called **alcohol dehydrogenase (ADH)** that breaks down acetaldehyde, a by-product of alcohol. If acetaldehyde is not broken down but builds up in the body, the person becomes very ill. The drug disulfiram (Antabuse) helps people stop drinking by chemically preventing the breakdown of acetaldehyde so that people feel sick when they drink. In 30 to 50 percent of people of Asian descent, ADH seems to be absent naturally, so they have difficulty metabolizing alcohol (Gordis, 2000b). The result is a physiological response, known as the skin-flushing response, characterized by reddening and warmth of the face, dizziness, and nausea. This response is thought to contribute to the relatively low rates of alcohol-related disorders in people of Asian descent (Newlin, 1989).

In 1990, a study suggested that alcoholism may be related to a particular gene, DRD2 (Blum et al., 1990). This gene appears to regulate the sensitivity of receptors to dopamine. As discussed next, the dopamine system affects the ability of drugs to provide pleasurable experiences, and the DRD2 gene was thought to influence alcoholism by increasing the positive quality of these experiences. However, more recent research disputes the role of this gene in alcoholism (Gordis, 2000b). Research is now examining whether certain genes affect the sedative-hypnotic effects of alcohol or how people experience withdrawal, and whether this influences who will ultimately become dependent (Prescott & Kendler, 1999). Genetic research to date tells us that substance abuse in general is affected by our genes, but no one gene seems to cause problematic substance use. Genetic factors may affect how people experience certain drugs, which in turn may partly determine who will or will not develop problems.

Neurobiological Influences

For the most part, the pleasurable experiences caused by psychoactive substances partly explain why people continue to use them. In behavioural terms, people are positively reinforced for using drugs. Complex and fascinating studies indicate the brain appears to have a natural pleasure pathway that mediates our experience of reward. All abused substances seem to affect this internal reward centre in the same way as you experience pleasure from certain foods or from sex (Ray, 2012). In other words, what psychoactive drugs may have in common is their ability to activate this reward centre and provide the user with a pleasurable experience, at least for a time.

The pleasure centre was discovered more than 50 years ago by James Olds and Peter Milner at McGill University, who studied the effects of electrical stimulation on rat brains (Olds, 1956; Olds & Milner, 1954). If certain areas were stimulated with very small amounts of electricity, the rats behaved as if they had received something very pleasant, such as food. The exact location of the area in the human brain is still subject to debate. It is believed that the dopaminergic system and its opioid-releasing neurons known as MOP-r receptors are involved. Opioids have an agonist effect at MOP-r receptors, which are spread throughout the central nervous system. Opioids encourage more production of the brains' own opioids. The pleasure centre of reward is made up of MOP-r receptors mostly found in ventral and dorsal striatal areas and is highly influenced by the downstream activation of the dopaminergic mesocorticolimbic and nigrostriatal systems (Berridge & Kringelbach, 2015; Borg et al., 2015).

How do different drugs that affect different neurotransmitter systems all converge to activate the pleasure pathway, which is primarily made up of dopamine-sensitive neurons? Researchers are only beginning to sort out the answers to this question, but some surprising findings have emerged in recent years. For example, we know that amphetamines and cocaine act directly on the dopamine system. Other drugs, however, appear to increase the availability of dopamine in more roundabout and intricate ways.

Another relevant issue in understanding the role of dopamine in drug rewards is the phenomenon of *sensitization*. This refers to the fact that, in animal studies, repeated exposure to stimulant drugs like amphetamines leads to an increased dopamine release when taking the drug. Isabelle Boileau, Alain Dagher, Marco Leyton, and their colleagues at the Montréal Neurological Institute have demonstrated this phenomenon in healthy humans. Ten participants were administered amphetamine in the laboratory on three occasions over five days. Their brain responses to amphetamine were examined using positron emission tomography (PET; see Chapter 3) on three occasions: the first day of exposure, two weeks following the third exposure, and one year following the third exposure. Consistent with sensitization, the PET scans showed increased dopamine release to amphetamine at the two later testing times relative to the first day of amphetamine exposure. They also found that novelty-seekers and impulsive individuals were most prone to amphetamine sensitization (Boileau et al., 2006).

This complicated picture is far from complete. Other pleasure pathways may exist in the brain. The future should yield even more interesting insights into the interaction of drugs and the brain. One aspect that awaits explanation is how drugs not only provide pleasurable experiences (positive reinforcement) but also how they help remove unpleasant experiences, such as pain, feelings of illness, or anxiety (negative reinforcement). Aspirin is a negative reinforcer: we take it not because it makes us feel good, but because it stops us from feeling bad. In much the same way, one property of the psychoactive drugs is that they stop people from feeling bad, an effect as powerful as making them feel good.

With several drugs, negative reinforcement is related to the anxiolytic effect, the ability to reduce anxiety (outlined briefly in our discussion on the sedative, hypnotic, and anxiolytic drugs). Alcohol has an anxiolytic effect. The neurobiology of how these drugs reduce anxiety seems to involve the septal–hippocampal system (Gray, 1987), which includes a large number of GABA-sensitive neurons. Certain drugs may reduce anxiety by enhancing the activity of GABA in this region, thereby inhibiting the brain's normal reaction (anxiety or fear) to anxiety-producing situations (Phil et al., 1993).

Researchers have identified individual differences in the way people respond to alcohol. Understanding these response differences is important because they may help explain why some people continue to use drugs until they acquire a dependence on them whereas others stop before this happens. A number of studies have compared individuals with and without a family history of alcoholism. For example, research by Robert Pihl, Jordan Peterson (yes, that one), and their colleagues suggests that individuals at high familial genetic risk for alcoholism may experience more of a pleasurable response to alcohol ingestion than do others. This pleasurable response is indexed through heart rate increases to alcohol and degree of beta-endorphin release to alcohol ingestion (Peterson et al., 1993, Peterson et al., 1996; Stewart et al., 1992). Thus, this laboratory-based research on the effects of alcohol suggests that what may be inherited among those genetically vulnerable to alcoholism is a propensity to experience the pleasurable consequences of drinking to a greater extent than others.

PSYCHOLOGICAL DIMENSIONS

Positive Reinforcement

We have shown that the substances people use to alter mood and behaviour have unique effects. The high from heroin differs substantially from the experience of smoking a cigarette, which in turn differs from the effects of amphetamines or LSD. Nevertheless, it is important to point out the similarities in the way people react to most of these substances. The feelings that result from using them are pleasurable in some way, and people will continue to take the drugs to recapture the pleasure. Many of the drugs used and abused by humans also seem to be pleasurable to animals (Young & Herling, 1986). Laboratory animals will work to have injected into their bodies such drugs as cocaine, amphetamines, opiates, sedatives, and alcohol, which demonstrates that even without social and cultural influences, these drugs are pleasurable.

Human research also indicates that to some extent all the psychoactive drugs provide a pleasurable experience (Ray, 2012). People are often very inventive in how they administer these drugs to maximize their euphoric effects. For example, individuals who are dependent on heroin sometimes combine it with benzodiazepines (such as Valium) to intensify their pleasure (American Psychiatric Association, 2000c). Cocaine users may heat the drug and inhale the fumes in a process known as "free-basing" or use the highly concentrated form known as crack to obtain a more rapid and intense experience. Such activities tend to increase as tolerance increases and more of the substance is needed to produce the high that is the hallmark of drug use. An interesting study by Sean Barrett of Dalhousie University and his colleagues investigated patterns of polysubstance use among Canadian university students: Tobacco use increased when an individual was also using alcohol, cannabis, psilocybin, MDMA,

cocaine, amphetamine, LSD, or methylphenidate. They also found that alcohol, tobacco, and cannabis are frequently mixed with other substances. The authors suggested that these patterns can be explained by students' attempts to enhance the pleasurable experience with one drug by simultaneously using another drug (Barrett et al., 2006a).

Negative Reinforcement

Most researchers have looked at how drugs help reduce unpleasant feelings through negative reinforcement. Many people are likely to initiate and continue drug use to escape from unpleasantness in their lives. In addition to the initial euphoria, many drugs provide escape from physical pain (opioids), from stress (alcohol), or from panic and anxiety (benzodiazepines). This phenomenon has been explored under a number of different names, including *tension reduction* and *self-medication* (Ray, 2012).

One premise is that substance use becomes a way for users to cope with the unpleasant feelings that go along with life circumstances (Cooper et al., 1988; Zack et al., 1999). Drug use by soldiers in the Vietnam War is one tragic example of this phenomenon. Almost 42 percent of these mostly young men experimented with heroin, half of whom became dependent, because the drug was readily available and because of the extreme stress of the war (Jaffe et al., 1997). It is interesting that only 12 percent of these soldiers were still using heroin three years after their return home (Robins et al., 1975), which suggests that once the stressors were removed, the men no longer needed the drug to relieve their pain. People who experience trauma, such as sexual abuse, are more likely to abuse alcohol (Stewart, 1996). This observation emphasizes the important role played by each aspect of abuse and dependence—biological, psychological, social, and cultural—in determining who will and who will not have difficulties with these substances. Research showing that adolescents tend to use drugs as a way to cope with unpleasant feelings (Chassin et al., 1993) suggests that to prevent people from using drugs, we may need to address such influences as stress and anxiety, a strategy we examine in our discussion on treatment.

Many people who use psychoactive substances experience an unpleasant crash after being high. So why don't they just stop taking drugs? One explanation involves an interesting integration of both the positive and negative reinforcement processes (Solomon, 1980; Solomon & Corbit, 1974). This *opponent-process theory* holds that an increase in positive feelings will be followed by an increase in negative feelings a short time later. Similarly, an increase in negative feelings will be followed by a period of positive feelings. Athletes often report feeling depressed after finally attaining a long-sought goal. The opponent-process theory claims that this mechanism is strengthened with use and weakened by disuse. So a person who has been using a drug for some time will need more of it to achieve the same results (tolerance). At the same time, the negative feelings that follow drug use tend to intensify. For many people, this is the point at which the motivation for using shifts from desiring the euphoric high to alleviating the increasingly unpleasant crash. Unfortunately, they come to believe that the best remedy is more of the same drug—referred to as "the hair of the dog that bit you" in the case of alcohol. People can become enslaved by this insidious cycle.

Researchers have also looked at substance abuse as a way of self-medicating for other problems (Bailey & Baillie, 2012; Conrod, Pihl, et al., 2000). If people have difficulties with anxiety, for example, they may be attracted to barbiturates, benzodiazepines, or alcohol because of their anxiety-reducing qualities. In one study, researchers were successful in treating a group of cocaine users who had ADHD with methylphenidate (Levin et al., 2007). They had hypothesized that these individuals used cocaine to help focus their attention. Once their ability to concentrate improved with the methylphenidate, the users reduced their use of cocaine. Research is just beginning to outline the complex interplay among stressors, negative feelings, other psychological disorders, and negative reactions to the drugs themselves as causative factors in psychoactive drug use.

Cognitive Factors

What people expect to experience when they use drugs influences how they react to them. A person who expects to be less inhibited when he or she drinks alcohol will act less inhibited whether that person actually drinks alcohol or a placebo he or she thinks is alcohol (Bailey & Baillie, 2012). This observation about the influence of how we think about drug use has been labelled an *expectancy effect* and has received considerable research attention.

Expectancies develop before people actually use drugs, perhaps as a result of parents' and peers' drug use, advertising, and media figures who model drug use (Campbell & Oei, 2013). In an important study, many students in Canada in Grades 7 to 11 were questioned each year for three years about their thoughts about alcohol and marijuana use (Fulton et al., 2012; Young, 2013). Included were instructions for them to list three or four things they expected would happen if they used a particular substance. Positive expectancies about the effects of alcohol or marijuana use predicted who was more likely to use and increase their use of these drugs three years later. These results suggest that adolescents may begin drinking or using other drugs partly because they believe these substances will have positive effects.

Expectations appear to change as people have more experience with drugs, although their expectations are similar for alcohol, nicotine, cannabis, and cocaine (Simons et al., 2009; Young 2013). Some evidence from the laboratory of Peter Finn, a clinical psychologist from Montréal, points to positive expectancies—believing you will feel good if you take a drug—as an indirect influence on drug problems. In other words, what these beliefs may do is to increase the likelihood you will take certain drugs, which in turn will increase the likelihood that problems will arise (Finn et al., 2000).

After people stop taking drugs after prolonged or repeated use, powerful urges called "cravings" can interfere with efforts to remain off these drugs (Hollander & Kenny, 2012; Young, 2013). The *DSM-5* includes cravings as one of the criteria for diagnosing a substance-related disorder. If you've ever tried to give up ice cream and then found yourself compelled to have some, you have a limited idea of what it might be like to crave a drug. These urges seem to be triggered by factors such as the availability of the drug, contact with things associated with drug taking (e.g., sitting in a bar), specific moods (e.g., being depressed), or having a small dose of the drug. For example, one study used a virtual reality apparatus to simulate visual, auditory, and olfactory (an

alcohol-dipped tissue) cues (Lee et al., 2009) for alcohol-dependent adults. The participants could choose among kinds of alcoholic beverages (e.g., beer, whisky, or wine), snacks, and drinking environments (beer garden, restaurant, and pub). The researchers found significant increases in cravings for alcohol under these conditions (Lee et al., 2009). This type of technology may make it easier for clinicians to assess potential problem areas for clients, which can then be targeted to help keep them from relapsing. Research is under way to determine how cravings may work in the brain and if certain medications can be used to reduce these urges and help supplement treatment (Hollander & Kenny, 2012).

Important research by Shep Seigel, Marvin Krank, and Riley Hinson at McMaster University in the 1980s examined the role of conditioning in addiction and overdosing. If a particular stimulus (e.g., sitting in a bar, seeing a needle for an injection drug user) is repeatedly paired with drug taking and consequent unconditioned drug effects, then that stimulus can become a conditioned stimulus signalling that the drug effect is coming (Siegel, 1982). Stimuli that can serve as such conditioned stimuli do not have to be external stimuli, such as drug paraphernalia; internal stimuli can also serve as conditioned stimuli. For example, negative emotions could serve as a conditioned stimulus, if the drug user frequently takes the drug in response to an unpleasant emotional state, such as anxiety (Westra & Stewart, 2002). According to the research of Shep Siegel and of many others since, with repeated learning opportunities involving pairing of the conditioned stimulus with drug taking, the drug taker will develop conditioned compensatory responses that are in the opposite direction to the drug's original (unconditioned) effect. For example, if decreased heart rate is the unconditioned drug effect, a conditioned compensatory response could involve increased heart rate. This conditioned compensatory response is initiated when the drug taker is exposed to the cues (conditioned stimulus) associated with drug taking.

This phenomenon can explain many aspects of addiction, including tolerance, craving, and overdose. With respect to tolerance, as the conditioned compensatory response develops, it works against the unconditioned drug effect, reducing the subjective experience of the drug effect for the user. With respect to craving, when the user is exposed to cues normally associated with drug taking, this initiates the conditioned compensatory response, which is experienced subjectively as craving for the drug. Finally, with respect to overdose, it is commonly observed that heroin users, for example, are more likely to overdose when injecting in an unfamiliar environment, even when using the same dose. From the perspective of conditioning theory, this happens because the usual drug cues are not present to initiate the conditioned compensatory response, and thus the user experiences the full unconditioned effect of the drug, resulting in an overdose (Siegel et al., 1982).

Another factor studied so far only in people who drink alcohol is a cognitive phenomenon called alcohol myopia. This condition has been defined as "a state of shortsightedness in which superficially understood, immediate aspects of experience have a disproportionate influence on behaviour and emotion" (Steele & Josephs, 1990, p. 923). Picture someone who is drunk, carefully and methodically placing one foot in front of the other as he or she walks so as not to fall, walking straight into the path of an oncoming truck. Although alcohol myopia may not explain why people drink in the first place, it may help us understand why they continue to drink when they know excessive drinking can have severe negative consequences. People under the influence of alcohol may not be able to evaluate properly the risks involved in their continued drinking. Tara MacDonald and her colleagues at Queen's University in Kingston have conducted some fascinating work demonstrating that alcohol myopia explains why people are more likely to take health risks (e.g., engaging in unprotected sex) when they are intoxicated (MacDonald, Fong, et al., 2000; MacDonald, MacDonald, et al., 2000; MacDonald et al., 1996, 1998).

SOCIAL DIMENSIONS

Exposure to psychoactive substances is a necessary prerequisite to their use and possible abuse, as previously discussed. You could probably list many ways in which people are exposed to these substances—through friends, through the media, and so on. For example, research on the consequences of cigarette advertising suggests the effects of media exposure may be more influential than peer pressure in determining whether teens smoke (Jackson et al., 2007). Research such as this has led to increasing restrictions by the Canadian government on how and where cigarette companies can advertise their product (Canadian Council on Smoking & Health and Physicians for a Smoke-Free Canada, 2003). Legislation that requires vendors to hide their "power wall" of cigarettes is implemented provincially and territorially rather than federally. In Nova Scotia, a law was put in place in March 2007 that required vendors to hide tobacco products in their stores and that did not allow in-store tobacco product advertising (Young, 2007). Manitoba, Saskatchewan, Alberta (Hall, 2007), and British Columbia (Blais, 2007) have all put similar legislation in place. Ontario has adopted legislation that bans all tobacco product displays and advertising ("Province-Wide Smoking Ban Adopted," 2005).

Drug-addicted parents spend less time monitoring their children than do parents without drug problems (Dishion et al., 1988), and this is an important contribution to early adolescent substance use (Kerr et al., 2010). When parents do not provide appropriate supervision, their children tend to develop friendships with peers who support drug use (Van Ryzin et al., 2012). Children influenced by drug use at home may be exposed to peers who use drugs as well. A self-perpetuating pattern seems to be associated with drug use that extends beyond the genetic influences we discussed previously.

The work of Alberta psychologist Nancy Galambos and her colleagues further affirms that parents' behaviour does matter in determining the alcohol use and drug-taking patterns of their teenage offspring. For example, Galambos, Barker, and Almeida (2003) followed more than 100 Canadian families for 3.5 years to examine the influence of parenting behaviours and of peers on children's adjustment in early adolescence. The results showed that parents who used firm behavioural control were able to stop the upward spiral of externalizing behaviours (i.e., acting-out behaviours, including substance abuse) among those teens who were affiliating with antisocial peers. Studies such as these suggest that parenting can exert an important influence on teenagers' use of alcohol and drugs and may do so even in the face of potentially negative peer influences.

How does our society view people who are dependent on drugs? This issue is of tremendous importance because it affects efforts to legislate the sale, manufacture, possession, and use of these substances. It also dictates how drug-dependent individuals are treated. Two views of substance-related disorders characterize contemporary thought: moral weakness and the disease model of dependence. According to the *moral weakness view*, drug use is seen as a failure of self-control in the face of temptation; this is a psychosocial perspective. Drug users lack the character or moral fibre to resist the lure of drugs. We saw earlier, for example, that the Catholic Church made drug abuse an official sin—an indication of its disdain. The *disease model of physiological dependence*, in contrast, assumes that drug use disorders are caused by an underlying physiological cause; this is a biological perspective. Just as diabetes or asthma can't be blamed on the individuals they affect, neither should drug use disorders. As noted by Canadian clinical psychologist G. Alan Marlatt, AA and similar organizations see drug dependence as an incurable disease over which the user has no control (Marlatt, 1985).

▲ Many young children are exposed to drug use.

Obviously, neither perspective does justice to the complex interrelationship between the psychosocial and biological influences that affect substance disorders. Viewing drug use as moral weakness leads to punishing those who have the disorder, whereas a disease model includes seeking treatment for a medical problem. Conversely, people certainly help determine the outcome of treatment for drug abuse and dependence, and messages that the disorder is out of their control can at times be counterproductive. A comprehensive view of substance-related disorders that includes both psychosocial and biological influences is needed for this important societal concern to be addressed adequately.

CULTURAL DIMENSIONS

When we examine a behaviour as it appears in different cultures, it is necessary to re-examine what is considered abnormal (Kohn et al., 2009). Each culture has its own preferences for psychoactive drugs as well as its own proscriptions for substances it finds unacceptable. Keep in mind that in addition to defining what is or is not acceptable, cultural norms affect the rates of substance use and abuse in important ways. For example, in certain cultures, including Korea, members are expected to drink alcohol heavily on certain social occasions (Lee, 1992). As we have seen before, exposure to these substances, in addition to social pressure for heavy and frequent use, may facilitate their abuse, and this may explain the high abuse rates in countries like Korea. However, poor economic conditions in certain parts of the world limit the availability of drugs, which appears in part to account for the relatively low prevalence of substance abuse in Mexico and Brazil (de Almeidia-Filho et al., 1991; Ortiz & Medicna-Mora, 1988).

Looking ahead to what we may find through future research, it is important for us to consider that biological factors may interact with cultural norms in a complex way. For example, it seems logical that cultural norms may develop over time as a consequence of biological differences. We have seen, however, that behaviour can also affect biology, and we may discover that the norms established by a society affect the biology of its people. Research on the cultural dimensions of problematic substance use is in its infancy, but it holds great promise for helping unravel the mysteries of this disorder.

AN INTEGRATIVE MODEL

Any explanation of substance use disorders must account for the basic issue raised earlier in this chapter: why can some people use drugs without abusing them or becoming dependent on them? ■ Figure 12.5 illustrates how the multiple influences we have discussed may interact to account for this process. Access to a drug is a necessary but obviously not sufficient condition for abuse or dependence. Exposure has many sources, including the media, parents, peers, and, indirectly, lack of supervision. Whether people use a drug depends also on social and cultural expectations, some encouraging and some discouraging, such as laws against possession or sale of the drug.

The path from drug use to abuse and dependence is more complicated. As major stressors aggravate many of the disorders we have discussed, so too do they increase the risk of abuse and dependence on psychoactive substances. Genetic influences may

▲ In many cultures, alcohol is used ceremonially.

be of several different types. Some individuals may inherit a greater sensitivity to the positively reinforcing effects of certain drugs and others to the negatively reinforcing effects (anxiolytic or analgesic) of certain drugs. Other psychiatric conditions may indirectly put someone at risk for substance abuse. For example, antisocial personality disorder, characterized by the frequent violation of social norms, is thought to include a lowered rate of arousal, which may account for the increased prevalence of substance abuse in this group.

Equifinality, the concept that a particular disorder may arise from multiple and different paths, is particularly appropriate to substance disorders. It is clear that abuse and dependence cannot be predicted from one factor, be it genetic, neurobiological, psychological, or cultural. For example, some people with the DRD2 gene common to many with substance abuse problems do not become abusers. Many people who experience the most crushing stressors, such as abject poverty or bigotry and violence, cope without resorting to drug use. There are different pathways to abuse, and we are only now beginning to identify their basic outlines.

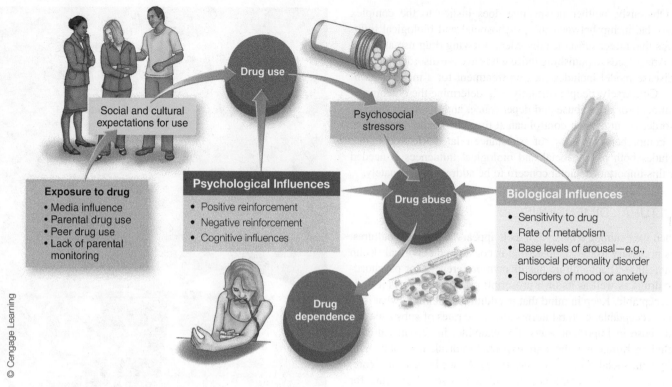

FIGURE 12.5 | An integrative model of substance-related disorders.

After a drug has been used repeatedly, biology and cognition conspire to create dependence. Continual use of most drugs causes tolerance, which requires the user to ingest more of the drug to produce the same effect. Conditioning is also a factor. If pleasurable drug experiences are associated with certain settings, a return to such a setting will later cause urges to develop, even if the drugs themselves are not available.

This obviously complex picture still does not convey the intricate lives of people who develop substance-related disorders (Wills et al., 1996). Each person has his or her own story and path to abuse and dependence. We have barely begun to discover the commonalities of substance disorders; we need to understand a great deal more about how all the factors interact to produce them.

TREATMENT

When we left Danny, he was in jail, awaiting the legal outcome of being arrested for robbery. At this point in his life, Danny needs more than legal help; he needs to free himself from his addiction to alcohol and cocaine. And the first step in his recovery has to come from him. Danny must admit he needs help, that he does indeed have a problem with drugs, and that he needs others to help him overcome his chronic dependence. The personal motivation to work on a drug problem appears to be important, and substance abusers arrive at treatment at different stages of readiness to change their substance use behaviour (Prochaska et al., 1997).

A specific psychological technique called *motivational enhancement therapy (MET)* (National Institute on Drug Abuse [NIDA], 2009), based on the work by Miller and Rollnick (2002, 2012), has been developed to help individuals with substance use disorders increase their motivation to change and move toward a stage where they are ready to work on modifying their problematic substance use (see also Brown et al., 2007). Recently, this type of approach has been successfully extended by researchers in Calgary to the treatment of pathological gambling (Hodgins et al., 2001; Hodgins et al., 2004). Fortunately, Danny's arrest seemed to shock him into realizing how serious his problems had become, and he was ready to confront his substance dependence head on.

Treating people who have substance-related disorders is a difficult task. Perhaps because of the combination of influences that often work together to keep people hooked, the outlook for those who are dependent on drugs is often not very positive. We will see in the case of heroin dependence, for example, that a best-case scenario is often just trading one addiction (heroin) for another (methadone). And even people who successfully cease taking drugs may feel all their lives the urge to resume drug use.

Treatment for substance-related disorders focuses on several areas (Higgins et al., 2014). The National Institute on Drug Abuse recommends 13 principles of effective treatment for illicit drug abuse based on more than 35 years of research (NIDA, 2009; see Table 12.1). Sometimes the first step is to help someone through the withdrawal process; and for some, the ultimate goal is abstinence. In other situations, the goal is to get a person to maintain a less harmful, more moderate level of drug use without escalating

TABLE 12.1 | Principles of Effective Treatment

1. No single treatment is appropriate for all individuals.

2. Treatment needs to be readily available.

3. Effective treatment attends to multiple needs of the individual, not just his or her drug use.

4. An individual's treatment and services plan must be assessed continually and modified as necessary to ensure that the plan meets the person's changing needs.

5. Remaining in treatment for an adequate period of time is critical for treatment effectiveness (i.e., three months or longer).

6. Counseling (individual and/or group) and other behavioral therapies are critical components of effective treatment for addiction.

7. Medications are an important element of treatment for many patients, especially when combined with counseling and other behavioral therapies.

8. Addicted or drug-abusing individuals with coexisting mental disorders should have both disorders treated in an integrated way.

9. Medical detoxification is only the first stage of addiction treatment and by itself does little to change long-term drug use.

10. Treatment does not need to be voluntary to be effective.

11. Possible drug use during treatment must be monitored continuously.

12. Treatment programs should provide assessment for HIV/AIDS, hepatitis B and C, tuberculosis and other infectious diseases, and counseling to help patients modify or change behaviors that place themselves or others at risk of infection.

13. Recovery from drug addiction can be a long-term process and frequently requires multiple episodes of treatment.

Source: Principles of Addiction Treatment: A Research-Based Guide (2nd ed.; NIH Publication No. 09-4180), by National Institute on Drug Abuse (NIDA), 2009.

its intake, and sometimes it is geared toward preventing exposure to drugs.

We discuss the treatment of substance-related disorders as a group because treatments have so much in common. For example, many programs that treat people for dependence on a variety of substances also teach skills for coping with life stressors. Biological treatments focus on how to mask the effects of the ingested substances. We discuss the obvious differences among substances as they arise.

BIOLOGICAL TREATMENTS

Agonist Substitution

Increased knowledge about how psychoactive drugs work on the brain has led researchers to explore ways of changing how they are experienced by people who are dependent on them. One method, **agonist substitution**, involves providing the person with a safer drug that has a chemical makeup similar to the addictive drug. Methadone is an opioid agonist that is often given as a heroin substitute (Kleber, 1999). Methadone is a synthetic narcotic developed in Germany during World War II when morphine was

not available for pain control; it was originally called *adolphine* after Adolf Hitler (Bellis, 1981). Although it does not give the quick high of heroin, methadone initially provides the same analgesic (pain-reducing) and sedative effects. When users develop a tolerance for methadone, however, it loses its analgesic and sedative qualities. Because heroin and methadone are *cross-tolerant*, acting on the same neurotransmitter receptors, a heroin user who takes methadone may become addicted to the methadone instead (O'Brien, 1996), trading a more harmful behavioural pattern for a much less harmful alternative (a notion referred to as **harm reduction**, as we will discuss in more detail later in this chapter). Methadone maintenance therapy is the most widely known and well-researched treatment for opioid dependency (Krambeer et al., 2001).

When users combine methadone with counselling, many reduce their use of heroin (Ball & Ross, 1991). In fact, methadone maintenance programs have effectively reduced heroin dependence and are available in most countries affected by heroin addiction (Murray, 1998). Additional benefits of methadone maintenance (especially in conjunction with psychotherapy) are decreased criminality, because the person is no longer engaging in illegal activities to get drugs, and decreased risk of HIV/AIDS and hepatitis (e.g., Millson et al., 2007), because the person is no longer injecting heroin and thus is no longer exposed to unsafe injection practices (see review by Murray, 1998).

Not all the news is good, however. A proportion of people under methadone treatment continue to abuse other substances, such as cocaine (Condelli et al., 1991) and benzodiazepines (Iguchi et al., 1990). Some people who use methadone as a substitute for heroin benefit significantly, but they may be dependent on methadone for the rest of their lives (O'Brien, 1996). Although some practitioners argue that methadone may be used continually without harmful side effects (e.g., Murray, 1998), the current trend in methadone treatment is to gradually wean the person off methadone in the final treatment phase (see Krambeer et al., 2001).

A newer substitution treatment for heroin dependence is with the drug *buprenorphine* (Jaffe & O'Keefe, 2003; Srivastava & Kahan, 2006). In France, high-dosage buprenorphine is currently the main substitution treatment for narcotic addiction (Poirier et al., 2004). According to Eder et al. (1998), buprenorphine may offer some advantages over methadone in the treatment of opioid dependence. For example, because buprenorphine is a partial opioid agonist (rather than a full agonist like methadone), it may involve less of a risk for dependence and produce fewer withdrawal symptoms on eventual discontinuation. In fact, some research suggests that buprenorphine treatment is as effective as, or more effective than, methadone maintenance in the treatment of opioid dependence. For example, an Austrian study by Giacomuzzi et al. (2003) showed that buprenorphine-maintained participants showed significantly less consumption of opioids and cocaine compared with participants in the methadone group at the end of the study. They also found that buprenorphine showed a slight advantage over methadone in terms of certain withdrawal symptoms (e.g., fewer stomach cramps, less fatigue, fewer chills, and less heart pounding with buprenorphine). Such results suggest promise for this newer substitute, but more research is needed (Giacomuzzi et al., 2003; Srivastava & Kahan, 2006).

Addiction to cigarette smoking is also treated by a substitution process. The drug—nicotine—is provided to smokers in the form of gum, a patch, an inhaler, or a nasal spray, which lack the carcinogens included in cigarette smoke; the dose is later tapered off to lessen withdrawal from the drug. In general, these replacement strategies successfully help people stop smoking, although they work best with supportive psychological therapy (Carpenter et al., 2013; Hughes, 2009). People must be taught how to use the gum properly, and a portion of the people who successfully quit smoking become dependent on the gum itself (Etter, 2009). The nicotine patch requires less effort and provides a steadier nicotine replacement (Hughes, 2009). Another medical treatment for smoking—bupropion (Zyban)—is also commonly prescribed, under the trade name Wellbutrin, as an antidepressant. This drug curbs the cravings without being an agonist for nicotine. All these medical treatments have approximately the same effectiveness in helping people quit smoking, with a six-month abstinence rate of approximately 20 to 25 percent (Litvin et al., 2012).

A controlled trial by researchers at the University of Western Ontario showed that combining physical exercise with nicotine replacement therapy not only facilitates smoking cessation, but also delays weight gain in women smokers, suggesting promise for this particular combination of behavioural and pharmacotherapies (Prapavessis et al., 2007).

Antagonist Treatments

We described how many of the psychoactive drugs produce euphoric effects through their interaction with the neurotransmitter systems in the brain. What would happen if the effects of these drugs were blocked, so that the drugs no longer produced the pleasant results? Would people stop using the drugs? **Antagonist drugs** block or counteract the effects of psychoactive drugs, and a variety of drugs that seem to cancel out the effects of opioids have been used with people dependent on a variety of substances (O'Brien & Cornish, 1999). The most often prescribed opioid-antagonist drug, naltrexone, has had only limited success with individuals who are not simultaneously participating in a structured treatment program (Goldstein, 1994). When it is given to a person who is dependent on opioids, it produces immediate withdrawal symptoms, an extremely unpleasant effect. A person must be withdrawn from the opioid completely before starting naltrexone, and because it removes the euphoric effects of the opioid, the user must be highly motivated to continue treatment.

Naltrexone has also been evaluated as a treatment for alcohol dependence because it prevents alcohol reinforcement by inhibiting dopamine release in the nucleus accumbens (O'Malley, 1996; Stewart et al., 2005). Naltrexone blocks alcohol-induced pleasurable stimulation in humans (Peterson et al., 2006). University of Calgary psychiatrists David Crockford and Nady el-Guebaly (1998) have described the results of a case study of a 49-year-old man with comorbid alcohol dependence and pathological gambling who was effectively treated for both disorders with naltrexone. The naltrexone was particularly beneficial in helping reduce this patient's cravings. Other drugs are now being studied to see if they can help improve the outcomes of people who want to reduce their drug use. For example, a relatively new drug—ondansetron—is being studied and may be particularly helpful for people who developed alcoholism in or before their early 20s (Johnson et al., 2000; Kranzler, 2000). Overall, naltrexone and the other drugs being explored are not magic bullets that shut off the person's response to psychoactive drugs and put an end to dependence. Antagonists may therefore be a useful addition to other therapeutic efforts.

Aversive Treatment

In addition to looking for ways to block the euphoric effects of psychoactive drugs, workers in this area may prescribe drugs that make ingesting the abused substances extremely unpleasant. The expectation is that a person who associates the drug with feelings of illness will avoid using the drug. The most commonly known aversive treatment uses disulfiram (Antabuse) with people who have an alcohol use disorder (Ivanov, 2009). Antabuse prevents the breakdown of acetaldehyde, a by-product of alcohol, and the resulting building of acetaldehyde causes feelings of illness. People who drink alcohol after taking Antabuse experience nausea, vomiting, and elevated heart rate and respiration. Ideally, Antabuse is taken each morning, before the desire to drink wins out (Nathan, 1993). Unfortunately, noncompliance is a major concern, and a person who skips the Antabuse for a few days is able to resume drinking (Ellis & Dronsfield, 2013).

Efforts to make smoking aversive have included the use of silver nitrate in lozenges or gum. This chemical combines with the saliva of a smoker to produce a bad taste in the mouth. Research has not shown it to be particularly effective (Jensen et al., 1991). Both Antabuse for alcohol abuse and silver nitrate for cigarette smoking have generally been less than successful as treatment strategies on their own, primarily because they require that people be extremely motivated to continue taking them outside the supervision of a mental health professional (Leccese, 1991).

Other Biological Treatments

Medication is frequently prescribed to help people deal with the often very disturbing symptoms of withdrawal. Clonidine, developed to treat hypertension, has been given to people withdrawing from opioids. Because withdrawal from certain prescribed medications, such as the sedatives, can cause cardiac arrest or seizures, these drugs are gradually tapered off to minimize dangerous reactions. In addition, sedative drugs (benzodiazepines) are often prescribed to help minimize discomfort for people withdrawing from other drugs such as alcohol (McCreery & Walker, 1993).

One of the few controlled studies of the use of medication to treat cocaine abuse (Gawin et al., 1989) found that desipramine, one of the antidepressant drugs, was more effective in increasing abstinence rates among cocaine users than lithium or a placebo. However, 41 percent of those receiving the medication were unable to achieve even a month of continuous cocaine abstinence, suggesting it may not be helpful for a large subgroup of users. Other medications—such as acamprosate (which affects the glutamate and GABA neurotransmitter systems) and several SSRIs (selective serotonin reuptake inhibitors), including Zoloft and Prozac—are now being tested for their potential therapeutic properties, especially for alcohol dependence (Gordis, 2000d).

PSYCHOSOCIAL TREATMENTS

Most of the biological treatments for substance abuse show some promise for people who are trying to eliminate their drug habit. None of these treatments alone is successful for most people, however. Most research indicates a need for social support or therapeutic intervention. Because so many people need help to overcome their substance disorder, a number of models and programs have been developed. Unfortunately, in no other area of psychology have unvalidated and untested methods of treatment been so widely accepted. A reminder: just because a program has not been subject to the scrutiny of research does not mean it doesn't work, but the sheer number of people receiving services of unknown value is cause for concern. We next review several therapeutic approaches that have been evaluated.

Inpatient Facilities

Inpatient treatment facilities are designed to help substance-dependent people get through the initial withdrawal period and to provide supportive therapy so they can go back to their communities (Morgan, 1981). Inpatient care can be extremely expensive (Miller & Hester, 1986). The question arises, then, as to how effective this type of care is compared with outpatient therapy, which can cost 90 percent less. Research suggests there may be no difference between intensive residential-setting programs and quality outpatient care in the outcomes for alcoholic patients (Miller & Hester, 1986) or for drug treatment in general (NIDA, 2009). Although some people do improve as inpatients, they may not need this expensive care.

Concept Check 12.3

Substance-related disorders are difficult to treat. See whether you understand how these treatments work. Read the examples and match them with the following terms: (a) dependent, (b) cross-tolerant, (c) agonist substitution, and (d) antagonist.

1. Methadone is used to help heroin users kick their habit in a method called _____.

2. Heroin and methadone are _____, which means they affect the same neurotransmitter receptors.

3. Unfortunately, the heroin user may become permanently _____ on methadone.

4. _____ drugs block or counteract the effects of psychoactive drugs and are sometimes effective in treating people with addictions.

Alcoholics Anonymous and Its Variations

Without question, the most popular model for the treatment of substance abuse is a variation of the 12-step program first developed by AA. Established in 1935 by two alcoholic professionals, William "Bill W." Wilson and Robert "Dr. Bob" Holbrook Smith, the foundation of AA is the notion that alcoholism is a disease and alcoholics must acknowledge their addiction to alcohol and its destructive power over them. The addiction is seen as more powerful than any individual, and therefore they must look to a higher power to help them overcome their shortcomings. Central to the design of AA is its independence from the established medical community and the freedom it offers from the stigmatization of alcoholism (Denzin, 1987; Robertson, 1988). An important component is the social support it provides through group meetings.

Since 1935, AA has steadily expanded to include almost 114 070 groups in more than 170 countries (White & Kurtz, 2008). In one survey conducted by researcher Robin Room, formerly of the Addiction Research Foundation in Toronto, more than 3 percent of the adult population has at one time attended an AA meeting (Room, 1993). The 12 steps of AA are the basis of its philosophy (see Table 12.2). In them you can see the reliance on prayer and a belief in God.

Many people credit AA and similar organizations, such as Cocaine Anonymous and Narcotics Anonymous (Miller, Gold, & Pottash, 1989), with saving their lives. Despite challenges conducting systematic research on AA because participants attend meetings anonymously and only when they feel the need to, there have

---

TABLE 12.2 | Twelve Steps of Alcoholics Anonymous

1. We admitted we were powerless over alcohol—that our lives had become unmanageable.

2. Came to believe that a power greater than ourselves could restore us to sanity.

3. Made a decision to turn our will and our lives over to the care of God as we understood Him.

4. Made a searching and fearless moral inventory of ourselves.

5. Admitted to God, to ourselves, and to another human being the exact nature of our wrongs.

6. Were entirely ready to have God remove all these defects of character.

7. Humbly asked Him to remove our shortcomings.

8. Made a list of all persons we had harmed, and became willing to make amends to them all.

9. Made direct amends to such people wherever possible, except when to do so would injure them or others.

10. Continued to take personal inventory and, when we were wrong, promptly admitted it.

11. Sought through prayer and meditation to improve our conscious contact with God as we understood Him, praying only for knowledge of His will for us and the power to carry that out.

12. Having had a spiritual awakening as the result of these steps, we tried to carry this message to alcoholics and to practise these principles in all our affairs.

Source: The Twelve Steps are reprinted with permission of Alcoholics Anonymous World Services (AAWS). Permission to reprint the Twelve Steps does not mean that AAWS has reviewed or approved the contents of this publication, or that AAWS necessarily agrees with the views expressed herein. AA is a program of recovery from alcoholism only—use of the Twelve Steps in connection with programs and activities which are patterned after AA, but which address other problems, or in any other non-AA context, does not imply otherwise.

been numerous attempts to evaluate the program's effect on alcoholism (McCrady & Tonigan, 2015). Research finds that those people who regularly participate in AA activities—or other similar supportive approaches—and follow its guidelines carefully are more likely to have positive outcomes, such as reduced drinking and improved psychological health (Kelly, 2013; Zemore et al., 2013). Those who are more likely to engage with AA tend to have more severe alcohol use problems and seem to be more committed to abstinence (McCrady & Tonigan, 2015). Thus, AA can be an effective treatment for highly motivated people with alcohol dependence. Research to date has not shown how AA compares to other treatments. However, preliminary evidence shows that AA can be helpful for individuals seeking to achieve total abstinence and may be more cost effective than other treatments. Researchers are still trying to understand exactly why AA and the 12-step program work but it seems that social support plays an important role (McCrady & Tonigan, 2015).

Some individuals have a more mixed experience with AA, and this includes agnostics and atheists, women, and minority groups (McCrady & Tonigan, 2015). Other groups now exist (e.g., Rational Recovery, Moderation Management, Women for Sobriety, SMART Recovery) for individuals who benefit from the social support of others but who may not want the abstinence-oriented 12-step program offered by groups modelled after AA (Tucker et al., 2011).

Controlled Use

One of the tenets of AA is total abstinence; recovering alcoholics who have just one sip of alcohol are believed to have slipped until they again achieve abstinence. Some researchers question this assumption, however, and believe at least a portion of abusers of several substances (notably alcohol and nicotine) may be capable of becoming social users without resuming their abuse of these drugs. Some people who smoke only occasionally are thought to react differently to nicotine than heavy users (Goldstein, 1994).

In the alcoholism treatment field, the notion of teaching people **controlled drinking** is extremely controversial. Mark and Linda Sobell conducted an important study in which people were assigned either to a program that taught them how to drink in moderation or to a group that was abstinence oriented. The Sobells followed the men for more than two years, maintaining contact with 98 percent of them. At the two-year follow-up, those who participated in the controlled drinking group were functioning well 85 percent of the time, whereas those in the abstinence group were doing well only 42 percent of the time. Nonetheless, some of the men in both groups had serious relapses and required rehospitalization, and some were incarcerated. Thus, controlled drinking may be a viable alternative to abstinence for some alcohol abusers although it clearly isn't a cure.

The controversy over this study began with a paper published by Pendery, Maltzman, and West (1982). The authors had contacted the men in the Sobell study after ten years and found that only one of the 20 men in the controlled drinking group maintained a pattern of controlled drinking. Although this re-evaluation made headlines, it had a number of flaws, as pointed out by Alan Marlatt and his colleagues (Marlatt et al., 1993). Most serious was the lack of data on the abstinence group over the same ten-year follow-up period.

▲ Mary Walsh, a well-known comedian, has struggled with an alcohol-related disorder and has publicly acknowledged being a member of AA.

The controversy over the Sobell study still had a chilling effect on controlled drinking as a treatment of alcohol abuse in the United States. In contrast, controlled drinking is widely accepted as a treatment for alcoholism in the United Kingdom (Rosenberg, 1993; Rosenberg & Melville, 2005). This approach is more widely accepted in Canada than in the United States but less so than in the United Kingdom. Research on this approach in the ensuing years (Marlatt et al., 1993; Orford & Keddie, 2006; van Amsterdam & van den Brink, 2013) seems to show that controlled drinking is at least as effective as abstinence, but that neither treatment is successful for 70 to 80 percent of patients over the long term—a rather bleak outlook for people with alcohol dependence.

Component Treatment

Most comprehensive treatment programs aimed at helping people with substance use disorders have several different components thought to boost the effectiveness of the treatment package. We saw in our review of biological treatments that their effectiveness is increased when psychologically based therapy is added. In aversion therapy, which uses a conditioning model, substance use is

▲ Linda and Mark Sobell conducted important research on substance use disorders during their time at the Addiction Research Foundation in Toronto. One of the Sobells' more important contributions was their work on the effectiveness of controlled drinking approaches.

paired with something extremely unpleasant, such as a brief electric shock or feelings of nausea. For example, a person might be offered a drink of alcohol and receive a painful shock when the glass reaches his or her lips. The goal is to counteract the positive associations of substance use with negative associations. The negative associations can also be made by imagining unpleasant scenes in a technique called *covert sensitization* (Cautela, 1966); the person might picture himself or herself beginning to snort cocaine and be interrupted with visions of becoming violently ill (Kearney, 2006).

One component that seems to be a valuable part of therapy for substance use is *contingency management* (Higgins et al., 2014; Petry et al., 2000). Here, the clinician and client together select the behaviours that the client needs to change and decide on the reinforcers that will reward reaching certain goals, perhaps money or small retail items. In a study of cocaine abusers, clients received cash vouchers (up to almost $2000) for having cocaine-negative urine specimens (Higgins et al., 2006). This study found greater abstinence rates among cocaine-dependent users with the contingency management approach and other skills training than among users in a more traditional counselling program that included a 12-step approach to treatment.

Another package of treatments is the *community reinforcement approach* (e.g., Campbell et al., 2012). Several different facets of the drug problem are addressed, to help identify and correct aspects of the person's life that might contribute to substance use, or interfere with efforts to abstain. First, a spouse, friend, or relative who is not a substance user is recruited to participate in relationship therapy to help the abuser improve his or her relationships with other important people. Second, clients are taught how to identify the antecedents and consequences that influence their drug taking. For example, if they are likely to use cocaine with certain friends, clients are taught to recognize the relationship and encouraged to avoid the associations. Third, clients are given assistance with employment, education, finances, or other social service areas that may help reduce their stress. Fourth, new recreational options help the person replace substance use with new

activities. There is now strong empirical support for the effectiveness of this approach with alcohol and cocaine abusers (Higgins et al., 2014).

Attempts to match treatments to the particular needs of individual clients (treatment matching) has received increased attention from workers in the area of substance abuse. Research by Canadian researcher Patricia Conrod and her colleagues in London, England, suggests that matching based on a substance-abusing client's personality and motivations for substance use improves outcomes for substance-abusing women (Conrod, Stewart, et al., 2000). In Conrod and colleagues' study, female substance abusers recruited from the community were randomly assigned to receive one of three brief interventions: (1) a motivation-matched intervention involving personality-specific motivational and coping skills training; (2) a motivational control intervention involving a film about substance abuse and a supportive discussion with a therapist; or (3) a motivation-mismatched intervention targeting a theoretically different personality profile.

The personality profiles targeted were (1) anxiety sensitivity (associated with benzodiazepine dependence and comorbid anxiety disorders), (2) hopelessness (associated with opioid analgesic dependence and comorbid depression), (3) impulsivity (associated with cocaine and alcohol dependence and comorbid antisocial personality disorder), and (4) sensation seeking (associated with exclusive alcohol dependence). Assessment at six months post-intervention indicated that only the matched intervention was superior to the motivational control intervention in reducing the severity and frequency of problematic substance abuse and in preventing the use of multiple medical services (see ■ Figure 12.6 for sample study result). These findings indicate promise for client-treatment matching approaches that match at the level of motivations for substance abuse.

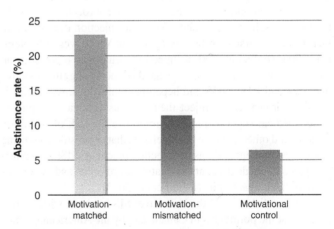

FIGURE 12.6 | Abstinence rates from alcohol following treatment in three groups: motivation-matched, motivation-mismatched, and motivational control intervention. Only the motivation-matched intervention resulted in an abstinence rate that was significantly higher than the motivational control intervention.

Source: Adapted from "Efficacy of Brief Coping Skills Interventions That Match Different Personality Profiles of Female Substance Abusers," by P. J. Conrod, S. H. Stewart, R. O. Pihl, S. Cote, V. Fontaine, and M. Dongier, 2000, *Psychology of Addictive Behaviors, 14*, pp. 231–242.

Relapse Prevention

Another kind of treatment directly addresses the problem of relapse. The **relapse prevention** treatment model developed by Alan Marlatt looks at the learned aspects of dependence and sees relapse as a failure of cognitive and behavioural coping skills (Marlatt & Gordon, 1985). Therapy involves helping people remove any ambivalence about stopping their drug use by examining their beliefs about the positive aspects of the drug ("There's nothing like a cocaine high") and confronting the negative consequences of its use ("I fight with my wife when I'm high"). High-risk situations are identified ("having extra money in my pocket") and strategies are developed to deal with potentially problematic situations, as well as with the craving that arises from abstinence. Incidents of relapse are dealt with as occurrences from which the person can recover; instead of looking on these episodes as inevitably leading to more drug use, people in treatment are encouraged to see them as episodes brought on by temporary stress or a situation that can be changed. Research on this technique suggests that it may be particularly effective for alcohol problems (McCrady, 2014), as well as in treating a variety of other substance-related disorders (Marlatt & Donovan, 2005).

HARM REDUCTION

In direct contrast to the current zero tolerance, "Just say no to drugs" approach taken by the United States government to combat substance abuse and dependence, a very different approach is currently predominant in Europe and elsewhere around the world (Marlatt, 1998). This approach is known as *harm reduction*—an approach also championed by Alan Marlatt (e.g., Roberts & Marlatt, 1999). The harm reduction approach recognizes that substance use occurs in society and seeks to minimize the harm associated with substance use as its primary goal. Abstinence can be the final goal of a substance-abusing client within a harm reduction approach, but it does not have to be. Thus, the controlled drinking interventions developed by the Sobells represent an example of the harm reduction approach.

Another example of the harm reduction approach is the establishment of safe injection sites (SISs) for injection drug users. In fact, Canada's first such facility opened in Vancouver in September 2003 (Follman, 2003). Injection drug use represents an increasing health problem in Canada—increasing the risk for overdose and HIV/AIDS and hepatitis C infections. At SISs, it is legal for drug users to inject their drug using clean equipment, under medical supervision. SISs minimize the risk of overdose, disease, and other negative health effects that can result from using unclean equipment and unsafe injecting practices. SISs also direct substance-dependent clients to treatment programs and operate as primary health-care units (Elliott et al., 2002).

The establishment of the Vancouver SIS has been widely criticized by some politicians in Canada and by the American government (Follman, 2003). Opponents argue that SISs condone or encourage drug use and that a strict abstinence-oriented approach would better contain drug use (Elliott et al., 2002). Proponents argue that SISs offer a safer, hygienic place to inject, with access to medical intervention and other health and social services, providing a positive message of concern for the drug user's health and well-being. Proponents argue that SISs can benefit the broader community as well, by reducing the public nuisance associated with drug taking in the streets of the community (e.g., discarded needles).

Scientific evidence lends support to the use of SISs. The experiences of countries such as Switzerland, Germany, the Netherlands, and Australia suggest that including SISs as part of a broader government drug policy will benefit both drug users and communities (Elliott et al., 2002). Results of the Vancouver SIS thus far appear favourable (e.g., Wood et al., 2004, 2006). For example, studies have shown that the presence of the SIS has led to an increased uptake of clients into detoxification programs and addiction treatment, to a reduction in public drug injection, and to a decrease in the amount of injection-related litter in the Vancouver downtown eastside area (Wood et al., 2004, 2006). A reduction of overdose-related deaths following the opening of the Vancouver SIS has been documented (Marshall et al., 2011). Moreover, the negative effects projected by critics do not appear to have materialized. The presence of the SIS in Vancouver has not led to an increase in drug-related crime, rates of arrest for drug trafficking, assaults, or robbery. In fact, rates of vehicle break-ins and theft have decreased in the area since the opening of the SIS (Wood et al., 2004).

PREVENTION

In education-based programs, harm reduction approaches to prevention and early intervention (e.g., Dimeff et al., 2002) appear more promising than programs encouraging a "no drug use" message (Pentz, 1999). And fortunately, more comprehensive programs that involve skills training to avoid or resist social pressures (such as peers) and environmental pressures (such as media portrayals of drug use) can be effective in preventing drug abuse among some.

Over the past several years, the strategies for preventing substance abuse and dependence have shifted from education-based approaches to more wide-ranging approaches, including the use of community-based interventions (Gordis, 2000c). For example, community-based intervention strategies to reduce binge drinking and alcohol-related injuries (e.g., car crashes, assaults) can involve mobilizing communities to encourage responsible beverage service (i.e., not serving too much alcohol to bar patrons), limiting alcohol access to underage drinkers, increasing local enforcement of drinking and driving laws, and using zoning laws to limit access to alcohol (Holder et al., 2000). But implementing this sort of intervention is obviously beyond the scope of one research investigator or even a consortium of researchers collaborating across many sites. It requires the cooperation of governmental, educational, and other social institutions. We may need to rethink our approach to preventing drug use and abuse.

GAMBLING DISORDER

Gambling has a long history—for example, dice have been found in Egyptian tombs (Greenberg, 2005). Many Indigenous groups in North America played games involving gambling before contact with Europeans. According to Gabriel Yanicki (2014, 2017), curator at the Canadian Museum of History, these games served, in part, as a way for members of different groups to socialize and to amicably compete. Today, gambling is growing in popularity, and in many places it is a legal and acceptable form of entertainment.

Gambling disorder, however, affects an increasing number of people, with a lifetime estimate of approximately 2 percent of adult Americans (Ashley & Boehlke, 2012). University of Lethbridge researcher Robert Williams and his colleagues (Williams, 2012) assessed the prevalence of problem gambling among adults (past year) worldwide and obtained an average of 2.3 percent, with Canada falling at 1.8 percent (ranging from 1.3 percent in Québec to 3.7 percent in New Brunswick).

Among pathological gamblers, 14 percent have lost at least one job, 19 percent have declared bankruptcy, 32 percent have been arrested, and 21 percent have been incarcerated (Gerstein et al., 1999) as a result of their gambling. Problem gamblers tend to have a taste for risk, engaging in many other risky behaviours (e.g., substance use, antisocial acts) and scoring high on measures of impulsivity, sensation seeking, and low self-control (Mishra et al., 2017). DSM Table 12.6 lists the *DSM-5* criteria for gambling disorder and the associated behaviours. These include the same pattern of urges we observe in the substance-related disorders. Note, too, the parallels with substance dependence, with the need to gamble increasing amounts of money over time and the withdrawal symptoms, such as restlessness and irritability, when attempting to stop. These parallels to substance-related disorders led to the recategorization of gambling disorder as an addictive disorder in the *DSM-5* (Denis et al., 2012).

There is a growing body of research on the nature and treatment of gambling. For example, work is under way to explore the biological origins of the urge to gamble among pathological gamblers. Research in this area and others (e.g., genetic research) show strong similarities in the biological origins of gambling disorders and substance use disorders. In one study, brain-imaging technology (echoplanar functional magnetic resonance imaging) was used to observe brain function while gamblers observed videotapes of other people gambling (Potenza et al., 2003). A decreased level of activity was observed in those regions of the brain that are involved in impulse regulation when compared with non-gamblers, suggesting an interaction between the environmental cues to gamble and the brain's response (which may be to decrease the ability to resist these cues). Studies have found that the ventromedial prefrontal cortex and orbitofrontal cortex ("the executive parts" of the brain) do not function as normal in those with gambling disorder. Poor impulse control and risky decisions are both processes that involve ventromedial prefrontal cortex and those individuals with higher problems in these areas also show poorer response to treatment and higher relapse rates (Yau et al., 2015).

Treatment of gambling problems is difficult. Those with gambling disorder exhibit a combination of characteristics—including denial of the problem, impulsivity, and continuing optimism ("One big win will cover my losses!")—that interfere with effective treatment. Pathological gamblers often experience cravings similar to those of people who have substance use disorders (Grant et al., 2015). Treatment is often similar, and there is a parallel Gamblers Anonymous that incorporates the same 12-step program we discussed previously. However, the evidence of effectiveness for Gamblers Anonymous suggests that 70 to 90 percent drop out of these programs and that the desire to quit must be present before intervention (Ashley & Boehlke, 2012).

DSM-5	**Table 12.6** Diagnostic Criteria for Gambling Disorder

A. Persistent and recurrent problematic gambling behavior leading to clinically significant impairment or distress, as indicated by the individual exhibiting four (or more) of the following in a 12-month period:

1. Needs to gamble with increasing amounts of money in order to achieve the desired excitement.
2. Is restless or irritable when attempting to cut down or stop gambling.
3. Has made repeated unsuccessful efforts to control, cut back, or stop gambling.
4. Is often preoccupied with gambling (e.g., having persistent thoughts of reliving past gambling experiences, handicapping or planning the next venture, or thinking of ways to get money with which to gamble).
5. Often gambles when feeling distressed (e.g., helpless, guilty, anxious, depressed).
6. After losing money gambling, often returns another day to get even ("chasing" one's losses).
7. Lies to conceal the extent of involvement with gambling.
8. Has jeopardized or lost a significant relationship, job, or educational or career opportunity because of gambling.
9. Relies on others to provide money to relieve desperate financial situations caused by gambling.

B. The gambling behavior is not better explained by a manic episode.

Specify current severity:

Mild: 4–5 criteria met.

Moderate: 6–7 criteria met.

Severe: 8–9 criteria met.

Source: Reprinted with permission from the *Diagnostic and Statistical Manual of Mental Disorders*, Fifth Edition (Copyright © 2013). American Psychiatric Association. All Rights Reserved.

Cognitive-behavioural interventions help reduce the symptoms of gambling disorder. Brief and full course treatments have both been found to help and both are recommended. Given the higher rates of impulsivity of those with these disorder and thus their high dropout rates from treatment, more research is starting to compare the brief versions to the full course ones (Grant et al., 2015).

In addition to gambling disorder being included under addictive disorders, the *DSM-5* includes another potentially addictive behaviour, Internet gaming disorder, as a condition for further study (American Psychiatric Association, 2013). There are indications that some individuals are so preoccupied with online games (sometimes in a social context with other players) that a similar pattern of tolerance and withdrawal develops (Petry & O'Brien, 2013). The goal of including this new category of addictive behaviour is to encourage additional research on its nature and treatment.

IMPULSE-CONTROL DISORDERS

A number of the disorders we describe in this book start with an irresistible impulse—usually one that will ultimately be harmful to the person affected. Typically, the person experiences increasing tension leading up to the act and, sometimes, pleasurable anticipation of acting on the impulse. For example, paraphilic

We see that the problem with drug abuse is not just use of the drug. A complicating factor in drug abuse includes the brain's desire to continue to use the drug, especially when in the presence of stimuli and situations usually associated with the drug. This drug seeking and relapse continue to interfere with successful treatment. Groundbreaking research is now exploring where in the brain these processes occur, which in turn may lead to new approaches to help people remain drug free (Kalivas, 2005).

Taking this one step further, new research with animals suggests the possibility of creating vaccines that would use the immune system to fight drugs, such as heroin, just as your body attacks infectious bacteria (Anton & Leff, 2006). A vaccine that would take away the pleasurable aspects of smoking is now being tested with humans (Moreno et al., 2010). What this means is that—theoretically—children could be vaccinated early in their lives, and if they tried a drug, it would not have the pleasurable effects that would encourage repeated use. These "vice vaccines" could hold the answer to one of our most pressing social issues.

On the other end of the intervention spectrum, new and more comprehensive prevention approaches may help many individuals avoid trying dangerous drugs. One such approach is being used in Montana—called the Montana Meth Project (Generations United, 2006). Initially funded by software billionaire

Timothy Siegel, this initiative supports advertising and community action programs to inform youth across the state about the devastating effects of methamphetamine use. The project uses dramatic and sometimes shocking pictures and video ads, and its surveys suggest that the methods were successful in changing attitudes about meth use in many 12- to 17-year-olds. Although no controlled research yet exists, this may be an additional powerful tool for reducing drug dependence.

▲ The Montana Meth Project used photos like these from Faces of Meth™, a project of the Multnomah County Sheriff's Office in Portland, Oregon.

disorders such as pedophilia (sexual attraction to children), eating disorders, and the substance-related disorders in this chapter often commence with temptations or desires that are destructive but difficult to resist. The *DSM-5* includes three additional impulse-control disorders: intermittent explosive disorder, kleptomania, and pyromania (Muresanu et al., 2012). In the *DMS-IV-TR*, gambling disorder was included as an impulse-control disorder, but it is now listed as an addictive disorder in the *DSM-5*. Tricho-tillomania (hair pulling disorder) was also moved out of this category and is now included under the obsessive-compulsive-related disorders (see Chapter 6).

INTERMITTENT EXPLOSIVE DISORDER

People with **intermittent explosive disorder** have episodes in which they act on aggressive impulses that result in serious assaults or destruction of property (Coccaro & McCloskey, 2010). Although

it is unfortunately common among the general population to observe aggressive outbursts, when you rule out the influence of other disorders (e.g., antisocial personality disorder, borderline personality disorder, a psychotic disorder, and Alzheimer's disease) or substance use, this disorder is not often diagnosed. In a rare but important large study of more than 9000 people, researchers found that the lifetime prevalence of this disorder was 7 percent (Kessler et al., 2006). Another study, of about 6500 adolescents, found a similar number, 8% (McLaughlin et al., 2012).

This diagnosis is controversial and has been debated through-out the development of the *DSM*. One concern, among others, is that by validating a general category that covers aggressive behaviour, it may be used as a legal defence for violent crimes (Coccaro & McCloskey, 2010).

Research is at the beginning stages for intermittent explosive disorder and focuses on brain regions involved, as well as the influence of neurotransmitters, such as serotonin and norepinephrine, and testosterone levels, along with their interaction with psychosocial influences (stress, disrupted family life, and parenting styles). Recent studies have proposed that there is a disruption of the orbital frontal cortex's role (the "executive parts" of the brain) in inhibiting amygdala activation (the "emotional part" of the brain) combined with changes in the serotonin system in those with this disorder (Yau et al., 2015). These and other influences are being examined to explain the origins of this disorder (Coccaro, 2012). Cognitive-behavioural interventions (e.g., helping the person identify and avoid triggers for aggressive outbursts) and approaches modelled after drug treatments appear the most effective for these individuals, although few controlled studies yet exist (McCloskey et al., 2008).

KLEPTOMANIA

The story of wealthy actor Winona Ryder stealing $5500 worth of merchandise from Saks Fifth Avenue in Beverly Hills, California, in December 2001 was as puzzling as it was titillating. Why risk a multimillion-dollar career over some clothes that she could easily afford? Was hers a case of **kleptomania**, which is defined as a recurrent failure to resist urges to steal things that are not needed for personal use or their monetary value? This disorder appears to be rare, but it is not well studied, partly because of the stigma associated with identifying oneself as acting out this illegal behaviour. Some studies suggest that that disorder may be more common in women than in men and that it typically starts in adolescence (Yau et al., 2015). One study has reported a lifetime prevalence rate of close to 1 percent in the United States (Grant, 2003). The patterns described by those with this disorder are strikingly similar—the person begins to feel a sense of tension just before stealing, which is followed by feelings of pleasure or relief while the theft is committed (Grant et al., 2010). People with kleptomania score high on assessments of impulsivity, reflecting their inability to judge the immediate gratification of stealing compared with the long-term negative consequences (e.g., arrest, embarrassment; Grant & Kim, 2002). Patients with kleptomania often report having no memory (amnesia) about the act of shoplifting (Hollander et al., 2009). Brain-imaging research supports these observations, with one study finding damage in areas of the brain associated with poor decision making (inferior frontal regions; Grant et al., 2006).

▲ In 2002, actor Winona Ryder was found guilty of shoplifting items worth several thousand dollars from a Beverly Hills department store.

There appears to be high comorbidity between kleptomania and mood disorders, and to a lesser extent with problematic substance use (Grant et al., 2010). Some refer to kleptomania as an "antidepressant" behaviour, or a reaction on the part of some to relieve unpleasant feelings through stealing (Fishbain, 1987). To date, few reports of treatment exist, and these involve either behavioural interventions or use of antidepressant medication. In one exception, naltrexone—the opioid antagonist used in the treatment of alcoholism—was somewhat effective in reducing the urge to steal in persons diagnosed with kleptomania (Grant et al., 2009).

DSM CONTROVERSIES — Are Substance Dependency and Substance Abuse the Same?

One of the changes to the *DSM-5* that caused concern among some in the field of substance-related disorders was dropping the distinction between dependence on a substance and abuse of that substance (G. Edwards, 2012; Hasin, 2012; Schuckit, 2012). Although there is general agreement that abusing a substance (e.g., binge drinking) and being dependent on that substance (e.g., increasing tolerance to alcohol and going through withdrawal symptoms if drinking is stopped) are different processes, research shows that, practically speaking, they tend to go together. In other words, if someone is routinely abusing a drug, that person will likely become dependent on it (O'Brien, 2011). From a scientific point of view, therefore, there is an obvious difference between abuse and dependence, but from a clinical perspective (which is the main function of the *DSM*), the argument was made that having these as separate diagnoses was more complicated than was necessary.

In addition, a second major change was the addition of addictive disorder, specifically, gambling disorder, to the substance-related disorders section.

Here again the science suggests that the phenomena are quite similar, with both substance-related disorders and gambling disorder showing patterns of dependence, cravings, and working on similar brain pathways (Ashley & Boehlke, 2012). However, this potentially opens up the category for the inclusion of many different kinds of "addictions." Other problems that cause real dysfunction among some people include "Internet gaming disorder," a new *DSM-5* disorder under further study (Block, 2008; Van Rooij et al., 2011) and even "tanning addiction" (Poorsattar & Hornung, 2010), and they are being taken seriously as similar types of problems. It is likely that many activities have the potential for causing dependence, because they activate the reward systems in our brains in much the same way as the substances described. The difference in whether or not they constitute a "disorder" may come back to whether or not they cause the harmful distress that is part of most psychological diagnoses.

PYROMANIA

Just as we know that someone who steals does not necessarily have kleptomania, it is also true that not everyone who sets fires is considered to have **pyromania**—an impulse-control disorder that involves having an irresistible urge to set fires. Again, the pattern parallels that of kleptomania, where the person feels a tension or arousal before setting a fire and a sense of gratification or relief while the fire burns. These individuals will also be preoccupied with fires and the associated equipment involved in setting and putting out these fires (Dickens & Sugarman, 2012). Research at an Ontario psychiatric hospital suggested that some arsonists experience sexual arousal at the thought of setting fires (Harris et al., 1992). Also rare, pyromania is diagnosed in only about 3 percent of arsonists (Lindberg et al., 2005), because arsonists can include people who set fires for monetary gain or revenge rather than to satisfy a physical or psychological urge. Because so few people are diagnosed with this disorder, research on etiology and treatment is limited (Dickens & Sugarman, 2012). Research that has been conducted follows the general group of arsonists (of which only a small percentage have pyromania) and examines the role of a family history of fire setting along with comorbid impulse disorders (antisocial personality disorder and alcoholism). Treatment is generally cognitive-behavioural and involves helping the person identify the signals that initiate the urges and teaching coping strategies to resist the temptation to start fires (Bumpass et al., 1983; McGrath et al., 1979).

Concept Check **12.4**

Match the following disorders with their corresponding symptoms: (a) intermittent explosive disorder, (b) kleptomania, and (c) pyromania.

1. This rarely diagnosed disorder is characterized by episodes of aggressive impulses and can sometimes be treated with cognitive-behavioural interventions, drug treatments, or both. _____

2. This disorder begins with the person feeling a sense of tension that is released and followed with pleasure after they have committed a theft. _____

3. Individuals with this disorder are preoccupied with fires and the equipment involved in setting and putting out fires. _____

SUMMARY

Perspectives on Substance-Related and Addictive Disorders

- In the *DSM-5*, substance-related and addictive disorders include problems with the use of depressants (alcohol, barbiturates, and benzodiazepines), stimulants (amphetamines, cocaine, nicotine, and caffeine), opioids (heroin, codeine, and morphine), and hallucinogens (cannabis and LSD), as well as gambling.

- Nonmedical drug use continues to cost Canadians billions of dollars and seriously impairs the lives of millions of Canadians each year.

Depressants, Stimulants, Opioids, Hallucinogens, and Other Drugs

- Depressants are a group of drugs that decrease central nervous system activity. The primary effect is to reduce our levels of physiological arousal and help us relax. Included in this group are alcohol, as well as the sedative, hypnotic, and anxiolytic drugs, such as those prescribed for insomnia.

- Stimulants, the most commonly consumed psychoactive drugs, include caffeine (in coffee, chocolate, and many soft drinks), nicotine (in tobacco products, such as cigarettes), amphetamines, and cocaine. In contrast to the depressant drugs, stimulants make us more alert and energetic.

- Opiates include opium, morphine, codeine, and heroin; they have a narcotic effect—relieving pain and inducing sleep. The broader term *opioids* is used to refer to the family of substances that includes these opiates as well as synthetic variations created by chemists (e.g., methadone, pethidine) and the similarly acting substances that occur naturally in our brains (enkephalins, beta-endorphins, and dynorphins).

- Hallucinogens essentially change the way the user perceives the world. Sight, sound, feelings, and even smell are distorted, sometimes in dramatic ways, in a person under the influence of drugs such as cannabis and LSD.
- A number of other substances that do not readily fit into the drug classes of depressants, stimulants, opiates, or hallucinogens are also used by individuals to alter sensory experiences. Examples of these other drugs of abuse are inhalants, steroids, and designer drugs like ketamine.

Causes and Treatments of Substance-Related Disorders

- Most psychotropic drugs seem to produce positive effects by acting directly or indirectly on the dopaminergic system (the pleasure pathway). In addition, psychosocial factors, such as expectations, stress, and cultural practices, interact with biology to influence drug use.

- Substance dependence is treated successfully for only a minority of those affected, and the best results reflect the motivation of the drug user and a combination of pharmacological and psychosocial treatments.
- Programs aimed at preventing drug use may have the greatest chance of significantly affecting the drug problem.

Gambling Disorder

- Problem gamblers display the same types of cravings and dependence as persons who have substance use disorders.
- Similar brain systems appear to be involved with those addicted to gambling as seen in persons with substance use disorders.

Impulse-Control Disorders

- In the *DSM-5*, impulse-control disorders include three separate disorders: intermittent explosive disorder, kleptomania, and pyromania.

KEY TERMS

agonist substitution, 373

alcohol dehydrogenase (ADH), 367

alcohol-related disorders, 349

antagonist drugs, 374

barbiturates, 354

benzodiazepines, 354

caffeine use disorder, 360

cannabis (marijuana), 363

controlled drinking, 376

delirium tremens (DTs), 351

depressants, 349

fetal alcohol syndrome (FAS), 351

gambling disorder, 379

gamma aminobutyric acid (GABA) system, 350

hallucinogens, 349

harm reduction, 373

impulse-control disorders, 345

intermittent explosive disorder, 380

kleptomania, 381

LSD (d-lysergic acid diethylamide), 362

opiate, 360

opioid-related disorders, 360

opioids, 360

physiological dependence, 347

polysubstance use, 345

psychoactive substances, 346

pyromania, 382

relapse prevention, 378

stimulants, 349

substance intoxication, 346

substance-related and addictive disorders, 345

substance use disorder, 347

tobacco-related disorders, 359

tolerance, 347

withdrawal, 347

withdrawal delirium, 351

ANSWERS TO CONCEPT CHECKS

12.1

1. b; **2.** a; **3.** c

12.2

1. hallucinogens; **2.** tolerance; **3.** psychoactive; **4.** withdrawal; **5.** depressants

12.3

1. c; **2.** b; **3.** a; **4.** d

12.4

1. a; **2.** b; **3.** c

MEDIA RESOURCES

CENGAGE | MINDTAP

Stay organized and efficient with MindTap—a single destination with all the course material and study aids you need to succeed. Built-in apps leverage social media and the latest learning technology. For example:

- ReadSpeaker will read the text to you.
- Flashcards are pre-populated to provide you with a jump start for review—or you can create your own.
- You can highlight text and make notes in your MindTap Reader. Your notes will flow into Evernote, the electronic notebook app that you can access anywhere when it's time to study for the exam.
- Self-quizzing allows you to assess your understanding.

Visit login.cengage.com to start using MindTap. Enter the Online Access Code from the card included with your text. If a code card is not provided, you can purchase instant access at Cengage.ca.

Exploring Substance Use Disorders

> Many kinds of problems can develop when people use and abuse substances that alter the way they think, feel, and behave.

> Once seen as caused by personal weakness, drug abuse and dependence are now thought to be influenced by both biological and psychosocial factors.

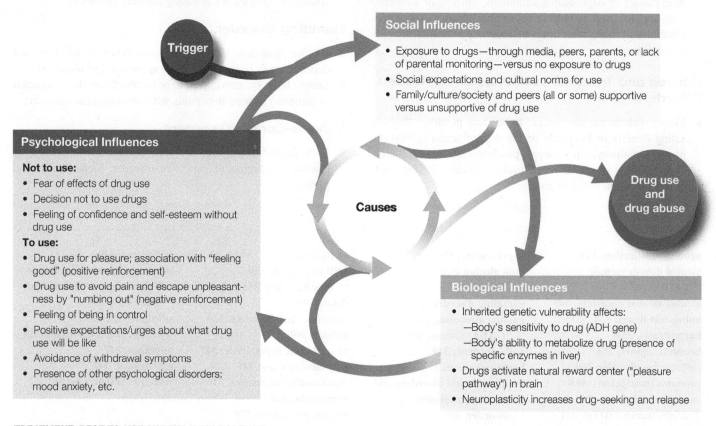

Social Influences

- Exposure to drugs—through media, peers, parents, or lack of parental monitoring—versus no exposure to drugs
- Social expectations and cultural norms for use
- Family/culture/society and peers (all or some) supportive versus unsupportive of drug use

Psychological Influences

Not to use:
- Fear of effects of drug use
- Decision not to use drugs
- Feeling of confidence and self-esteem without drug use

To use:
- Drug use for pleasure; association with "feeling good" (positive reinforcement)
- Drug use to avoid pain and escape unpleasantness by "numbing out" (negative reinforcement)
- Feeling of being in control
- Positive expectations/urges about what drug use will be like
- Avoidance of withdrawal symptoms
- Presence of other psychological disorders: mood anxiety, etc.

Biological Influences

- Inherited genetic vulnerability affects:
  —Body's sensitivity to drug (ADH gene)
  —Body's ability to metabolize drug (presence of specific enzymes in liver)
- Drugs activate natural reward center ("pleasure pathway") in brain
- Neuroplasticity increases drug-seeking and relapse

Trigger · **Causes** · **Drug use and drug abuse**

TREATMENT: BEST TO USE MULTIPLE APPROACHES

Psychosocial Treatments

- Aversion therapy—to create negative associations with drug use (shocks with drinking, imagining nausea with cocaine use)
- Contingency management to change behaviour by rewarding chosen behaviour
- Alcoholics Anonymous and its variations
- Inpatient hospital treatment (can be expensive)
- Controlled use
- Community reinforcement
- Relapse prevention

Biological Treatments

- Agonist substitution
  —Replacing one drug with a similar one (methadone for heroin, nicotine gum and patches for cigarettes)
- Antagonist treatment
  —Blocking one drug's effect with another drug (naltrexone for opioids and alcohol)
- Aversive treatments
  —Making taking drug's very unpleasant (using Antabuse, which causes nausea and vomiting when mixed with alcohol, to treat alcoholism)
- Drugs to help recovering person deal with withdrawal symptoms (clonidine for opioid withdrawal, sedatives for alcohol, etc.)

TYPES OF DRUGS

	Examples	Effects
Depressants	Alcohol, barbiturates (sedatives: Amytal, Seconal, Nembutal), benzodiazepines (antianxiety: Valium, Xanax, Halcion)	• Decreased central nervous system activity • Reduced levels of body arousal • Relaxation
Stimulants	Amphetamines, cocaine, nicotine, caffeine	• Increased physical arousal • User feels more alert and energetic
Opioids	Heroin, morphine, codeine	• Narcotic—reduce pain and induce sleep and euphoria by mirroring opioids in the brain (endorphins, etc.)
Hallucinogens	Cannabis, LSD, ecstasy	• Altered mental and emotional perception • Distortion (sometimes dramatic) of sensory perceptions

© Cengage Learning

Exploring Impulse-Control Disorders

Characterized by inability to resist acting on a drive or temptation. Sufferers often perceived by society as having a problem simply because of a lack of willpower.

TYPES OF IMPULSE-CONTROL DISORDERS

Disorder		Characteristics	Treatment
Intermittent Explosive		• Acting on aggressive impulses that result in assaults or destruction of property • Current research is focused on how neurotransmitters and testosterone levels interact with psychosocial influences (stress, parenting styles)	• Cognitive-behavioural interventions (helping person identify and avoid triggers for aggressive outbursts) and approaches modelled after drug treatments appear most effective
Kleptomania		• Recurring failure to resist urges to steal unneeded items • Feeling tense just before stealing, followed by feelings of pleasure or relief when committing the theft • High comorbidity with mood disorders and, to a lesser degree, with substance abuse/dependence	• Behavioural interventions or antidepressant medication
Pyromania		• Irresistible urge to set fires • Feeling aroused prior to setting fire, then a sense of gratification or relief while the fire burns	• Cognitive-behavioural interventions (helping person identify signals triggering urges, and teaching coping strategies to resist setting fires)

Ollyy/Shutterstock.com

Robert Kneschke/Shutterstock.com

Dale A Stork/Shutterstock.com

13 | Personality

I experienced a strong urge to harm myself. . . . I wanted to electrocute myself by putting a metal knife into a light socket. . . . I wanted to feel something that would "jolt" me back into a sense of feeling.

—JANE WANKLIN, Let Me Make It Good: A Chronicle of My Life with Borderline Personality Disorder

Use scientific reasoning to interpret behaviour:	› Identify basic biological, psychological, and social components of behavioural explanations (e.g., inferences, observations, operational definitions and interpretations) (APA SLO 2.1a)
Engage in innovative and integrative thinking and problem solving:	› Describe problems operationally to study them empirically (APA SLO 2.3A)
Describe applications that employ discipline-based problem solving:	› Correctly identify antecedents and consequences of behaviour and mental processes (APA SLO 1.3c)
	› Describe examples of relevant and practical applications of psychological principles to everyday life (APA SLO 1.3a)

*Portions of this chapter cover learning outcomes suggested by the American Psychological Association (2013) in its guidelines for the undergraduate psychology major. Chapter coverage of these outcomes is identified above by APA Goal and APA Suggested Learning Outcome (SLO).

We all think we know what a personality is. It's all the characteristic ways a person behaves and thinks: "Michael tends to be shy"; "Mindy likes to be very dramatic"; "Juan is always suspicious of others"; "Annette is very outgoing"; "Ahmed seems to be very sensitive and gets upset very easily over minor things"; "Sean has the personality of an eggplant!" We tend to type people as behaving in one way in many different situations. For example, like Michael, many of us are shy with people we don't know, but we aren't shy around our friends. A truly shy person is shy even among people he or she has known for some time. The shyness is part of the way the person behaves in most situations. We have all probably behaved in all the ways noted here (dramatic, suspicious, outgoing, easily upset). When personality characteristics interfere with relationships with others, cause the person distress, or in general disrupt activities of daily living, however, we consider these to be "personality disorders." In this chapter, we look at characteristic ways of behaving in relation to a number of specific personality disorders. First, we examine in some detail how we conceptualize personality disorders and the issues related to them; then we describe the disorders themselves.

AN OVERVIEW

What if a person's characteristic ways of thinking and behaving cause significant distress to the self or others? What if the person can't change this way of relating to the world and is unhappy? We might consider this person to have a "personality disorder." Unlike many of the disorders we have already discussed, personality disorders are chronic; they do not come and go but originate in childhood and continue throughout adulthood (Widiger, 2012). These chronic problems pervade every aspect of a person's life. If a man is overly suspicious, for example (a sign of a possible paranoid personality disorder), this trait will affect almost everything he does, including his employment (he may change jobs frequently if he believes co-workers conspire against him), his relationships (he may not be able to sustain a lasting relationship if he can't trust anyone), and even where he lives (he may move often if he suspects his landlord is out to get him).

A **personality disorder** is a persistent pattern of emotions, cognitions, and behaviour that results in enduring emotional distress for the person affected and for others and may cause difficulties with work and relationships (American Psychiatric Association, 2013). The *DSM-5* notes that having this disorder may distress the affected person. Some individuals with personality disorders may not feel any subjective distress, however; indeed, it may in fact be acutely felt by others because of the actions of the person with the disorder. As noted by forensic psychologist Robert Hare, professor emeritus at the University of British Columbia, this distress is particularly common with antisocial personality disorder, because the individual may show a blatant disregard for the rights of others yet exhibit no remorse (Hare, 1993). In certain cases, someone other than the person with the personality disorder must decide whether the disorder is causing significant functional impairment, because the affected person often cannot make such a judgment.

The *DSM-5* lists 10 specific personality disorders. Unfortunately, as we see later, many people who have personality disorders in addition to other psychological problems tend to do poorly in treatment. Data from several studies show that people who are depressed have a worse outcome in treatment if they also have a personality disorder (Sanderson & Clarkin, 1994; Shea et al., 1990). Michael Vallis and Janice Howes have suggested, however, that there are grounds to be cautiously optimistic about the potential uses of cognitive therapy in individuals with personality disorders (Vallis et al., 2000).

Before the *DSM-5*, most of the disorders we discuss in this book were in Axis I of the *DSM-IV-TR*, which included the traditional disorders. The personality disorders were included in a separate axis, Axis II, because as a group they were seen as distinct. It was thought that the characteristic traits were more ingrained and inflexible in people who have personality disorders, and the disorders themselves were less likely to be successfully modified. With the changes made with the *DSM-5*, these separate axes were eliminated and now the personality disorders are listed with the rest of the *DSM-5* disorders (American Psychiatric Association, 2013).

You may be surprised to learn that the category of personality disorders is controversial, because it involves several unresolved issues. Examining these issues can help us understand all the disorders described in this book.

CATEGORICAL AND DIMENSIONAL MODELS

Most of us are sometimes suspicious of others and a little paranoid, or overly dramatic, or too self-involved, or reclusive. Fortunately, these characteristics do not last long or are not overly intense; they don't significantly impair how we live and work.

People with personality disorders, however, display problem characteristics over extended periods and in many situations, which can cause great emotional pain for them, for others, or for both (Widiger, 2012). Their difficulty, then, can be seen as one of *degree* rather than *kind*; in other words, the problems of people with personality disorders may just be extreme versions of the problems many of us experience on a temporary basis, such as being shy or suspicious.

The distinction between problems of *degree* and problems of *kind* is usually described in terms of *dimensions* and *categories*. The issue that continues to be debated in the field is whether personality disorders are extreme versions of otherwise typical personality variations (dimensions) or ways of relating that are different from psychologically healthy behaviour (categories; Skodol, 2012). You can see the difference between dimensions and categories in everyday life. For example, we tend to look at gender categorically. Society generally views us as being in one category—"female"—or the other—"male." Yet many believe it is more accurate to look at gender in terms of dimensions. For example, we know that "male" and "female" may describe a range of choices in gender expression (e.g., personal grooming, attire, use of makeup, and other body modifications). We could just as easily place people along a continuum of maleness and femaleness rather than in the absolute categories of male or female. We also often label people's height categorically, as tall, average, or short. But height, too, can be viewed dimensionally, in inches or centimetres.

Most people in the field see personality disorders as extremes on one or more personality dimensions. Yet because of the way people are diagnosed with the *DSM*, the personality disorders—like most of the other disorders—end up being viewed in categories. You have two options—either you do or you do not have a disorder. For example, either you have antisocial personality disorder or you don't. The *DSM* doesn't rate *how* obsessive or compulsive you are; if you meet the criteria, you are labelled as having obsessive-compulsive personality disorder. No in-between is possible when it comes to personality disorders. Using categorical models of behaviour has advantages, the most important being convenience. With simplification, however, come problems. One is that the mere act of using categories leads clinicians to reify the disorders, that is, to view disorders as real things, comparable to the realness of an infection or a broken arm. Some argue that personality disorders are not things that exist but points at which society decides a particular way of relating to the world has become a problem.

Some had proposed that the *DSM-IV-TR* personality disorders section be replaced or at least supplemented by a dimensional model in which individuals would not only be given categorical diagnoses but also would be rated on a series of personality dimensions. Widiger and colleagues (Widiger, 2011; Widiger & Simonsen, 2005; Widiger & Trull, 2007) have argued for decades that such a system would have at least three advantages over a purely categorical system: (1) It would retain more information about each individual, (2) it would be more flexible because it would permit both categorical and dimensional differentiations among individuals, and (3) it would avoid the often arbitrary decisions involved in assigning a person to a diagnostic category. Currently, an alternative model of personality disorders is included in the section on "emerging measures and models" in the *DSM-5* that is included for further study (American Psychiatric Association, 2013). This model focuses on a continuum of disturbances of "self" (i.e., how you view yourself and your ability to be self-directed) and interpersonal functioning (i.e., your ability to empathize and be intimate with others). It remains to be seen how this alternative model will be used in the future.

Although no general consensus exists about what the basic personality dimensions might be, there are several contenders (South et al., 2011). One of the more widely accepted models is called the "Big Five" or the *five-factor model* of personality, and it is taken from work on "normal" personality (Hopwood & Thomas, 2012; McCrae & Costa Jr., 2008). In this model, people can be rated on a series of personality dimensions, and the combination of five components describes why people are so different. The five factors or dimensions are *extraversion* (talkative, assertive, and active versus silent, passive, and reserved); *agreeableness* (kind, trusting, and warm versus hostile, selfish, and mistrustful); *conscientiousness* (organized, thorough, and reliable versus careless, negligent, and unreliable); *neuroticism* (nervous, moody, and temperamental versus even-tempered); and *openness to experience* (imaginative, curious, and creative versus shallow and imperceptive; McCrae & Costa Jr., 2008). On each dimension, people are rated high, low, or somewhere in between.

Cross-cultural research establishes the relatively universal nature of the five dimensions—although there are individual differences across cultures (Carlo, Knight, Roesch et al., 2014; Valchev et al., 2013). One study examined the Big Five traits in high school students across six different cultures and found, for example, that young adults in Turkey reported higher levels of conscientiousness and extraversion than those in China, whereas students in Taiwan reported about as much openness as those in Slovenia (Vazsonyi et al., 2015). A number of researchers are trying to determine whether people with personality disorders can also be rated in a meaningful way along the Big Five dimensions and whether the system will help us better understand these disorders (Bagby et al., 2005; Costa & McCrae, 2013), as outlined in Table 13.1.

PERSONALITY DISORDER CLUSTERS

The *DSM-5* divides the personality disorders into three groups, or "clusters"; this will probably continue until a strong scientific basis is established for viewing them differently (American Psychiatric Association, 2013). The cluster division is based on resemblance (see Table 13.1). Cluster A is called the "odd" or "eccentric" cluster; it includes paranoid, schizoid, and schizotypal personality disorders. Cluster B is the "dramatic," "emotional," or "erratic" cluster; it consists of antisocial, borderline, histrionic, and narcissistic personality disorders. Montréal researchers Karl Looper and Joel Paris (2000) have found that all four disorders in this cluster are characterized by elevated impulsivity. Cluster C is the "anxious" or "fearful" cluster; it includes avoidant, dependent, and obsessive-compulsive personality disorders. Research by Michael Bagby and his colleagues in Toronto (Bagby et al., 1993) and by Birendra Sinha and David Watson (2004) in Edmonton supports the existence of these three clusters. More recent work shows, however, that the proposed three-cluster

TABLE 13.1 | Relationship between Each Personality Disorder and Characteristics of the Five-Factor Model of Personality

Disorder	N	E	O	A	C
Cluster A					
Paranoid		low	low	low*	
Schizoid		low*			
Schizotypal	high*	low*	high*		
Cluster B					
Borderline	high*	high		low	low
Narcissistic	high	high		low*	high
Histrionic	high*	high*	high*		low
Antisocial				low*	low*
Cluster C					
Dependent	high*			high*	
Avoidant	high*	low*			
Obsessive-compulsive	high	low	low		high*

Five-Factor Model Personality Trait (column group header above N, E, O, A, C)

Notes: N = neuroticism, E = extraversion, O = openness to experience, A = agreeableness, C = conscientiousness. Asterisks indicate defining features of a given personality disorder; otherwise features can be considered associated features. Blank spaces indicate that a given trait is not relevant to the personality disorder in question.

Source: Adapted from Widiger et al. (1994).

structure holds only when the personality disorders are assessed by clinicians, and not when they are assessed via patient self-reports (Yang et al., 2002). We follow this three-cluster order in our review.

STATISTICS AND DEVELOPMENT

Data on the prevalence of personality disorders in Canada are lacking, so we report on surveys conducted in the United States and elsewhere (see Table 13.2). The Canadian Institute for Health Information (CIHI, 2019), however, records information on hospitalization as a function of different psychological disorders in Canada. For 2017–2018, in general hospitals, 5.6 percent of patients discharged with a mental health diagnosis had a personality disorder. This was the second-lowest rate, after anxiety disorders at 4.4 percent, and far below the highest: mood disorders at 28.4 percent. In psychiatric hospitals, 7.8 percent of discharged patients had a personality disorder, with the lowest rate being again anxiety disorders at 2.0 percent, and the highest this time being schizophrenia and other psychotic disorders at 31.4 percent.

An impressive survey of over 40 000 American adults (Trull et al., 2010) found a prevalence of any *DSM-IV-TR* personality disorder to be 9.1 percent (2.1 percent for any disorders in Cluster A, 5.5 percent for any disorders in Cluster B, and 2.3 percent for any disorders in Cluster C). All ten personality disorders were associated with substance use problems. Having any of the ten diagnoses was associated with more suicide attempts, more trouble at work, being separated or divorced, having problems with friends and relatives, and having problems with the law. In a review of studies worldwide, Quirk et al. (2016) found that Clusters A and B diagnoses were associated with various physical diseases, such as cardiovascular diseases and arthritis. Clearly, people diagnosed with personality disorders experience significant life challenges.

In another U.S. survey (Lenzenweger et al., 2007), this time of nearly 10 000 adults, the prevalence of any *DSM-IV-TR* personality disorders was 11.9 percent (6.2 percent for Cluster A, 2.3 percent for Cluster B, and 6.8 percent for Cluster C). As you can see, numbers can vary from study to study, but both major surveys show personality disorders to be quite prevalent (at around 10 percent). In the Lenzenweger et al. (2007) survey, all personality disorders were comorbid with most other types of psychological disorders.

The prevalence of personality disorders varies across countries. Winsper et al. (2019) reported a worldwide prevalence of 7.8 percent, with some countries having near zero prevalence (e.g., China) and others having a prevalence of near one in five (e.g., Australia). Winsper et al. found that, overall, high-income countries had higher prevalences of personality disorders, for reasons that are not quite clear yet.

Personality disorders were once thought to originate in childhood or adolescence and continue into the adult years (Cloninger & Svakic, 2009). More sophisticated analyses suggest that personality disorders can remit over time; however, they may be replaced by other personality disorders (Torgersen, 2012; Zanarini et al., 2014). In other words, a person could receive a diagnosis of one personality disorder at one point in time but years later no longer meet the criteria for his or her original problem and now have characteristics of a second (or third) personality disorder. Our relative lack of information about such important features of personality disorders as their developmental course is a repeating theme. The gaps in our knowledge of the course of about half these disorders are visible in Table 13.2. One reason for this dearth of research is that many individuals do not seek treatment in the early developmental phases of their disorder, but only after years of distress. This delay makes it difficult to study people with personality disorders from the beginning, although a few research studies have helped us understand the development of several disorders (Kasen et al., 1999; Hecht et al., 2014).

People with borderline personality disorder are characterized by their volatile and unstable relationships; they tend to have persistent problems in early adulthood, with frequent hospitalizations, unstable personal relationships, depression, and suicidal gestures. Suicide attempts are extremely common, affecting more than 80 percent of individuals in some studies (e.g., Soloff et al., 2000), though only about 10 percent of these attempts are completed (Paris, 2014). On the bright side, their symptoms gradually improve if they survive into their 30s (Zanarini et al., 2014), although seniors may still experience higher than average interpersonal difficulties (Powers et al., 2013). People with

maureen rigdon/Shutterstock.com

▲ Personality disorders tend to begin in childhood.

antisocial personality disorder display a characteristic disregard for the rights and feelings of others; they tend to continue their destructive behaviours of lying and manipulation through adulthood. Fortunately, some tend to "burn out" in middle adulthood, reflected in a decline in the prevalence of antisocial personality disorder across the lifespan (Vachon et al., 2013). As a group, however, the problems of people with personality disorders continue, as shown when researchers follow their progress over the years (Torgersen, 2012).

GENDER DIFFERENCES

As shown in Table 13.2, some personality disorders are more common in one gender than the other. Not all surveys obtain the same gender differences, however, so readers should not make too much of these results. Men tend to be diagnosed with personality disorders more often than women overall (10.3 percent versus 8.0 percent in the Trull et al., 2010 study), and especially antisocial personality disorder. A higher prevalence is seen among women for Cluster C disorders, but the gender difference is not large. The largest gender difference for women is borderline personality disorder in most studies.

Do the gender disparities indicate differences between men and women in certain basic genetic or sociocultural experience, or do they represent biases on the part of the clinicians who make the diagnoses? Take, for example, a study by Ford and Widiger (1989), who sent fictitious case histories to clinical psychologists for diagnosis. One case described a person with *antisocial personality disorder*, which is characterized by irresponsible and reckless behaviour and usually diagnosed in males; the other case described a person with *histrionic personality disorder*, which is characterized by excessive emotionality and attention seeking and more often diagnosed in females. The patient was identified as

TABLE 13.2 | Statistics and Development of Personality Disorders

Disorder	Prevalence*	Gender Differences*	Course
Paranoid personality disorder	1.9%	F > M	Insufficient information
Schizoid personality disorder	0.6%	M > F	Insufficient information
Schizotypal personality disorder	0.6%	M = F	Chronic: some go on to develop schizophrenia
Antisocial personality disorder	3.8%	M > F	May dissipate after age 40 (Hare et al., 1988)
Borderline personality disorder	2.7 %	F > M	Symptoms gradually improve if individuals survive into their 30s (Dulit et al., 1993)
Histrionic personality disorder	0.3%	F > M	Chronic
Narcissistic personality disorder	1.0%	M > F	May improve over time (Cooper & Ronningstam, 1992; Gunderson et al., 1991)
Avoidant personality disorder	1.2%	F > M	Insufficient information
Dependent personality disorder	0.3%	F > M	Insufficient information
Obsessive-compulsive personality disorder	1.9%	F > M	Insufficient information

*Based on a survey of 40 000 American adults (Trull et al., 2010).
Source: Population data and gender data reported in "Epidemiology," by S. Torgersen, in T. A. Widiger (Ed.), *The Oxford Handbook of Personality Disorders* (pp. 186–205), 2012, Oxford University Press.

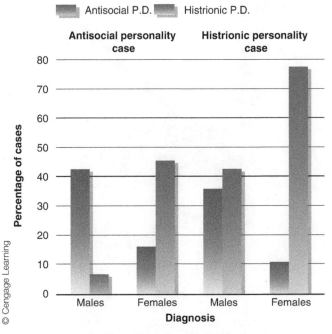

FIGURE 13.1 | Gender bias in diagnosing personality disorders. Data are shown for the percentage of cases clinicians rated as antisocial personality disorder or histrionic personality disorder, depending on whether the case was described as a male or a female.

Source: Adapted from "A Description of the DSM-III-R and DSM-IV Personality Disorders with the Five-Factor Model of Personality," by Widiger, Trull, Clarkin, Sanderson, and Costa, *Personality Disorders and the Five-Factor Model of Personality*, 2nd edition by Paul T. Costa and Thomas A. Widiger (Eds). © 2002 by the American Psychological Association.

male in some versions and as female in others, although everything else was identical. As the graph in ■ Figure 13.1 shows, when the antisocial personality disorder case was labelled male, most psychologists gave the correct diagnosis. When the same case was labelled female, however, most psychologists diagnosed it as histrionic personality disorder rather than antisocial personality disorder. This finding of an underdiagnosis of antisocial personality disorder in female clients was replicated in a similar study conducted in Toronto with psychiatry residents (Belitsky et al., 1996). In the original Ford and Widiger study, being labelled a woman increased the likelihood of a diagnosis of histrionic personality disorder.

Gender differences in diagnoses have been criticized by several authors. For example, some have argued that histrionic personality disorder, like several of the other personality disorders, is biased against females. Many of the features of histrionic personality disorder, such as overdramatization, vanity, seductiveness, and overconcern with physical appearance, are characteristic of the Western "stereotypical female" (Kaplan, 1983). This disorder may simply be the embodiment of extremely "feminine" traits (Chodoff, 1982); branding such an individual as having a mental illness, according to Kaplan, reflects society's inherent bias against females. Interestingly, the "macho" personality (Mosher & Sirkin, 1984; Pantony & Caplan, 1991), in which the individual possesses stereotypically masculine traits, is nowhere to be found in the *DSM*. What do you think the sex ratio would be for people diagnosed with this "personality disorder"?

Remember, however, that just because certain disorders are observed more in men or in women doesn't necessarily indicate bias (Lilienfeld et al., 1986). And when it is present, bias can occur at different stages of the diagnostic process. The criteria for the disorder may themselves be biased (*criterion gender bias*), or the assessment measures and the way they are used may be biased (*assessment gender bias*; Widiger & Spitzer, 1991). In general, the criteria themselves do not appear to have strong gender bias (Jane et al., 2007), although there may be some tendency for clinicians to have their own bias when using the criteria and therefore diagnose males and females differently (Oltmanns & Powers, 2012). As studies continue, researchers will try to make the diagnosis of personality disorders more accurate with respect to gender and more useful to clinicians.

COMORBIDITY

A major concern with the personality disorders is that people tend to be diagnosed with more than one. The term *comorbidity* historically describes the condition in which a person has multiple diseases (Caron & Rutter, 1991). A fair amount of disagreement exists about whether the term should be used with psychological disorders because of the frequent overlap of different disorders (e.g., Nurnberg et al., 1991). In just one example, Morey (1988) conducted a study of 291 persons who were diagnosed with personality disorder and found considerable overlap. In the far left column of Table 13.3 is the primary diagnosis, and across the table are the percentages of people who also meet the criteria for other disorders. For example, a person identified with borderline personality disorder also has a 32 percent likelihood (i.e., almost a one in three chance) of fitting the definition of another supposedly different personality disorder—paranoid personality disorder (Grove & Tellegen, 1991).

Do people really tend to have more than one personality disorder? Are the ways we define these disorders inaccurate, and do we need to improve our definitions so they do not overlap? Or did we divide the disorders in the wrong way to begin with and need to rethink the categories? Complicating this issue is the phenomenon that people will change diagnoses over time (Torgersen, 2012). Such questions about comorbidity are just a few of the important issues faced by researchers who study personality disorders.

CLUSTER A DISORDERS

PARANOID PERSONALITY DISORDER

Although it is probably very adaptive to be a little wary of other people and their motives, being too distrustful can interfere with making friends, working with others, and getting through daily interactions in a functional way. People with **paranoid personality disorder** are excessively mistrustful and suspicious of others, without any justification. They assume other people are out to harm or trick them, and therefore they tend not to confide in others. Consider the case of Jake.

▲ Gender bias may affect the diagnosis of clinicians who associate certain behavioural characteristics with one sex or the other.

TABLE 13.3 | Diagnostic Overlap of Personality Disorders

Odds Ratio* of People Qualifying for Other Personality Disorder Diagnoses										
Diagnosis	Paranoid	Schizoid	Schizotypal	Antisocial	Borderline	Histrionic	Narcissistic	Avoidant	Dependent	Obsessive-Compulsive
Paranoid		2.1	37.3*	2.6	12.3*	0.9	8.7*	4.0*	0.9	5.2*
Schizoid	2.1		19.2	1.1	2.0	3.9	1.7	12.3*	2.9	5.5*
Schizotypal	37.3*	19.2		2.7	15.2*	9.4	11.0	3.9*	7.0	7.1
Antisocial	2.6	1.1	2.7		9.5*	8.1*	14.0*	0.9	5.6	0.2
Borderline	12.3*	2.0	15.2*	9.5*		2.8	7.1*	2.5*	7.3*	2.0
Histrionic	0.9	3.9	9.4	8.1*	2.8		13.2	0.3	9.5	1.3
Narcissistic	8.7*	1.7	11.0	14.0*	7.1*	13.2*		0.3	4.0	3.7*
Avoidant	4.0*	12.3*	3.9*	0.9	2.5*	0.3	0.3		2.0	2.7
Dependent	0.9	2.9	7.0	5.6	7.3*	9.5	4.0	2.0		0.9
Obsessive-compulsive	5.2*	5.5*	7.1	0.2	2.0	1.3	2.0	2.7	0.9	

*The "odds ratio" indicates how likely it is that a person would have both disorders. The odds ratios with an asterisk (*) indicate that, statistically, people are likely to be diagnosed with both disorders—with a higher number meaning people are more likely to have both. Some higher odds ratios are not statistically significant because the number of people with the disorder in this study was relatively small.

Source: Reprinted, with permission, from Zimmerman, M., Rothschild, L., & Chelminski, I. (2005). The prevalence of DSM-IV personality disorders in psychiatric outpatients. *American Journal of Psychiatry*, 162, 1911–1918. Reprinted with permission from the American Journal of Psychiatry (Copyright © 2005). American Psychiatric Association. All Rights Reserved.

JAKE | Victim of Conspiracy?

Jake grew up in a middle-class neighbourhood, and although he never got into serious trouble, he had a reputation in high school for arguing with teachers and classmates. After high school he enrolled in the local community college but flunked out after the first year. Jake's lack of success in school was in part attributable to his failure to take responsibility for his poor grades. He began to develop conspiracy theories about fellow students and professors, believing they worked together to see him fail. Jake bounced from job to job, each time complaining that his employer was spying on him. His parents brought him to a psychologist, and he was diagnosed with paranoid personality disorder.

Clinical Description

The defining characteristic of people with paranoid personality disorder is a pervasive unjustified distrust. Certainly, there may be times when someone is deceitful and out to get you; however, people with paranoid personality disorder are suspicious in situations in which most other people would agree that their suspicions are unfounded. Even events that have nothing to do with them are interpreted as personal attacks. These people would view a neighbour's barking dog or a delayed airline flight as a deliberate attempt to annoy them. Unfortunately, such mistrust often extends to people close to them and makes meaningful relationships very difficult. Imagine what a lonely existence this must be. Suspiciousness and mistrust can show themselves in many ways. People with paranoid personality disorder may be argumentative, may complain, or may be quiet, but they are obviously hostile toward others. These individuals are very sensitive to criticism and have an excessive need for autonomy. Having this disorder increases the risk of suicide attempts and violent behaviour, and is related to having a poor overall quality of life (Hopwood & Thomas, 2012). The *DSM-5* criteria are outlined in DSM Table 13.1.

Paranoid personality disorder bears relationship to two disorders we will discuss in more detail in Chapter 14: (1) the paranoid type of schizophrenia and (2) delusional disorder. Both of the latter disorders involve delusions—persistent beliefs that are out of touch with reality. Although individuals with paranoid personality disorder are very suspicious of others, their suspiciousness does not reach delusional proportions. Another difference between the paranoid type of schizophrenia and paranoid personality disorder is that the former also involves other psychotic symptoms like hallucinations (e.g., hearing voices), whereas paranoid personality disorder does not (see Chapter 14).

Causes

Evidence for biological contributions to paranoid personality disorder is limited. Some research suggests the disorder may be slightly more common among the relatives of people who have schizophrenia, although the association does not seem to be strong (Tienari et al., 2003). Genetics appears to have a strong role

---

A. A pervasive distrust and suspiciousness of others such that their motives are interpreted as malevolent, beginning by early adulthood and present in a variety of contexts, as indicated by four (or more) of the following:

1. Suspects, without sufficient basis, that others are exploiting, harming, or deceiving him or her.
2. Is preoccupied with unjustified doubts about the loyalty or trustworthiness of friends or associates.
3. Is reluctant to confide in others because of unwarranted fear that the information will be used maliciously against him or her.
4. Reads hidden demeaning or threatening meanings into benign remarks or events.
5. Persistently bears grudges (i.e., is unforgiving of insults, injuries, or slights).
6. Perceives attacks on his or her character or reputation that are not apparent to others and is quick to react angrily or to counterattack.
7. Has recurrent suspicions, without justification, regarding fidelity of spouse or sexual partner.

B. Does not occur exclusively during the course of schizophrenia, a bipolar disorder or depressive disorder with psychotic features, or another psychotic disorder and is not attributable to the physiological effects of another medical condition.

Note: If criteria are met prior to the onset of schizophrenia, add "premorbid," i.e., "paranoid personality disorder (premorbid)."

in paranoid personality disorder (Kendler et al., 2015). As you will see later with the other odd or eccentric personality disorders in Cluster A, there seems to be some relationship with schizophrenia (Bolinskey et al., 2014), causing some to suggest eliminating it as a separate disorder from the *DSM* (Triebwasser et al., 2012).

Psychological contributions to this disorder are even less certain, although some interesting speculations have been made. Retrospective research—asking people with this disorder to recall events from their childhood—suggests that early mistreatment or traumatic childhood experiences may play a role in the development of paranoid personality disorder (Iacovino, 2014). Caution is warranted when interpreting these results because, clearly, there may be strong bias in the recall of these individuals, who are already prone to viewing the world as a threat.

Some psychologists point directly to the thoughts (also referred to as "schemas") of people with paranoid personality disorder as a way of explaining their behaviour. One view is that people with this disorder have the following basic mistaken assumptions about others: "People are malevolent and deceptive," "They'll attack you if they get the chance," and "You can be OK only if you stay on your toes" (Lobbestael & Arntz, 2012). This is a maladaptive way to view the world, yet it seems to pervade every aspect of the lives of these individuals. Although we don't know why they develop these perceptions, some speculation is that the roots are in their early upbringing. Their parents may teach them to be careful about making mistakes and to impress on them that they are different from other people. This vigilance causes them to see signs that other people are deceptive and malicious (Triebwasser, 2013). It is certainly true that people are not always benevolent and sincere, and our interactions are sometimes ambiguous enough to make other people's intentions unclear. Looking too closely at what other people say and do can sometimes lead to misinterpretation.

Cultural factors have also been implicated in paranoid personality disorder. Certain groups of people such as prisoners, refugees, people with hearing impairments, and the elderly are thought to be particularly susceptible because of their unique experiences (Iacovino et al., 2014; Raza, DeMarce, et al., 2014; Ryder et al., 2015). Imagine how you might view other people if you were an immigrant who had difficulty with the language and the customs of your new culture. Such innocuous things as other people laughing or talking quietly might be interpreted as somehow directed at you. We have seen how someone could misinterpret ambiguous situations as malevolent. Therefore, cognitive and cultural factors may interact to produce the suspiciousness observed in some people with paranoid personality disorder.

Treatment

Because people with paranoid personality disorder are mistrustful of everyone, they are unlikely to seek professional help when they need it, and they have difficulty developing the trusting relationships necessary for successful therapy (Sarkar & Adshead, 2012; Skodol & Gunderson, 2008). Establishing a meaningful therapeutic alliance between the client and the therapist therefore becomes an important first step (Bender, 2005). When they do seek therapy, the trigger is usually a crisis in their lives or other problems such as anxiety or depression, and not necessarily their personality disorder (Kelly et al., 2007).

Therapists try to provide an atmosphere conducive to developing a sense of trust (Bender, 2005). They often use cognitive therapy to counter the person's mistaken assumptions about others, focusing on changing the person's beliefs that all people are malevolent and most people cannot be trusted (Beck et al., 2015). Be forewarned, however, that to date there are no confirmed demonstrations that any form of treatment can significantly improve the lives of people with paranoid personality disorder (Bateman et al., 2015). Nonetheless, a review of the literature by Québec researcher Stephane Bouchard and his colleagues concluded that cognitive restructuring could be helpful in reducing paranoid beliefs (Bouchard et al., 1996). An Australian survey of mental health professionals indicated that only 11 percent of therapists who treat paranoid personality disorder thought these individuals would continue in therapy long enough to be helped (Quality Assurance Project, 1990).

SCHIZOID PERSONALITY DISORDER

Do you know someone who is a "loner"? Someone who would choose a solitary walk over an invitation to a party? A person who comes to class alone, sits alone, and leaves alone? Now, magnify this preference for isolation many times over and you can begin to grasp the impact of **schizoid personality disorder**. People with this personality disorder show a pattern of detachment from social relationships and a very limited range of emotions in inter-

personal situations. They seem aloof, cold, and indifferent to other people (see DSM Table 13.2). The term *schizoid* is relatively old, having been used by Bleuler (1924) to describe people who have a tendency to turn inward and away from the outside world. These people were said to lack emotional expressiveness and pursued vague interests. Consider the case of Mr. Z.

DSM-5 | **Table 13.2** Diagnostic Criteria for Schizoid Personality Disorder

A. A pervasive pattern of detachment from social relationships and a restricted range of expression of emotions in interpersonal settings, beginning by early adulthood and present in a variety of contexts, as indicated by four (or more) of the following:

1. Neither desires nor enjoys close relationships, including being part of a family.
2. Almost always chooses solitary activities.
3. Has little, if any, interest in having sexual experiences with another person.
4. Takes pleasure in few, if any, activities.
5. Lacks close friends or confidants other than first-degree relatives.
6. Appears indifferent to the praise or criticism of others.
7. Shows emotional coldness, detachment, or flattened affectivity.

B. Does not occur exclusively during the course of schizophrenia, a bipolar disorder or depressive disorder with psychotic features, another psychotic disorder, or autism spectrum disorder and is not attributable to the physiological effects of another medical condition.

Note: If criteria are met prior to the onset of schizophrenia, add "premorbid," *i.e.*, "*schizoid personality disorder (premorbid)*."

Source: Reprinted with permission from the *Diagnostic and Statistical Manual of Mental Disorders*, Fifth Edition (Copyright © 2013). American Psychiatric Association. All Rights Reserved.

MR. Z. | *All on His Own*

A 39-year-old scientist was referred after he returned from being stationed in Baffin Island where he had stopped cooperating with others, had withdrawn to his room, and begun drinking on his own. Mr. Z. was orphaned at age four, raised by an aunt until nine, and subsequently looked after by an aloof housekeeper. At university he excelled at physics, but chess was his only contact with others. Throughout his subsequent life, he made no close friends and engaged primarily in solitary activities. Until his move to Baffin Island, he had been quite successful in his research work in physics. He was now, some months after his return, drinking at least a bottle of Schnapps each day and his work had continued to deteriorate. He presented as self-contained and unobtrusive, and he was difficult to engage effectively. He was at a loss to explain his colleagues' anger at his aloofness in Baffin Island and appeared indifferent to their opinion of him. He did not appear to require any interpersonal relations.

Source: Quality Assurance Project, "Treatment Outlines for Paranoid, Schizotypal and Schizoid Personality Disorders," *Australian & New Zealand Journal of Psychiatry*, 24(3), 339–350. © 1990, Sage Publications.

As described in the book *The Stranger in the Woods* (Finkel, 2017), Christopher Knight spent 27 years living in a tent in a forest and not seeing anyone. He did it by choice and greatly missed his time there after he returned to society (he was caught stealing food). Although he has not been formally diagnosed, his choice and description of his life is consistent with some of the features of schizoid personality disorder.

Clinical Description

Individuals with schizoid personality disorder seem neither to desire nor enjoy closeness with others, including romantic or sexual relationships. As a result they appear cold, aloof, and detached (Loza & Hanna, 2006) and do not seem affected by praise or criticism. Unfortunately, homelessness appears to be prevalent among people with this personality disorder, perhaps as a result of their lack of close friendships and lack of dissatisfaction about not having a relationship with another person (Rouff, 2000; Angstman & Rasmussén, 2011).

The social deficiencies of people with schizoid personality disorder are similar to those of people with paranoid personality disorder, although the deficiencies are extreme. As Beck and Freeman (1990) put it, they "consider themselves to be observers rather than participants in the world around them" (p. 125). They do not seem to have the very unusual thought processes that characterize the other disorders in Cluster A (Kalus et al., 1993). For example, people with paranoid and schizotypal personality disorders often have ideas of reference, mistaken beliefs that meaningless events relate just to them. In contrast, those with schizoid personality disorder share the social isolation, poor rapport, and constricted affect (showing neither positive nor negative emotion) seen in people with paranoid personality disorder. We see in Chapter 14 that this distinction among psychotic-like symptoms is important to understanding people with schizophrenia, some of whom show the "positive" symptoms (actively unusual behaviours, such as ideas of reference) and others only the "negative" symptoms (the more passive manifestations of social isolation or poor rapport with others).

Causes

Extensive research on the genetic, neurobiological, and psychosocial contributions to schizoid personality disorder remains to be conducted. In fact, very little empirical research has been published on the nature and causes of this disorder (Triebwasser et al., 2012). Childhood shyness is reported as a precursor to later adult schizoid personality disorder. It may be that this personality trait is inherited and serves as an important determinant in the development of this disorder. Abuse and neglect in childhood are also reported among individuals with this disorder (Lobbestael et al., 2010; Carr et al., 2015). Research over the past several decades point to biological causes of autism (a disorder we discuss in more detail in Chapter 15), and research demonstrates significant overlap in the occurrence of autism spectrum disorder and schizoid personality disorder (Lugnegård et al., 2012; Hummelen et al., 2014; Coolidge et al., 2013; Vannucchi et al., 2014). It is possible that a biological dysfunction found in both autism and schizoid personality disorder combines with early learning or early problems with interpersonal relationships to produce the social deficits that define schizoid personality disorder (Hopwood & Thomas, 2012). For example, research on the neurochemical dopamine suggests that people with a lower density of dopamine receptors scored higher on a measure of detachment (Farde et al., 1997). It may be that dopamine (which seems to be involved with schizophrenia as well) may contribute to the social aloofness of people with schizoid personality disorder.

Treatment

It is rare for a person with this disorder to request treatment except in response to a crisis such as extreme depression or losing a job (Kelly et al., 2007). Therapists often begin treatment by pointing out the value in social relationships. The person with the disorder may even need to be taught the emotions felt by others to learn empathy (Skodol & Gunderson, 2008). Because their social skills were never established or have atrophied through lack of use, people with schizoid personality disorder often receive social skills training. The therapist takes the part of a friend or significant other in a technique known as *role-playing* and helps the patient practise establishing and maintaining social relationships (Skodol & Gunderson, 2008). This type of social skills training is helped by identifying a social network—a person or people who will be supportive (Bender, 2005). Outcome research on this type of approach is unfortunately quite limited, so we must be cautious in evaluating the effectiveness of treatment for people with schizoid personality disorder.

SCHIZOTYPAL PERSONALITY DISORDER

People with **schizotypal personality disorder** are typically socially isolated, like those with schizoid personality disorder. In addition, they also behave in ways that would seem unusual to many of us, and they tend to be suspicious and to have odd beliefs (Chemerenski et al., 2013; Rosell et al., 2014). Schizotypal personality disorder is considered by some to be on a continuum (i.e., on the same spectrum) with schizophrenia—the severe disorder we discuss in Chapter 14—but without some of the more debilitating symptoms, such as hallucinations and delusions. In fact, because of this close connection, the *DSM-5* includes this disorder under both the heading of a personality disorder and under the heading of a schizophrenia spectrum disorder (American Psychiatric Association, 2013). Consider the case of Mr. S.

MR. S. | *Man with a Mission*

Mr. S. was a 35-year-old chronically unemployed man who had been referred by a physician because of a vitamin deficiency. This problem was thought to have eventuated because Mr. S. avoided any foods that "could have been contaminated by a machine." He had begun to develop alternative ideas about diet in his 20s and soon left his family and began to study an Eastern religion. "It opened my third eye; corruption is all about," he said.

He lived by himself on a small farm in British Columbia, attempting to grow his own food, bartering for items he could not grow himself. He spent his days and evenings researching the origins and mechanisms of food contamination and, because of this knowledge, had developed a small band that followed his ideas. He had never married and maintained little contact with his family: "I've never been close to my father. I'm a vegetarian."

He said he intended to take a herbalism course to improve his diet before returning to his life on the farm. He had refused medication from the physician and became uneasy when the facts of his deficiency were discussed with him.

Source: Quality Assurance Project, "Treatment Outlines for Paranoid, Schizotypal and Schizoid Personality Disorders," *Australian & New Zealand Journal of Psychiatry*, 24(3), 339–350. © 1990, Sage Publications.

Clinical Description

People given a diagnosis of schizotypal personality disorder have psychotic-like (but not psychotic) symptoms (such as believing everything relates to them personally), social deficits, and sometimes cognitive impairments or paranoia (Kwapil & Barrantes-Vidal, 2012). These individuals are often considered odd or bizarre by others because of how they relate to other people, how they think and behave, and even how they dress. They have *ideas of reference*—for example, they may believe that somehow everyone on a passing city bus is talking about them, yet they may be able to acknowledge this is unlikely (Rosell et al., 2014). Again, as we see in Chapter 14, some people with schizophrenia also have ideas of reference, but they are usually not able to test reality or see the illogic of their ideas.

Individuals with schizotypal personality disorder also have odd beliefs or engage in "magical thinking," believing, for example, that they are clairvoyant or telepathic (Furnham & Crump, 2014). In addition, they report unusual perceptual experiences, including such *illusions* as feeling the presence of another person when they are alone. Notice the subtle but important difference between *feeling* as if someone else is in the room, and the more extreme perceptual distortion in people with schizophrenia who might report there is someone else in the room when there isn't. Only a small proportion of individuals with schizotypal personality disorder go on to develop schizophrenia (Wolff et al., 1991). Unlike people who simply have unusual interests or beliefs, those with schizotypal personality disorder tend to be suspicious and have paranoid thoughts, express little emotion, and may dress or behave in unusual ways (e.g., wear many layers of clothing in the summertime or mumble to themselves; Chemerinski et al., 2013). Prospective research on children who later develop schizotypal

personality disorder found that they tend to be passive and unengaged and are hypersensitive to criticism (Olin et al., 1997; see DSM Table 13.3).

Because persons with schizotypal personality disorder often have beliefs around religious or spiritual themes (Bennett et al., 2013), clinicians must be aware that different cultural beliefs or practices may lead to a mistaken diagnosis of this disorder. For example, some people who practise certain religious rituals—such as speaking in tongues, practising voodoo, or mind reading—may do so with such obsessiveness as to make them seem extremely unusual, thus leading to a misdiagnosis (American Psychiatric Association, 2013). Mental health workers have to be particularly sensitive to cultural practices that may differ from their own and can distort their view of certain seemingly unusual behaviours.

Causes

Historically, the word *schizotype* was used to describe people who were predisposed to develop schizophrenia (Meehl, 1962; Rado, 1962). Schizotypal personality disorder is viewed by some to be one phenotype of a schizophrenia genotype. Recall that a *phenotype* is one way a person's genetics are expressed. Your *genotype* is the gene or genes that make up a particular disorder. Depending on a variety of other influences, however, the way you turn

DSM-5	**Table 13.3** Diagnostic Criteria for Schizotypal Personality Disorder

A. A pervasive pattern of social and interpersonal deficits marked by acute discomfort with, and reduced capacity for, close relationships, as well as by cognitive or perceptual distortions and eccentricities of behavior, beginning by early adulthood and present in a variety of contexts, as indicated by five (or more) of the following:

1. Ideas of reference (excluding delusions of reference).
2. Odd beliefs or magical thinking that influences behavior and is inconsistent with subcultural norms (e.g., superstitiousness, belief in clairvoyance, telepathy, or "sixth sense"; in children and adolescents, bizarre fantasies or preoccupations).
3. Unusual perceptual experiences, including bodily illusions.
4. Odd thinking and speech (e.g., vague, circumstantial, metaphorical, overelaborate, or stereotyped).
5. Suspiciousness or paranoid ideation.
6. Inappropriate or constricted affect.
7. Behavior or appearance that is odd, eccentric, or peculiar.
8. Lack of close friends or confidants other than first-degree relatives.
9. Excessive social anxiety that does not diminish with familiarity and tends to be associated with paranoid fears rather than negative judgments about self.

B. Does not occur exclusively during the course of schizophrenia, a bipolar disorder or depressive disorder with psychotic features, another psychotic disorder, or autism spectrum disorder.

Note: If criteria are met prior to the onset of schizophrenia, add "premorbid," e.g., "schizotypal personality disorder (premorbid)."

Source: Reprinted with permission from the *Diagnostic and Statistical Manual of Mental Disorders*, Fifth Edition (Copyright © 2013). American Psychiatric Association. All Rights Reserved.

out—your phenotype—may vary from other people's phenotype, even if they have a similar genetic makeup to yours. Some people are thought to have "schizophrenia genes" (the genotype) and yet, because of the relative lack of biological influences (e.g., prenatal illnesses) or environmental stresses (e.g., poverty, maltreatment), some will have the less severe schizotypal personality disorder (the phenotype).

The idea of a relationship between schizotypal personality disorder and schizophrenia arises in part from the way people with the disorders behave. Many characteristics of schizotypal personality disorder, including ideas of reference, illusions, and paranoid thinking, are similar but milder forms of behaviours observed among people with schizophrenia. Genetic research also seems to support a relationship. Family, twin, and adoption studies, largely conducted in Norway, have shown an increased prevalence of schizotypal personality disorder among relatives of people with schizophrenia who do not also have schizophrenia themselves (Siever & Davis, 2004). These studies also tell us, however, that the environment can strongly influence schizotypal personality disorder. For example, research from the United Kingdom suggests that a woman's exposure to influenza in pregnancy may increase the chance of schizotypal personality disorder in her children (Venables, 1996). It may be that a subgroup of people with schizotypal personality disorder has a similar genetic makeup when compared with people with schizophrenia.

Biological theories of schizotypal personality disorder are receiving empirical support. For example, cognitive assessment of persons with this disorder point to mild to moderate decrements in their ability to perform on tests involving memory and learning, suggesting some damage in the left hemisphere (Voglmaier et al., 2000). Research by Roger Graves, professor emeritus at the University of Victoria, suggests that abnormalities in semantic association abilities may contribute to the thinking oddities displayed by schizotypal individuals. Graves and his colleagues examined people with high levels of *magical ideation* (MI)—a thinking style similar to that of schizotypal patients. High-MI participants were found to consider unrelated words as more closely associated than low-MI participants. Thus, for schizotypal people, "loose associations" may not be loose after all (Mohr et al., 2001). Other research using magnetic resonance imaging (MRI) points to generalized brain abnormalities in patients with schizotypal personality disorder (Lener et al., 2015).

Treatment

People with schizotypal personality disorder who request clinical help often seek assistance for anxiety or depression (American Psychiatric Association, 2013). Relatedly, the presence of schizotypal personality disorder significantly increases the risk for developing major depressive disorder even years later (Skodol et al., 2011). Treatment includes some of the medical and psychological treatments for depression (Cloninger & Svakic, 2009; Mulder et al., 2009).

Controlled studies of attempts to treat groups of people with schizotypal personality disorder are few. There is now growing interest in treating this disorder, however, because it is being viewed as a precursor to schizophrenia (McClure et al., 2010). One study used a combination of approaches, including antipsychotic medication, community treatment (a team of support professionals providing therapeutic services), and social skills training, to treat the symptoms experienced by individuals with this disorder. Researchers found that this combination of approaches either reduced their symptoms or postponed the onset of later schizophrenia. The idea of treating younger persons who have symptoms of schizotypal personality disorder with some combination of antipsychotic medication, cognitive behaviour therapy and social skills training in order to avoid the onset of schizophrenia may prove to be a promising prevention strategy (Nordentoft et al., 2015; Graff et al., 2014; Correll et al., 2010; Weiser, 2011).

CLUSTER B DISORDERS

ANTISOCIAL PERSONALITY DISORDER

People with **antisocial personality disorder** are among the most dramatic of the individuals a clinician will see in a practice and are characterized as having a history of failing to comply with social norms. They perform actions most of us would find unacceptable, such as stealing from friends and family. They also tend to be irresponsible, impulsive, and deceitful (Widiger & Corbitt, 1995). Robert Hare (1993), a pioneer in the study of people with **psychopathy** (a group of persons with antisocial personality disorder), describes them as

> social predators who charm, manipulate, and ruthlessly plow their way through life, leaving a broad trail of broken hearts, shattered expectations, and empty wallets. Completely lacking in conscience and empathy, they selfishly take what they want and do as they please, violating social norms and expectations without the slightest sense of guilt or regret. (p. xi)

The Trull et al. (2010) population study reported a prevalence of 5.7 percent for adult males. New male inmates in the Correctional Service of Canada system have a much higher rate of antisocial personality disorder: 44 percent overall, 36 percent in Ontario, 54 percent in the Atlantic region, 40 percent in the Prairies, and 64 percent in the Pacific region (Beaudette et al., 2015).

Although first identified as a "medical" problem by Philippe Pinel at the start of the 19th century (1801/1962), descriptions of individuals with these antisocial tendencies can be found in ancient stone texts from Mesopotamia dating as far back as 670 BCE (Abdul-Hamid & Stein, 2012). Just who are these people with antisocial personality disorder? Consider the case of Ryan.

RYAN | *The Thrill Seeker*

I first met Ryan on his 17th birthday. Unfortunately, he was celebrating the event in a psychiatric hospital. He had been truant from school for several months and had gotten into some trouble; the local judge who heard his case had recommended psychiatric evaluation one more time, though Ryan had been hospitalized six previous times, all for problems related to drug use and truancy. He was a veteran of the system and already knew most of the staff. I interviewed him to assess why he was admitted this time and to recommend treatment.

My first impression was that Ryan was cooperative and pleasant. He pointed out a tattoo on his arm that he had made himself, saying that it was a "stupid" thing to have done and that he now regretted it. In fact, he regretted many things and was looking forward to moving on with his life. I later found out that he was never truly remorseful for anything.

Our second interview was quite different. During those 48 hours, Ryan had done several things that showed why he needed a great deal of help. The most serious incident involved a 15-year-old girl named Ann who attended class with Ryan in the hospital school. Ryan had told her that he was going to get himself discharged, get in trouble, and be sent to the same correctional facility Ann's father was in, where he would rape her father. Ryan's threat so upset Ann that she hit her teacher and several of the staff. When I spoke to Ryan about this, he smiled slightly and said he was bored and that it was fun to upset Ann. When I asked whether it bothered him that his behaviour might extend her stay in the hospital, he looked puzzled and said, "Why should it bother me? She's the one who'll have to stay in this hellhole!"

Just before Ryan's admittance, a teenager in his town was murdered. A group of teens went to the local graveyard at night to perform satanic rituals, and a young man was stabbed to death, apparently over a drug purchase. Ryan was in the group, although he did not stab the boy. He told me that they occasionally dug up graves to get skulls for their parties; not because they really believed in the devil, but because it was fun and it scared the younger kids. I asked, "What if this was the grave of someone you knew, a relative or a friend? Would it bother you that strangers were digging up the remains?" He shook his head. "They're dead, man; they don't care. Why should I?"

Ryan told me he loved PCP, or "angel dust," and that he would rather be "dusted" than anything else. He routinely made the two-hour trip to Toronto to buy drugs in a particularly dangerous neighbourhood. He denied that he was ever nervous. This wasn't machismo; he really seemed unconcerned.

Ryan made little progress. I discussed his future in family therapy sessions and we talked about his pattern of showing supposed regret and remorse, and then stealing money from his parents and going back onto the street. In fact, most of our discussions centred on trying to give his parents the courage to say no to him and not to believe his lies.

One evening, after many sessions, Ryan said he had seen the "error of his ways" and that he felt bad that he had hurt his parents. If they would only take him home this one last time, he would be the son he should have been all these years. His speech moved his parents to tears, and they looked at me gratefully as if to thank me

for curing their son. When Ryan finished talking, I smiled, applauded, told him it was the best performance I had ever seen. His parents turned on me in anger. Ryan paused for a second, then he too smiled and said, "It was worth a shot!" Ryan's parents were astounded that he had once again tricked them into believing him; he hadn't meant a word of what he had just said. Ryan was eventually discharged to a drug rehabilitation program. Within four weeks, he had convinced his parents to take him home, and within two days he had stolen all their cash and disappeared; he apparently went back to his friends and to drugs.

When he was in his 20s, after one of his many arrests for theft, Ryan was diagnosed as having antisocial personality disorder. His parents never summoned the courage to turn him in or refuse him money, and he continues to con them into providing him with a means of buying more drugs.

Clinical Description

Individuals with antisocial personality disorder tend to have long histories of violating the rights of others. They are often described as being aggressive because they take what they want, indifferent to the concerns of other people. Lying and cheating seem to be second nature to them, and often they appear unable to tell the difference between the truth and the lies they make up to further their own goals. They show no remorse or concern over the sometimes devastating effects of their actions. Substance abuse is common, occurring in 60 percent of people with antisocial personality disorder; this appears to be a lifelong pattern among these individuals, who are also at increased risk for abusing multiple substances (Skodol et al., 2014; Taylor & Lang, 2006). The long-term outcome for people with antisocial personality disorder is usually poor, regardless of gender (Colman et al., 2009). One longitudinal study, for example, found that antisocial boys were more than twice as likely to die an unnatural death (e.g., accident, suicide, homicide) as their non-antisocial peers, which may be attributed to factors such as alcohol abuse and poor self-care (e.g., reckless behaviour; Laub & Vaillant, 2000).

Antisocial personality disorder has had a number of names over the years. Philippe Pinel (1801/1962) identified what he called *manie sans delire* (mania without delirium) to describe people with unusual emotional responses and impulsive rages but no deficits in reasoning ability (Charland, 2010). Other labels have included moral insanity, egopathy, sociopathy, and psychopathy. There continues to be debate in the field about whether antisocial personality disorder and psychopathy really are two distinct disorders (Douglas et al., 2015; Wall, 2015; Werner, 2015; Anderson, 2014; Venables, 2014). The diagnostic criteria for antisocial personality disorder are more liberal than those for psychopathy because in Canadian prisons and secure hospitals, 50 to 80 percent of male offenders are diagnosed with antisocial personality disorder (see DSM Table 13.4), but only 15 to 25 percent are diagnosed as psychopaths (Hare, 2003).

Earlier versions of the *DSM* criteria for antisocial personality focused almost entirely on observable behaviours (e.g., "impulsively and repeatedly changes employment, residence, or sexual partners"). The framers of the previous *DSM* criteria felt that trying to assess a personality trait—for example, whether someone was manipulative—would be more difficult than determining whether the person engaged in certain behaviours, such as repeated fighting. The *DSM-5*, however, moved closer to the trait-based criteria and includes such language as deceitfulness, impulsivity, and lack of remorse). Unfortunately, research on identifying persons with antisocial personality disorder suggests that this new definition reduces the reliability of the diagnosis (Regier et al., 2013). Additional work will be needed to improve the reliability of this diagnosis while maintaining the core traits that characterize these individuals.

Some people with antisocial personality traits manage to not get in trouble with the law. What separates many in this group from those who get into trouble with the law may be IQ, along with other factors. In a prospective, longitudinal study, White, Moffit, and Silva (1989) followed almost 1000 children, beginning at age five, to see what predicted antisocial behaviour at age 15. They found that of the five-year-olds determined to be at high risk for later delinquent behaviour, 16 percent did indeed have run-ins with the law by the age of 15 and 84 percent did not. What distinguished these two groups? In general, the at-risk children with lower IQs were the ones who got in trouble. This finding suggests that having a higher IQ may help protect some people from developing more serious problems or may at least prevent them from being caught.

The presence of antisocial traits among the criminal population seems to have important implications for predicting their future criminal behaviour (Vitacco et al., 2014). One study conducted in British Columbia by psychologist James Ogloff and his colleagues found that criminals who scored high on a measure of psychopathy put in less effort and showed fewer improvements in a therapy program than did criminals who were not psychopaths (Ogloff, 1990). Other studies have shown that psychopathic criminals are more likely than nonpsychopathic criminals to repeat their criminal offences, especially those that are violent or sexual in nature (Langton et al., 2006; Nicholls et al., 2004; Ogloff, 2006; Olver & Wong, 2006; Valliant et al., 1999).

It is important to note the developmental nature of antisocial behaviours and traits. The *DSM-5* provides a separate diagnosis for children who engage in behaviours that violate society's norms: *conduct disorder* (CD; DSM Table 13.5). It provides for the designation of two subtypes: *childhood-onset type* (the onset of at least one criterion characteristic of CD before age ten) or *adolescent-onset type* (the absence of any criteria characteristic of CD before age ten). An additional subtype, new to the *DSM-5*, is called "with a callous-unemotional presentation" (Barry et al., 2012). This designation is an indication that the young person presents in a way that suggests personality characteristics similar to an adult with psychopathy. Some children with CD do feel remorseful about their behaviour, hence the qualifier "with a callous-unemotional presentation" to better differentiate these two groups.

12. Has stolen items of nontrivial value without confronting a victim (e.g., shoplifting, but without breaking and entering; forgery).

Serious Violations of Rules

13. Often stays out at night despite parental prohibitions, beginning before age 13 years.

14. Has run away from home overnight at least twice while living in the parental or parental surrogate home, or once without returning for a lengthy period.

15. Is often truant from school, beginning before age 13 years.

B. The disturbance in behavior causes clinically significant impairment in social, academic, or occupational functioning.

C. If the individual is age 18 years or older, criteria are not met for antisocial personality disorder.

Specify whether:

Childhood-onset type: Individuals show at least one symptom characteristic of conduct disorder prior to age 10 years.

Adolescent-onset type: Individuals show no symptom characteristic of conduct disorder prior to age 10 years.

Unspecified onset: Criteria for a diagnosis of conduct disorder are met, but there is not enough information available to determine whether the onset of the first symptom was before age 10 years.

Specify current severity:

Mild: Few if any conduct problems in excess of those required to make the diagnosis are present, and conduct problems cause relatively minor harm to others (e.g., lying, truancy, staying out after dark without permission, other rule breaking).

Moderate: The number of conduct problems and the effect on others are intermediate between those specified "mild" and those in "severe" (e.g., stealing without confronting a victim, vandalism).

Severe: Many conduct problems in excess of those required to make the diagnosis are present, or conduct problems cause considerable harm to others (e.g., forced sex, physical cruelty, use of a weapon, stealing while confronting a victim, breaking and entering).

Source: Reprinted with permission from the *Diagnostic and Statistical Manual of Mental Disorders*, Fifth Edition (Copyright © 2013). American Psychiatric Association. All Rights Reserved.

Many children with conduct disorder—most often diagnosed in boys—become juvenile offenders and tend to become involved with drugs (Durand, 2014). Ryan fits in this category. More important, the research of Richard Tremblay and his colleagues at the Université de Montréal supports a stable, lifelong pattern of antisocial behaviour in a subgroup of antisocial children. Specifically, a group of young children who display antisocial behaviour has been shown to likely continue these behaviours as the members grow older, while many others desist (Charlebois et al., 1993). Some more recent longitudinal research from Tremblay and his colleagues shows that personality traits distinguish boys who show this stable pattern of antisocial behaviour over time. The most important personality characteristic that distinguished the boys who showed a stable and persistent pattern of physical aggression, theft, and vandalism, was "psychoticism" (Carrasco et al., 2006). Not to be confused with the psychotic disorders, like schizophrenia discussed in Chapter 14, psychoticism is an older label for a personality characterized by high impulsivity and low empathy (Carrasco et al., 2006).

Data from long-term follow-up research indicate that many adults with antisocial personality disorder or psychopathy had CD as children (Davidson, 2014; Kasen et al., 2014; Robins, 1978; Salekin, 2006); the likelihood increases if the child has both CD and attention-deficit/hyper-activity disorder (Lynam, 1996). There is a tremendous amount of interest in studying a group that causes a great deal of harm to society. Research has been conducted for many years, and so we know a great deal more about antisocial personality disorder than about the other personality disorders.

Genetic Influences

Family, twin, and adoption studies all suggest a genetic influence on both antisocial personality disorder and criminality (Checknita et al., 2015; Delisi & Vaughn, 2015; Ficks & Waldman, 2014; Kendler et al., 2015; Reichborn-Kjennerud et al., 2015). For example, Crowe (1974) examined adopted-away children of mothers who were felons and compared them with adopted-away children of noncriminal mothers. All were separated from their mothers as newborns, minimizing the possibility that environmental factors from their biological families were responsible for the results. Crowe found that the adopted-away offspring of felons had significantly higher rates of arrests, conviction, and antisocial personality than did the adopted-away offspring of noncriminal mothers, which suggests at least some genetic influence on criminality and antisocial behaviour.

Crowe (1974) also found something else quite interesting, however: the adopted children of felons who themselves later became criminals had spent more time in interim orphanages than either the adopted children of felons who did not become criminals or the adopted children of noncriminal mothers. As Crowe points out, this suggests a gene–environment interaction; in other words, genetic factors may be important only in the presence of certain environmental influences (alternatively, certain environmental influences are important only in the presence of certain genetic predispositions). Genetic factors may present a vulnerability, but actual development of criminality may require environmental factors, such as a deficit in early, high-quality contact with parents or parent-surrogates.

This gene–environment interaction was demonstrated most clearly by Cadoret, Yates, Troughton, Woodworth, and Stewart (1995), who studied adopted children and their likelihood of developing conduct problems. If the children's biological parents had a history of antisocial personality disorder and their adoptive families exposed them to chronic stress through marital, legal, or psychiatric problems, the children were at greater risk for conduct problems. Again, research shows that genetic influence does not necessarily mean certain disorders are inevitable. Genetic research on CD points to an interaction between genetic and environmental influences, such as academic difficulty, peer problems, low family income, neglect and harsh discipline from parents (Beaver et al., 2011; Kendler et al., 2013; Knopik et al. 2014; Silberg et al., 2012).

Neurobiological Influences

A great deal of research has focused on neurobiological influences that may be specific to antisocial personality disorder. Some researchers have used neuropsychological tests to determine if there are specific cognitive deficits that might contribute

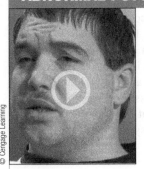

© Cengage Learning

Antisocial Personality Disorder: George

"I have hatred inside me. I don't care how much I beat somebody. . . . The more I hear somebody, the more anger I get inside me. . . . I used drugs when I was . . . probably nine or ten years old . . . smoked marijuana. . . . First time I drank some alcohol I think I was probably about three years old. . . . I assaulted a woman. . . . I had so much anger. . . . I was just like a bomb. . . . It's just ticking . . . and the way I'm going, that bomb was going to blow up in me. I wouldn't be able to get away from it . . . going to be a lot of people hurt. . . . I'm not going out without taking somebody with me."

Visit login.cengage.com to start using MindTap. Enter the Online Access Code from the card included with your text. If a code card is not provided, you can purchase instant access at Cengage.ca.

to antisocial personality disorder or psychopathy. For example, a study by Thierry Pham at the Pinel Institute in Montréal looked at the neuropsychological function of psychopaths and did find evidence of differences between the executive functions and attention-related abilities of incarcerated psychopaths and incarcerated nonpsychopathic patients. Specifically, Pham et al. (2003) found that, relative to others, psychopaths evidenced deficits in their abilities to maintain a plan and to inhibit irrelevant information. Similar results have been obtained by Blair et al. (2006), suggesting executive cognitive function deficits in psychopaths.

Two major neurobiological theories have attracted a great deal of attention in the area of antisocial personality and psychopathy: (1) the *underarousal hypothesis* and (2) the *fearlessness hypothesis*. According to the underarousal hypothesis, psychopaths have abnormally low levels of *cortical arousal* (Sylvers et al., 2009). There appears to be an inverted U-shaped relation between arousal and performance, the *Yerkes-Dodson* curve, which suggests that people with either very high or very low levels of arousal tend to experience negative affect and perform poorly in many situations, whereas individuals with intermediate levels of arousal tend to be relatively content and perform satisfactorily in most situations.

According to the underarousal hypothesis, the abnormally low levels of cortical arousal characteristic of psychopaths are the primary cause of their antisocial and risk-taking behaviours; they seek stimulation to boost their chronically low levels of arousal. This means that Ryan lied, took drugs, and dug up graves to achieve the same level of arousal we might get from talking on the phone with a good friend or watching television.

Low-frequency *theta* waves are found in brain wave measures of children and largely disappear in adulthood; their specific purpose is unknown. Evidence suggests that many psychopaths have excessive theta waves when they are awake. This finding led Robert Hare (1970) to generate another theory related to arousal levels, sometimes referred to as the *cortical immaturity*

hypothesis of psychopathy. Hare's theory holds that the cerebral cortex of psychopaths is at a relatively primitive stage of development. This hypothesis may help explain why the behaviour of psychopaths is often childlike and impulsive: their cerebral cortices, which play such a key role in the inhibition and control of impulses, may be insufficiently developed. But remember that many psychopaths are also quite planful, as indicated by the research of investigators like Adelle Forth and Stephen Porter (Brown & Forth, 1997; Woodworth & Porter, 2002).

The data on theta waves are open to an alternative and perhaps simpler explanation. Because theta waves also indicate states such as drowsiness or boredom, psychopaths' higher levels of theta waves may simply reflect their relative lack of concern regarding being hooked up to psychophysiological equipment! Picture yourself having your brain waves measured. You sit next to the intimidating polygraph machine, attached to a number of electrodes and wires. How will you react? As a nonpsychopath, you will probably feel anxiety and apprehension. In contrast, a psychopath, who is low in anxiety, will probably be bored, apathetic, and unresponsive. The excessive theta waves of psychopaths may simply reflect their relative absence of anxiety.

According to the *fearlessness hypothesis*, psychopaths possess a higher threshold for experiencing fear than most other individuals (Lykken, 1957, 1982). In other words, things that greatly frighten the rest of us have little or no effect on the psychopath (Syngelaki et al., 2013). Remember that Ryan was unafraid of going alone to dangerous neighbourhoods to buy drugs. According to proponents of this hypothesis, the fearlessness of the psychopath gives rise to all the other major features of the syndrome.

Early evidence for the fearlessness hypothesis came from a series of studies by Lykken (1957) using prison inmates. In one such study, Lykken constructed a classical conditioning task involving painful electric shock. His primary dependent measure was galvanic skin response (GSR), a reaction marked by an increase in palmar sweating and typically interpreted as a sign of autonomic

Gerhard Joren/LightRocket via Getty Images

▲ Many prisons allow visits between inmates and their children, partly to help reduce later problems in those children.

arousal. Lykken repeatedly paired a tone (the conditioned stimulus) with electric shock to the participants' fingertips (the unconditioned stimulus). Then, he presented the tone (conditioned stimulus) alone on multiple occasions. Nonpsychopaths showed a predictable and understandable pattern: when they heard the tone, their palms began to sweat, signalling that they expected the shock to come next. Moreover, their GSRs were quite slow to extinguish. In contrast, psychopaths showed a striking pattern: in most cases, they exhibited very weak GSRs to the tones alone, and their GSRs tended to extinguish rapidly.

This study by Lykken has important implications, suggesting that psychopaths may have difficulty associating certain cues or signals with impending punishment or danger, much as children are socialized to inhibit their behaviour. Most parents do not punish their children directly on every occasion for harmful or inappropriate behaviour, but instead rely on cues such as "no" or even a threatening stare to inhibit inappropriate behaviour. Largely because of classical conditioning, such cues tend to be quite effective substitutes for direct punishment. But if they have little or no impact on the prepsychopathic child, he or she will probably not acquire a well-developed capacity for impulse control.

Scientific research suggests the possibility that there may be a genetic component to one important aspect of psychopathy—aggression. Researchers in the Netherlands are cautiously optimistic after discovering that a gene mutation found in a large Dutch family may cause aggression (Brunner et al., 1993). Their study is important because it may tell us more about how genes affect behaviour. Brunner and his colleagues at the university hospital in Nijmegen have tracked the males of one family since 1978. Some of the men are prone to particularly violent outbursts. One raped his sister, two others were arsonists, and still another tried to run over his boss after being told his work wasn't good enough. None of the women in the family are given to violent outbursts.

The evidence for a genetic explanation of these behaviours is impressive. The observation that the condition occurs only in the males indicates the gene is probably on the X chromosome. Because men have only one X chromosome, any "bad" or mutated gene will show up. Because women have two X chromosomes, they tend to have a "good" or normal gene to balance the bad one.

To further narrow the location of the mutated gene, Brunner and his colleagues conducted a linkage study. As you may remember from Chapter 4, such studies try to identify marker genes that are inherited along with the gene you are trying to locate. Because we already know where the marker genes are, we can get a good idea of the approximate location of the mutated gene.

Based on the linkage study and biochemical analyses, Brunner and his fellow researchers believe the defect involves the gene that produces monoamine oxidase A, or MAOA. MAOA is an enzyme that helps break down neurotransmitters, specifically those involved in our fight-or-flight responses to threats and other stresses; they include serotonin, dopamine, and noradrenaline. If the MAOA enzyme isn't working properly, these neurotransmitters may build up and the affected people will have trouble handling stressful situations. For example, after the deaths of close relatives, the two arsonists in the Dutch family set fires.

A subsequent study confirmed that MAOA is deficient only in the affected males (Brunner et al., 1993). The possible genetic vulnerability to react violently, in combination with certain stressors, may result in aggression. But remember that this defect, to date, has been found only in one family. It is unlikely that all or even most aggressive behaviour will be traced to the same cause. Finally, social, economic, and cultural factors determine the type and severity of stresses. What this research suggests, however, is that just the right (or wrong) combination of genetic, neuro-biological, and psychosocial contributions came together to create devastating outcomes in one Dutch family.

A study by Caspi and colleagues (2002) in the United Kingdom found evidence suggesting that genetics may play a role in explaining why some males who are maltreated as children grow up to display antisocial behaviour, whereas others do not. There, researchers studied a large sample of male children from birth to adulthood. Once again, the genetic defect studied in this group involves the gene that produces the enzyme MAOA. Children who were maltreated but had the gene conferring high levels of MAOA expression (meaning they were less likely to have buildup of certain neurotransmitters during stress and thus better able to handle stress) were less likely to develop antisocial problems than maltreated children without this genotype. The authors claim that their findings may help explain why some but not all victims of abuse grow up to victimize others (Caspi et al., 2002). The findings also once again show how genetic and environmental factors can interact in the development of various forms of psychopathology—antisocial personality in this case (Caspi et al., 2002).

Psychological and Social Dimensions

What goes on in the mind of someone diagnosed with antisocial personality disorder or someone with the closely related condition called psychopathy? In one of several studies of how psychopaths process reward and punishment, Newman, Patterson, and Kosson (1987) set up a card-playing task on a computer; they provided five-cent rewards and fines for correct and incorrect answers to psychopathic and nonpsychopathic criminal offenders. The game was constructed so at first they were rewarded about 90 percent of the time and fined only about 10 percent of the time. Gradually, the odds changed until the probability of getting a reward was 0 percent. Despite feedback that reward was no longer forthcoming, the psychopaths continued to play and lose. As a result of this and other studies, the researchers hypothesized that once psychopaths set their sights on a reward goal, they are less likely than nonpsychopaths to be deterred despite signs that the goal is no longer achievable (Dvorak-Bertscha et al., 2009). Again, considering the reckless and daring behaviour of some psychopaths (robbing banks without a mask and being caught immediately), failure to abandon an unattainable goal fits the overall picture.

The influence of the family has also been of great interest to researchers. Gerald Patterson's influential work suggests that aggression in children may escalate in part because of their interactions with their parents (Granic & Patterson, 2006; Patterson, 1982). He found that the parents often give in to the problems displayed by their children. For example, parents ask their son to make his bed and he refuses. One parent yells at the boy. He yells back and becomes abusive. At some point his interchange becomes so aversive that the parent stops fighting and walks away, thereby ending the fight but also letting the son not make his bed. Giving in to these problems results in short-term gains for both the parent (calm is restored in the house) and the child (he gets what he wants), but it results in continuing problems. The child has learned to continue fighting and not give up, and the parent learns that the only way to "win" is to withdraw all demands. This coercive family process combines with other factors, such as genetic influences, parents' inept monitoring of their child's activities and less parental involvement, to help maintain the aggressive behaviours (Chronis et al., 2007; Patterson et al., 1989; Sansbury & Wahler, 1992). Coercive parenting—along with genetics—appears to be at least modestly involved with the callous-unemotional traits that seem related to later psychopathy (Waller et al., 2014).

Although little is known about which environmental factors play a direct role in causing antisocial personality disorder and psychopathy, evidence from adoption studies strongly suggests that shared environmental factors—that tend to make family members similar—are important to the etiology of criminality and to perhaps antisocial personality disorder. For example, in the Swedish adoption study by Sigvardsson, Cloninger, Bohman, and von Knorring (1982), low social status of the adoptive parents increased the risk of nonviolent criminality among females. Like children with CDs, individuals with antisocial personality disorder come from homes with inconsistent parental discipline (e.g., Robins, 1966).

One interesting study looked at the social environment and attitudes of neighbourhoods and their effect on violent crime. Sampson, Raudenbush, and Earls (1997) asked members of city neighbourhoods questions about the willingness of local residents to intervene for the common good, for example, whether neighbours would intervene if children were skipping school and hanging out on the street. The researchers found that the degree of mutual trust and solidarity in a neighbourhood was inversely related to violent crime. This study points out that factors outside the family can influence behaviours associated with antisocial personality disorder.

A final factor that has been implicated in antisocial personality disorder is the role of stress. One study found that trauma associated with combat may increase the likelihood of antisocial behaviour. In this study, more than 2000 army veterans of the Vietnam War were studied (Barrett et al., 1996). Even after adjusting for histories of childhood problems, the researchers found that those who had been exposed to the most traumatic events were most likely to engage in violence, illegal activities, lying, and the use of aliases. Stephen Porter has hypothesized that childhood trauma may play a role in the development of psychopathy. Specifically, when certain individuals are severely traumatized by loved ones, over time they might learn to "turn off" their emotions as a way of coping. The use of this coping skill could contribute to the emotional differences observed in psychopaths and even result in a psychopathic personality disorder (Porter, 1996). Consistent with this possibility, Campbell, Porter, and Santor (2004) found that higher psychopathy scores were associated with the experience of physical abuse in a large sample of male and female

incarcerated adolescent offenders. Porter's (1996) intriguing hypothesis is thus deserving of further study.

An Integrative Model

How can we put all this information together to get a better understanding of people with antisocial personality disorder? Remember that research in each area may involve people labelled as having antisocial personality disorder, people labelled as psychopathic, or criminals. Whatever the label, it appears these people have a genetic vulnerability to antisocial behaviours and personality traits. Perhaps this vulnerability results in underarousal or fearlessness. The genetic inheritance might be the propensity for weak inhibition systems and overactive reward systems that could partially account for the evidence of differences in cognitions and emotions (Newman & Wallace, 1993).

In a family that may already be under stress because of divorce or substance abuse (Hetherington et al., 1989; Patterson et al., 1989), there may be an interaction style that actually encourages antisocial behaviour on the part of the child (Wootton et al., 1997). The child's antisocial and impulsive behaviour alienates other children who might be good role models and attracts others who encourage antisocial behaviour (Vuchinich et al., 1992). These behaviours may also result in the child's dropping out of school and a poor occupational history in adulthood, which help create increasingly frustrating life circumstances that further incite acts against society (Caspi et al., 1987).

This is, admittedly, an abbreviated version of a complex and still incomplete scenario. Somehow, biological, psychological, and cultural factors combine in intricate ways to create someone like Ryan.

Treatment

One of the major problems with treating people in this group is typical of numerous personality disorders: these people rarely identify themselves as needing treatment. Because of this, and because they can be very manipulative even with their therapists, most clinicians are pessimistic about the outcome of treatment for adults who have antisocial personality disorder, and there are few documented success stories (National Collaborating Centre for Mental Health, 2009). Antisocial behaviour is predictive of poor prognosis even in childhood (Kazdin & Mazurick, 1994). Clinicians encourage identification of high-risk children so treatment can be attempted before they become adults (National Collaborating Centre for Mental Health, 2009; Patterson, 1982; Thomas, 2009). One large study with violent offenders found that cognitive behaviour therapy could reduce the likelihood of violence five years after treatment (Olver et al., 2013). Importantly, however, treatment success was negatively correlated with ratings of the psychopathy trait of "selfish, callous, and remorseless use of others." In other words, the higher the score on this trait, the less successful this group was in refraining from violence after their treatment.

The most common treatment strategy for children involves parent training (Scott et al., 2014; Patterson, 1986; Presnall et al., 2014). Parents are taught how to recognize behaviour problems early and how to use praise and privileges to reduce problem behaviour and encourage prosocial behaviours. Treatment studies typically show that these types of programs can significantly

▲ Children with conduct disorder may become adults with antisocial personality disorder.

improve the behaviours of many children who display antisocial behaviours (Conduct Problems Prevention Research Group, 2010; Fleischman, 1981; Patterson et al., 1982; Webster-Stratton & Hammond, 1997). A number of factors, however, put families at risk for either not succeeding in treatment or for dropping out early; these include cases with a high degree of family dysfunction, socioeconomic disadvantage, high family stress, parent's history of antisocial behaviour, and severe CD on the part of the child (Dumas & Wahler, 1983; Kaminski et al., 2008; Kazdin et al., 1993).

Some researchers are now examining how a multifaceted approach to treatment can help reduce delinquent behaviour on the part of juvenile offenders. Programs that combine the behavioural approaches just described with efforts to improve family relationships and provide services to the families in their communities are reporting some success. One study treating 155 violent and chronic juvenile offenders observed that by improving family relations and decreasing the child's associations with delinquent peers, significant reductions in delinquent behaviour were obtained (Huey et al., 2000).

Prevention

Some programs address these problems even earlier, in an attempt to prevent problems from arising. Typically preschool programs, they combine teaching good parenting skills with a variety of supports for families with social and economic disadvantages (Zigler et al., 1992). An obstacle to prevention efforts with this group is that we have relatively poor methods for identifying which children will grow up to have antisocial personality disorder (Bennett et al., 1999). It is too soon to assess the success of such programs in preventing the types of adult antisocial behaviours typically observed among people with this personality disorder (Ingoldsby et al., 2012). Given the low effectiveness of treatment for adults, however, prevention may be the best approach to this problem.

BORDERLINE PERSONALITY DISORDER

People with **borderline personality disorder** lead tumultuous lives. Their moods and relationships are unstable, and usually they have a very poor self-image. They often feel empty and are at great risk of dying by their own hands. Consider the case of Claire.

CLAIRE | *A Stranger among Us*

I have known Claire for more than 40 years and have watched her through the good but mostly bad times of her often shaky and erratic life as a person with borderline personality disorder. Claire and I went to school together from Grade 8 through high school, and we've kept in touch periodically. My earliest memory of her is of her hair, which was cut short and rather unevenly. She told me that when things were not going well she cut her own hair severely, which helped to "fill the void." I later found out that the long sleeves she usually wore hid scars and cuts that she had made herself.

Claire was the first of our friends to smoke. What was unusual about this and her later drug use was not that they occurred (this was in the 1960s!) or that they began early; it was that she didn't seem to use them to get attention, like everyone else. Claire was also one of the first whose parents divorced, and both of them seemed to abandon her emotionally. She later told me that her father was an alcoholic who had regularly beaten her and her mother. She did poorly in school and had very low self-esteem. She frequently said she was stupid and ugly, yet she was obviously neither.

Throughout our school years, Claire left town periodically, without any explanation. I learned many years later that she was in psychiatric facilities to get help with her suicidal depression. She often threatened to kill herself, although we didn't guess that she was serious.

In our later teens, we all drifted away from Claire. She had become increasingly unpredictable, sometimes berating us for a perceived slight ("You're walking too fast. You don't want to be seen with me!"), and at other times desperate to be around us. We were obviously confused by her behaviour. With some people, emotional outbursts can bring you closer together. Unfortunately for Claire, these incidents and her overall demeanour made us feel that we didn't know her at all. As we all grew older, the "void" she described in herself became overwhelming and eventually shut us all out.

Claire married twice, and both times had very passionate but stormy relationships interrupted by hospitalizations. She tried to stab her first husband during a particularly violent rage. She tried a number of drugs but mainly used alcohol to "deaden the pain."

Now, in her mid-50s, things have calmed down some, although she says she is rarely happy. Claire does feel a little better about herself and is doing well as a travel agent. Although she is seeing someone, she is reluctant to become very involved because of her personal history. Claire was ultimately diagnosed with depression and borderline personality disorder.

Clinical Description

Borderline personality disorder is one of the most common personality disorders observed in clinical settings. Claire's life illustrates the instability characteristic of people with borderline personality disorder (see DSM Table 13.6). They tend to have very turbulent relationships, fearing abandonment but lacking control over their emotions (Hooley et al., 2012). They frequently engage in suicidal or self-mutilating behaviours—cutting or burning or punching themselves. Claire sometimes used her cigarette to burn her palm or forearm, and she carved her initials in her arm. A significant proportion—approximately 10 percent—die by suicide (Paris, 2002). On the positive side, the long-term outcome for people with borderline personality disorder is encouraging, with nearly 75 percent achieving remission six years after initial treatment (Zanarini et al., 2014).

People with this personality disorder are often very intense, going from anger to deep depression in a short time. They also are characterized by impulsivity; Paul Links and his colleagues at Saint Michael's Hospital in Toronto have argued that impulsivity is the core aspect of borderline personality disorder (Links et al., 1999). This impulsiveness can be seen in their drug abuse and self-mutilation. Although not so obvious as to why, the self-injurious behaviours, such as cutting, sometimes are described as tension reducing by people who engage in these behaviours (Bohus et al., 2000). Claire's empty feeling is also common; these people are sometimes described as chronically bored and have difficulties with their own identities (Wilkinson-Ryan & Westen, 2000). The mood disorders we discussed in Chapter 8 are common among people with borderline personality disorder; a recent study of inpatients with this disorder found that more than 80 percent also had major depression and approximately 10 percent had bipolar II disorder (Zanarini et al., 2014). Eating disorders are also common, particularly bulimia (see Chapter 9): Approximately 25 percent of people with borderline personality disorder also have bulimia, while 20 percent meet criteria for anorexia (Zanarini et al., 2014). Up to 64 percent of the people with borderline personality disorder are also diagnosed with at least one substance use disorder (Zanarini et al., 2014). As with antisocial personality disorder, people with borderline personality disorder tend to improve during their 30s and 40s, although they may continue to have difficulties into old age (Zanarini et al., 2014).

Research by University of British Columbia psychologist Don Dutton and his colleagues indicates a link between borderline

Mikael Damkier/Shutterstock.com

▲ Borderline personality disorder is often accompanied by self-mutilation.

personality disorder and spousal abuse; several studies by his team indicate that men who abuse their spouses are high in borderline characteristics (e.g., Dutton, 2002, 2007; Dutton & Starzomski, 1993; Tweed & Dutton, 1998), with perhaps 40 percent of men who abuse their partners fit this borderline personality profile. Dutton (1995) argued that men with borderline personality disorder are susceptible to abusing their partners because they set excessively high standards for others and blame their partners when things go wrong.

Causes

The results from numerous family studies suggest that borderline personality disorder is more prevalent in families with the disorder and somehow linked with mood disorders (Amad et al., 2014). Studies of monozygotic (identical) and dizygotic (fraternal) twins indicated a higher concordance rate among monozygotic twins, further supporting the role of genetics in the expression of borderline personality disorder (Calati et al., 2013).

Cognitive factors in borderline personality disorder are just beginning to be explored. Here the question is, just how do people with this disorder process information, and does this contribute to their difficulties? One study that takes a look at the thought

A pervasive pattern of instability of interpersonal relationships, self-image, and affects, and marked impulsivity, beginning by early adulthood and present in a variety of contexts, as indicated by five (or more) of the following:

1. Frantic efforts to avoid real or imagined abandonment. (Note: Do not include suicidal or self-mutilating behavior covered in Criterion 5.)

2. A pattern of unstable and intense interpersonal relationships characterized by alternating between extremes of idealization and devaluation.

3. Identity disturbance: Markedly and persistently unstable self-image or sense of self.

4. Impulsivity in at least two areas that are potentially self-damaging (e.g., spending, sex, substance abuse, reckless driving, binge eating). (Note: Do not include suicidal or self-mutilating behavior covered in Criterion 5.)

5. Recurrent suicidal behavior, gestures, or threats, or self-mutilating behavior.

6. Affective instability due to a marked reactivity of mood (e.g., intense episodic dysphoria, irritability, or anxiety usually lasting a few hours and only rarely more than a few days).

7. Chronic feelings of emptiness.

8. Inappropriate, intense anger or difficulty controlling anger (e.g., frequent displays of temper, constant anger, recurrent physical fights).

9. Transient, stress-related paranoid ideation or severe dissociative symptoms.

Source: Reprinted with permission from the *Diagnostic and Statistical Manual of Mental Disorders*, Fifth Edition (Copyright © 2013). American Psychiatric Association. All Rights Reserved.

Courtesy of Dr. Paul Links

▲ Paul Links is the Chair of Psychiatry at Western University in London, Ontario. He and his colleagues have made many important contributions to understanding the nature, origins, and treatment of borderline personality disorder.

processes of these individuals asked people with and without borderline personality disorder to look at words projected on a computer screen and try to remember some of the words and try to forget others (Korfine & Hooley, 2000). When the words were not related to the symptoms of borderline personality disorder—for example, *celebrate*, *charming*, *collect*—both groups performed equally as well. However, when they were presented with words that might be relevant to the disorder—for example, *abandon*, *suicidal*, *emptiness*—individuals with borderline personality disorder remembered more of these words despite being instructed to forget them. This preliminary evidence for a memory bias may hold clues to the nature of this disorder and may someday be helpful in designing more effective treatment (Baer et al., 2012; Winter et al., 2014).

One psychosocial influence that has received a great deal of attention is the possible contribution of early trauma, especially sexual and physical abuse (Laporte & Guttman, 2001; Links & van Reekum, 1993; McLean & Gallop, 2003; Mitton et al., 1997). People with this disorder are more likely to report abuse than are individuals with other psychiatric conditions (Kuo et al., 2015; Lewis & Christopher, 1989; Ogata et al., 1990; Zanarini et al., 2014). Wagner and Linehan (1994) found that among women with both borderline personality disorder and parasuicidal behaviour (which includes both serious and minor suicide attempts), 76 percent reported some type of childhood sexual abuse and had made the most serious attempts to commit suicide. In a large study, researchers found an even higher rate of abuse histories in individuals with borderline personality disorder, with 91 percent reporting abuse and 92 percent reporting being neglected before the age of 18 (Zanarini et al., 1997). Although we obviously do not know whether abuse and neglect cause later borderline personality disorder, they may be predisposing factors in at least some cases. If childhood abuse or neglect does lead to most cases of borderline personality disorder, the connection may well explain why women are affected more often than men. Girls are two or three times as likely to be sexually abused as are boys (Herman et al., 1989). Moreover, the work of Harriet MacMillan at McMaster University and the Canadian Centre for Studies of Children at Risk has shown that the association between a history of abuse in childhood and psychopathology in adulthood (including personality disorders) is stronger for women than for men (MacMillan et al., 2001).

Building on the possible link to abuse, Gunderson and Sabo (1993) argued that borderline personality disorder is similar to post-traumatic stress disorder (PTSD); they see many resemblances in the two behaviour patterns. Herman et al. (1989) have drawn similar parallels—for example, difficulties in the regulation of mood, impulse control, and interpersonal relationships. This discussion about borderline personality disorder and PTSD can be viewed from a political perspective. Some writers argue that what the mental health profession calls borderline personality disorder is simply a case of PTSD among women, and a diagnosis of PTSD puts the emphasis on the victimization of women rather than on their mental illness. This distinction in assigning a diagnosis is an important one and represents a debate that will continue for some time. These observations all seem to support the hypothesis that borderline personality disorder may be caused by early trauma. It is important to remember, however, that not all cases of borderline personality disorder resemble PTSD (Zanarini et al., 1998).

Symptoms of borderline personality disorder have been observed among people who have gone through rapid cultural changes. The problems of identity, emptiness, fears of abandonment, and low anxiety threshold have been found in child and adult immigrants (Laxenaire et al., 1982; Skhiri et al., 1982). These observations further support the possibility that early trauma may, in some individuals, lead to borderline personality disorder.

Remember, however, that a history of childhood trauma, including sexual abuse and physical abuse, occurs in a number of other disorders, such as somatoform disorder, panic disorder, dissociative identity disorder, and substance use disorders.

Let Me Make It Good: A Chronicle of My Life with Borderline Personality Disorder
by Jane Wanklin

Jane Wanklin grew up in Halifax, Nova Scotia, and London, Ontario. She lives with borderline personality disorder, making it extremely difficult to maintain stable relationships with family and friends. In her memoir, *Let Me Make It Good: A Chronicle of My Life with Borderline Personality Disorder*, Wanklin examines her life experiences, attempting to put her mental illness into perspective.

She describes her frequent psychiatric hospitalizations starting at age 16. Passages of her autobiography clearly illustrate classic symptoms of borderline personality disorder, such as her unstable self-image and impulsive behaviour (e.g., binge eating). Like many borderline patients, Wanklin reports that she experienced childhood trauma, which she believes contributed to her mental illness. In addition to her personality pathology, Wanklin also suffered with an eating disorder, which research shows is commonly comorbid with borderline personality disorder.

In many parts of the book, Wanklin describes her frequent angry outbursts and difficulties controlling her rage. She came up with a name to describe her anger, as she explains in the following excerpt:

That's what I termed my extreme anger: The Beast. It became my constant companion and would spring from me, seemingly out of nowhere, disrupting the entire ward and causing fear and apprehension in the hearts of the other patients. (Wanklin, 1998, p. 152)

In the opening passage of this textbook chapter, we chose a quote from Wanklin's book that captures the borderline patient's experience of, and motivations for, self-harm. Wanklin's elaborate self-harm rituals (which involved cutting) were limited by staff during stays in the psychiatric hospital:

My cutting rituals [caused] the staff [to] forbid me to sit alone with a can of pop and [I] had to throw it away in front of them. This didn't stop me, for I only became more sneaky. I would get [pop cans] from the canteen and then hide in the sub-basement and cut myself to pieces in private. (Wanklin, 1998, p. 180)

She also provides some excellent examples of the borderline tendency to alternate between extremes of idealization and devaluation within her interpersonal relationships. For instance, Wanklin details how this pattern of alternating between these two extremes applied in her relationship with her psychiatrist:

I grew hostile toward Dr. Milo, who I saw as my captor. I would spit and fume at him when he came into my room. "I hate you," I sputtered, hollering at him to "Get the f_ away from me!" . . . [But] . . . by December, Dr. Milo was once again in my good books and we talked a lot out in the day-room. Some of his other patients resented all the time he was devoting to me and it made me feel special. I basked in the glow of his attention and chatted to him about matters such as running, music, and . . . philosophy. . . . He had a wonderful sense of humour and I soon discovered that I was falling in love with him. (Wanklin, 1998, p. 180)

Let Me Make It Good is a moving and enlightening memoir that takes a stark, unflinching, and sometimes cynical look at what it's like to live with borderline personality disorder. The book helps in showing people with the disorder that they are not alone. Reading Wanklin's vivid description of the symptoms she suffered will help readers recognize and understand borderline personality disorder in themselves, family members, friends, or co-workers.

Source: From *Let Me Make It Good: A Chronicle of My Life with Borderline Personality Disorder*, by J. Wanklin, 1998, Mosaic Press.

In addition, 20 to 40 percent of individuals with borderline personality disorder have no apparent history of such abuse (Gunderson & Sabo, 1993). Although childhood sexual abuse and physical abuse seem to play some role in the etiology of borderline personality disorder, neither appears to be necessary or sufficient to produce the syndrome. Zanarini and Frankenberg (1997) attempted to integrate the different aspects of etiology in borderline personality disorder. They suggest that childhood trauma combines with a predisposing temperament or personality and a stressful triggering event causes the unstable behaviours. The individuals abused as children who do not develop the disorder may lack the biological predisposition that, in this case, may be a volatile or impulsive personality style (Figueroa & Silk, 1997).

Concept Check   13.1

Which personality disorders are the following people displaying?

1. Homer, who seems eccentric, never shows much emotion. He does not have any close personal relationships and does not seek interactions with people.

   _____

2. Mohammed is 19 and has been in trouble with the law since he was 14. He lies to his parents, vandalizes buildings in his community, and, when caught, shows no

remorse. He frequently fights with others and doesn't care whom he injures. _____

3. Russell trusts no one and incorrectly believes other people want to harm him or spoil his plans. He is sure his wife is having an affair. He no longer confides in friends for fear that the information will be used against him. He dwells for hours on harmless comments by co-workers. _____

4. Nick is involved in drugs and has casual sexual encounters. He feels empty unless he does dangerous and exciting things. He threatens to commit suicide if his girlfriend suggests getting help or if she talks about leaving him. He alternates between loving her and hating her. He has low self-esteem and has recently experienced high levels of stress. _____

Treatment

In contrast to the extensive research on the nature of borderline personality disorder, relatively few studies have examined the effects of treatment. Efforts to provide successful treatment for people with borderline personality disorder are complicated by problems with drug abuse, compliance with treatment, and suicide attempts. As a result, many clinicians are reluctant to work with borderline personality disorder clients.

In terms of pharmacotherapy, many people with borderline personality disorder appear to respond positively to a variety of medications, including tricyclic antidepressants, lithium, and even antipsychotics (Soloff et al., 1989; Stone, 1986). For example, Paul Links and his colleagues have provided preliminary evidence on the efficacy of lithium therapy in the treatment of borderline personality disorder (Links et al., 1990). As another example, Québec researchers Evens Villeneuve and Sophie Lemelin (2005) have provided preliminary evidence that many symptoms of borderline personality disorder, including impulsivity, appear to respond favourably to treatment with the antipsychotic quetiapine.

Research on cognitive-behavioural treatment is limited. In one exception, Linehan (1987, 1993) used an approach she called *dialectical behaviour therapy* (DBT), which involves helping people cope with the stressors that seem to trigger suicidal behaviours and other maladaptive responses. Weekly individual sessions provide support, and patients are taught how to identify and regulate their emotions (Lau & McMain, 2005; McMain et al., 2001). Problem solving is emphasized so that they can handle difficulties more effectively. In addition, they receive treatment similar to that used for people with PTSD, in which prior traumatic events are re-experienced to help extinguish the fear associated with them. In the final stage of therapy, clients learn to trust their own responses rather than to depend on the validation of others, sometimes by visualizing themselves not reacting to criticism (Lynch & Cuper, 2012).

Results from a number of studies suggest that DBT may help reduce suicide attempts, drop-outs from treatment, and hospitalizations (Linehan, 2015; Linehan & Dexter-Mazza, 2008; McMain et al., 2014; Simpson et al., 1998). Of 39 women who received either dialectic behaviour therapy or general therapeutic support (called "treatment as usual") for one year showed that, during the first six months of follow-up, the women in the DBT group were less suicidal, less angry, and better adjusted socially (Linehan & Kehrer, 1993). Another study examined how treating these individuals with DBT in an inpatient setting—psychiatric hospital—for approximately three months before discharge to home would improve their outcomes (Bohus et al., 2000). The participants improved in a number of areas, such as with a reduction in depression, hopelessness, anger expression, and dissociation. A growing body of evidence is now available to document the effectiveness of this approach to aid many individuals with this debilitating disorder (Linehan, 2015).

Paul Links and Michelle Stockwell (2001) have suggested that, particularly given the pattern of unstable and intense interpersonal relationships characteristic of people with borderline personality disorder, couples therapy can be very beneficial for those borderline patients in a relationship. These authors identify three subtypes of borderline patients: (1) impulsive subtype (those with a history of impulsive, self-destructive, and treatment-threatening behaviours); (2) identity disturbance subtype (those with a markedly and persistently unstable self-image or sense of self); and (3) affective cluster (those with marked mood swings and difficulty controlling anger). They only recommend couples therapy for the latter two subtypes, and do not recommend that couples therapy be attempted for those in the impulsive subtype. Future research should evaluate the utility of this suggested subtyping scheme for borderline patients and evaluate the efficacy of couples treatment for the various subtypes (Links & Stockwell, 2001).

INNOVATIVE APPROACHES   When East Meets West

Dialectical behaviour therapy (DBT) as a treatment for borderline personality disorder combines traditional cognitive-behavioural therapy techniques with concepts from Eastern spiritual traditions, including Buddhism (Linehan & Dexter-Mazza, 2008). In addition to incorporating treatment techniques we have described for other disorders—including teaching problem-solving skills and cognitive-behavioural therapy—DBT uses aspects of "mindfulness" (the act of directing attention to the experiences occurring in the present moment in a nonjudgmental, accepting manner) (Baer & Krietemeyer, 2008). The idea of being mindful has a long tradition in Eastern spiritual practices and is increasingly being incorporated into a variety of interventions currently being used to address other psychological problems. These problems include stress in survivors of breast cancer (mindfulness-based stress reduction; Lengacher et al., 2009), preventing relapse among people treated for major depression (mindfulness-based cognitive therapy; Mathew et al., 2010), and reducing an individual's smoking (acceptance and commitment therapy; Bricker et al., 2010).

One of the advantages in practising mindfulness is that it encourages people to embrace their feelings and accept them in a neutral way. If you recall back to Chapter 5 where we discussed treatments for anxiety-related disorders, you will remember that one of the most important aspects of treating anxiety is exposure to the anxiety-provoking stimuli.

So, for example, if thoughts about being abandoned by a loved one (which are common in people with borderline personality disorder) make you upset, your natural tendency will be to avoid these thoughts and settings that might trigger them. However, by teaching someone to experience these thoughts in a relaxed manner, and accept them as natural but not dangerous, you increase the chance that the person will be exposed to these stimuli and therefore will have the opportunity to work toward reducing the anxiety surrounding them. We anticipate that many more approaches to helping people with complex problems will begin to incorporate Eastern concepts such as mindfulness as important therapeutic techniques.

HISTRIONIC PERSONALITY DISORDER

Individuals with **histrionic personality disorder** tend to be overly dramatic and often seem almost to be acting, which is why the term *histrionic*—which means theatrical in manner—is used. Consider the case of Pat.

PAT | *Always Onstage*

When we first met, Pat seemed to radiate enjoyment of life. She was single, in her mid-30s, and was going to university part-time for her master's degree. She often dressed very flamboyantly. During the day she taught children with disabilities, and when she didn't have class in the evening she was often out late on a date. When I first spoke with her, she enthusiastically told me how impressed she was with my work in the field of developmental disabilities and that she had been extremely successful in using some of my techniques with her students. She was clearly overdoing the praise, but who wouldn't appreciate such flattering comments?

Because some of our research included children in her classroom, I saw Pat frequently. Over a period of weeks, however, our interactions grew strained. She frequently complained of various illnesses and injuries (falling in the parking lot, twisting her neck looking out a window) that interfered with her work. She was disorganized, often leaving to the very last-minute tasks that required considerable planning. Pat made promises to other people that were impossible to keep but seemed to be aimed at winning their approval; when she broke the promise, she usually made up a story designed to elicit sympathy and compassion. For example, she promised the mother of one of her students that she would put on a "massive and unique" birthday party for her daughter, but completely forgot about it until the mother showed up with cake and juice. On seeing her, Pat flew into a rage and blamed the school principal for keeping her late after school, although there was no truth to this accusation.

Pat often interrupted meetings about research to talk about her latest boyfriend. The boyfriends changed almost weekly, but her enthusiasm ("Like no other man I have ever met!") and optimism about the future ("He's the guy I want to spend the rest of my life with!") remained high for each of them. Wedding plans were seriously discussed with almost every one, despite their brief acquaintance. Pat was very ingratiating, especially to the male teachers, who often helped her out of trouble she got into because of her disorganization.

When it became clear that she would probably lose her teaching job because of her poor performance, Pat managed to manipulate several of the male teachers and the principal into recommending her for a new job in a nearby school district. A year later she was still at the new school but had been moved twice to different classrooms. According to teachers she worked with, Pat still lacked close interpersonal relationships, although she described her current relationship as "deeply involved." After a rather long period of depression, Pat sought help from a psychologist, who diagnosed her as also having histrionic personality disorder.

Clinical Description

People with histrionic personality disorder are inclined to express their emotions in an exaggerated fashion, for example, hugging someone they have just met or crying uncontrollably during a sad movie (Blashfield et al., 2012; Ferguson & Negy, 2014). They also tend to be vain and self-centred, and uncomfortable when they are not in the limelight. They are often seductive in appearance and behaviour, and they are typically very concerned about their looks. (Pat, for example, spent a great deal of money on unusual jewellery and was sure to point it out to anyone who would listen.) In addition, people with histrionic personality disorder seek reassurance and approval constantly and may become upset or angry when others do not attend to them or praise them. People with histrionic personality disorder also tend to be impulsive and have great difficulty delaying gratification (see DSM Table 13.7).

The cognitive style associated with histrionic personality disorder is impressionistic (Beck et al., 2007), characterized by a tendency to view situations in global, black-and-white terms. Speech is often vague, lacking in detail, and characterized by exaggeration (APA, 2013; Nestadt et al., 2009). For example, when Pat was asked about a date she had had the night before, she might say it was "amazing" but fail to provide more detailed information.

The high rate of this diagnosis among women versus men raises questions about the nature of the disorder and its diagnostic criteria (Boysen et al., 2014). As we discussed in the beginning of this chapter, there is some thought that the features of histrionic personality disorder, such as overdramatization, vanity, seductiveness, and overconcern with physical appearance, are characteristic of the Western "stereotypical female" and may lead to an overdiagnosis among women. Sprock (2000) examined this important question and found some evidence for a bias among psychologists and psychiatrists to associate the diagnosis with women rather than men.

Causes

Despite its long history, very little research has been done on the causes or treatment of histrionic personality disorder. The ancient Greek philosophers believed that many unexplainable problems of women were caused by the uterus (*hysteria*) migrating within the body (Abse, 1987; see also Ussher, 2013). As we have seen, however, histrionic personality disorder also occurs among men.

One hypothesis involves a possible relationship with antisocial personality disorder. Evidence suggests that histrionic personality and antisocial personality co-occur more often than chance would account for. Lilienfeld and colleagues (1986), for example, found that roughly two-thirds of people with a histrionic personality also met the criteria for antisocial personality disorder. The evidence for this association has led to the suggestion (Cloninger, 1978; Lilienfeld, 1992) that histrionic personality and antisocial personality may be sex-typed alternative expressions of the same

unidentified underlying condition. Females with the underlying condition may be predisposed to exhibit a predominantly histrionic pattern, whereas males with the underlying condition may be predisposed to exhibit a predominantly antisocial pattern. Whether this association exists remains a controversial issue, however, and further research on this potential relationship is needed (Dolan & Vollm, 2009; Salekin et al., 1997), particularly given that borderline personality disorder has also been conceptualized as a female variant of psychopathy (Sprague et al., 2012).

Treatment

Although a great deal has been written about ways of helping people with this disorder, very little of the research demonstrates success (Cloninger & Svakic, 2009). Some therapists have tried to modify the attention-getting behaviour. Kass, Silvers, and Abrams (1972) worked with five women, four of whom had been hospitalized for suicide attempts and all of whom were later diagnosed with histrionic personality disorder. The women were rewarded for appropriate interactions and fined for attention-getting behaviour. The therapists noted improvement after an 18-month follow-up, but they did not collect scientific data to confirm their observation.

A large part of therapy for these individuals usually focuses on the problematic interpersonal relationships. They often manipulate others through emotional crises, using charm, sex, seductiveness, or complaining (Beck et al., 2007). People with histrionic personality disorder often need to be shown how the short-term gains derived from this interactional style result in long-term costs, and they need to be taught more appropriate ways of negotiating their wants and needs.

NARCISSISTIC PERSONALITY DISORDER

We all know people who think highly of themselves—perhaps exaggerating their real abilities. They consider themselves somehow different from others and deserving of special treatment. In **narcissistic personality disorder**, this tendency is taken to its extreme. In Greek mythology, Narcissus was a youth who spurned the love of Echo. So enamoured was he of his own beauty that he spent his days admiring his own image reflected in a pool of water. Psychoanalysts, including Sigmund Freud, used the term *narcissistic* to describe people who show an exaggerated sense of self-importance and are preoccupied with receiving attention (Ronningstam, 2012). Consider the case of David.

DSM-5	**Table 13.7** Diagnostic Criteria for Histrionic Personality Disorder

A pervasive pattern of excessive emotionality and attention seeking, beginning by early adulthood and present in a variety of contexts, as indicated by five (or more) of the following:

1. Is uncomfortable in situations in which he or she is not the centre of attention.
2. Interaction with others is often characterized by inappropriate sexually seductive or provocative behavior.
3. Displays rapidly shifting and shallow expression of emotions.
4. Consistently uses physical appearance to draw attention to self.
5. Has a style of speech that is excessively impressionistic and lacking in detail.
6. Shows self-dramatization, theatricality, and exaggerated expression of emotion.
7. Is suggestible (i.e., easily influenced by others or circumstances).
8. Considers relationships to be more intimate than they actually are.

Source: Reprinted with permission from the *Diagnostic and Statistical Manual of Mental Disorders*, Fifth Edition (Copyright © 2013). American Psychiatric Association. All Rights Reserved.

▲ People with histrionic personality disorder tend to be vain, extravagant, and seductive.

▲ In Greek mythology, Narcissus was so in love with his own image that he pined away and died of longing.

DAVID | *Taking Care of Number One*

David was a lawyer in his early 40s when he sought treatment for depressed mood. He appeared to be an outgoing man who paid meticulous attention to his appearance. He made a point of asking for the therapist's admiration of his new designer suit, his winter tan, and his new foreign convertible. He also asked the therapist what kind of car he drove and how many VIP clients he dealt with. David wanted to make sure that he was dealing with someone who was the best in the business. David spoke of being an "ace" student and a "super" athlete, but could not provide any details that would validate a superior performance in these areas.

During law school, David became a workaholic, fueled by fantasies of brilliant work and international recognition. He spent minimal time with his wife, and after their son was born, even less time with either of them. He waited until he felt reasonably secure in his first job so that he could let go of her financial support, and then he sought a divorce.

After his divorce, David decided he was totally free to just please himself. He loved spending all his money on himself, and he lavishly decorated his condominium and bought an attention-getting wardrobe. He constantly sought the companionship of different, attractive women.

David felt better when someone flattered him; when he was in a group social situation where he could easily grab the center of attention; and when he could fantasize about obtaining a high-level position, being honored for his great talent, or just being fabulously wealthy.

Source: Republished with permission of Guildford Publications, from *Cognitive therapy of personality disorders* by Beck, Aaron T. and Freeman, Arthur, © 1990; permission conveyed through Copyright Clearance Center, Inc.

Clinical Description

People with narcissistic personality disorder have an unreasonable sense of self-importance and are so preoccupied with themselves that they lack sensitivity and compassion for other people (Caligor et al., 2015; Ronningstam, 2012). They aren't comfortable unless someone is admiring them. Their exaggerated feelings and their fantasies of greatness, called grandiosity, create negative attributes. They require and expect a great deal of special attention—the best table in the restaurant, the illegal parking space in front of the movie theatre. They also tend to use or exploit others for their own interests and show little empathy. When confronted with other successful people, they can be extremely envious and arrogant. And because they often fail to live up to their own expectations, they are frequently depressed (see DSM Table 13.8).

Causes

We start out as infants being self-centred and demanding, which is part of our struggle for survival. Part of the socialization process, however, involves teaching children empathy and altruism. Some writers, including Austrian native Heinz Kohut (1971, 1977), believe that narcissistic personality disorder arises largely from a profound failure of empathic "mirroring" by the parents very early in a child's development. Consequently, the child remains fixated at a self-centred, grandiose stage of development.

DSM-5	**Table 13.8** Diagnostic Criteria for Narcissistic Personality Disorder

A pervasive pattern of grandiosity (in fantasy or behavior), need for admiration, and lack of empathy, beginning by early adulthood and present in a variety of contexts, as indicated by five (or more) of the following:

1. Has a grandiose sense of self-importance (e.g., exaggerates achievements and talents, expects to be recognized as superior without commensurate achievements).
2. Is preoccupied with fantasies of unlimited success, power, brilliance, beauty, or ideal love.
3. Believes that he or she is "special" and unique and can only be understood by, or should associate with, other special or high-status people (or institutions).
4. Requests excessive admiration.
5. Has a sense of entitlement (i.e., unreasonable expectations of especially favorable treatment or automatic compliance with his or her expectations).
6. Is interpersonally exploitative (i.e., takes advantage of others to achieve his or her own ends).
7. Lacks empathy: is unwilling to recognize or identify with the feelings and needs of others.
8. Is often envious of others or believes that others are envious of him or her.
9. Shows arrogant, haughty behaviors or attitudes.

Source: Reprinted with permission from the *Diagnostic and Statistical Manual of Mental Disorders*, Fifth Edition (Copyright © 2013). American Psychiatric Association. All Rights Reserved.

In addition, the child (and later the adult) becomes involved in an essentially endless and fruitless search for the ideal person who will meet his or her unfulfilled empathic needs.

In a sociological view, Christopher Lasch (1978) wrote in his popular book *The Culture of Narcissism* that this personality disorder is increasing in prevalence in most Western societies, primarily as a consequence of large-scale social changes, including greater emphasis on short-term hedonism, individualism, competitiveness, and success. According to Lasch, the "me generation" (baby boomers born between 1946 and 1964) has produced more than its share of individuals with narcissistic personality disorder. Indeed, reports confirm that narcissistic personality disorder is increasing in prevalence (Huang et al., 2009). However, this apparent rise may be a consequence of increased interest in and research on the disorder.

Some have questioned whether narcissism and psychopathy are redundant concepts. Researcher Delroy Paulhus and his colleagues at the University of British Columbia have conducted investigations of this issue. For example, Paulhus and Williams (2002) administered measures of psychopathy and narcissism to 245 students along with other measures, including a questionnaire measuring the features of the five-factor model of personality. They found that although psychopaths and narcissists shared elevated disagreeableness on the five-factor measure and a tendency to be self-enhancers, they did not share any other features. The authors thus concluded that narcissism and psychopathy are overlapping but distinct constructs.

Treatment

Treatment research is extremely limited in both the number of studies and the reports of success (Cloninger & Svakic, 2009; Dhawan et al., 2010; Ronningstam, 2014). When therapy is attempted with these individuals, it often focuses on their grandiosity, their hypersensitivity to evaluation, and their lack of empathy toward others (Beck et al., 2007; Campbell & Miller, 2011). Cognitive therapy aims at replacing their fantasies with a focus on the day-to-day pleasurable experiences that are truly attainable. Coping strategies, such as relaxation training, are used to help them face and accept criticism. Helping them focus on the feelings of others is also a goal. Because individuals with this disorder are vulnerable to severe depressive episodes, particularly in middle age, treatment is often initiated for the depression. It is impossible to draw any conclusions, however, about the impact of such treatment on the actual narcissistic personality disorder.

CLUSTER C DISORDERS

AVOIDANT PERSONALITY DISORDER

As the name suggests, people with **avoidant personality disorder** are extremely sensitive to the opinions of others and although they desire social relationships, their anxiety leads them to avoid such associations. Their extremely low self-esteem—coupled with a fear of rejection—causes them to be limited in their friendships and very dependent on those they feel comfortable with (Eikenaes et al., 2015; Sanislow et al., 2012). Consider the case of Jane.

JANE | *Not Worth Noticing*

Jane was raised by an alcoholic mother who had borderline personality disorder and who abused her verbally and physically. As a child she made sense of her mother's abusive treatment by believing that she (Jane) must be an intrinsically unworthy person to be treated so badly. As an adult in her late 20s, Jane still expected to be rejected when others found out that she was inherently unworthy and bad.

Jane was highly self-critical and predicted that she would not be accepted. She thought that people would not like her, that they would see she was a loser, and that she would not have anything to say. She became upset if she perceived that someone in even the most fleeting encounter was reacting negatively or neutrally. If a newspaper vendor failed to smile at her, or a sales clerk was slightly curt, Jane automatically thought it must be because she (Jane) was somehow unworthy or unlikable. She then felt quite sad. Even when she was receiving positive feedback from a friend, she discounted it. As a result, Jane had few friends and certainly no close ones.

Source: Republished with permission of Guildford Publications, from *Cognitive therapy of personality disorders* by Beck, Aaron T. and Freeman, Arthur, © 1990; permission conveyed through Copyright Clearance Center, Inc.

Clinical Description

Millon (1981), who initially proposed this diagnosis, notes that it is important to distinguish between individuals who are asocial because they are apathetic, affectively flat, and relatively uninterested in interpersonal relationships (comparable to what the *DSM-5* terms *schizoid personality disorder*) and individuals who are asocial because they are interpersonally anxious and fearful of rejection. It is the latter who fit the criteria of avoidant personality disorder (Millon & Martinez, 1995). These individuals feel chronically rejected by others and are pessimistic about their future (see DSM Table 13.9).

Causes

Several theories have been proposed that integrate biological and psychosocial influences as the cause of avoidant personality disorder. Millon (1981), for example, suggested that these individuals may be born with a difficult temperament or personality characteristics. As a result, their parents may reject them, or at least not provide them with enough early, uncritical love. This rejection, in turn, may result in low self-esteem and social alienation, conditions that persist into adulthood. Limited support does exist for psychosocial influences. Stravynski et al. (1989) questioned a group of people with avoidant personality disorder and a group of comparison subjects about their early treatment by their parents. Those with the disorder remembered their parents as more rejecting, more guilt engendering, and less affectionate than the comparison group did, suggesting parenting may contribute to the development of this disorder. Similarly, research has consistently found that these individuals are more likely to report childhood experiences of neglect, isolation, rejection, and conflict with others (Eikenaes et al., 2015; Meyer & Carver, 2000).

In interpreting the results of these studies, some caution is in order. You probably noticed that these are retrospective studies, relying on the participants' memories for a report of what happened. The differences in the reports could be a consequence of differences in their ability to remember their childhoods rather than of actual differences in the ways the participants were treated. Also, it could be that people with avoidant personality disorder are more sensitive to the way they are treated, and therefore their memories are different from what actually happened. The findings are intriguing nonetheless and should be followed up as a possible contributor to our understanding of this disorder.

Some have suggested that, given its similarity to social anxiety disorder (see Chapter 5), avoidant personality disorder is part of a social anxiety spectrum (e.g., Schneider et al., 2002). A growing body of research links *behavioural inhibition* (i.e., a heritable temperamental factor involving an avoidant response to unfamiliar situations; Smoller et al., 2003) quite specifically to this social anxiety disorder spectrum, including avoidant personality disorder (see Schneider et al., 2002). For example, research by Kenneth Bruce and his colleagues at the Douglas Hospital in Montréal shows that women with comorbid avoidant personality disorder displayed more behavioural inhibition in response to threat on a lab-based computer task (Bruce et al., 2004). Findings from a research group in Spain suggest that the behavioural inhibition system may be the core underlying vulnerability for Cluster C personality disorders more generally. More specifically, these researchers compared patients diagnosed with Cluster C personality disorders (including avoidant personality disorder) with two comparison groups (patients diagnosed with other personality disorders and non-patients) on measures of behavioural inhibition. Overall, the patients in the Cluster C personality disorders group showed scores on these measures that suggested an overactive behavioural inhibition system (Caseras et al., 2001). Additional research is needed to determine the degree to which elevated behavioural inhibition is characteristic of avoidant personality disorder, specifically, or Cluster C personality disorders more generally.

Treatment

In contrast to the scarcity of research into most of the other personality disorders, several well-controlled studies exist on approaches to therapy for people with avoidant personality disorder (Leahy & McGinn, 2012). Lynn Alden at the University of British Columbia and her colleagues have been at the forefront of the field, in developing effective approaches for treating individuals with avoidant personality disorder. Behavioural intervention techniques for anxiety and social skills problems have had some success (Alden, 1989; Alden & Capreol, 1993; Emmelkamp et al., 2006; Renneberg et al., 1990; Stravynski et al., 1989). In particular, Alden's work shows that social skills training within a support group is useful to help people with avoidant personality disorder become more assertive with others (e.g., Alden, 1989). Because the problems experienced by people with avoidant personality disorder resemble those of people with social anxiety disorder, many of the same treatments are used for both groups. For example, according to a recent review by Alden and her colleagues, the central element of cognitive-behavioural treatment for avoidant personality disorder is graduated exposure to feared situations (Alden et al., 2006).

Renneberg et al. (1990) identified areas that caused anxiety in a group of 17 people with avoidant personality disorder, including a fear of rejection, a fear of criticism, and anxiety about their appearance. In groups of five or six patients, they used *systematic desensitization*, which involves relaxing in the presence of feared situations (e.g., "You speak to a group of people at work, and you realize that your voice is not powerful enough; your voice is childish") and *behavioural rehearsal*, in which patients act out situations that cause anxiety. As a group, these people improved in such areas as fear of negative evaluation and social avoidance and distress. The improvements tended to be modest, although, given the usually poor outcomes found among people with personality disorders, even moderate improvement is encouraging.

DEPENDENT PERSONALITY DISORDER

We all know what it means to be dependent on another person. People with **dependent personality disorder**, however, rely on others to make ordinary decisions and important ones, which results in an unreasonable fear of abandonment. Consider the case of Karen.

KAREN | *Whatever You Say*

Karen was a 45-year-old married woman who was referred for treatment by her physician for problems with panic attacks. During the evaluation, she appeared to be very worried, sensitive, and naive. She was easily overcome with emotion and cried on and off throughout the session. She was self-critical at every opportunity throughout the evaluation. For example, when asked how she got along with other people, she reported that "others think I'm dumb and inadequate," although she could give no evidence as to what made her think that. She reported that she didn't like school because "I was dumb," and that she always felt that she was not good enough.

Karen described staying in her first marriage for ten years, even though "it was hell." Her husband had affairs with many other women and was verbally abusive. She tried to leave him many times, but gave in to his repeated requests to return. She was finally able to divorce him, and shortly afterward she met and married her current husband, whom she described as kind, sensitive, and supportive. Karen stated that she preferred to have others make important decisions and agreed with other people in order to avoid conflict. She worried about being left alone without anyone to take care of her and reported feeling lost without other people's reassurance. She also reported that her feelings were easily hurt, so she worked hard not to do anything that might lead to criticism.

Source: Republished with permission of Guildford Publications, from *Cognitive therapy of personality disorders* by Beck, Aaron T. and Freeman, Arthur, © 1990; permission conveyed through Copyright Clearance Center, Inc.

Clinical Description

Dependent personality disorder belongs in the anxious/fearful cluster of *DSM-5* personality disorders because interpersonally dependent behaviour is motivated by anxiety (e.g., fear of abandonment). Individuals with dependent personality disorder sometimes agree with other people when their own opinion differs so as not to be rejected. Their desire to obtain and maintain supportive and nurturing relationships may lead to their other behavioural characteristics, including submissiveness, timidity, and passivity. People with this disorder are similar to those with *avoidant personality disorder* in their feelings of inadequacy, sensitivity to criticism, and need for reassurance. However, people with avoidant personality disorder respond to these feelings by avoiding relationships, whereas those with dependent personality disorder respond by clinging to relationships (Bornstein, 2012; Disney, 2013). It is important to note that in certain cultures and philosophies (e.g., East Asian Confucianism) dependence and submission may be viewed as desired interpersonal states (Chen et al., 2009; see DSM Table 13.10).

Causes

We are all born dependent on other people for food, physical protection, and nurturance. Part of the socialization process in most cultures involves helping us live independently. It was thought such disruptions as the early death of a parent or neglect or rejection by caregivers could cause people to grow up fearing abandonment (Stone, 1993). It also is clear, however, that genetic

influences are important in the development of this disorder (Gjerde et al., 2012). What is not yet understood are the physiological factors underlying these genetic influences and how genetic factors interact with environmental influences (Sanislow et al., 2012).

Research by David A. Clark and his colleagues at the University of New Brunswick suggests that certain personality traits may be quite relevant to the etiology of dependent personality disorder as well. In particular, these researchers have been investigating the role of the personality constructs of sociotropy and autonomy in the Cluster C personality disorders. *Sociotropy* refers to a personality orientation involving a strong investment in positive social interactions, whereas autonomy refers to a personality style involving a strong investment in independence from others, mobility, and freedom of choice (Beck, 1983, 1987). Clark and colleagues tested more than 2000 psychiatric outpatients on a self-report measure of sociotropy and autonomy and with a structured interview for establishing *DSM* diagnoses (Clark et al., 1997). They found the sample was characterized by four clusters of patients in terms of their responses to the sociotropy–autonomy measure: an autonomous group, a sociotropic group, an individualistic achievement group, and a group of low-scoring individuals. They found that diagnoses of dependent personality disorder were significantly more common in the sociotropic group compared with the other three groups. Diagnoses of avoidant personality disorder were also significantly more common in the sociotropic group. Diagnoses of dependent personality disorder were significantly less common in the individualistic achievement group than in the other three groups. No other differences in personality disorders were found across the four groups (Clark et al., 1997).

DSM-5	**Table 13.10** Diagnostic Criteria for Dependent Personality Disorder

A pervasive and excessive need to be taken care of that leads to submissive and clinging behavior and fears of separation, beginning by early adulthood and present in a variety of contexts, as indicated by five (or more) of the following:

1. Has difficulty making everyday decisions without an excessive amount of advice and reassurance from others.
2. Needs others to assume responsibility for most major areas of his or her life.
3. Has difficulty expressing disagreement with others because of fear of loss of support or approval. (Note: Do not include realistic fears of retribution.)
4. Has difficulty initiating projects or doing things on his or her own (because of a lack of self-confidence in judgment or abilities rather than a lack of motivation or energy).
5. Goes to excessive lengths to obtain nurturance and support from others, to the point of volunteering to do things that are unpleasant.
6. Feels uncomfortable or helpless when alone because of exaggerated fears of being unable to take care of himself or herself.
7. Urgently seeks another relationship as a source of care and support when a close relationship ends.
8. Is unrealistically preoccupied with fears of being left to take care of himself or herself.

Source: Reprinted with permission from the *Diagnostic and Statistical Manual of Mental Disorders*, Fifth Edition (Copyright © 2013). American Psychiatric Association. All Rights Reserved.

Treatment

The treatment literature for this disorder is mostly descriptive; very little research exists to show whether a particular treatment is effective. On the surface, because of their attentiveness and eagerness to give responsibility for their problems to the therapist, people with dependent personality disorder can appear to be ideal patients. That very submissiveness, however, negates one of the major goals of therapy, which is to make the person more independent and personally responsible (Leahy & McGinn, 2012). Therapy therefore progresses gradually, as the patient develops confidence in his or her ability to make decisions independently (Beck & Freeman, 1990). There is a particular need for care that the patient does not become overly dependent on the therapist.

Concept Check 13.2

Review your ability to differentiate among the personality disorders.

1. John is very reluctant to talk to anyone, not to mention a therapist. His reluctance and mistrust of others seem to be unlimited. John gives the impression that everyone is out to get him. _____

2. The therapist immediately notices that Milagros displays a great deal of extreme emotional behaviour when she speaks, so much so that she seems to be acting.

    _____

3. Susan was brought in by her parents because they found her uncontrollable. She had been stealing from her parents and friends, and she's so impulsive that her parents don't know what she might try next. Some people call her a "psychopath." _____

4. Jaikumar is especially anxious at even the thought of social interactions. He reacts excessively to criticism, which only feeds his pervasive feelings of inadequacy.

    _____

OBSESSIVE-COMPULSIVE PERSONALITY DISORDER

People who have **obsessive-compulsive personality disorder** are characterized by a fixation on things being done the right way. Although many might envy their persistence and dedication, this preoccupation with details prevents them from actually completing much of anything. Consider the case of Daniel.

DANIEL | *Getting It Exactly Right*

Each day at exactly 8 a.m., Daniel arrived at his office at the university where he was a graduate student in psychology. On his way, he always stopped at Tim Hortons to buy coffee. After arriving at his office, he drank his coffee and read *The Globe and Mail* from 8 to 9:15 a.m. At 9:15 he reorganized the files that held the hundreds of papers related to his doctoral dissertation, now several years overdue. From 10 a.m. until noon, he read one of these papers, highlighting relevant passages. Then he took the paper bag that held his lunch (always a peanut butter and jelly sandwich and an apple) and went to the cafeteria to purchase a soft drink and eat by himself. From 1 p.m. until 5 p.m., he held meetings, organized his desk, made lists of things to do, and entered his references into a new database program on his computer. At home, Daniel had dinner with his wife, and then worked on his dissertation until after 11 p.m., although much of the time was spent trying out the new features of his home computer.

Daniel was no closer to completing his dissertation than he had been four and a half years ago. His wife was threatening to leave him because he was equally rigid about everything at home and she didn't want to remain in this limbo of graduate school forever. When Daniel eventually sought help from a therapist for his anxiety over his deteriorating marriage, he was diagnosed as having obsessive-compulsive personality disorder.

Clinical Description

Like many with this personality disorder, Daniel is very work oriented, spending little time going to movies or parties or doing anything that isn't related to psychology. Because of their general rigidity, these people tend to have poor interpersonal relationships (Samuels & Costa, 2012; see DSM Table 13.11).

DSM-5 | Table 13.11 Diagnostic Criteria for Obsessive-Compulsive Personality Disorder

A pervasive pattern of preoccupation with orderliness, perfectionism, and mental and interpersonal control, at the expense of flexibility, openness, and efficiency, beginning by early adulthood and present in a variety of contexts, as indicated by four (or more) of the following:

1. Is preoccupied with details, rules, lists, order, organization, or schedules to the extent that the major point of the activity is lost.
2. Shows perfectionism that interferes with task completion (e.g., is unable to complete a project because his or her own overly strict standards are not met).
3. Is excessively devoted to work and productivity to the exclusion of leisure activities and friendships (not accounted for by obvious economic necessity).
4. Is overconscientious, scrupulous, and inflexible about matters of morality, ethics, or values (not accounted for by cultural or religious identification).
5. Is unable to discard worn-out or worthless objects even when they have no sentimental value.
6. Is reluctant to delegate tasks or to work with others unless they submit to exactly his or her way of doing things.
7. Adopts a miserly spending style toward both self and others; money is viewed as something to be hoarded for future catastrophes.
8. Shows rigidity and stubbornness.

Source: Reprinted with permission from the *Diagnostic and Statistical Manual of Mental Disorders*, Fifth Edition (Copyright © 2013). American Psychiatric Association. All Rights Reserved.

▲ People with obsessive-compulsive personality disorder are preoccupied with doing things the right way.

We do not have much information on the successful treatment of individuals with this disorder. Therapy often attacks the fears that seem to underlie the need for orderliness (Pinto, 2015). These individuals are often afraid that what they do will be inadequate, so they procrastinate and excessively ruminate about both important issues and minor details. Therapists help the individual relax or use cognitive reappraisal techniques to reframe compulsive thoughts. Perfectionism (i.e., self-criticism, difficulty dealing with feedback, procrastination, and unrealistic goal setting) is an important aspect of obsessive-compulsive personality disorder, as indicated by the work of Toronto psychiatrists Allan Kaplan, Blake Woodside, and their colleagues (Halmi et al., 2005). A study by Alberta researchers Kirsten Ferguson and Margaret Rodway (1994) indicates that cognitive-behavioural therapy can be effective in treating this important feature of obsessive-compulsive personality disorder (Svartberg et al., 2004).

This personality disorder seems to be only distantly related to obsessive-compulsive disorder, a disorder we described in Chapter 6 (Samuels & Costa, 2012). People like Daniel tend not to have the obsessive thoughts and the compulsive behaviours seen in the like-named obsessive-compulsive disorder. Although people with the anxiety disorder sometimes show characteristics of the personality disorder, they also show the characteristics of other personality disorders as well (e.g., avoidant, histrionic, dependent; Melca et al., 2015; Trull et al., 2012).

An intriguing theory suggests that the psychological profiles of many serial killers point to the role of obsessive-compulsive personality disorder. Ferreira (2000) notes that these individuals do not often fit the definition of someone with a severe mental illness—such as schizophrenia—but are masters of control in manipulating their victims. Their need to control all aspects of the crime fits the pattern of people with obsessive-compulsive personality disorder, and some combination of this disorder and unfortunate childhood experiences may lead to this disturbing behaviour pattern. Obsessive-compulsive personality disorder may also play a role among some sex offenders—in particular, pedophiles. Brain-imaging research on pedophiles suggests that brain functioning in these individuals is similar to those with obsessive-compulsive personality disorder (Schiffer et al., 2007). At the other end of the behavioural spectrum, it is also common to find obsessive-compulsive personality disorder among gifted children, whose quest for perfectionism can be quite debilitating (Nugent, 2000).

Causes and Treatment

There seems to be a moderate genetic contribution to obsessive-compulsive personality disorder (Cloninger & Svakic, 2009; Gjerde et al., 2015). Some people may be predisposed to favouring structure in their lives, but to reach the level it did in Daniel may require parental reinforcement of conformity and neatness.

Concept Check 13.3

Check your understanding of these additional personality disorders by identifying the patterns described here as (a) dependent, (b) narcissistic, (c) obsessive-compulsive, (d) schizoid, or (e) histrionic.

1. Katherine thinks she is the best candidate for any job, thinks her performance is always excellent, and looks for admiration from others. _____

2. Manon is afraid to be alone and seeks constant reassurance from her family. She won't make any decisions or do things on her own. She thinks that if she shows any resolve or initiative she will be abandoned and have to take care of herself. _____

3. The therapist discovers that Filipe has yet to fill out the information form, although he was given at least 15 minutes. Filipe says he first had to resharpen the pencil, then clean it of debris, then he noticed that the pencil sharpener wasn't very clean. The paper also wasn't properly placed on the clipboard. _____

4. George is overly dramatic about everyday occurrences and likes to be the centre of attention. _____

PERSONALITY DISORDERS UNDER STUDY

We started this chapter by noting difficulties in categorizing personality disorders; for example, there is much overlap of the categories, which suggests there may be other ways to arrange these pervasive difficulties of character. It shouldn't surprise you to learn that other personality disorders have been studied for inclusion in the *DSM*—for example, sadistic personality disorder, which includes people who receive pleasure by inflicting pain on others (Morey et al., 2007), and passive-aggressive personality disorder, which includes people who are defiant and refuse to cooperate with requests—attempting to undermine authority figures (Wetzler & Jose, 2012). The existence of these disorders as distinct personality disorders remains controversial, however, so they were not included in the *DSM-5* (Wetzler & Jose, 2012).

DSM CONTROVERSIES | The Battle for the Personality Disorders

Discussion about the personality disorders in the *DSM-5* included proposals for a number of major changes to this category. As we have seen, the elimination of the distinction between Axis I and Axis II disorders elevated the personality disorders into the mainstream of problems experienced by individuals. However, other major changes that appeared to be ready for inclusion in *DSM-5* never occurred. The goal of creating dimensions of different personality traits along the lines of the Big Five rather than the specific disorders outlined in this chapter never materialized. In part, this proposal was not included in the *DSM-5* because of the difficulty in making a diagnosis (too many permutations) and potential problems in using that information to design treatments (Skodol, 2012).

However, one of the biggest changes proposed was to completely eliminate five of the personality disorders (paranoid, schizoid, histrionic, avoidant, and dependent personality disorders). Instead, people previously diagnosed with these disorders would be identified as having a general personality disorder with the traits specified (e.g., suspiciousness, emotional lability, hostility). The rationale for their removal included a relative lack of research on these disorders and significant overlap among the disorders (Skodol, 2012). In anticipation of this significant change, one set of researchers authored a paper with the title "The Death of Histrionic Personality Disorder" (Blashfield et al., 2012) and the personality disorders community of researchers in general was divided over this change (Pull, 2013). Ultimately, the final draft retained these disorders and left for a later time proposals for dealing with the problems of lack of research and specificity. This back and forth on how to carve up diagnoses exemplifies the difficulties that continue to exist for any diagnostic system, even after decades of arduous and dedicated research.

SUMMARY

An Overview

- The personality disorders represent long-standing and ingrained ways of thinking, feeling, and behaving that can cause significant distress. Because people may display two or more of these maladaptive ways of interacting with the world, considerable disagreement remains over how to categorize the personality disorders.
- The *DSM-5* includes ten personality disorders that are divided into three "clusters": Cluster A ("odd or eccentric") includes paranoid, schizoid, and schizotypal personality disorders; Cluster B ("dramatic, emotional, or erratic") includes antisocial, borderline, histrionic, and narcissistic personality disorders; Cluster C ("anxious or fearful") includes avoidant, dependent, and obsessive-compulsive personality disorder.
- Treating people with personality disorders is often difficult because they usually do not see that their difficulties are a result of the way they relate to others.
- Personality disorders are important for the clinician to consider because they may interfere with efforts to treat more specific problems, such as anxiety, depression, or substance abuse. Unfortunately, the presence of one or more personality disorders is associated with a poor treatment outcome and a generally negative prognosis.

Cluster A Disorders

- People with paranoid personality disorder are excessively mistrustful and suspicious of other people, without any justification. They tend not to confide in others and expect other people to do them harm.
- People with schizoid personality disorder show a pattern of detachment from social relationships and a very limited range of emotions in interpersonal situations. They seem aloof, cold, and indifferent to other people.
- People with schizotypal personality disorder are typically socially isolated and behave in ways that would seem unusual to most of us. Additionally, they tend to be suspicious and have odd beliefs about the world.

Cluster B Disorders

- People with antisocial personality disorder have a history of failing to comply with social norms. They perform actions most of us would find unacceptable, such as stealing from friends and family. They also tend to be irresponsible, impulsive, and deceitful.
- People with borderline personality disorder lack stability in their moods and in their relationships with other people, and

they usually have very poor self-esteem. These individuals often feel empty and are at great risk of suicide.

- Individuals with histrionic personality disorder tend to be overly dramatic and often appear almost to be acting.
- People with narcissistic personality disorder think highly of themselves—beyond their real abilities. They consider themselves somehow different from others and deserving of special treatment.

Cluster C Disorders

- People with avoidant personality disorder are extremely sensitive to the opinions of others and therefore avoid social relationships. Their extremely low self-esteem, coupled with a fear of rejection, causes them to reject the attention others crave.

- Individuals with dependent personality disorder rely on others to the extent of letting them make everyday decisions and major ones; this results in an unreasonable fear of being abandoned.
- People who have obsessive-compulsive personality disorder are characterized by a fixation on things being done "the right way." This preoccupation with details prevents them from actually completing much of anything.

Personality Disorders under Study

- Other personality disorders, such as sadistic personality disorder and passive-aggressive personality disorder, have been studied for inclusion in the *DSM*. Their existence as distinct personality disorders remains controversial.

KEY TERMS

antisocial personality disorder, 397

avoidant personality disorder, 412

borderline personality disorder, 404

dependent personality disorder, 413

histrionic personality disorder, 409

narcissistic personality disorder, 410

obsessive-compulsive personality disorder, 415

paranoid personality disorder, 391

personality disorder, 387

psychopathy, 397

schizoid personality disorder, 394

schizotypal personality disorder, 395

ANSWERS TO CONCEPT CHECKS

13.1

1. schizoid personality disorder; **2.** antisocial personality disorder; **3.** paranoid personality disorder; **4.** borderline personality disorder

13.2

1. paranoid personality disorder; **2.** histrionic personality disorder; **3.** antisocial personality disorder; **4.** avoidant personality disorder

13.3

1. b; **2.** a; **3.** c; **4.** e

⟐ CENGAGE | MINDTAP

Stay organized and efficient with MindTap—a single destination with all the course material and study aids you need to succeed. Built-in apps leverage social media and the latest learning technology. For example:

- ReadSpeaker will read the text to you.
- Flashcards are pre-populated to provide you with a jump start for review—or you can create your own.
- You can highlight text and make notes in your MindTap Reader. Your notes will flow into Evernote, the electronic notebook app that you can access anywhere when it's time to study for the exam.
- Self-quizzing allows you to assess your understanding.

Visit login.cengage.com to start using MindTap. Enter the Online Access Code from the card included with your text. If a code card is not provided, you can purchase instant access at Cengage.ca.

Exploring Personality Disorders

> People with personality disorders think and behave in ways that cause distress to themselves and/or the people who care about them.

> There are three main groups, or clusters, of personality disorders, which usually begin in childhood.

CLUSTER A

Odd or
Eccentric

Gazelle Technologies

Paranoid
extreme suspicion

Psychological Influences

- Thoughts that people are malicious, deceptive, and threatening
- Behaviour based on mistaken assumptions about others

Causes

Biological Influences

- Possible but unclear link with schizophrenia

Schizoid
social isolation

Psychological Influences

- Very limited range of emotions
- Apparently cold and unconnected
- Unaffected by praise or criticism

Biological Influences

- May be associated with lower density of dopamine receptors

Causes

Social/Cultural Influences

- "Outsiders" may be susceptible because of unique experiences (e.g., prisoners, refugees, people with hearing impairments, and the elderly)
- Parents' early teaching may influence

Treatment

- Difficult because of client's mistrust and suspicion
- Cognitive work to change thoughts
- Low success rate

Treatment

- Learning value of social relationships
- Social skills training with role playing

Social/Cultural Influences

- Preference for social isolation
- Lack of social skills
- Lack of interest in close relationships, including romantic or sexual

Psychological Influences

- Unusual beliefs, behaviour, or dress
- Suspiciousness
- Believing insignificant events are personally relevant ("ideas of reference")
- Expressing little emotion
- Symptoms of major depressive disorder

Schizotypal
suspicion and
odd behaviour

Biological Influences

- Genetic vulnerability for schizophrenia but without the biological or environmental stresses present in that disorder

Causes

CLUSTER C

Anxious or Fearful

Ghislain & Marie David de Lossy/
The Image Bank/Getty Images

Dependent
pervasive need to be taken
care of

Psychological Influences

- Early "loss" of caretaker (death, rejection, or neglect) leads to fear of abandonment
- Timidity and passivity

Biological Influences

- Each of us born dependent for protection, food, and nurturance

Causes

Treatment

- Teaching social skills to reduce isolation and suspicion
- Medication (haloperidol) to reduce ideas of reference, odd communication, and isolation
- Low success rate

Social/Cultural Influences

- Preference for social isolation
- Excessive social anxiety
- Lack of social skills

Social/Cultural Influences

- Agreement for the sake of avoiding conflict
- Similar to Avoidant in
  – inadequacy
  – sensitivity to criticism
  – need for reassurance
  BUT
  for those same shared reasons
- Avoidants withdraw
- Dependents cling

Treatment

- Very little research
- Appear as ideal clients
- Submissiveness negates independence

CLUSTER B

ThinkStock/Getty Images

Dramatic, Emotional, or Erratic

Note: Cluster B also includes Narcissistic Personality Disorder.

Antisocial
violation of others' rights

Histrionic
excessively emotional

Psychological Influences

- Difficulty learning to avoid punishment
- Indifferent to concerns of others

Causes

Biological Influences

- Genetic vulnerability combined with environmental influences
- Abnormally low cortical arousal
- High fear threshold

Psychological Influences

- Vain and self-centred
- Easily upset if ignored
- Vague and hyperbolic
- Impulsive; difficulty delaying gratification

Causes

Biological Influences

- Possible link to antisocial disorder
  - women histrionic/men antisocial

Social/Cultural Influences

- Criminality
- Stress/exposure to trauma
- Inconsistent parental discipline
- Socioeconomic disadvantage

Treatment

- Seldom successful (incarceration instead)
- Parent training if problems are caught early
- Prevention through preschool programs

Treatment

- Little evidence of success
- Rewards and fines
- Focus on interpersonal relations

Social/Cultural Influences

- Overly dramatic behaviour attracts attention
- Seductive
- Approval-seeking

Borderline
tumultuous instability

Psychological Influences

- Suicidal
- Erratic moods
- Impulsivity

Biological Influences

- Familial link to mood disorders
- Possibly inherited tendencies (impulsivity or volatility)

Causes

Social/Cultural Influences

- Early trauma, especially sexual/physical abuse
- Rapid cultural changes (immigration) may trigger symptoms

Treatment

- Dialectical behaviour therapy (DBT)
- Medication:
  - tricyclic antide-pressants
  - minor tranquilizers
  - lithium

Avoidant
inhibition

Psychological Influences

- Low self-esteem
- Fear of rejection, criticism leads to fear of attention
- Extreme sensitivity
- Resembles social phobia

Causes

Biological Influences

- Innate characteristics may cause rejection

Obsessive-compulsive
fixation on details

Biological Influences

- Distant relation to OCD
- Probable weak genetic role
  - predisposition to structure combined with parental reinforcement

Social/Cultural Influences

- Insufficient parental affection

Psychological Influences

- Generally rigid
- Dependent on routines
- Procrastinating

Causes

Treatment

- Behavioural intervention techniques sometimes successful
  - systematic desensitization
  - behavioural rehearsal
- Improvements usually modest

Social/Cultural Influences

- Very work-oriented
- Poor interpersonal relationships

Treatment

- Little information
- Therapy
  - attack fears behind need
  - relaxation or distraction techniques redirect compulsion to order

14 | Psychosis

Nick Dolding/Getty Images

The next day I awake and go to the Laundromat. But why are these cars making gestures as though guns are at their heads. They must all hate me. Someone is going to kill me. Maybe it is a warning. Maybe it is Emillio's plan. I run to my apartment. My God, what am I going to do? These people want me dead for some reason. . . . I run from the Laundromat to my apartment. . . . I hide under my Parson's table. But what's this? Everyone is honking? Are they angry?

—CHRISTINA ALEXANDRA, Five Lost Years: A Personal Exploration of Schizophrenia

Use scientific reasoning to interpret behaviour:	❭ Identify basic biological, psychological, and social components of behavioural explanations (e.g., inferences, observations, operational definitions, and interpretations) (APA SLO 2.1a)
Develop a working knowledge of the content domains of psychology:	❭ Summarize important aspects of history of psychology, including key figures, central concerns, methods used, and theoretical conflicts (APA SLO 1.2c)
Engage in innovative and integrative thinking and problem solving:	❭ Describe problems operationally to study them empirically (APA SLO 2.3a)
Describe applications that employ discipline-based problem solving:	❭ Correctly identify antecedents and consequences of behaviour and mental processes (APA SLO 1.3c) ❭ Describe examples of relevant and practical applications of psychological principles to everyday life (APA SLO 1.3a)

*Portions of this chapter cover learning outcomes suggested by the American Psychological Association (2013) in its guidelines for the undergraduate psychology major. Chapter coverage of these outcomes is identified above by APA Goal and APA Suggested Learning Outcome (SLO).

A middle-aged man walks the streets of Toronto with aluminum foil on the inside of his hat so Martians can't read his mind. A young woman sits in her college classroom and hears the voice of God telling her she is a vile and disgusting person. You try to strike up a conversation with the supermarket bagger, but he stares at you vacantly and will say only one or two words in a flat, toneless voice. Each of these people may have **schizophrenia**, the startling disorder characterized by a broad spectrum of cognitive and emotional dysfunctions, including delusions and hallucinations, disorganized speech and behaviour, and inappropriate emotions.

Schizophrenia is a complex syndrome that inevitably has a devastating effect on the lives of the person affected and on family members. This disorder can disrupt a person's perception, thought, speech, and movement—almost every aspect of daily functioning. And despite important advances in treatment, full recovery from schizophrenia is rare (Jääskeläinen et al., 2013). Obviously, this catastrophic disorder takes a tremendous emotional toll on everyone involved. In addition to the emotional costs, the financial drain is considerable. According to the Canadian National Outcomes Measurement Study in Schizophrenia, the majority of people with schizophrenia in our country are unemployed and living in poverty (Smith et al., 2006). The annual cost to Canadian society is in the billions of dollars when factors such as hospitalization, disability payments, welfare payments, and lost wages are considered (British Columbia Schizophrenia Society, 2001; Goeree et al., 2005). Because schizophrenia is so widespread, affecting approximately 1 out of every 100 people at some point in their lives, and because its consequences are so severe, research on its causes and treatment has proliferated. Given the attention it has received, you would think that the question "What is schizophrenia?" would by now be answered easily. It is not.

In this chapter, we explore this intriguing disorder and review efforts to determine whether schizophrenia is distinct in itself or a combination of disorders. As noted a long time ago by Walter Heinrichs and his colleagues at York University, the search is complicated by the presence of subtypes: different presentations and combinations of symptoms, such as hallucinations, delusions, and disorders of speech, cognition, emotion, and socialization (Heinrichs, 1993; Heinrichs & Awad, 1993; Heinrichs et al., 1997). In this chapter we discuss schizophrenia at length, along with other psychotic disorders.

PERSPECTIVES ON THE CONCEPT OF SCHIZOPHRENIA

EARLY FIGURES IN DIAGNOSING SCHIZOPHRENIA

Toward the end of the 19th century, German psychiatrist Emil Kraepelin (1899) provided what stands today as the most enduring description and categorization of schizophrenia. Two of Kraepelin's accomplishments are especially important. First, he combined several symptoms of insanity that had usually been viewed as reflecting separate and distinct disorders: **catatonia** (alternating immobility and excited agitation), **hebephrenia** (silly and immature emotionality), and **paranoia** (delusions of grandeur or persecution). Kraepelin thought these symptoms shared similar underlying features and included them under the Latin term **dementia praecox**. Although the clinical manifestation might differ from person to person, Kraepelin believed an early onset at the heart of each disorder ultimately develops into "mental weakness."

In a second important contribution, Kraepelin (1898) distinguished dementia praecox from manic-depressive illness (bipolar disorder). For people with dementia praecox, an early age of onset and a poor outcome were characteristic; in contrast, these patterns were not essential to manic depression. Kraepelin also noted the numerous symptoms in people with dementia praecox, including hallucinations, delusions, negativism, and stereotyped behaviour.

A second major figure in the history of schizophrenia was Kraepelin's contemporary, Eugen Bleuler (1908), a Swiss psychiatrist who introduced the term *schizophrenia*. The label was significant because it signalled Bleuler's departure from Kraepelin on what he thought was the core problem. "Schizophrenia," which comes from the combination of the Greek words for "split" (*skhizein*) and "mind" (*phren*), reflected Bleuler's belief that underlying all the unusual behaviours shown by people with this disorder was an **associative splitting** of the basic functions of personality. This concept emphasized the "breaking of associative threads," or the destruction of the forces that connect one function to the next. Furthermore, Bleuler believed that difficulty keeping a consistent train of thought, characteristic of all persons with this disorder, led to the many and diverse symptoms they displayed. Whereas Kraepelin focused on early onset and poor outcomes,

▲ Eugen Bleuler (1857–1939), a Swiss psychiatrist, introduced the term *schizophrenia* and was a pioneer in the field.

Bleuler highlighted what he believed to be the universal underlying problem. Unfortunately, the concept of "split mind" inspired the common but incorrect use of the term *schizophrenia* to mean split or multiple personality.

IDENTIFYING SYMPTOMS

What is schizophrenia? As you read about disorders in this book, you have learned that a particular behaviour, way of thinking, or emotion usually defines or is characteristic of each disorder. For example, depression always includes feelings of sadness, and panic disorder is always accompanied by intense feelings of anxiety. Surprisingly, this isn't the case for schizophrenia. Schizophrenia is actually a number of behaviours or symptoms that aren't necessarily shared by all the people who are given this diagnosis.

Despite significant variations, researchers have identified clusters of symptoms that make up the disorder of schizophrenia. Later, we describe these very dramatic symptoms, such as seeing or hearing things that others do not (hallucinations) or having beliefs that are unrealistic, bizarre, and not shared by others in the same culture (delusions). But first, consider the following case of an individual who had an intense but relatively rare short-term episode of psychotic behaviour.

ARTHUR | *Saving the Children*

We first met 22-year-old Arthur at an outpatient clinic in a psychiatric hospital. Arthur's family was extremely concerned and upset by his unusual behaviour and was desperately seeking help for him. They said that he was "sick" and "talking like a crazy man," and they were afraid he might harm himself.

Arthur had a normal childhood in a middle-class suburban neighbourhood. His parents had been happily married until his father's death several years earlier. Arthur was an average student throughout school and had completed an associate's degree in junior college. His family seemed to think he regretted not continuing on to receive a bachelor's degree. Arthur had worked in a series of temporary jobs, and his mother reported that he seemed satisfied with what he was doing. He lived and worked in a major city, some 15 minutes away from his mother and his married brother and sister.

Arthur's family said that about three weeks before he came to the clinic he had started speaking strangely. He had

been laid off from his job a few days before because of cutbacks and hadn't communicated with any of his family members for several days. When they next spoke with him, his behaviour startled them. Although he had always been idealistic and anxious to help other people, he now talked about saving all the starving children in the world with his "secret plan." At first his family assumed this was just an example of Arthur's sarcastic wit, but his demeanour changed to one of extreme concern, and he spoke nonstop about his plans. He began carrying several spiral notebooks that he claimed contained his scheme for helping starving children; he said he would reveal it only at the right time to the right person. Suspecting that Arthur might be taking drugs, which could explain the sudden and dramatic change in his behaviour, his family searched his apartment. Although they didn't find any evidence of drug use, they did find his chequebook and noticed a number of strange entries. Over the past several weeks, Arthur's handwriting had deteriorated, and he had written notes instead of the usual cheque information ("Start to begin now"; "This is important!" "They must be saved"). He had also made unusual notes in several of his most prized books, a particularly alarming development given his reverence for these books.

As the days went on, Arthur showed dramatic changes in emotion, often crying and acting very apprehensive. He stopped wearing socks and underwear and, despite the extremely cold weather, wouldn't wear a jacket when he went outdoors. At the family's insistence, he moved into his mother's apartment. He slept little and kept the family up until the early morning. His mother said it was like being in a living nightmare. Each morning she would wake up with a knot in her stomach, not wanting to get out of bed because she felt so helpless to do anything to rescue Arthur from his obvious distress.

The family's sense of alarm grew as Arthur revealed more details of his plan. He said that he was going to the German embassy because that was the only place people would listen to him. He would climb the fence at night when everyone was asleep and present his plan to the German ambassador. Fearing that Arthur would be hurt trying to enter the embassy grounds, his family contacted a local psychiatric hospital, described Arthur's condition, and asked that he be admitted. Much to their surprise and disappointment, they were told that Arthur could commit himself, but they couldn't bring him in involuntarily unless he was in danger of doing harm to himself or others. The fear that Arthur might be harmed wasn't sufficient reason to admit him involuntarily.

His family finally talked Arthur into meeting the staff at the outpatient clinic. In our interview, it was clear he was delusional, firmly believing in his ability to help all starving children. After some cajoling, I finally convinced him to let me see his books. He had written random thoughts (e.g., "The poor, starving souls"; "The moon is the only place") and made drawings of rocket ships. Parts of his plan involved building a rocket ship that would go to the moon, where he would create a community for all malnourished children, a place where they could live and be helped. After a few brief comments on his plan, I began to ask him about his health.

"You look tired. Are you getting enough sleep?"

"Sleep isn't really needed," he noted. "My plans will take me through, and then they can all rest."

"Your family is worried about you," I said. "Do you understand their concern?"

"It's important for all concerned to get together, to join together," he replied.

With that, he got up and walked out of the room and out of the building, after telling his family that he would be right back. After five minutes they went to look for him, but he had disappeared. He was missing for two days, which caused his family a great deal of concern about his health and safety. In an almost miraculous sequence of events, they found him walking the streets of the city. He acted as if nothing had happened. Gone were his notebooks and the talk of his secret plan.

What caused Arthur to act so strangely? Was it being laid off from his job? Was it the death of his father? Was it a genetic predisposition to have schizophrenia or another disorder that kicked in during a period of stress? Unfortunately, we will never know exactly what happened to Arthur to make him behave so bizarrely and then recover so quickly and completely. Research that we discuss next may shed some light on schizophrenia and related disorders and potentially help other Arthurs and their families.

CLINICAL DESCRIPTION

The case of Arthur shows the range of problems experienced by people with schizophrenia or other psychotic disorders. The term **psychosis** has been used to characterize many unusual behaviours, although in its strictest sense it usually involves delusions (irrational beliefs) and hallucinations (sensory experiences in the absence of external events). Schizophrenia is one of the disorders that involves psychosis, in which there is loss of contact with reality; we describe other disorders involving psychosis in more detail later.

Schizophrenia can affect all the functions we rely on each day. Before we describe the symptoms, it is important to look carefully at the specific characteristics of people who exhibit these behaviours, partly because we constantly see distorted images of people with schizophrenia. Headlines such as "Ex-Mental Patient Kills Family" falsely imply that everyone with schizophrenia is dangerous and violent. A Québec survey found that the majority of respondents thought that people with schizophrenia were dangerous or violent (Stip et al., 2001). But statistics show otherwise. A Canadian study examined nearly 700 cases from a forensic hospital and found that people with a schizophrenia diagnosis were far less likely to commit future violent crimes than those with a history of violent crime but no schizophrenia diagnosis

(Noonan, 2003). Nonetheless, media portrayals continue to frequently depict people with schizophrenia as violent. Like mistakenly assuming that "schizophrenia" means "split personality," the popular press also misrepresents people who experience these debilitating disorders.

Schizophrenia spectrum disorder constitutes the group of diagnoses we cover in this chapter, as recognized by those in the field of schizophrenia. In fact, Eugen Bleuler identified the different variants that were all included within this spectrum. (Ritsner & Gottesman, 2011). Previous editions of the DSM struggled with this concept in its varied presentations over the years, and, as we describe in this chapter, the *DSM-5* currently includes schizophrenia as well as other related psychotic disorders that fall under this heading (including schizophreniform, schizoaffective, delusional, and brief psychotic disorders). In addition, a personality disorder (schizotypal personality disorder, discussed in Chapter 13) also falls under this umbrella category of schizophrenia spectrum disorders. All these difficulties seem to share features of extreme reality distortion (e.g., hallucinations and delusions). Later, we discuss the symptoms the person experiences during the disorder (active-phase symptoms), the course of the disorder, and the spectrum of disorders included in this category.

Mental health workers typically distinguish between *positive* and *negative* symptoms of schizophrenia. A third dimension, *disorganized* symptoms, also appears to be an important aspect of the disorder. Positive symptoms generally refer to symptoms around distorted reality. Negative symptoms involve deficits in normal behaviour in such areas as speech, affect, and motivation. Disorganized symptoms include rambling speech, erratic behaviour, and inappropriate affect (Ho et al., 2003). A diagnosis of schizophrenia requires that two or more positive, negative, or disorganized symptoms be present for at least one month, with at least one of these symptoms including delusions, hallucinations, or disorganized speech (see DSM Table 14.1). The *DSM-5* also includes a dimensional assessment that rates the severity of the individual's symptoms on a 0–4 scale, with 0 indicating a symptom is not present, 1 indicating equivocal evidence (i.e., not sure), 2 indicating it is present but mild, 3 that it is present and moderate, and 4 that it is present and severe (American Psychiatric Association, 2013). A great deal of research has focused on the different symptoms of schizophrenia, each of which is described here in some detail.

POSITIVE SYMPTOMS

We next describe the **positive symptoms** of schizophrenia, which are the more obvious signs of psychosis. These include the disturbing experiences of delusions and hallucinations. Between 50 and 70 percent of people with schizophrenia experience hallucinations, delusions, or both (Lindenmayer & Khan, 2006).

Delusions

A belief that would be seen by most members of a society as a misrepresentation of reality is called a *disorder of thought content* or a **delusion**. Because of its importance in schizophrenia, delusion has been called "the basic characteristic of madness" (Jaspers, 1963). If, for example, you believe that squirrels really are aliens sent to Earth on a reconnaissance mission, you would

A. Two (or more) of the following, each present for a significant portion of time during a 1-month period (or less if successfully treated). At least one of these must be (1), (2), or (3):

  1. Delusions.

  2. Hallucinations.

  3. Disorganized speech (e.g., frequent derailment or incoherence).

  4. Grossly disorganized or catatonic behavior.

  5. Negative symptoms (i.e., diminished emotional expression or avolition).

B. For a significant portion of the time since the onset of the disturbance, level of functioning in one or more major areas, such as work, interpersonal relations, or self-care, is markedly below the level achieved prior to the onset (or when the onset is in childhood or adolescence, there is failure to achieve expected level of interpersonal, academic, or occupational functioning).

C. Continuous signs of the disturbance persist for at least 6 months. This 6-month period must include at least 1 month of symptoms (or less if successfully treated) that meet Criterion A (i.e., active-phase symptoms) and may include periods of prodromal or residual symptoms. During these prodromal or residual periods, the signs of the disturbance may be manifested by only negative symptoms or by two or more symptoms listed in Criterion A present in an attenuated form (e.g., odd beliefs, unusual perceptual experiences).

D. Schizoaffective disorder and depressive or bipolar disorder with psychotic features have been ruled out because either (1) no major depressive or manic episodes have occurred concurrently with the active-phase symptoms; or (2) if mood episodes have occurred during active-phase symptoms, they have been present for a minority of the total duration of the active and residual periods of the illness.

E. The disturbance is not attributable to the physiological effects of a substance (e.g., a drug of abuse, a medication) or another medical condition.

F. If there is a history of autistic spectrum disorder or a communication disorder of childhood onset, the additional diagnosis of schizophrenia is made only if prominent delusions or hallucinations, in addition to the other required symptoms of schizophrenia, are also present for at least 1 month (or less if successfully treated).

Specify if:

  With catatonia

be considered delusional. The media often portray people with schizophrenia as believing they are famous or important people (such as Napoleon or Jesus Christ). Arthur's belief that he could end starvation for all the world's children is also a *delusion of grandeur* (a mistaken belief that the person is famous or powerful) (Knowles et al., 2011).

A common delusion in people with schizophrenia is that others are out to get them. Called *delusions of persecution*, these beliefs can be most disturbing. One of us worked with a world-class cyclist who was on her way to making the Olympic team. Tragically, however, she believed other competitors were determined to sabotage her efforts, which forced her to stop riding for years. She believed that opponents would spray her bicycle with chemicals that would take her strength away and that they would slow her down by putting small pebbles in the road that only she would ride over. These thoughts created a great deal of anxiety, and she refused even to go near her bicycle for some time.

Other more unusual delusions include *Cotard's syndrome*, in which the person believes a part of his or her body (e.g., the brain) has changed in some impossible way, and *Capgras syndrome*, in which the person believes someone he or she knows has been replaced by a double (Black & Andreasen, 1999). An example of a celebrity who suffered from Capgras syndrome

was the tragic case of comedian Tony Rosato, former star of SCTV and *Saturday Night Live* (Brean, 2007; Freed, 2007). Rosato was arrested in 2005 on charges of criminal harassment of his wife after repeatedly complaining to police that his wife, Leah, and their infant daughter had gone missing and had been replaced by imposters (Brean, 2007; Freed, 2007).

Why do delusions persist in the face of contradictory information? One intriguing possibility is that delusions may serve a

▲ Toronto comedian Tony Rosato, of *SCTV* and *Saturday Night Live* fame, suffered from the unusual delusions characteristic of Capgras syndrome.

▲ Artist William Kurelek was born in 1927 near Whitford, Alberta. He painted this piece during a psychiatric hospitalization in 1953 where he was treated for schizophrenia. *The Maze* is an introspective work in which Kurelek portrays his persecutory and somatic delusions as scenes encapsulated within compartments in a human skull.

purpose for people with schizophrenia who are otherwise quite upset by the changes taking place within themselves. For example, Roberts (1991) studied 17 people who had elaborate delusions about themselves and the world, and compared them with a matched group of people who had previously had delusions but were now improving. The individuals with current delusions expressed a much stronger sense of purpose and meaning in life *and less depression*, all of which seemed related to their delusional belief systems. Compare this with the opposite situation we discussed in Chapter 8, in which we found that people who were depressed seemed sadder but wiser. That delusions may serve an adaptive function is at present just a theory with little support, but it may help us understand the phenomenon and its effect on those who experience it.

Hallucinations

Have you ever thought you heard someone call your name, only to discover that no one was there? Did you ever think you saw something move by you, yet nothing did? We all have fleeting moments when we think we see or hear something that isn't there. For many people with schizophrenia, however, these perceptions feel very real and occur on a regular basis. The experience of sensory events without any input from the surrounding environment is called a **hallucination** (Fischer et al., 2004). The case of David illustrates the phenomena of hallucinations and other disorders of thought that are common among people with schizophrenia.

David's conversational speech resembled a ball rolling down a rocky hill. Like an accelerating object, his speech gained momentum the longer he went on and, as if bouncing off obstacles, the topics almost always went in unpredictable directions. If he continued for too long, he often became agitated and spoke of harming others. David also said that his uncle's voice spoke to him repeatedly. He heard other voices also, but he couldn't identify them or tell what they said. We return to David's case later in this chapter when we discuss causes and treatments.

DAVID | *Missing Uncle Bill*

David was 25 years old when I met him; he had been living in a psychiatric hospital for about three years. He was a little overweight and of average height; he typically dressed in a T-shirt and jeans and tended to be active. I first encountered him while I was talking to another man who lived on the same floor. David interrupted us by pulling on my shoulder. "My Uncle Bill is a good man. He treats me well." Not wanting to be impolite, I said, "I'm sure he is. Maybe after I've finished talking to Michael here, we can talk about your uncle." David persisted, "He can kill fish with a knife. Things can get awfully sharp in your mind, when you go down the river. I could kill you with my bare hands—taking things into my own hands. . . . I know you know!" He was now speaking very quickly and had gained emotionality along with speed as he spoke. I talked to him quietly until he calmed down for the moment. Later, I looked into David's file for some information about his background.

David was brought up on a farm by his Aunt Katie and Uncle Bill. His father's identity is unknown and his mother, who had mental retardation (the term used at the time), couldn't care for him. David too was diagnosed as having mental retardation, although his functioning was only mildly impaired and he attended school. The year David's Uncle Bill died, his high school teachers first reported unusual behaviour. David occasionally talked to his deceased Uncle Bill in class. Later, he became increasingly agitated and verbally aggressive toward others and was diagnosed as having schizophrenia. He managed to graduate from high school but never obtained a job after that; he lived at home with his aunt for several years. Although his aunt really wanted him to stay with her, his threatening behaviour escalated to the point that she requested he be seen at the local psychiatric hospital.

I spoke with David again and had a chance to ask him a few questions. "Why are you here in the hospital, David?"

"I really don't want to be here," he told me "I've got other things to do. The time is right, and you know, when opportunity knocks. . . ."

He continued for a few minutes until I interrupted him. "I was sorry to hear that your uncle Bill died a few years ago. How are you feeling about him these days?"

"Yes, he died. He was sick and now he's gone. He likes to fish with me, down at the river. He's going to take me hunting. I have guns. I can shoot you and you'd be dead in a minute."

Hallucinations can involve any of the senses, although hearing things that aren't there, or *auditory hallucination*, is the most common form experienced by people with schizophrenia (Liddle, 2012). David had frequent auditory hallucinations, usually of his uncle's voice. When David heard a voice that belonged to his Uncle Bill, he often couldn't understand what his uncle was saying; on other occasions the voice was clearer. "He told me to turn off the TV. He said, 'It's too damn loud, turn it down, turn it down.' Other times he talks about fishing. 'Good day for fishing. Got to go fishing.'" You could tell when David was hearing voices. He was usually unoccupied, and he sat and smiled as if listening to someone next to him, but no one was there. This behaviour is consistent with research, which suggests that people tend to experience hallucinations more frequently when they are unoccupied or restricted from sensory input (e.g., Margo et al., 1981).

Exciting research on hallucinations uses sophisticated brain-imaging techniques to try to localize these phenomena in the brain. One theory of auditory verbal hallucinations states that people who are hallucinating are in fact not hearing the voices of others, but are listening to their own thoughts or their own voices and cannot recognize the difference. An alternative theory is that auditory verbal hallucinations arise from abnormal activation of the primary auditory cortex. A group of Montréal researchers (Ait Bentaleb et al., 2002) tested a woman with schizophrenia by using functional magnetic resonance imaging (fMRI) while she was experiencing her auditory verbal hallucinations and when she was listening to external speech; they compared her results with those of a matched control participant. They found that auditory verbal hallucinations were associated with increased metabolic activity in the left primary auditory cortex and in the right middle temporal gyrus. These results are consistent with both views regarding the origins of hallucinations (i.e., misinterpretation of inner speech and abnormal activation of the primary auditory cortex) and suggest that the two mechanisms are not necessarily mutually exclusive. More advanced imaging technology is allowing researchers to get a better view of just what is going on inside the brain during hallucinations and should help identify the role of the brain in the symptoms observed among people with schizophrenia (e.g., Silbersweig et al., 1995).

NEGATIVE SYMPTOMS

In contrast to the active presentations that characterize the positive symptoms of schizophrenia, the **negative symptoms** usually indicate the absence or insufficiency of normal behaviour. They include emotional and social withdrawal, apathy, and poverty of thought or speech. Approximately, 25 percent of people with schizophrenia display these symptoms (Cohen et al., 2013; Millan et al., 2014).

Avolition

Combining the prefix *a*, meaning "without," and *volition*, which means "an act of willing, choosing, or deciding," **avolition** is the inability to initiate and persist in activities. People with this symptom (also referred to as *apathy*) show little interest in performing even the most basic daily functions, including those associated with personal hygiene.

A study at the Centre for Addiction and Mental Health in Toronto examined the level of avolition in 28 patients with schizophrenia and its relationship to other symptoms of schizophrenia and to treatment outcome. Levels of avolition were significantly higher in the patients with schizophrenia than in a matched group of participants without schizophrenia. Avolition was not related to positive symptoms of schizophrenia. Unexpectedly, avolition was not related to negative symptoms of schizophrenia other than emotional withdrawal. Finally, avolition was more highly associated with poor outcome than were other schizophrenia symptoms—positive or negative (Kiang et al., 2003).

Alogia

Derived from the combination of *a* ("without") and *logos* ("words"), **alogia** refers to the relative absence of speech. A person with alogia may respond to questions with very brief replies that have little content and may appear uninterested in the conversation. For example, to the question, "Do you have any children?" most parents might reply, "Oh, yes, I have two beautiful children: a boy and a girl. My son is six and my daughter is twelve." In the following exchange, someone with alogia responds to the same question:

> INTERVIEWER: Do you have any children?
> CLIENT: Yes.
> INTERVIEWER: How many children do you have?
> CLIENT: Two.
> INTERVIEWER: How old are they?
> CLIENT: Six and twelve.

Such deficiency in communication is believed to reflect a negative thought disorder rather than inadequate communication skills. Some researchers, for example, suggest that people with alogia may have trouble finding the right words to formulate their thoughts (Alpert et al., 1994). Sometimes alogia takes the form of delayed comments or slow responses to questions. Talking with individuals who manifest this symptom can be extremely frustrating, making you feel as if you are "pulling teeth" to get them to respond.

ABNORMAL PSYCHOLOGY | **VIDEO**

© Cengage Learning

Schizophrenia: Andre

"I first started having problems . . . when I was about 15, . . . I saw a construction worker outside digging a hole . . . I seriously thought my mom was going to shoot me and . . . bury me where the hole was. . . . I have two boys and one girl. . . . No, I don't have any kids. I would remember I gave birth to kids. . . . My antipsychotic [meds] . . . make[s] me think more clearly. With the . . . [meds], I'm able to function. If I stop taking these medicines, then I probably would have a psychotic episode, leading me into further hospitalization. So, I'd have to say this is [inaudible]."

Visit login.cengage.com to start using MindTap. Enter the Online Access Code from the card included with your text. If a code card is not provided, you can purchase instant access at Cengage.ca.

Anhedonia

A related symptom is called **anhedonia**, which derives from the word *hedonic*, pertaining to pleasure. Anhedonia is the presumed lack of pleasure experienced by some people with schizophrenia. Like some mood disorders, anhedonia signals an indifference to activities that would typically be considered pleasurable, including eating, social interactions, and sexual relations. Given the similarities of the negative schizophrenia symptom of anhedonia to symptoms of depression, some researchers, such as David Romney and Carmie Candido at the University of Calgary, have questioned the distinctiveness of anhedonia and the mood disorders (e.g., Candido & Romney, 2002; Romney & Candido, 2001). A study by Ashok Malla at the University of Western Ontario and his colleagues provides mixed evidence on this issue. On the one hand, Malla et al. (2002) found a strong correlation between depression and a negative symptoms factor involving both anhedonia and avolition in a large sample of patients with schizophrenia. On the other hand, they also found that negative symptoms were present at a relatively high rate even after excluding the influence of depression. Regardless of the dependence or independence from depression, anhedonia is clinically meaningful in that it relates to a delay in seeking treatment for schizophrenia (Malla et al., 2002).

Asociality

This symptom may seem very similar to avolition or related to anhedonia. **Asociality** (*a* meaning "without" and *social* meaning "relating to society or its organization"), however, has been recognized as a separate symptom of schizophrenia spectrum disorders. This symptom captures a lack of interest in social interactions (APA, 2013). Unfortunately, this symptom can also result from or be worsened by limited opportunities to interact with others, particularly for severely ill patients (Reddy et al., 2016).

Research by University of Toronto researcher Jean Addington and her colleagues suggests that patients who have poor social or interpersonal functioning before the development of their psychosis also have greater levels of negative symptoms and greater social impairment at the time of their admission to a schizophrenia treatment program (Addington et al., 2003). In a review of the literature, Peter Liddle at the University of British Columbia found that the best predictor of asociality in people with schizophrenia is chronic cognitive impairment, suggesting that difficulties in processing information may contribute significantly to the social skills deficits and other social difficulties displayed by many patients (Liddle, 2000).

Affective Flattening

Imagine that people wore masks at all times: you could communicate with them but you wouldn't be able to see their emotional reactions. Approximately, two-thirds of the people with schizophrenia exhibit what is called **flat affect** (Simonsen et al., 2012). They are similar to people wearing masks because they do not show emotions when you would normally expect them to. They may stare at you vacantly, speak in a flat and toneless manner, and seem unaffected by things going on around them. However, although they do not react openly to emotional situations, they may still be experiencing emotions.

Berenbaum and Oltmanns (1992) compared people with schizophrenia who had flat (or blunted) affect with those who did not. The two groups were shown clips from films selected to create emotional reactions in the viewer. Berenbaum and Oltmanns found that the people with flat affect showed little change in facial expression, although they reported experiencing the appropriate emotions. The authors concluded that the flat affect in schizophrenia may represent difficulty expressing emotion, not a lack of feeling. In a more recent study, Montréal researchers Fahim et al. (2005) exposed schizophrenia patients with and without flat affect to negative and neutral images. Like the Berenbaum and Oltmanns findings, both groups experienced unpleasant emotions in response to the negative pictures; however, the negative emotions experienced were less intense in the patients with flat affect (Fahim et al., 2005). More research is thus needed to determine if it is the expression of emotion, the experience of emotion, or both, that is aberrant in schizophrenia patients suffering flat affect.

DISORGANIZED SYMPTOMS

Perhaps the least studied and therefore the least understood symptoms of schizophrenia are referred to as the **disorganized symptoms**. These include a variety of erratic behaviours that affect speech, motor behaviour, and emotional reactions. The prevalence of these behaviours among those with schizophrenia is unclear.

Disorganized Speech

A conversation with someone who has schizophrenia can be particularly frustrating. If you want to understand what is bothering or upsetting this person, eliciting relevant information is especially difficult. For one thing, people with schizophrenia often lack insight, an awareness that they have a problem. In addition, they experience "associative splitting" (Bleuler, 1908) and "cognitive slippage" (Meehl, 1962). These phrases help describe the speech problems of people with schizophrenia: Sometimes they jump from topic to topic and at other times they talk illogically. The *DSM-5* uses the term **disorganized speech** to describe such communication problems (Kerns & Berenbaum, 2002). Let's go back to our conversation with David to demonstrate the symptom.

> THERAPIST: Why are you here in the hospital, David?
> DAVID: I really don't want to be here. I've got other things to do. The time is right, and you know, when opportunity knocks . . .

David didn't really answer the question he was asked. This type of response is called *tangentiality*—that is, going off on a tangent instead of answering a specific question. David also abruptly changed the topic of conversation to unrelated areas, a behaviour that has been called loose association or derailment.

> THERAPIST: I was sorry to hear that your uncle Bill died a few years ago. How are you feeling about him these days?
> DAVID: Yes, he died. He was sick, and now he's gone. He likes to fish with me, down at the river. He's going to take me hunting. I have guns. I can shoot you and you'd be dead in a minute.

Again, David didn't answer the question. The therapist could not tell whether he didn't understand the question, couldn't focus his attention, or found it too difficult to talk about his uncle.

▲ Negative symptoms of schizophrenia include social withdrawal and apathy.

You can see why people spend a great deal of time trying to interpret all the hidden meanings behind this type of conversation. Unfortunately, however, such analyses have yet to provide us with useful information about the nature of schizophrenia or its treatment.

Concept Check 14.1

Identify the following terms associated with schizophrenia: affective flattening, avolition, delusions, hallucinations.

1. Beliefs that most people would describe as a misrepresentation of reality, called a disorder of thought content: _____

2. Apathy, or an inability to initiate or persist in important activities: _____

3. Lack of visible emotional response or reactivity: _____

4. Perceptions of sensory events that do not originate in the surrounding environment: _____

Inappropriate Affect and Disorganized Behaviour

Occasionally, people with schizophrenia display **inappropriate affect**, laughing or crying at improper times. Sometimes they exhibit bizarre behaviours, such as hoarding objects or acting in unusual ways in public. People with schizophrenia engage in several other "active" behaviours that are usually viewed as unusual. For example, catatonia is one of the most curious symptoms in some individuals with schizophrenia; it involves motor dysfunctions that range from wild agitation to immobility. The *DSM-5* now includes catatonia as a separate schizophrenia spectrum disorder. On the active side of the continuum, some people pace excitedly or move their fingers or arms in stereotyped ways. At the other end of the extreme, people hold unusual postures, as if they are fearful of something terrible happening if they move (**catatonic immobility**). This manifestation can also involve *waxy flexibility*, or the tendency to keep their bodies and limbs in the position they are put in by someone else.

Again, to receive a diagnosis of schizophrenia, a person must display two or more of the major symptoms (i.e., delusions, hallucinations, disorganized speech, grossly abnormal psychomotor behaviour—including catatonia—or negative symptoms such as diminished emotional expression or avolition) for a significant portion of time for one month. At least one of the symptoms must include delusions, hallucinations, or disorganized speech. Depending on the combination of symptoms displayed, two people could receive the same diagnosis but behave very differently, one having marked hallucinations and delusions and the other displaying disorganized speech and some of the negative symptoms. Proper treatment depends on differentiating individuals in terms of their varying symptoms.

OTHER PSYCHOTIC DISORDERS

The psychotic behaviours of some individuals do not fit neatly under the heading of schizophrenia as we have just described. Several other categories of disorders depict these significant variations.

Schizophreniform Disorder

Some people experience the symptoms of schizophrenia for a few months only; they can usually resume normal lives. The symptoms sometimes disappear as the result of successful treatment, but often for unknown reasons. The label **schizophreniform disorder** classifies these symptoms, but because relatively few studies are available on this disorder, data on important aspects of it are sparse. It appears, however, that the lifetime prevalence is approximately 0.2 percent (Erlich et al., 2014). The *DSM-5* diagnostic criteria for schizophreniform disorder (see DSM Table 14.2) include onset of psychotic symptoms within four weeks of the first noticeable change in usual behaviour, confusion at the height of the psychotic episode, good premorbid social and occupational functioning, and the absence of blunted or flat affect (Garrabe & Cousin, 2012).

Schizoaffective Disorder

Historically, people who had symptoms of schizophrenia and who also exhibited the characteristics of mood disorders (e.g., depression or bipolar affective disorder) were lumped together in the

For Robert K. Chapman, entering his 20s did not herald the beginning of exciting new adult pursuits, but rather the onset of symptoms of a major mental illness. Specifically, he was diagnosed with the paranoid type of schizophrenia. He struggled with this illness for more than a decade.

On Second Thought is a personal account of Chapman's struggles with many of the classic symptoms of paranoid schizophrenia. For example, he experienced delusions of influence, telepathy-like delusions of persecution, and problems with reality monitoring. Chapman also believed that his thoughts were being transmitted and that others could read his mind.

Not only does Chapman provide a lucid (and often humorous) account of his illness, but he also provides the reader with insights into the continuing social stigma associated with schizophrenia. He illustrates with examples from his own experience how people who have been diagnosed with this illness can be subject to such stigma, even after they have recovered. For Chapman, after he had recovered from schizophrenia, it took another two years to recuperate from the negative effects of the social stigma attached to mental illness.

Robert Chapman is now fully recovered from schizophrenia and resides in Ontario. He has been off antipsychotic medications for more than 15 years. His book contains a strong message of hope for those who have this disorder, their family members, and even for mental health professionals who work with clients who have schizophrenia. *On Second Thought* is largely a personal account of his courageous journey to full recovery. Chapman clearly describes how he made use of cognitive-behavioural therapy techniques to eliminate his paranoid delusions.

In addition to *On Second Thought*, he has written, researched, and illustrated several books on this subject. He also provides workshops and lectures at which he speaks about how he eliminated his paranoid delusions using cognitive-behavioural coping strategies, such as counterarguing against mind-reading ideas. He has given presentations from Ottawa, Ontario, to Oakland, California. A study conducted by researchers at McMaster University provides objective evidence that Chapman's message inspires hope for recovery among those who have schizophrenia. Specifically, the study showed that having a consumer like Chapman speak about cognitive-behavioural therapy is more effective in instilling hope for recovery than is having a mental health professional provide the same type of lecture (Zacharias et al., 1997).

Photo: From *On Second Thought: Eliminating Paranoid Delusions in Schizophrenia* by Robert K. Chapman, 1999. Reprinted with permission of Chapman Graphics.

---

category of schizophrenia. Now, however, this mixed bag of problems is diagnosed as **schizoaffective disorder** (Tsuang et al., 2012; see DSM Table 14.3). The prognosis is similar to the prognosis for people with schizophrenia—that is, individuals tend not to get better on their own and are likely to continue experiencing major life difficulties for many years. *DSM-5* criteria for schizoaffective disorder require that, in addition to the presence of a mood disorder, there have been delusions or hallucinations for at least two weeks in the absence of prominent mood symptoms (American Psychiatric Association, 2013).

Delusional Disorder

Delusions are beliefs that are not generally held by other members of a society. The major feature of **delusional disorder** is a persistent belief that is contrary to reality, in the absence of other characteristics of schizophrenia. For example, a woman who believes without any evidence that co-workers are tormenting her by putting poison in her food and spraying her apartment with harmful gases may have a delusional disorder. This disorder is characterized by a persistent delusion that is not the result of an organic factor, such as brain seizures, or of any severe psychosis. Individuals tend not to have flat affect, anhedonia, or other negative symptoms of schizophrenia; importantly, however, they may become socially isolated because they are suspicious of others. The delusions are often long-standing, sometimes persisting several years (Munro, 2012).

DSM-5 | **Table 14.2** Diagnostic Criteria for Schizophreniform Disorder

A. Two (or more) of the following, each present for a significant portion of time during a one-month period (or less if successfully treated). At least 1 of these must be (1), (2), or (3):

1. Delusions.
2. Hallucinations.
3. Disorganized speech (e.g., frequent derailment or incoherence).
4. Grossly disorganized or catatonic behavior.
5. Negative symptoms (i.e., diminished emotional expression or avolition).

B. An episode of the disorder lasts at least 1 month but less than 6 months. When the diagnosis must be made without waiting for recovery, it should be qualified as "provisional."

C. Schizoaffective disorder and depressive or bipolar disorder with psychotic features have been ruled out because either (1) no major depressive or manic episodes have occurred concurrently with the active-phase symptoms, or (2) if mood episodes have occurred during active-phase symptoms, they have been present for a minority of the total duration of the active and residual periods of the illness.

D. The disturbance is not attributable to the physiological effects of a substance (e.g., a drug of abuse, a medication) or another medical condition.

(continued)

▲ Homeless people who suffer from paranoid schizophrenia often bear the additional burden of persecutory delusions, which interferes with outside efforts to help.

The *DSM-5* recognizes the following delusional subtypes: erotomanic, grandiose, jealous, persecutory, and somatic (see DSM Table 14.4). An *erotomanic* delusion is someone's mistaken belief that a higher-status and unsuspecting person is in love with him or her. This delusional belief often motivates the patient to engage in an unrelenting pursuit of the person in attempts to

DSM-5	**Table 14.3** Diagnostic Criteria for Schizoaffective Disorder

A. An uninterrupted period of illness during which there is a major mood episode (major depressive or manic) concurrent with Criterion A of schizophrenia.

Note: The major depressive episode must include Criterion A1: Depressed mood.

B. Delusions or hallucinations for 2 or more weeks in the absence of a major mood episode (depressive or manic) during the lifetime duration of the illness.

C. Symptoms that meet criteria for a major mood episode are present for the majority of the total duration of the active and residual portions of the illness.

D. The disturbance is not attributable to the effects of a substance (e.g., a drug of abuse, a medication) or another medical condition.

Specify whether:

Bipolar type: This subtype applies if a manic episode is part of the presentation. Major depressive episodes may also occur.

Depressive type: This subtype applies only if only major depressive episodes are part of the presentation.

Specify if:

With catatonia

communicate with him or her. Several celebrities have been pursued by "stalkers" who likely have this form of delusional disorder. For example, in the 1980s, Canadian singer Anne Murray was relentlessly pursued by a Saskatchewan farmer named Charles Robert Kieling, despite several court orders that he stop attempting to contact her (MacFarlane, 1997). In another example, singer/songwriter Sarah McLachlan was pursued in the early 1990s by a computer programmer from Ottawa named Uwe Vandrei. He sent her flowers and hundreds of disturbing letters, and even made some comments to her in person. Vandrei took his own life in 1994, after he was unsuccessful in suing McLachlan for allegedly using his letters as the basis for her song "Possession" on her 1993 album *Fumbling Toward Ecstasy* (Fitzgerald, 2000).

The *grandiose* type of delusion involves believing in one's inflated worth, power, knowledge, identity, or special relationship to a deity or famous person. A person with the *jealous* type of delusion believes a sexual partner is unfaithful. The *persecutory* type of delusion involves the person believing that he or she (or someone close) is being malevolently treated in some way. Finally, with the *somatic* type of delusion, the person feels afflicted by a physical defect or general medical condition. Typically, these delusions differ from the more bizarre types often found in people with schizophrenia because in delusional disorder the imagined events could be happening but aren't (e.g., mistakenly believing you are being followed); in schizophrenia, however, the imagined events are not always possible (e.g., believing your brain waves broadcast your thoughts to other people around the world). The *DSM-5* allows for one bizarre delusion, which separates it from a diagnosis of schizophrenia, which requires more than one delusion to be present (Heckers et al., 2013)

Previous versions of the DSM included a separate delusional disorder—**shared psychotic disorder (folie à deux)**, the condition in which an individual develops delusions simply as a result of a close relationship with a delusional individual. The content and nature of the delusion originate with the partner and can range from the relatively bizarre, such as believing enemies are sending harmful gamma rays through your house, to the fairly ordinary, such as believing you are about to receive a major promotion despite evidence to the contrary. The *DSM-5* now includes this type of delusion under delusional disorder with a specifier to indicate if the delusion is shared (American Psychiatric Association, 2013).

Delusional disorder seems to be relatively rare, affecting 24 to 30 people out of every 100 000 in the general population (Suvisaari

et al., 2009). Among those people with psychotic disorders in general, between 2 and 8 percent are thought to have delusional disorder (Vahia & Cohen, 2009; Blaney, 2015). Researchers can't be confident about the percentages because they know that many of these individuals have no contact with the mental health system.

The onset of delusional disorder is relatively late: the average age of first admission to a psychiatric facility is between 40 and 49 (Vahia & Cohen, 2009). However, because many people with this disorder can lead relatively normal lives, they may not seek treatment until their symptoms become most disruptive. Delusional disorder seems to afflict more females than males (55 and 45 percent, respectively, of the affected population).

We know relatively little about either the biological or the psychosocial influences on delusional disorder (Vahia & Cohen, 2009). Research on families suggests that the characteristics of suspiciousness, jealousy, and secretiveness may occur more often among the relatives of people with delusional disorder than among the population at large, suggesting some aspect of this disorder may be inherited (Kendler & Walsh, 2007).

Several other disorders can cause delusions, and their presence should be ruled out before diagnosing delusional disorder. For example, abuse of amphetamines, alcohol, and cocaine can cause delusions, as can brain tumours, Huntington's disease, and Alzheimer's disease (Vahia & Cohen, 2009). The *DSM-5* includes two categories of these disorders: **substance-induced psychotic disorder** and **psychotic disorder due to another medical condition**—so that clinicians can qualify the nature of these difficulties.

Brief Psychotic Disorder

Recall the puzzling case of Arthur, who suddenly experienced the delusion that he could save the world and whose intense emotional swings lasted for only a few days. He would receive the *DSM-5* diagnosis of **brief psychotic disorder**, which is characterized by the presence of one or more positive symptoms, such as delusions, hallucinations, or disorganized speech or behaviour lasting one month or less (see DSM Table 14.5). Individuals like Arthur regain their previous ability to function well in day-to-day activities. Brief psychotic disorder is often precipitated by extremely stressful situations.

Attenuated Psychosis Syndrome

Some individuals who start to develop psychotic symptoms, such as hallucinations or delusions, are often sufficiently distressed to seek help from mental health professionals. They can be at high risk for developing schizophrenia and may be at an early stage of the disorder (called prodromal). Although they may not meet the full criteria for schizophrenia, they may be good candidates for early intervention in an effort to prevent symptoms from worsening. To focus attention on these individuals, the *DSM-5* is proposing a potentially new psychotic disorder for further study called **attenuated psychosis syndrome** (Fusar-Poli et al., 2014). Again, these people may have some of the symptoms of schizophrenia but they are aware of the troubling and bizarre nature of these symptoms.

Table 14.5 Diagnostic Criteria for Brief Psychotic Disorder

A. Presence of one (or more) of the following symptoms. At least 1 of these must be (1), (2), or (3):

1. Delusions.

2. Hallucinations.

3. Disorganized speech (e.g., frequent derailment or incoherence).

4. Grossly disorganized or catatonic behavior.

Note: Do not include a symptom if it is a culturally sanctioned response.

B. Duration of an episode of the disturbance is at least 1 day but less than 1 month, with eventual full return to premorbid level of functioning.

C. The disturbance is not better explained by major depressive or bipolar disorder with psychotic features, or another psychotic disorder such as schizophrenia or catatonia, and is not attributable to the physiological effects of a substance (e.g., a drug of abuse, a medication) or another medical condition.

Specify if:

With marked stressor(s) (brief reactive psychosis): If symptoms occur in response to events that, singly or together, would be markedly stressful to almost anyone in similar circumstances in the individual's culture.

Without marked stressor(s): If symptoms do not occur in response to events that, singly or together, would be markedly stressful to almost anyone in similar circumstances in the individual's culture.

With postpartum onset: If onset is during pregnancy or within 4 weeks postpartum.

Specify if:

With catatonia

Source: Reprinted with permission from the *Diagnostic and Statistical Manual of Mental Disorders*, Fifth Edition (Copyright © 2013). American Psychiatric Association. All Rights Reserved.

Schizotypal personality disorder, discussed in Chapter 13, is a related psychotic disorder. As you may recall, the characteristics are similar to those experienced by people with schizophrenia but are less severe. Some evidence also suggests that schizophrenia and schizotypal personality disorder may be genetically related as part of a schizophrenia spectrum.

Remember that although people with related psychotic disorders display many of the characteristics of schizophrenia, these disorders differ significantly. We now examine the nature of schizophrenia and learn how researchers have attempted to understand and treat people who have it.

PREVALENCE AND CAUSES OF SCHIZOPHRENIA

STATISTICS

Schizophrenia defies our desire for simplicity. We have seen how very different symptoms can be displayed by individuals who would all be considered to have the disorder; in some people the symptoms develop slowly, and in others they occur suddenly. Schizophrenia is generally chronic, and most people with the

disorder have a very difficult time functioning in society. This is especially true of their ability to relate to others; they tend not to establish or maintain significant relationships, and therefore many people with schizophrenia never marry or have children. Unlike the delusions of people with other psychotic disorders, the delusions of people with schizophrenia are likely to be outside the realm of possibility. Finally, even when individuals with schizophrenia improve with treatment, they are likely to experience difficulties throughout their lives.

Worldwide, the lifetime prevalence rate of schizophrenia is roughly equivalent for men and women, and it is estimated from 0.2 to 1.5 percent in the general population (Ho et al., 2003), which means the disorder will affect about 1 percent of the population at some point (Erlich et al., 2014). Simon Fraser University researcher Elliot Goldner and his colleagues suggested that the one-year prevalence of schizophrenic disorders in the British Columbia population was 0.4 percent (Goldner et al., 2003). The 2012 Canadian Community Health Survey—Mental Health (CCHS) estimated that 1.3 percent of Canadians 15 years of age and older had received a diagnosis of schizophrenia or psychosis in their lifetime, with similar rates for men and women (Statistics Canada, 2012). The CCHS does not cover First Nations people living on reserve. However, using Census and hospital discharge data, Statistics Canada estimates that First Nations people living both on and off reserve have almost double the acute care hospitalization rates for schizophrenic/psychotic disorders that Canadians of non-Aboriginal identity have (Carrière et al., 2018).

Life expectancy is slightly less than average, partly because of the higher rate of suicide and accidents among people with schizophrenia (Ho et al., 2003), but also because of higher rates of obesity, smoking, angina, and respiratory problems, as well as health problems associated with medication to treat schizophrenia (Seeman, 2007). One recent study out of the province of Ontario estimated that 11.7 percent of all suicide victims, more than 1 in 10, were individuals with schizophrenia spectrum disorder (Zaheer et al., 2018).

Concept Check 14.2

Diagnose the type of psychotic disorders described in each of the following. Choose from (a) schizophreniform disorder, (b) schizoaffective disorder, (c) delusional disorder, (d) shared psychotic disorder, and (e) brief psychotic disorder.

1. Lately Dom has become more isolated because he believes his co-workers are conspiring to get him fired. He becomes agitated whenever he sees a group of employees talking and laughing, because he believes that they are plotting against him. _____

2. Natalie reveals to her therapist that she hears numerous voices talking to her and giving her orders. Her doctor has just sent her to this therapist for what he believes to be a major depressive episode. She had begun to sleep all the time and contemplated suicide often.

_____

3. If Shawn's schizophrenic symptoms disappeared after about four months and he returned to his normal life, what diagnosis might he have received?

_____

4. Elias believes the government is out to get him. He thinks agents follow him daily, monitor his calls, and read his email. His roommate Cedric tried to convince him otherwise. After a year of this, however, Cedric began to believe the government was out to get him, too.

_____

Although some disagreement exists about the distribution of schizophrenia between men and women, the difference between the sexes in age of onset is clear. For men, the likelihood of onset diminishes with age. The onset for women is lower than for men until age 36, when the relative risk for onset switches, with more women than men being affected later in life (Howard et al., 1993). Women appear to have more favourable outcomes than men (Ho et al., 2003).

DEVELOPMENT

The more severe symptoms of schizophrenia first occur in late adolescence or early adulthood, although we saw that there may be signs of the development of the disorder in early childhood (Murray & Castle, 2012). Children who go on to develop schizophrenia show early clinical features, such as mild physical abnormalities, poor motor coordination, and mild cognitive and social problems (Golembo-Smith et al., 2012; Matheson et al., 2013; Welham et al., 2008). Unfortunately, these types of early problems are not specific enough to schizophrenia—meaning they could also be signs of other problems, such as the neurodevelopmental disorders we review in Chapter 15—to be able to say for sure that a particular child will later develop schizophrenia.

Up to 85 percent of people who later develop schizophrenia go through a **prodromal stage**—a one- to two-year period when less severe yet unusual behaviours start to show themselves but before serious symptoms occur (Jablensky, 2012). These behaviours (which you should recognize from Chapter 13 as symptoms seen in schizotypal personality disorders) include ideas of reference (thinking insignificant events relate directly to them), magical thinking (believing they have special abilities, such as being clairvoyant or telepathic), and illusions (such as feeling the presence of another person when they are alone). In addition, other symptoms are common, such as isolation, marked impairment in functioning, and a lack of initiative, interests, or energy (Addington et al., 2015).

Once symptoms begin to appear, it can take anywhere from 2 years to around 10 years before a person at high risk (e.g., mild positive symptoms, decline in functioning) meets the full criteria for a psychotic disorder (Nelson et al., 2013). The highest period of risk can be in the first two years for patients to develop a full-fledged psychotic disorder. Risk factors for going from high risk to developing the disorder include the length of duration of symptoms before seeking help, baseline functioning, as well as the presence of negative symptoms and disorganized symptoms (Addington et al., 2015, Nelson et al., 2013). Part of the delay in seeking help may be the result of hiding symptoms from others (sometimes because of increasing paranoia). Personality factors and the amount and quality of social support may also play a role in the amount of time it takes a person to first seek treatment for psychotic symptoms (Ruiz-Veguilla et al., 2012). Once treated, patients will often improve. Unfortunately, most will also go through a pattern of relapse and recovery (Emsley et al., 2013).

This relapse rate is important when discussing the course of schizophrenia. People with schizophrenia have a poorer prognosis than those with most of the other disorders we describe in this book—including a high risk of suicide—although a significant number of individuals can experience long periods of recovery (Jablensky, 2012). ■ Figure 14.1 illustrates the data from one study that show the course of schizophrenia among four prototypical groups (Shepherd et al., 1989). As you can see, about 22 percent of the group had one episode of schizophrenia and improved without lasting impairment. The remaining 78 percent experienced several episodes with differing degrees of impairment between them.

CULTURAL FACTORS

Because schizophrenia is so complex, the diagnosis itself can be controversial. Some have argued that "schizophrenia" does not really exist but is a pejorative label for people who behave in ways outside the cultural norm (e.g., Laing, 1967; Szasz, 1961). Although the idea that schizophrenia exists only in the minds of mental health professionals is certainly provocative, this extreme view is contradicted by experience. As clinicians, we have had a great deal of contact with people who have this disorder and with

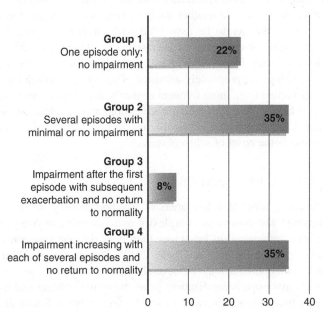

FIGURE 14.1 | The natural history of schizophrenia: A five-year follow-up.

Source: From "The Natural History of Schizophrenia: A Five-Year Follow-Up Study of Outcome and Prediction in a Representative Sample of Schizophrenics," by M. Shepherd, D. Watt, I. Falloon, and N. Smeeton, 1989, _Psychological Medicine, Monograph Supplement, 15_ (https://doi.org/10.1017/S026418010000059X). © 1989 by Cambridge University Press.

their families and friends, and the tremendous amount of emotional pain resulting from schizophrenia gives definite credence to its existence. In addition, many people in extremely diverse cultures have the symptoms of schizophrenia, which supports the notion that it is a reality for many people worldwide (Ihara et al., 2003; Patel & Andrade, 2003). Schizophrenia is thus universal, affecting all racial and cultural groups studied so far.

The course and outcome of schizophrenia vary from culture to culture. For example, in Colombia, India, and Nigeria, more people improve significantly or recover than in other countries (Leff et al., 1992). These differences may be due to cultural variations or biological influences, such as immunization, but we cannot yet explain these differences in outcomes. Surprisingly, outcomes are better in poor countries, and some have suggested the controversial idea that lack of access to pharmacological treatments may be the reason (Whitaker, 2011).

Research from England suggests that proportionately more blacks receive the diagnosis of schizophrenia than do whites. One possibility is that people from ethnic minority groups may be victims of bias and stereotyping (Lewis et al., 1990); in other words, they may be more likely to receive a diagnosis of schizophrenia than members of a dominant group. One prospective study of schizophrenia among different ethnic groups in London found that although the outcomes of schizophrenia appear similar across various ethnic groups, blacks were more likely to be detained against their will, brought to the hospital by police, and given emergency injections (Goater et al., 1999). A study by Eric Jarvis at McGill University similarly found that black immigrants with schizophrenia were more likely to have police contact and be subject to compulsory hospital admissions, and that Afro-Caribbean immigrants had the highest rates of schizophrenia of all immigrant groups (Jarvis, 1998). Anthony Feinstein of the University of Toronto disagrees with this conclusion. He and his colleague conducted another study in England and again found minority ethnicity to be associated with an increased risk for psychiatric hospitalization (Feinstein & Holloway, 2002). However, they found no evidence that ethnic minority patients were being inappropriately admitted. They suggest instead that other factors (e.g., more frequent cannabis abuse) may contribute to the higher rates of psychiatric admissions among ethnic minorities. Later in this chapter, we discuss the possible role of cannabis use in the onset of schizophrenia.

GENETIC INFLUENCES

We could argue that few areas of psychopathology so clearly illustrate the enormous complexity and intriguing mystery of genetic influences on behaviour than does the phenomenon of schizophrenia (Murray & Castle, 2012). Despite the possibility that schizophrenia may be several different disorders, we can safely make one generalization: genes are responsible for making some individuals vulnerable to schizophrenia. We will look at a range of research findings from family, twin, adoption, offspring of twins, and linkage and association studies (Faraone et al., 1999). We conclude by discussing the compelling reasons that no single gene is responsible for schizophrenia; rather, multiple gene variances combine to produce vulnerability (Murray & Castle, 2012).

Family Studies

In 1938, German researcher Franz Kallmann published a major study on the families of people with schizophrenia. Kallmann (1938) examined family members of more than 1000 persons diagnosed with schizophrenia in a Berlin psychiatric hospital. Several of his observations continue to guide research today. Kallmann showed that the severity of the parent's disorder influenced the likelihood of the children having schizophrenia: the more severe the parent's schizophrenia, the more likely the children were to develop it also. Another observation was important: all forms of schizophrenia (e.g., the historic categories such as catatonic and paranoid) were seen within the families. In other words, it does not appear that you inherit a predisposition for what was previously diagnosed as paranoid schizophrenia. Instead, you may inherit a general predisposition for schizophrenia that manifests in the same form or a different one from that of your parent. More recent research from Ireland confirms this observation and suggests that families that have a member with schizophrenia are at risk not just for schizophrenia alone or for all psychological disorders; instead, there appears to be some familial risk for a spectrum of psychotic disorders related to schizophrenia (Kendler et al., 1993).

Gottesman (1991) famously summarized the data from about 40 studies of schizophrenia, as shown in ■ Figure 14.2. The most striking feature of this graph is its orderly demonstration that the risk of having schizophrenia varies according to how many genes an individual shares with someone who has the disorder.

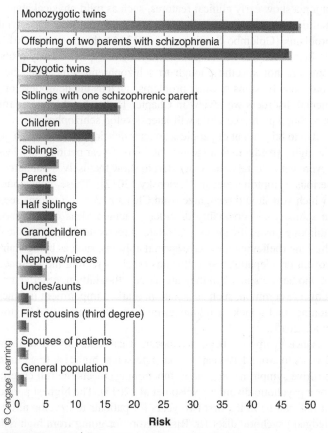

FIGURE 14.2 | Risk of developing schizophrenia.

Source: Based on Gottesman (1991).

For example, you have the greatest chance (approximately 48 percent) of having schizophrenia if it has affected your identical (monozygotic) twin, a person who shares 100 percent of your genetic information. Your risk drops to about 17 percent with a fraternal (dizygotic) twin, who shares about 50 percent of your genetic information. And having any relative with schizophrenia makes you more likely to have the disorder than someone in the general population without such a relative (about 1 percent).

Twin Studies

If they are raised together, identical twins share 100 percent of their genes and 100 percent of their environment, whereas fraternal twins share only about 50 percent of their genes and 100 percent of their environment. If the environment is solely responsible for schizophrenia, we would expect little difference between identical and fraternal twins with regard to this disorder. If only genetic factors are relevant, both identical twins would always have schizophrenia (be concordant) and the fraternal twins would both have it about 50 percent of the time. Research from twin studies indicates that the truth is somewhere in the middle (Braff et al., 2007; van Os et al., 2010).

In one of the most fascinating of nature's experiments, identical quadruplets, all of whom have schizophrenia, have been studied extensively. Nicknamed the "Genain" quadruplets (from the Greek, meaning "dreadful gene"), these women have been followed by researchers for years (e.g., Mirsky et al., 2000, 2013; Rosenthal, 1963). In a sense, the women embody the complex interaction between genetics and the environment. All four shared the same genetic predisposition, and all were brought up in the same particularly dysfunctional household; yet the time of onset for schizophrenia, the symptoms and diagnoses, the course of the disorder, and, ultimately, their outcomes differed significantly from sister to sister. For example, Hester was the first to experience severe symptoms of schizophrenia, at age 18; her sister Myra was not hospitalized until six years later. Hester never finished high school or lived independently. Myra was deemed to have a milder form of schizophrenia and had the most successful life course of the four sisters; she had the most education, was able to work, and was the only sister to marry and have children.

Dr. Allan F. Mirsky/National Institute of Mental Health

▲ The Genain quadruplets all had schizophrenia but exhibited different symptoms over the years.

In 2011, Hester was deceased, and Myra, at the age of 81, was still able to live independently with some assistance from community supports (Mirsky et al., 2013).

One genetic explanation for these differences may be the presence of *de novo* mutations in the sisters. These are genetic mutations that can occur as a result of a mutation in a germ cell (egg or sperm) of one of the parents or, perhaps in the case of these sisters, in the fertilized egg after conception. The case of the Genain quadruplets also reveals an important consideration in studying genetic influences on behaviour—*unshared environments* (Plomin, 1990). We tend to think that siblings, and especially identical multiples, are brought up the same way. The impression is that "good" parents expose their children to favourable environments, and "bad" parents give them unsound experiences. But even identical siblings can have very different prenatal and family experiences and can therefore be exposed to varying degrees of stress. For example, Hester, the last-born sister, was the smallest and was believed to have suffered more brain injury at birth than her sisters. Myra received preferential treatment from her parents, while Hester received harsh treatment. She was described by her parents as a habitual masturbator and was circumcised at the advice of a physician. This unusual case demonstrates that even siblings who are very close in every aspect of their lives can still have considerably different experiences physically and socially as they grow up, which may result in vastly different outcomes. The sisters also provide evidence that cognitive abilities may be maintained. A follow-up neuropsychological study showed the progression of their disorder stabilized, in fact may have improved, when they were assessed at age 66 (Mirsky et al., 2000). In 2011, a follow-up study of the two surviving sisters (Nora and Myra were 81 then) also showed maintenance of cognitive abilities (Mirskey et al., 2013).

Adoption Studies

Several adoption studies have distinguished the roles of the environment and genetics as they affect schizophrenia. These studies often span many years; because people often do not show the first signs of schizophrenia until early adulthood, researchers need to be sure all the offspring reach that point before drawing conclusions. Many schizophrenia studies are conducted in Europe, primarily because of the extensive and comprehensive records kept in many of these countries.

The largest adoption study was conducted in Finland (Tienari, 1991). From a sample of almost 20 000 women with schizophrenia, the researchers found 190 children who had been given up for adoption. The data from this study support the idea that schizophrenia represents a spectrum of related disorders, all of which overlap genetically. If an adopted child had a biological mother with schizophrenia, he or she had about a 5 percent chance of having the disorder (compared with about only 1 percent in the general population). However, if the biological mother had schizophrenia or one of the related psychotic disorders (e.g., delusional disorder, schizophreniform disorder), the risk that the adopted child would have one of these disorders rose to about 22 percent (Tienari et al., 2003, 2006). Even when raised away from their biological parents, children of parents with schizophrenia have a much higher chance of having the disorder themselves. At the same time, there appears to be a protective factor if these children are brought up in healthy, supportive homes. In other words, a gene–environment interaction was observed in this study, with a good home environment reducing the risk of schizophrenia (Gilmore, 2010; Wynne et al., 2006).

The Offspring of Twins

Twin and adoption studies strongly suggest a genetic component for schizophrenia, but what about children who develop schizophrenia even though their parents do not? For example, the study by Tienari and colleagues (2003, 2006) we just discussed found that 1.7 percent of the children with parents without schizophrenia developed schizophrenia. Does this mean you can develop schizophrenia without "schizophrenic genes"? Or are some people carriers, having the genes for schizophrenia but for some reason not showing the disorder themselves? An important clue to this question comes from research on the children of twins with schizophrenia.

In a study begun in 1971, 21 identical twin pairs and 41 fraternal twin pairs with a history of schizophrenia were identified along with their children (Fischer, 1971; Gottesman & Bertelsen, 1989). The researchers wanted to determine the relative likelihood that a child would have schizophrenia if his or her parent did, and if the parent's twin had schizophrenia but the parent did not. ■ Figure 14.3 illustrates the findings from this study. For example, if your parent is an identical (monozygotic) twin with schizophrenia, you have about a 17 percent chance of having the disorder yourself, a figure that holds if you are the child of an unaffected identical twin whose co-twin has the disorder.

Conversely, look at the risks for the child of a fraternal (dizygotic) twin. If your parent is the twin with schizophrenia, you have about a 17 percent chance of having schizophrenia yourself. If your parent does not have schizophrenia but your parent's fraternal twin does, your risk is only about 2 percent. The only way to explain this finding is through genetics. The data clearly indicate that you can have genes that predispose you to schizophrenia, not show the disorder yourself, but still pass on the genes to your children. In other words, you can be a carrier for schizophrenia. This is some of the strongest evidence yet that people are genetically vulnerable to schizophrenia. Remember, however, the chance of inheritance is only 17 percent, meaning that other factors help determine who will have this disorder.

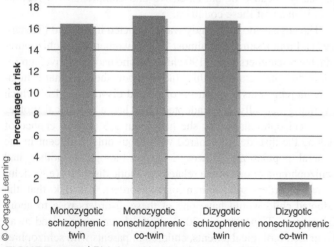

FIGURE 14.3 | Risk for schizophrenia among children of twins.
Source: Based on Gottesman (1991).

Concept Check 14.3

Genes are responsible for making some individuals vulnerable to schizophrenia. Check your understanding of genetic vulnerability by filling in the blanks of the statements provided associated with family, twin, and adoption studies. You may choose from the following words: (a) higher, (b) lower, (c) equal, (d) severity, (e) type, (f) identical twin, (g) specific, (h) fraternal twin, and (i) general.

1. The likelihood of a child's having schizophrenia is influenced by the _____ of the parent's disorder.

2. A child may inherit a(n) _____ predisposition for schizophrenia that is the same as or different from that of the parent.

3. The greatest risk of having schizophrenia is in those who have a(n) _____ with schizophrenia. Any relative with schizophrenia will make your chances (a) greater than, (b) less than, or (c) the same as the general population.

4. Children of people with schizophrenia adopted into families without schizophrenia have a(n) _____ than average chance of having schizophrenia.

Gene–Environment Interactions

An interesting study by Caspi and colleagues (2005), conducted with the large New Zealand sample described in Chapter 2, extended the study of genetic factors to examine the possibility of a gene by environment interaction in the development of schizophrenia. Cannabis use in youth is an established but modest risk factor for psychosis in adulthood. Yet, clearly, most people who use marijuana do not develop psychosis! Caspi and colleagues tested whether there might be certain genetically vulnerable individuals who are particularly susceptible to the effects of cannabis initiating psychosis. Indeed, they found that the combination of a particular genetic profile (i.e., carriers of the catechol-O-methyltransferase [COMT] valine [VAL] 158 allele as compared with those with two copies of the methionine [MET] allele) was particularly likely to develop schizophrenia in adulthood. But this was only true if these individuals had used cannabis as teenagers. This study suggests the interesting possibility that certain genes may act as vulnerability factors that interact with specific environmental pathogens at crucial developmental stages, leading to the development of schizophrenia (Caspi et al., 2005).

Linkage and Association Studies

Genetic linkage and association studies rely on traits, such as blood types (whose exact location on the chromosome is already known), that are inherited in families along with the disorder we are looking for—in this case, schizophrenia. Because we know the location of the genes for these traits (called marker genes), we can make a rough guess about the location of the disorder genes that are inherited along with them. To date, researchers have looked at several sites for genes that may be responsible for schizophrenia. For example, regions of chromosomes 1, 2, 3, 5, 6, 8, 10, 11, 13, 20, and 22 are implicated in this disorder (Kirov & Owen, 2009). Three of the most reliable genetic influences that make one susceptible to schizophrenia include sections on chromosome 8 called Neuregulin 1 (or NRG1), chromosome 6 (called dystrobrevin-binding protein 1 or DTNBP1), and chromosome 22 (called catecholamine O-methyl transferase or COMT) (Murray & Castle, 2012). The COMT gene is of particular interest to scientists, because it plays a role in dopamine metabolism, which we will see has been implicated in the etiology of schizophrenia. A recent study that combined one of the largest samples (i.e., 36 989 cases of individuals with schizophrenia and 113 075 controls) identified 128 independent associations and 108 loci that meet genome-wide significance, 83 of which were new. This further strengthens the theory that genetic risk arises from a large number of common genes each with a small effect that might be detected by genome-wide association studies (Ripke et al., 2014).

The Search for Markers

In the search for markers, researchers look for common traits other than the symptoms of the disorder itself. If some people have the positive symptoms of schizophrenia, others have the negative symptoms, and still others have a mixture of these symptoms, yet they all have a particular problem completing a certain task, the skill deficit would be very useful for identifying what else these people may have in common.

Several potential markers for schizophrenia have been studied over the years. As noted by McGill University psychologist Gillian O'Driscoll and her colleagues, one of the more highly researched markers is called *smooth-pursuit eye movement* or eye-tracking (O'Driscoll et al., 1998). While keeping your head still, you must be able to track a moving pendulum, back and forth, with your eyes. The ability to track objects smoothly across the visual field is deficient in many people who also have schizophrenia (e.g., Clementz & Sweeney, 1990); it does not appear to be the result of drug treatment or institutionalization (Lieberman et al., 1993). It also seems to be a problem for relatives of these people (Thaker & Avila, 2003). Although these eye-tracking deficits appear to be associated with both negative and positive symptoms, they are most strongly associated with positive symptoms (Holahan & O'Driscoll, 2005). When all these observations are combined, they suggest an eye-tracking deficit may be a marker for schizophrenia that could be used in further study (O'Driscoll et al., 1998).

Evidence for Multiple Genes

As we have seen, schizophrenia involves more than one gene, a phenomenon referred to as *quantitative trait loci* (Levinson et al., 1998; Plomin et al., 1994). The schizophrenia we see most often is probably caused by several genes located at different sites throughout the chromosomes. This model would also clarify why there can be gradations of severity in people with the disorder (from mild to severe), and why the risk of having schizophrenia increases with the number of affected relatives in the family.

NEUROBIOLOGICAL INFLUENCES

The belief that schizophrenia involves a malfunctioning brain goes back as far as the writings of Emil Kraepelin (1856–1926). It is therefore not surprising that a great deal of research has focused on the brain. Before we discuss some of this work, however, be forewarned: to study abnormalities in the brain for clues to the cause of schizophrenia is to face all the classic problems of doing correlational research, which we discussed in Chapter 4. For example, if a person has schizophrenia and too much of a neurotransmitter, (1) does too much neurotransmitter cause schizophrenia, (2) does schizophrenia create too much of the neurotransmitter, or (3) does something else cause both the schizophrenia and the chemical imbalance? Keep this caveat in mind as you review the following research.

Dopamine

One of the most enduring yet still controversial theories of the cause of schizophrenia involves the neurotransmitter *dopamine* (Harrison, 2012). Before we consider the research, however, let's review briefly how neurotransmitters operate in the brain and how they are affected by neuroleptic medications, which reduce hallucinations and delusions. In Chapter 2, we discussed the sensitivity of specific neurons to specific neurotransmitters and described how they cluster throughout the brain. The top of ■ Figure 14.4 shows two neurons and the important synaptic gap that separates them. Neurotransmitters are released from the storage vessels (synaptic vesicles) at the end of the axon, cross the gap, and are taken up by receptors in the dendrite of the next axon. Chemical messages are transported in this way from neuron to neuron throughout the brain.

This process can be influenced in a number of ways, and the rest of Figure 14.4 illustrates some of them. The chemical messages can be increased by agonistic agents or decreased by antagonistic agents. Antagonistic effects slow down or stop messages from being transmitted by preventing the release of the neurotransmitter, blocking uptake at the level of the dendrite, or causing leaks that reduce the amount of neurotransmitter ultimately released. Conversely, agonistic effects assist with the transference of chemical messages and, if extreme, can produce too much neurotransmitter activity by increasing production or release of the neurotransmitter, and by affecting more receptors at the dendrites.

What we've learned about antipsychotic medications points to the possibility that the dopamine system is too active in persons with schizophrenia. The simplified picture in Figure 14.4 does not show that there are actually different receptor sites and that a chemical, such as dopamine, produces different results depending on which of those sites it affects. In schizophrenia, attention has focused on two dopamine sites, referred to simply as D_1 and D_2. As we will see, D_2 is of particular interest to researchers in this field.

In a story that resembles a mystery plot, several pieces of circumstantial evidence are clues to the role of dopamine in schizophrenia:

1. Antipsychotic drugs (neuroleptics) that are often effective in treating people with schizophrenia are dopamine antagonists, partially blocking the brain's use of dopamine (Creese et al., 1976; Seeman et al., 1976).

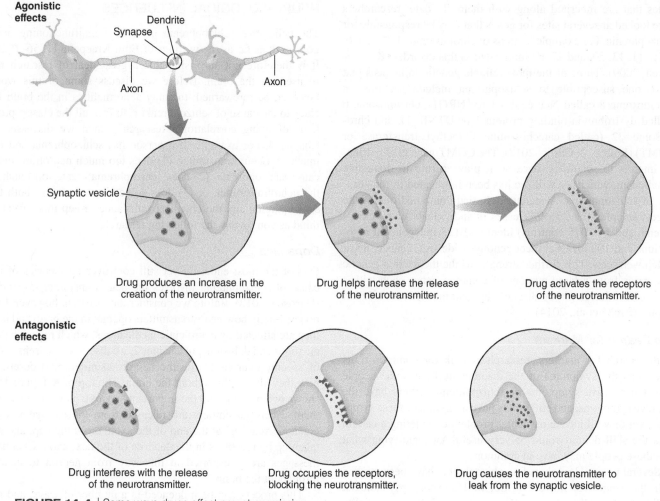

Agonistic effects

Dendrite
Synapse
Axon
Axon

Synaptic vesicle

Drug produces an increase in the creation of the neurotransmitter.

Drug helps increase the release of the neurotransmitter.

Drug activates the receptors of the neurotransmitter.

Antagonistic effects

Drug interferes with the release of the neurotransmitter.

Drug occupies the receptors, blocking the neurotransmitter.

Drug causes the neurotransmitter to leak from the synaptic vesicle.

FIGURE 14.4 | Some ways drugs affect neurotransmission.

2. These drugs can produce negative side effects similar to those in Parkinson's disease, a disorder known to be due to insufficient dopamine.

3. The drug L-dopa, a dopamine agonist used to treat people with Parkinson's disease, produces schizophrenia-like symptoms in some people (Davidson et al., 1987).

4. Amphetamines, which also activate dopamine, can make psychotic symptoms worse in some people with schizophrenia (van Kammen et al., 1982).

In other words, when drugs are administered that are known to increase dopamine (agonists), schizophrenic behaviour increases; when drugs that are known to decrease dopamine activity (antagonists) are used, schizophrenic symptoms tend to diminish. Taking these observations together, researchers theorized that schizophrenia in some people was attributable to excessive dopamine activity.

Despite these observations, some evidence is inconsistent with the dopamine theory (Javitt & Laruelle, 2006):

1. A significant number of people with schizophrenia are not helped by the use of dopamine antagonists.

2. Although the neuroleptics block the reception of dopamine quite quickly, the relevant symptoms subside only after several days or weeks, much more slowly than researchers would expect.

3. These drugs are only partly helpful in reducing the negative symptoms (e.g., flat affect, anhedonia) of schizophrenia.

In addition to these concerns, there is evidence of a double-edged sword with respect to schizophrenia. A medication called clozapine is effective with many people who were not helped with traditional neuroleptic medications (Agid et al., 2007; Tauscher et al., 2004; Wahlbeck et al., 1999). That's the good news. But as pointed out by Shitij Kapur and his colleagues in Toronto, the bad news for the dopamine theory is that clozapine is one of the weakest dopamine antagonists by far, much less able to block the dopamine sites than other drugs (Kapur et al., 1999). Why would a medication inefficient at blocking dopamine be effective as a treatment for schizophrenia if schizophrenia is caused by excessive dopamine activity?

The answer may be that although dopamine is involved in the symptoms of schizophrenia, its role is more complicated than we once thought (Potter & Manji, 1993). Current thinking points to at least three specific neurochemical abnormalities simultaneously at play in the brains of people with schizophrenia.

Strong evidence now leads us to believe that schizophrenia is partially the result of excessive stimulation of striatal dopamine D_2 receptors (Laruelle et al., 2003). Recall that the striatum is part of the basal ganglia found deep within the brain. These cells control movement, balance, and walking, and they rely on dopamine to

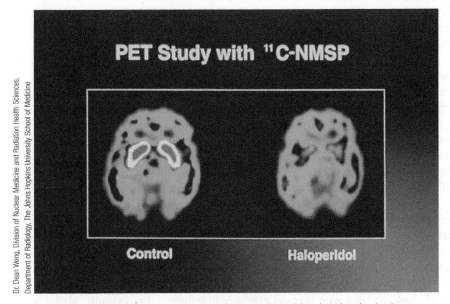

PET Study with ¹¹C-NMSP

Control   **Haloperidol**

▲ These PET images show the brain of a man with schizophrenia who had never been medicated (left) and after he received haloperidol (right). The red and yellow areas indicate activity in the D_2 receptors; haloperidol evidently reduced dopamine activity.

function. Huntington's disease (which involves problems in motor function) involves deterioration in this brain area. How do we know that excessive stimulation of D_2 receptors is involved in schizophrenia? One clue is that most effective antipsychotic drugs all share dopamine D_2 receptor antagonism (Ho et al., 2003), meaning they help block the simulation of the D_2 receptors.

A second area of interest to scientists investigating the cause of schizophrenia is the observation of a deficiency in the stimulation of prefrontal D_1 receptors (Koh et al., 2003). Therefore, although some dopamine sites may be overactive (e.g., striatal D_2), a second type of dopamine site in the part of the brain that we use for planning and organizing (prefrontal D_1 receptors) appears to be less active and may account for negative symptoms of schizophrenia, such as avolition. As we discuss later in this chapter, lower prefrontal activity in people with schizophrenia is referred to as *hypofrontality*.

Finally, a third and more recent area of neurochemical interest involves research on alterations in prefrontal activity involving glutamate transmission (Goff & Coyle, 2001). Glutamate is an excitatory neurotransmitter that is found in all areas of the brain and is only now being studied in earnest. Like dopamine, glutamate has different types of receptors. The ones being studied for their role in schizophrenia are the N-methyl-D-aspartate (NMDA) receptors. The effects of certain drugs that affect NMDA receptors point to clues to schizophrenia. Two recreational drugs described in Chapter 12—phencyclidine (PCP) and ketamine— can result in psychotic-like behaviour in people without schizophrenia and can exacerbate psychotic symptoms in those with schizophrenia. Both PCP and ketamine are NMDA antagonists, suggesting that a deficit in glutamate or blocking of NMDA sites may be involved in some of the symptoms of schizophrenia (Goff & Coyle, 2001).

You can see that research on these two neurotransmitters is complex and awaits clarification. However, advances in

technology are leading us closer to the clues behind this enigmatic disorder and closer still to better treatments.

Brain Structure

Evidence for neurological damage in people with schizophrenia comes from a number of observations. Many children with a parent who has the disorder, and who are therefore at risk, tend to show subtle but observable neurological problems, such as abnormal reflexes and inattentiveness (Buka et al., 2013). These difficulties are persistent: adults who have schizophrenia show deficits in their ability to perform certain tasks and to attend during reaction time exercises (Cleghorn & Albert, 1990). Such findings suggest that brain damage or dysfunction may cause or accompany schizophrenia, although no single site is probably responsible for the whole range of symptoms (Harrison, 2012).

One of the most reliable observations about the brain in people with schizophrenia involves the size of the ventricles (see ■ Figure 14.5). As early as 1927, researchers noted that these liquid-filled cavities showed enlargement in some but not all of the brains examined in people with schizophrenia (Jacobi & Winkler, 1927). Since then, more sophisticated techniques have been developed for observing the brain, and in the dozens of studies conducted on ventricle size, the great majority show abnormally large lateral and third ventricles in people with schizophrenia (Harrison, 2012). Ventricle size in itself may not be a problem, but the dilation (enlargement) of the ventricles indicates that either adjacent parts of the brain have not developed fully or have atrophied, thus allowing the ventricles to become larger.

Ventricle enlargement is not seen in everyone who has schizophrenia. Several factors seem to be associated with this finding. For example, enlarged ventricles are observed more often in men than in women (Abel et al., 2010). Ventricles seem to enlarge in

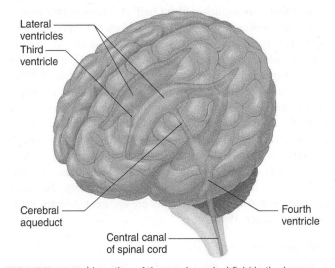

FIGURE 14.5 | Location of the cerebrospinal fluid in the human brain. This extracellular fluid surrounds and cushions the brain and spinal cord. It also fills the four interconnected cavities (cerebral ventricles) within the brain and the central canal of the spinal cord.

Lateral ventricles
Third ventricle
Cerebral aqueduct
Central canal of spinal cord
Fourth ventricle

proportion to age and to the duration of the schizophrenia. One study found that individuals with schizophrenia who were exposed to influenza prenatally may be more likely to have enlarged ventricles (Takei et al., 1996).

We touched on the concept of unshared environments in the section on genetics (Jang, 2005; Plomin, 1990). Although monozygotic twins are identical genetically, they can experience a number of environmental differences, even before they are born. For instance, in the intrauterine environment twins must compete for nutrients, and they may not be equally successful. In addition, birth complications, such as the loss of oxygen (anoxia), could affect only one of the twins (Murray & Castle, 2012). Obstetrical complications appear often among twins with schizophrenia in discordant identical pairs and among the more severely affected if both twins have schizophrenia (McNeil, 1987). Different experiences among twins who are already predisposed to the disorder could damage the brain and cause the types of symptoms we associate with schizophrenia (Williams et al., 2013).

The frontal lobes of the brain have also interested people looking for structural problems associated with schizophrenia. This area may be less active in people with schizophrenia than in people without the disorder, a phenomenon known as *hypofrontality* (*hypo* means "less active" or "deficient"). Neuropsychological research by several Canadian teams has shown that patients with schizophrenia perform poorly relative to comparison groups on cognitive tasks known to be related to functioning of the frontal lobes (e.g., Zakzanis et al., 2000). For example, James Everett and his colleagues at Laval University showed that patients with schizophrenia performed more poorly than healthy controls on a task called the Wisconsin Card Sorting Task—a test requiring planning and organization abilities subserved by the frontal lobes (Everett et al., 2001). Further research suggests that deficient activity in a particular area of the frontal lobes, the dorsolateral prefrontal cortex (DLPFC), may be implicated in schizophrenia (e.g., Berman & Weinberger, 1990). When people with and without schizophrenia are given tasks that involve the DLPFC, less activity (measured by cerebral blood flow) is recorded in the brains of those with schizophrenia. A meta-analytic study showed that hypofrontality distinguishes about half of schizophrenia patients from people without schizophrenia (Davidson & Heinrichs, 2003). Hypofrontality also seems to be associated with the negative symptoms of schizophrenia (Andreasen et al., 1992) and with the eye-tracking deficits mentioned earlier (O'Driscoll et al., 1999).

It appears that several brain sites are implicated in the cognitive dysfunction observed among people with schizophrenia, especially the prefrontal cortex, various other related cortical regions, and subcortical circuits including the thalamus and the stratum (Shenton & Kubicki, 2009). Remember that this dysfunction seems to occur before the onset of schizophrenia. In other words, brain damage may develop progressively, beginning before the symptoms of the disorder are apparent, perhaps prenatally (Weinberger, 1995).

Viral Infection

A curious fact about schizophrenia is that, according to some authors, no adequate descriptions of people having this disorder appear earlier than about 1800 (e.g., Gottesman, 1991). If you look at historic records or read ancient literature, you can find people with such disorders as intellectual disability, mania, depression, and dementia. Even William Shakespeare, who describes most human conditions, mentions nothing that resembles our current image of schizophrenia. Historically, such an obvious aberration of behaviour is puzzlingly absent. (However, there is now some evidence that at least a few cases of schizophrenia-like disorder may have existed as early as the 14th century; Heinrichs, 2003.)

One intriguing hypothesis is that schizophrenia is a recent phenomenon, appearing only during the past 200 years and that, like AIDS, it may involve some newly introduced virus (Gottesman, 1991). In other words, a "schizo-virus" could have caused some cases of this debilitating disorder (Torrey, 1988b). In fact, evidence suggests that a virus-like disease may account for some cases (Kirch, 1993). The higher prevalence of schizophrenia among men living in urban areas (Lewis et al., 1992) implies that they are more likely to have been exposed to infectious agents than are their peers in less populated areas.

Several studies have shown that schizophrenia may be associated with prenatal exposure to influenza. For example, Mednick and colleagues followed a large number of people after a severe Type A2 influenza epidemic in Helsinki, Finland, and found that those whose mothers were exposed to influenza during the second trimester of pregnancy were much more likely to have schizophrenia than others (Cannon et al., 1991). This observation has been confirmed by some researchers (e.g., O'Callaghan et al., 1991; Venables, 1996) but not by others (e.g., Buchanan & Carpenter, 2005; Selten et al., 2009).

A parasite has also been implicated in the etiology of schizophrenia. *Toxoplasma gondii* is most often found in cats and particularly in the feces of cats. Transmission to humans is done by ingestion of oocysts from litter boxes. In a recent meta-analysis of 23 studies, people diagnosed with schizophrenia were two to three times more likely to have antibodies in their blood, compared with people without schizophrenia (Torrey et al., 2007). The parasite is able to affect brain function in utero, so pregnant women are now asked in many places to remove litter boxes from their homes as a precaution.

Evidence that in utero events may be associated with schizophrenia has led researchers to look further into this area. Among the types of cells that normally migrate to the cortex during this period are the fingertip dermal cells, which are responsible for the number of fingerprint ridges. Although there is no such thing as an abnormal number of ridges, identical twins generally have the same number. However, if some interruption in second-trimester fetal development resulted in schizophrenia (when, according to the viral theory, a virus may have its effect), it would also affect the fingertip dermal cells. Researchers compared the fingerprint ridges of identical twins who were discordant for schizophrenia with those of identical twins without schizophrenia (Bracha et al., 1992). They found that the number of ridges on the fingertips of the twins without schizophrenia differed very little from each other; however, they differed a great deal among about one-third of the twin pairs who were discordant for schizophrenia. This study suggests that ridge count may be a marker of prenatal brain damage. Although there is no characteristic fingerprint for schizophrenia, this physical sign may add to our understanding of the second-trimester conditions that can trigger the genetic predisposition for schizophrenia (Weinberger, 1995).

PSYCHOLOGICAL AND SOCIAL INFLUENCES

That one identical twin may develop schizophrenia and the other may not suggests that schizophrenia involves something in addition to genes. We know that early brain trauma, perhaps resulting from a second-trimester virus-like attack or obstetrical complications, may generate physical stress that contributes to schizophrenia. All these observations show clearly that schizophrenia does not fall neatly into a few simple causal packages. For instance, not all people with schizophrenia have enlarged ventricles, nor do they all have hypofrontality or excessive activity in their dopamine systems. The causal picture may be further complicated by psychological and social factors. We next look at research into psychosocial factors. Do emotional stressors or family interaction patterns initiate the symptoms of schizophrenia? If so, how might those factors cause people to relapse after a period of improvement?

Stress

It is important to learn how much and what kind of stress makes a person with a predisposition for schizophrenia develop the disorder itself. Think back to the two cases we presented near the beginning of this chapter. Did you notice any precipitating events? Arthur's father had died several years earlier, and he was laid off from his job right around the time his symptoms first appeared. David's uncle had died the same year he began acting strangely. Were these stressful events just coincidences, or did they contribute to the men's later problems?

Researchers have studied the effects of a variety of stressors on schizophrenia. Living in a large city, for example, is associated with an increased risk of developing schizophrenia, suggesting that the stress of urban living may precipitate its onset (Boydell & Allardyce, 2011). Dohrenwend and Egri (1981) observed that otherwise healthy people who engage in combat during a war often display temporary symptoms that resemble those of schizophrenia. In an early study, Brown and Birley (1968; Birley & Brown, 1970) examined people whose onset of schizophrenia could be dated within a week. These individuals had experienced a high number of stressful life events in the three weeks just before they started showing signs of the disorder. In a large-scale study sponsored by the World Health Organization, researchers also looked at the role of life events in the onset of schizophrenia (Day et al., 1987). This cross-national study confirmed the findings of Brown and Birley across eight different research centres.

The *retrospective* nature of such research creates problems, however. Each study relies on after-the-fact reports, collected after the person showed signs of schizophrenia. We always wonder whether such reports are biased in some way and therefore misleading (Hirsch et al., 1992). One study used a *prospective* approach to examine the impact of stress on relapse. Ventura et al. (1989) identified 30 people with recent-onset schizophrenia and followed them for a year. The researchers interviewed the subjects every two weeks to learn whether they had experienced any stressful life events and whether their symptoms had changed. Notice that, unlike the previous studies, this research examines the factors that predict the recurrence of schizophrenic symptoms after a period of improvement. During the one-year assessment period, 11 of the 30 people had a significant relapse—that is, their symptoms returned or worsened. Like Brown and Birley,

Ventura et al. found that relapses occurred when stressful life events increased during the previous month. Other research demonstrates that stressful life events can increase depression among people with schizophrenia, which in turn may contribute to relapse (Ventura et al., 2000). An important finding from the first study is that, although the people experienced more stressful events as a group just before their relapse, 55 percent did not have a major life event during the previous month. Other factors must account for the return of symptoms among these people (Bebbington et al., 1993; Ventura et al., 1992).

Another important area in the study of the impact of stress on schizophrenia is research showing a significant negative correlation between social class and schizophrenia. In other words, there is a significant tendency for individuals with schizophrenia to be found in the lowest social classes. This finding has been replicated in a variety of cultures (e.g., Hollingshead & Redlich, 1958; Kohn, 1968). There are at least two possible explanations for this finding. The first explanation pertains to stress affecting schizophrenia rates: It could be that life in the lower social classes is stressful, predisposing those from the lower social classes to an increased likelihood of schizophrenia. This explanation is known as the *sociogenic hypothesis*. The second explanation pertains to the adverse effects of schizophrenia on a person's ability to hold a job. If the illness makes them less able to hold a job, individuals with schizophrenia may experience a downward social drift into the lower social classes. This second explanation is known as the *social selection hypothesis*. Although results have certainly been mixed, findings generally favour the social selection over the sociogenic hypothesis in terms of explaining the relation of social class and schizophrenia (see Dohrenwend et al., 1992). This should not be taken to mean that social environment does not play a role in schizophrenia, however. Take for example, the research on the role of social support, which we will examine next.

Elsewhere in this book, we examined how social support can exert a moderating influence in reducing the negative impact of stress in both physical and mental health disorders. Although investigations of social support in schizophrenia have been relatively sparse, some Canadian research supports its importance in this disorder as well. A longitudinal study by David Erickson and Morton Beiser at the University of Ottawa and the Centre for Addiction and Mental Health showed that higher levels of social support from non-family members in the social network predicted better outcomes five years later among patients experiencing their first episode of schizophrenia (Erickson et al., 1998). But what of the role of family members? We look at this important influence next.

Families and Relapse

A great deal of research has studied how interactions within the family affect people who have schizophrenia. For example, at one time the term **schizophrenogenic** was used to describe a mother whose cold, dominant, and rejecting nature was thought to cause schizophrenia in her children (Fromm-Reichmann, 1948). In addition, the term **double bind** was used to portray a type of communication style that produced conflicting messages, which, in turn, caused schizophrenia to develop (Bateson, 1959). Here, the parent presumably communicates messages that have two conflicting meanings; for example, a mother responds coolly to her child's embrace but says, "Don't you love me anymore?" when the child withdraws. Although these theories are no longer supported, they have been—and in some cases continue to be—destructive, producing guilt in parents who are persuaded that their early mistakes caused devastating consequences.

Recent work has focused more on how family interactions contribute not to the onset of schizophrenia itself, but to relapse after initial symptoms are observed. Research has focused on a particular emotional communication style known as **expressed emotion (EE)**. This concept was formulated by Brown and colleagues in London, England. Following a sample of people who had been discharged from the hospital after an episode of schizophrenic symptoms, the researchers found that former patients who had limited contact with their relatives did better than patients who spent longer periods with their families (Brown, 1959). Additional research results indicated that if the level of criticism (disapproval), hostility (animosity), and emotional over-involvement (intrusiveness) expressed by the families was high, patients tended to relapse (Brown et al., 1962).

Other researchers, including John Cole of the London Psychiatric Hospital and Shahe Kazarian of the University of Western Ontario, have since found that ratings of high EE in a family are a good predictor of relapse among people with chronic schizophrenia (Bebbington et al., 1995; Kazarian et al., 1990). In fact, if you have schizophrenia and live in a family with high EE, you are 3.7 times as likely to relapse as if you lived in a family with low EE (Kavanagh, 1992; Parker & Hadzi-Pavlovic, 1990).

Family communications involving high levels of EE are characterized by intrusiveness, high levels of emotional response, a negative attitude toward the illness on the part of family members, and low tolerance and unrealistic expectations of the patient (Cole & Kazarian, 1988). Research from Laval University researchers Helene Provencher and Frank Fincham (2000) demonstrates that, unfortunately, it is common for family members to see a patient's schizophrenia symptoms as being intentional. The literature on EE is valuable to our understanding of why symptoms of schizophrenia recur. It may also help people with this disorder to reduce the chance of further psychotic episodes (Cechnicki et al., 2013; Mueser et al., 1993).

An interesting issue that arises when studying family influences is whether what we see is unique to our culture or is universal. Looking at EE across different cultures may help us learn whether it is a cause of schizophrenia (Breitborde et al., 2010). Remember that schizophrenia is observed at about the same rate worldwide, with a prevalence of about 1 percent in the global population. If a factor like high EE in families is a causal agent, we should see the same rates in families across cultures; in fact, however, they differ, as you can see in ∎ Figure 14.6. These data come from an analysis of the concept of EE in several studies, from India, Mexico, Great Britain, and North America (Jenkins & Karno, 1992). The differences suggest there are cultural variations in how families react to someone with schizophrenia, and their reactions may not cause the disorder (Singh et al., 2013). And, what may appear to be overinvolvement in one culture may be viewed as supportive in other cultures. As pointed out by the research of Suzanne King at the Douglas Hospital in Montréal, however, it is also very important to consider the possibility that critical comments and emotional overinvolvement may

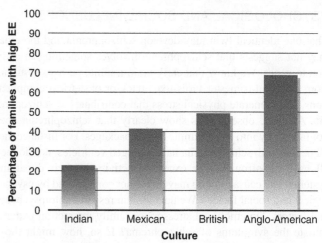

FIGURE 14.6 | Cultural differences in expressed emotion (EE).

Source: Jenkins & Karno (1992).

be family responses to a patient's unusual and disturbing behaviour rather than a cause (King, 2000). In fact, research does show that certain kinds of patient behaviours do evoke hostility in family members, supporting the position that the relation between the behaviour of patients with schizophrenia and EE in family members is indeed a reciprocal process (e.g., Cook et al., 1989; Miklowitz et al., 1989).

TREATMENT

If you remember our descriptions of Arthur and David, you will recall their families' concern for them. Arthur's mother spoke of the "living nightmare" and David's aunt expressed concern for both her safety and David's. In each case, the family was desperate to help, but what do you do for someone who has delusions, hears his dead uncle's voice, or can't communicate complete thoughts? The search for help has taken many paths, sometimes down some very disturbing roads; for example, in the 16th century, primitive surgery was conducted to remove the "stone of madness," which was thought to cause disturbed behaviour. As barbaric as this practice may seem today, it is not very different from the prefrontal lobotomies performed on people with schizophrenia as late as the 1950s. This procedure severed the frontal lobes from the lower portion of the brain, which sometimes calmed the patient but also caused cognitive and emotional deficits. Even today, some societies use crude surgical procedures to eliminate the symptoms of schizophrenia. In Kenya, for instance, Kisii tribal doctors listen to their patients to find the location of the noises in the patients' heads (hallucinations), then get them drunk, cut out a piece of scalp, and scrape the skull in the area of the voices (Mustafa, 1990).

In the Western world today, treatment usually begins with one of the neuroleptic drugs that help reduce the symptoms of schizophrenia for many people. They are typically used in combination with a variety of psychosocial treatments to reduce relapse, compensate for skills deficits, and improve cooperation for taking the medications (Cunningham Owens & Johnstone, 2012).

BIOLOGICAL INTERVENTIONS

Researchers have assumed for more than a century that schizophrenia requires some form of biological intervention. Emil Kraepelin, who so eloquently described dementia praecox in the late 19th century, saw the disorder as a brain disease. Lacking a biological treatment, he routinely recommended that the physician use "good patience, kindly disposition, and self-control" to calm excited patients (Nagel, 1991). This approach was seen as only a temporary way of helping the person through disturbing times and was not thought to be an actual treatment.

During the 1930s, several novel biological treatments were tried. One approach was to inject massive doses of insulin—the drug that given in smaller doses is used to treat diabetes—to induce comas in people who have schizophrenia. Insulin coma therapy was thought for a time to be helpful, but closer examination showed it carried great risk of serious illness and death. During this time psychosurgery, including prefrontal lobotomies, was introduced; and in the late 1930s, electroconvulsive therapy (ECT) was advanced as a treatment for schizophrenia. As with earlier drastic treatments, initial enthusiasm for ECT faded because it was found not to be beneficial for most people with schizophrenia—although it is still used with a limited number of people today (Fink & Sackeim, 1996; Zervas et al., 2012). As we explained in Chapter 8, ECT is sometimes recommended for people who experience very severe episodes of depression.

A breakthrough in the treatment of schizophrenia came during the 1950s with the introduction of several drugs that relieved symptoms in many people (Cunningham Owens & Johnstone, 2012; Lehmann & Ban, 1997; Potkin et al., 1993). Called *neuroleptics* (meaning "taking hold of the nerves"), these medications provided the first real hope that help was available for people with schizophrenia. The psychiatrist Heinz Lehmann is credited by many (e.g., Dongier, 1999) with introducing neuroleptic

medications for the treatment of schizophrenia to North America. Lehmann conducted a study demonstrating the effectiveness of chlorpromazine with about 200 patients who had schizophrenia at the Douglas Hospital in Montréal (Lehmann & Hanrahan, 1954). When they are effective, neuroleptics help people think more clearly and reduce or eliminate hallucinations and delusions. They work by affecting the positive symptoms (delusions, hallucinations, agitation) and to a lesser extent the negative and disorganized ones, such as social deficits.

Recall from our discussion of the dopamine theory of schizophrenia that the neuroleptics are dopamine antagonists. One of their major actions in the brain is to interfere with the dopamine neurotransmitter system. They can also affect other systems, however, such as the serotonergic system. We are just beginning to understand the mechanisms by which these drugs work.

In general, each drug is effective with some people and not with others. Clinicians and patients often must go through a trial-and-error process to find the medication that works best, and some individuals do not benefit significantly from any of them. The earliest neuroleptic drugs, called conventional antipsychotics, are effective for approximately 60 to 70 percent of persons who try them (American Psychiatric Association, 2000b; Cunningham Owens & Johnstone, 2012). Many people are not helped by antipsychotics, however, or they experience unpleasant side effects. Fortunately, some people respond well to newer medications; the most common are clozapine, risperidone, and olanzapine. First marketed in 1990, clozapine is now used widely, and risperidone and other newer drugs hold promise for helping patients who were previously unresponsive to medications (American Psychiatric Association, 2000b; Iskedjian et al., 1998; Malla et al., 2001; Wahlbeck et al., 1999). These newer antipsychotics are now prescribed to more than three-quarters of patients with schizophrenia in Canada (Smith et al., 2006). They tend to have fewer serious side effects than the conventional antipsychotics (Black & Andreasen, 1999; Levy et al., 2004). In fact, evidence from Howard Margolese and colleagues at McGill University shows that treatment with these newer antipsychotics can reduce the severity of longstanding *tardive dyskinesia*, discussed more below (Margolese et al., 2005).

Some limited evidence also suggests that these newer antipsychotics may be more effective than conventional antipsychotics in reducing both negative and positive symptoms (e.g., Chouinard et al., 1993). For example, University of Montréal researcher Emmanuel Stip and his colleagues have recently shown that the newer antipsychotic quetiapine may be effective in treating the negative symptom of flat affect (Stip et al., 2005). Moreover, research

Courtesy of Douglas Hospital, Montréal

▲ Psychiatrist Heinz Lehmann (1911–1999) is credited with introducing neuroleptic medications in the treatment of schizophrenia to North America in the 1950s. During his influential career, Lehmann was employed at the Douglas Hospital and McGill University in Montréal.

▲ An early 16th-century painting of psychosurgery, in which part of the brain is removed to treat mental illness.

© Bridgeman Art Library, London/SuperStock

by Kimberly Good and her colleagues at Dalhousie University provided evidence that these newer medications may be helpful in improving cognitive functioning, at least among patients experiencing their first episode of psychosis (Good et al., 2002; Kopala et al., 2006).

Despite the optimism generated by the effectiveness of antipsychotics, they work only when they are taken properly, and many people with schizophrenia do not routinely take their medication. David frequently "cheeked" the Haldol pills that were helpful in reducing his hallucinations, holding them in his mouth until he was alone, then spitting them out. Approximately, 7 percent of the people prescribed antipsychotic medication refuse to take it at all (Hoge et al., 1990). Research on the prevalence of occasional noncompliance suggests that a majority of people with schizophrenia stop taking their medication periodically. A follow-up study, for example, found that over a two-year period, three out of four patients studied refused to take their antipsychotic medication for at least one week (Weiden et al., 1991).

Several factors seem to be related to patients' noncompliance with a medication regimen, including negative doctor–patient relationships, cost of the medication, stigma, and poor social support (Haddad, Brain, and Scott, 2014). Not surprisingly, negative side effects are a major factor in patient refusal. Antipsychotics can produce a number of unwanted physical symptoms, such as grogginess, blurred vision, and dryness of the mouth. Because the drugs affect neurotransmitter systems, more serious side effects, called *extrapyramidal symptoms*, can also result (Cunningham Owens & Johnstone, 2012). These symptoms include the motor difficulties similar to those experienced by people with Parkinson's disease, sometimes called *parkinsonian symptoms* (Levy et al., 2004). *Akinesia* is one of the most common; it includes an expressionless face, slow motor activity, and monotonous speech (Blanchard & Neale, 1992). Another extrapyramidal symptom is tardive dyskinesia, which involves involuntary movements of the tongue, face, mouth, or jaw, and can include protrusions of the tongue, puffing of the cheeks, puckering of the mouth, and chewing movements. Tardive dyskinesia seems to result from long-term use of high doses of antipsychotic medication and is often irreversible. Studies have shown that 20 to 50 percent of all patients treated with antipsychotics develop tardive dyskinesia, with lower risk for younger people: only 3 to 5 percent of young people taking this medication display tardive dyskinesia, with the risk increasing over time (Waln & Jankovic, 2013). These serious negative side effects have justifiably concerned people who otherwise benefit from the drugs.

Concept Check 14.4

Read the descriptions and then match them to the following words: (a) clozapine, (b) extrapyramidal symptoms, (c) serotonin, and (d) dopamine.

1. Recent studies sometimes indicate that the relationship of the neurotransmitters _____ and _____ may explain some of the positive symptoms of schizophrenia.

2. Difficult cases of schizophrenia seem to improve with a serotonin and dopamine antagonist called _____.

3. Because antipsychotic medication may cause serious side effects, some patients stop taking them. One serious side effect is called _____, which may have parkinsonian symptoms.

To learn what patients themselves say, Windgassen (1992) questioned 61 people who had had recent onsets of schizophrenia. About half reported the feeling of sedation or grogginess as an unpleasant side effect: "I always have to fight to keep my eyes open," "I felt as though I was on drugs . . . drowsy, and yet really wound up" (p. 407). Other complaints included deterioration in the ability to think or concentrate (18 percent), problems with salivation (16 percent), and blurred vision (16 percent). Although a third of the patients felt the medications were beneficial, about 25 percent had a negative attitude toward them. A significant number of people who could benefit from antipsychotic medications find them unacceptable as a treatment, which may explain the relatively high rates of refusal and noncompliance (Sendt et al., 2015; Yamada et al., 2006).

Researchers have made this a major treatment issue in schizophrenia, realizing that medications can't be successful if they aren't taken regularly. Clinicians hoped that the new antipsychotics such as clozapine, which produce fewer negative side effects, would allay some legitimate patient concerns. However, even clozapine produces undesirable effects, and its use must be monitored closely to avoid rare effects that are potentially life threatening (Umbricht & Kane, 1996). Researchers hoped that compliance rates would improve with the introduction of injectable medications. Instead of taking an oral antipsychotic every day, patients can have their medications injected every few weeks. Unfortunately, noncompliance remains an issue, primarily because patients do not return to the hospital or clinic for repeated doses (Kane et al., 2009). Psychosocial interventions are now used not only to treat schizophrenia but also to increase medication-taking compliance by helping patients communicate better with professionals about their concerns.

An interesting treatment for the hallucinations experienced by many persons with schizophrenia involves exposing the individual to magnetic fields. Called *transcranial magnetic stimulation* (TMS), this technique uses wire coils to repeatedly generate magnetic fields—up to 50 times per second—that pass through the skull to the brain (see review by Daskalakis et al., 2002). This input seems to interrupt the normal communication temporarily to that part of the brain. Hoffman and colleagues (2000) used this technique to stimulate the area of the brain involved in hallucinations for 12 individuals with schizophrenia who experienced auditory hallucinations. They found that many of the individuals experienced improvement following TMS. A more recent study by Jeff Daskalakis at the Centre for Addiction and Mental Health in Toronto and his colleagues produced less promising results. They investigated whether TMS could help individuals with treatment-resistant auditory hallucinations. Unfortunately, TMS

Radius Images/Jupiter Images

▲ One of the major obstacles to drug treatment for schizophrenia is compliance. Patients discontinue their medication for a variety of reasons, including the negative side effects.

was generally ineffective in treating the auditory hallucinations except in decreasing their loudness (Fitzgerald et al., 2005). Subsequent studies have shown that TMS can modestly improve auditory hallucinations, but that its effects last less than one month (e.g., Slotema et al., 2012).

PSYCHOSOCIAL INTERVENTIONS

Historically, a number of psychosocial treatments have been tried for schizophrenia, reflecting the belief that the disorder results from problems in adapting to the world because of early experiences (Cunningham Owens & Johnstone, 2012). Many therapists have thought that individuals who could achieve insight into the presumed role of their personal histories could be safely led to deal with their existing situations. Although clinicians who take a psychodynamic or psychoanalytic approach to therapy continue to use this type of treatment, research suggests that their efforts at best may not be beneficial and at worst may be harmful (Mueser & Berenbaum, 1990; Scott & Dixon, 1995b).

Today, few believe that psychological factors cause people to have schizophrenia or that traditional psychotherapeutic approaches will cure them. We will see, however, that psychological methods do have an important role. Despite the great promise of drug treatment, the problems with ineffectiveness, inconsistent use, and relapse suggest that, by themselves, drugs may not be effective with many people. As with several other disorders discussed in this text, recent work in the area of psychosocial intervention has suggested the value of an approach that uses both kinds of treatment (Mueser & Marcello, 2010; Tarrier et al., 1999, 2000).

Until relatively recently, most people with severe and chronic cases of schizophrenia were treated in hospital settings. During the 19th century, inpatient care involved "moral treatment," which emphasized improving patients' socialization, helping them establish routines for self-control, and showing them the value of work and religion (Tenhula et al., 2009). Various types of such

milieu treatment have been popular but, with one important exception, none seems to have helped people with schizophrenia (Tucker et al., 1984).

In the 1970s, Gordon Paul and Robert Lentz (1977) conducted pioneering work that borrowed from the behavioural approaches used by Ted Ayllon and Nate Azrin (1968). Paul and Lentz designed an environment for inpatients that encouraged appropriate socialization, participation in group sessions, and self-care, such as bed-making, while discouraging violent outbursts. They set up an elaborate **token economy**, in which residents could earn access to meals and small luxuries by behaving appropriately. A patient could, for example, buy cigarettes with the tokens earned for keeping his or her room neat. Conversely, a patient would be fined (lose tokens) for being disruptive or otherwise acting inappropriately. This incentive system was combined with a full schedule of daily activities. Paul and Lentz compared the effectiveness of applied behavioural (or social learning) principles with traditional inpatient environments. In general, they found that patients who went through their program did better than others on social, self-care, and vocational skills, and more of them could be discharged from the hospital. This study was one of the first to show that people experiencing the debilitating effects of schizophrenia can learn to perform some of the skills they need to live more independently.

Since 1955, many efforts have combined to halt the routine institutionalization of people with schizophrenia in both Canada and the United States (Bachrach, 1994; Barnes & Toews, 1983; Talbott, 1990). This trend has occurred in part because of court rulings that limit involuntary hospitalization (as we saw in Arthur's case), in part because of the relative success of antipsychotic medication and in part because of fiscal crisis and ensuing cutbacks in health care (Hanna, 2001). In Canada, provincial psychiatric hospitals released thousands of patients and closed down more than 32 500 beds between 1960 and 1976, and this trend continues today (Nichols, 1995; Sealy & Whitehead, 2004). The bad news is that policies of deinstitutionalization have often been ill conceived so that the process has sometimes resulted in problems. For example, as a consequence of deinstitutionalization, many people who have schizophrenia or other serious psychological disorders are homeless (e.g., Stuart & Arboleda-Florez, 2000). As another example, women (and other family members) are increasingly expected to bear the burden of caring for a family member who has a mental illness (Chan & O'Brian, 2011). The good news is that more attention is being focused on supporting these people in their communities, among their friends and families (Richman & Harris, 1982–1983; Uditsky, 1994). In fact, when adequate community support is provided, these people fare no worse and sometimes fare better in the community than in institutions (Barnes & Toews, 1983). Thus, the trend is away from creating better hospital environments and toward the perhaps more difficult task of addressing complex problems in the less predictable and insecure world outside. So far, only a small fraction of the growing number of homeless individuals with mental disorders are being helped.

One of the more insidious effects of schizophrenia is its negative impact on a person's ability to relate to other people. Although not as dramatic as hallucinations and delusions, this problem can be the most visible impairment displayed by people with schizophrenia and can prevent them from getting and keeping jobs and making friends. Clinicians attempt to reteach social skills, such as basic conversation, assertiveness, and relationship building, to people with schizophrenia.

Therapists divide complex social skills into their component parts, which they model. Then the clients role-play and ultimately practise their new skills in the real world, all the while receiving feedback and encouragement at signs of progress. This isn't as easy as it may sound. For example, how would you teach someone to make a friend? Many skills are involved, such as maintaining eye contact when you talk to someone and providing the prospective friend with some (but not too much!) positive feedback on his or her own behaviour ("I really enjoy talking to you"). Such individual skills are practised and then combined until they can be used naturally (Swartz et al., 2006). Basic skills can be taught to people with schizophrenia, but there is some disagreement about how ultimately successful the treatment is (Bellack & Mueser, 1992; Hogarty et al., 1992). The problem is that the positive results of social skills training may fade after the training is over (Scott & Dixon, 1995b). The challenge of teaching social skills, as with all therapies, is to maintain the effects over a long time.

In addition to social skills, programs often teach a range of ways that people can adapt to their disorder yet still live in the community. In the Independent Living Skills Program developed by Eckman and colleagues (1992), the focus is on helping people take charge of their own care by such methods as identifying signs that warn of a relapse and learning how to manage their medication (Corrigan et al., 1994; Eckman et al., 1992). Preliminary evidence indicates that this type of training may help prevent the relapses of people with schizophrenia. For example, Ross Norman and his colleagues at the University of Western Ontario added a stress-management intervention to an existing medical and psychosocial treatment program for individuals with schizophrenia.

▲ A mother is glad to have her daughter home from a psychiatric hospital, but she acknowledges that now the real struggle begins.

Patients who participated in the stress-management program had fewer hospitalizations in the following year, particularly those who showed a high level of attendance at treatment sessions (Norman et al., 2002). Longer-term outcome research is needed to see how long these effects last (Cunningham Owens & Johnstone, 2012). To address some of the obstacles to this much-desired maintenance, such programs combine skills training with the support of a multidisciplinary team that provides services directly in the community, which seems to reduce hospitalization (Cunningham Owens & Johnstone, 2012; Scott & Dixon, 1995a). The more time and effort given to these services, the more likely the improvement (Brekke et al., 1997).

In our discussion of the psychosocial influences on schizophrenia, we reviewed some of the work linking the person's social and emotional environments to the recurrence of schizophrenic episodes (McNab et al., 2007). It is logical to ask whether families could be helped by learning to reduce their level of EE and whether this would result in fewer relapses and better overall functioning for people with schizophrenia. Several studies have addressed these issues in a variety of ways (Falloon et al., 1985; Hogarty et al., 1986, 1991), and behavioural family therapy has been used to teach the families of persons with schizophrenia to be more supportive (Dixon & Lehman, 1995; Mueser et al., 1990). Research on professionals who provide care for people who have schizophrenia, and who may also display high levels of EE, is also an active area of study (Barrowclough & Tarrier, 1998; Cunningham Owens & Johnstone, 2012; Tattan & Tarrier, 2000).

In contrast to traditional therapy, behavioural family therapy resembles classroom education (Falloon, 2015; Lefley, 2009). Family members are informed about schizophrenia and its treatment, relieved of the myth that they caused the disorder, and taught practical facts about antipsychotic medications and their side effects. They are also helped with communication skills so they can become more empathic listeners, and they learn constructive ways of expressing negative feelings to replace the harsh criticism that characterizes some family interactions. In addition, they learn problem-solving skills to help them resolve conflicts that arise. Like the research on social skills training, outcome research suggests that the effects of behavioural family therapy are significant during the first year but less robust two years after intervention (Cunningham Owens & Johnstone, 2012). This type of therapy, therefore, must be ongoing if patients and their families are to benefit from it.

Adults with schizophrenia face great obstacles to maintaining gainful employment. Their social skills deficits make reliable job performance and adequate employee relationships a struggle. To address these difficulties, some programs focus on vocational rehabilitation, such as supportive employment (Bustillo et al., 2001). Providing coaches who give on-the-job training may help some people with schizophrenia maintain meaningful jobs (Bond et al., 1997; Drake et al., 1996; Lehman, 1995). Social skills training, family intervention, and vocational rehabilitation may be helpful additions to biological treatments for schizophrenia, in terms of avoiding or delaying relapse.

A general trend in the treatment of schizophrenia today is toward early intervention. It is increasingly becoming recognized that intervening early can be important in affecting the course of the disorder over time. Getting help in the early stages of the

▲ Researchers are using virtual reality technology to better understand the complexity of schizophrenia. The photo at the top illustrates a participant in a study of paranoia. The bottom photo shows what the participants see. This technology allows researchers to closely control positions and facial expressions of the virtual people on the train.

TABLE 14.1 | Key Elements of Early Intervention

- Reduction of duration of untreated psychosis (DUP) through education. Raising psychosis awareness through educational initiatives with health professionals, teachers, families, and community members is a necessary step towards the reduction of DUP.

- Assessment and the context of care: building a therapeutic alliance. Once a psychosis is suspected, careful and comprehensive assessment of the individual by skilled professionals is the next step. For many, this will be the individual's first contact with the mental health system. This situation provides a significant opportunity for practitioners to begin to develop a positive, honest, mutually respectful relationship— a "therapeutic alliance"—with the young client and his or her family.

- Family engagement and support. Most young people experiencing psychosis for the first time are living in the family home. The family can play a significant role in promoting the recovery of their family member. But, in order to do so, the family also requires education, support, and inclusion in the therapeutic process.

- Comprehensive, phase-specific, individualized treatment including low-dose antipsychotic medications, psychoeducation, and psychosocial support. These three main components, when offered in the context of a therapeutic alliance with an attitude of "realistic optimism," are demonstrating positive outcomes in the lives of young people who experience psychosis.

- Prolonged engagement to sustain gains. Psychosis is a serious physiological event. Recovery takes time. Early psychosis intervention, even at its best, is not a magic bullet. Clients may need to receive services on an outpatient basis from an early psychosis clinical program for two years or more.

Source: Adapted from "Youth and Mental Illness: Early Intervention Project," an initiative of the CMHA National Office.

illness is critical. In fact, research has shown that getting patients onto the right medications and into effective psychotherapy as soon as possible, and providing information and support to affected families right away, can actually reduce the severity of future relapses (e.g., Drury et al., 1996). The key elements of early intervention are outlined in Table 14.1. Early psychosis clinical programs have now been developed at several sites across Canada (e.g., Halifax, Toronto, London, Hamilton, and Calgary; Lines,

2001). The first such centre, the First Episode Psychosis Clinic/ Early Psychosis Unit, was developed at the Centre for Addiction and Mental Health in Toronto (Nichols, 1995). It is designed to meet the needs of individuals experiencing a first episode of psychosis and assists such individuals and their families with the initial period of adjustment and recovery. The clinic provides a full assessment and psychosocial intervention to help such patients on an outpatient basis; inpatient services are also available. Priority is given to adults (aged 18 to 45) who have not yet received any antipsychotic treatment. For an example of early intervention in British Columbia see http://www.earlypsychosis.ca.

A relatively newer approach to the treatment of schizophrenia that has been applied over the past 20 years is cognitive-behavioural therapy (CBT; see reviews by Bouchard et al., 1996; Norman & Townsend, 1999; Rector & Beck, 2001). For example, British researchers David Kingdon and Douglas Turkington (1994) argued that people with schizophrenia are not inherently irrational but instead have a set of irrational beliefs that are amenable to intervention with cognitive and behavioural techniques. CBT has usually been applied to auditory hallucinations and delusions (i.e., positive symptoms; Birchwood et al., 1994; Norman & Townsend, 1999), although CBT strategies have been developed to treat both positive and negative symptoms (Beck & Rector, 2000). CBT strategies developed to treat symptoms of schizophrenia are essentially adaptations of CBT strategies successfully used in the treatment of depression and anxiety

(Beck et al., 2001). Take the case example of Thomas described by clinical psychologist Neil Rector—a case that was treated by Aaron Beck over 50 years ago, in the first application of CBT to the treatment of delusions (Rector & Beck, 2002).

THOMAS | *Examining the Evidence for a Conspiracy*

At the time he was seen by Beck, Thomas was a 28-year-old veteran of World War II who presented with a paranoid delusion that he had held for the last seven years. When he returned home from the war, he came to believe that members of his unit in the armed forces were working secretly with the government to monitor his activities. In treatment, Beck worked with Thomas to help him identify the antecedents or triggers of his delusional beliefs and to apply this knowledge to his current delusional system. Thomas's misperceptions of everyday events that were taken as evidence of this conspiracy (e.g., a stranger looking at him while he was on the bus) were identified by the therapist and gently questioned. The repeated questioning and testing of alternative explanations for such everyday events eventually led to changes in Thomas's beliefs. By the end of therapy, every time Thomas began to become suspicious that he was being watched, he was able to stand back and reason himself out of his erroneous thinking patterns. Thomas was taught to carefully question the evidence that supported his delusion both in the therapy session and between sessions. Through this careful examination of the evidence, he was eventually able to see his delusions as "hypotheses" about the meaning of things that happened in his life rather than as absolute, rigid "truths."

Source: Adapted from "Cognitive Therapy for Schizophrenia: From Conceptualization to Intervention," by N. A. Rector and A. T. Beck, 2002, *Canadian Journal of Psychiatry, 47*, pp. 39–48.

In the following excerpt, a patient from the Royal Ottawa Hospital, J. P. Lee, who has been living with schizophrenia for 20 years, describes how he learned to use CBT to effectively challenge his delusional paranoid thoughts. He attempts to describe a scenario where he used CBT to modify the sequence of his reactions:

My stimulating problematic thought may be that I am suspicious that my friends may be secretly criticizing and ridiculing me and doing that in my presence using cryptic language with each other. My interpretation is that my friends don't really like me and my reaction is one of resentment of this behavior. The consequence is that I am angry at my friends and choose not to socialize so much with them. Having recognized this pattern, I now attempt CBT. I will respond . . . with a different interpretation and reaction. . . . I will consider as a real possibility that my friends have not been ridiculing me using cryptic language. I will try harder not to sink into my paranoia but instead talk and interact with them and engage more enthusiastically with the activities at hand. . . .

The consequence is that I am no longer angry but more in synchrony with my friends. Having done one CBT exercise, I can mentally rehearse my way through future potential problematic/delusional thoughts in order to bypass the ravages of paranoid thinking. The next time when such stimuli trigger my mind I can quickly recognize the pattern and . . . relieve myself of confusion and harmful emotions. Hence, I am in charge of my symptoms, I am free from the strangulation of mental processes by excessive medication, and I am also free from the control of delusional thoughts. (Lee, 2005, p. 74)

Despite a good deal of initial skepticism as to whether symptoms of a such a severe disorder could be amenable to "talk therapy," more recent reviews of the literature are unanimous in supporting the potential of this approach in the treatment of patients with schizophrenia. For example, in a review of the literature conducted with CBT developer Aaron Beck, University of Toronto psychologist Neil Rector found that CBT produces large clinical effects on both positive and negative symptoms of schizophrenia (Rector & Beck, 2001). In one such study, 42 patients with schizophrenia were randomly assigned to either a treatment-as-usual control condition (i.e., specialized schizophrenia treatment services) or to treatment as usual with an additional 20 sessions of CBT. For patients in the experimental group receiving adjunctive CBT, significant benefits of treatment were observed at a six-month follow-up for positive symptoms, negative symptoms, and overall severity of the disorder. The most pronounced effect of the addition of CBT relative to the treatment-as-usual control group was in the reduction of negative symptoms at follow-up (Rector et al., 2003). In another example, Garety and colleagues at the Institute of Psychiatry in London, England, reported excellent outcome of a controlled trial of CBT for patients with schizophrenia who had not responded well to drug treatment in the past. They found that the treatment group improved more than the controls on the degree of conviction in their delusional beliefs, the severity of their overall symptoms, and their depression levels (Garety et al., 1994). Results such as these suggest promise for the impact of CBT in the treatment of schizophrenia.

TREATMENT ACROSS CULTURES

Treatment of schizophrenia and its delivery differ from one country to another and across cultures within countries. In China, for example, the most frequently used treatment is antipsychotic medication, although 7 to 9 percent of patients also receive traditional herbal medicine and acupuncture (Mingdao &

Courtesy of Neil A. Rector

▲ Neil Rector is a professor of psychiatry and psychological clinical science at the University of Toronto and director of the Mood and Anxiety Treatment and Research Program at the Sunnybrook Research Institute. He has worked closely with cognitive-behavioural therapy (CBT) originator Aaron Beck to develop and test the efficacy of CBT in the treatment of schizophrenia.

In China, acupuncture and herbal medicine are often used with antipsychotic medications for schizophrenia.

Zhenyi, 1990). For financial and cultural reasons, more people in China are treated outside the hospital than are in Western societies. The vast majority of the Xhosa people of South Africa who have schizophrenia report using traditional healers who sometimes recommend the use of oral treatments to induce vomiting, enemas, and the slaughter of cattle to appease the spirits (Koen et al., 2008). In one interesting study, beliefs about symptoms and treatments were compared between British and Chinese populations (Furnham & Wong, 2007). Native Chinese hold more religious beliefs about both the causes and the treatments of schizophrenia than those living in England—for example, endorsing statements such as "Schizophrenia is due to evil done in a previous life," and "Ancestor worship (burning candles and joss sticks) will help treat schizophrenia." These different beliefs translate into practice—with the British using more biological, psychological, and community treatments and the Chinese relying more on alternative medicine (Furnham & Wong, 2007). Supernatural beliefs about the cause of schizophrenia among family members in Bali lead to limited use of antipsychotic medication in treatment (Kurihara et al., 2006). In many countries in Africa, people with schizophrenia are kept in prisons, primarily because of the lack of adequate alternatives (Mustafa, 1990). In general, the movement from housing people in large institutional settings to community care is ongoing in most Western countries.

PREVENTION

One strategy for preventing a disorder such as schizophrenia—which typically first shows itself in early adulthood—is to identify and treat children who may be at risk for getting the disorder later in life. In our discussion of genetics, we noted that approximately 13 percent of the children born to parents who have schizophrenia are likely themselves to develop the disorder. These high-risk children have been the focus of several studies, both prospective (before and during an expected situation) and longitudinal (over long periods).

A classic at-risk study was initiated in the 1960s by Mednick and Schulsinger (1965, 1968) in Denmark. They identified 207 Danish children of mothers who had severe cases of schizophrenia and 104 comparison children born to mothers who had no history of the disorder. The average age of these children was about 15 when they were first identified, and the researchers followed them for 25 years to determine whether any factors had predicted who would and would not develop schizophrenia. The children of mothers with schizophrenia were at much greater risk to develop schizophrenia (16 percent) or personality disorders (21 percent) than children of non-affected mothers (2 and 5 percent; Parnas et al., 1993). We have already discussed pregnancy and delivery-related complications as predictors of schizophrenia. Mednick and Schulsinger also identified *instability of the early family-rearing environment*, which suggests that environmental influences may trigger the onset of schizophrenia (Carter et al., 2002). Poor parenting may place additional strain on a vulnerable person who is already at risk.

One approach to prevention of schizophrenia receiving increased attention is the treatment of persons in the prodromal stages of the disorder. Here, the individual is beginning to show early mild signs of schizophrenia (e.g., hallucinations, delusions) but is aware of these changes. Efforts to intervene with these individuals are being investigated as a means of either stopping the progression of the disorder or preventing relapses (Cunningham Owens & Johnstone, 2012).

SUMMARY

Perspectives on the Concept of Schizophrenia

- German psychiatrist Emil Kraepelin (1899) combined disparate symptoms of insanity under the Latin term dementia praecox and distinguished it from bipolar disorder. A contemporary of his, Swiss psychiatrist Eugen Bleuler introduced the term schizophrenia (meaning "split mind").

- Unlike other disorders, schizophrenia does not have defining behaviours, ways of thinking, or emotions, although researchers have identified clusters of symptoms that make up the disorder of schizophrenia.

Clinical Description

- Schizophrenia is characterized by a broad spectrum of cognitive and emotional dysfunctions that include delusions and hallucinations, disorganized speech and behaviour, and inappropriate emotions.

- The symptoms of schizophrenia can be divided into positive, negative, and disorganized. Positive symptoms are active manifestations of abnormal behaviour, or an excess or distortion of normal behaviour, and include delusions and hallucinations. Negative symptoms involve deficits in normal behaviour on such dimensions as affect, speech, and motivation. Disorganized symptoms include rambling speech, erratic behaviour, and inappropriate affect.

- Psychotic behaviours, such as hallucinations and delusions, characterize several other disorders; these include *schizophreniform disorder* (which includes people who experience the symptoms of schizophrenia for less than six months); *schizoaffective disorder* (which includes people who have symptoms of schizophrenia and who also exhibit the characteristics of mood disorders, such as depression and bipolar affective disorder); *delusional disorder* (which includes people with a persistent belief that is contrary to reality, in the absence of the other characteristics of schizophrenia); and *brief psychotic disorder* (which includes people with one or more positive symptoms, such as delusions, hallucinations, or disorganized speech or behaviour for less than a month).

Prevalence and Causes of Schizophrenia

- A number of causative factors have been implicated for schizophrenia, including genetic influences, neurotransmitter imbalances, structural damage to the brain caused by a prenatal viral infection or birth injury, and psychological stressors.

- Relapse appears to be triggered by hostile and critical family environments characterized by high expressed emotion.

Treatment

- Successful treatment for people with schizophrenia rarely includes complete recovery. The quality of life for these individuals can be meaningfully affected, however, by combining antipsychotic medications with psychosocial approaches, employment support, and community-based and family interventions.

- Treatment typically involves antipsychotic drugs that are usually administered in combination with a variety of psychosocial treatments, with the goal of reducing relapse and improving skills in deficits and compliance in taking the medications. The effectiveness of treatment is limited, as schizophrenia is typically a chronic disorder.

KEY TERMS

alogia, 428
anhedonia, 429
asociality, 429
associative splitting, 423
attenuated psychosis syndrome, 433
avolition, 428
brief psychotic disorder, 433
catatonia, 423
catatonic immobility, 430
delusion, 425

delusional disorder, 431
dementia praecox, 423
disorganized speech, 429
disorganized symptoms, 429
double bind, 443
expressed emotion (EE), 444
flat affect, 429
folie à deux, 433
hallucination, 427
hebephrenia, 423
inappropriate affect, 430

negative symptoms, 428
paranoia, 423
positive symptoms, 425
prodromal stage, 435
psychosis, 425
psychotic disorder due to another medical condition, 433
schizoaffective disorder, 431
schizophrenia, 423
schizophreniform disorder, 430

schizophrenogenic, 443
schizotypal personality disorder, 434
shared psychotic disorder, 433
substance-induced psychotic disorder, 433
token economy, 447

ANSWERS TO CONCEPT CHECKS

14.1

1. delusions; 2. avolition; 3. affective flattening; 4. hallucinations

14.2

1. c; 2. b; 3. a; 4. d

14.3

1. d; 2. i; 3. f, a; 4. a

14.4

1. c, d; 2. a; 3. b

CENGAGE | MINDTAP

Stay organized and efficient with MindTap—a single destination with all the course material and study aids you need to succeed. Built-in apps leverage social media and the latest learning technology. For example:

- ReadSpeaker will read the text to you.

- Flashcards are pre-populated to provide you with a jump start for review—or you can create your own.

- You can highlight text and make notes in your MindTap Reader. Your notes will flow into Evernote, the electronic notebook app that you can access anywhere when it's time to study for the exam.

- Self-quizzing allows you to assess your understanding.

Visit login.cengage.com to start using MindTap. Enter the Online Access Code from the card included with your text. If a code card is not provided, you can purchase instant access at Cengage.ca.

Exploring Schizophrenia

> Schizophrenia disrupts perception of the world, thought, speech, movement, and almost every other aspect of daily functioning.
> Usually chronic with a high relapse rate; complete recovery from schizophrenia is rare.

- Stressful, traumatic life event
- High expressed emotion (family criticism, hostility, and/or intrusion)
- Sometimes no obvious trigger

Trigger

Biological Influences

- Inherited tendency (multiple genes) to develop disease
- Prenatal/birth complications—viral infection during pregnancy/birth injury affects child's brain cells
- Brain chemistry (abnormalities in the dopamine and glutamate systems)
- Brain structure (enlarged ventricles)

Social Influences

- Environment (early family experiences) can trigger onset
- Culture influences interpretation of disease/symptoms (hallucinations, delusions)

Causes

Photodisc/Getty Images

© Cengage Learning

Behavioural Influences

- **Positive symptoms:**
  - Active manifestations of abnormal behaviour (delusions, hallucinations, disorganized speech, odd body movements, or catatonia)
- **Negative symptoms:**
  - Flat affect (lack of emotional expression)
  - Avolition (lack of initiative, apathy)
  - Alogia (relative absence in amount or content of speech)

Dynamic Graphics

Emotional and Cognitive Influences

- Interaction styles that are high in criticism, hostility, and emotional overinvolvement can trigger a relapse.

TREATMENT OF SCHIZOPHRENIA

Treatment		
Individual, Group, and Family Therapy	 Photodisc/ Getty Images	• Can help patients and family understand the disease and symptom triggers • Teaches families communication skills • Provides resources for dealing with emotional and practical challenges
Social Skills Training	Photodisc/ Getty Images	• Can occur in hospital or community settings • Teaches the person with schizophrenia social, self-care, and vocational skills
Medications	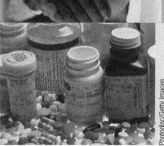 Photodisc/Getty Images	• Taking neuroleptic medications may help people with schizophrenia to – Clarify thinking and perceptions of reality – Reduce hallucinations and delusions • Drug treatment must be consistent to be effective. Inconsistent dosage may aggravate existing symptoms or create new ones.

SYMPTOMS OF SCHIZOPHRENIA

People with schizophrenia do not all show the same kinds of symptoms. Symptoms vary from person to person and may be cyclical. Common symptoms include:

Symptoms		
Delusions		• Unrealistic and bizarre beliefs not shared by others in the culture • May be delusions of grandeur (that you are really Mother Teresa or Napoleon) or delusions of persecution (the cyclist who believed her competitors were sabotaging her by putting pebbles in the road)
Hallucinations		• Sensory events that aren't based on any external event (hearing voices, seeing people who have died) • Many have auditory hallucinations (David hears his dead uncle talking to him)
Disorganized Speech		• Jumping from topic to topic • Talking illogically (not answering direct questions, going off on tangents) • Speaking in unintelligible words and sentences
Behavioural Problems		• Pacing excitably, wild agitation • Catatonic immobility • Waxy flexibility (keeping body parts in the same position when they are moved by someone else) • Inappropriate dress (coats in the summer, shorts in the winter) • Inappropriate affect • Ignoring personal hygiene
Withdrawal		• Lack of emotional response (flat speech, little change in facial expressions) • Apathy (little interest in day-to-day activities) • Delayed and brief responses in conversation • Loss of enjoyment in pleasurable activities (eating, socializing, sex)

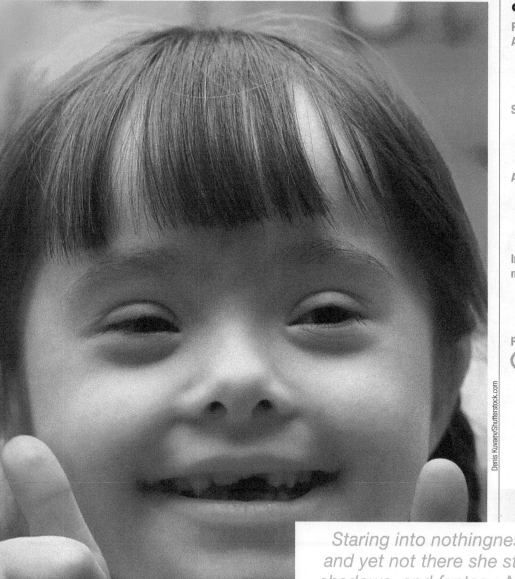

15 | Neurodevelopment

Denis Kuvaev/Shutterstock.com

Staring into nothingness since time began, There and yet not there she stood. In a world of dreams, shadows, and fantasy, Nothing more complex than colour and indiscernible sound. With the look of an angel no doubt, But also without the ability to love or Feel anything more complex than the sensation of cat's fur Against her face.

—AUSTRALIAN AUTHOR DONNA WILLIAMS, *Nobody Nowhere: The Extraordinary Autobiography of an Autistic*

STUDENT LEARNING OUTCOMES*

Use scientific reasoning to interpret behaviour:	⟩ Identify basic biological, psychological, and social components of behavioural explanations (e.g., inferences, observations, operational definitions and interpretations) (APA SLO 2.1a)
Engage in innovative and integrative thinking and problem solving:	⟩ Describe problems operationally to study them empirically (APA SLO 2.3a)
Describe applications that employ discipline-based problem solving:	⟩ Correctly identify antecedents and consequences of behaviour and mental processes (APA SLO 1.3c)
	⟩ Describe examples of relevant and practical applications of psychological principles to everyday life (APA SLO 1.3att)

*Portions of this chapter cover learning outcomes suggested by the American Psychological Association (2012) in its guidelines for the undergraduate psychology major. Chapter coverage of these outcomes is identified above by APA Goal and APA Suggested Learning Outcome (SLO).

Almost all the disorders described in this book are developmental disorders in the sense that they change over time. Many disorders originate in childhood, although the full presentation of the problem may not manifest until much later. Disorders that show themselves early in life often persist as the person grows older, so the term *childhood disorder* may be misleading. Because the developmental disorders in this group are all believed to be neurologically based, the *DSM-5* categorizes them as **neurodevelopmental disorders**. This is not to say that other disorders are not neurodevelopment in nature. Schizophrenia spectrum disorder, for example, is considered a neurodevelopmental disorder, but it is typically fully manifested in early adult years. In this chapter, we cover those disorders that are revealed in a clinically significant way during a child's developing years and that are of concern to families and the educational system. Remember, however, that these difficulties often persist through adulthood and are typically lifelong problems, not ones unique to children. In certain disorders, some children are fine except for difficulties with talking. Others have problems relating to their peers. Still other children have a combination of conditions that significantly hinder their development.

Before we discuss specific disorders, we need to address the broad topic of development in relation to disorders usually first diagnosed in infancy, childhood, or adolescence. Does it matter when in the developmental period certain problems arise? Are disruptions in development permanent, thus making any hope for treatment doubtful?

PERSPECTIVES

Recall that in Chapter 2, we described developmental psychopathology as the study of how disorders arise and how they change with time. Childhood is considered particularly important because the brain changes significantly for several years after birth; this is also the time when critical developments occur in social, emotional, cognitive, and other important competency areas. For the most part, these changes follow a pattern: the child develops one skill before acquiring the next, and subsequent skills often build on one another. Although this pattern of change is only one aspect of development, it is an important concept for us at this point because it implies that any disruption in the development of early skills will, by the very nature of this sequential process, disrupt the development of later skills. For

example, some researchers believe that people with autism spectrum disorder suffer from a disruption in early social development, which prevents them from developing important social relationships, even with their parents (Durand, 2014). From a developmental perspective, the absence of early and meaningful social relationships has serious consequences. Children whose motivation to interact with others is disrupted may have a more difficult time learning to communicate; that is, they may not want to learn to speak if other people are not important to them. We don't know whether a disruption in communication skills is a direct outcome of the disorder or a by-product of disrupted early social development.

Understanding this type of developmental relationship is important for several reasons. Knowing what processes are disrupted will help us understand the disorder better and may lead to more appropriate intervention strategies. It may be important to identify children with attention-deficit/hyperactivity disorder, for example, because their problems with impulsivity may interfere with their ability to create and maintain friendships, an important developmental consideration. Similarly, identifying a disorder such as autism spectrum disorder at an early age is important for these children so their social deficits can be addressed before they affect other skill domains, such as social communication.

One note of caution is appropriate here. There is real concern in the profession, especially among developmental psychologists, that some workers in the field may view aspects of normal development as symptoms of abnormality. For example, echolalia, which involves repeating the speech of others, was once thought to be a sign of autism spectrum disorder. When we study the development of speech in children without disorders, however, we find that repeating what someone else says is an intermediate step in language development. In children with autism spectrum disorder, therefore, echolalia is just a sign of relatively delayed language skills and not a symptom of their disorder (Roberts, 2014). Thus, as noted by developmental psychologist expert Jacob Burack from McGill University, knowledge of normal development is important for understanding the nature of childhood psychological disorders (Burack et al., 2002).

With that caveat in mind, we now examine several of the disorders usually diagnosed first in infancy, childhood, or adolescence, including *attention-deficit/hyperactivity disorder* (ADHD), which involves characteristics of inattention or hyperactivity and impulsivity, and *specific learning disorder*, which is characterized by one or more difficulties in areas such as reading and writing. We then focus on *autism spectrum disorder*, a more severe disability, in which a child shows significant impairment in social communication and restricted patterns of behaviour, interest, and activities. Finally, we examine *intellectual disability*, which involves significant deficits in cognitive abilities. Communication and motor disabilities, which are also considered neurodevelopmental disorders, are described later in the chapter (see Box 15.1).

ATTENTION-DEFICIT/ HYPERACTIVITY DISORDER

Do you know people who flit from activity to activity, who start many tasks but seldom finish one, who have trouble concentrating, and who don't seem to pay attention when others speak? These people may have **attention-deficit/hyperactivity disorder (ADHD)**, one of the most common reasons children are referred for mental health services (Popper et al., 2003; Taylor, 2012). The primary characteristics of such people include a pattern of inattention, such as being disorganized or forgetful about school- or work-related tasks, or of hyperactivity and impulsivity. These deficits can significantly disrupt academic efforts as well as social relationships. Consider the case of Danny.

DANNY | *The Boy Who Couldn't Sit Still*

Danny, a handsome nine-year-old boy, was referred to us because of the significant difficulties he was experiencing at school and at home. Danny had a great deal of energy and loved playing most sports, especially baseball. Academically, he was experiencing substantial difficulties with his grades. His teacher reported that Danny's performance was diminishing and she believed he would do better if he paid more attention in class. Danny rarely spent more than a few minutes on a task without some interruption: he would get up out of his seat, rifle through his desk, or constantly ask questions. His peers were frustrated with him because he was equally impulsive during their interactions: he never finished a game, and in sports he tried to play all the positions simultaneously.

At home, Danny was considered quite a handful. His room was in a constant mess because he became engaged in a game or an activity only to drop it and initiate something else. Danny's parents reported that they often scolded him for not carrying out some task, although the reason seemed to be that he forgot what he was doing rather than that he deliberately tried to defy them. They also said that, out of their own frustration, they sometimes grabbed him by the shoulders and yelled "Slow down!" because his hyperactivity drove them crazy.

CLINICAL DESCRIPTION

Danny has many of the characteristics of ADHD. People with this disorder have a great deal of difficulty sustaining their attention on a task or an activity. As a result, their tasks are frequently unfinished and they often seem not to be listening when someone else is speaking. In addition to this serious disruption in attention, some people with ADHD also display motor hyperactivity. Children with this disorder are often described as fidgety in school, unable to sit still for more than a few minutes. Danny's restlessness in his classroom was a considerable source of concern for his teacher and peers, who were frustrated by his impatience. In addition to hyperactivity and problems sustaining attention, impulsivity—acting apparently without thinking—is a common complaint made about people with ADHD. For instance, during meetings at his baseball practice, Danny often shouted out responses to the coach's questions even before the coach had finished his sentence.

For ADHD, the *DSM-5* differentiates two categories of symptoms (see DSM Table 15.1). The first includes problems of *inattention*. People may appear not to listen to others; they may lose necessary school assignments, books, or tools; and they may not pay enough attention to details, making careless mistakes. The second category of symptoms includes *hyperactivity and impulsivity*. Hyperactivity includes fidgeting, having trouble sitting for any length of time, and always being on the go. Impulsivity includes blurting out answers before questions have been completed and having trouble waiting turns. Either the first (inattention) or the second (hyperactivity and impulsivity) set of symptoms must be present for someone to be diagnosed with ADHD (American Psychiatric Association, 2013). These different presentations are called *subtypes*, and they include the inattentive subtype (what some may call *ADD*, noting the absence of hyperactivity, although this is not an official diagnostic label), and the hyperactive/impulsive subtype. Other individuals meet criteria for both inattention and hyperactivity/impulsivity, and these individuals are labelled with the *combined* subtype.

The work of clinical psychologist Virginia Douglas at McGill University was largely responsible for recognition that problems of inattention often accompany symptoms of hyperactivity (Douglas, 1972). Her work led to changes in the conceptualization of and diagnostic criteria for this disorder, which used to be called "hyperactive child syndrome." These two clusters of ADHD symptoms appear to be consistent across different cultural groups (Beiser et al., 2000).

Inattention, hyperactivity, and impulsivity often cause other problems that appear secondary to ADHD. Academic performance often suffers, especially as the child progresses in school. The cause of this poor performance is not known. It could be a result of inattention and impulsivity, and in some children this can be made worse by such factors as concurrent learning disabilities. Genetic research on both ADHD and learning disabilities suggests that they may share a common biological cause (DuPaul et al., 2013). Children with ADHD are likely to be unpopular and rejected by their peers (McQuade & Hoza, 2015).

A. A persistent pattern of inattention and/or hyperactivity-impulsivity that interferes with functioning or development, as characterized by (1) and/or (2):

  1. Inattention: Six (or more) of the following symptoms have persisted for at least 6 months to a degree that is inconsistent with developmental level and that negatively impacts directly on social and academic/occupational activities:

  Note: The symptoms are not solely a manifestation of oppositional behavior, defiance, hostility, or failure to understand tasks or instructions. For older adolescents and adults (age 17 and older), at least five symptoms are required.

    a. Often fails to give close attention to details or makes careless mistakes in schoolwork, at work, or during other activities (e.g., overlooks or misses details, work is inaccurate).

    b. Often has difficulty sustaining attention in tasks or play activities (e.g., has difficulty remaining focused during lectures, conversations, or lengthy reading).

    c. Often does not seem to listen when spoken to directly (e.g., mind seems elsewhere, even in the absence of any obvious distraction).

    d. Often does not follow through on instructions and fails to finish schoolwork, chores, or duties in the workplace (e.g., starts tasks but quickly loses focus and is easily sidetracked).

    e. Often has difficulty organizing tasks and activities (e.g., difficulty managing sequential tasks; difficulty keeping materials and belongings in order; messy, disorganized work; has poor time management; fails to meet deadlines).

    f. Often avoids, dislikes, or is reluctant to engage in tasks that require sustained mental effort (e.g., schoolwork or homework; for older adolescents and adults, preparing reports, completing forms, reviewing lengthy papers).

    g. Often loses things necessary for tasks or activities (e.g., school materials, pencils, books, tools, wallets, keys, paperwork, eyeglasses, mobile telephones).

    h. Is often easily distracted by extraneous stimuli (for older adolescents and adults, may include unrelated thoughts).

    i. Is often forgetful in daily activities (e.g., doing chores, running errands; for older adolescents and adults, returning calls, paying bills, keeping appointments).

  2. Hyperactivity and impulsivity: Six (or more) of the following symptoms have persisted for at least 6 months to a degree that is inconsistent with developmental level and that negatively impacts directly on social and academic/occupational activities:

  Note: The symptoms are not solely a manifestation of oppositional behavior, defiance, hostility, or failure to understand tasks or instructions. For older adolescents and adults (age 17 and older), at least five symptoms are required.

    a. Often fidgets with or taps hands or feet or squirms in seat.

    b. Often leaves seat in situations when remaining seated is expected (e.g., leaves his or her place in the classroom, in the office or other workplace, or in other situations that require remaining in place).

    c. Often runs about or climbs in situations where it is inappropriate. (Note: In adolescents or adults, may be limited to feeling restless.)

    d. Often unable to play or engage in leisure activities quietly.

    e. Is often "on the go," acting as if "driven by a motor" (e.g., is unable to be or uncomfortable being still for an extended time, as in restaurants, meetings; may be experienced by others as being restless or difficult to keep up with).

    f. Often talks excessively.

    g. Often blurts out an answer before a question has been completed (e.g., completes people's sentences; cannot wait for turn in conversation).

    h. Often has difficulty waiting his or her turn (e.g., while waiting in line).

    i. Often interrupts or intrudes on others (e.g., butts into conversations, games, or activities; may start using other people's things without asking or receiving permission; for adolescents or adults, may intrude into or take over what others are doing).

B. Several inattentive or hyperactive-impulsive symptoms were present prior to age 12 years.

C. Several inattentive or hyperactive-impulsive symptoms are present in two or more settings (e.g., at home, school or work; with friends or relatives; in other activities).

D. There is clear evidence that the symptoms interfere with, or reduce the quality of, social, academic, or occupational functioning.

E. The symptoms do not occur exclusively during the course of schizophrenia or another psychotic disorder and are not better explained by another mental disorder (e.g., mood disorder, anxiety disorder, dissociative disorder, personality disorder, substance intoxication or withdrawal).

Specify whether:

  Combined presentation: If both Criterion A1 (inattention) and Criterion A2 (hyperactivity-impulsivity) are met for the past 6 months.

  Predominantly inattentive presentation: If Criterion A1 (inattention) is met but Criterion A2 (hyperactivity-impulsivity) is not met for the past 6 months.

  Predominantly hyperactive/impulsive presentation: If Criterion A2 (hyperactivity-impulsivity) is met and Criterion A1 (inattention) is not met for the past 6 months.

STATISTICS

A recent meta-analytic review of community studies estimates that ADHD affects 3.4 percent of children and adolescents worldwide (Polanczyk et al., 2015). This matches the prevalence rate of ADHD among First Nations youth (12–17 years of age) living on reserve in Canada (FNIGC, 2018). With respect to gender distribution, boys outnumber girls roughly four to one (Popper et al., 2003). The 2012 Canadian Community Health Survey—Mental Health also demonstrated a gender difference among Canadians 15 years of age and over with ADD. ADD affected 2.6 percent of Canadians overall, 3.3 percent of men and 2.0 percent of women (Statistics Canada, 2012).

The reason for the gender difference is unknown. It may be that adults are more tolerant of hyperactivity among girls with ADHD, who tend to be less active than boys with ADHD. Whether ADHD has a different presentation in girls is as yet unknown, but this may account for the different prevalence rates for girls and boys. Children with ADHD are first identified as different from their peers around age three or four; their parents describe them as very active, mischievous, slow to toilet train, and oppositional (Conners et al., 2001; Taylor, 2012). The symptoms of inattention, impulsivity, and hyperactivity become increasingly obvious during the school years. Despite the perception that children grow out of ADHD, their problems usually continue: two-thirds of children with ADHD have ongoing difficulties through adulthood (Faraone, 2000). Over time, children with ADHD seem to be less impulsive, although inattention persists (Hart et al., 1995). Adults with ADHD are more likely than individuals without ADHD to have driving difficulties such as crashes, and they are more likely to be cited for speeding and to have their licences suspended (Barkley et al., 1996; Faraone et al., 2000).

What happens to children and adolescents with ADHD as they become adults? A recent Statistics Canada study raised concerns about educational achievement by demonstrating reduced rates of enrolment in postsecondary education for Canadian children who were diagnosed with ADHD during their school years (Arim & Frenette, 2019). As stated by Rubab Arim and Marc Frenette (2019), "ADHD is the most prevalent, long-term diagnosed MHC [mental health condition] in school years, and it poses the largest barrier to attending PSE [postsecondary education]" (p. 15). Rachel Klein and her colleagues followed up on more than 200 boys with ADHD and reported on their status 33 years later (Klein et al., 2012). When compared with a group without ADHD, the majority of these men (84 percent) were employed but in jobs with significantly lower positions than the comparison group. They also had 2.5 fewer years of education and were much less likely to hold higher degrees. These men were also more likely to be divorced and to have substance-use problems and antisocial personality disorder. In addition, the effects of their tendency to be impulsive may account for their increased risk of displaying risky driving, of having a sexually transmitted infection, of having a head injury, and of having more emergency department admissions (Ramos Olazagasti et al., 2013). In short, although the manifestations of ADHD change as people grow older, many of the problems persist.

In addition to the gender differences among children with ADHD, children are more likely to receive the label of ADHD in North America than anywhere else (Popper et al., 2003). This had led to concerns about overdiagnosis of ADHD in North America along with efforts to develop more objective measures that might assist in the diagnostic process (e.g., Leth-Steensen et al., 2000). With improvements in diagnosis worldwide, however, countries that previously reported lower rates of ADHD are finding similar numbers of these children being brought to the attention of helping professionals (Montiel-Nava et al., 2003). This change suggests that the disorder may not simply be a reflection of a lack of tolerance on the part of North American teachers or parents for active or impulsive children, but rather an indication that ADHD is a disorder that affects a significant number of children all over the world.

ADHD is frequently comorbid with other disruptive behaviour disorders, including oppositional defiant disorder (a pattern of negative, defiant, and hostile behaviour; e.g., refusing to obey adult, being angry, being argumentative) and conduct disorder (Waschbusch, 2002)—the childhood precursor to antisocial personality disorder that we discussed in Chapter 13. Additionally, research by Lily Hechtman and Gabrielle Weiss at the Montréal Children's Hospital and McGill University suggests that ADHD is a risk factor for antisocial outcomes in boys but not in girls (Herrero et al., 1994).

CAUSES

Important information about the genetics of ADHD is beginning to be uncovered (Barkley, 2015). Researchers have known for some time that ADHD is more common in families in which one person has the disorder. For example, the relatives of children with ADHD have been found to be more likely to have ADHD themselves than would be expected in the general population (Fliers et al., 2009). It is important to note that these families

display an increase in psychopathology in general, including conduct disorder, mood disorders, anxiety disorders, and substance abuse (Faraone et al., 2000). This research and the comorbidity in the children themselves suggest that some shared genetic deficits may contribute to the problems experienced by individuals with these disorders (Brown, 2009).

As with other disorders, multiple genes may be involved (Nikolas & Burt, 2010). In its simplest form, we tend to think of genetic problems in terms of having genes turned off (not making proteins) when they should be turned on and vice versa. Research on ADHD (and on other disorders) is finding that in many cases, however, mutations occur that either create extra copies of a gene on one chromosome or result in the deletion of genes, called **copy number variants** (Martin et al., 2015). Because our DNA is structured to function with corresponding or matching pairs of genes on each chromosome, the additions or deletions of one or more genes result in disrupted development.

Most attention to date focuses on genes associated with the neurochemical dopamine, although norepinephrine, serotonin, and gamma aminobutyric acid (GABA) are also implicated. More specifically, there is strong evidence that ADHD is associated with the dopamine D4 receptor gene, the dopamine transporter gene (DAT1), and the dopamine D5 receptor gene. DAT1 is of particular interest because methylphenidate (Ritalin)—one of the most common medical treatments for ADHD—inhibits this gene

and increases the amount of dopamine available (Davis et al., 2007; de Azeredo et al., 2014).

As with several other disorders we've discussed, researchers are looking for endophenotypes, those basic deficits—such as specific attentional problems—characteristic of ADHD. The goal is to link these deficits to specific brain dysfunctions. Not surprisingly, specific areas of current interest for ADHD are the brain's attention system, working memory functions, inattentiveness, and impulsivity. Researchers are now trying to tie specific genes to these cognitive processes to make the link between genes and behaviour. Some research indicates that poor inhibitory control (the ability to stop responding to a task when signalled) may be common among both children with ADHD and their unaffected family members (siblings and parents) and may be one genetic marker (an endophenotype) for this disorder (Goos et al., 2009; Nikolas & Nigg, 2015).

The strong genetic influence in ADHD does not rule out the role of the environment (Ficks & Waldman, 2009). In one of a growing number of gene–environment interaction studies

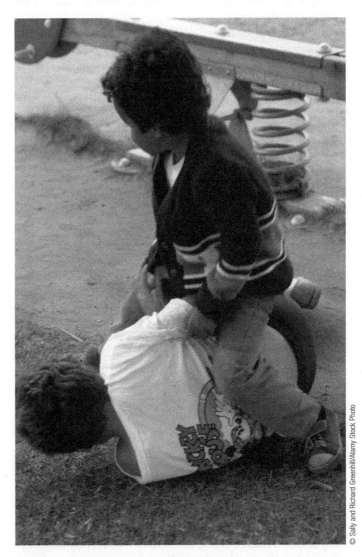

▲ ADHD is often comorbid with other disruptive behaviour disorders, such as conduct disorder, the childhood precursor to antisocial personality disorder.

▲ A child with ADHD is likely to behave inappropriately regardless of the setting.

of ADHD, for example, researchers found that children with a specific mutation involving the dopamine system (called the DAT1 genotype) were more likely to exhibit the symptoms of ADHD if their mothers smoked during pregnancy (Kahn et al., 2003). Prenatal smoking seemed to interact with this genetic predisposition to increase the risk for hyperactive and impulsive behaviour. Other research is now pointing to additional environmental factors, such as maternal stress and alcohol use, and parental marital instability and discord, as involved in these gene–environment interactions (Barkley, 2015; Ficks & Waldman, 2009). The association between ADHD and maternal smoking is one of the more consistent findings in this area.

In addition, a variety of other pregnancy complications (e.g., maternal alcohol consumption and low birth weight) may play a role in increasing the chance that a child with a genetic predisposition for ADHD will display the symptoms characteristic of this disorder (Barkley, 2006). Unfortunately, many of the studies in this area confound socioeconomic and genetic factors (e.g., there is an increased likelihood of smoking among women who also have low socioeconomic status or are under other stressors).

For several decades, ADHD has been thought to involve brain damage, and this notion is reflected in the previous use of labels such as "minimal brain damage" or "minimal brain dysfunction" (Ross & Pelham, 1981). In recent years, scanning technology has permitted a sophisticated assessment of the validity of this assumption. One thing is clear—several different brain mechanisms can likely lead to the attention deficits, along with the impulsivity and hyperactivity seen in individuals with ADHD. A general finding from brain-imaging studies of those with and without ADHD is that although no major damage is found in the brains of those with ADHD, there are subtle differences. One of the more reliable findings is that the volume (or overall size) of the brain is smaller (3 to 4 percent) in children with ADHD (Barclay, 2015). A number of areas in the brains of those with ADHD appear affected, especially those involved in self-organizational abilities (Valera et al., 2007). These changes seem less pronounced in persons who received medication (Taylor, 2012). In fact, a number of studies now point to a "growth enhancing effect" of stimulant medication, suggesting that brain development progresses in a more typical fashion in children receiving medication for ADHD versus those who do not (Frodl & Skokauskas, 2012; Rubia et al., 2014).

A variety of such toxins as allergens and food additives have been considered as possible causes of ADHD over the years, although very little evidence supports the association. The theory that food additives, such as artificial colours, flavourings, and preservatives, are responsible for the symptoms of ADHD has had a substantial impact. Feingold (1975) presented this view along with recommendations for eliminating these substances as a treatment for ADHD. As a result, hundreds of thousands of families have put their children on the Feingold diet, despite evidence that it has little or no effect on the symptoms of ADHD (Barkley, 1990). Some large-scale research now suggests that there may be a small but measurable impact of artificial food colours and additives on the behaviour of young children. One study found that three-year-old and eight- to nine-year-old children who consumed typical amounts of preservatives (sodium benzoate) and food colourings had increased levels of ADHD behaviours (inattention, impulsivity, and overactivity; McCann et al., 2007). Other research now points to the possible role of toxins, such as the pesticides found in foods, as contributing to an increased risk of ADHD (Barkley, 2015; Bouchard et al., 2010).

Canadian researchers have uncovered a potential role of sleep problems in ADHD. Some of the cognitive and behavioural problems typical of children with ADHD (e.g., inattention, impulsivity) are commonly seen among children experiencing sleep disruption (Guerrero et al., 2019; reviewed in Waldron et al., 2018). Could sleep problems be causally involved in the development of ADHD? We do not know, but we do know that sleep difficulties are particularly problematic for children with ADHD (Waldron et al., 2018). For example, using the Canadian Health Measures Survey, researchers determined that boys with a learning disability or ADHD were more likely to have short sleep and to sleep fewer hours than suggested by sleep guidelines (Chang et al., 2018). This knowledge has led to the development of sleep interventions for children with ADHD. In a randomized control study, for example, children receiving a brief specialized intervention to improve sleep showed improvement not only in their sleep but also in their behaviours during the day, compared to children receiving treatment as usual (Hiscock et al., 2015).

Psychological and social dimensions of ADHD further influence the disorder. Negative responses by parents, teachers, and peers to the affected child's impulsivity and hyperactivity may contribute to his or her feelings of low self-esteem, especially in children who are also depressed (Anastopoulos et al., 2009). Years of constant reminders by teachers and parents to behave, sit quietly, and pay attention may create a negative self-image in these children, which, in turn, can have a negative impact on their ability to make friends, and these effects can last into adulthood (Murphy, 2015). Thus, the possible biological influences on impulsivity, hyperactivity, and attention, combined with attempts to control these children, may lead to their being rejected and to their consequent poor self-image. An integration of the biological and psychological influences on ADHD suggests that both need to be addressed when designing effective treatments (Rapport, 2001; Taylor, 2012).

TREATMENT

Treatment for ADHD has proceeded on two fronts: biological and psychosocial interventions. Typically, the goal of biological treatments is to reduce the children's impulsivity and hyperactivity and to improve their attentional skills. Psychosocial treatments generally focus on broader issues, such as improving academic performance, decreasing disruptive behaviour, and improving social skills. Current thinking in this area points to using parent- or teacher-delivered behavioural interventions for young children before attempting medication (Subcommittee on Attention-Deficit/Hyperactivity Disorder & Management, 2011).

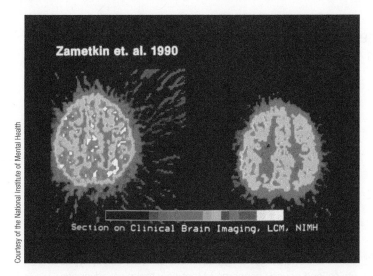

▲ Thanks to brain scan technology, we are beginning to understand the neurological aspects of ADHD.

Since the use of stimulant medication with children with ADHD was first described (Bradley, 1937), hundreds of studies have documented the short-term effectiveness of this kind of medication in reducing the core symptoms of the disorder. Drugs such as methylphenidate (Ritalin, Metadate, Concerta), d-amphetamine (Dexedrine, Dextrostat), and pemoline (Cylert) have proven helpful for approximately 70 percent of cases in at least temporarily reducing hyperactivity and impulsivity and improving concentration on tasks (e.g., Berman et al., 1999; Brodeur & Pond, 2001). A study by Gillian O'Driscoll and her colleagues (2005) showed that Ritalin improved both motor planning and response inhibition performance in children with ADHD. Cylert has a greater likelihood of negative side effects, so it is currently discouraged from routine use. Adderall, which is a longer-acting version of these psychostimulants, reduces the need for children to take multiple doses during the day but has similar positive effects (Grcevich et al., 2001).

Other drugs, such as certain antidepressants (bupropion, imipramine) and a drug used for treating high blood pressure (clonidine), may have similar effects on people with ADHD (Popper et al., 2003). All these drugs seem to improve compliance and decrease negative behaviours in many children, but they do not appear to produce substantial improvement in learning and academic performance, and their effects do not usually last over the long term when the drugs are discontinued.

Originally, it seemed paradoxical or contrary to expectation that children would calm down after taking a stimulant. However, on the same low doses, children and adults with and without ADHD react in the same way. It appears that stimulant medications reinforce the brain's ability to focus attention during problem-solving tasks (Volkow & Swanson, 2003). Without stimulant medications, children with ADHD perform more poorly on a variety of cognitive tasks than do children with other disorders, including anxiety or mood disorders (Szatmari et al., 1990). Although the use of stimulant medications remains controversial, especially for children, most clinicians recommend them temporarily, in combination with psychosocial inter-

ventions, to help improve children's social and academic skills (e.g., Douglas et al., 1995).

The use of stimulant medications in the treatment of children with ADHD raises two main concerns. The first concern pertains to stimulant drugs' potential for abuse. We saw in Chapter 12 that such drugs as methylphenidate are sometimes abused for their ability to create elation and reduce fatigue (Volkow & Swanson, 2003). This is of particular concern for children with ADHD because they are at increased risk for later substance abuse (Molina & Pelham, 2003). A second concern is that these medications may be overprescribed and their long-term effects are not well understood (Evenson, 2001). A survey showed that 80 percent of Canadian physicians had seen a patient with ADHD, 84 percent had prescribed methylphenidate, and 39 percent felt pressured to prescribe methylphenidate (Health Canada, 1999). A concern related to methylphenidate overprescription pertains to the medication's side effects, such as insomnia, irritability, and appetite suppression (Schachter et al., 2001). A longitudinal study by Alice Charach et al. (2006) at the Hospital for Sick Children in Toronto further suggests that long-term use of high doses of stimulants is likely to have measurable adverse effects on the growth of school-age children with ADHD.

In addition to these concerns, some portion of children with ADHD do not respond to medications, and most children who do respond do not show gains in the important areas of academics and social skills (Biederman et al., 2001; Pelham et al., 2001; B. Smith et al., 2006). Because of these findings, researchers have applied various behavioural interventions to help these children at home and in school (Fiore et al., 1993; Garber et al., 1996; Waschbusch et al., 2005). In general, the programs set such goals as increasing the amount of time the child remains seated, increasing the number of math papers completed, or engaging in appropriate play with peers. Reinforcement programs reward the child for improvements and, at times, punish misbehaviour with loss of rewards. Other programs incorporate parent training to teach families how to respond constructively to their child's behaviours and how to structure the child's day to help prevent difficulties (Sonuga-Barke et al., 2001). Although many children have benefited from these types of programs, others have not, and we have no way to predict which children will respond positively (Fiore et al., 1993). In sum, both medication and behavioural interventions have shortcomings. Most clinicians typically recommend a combination of approaches designed to individualize treatments for children with ADHD, targeting both short-term management issues (decreasing hyperactivity and impulsivity) and long-term concerns (preventing and reversing academic decline and improving social skills).

▲ Virginia Douglas is a clinical psychologist at McGill University. Her research has contributed substantially to our understanding of the nature of ADHD and the best ways to treat this childhood disorder.

Psychopharmacogenetics is the study of how your genetic makeup influences your response to certain drugs. The hope for this field is that medications can be matched or even "designed" for individuals to better complement their specific needs (Weinshilboum, 2003). For example, one study looked at the use of methylphenidate (Ritalin) for children and adolescents with ADHD (Polanczyk et al., 2007). For those who had a specific gene variation—the adrenergic alpha-2A receptor gene (ADRA2A)—methylphenidate had a strong positive effect, especially on their problems with inattention. This was not the case for those with ADHD who did not have the ADRA2A gene. Currently, the use of drug treatments tends to be by trial and error: a medication is attempted at a particular dose; if it is not effective, the dose is changed. If that does not work, a different medication is tried. This new study holds the promise of potentially eliminating this guesswork by tailoring the treatment to the individual.

This exciting new approach to medical treatment for mental illness brings with it some weighty concerns. Central to these concerns are issues of privacy and confidentiality. Genetic screening is likely to identify any number of potential genetic problems in each of us. How will schools, employment sites, and insurance companies view this information if they have access? The concern is that people will be discriminated against based on this information (e.g., having the genes that may or may not lead to having ADHD or another disorder). Will the desire to better target drug treatments outweigh these types of ethical and privacy concerns? Most new technical advances, like those promised with psychopharmacogenetics, also uncover new problems, and it is essential that ethical issues be part of the discussion as researchers move forward in this area.

To determine whether or not a combined approach to treatment is the most effective, a large-scale study initiated by the National Institute of Mental Health was conducted by six teams of researchers (Jensen et al., 2001). Labelled the Multimodal Treatment of Attention-Deficit/Hyperactivity Disorder (MTA) study, this 14-month study included 579 children who were randomly assigned to one of four groups. One group of the children received routine care without medication or specific behavioural interventions (community care). The three treatment groups consisted of medication management (usually methylphenidate), intensive behavioural treatment, and a combination of the two treatments. Initial reports from the study suggested that the combination of behavioural treatments and medication, and medication alone, were superior to behavioural treatment alone and community intervention for ADHD symptoms. For problems that went beyond the specific symptoms of ADHD, such as social skills, academics, parent–child relations, oppositional behaviour, and anxiety or depression, results suggested slight advantages of combination over single treatments (medication management, behavioural treatment) and community care.

SPECIFIC LEARNING DISORDER

Academic achievement is highly valued in our society. Because parents often invest a great deal of time and emotional energy in ensuring their children's academic success, it can be extremely upsetting when a child with no obvious intellectual deficits does not achieve as expected. In this section, we describe **specific learning disorder**, which is characterized by performance that is substantially below what would be expected given the person's age, IQ, and education (Pierce, 2016). We also look briefly at disorders that involve how we communicate. Consider the case of Alice.

CLINICAL DESCRIPTION

According to the *DSM-5* criteria (see DSM Table 15.2), Alice would be diagnosed as having a specific learning disorder (in her case especially in the area of reading), which is defined as a significant discrepancy between a person's academic achievement and what would be expected for someone of the same age. This particular learning disorder is also known as *dyslexia*. More specifically, the criteria require that the person perform academically at a level significantly below that of a typical person of the same age, cognitive ability (as measured on an IQ test), and educational background. In addition, this disability cannot be caused by a sensory difficulty, such as trouble with sight or hearing. *DSM-IV-TR* listed specific disorders in reading, mathematics, and written expression as separate disorders, but because of the significant overlap in these disabilities, they are now combined to assist clinicians in taking a broader view of the individual's learning abilities and difficulties (Pierce, 2016). Clinicians can use the specifiers for *disorders of reading*, *written expression*, or *mathematics* to highlight specific problems for remediation. As with other disorders, clinicians rate the disorder on levels of severity.

ALICE | *Taking a Learning Disorder to College*

Alice, a 20-year-old college student, sought help because of her difficulty in several of her classes. She reported that she had enjoyed school and had been a good student up until about Grade 6, when her grades suffered significantly. Her teacher informed her parents that Alice wasn't working up to her potential and that she needed to be better motivated. Alice had always worked hard in school but promised to try harder. However, with each report card her mediocre grades made her feel worse about herself. She managed to graduate from high school, but by that time she felt she was not as bright as her friends.

Alice enrolled in the local community college and again found herself struggling with the work. Over the years, she had learned several tricks that seemed to help her study and at least get passing grades. She read the material in her textbooks aloud to herself; she had earlier discovered that she could recall the material much better this way than if she just read silently to herself. In fact, reading silently, she could barely remember any of the details just minutes later.

After her second year in community college, Alice transferred to university, which she found even more demanding and where she failed most of her classes. After our first meeting, I suggested that she be formally assessed to identify the source of her difficulty. As suspected, Alice had a learning disability. Scores from an IQ test placed her above average, but she was also found to have significant difficulties with reading. Her comprehension was poor, and she could not remember most of the content of what she read. We recommended that she continue with her trick of reading aloud (Hinchley & Levy, 1988), because her comprehension for what she heard was adequate. In addition, Alice was taught how to analyze her reading—that is, how to outline and take notes. She was even encouraged to audiotape her lectures and play them back to herself as she drove around in her car. Although Alice did not become an A student, she was able to graduate from university, and she now works with young children who have learning disabilities.

STATISTICS

The prevalence of specific learning disorders has been estimated between 5 and 15 percent across youth of various ages and cultures (American Psychological Association, 2013). A study of more than 1600 German elementary schoolers found that approximately 7 percent showed significant deficits in reading, 9 percent in spelling (i.e., written expression), and 5 percent in arithmetic (Moll et al., 2014). Another study of Brazilian children in second through sixth grades estimated the prevalence of specific learning disorders to be between 5 and 8 percent across categories of written expression, reading, arithmetic, and global impairment (Fortes et al., 2015). In the United States, approximately 6.5 million students between the ages of 3 and 21 were receiving services for specific learning disorder between 2009 and 2010 (U.S. Department of Education, 2012).

According to school principals who participated in the National Longitudinal Survey of Children and Youth, an average of 12 percent of children in their schools had a learning disorder (Statistics Canada, 1996). Learning disability is one of the two most common disabilities in Canadian school-age children (5 to 14 years of age) (Human Resources and Skills Development Canada, 2011). In fact, 69 percent of Canadian school-age children with a disability have a learning disability. According to the 2017 Canadian Survey on Disability, 18 percent of Canadians over the age of 15 with a disability have a learning disability (Statistics Canada, 2017c).

Difficulties with reading are the most common of the learning disorders and occur in approximately 7 percent of the general population (Pennington & Bishop, 2009; Peterson & Pennington, 2012). Mathematics disorder appears in 5 to 6 percent of the population (Pierce, 2016), but we have very limited information about the prevalence of disorder of written expression among children and adults. Early studies suggested that boys were more likely to have a reading disorder than were girls, although other research indicates that boys and girls may be equally affected by this disorder (Feinstein & Phillips, 2006).

A learning disorder can lead to several different outcomes, depending on the extent of the disability and the extent of available support. Students with learning disabilities can drop out of school (Wagner, 1990; Kearney, 2008; Vogel & Reder, 1998). In addition, employment rates for students with learning disorders tend to be discouragingly low, ranging from 60 to 70 percent (Shapiro & Lentz, 1991). The low figure may be due in part to the students' low expectations; one study reported that only 50 percent of high school students with learning disabilities had post-graduation plans (Shapiro & Lentz, 1991). The low figure may also be due in part to difficulties these individuals have in holding a job. According to the Ontario Ministry of Labour, adults with learning disabilities who have not received appropriate education or training typically hold a job for only three months. Additionally, learning disorders may be related to the later development of other mental health problems. For example, a study by Toronto-based researcher Joseph Beitchman and his colleagues suggests that adolescents with learning disorders are at increased risk for substance-use disorders (Beitchman, Wilson, Douglas, et al., 2001). Another longitudinal study by this team showed that children with language disorders were at increased risk for the later development of psychiatric disorders (Beitchman, Wilson, Johnson, et al., 2001).

The negative outcomes for adults may be mitigated by providing the proper supports, such as having a positive relationship with caring adults and providing accommodations in postsecondary educational and employment settings (Gregg, 2013). Some individuals with learning disorders do attain their education or career goals. Psychologist Maggie Bruck notes a while ago that individuals with reading disorders can succeed in college or university if they are provided with instructional supports such as tutors, tape-recorded lectures, and tests without time limits (Bruck, 1987). However, completing college or university appears to be more difficult for people with severe learning disorders (Spreen, 1988). Interviews with adults who have specific learning disorder reveal that their school experiences were generally negative, and the effects often lasted beyond graduation. One man who did not have special assistance during school reports the following:

A. Difficulty learning and using academic skills, as indicated by the presence of at least one of the following symptoms that have persisted for at least 6 months, despite the provision of interventions that target those difficulties:

1. Inaccurate or slow and effortful word reading (e.g., reads single words aloud incorrectly or slowly and hesitantly, frequently guesses words, has difficulty sounding out words).

2. Difficulty understanding the meaning of what is read (e.g., may read text accurately but not understand the sequence, relationships, inferences, or deeper meanings of what is read).

3. Difficulties with spelling (e.g., may add, omit, or substitute vowels or consonants).

4. Difficulties with written expression (e.g., makes multiple grammatical or punctuation errors within sentences; employs poor paragraph organization; written expression of ideas lacks clarity).

5. Difficulties mastering number sense, number facts, or calculation (e.g., has poor understanding of numbers, their magnitude, and relationships; counts on fingers to add single-digit numbers instead of recalling the math fact as peers do; gets lost in the midst of arithmetic computation and may switch procedures).

6. Difficulties with mathematical reasoning (e.g., has difficulties applying mathematical concepts, facts, or procedures to solve quantitative problems).

B. The affected academic skills are substantially and quantifiably below those expected for the individual's chronological age, and cause significant interference with academic or occupational performance, or with activities of daily living, as confirmed by individually administered standardized achievement measures and comprehensive clinical assessment. For individuals age 17 years and older, a documented history of impairing learning difficulties may be substituted for the standardized assessment.

C. The learning difficulties begin during school-age years but may not become fully manifest until the demands for those affected academic skills exceed the individual's limited capacities (e.g., as in timed tests, reading or writing lengthy complex reports for a tight deadline, excessively heavy academic loads).

D. The learning difficulties are not better accounted for by intellectual disabilities, uncorrected visual or auditory acuity, other mental or neurological disorders, psychosocial adversity, lack of proficiency in the language of academic instruction, or inadequate educational instruction.

Note: The four diagnostic criteria are to be met based on clinical synthesis of the individual's history (developmental, medical, family, educational), school reports, and psychoeducational assessment.

Specify if:

With impairment in reading:

Word reading accuracy

Reading rate or fluency

Reading comprehension

With impairment in expression:

Spelling accuracy

Grammar and punctuation accuracy

Clarity or organization of written expression

With impairment in mathematics:

Number sense

Memorization of arithmetic facts

Accurate or fluent calculation

Accurate math reasoning

I faked my way through school because I was very bright. I resent most that no one picked up my weaknesses. Essentially I judge myself on my failures. . . . [I] have always had low self-esteem. In hindsight I feel that I had low self-esteem in college. . . . I was afraid to know myself. A blow to my self-esteem when I was in school was that I could not write a poem or a story. . . . I could not write with a pen or pencil. The computer has changed my life. I do everything on my computer. It acts as my memory. I use it to structure my life and for all of my writing since my handwriting and written expression has always been so poor. (Polloway et al., 1992, p. 521)

A group of disorders loosely identified as communication disorders seem closely related to specific learning disorder (American Psychiatric Association, 2013). These disorders can appear deceptively benign, yet their presence early in life can cause wide-ranging problems later on. For a brief overview of these disorders, which include childhood-onset fluency disorder (previously called **stuttering**) and **language disorder** (which combines *DSM-IV-TR* expressive and mixed receptive-expressive language disorders), see Box 15.1.

Concept Check	**15.1**

Assign a label to each of the following cases: (a) ADHD, (b) social (pragmatic) communication disorder, (c) Tourette's disorder, or (d) specific learning disorder.

1. Trent's developmental disorder is characterized by uncontrollable yelps, sniffs, and grunting noises.

   _____

2. Ten-year-old Cole can be frustrating to his parents, teachers, and friends. He has trouble waiting his turn during games and does things seemingly without thinking. He often calls out answers in school, sometimes before the complete question is asked.

   _____

3. In school, six-year-old Miley appears extremely awkward. She doesn't understand when other children are being sarcastic and misses any social communication cues. _____

4. Kelly was a good student until Grade 6. Her grades slowly began to drop, despite increased studying. Now, as a high school senior concerned about graduation, and with hopes of going to college, Kelly has sought help. She places above average on an IQ test but shows significant problems with reading and comprehension.

   _____

5. Eight-year-old Chandra is described by everyone as a handful. She fidgets constantly in class, drumming her fingers on the desk, squirming in her chair, and getting up and down. She has trouble waiting her turn at work or at play, and she sometimes has violent outbursts.

   _____

Box 15.1   Common Communication and Motor Disorders

CHILDHOOD-ONSET FLUENCY DISORDER

Clinical Description

A disturbance in speech fluency that includes a number of problems with speech, such as repeating syllables or words, prolonging certain sounds, making obvious pauses, or substituting words to replace ones that are difficult to articulate.

Statistics

Occurs twice as frequently among boys as among girls; begins most often in children under the age of three (Yairi & Ambrose, 1992); 98 percent of cases occur before the age of ten (Maguire et al., 2012); approximately 80 percent of children who stutter before they enter school will no longer stutter after they have been in school a year or so (Kroll & Beitchman, 2005).

Causes

Rather than anxiety causing childhood-onset fluency disorder, this problem makes people socially anxious (Ezrati-Vinacour & Levin, 2004); multiple brain pathways appear to be involved (Fox et al., 1996); genetic influences also may be a factor (Andrews et al., 1991; Maguire et al., 2012).

Treatment

Psychological: Parents are counselled about how to talk to their children; as noted by Mireille Gagnon and Robert Ladouceur, the *regulated-breathing method* is a promising behavioural treatment in which the person is instructed to stop speaking when a stuttering episode occurs and then to take a deep breath (exhale, then inhale) before proceeding (Gagnon & Ladouceur, 1992; Onslow et al., 2012); work by Marilyn Langevin of the University of Alberta and her colleagues suggests promise for an approach combining speech therapy with cognitive-behavioural therapy aimed at improving negative emotions surrounding the speech impediment (Huinck et al., 2006). Altered auditory feedback (electronically changing speech feedback to people who stutter) can improve speech, as can using forms of self-monitoring, in which people modify their own speech for the words they stutter (Onslow et al., 2012).
Pharmacological: The serious side effects of haloperidol outweigh any benefit it may offer; verapamil may decrease the severity of stuttering in some individuals (Brady, 1991).

LANGUAGE DISORDER

Clinical Description

Limited speech in all situations; *expressive language* (what is said) is significantly below *receptive language* (what is understood); the latter is usually average.

Statistics

Occurs in 10 to 15 percent of children younger than three years of age (Johnson & Beitchman, 2005) and is almost five times as likely to affect boys as girls (Whitehurst et al., 1988).

Causes

An unfounded psychological explanation is that the children's parents may not speak to them enough; a biological theory is that middle ear infection is a contributory cause.

Treatment

May be self-correcting and may not require special *intervention*.

SOCIAL (PRAGMATIC) COMMUNICATION DISORDER

Clinical Description

Difficulties with the social aspects of verbal and nonverbal communication, including verbosity, prosody, excessive switching of topics, and dominating conversations (Adams et al., 2012). Does not have the restricted and repetitive behaviours found in autism spectrum disorder.

Statistics

Exact estimates not yet available, but the number of cases identified appear to be rising with increasing awareness (Baird et al., 2006; D. V. M. Bishop, 2000).

Causes

Limited information.

Treatment

Individualized social skills training (e.g., modelling, role playing) with an emphasis on teaching important rules necessary for carrying on conversations with others (e.g., what is too much and too little information) (Adams et al., 2012).

TOURETTE'S DISORDER

Clinical Description

Involuntary motor movements (*tics*), such as head twitching, or vocalizations, such as grunts, that often occur in rapid succession, come on suddenly, and happen in idiosyncratic or stereotyped ways. Vocal tics often include the involuntary repetition of obscenities.

Statistics

Of all children, up to 20 percent show some tics during their growing years, and one to ten children out of every 1000 have Tourette's disorder (Jummani & Coffey, 2009). The disorder usually develops before the age of 14. There is high comorbidity between tics and ADHD, as well as obsessive-compulsive disorder (Jummani & Coffey, 2009).

Causes

There are likely multiple vulnerability genes that influence the form and severity of tics (Jummani & Coffey, 2009).

Treatment

Psychological: self-monitoring, relaxation training, and habit reversal.
Pharmacological: haloperidol; more recently, risperidone and ziprasidone.

Source: Adapted from "Disorders of Development," by V. M. Durand, in D. H. Barlow (Ed.), *Oxford Handbook of Clinical Psychology* (pp. 551–573), 2011, Oxford University Press.

CAUSES

Theories about the etiology of specific learning disorders assume a diverse and complex origin, and include genetic, neurobiological, and environmental factors. For example, some disorders of reading may have a genetic basis; the parents and siblings of people with reading disorders are more likely to display these disorders than are relatives of people without reading problems (Popper et al., 2003). When identical twins are studied, if one twin receives a diagnosis of a reading disorder, there appears to be an almost 100 percent chance that the second twin will receive the same diagnosis, further supporting a genetic influence (Vandenberg et al., 1986). As we saw with ADHD, the genetics of disorders of reading are complex, and genes on chromosomes 2, 3, 6, 15, and 18 have all been repeatedly linked to these difficulties (Cope et al., 2012; Kaminen et al., 2003; Zou et al., 2012). Remember, however, that problems in learning are extremely diverse and undoubtedly are influenced by multiple biological and psychosocial influences.

Various forms of subtle brain damage have also been thought responsible for learning disabilities; some of the earliest theories involve a neurological explanation (Hinshelwood, 1896). Studies show a link between phonological processing problems and reading disabilities in both children and adults (Bruck, 1992; Chiappe et al., 2002; Helenius et al., 2002; Stringer & Stanovich, 2000). For example, research by Ron Stringer at McGill University indicates that participants with dyslexia have difficulties performing a task in which they are asked to delete syllables from words spoken by the experimenter. For instance, they might be asked to delete a single phoneme from the initial or final position in a word (e.g., delete *bi-* from *bicycle*; Stringer & Stanovich, 2000). Research suggests structural and functional differences in the brains of people with learning disabilities. For example, the research of John Connolly and his colleagues at Dalhousie University shows weaker and delayed neural responses during reading of sentences among dyslexic readers compared with controls (Helenius et al., 1999). Such findings imply a neuropsychological deficit that interferes with the processing of certain essential language information. However, such physiological deficits are not consistent across individuals (Hynd & Semrud-Clikeman, 1989), which is not surprising, given that people with learning disorders display very different types of cognitive problems and therefore probably represent a number of etiological subgroups (Beitchman & Young, 1997; Popper et al., 2003; Young et al., 2002).

We saw that Alice persisted despite the obstacles caused by her specific learning disorder, as well as by the reactions of teachers and others. What helped her continue toward her goal when others choose, instead, to drop out of school? Psychological and motivational factors that have been reinforced by others seem to play an important role in the eventual outcome for people with learning disorders. Factors such as socioeconomic status, cultural expectations, parental interactions and expectations, and child management practices, together with existing neurological deficits and the types of support provided in the school, seem to influence outcome (Gregg, 2013).

TREATMENT

Before beginning treatment, an assessment must be conducted, typically by a school psychologist. The most common method of assessing learning disorders is to administer two types of tests (i.e., intelligence tests and achievement tests) and compare the scores on each. Intelligence tests, such as the Wechsler Intelligence Scales, are thought to tap academic aptitude or potential, whereas achievement tests tap performance in particular areas (reading, writing, math). If a significant discrepancy exists between aptitude and actual achievement in a particular subject, then a specific learning disorder is diagnosed (Kaufman & Kaufman, 2001). For example, when Alice was assessed, she scored one standard deviation above average on an intelligence test (IQ = 115) but one standard deviation below average on an achievement test tapping her reading performance. Thus, Alice was diagnosed with a reading disorder (dyslexia) and a treatment was planned with this diagnosis in mind.

As we will see in the case of intellectual disability, learning disorders primarily require educational intervention. Biological treatment is typically restricted to those individuals who may also have comorbid ADHD, which we have seen involves impulsivity and an inability to sustain attention, and which can be helped with certain stimulant medications such as methylphenidate (Ritalin or Adderall). Educational efforts can be broadly categorized into (1) efforts to remediate directly the underlying basic processing of problems (e.g., by teaching students visual and auditory perception skills); (2) efforts to *improve cognitive skills* through general instruction in listening, comprehension, and memory; and (3) targeting the *behavioural* skills needed to

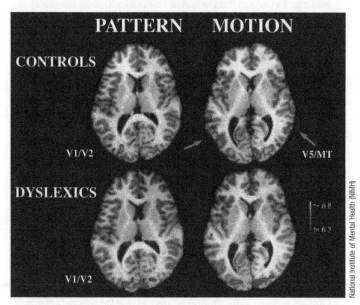

▲ These functional MRI scans of composite data from six adults with dyslexia and eight adults without dyslexia show a horizontal slice through the brain, with the face at the top. Imaging shows atypical brain activity associated with dyslexia. The scans were performed while participants tracked a pattern of moving dots on a computer screen. A brain area (V5/MT) normally active during such motion tasks did not switch on in adults with dyslexia (right). Their brain activity was more similar to that of adults without dyslexia during a pattern recognition task (left).

compensate for specific problems the student may have with reading, mathematics, or written expression—such as those we discussed in the case of Alice (Reeve & Kauffman, 1988). For example, Alice's reading disorder was helped by the behavioural skill of reading aloud (Hinchley & Levy, 1988).

For children with learning disorders who have difficulties processing language, treatment using exercises, such as specially designed computer games that help children distinguish among sounds, appears to be helpful (Merzenich et al., 1996). Considerable research also supports the usefulness of teaching the behavioural skills necessary to improve academic skills (Hammill, 1993). Maureen Lovett and her colleagues at the Hospital for Sick Children in Toronto have developed a new integrated program called the Phonology and Strategy Training Program (Lovett et al., 2000). They showed this combined program to be more effective than either phonological skills training or strategies training alone, in treating children with reading disorder (Lovett et al., 2000).

AUTISM SPECTRUM DISORDER

Autism spectrum disorder (ASD) is a neurodevelopmental disorder that, at its core, affects how one perceives and socializes with others (Durand, 2014). The *DSM-5* combined most of the disorders previously included under the umbrella term "pervasive developmental disorders" (e.g., autistic disorder, Asperger's disorder, and **childhood disintegrative disorder**) and included them into this one category (American Psychiatric Association, 2013). Moreover, Rett disorder, a genetic condition that affects mostly females, is diagnosed as ASD with the qualifier "associated with Rett syndrome" or "associated with MeCP2 mutation" (the gene involved in Rett syndrome). And the designation "not otherwise

specified," which was applied to other disorders before the *DSM-5*, was deleted. A disorder new to the *DSM-5*—social (pragmatic) communication disorder—includes the difficulties in social communication seen in ASD but without restricted, repetitive patterns of behaviour. Individuals with this disorder do not easily learn the social rules when communicating with others (e.g., interrupting, talking too loud, not listening to others). Certain individuals previously diagnosed with pervasive developmental disorder—not otherwise specified may fall into this category.

CLINICAL DESCRIPTION

Three major characteristics of ASD are expressed in the *DSM-5*: (1) impairments in social communication and social interaction, and (2) restricted, repetitive patterns of behaviour, interests, or activities (American Psychiatric Association, 2013; see DSM Table 15.3). In addition, the *DSM-5* recognizes that (3) the impairments are present in early childhood and that they limit daily functioning. It is the degree of impairment in each of these characteristics that presumably distinguish individuals previously diagnosed with the separate disorders of autistic disorder, Asperger's disorder, and pervasive developmental disorder—not otherwise specified.

To accommodate the range of difficulties in the two symptom clusters (social/communication interaction and restricted, repetitive patterns of behaviour, interests, or activities), the *DSM-5* introduced three levels of severity: Level 1— "Requiring support," Level 2—"Requiring substantial support," and "Level 3— "Requiring very substantial support." Separate ratings are provided for social/communication interaction and for restricted interests and repetitive behaviours. Each level of support is described qualitatively and, as yet, has no quantitative equivalent. This may make assigning the appropriate level of support needed somewhat problematic if the person with ASD does not perform at the extreme ends of these categories (Durand, 2014). Consider the case of Amy.

Impairment in Social Communication and Social Interaction

One of the defining characteristics of people with ASD is that they fail to develop age-appropriate social relationships (Davis & Carter, 2014). Amy never made any friends among her peers and often limited her contact with adults to using them as tools—for example, taking the adult's hand to reach for something she wanted. Research on the symptoms

© Ariel Skelley/Getty

▲ Specially designed computer games may help children with learning disorders improve their language skills.

of ASD, including communication difficulties and social difficulties, revealed the considerable overlap of these symptoms (Frazier et al., 2012; Skuse, 2012). The *DSM-5* combines these two areas into one general symptom cluster (social communication and social interaction). Difficulties with social communication and interaction are further defined by the inclusion of three aspects—problems with social reciprocity (a failure to engage in back-and-forth social interactions), nonverbal communication, and initiating and maintaining social relationships—all three of which must be present to be diagnosed with ASD (see DSM Table 15.3).

DSM-5	**Table 15.3** Diagnostic Criteria for Autism Spectrum Disorder

A. Persistent deficits in social communication and social interaction across multiple contexts, as manifested by the following, currently or by history (examples are illustrative, not exhaustive; see text):

1. Deficits in social-emotional reciprocity; ranging, for example from abnormal social approach and failure of normal back-and-forth conversation; to reduced sharing of interests, emotions, and affect; to failure to initiate or respond to social interactions.

2. Deficits in nonverbal communicative behaviors used for social interaction, ranging for example, from poorly integrated verbal and nonverbal communication; to abnormalities in eye contact and body language or deficits in understanding and use of gestures; to a total lack of facial expressions and nonverbal communication.

3. Deficits in developing, maintaining and understanding relationships, ranging for example, from difficulties adjusting behavior to suit various social contexts; to difficulties in sharing imaginative play and in making friends; to absence of interest in peers.

B. Restricted, repetitive patterns of behavior, interests, or activities, as manifested by at least two of the following, currently or by history (examples are illustrative, not exhaustive; see text):

1. Stereotyped or repetitive motor movements, use of objects, or speech (e.g., simple motor stereotypes, lining up toys or flipping objects, echolalia, idiosyncratic phrases).

2. Insistence on sameness, inflexible adherence to routines, or ritualized patterns of verbal or nonverbal behavior (e.g., extreme distress at small changes, difficulties with transitions, rigid thinking patterns, greeting rituals, need to take same route or eat same food every day).

3. Highly restricted, fixated interests that are abnormal in intensity or focus (e.g., strong attachment to or preoccupation with unusual objects, excessively circumscribed or perseverative interests).

4. Hyper- or hyporeactivity to sensory input or unusual interest in sensory aspects of the environment (e.g., apparent indifference to pain/temperature, adverse response to specific sounds or textures, excessive smelling or touching of objects, visual fascination with lights or movement).

C. Symptoms must be present in the early developmental period (but may not become fully manifest until social demands exceed limited capacities, or may be masked by learned strategies in later life).

D. Symptoms cause clinically significant impairment in social, occupational, or other important areas of current functioning.

E. These disturbances are not better explained by intellectual disability (intellectual developmental disorder) or global developmental delay. Intellectual disability and autism spectrum disorder frequently co-occur; to make comorbid diagnoses of autism spectrum disorder and intellectual disability, social communication should be below that expected for general developmental level.

Source: Reprinted with permission from the *Diagnostic and Statistical Manual of Mental Disorders*, Fifth Edition (Copyright © 2013). American Psychiatric Association. All Rights Reserved.

AMY | *In Her Own World*

Amy, three years old, spends much of her day picking up pieces of lint. She drops the lint in the air and then watches intently as it falls to the floor. She also licks the back of her hands and stares at the saliva. She hasn't spoken yet and can't feed or dress herself. Several times a day she screams so loudly that the neighbours at first thought she was being abused. She doesn't seem to be interested in her mother's love and affection but will take her mother's hand to lead her to the refrigerator. Amy likes to eat butter—whole pats of it, several at a time. Her mother uses the pats of butter that you get at some restaurants to help Amy learn and to keep her well behaved. If Amy helps with dressing herself, or if she sits quietly for several minutes, her mother gives her some butter. Amy's mother knows that the butter isn't good for her, but it is the only thing that seems to get through to the child. The family's pediatrician has been concerned about Amy's developmental delays for some time and has recently suggested that she be evaluated by specialists. The pediatrician thinks Amy may have autism and the child and her family will probably need extensive support.

Social reciprocity for individuals with more severe symptoms of ASD (previously diagnosed with autistic disorder) involves the inability to engage in **joint attention** (Gillespie-Lynch et al., 2012; Schietecatte et al., 2012). If a toddler without ASD sees a toy she likes, she might look at her mother, smile, look at the toy and look at her mother again. This social act communicates not only interest in the toy but also the desire to share this interest with another person. This action is limited in persons with ASD. Among persons with milder symptoms of ASD (previously diagnosed with Asperger's disorder), this lack of social reciprocity might present itself as appearing self-focused and not showing interest in things other people care about.

Research using sophisticated eye-tracking technology shows how social deficits evolve as the person develops. In one classic study, scientists showed an adult man with ASD some scenes from some movies and compared how he looked at social scenes with how a man without ASD did so (Klin et al., 2002). You can see from the photo that the man with ASD (indicated by the red lines) scanned nonsocial aspects of the scene (the actor's mouth and jacket), while the man without ASD looked at the socially meaningful sections (looking from eye to eye of the people conversing). This research suggests that people with ASD—for reasons not yet fully understood—may not be interested in social situations.

One current view on the social deficits of people with ASD is that they lack a theory of mind (i.e., the ability to appreciate that others have a point of reference that differs from their own; Baron-Cohen et al., 1994). However, some have been critical of the theory of mind perspective on ASD. For example, Philip Zelazo Jr. of the University of Toronto and Sophie Jacques of Dalhousie University have argued that autistic individuals' poor performance on theory of mind tasks may instead be attributed to more general difficulties with executive functioning (i.e., planning, organizing, sequencing, abstracting; Zelazo et al., 2001, 2002).

▲ Researchers are exploring how people with ASD view social interactions among other people.

Deficits in nonverbal communication can involve problems with a range of actions in persons with severe forms of ASD (e.g., not pointing to things you want) and among those with milder forms of ASD (e.g., standing too close to someone). Individuals with the less severe form of ASD may also lack appropriate facial expressions or tone of voice (also known as **prosody**; Durand, 2014) when speaking or just give the appearance of general nonverbal awkwardness. Finally, the deficits in social reciprocity and nonverbal communication can combine to influence the third symptom—problems maintaining social relationships.

Approximately, 25 percent of individuals with ASD do not develop speech proficiency sufficient to communicate their needs effectively (Anderson et al., 2007). In those with some speech, sometimes their communication is unusual. Some repeat the speech of others, a pattern called echolalia, which we referred to earlier as a sign of delayed speech development. If you say, "My name is Eileen. What's yours?" they will repeat all or part of what you said: "Eileen, what's yours?" Often, not only are your words repeated, but so is your intonation. On the other end of the autism spectrum, these individuals can be very verbal, but because of the social deficits and their tendency to have restricted interests, they often have one-sided conversations about the topics they want to discuss. Another aspect of the communication deficits of children with ASD is a lack of spontaneous pretend play or social imitative play appropriate to the child's development level, as shown in the work of Mel Rutherford and his colleagues at McMaster University (Rutherford & Rogers, 2003).

Restricted, Repetitive Patterns of Behaviour, Interests, or Activities

The more striking characteristics of ASD include restricted, repetitive patterns of behaviour, interests, or activities. The work of McMaster University's Peter Szatmari and his colleagues has shown that this broader category consists of two distinct dimensions: maintenance of sameness, and stereotyped and ritualistic behaviours (Szatmari et al., 2006). Exemplifying the first of these two dimensions, Amy appeared to like things to stay the same: she became extremely upset if even a small change was introduced (such as moving her toys in her room). One parent related that her son with ASD liked one particular helicopter from a toy set. She contacted the manufacturer and obtained more than 50 identical helicopters for her son. He would spend hours lining them up, and his mother reported that he could immediately tell if even one of the 50 was removed. This intense preference for the status quo has been called *maintenance of sameness*.

Often, people with ASD spend countless hours in stereotyped and ritualistic behaviours, making such stereotyped movements as spinning around in circles, waving their hands in front of their eyes with their heads cocked to one side, or biting their hands. The rituals are often complex: some people must touch each door as they walk down a hall; others touch each desk in a classroom. If they are interrupted or prevented from completing the ritual, they may have a severe tantrum. For individuals with less severe ASD, these behaviours can take the form of an almost obsessive interest in certain, very specific subjects (such as following airline schedules or memorizing postal codes). This tendency to be much more interested in esoteric facts than in people further interferes with social relationships.

STATISTICS

Current estimates of the rates of ASD are based on the previous *DSM-IV-TR* and *ICD-10* criteria (Lord & Bishop, 2010). ASD was once thought to be a rare disorder (e.g., one in 10 000 births), although more recent estimates of its occurrence show an increase in its prevalence. For example, 2013 estimates as reported by the Centers for Disease Control and Prevention suggest that an average of 1 in 68 eight-year-old children in the United States had a diagnosis under the category of ASD (Centers for Disease Control and Prevention, 2014). Similar estimates came out from the beginning stages of the Public Health Agency of Canada's (2018b) surveillance system for autism spectrum disorder. Its first report includes data from seven provinces and the three territories for 2015. It estimates that 1 in 66 Canadian children have ASD: 1 in 42 boys, and 1 in 165 girls. The majority of the rise in the rates may be the result of changes between versions of the *DSM* (Miller et al., 2013) and increased awareness on the part of professionals and general public (Frombonne et al., 2011). The reasons behind

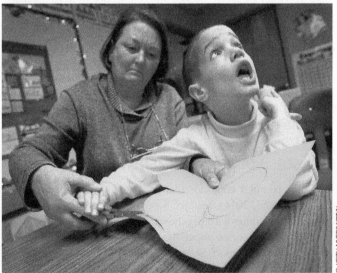

▲ In a pose typical of ASD, a boy's gaze is fixed on an overhead light.

▲ Football quarterback Doug Flutie was voted most valuable player in the Canadian Football League six times and led Calgary and Toronto to three Grey Cup titles in the 1990s. His son has autism spectrum disorder. In 2001, he and his wife started the Doug Flutie, Jr., Foundation for Autism to honour their son and to help other families facing childhood ASD through support and education.

▲ Timothy plays violin and piano as well as baseball. Autism spectrum disorder occurs in all cultures and races.

these changes are complex, however, and environmental factors (e.g., prenatal exposure to toxins) cannot yet be ruled out as partially contributing to the rise in rates (Frombonne et al., 2011; Liu & Bearman, 2012).

Gender differences are apparent in ASD, with the average reported male-to-female estimate being 4.5 to 1 (Centers for Disease Control and Prevention, 2014). ASD appears to be a universal phenomenon, identified in every part of the world, including Sweden (Gillberg, 1984), Japan (Sugiyama & Abe, 1989), Russia (Lebedinskaya & Nikolskaya, 1993), and Hong Kong (Chung et al., 1990).

People with ASD have a range of IQ scores. It is estimated that approximately 31 percent of individuals with ASD have intellectual disabilities (defined as an IQ score less than 70, comparable deficits in adaptive functioning, and present before the age of 18; Centers for Disease Control and Prevention, 2014).

IQ measures are used to determine prognosis: the higher children score on IQ tests, the less likely they are to need extensive support by family members or people in the helping professions. Conversely, young children with ASD who score lower on IQ tests are more likely to be severely delayed in acquiring communication skills and to need a great deal of educational and social support as they grow older. Usually, language abilities and IQ scores are reliable predictors of how children with ASD will fare later in life: the better the language skills and IQ test performance, the better the prognosis (Ben Itzchak et al., 2008).

CAUSES: BIOLOGICAL DIMENSIONS

ASD is a complex condition that does not appear to have a single cause (Durand, 2014). Instead, a number of biological contributions may combine with psychosocial influences.

Biological theories about the origins of ASD have received much empirical support. Several different medical conditions have been associated with ASD, including congenital rubella (German measles), hypsarrhythmia (a type of brain wave abnormality

sometimes observed in infants), tuberous sclerosis (a genetic disease characterized by benign tumour-like nodules in the brain, intellectual disability, and seizures), cytomegalovirus (an infection caused by a specific type of herpes virus), and difficulties during pregnancy and labour. However, although a small percentage of mothers exposed to the rubella virus have children with ASD, most often no ASD is present. Research by Lonnie Zwaigenbaum at McMaster University and his colleagues has similarly raised questions about the association of pregnancy and birth complications in ASD, suggesting that the association is not likely causal (Zwaigenbaum et al., 2002). Thus, more research is required on the role of various medical conditions in causing ASD.

Genetic Influences

It is now clear that ASD has a genetic component (Volkmar et al., 2005). What is also evident is that the genetics of ASD are highly complex (Wand et al., 2015) with a moderate genetic heritability (Hallmayer et al., 2011; Rutter, 2011a). Numerous genes on a number of our chromosomes have already been implicated in some way in the presentation of ASD (Li et al., 2012). And as with other psychological disorders, such as schizophrenia, many genes are involved but each one has only a relatively small effect.

Families that have one child with ASD have about a 20 percent chance of having another child with the disorder (Ozonoff et al., 2011). This rate is more than 100 times the risk in the general population, providing strong evidence of a genetic component in the disorder. The exact genes involved in the development of ASD remain elusive. One area that is receiving attention involves the genes responsible for the brain chemical oxytocin. Because oxytocin is shown to have a role in how we bond with others and in our social memory, researchers are looking at whether genes responsible for this neurochemical are involved with the disorder. Preliminary work identifies an association between ASD and an oxytocin receptor gene (Wermter et al., 2010).

There appears to be an increased risk of having a child with ASD among older parents. One group of researchers in Israel, for example, found that fathers 40 years old and up were more than five times as likely to have a child with ASD as fathers under the age of 30 (Reichenberg et al., 2006). The same correlation does

seem to hold up for maternal age (Croen et al., 2007; Durkin et al., 2008; Parner et al., 2012). These findings suggest that mutations may occur in the sperm of fathers or the eggs of mothers (called *de novo* mutations) that influence the development of ASD.

Neurobiological Influences

As in the area of genetics, many neurobiological influences are being studied to help explain the social communication and behaviour problems observed in ASD (Fein, 2011). One intriguing theory involves research on the amygdala—the area of the brain that, as you saw in Chapter 5, is involved in emotions, such as anxiety and fear. Researchers studying the brains of people with ASD after they died note that adults with and without the disorder have amygdalas of about the same size but that those with ASD have fewer neurons in this structure (Schumann & Amaral, 2006). Earlier research showed that young children with ASD actually have larger amygdalas. The theory being proposed is that the amygdala in children with ASD is enlarged early in life—causing excessive anxiety and fear (perhaps contributing to their social withdrawal). With continued stress, the release of the stress hormone cortisol damages the amygdala, causing the relative absence of these neurons in adulthood. The damaged amygdala may account for the different way people with ASD respond to social situations (Lombardo et al., 2009).

Other evidence that ASD is associated with some form of organic (brain) damage comes most obviously from the prevalence of data showing that a large percentage of people with ASD also have some level of intellectual disability. In addition, it has been estimated that between 30 and 75 percent of these people display some neurological abnormality such as clumsiness and abnormal posture or gait (Tsai & Ghaziuddin, 1992).

An additional neurobiological influence we mentioned in our discussion on genetics involves the neuropeptide oxytocin. Remember that this is an important social neurochemical that influences bonding and is found to increase trust and reduce fear. Some research on children with ASD found lower levels of oxytocin in their blood (Modahl et al., 1998), and giving people with ASD oxytocin improved their ability to remember and process information with emotion content (such as remembering happy faces), a problem that is symptomatic of ASD (Guastella et al., 2010). This is one of a number of theories being explored as possible contributors to this puzzling disorder.

One highly controversial theory is that mercury—specifically, the mercury previously used as a preservative in childhood vaccines (thimerosal)—is responsible for the increases seen in ASD. Large epidemiological studies conducted in Denmark show that, in fact, there is no increased risk of ASD in children who are vaccinated (Madsen et al., 2002; Parker et al., 2004). Additional research shows that the number of vaccinations—also cited as a cause for concern by some families—also does not contribute to an increased risk of ASD (DeStefano et al., 2013). Despite this and other convincing evidence, the coincidence between when a child is vaccinated for measles, mumps, and rubella (12 to 15 months) and when the symptoms of ASD first become evident (before three years), continues to fuel the belief by many families that there must be some connection. The negative consequence of this concern is that some parents are not vaccinating their children, and this is thought to contribute to a significant increase in cases of measles and mumps in Canada, the United States, and other countries (Centers for Disease Control and Prevention, 2011). For example, a recent large outbreak of measles in Québec's Lanaudière region occurred among a group of families that did not believe in the benefits of vaccination ("Quebec Measles Outbreak," 2015).

CAUSES: PSYCHOLOGICAL AND SOCIAL DIMENSIONS

Because historical context is important to research, it is helpful to examine past and more recent theories of ASD. Historically, ASD was (wrongly) seen as the result of failed parenting (Bettelheim, 1967; Ferster, 1961; Tinbergen & Tinbergen, 1972). Mothers and fathers of children with the more severe form of ASD were characterized as perfectionistic, cold, and aloof (Kanner, 1949), with relatively high socioeconomic status (Allen et al., 1971; Cox et al., 1975) and higher IQs than the general population (Kanner, 1943). Descriptions such as these inspired theories that held parents responsible for their children's unusual behaviours. These views were devastating to a generation of parents, who felt guilty and responsible for their children's problems. Imagine being accused of such coldness toward your own child as to cause serious and permanent disabilities! Later research contradicted these studies, suggesting that on a variety of personality measures, the parents of individuals with ASD may not differ substantially from parents of children without disabilities (Koegel et al., 1983; McAdoo & DeMyer, 1978).

Other theories about the origins of ASD were based on the unusual speech patterns of some individuals—namely, their tendency to avoid first-person pronouns, such as *I* and *me*, and to use *he* and *she* instead. For example, if you ask a child with ASD "Do you want something to drink?" he might say, "He wants something to drink" (meaning "I want something to drink"). This observation led some theorists to wonder whether ASD involves a lack of self-awareness (Goldfarb, 1963; Mahler, 1952). Imagine, if you can, not understanding that your existence is distinct. There is no "you," only "them." Such a debilitating view of the world was used to explain the unusual ways people with ASD behaved. Theorists suggested that the withdrawal seen among people with ASD reflected a lack of awareness of their own existence.

Later research has shown, however, that some people with ASD do seem to have self-awareness (Dawson & McKissick, 1984; Spiker & Ricks, 1984), and it follows a developmental progression. Just like children without a disability, those with cognitive abilities below the level expected for a child of 18 to 24 months show little or no self-recognition, but people with more advanced abilities do demonstrate self-awareness. Self-concept may be lacking when people with ASD also have cognitive disabilities or delays and not because of ASD itself.

Myths about people with ASD are perpetuated when the idiosyncrasies of the disorder are highlighted. These perceptions are furthered by portrayals such as Dustin Hoffman's in the movie *Rain Man*—his character could, for instance, instantly and accurately count hundreds of toothpicks falling to the floor. This type of exceptional mental ability—referred to as *savant skills*—does not occur in all individuals with ASD. It is estimated that approximately one-third of individuals with ASD have these unusual skills, although no persons with the more severe form of ASD appear to have savant abilities (Howlin et al., 2010; Rutter & Pickles, 2015). These exceptional skills appear to be the result of possessing superior working memory and highly focused attention (Bennett & Heaton, 2012). It is important always to separate myth from reality and to be aware that such portrayals do not accurately represent the full range of manifestations of this complex disorder.

As noted earlier, the phenomenon of *echolalia*, repeating a word or phrase spoken by another person, was once believed to be an unusual characteristic of this disorder. Subsequent work in developmental psychopathology, however, has demonstrated that repeating the speech of others is part of the typically developing language skills observed in most young children (Koegel, 1995; Prizant & Wetherby, 1989). Even a behaviour as disturbing as the self-injurious behaviour sometimes seen in people with ASD is observed in milder forms, such as head banging, among typically developing infants (de Lissovoy, 1961). This type of research has helped workers isolate the facts from the myths about ASD and clarify the role of development in the disorder. Primarily, it appears that what clearly distinguishes people with ASD from others are social deficiencies.

Deficits in such skills as social communication and the characteristic restricted and repetitive behaviours and interests have not reliably linked to psychosocial influences. The role of biological influences on the study of ASD is a relatively young field and still awaits an integrative theory.

TREATMENT

Most of the treatment research has focused on children with the more severe form of ASD, so we primarily discuss treatment research for these individuals. A growing number of studies are aimed at persons displaying less severe forms of ASD—typically focused on teaching social skills—and we describe this research as well. One generalization that can be made about ASD is that no completely effective treatment exists. We have not been successful in eliminating the social communication problems experienced by these individuals. Rather, most efforts at treating people with ASD focus on enhancing their communication and daily living skills and on reducing problem behaviours, such as tantrums and self-injury (Durand, 1999b). We describe some of these approaches next, including important work on early intervention for young children with ASD.

Psychosocial Treatments

Early psychodynamic treatments were based on the belief that ASD is the result of improper parenting, and these treatments encouraged ego development (Bettelheim, 1967). Given our current understanding about the nature of the disorder, we should not be surprised to learn that treatments based solely on ego development have not had a positive impact on the lives of people with ASD (Kanner & Eisenberg, 1955). Greater success has been achieved with behavioural approaches that focus on skill building and behavioural treatment of problem behaviours. A review by Susan Bryson and her colleagues concludes that the types of psychosocial interventions that are most successful are those that are very systematic and dedicated to teaching a specific skill (Bryson et al., 2003). Behavioural approaches are based on the early work of Ferster and Lovaas (e.g., Ferster, 1961; Lovaas, 1977). Although the work of these researchers has been greatly refined over the past few decades, the basic premise—that people with ASD can learn and that they can be taught some of the skills they lack—remains central. The treatment of ASD and the treatment of intellectual disability have a great deal of overlap. With that in mind, we highlight several treatment areas that are particularly important for people with ASD, including communication and socialization.

Problems with communication and language are among the defining characteristics of this disorder. A significant portion of people with ASD often do not acquire meaningful speech; they tend to have either very limited speech or use unusual speech such as echolalia. Teaching people to speak in a useful way is difficult. Think about how we teach languages: it mostly involves imitation. Imagine how you would teach a young girl to say the word *spaghetti*. You could wait for several days until she said a word that sounded something like "spaghetti" (maybe "confetti"), and then reinforce her. You could then spend several weeks trying to shape "confetti" into something closer to "spaghetti." Or you could just prompt, "Say 'spaghetti.'" Most children can imitate and learn to communicate very efficiently, but a child who has ASD can't or won't imitate.

In the mid-1960s, Lovaas and colleagues took a monumental first step toward addressing the difficulty of getting

▲ Susan Bryson holds an endowed chair in autism research at Dalhousie University. Her research efforts have contributed substantially to the understanding and treatment of autism spectrum disorder.

children with the more severe forms of ASD to respond. They used the basic behavioural procedures of *shaping* and *discrimination training* to teach these nonspeaking children to imitate others verbally (Lovaas et al., 1966). The first skill the researchers taught them was to imitate other people's speech. They began by reinforcing a child with food and praise for making any sound while watching the teacher. After the child had mastered that step, they reinforced the child only if she or he made a sound after the teacher made a request—such as the phrase "Say 'ball'" (a procedure known as discrimination training). Once the child reliably made some sound after the teacher's request, the teacher used shaping to reinforce only approximations of the requested sound, such as the sound of the letter "b." Sometimes the teacher helped the child with physical prompting—in this case, by gently holding the lips together to help the child make the sound of "b." After the child had responded successfully, a second word was introduced—such as "mama"—and the procedure was repeated. This continued until the child could correctly respond to multiple requests, demonstrating imitation by copying the words or phrases made by the teacher. Once a child could imitate, speech was easier, and progress was made in teaching some children to use labels, plurals, sentences, and other more complex forms of language (Lovaas, 1977).

More recently, several different approaches have used this type of teaching, bringing the instruction away from a desk with one child and one teacher to regular settings at home, in school, and in the community and attempting to use more child-directed versus adult-directed techniques (**naturalistic teaching strategies**; Durand, 2014). These teaching strategies include arranging the environment so that the child initiates an interest (e.g., placing a favourite toy just out of reach), and this is used as a teaching opportunity (e.g., Say, "I want truck."). Various evidence-based treatment packages use aspects of this approach, including incidental teaching (McGee et al., 1999), pivotal response training (Koegel & Koegel, 2012), and milieu teaching (Hancock & Kaiser, 2012). These techniques seem to increase a variety of social communication skills (e.g., making requests, interactions with peers, joint attention skills, play skills) among some children with more severe forms of ASD (Goldstein, 2002).

Despite the success of some children in learning speech, other children do not respond to this training, and workers sometimes use alternatives to vocal speech, such as sign pointing to pictures or using devices that have vocal output and can literally "speak" for the child (e.g., tablet computers; Johnson, Baumgart, Helmstetter, & Curry, 1996; van der Meer et al., 2012). One such alternative is the Picture Exchange Communication System developed by Bondy and Frost (2001, 2002) to teach functional communication to individuals with limited speech, such as children with ASD. This interesting new approach teaches children to initiate communicative interactions within a social framework. Children are taught to exchange a single picture for a desired item. Eventually, they learn to construct picture-based sentences and to use a variety of attributes in their requests.

One of the most striking features of people with ASD is their unusual reaction to other people. One study compared rates of interaction among adolescents with ASD, those with Down syndrome, and those developing normally; the adolescents with ASD showed significantly fewer interactions with their peers (Attwood et al., 1988). Although social deficits are among the

▲ The communication deficits typical of ASD often lead to social isolation.

more obvious problems experienced by people with ASD, limited progress has been achieved in developing social skills. Behavioural procedures have increased such behaviours as playing with toys or with peers, although the quality of these interactions appears to remain limited (Durand & Carr, 1988). In other words, behavioural clinicians have not found a way of teaching people with ASD the subtle social skills that are important for interactions with peers—including how to initiate and maintain social interactions that lead to meaningful friendships.

Lovaas and colleagues reported on their early intervention efforts with very young children (Lovaas, 1987). They used intensive behavioural treatment for communication and social skills problems for 40 hours or more per week, which seemed to improve intellectual and educational functioning. Follow-up suggests that these improvements are long lasting (Smith & Iadarola, 2015). Lovaas found that the children who improved most had been placed in regular classrooms, and children who did not do well had been placed in separate special education classes. As we will see in our discussion of intellectual disability, children with even the most severe disabilities are now being taught in regular classrooms. In addition, *inclusion*—helping children fully participate in the social and academic life of their peers—applies not only to school but also to all aspects of life. Many different models are being used to integrate people with ASD to normalize their experiences (Durand, 1999b). For instance, community homes are being recommended over separate residential settings, including special foster care programs (Smith, 1992), and supported employment options are being tested that would let individuals with ASD have regular jobs. The behavioural interventions discussed are essential to easing this transition to fully integrated settings.

Subsequent research on early intervention for toddlers with ASD includes programs specifically targeting joint attention and play skills—the absence of which are some of the earliest signs of problematic social development. Focusing on these skills in the early years is important for helping the child develop more sophisticated social repertoires (Poon et al., 2012). A growing research base suggests that these skills can be facilitated among very young children with ASD (Lawton & Kasari, 2012; Wong & Kasari,

2012), and preliminary follow-up data suggest that this approach may facilitate later development of language (Kasari et al., 2012). Some exciting research suggests that intensive early behavioural intervention may normalize the functioning of the developing brain in these children compared with children with ASD who do not receive this treatment (Dawson et al., 2012; Voos et al., 2013).

Individuals with less severe forms of ASD do not have the cognitive delays often found in persons with more severe forms, and can—with support—do well academically in school. However, their social difficulties and common comorbid problems (e.g., ADHD, anxiety) complicate their interactions with peers and teachers and can lead to disruptive behaviour problems. A number of programs exist to help school-age children improve such skills as appropriate social interaction, problem solving, self-control, recognizing emotions in others, expanding their often narrow range of interests, and improving their understanding of nonliteral idioms (e.g., understanding that the phrase "get off my back" means something very different from its literal meaning) (e.g., Karkhaneh et al., 2010; Koning et al., 2011). This work is in its infancy and future research should tell us how best to improve these abilities in persons with ASD.

Biological Treatments

No one medical treatment has been found to cure ASD. In fact, medical intervention has had little success. A variety of pharmacological treatments are used to decrease agitation, and the major tranquilizers and serotonin-specific reuptake inhibitors being most helpful (Greydanus et al., 2015). While psychotropic drugs may help to reduce some symptoms of ASD, Susan Bryson and her colleagues (2003) warned that they are neither curative nor a substitute for other forms of support and intervention. Although vitamins and dietary changes have been promoted as one approach to treating ASD and initial reports were very optimistic, research to date has found little support that they significantly help children with ASD (Holm & Varley, 1989).

Because ASD may result from a variety of different deficits, it is unlikely that one drug will work for everyone with this disorder. Much current work is focused on finding pharmacological treatments for specific behaviours or symptoms.

Integrating Treatments

Early intervention for very young children with ASD holds the most hope for significant changes in the core symptoms of this disorder. The treatment of choice for older children and those not responsive to early intervention combines various approaches to the many facets of this disorder. For children, most therapy consists of school education combined with special psychological supports for problems with communication and socialization. Behavioural approaches have been most clearly documented as benefiting children in this area. Pharmacological treatments can help some of them temporarily. Parents also need support because of the great demands and stressors involved in living with and caring for such children. As children with ASD grow older, intervention focuses on efforts to integrate them into the community, often with supported living arrangements and work settings. Because the range of abilities of people with ASD is so great, however, these efforts differ dramatically. Some people are able to live in their own apartments with only minimal support from family members. Others, with more severe forms of intellectual disability, require more extensive efforts to support them in their communities.

Determine how well you are able to diagnose the disorder in each of the following situations by labelling them (a) ASD requiring very substantial support, (b) ASD requiring support, and (c) social (pragmatic) communication disorder.

1. At an early age, Dwight became preoccupied with geography and could name all of the world capitals. His speech development was not delayed but he does not like to play with other children or to be touched or held.

   _____

2. Six-year old Tangelique has a low IQ and enjoys sitting in the corner by herself, where she arranges her toys or spins around in circles. She is unable to communicate verbally. She throws temper tantrums when her routine is changed even the slightest way or when her parents try to get her to do something she doesn't want to do.

   _____

3. Six-year-old Megan experiences many problems in communicating and does not seem to understand the "rules" when speaking with other children.

   _____

INTELLECTUAL DISABILITY (INTELLECTUAL DEVELOPMENTAL DISORDER)

Intellectual disability (ID) is a disorder evidenced in childhood as significantly below-average intellectual and adaptive functioning (Toth et al., 2016). People with ID experience difficulties with day-to-day activities, to an extent that reflects both the severity of their cognitive deficits and the type and amount of assistance they receive. The *DSM-5* identifies difficulties in three domains: conceptual (e.g., skill deficits in areas such as language, reasoning, knowledge, and memory), social (e.g., problems with social judgment and the ability to make and retain friendships), and practical (e.g., difficulties managing personal care or job responsibilities; American Psychiatric Association, 2013).

Perhaps more than any other group we have studied, people with ID have throughout history received treatment that can best be described as shameful (Scheerenberger, 1983). With notable exceptions, societies throughout the ages have devalued individuals whose intellectual abilities are deemed less than adequate. The *DSM-IV-TR* used the term "mental retardation," but this was changed in the *DSM-5* to "intellectual disability" (or intellectual developmental disorder) to be consistent with changes in terminology in this field (American Psychiatric Association, 2013).

The field of ID has undergone dramatic and fundamental changes during the past few decades. What it means to have an ID, how to define it, how to label it, and how people with this disorder are treated have been scrutinized, debated, and fought over by a variety of concerned groups. We describe the disorder in the context of these important changes, explaining both the status of people who have ID and our current understanding of its causes and treatment.

The manifestations of ID are varied. Some individuals function quite well, even independently, in our complex society, such as Canadian artist Jane Cameron, whose tapestries are found in galleries around the world. American actor Lauren Potter played a cheerleader in the popular television show *Glee*. Others with ID have significant cognitive and physical impairments and require considerable assistance to carry on daily activities. Consider the case of James.

Later, when we discuss treatment, we return to James, showing how we intervened at school and work to help him progress and become more independent.

JAMES | *Up to the Challenge*

James's mother contacted us because he was disruptive at school and at work. James was 17 and attended the local high school. He had Down syndrome and was described as very likeable and, at times, mischievous. He enjoyed skiing, bike riding, and many other activities common among teenage boys. In fact, his desire to participate was a source of some conflict between him and his mother: He wanted to take the driver's education course at school, which his mother felt would set him up for failure; and he had a girlfriend he wanted to date, a prospect that also caused his mother some concern.

School administrators complained because James didn't participate in activities such as physical education, and at the work site that was part of his school program, he was often sullen, sometimes lashing out at the supervisors. They were considering moving him to a program with more supervision and less independence.

James's family had moved frequently during his youth, and they had experienced striking differences in the way each community responded to James and his ID. In some school districts, he was immediately placed in classes with other children of his age and his teachers were provided with additional assistance and consultation. In others, it was just as quickly recommended that he be taught separately. Sometimes the school district had a special classroom in the local school for children with intellectual disabilities. Other districts had programs in other towns, and James would have to travel an hour to and from school each day. Every time he was assessed in a new school, the evaluation was similar to earlier ones. He received scores on his IQ tests in the range of 40 to 50, which placed him in the moderate range of ID. Each school gave him the same diagnosis: Down syndrome with moderate ID. At each school, the teachers and other professionals were competent and caring individuals who wanted the best for James and his mother. Yet some believed that to learn skills, James needed a separate program with specialized staff. Others felt they could provide a comparable education in a regular classroom and that to have peers without disabilities would be an added benefit.

In high school, James had several academic classes in a separate classroom for adolescents with learning problems, but he participated in some classes, such as gym, with students who did not have intellectual disabilities. His current difficulties in gym (not participating) and at work (being oppositional) were jeopardizing his placement in both programs. When I spoke with James's mother, she

expressed frustration that the work program was beneath him because he was asked to do boring, repetitive work, such as folding paper. James expressed a similar frustration, saying that he was treated like a baby. He could communicate fairly well when he wanted to, although he sometimes would get confused about what he wanted to say, and it was difficult to understand everything he tried to articulate. On observing him at school and at work, and after speaking with his teachers, we realized that a common paradox had developed. James resisted work he thought was too easy. His teachers interpreted his resistance to mean that the work was too hard for him, and they gave him even simpler tasks. He resisted or protested more vigorously, and they responded with even more supervision and structure.

CLINICAL DESCRIPTION

People with ID display a broad range of abilities and personalities. Individuals like James, who have mild or moderate impairments, can, with proper preparation, carry out most of the day-to-day activities expected of any of us. Many can learn to use public transportation, purchase groceries, and hold a variety of jobs. Those with more severe impairments may need help to eat, bathe, and dress themselves, although with proper training and support they can achieve a degree of independence. These individuals experience impairments that affect most areas of functioning. Language and communication skills are often the most obvious. James was only mildly impaired in this area, needing help with articulation. In contrast, people with more severe forms of ID may never learn to use speech as a form of communication, requiring alternatives, such as sign language or special communication devices, to express even their most basic needs. Because many cognitive processes are adversely affected, individuals with ID have difficulty learning. The level of challenge depends on how extensive the cognitive disability is.

Before examining the specific criteria for ID, note that, like the personality disorders we described in Chapter 13, ID was previously included on Axis II of the *DSM-IV-TR*. The rationale for placing these disorders on a separate axis was, first, that they tend to be more chronic and less amenable to treatment, and second, it was to remind clinicians to consider whether these disorders, if present, were affecting an Axis I disorder. People could be diagnosed on both Axis I (e.g., generalized anxiety disorder) and Axis II (e.g., mild ID). The *DSM-5* no longer has a separate axis for these disorders.

The *DSM-5* criteria for ID no longer include numeric cut-offs for IQ scores, which were present in previous versions (see DSM Table 15.4). They are still included in the narrative of the broader description, but the goal was to de-emphasize these numbers in favour of a comprehensive assessment of functioning. To be diagnosed with ID, a person must have *significantly subaverage intellectual functioning*, a determination made with one of several IQ tests with the cut-off score set by the *DSM-5* at approximately 70. The American Association on Intellectual and Developmental Disabilities (AAIDD), which has its own, similar definition of ID, has a cut-off score of approximately 70 to 75 (Toth et al., 2016).

Table 15.4 Diagnostic Criteria for Intellectual Disability (Intellectual Developmental Disorder)

Intellectual disability (intellectual developmental disorder) is a disorder with onset during the developmental period that includes both intellectual and adaptive functioning deficits in conceptual, social, and practical domains. The following three criteria must be met:

A. Deficits in intellectual functions, such as reasoning, problem solving, planning, abstract thinking, judgment, academic learning, and learning from experience, confirmed by both clinical assessment and individualized, standardized intelligence testing.

B. Deficits in adaptive functioning that result in failure to meet developmental and sociocultural standards for personal independence and social responsibility. Without ongoing support, the adaptive deficits limit functioning in one or more activities of daily life, such as communication, social participation, and independent living, across multiple environments such as home, school, work, and community.

C. Onset of intellectual and adaptive deficits during the developmental period.

Source: Reprinted with permission from the *Diagnostic and Statistical Manual of Mental Disorders*, Fifth Edition (Copyright © 2013). American Psychiatric Association. All Rights Reserved.

The second criterion calls for *concurrent deficits or impairments in adaptive functioning*. In other words, scoring "approximately 70 or below" on an IQ test is not sufficient for a diagnosis of ID; a person must also have significant difficulty in such areas as communication, self-care, home living, social and interpersonal skills, use of community resources, self-direction, functional academic skills, work, leisure, health, and safety. To illustrate, although James had many strengths, such as his ability to communicate and his social and interpersonal skills (he had several good friends), he was not as proficient as other teenagers at caring for himself in areas such as home living, health and safety, or in academic areas. This aspect of the definition is important because it excludes people who can function quite well in society but for various reasons do poorly on IQ tests. For instance, someone whose primary language is not English may do poorly on an IQ test but may still function at a level comparable with those of his or her peers. This person would not be considered to have ID even if he or she scored below 70 on the IQ test.

The final criterion for ID is the *age of onset*. The characteristic below-average intellectual and adaptive abilities must be evident before the person is 18. This cut-off is designed to identify affected individuals during the developmental period, when the brain is developing and therefore when any problems should become evident. The age criterion rules out the diagnosis of ID for adults who suffer from brain trauma or forms of dementia that impair their abilities. The age of 18 is somewhat arbitrary, but it is the age at which most children leave school and when our society considers a person an adult.

The imprecise definition of ID points to an important issue: intellectual disability, perhaps more than any of the other disorders, is defined by society. The cut-off IQ score of 70 or 75 is based on a statistical concept (two standard deviations from the mean) and not on qualities inherent in people who supposedly have ID. There is little disagreement about the diagnosis for people with the most severe disabilities; however, the majority of people diagnosed with ID are in the mild range of cognitive impairment. They need some support and assistance, but remember that the criteria for using the label of ID are based partly on a somewhat arbitrary cut-off score for IQ that can (and does) change with changing social expectations.

People with ID differ significantly in their degree of disability. Almost all classification systems have differentiated these individuals in terms of their ability or on the cause of the ID (Holland, 2012). Traditionally, classification systems have identified four levels of ID: *mild*, which is identified by an IQ score between 50 or 55 and 70; *moderate*, with a range of 35–40 to 50–55; *severe*, ranging from 20–25 up to 35–40; and *profound*, which includes people with IQ scores below 20–25. It is difficult to categorize each level of ID according to "average" individual achievements by people at each level. A person with severe or profound ID tends to have extremely limited formal communication skills (no spoken speech or only one or two words) and may require great or even total assistance in dressing, bathing, and eating. Yet people with these diagnoses have a wide range of skills that depend on training and the availability of other supports. Similarly, people like James, who have mild or moderate ID, should be able to live independently or with minimal supervision; again, however, their achievement depends in part on their education and the community support available to them.

Perhaps the most controversial change introduced in the AAIDD definition of ID is its description of different levels of this disorder, which are based on the level of support or assistance people need: *intermittent*, *limited*, *extensive*, or *pervasive* (Papazoglou et al., 2014; Thompson et al., 2009). The important difference is that the AAIDD system identifies the role of "needed supports" in determining level of functioning, whereas the *DSM-5* implies that the ability of the person is the sole determining factor. The AAIDD system focuses on specific areas of assistance a person needs that can then be translated into training goals. Whereas James's *DSM-5* diagnosis might be "moderate ID," he might receive the following

▲ The colourful tapestries of Canadian artist Jane Cameron, who had Down syndrome, hang in galleries all over the world. She flourished both as an artist and as a swimmer in the Paralympics.

AAIDD diagnosis: "a person with ID who needs limited supports in home living, health and safety, and in academic skills." The AAIDD definition emphasizes the types of support James and others require, and it highlights the need to identify what assistance is available when considering a person's abilities and potential.

STATISTICS

Approximately, 90 percent of people with ID fall under the label of mild intellectual disability (IQ of 50 to 70). When you add individuals with moderate, severe, and profound ID (IQ below 50), the total population of people with this disorder represents 1 to 3 percent of the general population (Toth et al., 2016). In Canada, about 70 babies a week are born with ID (Goldner, 2003). A study conducted with Ontario adolescents suggests that while the prevalence of severe ID is similar in Canada to rates obtained in studies conducted around the world, the rates of mild ID appear lower in Canada than in the United States, and more similar to rates found in the Scandinavian countries (Bradley et al., 2002).

The course of ID is chronic, meaning that people do not recover. However, the prognosis for people with this disorder varies considerably. Given appropriate training and support, individuals with less severe forms can live relatively independent and productive lives. People with more severe impairments require more assistance to participate in work and community life. ID is observed more often among males, with a male-to-female ratio of about 1.6 to 1 (Laxova et al., 1977). This difference may be present mainly among people with mild ID; no gender differences are found among people with severe forms (Richardson et al., 1986).

CAUSES

There are literally hundreds of known causes of ID, including the following:

- *Environmental*: for example, deprivation, abuse, and neglect
- *Prenatal*: for instance, exposure to disease or drugs while still in the womb
- *Perinatal*: such as difficulties during labour and delivery
- *Postnatal*: for example, infections, head injury

As we mentioned in Chapter 12, heavy use of alcohol among pregnant women can produce a disorder in their children called *fetal alcohol syndrome*, a condition that can lead to severe learning disabilities (Rangmar et al., 2015). Other prenatal factors that can produce ID include a pregnant woman's exposure to disease and chemicals, and poor nutrition. In addition, lack of oxygen (anoxia) during birth, and insults, such as malnutrition and head injuries, during the developmental period, can lead to severe cognitive impairments (Toth et al., 2016).

Biological Dimensions

Multiple genetic influences appear to contribute to ID, including chromosomal disorders (e.g., having an extra 21st chromosome, as in Down syndrome), single-gene disorders, mitochondrial disorders (defects in mitochondria, which are compartments found in most human cells that generate the majority of energy needed by the cells to function), and multiple genetic mutations (Toth et al., 2016). A portion of the people with more severe ID have identifi-

▲ Although this man cannot speak, he is learning to communicate with an eye-gaze board, pointing to or simply looking at the image that conveys his message.

▲ Intellectual disability can be defined in terms of the level of support people need.

Concept Check 15.3

In the following situations, label each level of intellectual disability as mild, moderate, severe, or profound. Also label the corresponding levels of necessary support: intermittent, limited, extensive, or pervasive.

1. Kevin received an IQ score of 20. He needs help with all his basic needs, including dressing, bathing, and eating. _____, _____

2. Adam received an IQ score of 45. He lives in a fully staffed group home and needs a great deal of help with many tasks. He is beginning to receive training for a job in the community. _____, _____

3. Jessica received an IQ score of 30. She lives in a fully staffed group home where she is trained in basic adaptive skills and communication. She is improving over time and can communicate by pointing or using her eye-gaze board. _____, _____

4. Ledel received an IQ score of 65. He lives at home, goes to school, and is preparing to work when he has finished school. _____, _____

able single-gene disorders, involving a *dominant gene* (which expresses itself when paired with a normal gene), a *recessive gene* (which expresses itself only when paired with another copy of itself), or an *X-linked gene* (present on the X or sex chromosome).

Before we discuss known genetic causes of ID, it is important to recognize that as many as 30 percent of cases of ID have no identified etiology (Toth et al., 2016). Important new research using sophisticated genetic analysis techniques is pointing to genetic causes that went previously undetected. One study of children from Germany and Switzerland found that a variety of genetic mutations, including *de novo* disorders (genetic mutations occurring in the sperm or egg or after fertilization), were present in those children with ID of unknown origin (Rauch et al., 2012). This work is important not only because it helps identify new causes of ID, but also because it helps explain why a child could have a genetically based disorder without that mutation being present in either parent. Mutations in genetic material can occur at various points in development, and this helps explain the causes of previously puzzling cases of ID.

Only a few dominant genes result in ID, probably as a result of natural selection: someone who carries a dominant gene that results in ID is less likely to have children and thus less likely to pass the gene to offspring. Therefore, this gene becomes less likely to continue in the population. Some people, however, especially those with mild ID, do marry and have children, thus passing on their genes. One example of a dominant gene disorder, *tuberous sclerosis*, is relatively rare, occurring in one in approximately every 30 000 births. About 60 percent of the people with this disorder have ID, and most have seizures (uncontrolled electrical discharges in the brain) and characteristic bumps on the skin that during their adolescence resemble acne (Samueli et al., 2015).

A recessive disorder called *phenylketonuria*, or PKU, affects one of every 10 000 newborns and is characterized by an inability to break down a chemical in our diets called phenylalanine (Schuck et al., 2015; Toth et al., 2016). For example, diet soft drinks contain phenylalanine. Until the mid-1960s, the majority of people with PKU had ID, seizures, and behaviour problems, resulting from high levels of this chemical. Infants are now routinely tested at birth, and any individuals identified with PKU can be successfully treated with a special diet that avoids the chemical phenylalanine. This is a rare example of the successful prevention of one form of ID.

Ironically, successful early identification and treatment of people with PKU during the past three decades has some worried that an outbreak of PKU-related ID will recur. The special diet to prevent symptoms is necessary only until the person reaches age six or seven. At this point, people tend to become lax and eat a regular diet—fortunately, with no harmful consequences for themselves. Because untreated maternal PKU can harm the developing fetus (Lenke & Levy, 1980), there is concern now that women with PKU who are of childbearing age may not stick to their diets and inadvertently cause PKU-related ID in their children before birth. Many physicians recommend dietary restriction through the person's lifetime, and especially during the childbearing period—thus the warnings on products with phenylalanine (Widaman, 2009).

Lesch-Nyhan syndrome, an X-linked disorder, is characterized by ID, signs of cerebral palsy (spasticity or tightening of the muscles), and self-injurious behaviour, including finger and lip biting (Nyhan, 1978). Only males are affected because a recessive gene is responsible; when it is on the X chromosome in males it does not have another gene to balance it, because males do not have a second X chromosome. Women with this gene are carriers and do not show any of the symptoms.

As our ability to detect genetic variations improves, more disorders will be identified genetically. The hope is that our increased knowledge will be accompanied by improvements in our ability to treat or, as in the case of PKU, prevent ID and other negative outcomes.

Approximately 60 years ago, the number of chromosomes—46—was correctly identified in human cells (Tjio & Levan, 1956). Three years later, researchers found that people with Down syndrome (the disorder James displayed) had an additional small chromosome (Lejeune et al., 1959). Since that time, a number of other chromosomal aberrations that result in ID have been identified. We describe Down syndrome and fragile X syndrome in some detail, but there are hundreds of other ways in which abnormalities among the chromosomes can lead to ID (Toth et al., 2016).

Down syndrome, the most common chromosomal form of ID, was first identified by the British physician Langdon Down in 1866. Down had tried to develop a classification system for people with ID based on their resemblance to people of other races; he described individuals with this particular disorder as "mongoloid" because they resembled people from Mongolia (Scheerenberger, 1983). The term *mongoloidism* was used for some time but has been replaced with the term *Down syndrome*. The disorder is caused by the presence of an extra 21st chromosome and is therefore sometimes referred to as trisomy 21. For reasons we don't completely understand, during cell division two of the 21st chromosomes stick together (a condition called *nondisjunction*), creating one cell with one copy that dies, and one cell with three copies that divide to create a person with *Down syndrome*.

People with Down syndrome have characteristic facial features, including folds in the corners of their upwardly slanting eyes, a flat nose, and a small mouth with a flat roof that makes the tongue protrude somewhat. Like James, they tend to have congenital heart malformations. Tragically, nearly all adults with Down syndrome past the age of 40 show signs of dementia of the Alzheimer's type, a degenerative brain disorder that causes impairments in memory and other cognitive disorders (Wiseman et al., 2015). This disorder among people with Down syndrome occurs earlier than usual (sometimes in their early 20s) and has led to the finding that at least one form of Alzheimer's disease is attributable to a gene on the 21st chromosome.

According to the Public Health Agency of Canada (2017a), for the years 2005 to 2013, the rate of Down syndrome in Canada (except Québec) was stable and averaged 15.8 for every 10 000 births. The incidence of children born with Down syndrome is tied to maternal age: as the age of the mother increases, so does her chance of having a child with this disorder (Evans & Hammerton, 1985; Hook, 1982). A woman at age 20 has a 1 in 2000 chance of having a child with Down syndrome; at the age of 35 this risk increases to 1 in 500, and at the age of 45 it increases again to 1 in every 30 births (Hook, 1982). Figure 15.1 shows that percentage of live births and the percentage of Down syndrome births in Canada (except Québec) for a nine-year period, highlighting the much higher rate of Down syndrome births for older women. (Despite these numbers, many more children with Down syndrome are born to younger mothers because, as women get older, they tend to have fewer children.) The reason for the rise in incidence with maternal age is not clear. Some suggest that because a woman's ova (eggs) are all produced in youth, the older ones have been exposed to toxins, radiation, and other harmful substances over longer periods of time. This exposure may interfere with the normal meiosis (division) of the chromosomes, creating an extra 21st chromosome (Pueschel & Goldstein, 1991). It may also be that the hormonal changes that occur as women age contribute to this particular cell division (Pandya et al., 2013).

For some time it has been possible to detect the presence of Down syndrome—but not the degree of ID—through **amniocentesis**, a procedure that involves removing and testing a sample of the fluid that surrounds the fetus in the amniotic sac. Down syndrome and a number of other disorders can be detected through amniocentesis.

The presence of this chromosomal abnormality does not convey information about the eventual severity of the disorder, however. Despite this lack of information, some estimate that a prenatal diagnosis of Down syndrome leads to a choice for an elective abortion more than 50 percent of the time (Natoli et al., 2012). Prenatal testing for Down syndrome cannot assist parents with information about the outcomes.

Fragile X syndrome is a second common chromosomally related cause of ID (Clarke & Deb, 2012). As its name suggests, this disorder is caused by an abnormality on the X chromosome, a mutation that makes the tip of the chromosome look as though it were hanging from a thread, giving it the appearance of fragility (Lubs et al., 2012). As with Lesch-Nyhan syndrome, which also involves the X chromosome, fragile X primarily affects males because they do not have a second X chromosome. Unlike Lesch-Nyhan carriers, however, women who carry fragile X syndrome commonly display mild to severe learning disabilities (Santoro et al., 2012). Men with the disorder display moderate to severe levels of ID and have higher rates of hyperactivity, short attention spans, gaze avoidance, and perseverative speech (repeating the same words again and again). In addition, such physical characteristics as large ears, testicles, and head circumference are common. Estimates are that one of every 4000 males and one of every 8000 females are born with fragile X syndrome (Toth & King, 2010).

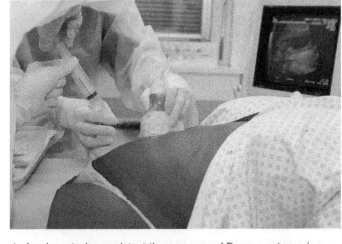

▲ Amniocentesis can detect the presence of Down syndrome in a fetus. Guided by an ultrasound image, the doctor withdraws amniotic fluid for analysis.

A study sponsored by the Canadian Paediatric Surveillance Program suggests that diagnoses of fragile X syndrome in Canada are in line with these estimates (Aubertin, 2015; Aubertin et al., 2015).

Psychological and Social Dimensions

Cultural influences that may contribute to ID can include abuse, neglect, and social deprivation. Sometimes referred to as **cultural-familial intellectual disability**, people with these characteristics are thought to have cognitive impairments that result from a combination of psychosocial and biological influences, although the specific mechanisms that lead to this type of ID are not yet understood. Fortunately, because of better child care systems and early identification of potential family difficulties, these cases are rare today (Kaski, 2012).

TREATMENT

Direct biological treatment of ID is currently not a viable option. Generally, the treatment of individuals with ID parallels that of people with more severe forms of ASD, attempting to teach them the skills they need to become more productive and independent. For individuals with mild ID, intervention is similar to that for people with learning disorders. Specific learning deficits are identified and addressed to help the person improve such skills as reading and writing. At the same time, these individuals often need additional support to live in the community. For people with more severe disabilities, the general goals are the same; however, the level of assistance they need is frequently more extensive. Remember that the expectation for all people with ID is that they will in some way

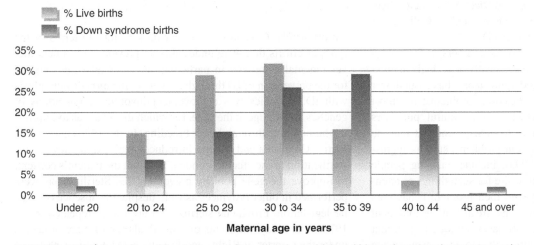

Legend:
% Live births
% Down syndrome births

y-axis: 35%, 30%, 25%, 20%, 15%, 10%, 5%, 0%
x-axis (Maternal age in years): Under 20, 20 to 24, 25 to 29, 30 to 34, 35 to 39, 40 to 44, 45 and over

FIGURE 15.1 | Proportion of live births and Down syndrome births within each maternal age category in Canada, excluding Québec, 2005–2013.

participate in community life, attend school and later hold a job, and have the opportunity for meaningful social relationships. Advances in electronic and educational technologies have made this goal realistic even for people with profound ID.

People with ID can acquire skills through the many behavioural innovations first introduced in the early 1960s to teach such basic self-care as dressing, bathing, feeding, and toileting to persons with even the most severe disabilities (Reid et al., 1991). The skill is broken into its component parts (a procedure called a *task analysis*) and the person is taught each part in succession until he or she can perform the whole skill. Performance on each step is encouraged by praise and by access to objects or activities the person desires (reinforcers). Success in teaching these skills is usually measured by the level of independence the person can attain by using them. Typically, most individuals, regardless of their disability, can be taught to perform some skills.

Communication training is very important for people with ID. Making their needs and wants known is essential for personal satisfaction and for participation in most social activities. The goals of communication training differ, depending on the existing skills. For people with mild levels of ID, the goals may be relatively minor (e.g., improving articulation) or more extensive (e.g., organizing a conversation; Berney, 2012; Heath et al., 2015). Some, like James, have communication skills that are already adequate for day-to-day needs.

For individuals with the most severe disabilities, this type of training can be particularly challenging, because they may have multiple physical or cognitive deficits that make spoken communication difficult or impossible (Warren & Reichle, 1992). Creative researchers, however, use alternative systems that may be easier for these individuals, including the sign language used primarily by people with hearing disabilities and *augmentative communication strategies*. Augmentative strategies may use picture books, teaching the person to make a request by pointing to a picture—for instance, pointing to a picture of a cup to request a drink (Heath et al., 2015). A variety of computer-assisted devices, including tablet computers, can be programmed so that the individual presses a button to produce complete spoken sentences (e.g., "Would you come here? I need your help"). People with very limited communication skills can be taught to use these devices, which helps them reduce the frustration of not being able to relate their feelings and experiences to other people (Durand, 2011).

Concern is often expressed by parents, teachers, and employers that some people with ID can be physically or verbally aggressive or may hurt themselves. Considerable debate has ensued over the proper way to reduce these behaviour problems; the most heated discussions involve whether to use painful punishers (Repp & Singh, 1990). Alternatives to punishment that may be equally effective in reducing behaviour problems, such as aggression and self-injury (Durand, 1999a), include teaching people how to communicate their need or desire for such things as attention that they seem to be getting with their problem behaviours (Durand, 2012). To date, however, no treatment or treatment package has proven successful in all cases, although important advances are being made in significantly reducing even severe behaviour problems for some people.

In addition to ensuring that people with ID are taught specific skills, caretakers focus on the important task of supporting them

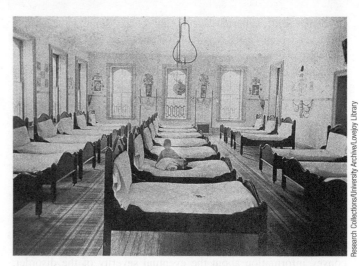

▲ In the 19th century, children with ID were housed in asylums for the "feeble-minded" like the one illustrated here. Today, great efforts are made to keep children with ID in their homes and communities.

in their communities. "Supported employment" involves helping an individual find and participate satisfactorily in a competitive job (Drake et al., 2012). People with ID can be placed in meaningful jobs and, despite the costs associated with supported employment, these placements are cost-effective (Cimera, 2012). The benefits to people who achieve the satisfaction of being a productive part of society are incalculable.

There is general agreement about *what* should be taught to people with ID. The controversy in recent years has been over *where* this teaching should take place. Should people with ID, especially the severe forms, be taught in specially designed separate classrooms or workshops, or should they attend their neighbourhood public schools and work at local businesses? Increasingly, teaching strategies to help these students learn are being used in regular classrooms and in preparing them to work at jobs in the community (Foley et al., 2012).

PREVENTION OF NEURODEVELOPMENTAL DISORDERS

Unfortunately, Canada has a rather dark history in terms of the types of efforts that were undertaken to prevent certain neurodevelopmental disorders. In particular, eugenics advocates argued for the prevention of ID through sexual sterilization of individuals with ID. Eugenics was a movement involving applications of genetics knowledge at the time, for which the goal was to improve the human race through better breeding. In the 1920s and 1930s, British Columbia and Alberta introduced legislation allowing for sterilization of the "feeble-minded," without the patient's consent, to improve the gene pool by preventing ID. Sterilizations were performed in other provinces as well, despite the absence of similar legislation. Provincial sterilization laws were repealed in the 1970s, and today, the rights of individuals with ID are protected under the Charter of Rights and Freedoms (McLaren, 1990).

Current efforts to prevent neurodevelopmental disorders are in their early stages. One such effort—early intervention—has been described for ASD and appears to hold considerable promise for

Research Collections/University Archive/Lovejoy Library

some children. Additionally, early interventions combining educational, medical, and social supports can target and assist children and their families where the child is at risk for developing cultural-familial ID because of an inadequate environment (Eldevik et al., 2010). One such effort at early intervention identified a group of children shortly after birth and provided them with an intensive preschool program, along with medical and nutritional supports. This intervention continued until the children began formal education (Martin et al., 1990). The authors of this study found that for all but one of the children in a control group who received medical and nutritional support but not the intensive educational experiences, each had an IQ score below 85 at age three. The children in the experimental group all tested above 85 at age three. Such findings are important because they show the potential for creating a lasting impact on the lives of these children and their families.

Although it appears that many children can make significant progress if interventions are initiated early in life (Eldevik et al., 2010), a number of important questions remain regarding early intervention efforts. Not all children, for example, benefit significantly from such efforts, and future research will need to resolve a number of lingering concerns. For instance, researchers need to determine how best to identify children and families who will benefit from such programs, how early in the child's development programs should begin, and how long to continue these early intervention programs to produce desirable outcomes.

Given recent advances in genetic screening and technology, it may someday be possible to detect and correct genetic and chromosomal abnormalities; related ongoing research could fundamentally change our approach to children with neurodevelopmental disorders. For example, one study used mice that were genetically engineered to model fragile X syndrome found in many individuals with ID (Suvrathan et al., 2010). Researchers found that they could improve the functioning of certain glutamate receptors in the amygdala of the mice with a drug that blocks these receptors. This resulted in more normalized functioning between these neurons, a potential early medical intervention for children with fragile X disorder (Krueger & Bear, 2011; Suvrathan et al., 2010). Someday, it may be possible for similar research to be performed prenatally on children identified as having syndromes associated with ID. For example, it may soon be possible to conduct prenatal gene therapy, where a developing fetus that has been screened for a genetic disorder may be the target of intervention before birth (Ye et al., 2001). This prospect is not without its difficulties, however.

Advances in biomedical technology will need support from psychological researchers to make sure that any needed treatments are carried out properly. For example, biological risk factors for several neurodevelopmental disorders include malnutrition and exposure to toxins, such as lead and alcohol. Although medical researchers can identify the role of these biological events in cognitive development, psychologists will need to support these efforts. Behavioural intervention for safety training (e.g., involving lead-based paints in older homes), substance-use treatment and prevention, and behavioural medicine (e.g., "wellness" efforts) are examples of crucial roles played by psychologists in helping to prevent certain forms of neurodevelopmental disorders.

DSM CONTROVERSIES   Losing a Valued Label

One of the most talked-about and debated changes in the *DSM-5* was the elimination of separate categories for "autistic disorder" and "Asperger's disorder," which were present in the *DSM-IV*. The rationale behind this reorganization of the separate autism-related disorders under one rubric was that ASD could be reliably distinguished from other disorders. But within this category were considerable inconsistencies (Frazier et al., 2012; Rutter, 2011b). In other words, it was not always clear whether someone had a milder form of autistic disorder (e.g., with more speech) or whether it was Asperger's disorder. They all share the pervasive deficits in social communication skills and the restricted patterns of behaviours. It was argued that the main differences between the disorders involve the severity of the symptoms, language level, and levels of intellectual deficit and, therefore, could be grouped together as autism spectrum disorder—with varying degrees of severity.

One of the first concerns was that these new criteria might exclude some individuals who previously met *DSM-IV* criteria; in turn, it might result in the denial of treatment services for those left out. This concern was precipitated by researchers who evaluated cases that received a *DSM-IV* diagnosis of autism or a related disorder and tried to see how many would now fall into the new ASD category (McPartland et al., 2012). Their initial findings caused considerable alarm, since they concluded that almost 40 percent of individuals would not meet the *DSM-5* criteria. Although subsequent analyses found this number to be lower (e.g., approximately 9 percent in one study; Huerta et al., 2012), there remains a concern that some individuals will no longer be eligible for needed services.

In addition to the concern about combining this disorder into the generic ASD, many of those individuals who have been previously diagnosed with Asperger's disorder feel that this decision takes away part of their identity (Pellicano & Stears, 2011). Rather than feeling shame or embarrassment about receiving this diagnosis, a good number of these individuals embrace their distinctiveness. Some advocate for seeing these differences in terms of "neurodiversity," or viewing their "disorder" as just a different and not abnormal way to view the world (Armstrong, 2010; Singer, 1999). In fact, the word "Aspies" is sometimes used with pride by individuals with this label (e.g., Beardon & Worton, 2011), and those who do not have this disorder are often referred to as "neurotypical"—sometimes in a sarcastic way. It is likely that despite the elimination of Asperger's disorder from the *DSM-5*, some in this community will continue to hold on to the label with pride.

SUMMARY

Perspectives

■ Developmental psychopathology is the study of how disorders arise and change with time. These changes usually follow a pattern, with the child mastering one skill before acquiring the next. This aspect of development is important, because it implies that any disruption in the acquisition of early skills will, by the very nature of the developmental process, also disrupt the development of later skills.

Attention-Deficit/Hyperactivity Disorder

■ The primary characteristics of people with attention-deficit/hyperactivity disorder are a pattern of inattention (such as not paying attention to school- or work-related tasks), impulsivity, and/or hyperactivity. These deficits can significantly disrupt academic efforts and social relationships.

Specific Learning Disorder

■ The *DSM-5* describes specific learning disorder as academic performance that is substantially below what would be expected given the person's age, intelligence quotient (IQ) score, and education. These problems can be seen as difficulties with reading, mathematics, or written expression. All are defined by performance that falls far short of expectations based on intelligence and school preparation.

■ Communication and motor disorders seem closely related to specific learning disorder. They include childhood speech fluency disorder (stuttering), a disturbance in speech fluency, language disorder, very limited speech in all situations but without the types of cognitive deficits that lead to language problems in people with intellectual disability or autism spectrum disorder, and Tourette's disorder, which includes involuntary motor movements, such as head twitching and vocalizations, such as grunts that occur suddenly, in rapid succession, and in very idiosyncratic or stereotyped ways.

Autism Spectrum Disorder

■ People with ASD all experience trouble progressing in language, socialization, and cognition. ASD is a condition that significantly affects how individuals live and interact with each other.

■ ASD is a childhood disorder characterized by significant impairment in social communication skills and restricted, repetitive patterns of behaviour, interests, or activities. This disorder does not have a single cause; instead, a number of biological conditions may contribute, and these, in combination with psychosocial influences, result in the unusual behaviours displayed by people with ASD.

■ Impressive advances have been made in improving outcomes for many young children with ASD using early intervention programs. Treatment for older children involves behavioural interventions focused on their social communication deficits and the restricted, repetitive patterns of behaviour, interests, or activities.

Intellectual Disability (Intellectual Development Disorder)

■ The definition of intellectual disability has three parts: significantly subaverage intellectual functioning, concurrent deficits or impairments in present adaptive functioning, and an onset before the age of 18.

■ Down syndrome is a type of intellectual disability caused by the presence of an extra 21st chromosome. It is possible to detect the presence of Down syndrome in utero through a process known as amniocentesis.

■ Two other types of intellectual disability are fragile X syndrome, which is caused by a chromosomal abnormality of the tip of the X chromosome, and cultural-familial intellectual disability, a rare problem resulting from adverse environmental conditions.

KEY TERMS

amniocentesis, 481
attention-deficit/hyperactivity disorder (ADHD), 458
autism spectrum disorder (ASD), 469
childhood disintegrative disorder, 469

copy number variants, 461
cultural-familial intellectual disability, 481
Down syndrome, 480
fragile X syndrome, 481
intellectual disability (ID), 476

joint attention, 470
language disorder, 466
naturalistic teaching strategies, 475
neurodevelopmental disorders, 457
prosody, 471

specific learning disorder, 464
stuttering, 466

ANSWERS TO CONCEPT CHECKS

15.1

1. c; 2. a; 3. b; 4. d; 5. a

15.2

1. b; 2. a; 3. c

15.3

1. profound/pervasive support;
2. moderate/limited support;
3. severe/extensive support;
4. mild/intermittent support

CENGAGE | MINDTAP

Stay organized and efficient with MindTap—a single destination with all the course material and study aids you need to succeed. Built-in apps leverage social media and the latest learning technology. For example:

- ReadSpeaker will read the text to you.
- Flashcards are pre-populated to provide you with a jump start for review—or you can create your own.
- You can highlight text and make notes in your MindTap Reader. Your notes will flow into Evernote, the electronic notebook app that you can access anywhere when it's time to study for the exam.
- Self-quizzing allows you to assess your understanding.

Visit login.cengage.com to start using MindTap. Enter the Online Access Code from the card included with your text. If a code card is not provided, you can purchase instant access at Cengage.ca.

Exploring Developmental Disorders

Disorders that appear early in life disrupt the normal course of development.

> Interrupting or preventing the development of one skill impedes mastery of the skill that is normally acquired next.
> Knowing what skills are disrupted by a particular disorder is essential to developing appropriate intervention strategies.

© Cengage Learning

COGNITION

LANGUAGE

SOCIALIZATION

Photodisc/Getty Images

TYPES OF DEVELOPMENTAL DISORDERS

		Description	Causes	Treatment

Attention-Deficit/Hyperactivity Disorder (ADHD)	© baona/iStock	• Inattentive, overactive, and impulsive behaviour
		• Disrupted schooling and relationships
		• Symptoms may change with maturity, but problems persist
		• More prevalent in boys than girls
			• Research suggests hereditary factor
			• Abnormal neurology
			• Possible link with maternal smoking
			• Negative responses by others create low self-esteem
				• Biological (medication)
				  –improves compliance
				  –decreases negative behaviours
				  –effects not long term
				• Psychological (behavioural)
				  –goal setting and reinforcement

Specific Learning Disorder	© Ariel Skelley/Getty	• Reading, math, and written expression fall behind IQ, age, and education
		• May also be accompanied by ADHD
			• Theories assume genetic, neurobiological, and environmental factors	• Education intervention
				  –basic processing
				  –cognitive and behavioural skills

TYPES OF NEURODEVELOPMENTAL DISORDERS

		Types	Description	Treatment
Communication and Motor Disorders Closely related to learning disorders, but comparatively benign. Early appearance, wide range of problems later in life.	Photodisc/Getty Images	• Childhood-Onset Fluency • Disorder (Stuttering)	• Disturbance in speech fluency (repeating words, prolonging sounds, extended pauses)	• Psychological • Pharmacological
		• Language Disorder	• Limited speech in all situations	• Some cases may be self-correcting
		• Social (Practical) Communication Disorder	• Problems with the social aspects of verbal and nonverbal communication	• Psychological • Pharmacological
		• Tourette's Disorders	• Involuntary motor movements (tics), such as physical twitches or vocalizations	• Psychological • Pharmacological

PERVASIVE DEVELOPMENTAL DISORDERS

		Description	Causes	Treatment

Autism Spectrum Disorder	Photodisc/Getty Images	• Severely impaired socialization and communication
		• Restricted, repetitive patterns of behaviour
		• Symptoms almost always develop before 36 months of age.
			• Little conclusive data
			• Numerous biological factors
			  −clear genetic component
			  −evidence of brain damage (cognitive deficits) combined with psychosocial influences
				• Behavioural focus
				  −communication
				  −socialization
				  −living skills
				• Inclusive schooling
				• Temporary benefits from medication

INTELLECTUAL DISABILITY

		Description	Causes	Treatment

	Moodboard Stock Photography Ltd./Getty Images	• Adaptive and intellectual functioning significantly below average
		  −language and communication impairments
		• Wide range of impairment—from mild to profound—in daily activities (90 percent of affected individuals have mild impairments)
			• Hundreds of identified factors
			  −genetic
			  −prenatal
			  −perinatal
			  −postnatal
			  −environmental
			• Nearly 75 percent of cases cannot be attributed to any known cause
				• No biological intervention
				• Behavioural focus similar to that for autism
				• Prevention
				  −genetic counselling
				  −biological screening
				  −maternal care

16 | Aging and Neurocognition

Christian Martinez Kempin/E+ /Getty Images

myself

As my grip upon the present slips, more and more comfort is found within my memories of the past. Childhood nostalgia is so keen I can actually smell the aroma of the small town library where I spent so many childhood hours.

—DIANA FRIEL MCGOWIN, Living in the Labyrinth:
A Personal Journey, Through the Maze of
Alzheimer's

Use scientific reasoning to interpret behaviour:	›	Identify basic biological, psychological, and social components of behavioural explanations (e.g., inferences, observations, operational definitions, and interpretations) (APA SLO 2.1a)
Engage in innovative and integrative thinking and problem solving:	›	Describe problems operationally to study them empirically (APA SLO 2.3A)
Describe applications that employ discipline-based problem solving:	›	Correctly identify antecedents and consequences of behaviour and mental processes (APA SLO 1.3c) Describe examples of relevant and practical applications of psychological principles to everyday life (APA SLO 1.3a)

* Portions of this chapter cover learning outcomes suggested by the American Psychological Association (2013) in its guidelines for the undergraduate psychology major. Chapter coverage of these outcomes is identified above by APA Goal and APA Suggested Learning Outcome (SLO).

Research on the brain and its role in psychopathology has increased at a rapid pace, and we have described many of the latest advances throughout this book. All the disorders we have reviewed are in some way influenced by the brain, or at least involve the brain. You have seen, for example, that relatively subtle changes in neurotransmitter systems can significantly affect mood, cognition, and behaviour. Unfortunately, the brain is sometimes affected profoundly, and when this happens, drastic changes occur. In earlier editions of this book, the tone of this chapter was quite dark given the lack of information on these cognitive disorders that impair all aspects of mental functioning. The typically poor prognosis of the people afflicted led to pessimistic conclusions. A great deal of new research is leading us to be more optimistic about the future, however. For example, we used to think that once neurons died, there was no hope of any replacement, yet we now know brain cells can regenerate even in the aging brain (Seib & Martin-Villalba, 2015; Stellos et al., 2010). In this chapter, we examine this exciting new work related to the brain disorders that affect cognitive processes, such as learning, memory, and consciousness, with a focus on aging.

PERSPECTIVES

Most neurocognitive disorders develop much later in life, whereas intellectual disability and specific learning disorders are believed to be present from birth (see Chapter 15). In this section, we review two classes of cognitive disorders: *delirium*, an often temporary condition displayed as confusion and disorientation, and *mild or major neurocognitive disorder*, a progressive condition marked by gradual deterioration of a broad range of cognitive abilities.

The *DSM-5* label "neurocognitive disorders" reflects a shift in the way these disorders are viewed (American Psychiatric Association, 2013). In early editions of the *DSM* they were defined as "organic mental disorders," along with mood, anxiety, personality, hallucinosis, and delusional disorders. The word *organic* indicated that brain damage or dysfunction was believed to be involved. The "organic mental disorders" category, however, covered so many disorders that the distinction was meaningless. Consequently, the traditional organic disorders—delirium, dementia, and amnestic disorders—were kept together, and the others—organic mood, anxiety, personality, hallucinosis, and delusional disorders—were categorized with disorders that shared their symptoms (such as anxiety and mood disorders).

After the term *organic* was dropped, attention moved to developing a better label for delirium, dementia, and the amnestic disorders. The label "cognitive disorders" was used in the *DSM-IV* to signify that their predominant feature is the impairment of such cognitive abilities as memory, attention, perception, and thinking. Although disorders such as schizophrenia, autism spectrum disorder, and depression also involve cognitive problems, cognitive issues are not believed to be primary characteristics (Ganguli et al., 2011; Sachdev et al., 2014). Problems still existed with the "cognitive disorder" label, however, because although the cognitive disorders usually first appear in older adults, intellectual disability and specific learning disorders (which are apparent early) also have cognitive impairment as a predominant characteristic. Thus, in the *DSM-5*, *neurocognitive disorders* is the category name for the various forms of dementia and amnestic disorders, with "major" or "minor" subtypes; the *DSM-5* retains the "delirium" label (American Psychiatric Association, 2013). This new categorization was created because of the overlap of the different types of dementia (e.g., Alzheimer's disease) and amnestic disorder found in people such that one person may actually suffer from multiple types of neurocognitive problems (Ganguli et al., 2011; Sachdev et al., 2014).

■ Figure 16.1 illustrates how the incidence of disability caused by cognitive functions (learning and memory) rises with increasing age, with rates being highest for these types of disability in those ages 65 years and older. In contrast, the prevalence of disability related to mental health does not follow this age pattern and rates decline after age 65. This finding should be interpreted with caution, however, because it may be related to the lack of survey participation for individuals living in institutions (Statistics Canada, 2015a). As our life expectancy increases, cognitive disorders become more prevalent and have emerged as a major concern for mental health professionals. In 2017, the percentage of Canadians (15 and older) with a memory-related disability was 3.8 percent, 2.5 percent for people 15 to 24 years old, 3.5 percent for people 25 to 64 years old, and 5.4 percent for people 65 years and older (Morris et al., 2018).

As with certain other disorders, it may be useful to clarify why neurocognitive disorders are discussed in a textbook on abnormal psychology. Because they so clearly have organic causes, you could argue that they are purely medical concerns. We will see, however, that the consequences of a neurocognitive disorders often include profound changes in a person's behaviour and personality. Intense anxiety or depression is common, especially among people with major neurocognitive disorder. In addition,

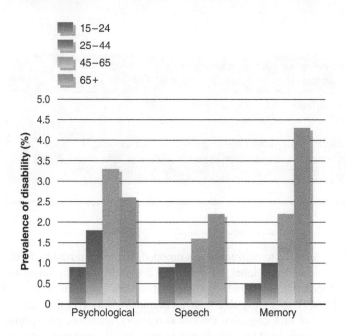

FIGURE 16.1 | Rates for disability among Canadians ages 15 years and over, specific for age and source of disability.

Source: Adapted from *A Profile of Disability in Canada, 2001,* 89–577-XIE2001001, by Statistics Canada, December 2003.

paranoia is frequently reported, as are extreme agitation and aggression. Families and friends are also deeply affected by such changes. Imagine your emotional distress as a loved one is transformed into a different person, often one who no longer remembers who you are or your history together. The deterioration of cognitive ability, behaviour, and personality and the effects on others are a major concern for mental health professionals.

DELIRIUM

The disorder known as **delirium** is characterized by impaired consciousness and cognition during the course of several hours or days (Cole, 2004; Conn & Lieff, 2001; Rahkonen et al., 2000). Delirium is one of the earliest recognized mental disorders: descriptions of people with these symptoms were written more than 2500 years ago (Lipowski, 1990). Consider the case of Mr. J.

MR. J. | *Sudden Distress*

Mr. J., an older man, was brought to the hospital emergency room. He didn't know his own name and at times he didn't seem to recognize his daughter, who was with him. Mr. J. appeared confused, disoriented, and a little agitated. He had difficulty speaking clearly and could not focus his attention to answer even the most basic questions. Mr. J.'s daughter reported that he had begun acting this way the night before, had been awake most of the time since then, was frightened, and seemed even more confused today. She told the nurse that this behaviour was not normal for him and she was worried that he was becoming senile. She mentioned that

his doctor had just changed his hypertension medication and wondered whether the new medication could be causing her father's distress. Mr. J. was ultimately diagnosed as having substance-induced delirium (a reaction to his new medication); once the medication was stopped, he improved significantly over the next two days. This scenario is played out daily in most major metropolitan hospital emergency rooms.

CLINICAL DESCRIPTION AND STATISTICS

People with delirium appear confused, disoriented, and out of touch with their surroundings. They cannot focus and sustain their attention on even the simplest tasks. They have marked impairments in memory and language (Meagher & Trzapacz, 2012). Mr. J. had trouble speaking; he was not only confused but also couldn't remember basic facts such as his own name. As we saw, the symptoms of delirium do not come on gradually; they develop over hours or a few days, and they can vary over the course of a day.

Delirium is estimated to be present in as many as 10 to 30 percent of the people who come into acute care facilities such as emergency rooms (American Psychiatric Association, 2000e). Michel Elie and his colleagues (2000) at McGill University determined the prevalence of delirium in emergency department patients ages 65 years and above to be about 10 percent. It is most prevalent among older adults, people undergoing medical procedures, cancer patients, and people with acquired immune deficiency syndrome (AIDS; Bourgeois et al., 2003). According to a study by a group of researchers in Québec, common risk factors for delirium in older patients include major neurocognitive disorder (formerly called dementia, a neurocognitive disorder to be discussed in the next section of this chapter), medication, and medical illness (Voyer et al., 2007).

Delirium usually subsides relatively quickly. Once thought to be only a temporary problem, more recent work indicates that the effects of delirium may be more lasting (Cole et al., 2009; Meagher et al., 2012). Some individuals continue to have problems on and off; some even lapse into a coma and may die. Concern by medical professionals is increasing—perhaps because of the increased number of adults living longer—leading some to recommend that delirium be included as one of the vital signs (along with heartbeat, breathing rate, temperature, and blood pressure) that physicians routinely check when seeing older adults (Flaherty, 2011).

Many conditions that impair brain function have been linked to delirium, including intoxication by drugs and poisons; withdrawal from drugs, such as alcohol and sedative, hypnotic, and anxiolytic drugs; infections; head injury; and various other types of brain trauma (Meagher & Trzapacz, 2012). Delirium often occurs during dementia; as many as 50 percent of people with dementia suffer at least one episode of delirium (Fong et al., 2015; Kwok et al., 2008). The *DSM-5* (see DSM Table 16.1) recognizes several causes of delirium among its subtypes. The diagnosis received by Mr. J.—substance-induced delirium—as well as delirium not otherwise specified all include disruptions in the person's ability to direct, focus, sustain, and shift attention. The rise in the use of designer drugs, such as ecstasy or molly (methylenedioxymethamphetamine) and more recently bath salts (methylenedioxypyrovalerone), is of particular concern because of such drugs' potential to produce delirium (Penders et al., 2012; Solai, 2009). Substance-induced delirium indicates the often complex nature of this condition.

That delirium can be brought on by the improper use of medication can be a particular problem for older adults, because they tend to use prescription medications more than any other age group (Cole, 2004). Medications with anticholinergic effects (e.g., those used to counteract extrapyramidal side effects of neuroleptic medications; see Chapter 14) appear particularly associated with severe delirium in seniors (Han et al., 2001). This suggests the possibility that a cholinergic deficit may contribute to delirium. Moreover, seniors also tend to be multiple medication users (Millar, 1998), putting them at risk for adverse drug interactions. The risk of problems among older adults is increased further because they tend to eliminate drugs from their systems less efficiently than younger individuals. It is not surprising, then, that adverse drug reactions resulting in hospitalization are almost six times higher among seniors than in other age groups (Budnitz et al., 2011; Olivier et al., 2009). And it is believed that delirium is responsible for many of the falls that cause debilitating hip fractures in older adults (Seitz et al., 2011; Stenvall et al., 2006). Although there has been some improvement in the use of medication among older adults—with physicians using more care with drug dosages and the use of multiple drugs—improper use continues to produce serious side effects, including symptoms of delirium (Budnitz et al., 2011; Olivier et al., 2009). Because possible combinations of illnesses and medications are so numerous, determining the cause of delirium is extremely difficult (Solai, 2009).

Other factors can trigger delirium. Age itself is an important factor; older adults are more susceptible to developing delirium as a result of mild infections or medication changes (Inouye et al., 2014). Sleep deprivation, immobility, and excessive stress can also cause delirium (Solai, 2009). Delirium may be experienced by children who have high fevers or who are taking certain medications and is often mistaken for noncompliance (Kelly & Frosch, 2012; Smeets et al., 2010).

Environmental factors can also play a role in the risk for severe delirium in hospitalized seniors. In a prospective study of hospitalized older adults, Jane McCusker of McGill University and her colleagues found environmental variables such as the number of room changes and absence of a clock, watch, or reading glasses, were related to an increase in delirium severity over time. Hospital room changes, for example, can disrupt older patients' ability to correctly perceive environmental cues, resulting in their misinterpretation of stimuli around them (McCusker et al., 2001). Since these environmental factors are modifiable, they can be targeted in treatment or prevention.

Researchers studying the brain functioning of persons with and without delirium are beginning to understand the mechanisms underlying this disorder of attention. In one study, scientists assessed brain activity using fMRI scanning during active episodes of delirium and after these episodes and found both lasting disruption of connectivity (between the dorsolateral prefrontal cortex with the posterior cingulate cortex) and reversible disruptions (such as between the thalamus with the reticular activating system; S.-H. Choi et al., 2012; Slooter & de Groot, 2014). Although such research is potentially important for efforts to both prevent and treat delirium, there are potential ethical concerns. For example, a person experiencing delirium is not capable of providing informed consent for participating in such research; therefore, someone else (e.g., a spouse or relative) must agree. In addition, fMRI testing can be anxiety-provoking for many people and is possibly very frightening for someone already so disoriented (Gaudreau, 2012).

TREATMENT

Rapid treatment of delirium is important, as quicker in-hospital recovery is associated with better long-term outcomes (Cole & McCusker, 2002). The first step for the treatment of delirium is addressing underlying causes. For example, delirium brought on by withdrawal from alcohol or other drugs is usually treated with haloperidol or other antipsychotic medications, which help calm the individual. Infections, brain injury, and tumours are given the necessary and appropriate medical intervention, which often then resolves the accompanying delirium. The antipsychotic drugs haloperidol and olanzapine are also prescribed for individuals in acute delirium when the cause is unknown (Meagher & Trzapacz, 2012).

The inclusion of a family member in the care for patients with delirium, such as overnight stays with the patient, may be a great comfort to the patient. Similarly, familiar personal belongings, such as family photographs, may also be an easy and comforting intervention (Fearing & Inouye, 2009; van Munster & de Rooij, 2014). Also, a patient who is included in all treatment decisions retains a sense of control that can aid patients cope with anxiety and agitation due to the delirium (Katz, 1993). This type of psychosocial treatment can help the person manage during this disruptive period until the medical causes are identified and addressed (Breitbart & Alici, 2012). Some evidence suggests that this type of support can also delay institutionalization for older patients (Rahkonen et al., 2001).

PREVENTION

Preventive efforts may be most successful in assisting people who are susceptible to delirium. Proper medical care for illnesses and therapeutic drug monitoring can play a significant role in preventing delirium (Breitbart & Alici, 2012). According to Montréal psychiatrist Martin Cole (2004), the evidence suggests that a broad spectrum of interventions (education, support, reorientation, anxiety reduction, preoperative medical assessment) may be moderately effective in preventing delirium in surgical patients. In fact, structured multidisciplinary interventions that target the prevention of delirium during hospital stays in older patients are very effective (for more information, see Hospital Elder Life Program; Inouye et al., 2014). These types of programs are implemented by an interdisciplinary team of doctors, nurses, and volunteers and consists reorientating the patient, providing vision and hearing aids as needed, increasing sleep and physical activity, maintaining proper hydration and nutrition, involving the patient in therapeutic activities, and reducing dosages of psychoactive drugs. One downside is that these programs require a lot of resources from hospitals to put it into place consistently with all those who are at risk for delirium.

MAJOR AND MILD NEUROCOGNITIVE DISORDERS

Few things are more frightening than the possibility of one day not recognizing those you love, not being able to perform the most basic of tasks, and, worse yet, being acutely aware of this failure of your mind. And when family members show these signs, adult children often deny any difficulty, coming up with excuses ("I forget things too") for their parents' failing abilities. **Major neurocognitive disorder** (previously labelled **dementia**) is a gradual deterioration of brain functioning that affects judgment, memory, language, and other advanced cognitive processes (see DSM Table 16.2). **Mild neurocognitive disorder** is a new *DSM-5* disorder that was created to focus attention on the early stages of cognitive decline (see DSM Table 16.3). Here, the person has modest impairments in cognitive abilities but can, with some accommodations (e.g., making extensive lists of things to do or creating elaborate schedules), continue to function independently.

Causes of neurocognitive disorders include several medical conditions and the abuse of drugs or alcohol, which produce negative changes in cognitive functioning. Some of these conditions—for instance, infection or depression—can cause neurocognitive impairment, although it is often reversible through treatment of the primary condition. Some forms of the disorder, such as Alzheimer's disease, are at present irreversible. Although delirium and

DSM-5 | **Table 16.2** Diagnostic Criteria for Major Neurocognitive Disorder

A. Evidence of significant cognitive decline from a previous level of performance in one or more cognitive domains (complex attention, executive function, learning and memory, language, perceptual-motor, or social cognition) based on:

   1. Concern of the individual, a knowledgeable informant, or the clinician that there has been a significant decline in cognitive function; and

   2. A substantial impairment in cognitive performance, preferably documented by standardized neuropsychological testing or, in its absence, another quantified clinical assessment.

B. The cognitive deficits interfere with independence in everyday activities (i.e., at a minimum, requiring assistance with complex instrumental activities of daily living such as paying bills or managing medications).

C. The cognitive deficits do not occur exclusively in the context of a delirium.

D. The cognitive deficits are not better explained by another mental disorder (e.g., major depressive disorder, schizophrenia).

Specify whether due to:

Alzheimer's disease

Frontotemporal lobar degeneration

Lewy body disease

Vascular disease

Traumatic brain injury

Substance/medication use

HIV infection

Prion disease

Parkinson's disease

Huntington's disease

Another medical condition

Multiple etiologies

Unspecified

Source: Reprinted with permission from the *Diagnostic and Statistical Manual of Mental Disorders*, Fifth Edition (Copyright © 2013). American Psychiatric Association. All Rights Reserved.

neurocognitive disorder can occur together, neurocognitive disorder has a gradual progression as opposed to delirium's acute onset; people with neurocognitive disorder are not disoriented or confused in the early stages, unlike people with delirium. Like delirium, however, neurocognitive disorder has many causes, including a variety of insults to the brain, such as stroke (which destroys blood vessels), the infectious diseases of syphilis and HIV, severe head injury, the introduction of certain toxic or poisonous substances, and diseases, such as Parkinson's, Huntington's, and the most common cause of major neurocognitive disorder, Alzheimer's disease. Consider the personal account by Pat Summitt, the most successful NCAA basketball coach of all time. She coached the Tennessee Lady Vols basketball team from 1974 to 2012—winning a record-setting 1098 games—until her symptoms of neurocognitive disorder due to Alzheimer's disease prevented her from working with the team full-time. She courageously writes of her experiences with this disorder (Summitt, 2013).

A. Evidence of modest cognitive decline from a previous level of performance in one or more cognitive domains (complex attention, executive function, learning and memory, language, perceptual motor, or social cognition) based on:

1. Concern of the individual, a knowledgeable informant, or the clinician that there has been a mild decline in cognitive function; and

2. A modest impairment in cognitive performance, preferably documented by standardized neuropsychological testing or, in its absence, another quantified clinical assessment.

B. The cognitive deficits do not interfere with capacity for independence in everyday activities (i.e., complex instrumental activities of daily living such as paying bills or managing medications are preserved, but greater effort, compensatory strategies, or accommodation may be required).

C. The cognitive deficits do not occur exclusively in the context of a delirium.

D. The cognitive deficits are not better explained by another mental disorder (e.g., major depressive disorder, schizophrenia).

Specify whether due to:

Alzheimer's disease

Frontotemporal lobar degeneration

Lewy body disease

Vascular disease

Traumatic brain injury

Substance/medication use

HIV infection

Prion disease

Parkinson's disease

Huntington's disease

Another medical condition

Multiple etiologies

Unspecified

Source: Reprinted with permission from the *Diagnostic and Statistical Manual of Mental Disorders*, Fifth Edition (Copyright © 2013). American Psychiatric Association. All Rights Reserved.

PAT SUMMITT | *Grit and Determination*

At the age of 57, Pat Summitt was a highly successful basketball coach and mother, but she was beginning to experience lapses in her memory.

Friends started asking, "Are you having trouble with your memory?" Finally I admitted, "Sometimes I draw blanks." I grew uncertain, and then a little frightened. I began staying in bed until late in the morning, which was unlike me. I'd always been a bolter, the first person up and the most energetic one, too, and I'd always gone to work earlier than anyone on my staff. But I began to dread going into the office. (p. 11)

Despite having cognitive difficulties, not all of her memories are lost to her in this initial stage of the disease. She begins her memoir with the things she remembers.

Simon Bruty/Sports Illustrated/Getty Images

I remember a tiny saloon in the Tennessee hills where the bartender squirted bourbon shots from a squeeze bottle, straight into the customers' mouths.

I remember teaching a clinic to other coaches and opening the floor for questions, and a guy raised his hand and asked if I had any advice when it came to "coaching women." I remember leveling him with a death ray stare and then relaxing and curling up the corner of my mouth and saying, "Don't worry about coaching 'women.' Just go home and coach 'basketball.'" (p. 6)

I remember the night my son was born. The doctor placed him on my chest and I said, "Hey, Tyler, I've been waitin' on you." (pp. 6–7)

Her memory for important experiences that occurred years ago remains intact. However, recent experiences and facts are more elusive. She then goes on to describe some of the things she no longer remembers.

Sometimes, when I first wake up, I don't remember where I am. For a moment I'm disoriented and uneasy, and I have to lie there until it comes to me.

Occasionally when I'm asked a question, I begin to answer it but then I forget the subject—it slips away like a thread through my fingers.

I struggle to remember directions. There are moments when I'm driving to someplace I should know, and I have to ask, "Do I go left or right here?"

I tend not to remember what hotel room I'm in. I don't remember what time my appointments are for. (p. 7)

Many people who begin to have these cognitive difficulties retell these initial experiences as incredibly frightening. However, Pat Summitt is known for her tough determination both on the basketball court and now battling Alzheimer's disease. Her reaction to her diagnosis and her doctor's recommendations show an incredible level of courage and strength.

In my case, symptoms began to appear when I was only fifty-seven. In fact, the doctors believe early-onset Alzheimer's has a strong genetic predictor, and that it may have been progressing hidden in me for some years before I was diagnosed. I'd been walking around with a slow-ticking, slow-exploding bomb in my brain cells, and it only became apparent when it began to seriously interfere with my work. (p. 9)

The doctor told me that given my diagnosis, frankly, he felt I could no longer work at all. I should step down immediately, because in his opinion the dementia would progress rapidly. I needed to quit, and get myself out of the public eye as quickly as possible, or I would "embarrass" myself and ruin my legacy. As he spoke, I felt my fist clench. It was all I could do not to lunge across the desk and drop him with one punch. Who did he think he was? Even if I had an irreversible brain disease—even if I did—what right did he have to tell me how to cope with it? Quit? Quit? (pp. 17–18)

She goes on to write about her unusually practical and optimistic perspective on having Alzheimer's disease—a view of this degenerative disease that should serve as a role model for the millions of people affected by this disorder.

Above all, I know that Alzheimer's has brought me to a point that I was going to arrive at someday anyway. With or without this diagnosis, I was going to experience diminishment. We all do. It's our fate. No, I can't size up a court of ten players anymore, see the clock out of one eye and the shifting schemes of opposing players with the other, and order up a countermove by hollering "Five!" or "Motion!" But I can suggest that people with mild to moderate stages of dementia have far more abilities than incapacities. I can suggest that just because certain circuits of memory or swiftness of synapses may fail, thought and awareness and consciousness do not. (p. 375)

Source: Excerpt(s) from SUM IT UP: A THOUSAND AND NINETY-EIGHT VICTORIES, A COUPLE OF IRRELEVANT LOSSES, AND A LIFE IN PERSPECTIVE by Pat Head Summitt, copyright © 2013 by Pat Head Summitt. Used by permission of Crown Archetype, an imprint of the Crown Publishing Group, a division of Random House LLC. All rights reserved.

After several evaluations, which included neurological evaluations, magnetic resonance imaging (MRI) showing some damage in several parts of her brain, and a spinal tap that showed the presence of beta-amyloid protein, Pat Summitt's neurologist concluded that she had early-onset neurocognitive disorder from Alzheimer's disease. People at the same stage of decline as Summitt will continue to deteriorate and eventually may die from complications of their disorder.

CLINICAL DESCRIPTION AND STATISTICS

Depending on the individual and the cause, the gradual progression of neurocognitive disorder may have somewhat different symptoms, although all aspects of cognitive functioning are eventually affected. In the initial stages, memory impairment is typically seen as an inability to register ongoing events. In other words, a person can remember how to talk and may remember events from many years ago, but have trouble remembering what happened in the past hour. For example, Pat Summitt had vivid recollections about her childhood but could not remember which direction to drive in familiar places.

Pat Summitt couldn't find her way home because *visuospatial* skills are impaired among people with neurocognitive disorder.

Agnosia, the inability to recognize and name objects, is one of the most familiar symptoms. **Facial agnosia**, the inability to recognize even familiar faces, can be extremely distressing to family members. A general deterioration of intellectual function results from impairment in memory, planning, and abstract reasoning.

Perhaps because victims of neurocognitive disorder are aware that they are deteriorating mentally, emotional changes often occur as well. Common side effects are delusions (irrational beliefs), depression, agitation, aggression, and apathy (Lovestone, 2012). Again, it is difficult to establish the cause-and-effect relationship. We don't know how much behavioural change is due to progressive brain deterioration directly and how much is a result of the frustration and discouragement that inevitably accompany the loss of function and the isolation of "losing" loved ones. Cognitive functioning continues to deteriorate until the person requires almost total support to carry out day-to-day activities. Ultimately, death occurs as the result of inactivity combined with the onset of other illnesses, such as pneumonia.

Major neurocognitive disorder can develop at almost any age, although major neurocognitive disorder of the Alzheimer's type rarely occurs in people under 45 years of age (American Psychiatric Association, 2000f). The incidence of major neurocognitive disorder is thus highest in older adults. The Public Health Agency of Canada uses the Canadian Chronic Disease Surveillance System (CCDSS) to understand the prevalence of dementia (including Alzheimer's disease). The CCDSS accesses administrative health databases from the provinces and territories (e.g., physician billing, hospital discharge records). In 2013–2014, it was estimated that 7.1 percent of Canadians 65 years of age and older were living with dementia, and two-thirds were women (Public Health Agency of Canada, 2017b). The prevalence of dementia increases steadily with age: 0.8 percent among those 65 to 69, 2.4 percent among those 70 to 74, 5.9 percent among those 75 to 79, 12.4 percent among those 80 to 84, and 24.6 percent among those over 85 (see ■ Figure 16.2). Canadians can view

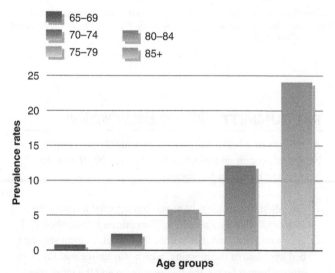

FIGURE 16.2 | Prevalence of dementia increases steadily with age.

Source: Dementia in Canada, Including Alzheimer's Disease: Highlights from the Canadian Chronic Disease Surveillance System, by Public Health Agency of Canada, 2017 (https://www.canada.ca/en/public-health/services/publications/diseases-conditions/dementia-highlights-canadian-chronic-disease-surveillance.html).

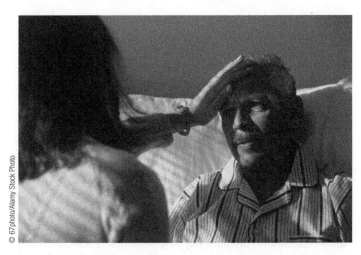

▲ People with facial agnosia, a common symptom of neurocognitive disorder, are unable to recognize faces, even of their closest friends and relatives.

regularly updated prevalence rates with a data tool on the CCDSS website (https://health-infobase.canada.ca/ccdss/data-tool/).

The National Population Health Study of Neurological Conditions in Canada (Caesar-Chavannes & MacDonald, 2013) also found evidence that Alzheimer's disease and other types of dementias increase in prevalence with age, the rate close to doubling every five years after individuals reach the age of 70 (Public Health Agency of Canada & Neurological Health Charities Canada, 2014). One study focused on prevalence among Canadians 45 years of age and older living in long-term residential care homes in 2011. Compared to only 0.8 percent of Canadians living in private homes, 45 percent of Canadians living in long-term care had a diagnosis of dementia; 12 percent of residents between the ages of 45 to 64 had been diagnosed with dementia, rising to 42 percent for those 65 to 79, and reaching more than half (56 percent) for residents 80 years of age or older (Wong et al., 2016). Furthermore, it was estimated that the number of Canadians with Alzheimer's disease and other types of dementia would virtually double between 2011 and 2031 with 674 000 Canadians affected. Now, a dramatic rise in Alzheimer's disease is predicted through the year 2050, because larger numbers of people are expected to live beyond 85 years of age.

The actual rate may be considerably higher, however, especially among older adults. Evans and colleagues (1989) found that as many as 47 percent of adults over the age of 85 may have neurocognitive disorder of the Alzheimer's type, and a study of centenarians (people 100 years and older) found that almost 90 percent showed signs of neurocognitive disorder (Blansjaar et al., 2000). Thus, prevalence rates have varied considerably across studies. This discrepancy in estimates may result from several factors. Using data from the Canadian Study of Health and Aging, researchers at the University of Western Ontario and the London Health Sciences Centre have demonstrated how the use of different diagnostic criteria can dramatically affect prevalence estimates for neurocognitive disorder (Erkinjuntti et al., 1997).

A problem with confirming prevalence figures for neurocognitive disorders is that survival rates alter the outcomes. Incidence studies, which count the number of new cases in a year, may thus be the most reliable method for assessing the frequency of neurocognitive disorder, especially among seniors. The Public Health Agency of Canada also uses the CCDSS to track incidence rates of dementia. In 2013–2014, it estimated 14.3 new dementia diagnoses for every 1000 Canadian seniors (Public Health Agency of Canada, 2017b). The incidence rates increased dramatically with age (e.g., 2.9/1000 for 65- to 69-year-olds, compared to 50.4/1000 for seniors 85 years of age and older), and were higher among women than men (12.4/1000 for men compared to 15.8/1000 for women).

In addition to the human costs of neurocognitive disorder, the medical costs are staggering (Getsios et al., 2001). For example, for the fiscal year 2010–2011, it was estimated that the direct health care cost for Alzheimer's disease and other types of dementia exceeded $525 million for British Columbia alone. This cost is three times higher than among age-standardized individuals without this condition. Estimates for other neurocognitive disorders included Parkinsonism at over $120 million (six times higher cost) and traumatic brain injury at over $86 million (14 times higher cost) (Public Health Agency of Canada & Neurological Health Charities Canada, 2014). Estimates suggest that such direct health care costs for dementia will double by the year 2031. But direct medical costs (e.g., hospital and doctor's visits, medication) are only a fraction of the total financial burden of caring for a person with neurocognitive disorder. Yearly nursing home costs are astounding. Often family members care for an afflicted person around the clock, which is an inestimable personal and financial commitment (Hermann et al., 2006). In a review of the literature, a team of researchers in Hong Kong found that the economic costs associated with the care of individuals with neurocognitive disorder due to Alzheimer's disease were highly variable across studies. This variation was mostly due to differences in the methods that researchers used to calculate economic costs and to variations in care patterns in different areas of the world. The researchers concluded, however, that there is little doubt that the economic impact of neurocognitive disorder is substantial (Leung et al., 2003). The economic impact is likely to worsen worldwide as a greater proportion of the world's population becomes elderly.

The *DSM-5* identifies classes of neurocognitive disorder based on etiology: (1) Alzheimer's disease, (2) vascular injury, (3) frontotemporal degeneration, (4) traumatic brain injury, (5) Lewy body disease, (6) Parkinson's disease, (7) HIV infection, (8) substance use, (9) Huntington's disease, (10) prion disease, and (11) another medical condition. We emphasize neurocognitive disorder from Alzheimer's disease because of its prevalence (almost half of those with neurocognitive disorder exhibit this type) and the relatively large amount of research conducted on its etiology and treatment.

NEUROCOGNITIVE DISORDER OF THE ALZHEIMER'S TYPE

Description and Statistics

In 1907, the German psychiatrist Alois Alzheimer first described the disorder that bears his name. He wrote of a 51-year-old woman who had a "strange disease of the cerebral cortex" that manifested as progressive memory impairment and other behavioural and cognitive problems, including suspiciousness (Richards & Sweet, 2009). He called the disorder an "atypical form of senile dementia," and thereafter it was referred to as **Alzheimer's disease**.

The *DSM-5* diagnostic criteria for **neurocognitive disorder due to Alzheimer's disease** include multiple cognitive deficits that develop gradually and steadily (see DSM Table 16.4). Predominant is the impairment of *memory*, *orientation*, *judgment*, and *reasoning*. The inability to integrate new information results in failure to learn new associations. Individuals with neurocognitive

DSM-5	**Table 16.4** Diagnostic Criteria for Major or Mild Neurocognitive Disorder Due to Alzheimer's Disease

A. The criteria are met for major or mild neurocognitive disorder.

B. There is insidious onset and gradual progression of impairment in one or more cognitive domains (for major neurocognitive disorder, two domains must be impaired).

C. Criteria are met for either probable or possible Alzheimer's disease as follows:

For major neurocognitive disorder:

Probable Alzheimer's disease is diagnosed if either of the following is present; otherwise, **possible Alzheimer's disease** should be diagnosed.

1. Evidence of a causative Alzheimer's disease genetic mutation from family history or genetic testing.

2. All three of the following are present:

    a. Clear evidence of decline in memory and learning and at least one other cognitive domain (based on detailed history or serial neuropsychological testing).

    b. Steadily progressive, gradual decline in cognition, without extended plateaus.

    c. No evidence of mixed etiology (i.e., absence of other neurodegenerative or cerebrovascular disease, or another neurological, mental, or systemic disease or condition likely contributing to cognitive decline).

For mild neurocognitive disorder:

Probable Alzheimer's disease is diagnosed if there is evidence of a causative Alzheimer's disease genetic mutation from either genetic testing or family history.

Possible Alzheimer's disease is diagnosed if there is no evidence of a causative Alzheimer's disease genetic mutation from either genetic testing or family history, and all three of the following are present:

1. Clear evidence of decline in memory and learning.

2. Steadily progressive, gradual decline in cognition, without extended plateaus.

3. No evidence of mixed etiology (i.e., absence of other neurodegenerative or cerebrovascular disease, or another neurological or systemic disease or condition likely contributing to cognitive decline).

D. The disturbance is not better explained by cerebrovascular disease, another neurodegenerative disease, the effects of a substance, or another mental, neurological, or systemic disorder.

disorder due to Alzheimer's disease forget important events and lose objects. Their interest in nonroutine activities narrows. They tend to lose interest in others and, as a result, become more socially isolated. As the disorder progresses, they can become agitated, confused, depressed, anxious, or even combative. Many of these difficulties become more pronounced late in the day—in a phenomenon referred to as "sundowner syndrome"—perhaps as a result of fatigue or a disturbance in the brain's biological clock (Ferrazzoli et al., 2013; Lemay & Landreville, 2010).

As noted in a review by University of Western Ontario researchers Edward Helmes and Truls Ostbye (2002), people with neurocognitive disorder due to Alzheimer's disease also display one or more other cognitive disturbances, including **aphasia** (difficulty with language), *apraxia* (impaired motor functioning), *agnosia* (failure to recognize objects), or difficulty with activities, such as planning, organizing, sequencing, or abstracting information. One example of the language difficulties experienced by people with neurocognitive disorder due to Alzheimer's disease is *anomia* (problems with naming objects; Auchterlonie et al., 2002). These cognitive impairments also have a serious negative impact on social and occupational functioning, and they represent a significant decline from previous abilities.

A definitive diagnosis of neurocognitive disorder due to Alzheimer's disease can be made only after an autopsy determines that certain characteristic types of damage are present in the brain, although clinicians are accurate in identifying this condition in living patients 70 to 90 percent of the time (Bourgeois et al., 2003). To make a diagnosis without direct examination of the brain, a simplified version of a mental status exam, called the Mini Mental State Examination (Folstein et al., 1975), is used to assess language and memory problems. This simple exam has been shown to be quite accurate in identifying people with dementia (Mcdowell et al., 1997).

A test that is often used to supplement the mental status exam for detecting neurocognitive disorders (Shulman, 2000) is the clock drawing subtest of the Clock Test (Tuokko et al., 1995, 2000). In this test, the patient is presented with a drawing of a circle and is instructed to

▲ Holly Tuokko at the University of Victoria has conducted considerable research on various aspects of neurocognitive disorders. She is probably best known for her work in developing and evaluating the Clock Test (Tuokko et al., 1992, 1995, 2000) as a measure for detecting neurocognitive disorders.

imagine that the circle is a clock. The patient is then asked to put the numbers on the clock and to place the clock's hands in the position to show the time as 11:10. The test is scored according to the number and types of errors that the patient makes to assist in identifying patients with neurocognitive disorder due to

Alzheimer's disease (Shulman et al., 1986). Patients with neurocognitive disorder due to Alzheimer's disease make more errors of omission and misplacements of numbers, as compared with controls (Tuokko et al., 1992). Samples of clocks drawn by three patients with neurocognitive disorder due to Alzheimer's disease are displayed in ■ Figure 16.3. Additionally, longitudinal research suggests that scores on the Clock Test may also be useful in identifying which elderly individuals will develop neurocognitive disorder in the future (O'Rourke et al., 1997).

Cognitive deterioration with Alzheimer's disease is slow during the early and later stages but more rapid during the middle stages (Ito et al., 2011; Richards & Sweet, 2009). The average survival time is estimated to be about four to eight years, although many individuals live dependently for more than 20 years. Canadian data suggest that the survival time may be much shorter. Christina Wolfson of McGill University and her colleagues made use of data from the Canadian Study of Health and Aging and found that the median survival after the onset of neurocognitive disorder due to Alzheimer's disease was only three years (Wolfson et al., 2001). In some forms, the disease can occur relatively early, during the 40s or 50s (sometimes referred to as early onset), but it usually appears during the 60s or 70s (Wise et al., 1999).

Some research suggests that education may be a protective factor for Alzheimer's disease (Amieva et al., 2014; Fratiglioni et al., 1991; Korczyn et al., 1991; Stern et al., 1994). Stern and colleagues (1994) suggested that educational attainment may somehow create a mental "reserve," a learned set of skills that helps someone cope for longer with the cognitive deterioration that marks the beginning of neurocognitive deficits. Some people may adapt more successfully than others and thus escape detection longer. Brain deterioration may thus be comparable for individuals with varied education, but better educated individuals may be able to function successfully on a day-to-day basis for longer.

A biological version of this theory—called the *cerebral reserve hypothesis*—suggests that the more synapses a person develops throughout life, the more neuronal death must take place before the signs of neurocognitive disorder are obvious (Stern, 2009). Mental activity that occurs with education presumably builds up this reserve of synapses and serves as a protective factor in the development of the disorder. It is likely that both skill development and the changes in the brain with education may contribute to how quickly the disorder progresses.

Neurocognitive disorder due to Alzheimer's disease may be more prevalent among women (Craig & Murphy, 2009), even when women's higher survival rate is factored into the statistics. In other words, because women live longer than men on average, they are more likely to experience neurocognitive disorder due to Alzheimer's and other diseases, but longevity alone does not account for the higher prevalence of the disorder among women. A tentative explanation involves the hormone estrogen. Women lose estrogen as they grow older, so perhaps estrogen is protective against the disease. A large and important study—the Women's Health Initiative Memory Study—looked at hormone use among women and its effect on neurocognitive disorder due to Alzheimer's disease (Lobo, 2013; Shumaker et al., 2004). The study followed women over age 65 using a type of combined estrogen plus progestin known as Prempro and, contrary to the belief that giving women estrogen would decrease their chance of developing neurocognitive disorder, they observed an *increased* risk for Alzheimer's disease (Coker et al., 2010; Maki & Henderson, 2012). Research is ongoing into the individual effects of these two types of hormones on neurocognitive disorders.

Finally, there appear to be questions about the prevalence of neurocognitive disorder due to Alzheimer's disease according to cultural or racial identity. Early research seemed to suggest that certain populations (such as those with Japanese, Nigerian, certain First Nations, and Amish backgrounds) were less likely to be affected (e.g., see Pericak-Vance et al., 1996; Rosenberg et al., 1996). Similarly, prevalence rates of Alzheimer's disease in low- and middle-income countries have also been reportedly lower than higher-income countries (Sosa-Ortiz et al., 2012). More recent work indicates, however, that some of these differences may be due to lower numbers in those who seek assistance (possibly because of stigma and high levels of social care from family members), as well as differences in education, and how the disorders were measured (Sosa-Ortiz et al., 2012; Wilson et al., 2010). For example, individuals in low- and middle-income countries did not meet *DSM* criteria for the disorder because they did not have the social or occupational interference since their families

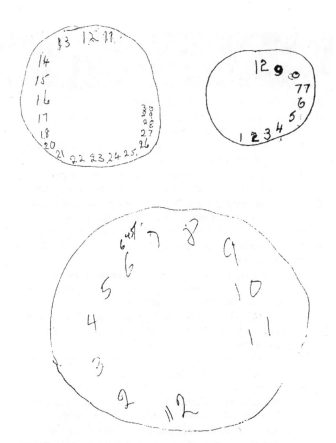

FIGURE 16.3 | Samples of the clock drawing subtest of the Clock Test developed by Holly Tuokko, as drawn by three patients with neurocognitive disorder due to Alzheimer's disease.

Source: Adapted from *Clock Drawing: A Neuropsychological Analysis*, by M. Freedman, L. Leach, E. Kaplan, G. Winocur, K. I. Shulman, and D. C. Delis, 1994, Oxford University Press.

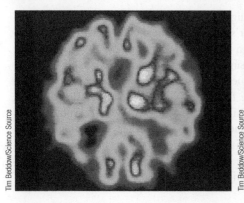

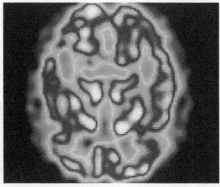

▲ The PET scan of a brain with neurocognitive disorder due to Alzheimer's disease (left) shows significant tissue deterioration in comparison with a normal brain (right).

were taking care of them (Sosa-Ortiz et al., 2012). Neurocognitive disorder due to Alzheimer's disease is found in roughly the same numbers across all ethnic groups, with one study finding a slightly lower rate among First Nations groups (Weiner et al., 2007). However, rates of dementia, including Alzheimer's disease, seem to be increasing more rapidly for Indigenous peoples, and age of onset might be earlier (reviewed in Petrasek MacDonald et al., 2018; Warren et al., 2015). Good information on dementia in Indigenous people is scarce, and almost nothing is known about rates or progression in Métis and Inuit people.

particular pattern of skills that are impaired—differs from person to person. *DSM-5* lists as criteria for vascular neurocognitive disorder cognitive disturbances, such as declines in speed of information processing and executive functioning (e.g., complex decision making) (Erkinjuntti, 2012; see DSM Table 16.5). In contrast, those with neurocognitive disorder due to Alzheimer's disease have memory problems as their initial cognitive disturbance.

Compared with research on neurocognitive disorder due to Alzheimer's disease, there are fewer studies on vascular neurocognitive disorder. One study of people living in a Swedish city suggests that the lifetime risk of having vascular neurocognitive disorder is 4.7 percent among men and 3.8 percent among women (Hagnell et al., 1992). The higher risk for men is typical for this disorder, in contrast with the higher risk among women for neurocognitive disorder due to Alzheimer's disease (Alzheimer's Society of Canada, 2004). The relatively high rate of cardiovascular disease among men in general may account for their increased risk of vascular neurocognitive disorder. Indeed, in Canada, the incidence of strokes is higher in men (329 per 100 000 in 2015) than

---

Concept Check 16.1

Identify the following symptoms of neurocognitive disorder from the descriptions (a) facial agnosia, (b) agnosia, (c) apraxia, and (d) aphasia.

1. Timmy's grandmother does not recognize her own home anymore. _____

2. She can no longer form complete, coherent sentences. _____

3. She no longer recognizes Timmy when he visits, even though he is her only grandchild. _____

4. She has trouble walking from a bed to the bathroom. _____

VASCULAR NEUROCOGNITIVE DISORDER

Each year, thousands of people die from strokes (any diseases or insults to the brain that result in restriction or cessation of blood flow). Although stroke is one of the top causes of death in Canadian seniors (Statistics Canada, 2014), many people survive, but one potential long-term consequence can be severely debilitating. **Vascular neurocognitive disorder** is a progressive brain disorder that is second only to Alzheimer's disease as a cause of neurocognitive deficits (Stuss & Cummings, 1990). The word *vascular* refers to blood vessels. When the blood vessels in the brain are blocked or damaged and no longer carry oxygen and other nutrients to certain areas of brain tissue, damage results. Because multiple sites in the brain can be damaged, the profile of degeneration—the

---

DSM-5 | **Table 16.5** Diagnostic Criteria for Major or Mild Vascular Neurocognitive Disorder

A. The criteria are met for major or mild neurocognitive disorder.

B. The clinical features are consistent with a vascular etiology as suggested by either of the following:

  1. Onset of the cognitive deficits is temporally related to one or more cerebrovascular events.

  2. Evidence for decline is prominent in complex attention (including processing speed) and frontal-executive function.

C. There is evidence of the presence of cerebrovascular disease from history, physical examination, and/or neuroimaging considered sufficient to account for the neurocognitive deficits.

D. The symptoms are not better explained by another brain disease or systemic disorder.

Probable vascular neurocognitive disorder is diagnosed if one of the following is present; otherwise, possible vascular neurocognitive disorder should be diagnosed:

  1. Clinical criteria are supported by neuroimaging evidence of significant parenchymal injury attributed to cerebrovascular disease (neuroimaging-supported).

  2. The neurocognitive syndrome is temporally related to one or more documented cerebrovascular events.

  3. Both clinical and genetic (e.g., cerebral autosomal dominant arteriopathy with subcortical infarcts and leukoencephalopathy) evidence of cerebrovascular disease is present.

Possible vascular neurocognitive disorder is diagnosed if the clinical criteria are met but neuroimaging is not available and the temporal relationship of the neurocognitive syndrome with one or more cerebrovascular events is not established.

Source: Reprinted with permission from the *Diagnostic and Statistical Manual of Mental Disorders,* Fifth Edition (Copyright © 2013). American Psychiatric Association. All Rights Reserved.

in women (271 per 100 000 in 2015; CCDSS, 2018). The onset of vascular neurocognitive disorder is typically more sudden than for neurocognitive disorder due to Alzheimer's type (King et al., 2005, 2006), probably because the disorder is the result of stroke, which inflicts brain damage immediately. The outcome, however, is similar for people with both types: ultimately, they will require formal nursing care until they succumb to an infectious disease, such as pneumonia.

OTHER MEDICAL CONDITIONS THAT CAUSE NEUROCOGNITIVE DISORDER

In addition to Alzheimer's disease and vascular damage, several other neurological and biochemical processes can lead to neurocognitive disorder. The *DSM-5* lists eight specific causes in addition to Alzheimer's disease and vascular damage: frontotemporal degeneration, traumatic brain injury, Lewy body disease, Parkinson's disease, HIV infection, substance use, Huntington's disease, and prion disease. Each of these types is briefly discussed here. In addition, a last category—neurocognitive disorder due to another medical condition—is provided for other causes. Other medical conditions that can lead to neurocognitive disorder include normal-pressure hydrocephalus (excessive water in the cranium, caused by brain shrinkage), hypothyroidism (an underactive thyroid gland), brain tumour, and vitamin B12 deficiency. There is increasing recognition of neurocognitive disorder among athletes who receive repeated blows to the head. In the past this type of neurocognitive disorder was referred to as dementia pugilistica (which suggested that it was restricted to boxers), but it is currently referred to as chronic traumatic encephalopathy (CTE). CTE is caused by repetitive head trauma that can provoke distinctive neurodegeneration (Baugh et al., 2012). In their effect on cognitive ability, these disorders are comparable to the other forms of neurocognitive disorder we have discussed so far.

Frontotemporal neurocognitive disorder is an overarching term used to categorize a variety of brain disorders that damage the frontal or temporal regions of the brain—areas that affect personality, language, and behaviour (Gustafson & Brun, 2012). The *DSM-5* identifies two variants of frontotemporal neurocognitive disorder—through declines in appropriate behaviour (e.g., socially inappropriate actions, apathy, making poor judgments) or language (e.g., problems with speech, finding the right word, naming objects). One of the disorders in this category of neurocognitive disorders is **Pick's disease**, a rare neurological condition—occurring in about 5 percent of those people with neurocognitive impairment—that produces symptoms similar to that of Alzheimer's disease. The course of this disease is believed to last from five to ten years and appears to have a genetic component (Gustafson & Brun, 2012). Pick's disease usually occurs relatively early in life—during a person's 40s or 50s—and is therefore considered an example of early-onset neurocognitive disorder.

Severe trauma to the head causes the brain to sustain lasting injuries (called **traumatic brain injury** or **TBI**), which can lead to neurocognitive disorder (Fleminger, 2012). **Neurocognitive disorder due to traumatic brain injury** includes symptoms that persist for at least a week following the trauma, including executive dysfunction (e.g., difficulty planning complex activities) and

problems with learning and memory. Those that are at greatest risk for TBI are teens and young adults, especially accompanied by alcohol abuse or lower socioeconomic status (Fleminger, 2012). Traffic accidents, assaults, falls, and suicide attempts are common causes, as is being exposed to bomb blasts in combat.

A common type of neurocognitive disorders is **neurocognitive disorder due to Lewy body disease** (Aarsland et al., 2012; McKeith et al., 2005). Lewy bodies are microscopic deposits of a protein that damage brain cells over time. The signs of this disorder come on gradually and include impairment in alertness and attention, vivid visual hallucinations, and motor impairment as seen in Parkinson's disease. In fact, there is some overlap between this disorder and **neurocognitive disorder due to Parkinson's disease** (Mindham & Hughes, 2012).

Parkinson's disease is a degenerative brain disorder that affects about one out of every 1000 people worldwide (Marsh & Margolis, 2009). According to a recent study, 55 000 (0.2 percent) of Canadians over the age of 18 reported a diagnosis of Parkinson's disease in 2010–2011 (Wong et al., 2014). These individuals were not living in institutions and the majority (79 percent) were over 65 years of age. Among Canadian adults living in long-term care facilities, 4.9 percent (12 500) reported a diagnosis of Parkinson's in 2011. Similar to the estimates for Canadians with neurocognitive disorder due to Alzheimer's disease, the number of Canadians living with Parkinson's disease is expected to almost double between 2011 and 2031 and surpass 160 000 (0.7 percent) Canadians (Public Health Agency of Canada & Neurological Health Charities Canada, 2014). The most current Canadian estimates come out of the CCDSS. In 2013–2014, 0.4 percent of Canadians over the age of 40 were living with Parkinsonism, including Parkinson's disease, and 10 000 Canadians first received this diagnosis in that period (Public Health Agency of Canada, 2018c). Canadians can access updated prevalence and incidence rates by accessing the CCDSS website (https://health-infobase .canada.ca/ccdss/data-tool/).

Motor problems are characteristic among people with Parkinson's disease, who tend to have stooped posture, slow body movements (called *bradykinesia*), tremors, and jerkiness in walking. The voice is also affected; afflicted individuals speak in a very soft monotone. The changes in motor movements are the result of damage to dopamine pathways. Because dopamine is involved in complex movement, a reduction in this neurotransmitter makes affected individuals increasingly unable to control their muscle movements, which leads to tremors and muscle weakness. In addition to degeneration of these pathways, Lewy bodies are also present in the brains of affected persons. Some people with Parkinson's develop neurocognitive disorder (La Rue, 1992); conservative estimates place the rate at twice that found in the general population (Gibb, 1989).

The **human immunodeficiency virus-type-1**, which causes **acquired immune deficiency syndrome (AIDS)**, can also cause neurocognitive disorder (called **neurocognitive disorder due to HIV infection**; Maj, 2012). This impairment seems to be independent of the other infections that accompany HIV; in other words, the HIV infection itself seems to be responsible for the neurological impairment. The early symptoms of neurocognitive disorder resulting from HIV are cognitive slowness, impaired attention, and forgetfulness. Affected individuals also tend to be

© Nicholas Hunt/Getty

▲ Actor Michael J. Fox provides his time and celebrity status to efforts to cure Parkinson's disease, a degenerative disease that is severely affecting his life. Despite his worsening symptoms, Fox continues his advocacy efforts. More detail on his struggles with Parkinson's disease can be found in his autobiography, described in this chapter's From the Inside box.

clumsy, to show repetitive movements, such as tremors and leg weakness, and to become apathetic and socially withdrawn (Navia, 1990).

People with HIV seem particularly susceptible to cognitive impairments in the later stages of HIV infection, although significant impairment of cognitive abilities may occur earlier (Heaton et al., 1994). Cognitive impairments are observed in 29 to 87 percent of people with AIDS (Lipton & Weiner, 2003), and approximately one-third of the infected people ultimately meet the criteria for neurocognitive disorder resulting from HIV disease (Day et al., 1992; Price & Brew, 1988). HIV-1 accounts for a relatively small percentage of people with neurocognitive disorder compared with Alzheimer's disease and vascular causes, but its presence complicates an already devastating and ultimately fatal set of conditions.

Like neurocognitive disorder from Parkinson's disease and several other causes, neurocognitive disorder resulting from HIV is sometimes referred to as subcortical dementia, because it affects primarily the inner areas of the brain, below the outer layer called the *cortex* (Clifford & Ances, 2013). The distinction between "cortical" (including neurocognitive disorder due to Alzheimer's disease) and "subcortical" dementia is important because of the different expressions of neurocognitive disorder in these two categories. Aphasia, which involves impaired language skills, occurs among people with neurocognitive disorder due to Alzheimer's disease but not among people with subcortical dementia. In contrast, people with subcortical dementia are more likely to experience severe depression and anxiety than those with neurocognitive disorder due to Alzheimer's disease. The differing patterns of impairment can be attributed to the different areas of the brain affected by the disorders causing the neurocognitive disorder.

Huntington's disease is a genetic disorder that initially affects motor movements, typically in the form of *chorea*,

---

FROM THE INSIDE

Lucky Man: A Memoir
by Michael J. Fox

From Lucky Man: A Memoir by Michael J. Fox, copyright © 2002. Reprinted by permission of Hachette Books, an imprint of Hachette Book Group, Inc.

In 1998, during an interview with Barbara Walters, Canadian actor Michael J. Fox first revealed to the public that he had been diagnosed with Parkinson's disease (PD) seven years earlier. Although Fox initially attempted to hide the symptoms of his illness from his co-workers and fans, he is now using his celebrity status to give hope to those with the illness and to attempt to find a cure. *Lucky Man* is his autobiography in which he courageously shares with his readers many of the problems he has faced—problems that many PD patients face. He describes not only the

debilitating physical effects of the disease but also the sense of mourning he experienced on the discovery of his illness. The book is an engaging read as is illustrated by the following excerpts:

I need to explain the "on-off" phenomenon. This Jekyll-and-Hyde melodrama is a constant vexation for the PD patient, especially one as determined as I was to remain closeted. "On" refers to the time when the medication is telling my brain everything it wants to hear. I'm relatively loose and fluid, my mind clear and movements under control. Only a trained observer could detect my Parkinson's. . . . When I'm "off," the disease has complete authority over my physical being. I'm utterly in its possession. Sometimes there are flashes of function, and I can be effective at performing basic physical tasks, certainly feeding and dressing myself (though I'll lean toward loafers and pullover sweaters), as well as any chore calling for more brute force involuntary limb movements (Pringsheim et al., 2012). People with Huntington's can live for 20 years after the first signs of the disease appear, although nursing care is often required during the last stages. Just as with Parkinson's disease, only a portion of persons with Huntington's disease go on to display cognitive deficits—43 percent of new Huntington's disorder cases also present with *mild* cognitive impairment (Robbins & Cools, 2014). Estimates of how many individuals go on to develop neurocognitive disorders vary widely from 20 to 80 percent—although some researchers believe that all Huntington's patients would eventually display neurocognitive disorder if they lived long enough (Marsh & Margolis, 2009). **Neurocognitive disorder due to Huntington's disease** also follows the subcortical pattern.

The search for the gene responsible for Huntington's disease reads like a detective story. For some time, researchers have known that the disease is inherited as an autosomal dominant disorder, meaning that approximately 50 percent of the offspring of an adult with Huntington's will develop the disease. Since 1979, behavioural scientist Nancy Wexler and a team of researchers have been studying the largest known extended family in the world with Huntington's disease, in small villages in Venezuela. The villagers have cooperated with the research, partly because Wexler herself lost her mother, three uncles, and her maternal grandfather to Huntington's disease, and she, too, may develop the disorder (Wexler, 2012). Using genetic linkage analysis techniques, these researchers first mapped the deficit to an area on chromosome 4 (Gusella et al., 1983) and then identified the elusive gene (Huntington's Disease Collaborative Research Group, 1993). Finding that one gene causes a disease is unusual; research on other inherited mental disorders typically points to multiple gene (polygenic) influences.

Neurocognitive disorder due to prion disease is a rare progressive neurodegenerative disorder caused by *prions*—proteins that can reproduce themselves and cause damage to brain cells leading to neurocognitive decline (Collinge, 2012). Unlike other infectious agents, such as bacteria or viruses, prions are thought by some to have no DNA or RNA that can be destroyed by chemicals or radiation. As a result, there is no known treatment for prion disease, and this disorder is always fatal. On the positive side, prions

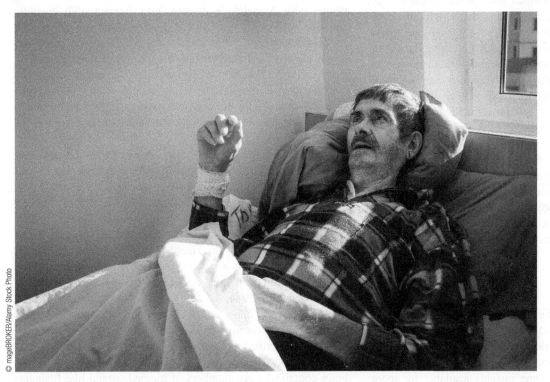

▲ The AIDS virus may cause neurocognitive disorder in the later stages.

are not contagious in humans and have only been contracted through cannibalism (causing *kuru*) or accidental inoculations (e.g., through blood transfusions from an infected person; Collinge, 2012). One type of prion disease, **Creutzfeldt-Jakob disease**, is believed to affect only one in every million individuals (Heath et al., 2010; Sikorska et al., 2012). An alarming development in the study of Creutzfeldt-Jacob disease is the finding of ten cases of a new variant that may be linked to bovine spongiform encephalopathy (BSE), more commonly referred to as "mad cow disease" (Ebringer, 2015; Neugroschi et al., 2005). This discovery led to a ban on exporting beef from the United Kingdom for a number of years, because the disease might be transmitted from infected cattle to humans. We have experienced similar problems in Canada. In May 2003, veterinary officials in Alberta identified a single sick cow. This announcement led the United States and Mexico to institute a ban on Canadian beef, which resulted in a severe slump in the Canadian beef industry ("Timeline of BSE," 2004); the U.S. ban continued for more than two years ("U.S. to Allow Import," 2007). We do not yet have definitive information about the link between mad cow disease and the new form of Creutzfeldt-Jacob disease.

SUBSTANCE/MEDICATION-INDUCED NEUROCOGNITIVE DISORDER

Prolonged drug use, especially in combination with poor diet, can damage the brain and, in some circumstances, can also lead to neurocognitive disorder. As many as 50 to 70 percent of chronic heavy alcohol users show cognitive impairment (Sico et al., 2014), and 7 percent of those with an alcohol use disorder also meet criteria for a neurocognitive disorder (Neugroschi et al., 2005). The long-term abuse of a number of drugs can lead to symptoms of neurocognitive disorder, including alcohol; inhalants, such as glue or gasoline (which some people inhale for the euphoric feeling they produce); and the sedative, hypnotic, and anxiolytic drugs (see Chapter 12). These drugs pose a threat because they create physiological dependence, making it difficult for a user to stop ingesting them. The resulting brain damage can be permanent and can cause the same symptoms seen in neurocognitive disorder due to Alzheimer's disease (Parsons & Nixon, 1993). The *DSM-5* criteria for **substance/medication-induced neurocognitive disorder** are essentially the same as many of the other forms of neurocognitive disorder; they include memory impairment and at least one of the following cognitive disturbances: aphasia (language disturbance), apraxia (inability to carry out motor activities despite intact motor function), agnosia (failure to recognize or identify objects despite intact sensory function), or a disturbance in executive functioning (such as planning, organizing, sequencing, and abstracting).

CAUSES

As our technology for studying the brain advances, so does our understanding of the many and varied causes of neurocognitive disorder. A complete description of what is known about the origins of this type of brain impairment is beyond the scope of this book, but we highlight some insights available for more common forms of this disorder.

Biological Influences

Cognitive abilities can be adversely compromised in many ways. As we have seen, neurocognitive disorder can be caused by a number of processes: Alzheimer's disease, Huntington's disease, Parkinson's disease, head trauma, substance abuse, and others. The most common cause of neurocognitive disorder, Alzheimer's disease, is also the most mysterious. Because of its prevalence and our relative ignorance about the factors responsible for it, Alzheimer's disease has held the attention of a great many researchers who are trying to find the cause and ultimately a treatment or cure for this devastating condition.

Findings from Alzheimer's research seem to appear almost daily. We should be cautious when interpreting the output of this fast-paced and competitive field; too often, as we have seen in other areas, findings are heralded prematurely as conclusive and important. Remember that "discoveries" of a single gene for bipolar disorder, schizophrenia, and alcoholism were later shown to be based on overly simplistic accounts. Similarly, findings from Alzheimer's research are sometimes too quickly sanctioned as accepted truths before they have been replicated by other researchers, an essential validation process.

One lesson in scientific caution comes from research that demonstrates a negative correlation between cigarette smoking and Alzheimer's disease (Brenner et al., 1993). In other words, the study found that smokers are less likely than nonsmokers to develop Alzheimer's disease. Does this mean smoking has a protective effect, shielding a person against the development of this disease? On close examination, the finding may instead be the result of the differential survival rates of those who smoke and those who do not. In general, nonsmokers tend to live longer and are thereby more likely to develop Alzheimer's disease, which appears later in life. Some believe the relative inability of cells to repair themselves, a factor that may be more pronounced among people with Alzheimer's disease, may interact with cigarette smoking to shorten the lives of smokers who are at risk for Alzheimer's (Riggs, 1993). Put another way, smoking may exacerbate the degenerative process of Alzheimer's disease, causing people with the disease who also smoke to die much earlier than nonsmokers who have Alzheimer's (Ashare et al., 2012). These types of studies and the conclusions drawn from them should make us sensitive to the complicated nature of the disorders we study.

Another theory about Alzheimer's disease that remains largely unsubstantiated is the aluminum hypothesis, which asserts that exposure to aluminum (e.g., through occupational exposure) is involved in causing Alzheimer's disease. However, many studies, such as the large-scale Canadian Study of Health and Aging, have failed to support a strong role of aluminum exposure as a risk factor (Canadian Study of Health and Aging Working Group, 1994). Most scientists now conclude that if aluminum exposure plays any role in Alzheimer's disease, the role is small (Alzheimer's Association, 2004).

What do we know about Alzheimer's disease, the most common cause of neurocognitive disorder? After the death of the patient he described as having a "strange disease of the cerebral cortex," Alois Alzheimer performed an autopsy. He found that the brain contained large numbers of tangled, strand-like filaments (referred to as *neurofibrillary tangles*). This type of damage occurs in everyone with Alzheimer's disease, although we do not know what causes it. A second type of degeneration results from gummy protein deposits—called *amyloid plaques* (also called *senile* or *neuritic plaques*)—that accumulate in the brains of people with this disorder. Amyloid plaques are also found in older adults who do not have symptoms of neurocognitive disorder, but they have far fewer of them than individuals with Alzheimer's disease (Richards & Sweet, 2009). Both forms of damage—neurofibrillary tangles and amyloid plaques—accumulate over the years and are believed to produce the characteristic cognitive disorders we have been describing (Weiner et al., 2012a).

These two types of degeneration affect extremely small areas and can be detected only by a microscopic examination of the brain. Even sophisticated brain-scan techniques are not yet powerful enough to observe these changes in the living brain, which is why a definitive diagnosis of Alzheimer's disease requires an autopsy (Weiner et al., 2010). In addition to having neurofibrillary tangles and amyloid plaques, over time the brains of many people with Alzheimer's disease atrophy (shrink) to a greater extent than would be expected through normal aging (Lovestone, 2012). Because brain shrinkage has many causes, however, only by observing the tangles and plaques can a diagnosis of Alzheimer's disease be properly made.

Rapid advances are being made toward uncovering the genetic bases of Alzheimer's disease (e.g., Seshadri et al., 2010). Because important discoveries happen almost daily, we cannot speak conclusively; however, certain overall themes have arisen from genetic research. As with most of the other behavioural disorders we have examined, multiple genes seem to be involved in the development of Alzheimer's disease. Table 16.1 illustrates what we know so far. Genes on chromosomes 21, 19, 14, 12, and 1 have all been linked to certain forms of Alzheimer's disease (Devi et al., 2000; Marx, 1998; Rogaeva et al., 2001). The link to chromosome 21 was discovered first and resulted from the unfortunate observation that individuals with Down syndrome, who

TABLE 16.1 | Examples of Genetic Factors in Alzheimer's Disease

Gene	Chromosome	Age of Onset (years)
APP	21	43 to 59
Presenilin 1	14	33 to 60
Presenilin 2	1	50 to 90
apo E4	19	60

APP = amyloid precursor protein; *apo E4* = *apolipoprotein E4*.
Source: From "Dementia: Alzheimer's Disease," by S. Lovestone, in M. G. Gelder, N. C. Andreasen, J. J. Lopez Jr., and J. R. Geddes (Eds.), *New Oxford Textbook of Psychiatry* (2nd ed., Vol. 1, pp. 333–343), 2012, Oxford University Press.

© Cengage Learning

have three copies of chromosome 21 instead of the usual two, developed the disease at an unusually high rate (Report of the Advisory Panel on Alzheimer's Disease, 1995). More recent work has located relevant genes on other chromosomes. These discoveries indicate that there is more than one genetic cause of Alzheimer's disease. Some forms, including the one associated with chromosome 14, have an early onset. A team of researchers at the University of Toronto headed by geneticist and neurologist Peter St. George-Hyslop were the first to uncover gene mutations on chromosome 14 in the early-onset familial form of Alzheimer's disease (Jeffrey, 1995; Sherrington et al., 1995). Pat Summitt was diagnosed with an early-onset form. In contrast, Alzheimer's disease associated with chromosome 19 seems to be a late-onset form of the disease that has an effect only after about age 60.

Some genes that are now identified are **deterministic**, meaning that if you have one of these genes you have a nearly 100 percent chance of developing Alzheimer's disease (Bettens et al., 2010). Deterministic genes such as the precursor gene for small proteins called *amyloid beta peptides* (also referred to as beta-amyloid or Aβ) and the *Presenilin 1* and *Presenilin 2* genes will inevitably lead to Alzheimer's disease, but, fortunately, these genes are also rare in the general population. For treatment purposes, this means that even if researchers can find a way to prevent these genes from leading to Alzheimer's disease, it will only help a relatively small number of people. On the other hand, some genes—including the *apolipoprotein E4* (*apo E4*) gene—are known as **susceptibility** genes. These genes only slightly increase the risk of developing Alzheimer's disease, but in contrast to the deterministic genes, these are more common in the general population (Lovestone, 2012). If future research can find ways to interfere with the *apo E4* gene, many people will be helped.

Although closing in on the genetic origins of Alzheimer's disease has not brought immediate treatment implications, researchers are nearer to understanding how the disease

Ron Scherl/Redferns/Getty Images

▲ Maureen Forrester, a famous Canadian opera singer who died in 2010, suffered from a neurocognitive disorder brought on by prolonged alcohol abuse.

develops, which may result in medical interventions. Genetic research has advanced our knowledge of how the amyloid plaques develop in the brains of people with Alzheimer's disease and may hold a clue to its origins. In the core of the plaques is a solid waxy substance made up of A peptide called amyloid beta or Aβ. Just as cholesterol buildup on the walls of blood vessels chokes the blood supply, deposits of Aβ are believed by some researchers to cause the cell death associated with Alzheimer's disease (Lovestone, 2012). An important question, then, is: Why does this protein accumulate in the brain cells of some people but not of others?

Two mechanisms that may account for amyloid protein buildup are being studied. The first involves *amyloid precursor protein* (APP), a large protein that is eventually broken down into the *amyloid protein* found in the amyloid plaques. Important work resulted in identifying the gene responsible for producing APP, on chromosome 21 (Lovestone, 2012). This finding may help integrate two observations about Alzheimer's disease: (1) APP produces the amyloid protein found in the amyloid plaques, and (2) Down syndrome, associated with an extra 21st chromosome, results in a higher incidence of the disease (see Chapter 15). The gene responsible for producing APP and, ultimately, amyloid protein, may be responsible for the relatively infrequent early-onset form of the disease, and its location could explain why people with Down syndrome—who have an extra 21st chromosome and therefore an extra APP gene—are more likely than the general population to develop Alzheimer's disease.

A second, more indirect way that amyloid protein may build up in brain cells is through apolipoprotein E (apo E), which normally helps transport cholesterols, including amyloid protein, through the bloodstream. There are at least three forms of this transporter protein: apo E2, apo E3, and apo E4. Individuals who have late-onset Alzheimer's disease, the most common form, are likely to carry the gene associated with apo E4, located on chromosome 19. The majority of people with Alzheimer's disease who also have a family history of the disease will have at least one gene for apo E4 (Lovestone, 2012). In contrast, approximately 64 percent of individuals with Alzheimer's disease who have no family history of the disease have at least one gene for apo E4, and only 31 percent of nonaffected individuals have the gene. Having two genes for apo E4 (one on each member of the chromosome 19 pair) increases the risk for Alzheimer's disease: As many as 90 percent of people with two genes developed Alzheimer's disease (Reiman et al., 2007). In addition, having two apo E4 genes seemed to decrease the mean age of onset from 84 years to 68 years. These results suggest that apo E4 may be responsible for late-onset Alzheimer's disease and that a gene on chromosome 19 is responsible.

What is still not completely understood is how apo E4 causes amyloid proteins to build up in the neurons of people who ultimately exhibit Alzheimer's disease and whether this process is responsible for the disease. One study examined the role of high blood pressure in creating amyloid proteins when interacting with *apo E4* genotype in healthy adults. The study found that hypertension alone or apo E4 alone did not increase amyloid deposits. However, healthy individuals with at least one *apo E4* gene and untreated high blood pressure had the greatest risk for amyloid protein deposits. And the higher the blood pressure, the more

amyloid protein deposits were found. On the other hand, those with high blood pressure under medical control had only slightly higher levels of amyloid deposits than people without it (Rodrigue et al., 2013).

Researchers are also examining potential gene–environment interactions in development of Alzheimer's disease. Several studies suggest a few areas of promise. One study found that having the apo E4 genotype was more likely to produce cognitive decline in those persons living in stressful environments—suggesting a gene (*apo E4*)–environment (stress) interaction (Boardman et al., 2012). Another study found that among those of African descent, having low levels of cholesterol seemed to reduce the risk of Alzheimer's disease, but only among those who did not carry the *apo E4* gene (Evans et al., 2000). Finally, physical exercise may reduce the likelihood of developing the disease but, like the previous study, only among those without the *apo E4* gene (Podewils et al., 2005). This type of research holds the potential for better understanding the complex nature of Alzheimer's disease and may lead to important prevention strategies (such as lowering cholesterol levels and exercising regularly; Pedersen, 2010).

For all disorders described in this book, we have identified the role of biological, psychological, or both types of stressors as partially responsible for the onset of the disorder. Does neurocognitive disorder due to Alzheimer's disease—which appears to be a strictly biological event—follow the same pattern? One of the leading candidates for an external contributor to this disorder is head trauma. As we have seen, it appears that repeated blows to the head can bring on *neurocognitive disorder (chronic traumatic encephalopathy or CTE)*. Fighters who carry the *apo E4* gene may be at greater risk for developing *neurocognitive disorder* attributed to head trauma (Jordan et al., 1997). In addition to boxers, the trauma experienced by football players may lead to the development of CTE (Stamm et al., 2015). Head trauma may be one of the stressors that initiates the onset of neurocognitive disorder of varying types. Other such stressors include having diabetes, high blood pressure, or herpes simplex virus-1 (Richards & Sweet, 2009). As with each of the disorders discussed, psychological and biological stressors may interact with physiological processes to produce Alzheimer's disease.

Psychological and Social Influences

For the most part, research has focused on the biological conditions that produce neurocognitive disorder. Although few would claim that psychosocial influences directly cause the type of brain deterioration seen in people with neurocognitive disorder, they may help determine onset and course. For example, a person's lifestyle may involve contact with factors that can cause neurocognitive disorder. We saw, for instance, that substance abuse can lead to neurocognitive disorder and, as we discussed previously (see Chapter 12), whether a person abuses drugs is determined by a combination of biological and psychosocial factors. In the case of vascular neurocognitive disorder, a person's biological vulnerability to vascular disease will influence the chances of strokes that can lead to this form of disorder. Lifestyle issues, such as diet, exercise, and stress, influence cardiovascular disease, and therefore help determine who ultimately experiences vascular neurocognitive disorder.

Cultural factors may also affect this process. For example, hypertension and strokes are more prevalent among some groups of people with African or Asian heritage (Howard et al., 2013; King et al., 2007), compared with non-hispanic whites. This may explain why vascular neurocognitive disorder is also more often observed in members of these groups. In an extreme example, exposure to prion disease can lead to neurocognitive disorder described previously as *kuru*. Prions can be passed on through a ritual form of cannibalism practised in Papua New Guinea as a part of mourning (Collinge et al., 2006, 2008). In yet another example of how cultural factors may play a role, neurocognitive disorder caused by head trauma and malnutrition are relatively prevalent in preindustrial rural societies (Del Parigi et al., 2006), which suggests that social engineering in the form of occupational safety and economic conditions influencing diet also affect the prevalence of certain forms of neurocognitive disorders. It is apparent that psychosocial factors help influence who does and who does not develop certain forms of neurocognitive disorder. Brain deterioration is a biological process but, as we have seen throughout this text, even biological processes are influenced by psychosocial factors.

Psychosocial factors also influence the course of neurocognitive disorder. Recall that educational attainment may affect the onset of dementia (Amieva et al., 2014). Having certain skills may help some people cope better than others with the early stages of neurocognitive disorder. The early stages of confusion and memory loss may be better tolerated in cultures with lowered expectations of older adults. In certain cultures, including the Chinese, younger people are expected to take the demands of work and care from older adults after a certain age, and symptoms of neurocognitive disorder are viewed as a sign of normal aging (Hinton et al., 2000; Sun, Ong, & Burnette, 2012). Neurocognitive disorder may go undetected for years in these societies (Sosa-Ortiz et al., 2012).

Much remains to be learned about the cause and course of most types of neurocognitive disorder. As we saw in Alzheimer's and Huntington's disease, certain genetic factors make some individuals vulnerable to progressive cognitive deterioration. In addition, brain trauma, some diseases, and exposure to certain drugs, such as alcohol, inhalants, and sedative, hypnotic, and anxiolytic drugs can cause the characteristic decline in cognitive abilities. We also noticed that psychosocial factors can help determine who is subject to these causes and how they cope with the condition. Looking at neurocognitive disorder from this integrative perspective should help us view treatment approaches in a more optimistic light. It may be possible to protect people from conditions that lead to neurocognitive disorder and to support them in dealing with the devastating consequences of having it. We next review attempts to help from both biological and psychosocial perspectives.

TREATMENT

For many of the disorders we have considered in this book, treatment prospects are fairly good. Clinicians can combine various strategies to reduce suffering significantly. Even when treatment does not bring expected improvements, mental health professionals have usually been able to stop problems from progressing. This is not the case in the treatment of neurocognitive disorder.

One factor preventing major advances in the treatment of neurocognitive disorder is the nature of the damage caused by this disorder. The brain contains billions of neurons, many more than are used. Damage to some can be compensated for by others, due to plasticity. There is a limit to where and how many neurons can be destroyed, however, before vital functioning is disrupted. Researchers are closing in on how to use the brain's natural process of regeneration to potentially reverse the damage caused in neurocognitive disorder (e.g., Wright et al., 2015). Currently, however, with extensive brain damage, no known treatment can restore lost abilities. The goals of treatment therefore become (1) trying to prevent certain conditions, such as substance abuse or strokes, that may bring on neurocognitive disorder; (2) trying to delay the onset of symptoms to provide better quality of life; and (3) attempting to help individuals and their caregivers cope with the advancing deterioration. Most efforts in treating neurocognitive disorder have focused on the second and third goals, with biological treatments aimed at stopping the cerebral deterioration and psychosocial treatments directed at helping patients and caregivers cope.

A troubling fact further clouds the tragic circumstances of neurocognitive disorder: many of the caregivers of people with neurocognitive disorder—usually relatives—eventually become clinically depressed (Joling et al., 2015; Public Health Agency of Canada, 2019). Compared with the general public, these caregivers

▲ The film *Away from Her* (2006) is a beautiful and moving love story about a couple dealing with the wife's cognitive decline as she becomes increasingly debilitated by Alzheimer's disease. Directed by Sarah Polley, and starring Gordon Pinsent and Julie Christie, the film is a screenplay adaptation of celebrated author Alice Munro's 1999 short story "The Bear Came over the Mountain."

Collection Christophel/Alamy Stock Photo

Major and Mild Neurocognitive Disorders   **505**

are twice as likely to develop depression (Canadian Study of Health and Aging Working Group, 1994; O'Rourke et al., 2003), and they use more psychotropic medications and report stress symptoms at three times the normal rate (George, 1984). Caring for people with neurocognitive disorder, especially in its later stages, is a trying experience (O'Rourke & Cappeliez, 2002). The stress experienced by such caregivers is illustrated in the film *Away from Her* (Polley, 2006)—a film that depicts the decline of Fiona (played by Julie Christie) as her cognitive abilities become increasingly compromised by Alzheimer's disease. The film is particularly compelling in its depiction of the caregiver burden experienced by her loving husband Grant (played by Gordon Pinsent) and the couple's ultimate decision to place Fiona in a nursing home specializing in neurocognitive disorder, to relieve Grant of the burden of caring for her on his own. Clinicians are becoming increasingly sensitive to the needs of caregivers, and research is now exploring interventions that are easy to disseminate (such as over the Internet) to assist them in caring for people with neurocognitive disorder. Preliminary results from such interventions are promising and have important implications for the caregivers of the baby-boomer generation (Blom et al., 2013).

Another difficult issue is access to treatment and support. Remote communities, including many Indigenous communities, do not have access to diagnostic and care services. Many families do not have the resources to care for or support someone with a neurocognitive disorder, including accessing health care services. Health care providers may not have the cultural competence to care for minority and Indigenous people dealing with neurocognitive issues. All these challenges add to the already daunting task of coping with neurocognitive disorders and are recognized in the Canadian national dementia strategy (Public Health Agency of Canada, 2019).

Biological Treatments

Neurocognitive disorder due to known infectious diseases, nutritional deficiencies, and depression can be treated if it is caught early. Unfortunately, however, no known treatment exists for most of the different types of neurocognitive disorder that account for the vast majority of cases. Neurocognitive disorder due to stroke, Parkinson's disease, and Huntington's disease is not currently treatable because we have no effective treatment for the primary disorder. However, new research in several related areas has brought us closer to helping individuals with these forms of neurocognitive disorder. Substances that may help preserve and perhaps restore neurons—called *glial cell-derived neurotrophic factor*, or GDNF—may someday be used to help reduce or reverse the progression of degenerative brain diseases (Lu et al., 2013). Researchers are also looking into the possible benefits of transplanting stem cells (from fetal brain tissue) into the brains of people with such diseases. Initial results from these studies appear promising (Pen & Jensen, 2016). Neurocognitive disorder

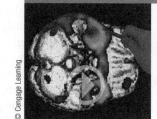

brought on by strokes may now be more preventable by new drugs that help prevent much of the damage inflicted by the blood clots characteristic of stroke (Erkinjuntti, 2012). Most current attention is on a treatment for neurocognitive disorder due to Alzheimer's disease, because it affects so many people. Here, too, however, success has been modest at best.

Much work has been directed at developing drugs that will enhance the cognitive abilities of people with neurocognitive disorder due to Alzheimer's disease. Many seem to be effective initially, but long-term improvements have not been observed in placebo-controlled studies (Richards & Sweet, 2009). Several drugs (called *cholinesterase inhibitors*) have had a modest impact on cognitive abilities in some patients and include donepezil (Aricept), rivastigmine (Exelon), and galantamine (Reminyl; Trinh et al., 2003). *Tacrine hydrochloride* (Cognex), another in this family of drugs, is rarely used today because of the potential for liver damage (Rabins, 2006). These drugs prevent the breakdown of the neurotransmitter acetylcholine (which is deficient in people with Alzheimer's disease), thus making more acetylcholine available to the brain. Research suggests that, when using these drugs, people's cognitive abilities improve to the point where they were six months earlier (Kimchi & Lyketos, 2015). But the gain is not permanent. Even people who respond positively do not stabilize but continue to experience the cognitive decline associated with Alzheimer's disease. In addition, if they stop taking the drug—as almost three-quarters of the patients do because of negative side effects such as liver damage and nausea—they lose even that six-month gain (Kimchi & Lyketos, 2015). Newer drugs are now being investigated for the treatment of Alzheimer's disease. These include drugs that target the beta-amyloid (plaques) in the brain, and it is hoped that these advances will finally provide a positive prognosis for this devastating disease (Lukiw, 2012; McClam et al., 2015).

Several other medical approaches are being explored to slow the course of Alzheimer's disease, but initial excitement generated by these approaches tends to wane over time. For example, you have probably heard of using *Ginkgo biloba* (maidenhair) to improve memory. Initial research suggested that this herbal remedy may produce modest improvements in the memory of people with Alzheimer's disease, but other studies have not replicated this benefit (Vellas et al., 2012). Similarly, the effects of vitamin E have been evaluated. A few large studies have found that among individuals with moderately severe impairment, high doses of the vitamin (2000 international units per day) delayed progression compared with a placebo (Dysken et al., 2014; Sano et al., 1997), but it did not prevent the development of the disease. Further research, in fact, indicates that taking high doses of vitamin E may actually increase mortality and therefore this intervention is no longer recommended (Richards & Sweet, 2009). Modest slowing of the progression of the disease also may be obtained by introducing exercise to patients (Paillard et al., 2015). To date, however, no medical interventions are available that directly treat and therefore stop the progression of the conditions that cause the cerebral damage in Alzheimer's disease.

Medical interventions for neurocognitive disorder also include the use of drugs to help with some associated symptoms. A variety of antidepressants—such as serotonin-specific reuptake inhibitors—are commonly recommended to alleviate the depression and anxiety that too often accompany the cognitive decline. Antipsychotic medication is sometimes used for those who become unusually agitated (Richards & Sweet, 2009).

Other researchers are targeting vaccines that would potentially treat and prevent—rather than just delay—the symptoms of Alzheimer's disease. Much of the research is attempting to get the immune system to attack the process that overproduces the small proteins (Aβ) that lead to cell death. Prior efforts had to be abandoned because of the severe negative side effects of the vaccine, which included serious brain inflammation. More recent research with humans and animals indicates that there may be several vaccines that could be effective in preventing the damage caused by Aβ formation and therefore represent the first glimmer of hope for patients and their families (Davtyan et al., 2013).

This type of research currently begins with transgenic mice— mice in which the DNA has been altered. In the case of testing an Alzheimer's vaccine, the mice DNA is engineered to produce the same small proteins thought to be responsible for the neurocognitive disorder. Mice are good subjects because they age rapidly, with a 22-month-old mouse equivalent to a 65-year-old human (Davtyan et al., 2013; Morgan, 2007). This allows researchers to study how the brain reacts to the potential vaccine if it has already started the progression of Alzheimer's. If the results are promising in these transgenic mice, only then do researchers try small studies with humans. Researchers are optimistic that there may finally be intervention approaches that would reverse the current trend of increasing numbers of people with neurocognitive disorder. Next, we describe psychosocial approaches that are used with medication to address the variety of problems that accompany memory difficulties.

Psychosocial Treatments

Psychosocial treatments are now receiving a great deal of attention for their ability to delay the onset of severe cognitive decline. These efforts focus on enhancing the lives of people with dementia, as well as those of their families.

People with neurocognitive disorder can be taught skills to compensate for their lost abilities. Some researchers have evaluated more formal

adaptations to help people in the early stages of dementia. Michelle Bourgeois (2007) created "memory wallets" to help people with Alzheimer's disease carry on conversations. On white index cards inserted into a plastic wallet are printed declarative statements, such as "My husband, John, and I have three children," or "I was born on January 6, 1921, in Winnipeg." In one study, Bourgeois (1992) found that adults with neurocognitive disorder could, with minimal training, use this memory aid to improve their conversations with others. With advances in technology, such as tablet computers, that can be programmed to "speak" for the person, adaptations such as these help people communicate with others, help them remain aware of their surroundings, and can reduce the frustration that comes with the awareness of their own decline (Fried-Oken et al., 2012).

Cognitive stimulation—encouraging people with neurocognitive disorder to practise learning and memory skills—seems to be an effective method for delaying the onset of the more severe cognitive effects of this disorder (Aguirre et al., 2013; Woods et al., 2012). These activities include word games, tests of memory of famous and familiar faces, and practice with numbers (e.g., how much change you would receive from a purchase). These types of skill-building exercises can maintain cognitive activity and improve the quality of life in those patients when compared with controls (J. Choi & Twamley, 2013).

What impact do the medical and nonmedical treatments have on those with Alzheimer's disease? ■ Figure 16.4 illustrates how these interventions may delay the worst of the symptoms—essentially compressing the time when the person is most impaired (Becker et al., 2007). The red line illustrates the typical course of the disease, which results in three to five years of severe impairment before death. However, with the interventions we highlighted (illustrated by the purple line), people are able to live more fully for a longer period, despite the still-inevitable impairment and death. Families find this extra time with their loved ones to be

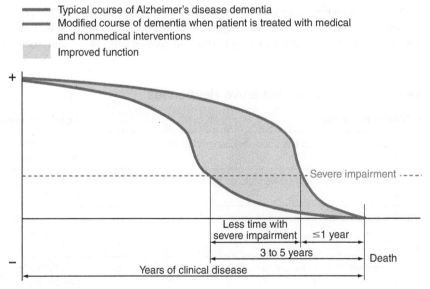

FIGURE 16.4 | Improving the course of Alzheimer's disease with medical and nonmedical interventions.

Source: From Becker, J. T., Mestre, L. T., Ziolko, S., & Lopez, O. L. [2007]. Gene–environment interactions with cognition in late life and compression of morbidity. *American Journal of Psychiatry, 164*, 849–852. Reprinted with permission from the American Journal of Psychiatry, (Copyright ©1997). American Psychiatric Association. All Rights Reserved.

invaluable, and hopefully with more advancements we will see progress on improving mortality rates of this progressive disease.

Individuals with advanced neurocognitive disorder are not able to feed, bathe, or dress themselves. They cannot communicate with or recognize even familiar family members. They may wander away from home and become lost. Because they are no longer aware of social stigma, they may engage in public displays of sexual behaviour. They may be frequently agitated or even physically violent. To help both the person with dementia and the caregiver, researchers have explored interventions for dealing with these consequences of the disorder (Lovestone, 2012). For example, some research indicates that a combination of exercise for patients and instruction for caregivers on how to handle behaviour problems can improve the overall health and the depression in people with Alzheimer's disease (Potter et al., 2011; Teri et al., 2003).

Of great concern is the tendency of people with neurocognitive disorder to wander. Sometimes they wind up in places or situations that may be dangerous (e.g., stairwells, the street). This tendency to wander was depicted in a scene in the film *Away from Her*, where the central character, Fiona, wanders away from her home, sending her caregiver husband, Grant, on a frantic search to find her (Polley, 2006). Often, the person with neurocognitive disorder is tied to a chair or bed, or sedated, to prevent roaming. Unfortunately, physical and medical restraints have their own risks, including additional medical complications; they also add greatly to the loss of control and independence that already plague the person with neurocognitive disorder. Psychological treatment as an alternative to restraint sometimes involves providing cues for people to help them safely navigate around their home or other areas. New innovations in surveillance technology—creating a "smart home" that can monitor the location of the patient and warn caregivers—may provide more peace of mind for those who care for these patients. At the same time, ethical concerns are being raised about the use of this technology because of its ability to invade privacy (Bharucha et al., 2009; Chung et al., 2016).

Someone with neurocognitive disorder can become agitated and is sometimes verbally and physically aggressive. This behaviour is understandably very stressful for people trying to provide care. In these situations, medical intervention is often used, although frequently with only modest results (Testad et al., 2010). Teaching communication skills in a manner similar to programs for persons with autism spectrum disorder (Durand, 2012) may help reduce aggressive behaviour in persons with neurocognitive disorder (Livingston et al., 2014). In addition, caregivers are often given assertiveness training to help them deal with hostile behaviours (see Table 16.2). Otherwise, caregivers may either passively accept all the criticism inflicted by the person with neurocognitive disorder, which increases stress, or become angry and aggressive in return.

This last response is of particular concern because of the potential for *elder abuse*. Withholding food or medication or inflicting physical abuse is most common among caregivers of older adults who have cognitive deficits (Post et al., 2010). Given the established role of caregiver stress in many such cases of elder abuse (Statistics Canada, 2004), it is important to teach caregivers how to handle stressful circumstances so they do not escalate into abusive situations. Little objective evidence supports the usefulness of assertiveness training for reducing caregiver stress, and we await research to guide future efforts.

In general, families of people with mild to moderate neurocognitive disorder can benefit from supportive counselling to help them cope with the frustration, depression, guilt, and loss that take a heavy emotional toll. Clinicians must first recognize, however, that the ability to adapt to stressors differs among people. One study, for example, found cultural differences in the coping styles of caregivers. In one area of rural Alabama, white caregivers used acceptance and humour as coping strategies, and black caregivers used religion and denial (Kosberg et al., 2007). Another large-scale study of 555 principal caregivers over three years identified a number of steps that can be taken to support caregivers through this difficult time (Aneshensel et al., 1995). Despite numerous studies aimed at supporting caregivers, however, the results remain weak and additional work is needed to determine how best to support these individuals (Schoenmakers et al., 2010; Tremont et al., 2015). A new and interesting concept is that of dementia-friendly communities, in which the physical and social environment is designed to support the needs and

TABLE 16.2 | Sample Assertive Responses

Patient Behaviour	Assertive Response
1. The patient refuses to eat, bathe, or change clothes.	Calmly but firmly say the following: "We agreed to do this at this time so that we will be able to (give specific activity or reward)."
2. The patient says she or he wants to go home.	"I know you miss some of the places we used to be. This is our home now and together we are safe and happy here."
3. The patient demands immediate gratification.	"It's not possible to have everything we want. As soon as I've finished (describe your task or actions), we can discuss other things we want to do."
4. The patient accuses the caregiver of taking his or her possessions.	"We both enjoy our own things. I'll help you look for (specific item missing) so you can enjoy it, just as soon as I have finished (describe specific task or action)."
5. The patient is angry or rebellious.	"I like to be treated fairly just as you do. Let's discuss what's bothering you so we can go back to our usual good relationship."

Source: Adapted from *When Memory Fails: Helping the Alzheimer's and Dementia Patient* (p. 174), by A. J. Edwards, 1994, Plenum Press. © 1994 Plenum Press.

© Cengage Learning

independence of people living with dementia, along with caregivers (Public Health Agency of Canada, 2019).

Early on, caregivers need basic information on the causes and treatment of neurocognitive disorder, as well as on financial and legal issues, and on locating help for the patient and the family. As the neurocognitive disorder progresses, and the affected person requires more and more assistance, caregivers will need help managing behavioural difficulties (wandering away, violent outbursts) and developing effective ways to communicate with the patient. Clinicians also assist the family with decisions about hospitalizations and, finally, help them adjust during bereavement. However, the best methods to help caregivers help others are still being explored (Peeters et al., 2010; Zabalegui et al., 2014).

Overall, the outlook for slowing (but not stopping) the cognitive decline characteristic of neurocognitive disorder is mildly optimistic. The best available medications provide some recovery of function, but they do not stop the progressive deterioration. Psychological interventions may help people cope more effectively with the loss of cognitive abilities, especially in the earlier stages of this disorder. In addition, emphasis is placed on helping caregivers—the other victims of neurocognitive disorder—as the person they care for continues to decline.

PREVENTION

Without treatment, we need to rely even more heavily on prevention strategies for neurocognitive disorder. You can imagine that it is difficult to study prevention efforts for neurocognitive disorder because of the need to follow individuals for long periods to see whether the efforts are effective. One major study conducted in Sweden looked at many of the risk factors (those factors that increase the chance of having neurocognitive disorder) and protective factors (those that decrease the risk) under study today (Fratiglioni & Qiu, 2009; Fratiglioni et al., 2007). They looked at the medical records of 1810 participants who were older than 75 at the time and followed them for about 13 years. Through interviews and medical histories, they came to three major conclusions: control your blood pressure, do not smoke, and lead an active physical and social life. These recommendations came out as the major factors that individuals can change—because you cannot change your genetic makeup, for example—that will decrease the chances of developing neurocognitive disorder (Rizzuto et al., 2012). Additional prevention research is ongoing, and there may be other potentially fruitful research areas that can lead to the successful prevention of this devastating disorder.

| DSM-5 CONTROVERSIES | Is Normal Aging a Mental Disorder? |

Researchers and clinicians have, for some time, recognized that many older adults begin to show cognitive decline in areas such as memory that is more pronounced than expected for their age and that begins to affect their daily functioning (Petersen et al., 1999). This interest in the distinction between the normal forgetting that occurs as we age and the onset of neurocognitive disorder is motivated by a desire both to understand the progression of the cognitive changes that accompany neurocognitive disorder and to attempt early intervention. In response to this concern, the DSM-5 introduced a new psychiatric disorder—mild neurocognitive disorder—to categorize the condition and bring it to the attention of clinicians (Ganguli et al., 2011).

This proposed distinction is consistent with some of the breakthroughs in diagnoses involving improved brain scanning and identification of biomarkers that we covered earlier in this chapter (Weiner et al., 2012). Researchers are becoming more sophisticated in their ability to identify beginning signs of neurocognitive disorder, which not only allows for early diagnosis but also can highlight for clinicians the need to track cognitive abilities over time. However, this new disorder has raised concerns among some in the field (Rabins & Lyketsos, 2011).

First, the distinction between "major" and "mild" neurocognitive disorder is a difficult one to make. The DSM-5 attempts to quantify the declines by tying the diagnosis to cognitive test performance in the range of one to two standard deviations below what would be expected for a person of that age (American Psychiatric Association, 2013). Below-average performance does not necessarily mean, however, that the person has declining cognitive function. That can be assessed only if performance was measured through cognitive assessment before the decline occurred. But, it has been argued, routine cognitive testing is not typically done on adults until after some concern is raised, making conclusions about changes in functioning problematic (Frances, 2010).

A second concern is one that is relevant for a number of other disorders as well. The addition of new disorders (such as mild neurocognitive disorder as well as others such as premenstrual mood dysphoric disorder) and the broadening of the definitions of others have some concerned that eventually most people will meet the criteria for one or more psychiatric disorders. In the case of mild neurocognitive disorder, will we be labelling people—and perhaps prescribing drugs—to those who exhibit normal forgetting related to age? As a whole, the consequences of these changes across the DSM-5 are not trivial (Frances, 2010). Pharmaceutical companies are incentivized to find more customers for psychiatric drugs and therefore expanding the number of people with a diagnosis could increase business. The legal system could be affected with a greater number of people using "mental illness" as a mitigating factor in their defence. These issues are far from being resolved, and it is important to note that DSM-5 is a work in progress that will hopefully evolve with our expanding scientific understanding of the nature and causes of all of the maladies affecting us.

Identify the cognitive disorders described.

1. Julian is a recovering alcoholic. When asked about his wild adventures as a young man, his stories usually end quickly because he can't remember the whole tale. He even has to write down things he has to do in a notebook; otherwise, he's likely to forget. _____

2. Mr. Brown has suffered from a number of strokes but can still care for himself. His ability to remember important things, however, has been declining steadily for the past few years. _____

3. A decline in cognitive functioning that is gradual and continuous and has been associated with neurofibrillary tangles and amyloid plaques. _____

SUMMARY

Perspectives

- Most neurocognitive disorders develop late in life and the incidence of disability rises with age.

- In the *DSM-5*, delirium and dementia and amnestic disorders, with major or minor subtypes, were given the umbrella label of *neurocognitive disorders* to signify that impairment of cognitive abilities, such as memory, attention, perception, and thinking, is the primary characteristic.

- Although neurocognitive disorders clearly have organic causes, the consequences of the disorders often include changes in a person's behaviour and personality; anxiety or depression is common, paranoia is frequently reported, as are extreme agitation and aggression, and families and friends are also affected by such changes. These are all concerns for mental health professionals.

Delirium

- Delirium is a temporary state of confusion and disorientation that can be caused by brain trauma, intoxication by drugs or poisons, surgery, and a variety of other stressful conditions, especially among older adults.

Major and Mild Neurocognitive Disorders

- Neurocognitive disorder is a progressive and degenerative condition marked by gradual deterioration of a broad range of cognitive abilities, including memory, language, and planning, organizing, sequencing, and abstracting information.

- Mild neurocognitive disorder is a condition in which there are early signs of cognitive decline such that it begins to interfere with the activities of daily living.

- Alzheimer's disease is the leading cause of neurocognitive disorder; there is currently no known cause or cure.

- To date, there is no effective treatment for the irreversible neurocognitive disorder caused by Alzheimer's disease, Lewy bodies, vascular disease, Parkinson's disease, Huntington's disease, and the various other less common conditions that produce this progressive cognitive impairment. Treatment often focuses on helping the patient cope with the continuing loss of cognitive skills and helping caregivers deal with the stress of caring for the affected individuals.

KEY TERMS

acquired immune deficiency syndrome (AIDS), 499
agnosia, 494
Alzheimer's disease, 496
aphasia, 496
Creutzfeldt-Jakob disease, 502
delirium, 490
dementia, 492
deterministic, 503
facial agnosia, 494

frontotemporal neurocognitive disorder, 499
human immunodeficiency virus-type-1, 499
Huntington's disease, 500
major neurocognitive disorder, 492
mild neurocognitive disorder, 492
neurocognitive disorder due to Alzheimer's disease, 496

neurocognitive disorder due to HIV infection, 499
neurocognitive disorder due to Huntington's disease, 501
neurocognitive disorder due to Lewy body disease, 499
neurocognitive disorder due to Parkinson's disease, 499
neurocognitive disorder due to prion disease, 501

neurocognitive disorder due to traumatic brain injury, 499
Parkinson's disease, 499
Pick's disease, 499
substance/medication-induced neurocognitive disorder, 502
susceptibility, 503
traumatic brain injury (TBI), 499
vascular neurocognitive disorder, 498

ANSWERS TO CONCEPT CHECKS

16.1

1. b; **2.** d; **3.** a; **4.** c

16.2

1. substance-induced neuro-cognitive disorder; **2.** vascular neurocognitive disorder; **3.** neurocognitive disorder due to Alzheimer's disease

MEDIA RESOURCES

CENGAGE | MINDTAP

Stay organized and efficient with MindTap—a single destination with all the course material and study aids you need to succeed. Built-in apps leverage social media and the latest learning technology. For example:

- ReadSpeaker will read the text to you.
- Flashcards are pre-populated to provide you with a jump start for review—or you can create your own.
- You can highlight text and make notes in your MindTap Reader. Your notes will flow into Evernote, the electronic notebook app that you can access anywhere when it's time to study for the exam.
- Self-quizzing allows you to assess your understanding.

Visit login.cengage.com to start using MindTap. Enter the Online Access Code from the card included with your text. If a code card is not provided, you can purchase instant access at Cengage.ca.

Exploring Neurocognitive Disorders

> When the brain is damaged, the effects are often irreversible, accumulating until learning, memory, or consciousness are obviously impaired.
> Neurocognitive disorders develop much later than intellectual disability and other learning disorders, which are believed to be present at birth.

		Description	Causes (subtypes)	Treatment
Delirium		• Impaired consciousness and cognition for several hours or days – confusion, disorientation, inability to focus • Most prevalent among older adults, people with AIDS, and patients on medication	• Due to a general medical condition • Due to medication • Substance-induced • Due to multiple etiologies	• Pharmacological – benzodiazepines – antipsychotics • Psychosocial – reassurance • presence of personal objects • inclusion in treatment decisions

Photodisc/Getty Images

Photodisc/Getty Images

© Cengage Learning

Major and Mild Neurocognitive Disorders

> Gradual deterioration of brain functioning that affects judgment, memory, language, and other advanced cognitive processes
> Caused by medical condition or drug abuse
> Some forms are irreversible; some are resolved by treatment of primary condition.

		Description	Causes	Treatment
Neurocognitive Disorder Due to Alzheimer's Disease	 Christian Martinez Kempin/E+/Getty Images	• Increasing memory impairment and other multiple behavioural and cognitive deficits, affecting language, motor functioning, ability to recognize people or things, and/or planning • Most prevalent neurocognitive disorder • Subject of most research	• Progressive brain damage, evident in neurofibrillary tangles and neuritic plaque, confirmed by autopsy but assessed by simplified mental status exam • Involves multiple genes	• No cure so far, but hope lies in genetic research and amyloid protein. • Management may include lists, maps, and notes to help maintain orientation. • New medications that prevent acetylcholine breakdown delay but do not stop progression of decline.
Substance-Induced Neurocognitive Disorder	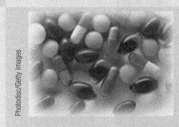 Photodisc/Getty Images	• Caused by brain damage due to prolonged drug use, especially in combination with poor diet, as in problematic alcohol use; other substances may include inhalants, and the sedative, hypnotic, and anxiolytic drugs • Treatment focuses on prevention.		
Vascular Neurocognitive Disorder	 Photodisc/Getty Images	• Permanent deterioration due to blocked or damaged blood vessels in the brain (stroke) • Symptoms include declines in speed of information processing and executive functioning (e.g., complex decision making) and may also include problems with walking and weakness of limbs. • Treatment focuses on coping.		
Neurocognitive Disorders Due to Other Medical Conditions	 Simon Fraser/Royal Victoria Infirmary, Newcastle upon Tyne/Science Source	• Similar in effect to other cognitive disorders, but caused by — head trauma — Lewy bodies, HIV, Parkinson's, Huntington's, Pick's, or Creutzfeldt-Jakob disease — hydrocephalus, hypothyroidism, brain tumour, and vitamin B12 deficiency • Treatment of primary condition is sometimes possible.		

17 | Mental Health and the Law

Wolfgang Lienbacher/Getty Images

Be kind, for everyone you meet is fighting a harder battle.

—PLATO

Describe applications that employ discipline-based problem solving:	⟩ Describe examples of relevant and practical applications of psychological principles to everyday life (APA SLO 1.3a)
	⟩ Articulate how psychological principles can be used to explain social issues, address pressing societal needs, and inform public policy (APA SLO 1.3A)

*Portions of this chapter cover learning outcomes suggested by the American Psychological Association (2013) in its guidelines for the undergraduate psychology major. Chapter coverage of these outcomes is identified above by APA Goal and APA Suggested Learning Outcome (SLO).

We begin this chapter with a return to Arthur, whom we described in Chapter 14 as having psychotic symptoms. Revisiting the case from his family's perspective reveals the complexities of mental health law and the ethical aspects of working with people who have psychological disorders.

ARTHUR | A Family's Dilemma

As you remember, Arthur's family members brought him to one of our clinics because he was speaking and acting strangely. He talked incessantly about his "secret plan" to save all the starving children in the world. His family's concern intensified when Arthur said he was planning to break into the German embassy and present his plan to the German ambassador. Alarmed by his increasingly inappropriate behaviour and fearing he would be hurt, the family was astounded to learn they could not force him into a psychiatric hospital. Arthur could admit himself—which was not likely, given his belief that nothing was wrong with him—but they had no power to admit him involuntarily unless he was in danger of doing harm to himself or others. The family coped with this emergency as best they could for several weeks until the worst of Arthur's behaviours began to diminish.

Arthur experienced what is known as brief psychotic disorder (see Chapter 14). Fortunately for him, this is one of the few psychotic disorders that are not chronic. What is important here is to see how the mental health system responded. Because Arthur had not hurt himself or someone else, he had to seek help on his own before the hospital would assist him, even though everyone involved realized that such action on his part was very unlikely. This response by the mental health system added one more layer of helplessness to the family's already desperate emotional state.

Why wouldn't the mental health facility admit Arthur, who was clearly out of touch with reality and in need of help? Why couldn't his family authorize the mental health facility to act? What would have happened if Arthur had entered the German embassy and hurt or, worse, killed someone? Would he have gone to jail, or would he have finally received help from the mental health community? Would Arthur have been held responsible if he hurt other people while he was delusional? These are just a few of the many issues that surface when we try to balance the rights of people who have psychological disorders with the responsibilities of society to provide care.

Mental health professionals face such questions daily. They must both diagnose and treat people and consider individual and societal rights and responsibilities. As we describe how systems of ethics and legal concepts have developed, remember that they change with time and with shifting societal and political perspectives on mental illness. How we treat people with psychological disorders is in part a function of how society views them. For example, do people with mental illness need help and protection, or does society need protection from them? As public opinion of people with mental illness changes, so do the laws affecting them, and legal and ethical issues have an effect on both research and practice. As you will see, the issues affecting research and practice are often complementary. For example, confidentiality (i.e., that no information will be released to a third party) is required to protect the identity of a participant in a research study and of a patient seeking help for a psychological disorder. Because people who receive mental health services often simultaneously participate in research studies, we must consider the concerns of both constituencies.

CIVIL COMMITMENT

The legal system exercises significant influence over the mental health system, for better or for worse. Laws have been designed to protect people who display abnormal behaviour and to protect society. Often, achieving this protection is a delicate balancing act, with the scales sometimes thought to be tipped in favour of the rights of individuals and at other times in favour of society as a whole. For example, each province and territory has **civil commitment laws** under the provincial or territorial Mental Health Acts that detail when a person can be legally detained in a psychiatric institution— even against his or her will. When Arthur's family tried to have him involuntarily committed to a mental health facility, hospital officials decided that because he was not in imminent danger of hurting himself or others, he could not be committed against his will. In this case, the laws of his provincial Mental Health Act protected Arthur from involuntary commitment, but they also put him and others at potential risk by not compelling him to get help. In civil commitment law, the rights of people are pitted against the responsibility of the government (in this case, the provinces and territories) to care for its citizens.

CRITERIA FOR CIVIL COMMITMENT

Although there is variability across provinces and territories, most provincial legislation permits commitment when the following three conditions have been met: (1) The person has a mental disorder, (2) the person is dangerous to himself or herself or others, and (3) the person is in need of treatment. All Canadian jurisdictions require the second of these three criteria and some, but not all, also require the first and third. Although every Canadian jurisdiction but Québec requires that a person have a mental illness before he or she can be detained under civil commitment legislation, the definition of mental illness differs across jurisdictions, as we will see in the next section of this chapter. Similarly, although every Canadian jurisdiction also requires that a person be a danger to himself or herself or others, or that the person needs to be hospitalized for his or her safety or protection or for the safety or protection of others, the provinces and territories vary considerably in how they define safety and protection.

For example, British Columbia defines these terms very broadly (i.e., the person requiring hospitalization to prevent his or her substantial mental or physical deterioration). Broad definitions, such as this, one can require a great deal of judgment from the court and from mental health professionals. In contrast, Ontario defines these terms much more strictly (i.e., requiring that the person's mental disorder will likely result in serious bodily harm or imminent and serious physical impairment to him or her or to another person). With these differences across jurisdictions in how strictly dangerousness is defined, you can see how it would have been easier for Arthur to have been committed under the legislation in British Columbia than under the legislation in Ontario. Some have argued that less strict definitions of dangerousness are actually in the patient's best interest. For example, John Gray and Richard O'Reilly of the British Columbia Ministry of Health and the University of Western Ontario, respectively, argue that if a patient cannot be legally admitted until he or she has demonstrated dangerousness, not only will the patient's prognosis be worse for the lost treatment time, but the patient will also likely have legal issues to deal with because he or she has broken the law (Gray & O'Reilly, 2001). But others, such as the Québec patient advocacy group Action Autonomie, have argued that less strict definitions of dangerousness can result in decisions that compromise a patient's autonomy. For example, such a definition of dangerousness could result in a psychiatrist deciding to detain a schizophrenic patient because he refuses to take his medications. This could happen if the psychiatrist feels the medication noncompliance could result in the patient directing traffic, for example, thus putting the patient and others in danger—even when the patient is not actively dangerous to others in the sense of wanting to hurt someone (Bratulic, 2007).

The Canadian jurisdictions also differ on several other issues pertaining to civil commitment, such as whether the patient has the right to refuse treatment, the right to be informed of the reasons for the hospital detention, the right to apply to a review panel that can grant a discharge from the hospital, and the specified right to legal counsel. These safeguards are built into the civil commitment process to guarantee the rights of the person being examined and to ensure that no one is involuntarily committed to a psychiatric facility for other than legitimate reasons.

The legislations relevant to civil commitment across Canada also vary in terms of how long a person can be detained.

How the conditions for civil commitment are interpreted has varied over the years and has always been controversial. Two types of authority permit the government to take actions that are against a citizen's will: police power and *parens patriae* ("state as the parent") power. Under police power, the government takes responsibility for protecting the public health, safety, and welfare and can create laws and regulations to ensure this protection. Criminal offenders are held in custody if they are a threat to society. This first rationale for civil commitment has a long history under Canadian law. Even as Europeans were settling Canada, people with mental illnesses could be detained to prevent them from harming others. The provinces and territories apply the second rationale for civil commitment—*parens patriae* power—in circumstances in which citizens are not likely to act in their own best interest. For example, it is used to commit individuals with severe mental illness to mental health facilities when it is believed that they might be harmed because they are unable to secure the basic necessities of life, such as food and shelter, or because they do not recognize their need for treatment (Perlin, 2000).

Under *parens patriae* power, the government acts as a surrogate parent, presumably in the best interests of a person who needs help.

▲ The government can exert *parens patriae* to protect people from hurting themselves.

▲ People with mental illness are treated differently in different cultures.

"disease or disability of the mind" (Douglas & Koch, 2001, p. 355).

Mental illness is *not* synonymous with psychological disorder; in other words, receiving a *DSM-5* diagnosis does not necessarily mean that a person fits the legal definition of someone having a mental illness. Although the *DSM* is quite specific about criteria that must be met for diagnosis, considerable ambiguity exists about what constitutes a "disease or disability of the mind" and what are "adverse effects on a person's ability to function" as required in a functional definition of mental illness. This ambiguity allows for flexibility in making decisions about individual cases, but it also creates the possibility of subjective impression and bias influencing these decisions.

A person in need of help can always voluntarily request admission to a mental health facility; after an evaluation by a mental health professional, he or she may be accepted for treatment. When an individual does not voluntarily seek help, but others feel that treatment or protection is necessary, however, the process of civil commitment may be initiated. The specifics of this process differ across jurisdictions, but typically one or two physicians or psychiatrists must conduct an assessment and agree that the person meets the criteria for commitment outlined in the relevant jurisdiction's legislation.

In Canada, people deemed suitable for commitment are not necessarily committed to a hospital. Instead, there are also options for compulsory community treatments (CCT) for the mentally ill. CCT's main goals are to prevent relapse and to provide care in a less restrictive environment. Unlike Australia, where CCT is allowed as a first form of treatment, CCT is not permitted in Canada until there has already been previous inpatient treatment. In Canadian jurisdictions, the patient must satisfy one of two necessary criteria for CCT: the patient must have some risk of increased mental deterioration or possibly pose harm to himself or herself or others (Gray & O'Reilly, 2005).

DEFINING MENTAL ILLNESS

The concept of mental illness figures prominently in civil commitment, and it is important to understand how it is defined. In this context, **mental illness** is a legal concept, typically meaning severe emotional or thought disturbances that negatively affect an individual's health and safety. As we mentioned earlier, each Canadian jurisdiction has its own definition. For example, in Saskatchewan, mental illness means "a disorder of thought, perceptions, feelings or behaviour that seriously impairs a person's judgement, capacity to recognize reality, ability to associate with others, or ability to meet the ordinary demands of life, in respect of which treatment is advisable" (Douglas & Koch, 2001, p. 355). Robertson (1994) refers to this type of definition of mental illness as a functional definition, because it specifies the effect of the illness on the patient's thoughts and behaviour. In contrast, some other provinces, like Ontario, do not use a functional definition of mental illness; they instead define mental disorder more traditionally as a

DANGEROUSNESS

Assessing whether someone is a danger to himself, herself, or others is a critical determinant of the civil commitment process. **Dangerousness** is a particularly controversial concept for people with mental illnesses: according to popular opinion, people who have a mental illness are more dangerous than those who do not (Kobau et al., 2010; Schomerus et al., 2012). The belief is still widespread, in part because of sensational media reports. Such views are important to the process of civil commitment if they bias a determination of dangerousness and unfairly link it with severe mental illness.

The results of research on dangerousness and mental illness are often mixed, but evidence points to a small increased rate of violence among people with mental illness (Elbogen & Johnson, 2009; Elbogen et al., 2016). Closer examination of this kind of research reveals that although having a serious mental illness (e.g., schizophrenia, depression) generally does increase the likelihood of future violence, specific factors such as a high anger predisposition, recent stressors (e.g., victimization) and especially substance use are likely responsible for the increased risk of violence (Elbogen et al., 2016; Fazel et al., 2015; Tiihonen et al., 1997). It is also the presence of these risk factors that may predict the reoccurrence of violent crimes by individuals with mental illness. Among incarcerated individuals, inmates with serious mental illnesses like schizophrenia are less likely to commit a new violent offence on release than inmates without serious mental illnesses (reviewed in Harris et al., 2015).

How do you determine whether a person is dangerous to others? How accurate are mental health professionals at assessing who will and who will not later be violent? The answers directly affect the process of civil commitment and the protection of society. If we can't accurately assess dangerousness, how can we justify involuntary commitment?

Early research on this issue suggested that psychiatrists and psychologists were actually rather poor at assessing

Grant T. Harris

▲ Grant T. Harris (1950–2014), past director of the Research Department of the Waypoint Mental Centre in Ontario, was an internationally acclaimed expert on the assessment of dangerousness.

dangerousness (see review by Harris et al., 2015). However, more recent research has shown that accurate assessments of the risk for violence are indeed possible (Harris & Rice, 2010; Harris et al., 2015; Ogloff & Daffern, 2006; Rice, 1997). Many advances in assessing dangerousness have been made by Canadian research teams. One example is a series of studies that showed that a rating scale based on important predictors of violence (e.g., psychopathy score, age at first arrest, failure on prior conditional release) can reliably predict violent recidivism among individuals who have already been violent (Harris et al., 2015). Clinical judgment is required to score the person on the scale, but the summation of the scores and the differential importance of each item are determined by prior statistical analyses, making the risk assessment actuarial in nature. Canadian teams have also made important advances in the prediction of violence in women (e.g., Nicholls et al., 2005; Olver et al., 2018).

Similarly, since risk for self-harm is one of the common criteria used for decisions about civil commitment, one might ask whether psychologists can accurately assess risk for suicidal behaviour. The job of assessing patients' risk for suicide and other self-harm is an important and common activity for many mental health professionals. A good deal of research, again much of which has been done by Canadian teams (e.g., Cochrane-Brink et al., 2000), shows that several important variables should be assessed in evaluating a patient's risk for self-injury. For example, a study done by forensic psychologist James Ogloff and his colleagues investigated nearly 300 psychiatric patients who had been involuntarily committed to the Riverview Psychiatric Hospital in British Columbia. These researchers investigated what variables predicted which patients would display self-injurious behaviour while in hospital. They found that those patients who reported suicidal thoughts while in hospital, those who showed verbal and physical aggression toward others in hospital, those with a history of self-harm, and those who had engaged in a suicide attempt or other form of self-injurious behaviour within the two weeks before being committed to hospital were most likely to harm themselves while in hospital (Jack et al., 1998; Nicholls et al., 1998). More recently, a scale called the Suicide Risk Assessment Scale (SRAS) for prisoners was developed by a group of researchers at the Correctional Service of Canada (Wichmann et al., 2000). The SRAS was subsequently validated by a research group in Trois-Rivières, Québec. Specifically, the SRAS performed better than a more elaborate test in assessing suicide risk in two samples of inmates (Daigle et al., 2006). Research like this has led to guidelines to help clinicians make decisions about predicting self-harm that are more accurate than clinicians' global judgments and far better than chance (Douglas & Koch, 2001; Murray & Wright, 2006).

DEINSTITUTIONALIZATION AND HOMELESSNESS

Two trends have influenced the number of people in Canada who are involuntarily committed each year: (1) the increase in the number of people who are homeless and (2) **deinstitutionalization**, the movement of people with severe mental illness out of institutions. Homelessness, although not exclusively a problem of the mentally ill, is largely determined by social views of people with mental illness.

The 2016 Census enumerated Canadians spending the night of May 9 in a homeless shelter. The 965 shelters had 22 190 residents, of whom 61 percent were men (McDermott et al., 2019). These numbers only begin to estimate the homeless population in Canada. It is estimated that 235 000 Canadians will experience homelessness in a given year (Gaetz et al., 2014). Shelter residents are considered homeless individuals receiving emergency shelter (e.g., shelters for abused women and their children). The majority, 180 000 persons, use this type of emergency shelter while 50 000 have provisional shelter (e.g., are couch surfing, in prison, in hospital). An estimated 5000 are unsheltered (e.g., living in their car or outside).

Stuart and Arboldea-Florez (2000) from Queen's University interviewed homeless people using inner-city shelters in Calgary in the late summer of 1997. Three-quarters of them had some kind of mental health issue, with 33 percent displaying significant mental health problems. Lifetime alcohol abuse was evident for one-third. Those with mental health problems were having a harder time living on the streets (e.g., being victimized, stressed, having a harder time finding food and work) than those without mental health problems. These researchers also reported that the face of the homeless person in Canada has changed from the image of an older male with an alcohol use disorder; today, there are also many younger people, women, and families living on the streets (Stuart & Arboldea-Florez, 2000). As University of Lethbridge researchers have noted, Indigenous people, refugees, and ethnic minorities are overrepresented among the homeless in Canada (Belanger et al., 2012; Hargrave, 1999).

Deinstitutionalization caused by the closing of many large psychiatric hospitals and reductions in the number of beds in hospitals are factors that many believe have contributed to increasing rates of homelessness in Canada. Deinstitutionalization had two goals: (1) to downsize or even close the large provincial and territorial psychiatric hospitals and (2) to create a network of community mental health services in which the released individuals could be treated. As explained by Douglas and Koch (2001), the deinstitutionalization movement led to the rapid downsizing of psychiatric facilities across Canada. In 1957, some 70 300 persons were detained in psychiatric institutions in Canada (Dominion Bureau of Statistics, 1955–1957). In 1975, this figure was down to 44 847 inpatients (Statistics Canada, 1975). Further decreases ensued. For example, in 1992–1993 alone, 29 991 patients were discharged from psychiatric hospitals, and the number detained was even lower (Douglas & Koch, 2001; Statistics Canada, 1995). Some argue that the deinstitutionalization movement continues into the present-day era of "community integration" (Jones, 2007).

As we can see, the first goal of the deinstitutionalization movement (i.e., downsizing or closing the large provincial and territorial mental hospitals) appears to have been substantially accomplished. However, the second goal of providing alternative community care has not. Instead, there was **transinstitutionalization**, or the movement of people with severe mental illness from large psychiatric hospitals to nursing homes or other group residences, including jails and prisons, many of which provide only marginal services (Sealy & Whitehead, 2004). Because of the deterioration in care for many people who had previously been served by the provincial or territorial mental hospital system, deinstitutionalization is largely considered a failure. Although many praise the ideal of providing community care for people with severe mental illness, the support needed to provide this type of care has been severely deficient. And many remain concerned about continuity of care (i.e., how the many different agencies and services should best work together) in this new era of community integration (e.g., Durbin et al., 2006).

As noted by Patricia Sealy and Paul Whitehead (2004) of the University of Western Ontario, since the deinstitutionalization movement began over 40 years ago, community care continues to

grow and the number of hospital beds continues to decrease. They fear this trend will continue until the appropriate balance of community care and inpatient psychiatric services is definitively determined. However, others argue that deinstitutionalization does not lead to homelessness or patient abandonment in the community. For example, a study by researchers at the University of Montréal examined the effects of deinstitutionalization in a sample of 96 patients discharged from Louis H. Lafontaine Hospital between 1989 and 1998, as compared with a sample of 96 patients who were hospitalized during the same interval. They did not find higher rates of homelessness in the deinstitutionalized sample (only two ended up on the streets). Most discharged patients moved to some form of group residential supervised care in the community (Lesage et al., 2000).

CRIMINAL COMMITMENT

What would have happened if Arthur had been arrested for trespassing on embassy grounds or, worse yet, if he had hurt or killed someone in his effort to present his plan for saving the starving children? Would he have been held responsible for his actions, given his obviously disturbed mental state? How would a jury have responded to him when he seemed fine just several days later? If he was not responsible for his behaviour then, why does he seem so normal now?

These questions are of enormous importance as we debate whether people should be held responsible for their criminal behaviour despite the possible presence of mental illness. For example, Nova Scotian Jane Hurshman admitted to shooting her common-law husband, Billy Stafford, to death but claimed she was driven to it by years of severe abuse perpetrated by Stafford (Vallee, 1986). She was acquitted by a jury, but on appeal, a new trial was ordered. Rather than go through another trial, Hurshman pleaded guilty to manslaughter and served a short jail term. Cases such as this have ignited considerable controversy about the conditions under which people should be responsible for criminal behaviour. Jane Hurshman's experience and other similar cases (e.g., *Regina v. Lavallee*; see Regehr & Glancy, 1995) led to the recognition of *battered woman syndrome* in Canadian law (Schuller & Yarmey, 2001).

Battered woman syndrome is not specifically mentioned in the *DSM-5*. The term refers to a state of learned helplessness or post-traumatic stress that results from chronic abuse within a relationship such that a woman feels unable to leave. The Supreme Court of Canada has acknowledged that in certain extreme cases involving battered woman syndrome, an accused may well be under a reasonable apprehension of death even though she is not in danger of "imminent or immediate harm" at the moment that force is used to protect herself. This is an expansion of the self-defence legal defence that is always available to any person accused of murder who reasonably believes that his or her life was in danger from an assault. A battered woman's apprehension about dying may be quite realistic; one study conducted in Ontario found that nearly 80 percent of female murder victims are killed by their spouses or intimate partners (Crawford & Gartner, 1992). Nonetheless, the battered woman syndrome defence has its critics, with some calling it the "abuse excuse" (e.g., Dershowitz, 1994).

▲ People become homeless because of many factors, including economic conditions, mental health status, and alcohol or other drug abuse.

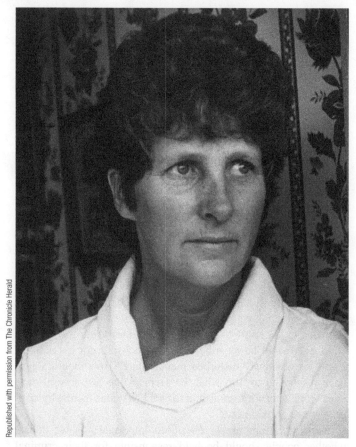

▲ Nova Scotian Jane Hurshman was severely abused over a number of years by her common-law husband, Billy Stafford, whom she eventually killed. Cases like Hurshman's led to the acceptance of battered woman syndrome as a murder defence in Canadian courts in 1990.

Criminal commitment is the process by which people are held because (1) they have been accused of committing a crime and are detained in a mental health facility until they can be determined to be fit to participate in legal proceedings against them, or (2) they have been found not criminally responsible on account of a mental disorder (NCRMD).

THE INSANITY DEFENCE

Not all people are punished for criminal behaviour. Why not? Because the law recognizes that, under certain circumstances, people are not responsible for their behaviour and it would be unfair to punish them. Current views originate from a case recorded more than 150 years ago in England. Daniel M'Naghten today might receive the diagnosis of schizophrenia. He held the delusion that the English Tory party was persecuting him, and he set out to kill the British prime minister. He mistook the man's secretary for the prime minister and killed the secretary instead. In what has become known as the *M'Naghten rule*, the English court decreed that people are not responsible for their criminal behaviour if they do not know what they are doing or if they don't know that what they are doing is wrong. An adaptation of this standard became part of Canadian law in 1894.

The M'Naghten rule was the most common insanity defence standard used in the last half of the 19th century and well into the 20th century. The requirements of the M'Naghten rule are still being used by numerous jurisdictions worldwide, including in Canada and in many states in the United States. Other standards have been proposed in the United States to modify the M'Naghten rule, because many critics feel that simply relying on an accused person's knowledge of right or wrong is too limiting and a broader definition is needed (Guttmacher & Weihofen, 1952). For example, a person with a compulsion may know what he or she is doing is considered wrong by society and yet not be able to resist the compulsion.

There have been changes to the insanity defence in Canada as well. Originally, under the 1985 Canadian Criminal Code, a person found not guilty by reason of insanity would be automatically detained in a psychiatric hospital until the mental disorder improved sufficiently to justify the patient's release. The purpose of this criminal commitment was to protect the public and to allow the patient to recover from his or her mental disorder. However, concerns were raised about whether patients detained under criminal commitment were actually receiving sufficient treatment. Concerns were also expressed that the detention periods in psychiatric facilities were often much longer than the prison sentence the person would have served if convicted of the offence (Gelinas, 1994). Thus, in 1991, in the case of *Regina v. Swain* (1991), the Supreme Court ruled that this indeterminate detention infringed on the rights of the accused. There were also changes in the insanity defence. Specifically, the name of the defence was changed from not guilty by reason of insanity (NGRI) to not criminally responsible on account of mental disorder (NCRMD). The wording of the standard was also revised, as follows:

No person is criminally responsible for an act committed or an omission made while suffering from a mental disorder that rendered the person incapable of appreciating the nature and quality of the act or omission or of knowing that it was wrong. (Criminal Code of Canada, Section 16, 1992)

There are three main differences between the NGRI and the NCRMD defences. First, the term *insanity* has been replaced by *mental disorder*. Second, the defendant is now considered "not criminally responsible" as opposed to "not guilty." This difference may appear subtle, but the change recognizes explicitly that the defendant did commit the crime as opposed to being "not guilty" of the crime. Finally, the meaning of "wrong" has changed. Unlike NGRI, which was concerned only with legal wrongs, NCRMD judgments can be made if the person is incapable of knowing that his or her actions were either legally or morally wrong (Davis, 1993).

A well-known example of the successful use of the NCRMD defence in Canada is the case of André Dallaire in 1995. In November of that year, Dallaire attempted to assassinate the Canadian prime minister at the time, Jean Chrétien. Dallaire broke into the prime minister's home armed with a knife, intending to slit Chrétien's throat. Chrétien and his wife were able to hide safely in a locked bedroom until the police came to arrest Dallaire. A psychiatric assessment revealed that Dallaire was suffering from a psychotic disorder, specifically paranoid schizophrenia. His hallucinations consisted of hearing voices that commanded him to kill the prime minister. He also displayed delusions of grandeur that he was a secret agent with a mission to avenge the outcome of the Québec independence referendum (Fisher, 1996). Although Dallaire was found guilty of the crime of attempted murder of the prime minister, he was also found not to be criminally responsible for his actions because his intention to kill the prime minister was ruled to be the product of a mental disorder and because his mental disorder prevented him from comprehending the nature of his actions or the fact that his actions were wrong (Fisher, 1996). He was committed to the Royal Ottawa Mental Health Centre, where he received treatment, including antipsychotic medication. Once Dallaire was no longer delusional or hallucinating, he was conditionally released to a group home and finally into the community with continued psychiatric care (Fisher, 1996).

Another example is that of David Carmichael, a well-known fitness expert who strangled his 11-year-old son in a London, Ontario, hotel room in July 2004. He was charged with first-degree murder. Two leading forensic psychiatrists assessed Carmichael as having been in a major depression with psychotic features, including delusions, at the time when he killed his son. Carmichael was judged to be NCRMD and was sentenced to the Brockville Mental Health Centre where he received the treatment he needed. One year later, he was released into the community where he continued as an outpatient and worked with his wife and daughter to rebuild their family (Mandel, 2007).

▲ In his 2009 trial for the murder of Tim McLean on a Greyhound bus, Vince Li successfully used the NCRMD defence, as he was found to have been suffering from paranoid schizophrenia at the time.

A third example of the use of the NCRMD defence is the case of Vince Li, who beheaded and cannibalized a man on a Greyhound bus near Portage la Prairie, in Manitoba, in 2008. Li was delusional at the time of the offence, and he believed that the victim, who was sleeping in the seat next to him, was possessed by the devil and was going to kill him. After being found NCRMD, Li was treated for his mental illness and is now not considered dangerous and allowed to live in a group home ("Bus Beheader," 2015).

University of Alberta researchers recently examined the long-term criminal outcomes of all 528 Albertans (84 percent male) who were found NGRI or NCRMD between 1941 and 2015. The overall reconviction rate was 20 percent, and of those reconvicted for a crime, only 13 percent committed a new violent crime; these numbers are much lower than those seen for offenders not designated NGRI or NCRMD. Overall, then, this was not a very dangerous group, a finding in line with other research in Canada and elsewhere. In fact, in that and other studies, having a severe mental disorder (e.g., schizophrenia) was associated with a lower reconviction risk (Richer et al., 2018).

REACTIONS TO THE INSANITY DEFENCE

The successful use of concepts such as insanity or mental disorder in criminal cases alarmed large segments of the population, however, just as have defences involving battered woman syndrome discussed earlier in this chapter. As noted by Ogloff and Whittemore (2001), when someone is found NCRMD, there is often a public outcry that the person has "got off" too easily. Research supports that the public often holds negative perceptions about the NCRMD defence. One telephone survey study found that 91 percent of people who responded agreed with the statement that "judges and juries have a hard time telling whether the defendants are really sane or insane" (Hans, 1986). Almost 90 percent agreed the "insanity plea is a loophole that allows too many guilty people to go free." In a similar study, 90 percent of people agreed that "the insanity plea is used too much. Too many people escape responsibilities for crimes by pleading insanity" (Pasewark & Seidenzahl, 1979). In a recent Canadian survey, one-third of respondents disagreed with the availability of the NCRMD defence (Fraser & Desjardins, 2009). Do you think that Dallaire, Carmichael, or Li "got off too easily"? Is there hard evidence that the insanity defence is used too often?

You will probably be surprised to learn that the NGRI defence was used relatively infrequently in Canadian courts. For example, in 1991, only about 1000 individuals who had been found NGRI were being held in institutions across Canada (Roesch et al., 1997). Although the NCRMD defence is used more often than the NGRI defence (Livingston et al., 2003), its use is still relatively uncommon (Roesch et al., 1997). For example, in British Columbia, in the two years following the legal change to the NCRMD defence, among those cases remanded for assessment of criminal responsibility, psychiatrists' recommendations favoured NCRMD only 29 percent of the time—a total of only 53 cases over two years. In a review of NCRMD and unfit to stand trial (see below) cases under the Québec and Ontario Review Boards, there were only 486 and 215 new cases in 2004, respectively (Latimer & Lawrence, 2006).

Negative public perceptions of the NCRMD defence reflect a lack of appreciation by the public about just how serious the consequences are of using this defence (Ogloff & Whittemore, 2001). Although the NCRMD defence does not entail automatic detention in a psychiatric hospital, some defendants end up being kept in psychiatric institutions for much longer periods than they would have been sentenced to prison if they had not employed this defence (Davis, 1994; Holley et al., 1998); correctional sentences are finite, whereas NCRMD detainments in a hospital can continue indefinitely if the patient is considered dangerous, for example. People with mental illness apparently do not often "beat the system" as a result of being judged NCRMD.

Perhaps because of the negative public perception of NCRMD, and also because of a few very high-profile cases, the Canadian Criminal Code was amended in 2014 to designate some NCRMD individuals as high-risk accused. High-risk accused face more restrictions and are more likely to stay in secure settings, rather than transitioning into the community like most NCRMD people do. A pan-Canadian team of researchers recently examined the effectiveness of this amendment to the law by studying all individuals who would have been designated as high-risk accused in British Columbia, Ontario, and Québec between 2000 and 2005. They found that NCRMD high-risk accused were not more likely to commit a new crime, compared with NCRMD who were not considered high-risk accused (Goossens et al., 2018). High-risk accused were already being managed carefully in the forensic system. Thus, the amended law will likely do little to improve public safety, beyond what was already done.

An important issue concerns where such people should be cared for once they have been judged NCRMD. A recent Canadian review suggests that forensic community programs are generally one of the best tools for helping people deemed NCRMD (Woodworth et al., 2003). These authors recommend that to best implement such community-based programs for NCRMD individuals, people in the community must be aware of the program and be appropriately educated about the risk that these individuals pose and that there be high levels of monitoring of these people, assessment of psychopathic traits (see Chapter 14), and routine use made of validated risk assessment tools, such as those discussed earlier in this chapter (Woodworth et al., 2003).

A final issue relates to the legal concept of burden of proof, the weight of evidence needed to win a case. With respect to the defence of NCRMD, according to Canadian law, the defendant can raise the issue of NCRMD at any time. In contrast, the prosecution can only raise the possibility of NCRMD after the defendant has been found guilty or after the defence, for any reason (Ogloff & Whittemore, 2001).

Society has long recognized the need to identify criminals who may not be in control of their behaviour. The challenge is in trying to do what may be impossible: determining whether the person knew what he or she was doing, knew right from wrong, and could control his or her behaviour at the time of the offence. Mental health professionals cannot assess mental health retrospectively. An additional dilemma is the desire, on the one hand, to provide care to people with mental illness and, on the other, to treat them as responsible individuals. Finally, we must resolve the simultaneous and conflicting interests of wanting to assist people with mental illness and wanting to be protected from those who

might be dangerous. By evaluating the effects of various consequences, science may be able to help resolve some of these issues. Concerns about law and order must be balanced with the rights of people with mental illness, providing adequate attention to both concerns.

FITNESS TO STAND TRIAL

Before people can be tried for a criminal offence, they must be able to understand the charges against them and to assist with their own defence—criteria outlined by the Canadian Criminal Code in 1992. Thus, in addition to interpreting a person's state of mind during the criminal act, experts must also anticipate his or her state of mind during the subsequent legal proceedings. A person could be ruled NCRMD because of his or her mental illness at the time of the criminal act yet still be fit to stand trial.

The classic case for the determination of fitness in Canada is *Regina v. Pritchard* (1836). Lindsay (1977) describes three issues emerging from the criteria defined in the *Pritchard* ruling that need to be addressed in a fitness assessment: (1) Is the accused able to assist in his or her defence? (2) Does the accused understand his or her role in the proceedings? (3) Does the accused understand the nature or object of the proceedings? According to the Canadian Criminal Code: "Unfit to stand trial means . . . in particular, unable on account of mental disorder to: (a) understand the nature or object of the proceedings, (b) understand the possible consequences of the proceedings, or (c) communicate with counsel" (Ogloff & Whittemore, 2001, p. 294).

A person determined not fit to stand trial typically loses the authority to make decisions and faces commitment. If the defendant is found to be unfit to stand trial, the court may decide the next step (e.g., detention in hospital) if it can do so readily, and if not, a review board must reach a decision in 45 days. The review board's three options are to (1) conditionally discharge the accused, (2) detain the accused in hospital, or (3) order that the accused receive treatment (Ogloff & Whittemore, 2001).

Canadian researchers have contributed substantially to developing sound instruments and methods for assessing a defendant's **fitness to stand trial** (Ogloff & Whittemore, 2001). For example, the Fitness Interview Test–Revised is a three-part instrument developed by Christopher Webster and his colleagues (Roesch et al., 1999) that specifies the particular abilities required by an individual to demonstrate that he or she is fit to stand trial. In the first section, the individual's understanding of the nature and object of the proceedings is assessed (e.g., does the individual understand key components, such as the arrest process, pleas available, court procedures?).

In the second section, the individual's understanding of the possible consequences of the proceedings is measured (e.g., the range of possible penalties, legal defences available). In the final section, the individual's capacity to contribute to his or her own defence is tapped (e.g., can he or she communicate with a lawyer, plan a legal strategy?). This test reliably screens out those individuals who are clearly fit to stand trial (Viljoen et al., 2002; Zapf, 2001; Zapf & Roesch, 1997).

In Canada, most criminal responsibility and fitness to stand trial evaluations are done by psychiatrists, not psychologists. It has been suggested (correctly, we think) that forensic psychologists are particularly qualified to perform these assessments, and calls have been made for changes in the law to allow all qualified mental health professionals to perform these assessments. This change would likely increase timely access to these services (Roesch et al., 2019).

Concept Check   17.1

Commitment laws determine the conditions under which a person is certified to have a mental disorder and therefore placed in a hospital, sometimes in conflict with the person's own wishes. The following paragraph is about civil commitment and criminal commitment. Check your understanding by filling in the blanks.

Several conditions must be met before the government is permitted to commit a person involuntarily: The person has a(n) (1)_____; the person is considered (2) _____ to herself or himself or others, and the person is in need of (3) _____. In the case of criminal commitment, people are held for two reasons: (4) _____ or (5) _____.

DUTY TO WARN AND PROTECT

Do mental health professionals have any responsibility for the actions of the people they serve? This question is especially important when we consider the dangerous behaviour exhibited by a minority of people with severe mental illness. What are the responsibilities of professionals who suspect that someone with whom they are working may hurt or even kill another person? Must they contact the appropriate authority or the person who may be harmed, or are they forbidden to discuss information disclosed during therapy sessions?

These issues are the subject of a tragic and influential case in the United States known as *Tarasoff v. Regents of the University of California* (1974, 1976). In 1969, Prosenjit Poddar, a graduate student at the University of California, Berkeley, killed a fellow student, Tatiana Tarasoff, who had previously rejected his romantic advances. At the time of the murder, he was being seen by two therapists at the University Health Center and had received a diagnosis of paranoid schizophrenia. At his last session, Poddar hinted that he was going to kill Tarasoff. His therapist believed this threat was serious and contacted the campus police, who investigated the allegation and received assurances from Poddar that he would leave Tarasoff alone. Weeks later, after repeated attempts to contact her, Poddar shot and stabbed Tarasoff until she died.

After learning of the therapists' role in the case, Tatiana Tarasoff's family sued the university, the therapists, and the university police, saying they should have warned Tatiana that she was in danger. The court agreed, and the *Tarasoff* case has been used ever since as a standard in the United States for therapists concerning their **duty to warn** a client's potential victims. Nonetheless, it is still difficult for therapists to know their exact responsibilities for protecting third parties from their clients. Good clinical practice dictates that any time they are in doubt, they should consult with colleagues. A second opinion can be just as helpful to a therapist as to a client. We have not had a legal precedent in Canada like the ruling in the *Tarasoff* case in the United States. Nonetheless, the Alberta Court of Queen's Bench stated in *Wenden v. Trikha* (1991) that a duty to warn might be imposed for psychologists under some circumstances (Lyon et al., 2001; Schuller & Ogloff, 2001).

In addition to this legal warning, the code of ethics of the Canadian Psychological Association dictates how mental health practitioners should behave in such cases. The code is quite clear that psychologists have an ethical duty to protect a third party of impending danger from a client, very similar to the legal requirements imposed by the ruling in the *Tarasoff* case in the United States (Ogloff & Olley, 1998). Specifically, the Canadian Psychological Association Code requires that psychologists should do everything within reason to stop or offset the harmful or lethal consequences of a client's actions. According to the Code, the ethical response can include making a report to appropriate authorities (e.g., the police) or warning an intended victim or a family member. Moreover, the psychologist should take such actions even when a confidential relationship, like a patient–therapist relationship, is involved (Canadian Psychological Association [CPA], 2017).

Communications between a therapist and client are required to be held completely confidential, except in a very few exceptional situations (CPA, 2017). These exceptions are called "limits to confidentiality." One such limit to confidentiality occurs when the psychologist must break confidentiality to allow for the protection of identifiable third parties at risk for harm (Schuller & Ogloff, 2001). Another such limit to confidentiality involves suspected cases of child abuse. In virtually every Canadian jurisdiction, psychologists have an affirmative duty to report suspected cases of child abuse, even when information pertaining to this suspicion was obtained within the otherwise confidential patient–therapist relationship. A further situation in which limits to confidentiality apply occurs when the psychologist judges the patient to be a risk to himself or herself. The therapist may need to break confidentiality to arrange for proper care for a highly suicidal patient who does not want to enter hospital, for example.

MENTAL HEALTH PROFESSIONALS AS EXPERT WITNESSES

Judges and juries often have to rely on **expert witnesses**, individuals who have specialized knowledge, to assist them in making decisions. The Canadian legal system has been relying increasingly often on expert witness testimony in such areas as child custody disputes (Austin et al., 1994). We have alluded to several instances in which mental health professionals serve in such a capacity, providing information about a person's dangerousness or ability to understand and participate in the defence. The public perceives expert witnesses ambivalently. On one hand, they see the value of persuasive expert testimony in educating a jury; on the other, they see expert witnesses as "hired guns" whose opinions suit the side that pays their bills. How reliable are the judgments of mental health professionals who act as expert witnesses?

To take one example, in deciding whether someone should be civilly committed, the assessor must determine the person's

▲ Dr. John Yuille, a forensic psychologist and emeritus professor at the University of British Columbia, has provided a good deal of expert witness testimony in his areas of expertise. For example, he testified for the defence during the trial of a group of childcare workers in Martensville, Saskatchewan, in the early 1990s, who were alleged to have perpetrated multiple counts of child abuse.

potential for future violence. As we discussed earlier in this chapter, mental health professionals can now make reliable assessments of dangerousness by using appropriate tools (Ogloff & Daffern, 2006; Harris et al., 2015; Rice, 1997). A second area in which mental health professionals are frequently asked to provide consultation is in assigning a diagnosis. In Chapter 3, we discussed the development of systems to ensure the reliability of diagnoses. Recent revisions of diagnostic criteria, including the *DSM-IV-TR* and *DSM-5*, have addressed this issue directly, thus helping clinicians make diagnoses that are generally reliable. Remember, however, that the legal definition of mental illness is not matched by a comparable disorder in the *DSM-5*. Therefore, statements about whether someone has a "mental illness" reflect determinations made by the court and not by mental health professionals.

Mental health professionals appear to have expertise in identifying **malingering** and in assessing competence. Remember, as we discussed in Chapter 7, that to malinger is to fake or grossly exaggerate symptoms, usually to be absolved from blame. For example, a person might claim to have been actively hallucinating at the time of the crime and therefore not be responsible. A good deal of research suggests that malingering is detectable using validated instruments like the Minnesota Multiphasic Personality Inventory (MMPI; e.g., Bacchiochi & Bagby, 2006; Bagby, Marshall, & Bacchiochi, 2005; Bagby, Nicholson, et al., 2002). For example, the MMPI test is almost 90 percent accurate in revealing malingering in people claiming to have post-traumatic stress disorder (PTSD; McCaffrey & Bellamy-Campbell, 1989). However, recent work cautions that people who have knowledge about the MMPI validity scales can be quite successful in avoiding detection that they are faking PTSD (Bury & Bagby, 2002). Mental health professionals also appear capable of providing reliable information about a person's competence or ability to understand and assist with a defence (Melton et al., 1987). Overall, mental health professionals can provide judges and juries with reliable and useful information in specific areas.

The research described here does not indicate how accurate expert testimony actually is under everyday conditions. In other words, under the right circumstances, experts can make accurate determinations of the risks that a person will commit an act of violence, is faking certain symptoms, or is fit to stand trial, and of what diagnosis should be made. Yet other factors conspire to influence expert testimony. Personal and professional opinions

that exceed the competence of the expert witness can influence what information is or is not presented, as well as how it is relayed to the court (Drogin et al., 2012). For instance, if the expert witness believes in general that people should not be involuntarily committed to mental health facilities, this opinion will likely influence how the witness presents clinical information in civil commitment court proceedings. Carleton University researchers studied expert witnesses retained during dangerous offender hearings (hearings to determine if someone is very dangerous and thus should receive an indeterminate sentence). Expert witnesses retained by the prosecution rated offenders as more psychopathic on the Psychopathy-Checklist Revised, compared with expert witnesses retained by the defence (Lloyd et al., 2010).

ETHICS AND TREATMENT OF MENTAL ILLNESS

Psychologists who are providing treatment to individuals with mental disorders are bound by the ethical principles set out by their professional organization to protect the dignity of the individuals they are treating and to ensure that caring for them occurs in a responsible fashion. Canadian psychologists follow the ethical principles laid out in the Canadian Code of Ethics for Psychologists, published by the CPA (2017). These ethical principles cover a variety of issues including boundary issues, the requirement that the psychologist do no harm, and the need for psychologists to practise within their areas of competence. Let us first turn our attention to a case in which two of these principles were broken.

The ethical principles of maintaining clear boundaries with patients and doing no harm were breached in a case that occurred in Toronto in the 1980s. Psychologist David Garner lost his licence to practise in Ontario after engaging in sexual relations with two clients he was treating for eating disorders. You may remember Garner's name from Chapter 9, as he was a very productive researcher in the area of eating disorders. At the time his licence to practise was revoked, Garner was already serving a two-year suspension of his registration after it was learned that he had engaged in sexual relations with another 18-year-old client with anorexia nervosa in 1985. The original two-year suspension of Garner's licence forced him to resign from his position as a clinical psychologist at the Toronto General Hospital and from his academic appointment at the University of Toronto. He moved to the United States, where he engaged in research until he was once again issued a licence to practise psychology by the Ohio psychology board in 1994 (Goodman, 2003; Mahr, 2003).

BOUNDARY ISSUES

The Canadian Code of Ethics for Psychologists (CPA, 2017) clarifies that psychologists must be clear about professional boundaries with their clients to avoid conflict of interest. This means that psychologists should avoid dual relationships (e.g., acting as therapist to someone they have interactions with in another context) whenever possible. It also means that psychologists must not exploit any relationship established with them as psychologists to further their own personal, business, or political interests at the expense of the best interests of their client. This means a psychologist cannot take advantage of a client's trust or dependency to encourage or engage in sexual relations with clients or with a client's partner or relatives.

DO NO HARM

Psychologists are also bound by the ethical principle of minimizing harm to their clients. This is quite a broad ethical principle that applies to such activities as record keeping (not recording information that could be misinterpreted and misused), psychological report writing (using clear language in reports that can be understood by the person who receives the report), and making referrals to other mental health professionals (giving reasonable assistance to help a person secure needed services if a therapist is unable to treat the person). The do-no-harm imperative also prohibits sexual intimacy between a therapist and a client. The Canadian Code of Ethics for Psychologists stipulates that the psychologist must be "acutely aware of the power relationship in therapy and, therefore, not encourage or engage in sexual intimacy with therapy clients" (CPA, 2017, principle II.28, p. 22). This prohibition against sexual relations with therapy clients applies not only to the period while therapy is taking place but also to any period after therapy has ended when the power relationship could reasonably be expected to still be influencing the client's decision making. It was Garner's failure to attend to the power relationship that was present with his two female clients, and his consequent failure to minimize harm to them by engaging in sexual relations with them despite the power relationship, that resulted in the revoking of Garner's psychologist's licence in Ontario.

RECOGNIZING LIMITS OF COMPETENCE

According to the Canadian Code of Ethics for Psychologists (CPA, 2017), psychologists must practise within the limits of their competence. A neuropsychologist would not treat an individual with a substance use disorder, unless he or she had the proper training to work with a client with addictions, for example. Psychologists must obtain specific training (coursework, research, individual study, applied training, or supervision) in the particular areas of expertise in which they provide clinical services. If a neuropsychologist wanted to begin working with clients with substance use disorders, he or she would need to obtain specialized training in this new area to establish competence before providing clinical services in this new area. Clients have the right to receive treatment from competent and well-trained professionals. This brings us to a discussion of specific examples of patients' rights and how they are, and have come to be, protected by law in Canada today.

PATIENTS' RIGHTS

Until about 40 years ago, people in mental health facilities were accorded few rights. What treatment they received and whether they could make phone calls, send and receive mail, or have visitors were typically decided by hospital personnel who rarely consulted with the patient. Abuses of this authority, however, led to legal action and subsequent rulings by the courts concerning the rights of people in these facilities. Over the past four decades, constitutional protection of the rights of Canadian citizens has been explicitly extended to patients in psychiatric institutions (Olley & Ogloff, 1995).

THE RIGHT TO TREATMENT

One of the most fundamental rights of people in mental health facilities is, obviously, the right to treatment (Bloch & Green, 2012). For too many and for too long, conditions were poor and treatment was lacking in numerous large mental health facilities. In Canada, the right to treatment of people with mental illness and intellectual disability has been more explicitly recognized in Canadian law over the last four decades (Olley & Ogloff, 1995).

A separate but related right is the right to treatment in the least restrictive setting possible (Olley & Ogloff, 1995). For example, those with intellectual disability should have a right to the least restrictive conditions necessary to achieve the purpose of habilitation (i.e., maximizing their independence). This right was established by a landmark case in the United States, *Wyatt v. Stickney* (1972). This case grew out of a lawsuit filed by the employees of large institutions in Alabama who were fired because of funding difficulties. The case mandated that facilities make positive efforts to attain treatment goals for their patients. To this end, it was ruled that institutions should make every attempt to move residents with intellectual disability from (1) more to less structured living, (2) large to smaller facilities, (3) large to smaller living units, (4) group to individual residences, (5) segregated from the community to integrated into the community, and (6) dependent living to independent living. In Canada, advocacy efforts and constitutional provisions (e.g., the Canadian Charter of Rights and Freedoms, 1982) protect the rights of people with mental illness, such as the right to treatment in the least restrictive environment and the right to refuse treatment, which we discuss next (Olley & Ogloff, 1995).

THE RIGHT TO REFUSE TREATMENT

One of the most controversial issues in mental health today is the right of people, especially those with severe mental illness, to refuse treatment. Along with the development of the Canadian Charter of Rights and Freedoms in 1982, provinces like Manitoba and Ontario now explicitly recognize the right of involuntary but competent patients (e.g., someone who is involuntarily committed because of suicidality who nonetheless understands the risks and benefits of a proposed treatment) to refuse treatment. Some provinces, such as British Columbia, continue to fail to recognize this right and leave the decision in the hands of individual physicians treating a given patient. It should be noted that this condition arises rarely: fewer than 10 percent of involuntary patients persist in refusing treatment (Gratzer & Matas, 1994). Nonetheless, the issues involved can

GEORGE REID | *Asserting the Right to Refuse Treatment*

In the early 1980s, George Reid committed a violent robbery, was arrested, and later found not guilty by reason of insanity. He was held in a maximum-security psychiatric facility, having been declared under the Ontario Mental Health Act to be an involuntary patient who was incompetent to make treatment decisions for himself. He was diagnosed with schizophreniform psychosis. His psychiatrist, Dr. Russell Fleming, proposed to treat him with antipsychotic medication. Such medication usually has a beneficial effect on symptoms of psychosis, as well as on restoring cognitive capacity to some extent. However, it also has side effects that many people find highly undesirable.

Under the legislation at the time, a substitute decision maker, in this case a designate of the province, could provide consent to treatment on the behalf of an incompetent person. The psychiatrist applied to this person for consent to treat Mr. Reid. The substitute decision maker refused, as Mr. Reid had earlier expressed (when he was competent) that he did not want to take psychotropic medication. The psychiatrist appealed this decision to the psychiatric review board in Ontario, which granted consent to treatment. This decision was upheld by the Ontario District Court but later overturned by the Ontario Court of Appeal. The Court of Appeal held that treatment provided against the consent (even if given earlier) of a person is unconstitutional, violating the right to security of the person under section 7 of the Canadian Charter of Rights and Freedoms.

This decision introduced a conundrum into the law: Although people could be admitted to hospital involuntarily, the mental illness that gave rise to their involuntary hospitalization could not be treated. Without treatment, patients' illnesses may never remit, and patients could then be hospitalized indefinitely. Although Ontario has dealt with this problem by revising its legislation, the Fleming case has dramatic implications for other provinces and territories that may treat patients without their consent, or even against their express wishes. The inherent dilemma is that to provide treatment may be unconstitutional, but to withhold it may give rise to indefinite hospitalization, because the very basis for hospitalization—mental illness—may not remit without treatment.

Source: From "Civil Commitment and Civil Competence: Psychological Issues," by Kevin S. Doulas and William J. Koch, from *Introduction to Psychology and Law: Canadian Perspectives,* edited by Regina A. Schuller and James R.P. Ogloff, © University of Toronto Press 2001. Reprinted with permission of the publisher.

be quite complex when an involuntary patient does persist in refusing treatment, as is illustrated in the following case described by Douglas and Koch (2001).

As illustrated in the preceding case, today, the argument about patients' rights to refuse treatment has often centred on the use of antipsychotic medications. On one side of the issue is the mental health professional who believes that, under certain circumstances, people with severe mental illness are not capable of making a decision in their own best interest and that the clinician is therefore responsible for providing treatment, despite the protestations of the affected person. On the other side, patients and their advocates argue that all people have a fundamental right to make decisions about their own treatment, even if doing so is not in their own best medical interests. This controversy is not yet completely resolved.

THE RIGHTS OF RESEARCH PARTICIPANTS

Throughout this book we have described research conducted worldwide with people who have psychological disorders, and we touched briefly in Chapter 4 on the issue of the ethical issues involved in conducting research with these individuals. In general, research involving human participants should be guided by the following three core ethical principles: respect for persons, concern for welfare, and justice.

According to the principles outlined in the Tri-Council policy statement (2014), the researcher must be respectful of the dignity of all research participants. Protecting participants' autonomy is particularly important for people with psychological disorders who may not be able to understand the research fully. One of the most important concepts in research is that those who participate must be fully informed about the risks and benefits of the study. Simple consent is not sufficient; it must be **informed consent**, or formal agreement by the subject to participate after being fully apprised of all important aspects of the study, including any possibility of harm. The possibility of harm occurring because of the research must be minimized, and participants must be made aware of the risk of harm, as well as the possible benefits, of the research. The burden and benefits of the research must be distributed across the population such that one particular group may not bear the burden of research (we're looking at you, psychology undergrads!), or benefit from the research, more than other groups.

Unfortunately, there are many examples in history where researchers have not followed ethical principles in the conduct of their research on various forms of abnormal behaviour. Take, for example, the brainwashing research of Dr. Ewan Cameron, which was conducted on psychiatric patients at the Allan Memorial Institute in Montréal in the 1950s and 1960s. As mentioned in Chapter 4, patients and their families were not asked for their consent to participate in Cameron's studies on experimental treatments for mental illness, nor were they adequately informed that his treatments were experimental and not standard practice. His treatments included multiple courses of shock treatment daily and a technique called "psychic driving," where patients listened to subliminal messages repeatedly while in a drug-induced coma. These experimental procedures unfortunately resulted in horrific consequences for many, including patients becoming confused, unable to feed themselves, and unable to control their bladders (Collins, 1988).

▲ The Allan Memorial Institute in Montréal was the site of the notorious brainwashing research of Dr. Ewan Cameron in the 1950s and 1960s. His "psychic driving" experiments resulted in horrific consequences for many of his psychiatric patient participants, who did not provide informed consent for their participation in Cameron's research.

Concept Check 17.2

Psychological professionals assume many roles and responsibilities. Identify the following situations using one of these terms: (a) informed consent, (b) duty to warn, (c) expert witness, (d) deinstitutionalization, and (e) malingering.

1. Dr. X testified in court that the defendant was faking and exaggerating symptoms to evade responsibility. Dr. X is acting as a(n) _____ and the defendant is _____.

2. The therapist has learned he is required to release more mentally ill patients from the hospital. He is worried that many of them will end up homeless and without continuing treatment as a result of _____.

3. One of my clients threatened his mother's life during his session today. Now I must decide whether I have a(n) _____.

4. The clinical researcher knows the potential for harm of the participants is very slight, but is nevertheless careful to tell them about it and asks them whether they agree to give their _____.

CLINICAL PRACTICE GUIDELINES

Over the past three decades, attempts have been made to establish greater uniformity in the delivery of effective mental health care and to better communicate the latest developments in treating certain disorders effectively to practitioners. A greater emphasis has also been placed on research focused on improving systems for the delivery of mental health services.

To accomplish these goals, some clinical practice guidelines have been published for specific health problems, including sickle cell disease, management of cancer pain, unstable angina, and depression in primary care settings. The hope is not only to reduce costs by eliminating unnecessary or ineffective treatments but also to facilitate the dissemination of effective interventions based on the latest research evidence. Treating people effectively—alleviating their pain and distress—is ultimately the most important way to reduce health-care costs, because these individuals will no longer request one treatment after another in an unending search for relief.

A task force of the American Psychological Association (APA) composed a template, or set, of principles for constructing and evaluating guidelines for clinical interventions for both psychological disorders and psychosocial aspects of physical disorders, which were published in 1995. These principles help ensure that future clinical practice guidelines will be comprehensive and consistent. As envisioned by the APA task force, the guidelines developed from this template should help both the practitioner and the patient make decisions about appropriate treatment interventions for psychological disorders, as well as psychosocial aspects of physical disorders. The CPA has been engaging in a similar exercise. Specifically, the clinical psychology section of the CPA has developed a task force on empirically supported treatments. The task force produced recommendations for Canadian professional psychologists regarding the use of empirically supported treatments in psychology (Dozois et al., 2014).

The APA task force decided that clinical practice guidelines for specific disorders should be constructed based on two simultaneous considerations, or axes. The **clinical efficacy** axis is a thorough consideration of the scientific evidence to determine whether the intervention in question is effective. This evidence would answer the question: "Is the treatment effective when compared with an alternative treatment or to no treatment in a controlled clinical research context?" In Chapter 4, we reviewed the various research strategies used to determine whether an intervention is effective. For many reasons, a treatment might seem effective when it is not effective at all. For instance, if patients improve on their own while being treated simply because of the passage of time or the natural healing process, the treatment had little to do with the improvement. It is possible that nonspecific effects of the treatment—perhaps just meeting with a caring health professional—are enough to make someone feel better without any contribution from the particular treatment technique.

To determine clinical efficacy, experiments must establish whether the intervention in question is better than no therapy, better than a nonspecific therapy, or better than an alternative therapy. (The latter finding provides the highest level of evidence for a treatment's effectiveness.) We might also rely on information collected from various clinics in which a large number of practitioners are treating the disorder in question. If these clinicians collect systematic data on the outcomes of their patients, they can ascertain how many are "cured," how many improve somewhat without recovering totally, and how many fail to respond to the intervention. Such data are referred to as quantified clinical observations or clinical replication series. Finally, a clinical consensus of leading experts is also a valuable additional source of information.

The **clinical utility** axis is concerned with the effectiveness of the intervention in the practice setting in which it is to be applied; in other words, will an intervention with proven efficacy in a research setting also be effective in the various frontline clinical settings in which it will be most frequently applied? For example, randomized controlled trials of therapy efficacy are often conducted with a very homogeneous group of patients who only have the disorder in question; those patients with comorbid disorders are typically excluded. But as we have discussed throughout this textbook, co-occurrence of more than one disorder (i.e., comorbidity) is a common phenomenon, making it difficult to know whether the results of the randomized controlled trial generalize to more complicated types of patients seen in frontline clinical settings. Also, is application of the intervention in the settings where it is needed feasible and cost effective? This axis is concerned with external validity, the extent to which an internally valid intervention is effective in different settings or under different circumstances from those under which it was tested.

The first major issue to consider on the clinical utility axis is feasibility. Will patients accept the intervention and comply with its requirements, and is it relatively easy to administer? As noted in Chapter 8, electroconvulsive therapy (ECT) is an effective treatment for very severe depression in many cases, but it is extremely frightening to patients, many of whom refuse it. The treatment also requires sophisticated procedures and close supervision by medical personnel, usually in a hospital setting. Therefore, it is not particularly feasible.

A second issue on the clinical utility axis is generalizability—the extent to which an intervention is effective with patients of differing backgrounds (ethnicity, age, sex) and in different settings (inpatient, outpatient, community) or with different therapists. Once again, an intervention could be very effective in a research setting with one group of patients but generalize very poorly across different ethnic groups. John Hunsley and Catherine Lee from the University of Ottawa published a review of effectiveness studies with adults and children and conclude that the size of the treatment effects were for the most part comparable to those observed in efficacy studies (Hunsley & Lee, 2007).

In reading the chapters of this book, you will have noted a number of effective treatments, both psychosocial and medical. In the future, we will see a great deal of additional research to establish both the clinical efficacy and the clinical utility of various interventions for psychological disorders, and the development of ever more sophisticated clinical practice guidelines. In 2010, the APA decided to develop its own set of clinical practice guidelines on providing the best evidence-based psychological care for people with psychological disorders; guidelines documents for specific disorders are now starting to be made available (http://www.apa.org/about/offices/directorates/guidelines/news.aspx). The Cochrane website provides updated review on the efficacy and effectiveness of various psychological treatments (http://www.cochrane.org).

In Chapter 1, we reviewed various activities that make up the role of scientist-practitioners in the mental health professions, who take a scientific approach to their clinical work to provide the most effective assessment procedures and interventions. Changes in the delivery of mental health services are likely to be accompanied by considerable disruption, because this is a major system that affects millions of people. But the change will also bring opportunities. Scientist-practitioners will contribute to the process of guidelines development in several ways. For example, most of the information relevant to clinical utility or external validity of interventions will be collected by mental health professionals in the course of their practice. Thus, they will truly fulfill the scientist-practitioner role to the benefit of patients in our field.

CONCLUSIONS

Therapy and scientific progress do not occur in a vacuum. People who study and treat abnormal behaviour are responsible not only for mastering the wealth of information we have only touched on in this book but also for understanding and appreciating their role in Canadian society and in the world at large. Every facet of life—from the biological to the social, political, and legal—interacts with every other; if we are to help people, we must appreciate this complexity.

We hope we have given you a good sense of the challenges faced by workers in the field of mental health and have spurred some of you to join us in this rewarding work.

SUMMARY

- Mental health law must balance a commitment to individual rights and fairness against majority concerns and a commitment to law and order.

☆ Civil Commitment

- Civil commitment laws determine the conditions under which a person may be certified legally to have a mental illness and therefore to be placed in a hospital, sometimes in conflict with the person's own wishes.

- Most Canadian jurisdictions permit commitment when several conditions have been met: (1) the person has a mental illness, (2) the person is dangerous to himself or herself or to others, and (3) the person is in need of treatment.

- "Mental illness" as used in legal system language is not synonymous with "psychological disorder"; each Canadian jurisdiction has its own definition of mental illness. Those provinces and territories using functional definitions of mental illness include people with very severe disturbances that negatively affect their health and safety.

- Having a severe mental illness seems to increase, but only slightly, the likelihood of violence, especially in the context of substance abuse.
- Strict civil commitment laws were designed to protect individual rights and freedoms. However, the combination of strict civil commitment laws and the lack of success with deinstitutionalization has resulted instead in transinstitutionalization and a rise in homelessness.

Criminal Commitment

- Criminal commitment is the process by which people are held for one of two reasons: (1) they have been accused of committing a crime and are detained in a mental health facility until they can be determined as fit or unfit to participate in legal proceedings against them, or (2) they have been found not criminally responsible on account of a mental disorder (NCRMD).
- The insanity defence in Canada is currently the not criminally responsible on account of a mental disorder (NCRMD) defence. It is primarily determined by the following legal ruling from a historical case in England: The M'Naghten rule states that people are not responsible for criminal behaviour if they do not know what they are doing, or if they do know what they are doing but don't know it is wrong. Other rulings have influenced the insanity defence in the United States.
- A determination of fitness must be made before an individual can be tried for a criminal offence: to stand trial, people must be fit to do so—able to understand the charges against them and to assist with their own defence.
- Duty to warn is an American legal standard that sets forth the responsibility of the therapist to warn potential victims that a client may attempt to hurt or kill them. In Canadian professional ethical standards, a better description of this principle might be duty to protect, which would include warning of imminent violence.

- Individuals who have specialized knowledge and who assist judges and juries in making decisions, especially about such issues as competence and malingering, are called expert witnesses.

Ethics and Treatment of Mental Illness

- Canadian psychologists are bound by the Canadian Code of Ethics for Psychologists to protect the dignity of clients and treat them responsibly. These ethical principles including boundary issues, the requirement that the psychologist do no harm, and the need for psychologists to practise within their areas of competence.

Patients' Rights

- One of the more fundamental rights of patients in mental facilities is their right to treatment; that is, they have a legal right to some sort of ongoing effort to both define and strive toward treatment goals. By contrast, a great deal of controversy exists over whether all patients are capable of making a decision to refuse treatment. This is an especially difficult dilemma in the case of antipsychotic medications that may improve patients' symptoms but also bring with them severe negative side effects.
- Those who participate in any research study must be fully informed of the risks and benefits and must formally and freely give their informed consent.

Clinical Practice Guidelines

- Clinical practice guidelines can play a major role in providing information about types of interventions that are likely to be effective for a specific disorder. Critical to such a determination are measures of clinical efficacy (internal validity) and clinical utility (external validity); in other words, the former is a measure of whether a treatment works, and the latter is a measure of whether the treatment is effective in a variety of settings.

KEY TERMS

civil commitment laws, 515
clinical efficacy, 527
clinical utility, 528
criminal commitment, 520

dangerousness, 517
deinstitutionalization, 518
duty to warn, 523
expert witnesses, 523

fitness to stand trial, 522
informed consent, 526
malingering, 524
mental illness, 517

transinstitutionalization, 519

ANSWERS TO CONCEPT CHECKS

17.1
1. mental disorder; 2. dangerous; 3. treatment; 4. They have been accused of committing crimes and they are waiting to be determined fit to stand trial; 5. They have been found not criminally responsible on account of a mental disorder (NCRMD)
17.2
1. c, e; 2. d; 3. b; 4. a

⁙ CENGAGE | MINDTAP

Stay organized and efficient with MindTap—a single destination with all the course material and study aids you need to succeed. Built-in apps leverage social media and the latest learning technology. For example:

- ReadSpeaker will read the text to you.
- Flashcards are pre-populated to provide you with a jump start for review—or you can create your own.
- You can highlight text and make notes in your MindTap Reader. Your notes will flow into Evernote, the electronic notebook app that you can access anywhere when it's time to study for the exam.
- Self-quizzing allows you to assess your understanding.

Visit login.cengage.com to start using MindTap. Enter the Online Access Code from the card included with your text. If a code card is not provided, you can purchase instant access at Cengage.ca.

GLOSSARY

Note: *OLC* refers to page numbers within the online chapter.

acquired immune deficiency syndrome (AIDS) Final stage of disease caused by HIV, which attacks and destroys the immune system. (499)

acute pain Pain that typically follows an injury and disappears once the injury heals or is effectively treated. (OLC–21)

acute stress disorder Severe reaction immediately following a terrifying event, often including amnesia about the event, emotional numbing, and **derealization**. Many victims later develop **post-traumatic stress disorder**. (191)

adjustment disorders Anxious or depressive reactions to life stress that are generally milder than in acute stress disorder or **post-traumatic stress disorder** but that are nevertheless impairing in terms of interfering with work or school performance, interpersonal relationships, or other areas of living. (196)

adoption studies In genetics research, the study of first-degree relatives reared in different families and environments. If they share common characteristics, such as a disorder, this finding suggests that those characteristics have a genetic component. (110)

affect Conscious, subjective aspect of an **emotion** that accompanies an action at a given time. (58)

agnosia Inability to recognize and name objects; may be a symptom of **dementia** or other brain disorders. (494)

agonist substitution Replacement of a drug on which a person is dependent with one having a similar chemical makeup, an **agonist**. Used as a treatment for **substance dependence**. (373)

agonists Chemical substances that effectively increase the activity of a **neurotransmitter** by imitating its effects. (46, 494)

agoraphobia Anxiety about being in places or situations from which escape might be difficult. (133)

AIDS-related complex (ARC) Group of minor health problems such as weight loss, fever, and night sweats that appears after HIV infection but before development of full-blown AIDS. (OLC–11)

alcohol dehydrogenase (ADH) Enzyme that helps humans metabolize alcohol. Different levels of its subtypes may account for different susceptibilities to disorders such as **fetal alcohol syndrome (FAS)**. (367)

alcohol-related disorders Cognitive, biological, behavioural, and social problems associated with alcohol use and abuse. (349)

alogia Deficiency in the amount or content of speech; a disturbance often seen in people with **schizophrenia**. (428)

alters Shorthand term for alter **egos**, the different personalities or identities in **dissociative identity disorder**. (201)

Alzheimer's disease "Strange disease of the cerebral cortex" that causes an "atypical form of senile **dementia**," discovered by German psychiatrist Alois Alzheimer. (496)

amniocentesis Prenatal medical procedure that allows the detection of abnormalities (e.g., **Down syndrome**) in the developing fetus. It involves removal and analysis of amniotic fluid from the mother. (481)

analogue models Approaches to research that use subjects who are similar to clinical clients, allowing replication of a clinical problem under controlled conditions. (101)

anhedonia Inability to experience pleasure, associated with some schizophrenic and **mood disorders**. (429)

animal phobia Unreasonable, enduring **fear** of animals or insects that usually develops early in life. (143)

anorexia nervosa Eating disorder characterized by recurrent food refusal leading to dangerously low body weight. (263)

antagonist drugs Medications that block or counteract the effects of psychoactive drugs. (374)

antagonists In neuroscience, chemical substances that decrease or block the effects of a **neurotransmitter**. (46, 374)

antidepressant Medication used to treat depressive disorders, such as tricyclic antidepressants, monoamine oxidase (MAO) inhibitors, and selective serotonin reuptake inhibitors. (243)

antigens Foreign materials that enter the body, including bacteria and parasites. (OLC–8)

antisocial personality disorder Cluster B (dramatic, emotional, or erratic) **personality disorder** involving a pervasive pattern of disregard for and violation of the rights of others. Similar to the non-*DSM*-label **psychopathy**, but with greater emphasis on overt behaviour rather than on personality traits. (397)

anxiety State of **mood** characterized by marked negative **affect** and bodily symptoms of tension in which a person apprehensively anticipates future danger or misfortune. Anxiety may involve feelings, behaviours, and physiological responses. (121)

aphasia Impairment or loss of language skills resulting from brain damage caused by **stroke, Alzheimer's disease**, or other illness or trauma. (496)

asociality Lack of interest in or motivation for social interactions; a preference for solitary activities. (429)

association studies Research strategies for comparing **genetic markers** in groups of people with and without a particular disorder. (111)

associative splitting Separation among basic functions of human personality (e.g., cognition, **emotion**, perception) that is seen by some as the defining characteristic of **schizophrenia**. (423)

attachment disorders Developmentally inappropriate behaviours in which a child is unable or unwilling to form normal attachment relationships with caregiving adults. (196)

attention-deficit/hyperactivity disorder (ADHD) Developmental disorder featuring maladaptive levels of inattention, excessive activity, and impulsiveness. (458)

attenuated psychosis syndrome Disorder involving the onset of psychotic symptoms such as hallucinations and delusions, which puts a person at high risk for schizophrenia; designated for further study by the *DSM-5*. (433)

autism spectrum disorder (ASD) Neurodevelopmental disorder characterized by significant impairment in social interactions and communication and restricted patterns of behaviour, interest, and activity. (469)

autoimmune disease Condition in which the body's **immune system** attacks healthy tissue rather than **antigens**. (OLC–9)

avoidant personality disorder Cluster C (anxious or fearful) **personality disorder** featuring a pervasive pattern of social inhibition, feelings of inadequacy, and hypersensitivity to criticism. (412)

avolition Apathy, or the inability to initiate or persist in important activities. (428)

barbiturates Sedative (and addictive) drugs including Amytal, Seconal, and Nembutal that are used as sleep aids. (354)

baseline Measured rate of a behaviour before introduction of an intervention that allows comparison and assessment of the effects of the intervention. (107)

behaviour therapy Array of therapy methods based on the principles of behavioural and **cognitive science** as well as principles of learning as applied to clinical problems. It considers specific behaviours rather than inferred conflict as legitimate targets for change. (25)

behavioural assessment Measuring, observing, and systematically evaluating (rather than inferring) the client's thoughts, feelings, and behaviour in the actual problem situation or context. (74)

behavioural inhibition system (BIS) Brain circuit in the limbic system that responds to threat signals by inhibiting activity and causing **anxiety**. (124)

behavioural medicine Interdisciplinary approach applying behavioural science to the prevention, **diagnosis**, and treatment of medical problems. (OLC–4)

behavioural model Explanation of human behaviour, including dysfunction, based on principles of learning and adaptation derived from experimental psychology. (23)

behaviourism Explanation of human behaviour, including dysfunction, based on principles of learning and adaptation derived from experimental psychology. (17)

benzodiazepines Anti-anxiety drugs, including Valium, Xanax, Dalmane, and Halcion, also used to treat insomnia. Effective against **anxiety** (and, at high potency, panic disorder), they show some side effects, such as some cognitive and motor impairment, and may result in dependence and addiction. Relapse rates are extremely high when the drug is discontinued. (354)

binge-eating disorder (BED) Pattern of eating involving distress-inducing **binges** not followed by purging behaviours. (269)

binges Relatively brief episodes of uncontrolled, excessive consumption, usually of food or alcohol. (263)

biofeedback Use of physiological monitoring equipment to make individuals aware of their own bodily functions, such as blood pressure or brain waves, that they cannot normally access, with the purpose of controlling these functions. (OLC–27)

bipolar I disorder Alternation of **major depressive** episodes with full manic episodes. (224)

bipolar II disorder Alternation of **major depressive** episodes with **hypomanic episodes** (not full manic episodes). (224)

blood-injury-injection phobia Unreasonable **fear** and avoidance of exposure to blood, injury, or the possibility of an injection. Victims experience fainting and a drop in blood pressure. (142)

body dysmorphic disorder (BDD) **Somatoform disorder** featuring a disruptive preoccupation with some imagined defect in appearance ("imagined ugliness"). (178)

borderline personality disorder Cluster B (dramatic, emotional, or erratic) **personality disorder** involving a pervasive pattern of instability of interpersonal relationships, self-image, **affects**, and control over impulses. (404)

brain circuits Neural pathways or **neurotransmitter** currents in the brain. (46)

breathing-related sleep disorders Sleep disruption leading to excessive sleepiness or insomnia, caused by a breathing problem such as interrupted (apnea) or laboured (hypoventilation) breathing. (298)

brief psychotic disorder Psychotic disturbance involving **delusions**, **hallucinations**, or **disorganized speech** or behaviour, but lasting less than one month; often occurs in reaction to a stressor. (433)

bulimia nervosa Eating disorder involving recurrent episodes of uncontrolled excessive (**binge**) eating followed by compensatory actions to remove the food (e.g., deliberate vomiting, laxative abuse, excessive exercise). (263)

caffeine use disorder Cognitive, biological, behavioural, and social problem associated with the use and abuse of caffeine. (360)

cannabis (marijuana) Dried part of the hemp plant, a **hallucinogen** that is the most widely used illegal substance. (363)

cardiovascular disease Afflictions in the mechanisms, including the heart, blood vessels, and their controllers, that are responsible for transporting blood to the body's tissues and organs. Psychological factors may play important roles in such diseases and their treatments. (OLC–16)

case study method Research procedure in which a single person or small group is studied in detail. The method does not allow conclusions about cause-and-effect relationships, and findings can be generalized only with great caution. (102)

catatonia Disorder of movement involving immobility or excited agitation. (423)

catatonic immobility Disturbance of motor behaviour in which the person remains motionless, sometimes in an awkward posture, for extended periods of time. (430)

catharsis Rapid or sudden release of emotional tension thought to be an important factor in psychoanalytic therapy. (18)

cerebral vascular accident (CVA) Temporary blockage of blood vessels supplying the brain, or a rupture of vessels in the brain, resulting in temporary or permanent loss of brain functioning. Also called a stroke. (OLC–16)

childhood disintegrative disorder Pervasive developmental disorder involving severe regression in language, adaptive behaviour, and motor skills after a two-year to four-year period of normal development. (469)

chronic fatigue syndrome (CFS) Incapacitating exhaustion following only minimal exertion, accompanied by fever, headaches, muscle and joint pain, depression, and **anxiety**. (OLC–24)

chronic pain Enduring pain that does not decrease over time; may occur in muscles, joints, and the lower back, and may be due to enlarged blood vessels, or degenerating or cancerous tissue. Other significant factors are social and psychological. (OLC–21)

circadian rhythm sleep-wake disorders Sleep disturbances resulting in sleepiness or insomnia caused by the body's inability to synchronize its sleep patterns with the current pattern of day and night. (299)

civil commitment laws Legal proceedings that determine a person has a mental disorder and may be hospitalized, even involuntarily. (515)

classical categorical approach Classification method founded on the assumption of clear-cut differences among disorders, each with a different known cause. (85)

classical conditioning Fundamental learning process first described by Ivan Pavlov. An event that automatically elicits a response is paired with another stimulus event that does not (a neutral stimulus). After repeated pairings, the neutral stimulus becomes a conditioned stimulus that by itself can elicit the desired response. (23)

classification Assignment of objects or people to categories based on shared characteristics. (84)

clinical assessment Systematic evaluation and measurement of psychological, biological, and social factors in a person presenting with a possible **psychological disorder**. (69)

clinical description Details of the combination of behaviours, thoughts, and feelings of an individual that make up a particular disorder. (8)

clinical efficacy One of a proposed set of guidelines for evaluating clinical interventions on the evidence of their effectiveness. (527)

clinical significance Degree to which research findings have useful and meaningful applications to real problems. (101)

clinical utility One of a proposed set of guidelines for evaluating clinical interventions by whether they can be applied effectively and cost effectively in real clinical settings. (528)

cognitive science Field of study that examines how humans and other animals acquire, process, store, and retrieve information. (52)

cognitive therapy Treatment approach that involves identifying and altering negative thinking styles related to **psychological disorders**, such as depression and **anxiety**, and replacing them with more positive beliefs and attitudes and, ultimately, more adaptive behaviour and coping styles. (246)

cognitive triad Aaron T. Beck's theory that depression may result from a tendency to think negatively about three areas: the self, the immediate world, and the future. (238)

cognitive-behavioural therapy (CBT) Group of treatment procedures aimed at identifying and modifying faulty thought processes, attitudes and attributions, and problem behaviours; often used synonymously with **cognitive therapy**. (56)

cohort effect Observation that people of different age groups also differ in their values and experiences. (112)

cohorts Participants in each age group of a cross-sectional research study. (112)

comorbidity Presence of two or more disorders in an individual at the same time. (90)

comparative treatment research Outcome research that contrasts two or more treatment methods to determine which is most effective. (106)

complicated grief Grief characterized by debilitating feelings of loss and emotions so painful that a person has trouble resuming a normal life; designated for further study as a disorder by the *DSM-5*. (221)

compulsions Repetitive, ritualistic, time-consuming behaviours or mental acts a person feels driven to perform. (173)

confound (confounding variable) Any factor occurring in a research study that makes the results uninterpretable because its effects cannot be separated from those of the variables being studied. (100)

control group Group of individuals in a research study who are similar to the experimental subjects in every way but are not exposed to the treatment received by the experimental group; their presence allows for a comparison of the differential effects of the treatment. (100)

controlled drinking Extremely controversial treatment approach to alcohol dependence in which severe abusers are taught to drink in moderation. (376)

conversion disorders Physical malfunctions, such as blindness or paralysis, suggesting neurological impairment, with no organic pathology to account for it. (168)

copy number variant Base pairs that are added or deleted as a result of mutations; these variants may play a role in the development of ADHD and other disorders. (461)

coronary heart disease (CHD) Blockage of the arteries supplying blood to the heart muscle, a major cause of death in Western culture, with social and psychological factors involved. (OLC–18)

correlation Degree to which two variables are associated. In a **positive correlation**, the two variables increase or decrease together; in a **negative correlation**, one variable decreases as the other increases. (103)

correlation coefficient Computed statistic reflecting the strength and direction of any association between two variables. It can range from +1.000 through zero (indicating no association) to −1.000, with the absolute value indicating the strength, and the sign reflecting the direction. (103)

course Pattern of development and change of a disorder over time. (8)

covert sensitization Cognitive-behavioural intervention to reduce unwanted behaviours by having clients imagine the extremely aversive consequences of the behaviours and establish negative rather than positive associations with them. (332)

Creutzfeldt-Jakob disease Extremely rare condition that causes **dementia**. (502)

criminal commitment Legal procedure by which a person who is found not criminally responsible on account of a mental disorder must be confined in a psychiatric hospital. (520)

cross-generational effect Limit to the **generalizability** of longitudinal research because the group under study may differ from others in culture and experience. (113)

cross-sectional design Methodology to examine a characteristic by comparing different individuals of different ages. Contrast with **longitudinal design**. (112)

cultural-familial intellectual disability Mild intellectual disability that may be caused largely by environmental influences. (481)

cyclothymic disorder Chronic (at least two years) **mood disorder** characterized by alternating **mood** elevation and depression levels that are not as severe as manic or **major depressive episodes**. (225)

dangerousness Tendency to violence that, contrary to popular opinion, is not more likely among mental patients. (517)

defence mechanisms Common patterns of behaviour, often adaptive coping styles when they occur in moderation, observed in response to particular situations. In **psychoanalysis**, these are thought to be **unconscious** processes originating in the **ego**. (19)

deinstitutionalization Systematic removal of people with severe **mental illness** or intellectual disability from institutions like psychiatric hospitals. (518)

delayed ejaculation Disorder in which a man achieves orgasm only with great difficulty. (313)

delirium Rapid-onset reduced clarity of consciousness and cognition, with confusion, disorientation, and deficits in memory and language. (490)

delirium tremens (DTs) Frightening **hallucinations** and body tremors that result when a heavy drinker withdraws from alcohol. Also called **withdrawal delirium**. (351)

delusion Psychotic symptom involving disorder of thought content and presence of strong beliefs that are misrepresentations of reality. (425)

delusional disorder Psychotic disorder featuring a persistent belief contrary to reality (**delusion**) but no other symptoms of **schizophrenia**. (431)

dementia Gradual-onset deterioration of brain functioning, involving memory loss, inability to recognize objects or faces, and problems in planning and abstract reasoning. These are associated with frustration and discouragement. (492)

dementia praecox Latin term meaning "premature loss of mind," an early label for what is now called **schizophrenia**, emphasizing the disorder's frequent appearance during adolescence. (423)

dependent personality disorder Cluster C (anxious or fearful) **personality disorder** characterized by a person's pervasive and excessive need to be taken care of, a condition that leads to submissive and clinging behaviour and **fears** of separation. (413)

dependent variable In an experimental research study, the phenomenon that is measured and expected to be influenced. (99)

depersonalization Term given to an alteration in perception that causes someone to temporarily lose the sense of their own reality. (198)

depersonalization-derealization disorder **Dissociative disorder** in which feelings of **depersonalization** are so severe they dominate the client's life and prevent normal functioning. (198)

depressants **Psychoactive substances** that result in behavioural sedation, including alcohol and the sedative, hypnotic, and anxiolytic drugs. (349)

derealization Situation in which the individual loses his or her sense of the reality of the external world. (198)

deterministic In genetics, **genes** that lead to nearly a 100 percent chance of developing the associated disorder. These are rare in the population. (503)

diagnosis Process of determining whether a **presenting problem** meets the established criteria for a specific **psychological disorder**. (69)

diathesis–stress model Hypothesis that both an inherited tendency (a vulnerability) and specific stressful conditions are required to produce a disorder. (37)

dimensional approach Method of categorizing characteristics on a continuum rather than on a binary, either-or, or all-or-none basis. (85)

disorganized speech Style of talking often seen in people with **schizophrenia** that involves incoherence and a lack of typical logic patterns. (429)

disorganized symptoms Least understood symptoms of schizophrenia that include erratic behaviours that affect speech, motor behaviour, and emotional reactions. (429)

disruptive mood dysregulation disorder Condition in which a child has chronic negative moods such as anger and irritability without any accompanying mania. (221)

dissociative amnesia **Dissociative disorder** featuring the inability to recall personal information, usually of a stressful or traumatic nature. (199)

dissociative disorders Disorders in which individuals feel detached from themselves or their surroundings, and reality, experience, and identity may disintegrate. (198)

dissociative fugue **Dissociative disorder** featuring sudden, unexpected travel away from home, along with an inability to recall the past, sometimes with assumption of a new identity. (200)

dissociative identity disorder (DID) Formerly known as *multiple personality disorder*, a disorder in which as many as one hundred personalities or fragments of personalities coexist within one body and mind. (201)

dissociative trance disorder (DTD) Altered state of consciousness in which the person believes firmly that he or she is possessed by spirits; considered a disorder only where there is distress and dysfunction. (201)

dopamine **Neurotransmitter** whose generalized function is to activate other neurotransmitters and to aid in exploratory and pleasure-seeking behaviours (thus balancing **serotonin**). A relative excess of dopamine is implicated in **schizophrenia** (though contradictory evidence suggests the connection is not simple) and its deficit is involved in **Parkinson's disease**. (48)

double bind According to an obsolete, unsupported theory, the practice of transmitting conflicting messages that was thought to cause **schizophrenia**. (443)

double depression Severe **mood disorder** typified by **major depressive episodes** superimposed over a background of dysthymic disorder. (218)

double-blind control Procedure in outcome studies that prevents bias by ensuring that neither the subjects nor the providers of the experimental treatment know who is receiving treatment and who is receiving placebo. (106)

Down syndrome Type of intellectual disability caused by a chromosomal aberration (on chromosome 21) and involving characteristic physical appearance. (480)

dream analysis Psychoanalytic therapy method in which dream contents are examined as symbolic of **id** impulses and **intrapsychic conflicts**. (21)

duty to warn Mental health professionals' responsibility to break confidentiality and notify the potential victim whom a client has specifically threatened. (523)

dyssomnias Problems in getting to sleep or in obtaining sufficient quality sleep. (293)

effect size Statistical measure that shows the amount of difference among the members of a group in a clinical study. (101)

ego In **psychoanalysis**, the psychical entity responsible for finding realistic and practical ways to satisfy **id** drives. (19)

ego psychology Derived from **psychoanalysis**, this theory emphasizes the role of the **ego** in development and attributes **psychological disorders** to failure of the ego to manage impulses and internal conflicts. (21)

electroconvulsive therapy (ECT) Biological treatment for severe, chronic depression involving the application of electrical impulses through the brain to produce seizures. The reasons for its effectiveness are unknown. (243)

electroencephalogram (EEG) Measure of electrical activity patterns in the brain taken through electrodes placed on the scalp. (83)

emotion Pattern of action elicited by an external event and a feeling state, accompanied by a characteristic physiological response. (58)

endogenous opioids Substances occurring naturally throughout the body that function like **neurotransmitters** to shut down pain sensation even in the presence of marked tissue damage. These may contribute to psychological problems such as eating disorders. Also known as *endorphins* or *enkephalins*. (OLC–23)

endophenotypes Genetic mechanisms that contribute to the underlying problems causing the symptoms and difficulties experienced by people with psychological **disorders**. (109)

epidemiology **Psychopathology** research method examining the **prevalence**, distribution, and consequences of disorders in populations. (103)

epigenetics Study of factors other than inherited DNA sequence, such as new learning or **stress**, that alter the phenotypic expression of **genes**. (40)

equifinality Developmental **psychopathology** principle that a behaviour or disorder may have several different causes. (63)

erectile disorder Recurring inability in some men to attain or maintain adequate penile erection until completion of sexual activity. (311)

essential hypertension High blood pressure with no verifiable physical cause, which makes up the overwhelming majority of high blood pressure cases. (OLC–17)

etiology Cause or source of a disorder. (8)

excoriation Recurrent, difficult-to-control picking of one's skin leading to significant impairment or distress. (183)

exhibitionistic disorder Disorder in which sexual gratification is attained by exposing the genitals to unsuspecting strangers. (326)

experiment Research method that can establish causation by manipulating the variables in question and controlling for other alternative explanations of any observed effects. (105)

expert witness Person who because of special training and experience is allowed to offer opinion testimony in legal trials. (523)

expressed emotion (EE) Hostility, criticism, and overinvolvement demonstrated by some families toward a family member with a **psychological disorder**; this can often contribute to the person's relapse. (444)

external validity Extent to which research study findings generalize, or apply, to people and settings not involved in the study. (99)

extinction Learning process in which a response maintained by **reinforcement** in operant conditioning or pairing in **classical conditioning** decreases when that reinforcement or pairing is removed; also the procedure of removing that reinforcement or pairing. (24)

facial agnosia Type of **agnosia** characterized by a person's inability to recognize even familiar faces. (494)

factitious disorders Nonexistent physical or **psychological disorders** deliberately faked for no apparent gain except possibly sympathy and attention. (169)

false negative Assessment error in which no pathology is noted (i.e., test results are negative) when it is actually present. (81)

false positive Assessment error in which pathology is reported (i.e., test results are positive) when none is actually present. (81)

family studies Genetic studies that examine patterns of traits and behaviours among relatives. (109)

fear Immediate emotional alarm reaction to present danger or life-threatening emergencies. (121)

female orgasmic disorder Recurring delay or absence of orgasm in some women following a normal sexual excitement phase, relative to their prior experience and current stimulation. Also known as *inhibited female orgasm*. (313)

female sexual interest/arousal disorder Recurrent inability in some women to attain or maintain adequate lubrication and swelling sexual excitement responses until completion of sexual activity. (309)

fetal alcohol syndrome (FAS) Pattern of problems including learning difficulties, behaviour deficits, and characteristic physical flaws, resulting from heavy drinking by the victim's mother when she was pregnant with the victim. (351)

fetishistic disorder Long-term, recurring, intense, sexually arousing urges, fantasies, or behaviour involving the use of nonliving, unusual objects, which cause distress or impairment in life functioning. (326)

fight/flight system (FFS) **Brain circuit** in animals that, when stimulated, causes an immediate alarm and escape response resembling human **panic**. (124)

fitness to stand trial To stand trial, people must be able to understand the charges against them and to assist with their own defence. (522)

flat affect Apparently emotionless demeanour (including toneless speech and vacant gaze) when a reaction would be expected. (429)

flight-or-fight response Biological reaction to alarming stressors that musters the body's resources (e.g., blood flow, respiration) to resist or flee the threat. (57)

folie à deux Psychotic disturbance in which an individual develops a **delusion** similar to that of a person with whom he or she shares a close relationship. Also called **shared psychotic disorder**. (433)

fragile X syndrome Pattern of abnormality caused by a defect in the X chromosome that results in intellectual disability, learning problems, and unusual physical characteristics. (481)

free association Psychoanalytic therapy technique intended to explore threatening material repressed into the **unconscious**. The patient is instructed to say whatever comes to mind without censoring. (21)

frontotemporal neurocognitive disorder Condition that damages the frontal or temporal regions of the brain; behaviour or language is negatively affected. (499)

frotteuristic disorder Sexual arousal from touching or rubbing against a nonconsenting person, such as in a crowded subway. (325)

gambling disorder Condition in which individuals are unable to resist the urge to gamble, which results in negative personal consequences (e.g., divorce, loss of employment). (379)

gamma aminobutyric acid (GABA) **Neurotransmitter** that reduces activity across the synapse and thus inhibits a range of behaviours and **emotions**, especially generalized **anxiety**. (350)

gamma aminobutyric acid (GABA) system Inhibitory **neurotransmitter** system that is thought to be associated with excessive **anxiety**. (47)

gender dysphoria Psychological dissatisfaction with biological gender, a disturbance in the sense of identity as a male or female. The primary goal is not sexual arousal but rather to live the life of the opposite gender. (334)

gender nonconformity Phenomenon in which prepubescent children do not identify with their biological sex, but instead identify strongly with the gender of the opposite sex and display varying degrees of behaviour more characteristic of the opposite sex. (336)

gender reassignment surgery Physically altering anatomy to be consistent with gender identity. This procedure is also sometimes called sex reassignment surgery and gender confirming surgery. (338)

gene–environment correlation model Hypothesis that people with a genetic predisposition for a disorder may also have a genetic tendency to create environmental risk factors that promote the disorder. (39)

general adaptation syndrome (GAS) Sequence of reactions to sustained **stress** described by Hans Selye. These stages are alarm, resistance, and exhaustion, which may lead to death. (OLC–5)

generalizability Extent to which research results apply to a range of individuals not included in the study. (101)

generalized amnesia Condition in which a person loses memory of all personal information, including his or her own identity. (199)

generalized anxiety disorder (GAD) **Anxiety** disorder characterized by intense, uncontrollable, unfocused, chronic, and continuous worry that is distressing and unproductive accompanied by physical symptoms of tenseness, irritability, and restlessness. (128)

genes Long deoxyribonucleic acid (DNA) molecules, the basic physical units of heredity, that appear as locations on chromosomes. (35)

genetic linkage analysis Studies that seek to match the inheritance pattern of a disorder to that of a **genetic marker**; this helps researchers establish the location of the **gene** responsible for the disorder. (111)

genetic marker Inherited characteristic for which the chromosomal location of the responsible **gene** is known. (111)

genito-pelvic pain/penetration disorder Sexual dysfunction in which a woman experiences pain or difficulty with penetration during intercourse; may include **vaginismus**. (315)

genotypes Specific genetic makeup of individuals. (108)

glutamate Amino acid neurotransmitter that excites many different neurons, leading to action. (47)

hallucination Psychotic symptom of a perceptual disturbance in which things are seen or heard or otherwise sensed although they are not real or actually present. (427)

hallucinogens Any **psychoactive substances** such as LSD or **marijuana** that can produce **delusions, hallucinations, paranoia,** and altered sensory perception. (349)

harm reduction Approach to **substance abuse** prevention and treatment that seeks to minimize the harm associated with substance use as its primary goal (e.g., **controlled drinking** interventions, safe injection sites for injection drug users). (373)

health psychology Subfield of **behavioural medicine** that studies psychological factors important in health promotion and mainte-nance. (OLC–4)

hebephrenia Silly and immature emotionality, a characteristic of some types of **schizophrenia**. (423)

histrionic personality disorder Cluster B (dramatic, emotional, or erratic) **personality disorder** involving a pervasive pattern of excessive emotionality and atten-tion seeking. (409)

hormone Chemical messenger produced by the endocrine glands. (45)

human genome project Ongoing scientific attempt to develop a comprehensive map of all human **genes**. (109)

human immunodeficiency virus-type-1 Virus that causes **acquired immune deficiency syndrome (AIDS)** and can also cause neu-rocognitive disorder. (499)

Huntington's disease Genetic disorder marked by involuntary limb movements and progressing to **dementia**. (500)

hypersomnolence disorders Sleep dysfunc-tion involving an excessive amount of sleep that disrupts normal routines. (296)

hypertension Also known as *high blood pres-sure*; a major risk factor for **stroke** and heart and kidney disease that is intimately related to psychological factors. (OLC–16)

hypomanic episode Less severe and less dis-ruptive version of a manic episode that is one of the criteria for several **mood disorders**. (216)

hypothesis Educated guess or statement to be tested by research. (99)

id In **psychoanalysis**, the **unconscious** psy-chical entity present at birth representing basic drives. (19)

illness anxiety disorder Involves severe **anxiety** over belief in having a disease without any evident physical cause. (161)

immune system Body's means of identifying and eliminating any foreign materials (e.g., bacteria, parasites, even transplanted organs) that enter. (OLC–8)

implicit cognition Cognitive processes of the **unconscious** that are difficult to measure because people cannot verbalize them, as they are not even aware of them. (55)

implicit memory Condition of memory in which a person cannot recall past events even though he or she acts in response to them. (55)

impulse-control disorders Disorders in which a person acts on an irresistible, but poten-tially harmful, impulse. (345)

inappropriate affect Emotional displays that are improper for the situation. (430)

incidence Number of new cases of a disorder appearing during a specific time period (compare with **prevalence**). (104)

independent variable Phenomenon that is manipulated by the experimenter in a research study and expected to influence the **dependent variable**. (99)

informed consent Ethical requirement whereby research subjects agree to participate in a research study only after they receive full disclosure about the nature of the study and their own role in it. (116)

insomnia disorder Condition in which insuf-ficient sleep interferes with normal func-tioning. (294)

integrated grief Grief that evolves from acute grief into a condition in which the indi-vidual accepts the finality of a death and adjusts to the loss. (221)

intellectual disability (ID) Significantly sub-average intellectual functioning paired with deficits in adaptive functioning such as self-care or occupational activities, appearing before age. (476)

intelligence quotient (IQ) Score on an intelli-gence test, abbreviated IQ, estimating a person's deviation from average test per-formance. (80)

intermittent explosive disorder Episodes during which a person acts on aggressive impulses that result in serious assaults or destruction of property. (380)

internal validity Extent to which the results of a research study can be attributed to the **independent variable** after confounding alternative explanations have been ruled out. (99)

interpersonal psychotherapy (IPT) Therapy that focuses on resolving problems in existing relationships and learning to form important new interpersonal relationships. (247)

intrapsychic conflict In **psychoanalysis**, the struggles among the **id**, **ego**, and **superego**. (19)

introspection Early, nonscientific approach to the study of psychology involving systematic attempts to report thoughts and feelings that specific stimuli evoked. (24)

inverse agonists Chemical substances that produce effects opposite those of a partic-ular **neurotransmitter**. (46)

joint attention Attention shared by two per-sons toward an object after one person has indicated interest in the object to the other person; this social interaction is limited or absent in people with **autism spectrum disorder**. (470)

kleptomania Recurrent failure to resist urges to steal things not needed for personal use or their monetary value. (381)

labelling Applying a name to a phenomenon or a pattern of behaviour. The label may acquire negative connotations or be applied erroneously to the person rather than his or her behaviours. (90)

language disorder Limited speech in all situ-ations; *expressive language* (what is said) is significantly below *receptive language* (what is understood); receptive language is usually average. (466)

learned helplessness Condition in which a person begins to believe that he or she has no control over his or her life. (53)

learned helplessness theory of depression Seligman's theory that people become anx-ious and depressed when they make an attribution that they have no control over the **stress** in their lives (whether in reality they do or not). (237)

level Degree of behaviour change with dif-ferent interventions (e.g., high, low). (107)

lifetime prevalence Number of people in the population who have ever had the disorder. (8)

localized amnesia Memory loss limited to specific times and events, particularly trau-matic events. Also known as **selective amnesia**. (199)

longitudinal design Systematic study of changes in the same individual or group examined over time. (112)

LSD (d-lysergic acid diethylamide) Most common hallucinogenic drug; a synthetic version of the grain fungus ergot. (362)

maintenance treatment Combination of con-tinued **psychosocial** treatment or medica-tion designed to prevent relapse following therapy. (248)

major depressive disorder Mood disorder involving one *(single episode)* or more (separated by at least two months without depression, *recurrent*) **major depressive episodes**. (216)

major depressive episode Most common and severe experience of depression, including feelings of worthlessness, distur-bances in bodily activities such as sleep, loss of interest, and the inability to experi-ence pleasure, persisting at least two weeks. (214)

major neurocognitive disorder Gradual deterioration of brain functioning that affects memory, judgment, language, and other advanced cognitive processes. (492)

male hypoactive sexual desire disorder Dysfunction in which a man feels distress from having little or no sexual interest. (309)

male orgasmic disorder Recurring delay in or absence of orgasm in some men following a normal sexual excitement phase, relative to age and current stimulation. Also known as *inhibited male orgasm*. (313)

malingering Deliberate faking of a physical or **psychological disorder** motivated by gain. (169)

mania Period of abnormally excessive elation or euphoria, associated with some **mood disorders**. (215)

marijuana (cannabis) Dried part of the hemp plant, a **hallucinogen** that is the most widely used illegal substance. (363)

mental hygiene movement Mid-20th-century effort to improve care of the mentally disordered by informing the public of their mistreatment. (16)

mental illness Term formerly used to mean **psychological disorder** but less preferred because it implies that the causes of the disorder can be found in a medical disease process. (517)

mental status exam Relatively coarse preliminary test of a client's judgment, orientation to time and place, and emotional and mental state; typically conducted during an initial interview. (71)

microsleeps Short, seconds-long periods of sleep that occur in people who have been deprived of sleep. (293)

mild neurocognitive disorder Modest impairment in cognitive abilities that can be overcome with accommodations such as extensive lists or elaborate schedules. (492)

mixed features Condition in which the individual experiences both elation and depression or **anxiety** at the same time. Also known as *dysphoric manic episode* or *mixed manic episode*. (216)

modelling Learning through observation and imitation of the behaviour of other individuals and the consequences of that behaviour; also known as **observational learning**. (54)

mood Enduring period of emotionality. (58)

mood disorders Group of disorders involving severe and enduring disturbances in emotionality ranging from elation to severe depression. (58, 214)

moral therapy Nineteenth-century **psychosocial** approach to treatment that involved treating patients as normally as possible in normal environments. (15)

multidimensional integrative approach Approach to the study of **psychopathology** that holds that **psychological disorders** are always the products of multiple interacting causal factors. (33)

multiple baseline Single-case experimental **design** in which measures are taken on two or more behaviours, or on a single behaviour in two or more situations. A particular intervention is introduced for each at different times. If behaviour change is coincident with each introduction, this is strong evidence the intervention caused the change. (108)

narcissistic personality disorder Cluster B (dramatic, emotional, or erratic) personality disorder involving a pervasive pattern of grandiosity in fantasy or behaviour, need for admiration, and lack of empathy. (410)

narcolepsy Sleep disorder involving sudden and irresistible sleep attacks. (297)

natural environment phobia Extreme **fear** of situations or events in nature, especially heights, storms, and water. (143)

naturalistic teaching strategies Instructional techniques that are used with children having neurodevelopmental disorders and that move away from traditional desk instruction toward more natural social interactions. (475)

negative correlation Association between two variables in which one increases as the other decreases. (103)

negative symptoms Less outgoing symptoms, such as **flat affect** and poverty of speech, displayed by some people with **schizophrenia**. (428)

neurocognitive disorder due to Alzheimer's disease Condition resulting from a disease that develops most often in people 50 and older; characterized by multiple cognitive defects that develop gradually and steadily. (499)

neurocognitive disorder due to HIV infection Less common type of neurocognitive disorder that affects people who have HIV; may lead to impaired thinking in advanced stages. (499)

neurocognitive disorder due to Huntington's disease Neurological disorder that follows a subcortical pattern and is notable for causing involuntary limb movements. (501)

neurocognitive disorder due to Lewy body disease Neurological impairment that affects people with Lewy body disease, in which protein deposits damage brain cells and gradually cause motor impairments and loss of alertness. (499)

neurocognitive disorder due to Parkinson's disease Disorder characterized by progressive decline in motor movements; results from damage to dopamine pathways. (499)

neurocognitive disorder due to prion disease Rare progressive neurodegenerative disorder caused by prions, proteins that can reproduce themselves and cause damage to brain cells. (501)

neurocognitive disorder due to traumatic brain injury Condition resulting from jarring of the brain caused by a blow to the head or other impact; symptoms persist for at least a week after the initial trauma. (499)

neurodevelopmental disorders Neurologically based disorders that are revealed in a clinically significant way during a child's developing years. (457)

neurohormones Hormones that affect the brain and are increasingly the focus of study in **psychopathology**. (234)

neuroimaging Sophisticated computer-aided procedures that allow nonintrusive examination of nervous system structure and function. (81)

neuropsychological testing Assessment of brain and nervous system functioning by testing an individual's performance on behavioural tasks. (80)

neuroscience Study of the nervous system and its role in behaviour, thoughts, and **emotions**. (41)

neurosis (neuroses, plural) Obsolete psychodynamic term for a **psychological disorder** thought to result from **unconscious** conflicts and the **anxiety** they cause. (20)

neurotransmitters Chemicals that cross the **synaptic cleft** between nerve cells to transmit impulses from one **neuron** to the next. Their relative excess or deficiency is involved in several **psychological disorders**. (42)

nightmares Frightening and **anxiety**-provoking dreams occurring during rapid eye movement (REM) sleep. The individual recalls the bad dreams and recovers alertness and orientation quickly. (303)

nomenclature In a naming system or **nosology**, the actual labels or names that are applied. In **psychopathology** these include, for example, mood disorders and eating disorders. (84)

noradrenaline See **norepinephrine**. (48)

norepinephrine (also noradrenaline) **Neurotransmitter** that is active in the central and peripheral nervous systems controlling heart rate, blood pressure, and respiration, among other functions. Because of its role in the body's alarm reaction, it may also contribute in general and indirectly to **panic attacks** and other disorders. (48)

nosology Classification and naming system for medical and psychological phenomena. (84)

observational learning Type of learning that does not require direct experience; rather, an organism can learn by observing what happens to another organism and later imitating the other organism's behaviour (also known as **modelling**). (54)

obsessions Recurrent intrusive thoughts or impulses the client seeks to suppress or neutralize while recognizing they are not imposed by outside forces. (173)

obsessive-compulsive disorder (OCD) **Anxiety** disorder involving unwanted, persistent, intrusive thoughts and impulses as well as repetitive actions intended to suppress them. (173)

obsessive-compulsive personality disorder Cluster C (anxious or fearful) **personality disorder** featuring a pervasive pattern of preoccupation with orderliness, perfectionism, and mental and interpersonal control at the expense of flexibility, openness, and efficiency. (415)

opiates Natural chemicals in the opium poppy that have a narcotic effect. (349)

opioid-related disorders Cognitive, biological, behavioural, and social problems associated with the use and abuse of **opiates** and their synthetic variants. (360)

opioids Family of addictive **psychoactive substances** that includes natural opiates, synthetic variations (methadone, pethidine), and the comparable substances that occur naturally in the brain (enkephalins, beta-endorphins, and dynorphins) and that cause temporary euphoria and analgesia (pain reduction). (360)

orgasmic reconditioning Learning procedure to help clients strengthen appropriate patterns of sexual arousal by pairing appropriate stimuli with the pleasurable sensations of masturbation. (333)

other drugs Other substances that are abused but do not fit into typical categories; include inhalants (e.g., airplane glue), anabolic steroids, and other over-the-counter and prescription medications (e.g., nitrous oxide). (383)

pain catastrophizing Exaggerated negative response during an actual or anticipated painful experience. Catastrophizers ruminate on and magnify the pain, and they often feel helpless in the face of the pain. (OLC–22)

panic Sudden overwhelming fright or terror. (122)

panic attack Abrupt experience of intense **fear** or discomfort accompanied by physical symptoms such as dizziness or heart palpitations. (122)

panic control treatment (PCT) Cognitive-behavioural treatment for **panic attacks**, involving gradual exposure to feared somatic sensations and modification of perceptions and attitudes about them. (140)

panic disorder Recurrent unexpected panic attacks accompanied by concern about future attacks and/or a lifestyle change to avoid future attacks. (133)

paranoia Person's irrational beliefs that he or she is especially important (**delusions** of grandeur) or that other people are seeking to do him or her harm. (423)

paranoid personality disorder Cluster A (odd or eccentric) **personality disorder** involving pervasive distrust and suspiciousness of others such that their motives are interpreted as malevolent. (391)

paraphilic disorders Sexual disorders in which sexual arousal occurs almost exclusively in the context of inappropriate objects or individuals. (325)

parasomnias Abnormal behaviours such as **nightmares** or **sleepwalking** that occur during sleep. (293)

Parkinson's disease Degenerative brain disorder principally affecting motor performance (e.g., tremors, stooped posture) associated with reduction in **dopamine**. **Dementia** may be a result as well. (499)

patient uniformity myth Tendency to consider all members of a category as more similar than they are, ignoring their individual differences. (101)

pedophilic disorder Paraphilic disorder involving strong sexual attraction toward children. (329)

persistent depressive disorder (dysthymia) Mood disorder involving persistently depressed **mood**, with low self-esteem, **withdrawal**, pessimism, or despair; present for at least two years, with no absence of symptoms for more than two months. (216)

personality disorder Enduring maladaptive pattern for relating to the environment and oneself, exhibited in a wide range of contexts that cause significant functional impairment or subjective distress. (387)

personality inventories Self-report questionnaires that assess personal traits by asking respondents to identify descriptions that apply to them. (77)

person-centred therapy Therapy method in which the client, rather than the counsellor, primarily directs the course of discussion, seeking self-discovery and self-responsibility. (22)

phenotypes Observable characteristics or behaviours of individuals. (108)

phobia Any **psychological disorder** characterized by marked and persistent fear of an object or situation. (3)

physiological dependence One symptom of substance use disorders; includes the use of increasingly greater amounts of the drug to experience the same effect (**tolerance**), and a negative physical response when the substance is no longer ingested (**withdrawal**). (347)

Pick's disease Very rare neurological disorder that results in presenile (early onset) **dementia**. (499)

placebo control groups In outcome **experiments**, **control groups** that do not receive the experimental manipulation but are given a similar procedure with an identical expectation of change, allowing the researcher to assess any **placebo effect**. (105)

placebo effect Behaviour change resulting from the person's expectation of change rather than from the experimental manipulation itself. (105)

polysomnographic (PSG) evaluation Assessment of sleep disorders in which a client sleeping in the lab is monitored for heart, muscle, respiration, brain wave, and other functions. (293)

polysubstance use Use of multiple mind-altering and behaviour-altering substances, such as drugs. (345)

positive correlation Association between two variables in which one increases as the other increases. (103)

positive symptoms More overt symptoms, such as **delusions** and **hallucinations**, displayed by some people with **schizophrenia**. (425)

post-traumatic stress disorder (PTSD) Enduring, distressing emotional disorder that follows exposure to a severe helplessness- or **fear**-inducing threat. The victim re-experiences the trauma, avoids stimuli associated with it, and develops a numbing of responsiveness and an increased vigilance and arousal. (189)

premature ejaculation Recurring ejaculation before the person wants it, with minimal sexual stimulation. (314)

premenstrual dysphoric disorder (PMDD) Disorder of mood whose symptoms include physical symptoms, severe mood swings, and anxiety that cause incapacitation during most menstrual cycles, starting in the final week before the onset of menses, improving within a few days after the onset of menses, and becoming absent in the week post-menses. (221)

prepared learning Certain associations can be learned more readily than others because this ability has been adaptive for evolution. (55)

presenting problem Original complaint reported by the client to the therapist. The actual treated problem may sometimes be a modification derived from the presenting problem. (8)

prevalence Number of people displaying a disorder in the total population at any given time (compare with **incidence**). (8, 104)

proband In genetics research, the individual displaying the trait or characteristic being studied. Also known as *index case*. (109)

prodromal stage Period during which some symptoms appear but before development of full symptoms. (435)

prognosis Predicted future development of a disorder over time. (8)

projective tests Psychoanalytically based measures that present ambiguous stimuli to clients on the assumption that their responses will reveal their **unconscious** conflicts. Such tests are inferential and lack high **reliability** and **validity**. (76)

prosody Vocal characteristics such as tone and stress; people with **autism spectrum disorder** often have trouble recognizing and interpreting these vocal cues. (471)

prototypical approach System for categorizing disorders using both essential, defining characteristics and a range of variation on other characteristics. (85)

psychoactive substances Substances, such as drugs, that alter **mood** or behaviour. (346)

psychoanalysis Psychoanalytic assessment and therapy, which emphasizes exploration of, and insight into, **unconscious** processes and conflicts, pioneered by Sigmund Freud. (17)

psychoanalyst Therapist who practises **psychoanalysis** after earning either an M.D. or Ph.D. degree and then receiving additional specialized postdoctoral training. (21)

psychoanalytic model Complex and comprehensive theory originally advanced by Sigmund Freud that seeks to account for the development and structure of personality, as well as the origin of abnormal behaviour, based primarily on inferred inner entities and forces. (18)

psychodynamic psychotherapy Contemporary version of **psychoanalysis** that still emphasizes **unconscious** processes and conflicts but is briefer and more focused on specific problems. (22)

psychological autopsy Post-mortem psychological profile of a suicide victim constructed from interviews with people who knew the person before death. (254)

psychological disorder Psychological dysfunction associated with distress or impairment in functioning that is not a typical or culturally expected response. (3)

psychological factors affecting medical condition Somatic condition in which a psychological characteristic affects a diagnosed medical condition, such as asthma being exacerbated by **anxiety**. (168)

psychoneuroimmunology Study of psychological influences on the neurological responding involved in the body's immune response. (OLC–10)

psycho-oncology Study of psychological factors involved in the **course** and treatment of **cancer**. (OLC–13)

psychopathology Scientific study of **psychological disorders**. (6)

psychopathy Non-*DSM* category similar to **antisocial personality disorder** but with less emphasis on overt behaviour; indicators include superficial charm, lack of remorse, and other personality characteristics. (397)

psychophysiological assessment Measurement of changes in the nervous system reflecting psychological or emotional events, such as anxiety, stress, and sexual arousal. (83)

psychosexual stages of development In **psychoanalysis**, the sequence of phases a person passes through during development. Each stage is named for the location on the body where **id** gratification is maximal at that time. (20)

psychosocial Social and cultural factors (such as family experience) and psychological influences. (15)

psychosis Term used to characterize many unusual behaviours, although in its strictest sense it usually involves **delusions** and **hallucinations**. (425)

psychotherapy process How psychotherapy works. (23)

psychotic disorder due to another medical condition Condition that is characterized by hallucinations or delusions and that is the direct result of another physiological disorder, such as stroke or brain tumour. (433)

purging techniques In the eating disorder **bulimia nervosa**, the self-induced vomiting or laxative abuse used to compensate for excessive food ingestion. (265)

pyromania Impulse-control disorder that involves having an irresistible urge to set fires. (382)

randomization Method for placing individuals into research groups that assures each one of an equal chance of being assigned to any group, to eliminate any systematic differences across groups. (101)

rapid eye movement (REM) sleep Periodic intervals of sleep during which the eyes move rapidly from side to side, and dreams occur, but the body is inactive. (292)

reactive attachment disorder Attachment disorder in which a child with disturbed behaviour neither seeks out a caregiver nor responds to offers of help from one; fearfulness and sadness are often evident. (197)

rebound insomnia In a person with insomnia, the worsened sleep problems that can occur when medications are used to treat insomnia and then withdrawn. (296)

reinforcement In operant conditioning, consequences for behaviour that strengthen it or increase its frequency. Positive reinforcement involves the contingent delivery of a desired consequence; negative reinforcement is the contingent escape from an aversive consequence. Unwanted behaviours may result from their reinforcement, or the failure to reinforce desired behaviours. (26)

relapse prevention Extending therapeutic progress by teaching the client how to cope with future troubling situations. (334, 378)

relaxation response Active components of meditation methods, including repetitive thoughts of a sound to reduce distracting thoughts, and closing the mind to other intruding thoughts, that decrease the flow of stress hormones and neurotransmitters and cause a feeling of calm. (OLC–27)

reliability Degree to which a measurement is consistent—for example, over time or among different raters. (70)

repeated measurement When responses are measured on more than two occasions (not just before and after intervention) to assess trends. (106)

research design Plan of experimentation used to test a **hypothesis**. (99)

retrospective information Literally "the view back," data collected by examining records or recollections of the past. It is limited by the accuracy, **validity**, and thoroughness of the sources. (112)

reuptake Action by which a **neurotransmitter** is quickly drawn back into the discharging **neuron** after being released into a **synaptic cleft**. (46)

rheumatoid arthritis Painful, degenerative disease in which the **immune system** essentially attacks itself, resulting in stiffness, swelling, and even destruction of the joints. Cognitive-behavioural treatments can help relieve pain and stiffness. (OLC–9)

schizoaffective disorder Psychotic disorder featuring symptoms of both **schizophrenia** and major **mood disorder**. (431)

schizoid personality disorder Cluster A (odd or eccentric) **personality disorder** featuring a pervasive pattern of detachment from social relationships and a restricted range of expression of **emotions**. (394)

schizophrenia Devastating psychotic disorder that may involve characteristic disturbances in thinking (**delusions**), perception (**hallucinations**), speech, **emotions**, and behaviour. (423)

schizophreniform disorder Psychotic disorder involving the symptoms of **schizophrenia** but lasting less than six months. (430)

schizophrenogenic According to an obsolete, unsupported theory, a cold, dominating, rejecting parent who was thought to cause **schizophrenia** in his or her offspring. (443)

schizotypal personality disorder Cluster A (odd or eccentric) **personality disorder** involving a pervasive pattern of interpersonal deficits featuring acute discomfort with, and reduced capacity for, close relationships, as well as by cognitive or perceptual distortions and eccentricities of behaviour. (395)

scientist-practitioner model Expectation that mental health professionals will apply scientific methods to their work. They must keep current in the latest research on **diagnosis** and treatment, they must evaluate their own methods for effectiveness, and they may generate their own research to discover new knowledge of disorders and their treatment. (7)

seasonal affective disorder (SAD) Mood disorder involving a cycling of episodes corresponding to the seasons of the year, typically with depression occurring during the winter. (220)

selective amnesia Memory loss limited to specific times and events, particularly traumatic events. Also known as **localized amnesia**. (199)

self-actualizing Process emphasized in humanistic psychology in which people strive to achieve their highest potential against difficult life experiences. (22)

self-efficacy Person's perception that he or she has the ability to cope with **stress** or challenges. (OLC–7)

self-monitoring Action by which clients observe and record their own behaviours as either an assessment of a problem and its change or a treatment procedure that makes them more aware of their responses. Also called self-observation. (75)

separation anxiety disorder Excessive enduring **fear** in some children that harm will come to them or their parents while they are apart. (147)

sequential design Combination of the cross-sectional and longitudinal research methods involving repeated study of different **cohorts** over time. (113)

serotonin Neurotransmitter involved in processing information and coordination of movement as well as inhibition and restraint; it also assists in the regulation of eating, sexual, and aggressive behaviours, all of which may be involved in different **psychological disorders**. Its interaction with **dopamine** is implicated in **schizophrenia**. (47)

sexual dysfunctions Sexual disorders in which the client finds it difficult to function adequately while having sex. (309)

sexual masochism disorder Paraphilic disorder in which sexual arousal is associated with experiencing pain or humiliation. (328)

sexual sadism disorder Paraphilic disorder in which sexual arousal is associated with inflicting pain or humiliation. (328)

shaping In operant conditioning, the development of a new response by reinforcing successively more similar versions of that

response. Both desirable and undesirable behaviours may be learned in this manner. (26)

shared psychotic disorder Psychotic disturbance in which an individual develops a delusion similar to that of a person with whom he or she shares a close relationship. Also called **folie à deux**. (443)

single-case experimental design Research tactic in which an **independent variable** is manipulated for a single individual, allowing cause-and-effect conclusions, but with limited **generalizability** (contrast with **case study method**). (106)

situational phobias Anxieties involving enclosed places (e.g., claustrophobia) or public transportation (e.g., **fear** of flying). (143)

sleep apnea Disorder involving brief periods when breathing ceases during sleep. (297)

sleep efficiency (SE) Percentage of time actually spent sleeping of the total time spent in bed. (293)

sleep terrors Episodes of apparent awakening from sleep, accompanied by signs of **panic**, followed by disorientation and amnesia for the incident. These occur during non-REM sleep and so do not involve frightening dreams. (303)

sleepwalking (or somnambulism) Parasomnia that involves leaving the bed during NREM—deep, nondreaming—sleep. (304)

social anxiety disorder Extreme, enduring, irrational **fear** and avoidance of social or performance situations. (143)

somatic symptom disorders Disorders involving extreme and long-lasting focus on multiple physical symptoms for which no medical cause is evident; previously known as *somatization disorders*. (161)

specific learning disorder Neurodevelopmental disorder characterized by academic performance that is substantially below what would be expected given the person's age, **intelligence quotient (IQ)** score, and education. (464)

specific phobia Unreasonable **fear** of a specific object or situation that markedly interferes with daily life functioning. (141)

standardization Process of establishing specific norms and requirements for a measurement technique to ensure it is used consistently across measurement occasions. This includes instructions for administering the measure, evaluating its findings, and comparing these to data for large numbers of people. (70)

statistical significance Probability that obtaining the observed research findings merely by chance is small. (101)

stigma Combination of stereotypic negative beliefs, prejudices, and attitudes resulting

in reduced life opportunities for the devalued group in question. (90)

stimulants Group of **psychoactive substances** that elevate **mood**, activity, and alertness, including amphetamines, caffeine, cocaine, and nicotine. (349)

stress Body's physiological response to a stressor, which is any event or change that requires adaptation. (OLC–5)

strokes Temporary blockages of blood vessels supplying the brain, or ruptures of vessels in the brain, resulting in temporary or permanent loss of brain functioning. Also called **cerebral vascular accidents (CVA)**. (OLC–16)

stuttering Now referred to as childhood-onset fluency disorder; a disturbance in speech fluency that causes the speaker to repeat words, prolong sounds, and extend pauses. (466)

substance intoxication Physiological reactions, such as impaired judgment and motor ability as well as **mood** changes, resulting from the ingestion of **psychoactive substances**. (346)

substance use disorder Defined in terms of how significantly the use of any substance interferes with the user's life; use disrupts the user's education, job, or relationships, and put him or her in physically dangerous situations. (347)

substance-induced psychotic disorder Psychosis caused by the ingestion of medications, psychoactive drugs, or toxins. (433)

substance/medication-induced neurocognitive disorder Brain damage caused by prolonged use of drugs, often in combination with a poor diet. (502)

substance-related and addictive disorders Range of problems associated with the use and abuse of drugs such as alcohol, cocaine, heroin, and other substances people use to alter the way they think, feel, and behave. These are extremely costly in human and financial terms. (345)

suicidal attempts Efforts made to kill oneself. (252)

suicidal ideation Serious thoughts about committing suicide. (252)

superego In **psychoanalysis**, the psychical entity representing the internalized moral standards of parents and society. (19)

susceptibility Slightly increased risk of developing a disease because of the genes a person has. (503)

synaptic cleft Space between nerve cells where chemical transmitters act to move impulses from one **neuron** to the next. (42)

systematic desensitization Behavioural therapy technique to diminish excessive **fears**, involving gradual exposure to the feared stimulus paired with a positive coping experience, usually relaxation. (25)

taxonomy System of naming and classification (e.g., of specimens) in science. (84)

testability Ability of a **hypothesis**, for example, to be subjected to scientific scrutiny and to be accepted or rejected, a necessary condition for the hypothesis to be useful. (100)

tobacco-related disorders Cognitive, biological, behavioural, and social problems associated with the use and abuse of nicotine. (359)

token economy Social learning behaviour modification system in which individuals earn items they can exchange for desired rewards by displaying appropriate behaviours. (447)

tolerance Need for increased amounts of a substance to achieve the desired effect, and a diminished effect with continued use of the same amount. (347)

transference Psychoanalytic concept suggesting that clients may seek to relate to the therapist as they do to important authority figures, particularly their parents. (21)

transinstitutionalization Movement of people with severe **mental illness** from large psychiatric hospitals to smaller group residences. (519)

transvestic disorder Paraphilic disorder in which individuals, usually males, are sexually aroused or receive gratification by wearing clothing of the opposite sex. (327)

traumatic brain injury (TBI) Brain damage caused by a blow to the head or other trauma that injures the brain and results in diminished neurocognitive capacity. (499)

treatment outcome research Studies of the effectiveness of clinical interventions, including the comparison of competing treatments. (105)

trend Direction of change of a behaviour or behaviours (e.g., increasing, decreasing). (107)

trichotillomania People's urge to pull out their own hair from anywhere on the body, including the scalp, eyebrows, and arms. (183)

twin studies In genetics research, the comparison of twins with unrelated or less closely related individuals. If twins, particularly monozygotic twins who share identical **genotypes**, share common characteristics such as a disorder, even if they were reared in different environments, this is strong evidence of genetic involvement in those characteristics. (110)

type A behaviour pattern Cluster of behaviours including excessive competitiveness, time-pressured impatience, accelerated speech, and anger, originally thought to promote high risk for heart disease. (OLC–19)

type B behaviour pattern Cluster of behaviours including a relaxed attitude, indifference to time pressure, and less forceful ambition; originally thought to cause low risk for heart disease. (OLC–19)

unconditional positive regard Acceptance by the counsellor of the client's feelings and actions without judgment or condemnation. (22)

unconscious Part of the psychic makeup that is outside the person's awareness. (18)

vaginismus Recurring involuntary muscle spasms in the outer third of the vagina that interfere with sexual intercourse. (315)

validity Degree to which a technique actually measures what it purports to measure. (70)

variability Degree of change in a phenomenon over time. (107)

vascular neurocognitive disorder Progressive brain disorder involving loss of cognitive functioning, caused by blockage of blood flow to the brain, that appears concurrently with other neurological signs and symptoms. (498)

voyeuristic disorder Paraphilic disorder in which sexual arousal is derived from observing unsuspecting individuals undressing or naked. (326)

vulnerability Susceptibility or tendency to develop a disorder. (37)

withdrawal Severely negative physiological reaction to removal of a **psychoactive substance**, which can be alleviated by the same or a similar substance. (347)

withdrawal delirium Frightening **hallucinations** and body tremors that result when a heavy drinker withdraws from alcohol. Also called **delirium tremens (DTs)**. (351)

withdrawal design Removing a treatment to note whether it has been effective. In single-case experimental designs, a behaviour is measured (**baseline**), an independent variable is introduced (intervention), and then the intervention is withdrawn. Because the behaviour continues to be measured throughout (repeated measurement), any effects of the intervention can be noted. Also called *reversal design*. (107)

REFERENCES

Aaronson, C. J., Shear, M. K., Goetz, R. R., Allen, L. B., Barlow, D. H., White, K. S., & Gorman, J. M. (2008). Predictors and time course of response among panic disorder patients treated with cognitive-behavioral therapy. *Journal of Clinical Psychiatry, 69*(3), 418–424.

Aarsland, D., Ballard, C., Rongve, A., Broadstock, M., & Svenningsson, P. (2012). Clinical trials of dementia with Lewy bodies and Parkinson's disease dementia. *Current Neurology and Neuroscience Reports, 12*(5), 492–501.

Aarsland, D., & Kurz, M. W. (2010). The epidemiology of dementia associated with Parkinson disease. *Journal of the Neurological Sciences, 289*(1–2), 18–22.

Abba, S. M., Soca, R., & Zee, P. C. (2014). Circadian rhythm sleep disorders. In *Primary care sleep medicine* (pp. 297–309). Springer New York.

Abbey, S. E., & Garfinkel, P. E. (1991a). Neurasthenia and chronic fatigue syndrome: The role of culture in the making of a diagnosis. *American Journal of Psychiatry, 148*, 1638–1646.

Abbott, D. W., de Zwaan, M., Mussell, M. P., Raymond, N. C., Seim, H. C., Crow, S. J., . . . Mitchell, J. E. (1998). Onset of binge eating and dieting in overweight women: Implications for etiology, associated features and treatment. *Journal of Psychosomatic Research, 44*, 367–374.

Abdul-Hamid, W. K., & Stein, G. (2012). The Surpu: Exorcism of antisocial personality disorder in ancient Mesopotamia. *Mental Health, Religion & Culture, 16*(7). https://doi.org/10.1080/13674676.2012.713337

Abel, G. G., Becker, J. V., Cunningham-Rathner, J., Mittelman, M., & Rouleau, J. L. (1988). Multiple paraphilic diagnoses among sex offenders. *Bulletin of the American Academy of Psychiatry and Law, 16*, 153–168.

Abel, K. M., Drake, R., & Goldstein, J. M. (2010). Sex differences in schizophrenia. *International Review of Psychiatry, 22*(5), 417–428.

Abela, J. R. Z., & Sarin, S. (2002). Cognitive vulnerability to hopelessness depression: A chain is only as strong as its weakest link. *Cognitive Therapy & Research, 26*, 811–829.

Abela, J. R. Z., Aydin, C., & Auerbach, R. P. (2006). Operationalizing the "vulnerability" and "stress" components of the hopelessness theory of depression: A multi-wave longitudinal study. *Behaviour Research and Therapy, 44*, 1565–1583.

Abela, J. R., & Hankin, B. L. (2011). Rumination as a vulnerability factor to depression during the transition from early to middle adolescence: A multiwave longitudinal study. *Journal of Abnormal Psychology, 120*(2), 259–271.

Abela, J. R., Stolow, D., Mineka, S., Yao, S., Zhu, X. Z., & Hankin, B. L. (2011). Cognitive vulnerability to depressive symptoms in adolescents in urban and rural Hunan, China: A multiwave longitudinal study. *Journal of Abnormal Psychology, 120*(4), 765–778.

Abramowitz, J. S., Jacoby, R. J. (2015). Obsessive–compulsive and related disorders: A critical review of the new diagnostic class. *Annual Review of Clinical Psychology, 11*, 165–186.

Abramowitz, J. S., Taylor, S., & McKay, D. (2012). Exposure-based treatment for obsessive compulsive disorder. In G. Steketee (Ed.), *The Oxford handbook of obsessive compulsive and spectrum disorders* (pp. 322–364). New York, NY: Oxford University Press.

Abramson, L. Y., Bardone-Cone, A. M., Vohs, K. D., Joiner, T. E., Jr., & Heatherton, T. F. (2006). Cognitive vulnerability to bulimia. In L. B. Alloy & J. H. Riskind (Eds.), *Cognitive vulnerability to emotional disorders* (pp. 329–364). Mahwah, NJ: Lawrence Erlbaum Associates Publishers.

Abramson, L. Y., Metalsky, G. I., & Alloy, L. B. (1989). Hopelessness depression: A theory-based subtype of depression. *Psychological Review, 96*(2), 358–372.

Abramson, L. Y., Seligman, M. E. P., & Teasdale, J. D. (1978). Learned helplessness in humans: Critique and reformulation. *Journal of Abnormal Psychology, 87*, 49–74.

Abse, D. W. (1987). *Hysteria and related mental disorders: An approach to psychological medicine.* Bristol, UK: Wright.

Adachi, Y., Sato, C., Nishino, N., Ohryoji, F., Hayama, J., & Yamagami, T. (2009). A brief parental education for shaping sleep habits in 4-month-old infants. *Clinical Medicine & Research, 7*(3), 85–92.

Adair, R., Bauchner, H., Philipp, B., Levenson, S., & Zuckerman, B. (1991). Night waking during infancy: Role of parent presence at bedtime. *Pediatrics, 87*, 500–504.

Adams, T. D., Davidson, L. E., Litwin, S. E., Kolotkin, R. L., LaMonte, M. J., Pendleton, R. C., & Hunt, S. C. (2012). Health benefits of gastric bypass surgery after 6 years. *JAMA, 308*(11), 1122–1131.

Addington, A. M., & Rapoport, J. L. (2012). Annual research review: Impact of advances in genetics in understanding developmental psychopathology. *Journal of Child Psychology and Psychiatry, 53*(5), 510–518.

Addington, J., Liu, L., Buchy, L., Cadenhead, K. S., Cannon, T. D., Cornblatt, B. A., . . . Woods, S. W. (2015). North American prodrome longitudinal study (NAPLS 2): The prodromal symptoms. *Journal of Nervous and Mental Disease, 203*(5), 328–335.

Addington, J., van Mastrigt, S., & Addington, D. (2003). Patterns of premorbid functioning in first-episode psychosis: Initial presentation. *Schizophrenia Research, 62*, 23–30.

Addis, M. E. (2008). Gender and depression in men. *Clinical Psychology: Science and Practice, 15*(3), 153–168.

Ader, R., & Cohen, N. (1975). Behaviorally conditioned immunosuppression. *Psychosomatic Medicine, 37*, 333–340.

Ader, R., & Cohen, N. (1993). Psychoneuroimmunology: Conditioning and stress. *Annual Review of Psychology, 44*, 53–85.

Adinoff, B., & Stein, E. A. (2011). *Neuroimaging in addiction.* Hoboken, NJ: Wiley.

Adler, C. M., Côté, G., Barlow, D. H., & Hillhouse, J. J. (1994). Phenomenological relationships between somatoform, anxiety, and psychophysiological disorders. Unpublished manuscript.

Adler, N. E. (2013). Health disparities: Taking on the challenge. *Perspectives on Psychological Science, 8*(6), 679–681.

Adler, P. S. J., Ditto, B., France, C., & France, J. (1994). Cardiovascular reactions to blood donation in offspring of hypertensives and normotensives. *Journal of Psychosomatic Research, 38*, 429–439.

Agid, O., Remington, G., Kapur, S., Arenovich, T., & Zipursky, R. B. (2007). Early use of clozapine for poorly responding first-episode psychosis. *Journal of Clinical Psychopharmacology, 27*(4), 369–373.

Aggarwal, N. K., Nicasio, A. V., DeSilva, R., Boiler, M., & Lewis-Fernández, R. (2013). Barriers to implementing the DSM-5 cultural formulation interview: A qualitative study. *Culture, Medicine, and Psychiatry, 37*(3), 505–533.

Agras, W. S. (1987). *Eating disorders: Management of obesity, bulimia, and anorexia nervosa.* Elmsford, NY: Pergamon Press.

Agras, W. S. (2001). The consequences and costs of eating disorders. *Psychiatric Clinics of North America, 24*, 371–379.

Agras, W. S., Barlow, D. H., Chapin, H. N., Abel, G. G., & Leitenberg, H. (1974). Behavior modification of anorexia nervosa. *Archives of General Psychiatry, 30*, 279–286.

Agras, W. S., & Kirkley, B. G. (1986). Bulimia: Theories of etiology. In K. D. Brownell & J. P. Foreyt (Eds.), *Handbook of eating disorders: Physiology, psychology, and treatment of obesity, anorexia, and bulimia* (pp. 367–378). New York, NY: Basic Books.

Agras, W. S., Lock, J., Brandt, H., Bryson, S. W., Dodge, E., Halmi, K. A., . . . Woodside, B. (2014). Comparison of 2 family therapies for adolescent anorexia nervosa: A randomized parallel trial. *JAMA Psychiatry, 71*(11), 1279–1286.

Agras, W. S., Sylvester, D., & Oliveau, D. (1969). The epidemiology of common fears and phobia. *Comprehensive Psychiatry, 10*, 151–156.

Agras, W. S., Telch, C. F., Arnow, B., Eldredge, K., & Marnell, M. (1997). One year follow-up of cognitive-behavioral therapy of obese individuals with binge eating disorder. *Journal of Consulting and Clinical Psychology, 65*, 343–347.

Agras, W. S., Walsh, B. T., Fairburn, C. G., Wilson, G. T., & Kraemer, H. C. (2000). A multicenter comparison of cognitive-behavioral therapy and interpersonal psychotherapy for bulimia nervosa. *Archives of General Psychiatry, 57*, 459–466.

Agrawal, P. (1978). Diazepam addiction: A case report. *Canadian Psychiatric Association Journal, 23*, 35–37.

Aguirre, E., Woods, R. T., Spector, A., & Orrell, M. (2013). Cognitive stimulation for dementia: A systematic review of the evidence of effectiveness from randomised controlled trials. *Ageing Research Reviews, 12*(1), 253–262.

Ahlers, C. J., Schaefer, G. A., Mundt, I. A., Roll, S., Englert, H., Willich, S. N., & Beier, K. M. (2011). How unusual are the contents of paraphilias? Paraphilia-associated sexual arousal patterns in a community based sample of men. *Journal of Sexual Medicine, 8*(5), 1362–1370.

Ahmed, A. O., Green, B. A., Goodrum, N. M., Doane, N. J., Birgenheir, D., & Buckley, P. F. (2013). Does a latent class underlie schizotypal personality disorder? Implications for schizophrenia. *Journal of Abnormal Psychology, 122*, 475–491.

Ahmed, I., & Thorpy, M. (2012). Narcolepsy and idiopathic hypersomnia. In M. S. Badr (Ed.), *Essentials of sleep medicine: An approach for clinical pulmonology* (pp. 297–314). New York, NY: Humana Press.

Aigner, M., & Bach, M. (1999). Clinical utility of DSM-IV pain disorder. *Comprehensive Psychiatry, 40*(5), 353–357.

Aiken, A., Human, L. J., Alden, L. E., & Biesanz, J. C. (2014). Try to find me: Social anxiety and peer first impressions. *Behavior Therapy, 45*(6), 841–862. http://dx.doi.org/10.1016/j.beth.2014.08.001

Ait Bentaleb, L., Beauregard, M., Liddle, P., & Stip, E. (2002). Cerebral activity associated with auditory verbal hallucinations: A functional magnetic resonance imaging case study. *Journal* of *Psychiatry & Neuroscience, 27*, 110–115.

Åkerstedt, T., & Wright Jr., K. P. (2009). Sleep loss and fatigue in shift work and shift work disorder. *Sleep Medicine Clinics, 4*(2), 257–271.

Akiskal, H. S. (1997). Overview of chronic depressions and their clinical management. In H. S. Akiskal & G. B. Cassano (Eds.), *Dysthymia and the spectrum of chronic depressions* (pp. 1–34). New York, NY: Guilford Press.

Akiskal, H. S. (2009). Dysthymia, cyclothymia, and hyperthymia. In M. G. Gelder, N. C. Andreasen, J. J. López-Ibor, Jr., & J. R. Geddes (Eds.), *New Oxford textbook of psychiatry* (2nd ed., Vol. 1, pp. 680–692). Oxford, UK: Oxford University Press.

Aktar, S., & Brenner, I. (1979). Differential diagnosis of fugue-like states. *Journal of Clinical Psychiatry, 40*, 381–385.

Albano, A. M., & Barlow, D. H. (1996). Breaking the vicious cycle: Cognitive-behavioral group treatment for socially anxious youth. In E. D. Hibbs & P. S. Jensen (Eds.), *Psychosocial treatment research and adolescent disorders* (pp. 43–62). Washington, DC: APA Press.

Albano, A. M., Chorpita, B. F., & Barlow, D. H. (1996). Childhood anxiety disorders. In E. J. Mash & R. A. Barkley (Eds.), *Child psychopathology* (pp. 196–241). New York, NY: Guilford Press.

Albano, A. M., & Hack, S. (2004). Children and adolescents. In R. G. Heimberg, C. L. Turk, & D. S. Mennin (Eds.), *Generalized anxiety disorder: Advances in research and practice* (pp. 383–408). New York, NY: Guilford Press.

Albee, G. W. (1998). Fifty years of clinical psychology: Selling our soul to the devil. *Applied & Preventive Psychology, 7*, 189–194.

Albee, G. W. (2000). The Boulder model's fatal flaw. *American Psychologist, 55*, 247–248.

Albert, C., Chae, C., Rexrode, K., Manson, J., & Kawachi, I. (2005). Phobic anxiety and risk of coronary heart disease and sudden cardiac among women. *Circulation, 111*, 480–487.

Alberta Family and Social Services. (1990). *Elder abuse: What is it? What to do about it?* http://www.acjnet.org/docs/eldabpfv.html

Albertini, R. S., & Phillips, K. A. (1999). Thirty-three cases of body dysmorphic disorder in children and adolescents. *Journal of the American Academy of Child and Adolescent Psychiatry, 38*(4), 453–459.

Alcoholics Anonymous. (1990). *Comments on A. A.'s triennial surveys.* New York, NY: Alcoholics Anonymous World Services.

Alda, M. (2015). Lithium in the treatment of bipolar disorder: Pharmacology and pharmacogenetics. *Molecular Psychiatry, 20*, 661–670.

Alden, L. (1989). Short-term structured treatment for avoidant personality disorder. *Journal of Consulting and Clinical Psychology, 57*, 756–764.

Alden, L. E. (2001). Interpersonal perspectives on social phobia. In W. R. Crozier & L. E. Alden (Eds.), *International handbook of social anxiety: Research and interventions* (pp. 381–404). New York, NY: Wiley.

Alden, L. E., Bieling, P. J., & Meleshko, K. G. (1995). An interpersonal comparison of depression and social anxiety.

In K. Craig & K. S. Dobson (Eds.), *Anxiety and depression in adults and children* (pp. 57–81). Thousand Oaks, CA: Sage Publications.

Alden, L. E., & Capreol, M. J. (1993). Avoidant personality disorder: Interpersonal problems as predictors of treatment response. *Behavior Therapy, 24*, 357–376.

Alden, L. E., & Taylor, C. T. (2004). Interpersonal processes in social phobia [Special issue: Social phobia and social anxiety]. *Clinical Psychology Review, 24*, 857–882.

Alden, L. E., & Wallace, S. T. (1995). Social phobia and social appraisal in successful and unsuccessful interactions. *Behaviour Research and Therapy, 33*, 497–506.

Alden, L. E., Laposa, J. M., & Taylor, C. T. (2006). Avoidant personality disorder. In J. E. Fisher & W. T. O'Donohue (Eds.), *Practitioner's guide to evidence-based psychotherapy* (pp. 115–121). New York, NY: Springer Science + Business Media.

Alderwoman to seek therapy to avoid charges. (2003). *CTV News.* http://www.ctv.ca/servlet/ArticleNews/story/CTVNews/1053451733897_24//

Alexander, F. (1950). *Psychosomatic medicine.* New York, NY: Norton.

Alexander, F. G. (1939). Emotional factors in essential hypertension: Presentation of a tentative hypothesis. *Psychosomatic Medicine, 1*, 175–179.

Alexander, F. G., & Selesnick, S. T. (1966). *The history of psychiatry: An evaluation of psychiatric thought and practice from prehistoric times to the present.* New York, NY: Harper & Row.

Ali, S. R., Liu, W. M., & Humedian, M. (2004). Islam 101: Understanding the religion and therapy implications. *Professional Psychology: Research and Practice, 35*(6), 635.

Allan, R., & Unger, M. (2014). Resilience-building interventions with children, adolescents, and their families. In *Resilience interventions for youth in diverse populations* (pp. 447–462). New York, NY: Springer.

Allen, D., & Midwinter, J. (1990, September 30). The debunking of a myth. *Satanic MediaWatch and News Exchange.* From http://www.smwane.dk/content/view/173/34/

Allen, J. M., Lam, R. W., Remick, R. A., & Sadovnick, A. D. (1993). Depressive symptoms and family history in seasonal and nonseasonal mood disorders. *American Journal of Psychiatry, 150*(3), 443–448.

Allen, J., DeMyer, M., Norton, J., Pontius, W., & Yang, G. (1971). Intellectuality in parents of psychotic, subnormal, and normal children. *Journal of Autism and Childhood Schizophrenia, 1*, 311–326.

Allen, K. L., Byrne, S. M., Oddy, W. H., & Crosby, R. D. (2013). DSM–IV–TR and DSM-5 eating disorders in adolescents: Prevalence, stability, and psychosocial correlates in a population-based sample of male and female adolescents. *Journal of Abnormal Psychology, 122*(3), 720.

Allen, K., Blascovitch, J., & Mendes, W. B. (2002). Cardiovascular reactivity in the presence of pets, friends, and spouses: The truth about cats and dogs. *Psychosomatic Medicine, 64*, 727–739.

Allen, L. A., Woolfolk, R. L., Escobar, J. I., Gara, M. A., & Hamer, R. M. (2006). Cognitive-behavioral therapy for

somatization disorder: A randomized controlled trial. *Archives of Internal Medicine, 166*(14), 1512–1518.

Allen, L. B., White, K. S., Barlow, D. H., Shear, M. K., Gorman, J. M., & Woods, S. W. (2010). Cognitive-behavior therapy (CBT) for panic disorder: Relationship of anxiety and depression comorbidity with treatment outcome. *Journal of Psychopathology & Behavioral Assessment, 32*(2), 185–192.

Allender, S., Peto, V., Scarborough, P., Boxer, A., & Rayner, M. (2007). *Coronary heart disease statistics.* Oxford, England: British Heart Foundation & Stroke Association.

Alloy, L., & Abramson, L. (2006). Prospective incidence of first onsets and recurrences of depression individuals at high and low cognitive risk for depression. *Journal of Abnormal Psychology, 115*, 145–156.

Alloy, L., Abramson, L. Y., Hogan, M. E., Whitehouse, W. G., Rose, D. T., Robinson, M. S., & Lapkin, J. B. (2000). The Temple-Wisconsin cognitive vulnerability to depression project: Lifetime history of axis I psychopathology in individuals at high and low cognitive risk for depression. *Journal of Abnormal Psychology, 109*, 403–418.

Alloy, L. B., Bender, R. E., Whitehouse, W. G., Wagner, C. A., Liu, R. T., Grant, D. A., & Abramson, L. Y. (2012). High Behavioral Approach System (BAS) sensitivity, reward responsiveness, and goal-striving predict first onset of bipolar spectrum disorders: A prospective behavioral high-risk design. *Journal of Abnormal Psychology, 121*(2), 339–351.

Alloy, L. B., Nusslock, R., & Boland, E. M. (2015). The development and course of bipolar spectrum disorders: An integrated reward and circadian rhythm dysregulation model. *Annual Review of Clinical Psychology, 11*, 213.

Almklov, E. L., Drummond, S. P., Orff, H., & Alhassoon, O. M. (2015). The effects of sleep deprivation Alpert, M., Clark, A., & Pouget, E. R. (1994). The syntactic role of pauses in the speech of schizophrenic patients with alogia. *Journal of Abnormal Psychology, 103*, 750–757.

Alpers, G. W. (2009). Ambulatory assessment of panic disorder and specific phobia. *Psychological Assessment, 21*, 476–485.

Alpert, M., Clark, A., & Pouget, E. R. (1994). The syntactic role of pauses in the speech of schizophrenic patients with alogia. *Journal of Abnormal Psychology, 103*, 750–757.

Alter, H. J., Mikovits, J. A., Switzer, W. M., Ruscetti, F. W., Lo, S. C., Klimas, N., . . . Lipkin, W. I. (2012). A multicenter blinded analysis indicates no association between chronic fatigue syndrome/myalgic encephalomyelitis and either xenotropic murine leukemia virus-related virus or polytropic murine leukemia virus. *MBio, 3*(5), e00266–12.

Althof, S. (2006). The psychology of premature ejaculation: Therapies and consequences. *Journal of Sexual Medicine, 3*, 324–331.

Althof, S. E. (2007). Treatment of rapid ejaculation: Psychotherapy, pharmacotherapy, and combined therapy. In S. R. Leiblum (Ed.), *Principles and practice of sex therapy* (4th ed.,

pp. 212–240). New York, NY: Guilford Press.

Altshuler, L. L., Kupka, R. W., Hellemann, G., Frye, M. A., Sugar, C. A., McElroy, S. L., & Suppes, T. (2010). Gender and depressive symptoms in 711 patients with bipolar disorder evaluated prospectively in the Stanley Foundation bipolar treatment outcome network. *American Journal of Psychiatry, 167*(6), 708–715.

Alzheimer's Association. (2004). *Aluminum and Alzheimer: Does aluminum play a role in causing Alzheimer's disease?* http://www.corrosion-doctors.org/Pollution/Alumin-Alzheimer.htm

Alzheimer's Society of Canada. (2004). *People with Alzheimer disease and related dementias.* http://www.alzheimers.ca/english/disease/stats-people.htm

Amad, A., Ramoz, N., Thomas, P., Jardri, R., & Gorwood, P. (2014). Genetics of borderline personality disorder: Systematic review and proposal of an integrative model. *Neuroscience and Biobehavioral Review, 40*, 6–19.

Amat, J., Baratta, B. V., Paul, E., Bland, S. T., Watkins, L. R., & Maier, S. F. (2005). Medial prefrontal cortex determines how stressor controllability affects behavior and dorsal raphe nucleus. *Nature Neuroscience, 8*, 365–371.

American College Health Association. (2013). *American College Health Association-National College Health Assessment II: Canadian Reference Group Executive Summary Spring 2013.* Hanover, MD: Author. Retrieved from http://www.acha-ncha.org/docs/ACHA-NCHA-II_CANADIAN_ReferenceGroup_ExecutiveSummary_Spring2013.pdf

American College of Obstetricians and Gynecologists. (2002). Clinical management guidelines for obstetricians-gynecologists: Premenstrual syndrome. *ACOG Practice Bulletin, 15.* Washington, DC: American College of Obstetricians and Gynecologists.

American Psychiatric Association. (1980). *Diagnostic and statistical manual of mental disorders* (3rd ed.). Washington, DC: Author.

American Psychiatric Association. (2000a). *Diagnostic and statistical manual of mental disorders* (4th ed., Text Revision). Washington, DC: Author.

American Psychiatric Association. (2000b). Practice guidelines for the treatment of patients with major depressive disorder (revision). Supplement to *American Journal of Psychiatry, 157*(4).

American Psychiatric Association. (2000c). Substance use disorders: Alcohol, cocaine, opioids. In *Practice guidelines for the treatment of psychiatric disorders: Compendium 2000* (pp. 139–238). Washington, DC: Author.

American Psychiatric Association. (2000d). Schizophrenia. In *Practice guidelines for the treatment of psychiatric disorders: Compendium 2000* (pp. 200–412). Washington, DC: Author.

American Psychiatric Association. (2000e). In *Practice guidelines for the treatment of patients with delirium: Compendium 2000* (pp. 31–68). Washington, DC: Author.

American Psychiatric Association. (2000f). In *Practice guidelines for the treatment of patients with Alzheimer's disease and other dementias of late* life: *Compendium 2000* (pp. 69–137). Washington, DC: Author.

American Psychiatric Association. (2001). *The practice of electroconvulsive therapy: Recommendations for treatment, training, and privileging: A task force report of the American Psychiatric Association* (2nd ed.). Washington, DC: Author.

American Psychiatric Association. (2003). Practice guideline for the assessment and treatment of patients with suicidal behaviors. *American Journal of Psychiatry, 160*(Suppl.), 1–44.

American Psychiatric Association. (2006). Practice guideline for the psychiatric evaluation of adults (2nd ed.). *American Journal of Psychiatry, 163*(Suppl.), 1–36.

American Psychiatric Association. (2010a). *APA practice guidelines for treatment of patients with eating disorders* (3rd ed.). Retrieved from http://www.psychiatry-online.com/content.aspx?aID5138866

American Psychiatric Association. (2010b). *DSM development: Sleep-wake disorders.* http://www.dsm5.org/ProposedRevision/Pages/Sleep-WakeDisorders.aspx

American Psychiatric Association. (2010c). *DSM-5 development: Personality and personality disorders.* http://www.dsm5.org/ProposedRevisions/Pages/PersonalityandPersonalityDisorders.aspx

American Psychiatric Association. (2013). *Diagnostic and statistical manual of mental disorders* (5th ed.). Washington, DC: Author.

American Psychological Association. (2013). *APA guidelines for the undergraduate psychology major: Version 2.0.* Washington, DC: Author.

American Psychological Association Task Force on Gender Identity and Gender Variance. (2008). *Report of the task force on gender identity and gender variance.* Washington, DC: Author.

American Society of Plastic Surgeons. (2012). *National cosmetic procedures.* Retrieved from: http://www.plasticsurgery.org/news-and-resources/2012-plastic-surgery-statistics.html

Amering, M., & Katschnig, H. (1990). Panic attacks and panic disorder in cross-cultural perspective. *Psychiatric Annals, 20,* 511–516.

Amieva, H., Mokri, H., Le Goff, M., Meillon, C., Jacqmin-Gadda, H., Foubert-Samier, A., . . . Dartigues, J. F. (2014). Compensatory mechanisms in higher-educated subjects with Alzheimer's disease: A study of 20 years of cognitive decline. *Brain, 137*(4), 1167–1175.

Anastasi, A. (1988). *Psychological testing* (6th ed.). New York, NY: Oxford University Press.

Anastopoulos, A., Sommer, J., & Schatz, N. (2009). ADHD and family functioning. *Current Attention Disorders Reports, 1*(4), 167–170.

Ancoli-Israel, S. (2000). Insomnia in the elderly: A review for the primary care practitioner. *Sleep, 23*(Suppl. 1), S23–S30.

Ancoli-Israel, S., & Ayalon, L. (2009). Diagnosis and treatment of sleep disorders in odler adults. *Focus, 7,* 98–105.

Andersen, B. L., Farrar, W. B., Golden-Kreutz, D., Emery, C. F., Glaser, R., Crespin, T., & Carson, W. E., III. (2007). Distress reduction from a psychological intervention contributes to improved health for cancer patients. *Brain, Behavior, and Immunity, 21,* 953–961.

Andersen, B. L., Kiecolt-Glaser, J. K., & Glaser, R. (1994). A biobehavioral model of cancer stress and disease course. *American Psychologist, 49,* 389–404.

Anderson, B., & Baum, A. (2001). *Psychosocial intervention for cancer.* Washington, DC: American Psychological Association.

Anderson, D. K., Lord, C., Risi, S., DiLavore, P. S., Shulman, C., Thurm, A., & Pickles, A. (2007). Patterns of growth in verbal abilities among children with autism spectrum disorder. *Journal of Consulting and Clinical Psychology, 75*(4), 594–604.

Anderson, J. L., Sellborn M., Wygant, D. B., Salekin, R. T., & Krueger, R. F. (2014). Examining the associations between DSM-5 Section III antisocial personality disorder traits and psychopathy in community and university samples. *Journal of Personality Disorders, 28*(5), 675–697.

Anderson-Fye, E. (2009). Cross-cultural issues in body image among children and adolescents. In L. Smolak & J. K. Thompson (Eds.), *Body image, eating disorders, and obesity in youth: Assessment, prevention, and treatment* (2nd ed., pp. 113–133). Washington, DC: American Psychological Association.

Andersson, E., Hedman, E., Enander, J., Djurfeldt, D. R., Ljótsson, B., Cervenka, S., . . . Rück, C. (2015). D-Cycloserine vs placebo as adjunct to cognitive behavioral therapy for obsessive–compulsive disorder and interaction with antidepressants: A randomized clinical trial. *JAMA Psychiatry, 72*(7), 659–667. https://doi.org/10.1001/jamapsychiatry.2015.0546

Andrade, L., Caraveo-Anduaga, J. J., Berglund, P., Bijl, R. V., de Graaf, R., Vollegergh, W., . . . Wittchen, H. U. (2003). The epidemiology of major depressive episodes: Results from the International Consortium of Psychiatric Epidemiology (ICPE) Surveys. *International Journal of Methods in Psychiatric Research, 12*(1), 3–21.

Andrasik, F. (2000). Biofeedback. In D. I. Mostofsky & D. H. Barlow (Eds.), *The management of stress and anxiety in medical practice* (pp. 66–83). Needham Heights, MA: Allyn & Bacon.

Andreasen, N. C. (1979). Thought, language, and communication disorders: I. Clinical assessment, definition of terms, and evaluation of their reliability. *Archives of General Psychiatry, 36,* 1315–1321.

Andreasen, N. C., Rezai, K., Alliger, R., Swayze, V. W., Flaum, M., Kirchner, P., . . . O'Leary, D. S. (1992). Hypofrontality in neuroleptic naive patients and in-patients with chronic schizophrenia: Assessment with xenon 133 single-photon emission computed tomography with the Tower of London. *Archives of General Psychiatry, 49,* 943–958.

Andrews, G., Hobbs, M. J., Borkovec, T. D., Beesdo, K., Craske, M. G., Heimberg, R. G., Rapee, R. M., Ruscio, A. M., & Stanley, M. A. (2010). Generalized worry disorder: A review of DSM-IV generalized anxiety disorder and options for DSM-V. *Depression and Anxiety, 27*(2), 134–147. https://doi.org/10.1002/da.20658

Andrews, G., Morris-Yates, A., Howie, P., & Martin, N. G. (1991). Genetic factors in stuttering confirmed. *Archives of General Psychiatry, 48,* 1034–1035.

Aneshensel, C. S., Pearlin, L. I., Mullan, J. T., Zarit, S. H., & Whitlatch, C. J. (1995). *Profiles in caregiving: The unexpected career.* San Diego, CA: Academic Press.

Angst, A., Angst, F., Gerber-Werder, R., & Gamma, A. (2005). Suicide in 406 mood disordered patients with and without long-term medication: A 40 to 44 years' follow-up. *Archives Suicide Research, 9,* 279–300.

Angst, J. (2009). Course and prognosis of mood disorders. In M. G. Gelder, N. C. Andreasen, J. J. López-Ibor, Jr., & J. R. Geddes (Eds.), *New Oxford textbook of psychiatry* (2nd ed., Vol. 1, pp. 665–669). Oxford, UK: Oxford University Press.

Angst, J., Azorin, J. M., Bowden, C. L., Perugi, G., Vieta, E., Gamma, A., & Young, A. H. (2011). Prevalence and characteristics of undiagnosed bipolar disorders in patients with a major depressive episode. *Archives of General Psychiatry, 68*(8), 791–798.

Angst, J., & Grobler, C. (2015). Unipolar mania: A necessary diagnostic concept. *European Archives of Psychiatry and Clinical Neuroscience, 265,* 273–280.

Angst, J., & Preizig, M. (1996). Course of a clinical cohort of unipolar, bipolar and schizoaffective patients: Results of a prospective study from 1959 to 1985. *Schweizer Archiv fur Neurologie und Psychiatrie, 146,* 1–16.

Angst, J., & Sellaro, R. (2000). Historical perspectives and natural history of bipolar disorder. *Biological Psychiatry, 48*(6), 445–457.

Angstman, K. B., & Rasmussen, N. H. (2011). Personality disorders: Review and clinical application in daily practice. *American Family Physician, 84*(11), 1253.

Anisman, H., Zaharia, M. D., Meaney, M. J., & Merali, Z. (1998). Do early life events permanently alter behavioral and hormonal responses to stressors? *International Journal of Developmental Neuroscience, 16,* 149–164.

Anson, M., Veale, D., & de Silva, P. (2012). Social-evaluative versus self-evaluative appearance concerns in body dysmorphic disorder. *Behavior Research and Therapy, 50*(12), 753–760.

Antle, M. C., & Silver, R. (2005). Orchestrating time: Arrangements of the brain circadian clock. *Trends in Neurosciences, 28,* 145–151.

Anton, B., & Leff, L. P. (2006). A novel bivalent morphine/heroin vaccine that prevents relapse to heroin addiction in rodents. *Vaccine, 24*(16), 3232–3240.

Anton, R. F. (1999). What is craving? Models and implications for treatment. *Alcohol Research & Health, 23*(3), 165–173.

Antoni, M. H. (2012). Stress, coping, and health in HIV/AIDS. *The Oxford Handbook of Stress, Heath, and Coping.* Oxford, UK: Oxford University Press.

Antoni, M. H., Baggett, L., Ironson, G., LaPerriere, A., August, S., Klimas, N., . . . Fletcher, M. A. (1991). Cognitive-behavioral stress management intervention buffers distress responses and immunologic changes following notification of HIV-1 sero-positivity. *Journal of Consulting and Clinical Psychology, 59*(6), 906–915.

Antoni, M. H., Cruess, D. G., Cruess, S., Lutgendorf, S., Kumar, M., Ironson, G., . . . Schneiderman, N. (2000). Cognitive-behavioral stress management intervention effects on anxiety, 24-hr urinary norepinephrine output, and T-cytotoxic/suppressor cells over time among symptomatic HIV-infected gay men. *Journal of Consulting and Clinical Psychology, 68,* 31–45.

Antoni, M. H., Lechner, S., Kazi, A., Wimberly, S., Sifre, T., Urcuyo, K., & Carver, C. S. (2006). How stress management improves quality of life after treatment for breast cancer. *Journal of Consulting and Clinical Psychology, 74,* 1143–1152.

Antony, M. M., & Barlow, D. H. (2002). Specific phobias. In D. H. Barlow (Ed.), *Anxiety and its disorders: The nature and treatment of anxiety and panic* (2nd ed., pp. 380–417). New York, NY: Guilford Press.

Antony, M. M., & Barlow, D. H. (Eds.). (2010). *Handbook of assessment and treatment planning for psychological disorders* (2nd ed.). New York, NY: Guilford Press.

Antony, M. M., Brown, T. A., & Barlow, D. H. (1997a). Heterogeneity among specific phobia types in DSM-IV. *Behavior Research and Therapy, 35,* 1089–1100.

Antony, M. M., Brown, T. A., & Barlow, D. H. (1997b). Response to hyperventilation and 5.5% CO_2 inhalation of subjects with types of specific phobia, panic disorder, or no mental disorder. *American Journal of Psychiatry, 154,* 1089–1095.

Antony, M. M., Craske, M. G., & Barlow, D. H. (2006). *Mastering your fears and phobias: Workbook.* New York, NY: Oxford University Press.

Antony, M. M., & McCabe, R. E. (2002). Empirical basis of panic control treatment. *Scientific Review of Mental Health Practice, 1,* 189–194.

Antony, M. M., Rowa, K., Liss, A., Swallow, S. R., & Swinson, R. P. (2005). Social comparison processes in social phobia. *Behavior Therapy, 36,* 65–75.

Anzengruber, D., Klump, K. L., Thornton, L., Brandt, H., Crawford, S., Fichter, M. M., . . . Bulik, C. M. (2006). Smoking in eating disorders. *Eating Behaviors, 7,* 291–299.

Aouizerate, B., Rotge, J., Martin-Guehl, C., Cuny, E., Rougier, A., Guehl, D., . . . Tignol, J. (2006). A systematic review of psychsurgical treatments for obsessive–compulsive disorder: Does deep brain stimulation represent the future trend in psychosurgery? *Clinical Neuropsychiatry, 3*(6), 391–403.

Apfelbaum, B. (2000). Retarded ejaculation: A much misunderstood syndrome. In S. R. Leiblum & R. C. Rosen (Eds.), *Principles and practice of sex therapy* (3rd ed., pp. 205–241). New York, NY: Guilford Press.

Arai, J. A., Li, S., Hartley, D. M., & Feig, L. A. (2009). Transgenerational rescue of a genetic defect in long-term potentiation and memory formation by juvenile enrichment. *Journal of Neuroscience, 29*(5), 1496–1502.

Arcelus J., Mitchell, A. J., Wales, J., & Nielsen, S. (2011). Mortality rates in patients with anorexia nervosa and other eating disorders: A meta-analysis of 36 studies. *Archives of General Psychiatry, 68*(7), 724–731.

Arenas, E. (2010). Towards stem cell replacement therapies for Parkinson's disease. *Biochemical and Biophysical Research Communications, 396*(1), 152–156.

Arenkiel, B. R., & Ehlers, M. D. (2009). Molecular genetics and imaging technologies for circuit-based neuro-anatomy. *Nature, 461*(7266), 900–907.

Arim, R., & Frenette, M. (2019). Are mental health and neurodevel-opmental conditions barriers to postsecondary access? *Analytical Studies Branch Research Paper Series* (Catalogue No. 11F0019M). https://www150.statcan.gc.ca/n1/en/catalogue/11F0019M2019005

Armbruster, D., Mueller, A., Moser, D. A., Lesch, K. P., Brocke, B., & Kirschbaum, C. (2009). Interaction effect of D4 dopamine receptor gene and serotonin transporter promoter polymorphism on the cortisol stress response. *Behavioral Neuroscience, 123*(6), 1288–1295.

Armstrong, T. (2010). *Neurodiversity: Discovering the extraordinary gifts of autism, ADHD, dyslexia, and other brain differences.* Cambridge, MA: Da Capo Lifelong Books.

Arria, A. M., Garnier-Dykstra, L. M., Cook, E. T., Caldeira, K. M., Vincent, K. B., Baron, R. A., & O'Grady, K. E. (2013). Drug use patterns in young adulthood and post-college employment. *Drug and Alcohol Dependence, 127*(1–3), 23–30.

Arrindell, W. A., Eisemann, M., Richter, J., Oei, T. P. S., Caballo, V. E., van der Ende, J., . . . Hudson, B. L. (2003). Phobic anxiety in 11 nations Part I: Dimensional constancy of the five-factor model. *Behaviour Research and Therapy, 41*, 461–479.

Asarnow, J. R. (1994). Annotation: Childhood-onset schizophrenia. *Journal of Child Psychology and Psychiatry, 35*, 1345–1371.

Asberg, M., Nordstrom, P., & Traskman-Bendz, L. (1986). Cerebrospinal fluid studies in suicide: An overview. *Annals of the American Academy of Science, 487*, 243–255.

Aschoff, J., & Wever, R. (1962). Spontanperiodik des Menschen die Ausschulus aller Zeitgeber. *Die Naturwissenschaften, 49*, 337–342.

Ashare, R. L., Karlawish, J. H., Wileyto, E. P., Pinto, A., & Lerman, C. (2012). APOE ε4, an Alzheimer's disease susceptibility allele, and smoking cessa-tion. *The Pharmacogenomics Journal, 13*, 538–543. https://doi.org/10.1038/tpj.2012.49

Ashbaugh, A. R., McCabe, R. E., Antony, M. M., Schmidt, L. A., & Swinson, & R. P. (2005). Evaluative biases in social anxiety. *Cognitive Therapy and Research, 29*, 387–398.

Ashley, L. L., & Boehlke, K. K. (2012). Pathological gambling: A general over-view. *Journal of Psychoactive Drugs, 44*(1), 27–37.

Askew, C., Hagel, A., & Morgan, J. (2015). Vicarious learning of children's social-anxiety-related fear beliefs and emotion Stroop bias. *Emotion, 15*, 501–510.

Asmundson, G. J. G., & Carleton, R. N. (2009). Fear of pain. In M. M. Antony & M. B. Stein (Eds.), *Oxford hand-book of anxiety and related disorders*

(pp. 551–561). Oxford, UK: Oxford University Press.

Asmundson, G. J. G., Carleton, R. N., Wright, K. D., & Taylor, S. (2004). Psychological sequelae of remote exposure to the September 11th terrorist attacks in Canadians with and without panic. *Cognitive Behaviour Therapy, 33*(2), 49–50.

Asmundson, G. J. G., Jacobson, S. J., Allerdings, M. D., & Norton, G. R. (1996). Social phobia in disabled workers with chronic musculoskeletal pain. *Behaviour Research & Therapy, 34*, 939–943.

Asmundson, G. J. G., Norton, G. R., & Stein, M. B. (2002). *Clinical research in mental health: A practical guide.* Thousand Oaks, CA: Sage Publications.

Asmundson, G. J. G., & Stein, M. B. (1994). Selective processing of social threat in patients with generalized social phobia: Evaluation using a dot-probe paradigm. *Journal of Anxiety Disorders, 8*, 107–117.

Asmundson, G. J. G., & Taylor, S. (2005). *It's not all in your head: How worrying about your health could be making you sick—and what you can do about it.* New York, NY: Guilford Press.

Asnaani, A., Gutner, C., Hinton, D., & Hofmann, S. G. (2009). Panic disorder, panic attacks, and panic attack symptoms across race-ethnic groups: Results of the Collaborative Psychiatric Epidemiology Survey. *CNS Neuroscience and Therapeutics, 15*, 249–254.

Asnaani, A., Richey, J. A., Dimaite, R., Hinton, D. E., & Hofmann, S. G. (2010). A cross-ethnic comparison of lifetime prevalence rates of anxiety dis-orders. *Journal of Nervous and Mental Disease, 198*(8), 551–555.

Assembly of First Nations & Health Canada (2015). *First Nations mental wellness continuum framework: Summary report.* https://www.canada.ca/en/indigenous -services-canada/services/first-nations -inuit-health/reports-publications/ health-promotion/first-nations-mental -wellness-continuum-framework -summary-report.html

Assumpção, A. A., Garcia, F. D., Garcia, H. D., Bradford, J. M., & Thibault, F. (2014). Pharmacologic treatment of paraphilias. *Psychiatric Clinics of North America, 37*(2), 173–181.

Attia, E., & Roberto, C. A. (2009). Should amenorrhea be a diagnostic criterion for anorexia nervosa? *International Journal of Eating Disorders, 42*(7), 581–589.

Attie, I., & Brooks-Gunn, J. (1995). The development of eating regulation across the life span. In D. Cicchetti & D. J. Cohen (Eds.), *Developmental psychopathology* (Vol. 2). New York, NY: Wiley.

Attwood, A., Frith, J., & Hermelin, B. (1988). The understanding and use of interpersonal gesture by autistic and Down syndrome children. *Journal of Autism and Developmental Disorders, 18*, 241–258.

Aubertin, G. (2015). 136: Fragile X syndrome in Canada: A Canadian Paediatric Surveillance Program Study. *Paediatrics and Child Health, 20*(5), e83–e84. https://doi.org/10.1093/pch/20.5.e83a

Aubertin, G., Down, J., Graham, G., Nelson, T., Ofner, C., & Paribello, C. (2015). Fragile X syndrome: April 2012 to March 2014—Final deport.

In *Canadian Paediatric Surveillance Program, 2014 Results* (pp. 28–29). Canadian Paediatric Society. https://www.cpsp.cps.ca/uploads/publications/Results-2014.pdf

Auchterlonie, S., Phillips, N. A., & Chertkow, H. (2002). Behavioral and electrical brain measures of semantic priming in patients with Alzheimer's disease: Implications for access failure versus deterioration hypotheses. *Brain & Cognition, 48*, 264–267.

Augedal, A. W., Hansen, K. S., Kronhaug, C. R., Harvey, A. G., & Pallesen, S. (2013). Randomized controlled trials of psychological and pharmacological treatments for nightmares: A meta-analysis. *Sleep Medicine Reviews 17*(2), 143–152.

Aurora, R. N., Zak, R. S., Auerbach, S. H., Casey, K. R., Chowdhuri, S., Karippot, A., & Bista, S. R. (2010). Best practice guide for the treatment of nightmare disorder in adults. *Journal of Clinical Sleep Medicine: JCSM: Official Publication of the American Academy of Sleep Medicine, 6*(4), 389.

Austin, G. W., Jaffe, P., & Friedman, B. (1994). Custody and access assessors: Effects of background and experience on analogue case judgement. *Canadian Journal of Behavioural Science, 26*(4), 463–475.

Ausubel, D. (1971). The peer group and adolescent conformity. *Delta* (Nov.), 50–64.

Auyeung, B., Baron-Cohen, S., Ashwin, E., Knickmeyer, R., Taylor, K., Hackett, G., & Hines, M. (2009). Fetal testos-terone predicts sexually differentiated childhood behavior in girls and boys. *Psychological Science, 20*, 144–148.

Ayala, E. S., Meuret, A. E., & Ritz, T. (2009). Treatments for blood-injury-injection phobia: A critical review of current evidence. *Journal of Psychiatric Research, 43*(15), 1235–1242.

Ayers, C. R., Saxena, S., Golshan, S., & Wetherell, J. L. (2010). Age at onset and clinical features of late life compul-sive hoarding. *International Journal of Geriatric Psychiatry, 25*(2), 142–149.

Ayers, C. R., Thorp, S. R., & Wetherell, J. L. (2009). Anxiety disorders and hoarding in older adults. In M. M. Antony & M. B. Stein (Eds.), *Oxford handbook of anxiety and related dis-orders* (pp. 625–635). New York, NY: Oxford University Press.

Ayllon, T., & Azrin, N. H. (1968). *The token economy: A motivational system for therapy and rehabilitation.* New York, NY: Appleton-Century-Crofts.

Ayllon, T., & Michael, J. (1959). The psy-chiatric nurse as a behavioral engineer. *Journal of the Experimental Analysis of Behavior, 2*, 323–334.

Azmitia, E. C. (1978). The serotonin-producing neurons of the midbrain median and dorsal raphe nuclei. In L. Iverson, S. Iverson, & S. Snyder (Eds.), *Handbook of psychopharmacology: Vol. 9. Chemical pathways in the brain* (pp. 233–314). New York, NY: Plenum Press.

Bacchiochi, J. R., & Bagby, R. M. (2006). Development and validation of the malingering discriminant function index for the MMPI-2. *Journal of Personality Assessment, 87*, 51–61.

Bach, A. K., Brown, T. A., & Barlow, D. H. (1999). The effects of false negative feedback on efficacy expec-tancies and sexual arousal in sexually

functional males. *Behavior Therapy, 30*, 79–95.

Bach, A. K., Wincze, J. P., & Barlow, D. H. (2001). Sexual dysfunction. In D. H. Barlow (Ed.), *Clinical handbook of psychological disorders: A step-by-step treatment manual* (3rd ed.). New York, NY: Guilford Press.

Bachrach, L. L. (1994). Deinstitutionalization and service priorities in Canada and the United States. In L. L. Bachrach & P. Goering (Eds.), *Mental health care in Canada* (pp. 3–9). San Francisco, CA: Jossey-Bass.

Badr, M. S. (2012). Central sleep apnea. In M. S. Badr (Ed.), *Essentials of sleep medicine* (pp. 219–232). New York, NY: Humana Press.

Baek, J. H., Eisner, L. R., & Nierenberg, A. A. (2014). Epidemiology and course of unipolar mania: Results from the National Epidemiologic Survey on Alcohol and Related Conditions (NESARC). *Depression and Anxiety, 31*, 746–755.

Baer, D. M., Wolf, M. M., & Risley, T. R. (1968). Some current dimensions of applied behavior analysis. *Journal of Applied Behavior Analysis, 1*, 91–97.

Baer, R. A., & Krietemeyer, J. (2008). Overview of mindfulness- and acceptance-based treatment approaches. In R. A. Baer (Ed.), *Mindfulness-based treatment approaches: Clinician's guide to evidence base and applications* (pp. 3–27). Burlington, MA: Academic Press.

Baer, R. A., Peters, J. R., Eisenlohr-Moul, T. A., Geiger, P. J., & Sauer, S. E. (2012). Emotion-related cognitive processes in borderline personality disorder: A review of the empirical literature. *Clinical Psychology Review, 32*(5), 359–369. https://doi.org/10.1016/j.cpr.2012.03.002

Bagby, R. M., Joffe, R. T., Parker, J. D. A., & Schuller, D. R. (1993). Re-examination of the evidence for the DSM-III personality disorder clusters. *Journal of Personality Disorders, 7*, 320–328.

Bagby, R. M., Marshall, M. B., & Bacchiochi, J. R. (2005). The validity and clinical utility of the MMPI-2 malingering depression scale. *Journal of Personality Assessment, 85*, 304–311.

Bagby, R. M., Marshall, M. B., & Georgiades, S. (2005). Dimensional personality traits and the prediction of DSM-IV personality disorder symptom counts in a nonclinical sample. *Journal of Personality Disorders, 19*, 53–67.

Bagby, R. M., Nicholson, R. A., Bacchiochi, J. R., Ryder, A. G., & Bury, A. S. (2002). The predictive capacity of the MMPI-2 and PAI validity scales and indexes to detect coached and uncoached feigning. *Journal of Personality Assessment, 78*, 69–86.

Baglioni, C., Nanovska, S., Regen, W., Spiegelhalder, K., Feige, B., Nissen, C., Reynolds III, C. F., & Riemann, D. (2016). Sleep and mental disorders: A meta-analysis of polysomnographic research. *Psychological Bulletin, 142*(9), 969.

Bagby, R. M., Ryder, A. G., & Cristi, C. (2002). Psychosocial and clinical pre-dictors of response to pharmacotherapy for depression. *Journal of Psychiatry & Neuroscience, 27*, 250–257.

Bailey, J. A. (2009). Addressing common risk and protective factors can prevent a wide range of adolescent risk behaviors. *Journal of Adolescent Health, 45*(2), 107–108.

Bailey, J. M. (2003). *The man who would be queen: The science of gender-bending and transsexualism.* Washington, DC: National Academy Press.

Bailey, R. C., & Baillie, A. J. (2012). The relationship between placebo alcohol and affect: Motives for drinking. *Drug and Alcohol Review, 32,* 162–169. https://doi.org/10.1111/j.1465-3362.2012.00500.x

Baird, G., Simonoff, E., Pickles, A., Chandler, S., Loucas, T., Meldrum, D., & Charman, T. (2006). Prevalence of disorders of the autism spectrum in a population cohort of children in South Thames: The Special Needs and Autism Project (SNAP). *The Lancet, 368*(9531), 210–215.

Baker, B., Richter, A., & Anand, S. S. (2001). From the heartland: Culture, psychological factors, and coronary heart disease. In S. S. Kazarian & D. R. Evans (Eds.), *Handbook of cultural health psychology* (pp. 141–162), San Diego, CA: Academic Press.

Baker, J. C., & LeBlanc, L. A. (2011). Acceptability of interventions for aggressive behavior in long-term care settings: Comparing ratings and hierarchical selection. *Behavior Therapy, 42*(1), 30–41.

Baldessarini, R. J. (1989). Current status of antidepressants: Clinical pharmacology and therapy. *Journal of Clinical Psychiatry, 50*(4), 117–126.

Balfour, L., Kowal, J., Silverman, A., Tasca, G. A., Angel, J. B., Macpherson, P. A., . . . Cameron, D. W. (2006). A randomized controlled psycho-education intervention trial: Improving psychological readiness for successful HIV medication adherence and reducing depression before initiating HAART. *AIDS Care, 18*(7), 830–838.

Ball, J. C., & Ross, A. (1991). *The effectiveness of methadone maintenance treatment.* New York, NY: Springer-Verlag.

Balon, R. (2006). SSRI-associated sexual dysfunction. *American Journal of Psychiatry, 163,* 1504–1512.

Balon, R., Segraves, R., & Clayton, A. (2007). Issues for DSM-V: Sexual dysfunction, disorder, or variation along normal distribution—Toward rethinking DSM criteria of sexual dysfunctions. *American Journal of Psychiatry, 164,* 198–200.

Bancroft, J. (1989). *Human sexuality and its problems* (2nd ed.). Edinburgh, UK: Churchill Livingstone.

Bancroft, J. (1997). Sexual problems. In D. M. Clark & C. G. Fairburn (Eds.), *Science and practice of cognitive behavior therapy* (pp. 243–257). New York, NY: Oxford University Press.

Bandura, A. (1973). *Aggression: A social learning analysis.* Englewood Cliffs, NJ: Prentice-Hall.

Bandura, A. (1986). *Social foundations of thought and action: A social cognitive theory.* Englewood Cliffs, NJ: Prentice-Hall.

Bandura, A., Jeffery, R., & Bachicha, D. L. (1974). Analysis of memory codes and cumulative rehearsal in observational learning. *Journal of Research in Personality, 7,* 295–305.

Bandura, A., & McDonald, F. J. (1963). Influence of social reinforcement and the behavior of models in shaping

children's moral judgment. *Journal of Abnormal & Social Psychology, 67,* 274–281.

Bandura, A., O'Leary, A., Taylor, C. B., Gauthier, J., & Gossard, D. (1987). Perceived self-efficacy and pain control: Opioid and nonopioid mechanisms. *Journal of Personality and Social Psychology, 53,* 563–571.

Bandura, A., Ross, D., & Ross, S. A. (1961). Transmission of aggression through imitation of aggressive models. *Journal of Abnormal & Social Psychology, 63,* 575–582.

Bandura, A., Ross, D., & Ross, S. A. (1963). Imitation of film-mediated aggressive models. *Journal of Abnormal & Social Psychology, 66,* 3–11.

Bankert, E. A., & Amdur, R. J. (2006). *Institutional Review Board: Management and function.* Boston, MA: Jones and Bartlett Publishers.

Barbaree, H. E., & Seto, M. C. (1997). Pedophilia: Assessment and treatment. In D. R. Laws & W. O. O'Donohue (Eds.), *Sexual deviance: Theory, assessment, and treatment* (pp. 175–193). New York, NY: Guilford Press.

Barclay, N. L., & Gregory, A. M. (2013). Quantitative genetic research on sleep: A review of normal sleep, sleep disturbances and associated emotional, behavioural, and health-related difficulties. *Sleep Medicine Reviews, 17*(1), 29–40.

Barclay, P. (2015). Reputation. In D. Buss (Ed.), *Handbook of evolutionary psychology* (2nd ed., pp. 810–828). Hoboken, NJ: J. Wiley & Sons.

Bargh, J. A., & Chartrand, T. L. (1999). The unbearable automaticity of being. *American Psychologist, 54,* 462–479.

Bar-Haim, Y., Lamy, D., Pergamin, L., Bakermans-Kranenburg, M. J., & Van Ijzendoorn, M. H. (2007). Threat-related attentional bias in anxious and nonanxious individuals: A meta-analytic study. *Psychological Bulletin, 133,* 1–24.

Barik, J., Marti, F., Morel, C., Fernandez, S. P., Lanteri, C., Godeheu, G., & Tronche, F. (2013). Chronic stress triggers social aversion via glucocorticoid receptor in dopaminoceptive neurons. *Science, 339*(6117), 332–335.

Barkley, R. A. (1990). *Attention deficit hyperactivity disorder: A handbook for diagnosis and treatment.* New York, NY: Guilford Press.

Barkley, R. A. (2006). Etiologies. In R. A. Barkley (Ed.), *Attention-deficit hyperactivity disorder: A handbook for diagnosis and treatment* (3rd ed., pp. 219–247). New York, NY: Guilford Press.

Barkley, R. A. (2015a). Etiologies of ADHD. In R. A. Barkley (Ed.), *Attention-deficit hyperactivity disorder: A handbook for diagnosis & treatment* (4th ed., pp. 356–390). New York, NY: Guilford Press.

Barkley, R. A., Murphy, K. R., & Kwasnik, D. (1996). Motor vehicle driving competencies and risks in teens and young adults with attention deficit hyperactivity disorder. *Pediatrics, 98,* 1089–1095.

Barlow, D. H. (1986). Causes of sexual dysfunction: The role of anxiety and cognitive interference. *Journal of Consulting and Clinical Psychology, 54,* 140–148.

Barlow, D. H. (1988). *Anxiety and its disorders: The nature and treatment of anxiety and panic.* New York, NY: Guilford Press.

Barlow, D. H. (1991). Disorders of emotion. *Psychological Inquiry, 2*(1), 58–71.

Barlow, D. H. (2000). Unraveling the mysteries of anxiety and its disorders from the perspective of emotion theory. *American Psychologist, 55,* 1245–1263.

Barlow, D. H. (2002). *Anxiety and its disorders: The nature and treatment of anxiety and panic* (2nd ed.). New York, NY: Guilford Press.

Barlow, D. H. (2004). Covert sensitization for paraphilia. In D. Wedding & R. J. Corsini (Eds.), *Case studies in psychotherapy* (4th ed., pp. 105–113). Belmont, CA: Thomson. (Reprinted from Covert conditioning casebook (1st ed., pp. 187–207) by J. R. Cautela & A. J. Kearney, Eds., 1993, Belmont, CA: Brooks/Cole.

Barlow, D. H., Bullis, J. R., Comer, J. S., & Ametaj, A. A. (2013). Evidence-based psychological treatments: An update and a way forward. In S. Nolen-Hoeksema, T. D. Cannon, & T. Widiger (Eds.), *Annual review of clinical psychology* (Vol. 9, pp. 1–27). Palo Alto, CA: Annual Reviews.

Barlow, D. H., & Craske, M. G. (2007). *Mastery of your anxiety and panic* (4th ed.). New York, NY: Oxford University Press.

Barlow, D. H., & Lehman, C. L. (1996). Advances in the psychosocial treatment of anxiety disorders: Implications for national health care. *Archives of General Psychiatry, 53,* 727–735.

Barlow, D. H., & Liebowitz, M. R. (1995). Specific and social phobias. In H. I. Kaplan & B. J. Sadock (Eds.), *Comprehensive textbook of psychiatry: VI* (pp. 1204–1217). Baltimore, MD: Williams & Wilkins.

Barlow, D. H., & Wincze, J. P. (1980). Treatment of sexual deviations. In S. R. Leiblum & L. A. Pervin (Eds.), *Principles and practice of sex therapy* (pp. 347–375). New York, NY: Guilford Press.

Barlow, D. H., Allen, L. B., & Basden, S. (2007). Psychological treatments for panic disorders, phobias, and generalized anxiety disorder. In P. E. Nathan & J. M. Gorman (Eds.), *A guide to treatments that work* (3rd ed.). New York, NY: Oxford University Press.

Barlow, D. H., Allen, L. B., & Choate, M. L. (2004). Toward a unified treatment for emotional disorders. *Behavior Therapy, 35,* 205–230.

Barlow, D. H., Brown, T. A., & Craske, M. G. (1994). Definitions of panic attacks and panic disorder in DSM-IV: Implications for research. *Journal of Abnormal Psychology, 103,* 553–554.

Barlow, D. H., Chorpita, B. F., & Turovsky, J. (1996). Fear, panic, anxiety, and disorders of emotion. In D. A. Hope (Ed.), *The 43rd Annual Nebraska Symposium on Motivation. Perspectives on anxiety, panic and fear* (pp. 251–328). Lincoln, NE: Nebraska University Press.

Barlow, D. H., Gorman, J. M., Shear, K. M., & Woods, S. W. (2000). Cognitive-behavioral therapy, imipramine, or their combination for panic disorder: A randomized controlled trial. *JAMA: Journal of the American Medical Association, 283*(19), 2529–2536.

Barlow, D. H., Hayes, S. C., & Nelson, R. O. (1984). *The scientist practitioner: Research and accountability in clinical and educational settings.* Boston, MA: Allyn & Bacon.

Barlow, D. H., Levitt, J. T., & Bufka, L. F. (1999). The dissemination of empirically supported treatments: A view to the future. *Behaviour Research and Therapy, 37*(Suppl. 1), S147–162.

Barlow, D. H., Nock, M. K., & Hersen, M. (2009). *Single case experimental designs: Strategies for studying behavior change* (3rd ed.). New York, NY: Allyn & Bacon.

Barlow, D. H., Pincus, D. B., Heinrichs, N., & Choate, M. L. (2003). Anxiety disorders: A lifespan developmental perspective. In I. Weiner (Ed.), *Comprehensive handbook of psychology* (Vol. 8, pp.119–147). New York, NY: John Wiley & Sons.

Barlow, D. H., Rapee, R. M., & Reisner, L. C. (2001). *Mastering stress 2001: A lifestyle approach.* Dallas, TX: American Health.

Barlow, D. H., Sauer-Zavala, S., Carl, J. R., Bullis, J. R., & Ellard, K. K. (2014). The nature, diagnosis, and treatment of neuroticism: Back to the future. *Clinical Psychological Science, 2*(3), 344–365. https://doi.org/10.1177/2167702613505532

Barmish, A. J., & Kendall, P. C. (2005). Should parents be co-clients in cognitive behavioral therapy for anxious youth? *Journal of Clinical Child and Adolescent Psychology, 34*(3), 69–581.

Barnard, A. (2000, September 12). When plastic surgeons should just say "no." *Boston Globe,* pp. E1, E3.

Barnes, G. E., & Toews, J. (1983). Deinstitutionalization of chronic mental patients in the Canadian context. *Canadian Psychology, 24,* 22–36.

Barnes, J. (1981). Non-consummation of marriage. *Irish Medical Journal, 74,* 19–21.

Barnett, P. A., & Gotlib, I. H. (1988). Psychosocial functioning and depression: Distinguishing among antecedents, concomitants and consequences. *Psychological Bulletin, 104*(1), 97–126.

Baron, M., Gruen, R., Asnis, L., & Lord, S. (1985). Familial transmission of schizotypal and borderline personality disorders. *American Journal of Psychiatry, 142,* 927–934.

Baron, M., Risch, N., Hamburger, R., Mandel, B., Kushner, S., Newman, M., . . . Belmaker, R. H. (1987). Genetic linkage between X-chromosome markers and bipolar affective illness. *Nature, 326,* 289–292.

Baron-Cohen, S., Tager-Flusberg, H., & Cohen, D. J. (Eds.). (1994). *Understanding other minds: Perspectives from autism.* London, UK: Oxford University Press.

Barr, H. M., & Streissguth, A. P. (2001). Identifying maternal self-reported alcohol use associated with fetal alcohol spectrum disorders. *Alcoholism, Clinical and Experimental Research, 25,* 283–287.

Barrett, D. H., Resnick, H. S., Foy, D. W., Dansky, B. S., Flanders, W. D., & Stroup, N. E. (1996). Combat exposure and adult psychosocial adjustment among U.S. army veterans serving in Vietnam, 1965–1971. *Journal of Abnormal Psychology, 105,* 575–581.

Barrett, L. F. (2009). Variety is the spice of life: A psychological construction approach to understanding variability in emotion. *Cognition and Emotion, 23*(7), 1284–1306.

Barrett, L. F. (2012). Emotions are real. *Emotion, 12*(3), 413–429.

Barrett, P. M., Dadds, M. R., & Rapee, R. M. (1996). Family treatment of childhood anxiety: A controlled trial. *Journal of Consulting and Clinical Psychology, 64*, 333–342.

Barrett, R., Loa, P., Jerah, E., Nancarrow, D., Chant, D., & Mowry, B. (2005). Rates of treated schizophrenia and its clinical and cultural features in the population isolate of the Iban of Sarawak: A tri-diagnostic approach. *Psychological Medicine, 35*, 281–293.

Barrett, S. P., Darredeau, C., & Pihl, R. O. (2006a). Patterns of simultaneous poly-substance use in drug using university students. *Human Psychopharmacology: Clinical and Experimental, 21*(4), 255–263.

Barrett, S. P., Tichauer, M., Leyton, M., & Pihl, R. O. (2006b). Nicotine increases alcohol self-administration in non-dependent male smokers. *Drug and Alcohol Dependence, 81*(2), 197–204.

Barrowclough, C., & Tarrier, N. (1998). The application of expressed emotion to clinical work in schizophrenia. *In Session: Psychotherapy in Practice, 4*(3), 7–23.

Barry, C. T., Golmaryami, F. N., Rivera-Hudson, N., & Frick, P. J. (2012). Evidence-based assessment of conduct disorder: Current considerations and preparation for DSM-5. *Professional Psychology: Research and Practice, 44*(1), 56–63.

Barsaglini, A., Sartori, G., Benetti, S., Pettersson-Yeo, W., & Mechelli, A. (2014). The effects of psychotherapy on brain function: A systematic and critical review. *Progress in Neurobiology, 114*, 1–4.

Barsky, A. J., & Ahern, D. K. (2005). Cognitive behavior therapy for hypochondriasis: A randomized controlled trial. *JAMA. 291*, 1464–1470.

Barsky, A. J., Wyshak, G., & Klerman, G. L. (1986). Hypochondriasis: An evaluation of the DSM-III criteria in medical outpatients. *Archives of General Psychiatry, 43*, 493–500.

Bartlett, N., & Vasey, P. (2006). A retrospective study of childhood gender-atypical behavior in Samoan Fa'afafine. *Archives of Sexual Behaviour, 39*(4), 821–830. https://doi.org/10.1007/s10508-008-9404-3

Bartlik, B., & Goldberg, J. (2000). Female sexual arousal disorder. In S. R. Leiblum & R. C. Rosen (Eds.), *Principles and practice of sex therapy* (3rd ed., pp. 85–117). New York, NY: Guilford Press.

Basoglu, M., Marks, I., Livanou, M., & Swinson, R. (1997). Double-blindness procedures, rater blindness, and ratings of outcome: Observations from a controlled trial. *Archives of General Psychiatry, 54*, 744–748.

Basson, R. (2001). Using a different model for female sexual response to address women's problematic low sexual desire. *Journal of Sex & Marital Therapy, 27*, 395–403.

Basson, R. (2006). Sexual desire and arousal disorders in women. *New England Journal of Medicine, 354*, 1497–1506.

Basson, R. (2007). Sexual desire/arousal disorders in women. In S. R. Leiblum (Ed.), *Principles and practice of sex therapy* (4th ed., pp. 25–53). New York, NY: Guilford Press.

Basson, R., Althof, S., Davis, S., Fugl-Meyer, K., Goldstein, I., Leiblum, S., . . .

Wagner, G. (2004a). Summary of the recommendations on sexual dysfunctions in women. *Journal of Sexual Medicine, 1*, 24–34.

Basson, R., Brotto, L. A., Laan, E., Redmond, G., & Utian, W. H. (2005). Assessment and management of women's sexual dysfunctions: Problematic desire and arousal. *Journal of Sexual Medicine, 2*, 291–300.

Basson, R., Leiblum, S., Brotto, L., Derogatis, L., Fourcroy, J., Fugl-Meyer, K., . . . Weijmar Schultz, W. (2004b). Definitions of women's sexual dysfunction reconsidered: Advocating expansion and revision. *Journal of Psychosomatic Obstetrics & Gynecology, 24*, 221–229.

Basson, R., Wierman, M., van Lankveld, J., & Brotto, L. (2010). Summary of the recommendations on sexual dysfunctions in women. *Journal of Sexual Medicine, 7*(1, pt. 2), 314–326.

Bastien, C. H., Vallières, A., & Morin, C. M. (2004). Precipitating factors of insomnia. *Behavioral Sleep Medicine, 2*, 50–62.

Bateman, A. W., Gunderson, J., & Mulder, R. (2015). Personality Disorder 2: Treatment of personality disorder. *Lancet, 385*, 735–743.

Bateson, G. (1959). Cultural problems posed by a study of schizophrenic process. In A. Auerback (Ed.), *Schizophrenia: An integrated approach*. New York, NY: Ronald Press.

Baugh, C. M., Stamm, J. M., Riley, D. O., Gavett, B. E., Shenton, M. E., Lin, A., . . . Stern, R. A. (2012). Chronic traumatic encephalopathy: Neurodegeneration following repetitive concussive and subconcussive brain trauma. *Brain Imaging and Behavior, 6*(2), 244–254.

Bausell, R. B. (2007). *Snake oil science*. Oxford: Oxford University Press.

Baxter, L. R., Jr., Schwartz, J. M., Bergman, K. S., Szuba, M. P., Guze, B. H., Mazziotta, J. C., . . . Phelps, M. E. (1992). Caudate glucose metabolic rate changes with both drug and behavior therapy for obsessive–compulsive disorder. *Archives of General Psychiatry, 49*, 681–689.

Beach, S. R. H., Jones, D. J., & Franklin, K. J. (2009). Marital, family, and interpersonal therapies for depression in adults. In I. H. Gotlib & C. L. Hammen (Eds.), *Handbook of depression* (2nd ed., pp. 624–641). New York, NY: Guilford Press.

Beach, S. R. H., Sandeen, E. E., & O'Leary, K. D. (1990). Depression in marriage: A model for etiology and treatment. In D. H. Barlow (Ed.), *Treatment manuals for practitioners*. New York, NY: Guilford Press.

Bear, R. E., Fitzgerald, P., Rosenfeld, J. V., & Bittar, R. G. (2010). Neurosurgery for obsessive–compulsive disorder: Contemporary approaches. *Journal of Clinical Neuroscience, 17*(1), 1–5.

Beard, G. M. (1869). Neurasthenia or nervous exhaustion. *Boston Medical Surgical Journal, 3*, 217–221.

Beard, J. H., Malamud, T. J., & Rossman, E. (1978). Psychiatric rehabilitation and long-term rehospitalization rates: The findings of two research studies. *Schizophrenia Bulletin, 4*, 622–635.

Beard, J. H., Propst, R. N., & Malamud, T. J. (1982). The Fountain House model of psychiatric rehabilitation. *Psychosocial Rehabilitation Journal, 5*, 47–53.

Beardon, L., & Worton, D. (2011). *Aspies on mental health: Speaking for ourselves*. London, UK: Jessica Kingsley.

Beardslee, W. R., Salt, P., Versage, E. M., Gladstone, T. R. G., Wright, E. J., & Rothberg, P. C. (1997). Sustained change in parents receiving preventive interventions for families with depression. *American Journal of Psychiatry, 154*(4), 510–515.

Beaudette, J. (2013). Prevalence of mental health disorders among incoming federal offenders: Atlantic, Ontario, & Pacific Regions. *Emerging Research Results*, 13–3. Correctional Services Canada. http://www.csc-scc.gc.ca/005/008/092/err13-3-eng.pdf

Beaudette, J. N., Power, J., & Stewart, L. A. (2015). *National Prevalence of Mental Disorders among Incoming Federally-Sentenced Men Offenders* (Research Report, R-357). Correctional Service Canada.

Beaulieu, J. M., & Gainetdinov, R. R. (2011). The physiology, signaling, and pharmacology of dopamine receptors. *Pharmacological Reviews, 63*, 182–217.

Beaver, K. M., Barnes, J. C., May, J. S., & Schwartz, J. A. (2011). Psychopathic personality traits, genetic risk, and gene–environment correlations. *Criminal Justice and Behavior, 38*(9), 896–912.

Bebbington, P. E., Bowen, J., Hirsch, S. R., & Kuipers, E. A. (1995). Schizophrenia and psychosocial stresses. In S. R. Hirsch & D. R. Weinberger (Eds.), *Schizophrenia* (pp. 587–604). Oxford, UK: Blackwell Science.

Bebbington, P., Wilkins, S., Jones, P., Foerster, A., Murray, R., Toone, B., & Lewis, S. (1993). Life events and psychosis: Initial results from the Camberwell Collaborative Psychosis Study. *British Journal of Psychiatry, 162*, 72–79.

Bech, P. (2009). Clinical features of mood disorders and mania. In M. G. Gelder, N. C. Andreasen, J. J. López-Ibor, Jr., & J. R. Geddes (Eds.), *New Oxford textbook of psychiatry* (2nd ed., Vol. 1, pp. 632–637). Oxford, UK: Oxford University Press.

Beck, A. T. (1967). *Depression: Clinical, experimental and theoretical aspects*. New York, NY: Harper & Row.

Beck, A. T. (1976). *Cognitive therapy and the emotional disorders*. New York, NY: International Universities Press.

Beck, A. T. (1983). Cognitive therapy of depression: New perspectives. In P. Clayton & J. E. Barrett (Eds.), *Treatment of depression: Old controversies and new approaches* (pp. 265–290). New York, NY: Raven Press.

Beck, A. T. (1986). Hopelessness as a predictor of eventual suicide. *Annals of the New York Academy of Science, 487*, 90–96.

Beck, A. T. (1987). Cognitive models of depression. *Journal of Cognitive Psychotherapy, 1*, 5–37.

Beck, A. T., & Freeman, A. (1990). *Cognitive therapy of personality disorders*. New York, NY: Guilford Press.

Beck, A. T., Davis, D. D., & Freeman, A. (2015). *Cognitive therapy of personality disorders* (3rd ed.). New York, NY: Guilford Press.

Beck, A. T., Epstein, N., & Harrison, R. (1983). Cognitions, attitudes and personality dimensions in depression.

British Journal of Cognitive Psychotherapy, 1(1), 1–16.

Beck, A. T., Freeman, A., & Davis, D. D. (2007). *Cognitive therapy of personality disorders* (2nd ed.). New York, NY: Guilford Press.

Beck, A. T., Hollon, S. D., Young, J. E., Bedrosian, R. C., & Budenz, D. (1985). Treatment of depression with cognitive therapy and amitriptyline. *Archives of General Psychiatry, 42*, 142–148.

Beck, A. T., & Rector, N. A. (2000). Cognitive therapy of schizophrenia: A new therapy for the new millennium. *American Journal of Psychotherapy, 54*, 291–300.

Beck, A. T., Rector, N. A., Stolar, N., & Grant, P. (2001). *Schizophrenia: Cognitive theory, research, and therapy*. New York, NY: Guilford Press.

Beck, A. T., Steer, R., Kovacs, M., & Garrison, B. (1985). Hopelessness and eventual suicide: A 10-year prospective study of patients hospitalized with suicidal ideation. *American Journal of Psychiatry, 142*, 559–563.

Beck, C. A., Patten, S. B., Williams, J. V. A., Wang, J. L., Currie, S. R., Maxwell, C. J., & El-Guebaly, N. (2005). Anti-depressant utilization in Canada. *Social Psychiatry and Psychiatric Epidemiology, 40*, 799–807.

Beck, C. A., Williams, J. V. A., Wang, J. L., Kassam, A., El-Guebaly, N., Currie, S. R., . . . Patten, S. B. (2005). Psychotropic medication use in Canada [Special issue: The Canadian Academy of Psychiatric Epidemiology (CAPE) look at the Canadian Community Health Survey, Cycle 1. 2]. *Canadian Journal of Psychiatry, 50*, 605–613.

Beck, J. G. (1993). Vaginismus. In W. O'Donohue & J. H. Geer (Eds.), *Handbook of sexual dysfunctions: Assessment and treatment* (pp. 381–397). Boston, MA: Allyn & Bacon.

Beck, J. G., & Averill, P. M. (2004). Older adults. In R. G. Heimberg, C. L. Turk, & D. S. Mennin (Eds.), *Generalized anxiety disorder: Advances in research and practice* (pp. 409–433). New York, NY: Guilford Press.

Beck, J. G., & Sloan, D. M. (Eds.). (2012). *The Oxford handbook of traumatic stress disorders*. New York, NY: Oxford University Press.

Beck, J. G., & Stanley, M. A. (1997). Anxiety disorders in the elderly: The emerging role of behavior therapy. *Behavior Therapy, 28*, 83–100.

Becker, D. (2000). When she was bad: Borderline personality disorder in a posttraumatic age. *American Journal of Orthopsychiatry, 70*, 422–432.

Becker, J. T., Mestre, L. T., Ziolko, S., & Lopez, O. L. (2007). Gene–environment interactions with cognition in late life and compression of morbidity. *American Journal of Psychiatry, 164*(6), 849–852.

Becvar, D. S. (2013). *Handbook of family resilience*. New York, NY: Springer.

Beesdo, K., Pine, D. S., Lieb, R., & Wittchen, H. U. (2010). Incidence and risk patterns of anxiety and depressive disorders and categorization of generalized anxiety disorder. *Archives of General Psychiatry, 67*(1), 47–57.

Beiser, M., & Gotowiec, A. (2000). Accounting for Native/non-Native differences in IQ scores. *Psychology in the Schools, 3*(3), 237–252.

Beiser, M., Dion, R., & Gotowiec, A. (2000). The structure of attention-deficit and hyperactivity symptoms among Native and non-Native elementary school children. *Journal of Abnormal Child Psychology, 28,* 425–437.

Beitchman, J. H., & Young, A. R. (1997). Learning disorders with a special emphasis on reading disorders: A review of the past 10 years. *Journal of the American Academy of Child & Adolescent Psychiatry, 36,* 1020–1032.

Beitchman, J. H., Davidge, K. M., Kennedy, J. L., Atkinson, L., Lee, V., Shapiro, S., & Douglas, L. (2003). The serotonin transporter gene in aggressive children with and without ADHD and nonaggressive matched controls. *Annals of the New York Academy of Sciences, 1008,* 248–251.

Beitchman, J. H., Wilson, B., Douglas, L., Young, A., & Adlaf, E. (2001). Substance use disorders in young adults with and without LD: Predictive and concurrent relationships. *Journal of Learning Disabilities, 34,* 317–332.

Beitchman, J. H., Wilson, B., Johnson, C. J., Atkinson, L., Young, A., Adlaf, E., Escobar, M., & Douglas L. (2001). Fourteen-year follow-up of speech/language-impaired and control children: Psychiatric outcome. *Journal of the American Academy of Child & Adolescent Psychiatry, 40,* 75–82. https://doi.org/10.1097/00004583-200101000-00019

Béjot, Y., Juenet, N., Garrouty, R., Maltaverne, D., Nicolleau, L., Giroud, M., & Didi-Roy, R. (2010). Sexsomnia: An uncommon variety of parasomnia. *Clinical Neurology and Neurosurgery, 112*(1), 72–75.

Bélanger, L., Savard, J., & Morin, C. M. (2006). Clinical management of insomnia using cognitive therapy. *Behavioral Sleep Medicine, 4,* 179–202.

Belanger, Y., Weasel Head, G., & Awosoga, O. (2012). *Assessing Urban Aboriginal Housing and Homelessness in Canada.* National Association of Friendship Centres and the Office of the Federal Interlocuter for Métis and Non- Status Indians. https://www.homelesshub.ca/sites/default/files/attachments/Final_Belanger_Housing_and_Homeless_-_6_May_2012.pdf

Belik, S. L., Sareen, J., & Stein, M. B. (2009). Anxiety disorders and physical comorbidity. In M. M. Antony & M. B. Stein (Eds.), *Oxford handbook of anxiety and related disorders* (pp. 596–610). New York, NY: Oxford University Press.

Belitsky, C. A., Toner, B. B., Ali, A., Yu, B., Osborne, S. L., & deRooy, E. (1996). Sex-role attitudes and clinical appraisal in psychiatry residents. *Canadian Journal of Psychiatry, 41,* 503–508.

Belitsky, R., & McGlashan, T. H. (1993). The manifestations of schizophrenia in late life: A dearth of data. *Schizophrenia Bulletin, 19,* 683–685.

Belke, T. W., Pierce, W. D., & Duncan, I. D. (2006). Reinforcement value and substitutability of sucrose and wheel running: Implications for a activity anorexia. *Journal of the Experimental Analysis of Behavior, 86*(2), 131–158.

Bell Canada. (2019). *Bell let's talk: Our initiatives.* https://letstalk.bell.ca/en/our-initiatives/#stories

Bell, C. C., Dixie-Bell, D. D., & Thompson, B. (1986). Further studies on the prevalence of isolated sleep paralysis in black subjects. *Journal of the National Medical Association, 75,* 649–659.

Bell, I. R. (1994). Somatization disorder: Health care costs in the decade of the brain. *Biological Psychiatry, 35,* 81–83.

Bellack, A. S., & Mueser, K. T. (1992). Social skills training for schizophrenia? *Archives of General Psychiatry, 49,* 76.

Bellak, L. (1975). *The thematic apperception test, the children's apperception test, and the senior apperception technique in clinical use* (3rd ed.). New York, NY: Grune & Stratton.

Bellis, D. J. (1981). *Heroin and politicians: The failure of public policy to control addiction in America.* Westport, CT: Greenwood Press.

Belzak, L., & Halverson, J. (2018). The opioid crisis in Canada: A national perspective. *Health Promotion and Chronic Disease Prevention in Canada, 38*(6), 224–233.

Ben Itzchak, E., Lahat, E., Burgin, R., & Zachor, A. D. (2008). Cognitive, behavior and intervention outcome in young children with autism. *Research in Developmental Disabilities, 29*(5), 447–458.

Benbadis, R. R., & Allen-Hauser, W. (2000). An estimate of the prevalence of psychogenic non-epileptic seizures. *Seizure, 9*(4), 280–281.

Benca, R. M., Obermeyer, W. H., Thisted, R. A., & Gillin, J. C. (1992). Sleep and psychiatric disorders: A meta-analysis. *Archives of General Psychiatry, 49,* 651–668.

Bender, D. S. (2005). Therapeutic alliance. In J. M. Oldham, A. E. Skodol, & D. S. Bender (Eds.), *Textbook of personality disorders* (pp. 405–420). Washington, DC: American Psychiatric Publishing.

Benedetti, A., Perugi, G., Toni, C., Simonetti, B., Mata, B., & Cassano, G. B. (1997). Hypochondriasis and illness phobia in panic-agoraphobic patients. *Comprehensive Psychiatry, 38*(2), 124–131.

Benedetti, F. (2012). Antidepressant chronotherapeutics for bipolar depression. *Dialogues in Clinical Neuroscience, 14*(4), 401. https://doi.org/10.1177/1363461513503380

Benight, C. C., & Bandura, A. (2004). Social cognitive theory of posttraumatic recovery: The role of perceived self-efficacy. *Behaviour Research and Therapy, 42*(10), 1129–1148.

Benjamin, C. L., Harrison, J. P., Settipani, C. A., Brodman, D. M., & Kendall, P. C. (2013). Anxiety and related outcomes in young adults 7 to 19 years after receiving treatment for child anxiety. *Journal of Consulting and Clinical Psychology, 81,* 865.

Bennett, E., & Heaton, P. (2012). Is talent in autism spectrum disorders associated with a specific cognitive and behavioural phenotype? *Journal of Autism and Developmental Disorders, 42*(12), 2739–2753.

Bennett, K. J., Lipman, E. L., Brown, S., Racine, Y., Boyle, M. H., & Offord, D. R. (1999). Predicting conduct problems: Can high-risk children be identified in kindergarten and grade 1? *Journal of Consulting and Clinical Psychology, 67,* 470–480.

Bennett, K., Shepherd, J., & Janca, A. (2013). Personality disorders and spirituality. *Current Opinion in Psychiatry, 26*(1), 79–83.

Bennett-Branson, S. M., & Craig, K. D. (1993). Postoperative pain in children: Developmental and family influences on spontaneous coping strategies. *Canadian Journal of Behavioural Science, 25,* 355–383.

Benowitz, N. L. (1996). Pharmacology of nicotine: Addiction and therapeutics. *Annual Review of Pharmacology and Toxicology, 36,* 597–613.

Benson, H. (1975). *The relaxation response.* New York, NY: William Morrow.

Benson, H. (1984). *Beyond the relaxation response.* New York, NY: Times Books.

Berenbaum, H., & Oltmanns, T. F. (1992). Emotional experience and expression in schizophrenia and depression. *Journal of Abnormal Psychology, 101,* 37–44.

Berkman, L. F., & Syme, S. L. (1979). Social networks, host resistance, and mortality: A nine-year follow-up study of Alameda county residents. *American Journal of Epidemiology, 109,* 186.

Berman, A. L. (2009). Depression and suicide. In I. H. Gotlib & C. L. Hammen (Eds.), *Handbook of depression* (2nd ed., pp. 510–530). New York, NY: Guilford Press.

Berman, A. L., & Jobes, D. A. (1991). *Adolescent suicide: Assessment and intervention.* Washington, DC: American Psychological Association.

Berman, K. F., & Weinberger, D. R. (1990). Lateralization of cortical function during cognitive tasks: Regional cerebral blood flow studies of normal individuals and patients with schizophrenia. *Journal of Neurology, Neurosurgery and Psychiatry, Neurology, 53,* 150–160.

Berman, M. E., McCloskey, M. S., Fanning, J. R., Schumacher, J. A., & Coccaro, E. F. (2009). Serotonin augmentation reduces response to attack in aggressive individuals. *Psychological Science, 20*(6), 714–720.

Berman, T., Douglas, V. I., & Barr, R. G. (1999). Effects of methylphenidate on complex cognitive processing in attention-deficit hyperactivity disorder. *Journal of Abnormal Psychology, 108,* 90–105.

Berner, L. A., Shaw, J. A., Witt, A. A., & Lowe, M. R. (2013). The relation of weight suppression and body mass index to symptomatology and treatment response in anorexia nervosa. *Journal of Abnormal Psychology, 122*(3), 694.

Berney, S., Sookman, D., Leyton, M., Young, S. N., & Benkelfat, C. (2006). Lack of effects on core obsessive-compulsive symptoms of tryptophan depletion during symptom provocation in remitted obsessive–compulsive disorder patients. *Biological Psychiatry, 59,* 853–857.

Berney, T. P. (2012). Methods of treatment. In M. G. Gelder, N. C. Andreasen, J. J. Lopez-Ibor, Jr., & J. R. Geddes (Eds.), *New Oxford textbook of psychiatry* (2nd ed., Vol. 2, pp. 1871–1877). New York, NY: Oxford University Press.

Bernstein, D. A., & Borkovec, T. D. (1973). *Progressive relaxation training: A manual for the helping professions.* Champaign, IL: Research Press.

Bernstein, D. A., Borkovec, T. D., & Hazlett-Stevens, H. (2000). *New directions in progressive relaxation training: A guidebook for helping professionals.* Westport, CT: Praeger.

Bernstein, D. M., & Loftus, E. F. (2009). How to tell if a particular memory is true or false. *Perspectives on Psychological Science, 4*(4), 370–374.

Bernstein, D. P., & Useda, J. (2007). Paranoid personality disorder. In W. O'Donohue, K. Fowler, & S. Lilienfeld (Eds.), *Personality disorders: Toward the DSM-V* (pp. 41–62). Thousand Oaks, CA: Sage Publications.

Bernstein, D. P., Useda, D., & Siever, L. J. (1993). Paranoid personality disorder: Review of the literature and recommendations for DSM-IV. *Journal of Personality Disorders, 7,* 53–62.

Bernstein, J., Adlaf, E., & Paglia, A. (2002). *Drug use in Toronto—2000.* Retrieved October 25, 2003, from http://www.city.toronto.on.ca/drugcentre/rgdu00/rgdu1.htm

Berntsen, D., Johannessen, K. B., Thornsen, Y. D., Bertelsen, M., Hoyle, R. H., & Rubin, D. C. (2012). Peace and war: Trajectories of posttraumatic stress disorder symptoms before, during, and after military deployment in Afghanistan. *Psychological Science, 23,* 1557–1565.

Berridge, K. C., & Kringelbach, M. L. (2015). Pleasure systems in the brain. *Neuron, 86*(3), 646–664. https://doi.org/10.1016/j.neuron.2015.02.018

Berrios, G. E. (2011). Eugen Bleuler's place in the history of psychiatry. *Schizophrenia Bulletin, 37*(6), 1095–1098.

Berry, J. W. (2003). Origins of cross-cultural similarities and differences in human behavior: An ecocultural perspective. In A. Toomela (Ed.), *Cultural guidance in the development of the human mind* (pp. 97–109). Westport, CT: Ablex.

Berthiaume, L. (2006, May 6). Margaret Trudeau's secret war. *Canada.com.* Retrieved September 22, 2007, from http://www.canada.com/topics/bodyandhealth/story.html?id8cf493ee-f0d4–421c-bfce-92adb8b2ea0b&k22306

Bettelheim, B. (1967). *The empty fortress.* New York, NY: Free Press.

Bettens, K., Sleegers, K., & Van Broeckhoven, C. (2010). Current status on Alzheimer disease molecular genetics: From past, to present, to future. *Human Molecular Genetics, 19*(R1), R4–R11.

Bhagwanjee, A., Parekh, A., Parvk, Z., Petersen, I., & Sudebar, H. (1998). Prevalence of minor psychiatric disorders in an adult African rural community in South Africa. *Psychological Medicine, 28,* 1137–1147.

Bharucha, A., Anand, V., Forlizzi, J., Dew, M., Reynolds, C., III, Stevens, S., & Wactlar, M. S. (2009). Intelligent assistive technology applications to dementia care: Current capabilities, limitations, and future challenges. *The American Journal of Geriatric Psychiatry: Official Journal of the American Association for Geriatric Psychiatry, 17*(2), 88.

Biederman, J., Faraone, S. V., Wozniak, J., Mick, E., Kwon, A., Cayton, G. A., & Clark, S. V. (2005). Clinical correlates of bipolar disorder in a large, referred sample of children and adolescents. *Journal of Psychiatric Research, 39*(6), 611–622.

Biederman, J., Mick, E., Faraone, S. V., Spencer, T., Wilens, T. E., & Wozniak, J. (2000). Pediatric mania: A developmental subtype of bipolar disorder? *Biological Psychiatry, 48*(6), 458–466.

Biederman, J., Spencer, T., Wilens, T., & Greene, R. (2001). Attention-deficit/hyperactivity disorder. In G. O. Gabbard (Ed.), *Treatment of psychiatric disorders* (3rd ed., Vol. 1, pp. 145–176). Washington, DC: American Psychiatric Press.

Bierut, L. J., Heath, A. C., Bucholz, K. K., Dinwiddie, S. H., Madden, P. A., Statham, D. J., . . . Martin, N. G. (1999). Major depressive disorder in a community-based twin sample: Are there different genetic and environmental contributions for men and women? *Archives of General Psychiatry, 56*(6), 557–563.

Billingsley, R. L., McAndrews, M. P., & Smith, M. L. (2002). Intact perceptual and conceptual priming in temporal lobe epilepsy: Neuroanatomical and methodological implications. *Neuropsychology, 16*(1), 92–101.

Billingsley, R. L., Smith, M. L., & McAndrews, M. P. (2002). Developmental patterns in priming and familiarity in explicit recollection. *Journal of Experimental Child Psychology, 82,* 251–277.

Billy, J. O. G., Tanfer, K., Grady, W. R., & Klepinger, D. H. (1993). The sexual behavior of men in the United States. *Family Planning Perspectives, 25,* 52–60.

Binder, E. B., Bradley, R. G., Liu, W., Epstein, M. P., Deveau, T. C., Mercer, K. B., . . . Ressler, K. J. (2008). Association of FKBP5 polymorphisms and childhood abuse with risk of post-traumatic stress disorder symptoms in adults. *JAMA, 299*(11), 1291–1305.

Binik, Y. M. (2010). The DSM diagnostic criteria for dyspareunia. *Archives of Sexual Behavior, 39,* 292–303.

Binik, Y. M., Bergeron, S., & Kalifé, S. (2007). Dyspareunia and vaginismus: So-called sexual pain. In S. R. Leiblum (Ed.), *Principles and practice of sex therapy* (4th ed., pp. 124–156). New York, NY: Guilford Press.

Binzer, M., Andersen, P. M., & Kullgren, G. (1997). Clinical characteristics of patients with motor disability due to conversion disorder: A prospective control group study. *Journal of Neurology, Neurosurgery, and Psychiatry, 63*(1), 83–88.

Birch, D. E. (1992). Duty to protect: Update and Canadian perspective. *Canadian Psychology, 33,* 94–104.

Birchwood, M., Smith, J., Drury, V., Healy, J., MacMillan, F., & Slade, M. A. (1994). A self-report insight scale for psychosis: Reliability, validity and sensitivity to change. *Acta Psychiatrica Scandinavica, 89,* 62–67.

Birley, J., & Brown, G. W. (1970). Crisis and life changes preceding the onset or relapse of acute schizophrenia: Clinical aspects. *British Journal of Psychiatry, 16,* 327–333.

Bishop, D. V. M. (2000). Pragmatic language impairment: A correlate of SLI, a distinct subgroup, or part of the autistic continuum. In D. V. M. Bishop & L. B. Leonard (Eds.), *Speech and language impairments in children: Causes, characteristics, intervention and outcome* (pp. 99–113). East Sussex, UK: Psychology Press.

Bishop, J., Huether, C. A., Torfs, C., Lorey, F., & Deddens, J. (1997). Epidemiologic study of Down syndrome in a racially diverse California population, 1989–1991. *American Journal of Epidemiology, 145*(2), 134–147.

Bjorklund, D. F. (1989). Children's thinking: Developmental function and individual differences. Pacific Grove, CA: Brooks/Cole.

Black, D. W. (2013). *Bad boys, bad men: Confronting Antisocial Personality Disorder (sociopathy).* New York, NY: Oxford University Press.

Black, D. W., & Andreasen, N. C. (1999). Schizophrenia, schizophreniform disorder, and delusional (paranoid) disorders. In R. E. Hales, S. C. Yudofsky, & J. A. Talbott (Eds.), *Textbook of psychiatry* (3rd ed., pp. 425–477). Washington, DC: American Psychiatric Press.

Blackburn, I. M., & Moore, R. G. (1997). Controlled acute and follow-up trial of cognitive therapy and pharmacotherapy in outpatients with recurrent depression. *British Journal of Psychiatry, 171,* 328–334.

Blacker, D. (2005). Psychiatric rating scales. In B. J. Sadock & V. A. Sadock (Eds.), *Kaplan & Sadock's comprehensive textbook of psychiatry* (pp. 929–955). Philadelphia, PA: Lippincott Williams & Wilkins.

Blackshaw, S., Chandarana, P., Garneau, Y., Merskey, H., & Mescarello, R. (1996). Adult recovered memories of childhood sexual abuse. *The Canadian Journal of Psychiatry, 41,* 305–306.

Blagys, M. D., & Hilsenroth, M. J. (2000). Distinctive features of short-term psychodynamic-interpersonal psychotherapy: A review of the comparative psychotherapy process literature. *Clinical Psychology: Science and Practice, 7,* 167–188.

Blair, K. S., Newman, C., Mitchell, D. G. V., Richell, R. A., Leonard, A., Morton, J., & Blair, R. J. R. (2006). Differentiating among prefrontal substrates in psychopathy: Neuropsychological test findings. *Neuropsychology, 20,* 153–165.

Blair, K., Shaywitz, J., Smith, B. W., Rhodes, R., Geraci, M., Jones, M., . . . Pine, D. S. (2008). Response to emotional expressions in generalized social phobia and generalized anxiety disorder: Evidence for separate disorders. *American Journal of Psychiatry, 165*(9), 1193–1202.

Blais, S. (2007, March 14). Pharmacist praises changes in how tobacco can be displayed. *Coquitlam Now,* p. 20.

Blanchard, E. B. (1987). Long-term effects of behavioral treatment of chronic headache. *Behavior Therapy, 18,* 375–385.

Blanchard, E. B. (1992). Psychological treatment of benign headache disorders. [Special issue: Behavioral medicine: An update for the 1990s.] *Journal of Consulting and Clinical Psychology, 60*(4), 537–551.

Blanchard, E. B., & Andrasik, F. (1982). Psychological assessment and treatment of headache: Recent developments and emerging issues. *Journal of Consulting and Clinical Psychology, 50*(6), 859–879.

Blanchard, E. B., & Epstein, L. H. (1977). *A biofeedback primer.* Reading, MA: Addison-Wesley.

Blanchard, E. B., Andrasik, F., Ahles, T. A., Teders, S. J., & O'Keefe, D. (1980). Migraine and tension headache: A meta-analytic review. *Behavior Therapy, 11,* 613–631.

Blanchard, E. B., Appelbaum, K. A., Radnitz, C. L., Michultka, D., Morrill, B., Kirsh, C., . . . Dentinger, M. P. (1990). Placebo-controlled evaluation of abbreviated progressive muscle relaxation combined with cognitive therapy in the treatment of tension headache. *Journal of Consulting and Clinical Psychology, 58*(2), 210–215.

Blanchard, E. B., Kuhn, E., Rowell, D. L., Hickling, E. J., Wittrock, D., Rogers, R. L., . . . Steckler, D. C. (2004). Studies of the vicarious traumatization of college students by the September 11th attacks: Effects of proximity, exposure and connectedness. *Behaviour Research & Therapy, 42,* 191–205.

Blanchard, J. J., & Neale, J. M. (1992). Medication effects: Conceptual and methodological issues in Schizophrenia Research. *Clinical Psychology Review, 12,* 345–361.

Blanchard, R. (2010). The DSM diagnostic criteria for pedophilia. *Archives of Sexual Behavior, 39,* 304–314.

Blanchard, R., & Steiner, B. W. (Eds.). (1990). *Clinical management of gender identity disorders in children and adults.* Washington, DC: American Psychiatric Association.

Blanchard, R., & Steiner, B. W. (1992). *Clinical management of gender identity disorders in children and adults.* Washington, DC: American Psychiatric Press.

Blanco, C., Goodwin, R., Liebowitz, M. R., Schmidt, A. B., Lewis-Fernandez, R., & Olfson, M. (2004). Use of psychotropic medications for patients with office visits who receive a diagnosis of panic disorder. *Medical Care, 42*(12), 1242–1246.

Blanco, C., Vesga-Lopez, O., Stewart, J. W., Liu, S. M., Grant, B. F., & Hasin, D. S. (2012). Prevalence, correlates, comorbidity and treatment-seeking among individuals with a lifetime major depressive episode with and without atypical features: Results from the National Epidemiologic Survey on Alcohol and Related Conditions. *Journal of Clinical Psychiatry, 73*(2), 224–232.

Bland, R. C. (1997). Epidemiology of affective disorders: A review. *Canadian Journal of Psychiatry, 42,* 367–377.

Bland, R. C., Newman, S. C., & Orn, H. (1988). Period prevalence of psychiatric disorders in Edmonton. *Acta Psychiatrica Scandinavica, 77*(Suppl. 338), 33–42.

Blaney, P. H. (2015). Paranoid and delusional disorders. In P. H. Blaney, R. F. Krueger, Robert F., & T. Millon (Eds.), *Oxford textbook of psychopathology* (3rd ed., pp. 383–417). New York, NY: Oxford University Press.

Blansjaar, B. A., Thomassen, R., & Van Schaick, H. W. (2000). Prevalence of dementia in centenarians. *International Journal of Geriatric Psychiatry, 15*(3), 219–225.

Blasco-Fontecilla, H. (2012). The addictive hypothesis of suicidal behavior. *Medical Hypotheses, 78*(2), 305.

Blasco-Fontecilla, H. (2013). On suicide clusters: More than contagion. *The Australian and New Zealand Journal of Psychiatry, 47*(5), 490–491.

Blascovich, J., Spencer, S. J., Quinn, D., & Steele, C. (2001). African Americans and high blood pressure: The role of stereotype threat. *Psychological Science, 12*(3), 225–229.

Blashfield, R. K., Keeley, J. W., Flanagan, E. H., & Miles, S. R. (2014). The cycle of classification: DSM-I through DSM-5. *Annual Review of Clinical Psychology, 10,* 25–51. https://doi.org/10.1146/annurev-clinpsy-032813-153639

Blashfield, R. K., Reynolds, S. M., & Stennett, B. (2012). The death of histrionic personality disorder. In T. A. Widiger (Ed.), *The Oxford handbook of personality disorders* (pp. 603–627). New York, NY: Oxford University Press.

Blazer, D. G. (1989). Current concepts: Depression in the elderly. *New England Journal of Medicine, 320,* 164–166.

Blazer, D. G., George, L., & Hughes, D. (1991). The epidemiology of anxiety disorders: An age comparison. In C. Salzman & B. Liebowitz (Eds.), *Anxiety disorders in the elderly* (pp. 17–30). New York, NY: Springer.

Blazer, D. G., Hughes, D., George, L. K., Swartz, M., & Boyer, R. (1991). Generalized anxiety disorder. In L. N. Robins & D. A. Regier (Eds.), *Psychiatric disorders in America* (pp. 180–203). New York, NY: Free Press.

Bleackley, C., Green, D., Lockshin, R. A., Melino, G., & Zakeri, Z. (2001). Arnold H. Greenberg, 1941–2001. Retrieved June 25, 2004, from http://www.celldeath-apoptosis.org/arnold_h.htm

Bleiberg, K. L., & Markowitz, J. C. (2014). Interpersonal psychotherapy for depression. In D. H. Barlow (Ed.), *Clinical handbook of psychological disorders: A step-by-step treatment manual* (5th ed.). New York, NY: Guilford Press.

Bleuler, E. (1908). Die Prognosder Dementia praecox (Schizophreniegruppe). *Allgemeine Zeitschrift für Psychiatrie, 65,* 436–464.

Bleuler, E. (1924). *Textbook of psychiatry* (A. A. Brill, Trans.). New York, NY: Macmillan.

Bliss, E. L. (1984). A symptom profile of patients with multiple personalities including MMPI results. *Journal of Nervous and Mental Diseases, 172,* 197–211.

Bloch, M., Schmidt, P. J., & Rubinow, D. R. (2014). Premenstrual syndrome: Evidence for symptom stability across cycles. *American Journal of Psychiatry, 154*(12), 1741–1746.

Bloch, M. H., Landeros-Weisenberger, A., Rosario, M. C., Pittenger, C., & Leckman, J. F. (2008). Meta-analysis of the symptom structure of obsessive–compulsive disorder. *American Journal of Psychiatry, 165*(12), 1532–1542.

Bloch, S., & Green, S. (2012). Psychiatric ethics. In M. G. Gelder, N. C. Andreasen, J. J. Lopez-Ibor, & J. R. Geddes (Eds.), *New Oxford textbook of psychiatry* (2nd ed., Vol. 1, pp. 28–32). New York, NY: Oxford University Press.

Block, J. J. (2008). Issues for DSM-V: Internet addiction. *American Journal of Psychiatry, 165*(3), 306–307.

Blom, M. M., Bosmans, J. E., Cuijpers, P., Zarit, S. H., & Pot, A. M. (2013). Effectiveness and cost-effectiveness of an internet intervention for family caregivers of people with dementia: Design of a randomized controlled trial. *BMC Psychiatry, 13*(1), 1.

Bloom, F. E., & Kupfer, D. J. (1995). *Psychopharmacology: The fourth* generation of progress. New York, NY: Raven Press.

Bloom, F. E., Nelson, C. A., & Lazerson, A. (2001). *Brain, mind, and behavior* (3rd ed.). New York, NY: Worth.

Blum, K., Noble, E. P., Sheridan, P. J., Montgomery, A., Ritchie, T., Jagadeeswaran, P., . . . Cohn, J. B. (1990). Allelic association of human dopamine D2 receptor gene in alcoholism. *JAMA, 263*, 2055–2060.

Blumberg, S. J., Bramlett, M. D., Kogan, M. D., Schieve, L. A., & Jones, J. R. (2013). Changes in prevalence of parent-reported autism spectrum disorder in school-aged U.S. children: 2007 to 2011–2012. *National Health Statistics Reports, 65*, 1–11.

Blumenthal, J. A., Sherwood, A., Babyak, M. A., Watkins, L. L., Waugh, R., Georgiades, A., . . . Hinderliter, A. (2005). Effects of exercise and stress management training on markers of cardiovascular risk in patients with ischemic heart disease: A randomized controlled trial. *JAMA, 293*(13), 1626–1634.

Blumenthal, S. J. (1990). An overview and synopsis of risk factors, assessment, and treatment of suicidal patients over the life cycle. In S. J. Blumenthal & D. J. Kupfer (Eds.), *Suicide over the life cycle: Risk factors, assessment and treatment of suicidal patients.* Washington, DC: American Psychiatric Press.

Boachie, A., Goldfield, G. S., & Spettigue, W. (2003). Olanzapine use as an adjunctive treatment for hospitalized children with anorexia nervosa: Case reports. *International Journal of Eating Disorders, 33*, 98–103.

Boardman, J. D., Barnes, L. L., Wilson, R. S., Evans, D. A., & de Leon, C. F. M. (2012). Social disorder, APOE-E4 genotype, and change in cognitive function among older adults living in Chicago. *Social Science & Medicine, 74*(10), 1584–1590.

Bob, P. (2003). Dissociation and neuroscience: History and new perspectives. *International Journal of Neuroscience, 113*, 903–914.

Bockoven, J. S. (1963). *Moral treatment in American psychiatry.* New York, NY: Springer.

Bodell, L. P., & Keel, P. K. (2015). Weight suppression in bulimia nervosa: Associations with biology and behavior. *Journal of Abnormal Psychology, 124*(4), 994.

Boden, J. M., Fergusson, D. M., & Horwood, L. J. (2012). Alcohol misuse and violent behavior: Findings from a 30-year longitudinal study. *Drug and Alcohol Dependence, 122*, 135–141. https://doi.org/10.1016/j.drugalcdep.2011.09.023

Bodlund, O., & Kullgren, G. (1996). Transsexualism—General outcome and prognostic factors: A five-year follow-up study of nineteen transsexuals in the process of changing sex. *Archives of Sexual Behavior, 25*, 303–316.

Bodnar, R. J. (2012). Endogenous opiates and behavior. *Peptides, 38*(2), 463–522.

Boehm, J. K., & Kubzansky, L. D. (2012). The heart's content: The association between positive psychological well-being and cardiovascular health. *Psychological bulletin, 138*(4), 655–691.

Bogan, R. K., Roth, T., Schwartz, J., & Miloslavsky, M. (2014). Time to

response with sodium oxybate for the treatment of excessive daytime sleepiness and cataplexy in patients with narcolepsy. *Journal of Clinical Sleep Medicine: JCSM: Official Publication of the American Academy of Sleep Medicine, 11*(4), 427–432.

Bögels, S. M., Alden, L., Beidel, D. C., Clark, L. A., Pine, D. S., Stein, M. B., & Voncken, M. (2010). Social anxiety disorder: Questions and answers for the DSM-V. *Depression and Anxiety, 27*(2), 168–189.

Bohman, M., Cloninger, C. R., von Knorring, A. L., & Sigvardsson, S. (1984). An adoption study of somatoform disorders: III. Cross-fostering analysis and genetic relationship to alcoholism and criminality. *Archives of General Psychiatry, 41*, 872–878.

Bohus, M., Haaf, B., Stiglmayr, C., Pohl, U., Bohme, R., & Linehan, M. (2000). Evaluation of inpatient dialectical-behavioral therapy for borderline personality disorder—A prospective study. *Behavior Research and Therapy, 38*(9), 875–887.

Boileau, I., Dagher, A., Leyton, M., Gunn, R. N., Baker, G. B., Diksic, M., & Benkelfat, C. (2006). Modelings sensitization to stimulants in humans: An [11C]raclopride/positron emission tomography study in healthy men. *Archives of General Psychiatry, 63*(12), 1386–1395.

Boivin, D. B., Czeisler, D. A., Dijk, D. J., Duffy, J. E., Folkard, S., Minors, D. S., . . . Waterhouse, J. M. (1997). Complex interaction of the sleep-wake cycle and circadian phase modulates mood in healthy subjects. *Archives of General Psychiatry, 54*, 145–152.

Boland, R. J., & Keller, M. B. (2009). Course and outcome of depression. In I. H. Gotlib & C. L. Hammen (Eds.), *Handbook of depression* (2nd ed., pp. 23–43). New York, NY: Guilford Press.

Bolinskey, P. K., James, A. V., Cooper-Bolinskey, D., Novi, J. H., Hunter, H. K., Hudak, D. V., . . . Lenzenweger, M. F. (2015). Revisiting the blurry boundaries of schizophrenia: Spectrum disorders in psychometrically identified schizotypes. *Psychiatry Research, 225*(3), 335–340.

Boll, T. J. (1985). Developing issues in clinical neuropsychology. *Journal of Clinical and Experimental Neuropsychology, 7*(5), 473–485.

Bombay, A., Matheson, K., & Anisman, H. (2014). The intergenerational effects of Indian Residential Schools: Implications for the concept of historical trauma. *Transcultural Psychiatry, 51*(3), 320–338.

Bonanno, G. A., & Kaltman, S. (1999). Toward an integrative perspective on bereavement. *Psychological Bulletin, 125*(6), 1004–1008.

Bonanno, G. A., & Kaltman, S. (2001). The varieties of grief experience. *Clinical Psychology Review, 21*, 705–734.

Bonanno, G. A., Wortman, C. B., Lehman, D. R., Tweed, R. G., Haring, M., Sonnega, J., . . . Nesse, R. M. (2002). Resilience to loss and chronic grief: A prospective study from preloss to 18-months postloss. *Journal of Personality and Social Psychology, 83*, 1150–1164.

Bonanno, G. A., Wortman, C., & Nesse, R. (2004). Prospective patterns of resilience and maladjustment during

widowhood. *Psychology and Aging, 19*, 260–271.

Bond, A., & Lader, M. (2012). Anxiolytics and sedatives. In J. C. Verster, K. Brady, M. Galanter, & P. Conrod (Eds.), *Drug abuse and addiction in medical illness: Causes, consequences and treatment* (pp. 231–239). New York, NY: Springer.

Bond, A., & Lader, M. L. (1979). Benzodiazepines and aggression. In M. Sandler (Ed.), *Psychopharmacology of aggression.* New York, NY: Raven Press.

Bond, G. R., Drake, R. E., Mueser, K. T., & Becker, D. R. (1997). An update on supported employment for people with severe mental illness. *Psychiatric Services, 48*, 335–346.

Bondy, A., & Frost, L. (2001). The picture exchange communication system. *Behavior Modification, 25*, 725–744.

Bondy, A., & Frost, L. (2002). A picture's worth: PECS and other visual communication strategies in autism. Bethesda, MD: Woodbine House.

Bongaarts, J., & Over, M. (2010). Global HIV/AIDS policy in transition. *Science, 328*, 1359–1360.

Bonnano, G. A. (2004). Loss, trauma, and human resilience: Have we underestimated the human capacity to thrive after extremely aversive events? *American Psychologist, 59*, 20–28.

Bonnet, M. H. (2000). Sleep deprivation. In M. H. Kryger, T. Roth, & W. C. Dement (Eds.), *Principles and practice of sleep medicine* (3rd ed., pp. 53–71). Philadelphia, PA: W. B. Saunders.

Boon, S., & Draijer, N. (1991). Diagnosing dissociative disorders in the Netherlands: A pilot study with the Structured Clinical Interview for DSM-III-R dissociative disorders. *American Journal of Psychiatry, 148*, 458–462.

Boon, S., & Draijer, N. (1993). Multiple personality disorder in the Netherlands: A clinical investigation of 71 cases. *American Journal of Psychiatry, 150*, 489–494.

Boone, L., Soenens, B., Vansteenkiste, M., & Braet, C. (2012). Is there a perfectionist in each of us? An experimental study on perfectionism and eating disorder symptoms. *Appetite, 59*(2), 531–540.

Boot, W. R., Simons, D. J., Stothart, C., & Stutts, C. (2013). The pervasive problem with placebos in psychology why active control groups are not sufficient to rule out placebo effects. *Perspectives on Psychological Science, 8*(4), 445–454. https://doi.org/10.1177/1745691613491271

Boothroyd, L. J., Kirmayer, L. J., Spreng, S., Malus, M., & Hodgins, S. (2001). Completed suicides among the Inuit of northern Québec, 1982–1996: A case–control study. *Canadian Medical Association Journal, 165*, 749–755.

Borckardt, J. J., Nash, M. R., Murphy, M. D., Shaw, D., O'Neil, P., & Moore, M. (2008). Clinical practice as natural laboratory for psychotherapy research: A guide to case-based time-series analysis. *American Psychologist, 63*(2), 77–95.

Border, R., Johnson, E. C., Evans, L. M., Smolen, A., Berley, N., Sullivan, P. F., & Keller, M. (2019). No support for historical candidate gene or candidate gene-by-interaction hypotheses for major depression across multiple large

samples. *American Journal of Psychiatry, 176*(5), 376–387. https://doi.org/10.1176/appi.ajp.2018.18070881

Borg, L., Buonora, M., Butelman, E. R., Ducat, E., Ray, B. M., & Kreek, M. J. (2015). The pharmacology of opioids. In R. K. Ries, D. A. Fiellin, S. C. Miller, & R. Saitz (Eds.), *The ASAM principles of addiction medicine* (5th ed., pp. 135–150). New York, NY: Wolters Kluwer.

Borgelt, L. M., Franson, K. L., Nussbaum, A. M., & Wang, G. S. (2013). The pharmacologic and clinical effects of medical cannabis. *Pharmacotherapy, 33*(2), 195–209. https://doi.org/10.1002/phar.1187

Borges, G., Nock, M. K., Abad, J. M. H., Hwang, I., Sampson, N. A., Alonso, J., & Kessler, R. C. (2010). Twelve month prevalence of and risk factors for suicide attempts in the WHO World Mental Health Surveys. *Journal of Clinical Psychiatry, 71*(12), 1617–1628.

Borkovec, T. D., & Costello, E. (1993). Efficacy of applied relaxation and cognitive-behavioral therapy in the treatment of generalized anxiety disorder. *Journal of Consulting and Clinical Psychology, 61*(4), 611–619.

Borkovec, T. D., Alcaine, O. M., & Behar, E. (2004). Avoidance theory of worry and generalized anxiety disorder. In R. G. Heimberg, C. L. Turk, & D. S. Mennin (Eds.), *Generalized anxiety disorder: Advances in research and practice* (pp. 77–108). New York, NY: Guilford Press.

Borkovec, T. D., & Hu, S. (1990). The effect of worry on cardiovascular response to phobic imagery. *Behaviour Research and Therapy, 28*, 69–73.

Borkovec, T. D., & Inz, J. (1990). The nature of worry in generalized anxiety disorder: A predominance of thought activity. *Behaviour Research and Therapy, 28*, 153–158.

Borkovec, T. D., & Ruscio, A. (2001). Psychotherapy for generalized anxiety disorder. *Journal of Clinical Psychiatry, 62*, 37–45.

Borkovec, T. D., Shadick, R., & Hopkins, M. (1991). The nature of normal and pathological worry. In R. M. Rapee & D. H. Barlow (Eds.), *Chronic anxiety, generalized anxiety disorder, and mixed anxiety depression.* New York, NY: Guilford Press.

Bornath, L. M. (2002). *Elaine Tanner: Best female Canadian swimmer in the late 1960s.* Retrieved June 25, 2004, from http://www.almostfabulous.com/canadians/name/t/tannerelaine.php

Bornstein, R. F. (1992). The dependent personality: Developmental, social, and clinical perspectives. *Psychological Bulletin, 112*, 3–23.

Bornstein, R. F. (1997). Dependent personality disorder in the DSM-IV and beyond. *Clinical Psychology: Science and Practice, 4*, 175–187.

Bornstein, R. F. (2012). Dependent personality disorder. In T. A. Widiger (Ed.), *The Oxford handbook of personality disorders* (pp. 505–526). New York, NY: Oxford University Press.

Borodinsky, L. N., Root, C. M., Cronin, J. A., Sann, S. B., Gu, X., & Spitzer, N. C. (2004). Activity-dependent homeostatic specification of transmitter expression in embryonic neurons. *Nature, 429*, 523–530.

Boskind-Lodahl, M. (1976). Cinderella's stepsisters: A feminist perspective on anorexia nervosa and bulimia. *Signs, 2,* 342–356.

Bouchard, M. F., Bellinger, D. C., Wright, R. O., & Weisskopf, M. G. (2010). Attention-deficit/hyperactivity disorder and urinary metabolites of organophosphate pesticides. *Pediatrics, 125*(6), e1270–e1277.

Bouchard, S., Dumoulin, S., Robillard, G., Guitard, T., Klinger, É., Forget, H., Loranger, C., & Roucaut, F. X. (2016). Virtual reality compared with in vivo exposure in the treatment of social anxiety disorder: A three-arm randomised controlled trial. *British Journal of Psychiatry.* https://doi.org/10.1192/bjp.bp.116.184234

Bouchard, S., Vallieres, A., Roy, M. A., & Maziade, M. (1996). Cognitive restructuring in the treatment of psychotic symptoms in schizophrenia: A critical analysis. *Behavior Therapy, 27,* 257–277.

Bouchard, T. J., Jr., Lykken, D. T., McGue, M., Segal, N. L., & Tellegen, A. (1990). Sources of human psychological differences: The Minnesota study of twins reared apart. *Science, 250,* 223–228.

Boulos, C., Kutcher, S., Marton, P., Simeon, J., Ferguson, B., & Roberts, N. (1991). Response to desipramine treatment in adolescent major depression. *Psychopharmacology Bulletin, 27,* 59–65.

Bouman, T. K. (2014). Psychological treatments for hypochondriasis: A narrative review. *Current Psychiatry Reviews, 10,* 58–69.

Bourgeois, J. A., Seaman, J. S., & Servis, M. E. (2003). Delirium, dementia, and amnestic disorders. In R. E. Hales & S. C. Yudofsky (Eds.), *Textbook of clinical psychiatry* (4th ed., pp. 259–308). Washington, DC: American Psychiatric Press.

Bourgeois, M. S. (1992). Evaluating memory wallets in conversations with persons with dementia. *Journal of Speech and Hearing Research, 35,* 1344–1357.

Bourgeois, M. S. (2007). *Memory books and other graphic cuing systems: Practical communication and memory aids for adults with dementia.* Baltimore, MD: Health Professions.

Bouton, M. E. (2005). Behavior systems and the contextual control of anxiety, fear, and panic. In L. Feldman-Barrett, P. Niedenthal, & P. Winkielman (Eds.), *Emotion: Conscious and unconscious* (pp. 205–227). New York, NY: Guilford Press.

Bouton, M. E., Mineka, S., & Barlow, D. H. (2001). A modern learning-theory perspective on the etiology of panic disorder. *Psychological Review, 108,* 4–32.

Bowers, J. S., & Marsolek, C. J. (2003). *Rethinking implicit memory.* New York, NY: Oxford University Press.

Bowlby, J. (1980). *Attachment and loss.* New York, NY: Basic Books.

Bowman, E. S., & Coons, P. M. (2000). The differential diagnosis of epilepsy, pseudoseizures, dissociative identity disorder, and dissociative disorder not otherwise specified. *Bulletin of the Menninger Clinic, 64,* 164–180.

Boyce, N. (2011). Suicide clusters: The undiscovered country. *The Lancet, 378*(9801), 1452.

Boyce, W., Doherty-Poirier, M., MacKinnon, D., Fortin, C., Saab, H.,

King, M., & Gallupe, O. (2006). Sexual health of Canadian youth: Findings from the Canadian youth, sexual health and HIV/AIDS study. *Canadian Journal of Human Sexuality, 15,* 59–68.

Boydell, J., & Allardyce, J. (2011). Does urban density matter? In A. S. David, S. Kapur, P. McGuffin, & R. M. Murray (Eds.), *Schizophrenia: The final frontier—A fest-schrift for Robin M. Murray* (pp. 273–280). New York, NY: Routledge.

Boyer, P., & Liénard, P. (2008). Ritual behavior in obsessive and normal individuals: Moderating anxiety and reorganizing the flow of action. *Current Directions in Psychological Science, 17*(4), 291–294.

Boyle, W., Doherty, M., Fortin, C., & MacKinnon, D. (2002). *Canadian youth, sexual health and AIDS study.* Toronto, ON: Council Ministers of Education Canada.

Boysen, G., Ebersole, A., Casner, R., & Coston, N. (2014). Gendered mental disorders: Masculine and feminine stereotypes about mental disorders and their relation to stigma. *Journal of Social Psychology, 154*(6), 546–565. https://doi.org/10.1080/00224545.2014.953028

Bracha, H. S., Torrey, E. F., Gottesman, I. I., Bigelow, L. B., & Cunniff, C. (1992). Second-trimester markers of fetal size in schizophrenia: A study of monozygotic twins. *American Journal of Psychiatry, 149,* 1355–1361.

Bradford, A., & Meston, C. M. (2011). Sex and gender disorders. In D. H. Barlow (Ed.), *Oxford handbook of clinical psychology.* New York, NY: Oxford University Press.

Bradford, J. (1997). Medical interventions in sexual deviance. In D. R. Laws & W. O'Donohue (Eds.), *Sexual deviance: Theory, assessment and treatment* (pp. 449–464). New York, NY: Guilford Press.

Bradley, B. P., & Mathews, A. (1988). Memory bias in recovered clinical depressives. [Special issue: Information processing and the emotional disorders.] *Cognition and Emotion, 2*(3), 235–245.

Bradley, B. P., Mogg, K., White, J., Groom, C., & de Bono, J. (1999). Attentional bias for emotional faces in generalized anxiety disorder. *British Journal of Clinical Psychology, 38,* 267–278.

Bradley, E. A., Thompson, A., & Bryson, S. E. (2002). Mental retardation in teenagers: Prevalence data from the Niagara region, Ontario. *Canadian Journal of Psychiatry, 47,* 652–659.

Bradley, R. G., Binder, E. B., Epstein, M. P., Tang, Y., Nair, H. P., Liu, W., . . . Ressler, K. J. (2008). Influence of child abuse on adult depression: Moderation by the corticotropin-releasing hormone receptor gene. *Archives of General Psychiatry, 65*(2), 190–200.

Bradley, W. (1937). The behavior of children receiving benzedrine. *American Journal of Psychiatry, 94,* 577–585.

Brady, J. P. (1991). The pharmacology of stuttering: A critical review. *American Journal of Psychiatry, 148,* 1309–1316.

Brady, J. P., & Lind, D. L. (1961). Experimental analysis of hysterical blindness. *Archives of General Psychiatry, 4,* 331–339.

Braff, D., Schork, N. J., & Gottesman, I. I. (2007). Endophenotyping

schizophrenia. *American Journal of Psychiatry, 164,* 705–707.

Brand, B., Classen, C., Lanins, R., Loewenstein, R., McNary, S., Pain, C., & Putnam, F. (2009). A naturalistic study of dissociative identity disorder and dissociative disorder not otherwise specified patients treated by community clinicians. *Psychological Trauma: Theory, Research, Practice, and Policy, 1*(2), 153–171.

Brandon, K. O. (1995). A multivariate twin family study of the genetic and environmental structure of personality, beliefs, and alcohol use. *Dissertation Abstracts International: Section B: The Sciences & Engineering, 55*(10-B), 4599.

Brannon, L., & Feist, J. (1997). *Health psychology: An introduction to behavior and health.* Pacific Grove, CA: Brooks/Cole.

Braswell, L., & Bloomquist, M. (1994). *Cognitive behavior therapy of ADHD.* New York, NY: Guilford Press.

Bratulic, A. (2007, October 3). Law used for medical blackmail: Rights group. *The Suburban.* Retrieved October 12, 2007, from http://www.thesuburban.com/content.jsp?sid16308699675863003019134240012&ctid1000000&cnid1013020

Brawman-Mintzer, O. (2001). Pharmacologic treatment of generalized anxiety disorder. *Psychiatric Clinics of North America, 24,* 119–137.

Brean, J. (2007, September 6). Judge's verdict reveals comic's sad descent. *National Post.* Retrieved October 1, 2007, from http://www.nationalpost.com/news/story.html?id2fc21502-f905-4409-8a86-603c4632f2e9&k48220

Breitbart, W., & Alici, Y. (2012). Evidence-based treatment of delirium in patients with cancer. *Journal of Clinical Oncology, 30*(11), 1206–1214.

Breitborde, N. J., López, S. R., & Kopelowicz, A. (2010). Expressed emotion and health outcomes among Mexican-Americans with schizophrenia and their caregiving relatives. *Journal of Nervous and Mental Disease, 198*(2), 105–109.

Brekke, J. S., Long, J. D., Nesbitt, N., & Sobell, E. (1997). The impact of service characteristics on functional outcomes from community support programs for persons with schizophrenia: A growth curve analysis. *Journal of Consulting and Clinical Psychology, 65,* 464–475.

Bremner, J. D. (1999). Does stress damage the brain? *Biological Psychiatry, 45,* 797–805.

Bremner, J. D., Randall, P. R., Scott, T. M., Bronen, R. A., Seibyl, J. P., Southwick, S. M., . . . Innis, R. B. (1995). MRI-based measurement of hippocampal volume in patients with combat-related posttraumatic stress disorder. *American Journal of Psychiatry, 152,* 973–981.

Brenes, G. A., Miller, M. E., Stanley, M. A., Williamson, J. D., Knudson, M., & McCall, W. V. (2009). Insomnia in older adults with generalized anxiety disorder. *American Journal of Geriatric Psychiatry, 17,* 465–472.

Brennen, S. (2012). *Victimization of older Canadians, 2009* (Catalogue no. 85–002-X). Ottawa, ON: Statistics Canada. Retrieved from http://www.statcan.gc.ca/pub/85–002-x/2012001/article/11627-eng.pdf

Brenner, D. E., Kukull, W. A., van Belle, G., Bowen, J. D., McCormick, W. C., Teri, L., & Larson, E. B. (1993).

Relationship between cigarette smoking and Alzheimer's disease in a population-based case–control study. *Neurology, 43,* 293–300.

Brent, D., & Birmaher, B. (2009). Paediatric mood disorders. In M. G. Gelder, N. C. Andreasen, J. J. López-Ibor, Jr., & J. R. Geddes (Eds.), *New Oxford textbook of psychiatry* (2nd ed., Vol. 2, pp. 1669–1680). Oxford, UK: Oxford University Press.

Brent, D. A., Kerr, M. M., Goldstein, C., Bozigar, J., Wartella, M., & Allan, M. J. (1989). An outbreak of suicide and suicidal behavior in a high school. *Journal of the American Academy of Child and Adolescent Psychiatry, 28*(6), 918–924.

Brent, D. A., & Kolko, D. J. (1990). The assessment and treatment of children and adolescents at risk for suicide. In S. J. Blumenthal & D. J. Kupfer (Eds.), *Suicide over the life cycle: Risk factors, assessment and treatment of suicidal patients.* Washington, DC: American Psychiatric Press.

Brent, D. A., & Mann, J. J. (2005). Family genetic studies, suicide, and suicidal behavior. *American Journal of Medical Genetics, 133*(1), 13–24.

Brent, D., Melhem, N., Donohoe, M. B., & Walker, M. (2009). The incidence and course of depression in bereaved youth 21 months after the loss of a parent to suicide, accident, or sudden natural death. *American Journal of Psychiatry, 166*(7), 786–794.

Brent, D. A., Melhem, N. M., Oquendo, M., Burke, A., Birmaher, B., Stanley, B., Biernesser, C., Keilp, J., Kalka, D., Ellis, S., Porta, G., Zelazny, J., Iyengar, S., & Mann, J. J. (2015). Familial pathways to early-onset suicide attempt: A 5.6-year prospective study. *JAMA Psychiatry, 72,* 160–168.

Brent, D. A., Oquendo, M., Birmaher, B., Greenhill, L., Kolko, D., Stanley, B., & Mann, J. J. (2002). Familial pathways to early-onset suicide attempt risk for suicidal behavior in offspring of mood-disordered suicide attempters. *Archives of General Psychiatry, 59,* 801–807.

Brent, D. A., Perper, J. A., Goldstein, C. E., Kolko, D. J., Allan, M. J., Allman, C. J., & Zelenak, J. P. (1988). Risk factors for adolescent suicide: A comparison of adolescent suicide victims with suicidal inpatients. *Archives of General Psychiatry, 45,* 581–588.

Breslau, N. (2012). Epidemiology of posttraumatic stress disorder in adults. In J. G. Beck & D. M. Sloan (Eds.), *The Oxford handbook of traumatic stress disorders* (pp. 84–97). New York, NY: Oxford University Press.

Breslau, N., Davis, G. C., & Andreski, M. A. (1995). Risk factors for PTSD-related traumatic events: A prospective analysis. *American Journal of Psychiatry, 152,* 529–535.

Breslau, N., Lucia, V. C., & Alvarado, G. F. (2006). Intelligence and other predisposing factors in exposure to trauma and posttraumatic stress disorder. *Archives of General Psychiatry, 63,* 1238–1245.

Breuer, J., & Freud, S. (1957). *Studies on hysteria.* New York, NY: Basic Books. (Original work published 1895).

Brewerton, T. D., Rance, S. J., Dansky, B. S., O'Neil, P. M., & Kilpatrick, D. G. (2014). A comparison of women with child-adolescent versus adult onset binge eating: Results from the National

Women's Study. *International Journal of Eating Disorders, 47*(7), 836–843.

Bricker, J., Mann, S., Marek, P., Liu, J., & Peterson, A. (2010). Telephone-delivered Acceptance and Commitment Therapy for adult smoking cessation: A feasibility study. *Nicotine & Tobacco Research: Official Journal of the Society for Research on Nicotine and Tobacco, 12*(4), 454–458.

Bridges, F. S., & Kunselman, J. C. (2005). Premature mortality due to suicide, homicide, and motor vehicle accidents in health service delivery areas: Comparison of status Indians in British Columbia, Canada, with all other residents. *Psychological Reports, 97*(3), 739–749.

Briere pleads guilty to Holly Jones's murder. (2004). *The Globe and Mail.* Retrieved August 5, 2004, from http://www.theglobeandmail.com/servlet/story/RTGAM.20040617.wbrier0617B/BNStory/Nationl

Brinker, J. K., Harris, J. A., Guyitt, B., & Dozois, D. J. A. (2006). The importance of importance: Self-descriptors in dysphoria. *Journal of Individual Differences, 27*, 193–198.

British Columbia Schizophrenia Society. (2001). *Basic facts about schizophrenia.* Retrieved November 3, 2004, from http://www.mentalhealth.com/book/p40-sc02.html

Britton, A., Ben-Shlomo, Y., Benzeval, M., Kuh, D., & Bell, S. (2015). Life course trajectories of alcohol consumption in the United Kingdom using longitudinal data from nine cohort studies. *BMC Medicine, 13*, 47.

Britton, J. C., & Rauch, S. L. (2009). Neuroanatomy and neuroimaging of anxiety disorders. In M. M. Antony & M. B. Stein (Eds.), *Oxford handbook of anxiety and related disorders* (pp. 97–110). Oxford, UK: Oxford University Press.

Britton, J. C., Grillon, C., Lissek, S., Norcross, M. A., Szuhany, K., Chen, G., Ernst, M., Nelson, E. E., Leibenluft, E., Shechner, T., & Pine, D. S. (2013). Response to learned threat: An fMRI study in adolescent and adult anxiety. *American Journal of Psychiatry, 170*, 1195–1204.

Brodeur, D. A., & Pond, M. (2001). The development of selective attention in children with attention deficit hyperactivity disorder. *Journal of Abnormal Child Psychology, 29*, 229–239.

Brody, A. L., Saxena, S., Stoessel, P., Gillies, L. A., Fairbanks, L. A., Alborzian, S., . . . Baxter, L. R., Jr. (2001). Regional brain metabolic changes in patients with major depression treated with either paroxetine or interpersonal therapy. *Archives of General Psychiatry, 48*, 631–640.

Brody, H., & Miller, F. G. (2011). Lessons from recent research about the placebo effect—From art to science. *JAMA, 306*(23), 2612–2613.

Brody, M. J., Walsh, B. T., & Devlin, M. J. (1994). Binge eating disorder: Reliability and validity of a new diagnostic category. *Journal of Consulting and Clinical Psychology, 62*, 381–386.

Broft, A., Berner, L. A., & Walsh, B. T. (2010). Pharmacotherapy for bulimia nervosa. In C. M. Grilo & J. E. Mitchell (Eds.), *The treatment of eating disorders: A clinical handbook* (pp. 388–401). New York, NY: Guilford Press.

Brondolo, E., Grantham, K. I., Karlin, W., Taravella, J., Mencia-Ripley, A., Schwartz, J. E., & Contrada, R. J. (2009). Trait hostility and ambulatory blood pressure among traffic enforcement agents: The effects of stressful social interactions. *Journal of Occupational Health Psychology, 14*(2), 110–121.

Brotman, M. A., Schmajuk, M., Rich, B. A., Dickstein, D. P., Guyer, A. E., Costello, E. J., & Leibenluft, E. (2006). Prevalence, clinical correlates, and longitudinal course of severe mood dysregulation in children. *Biological Psychiatry, 60*(9), 991–997.

Brotto, L. A. (2006). Psychologic-based desire and arousal disorders: Treatment strategies and outcome results. In I. Goldstein, C. M. Meston, S. R. Davis, & A. M. Traish (Eds.), *Women's sexual function and dysfunction: Study, diagnosis, and treatment* (pp. 441–448). New York, NY: Taylor & Francis.

Brotto, L. A. (2010a). The DSM diagnostic criteria for hypoactive sexual desire disorder in women. *Archives of Sexual Behavior, 39*, 222–239.

Brotto, L. A. (2015, June 5). "Female Viagra" won't help many but that's not stopping the drug company. *The Globe and Mail.* Retrieved from http://www.theglobeandmail.com/life/health-and-fitness/health-advisor/female-viagra-wont-help-many-but-thats-not-stopping-the-drug-company/article24820653/

Brotto, L. A. (2018). *Better sex through mindfulness: How women can cultivate desire.* Greystone Books.

Brotto, L. A., Bergeron, S., Zdaniuk, B., Driscoll, M., Grabovac, A., Sadownik, L. A., Smith, K. B., & Basson, R. (2019). A comparison of mindfulness-based cognitive therapy vs cognitive behavioral therapy for the treatment of provoked vestibulodynia in a hospital clinic setting. *Journal of Sexual Medicine, 16*(6), 909–923. https://doi.org/10.1016/j.jsxm.2019.04.002

Brotto, L. A., Chik, H. M., Ryder, A. G., Gorzalka, B. B., & Seal, B. N. (2005). Acculturation and sexual function in Asian women. *Archives of Sexual Behavior, 34*, 613–626.

Brotto, L., & Luria, M. (2014). Sexual interest/arousal disorder in women. In Y. M. Binik & K. S. K. Hall (Eds.), *Principles and practices of sex therapy* (5th ed., pp. 17–41). New York, NY: Guilford Press.

Broude, G. J., & Greene, S. J. (1980). Cross-cultural codes on 20 sexual attitudes and practices. In H. Barry, III & A. Schlegel (Eds.), *Cross-cultural samples and codes* (pp. 313–333). Pittsburgh, PA: University of Pittsburgh Press.

Broughton, R. J. (2000). NREM arousal parasomnias. In M. H. Kryger, T. Roth, & W. C. Dement (Eds.), *Principles and practice of sleep medicine* (3rd ed., pp. 693–706). Philadelphia, PA: W. B. Saunders.

Broughton, R., Billings, R., & Cartwright, R. (1994). Homicidal somnambulism: A case report. *Sleep, 17*, 253–264.

Brown, G. K., Beck, A. T., Steer, R. A., & Grisham, J. R. (2000). Risk factor for psychiatric outpatients: A 20-year perspective study. *Journal of Consulting and Clinical Psychology, 63*(3), 371–377.

Brown, G. W. (1959). Experiences of discharged chronic schizophrenic mental hospital patients in various types of living group. *Millbank Memorial Fund Quarterly, 37*, 105–131.

Brown, G. W. (1989). Depression. In G. W. Brown & T. O. Harris (Eds.), *Life events and illness* (pp. 49–93). New York, NY: Guilford Press.

Brown, G. W., & Birley, J. L. T. (1968). Crisis and life change and the onset of schizophrenia. *Journal of Health and Social Behavior, 9*, 203–214.

Brown, G. W., & Harris, T. O. (1978). *Social origins of depression: A study of psychiatric disorder in women.* London, UK: Tavistock.

Brown, G. W., Harris, T. O., & Hepworth, C. (1994). Life events and endogenous depression. *Archives of General Psychiatry, 51*, 525–534.

Brown, G. W., Monck, E. M., Carstairs, G. M., & Wing, J. K. (1962). Influence of family life on the course of schizophrenic illness. *British Journal of Preventive and Social Medicine, 16*, 55–68.

Brown, J., & Finn, P. (1982). Drinking to get drunk: Findings of a survey of junior and senior high school students. *Journal of Alcohol and Drug Education, 27*, 13–25.

Brown, P. L. (2006, December 2). Supporting boys or girls when the line isn't clear. *New York Times.* Retrieved from http://www.nytimes.com/2006/12/02/us/02child.html

Brown, R. E. (1994). *An introduction to neuroendocrinology.* Cambridge, NY: Cambridge University Press.

Brown, R. J., & Lewis-Fernandez, R. (2011). Culture and conversion disorder: Implications for DSM-5. *Psychiatry, 74*(3), 187–206.

Brown, S. L., & Forth, A. E. (1997). Psychopathy and sexual assault: Static risk factors, emotional precursors, and rapist subtypes. *Journal of Consulting & Clinical Psychology, 65*, 848–857.

Brown, T. A., & Barlow, D. H. (2002). Classification of anxiety and mood disorders. In D. H. Barlow (Ed.), *Anxiety and its disorders: The nature and treatment of anxiety and panic* (2nd ed.). New York, NY: Guilford Press.

Brown, T. A., & Barlow, D. H. (2005). Dimensional versus categorical classification of mental disorders in the fifth edition of the *Diagnostic and statistical manual of mental disorders* and beyond: Comment on the special issue [Special issue: Toward a dimensionally based taxonomy of psychopathology]. *Journal of Abnormal Psychology, 114*(4), 551–556.

Brown, T. A., & Barlow, D. H. (2009). A proposal for a dimensional classification system based on the shared features of the DSM-IV anxiety and mood disorders: Implications for assessment and treatment. *Psychological Assessment, 21*(3), 256–271.

Brown, T. A., & Barlow, D. H. (2014). *Anxiety and related disorders interview schedule for DSM-5 (ADIS-5L)—Lifetime version: Client interview schedule 5.* New York, NY: Oxford University Press.

Brown, T. A., & Naragon-Gainey, K. (2012). Evaluation of the unique and specific contributions of dimensions of the triple vulnerability model to the prediction of DSM-IV anxiety and mood

disorder constructs. *Behavior Therapy, 44*(2), 277–292.

Brown, T. A., Barlow, D. H., & Liebowitz, M. R. (1994). The empirical basis of generalized anxiety disorder. *American Journal of Psychiatry, 15*(9), 1272–1280.

Brown, T. A., Campbell, L. A., Lehman, C. L., Grisham, J. R., & Mancill, R. B. (2001). Current and lifetime comorbidity of the DSM-IV anxiety and mood disorders in a large clinical sample. *Journal of Abnormal Psychology.*

Brown, T. A., Chorpita, B. F., & Barlow, D. H. (1998). Structural relationships among dimensions of the DSM-IV anxiety and mood disorders and dimensions of negative affect, positive affect, and autonomic arousal. *Journal of Abnormal Psychology, 107*(2), 179–192.

Brown, T. A., Marten, P. A., & Barlow, D. H. (1995). Discriminant validity of the symptoms comprising the DSM-III-R and DSM-IV associated symptom criterion of generalized anxiety disorder. *Journal of Anxiety Disorders, 9*, 317–328.

Brown, T. A., White, K. S., & Barlow, D. H. (2005). A psychometric reanalysis of the Albany panic and phobia questionnaire. *Behaviour Research and Therapy, 43*, 337–355.

Brown, T. E. (Ed.). (2009). *ADHD comorbidities: Handbook for ADHD complications in children and adults.* Arlington, VA: American Psychiatric Publishing.

Brown, T. G., Dongier, M., Latimer, E., Legault, L., Seraganian, P., Kokin, M., & Ross, D. (2007). Group-delivered brief intervention versus standard care for mixed alcohol/other drug problems: A preliminary study. *Alcoholism Treatment Quarterly, 24*(4), 23–40.

Browne, H. A., Hansen, S. N., Buxbaum, J. D., Gair, S. L., Nissen, J. B., Nikolajsen, K. H., . . . Grice, D. E. (2015). Familial Clustering of Tic Disorders and Obsessive–Compulsive Disorder. *JAMA Psychiatry, 72*, 359–366.

Brownell, K. D. (1991). Dieting and the search for the perfect body: Where physiology and culture collide. *Behavior Therapy, 22*, 1–12.

Brownell, K. D., & Fairburn, C. G. (Eds.). (1995). *Eating disorders and obesity: A comprehensive handbook.* New York, NY: Guilford Press.

Brownell, K. D., & Fairburn, C. G. (2002). *Eating disorders and obesity: A comprehensive handbook* (2nd ed.). New York, NY: Guilford Press.

Brownell, K. D., Hayes, S. C., & Barlow, D. H. (1977). Patterns of appropriate and deviant sexual arousal: The behavioral treatment of multiple sexual deviations. *Journal of Consulting and Clinical Psychology, 45*(6), 1144–1155.

Brownell, K. D., & Rodin, J. (1994). The dieting maelstrom: Is it possible and advisable to lose weight? *American Psychologist, 49*(9), 781–791.

Brownlee, K., Devins, G. M., Flanigan, M., Fleming, J. A. E., Morehouse, R., Moscovitch, A., . . . Shapiro, C. M. (2003). Are there gender differences in the prescribing of hypnotic medications for insomnia? *Human Psychopharmacology Clinical and Experimental, 18*, 69–73.

Brownridge, D. A. (2003). Male partner violence against Aboriginal women in

Canada: An empirical analysis. *Journal of Interpersonal Violence, 18*(1), 65–83.

Bruce, K. R., Koerner, N. M., Steiger, H., & Young, S. N. (2003). Laxative misuse and behavioral disinhibition in bulimia nervosa. *International Journal of Eating Disorders, 33*, 92–97.

Bruce, K. R., Steiger, H., Koerner, N. M., Israel, M., & Young, N. (2004). Bulimia nervosa with co-morbid avoidant personality disorder: Behavioural characteristics and serotonergic function. *Psychological Medicine, 34*, 113–124.

Bruce, M. L., & Kim, K. M. (1992). Differences in the effects of divorce on major depression in men and women. *American Journal of Psychiatry, 149*(7), 914–917.

Bruce, S. E., Yonkers, K. A., Otto, M. W., Eisen, J. L., Weisberg, R. B., Pagano, M., . . . Keller, M. B. (2005). Influence of psychiatric comorbidity on recovery and recurrence in generalized anxiety disorder, social phobia, and panic disorder: A 12-year prospective study. *American Journal of Psychiatry, 162*, 1179–1187.

Bruch, H. (1973). *Eating disorders: Obesity, anorexia nervosa, and the person within*. New York, NY: Basic Books.

Bruch, H. (1985). Four decades of eating disorders. In D. M. Garner & P. E. Garfinkel (Eds.), *Handbook of psychotherapy for anorexia nervosa and bulimia* (pp. 7–18). New York, NY: Guilford Press.

Bruch, H. (1986). Anorexia nervosa: The therapeutic task. In K. D. Brownell & J. P. Foreyt (Eds.), *Handbook of eating disorders: Physiology, psychology, and treatment of obesity, anorexia, and bulimia* (pp. 328–332). New York, NY: Basic Books.

Bruch, M. A., & Heimberg, R. G. (1994). Differences in perceptions of parental and personal characteristics between generalized and non-generalized social phobics. *Journal of Anxiety Disorders, 8*, 155–168.

Bruck, M. (1987). The adult outcomes of children with learning disabilities. *Annals of Dyslexia, 37*, 252–263.

Bruck, M. (1992). Persistence of dyslexics' phonological deficits. *Developmental Psychology, 28*, 874–886.

Brunet, A., & Monson, E. (2014). Suicide risk among active and retired Canadian soldiers: The role of posttraumatic stress disorder. *Canadian Journal of Psychiatry, 59*, 457–459.

Brunner, H. G., Nelen, M. R., Van Zandvoort, P., Abeling, N. G. G. M., van Gennip, A. H., Wolters, E. C., . . . van Oost, B. A. (1993). X-linked borderline mental retardation with prominent behavioral disturbance: Phenotype, genetic localization, and evidence for disturbed monoamine metabolism. *American Journal of Human Genetics, 52*, 1032–1039.

Brunoni, A. R., Valiengo, L., Baccaro, A., Zanao, T., de Oliveira, J. F., Goulart, A., & Fregni, F. (2013). The sertraline versus electrical current therapy for treating depression clinical study: Results from a factorial, randomized, controlled trial. *JAMA Psychiatry, 70*(4), 383–391.

Bryant, R. A. (2010). The complexity of complex PTSD. *American Journal of Psychiatry, 167*, 879–881.

Bryant, R. A., Friedman, M. J., Spiegel, D., Ursano, R., & Strain, J. (2011). A review of acute stress disorder in DSM-5. *Depression and Anxiety, 28*(9), 802–817.

Bryant, R. A., Moulds, M. L., & Nixon, R. V. D. (2003). Cognitive behavior therapy of acute stress disorder: A four-year follow-up. *Behaviour Research and Therapy, 41*, 489–494.

Bryant, R. A., O'Donnell, M. L., Creamer, M., McFarlane, A., & Silove, D. (2013). A multisite analysis of the fluctuating course of posttraumatic stress disorder. *JAMA Psychiatry, 70*, 839–846.

Bryson, S., Rogers, S. J., & Fombonne, E. (2003). Autism spectrum disorders: Early detection, intervention, education, and psychopharmacological management. *Canadian Journal of Psychiatry, 48*, 506–516.

Buchanan, R. W., & Carpenter, W. T. (2005). Schizophrenia and other psychotic disorders. In B. J. Sadock & V. A. Sadock (Eds.), *Kaplan & Sadock's comprehensive textbook of psychiatry* (pp. 1329–1345). Philadelphia, PA: Lippincott, Williams & Wilkins.

Buchwald, A. M., & Rudick-Davis, D. (1993). The symptoms of major depression. *Journal of Abnormal Psychology, 102*(2), 197–205.

Buda, M., & Tsuang, M. T. (1990). The epidemiology of suicide: Implications for clinical practice. In S. J. Blumenthal & D. J. Kupfer (Eds.), *Suicide over the life cycle: Risk factors, assessment and treatment of suicidal patients*. Washington, DC: American Psychiatric Press.

Budnitz, D. S., Lovegrove, M. C., Shehab, N., & Richards, C. L. (2011). Emergency hospitalizations for adverse drug events in older Americans. *New England Journal of Medicine, 365*(21), 2002–2012.

Buffett-Jerrott, S., & Stewart, S. H. (2002). Cognitive and sedative effects of benzodiazepine use. *Current Pharmaceutical Design, 8*, 45–58.

Buffum, J. (1982). Pharmacosexology: The effects of drugs on sexual function—A review. *Journal of Psychoactive Drugs, 14*, 5–44.

Buhle, J. T., Stevens, B. L., Friedman, J. J., & Wager, T. D. (2012). Distraction and placebo: Two separate routes to pain control. *Psychological Science, 23*(3), 246–253.

Buhlmann, U., Reese, H. E., Renaud, S., & Wilhelm, S. (2008). Clinical considerations for the treatment of body dysmorphic disorder with cognitive-behavioral therapy. *Body Image, 5*(1), 39–49.

Buka, S. L., Seidman, L. J., Tsuang, M. T., & Goldstein, J. M. (2013). The New England family study high-risk project: Neurological impairments among offspring of parents with schizophrenia and other psychoses. *American Journal of Medical Genetics Part B: Neuropsychiatric Genetics, 162*(7), 653–660.

Bulik, C. M., Sullivan, P. F., & Kendler, K. S. (2000). An empirical study of the classification of eating disorders. *American Journal of Psychiatry, 157*(6), 886–895.

Bulik, C. M., Sullivan, P. F., Tozzi, F., Furberg, H., Lichtenstin, P., & Pedersen, N. L. (2006). Prevalence, heritability, and prospective risk factors, for anorexia nervosa. *Archives of General Psychiatry, 63*(3), 305–312.

Bulik, C. M., Thornton, L., Pinheiro, A. P., Plotnicov, K., Klump, K. L., Brandt, H., . . . Kaye, W. H. (2008). Suicide attempts in anorexia nervosa. *Psychosomatic Medicine, 70*(3), 378–383.

Bulik, C. M., Tozzi, F., Anderson, C., Mazzeo, S. E., Aggen, S., & Sullivan, P. F. (2003). The relation between eating disorders and components of perfectionism. *American Journal of Psychiatry, 160*(2), 366–368.

Bulloch, A. G., Williams, J. V., Lavorato, D. H., & Patten, S. B. (2009). The relationship between major depression and marital disruption is bidirectional. *Depression and Anxiety, 26*, 1172–1177.

Bumpass, E. R., Fagelman, F. D., & Brix, R. J. (1983). Intervention with children who set fires. *American Journal of Psychotherapy, 37*(3), 328–345.

Burack, J. A., Iarocci, G., Bowler, D., & Mottron, L. (2002). Benefits and pitfalls in the merging of disciplines: The example of developmental psychopathology and the study of persons with autism. *Development & Psychopathology, 14*, 225–237.

Burke, K. C., Burke, J. D., Jr., Regier, D. A., & Rae, D. S. (1990). Age at onset of selected mental disorders in five community populations. *Archives of General Psychiatry, 47*, 511–518.

Burkhalter, H., Wirz-Justice, A., Denhaerynck, K., Fehr, T., Steiger, J., Venzin, R. M., . . . & De Geest, S. (2015). The effect of bright light therapy on sleep and circadian rhythms in renal transplant recipients: A pilot randomized, multicentre wait-list controlled trial. *Transplant International, 28*(1), 59–70.

Burnham, M. M., & Gaylor, E. E. (2011). Sleep environments of young children in post-industrial societies. In M. El-Sheikh (Ed.), *Sleep and development: Familial and sociocultural considerations* (pp. 195–218). New York, NY: Oxford University Press.

Burns, A. (2000). The burden of Alzheimer's disease. *International Journal of Neuropsychopharmacology, 3*(7), 31–38.

Burri, A., Spector, T., & Rahman, Q. (2013). A discordant monozygotic twin approach to testing environmental influences on sexual dysfunction in women. *Archives of Sexual Behavior, 42*(6), 961–972.

Burton, R. (1977). *Anatomy of melancholy* (reprinted). New York, NY: Random House. (Original work published 1621.)

Bury, A. S., & Bagby, R. M. (2002). The detection of feigned uncoached and coached posttraumatic stress disorder with the MMPI-2 in a sample of workplace accident victims. *Psychological Assessment, 14*, 472–484.

Bus beheader Vince Li gets approval to live in Winnipeg group home. (2015, May 8). *The Globe and Mail*. Retrieved from http://www.theglobeandmail.com/news/national/bus-beheader-vince-li-gets-approval-to-live-in-winnipeg-group-home/article24355111/

Busatto, G. F. (2013). Structural and functional neuroimaging studies in major depressive disorder with psychotic features: A critical review. *Schizophrenia Bulletin, 39*(4), 776–786.

Buscher, A. L., & Giordano, T. P. (2010). Gaps in knowledge in caring for HIV survivors long-term. *JAMA, 304*, 340–341.

Bushman, B. J. (1993). Human aggression while under the influence of alcohol and other drugs: An integrative research review. *Psychological Science, 2*, 148–152.

Bushnell, J. A., Wells, J. E., Hornblow, A. R., Oakley-Browne, M. A., & Joyce, P. (1990). Prevalence of three bulimia syndromes in the general population. *Psychological Medicine, 20*, 671–680.

Bustillo, J., Lauriello, J., Horan, W., & Keith, S. (2001). The psychosocial treatment of schizophrenia: An update. *American Journal of Psychiatry, 158*(2), 163–175.

Butcher, J. N. (2009). Clinical personality assessment: History, evolution, contemporary models, and practical applications. In J. N. Butcher (Ed.), *Oxford handbook of personality assessment* (pp. 5–21). New York, NY: Oxford University Press.

Butcher, J. N., Graham, J. R., Williams, C. L., & Ben-Porath, Y. S. (1990). *Development and use of the MMPI-2 content scales*. Minneapolis, MN: University of Minnesota Press.

Butler, G., & Mathews, A. (1983). Cognitive processes in anxiety. *Advances in Behaviour Research and Therapy, 5*, 51–62.

Butler, L. D., Duran, R. E. F., Jasiukaitis, P., Koopman, C., & Spiegel, D. (1996). Hypnotizability and traumatic experience: A diathesis stress model of dissociative symptomatology. *American Journal of Psychiatry, 153*, 42–63.

Buxton, J. (2005). *Vancouver drug use epidemiology: Vancouver site report for the Canadian Community Epidemiology Network on Drug Use (CCENDU)*. Ottawa, ON: Canadian Community Epidemiology Network on Drug Use. Retrieved December 1, 2007, from http://www.ccsa.ca/NR/rdonlyres/E8864A4A-6225-4EF9-B4A9-9C391AC60B91/0/CCENDUVancouverhighlights2005e.pdf

Buysse, D. J., Reynolds, C. F., & Kupfer, D. J. (1993). Classification of sleep disorders: A preview of the DSM-IV. In D. L. Dunner (Ed.), *Current psychiatric therapy* (pp. 360–361). Philadelphia, PA: W. B. Saunders.

Buysse, D. J., Strollo, P. J., Black, J. E., Zee, P. G., & Winkelman, J. W. (2008). Sleep disorders. In R. E. Hales, S. C. Yudofsky, & G. O. Gabbard (Eds.), *The American Psychiatric Publishing textbook of psychiatry* (5th ed., pp. 921–969). Arlington, VA: American Psychiatric Publishing.

Buysse, D. J., Tu, X. M., Cherry, C. R., Begley, A. E., Kowalski, J., Kupfer, D. J., & Frank, E. (1999). Pretreatment REM sleep and subjective sleep quality distinguish depressed psychotherapy remitters and nonremitters. *Biological Psychiatry, 45*(2), 205–213.

Buzzella, B. A., Ehrenreich-May, J. T., & Pincus, D. B. (2011). Comorbidity and family factors associated with selective mutism. *Child Development Research, 2011*, 1–9.

Bye, E. K. (2007). Alcohol and violence: Use of possible confounders in a time-series analysis. *Addiction, 102*, 369–376.

Byers, A. L., Yaffe, K., Covinsky, K. E., Friedman, M. B., & Bruce, M. L. (2010). High occurrence of mood and anxiety disorders among older adults: The National Comorbidity Survey Replication. *Archives of General Psychiatry, 67*(5), 489–496.

Byne, W., Bradley, S. J., Coleman, E., Eyler, A. E., Green, R., Menvielle, E. J., & Tompkins, D. A. (2012). Report of the American Psychiatric Association Task Force on treatment of gender identity disorder. *Archives of Sexual Behavior, 41*(4), 759–796.

Byrd, A. L., Loeber, R., & Pardini, D. A. (2014). Antisocial behavior, psychopathic features and abnormalities in reward and punishment processing in youth. *Clinical Child and Family Psychology Review, 17*(2), 125–156.

Byrne, D., & Schulte, L. (1990). Personality dispositions as mediators of sexual responses. *Annual Review of Sex Research, 1*, 93–117.

Byrne, E. M., Johnson, J., McRae, A. F., Nyholt, D. R., Medland, S. E., Gehrman, P. R., & Chenevix-Trench, G. (2012). A genome-wide association study of caffeine-related sleep disturbance: Confirmation of a role for a common variant in the adenosine receptor. *Sleep, 35*(7), 967–975.

Byrne, J. M., Bawden, H. N., Beattie, T., DeWolfe, N. A. (2003). Risk for injury in preschoolers: Relationship to attention deficit hyperactivity disorder. *Child Neuropsychology, 9*, 142–151.

Cabeza, R., & Nyberg, L. (2000). Imaging cognition II: An empirical review of 275 PET and fMRI studies. *Journal of Cognitive Neuroscience, 12*(1), 1–47.

Cacioppo, J. T., & Patrick, W. (2008). *Loneliness: Human nature and the need for social connection.* New York, NY: Norton.

Cacioppo, J. T., Amaral, D. G., Blanchard, J. J., Cameron, J. L., Carter, C. S., Crews, D., . . . Quinn, K. J. (2007). Social neuroscience: Progress and implications for mental health. *Perspectives on Psychological Science, 2*(2), 99–123.

Cacioppo, S., Grippo, A. J., London, S., Goossens, L., & Cacioppo, J. T. (2015). Loneliness: Clinical Import and Interventions. *Perspectives on Psychological Science, 10*, 238–249.

Cadoret, R. J. (1978). Psychopathology in the adopted-away offspring of biologic parents with antisocial behavior. *Archives of General Psychiatry, 35*, 176–184.

Cadoret, R. J., Yates, W. R., Troughton, E., Woodworth, G., & Stewart, M. A. (1995). Genetic-environment interaction in the genesis of aggressivity and conduct disorders. *Archives of General Psychiatry, 52*, 916–924.

Caesar-Chavannes, C. R., & MacDonald, S. (2013). National Population Health Study of Neurological Conditions in Canada. *Chronic Diseases and Injuries in Canada, 33*, 183–191.

Cafri, G., Yamamiya, Y., Brannick, M., & Thompson, J. K. (2005). The influence of sociocultural factors on body image: A meta-analysis. *Clinical Psychology: Science and Practice, 12*, 421–433.

Caglayan, A. O. (2010). Genetic causes of syndromic and non-syndromic autism. *Developmental Medicine & Child Neurology, 52*(2), 130–138.

Cain, A. S., Epler, A. J., Steinley, D., & Sher, K. J. (2010). Stability and change in patterns of concerns related to eating, weight, and shape in young adult women: A latent transition analysis. *Journal of Abnormal Psychology, 119*(2), 255–267.

Cain, V. S., Johannes, C. B., Avis, N. E., Mohr, B., Schocken, M., Skurnick, J., & Ory, M. (2003). Sexual functioning and practices in a multi-ethnic study of midlife women: Baseline results from swan. *Journal of Sex Research, 40*(3), 266–276.

Cairney, J., Thorpe, C., Rietschlin, J., & Avison, W. R. (1999). 12-month prevalence of depression among single and married mothers in the 1994 National Population Health Survey. *Canadian Journal of Public Health, 90*, 320–324.

Calabrese, J., Shelton, M., Rapport, D., Youngstrom, E., Jackson, K., Bilali, S., . . . Findling, R. L. (2005). A 20-month, double-blind, maintenance trial of lithium versus divalproex, in rapid-cycling bipolar disorder. *American Journal of Psychiatry, 162*, 2152–2161.

Calamari, J. E., Chik, H. M., Pontarelli, N. K., & DeJong, B. L. (2012). Phenomenology and epidemiology of obsessive compulsive disorder. In G. Steketee (Ed.), *The Oxford handbook of obsessive compulsive and spectrum disorders* (pp. 11–47). New York, NY: Oxford University Press.

Calamari, J. E., Wiegartz, P. S., Riemann, B. C., Cohen, R. J., Greer, A., Jacobi, D. M., . . . Carmin, C. (2004). Obsessive–compulsive disorder subtypes: An attempted replication and extension of symptom-based taxonomy. *Behavior Research and Therapy, 42*, 647–670.

Calati, R., Gressier, F., Balestri, M., & Serretti, A. (2013). Genetic modulation of borderline personality disorder: Systematic review and meta-analysis. *Journal of Psychiatric Research, 47*(10), 1275–1287.

Calhoun, S. L., Fernandez-Mendoza, J., Vgontzas, A. N., Liao, D., & Bixler, E. O. (2014). Prevalence of insomnia symptoms in a general population sample of young children and preadolescents: Gender effects. *Sleep Medicine, 15*(1), 91–95.

Caligor, E., Levy, K. N., & Yeomans, F. E. (2015). Narcissistic personality disorder: Diagnostic and clinical challenges. *American Journal of Psychiatry, 172*(5), 415–22. https://doi.org/10.1176/appi.ajp.2014.14060723

Callanan, V. J., & Davis, M. S. (2012). Gender differences in suicide methods. *Social Psychiatry and Psychiatric Epidimiology, 47*(6), 857–869.

Cameron, N. M., Champagne, F. A., Parent, C., Fish, E. W., Ozaki-Kuroda, K., & Meaney, M. J. (2005). The programming of individual differences in defensive responses and reproductive strategies in the rat through variations in maternal care. *Neuroscience and Biobehavioral Reviews, 29*, 843–865.

Campbell, A. N., Miele, G. M., Nunes, E. V., McCrimmon, S., & Ghitza, U. E. (2012). Web-based, psychosocial treatment for substance use disorders in community treatment settings. *Psychological Services, 9*(2), 212.

Campbell, D. (2003, January 15). Pep pills blamed in friendly fire case. *The Guardian.* Retrieved October 25, 2003, from http://www.guardian.co.uk/afghanistan/story/0,1284,874923,00.html

Campbell, J. M., & Oei, T. P. (2010). A cognitive model for the intergenerational transference of alcohol use behavior. *Addictive Behaviors, 35*(2), 73–83.

Campbell, M. A., Porter, S., & Santor, D. (2004). Psychopathic traits in adolescent offenders: An evaluation of criminal history, clinical, and psychosocial correlates. *Behavioral Sciences & The Law, 22*, 23–47.

Campbell, W. K., & Miller, J. D. (2011). *The handbook of narcissism and narcissistic personality disorder: Theoretical approaches, empirical findings, and treatments.* John Wiley & Sons.

Campbell-Sills, L., & Barlow, D. H. (2007). Incorporating emotion regulation into conceptualization and treatment of anxiety and mood disorders. In J. J. Gross (Ed.), *Handbook of emotion regulation* (pp. 542–560). New York, NY: Guilford Press.

Campbell-Sills, L., & Brown, T. A. (2010). Generalized anxiety disorder. In M. M. Antony & D. H. Barlow (Eds.), *Handbook of assessment and treatment planning for psychological disorders* (2nd ed., pp. 224–266). New York, NY: Guilford Press.

Campo, J. A., Nijman, H., Merckelbach, H., & Evers, C. (2003). Psychiatric comorbidity of gender identity disorders: A survey among Dutch psychiatrists. *American Journal of Psychiatry, 160*, 1332–1336.

Campo, J. V., & Negrini, B. J. (2000). Case study: Negative reinforcement and behavioral management of conversion disorder. *Journal of the American Academy of Child and Adolescent Psychiatry, 39*(6), 787–790.

Canadian Centre on Substance Abuse. (2004, November). *A national survey of Canadians' use of alcohol and other drugs: Prevalence of use and related harms.* Retrieved March 3, 2008, from http://www.ccsa.ca/NR/rdonlyres/B2C820A2-C987–4F08–86052BE999FE4DFC/0/ccsa0048042004.pdf

Canadian Centre on Substance Abuse. (2015). *Canadian drug summary: Cannabis.* Retrieved from http://www.ccsa.ca/Resource%20Library/CCSA-Canadian-Drug-Summary-Cannabis-2015-en.pdf

Canadian Centre on Substance Abuse and Addiction. (2017). *Ecstasy or molly (MDMA)* (Canadian drug summary). https://www.ccsa.ca/ecstasy-or-molly-mdma-canadian-drug-summary

Canadian Charter of Rights and Freedoms, being Part I of the Constitution Act, *1982*, enacted by the Canada Act 1982 (U.K.), c. 11, Sched. B. (R. S. C. (1985), Appendix II, No. 44.

Canadian Chronic Disease Surveillance System. (2018). *Summary table: Acute myocardial infarction, age-standardized incidence rate, per 100,000, age 20 years and older, Canada.* Retrieved on August 30, 2019 from https://health-infobase.canada.ca/ccdss/data-tool/

Canadian Council on Smoking & Health and Physicians for a Smoke-Free Canada. (2003). *Number of deaths in Canada caused by smoking.* Retrieved August 16, 2003, from http://www.mediaawareness.ca/english/resources/educational/handouts/tobacco_advertising/number_of_deaths.cfm

Canadian Down Syndrome Society. (2000). New Down syndrome statistics. *CDSS Quarterly, 13.* Retrieved May 20, 2004, from http://www.cdss.ca/Newsletter%20Articles/medical%20and%20health/2000vol13–1,8.html

Canadian Institute for Health Information. (2011). *Canada's health care providers, 2000 to 2009: A reference guide. Health personnel trends in Canada.* Retrieved from https://secure.cihi.ca/estore/productFamily.htm?locale=en&pf=PFC1661

Canadian Institute for Health Information. (2013). *Canada's health care providers, 1997 to 2011: A reference guide.* Retrieved from https://secure.cihi.ca/estore/productFamily.htm?pf=PFC2161&lang=en&media=0

Canadian Institute for Health Information. (2014). *Canada's health care providers—Provincial profiles—2012.* Retrieved from https://secure.cihi.ca/estore/productFamily.htm?pf=PFC2500&lang=en&media=0

Canadian Institute for Health Information. (2017a). *Health workforce database, 2016: Methodology guide.* https://www.cihi.ca/sites/default/files/document/hwdb-meth-guide-2017-en-web.pdf

Canadian Institute for Health Information. (2017b). *Canada's health care providers: Provincial profiles, 2007 to 2016—Data tables.* https://secure.cihi.ca/free_products/HCP-2016-provincial-profiles-data-tables-en-web.xlsx

Canadian Institute for Health Information. (2017c). *Supply, distribution and migration of physicians in Canada, 2016: Data tables.* https://www.cihi.ca/sites/default/files/document/smdb_data_tables_phys2016_en.zip

Canadian Institute for Health Information. (2017d). *Supply, distribution and migration of physicians in Canada, 2016: Methodological notes.* https://www.cihi.ca/sites/default/files/document/smdb_data_release_methodology_notes_phys2016_en.pdf

Canadian Institute for Health Information. (2018). *Pan-Canadian trends in the prescribing of opioids and benzodiazepines, 2012 to 2017.* https://www.cihi.ca/sites/default/files/document/opioid-prescribing-june2018-en-web.pdf

Canadian Institute for Health Information. (2019). *Hospital mental health database (HMHDB) quick stats: Mental health and addictions hospitalizations in Canada, supplementary tables, 2017–2018.* https://www.cihi.ca/sites/default/files/document/hmhdb-qs-preformatted-2017-18-en.xlsx

Canadian Press. (2003, December 30). *Questions about the herb ephedra and its ban by the FDA.* Retrieved August 6, 2004, from http://www.medbroadcast.com/channel_health_news_details.asp?news_channel_id1000&news_id2957&channel_id1012&relation_id0

Canadian Press. (2004, May 11). Boy raised as girl has tragic demise: Doctor advised gender switch. *The Chronicle Herald, 56*, A1–A2.

Canadian Psychological Association. (2000). *Canadian code of ethics for psychologists* (3rd ed.). Ottawa, ON: Canadian Psychological Association.

Canadian Psychological Association. (2004). *Deciding to see a psychologist: How to choose one and what to expect.* Retrieved July 5, 2004, from http://www.cpa.ca/Psychologist/psychologist.htm

Canadian Study of Health and Aging Working Group. (1994). Canadian Study of Health and Aging: Study methods and prevalence of dementia. *Canadian Medical Association Journal, 150,* 899–913.

Canadian Study of Health and Aging Working Group. (2000). The incidence of dementia in Canada. *Neurology, 55,* 66–73.

Canadian Study of Health and Aging Working Group. (2001). Disability and frailty among elderly Canadians: A comparison of six surveys. *International Journal of Psychogeriatrics, 13*(Suppl. 1), 159–167.

Candido, C. L., & Romney, D. M. (2002). Depression in paranoid and nonparanoid schizophrenic patients compared with major depressive disorder. *Journal of Affective Disorders, 70,* 261–271.

Canli, T., & Lesch, K.-P. (2007). Long story short: The serotonin transporter In emotion regulation and social cognition. *Nature Neuroscience, 10,* 1103–1109.

Cannon, T. D., Barr, C. E., & Mednick, S. A. (1991). Genetic and perinatal factors in the etiology of schizophrenia. In E. F. Walker (Ed.), *Schizophrenia: A life-course developmental perspective* (pp. 9–31). New York, NY: Academic Press.

Cannon, W. B. (1929). *Bodily changes in pain, hunger, fear and rage* (2nd ed.). New York, NY: Appleton-Century-Crofts.

Cannon, W. B. (1942). Voodoo death. *American Anthropologist, 44,* 169–181.

Canter, A. (1996). The Bender-Gesalt Test (BGT). In C. S. Newmark (Ed.), *Major psychological assessment instruments* (pp. 400–430). Boston, MA: Allyn & Bacon.

Canterbury Farms. (1997). *The new wonder herb that has been around for 2500 years!* Retrieved July 7, 2004, from http://www.nwgardening.com/stjohnsworth.html

Cantor, J. M. (2017). How man transgender kids grow up to stay trans? *PsyPost.org.* https://www.psypost.org/2017/12/many-transgender-kids-grow-stay-trans-50499

Cantor, J. M., Kabani, N., Christensen, B. K., Zipursky, R. B., Barbaree, H. E., Dickey, R., . . . Blanchard, R. (2008). Cerebral white matter deficiencies in pedophilic men. *Journal of Psychiatric Research, 42*(3), 167–183.

Caprara, D. L., Nash, K., Greenbaum, R., Rovet, J., & Koren, G. (2007). Novel approaches to the diagnosis of fetal alcohol spectrum disorder. *Neuroscience & Biobehavioral Reviews, 31*(2), 254–260.

Cardena, E. A., & Gleaves, D. H. (2003). Dissociative disorders: Phantoms of the self. In M. Hersen & S. M. Turner (Eds.), *Adult psychopathology and diagnosis* (4th ed., pp. 476–505). New York, NY: John Wiley & Sons.

Cardeña, E., & Carlson, E. (2011). Acute stress disorder revisited. *Annual Review of Clinical Psychology, 7,* 245–267. https://doi.org/10.1146/annurev-clinpsy-032210–104502

Cardeña, E., Lewis-Fernandez, R., Bear, D., Pakianathan, I., & Spiegel, D. (1996). Dissociative disorders. In T. A. Widiger, A. J. Frances, H. A. Pincus, R. Ross, et al. (Eds.), *DSM-IV sourcebook* (Vol. 2, pp. 973–1005). Washington, DC: American Psychiatric Press.

Carey, G. (1992). Twin imitation for antisocial behavior: Implications for genetic and family environment research. *Journal of Abnormal Psychology, 101,* 18–25.

Carey, M. P., & Johnson, B. T. (1996). Effectiveness of yohimbine in the treatment of erectile disorder: Four meta-analytic integrations. *Archives of Sexual Behavior, 25,* 341–360.

Carey, M. P., Wincze, J. P., & Meisler, A. W. (1993). Sexual dysfunction: Male erectile disorder. In D. H. Barlow (Ed.), *Clinical handbook of psychological disorders* (2nd ed., pp. 442–480). New York, NY: Guilford Press.

Carlat, D. J., & Camargo, C. A. (1991). Review of bulimia nervosa in males. *American Journal of Psychiatry, 148,* 831–843.

Carlat, D. J., Camargo, C. A., Jr., & Herzog, D. B. (1997). Eating disorders in males: A report on 135 patients. *American Journal of Psychiatry, 154,* 1127–1132.

Carlo, G., Knight, G. P., Roesch, S. C., Opal, D., & Davis, A. (2014). Personality across cultures: A critical analysis of Big Five research and current directions. In A Leong, T. L. Frederick, L. Comas-Díaz, N. Hall, C. Gordon, & V. C. McLoyd (Eds.), *APA handbook of multicultural psychology, Vol. 1: Theory and research* (pp. 285–298). Washington, DC: American Psychological Association.

Carlson, G. A. (1990). Annotation: Child and adolescent mania—Diagnostic considerations. *Journal of Child Psychology and Psychiatry, 31*(3), 331–341.

Carlson, L. E., & Garland, S. N. (2005). Impact of mindfulness-based stress reduction (MBSR) on sleep, mood, stress and fatigue symptoms in cancer outpatients. *International Journal of Behavioral Medicine, 12*(4), 278–285.

Carlson, L. E., Speca, M., Patel, K. D., & Goodey, E. (2004). Mindfulness-based stress reduction in relation to quality of life, mood, symptoms of stress and levels of cortisol, dehydroepiandrosterone sulfate (DHEAS) and melatonin in breast and prostate cancer outpatients. *Psychoneuroendocrinology, 9*(4), 448–474.

Carney, C. E., Edinger, J. D., Kuchibhatla, M., Lachowski, A. M., Bogouslavsky, O., Krystal, A. D., & Shapiro, C. M. (2017). Cognitive behavioral insomnia therapy for those with insomnia and depression: A randomized controlled clinical trial. *Sleep, 40*(4), zsx019. https://doi.org/10.1093/sleep/zsx019

Caron, C., & Rutter, M. (1991). Comorbidity in childhood psychopathology: Concepts, issues, and research strategies. *Journal of Child Psychology and Psychiatry, 32,* 1063–1080.

Caron, J., & Liu, A. (2010). A descriptive study of the prevalence of psychological distress and mental disorders in the Canadian population: Comparison between low-income and non-low-income populations. *Chronic Diseases in Canada, 30,* 84–94.

Carpenter, A. L., Puliafico, A. C., Lurtz, S. M., Pincus, D. B., & Comer, J. S. (2014). Extending parent–child interaction therapy for early childhood internalizing problems: New advances for an overlooked population. *Clinical Child and Family Psychology Review, 17,* 340–356.

Carpenter, M. J., Jardin, B. F., Burris, J. L., Mathew, A. R., Schnoll, R. A., Rigotti, N. A., & Cummings, K. M. (2013). Clinical strategies to enhance the efficacy of nicotine replacement therapy for smoking cessation: A review of the literature. *Drugs, 73*(5), 407–426.

Carpenter,.W. T. (1992). The negative symptom challenge. *Archives of General Psychiatry, 49,* 236–237.

Carpenter, W. T., & van Os, J. (2011). Should attenuated psychosis syndrome be a DSM-5 diagnosis? *American Journal of Psychiatry, 168*(5), 460–463.

Carr, A., Keenlyside, M., & Fitzhenry, M., O'Hanrahan, K., Harte, E., White, W., . . . Browne, S. (2015). *The Waterford mental health survey.* Dublin, Ireland: University College Dublin, School of Psychology, Health Services Executive. Retrieved from http://researchrepository.ucd.ie/bitstream/handle/10197/6512/WMHS_Report.pdf

Carr, E. G., & Durand, V. M. (1985). Reducing behavior problems through functional communication training. *Journal of Applied Behavior Analysis, 18,* 111–126.

Carrasco, M., Barker, E. D., Tremblay, R. E., & Vitaro, F. (2006). Eysenck's personality dimensions as predictors of male adolescent trajectories of physical aggression, theft and vandalism. *Personality and Individual Differences, 41,* 1309–1320.

Carrico, A. W., & Antoni, M. H. (2008). Effects of psychological interventions on neuroendocrine hormone regulation and immune states in HIV-positive persons: A review of randomized controlled trials. *Psychosomatic Medicine, 70,* 575–584.

Carrier, S., Brock, G. B., Pommerville, P. J., Shin, J., Anglin, G., Whittaker, S., & Beasley, C. M., Jr. (2005). Efficacy and safety of oral tadalafil in the treatment of men in Canada with erectile dysfunction: A randomized, double-blind, parallel, placebo-controlled clinical trial. *Journal of Sexual Medicine, 2,* 685–698.

Carrière, G., Bougie, E., & Kohen, D. (2018). Acute care hospitalizations for mental and behavioural disorders among First Nations people. *Health Reports, 29*(6), 11–19. https://www150.statcan.gc.ca/n1/en/catalogue/82-003-X201800654971

Carrigg, D., & Luymes, G. (2017, July 11). Decriminalize pot: Campbell, B.C. senator and ex-mayor says possession should result in fine. *The Province,* p. A.3.

Carrington, P. J. (1999). Gender, gun control, suicide and homicide in Canada. *Archives of Suicide Research, 5,* 71–75.

Carroll, A. (2009). Are you looking at me? Understanding and managing paranoid personality disorder. *Advances in Psychiatric Treatment, 15*(1), 40.

Carroll, B. J., Feinberg, M., Greden, J. F., Haskett, R. F., James, N. M., Steiner, M., & Tarika, J. (1980). Diagnosis of endogenous depression: Comparison of clinical, research, *and neuroendocrine criteria. Journal of Affective Disorders, 2,* 177–194.

Carroll, B. J., Martin, F. I., & Davies, B. (1968). Resistance to suppression by dexamethasome of plasma 11-O.H.C.S. levels in severe depressive illness. *BMJ, 3,* 285–287.

Carroll, K. M. (1992). Psychotherapy for cocaine abuse: Approaches, evidence, and conceptual models. In T. R. Kosten &

H. D. Kleber (Eds.), *Clinician's guide to cocaine addiction: Theory, research, and treatment* (pp. 290–313). New York, NY: Guilford Press.

Carroll, R. A. (2007). Gender dysphoria and transgender experiences. In S. R. Leiblum (Ed.), *Principles and practice of sex therapy* (4th ed., pp. 477–508). New York, NY: Guilford Press.

Carson, R. C. (1991). Discussion: Dilemmas in the pathway of DSM-IV. *Journal of Abnormal Psychology, 100,* 302–307.

Carson, R. C. (1996). Aristotle, Galileo, and the DSM taxonomy: The case of schizophrenia. *Journal of Consulting and Clinical Psychology, 64*(6), 1133–1139.

Carstensen, L. L., Charles, S. T., Isaacowitz, D., & Kennedy, Q. (2003). Life-span personality development and emotion. In R. J. Davidson, K. Scherer, & H. H. Goldsmith (Eds.), *Handbook of affective sciences* (pp. 726–746). Oxford, UK: Oxford University Press.

Carter, J. C., & Fairburn, C. G. (1998). Cognitive-behavioral self-help for binge eating disorder: A controlled effectiveness study. *Journal of Consulting and Clinical Psychology, 66,* 616–623.

Carter, J. C., McFarlane, T. L., Bewell, C., Olmsted, M. P., Woodside, D. B., Kaplan, A. S., & Crosby, R. D. (2009). Maintenance treatment for anorexia nervosa: A comparison of cognitive behavior therapy and treatment as usual. *International Journal of Eating Disorders, 42*(3), 202–207.

Carter, J. S., & Garber, J. (2011). Predictors of the first onset of a major depressive episode and changes in depressive symptoms across adolescence: Stress and negative cognitions. *Journal of Abnormal Psychology, 120*(4), 779–796.

Carter, J. W., Schulsinger, F., Parnas, J., Cannon, T., Mednick, S. A. (2002). A multivariate prediction model of schizophrenia. *Schizophrenia Bulletin, 28,* 649–682

Cartwright, R. D. (2006). Sleepwalking. In T. Lee-Chiong (Ed.), *Sleep: A comprehensive handbook* (pp. 429–433). Hoboken, NJ: John Wiley & Sons.

Carvalho, M., Carmo, H., Costa, V., Capela, J., Capela, J. P., Pontes, H., Remião, F., & Bastos, M. D. (2012). Toxicity of amphetamines: An update. *Archives of Toxicology, 86*(8), 1167–1231.

Carver, C. S., Johnson, S. L., & Joormann, J. (2009). Two-mode models of self-regulation as a tool for conceptualizing effects of the serotonin system in normal behavior and diverse disorders. *Current Directions in Psychological Science, 18*(4), 195–199.

Caseras, X., Torrubia, R., & Farre, J. M. (2001). Is the behavioral inhibition system the core vulnerability for cluster C personality disorders? *Personality and Individual Differences, 31,* 349–359.

Cash, T. F., & Pruzinsky, T. (2002). Understanding body images. In T. F. Cash & T. Pruzinsky (Eds.), *Body image: A handbook of theory, research and clinical practice* (pp. 3–12). New York, NY: Guilford Press.

Caspi, A., Elder, G. H., Jr., & Bem, D. L. (1987). Moving against the world: Life-course patterns of explosive children. *Developmental Psychology, 23,* 308–313.

Caspi, A., McClay, J., Moffitt, T., Mill, J., Martin, J., Craig, I. W., . . . Poulton, R.

(2002). Role of genotype in the cycle of violence in maltreated children. *Science, 297,* 851–854.

Caspi, A., Moffitt, T. E., Cannon, M., McClay, J., Murray, R., Harrington, H. L., . . . Craig, I. W. (2005). Moderation of the effect of adolescent-onset cannabis use on adult psychosis by a functional polymorphism in the catechol-o-methyltransferase gene: Longitudinal evidence of a gene X environment interaction. *Biological Psychiatry, 57,* 1117–1127.

Caspi, A., Sugden, K., Moffitt, T. E., Taylor, A., Craig, I. W., Harrington, H., . . . Poulton, R. (2003). Influence of life stress on depression: Moderation by a polymorphism in the 5-HTT gene. *Science, 301,* 386–389.

Cassidy, F., Forest, K., Murry, E., & Carroll, B. J. (1998). A factor analysis of the signs and symptoms of mania. *Archives of General Psychiatry, 55,* 27–32.

Cassidy, F., Yatham, L. N., Berk, M., & Grof, P. (2008). Pure and mixed manic subtypes: A review of diagnostic classification and validation. *Bipolar Disorders, 10,* 131–143.

Cassin, S. E., & von Ranson, K. M. (2005). Personality and eating disorders: A decade in review. *Clinical Psychology Review, 25,* 895–916.

Castellanos, F. X., Sharp, W. S., Gottesman, R. F, Greenstein, D. K., Giedd, J. N., & Rapoport, J. L. (2003). Anatomic brain abnormalities in monozygotic twins discordant for attention deficit hyperactivity disorder. *American Journal of Psychiatry, 160,* 1693–1696.

Castonguay, L. G., Eldredge, K. L., & Agras, W. S. (1995). Binge eating disorder: Current state and directions. *Clinical Psychology Review, 15,* 815–890.

Catania, J. A., Morin, S. F., Canchola, J., Pollack, L., Chang, J., & Coates, T. J. (2000). U.S. priorities—HIV prevention. *Science, 290,* 717.

Cautela, J. R. (1966). Treatment of compulsive behavior by covert sensitization. *Psychological Record, 16,* 33–41.

Cautela, J. R. (1967). Covert sensitization. *Psychological Reports, 20,* 459–468.

CBS News. (1999, February 25). *Obsessions* [Television series episode]. Retrieved from http://www.ocfoundation.org/ ocf1420q.htm

Cechnicki, A., Bielańska, A., Hanuszkiewicz, I., & Daren, A. (2013). The predictive validity of expressed emotions (EE) in schizophrenia. A 20-year prospective study. *Journal of Psychiatric Research, 47*(2), 208–214.

Ceci, S. J. (2003). Cast in six ponds and you'll reel in something: Looking back on 25 years of research. *American Psychologist, 58,* 855–867.

Cederlöf, M., Thornton, L. M., Baker, J., Lichtenstein, P., Larsson, H., Rück, C., . . . Mataix-Cols, D. (2015). Etiological overlap between obsessive-compulsive disorder and anorexia nervosa: A longitudinal cohort, multigenerational family and twin study. *World Psychiatry, 14*(3), 333–338.

Celio, A. A., Zabinski, M. F., & Wilfley, D. E. (2002). African American body images. In T. F. Cash & T. Pruzinsky (Eds.), *Body image: A handbook of theory, research and clinical practice* (pp. 234–242). New York, NY: Guilford Press.

Centers for Disease Control and Prevention. (2003). *Deaths, percent of total deaths, and death rates for the 15 leading causes of death in 5-year age groups, by race and sex: United States, 2000.* Centers for Disease Control and National Center for Health Statistics, National Vital Statistics System.

Centers for Disease Control and Prevention. (2010b). *Fatal injury data.* Retrieved from http://www.cdc.gov/injury/ wisqars/fatal.html

Centers for Disease Control and Prevention. (2011). Measles—United States, January–May 20, 2011. *Morbidity and Mortality Weekly Report, 60*(20), 666–668.

Centers for Disease Control and Prevention. (2014). Prevalence of autism spectrum disorders among children 8 years—Autism and Developmental Disabilities Monitoring Network, 11 Sites, *United States, 2010. MMWR, 63*(No. SS-02), 1–19. Retrieved from http://www. cdc.gov/mmwr/preview/mmwrhtml/ ss6103a1.htm?s_cid=ss6103a1_e

Chachamovich, E., Kirmayer, L. J., Haggarty, J. M., Cargo, M., McCormick, R., & Turecki, G. (2015). Suicide among Inuit: Results from a large, epidemiologically representative follow-back study in Nunavut. *Psychiatry, 60*(6), 268–275.

Chalder, T., Cleare, A., & Wessely, S. (2000). The management of stress and anxiety in chronic fatigue syndrome. In D. I. Mostofsky & D. H. Barlow (Eds.), *The management of stress and anxiety in medical disorders* (pp. 160–179). Needham Heights, MA: Allyn & Bacon.

Challacombe, L. (2018). *CATIE fact sheet: The epidemiology of HIV in people who inject drugs in Canada.* https:// www.catie.ca/fact-sheets/epidemiology/ injection-drug-use-and-hiv-canada

Chamberlain, S. R., Menzies, L., Hampshire, A., Suckling, J., Fineberg, N. A., del Campo, N., . . . Sahakian, B. J. (2008). Orbitofrontal dysfunction in patients with obsessive–compulsive disorder and their unaffected relatives. *Science, 321,* 421–422.

Chamberlain, S. R., Menzies, L., Sahakian, B. J., & Fineberg, N. A. (2007). Lifting the veil on trichotillomania. *American Journal of Psychiatry, 164,* 568–574.

Chan, B. W. Y., & O'Brian, A. M. (2011). The right of caregivers to access health information of relatives with mental illness. *International Journal of Law and Psychiatry, 34,* 386–392.

Chandler, M. J., & Lalonde, C. (1998). Cultural continuity as a hedge against suicide in Canada's First Nations. *Transcultural Psychiatry, 35,* 191–219.

Chang, V. C., Chaput, J.-P., Roberts, K. C., Jayaraman, G., & Do, M. T. (2018). Factors associated with sleep duration across life stages: Results from the Canadian Health Measures Survey. *Health Promotion and Chronic Disease Prevention in Canada, 38*(11), 404–418. https://www.canada.ca/ content/dam/phac-aspc/documents/ services/reports-publications/health-promotion-chronic-disease-prevention-canada-research-policy-practice/ vol-38-no-11-2018/ar02-eng.pdf

Chaouloff, F., & Groc, L. (2010). Temporal modulation of hippocampal excitatory transmission by corticosteroids and stress. *Frontiers in Neuroendocrinology.* Advance online publication. https://doi.org/10.1016/ j.yfrne.2010.07.004

Chaput, J.-P., Wong, S. L., & Michaud, I. (2017). Duration and quality of sleep among Canadians aged 18 to 79. *Health Reports, 28*(9), 28–33. https:// www150.statcan.gc.ca/n1/pub/82 -003-x/2017009/article/54857-eng.htm

Chaput, J.-P., Yau, J., Rao, D. P., & Morin, C. M. (2018). Prevalence of insomnia for Canadians aged 6 to 79. *Health Reports, 29*(12), 16–20. https://www150.statcan.gc.ca/n1/en/ catalogue/82-003-X201801200002

Charach, A., Figueroa, M., Chen, S., Ickowicz, A., & Schachar, R. (2006). Stimulant treatment over 5 years: Effects on growth. *Journal of the American Academy of Child and Adolescent Psychiatry, 45,* 415–421.

Charbonneau, J., & O'Connor, K. (1999). Depersonalization in a non-clinical sample. *Behavioural and Cognitive Psychotherapy, 27,* 377–381.

Charland, L. C. (2010). Science and morals in the affective psychopathology of Philippe Pinel. *History of Psychiatry, 21*(1), 38–53.

Charlebois, P., LeBlanc, M., Gagnon, C., Larivee, S., & Tremblay, R. (1993). Age trends in early behavioral predictors of serious antisocial behaviors. *Journal of Psychopathology and Behavioral Assessment, 15,* 23–41.

Charles, S. T., & Carstensen, L. L. (2010). Social and emotional aging. *Annual Review of Psychology, 61,* 383–409.

Charney, D. S., & Drevets, W. C. (2002). Neurobiological basis of anxiety disorders. In K. L. Davis, D. Charney, J. T. Coyle, & C. Nemeroff (Eds.), *Neuropsychopharmacology: The fifth generation of progress* (pp. 901–951). Philadelphia, PA: Lippincott Williams & Wilkins.

Charney, D. S., Barlow, D. H., Botteron, K., Cohen, J. D., Goldman, D., Gur, R. E., . . . Zalcman, S. J. (2002). Neuroscience research agenda to guide development of a pathophysiologically based classification system. In D. J. Kupfer, M. B. First, & D. A. Regier (Eds.), *A research agenda for DSM-V* (pp. 31–83). Washington, DC: American Psychiatric Association.

Charney, D. S., Deutch, A. Y., Krystal, J. H., Southwick, S. M., & Davis, M. (1993). Psycho-biological mechanisms of post-traumatic stress disorder. *Archives of General Psychiatry, 50,* 294–305.

Charney, D. S., Woods, S. W., Price, L. H., Goodman, W. K., Glazer, W. M., & Heninger, G. R. (1990). Noradrenergic dysregulation in panic disorder. In J. C. Ballenger (Ed.), *Neurobiology of panic disorder* (pp. 91–105). New York, NY: Wiley-Liss.

Chartrand, H., Sareen, J., Toews, M., & Bolton, J. M. (2012). Suicide attempts versus nonsuicidal self-injury among individuals with anxiety disorders in a nationally representative sample. *Depression and Anxiety, 29,* 172–179.

Chassin, L., Pillow, D. R., Curran, P. J., Molina, B. S. G., & Barrera, M. (1993). Relation of parental alcoholism to early adolescent substance use: A test of three mediating mechanisms. *Journal of Abnormal Psychology, 102,* 3–19.

Chasson G. S., Buhlmann U., Tolin D. F., Rao, S. R., Reese, H. E., Welsh, K. S., & Wilhelm, S. (2010). Need for speed: Evaluating slopes of OCD recovery in behavior therapy enhanced with d-cycloserine. *Behaviour Research and Therapy, 48,* 675–679.

Chavez, M., & Insel, T. R. (2007). Eating disorders: National Institute of Mental Health perspective. *American Psychologist, 62,* 159–166.

Check, J. R. (1998). Munchausen syndrome by proxy: An atypical form of child abuse. *Journal of Practical Psychology and Behavioral Health, 4,* 340–345.

Checknita, D., Maussion, G., Labonté, B., Comai, S., Tremblay, R. E., Vitaro, F., . . . Turecki, G. (2015). Monoamine oxidase A gene promoter methylation and transcriptional downregulation in an offender population with antisocial personality disorder. *British Journal of Psychiatry, 206*(3), 216–222.

Chemerenski, E., Triebwasser, J., Roussos, P., & Siever, L. J. (2012). Schizotypal personality disorder. *Journal of Personality Disorders, 27*(5), 652–679. https://doi.org/10.1521/ pedi_2012_26_053

Chen, H., & Jackson, T. (2008). Prevalence and sociodemographic correlates of eating disorder endorsements among adolescents and young adults from China. *European Eating Disorders Review, 16*(5), 375–385.

Chen, Y., Nettles, M. E., & Chen, S. W. (2009). Rethinking dependent personality disorder: Comparing different human relatedness in cultural contexts. *Journal of Nervous and Mental Disease, 197*(11), 793–800.

Cheng, C., & Tang, C. S. K. (2004). The psychology behind the masks: Psychological responses to the severe acute respiratory syndrome outbreak in different regions [Special issue: Special issue on psychology of severe acute respiratory syndrome (SARS)]. *Asian Journal of Social Psychology, 7,* 3–7.

Cheung, F. M. (2012). Mainstreaming culture in psychology. *American Psychologist, 67*(8), 721–730.

Cheung, F. M., van de Vijver, F. J., & Leong, F. T. (2011). Toward a new approach to the study of personality in culture. *American Psychologist, 66*(7), 593–603.

Chiappe, P., Stringer, R., Siegel, L. S., & Stanovich, K. E. (2002). Why the timing deficit hypothesis does not explain reading disability in adults. *Reading and Writing, 15,* 73–107.

Chida, Y., & Steptoe, A. (2009). The association of anger and hostility with future coronary heart disease: A meta-analytic review of prospective evidence. *Journal of the American College of Cardiology, 53*(11), 936–946.

Chida, Y., & Steptoe, A. (2010). Greater cardiovascular responses to laboratory mental stress are associated with poor subsequent cardiovascular risk status: A meta-analysis of prospective evidence. *Hypertension, 55*(4), 1026–1032.

Chilcott, L. A., & Shapiro, C. M. (1996). The socio-economic impact of insomnia: An overview. *Pharmacoeconomics, 10,* 1–14.

Chisuwa, N., & O'Dea, J. A. (2010). Body image and eating disorders amongst Japanese adolescents: A review of the literature. *Appetite, 54,* 5–15.

Chivers, M. L., & Bailey, J. M. (2000). Sexual orientation of female-to-male transsexuals: A comparison of homosexual and nonhomosexual types. *Archives of Sexual Behavior, 29*(3), 259–279.

Chivers, M. L., Rieger, G., Latty, E., & Bailey, M. (2004). A sex difference in the specificity of sexual arousal. *Psychological Science, 15,* 736–744.

Chivers, M. L., Seto, M. C., Lalumière, M. L., Laan, E., & Grimbos, T. (2010). Agreement of self-reported and genital measures of sexual arousal among men and women: A meta-analysis. *Archives of Sexual Behavior, 39*, 5–56. https://doi.org/10.1007/s10508-009-9556-9

Chmielewski, M., Clark, L. A., Bagby, R. M., & Watson, D. (2015). Method matters: Understanding diagnostic reliability in DSM-IV and DSM-5. *Journal of Abnormal Psychology, 124*(3), 764–769. https://doi.org/10.1037/abn0000069

Cho, H. J., Lavretsky, H., Olmstead, R., Levin, M. J., Oxman, M. N., & Irwin, M. R. (2008). Sleep disturbance and depression recurrence in community-dwelling older adults: A prospective study. *American Journal of Psychiatry, 165*(12), 1543–1550.

Choate, M. L., Pincus, D. B., Eyberg, S. M., & Barlow, D. B. (2005). Parent–child interaction therapy for treatment of separation anxiety disorder: A pilot study. *Cognitive and Behavioral Practice, 12*(1), 126–135.

Chodoff, P. (1982). Hysteria in women. *American Journal of Psychiatry, 139*, 545–551.

Choi, J., & Twamley, E. W. (2013). Cognitive rehabilitation therapies for Alzheimer's disease: A review of methods to improve treatment engagement and self-efficacy. *Neuropsychology Review, 23*(1), 48–62.

Choi, S. H., Lee, H., Chung, T. S., Park, K. M., Jung, Y. C., Kim, S. I., & Kim, J.-J. (2012). Neural network functional connectivity during and after an episode of delirium. *American Journal of Psychiatry, 169*(5s), 498–507.

Chorpita, B. F., & Barlow, D. H. (1998). The development of anxiety: The role of control in the early environment. *Psychological Bulletin, 124*(1), 3–21.

Chosak, A., Marques, L., Greenberg, J. L., Jenike, E., Dougherty, D. D., & Wilhelm, S. (2008). Body dysmorphic disorder and obsessive–compulsive disorder: Similarities, differences and the classification debate. *Expert Review of Neurotherapeutics, 8*(8), 1209–1218.

Chouinard, G., Jones, B., Remington, G., Bloom, D., Addington, D., MacEwan, G. W., . . . Arnott, W. (1993). A Canadian multicenter placebo-controlled study of fixed doses of risperidone and haloperidol in the treatment of chronic schizophrenic patients. *Journal of Clinical Psychopharmacology, 13*, 25–40.

Christopher, J. C., Wendt, D. C., Marecek, J., & Goodman, D. M. (2014). Critical cultural awareness: Contributions to a globalizing psychology. *American Psychologist, 69*(7), 645–655.

Chronic Pain Association of Canada. (2003). *Painful facts.* Retrieved July 15, 2004, from http://ecn.ab.ca/cpac/page5.html

Chronis, A. M., Lahey, B. B., Pelham, W. E., Jr., Williams, S. H., Baumann, B. L., Kipp, H., . . . Rathouz, P. J. (2007). Maternal depression and early positive parenting predict future conduct problems in young children with attention-deficit/hyperactivity disorder. *Developmental Psychology, 43*, 70–82.

Chung, J., Demiris, G., & Thompson, H. J. (2016). Ethical considerations regarding the use of smart home technologies for older adults: An integrative review. *Annual Review of Nursing Research, 34*(1), 155–181.

Chung, K. F., Yeung, W. F., Ho, F. Y. Y., Yung, K. P., Yu, Y. M., & Kwok, C. W. (2015). Cross-cultural and comparative epidemiology of insomnia: The Diagnostic and Statistical Manual (DSM), International Classification of Diseases (ICD) and International Classification of Sleep Disorders (ICSD). *Sleep Medicine, 16*(4), 477–482.

Chung, S. Y., Luk, S. L., & Lee, P. W. H. (1990). A follow-up study of infantile autism in Hong Kong. *Journal of Autism and Developmental Disorders, 20*, 221–232.

Chung, T., & Martin, C. S. (2009). Subjective stimulant and sedative effects of alcohol during early drinking experiences predict alcohol involvement in treated adolescents. *Journal of Studies on Alcohol and Drugs, 70*(5), 660–667.

Church, E., & Friesen, J. (2013, November 5). Toronto Mayor Rob Ford apologizes, but will not step down, after admitting to smoking crack cocaine. *Globe and Mail.* Retrieved from http://www.theglobeandmail.com/news/toronto/rob-ford-councillors/article15263319/

Cicchetti, D. (1991). A historical perspective on the discipline of developmental psychopathology. In J. Rolf, A. S. Masten, D. Cicchetti, K. H. Nuechterlein, et al. (Eds.), *Risk and protective factors in the development of psychopathology* (pp. 2–28). New York, NY: Cambridge University Press.

Cimera, R. E. (2012). The economics of supported employment: What new data tell us. *Journal of Vocational Rehabilitation, 37*(2), 109.

Cipani, E. (1991). Educational classification and placement. In J. L. Matson & J. A. Mulick (Eds.), *Handbook of mental retardation* (2nd ed., pp. 181–191). Elmsford, NY: Pergamon Press.

Ciraulo, D. A., Barlow, D. H., Gulliver, S. B., Farchione, T., Morissette, S. B., Kamholz, B. W., . . . Knapp, C. M. (2013). The effects of venlafaxine and cognitive behavioral therapy alone and combined in the treatment of co-morbid alcohol use-anxiety disorders. *Behaviour Research and Therapy, 51*, 729–735.

Clark, C. J., Henderson, K. M., de Leon, C. F., Guo, H., Lunos, S., Evans, D. A., & Everso Rose, S. A. (2012). Latent constructs in psychosocial factors associated with cardiovascular disease: An examination by race and sex. *Frontiers in Psychiatry, 3*, 5.

Clark, D. A., & O'Connor, K. (2005). Thinking is believing: Ego-dystonic intrusive thoughts in obsessive–compulsive disorder. In D. A. Clark (Ed.), *Intrusive thoughts in clinical disorders* (pp. 145–174). New York, NY: Guilford Press.

Clark, D. A., & Purdon, C. L. (1995). The assessment of unwanted intrusive thoughts: A review and critique of the literature. *Behaviour Research and Therapy, 33*, 967–976.

Clark, D. A., & Rhyno, S. (2005). Unwanted intrusive thoughts in non-clinical individuals: Implications for clinical disorders. In D. A. Clark (Ed.), *Intrusive thoughts in clinical disorders* (pp. 1–29). New York, NY: Guilford Press.

Clark, D. A., Beck, A. T., & Alford, B. A. (1999). *Scientific foundations of cognitive theory and therapy of depression.* New York, NY: John Wiley & Sons.

Clark, D. A., Steer, R. A., Haslam, N., Beck, A. T., & Brown, G. K. (1997). Personality vulnerability, psychiatric diagnoses, and symptoms: Cluster analyses of the sociotropy-autonomy subscales. *Cognitive Therapy & Research, 21*, 267–283.

Clark, D. M. (1986). A cognitive approach to panic. *Behaviour Research and Therapy, 24*, 461–470.

Clark, D. M. (1996). Panic disorder: From theory to therapy. In P. Salkovskis (Ed.), *Frontiers of cognitive therapy* (pp. 318–344). New York, NY: Guilford Press.

Clark, D. M., Ehlers, A., Hackman, A., McManus, F., Fennell, M., Grey, N., & Wild, J. (2006). Cognitive therapy versus exposure and applied relaxation in social phobia: A randomized controlled trial. *Journal of Consulting and Clinical Psychology, 74*, 568–578.

Clark, D. M., Ehlers, A., McManus, F., Hackman, A., Fennell, M. J. V., Campbell, H., . . . Louis, B. (2003). Cognitive therapy versus fluoxetine in generalized social phobia: A randomized placebo-controlled trial. *Journal of Consulting and Clinical Psychology, 71*, 1058–1067.

Clark, D. M., Salkovski, P. M. N., Hackmann, A., Wells, A., Fennell, M., Ludgate, S., . . . Gelder, M. (1998). Two psychological treatments for hypochondriasis: A randomised controlled trial. *British Journal of Psychiatry, 173*, 218–225.

Clark, D. M., Salkovskis, P. M., Hackmann, A., Middleton, H., Anastasiades, P., & Gelder, M. (1994). A comparison of cognitive therapy, applied relaxation and imipramine in the treatment of panic disorder. *British Journal of Psychiatry, 164*(6), 759–769.

Clark, L. A. (1993). *Manual for the schedule of non-adaptive and adaptive personality.* Minneapolis, MN: University of Minnesota Press.

Clark, L. A. (1999). Introduction to the special section on the concept of disorder. *Journal of Abnormal Psychology, 108*, 371–373.

Clark, L. A. (2005). Temperament as a unifying basis for personality and psychopathology [Special issue]. *Journal of Abnormal Psychology, 114*, 505–521.

Clark, R. (2003). Parental history of hypertension and coping responses predict blood pressure changes in black college volunteers undergoing a speaking task about perceptions of racism. *Psychosomatic Medicine, 65*, 1012–1019.

Clarke, D. M., & Deb, S. (2012). Syndromes causing intellectual disability. In M. G. Gelder, N. C. Andreasen, J. J. Lopez, & J. R. Geddes (Eds.), *New Oxford textbook of psychiatry* (2nd ed., Vol. 2, pp. 1838–1848). New York, NY: Oxford University Press.

Clarkin, J. F., Carpenter, D., Hull, J., Wilner, P., & Glick, I. (1998). Effects of psychoeducational intervention for married patients with bipolar disorder and their spouses. *Psychiatric Service, 49*(4), 531–533.

Clarkin, J. F., Haas, G. L., & Glick, I. D. (1988). *Affective disorders in the family.* New York, NY: Guilford Press.

Clarkin, J. F., Howieson, D. B., & McClough, J. (2008). The role of psychiatric measures in assessment and treatment. In R. E. Hales, S. C. Yudofsky, & G. O. Gabbard (Eds.), *The American Psychiatric Publishing textbook of psychiatry* (5th ed., pp. 73–110). Arlington, VA: American Psychiatric Publishing, Inc.

Classen, C., Sephton, S. E., Diamond, S., & Spiegel, D. (1998). Studies of life-extending psychosocial interventions. In J. Holland (Ed.), *Psychooncology* (pp. 730–742). Oxford, UK: Oxford University Press.

Clayton, A. H., Croft, H. A., & Handiwala, L. (2014). Antidepressants and sexual dysfunction: Mechanisms and clinical implications. *Postgraduate Medicine, 126*(2), 91–99.

Cleckley, H. M. (1982). *The mask of sanity* (6th ed.). St. Louis, MO: Mosby. (Original work published 1941).

Cleghorn, J. M., & Albert, M. L. (1990). Modular disjunction in schizophrenia: A framework for a pathological psychophysiology. In A. Kales, C. N. Stefanis, & J. A. Talbot (Eds.), *Recent advances in schizophrenia* (pp. 59–80). New York, NY: Springer-Verlag.

Clement, U. (1990). Surveys of heterosexual behavior. *Annual Review of Sex Research, 1*, 45–74.

Clementz, B. A., & Sweeney, J. A. (1990). Is eye movement dysfunction a biological marker for schizophrenia? A methodological review. *Psychological Bulletin, 108*, 77–92.

Clifford, D. B., & Ances, B. M. (2013). HIV-associated neurocognitive disorder. *The Lancet Infectious Diseases, 13*(11), 976–986.

Cloninger, C. R. (1978). The link between hysteria and sociopathy: An integrative model of pathogenesis based on clinical, genetic, and neurophysiological observations. In H. S. Akiskal & W. L. Webb (Eds.), *Psychiatric diagnosis: Exploration of biological predictors* (pp. 189–218). New York, NY: Spectrum.

Cloninger, C. R. (1987). A systematic method for clinical description and classification of personality variants: A proposal. *Archives of General Psychiatry, 44*, 573–588.

Cloninger, C. R., & Svakic, D. M. (2009). Personality disorders. In B. J. Sadock, V. A. Sadock, & P. Ruiz (Eds.), *Kaplan & Sadock's comprehensive textbook of psychiatry* (9th ed., Vol. 2, pp. 2197–2240). Philadelphia, PA: Lippincott Williams & Wilkins.

Closser, M. H. (1992). Cocaine epidemiology. In T. R. Kosten & H. D. Kleber (Eds.), *Clinician's guide to cocaine addiction: Theory, research, and treatment* (pp. 225–240). New York, NY: Guilford Press.

Clyburn, L. D., Stones, M. J., Hadjistavropoulos, T., & Tuokko, H. (2000). Predicting caregiver burden and depression in Alzheimer's disease. *Journals of Gerontology Series B: Psychological Sciences and Social Sciences, 55*, 2–13.

Cobb, S. (1976). Social support as a moderator of life stress. *Psychosomatic Medicine, 38*, 300.

Cobham, V. E., Dadds, M. R., Spence, S. H., & McDermott, B. (2010). Parental anxiety in the treatment of childhood anxiety: A different story three years later. *Journal of Clinical Child* and Adolescent Psychology, 39(3), 410–420.

Coccaro, E. F. (2012). Intermittent explosive disorder as a disorder of impulsive aggression for DSM-5. American Journal of Psychiatry, 169(6), 577–588.

Coccaro, E., & McCloskey, M. (2010). Intermittent explosive disorder: Clinical aspects. In E. Aboujaoude & L. M. Koran (Eds.), Impulse control disorders (pp. 221–232). New York, NY: Cambridge University Press.

Cochran, S. D. (1984). Preventing medical non-compliance in the outpatient treatment of bipolar affective disorders. Journal of Consulting and Clinical Psychology, 52(5), 873–878.

Cochrane-Brink, K. A., Lofchy, J. S., & Sakinofsky, I. (2000). Clinical rating scales in suicide risk assessment. General Hospital Psychiatry, 22, 445–451.

Cocores, J. A., Miller, N. S., Pottash, A. C., & Gold, M. S. (1988). Sexual dysfunction in abusers of cocaine and alcohol. American Journal of Drug and Alcohol Abuse, 14, 169–173.

Coderre, T. J., Katz, J., Vaccarino, A. L., & Melzack, R. (1993). Contribution of central neuroplasticity to pathological pain: Review of clinical and experimental evidence. Pain, 52, 259–285.

Coe, C. L. (2010). Immunity in primates within a psychobiological perspective. In G. E. Demas & R. J. Nelson (Eds.), Ecoimmunology. New York, NY: Oxford University Press.

Cohen, C. I., Natarajan, N., Araujo, M., & Solanki, D. (2013). Prevalence of negative symptoms and associated factors in older adults with schizophrenia spectrum disorder. American Journal of Geriatric Psychiatry, 21(2), 100–107.

Cohen, D., & Pressman, S. D. (2006). Positive affect and health. Current Directions in Psychological Science, 15, 122–125.

Cohen, J. (2002). Confronting the limits of success. Science, 296, 2320–2324.

Cohen, J. (2006). The overlooked epidemic. Science Magazine, 313, 468–469.

Cohen, J. (2011). AIDS research: Complexity surrounds HIV prevention advances. Science, 333(6041), 393.

Cohen, J. B., & Reed, D. (1985). Type A behavior and coronary heart disease among Japanese men in Hawaii. Journal of Behavioral Medicine, 8, 343–352.

Cohen, J. S., Edmunds, J. M., Brodman, D. M., Benjamin, C. L., & Kendall, P. C. (2012). Using self-monitoring: Implementation of collaborative empiricism in cognitive-behavioral therapy. Cognitive and Behavioral Practice, 20(4), 419–428. https://doi.org/10.1016/j.cbpra.2012.06.002

Cohen, S. (1996). Psychological stress, immunity, and upper respiratory infections. Current Directions in Psychological Science, 5, 86–90.

Cohen, S., Doyle, W. J., & Skoner, D. P. (1999). Psychological stress, cytokine production, and severity of upper respiratory illness. Psychosomatic Medicine, 61, 175–180.

Cohen, S., Doyle, W. J., Skoner, D. P., Fireman, P., Gwaltney, J. M., Jr., & Newsome, J. T. (1995). State and trait negative affect as predictors of objective and subjective symptoms of respiratory viral infections. Journal of Personality and Social Psychology, 68, 159–169.

Cohen, S., Doyle, W. J., Skoner, D. P., Rabin, B. S., & Gwaltney, J. M. (1997). Social ties and susceptibility to the common cold. Journal of the American Medical Association, 277, 1940–1944.

Cohen, S., Doyle, W. J., Turner, R., Alper, C. M., & Skoner, D. P. (2003). Sociability and susceptibility to the common cold. Psychological Science, 14(5), 389–395.

Cohen, S., & Herbert, T. B. (1996). Health psychology: Psychological factors and physical disease from the perspective of human psychoneuroimmunology. Annual Review of Psychology, 47, 113–142.

Cohen, S., & Janicki-Deverts, D. (2009). Can we improve our physical health by altering our social networks? Perspectives on Psychological Science, 4, 375–378.

Cohen-Kettenis, P. T., & Pfäfflin, F. (2010). The DSM diagnostic criteria for gender identity disorder in adolescents and adults. Archives of Sexual Behavior, 39, 499–513.

Coker, L. H., Espeland, M. A., Rapp, S. R., Legault, C., Resnick, S. M., Hogan, P., . . . Shumaker, S. A. (2010). Postmenopausal hormone therapy and cognitive outcomes: The Women's Health Initiative Memory Study (WHIMS). Journal of Steroid Biochemistry and Molecular Biology, 118(4–5), 304–310.

Colapinto, J. (2001). As nature made him: The boy who was raised as girl. New York, NY: HarperCollins.

Cole, J. D., & Kazarian, S. S. (1988). The Level of expressed emotion scale: A new measure of expressed emotion. Journal of Clinical Psychology, 44, 392–397.

Cole, J. T., Mitala, C. M., Kundu, S., Verma, A., Elkind, J. A., Nissim, I., & Cohen, A. S. (2010). Dietary branched chain amino acids ameliorate injury-induced cognitive impairment. Proceedings of the National Academy of Sciences, 107, 366–371.

Cole, M. G. (2004). Delirium in elderly patients. American Journal of Geriatric Psychiatry, 12, 7–21.

Cole, M. G., Ciampi, A., Belzile, E., & Zhong, L. (2009). Persistent delirium in older hospital patients: A systematic review of frequency and prognosis. Age and Ageing, 38(1), 19–26.

Cole, M. G., & McCusker, J. (2002). Treatment of delirium in older medical inpatients: A challenge for geriatric specialists [Letter to the Editor]. Journal of the American Geriatrics Society, 50, 2101–2103.

Cole, S. W. (2008). Psychosocial influences on HIV-1 disease progression: Neural, endocrine, and virologic mechanisms. Psychosomatic Medicine, 70, 562–568.

Cole, S. W. (2011). Socio-environmental effects on gene expression. In K. S. Kendler, S. Jaffee, & D. Romer (Eds.), The dynamic genome and mental health: The role of genes and environments in youth development (pp. 195–228). New York, NY: Oxford University Press.

Coleman, E., & Bockting, W. O., & Gooren, L. (1993). Homosexual and bisexual identity in sex-reassigned female-to-male transsexuals. Archives of Sexual Behavior, 22, 37–50.

Coleman, E., Colgan, P., & Gooren, L. (1992). Male cross-gender behavior in Myanmar (Burma): A description of

the acault. Archives of Sexual Behavior, 21(3), 313–321.

Coleman, H., Charles, G., & Collins, J. (2001). Inhalant use by Canadian aboriginal youth. Journal of Child & Adolescent Substance Abuse, 10(3), 1–20.

Collinge, J. (2012). Prion disease. In M. G. Gelder, N. C. Andreasen, J. J. Lopez, & J. R. Geddes (Eds.), New Oxford textbook of psychiatry (2nd ed., Vol. 1, pp. 351–361). New York, NY: Oxford University Press.

Collinge, J., Whitfield, J., McKintosh, E., Beck, J., Mead, S., Thomas, D. J., & Alpers, M. P. (2006). Kuru in the 21st century: An acquired human prion disease with very long incubation periods. Lancet, 367(9528), 2068–2074.

Collinge, J., Whitfield, J., McKintosh, E., Frosh, A., Mead, S., Hill, A. F., . . . & Alpers, M. P. (2008). A clinical study of kuru patients with long incubation periods at the end of the epidemic in Papua New Guinea. Philosophical Transactions of the Royal Society of London B: Biological Sciences, 363(1510), 3725–3739.

Collins, A. (1988). In the sleeproom: The story of the CIA brainwashing experiments in Canada. Toronto, ON: Lester and Orpen Dennys Limited.

Colloca, L., Lopiano, L., Lanotte, M., & Benedetti, F. (2004). Overt versus covert treatment for pain, anxiety, and Parkinson's disease. Lancet Neurology, 3(11), 679–684.

Colman, I., Murray, J., Abbott, R., Maughan, B., Kuh, D., Croudace, T., & Jones, P. B. (2009). Outcomes of conduct problems in adolescence: 40 year follow-up of national cohort. British Medical Journal, 338, a2981.

Colp, R. (2009). History of psychiatry. In B. J. Sadock, V. A. Sadock, & P. Ruiz (Eds.), Kaplan & Sadock's comprehensive textbook of psychiatry (9th ed., Vol. 2, pp. 4474–4509). Philadelphia, PA: Lippincott Williams & Wilkins.

Comas-Diaz, L. (1981). Puerto Rican espiritismo and psychotherapy. American Journal of Orthopsychiatry, 51(4), 636–645.

Comer, J. S., Blanco, C., Hasin, D. S., Liu, S. M., Grant, B. F., Turner, J. B., & Olfson, M. (2011). Health-related quality of life across the anxiety disorders: Results from the national epidemiologic survey on alcohol and related conditions (NESARC). Journal of Clinical Psychiatry, 72, 43–50.

Comer, J. S., Mojtabai, R., & Olfson, M. (2011). National trends in the antipsychotic treatment of psychiatric outpatients with anxiety disorders. American Journal of Psychiatry, 168, 1057–1065.

Compare, A., Bigi, R., Orrego, P. S., Proietti, R., Grossi, E., & Steptoe, A. (2013). Type d personality is associated with the development of stress cardiomyopathy following emotional triggers. Annals of Behavioral Medicine, 45(3), 299–307.

Compas, B. E., Boyer, M., Stanger, C., Colletti, R., & Thomsen, A. (2006). Latent variable analysis of coping, anxiety/depression, and somatic symptoms in adolescents with chronic pain. Journal of Consulting and Clinical Psychology, 74, 1132–1142.

Compas, B. E., Oppedisano, G., Connor, J. K., Gerhardt, C. A., Hinden, B. R., Achenbach, T. M., & Hammen, C. (1997). Gender differences in

depressive symptoms in adolescence: Comparison of national samples of clinically referred and nonreferred youths. Journal of Consulting and Clinical Psychology, 65, 617–626.

Compton, S. N., Peris T. S., Almirall, D., Birmaher, B., Sherrill, J., Kendall, P. C., . . . Albano, A. M. (2014). Predictors and moderators of treatment response in childhood anxiety disorders: Results from the CAMS trial. Journal of Consultative Clinical Psychology, 82(2), 212–224.

Compton, W. M., Cottler, L. B., Jacobs, J. L., Ben-Abdallah, A., & Spitznagel, E. L. (2003). The role of psychiatric disorders in predicting drug dependence treatment outcomes. American Journal of Psychiatry, 160, 890–895.

Condelli, W. S., Fairbank, J. A., Dennis, M. L., & Rachal, J. V. (1991). Cocaine use by clients in methadone programs: Significance, scope, and behavioral interventions. Journal of Substance Abuse Treatment, 8, 203–212.

Condon, W., Ogston, W., & Pacoe, L. (1969). Three faces of Eve revisited: A study of transient microstrabismus. Journal of Abnormal Psychology, 74, 618–620.

Conduct Problems Prevention Research Group. (2010). The effects of a multiyear universal social-emotional learning program: The role of student and school characteristics. Journal of Consulting and Clinical Psychology, 78(2), 156–168.

Conn, D. K., & Lieff, S. (2001). Diagnosing and managing delirium in the elderly. Canadian Family Physician, 47, 101–108.

Conners, C. K., March, J. S., Frances, A., Wells, K. C., & Ross, R. (2001). Treatment of attention-deficit/hyperactivity disorder: Expert consensus guidelines. Journal of Attention Disorders, 4(Suppl. 1). https://doi.org/10.1177/108705470000401s02

Connor, D. F. (2015). Stimulant and nonstimulant medications for childhood ADHD. In R. A. Barkley (Ed.), Attention-deficit hyperactivity disorder: A handbook for diagnosis & treatment (4th ed., pp. 666–685). New York: Guilford Press.

Conrod, P. J., & Stewart, S. H. (2005). A critical look at dual-focused cognitive-behavioural treatment for comorbid substance abuse and psychiatric disorders: Strengths, limitations and future directions. Journal of Cognitive Psychotherapy, 19, 265–289.

Conrod, P. J., Peterson, J. B., Pihl, R. O., & Mankowski, S. (1997). Biphasic effects of alcohol on heart rate are influenced by alcoholic family history and rate of alcohol ingestion. Alcoholism: Clinical & Experimental Research, 21, 140–149.

Conrod, P. J., Pihl, R. O., Stewart, S. H., & Dongier, M. (2000). Validation of a system of classifying female substance abusers on the basis of personality and motivational risk factors for substance abuse. Psychology of Addictive Behaviors, 14, 243–256.

Conrod, P. J., Stewart, S. H., Pihl, R. O., Côté, S., Fontaine, V., & Dongier, M. (2000). Efficacy of brief coping skills interventions that match different personality profiles of female substance abusers. Psychology of Addictive Behaviors, 14, 231–242.

Constantino, J., Abbacchi, A., Lavesser, P., Reed, H., Givens, L., Chiang, L., . . . Todd, R. D. (2009). Developmental course of autistic social impairment in males. *Development and psychopathology, 21*(1), 127–138.

Conti, C. R., Pepine, C. J., & Sweeney, M. (1999). Efficacy and safety of sildenafil citrate in the treatment of erectile dysfunction in patients with ischemic heart disease. *American Journal of Cardiology, 83*, 29C–34C.

Conwell, Y., Duberstein, P. R., & Caine, E. D. (2002). Risk factors for suicide in later life. *Biological Psychiatry, 52*, 193–204.

Conwell, Y., Duberstein, P. R., Cox, C., Hermmann, J. H., Forbes, N. T., & Caine, E. D. (1996). Relationships of age and axis I diagnoses in victims of completed suicide: A psychological autopsy study. *American Journal of Psychiatry, 153*, 1001–1008.

Cook, E. H., Jr. (2001). Genetics of autism. *Child and Adolescent Psychiatric Clinics of North America, 10*(2), 333–350.

Cook, E. W., Hodes, R. L., & Lang, P. J. (1986). Preparedness and phobia: Effects of stimulus content on human visceral conditioning. *Journal of Abnormal Psychology, 95*(3), 195–207. https://doi.org/10.1037/0021-843X.95.3.195

Cook, W. L., Strachan, A. M., Goldstein, M. J., & Miklowitz, D. J. (1989). Expressed emotion and reciprocal affective relationships in families of disturbed adolescents. *Family Process, 28*, 337–348.

Coolidge, F. L., Marle, P. D., Rhoades, C. S., Monaghan, P., & Segal, D. L. (2013). Psychometric properties of a new measure to assess autism spectrum disorder in DSM-5. *American Journal of Orthopsychiatry, 83*(1), 126.

Coolidge, F., Thede, L., & Young, S. (2002). The heritability of gender identity disorder in a child and adolescent twin sample. *Behavior Genetics, 32*, 251–257.

Coon, P. M. (1986). Treatment progress in 20 patients with multiple personality disorder. *Journal of Nervous and Mental Disease, 174*, 715–721.

Coons, P. M. (1991) Iatrogenesis and malingering of multiple personality disorder in the forensic evaluation of homicide defendants. *Psychiatric Clinics of North America, 14*(3), 757–768.

Coons, P. M. (1994). Confirmation of childhood abuse in child and adolescent cases of multiple personality disorder not otherwise specified. *Journal of Nervous & Mental Disease, 182*, 461–464.

Coons, P. M., Bowman, E. S., Kluft, R. P., & Milstein, V. (1991). The cross-cultural occurrence of NPD: Additional cases from a recent survey. *Dissociation, 4*, 124–128.

Coons, W. H. (1957). Interaction and insight in group psychotherapy. *Canadian Journal of Psychology, 11*, 1–8.

Coons, W. H. (1967). The dynamics of change in psychotherapy. *Canadian Psychiatric Association Journal, 12*, 239–245.

Coons, W. H., & Peacock, E. P. (1970). Interpersonal interaction and personality change in group psychotherapy. *Canadian Psychiatric Association Journal, 15*, 347–355.

Cooper, A. J. (1988). Sexual dysfunction and cardiovascular disease. *Stress Medicine, 4*, 273–281.

Cooper, A. M., & Ronningstam, E. (1992). Narcissistic personality disorder.

In A. Tasman & M. B. Riba (Eds.), *Review of psychiatry* (Vol. 11, pp. 80–97). Washington, DC: Psychiatric Press.

Cooper, J., Kapur, N., Webb, R., Lawlor, M., Guthrie, E., Mackway-Jones, K., & Appleby, L. (2005). Suicide after deliberate self-harm: A 4-year cohort study. *American Journal of Psychiatry, 162*, 297–303.

Cooper, M., Corrado, R., Karlberg, A. M., & Adams, L. P. (1992). Aboriginal suicide in British Columbia: An overview. *Canada's Mental Health, 40*(3), 19–23.

Cooper, M. L., Russell, M., & George, W. H. (1988). Coping, expectancies, and alcohol abuse: A test of social learning formulations. *Journal of Abnormal Psychology, 97*, 218–230.

Cooper, N. S., Feder, A., Southwick, S. M., & Charney, D. S. (2007). Resilience and vulnerability to trauma: Psychobiological mechanisms. In D. Romer & E. F. Walker (Eds.), *Adolescent psychopathology and the developing brain: Integrating brain and prevention science* (pp. 347–372). New York, NY: Oxford University Press.

Cooper, S. A., & Smiley, E. (2012). Prevalence of intellectual disabilities and epidemiology of mental ill-health in adults with intellectual disabilities. In M. G. Gelder, N. C. Andreasen, J. J. Lopez-Ibor, & J. R. Geddes (Eds.), *New Oxford textbook of psychiatry* (2nd ed., Vol. 2, pp. 1825–1829). New York, NY: Oxford University Press.

Cooperstock, R., & Hill, J. (1982). *The effects of tranquillization: Benzodiazepine use in Canada.* Ottawa, ON: Health Canada.

Cope, N., Eicher, J. D., Meng, H., Gibson, C. J., Hager, K., Lacadie, C., & Gruen, J. R. (2012). Variants in the DYX2 locus are associated with altered brain activation in reading-related brain regions in subjects with reading disability. *NeuroImage, 63*(1), 148–156.

Copeland, W. E., Shanahan, L., Egger, H., Angold, A., & Costello, E. J. (2014). Adult diagnostic and functional outcomes of DSM-5 disruptive mood dysregulation disorder. American *Journal of Psychiatry, 171*, 668–674.

Coplan, J. D., Trost, R. C., Owens, M. J., Cooper, T. B., Gorman, J. M., Nemeroff, C. B., & Rosenblum, L. A. (1998). Cerebrospinal fluid concentrations of somatostatin and biogenic amines in grown primates reared by mothers exposed to manipulated foraging conditions. *Archives of General Psychiatry, 55*, 473–477.

Coren, S. (1996). *Sleep thieves: An eye-opening exploration into the science and mysteries of sleep.* New York, NY: Free Press.

Corkum, P., Tannock, R., & Moldofsky, H. (1998). Sleep disturbances in children with attention-deficit/hyperactivity disorder. *Journal of the American Academy of Child & Adolescent Psychiatry, 37*, 637–646.

Correll, C. U., Hauser, M., Auther, A. M., & Cornblatt, B. A. (2010). Research in people with psychosis risk syndrome: A review of the current evidence and future directions. *Journal of Child Psychology and Psychiatry, 51*(4), 390–431. https://doi.org/10.1111/j.1469-7610.2010.02235.x

Corrigan, P. W., Druss, B. G., & Perlick, D. A. (2014). The impact of mental

illness stigma on seeking and participating in mental health care. *Psychological Science in the Public Interest, 15*(2), 37–70. https://doi.org/10.1177/1529100614531398

Corrigan, P. W., Wallace, C. J., Schade, M. L., & Green, M. F. (1994). Learning medication self-management skills in schizophrenia: Relationships with cognitive deficits and psychiatric symptoms. *Behavior Therapy, 25*, 5–15.

Cortoni, F., & Gannon, T. A. (2016). Female Sexual Offenders: An Overview. In *Sexual offending* (pp. 213–224). Springer New York.

Cory Monteith's overdose detailed in coroner's report. (2013, October 2). *CBC News*. https://www.cbc.ca/news/canada/british-columbia/cory-monteith-s-overdose-detailed-in-coroner-s-report-1.1876597

Coryell, W., Endicott, J., & Keller, M. (1992). Rapid cycling affective disorder: Demographics, diagnosis, family history, and course. *Archives of General Psychiatry, 49*, 126–131.

Coryell, W., Endicott, J., Maser, J. D., Keller, M. B., Leon, A. C., & Akiskal, H. S. (1995). Long-term stability of polarity distinctions in the affective disorders. *American Journal of Psychiatry, 152*, 385–390.

Coryell, W., Solomon, D., Turvey, C., Keller, M., Leon, A. C., Endicott, J., . . . Mueller, T. (2003). The long-term course of rapid-cycling bipolar disorder. *Archives of General Psychiatry, 60*, 914–920.

Costa, E. (1985). Benzodiazepine-GABA interactions: A model to investigate the neurobiology of anxiety. In A. H. Tuma & J. D. Maser (Eds.), *Anxiety and the anxiety disorders.* Hillsdale, NJ: Erlbaum.

Costa Jr, P. T., & McCrae, R. R. (2013). The five-factor model of personality and its relevance to personality disorders. *Personality and Personality Disorders: The Science of Mental Health, 7*, 17.

Costa e Silva, J. A., & de Girolamo, G. (1990). Neurasthenia: History of a concept. In N. Sartorius, D. Goldberg, G. de Girolamo, J. A. Costa e Silva, et al. (Eds.), *Psychological disorders in general medical settings* (pp. 699–781). Toronto, ON: Hogrefe and Huber.

Costantino, A., Cerpolini, S., Alvisi, S., Morselli, P. G., Venturoli, S., & Meriggiola, M. C. (2013). A prospective study on sexual function and mood in female-to-male transsexuals during testosterone administration and after sex reassignment surgery. *Journal of Sex & Marital Therapy, 39*(4), 321–335.

Côté, G., O'Leary, T., Barlow, D. H., Strain, J. J., Salkovskis, P. M., Warwick, H. M. C., . . . Rasmussen, S. A. (1996). Hypochondriasis. In T. A. Widiger, A. J. Frances, H. A. Pincus, R. Ross, et al. (Eds.), *DSM-IV sourcebook* (Vol. 2, pp. 933–947). Washington, DC: American Psychiatric Association.

Côté, J. K., & Pepler, C. (2002). A randomized trial of a cognitive coping intervention for acutely ill HIV-positive men. *Nursing Research, 51*, 237–244.

Cottone, P., Sabino, V., Roberto, M., Bajo, M., Pockros, L., Frihauf, J. B., & Zorrilla, E. P. (2009). CRF system recruitment mediates dark side of compulsive eating. *PNAS: Proceedings of the National Academy of Sciences of the United States of America, 106*, 20016–20020.

Courchesne, E. (1991). Neuroanatomic imaging in autism. *Pediatrics, 87*, 781–790.

Courchesne, E., Hesselink, J. R., Jernigan, T. L., & Yeung-Courchesne, R. (1987). Abnormal neuroanatomy in a nonretarded person with autism: Unusual findings with magnetic resonance imaging. *Archives of Neurology, 44*, 335–341.

Courneya, K. S., Friedenreich, C. M., Sela, R. A., Quinney, H. A., Rhodes, R. E., & Handman, M. (2003). The group psychotherapy and home-based physical exercise (group-hope) trial in cancer survivors: Physical fitness and quality of life outcomes. *Psycho-oncology, 12*, 357–374.

Couturier, J. L., & Lock, J. (2006). Denial and minimization in adolescents with anorexia nervosa. *International Journal of Eating Disorders, 39*, 212–216.

Covin, R., Ouimet, A. J., Seeds, P. M., & Dozois, D. J. A. (2008). A meta-analysis of CBT for pathological worry among clients with GAD. *Journal of Anxiety Disorders, 22*(1), 108–116. http://doi.org/10.1016/j.janxdis.2007.01.002

Cox, A. C., Weed, N. C., & Butcher, J. N. (2009). The MMPI-2: History, interpretation, and clinical issues. In J. N. Butcher (Ed.), *Oxford handbook of personality assessment* (pp. 250–276). New York, NY: Oxford University Press.

Cox, A., Rutter, M., Newman, S., & Bartak, L. (1975). A comparative study of infantile autism and specific developmental receptive language disorder: II. Parental characteristics. *British Journal of Psychiatry, 126*, 146–159.

Cox, B. J., Norton, G. R., Swinson, R. P., & Endler, N. S. (1990). Substance abuse and panic related anxiety: A critical review. *Behaviour Research and Therapy, 28*, 385–393.

Cox, B. J., Swinson, R. P., Shulman, I. D., Kuch, K., & Reichman, J. T. (1993). Gender effects in alcohol use in panic disorder with agoraphobia. *Behaviour Research & Therapy, 31*, 413–416.

Craddock, N., & Jones, I. (2001). Molecular genetics of bipolar disorder. *British Journal of Psychiatry, 41*, 128–133.

Crafti, N. A. (2002). Integrating cognitive-behavioural and interpersonal approaches in a group program for the eating disorders: Measuring effectiveness in a naturalistic setting. *Behaviour Change, 19*, 22–38.

Crago, M., Shisslak, C. M., & Estes, L. S. (1997). Eating disturbances among American minority groups: A review. *The International Journal of Eating Disorders, 19*, 239–248.

Craig, M. C., & Murphy, D. G. M. (2009). Alzheimer's disease in women. *Best Practice & Research Clinical Obstetrics & Gynaecology, 23*(1), 53–61.

Craighead, L. W., & Agras, W. S. (1991). Mechanisms of action in cognitive-behavioral and pharmacological interventions for obesity and bulimia nervosa. *Journal of Consulting and Clinical Psychology, 59*, 115–125.

Craske, M. G. (1999). *Anxiety disorders: Psychological approaches to theory and treatment.* Boulder, CO: Westview Press.

Craske, M. G., Antony, M. M., & Barlow, D. H. (2006). *Mastering your fears and phobias: Therapist guide.* New York, NY: Oxford University Press.

Craske, M. G., & Barlow, D. H. (1988). A review of the relationship between panic and avoidance. *Clinical Psychology Review, 8,* 667–685.

Craske, M. G., & Barlow, D. H. (2001). Panic disorder and agoraphobia. In D. H. Barlow (Ed.), *Clinical handbook of psychological disorders* (3rd ed.). New York, NY: Guilford Press.

Craske, M. G., & Barlow, D. H. (2006). *Mastery of your anxiety and worry.* New York, NY: Oxford University Press.

Craske, M. G., & Barlow, D. H. (2014). Panic disorder and agoraphobia. In D. H. Barlow (Ed.), *Clinical handbook of psychological disorders: A step-by-step treatment manual* (5th ed., pp. 1–61). New York, NY: Guilford Press.

Craske, M. G., Barlow, D. H., Clark, D. M., Curtis, G. C., Hill, E. M., Himle, J. A., . . . Warwick, H. M. C. (1996). Specific (simple) phobia. In T. A. Widiger, A. J. Frances, H. A. Pincus, R. Ross, et al. (Eds.), *DSM-IV sourcebook* (Vol. 2, pp. 473–506). Washington, DC: American Psychiatric Association.

Craske, M. G., Barlow, D. H., & O'Leary, T. A. (1992). *Mastery of your anxiety and worry.* Albany, NY: Graywind Publications.

Craske, M. G., Brown, T. A., & Barlow, D. H. (1991). Behavioral treatment of panic disorder: A two-year follow-up. *Behavior Therapy, 22,* 289–304.

Craske, M. G., Golinelli, D., Stein, M. B., Roy-Byrne, P., Bystritsky, A., Sherbourne, C. (2005). Does the addition of cognitive behavioral therapy improve panic disorder treatment outcome relative to medication alone in the primary-care setting? *Psychological Medicine, 35*(11), 1645–1654. doi:10.1017/S003329170500557X

Craske, M. G., Hermans, D., & Vansteenwegen, D. (2006). *Fear and learning.* Washington, DC: American Psychological Association.

Craske, M. G., Kircanski, K., Epstein, A., Wittchen, H. U., Pine, D. S., Lewis-Fernández, R., & Hinton, D. (2010). Panic disorder: A review of DSM-IV panic disorder and proposals for DSM-V. *Depression and Anxiety, 27*(2), 93–112.

Craske, M. G., Lang, A. J., Mystkowski, J. L., Zucker, B. G., & Bystritsky, A. (2002). Does nocturnal panic represent a more severe form of panic disorder? *Journal of Nervous and Mental Disease, 190,* 611–618.

Craske, M. G., Rauch, S. L., Ursano, R., Prenoveau, J., Pine, D. S., & Zinbarg, R. E. (2009). What is an anxiety disorder? *Depression and Anxiety, 26,* 1066–1085.

Craske, M. G., & Rowe, M. K. (1997). Nocturnal panic. *Clinical Psychology: Science & Practice, 4,* 153–174.

Craske, M. G., Stein, M. B., Sullivan, G., Sherbourne, C., Bystritsky, A., Rose, R. D., & Roy-Byrne, P. (2011). Disorder-specific impact of coordinated anxiety learning and management treatment for anxiety disorders in primary care. *Archives of General Psychiatry, 68,* 378–388.

Crasson, M., Kjiri, S., Colin, A., Kjiri, K., L'Hermite-Baleriaux, M., Ansseau, M., & Legros, J. J. (2004). Serum melatonin and urinary 6-sulfatoxymelatonin in major depression. *Psychoneuroendocrinology, 29,* 1–12.

Crawford, M., & Gartner, R. (1992). *Woman killing: Intimate femicide in Ontario,*

1974–1990. Toronto, ON: Women We Honour Action Committee.

Creed, F. H. (2012). Somatization and health anxiety as predictors of health care use. *Psychosomatic Medicine, 74*(6), 656–664.

Creed, F., & Barsky, A. (2004). A systematic review of the epidemiology of somatisation disorder and hypochondriasis. *Journal of Psychosomatic Research, 56,* 391–408.

Creese, I., Burt, D. R., & Snyder, S. H. (1976). Dopamine receptor binding predicts clinical and pharmacological potencies of antischizophrenic drugs. *Science, 192,* 481–483.

Cremniter, D., Jamin, S., Kollenbach, K., Alvarez, J. C., Lecruibier, Y., Gilton, A., . . . Spreux-Varoquaux, O. (1999). CSF 5–HIAA levels are lower in impulsive as compared to nonimpulsive violent suicide attempts and control subjects. *Biological Psychiatry, 45*(12), 1572–1579.

Crerand, C., Sarwer, D., Magee, L., Gibbons, L., Lowe, M., Bartlett, S., . . . Whitaker, L. A. (2004). Rate of body dysmorphic disorder among patients seeking facial plastic surgery. *Psychiatric Annals, 34,* 958–965.

Crichton, P., & Morey, S. (2003). Treating pain in cancer patients. In D. C. Turk & R. J. Gatchel (Eds.), *Psychological approaches to pain management: A practitioner's handbook* (2nd ed., pp. 501–514). New York, NY: Guilford Press.

Crisp, A. H., Callender, J. S., Halek, C., & Hsu, L. K. G. (1992). Long-term mortality in anorexia nervosa: A 20-year follow-up of the St. George's and Aberdeen cohorts. *British Journal of Psychiatry, 161,* 104–107.

Cristancho, M. A., Kocsis, J. H., & Thase, M. E. (2012). Dysthymic disorder and other chronic depressions. *FOCUS, 10,* 422–427.

Crockford, D. N., & el-Guebaly, N. (1998). Psychiatric comorbidity in pathological gambling: A critical review. *Canadian Journal of Psychiatry, 43,* 43–50.

Croen, L. A., Najjar, D. V., Fireman, B., & Grether, J. K. (2007). Maternal and paternal age and risk of autism spectrum disorders. *Archives of Pediatrics & Adolescent Medicine, 161*(4), 334.

Cross-National Collaborative Group. (1992). The changing rate of major depression. Cross-national comparisons. *JAMA, 268*(21), 3098–3105.

Cross-National Collaborative Panic Study, Second Phase Investigators. (1992). Drug treatment of panic disorder. Comparative efficacy of alprazolam, imipramine, and placebo. *British Journal of Psychiatry, 160,* 191–202.

Crouse, K. (2013, January 3). A fun-loving, carefree, spirit becomes the face of anxiety. *New York Times.* Retrieved from http://www.nytimes.com/2013/01/04/ sports/golf/charlie-beljan-lives-a-life -of-high-anxiety-and-low-golf-scores .html?pagewanted=all

Crow, S. J., Mitchell, J. E., Roerig, J. D., & Steffen, K. (2009). What potential role is there for medication treatment in anorexia nervosa? *International Journal of Eating Disorders, 42*(1), 1–8.

Crow, S. J., Thuras, P., Keel, P. K., & Mitchell, J. E. (2002). Long-term menstrual and reproductive function in patients with bulimia nervosa. *American Journal of Psychiatry, 159,* 1048–1050.

Crowe, R. R. (1974). An adoption study of antisocial personality. *Archives of General Psychiatry, 31,* 785–791.

Crowley, P. H., Hayden, T. L., & Gulati, D. K. (1982). Etiology of Down syndrome. In S. M. Pueschel & J. E. Rynders (Eds.), *Down syndrome: Advances in biomedicine and behavioral sciences* (pp. 89–131). Cambridge, MA: Ware Press.

Crowley, T., Richardson, D., & Goldmeir, D. (2006). Recommendation for the management of vaginismus: BASHH special interest group for sexual dysfunction. *International Journal of STD and AIDS, 17,* 14–18.

Crump, C., Winkleby, M. A., Sundquist, K., & Sundquist, J. (2013). Comorbidities and mortality in persons with schizophrenia: A Swedish national cohort study. *American Journal of Psychiatry, 170*(3), 324–333.

Csordas, T. J. (2015). Cultural phenomenology and psychiatric illness. In L. J. Kirmayer, R. Lemelson, & C. A. Cummings (Eds.), *Re-visioning psychiatry: Cultural phenomenology, critical neuroscience, and global mental health* (pp. 117–140). New York, NY: Cambridge University Press.

Cuffee, Y., Ogedegbe, C., Williams, N. J., Ogedegbe, G., & Schoenthaler, A. (2014). Psychosocial risk factors for hypertension: An update of the literature. *Current Hypertension Reports, 16*(10), 1–11.

Cuijpers, P. (2015). Psychotherapies for adult depression: Recent developments. *Current Opinion in Psychiatry, 28,* 24–29.

Cuijpers, P., Geraedts, A. S., van Oppen, P., Andersson, G., Markowitz, J. C., & van Straten, A. (2011). Interpersonal psychotherapy for depression: A meta-analysis. *American Journal of Psychiatry, 168*(6), 581–592.

Cuijpers, P., Sijbrandi, M., Koole, S., Huibers, M.., Berking, M., & Andersson, G. (2014). Psychological treatment of generalized anxiety disorder: A meta-analysis. *Clinical Psychology Review, 34,* 130–140.

Culos-Reed, S. N., Carlson, L. E., Daroux, L. M., & Hately-Aldous, S. (2006). A pilot study of yoga for breast cancer survivors: Physical and psychological benefits. *Psychooncology, 15*(10), 891–897.

Cunningham Owens, D. G., & Johnstone, E. C. (2012). Treatment and management of schizophrenia. In M. G. Gelder, N. C., Andreasen, J. J. López-Ibor, & Geddes, J. R. (Eds.), *New Oxford textbook of psychiatry* (2nd ed., Vol. 1, pp. 578–595). New York, NY: Oxford University Press.

Cunningham, J., Yonkers, K. A., O'Brien, S., & Eriksson, E. (2009). Update on research and treatment of premenstrual dysphoric disorder. *Harvard Review of Psychiatry, 17*(2), 120–137.

CUPE. (2005, November 17). Ontario tribunal rules on sex reassignment surgery. *CUPE News.* Retrieved July 1, 2007, from http://www.cupe.ca/www/ news/stonehouse_tribunal

Curatolo, P., Bombardieri, R., & Jozwiak, S. (2008). Tuberous sclerosis. *The Lancet, 372*(9639), 657–668.

Currier, J. M., Neimeyer, R. A., & Berman, J. S. (2008). The effectiveness of psychotherapeutic interventions for bereaved persons: A comprehensive quantitative review. *Psychological Bulletin, 134*(5), 648–661.

Curtis, G. C., Hill, E. M., & Lewis, J. A. (1990). *Heterogeneity of DSM-III-R simple phobia and the simple phobia/ agoraphobia boundary: Evidence from the ECA study.* Preliminary report to the Simple Phobia subcommittee of the DSM-IV Anxiety Disorders Work Group.

Cuthbert, B. N. (2014). The RDoC framework: Facilitating transition from ICD/ DSM to dimensional approaches that integrate neuroscience and psychopathology. *World Psychiatry, 13*(1), 28–35.

Cutrona, C. E. (1984). Social support and stress in the transition to parenthood. *Journal of Abnormal Psychology, 93*(4), 378–390.

Cutting, J. (1985). *The psychology of schizophrenia.* New York, NY: Churchill Livingstone.

Cyranowski, J. M., Aarestad, S. L., & Andersen, B. L. (1999). The role of sexual self-schema in a diathesis-stress model of sexual dysfunction. *Applied & Preventative Psychology, 8,* 217–228.

Cyranowski, J. M., Frank, E., Young, E., & Shear, M. K. (2000). Adolescent onset of the gender difference in lifetime rates of major depression. *Archives of General Psychiatry, 57,* 21–27.

Czeisler, C. A., & Allan, J. S. (1989). Pathologies of the sleep-wake schedule. In R. L. Williams, I. Karacan, & C. A. Morre (Eds.), *Sleep disorders: Diagnosis and treatment* (pp. 109–129). New York, NY: John Wiley & Sons.

D'Hulst, C., Atack, J. R., & Kooy, R. F. (2009). The complexity of the GABAA receptor shapes unique pharmacological profiles. *Drug Discovery Today, 14* (17–18), 866–875.

D'Onofrio, B. M., Rickert, M. E., Langström, N., Donahue, K. L., Coyne, C. A., Larsson, H., & Rathouz, P. J. (2012). Familial confounding of the association between maternal smoking during pregnancy and offspring substance use and problems. *JAMA Psychiatry, 69*(11), 1140–1150.

D'Onofrio, B. M., Turkheimer, E., Emery, R. E., Slutske, W. S., Heath, A. C., Madden, P. A., & Martin, N. G. (2006). A genetically informed study of the processes underlying the association between parental marital instability and offspring adjustment. *Developmental Psychology, 42,* 486–499.

Daamen, A. P., Penning, R., Brunt, T., & Verster, J. C. (2012). Cocaine. In J. C. Verster, K. Brady, M. Galanter, & P. Conrod (Eds.), *Drug abuse and addiction in medical illness* (pp. 163–173). New York, NY: Springer.

Dadds, M. R., Sanders, M. R., Morrison, M., & Rebgetz, M. (1992). Childhood depression and conduct disorder: II. An analysis of family interaction patterns in the home. *Journal of Abnormal Psychology, 101*(3), 505–513.

Dahl, A. A. (1993, Spring). The personality disorders: A critical review of family, twin, and adoption studies. *Journal of Personality Disorders* (Supplement), 86–99.

Daigle, M. S., Labelle, R., & Côté, G. (2006). Further evidence of the validity of the suicide risk assessment scale for prisoners. *International Journal of Law and Psychiatry, 29,* 343–354.

Dailey, R. C. (1968). The role of alcohol among North American Indian Tribes as reported in the Jesuit Relations. *Anthropologia, 10,* 45–49.

Dalack, G. W., Glassman, A. H., & Covey, L. S. (1993). Nicotine use. In

D. L. Dunner (Ed.), *Current psychiatric therapy* (pp. 114–118). Philadelphia, PA: W. B. Saunders.

Dahlenberg, C. J., Brand, B. L., Gleaves, D. H., Dorahy, M. J., Loewenstein, R. J., Cardeña, E., … Spiegel, D. (2012). Evaluation of the evidence for the trauma and fantasy models of dissociation. *Psychological Bulletin, 138*(3), 550–588. https://doi.org/10.1037/a0027447

Dallaire, R. (2003a). PTSD and military peace-keeping. Invited address at the Annual Meeting of the Anxiety Disorders Association of America, Toronto, March.

Dallaire, R. (2003b). *Shake hands with the Devil: The failure of humanity in Rwanda*. Toronto, ON: Random House Canada.

Dalle Grave, R., Calugi, S., Doll, H. A., & Fairburn, C. G. (2013). Enhanced cognitive behaviour therapy for adolescents with anorexia nervosa: An alternative to family therapy? *Behaviour Research and Therapy, 51*, R9–R12.

Daly, R. J. (1983). Samuel Pepys and post-traumatic stress disorder. *British Journal of Psychiatry, 143*, 64–68.

Dan, O., Sagi-Schwartz, A., Bar-Haim, Y., & Eshel, Y. (2011). Effects of early relationships on children's perceived control: A longitudinal study. *International Journal of Behavioral Development, 35*(5), 449–456.

Dana, R. H. (1996). The thematic apperception test (TAT). In C. S. Newmark (Ed.), *Major psychological assessment instruments* (pp. 166–205). Boston, MA: Allyn & Bacon.

Daniels, A., Adams, N., Carroll, C., & Beinecke, R. (2009). A conceptual model for behavioral health and primary care integration: Emerging challenges and strategies for improving international mental health services. *International Journal of Mental Health, 38*(1), 100–112.

Darwin, C. R. (1872). *The expression of emotions in man and animals*. London, UK: John Murray.

Daskalakis, Z. J., Christensen, B. K., Fitzgerald, P. B., Chen, R. (2002). Transcranial magnetic stimulation: A new investigational and treatment tool in psychiatry. *Journal of Neuropsychiatry & Clinical Neurosciences, 14*(4), 406–415.

Davey, G. (2006). Cognitive mechanisms in fear acquisition and maintenance. In M. G. Craske, D. Hermans, & D. Vansteenwegen (Eds.), *Fear and learning from basic processes to clinical implications.* (pp. 99–116). Washington, DC: American Psychological Association.

David Klonsky, E., Kotov, R., Bakst, S., Rabinowitz, J., & Bromet, E. J. (2012). Hopelessness as a predictor of attempted suicide among first admission patients with psychosis: A 10-year cohort study. *Suicide and Life-Threatening Behavior, 42*(1), 1–10.

Davidson, A. J., Sellix, M. T., Daniel, J., Yamazaki, S., Menaker, M., & Block, G. D. (2006). Chronic jet-lag increases mortality in aged mice. *Current Biology, 16*, R914–R916.

Davidson, J. R. T., Foa, E. B., & Huppert, J. D. (2004). Fluoxetine, comprehensive cognitive behavioral therapy, and placebo in generalized social phobia. *Archives of General Psychiatry, 61*, 1005–1013.

Davidson, J. R. T., Hughes, D. L., Blazer, D. G., & George, L. K. (1991). Posttraumatic stress in the community: An epidemiological study. *Journal of Psychological Medicine, 21*, 713–721.

Davidson, L. L., & Heinrichs, R. W. (2003). Quantification of frontal and temporal lobe brain-imaging findings in schizophrenia: A meta-analysis. *Psychiatry Research: Neuroimaging, 122*, 69–87.

Davidson, M., Keefe, R. S. E., Mohs, R. C., Siever, L. J., Losonczy, M. F., Horvath, T. B., & Davis, K. L. (1987). l-Dopa challenge and relapse in schizophrenia. *American Journal of Psychiatry, 144*, 934–938.

Davidson, R. D. (1993). The neuropsychology of emotion and affective style. In M. Lewis & J. Haviland (Eds.), *Handbook of emotions* (pp. 143–154). New York, NY: Guilford Press.

Davidson, R. J. (1993). Cerebral asymmetry and emotion: Methodological conundrums. *Cognition and Emotion, 7*, 115–138.

Davidson, R. J., Pizzagalli, D. A., & Nitschke, J. B. (2009). Representation and regulation of emotion in depression: Perspectives from affective neuroscience. In I. H. Gotlib & C. L. Hammen (Eds.), *Handbook of depression* (2nd ed., pp. 218–248). New York, NY: Guilford Press.

Davidson, R., Pizzagalli, D., Nitschke, J., & Putnam, K. (2002). Depression: Perspectives from affective neuroscience. *Annual Review of Psychology, 53*, 545–574.

Davidson, S. L. (2014). Relationship between childhood conduct disorder and antisocial personality disorder in adulthood: An argument in favor of mandatory life sentences without parole for juvenile homicide offenders. *Law and Psychology Review, 39*, 239.

Davies, M. N., Verdi, S., Burri, A., Trzaskowski, M., Lee, M., Hettema, J. M., Jansen, R., Boomsma, D. I.,, & Spector, T. D. (2015). Generalized anxiety disorder: A twin study of genetic architecture, genome-wide association and differential gene expression. *PLoS One, 10*(8), e0134865.

Davila, J., Stroud, C. B., & Starr, L. R. (2009). Depression in couples and families. In I. H. Gotlib & C. L. Hammen (Eds.), *Handbook of depression* (2nd ed., pp. 467–491). New York, NY: Guilford Press.

Davis, C. (1997). Normal and neurotic perfectionism in eating disorders: An interactive model. *International Journal of Eating Disorders, 22*, 421–426.

Davis, C., & Strachan, S. (2001). Elite female athletes with eating disorders: A study of psychopathological characteristics. *Journal of Sport & Exercise Psychology, 23*, 245–253.

Davis, C., Blackmore, E., Katzman, D. K., & Fox, J. (2005). Female adolescents with anorexia nervosa and their parents: A case–control study of exercise attitudes and behaviours. *Psychological Medicine, 35*, 377–386.

Davis, C., Katzman, D. K., Kaptein, S., Kirsh, C., Brewer, H., Kalmbach, K., … Kaplan, A. S. (1997). The prevalence of high-level exercise in the eating disorders: Etiological implications. *Comprehensive Psychiatry, 38*, 321–326.

Davis, C., Levitan, R. D., Kaplan, A. S., Carter, J., Reid, C., Curtis, C., & Kennedy, J. L. (2007). Dopamine

transporter gene (DAT1) associated with appetite suppression to methylphenidate in a case–control study of binge eating disorder. *Neuropsychopharmacology, 32*(10), 2199–2206.

Davis, C., Shuster, B., Blackmore, E., & Fox, J. (2004). Looking good: Family focus on appearance and the risk for eating disorders. *International Journal of Eating Disorders, 35*, 136–144.

Davis, L. (2014). Paraphilic disorders in women: Mental illness or a reaction to untreated trauma? In N. L. Ishibashi (Ed.), *Arguing with the DSM-5: Reflections from the perspective of social work* (pp. 29–39). Lulu.com.

Davis, M. (2002). Neural circuitry of anxiety and stress disorders. In K. L. Davis, D. Harney, J. T. Coyle, & C. Nemeroff (Eds.), *Neuropsychopharmacology: The fifth generation of progress* (pp. 901–930). Philadelphia, PA: Lippincott Williams & Wilkins.

Davis, R., & Olmsted, M. P. (1992). Cognitive-behavioral group treatment for bulimia nervosa: Integrating psychoeducation and psychotherapy. In H. Harper-Giuffre & K. R. MacKenzie (Eds.), *Group psychotherapy for eating disorders* (pp. 71–103). Washington, DC: American Psychiatric Association.

Davis, R., Freeman, R. J., & Garner, D. M. (1988). A naturalistic investigation of eating behavior in bulimia nervosa. *Journal of Consulting & Clinical Psychology, 56*, 273–279.

Davis, R., McVey, G., Heinmaa, M., Rockert, W., & Kennedy, S. (1999). Sequencing of cognitive-behavioral treatments for bulimia nervosa. *International Journal of Eating Disorders, 25*, 361–374.

Davis, R., Olmsted, M. P., & Rockert, W. (1990). Brief group psychoeducation for bulimia nervosa: Assessing the clinical significance of change. *Journal of Consulting & Clinical Psychology, 58*, 882–885.

Davis, R., Olmsted, M. P., & Rockert, W. (1992). Brief group psychoeducation for bulimia nervosa: II. Prediction of clinical outcome. *International Journal of Eating Disorders, 11*, 205–211.

Davis, S. (1993). Changes to the Criminal Code provisions for mentally disordered offenders and their implications for Canadian psychiatry. *Canadian Journal of Psychiatry, 38*, 122–126.

Davis, S. (1994). Fitness to stand trial in Canada in light of the recent Criminal Code amendments. *International Journal of Law and Psychiatry, 17*, 319–329.

Davison, G. C. (1968). Elimination of a sadistic fantasy by a client-controlled counter-conditioning technique: A case study. *Journal of Abnormal Psychology, 73*, 91–99.

Davtyan, H., Ghochikyan, A., Petrushina, I., Hovakimyan, A., Davtyan, A., Poghosyan, A., … Larsen, A. K. (2013). Immunogenicity, efficacy, safety, and mechanism of action of epitope vaccine (Lu AF20513) for Alzheimer's disease: Prelude to a clinical trial. *Journal of Neuroscience, 33*(11), 4923–4934.

Dawson, D. A., Goldstein, R. B., & Grant, B. F. (2012). Differences in the profiles of DSM-IV and DSM-5 alcohol use disorders: Implications for clinicians. *Alcoholism: Clinical and Experimental Research, 37*(s1), E305–E315. https://doi.org/10.1111/j.1530-0277.2012.01930.x

Dawson, G., & McKissick, F. C. (1984). Self-recognition in autistic children. *Journal of Autism and Developmental Disorders, 14*, 383–394.

Dawson, G., Jones, E. J. H., Merkle, K., Venema, K., Lowy, R., Faja, S., & Webb, S. J. (2012). Early behavioral intervention is associated with normalized brain activity in young children with autism. *Journal of the American Academy of Child and Adolescent Psychiatry, 51*(11), 1150–1159.

Dawson, S. J., Bannerman, B. A., & Lalumière, M. L. (2016). Paraphilic interests: An examination of sex differences in a nonclinical sample. *Sexual Abuse, 28*, 20–45. https://doi.org/10.1177/1079063214525645

Day, J. J., Grant, I., Atkinson, J. H., Brysk, L. T., McCutchan, J. A., Hesselink, J. R., … Richman, D. D. (1992). Incidence of AIDS dementia in a two-year follow-up of AIDS and ARC patients on an initial phase II AZT placebo-controlled study: San Diego cohort. *Journal of Neuropsychiatry and Clinical Neuroscience, 4*, 15–20.

Day, R., Nielsen, J. A., Korten, A., Ernberg, G., Dube, K. C., Gebhart, J., … Olatawura, M. M. (1987). Stressful life events preceding the acute onset of schizophrenia: A cross-national study from the World Health Organization. *Cultural Medicine and Psychiatry, 11*, 123–205.

de Almeidia-Filho, N., Santana, V. S., Pinto, I. M., & de Carvalho-Neto, J. A. (1991). Is there an epidemic of drug misuse in Brazil? A review of the epidemiological evidence (1977–1988). *International Journal of the Addictions, 26*, 355–369.

de Azeredo, L. A., Rovaris, D. L., Mota, N. R., Polina, E. R., Marques, F. Z., Contini, V., … Grevet, E. H. (2014). Further evidence for the association between a polymorphism in the promoter region of SLC6A3/DAT1 and ADHD: Findings from a sample of adults. *European Archives of Psychiatry and Clinical Neuroscience, 264*(5), 401–408.

De Dios, J. A. A., & Brass, S. D. (2012). New and unconventional treatments for obstructive sleep apnea. *Neurotherapeutics, 9*(4), 702–709.

de Lissovoy, V. (1961). Head banging in early childhood. *Child Development, 33*, 43–56.

deMaat, S., de Jonghe, F., de Kraker, R., Leichsenring, F., Abbass, A., Luyten, P., Barber, J. P., Van, R., & Dekker, J. (2013). The current state of the empirical evidence for psychoanalysis: A meta-analytic approach. *Harvard Review of Psychiatry, 21*, 107–137.

De Marco, R. R. (2000). The epidemiology of major depression: Implications of occurrence, recurrence, and stress in a Canadian community sample. *Canadian Journal of Psychiatry, 45*, 67–74.

De Raedt, R., Vanderhasselt, M.-A., & Baeken, C. (2015). Neurostimulation as an intervention for treatment resistant depression: From research on mechanisms towards targeted neurocognitive strategies. *Clinical Psychology Review, 41*, 61–69.

de Silva, P., Rachman, S., & Seligman, M. E. (1977). Prepared phobias and obsessions: Therapeutic outcome. *Behaviour Research and Therapy, 15*(1), 65–77.

Deakin, J. F. W., & Graeff, F. G. (1991). Critique: 5-HT and mechanisms of defence. *Journal of Psychopharmacology, 5*(4), 305–315.

Deale, A., Chalder, T., Marks, I., & Wessely, S. (1997). Cognitive behavior therapy for chronic fatigue syndrome: A randomized controlled trial. *American Journal of Psychiatry, 154,* 408–414.

Dean, R. R., Kelsey, J. E., Heller, M. R., & Ciaranello, R. D. (1993). Structural foundations of illness and treatment: Receptors. In D. L. Dunner (Ed.), *Current psychiatric therapy.* Philadelphia, PA: W. B. Saunders.

DeBacker, G., Kittel, F., Kornitzer, M., & Dramaix, M. (1983). Behavior, stress, and psychosocial traits as risk factors. *Preventative Medicine, 12,* 32–36.

Debruille, J. B., Kumar, N., Saheb, D., Chintoh, A., Gharghi, D., Lionnet, C., & King, S. (2007). Delusions and processing of discrepant information: An event-related brain potential study. *Schizophrenia Research, 89*(1–3), 261–277.

Deckersbach, T., Moshier, S. J., Tuschen-Caffier, B., & Otto, M. W. (2011). Memory dysfunction in panic disorder: An investigation of the role of chronic benzodiazepine use. *Depression and Anxiety, 28,* 999–1007.

Deckersbach, T., Peters, A. T., Sylvia, L., Urdahl, A., Magalhães, P. V., Otto, M. W., ... Nierenberg, A. (2014). Do comorbid anxiety disorders moderate the effects of psychotherapy for bipolar disorder? Results from STEP-BD. *American Journal of Psychiatry, 171*(2), 178–186.

Decriminalization of marijuana in Canada: Canadian government plans to ease marijuana laws. (2003, May 26). *Canada Online.* Retrieved October 26, 2003, from http://www.canaadaonline.about.com/library/issues/blimj.htm

DeKosky, S. T., Williamson, J. D., Fitzpatrick, A. L., Kronmal, R. A., Ives, D. G., Saxton, J. A., ... Furberg, C. D. (2008). Ginkgo biloba for prevention of dementia: A randomized controlled trial. *JAMA, 300*(19), 2253–2262.

Del Parigi, A., Panza, F., Capurso, C., & Solfrizzi, V. (2006). Nutritional factors, cognitive decline, and dementia. *Brain Research Bulletin, 69*(1), 1–19.

DeLamater, J., & Sill, M. (2005). Sexual desire in latter life. *Journal of Sex Research, 42,* 138–149.

Delano-Wood, L., & Abeles, N. (2005). Late-life depression: Detection, risk, reduction, and somatic intervention. *Clinical Psychology Science Practice, 12,* 207–217.

DeLisi, M., & Vaughn, M. G. (2015). Ingredients for criminality require genes, temperament, and psychopathic personality. *Journal of Criminal Justice, 43*(4), 290–294.

Delizonna, L. L., Wincze, J. P., Litz, B. T., Brown, T. A., & Barlow, D. H. (2001). A comparison of subjective and physiological measures of mechanically produced and erotically produced erections (or, is an erection an erection?). *Journal of Sex and Marital Therapy, 27,* 21–31.

Dell, P. F. (1998). Axis II pathology in outpatients with dissociative identity disorder. *Journal of Nervous and Mental Disease, 186*(6), 352–356.

Dembroski, T. M., & Costa, P. T., Jr. (1987). Coronary prone behavior: Components of the type A pattern and hostility. *Journal of Personality, 55*(2), 211–235.

Denis, C., Fatséas, M., & Auriacombe, M. (2012). Analyses related to the development of DSM-5 criteria for substance use related disorders: 3. An assessment of Pathological Gambling criteria. *Drug and Alcohol Dependence, 122*(1–2), 22–27.

Dent, M. F., & Bremner, J. D. (2009). Pharmacotherapy for posttraumatic stress disorder and other trauma-related disorders. In M. M. Antony & M. B. Stein (Eds.), *Oxford handbook of anxiety and related disorders.* (pp. 405–416). New York, NY: Oxford University Press.

Denton, F. T., Feaver, C. H., & Spencer, B. G. (1998). The future population of Canada, its age distribution and dependency relations. *Canadian Journal on Aging, 17,* 83–109.

Denys, D., Mantione, M., Figee, M., van den Munckhof, P., Koerselman, F., Westenberg, H., & Schuurman, R. (2010). Deep brain stimulation of the nucleus accumbens for treatment-refractory obsessive–compulsive disorder. *Archives of General Psychiatry, 67*(10), 1061–1068.

Denzin, N. K. (1987). *The recovering alcoholic.* Newbury Park, CA: Sage Publications.

Department of Justice. (2018). *Cannabis legalization and regulation.* https://www.justice.gc.ca/eng/cj-jp/cannabis/

Depression Guideline Panel. (1993, April). Depression in primary care: Vol. 1. Detection and diagnosis (AHCPR Publication No. 93-0550). *Clinical practice guideline, No. 5.* Rockville, MD: U.S. Department of Health and Human Services, Public Health Service, Agency for Health Care Policy and Research.

Deptula, D., & Pomara, N. (1990). Effects of anti-depressants on human performance: A review. *Journal of Clinical Psychopharmacology, 10,* 105–111.

Depue, R. A., Luciana, M., Arbisi, P., Collins, P., & Leon, A. (1994). Dopamine and the structure of personality: Relation of agonist-induced dopamine activity to positive emotionality. *Journal of Personality and Social Psychology, 67,* 485–498.

Derry, P. A., & Kuiper, N. A. (1981). Schematic processing and self-reference in clinical depression. *Journal of Abnormal Psychology, 90,* 286–297.

Dersh, J., Polatin, P. B., & Gatchel, R. J. (2002). Chronic pain and psychopathology: Research findings and theoretical considerations. *Psychosomatic Medicine, 64,* 773–786.

Dershewitz, R. A., & Williamson, J. W. (1977). Prevention of childhood household injuries: A controlled clinical trial. *American Journal of Public Health, 67,* 1148–1153.

Dershowitz, A. (1994). *The abuse excuse and other cop-outs, sob stories, and evasions of responsibility.* Boston, MA: Little Brown.

DeRubeis, R. J., Gelfand, L. A., Tang, T. Z., & Simons, A. D. (1999). Medications versus cognitive behavior therapy for severely depressed outpatients: Mega-analysis of four randomized comparisons. *American Journal of Psychiatry, 156,* 1007–1013.

DeStefano, F., Price, C. S., & Weintraub, E. S. (2013). Increasing exposure to antibody-stimulating proteins and polysaccharides in vaccines is not

associated with risk of autism. *Journal of Pediatrics, 163*(2), 561–567.

Deveci, A., Taskin, O., Dinc, G., Yilmaz, H., Demet, M. M., Erbay-Dundar, P., ... Ozmen, E. (2007). Prevalence of pseudoneurologic conversion disorder in an urban community in Manisa, Turkey. *Social Psychiatry and Psychiatric Epidemiology, 42*(11), 857–864.

Devi, G., Fotiou, A., Jyrinji, D., Tycko, B., DeArmand, S., Rogaeva, E., ... Mayeux, R. (2000). Novel presenilin 1 mutations associated with early onset of dementia in a family with both early-onset and late-onset Alzheimer disease. *Archives of Neurology, 57,* 1454–1457.

Devinsky, O., Feldman, E., Burrowes, K., & Bromfield, E. (1989). Autoscopic phenomena with seizures. *Archives of Neurology, 46*(10), 1080–1088.

DeWall, C. N., MacDonald, G., Webster, G. D., Masten, C. L., Baumeister, R. F., Powell, C., & Eisenberger, N. I. (2010). Acetaminophen reduces social pain: Behavioral and neural evidence. *Psychological Science, 21,* 931–937.

DeWit, D. J., Adlaf, E. M., Offord, D. R., & Ogborne, A. C. (2000). Age at first alcohol use: A risk factor for the development of alcohol disorders. *American Journal of Psychiatry, 157,* 745–750.

Dhawan, N., Kunik, M. E., Oldham, J., & Coverdale, J. (2010). Prevalence and treatment of narcissistic personality disorder in the community: A systematic review. *Comprehensive Psychiatry, 51*(4), 333–339.

Dhejne, C., Öberg, K., Arver, S., & Landén, M. (2014). An analysis of all applications for sex reassignment surgery in Sweden, 1960–2010: Prevalence, incidence, and regrets. *Archives of Sexual Behavior, 43*(8), 1535–1545.

Di Guilio, G., & Reissing, E. D. (2006). Premenstrual dysphoric disorder: Prevalence, diagnostic considerations, and controversies. *Journal of Psychosomatic Obstetrics & Gynecology, 27*(4), 201–210.

Diamond, L. M., Butterworth, M. R., & Savin-Williams, R. C. (2011). Working with sexual-minority individuals. In D. H. Barlow (Ed.), *Oxford handbook of clinical psychology.* New York, NY: Oxford University Press.

Diamond, M., & Sigmundson, K. (1997). Sex reassignment at birth: Long-term review and clinical implications. *Archives of Pediatric and Adolescent Medicine, 151,* 298–304.

Dick, D. M. (2011). Gene–environment interaction in psychological traits and disorders. *Annual Review of Clinical Psychology, 7,* 383–409. https://doi.org/10.1146/annurev-clinpsy-032210-104518

Dickens, G., & Sugarman, P. (2012). Adult firesetters: Prevalence, characteristics and psychopathology. In G. L. Dickens, P. A. Sugarman, & T. A. Gannon (Eds.), *Firesetting and mental health: Theory, research and practice* (pp. 3–27). London, UK: RCPsych Publications.

Dickens, W. T., Turkheimer, E., & Beam, C. (2011). The social dynamics of the expression of genes for cognitive ability. In K. S. Kendler, S. Jaffee, & D. Romer (Eds.), *The dynamic genome and mental health: The role of genes and environments in youth development* (pp. 103–127). New York, NY: Oxford University Press.

DiClemente, R. J., Crittenden, C. P., Rose, E., Sales, J. M., Wingood, G. M., Crosby, R. A., & Salazar, L. F. (2008). Psychosocial predictors of HIV-associated sexual behaviors and the efficacy of prevention interventions in adolescents at-risk for HIV infection: What works and what doesn't work? *Psychosomatic Medicine, 70,* 598–605.

DiClemente, R. J., Wingwood, G. M., Harrington, K. F., Lang, D. L., Davies, S. L., Hook, E. W., ... Robillard, A. (2004). Efficacy of an HIV prevention intervention for African American adolescent girls: A randomized controlled trial. *JAMA, 292,* 171–179.

Diener, E. (2000). Subjective well-being: The science of happiness and a proposal for a national index. *American Psychologist, 55,* 34–43.

Diener, E., Oishi, S., & Lucas, R. E. (2003). Personality, culture, and subjective well-being: Emotional and cognitive evaluations of life. *Annual Review of Psychology, 54,* 403–425.

Dimberg, U., & Öhman, A. (1983). The effects of directional facial cues on electrodermal conditioning to facial stimuli. *Psychophysiology, 20,* 160–167.

Dimeff, L. A., Baer, J. S., Kivlahan, D. R., & Marlatt, G. A. (2002). Brief alcohol screening and intervention for college students (BASICS): A harm reduction approach. *Journal of Psychiatry & Law, 30,* 275–278.

Dimidjian, S., Barrera, M. Jr., Martell, C., Muñoz, R. F., & Lewinsohn, P. M. (2011). The origins and current status of behavioral activation treatments for depression. *Annual Review of Clinical Psychology, 7,* 1–38.

Dimidjian, S., Martell, C., Herman-Dunn, R., & Hubley, S. (2014). Behavior activation for depression. In D. H. Barlow (Ed.), *Clinical handbook of psychological disorders: A step-by-step treatment manual* (5th ed.). New York, NY: Guilford Press.

Dimmock, G. (2019, July 27). Sexsomnia case: Dad who molested young teen daughter found not criminally responsible. *Ottawa Citizen.* https://ottawacitizen.com/news/local-news/sexsomnia-case-dad-who-molested-young-teen-daughter-found-not-criminally-responsible

DiNardo, P. A., Brown, T. A., & Barlow, D. H. (1994). *Anxiety disorders interview schedule for DSM-IV (ADIS-IV).* Albany, NY: Graywind Publications.

Dineen, T. (2002, August 15). Peggy Claude-Pierre: Angel for anorexics or misguided amateur? *The Vancouver Sun.* Retrieved June 24, 2004, from http://tanadineen.com/COLUMNIST/Columns/MontreuxClinic.htm

Dinnel, D. L., Kleinknecht, R. A., & Tanaka-Matsumi, J. (2002). A cross-cultural comparison of social phobia symptoms. *Journal of Psychopathology and Behavioral Assessment, 24,* 75–84.

Dishion, T. J., Patterson, G. R., & Reid, J. R. (1988). Parent and peer factors associated with drug sampling in early adolescence: Implications for treatment. In E. R. Rahdert & J. Gabowski (Eds.), *Adolescent drug abuse: Analyses of treatment research* (NIDA Research Monograph No. 77, DHHS Publication No. ADM88-1523, pp. 69–93). Rockville, MD: National Institute on Drug Abuse.

Disney, K. L. (2013). Dependent personality disorder: A critical review. *Clinical Psychology Review, 33*(8), 1184–1196.

Distel, M. A., Trull, T. J., & Boomsma, D. I. (2009). Genetic epidemiology of borderline personality disorder. In M. H. Jackson & L. F. Westbrook (Eds.), *Borderline personality disorder: New research* (pp. 1–31). Hauppage, NY: Nova Science Publishers.

Ditto, B., Wilkins, J. A., France, C. R., Lavoie, P., & Adler, P. S. (2003). On-site training in applied muscle tension to reduce vasovagal reactions to blood donation. *Journal of Behavioral Medicine, 26*, 53–65.

Dixon, J. C. (1963). Depersonalization phenomena in a sample population of college students. *British Journal of Psychiatry, 109*, 371–375.

Dixon, L. B., & Lehman, A. F. (1995). Family interventions for schizophrenia. *Schizophrenia Bulletin, 21*, 631–643.

Dobson, D. J. G., McDougall, G., Busheikin, J., & Aldous, J. (1995). Effects of social skills training and social milieu treatment on symptoms of schizophrenia. *Psychiatric Services, 46*, 376–380.

Dobson, K. S., & Dozois, D. J. A. (2004). Attentional biases in eating disorders: A meta-analytic review of Stroop performance. *Clinical Psychology Review, 23*, 1001–1022.

Dobson, K. S., & Shaw, B. F. (1987). Specificity and stability of self-referent encoding in clinical depression. *Journal of Abnormal Psychology, 96*, 34–40.

Docter, R. F., & Prince, V. (1997). Transvestism: A survey of 1032 cross-dressers. *Archives of Sexual Behavior, 26*, 589–605.

Doehrmann, O., Ghosh, S. S., Polli, F. E., Reynolds, G. O., Whitfield-Gabrieli, S., Hofmann, S. G., Pollack, M., & Gabrieli, J. D. (2013). Predicting treatment response in social anxiety disorder from functional magnetic resonance imaging. *JAMA Psychiatry, 70*, 87–97.

Does the addition of cognitive behavioral therapy improve panic disorder treatment outcome relative to medication alone in the primary-care setting? *Psychological Medicine, 35*(11), 1645–1654.

Doğan, S. (2009). Vaginismus and accompanying sexual dysfunctions in a Turkish clinical sample. *Journal of Sexual Medicine, 6*, 184–192.

Doğan, S., & Doğan, M. (2006). Possible gender identity disorder in an extremely religious Muslim family. *Archives of Sexual Behavior, 35*, 645–646.

Doghramji, K. (2000). The need for flexibility in dosing of hypnotic agents. *Sleep, 23*(Suppl. 1), S16–S20.

Dohrenwend, B. P., Yager, T. J., Wall, M. M., & Adams, B. G. (2012). The roles of combat exposure, personal vulnerability, and involvement in harm to civilians or prisoners in Vietnam-war-related posttraumatic stress disorder. *Clinical Psychological Science, 1*, 223–238.

Dohrenwend, B. P., & Dohrenwend, B. S. (1981). Socioenvironmental factors, stress and psychopathology. *American Journal of Community Psychology, 9*(2), 128–164.

Dohrenwend, B. P., & Egri, G. (1981). Recent stressful life events and episodes of schizophrenia. *Schizophrenia Bulletin, 7*, 12–23.

Dohrenwend, B. P., Levav, I., Shrout, P. E., Schwartz, S., Naveh, G., Link, B. G., … Stueve, A. (1992). Socioeconomic status and psychiatric disorders: The causation-selection issue. *Science, 255*, 946–952.

Dohrenwend, B. P., Turner, J. B., & Turse, N. A. (2006). The psychological risks of Vietnam for U.S. veterans: A revisit with new data and methods. *Science, 313*, 979–982.

Doidge, N., Simon, B., Brauer, L., Grant, D. C., First, M., Brunshaw, J., … Mosher, P. (2002). Psychoanalytic patients in the U.S., Canada, and Australia: I. DSM-III-R disorders, indications, previous treatment, medications, and length of treatment. *Journal of the American Psychoanalytic Association, 50*, 575–614.

Dolan, M., & Vollm, B. (2009). Antisocial personality disorder and psychopathy in women: A literature review on the reliability and validity of assessment instruments. *International Journal of Law and Psychiatry, 32*(1), 2–9.

Dominé, F., Berchtold, A., Akré, C., Michaud, P.-A., & Suris, J.-C. (2009). Disordered eating behaviors: What about boys? *Journal of Adolescent Health, 44*(2), 111–117.

Domino, E. F., & Miller, S. C. (2015). The pharmacology of dissociatives. In R. K. Ries, D. A. Fiellin, S. C. Miller, & R. Saitz (Eds.), *The ASAM principles of addiction medicine* (5th ed., pp. 256–266). New York, NY: Wolters Kluwer.

Dominus, S. (2011, May 25). Could conjoined twins share a mind? *The New York Times Magazine*. Retrieved from http://www.nytimes.com/2011/05/29/magazine/could-conjoined-twins-share-a-mind.html

Domschke, K., & Dannlowski, U. (2010). Imaging genetics of anxiety disorders. *NeuroImage, 53*, 822–831.

Dongen, J., Ehli, E. A., Slieker, R. C., Bartels, M., Weber, Z. M., Davies, G. E., … Boomsma, D. I. (2014). Epigenetic variation in monozygotic twins: A genome-wide analysis of DNA methylation in buccal cells. *Genes, 5*(2), 347–365. https://doi.org/10.3390/genes5020347

Dongier, M. (1999). In memoriam—Heinz E. Lehmann, 1911–1999. *Journal of Psychiatry and Neuroscience, 24*, 362.

Dougherty, D. D., Rauch, S. L., & Jenike, M. A. (2012). Pharmacological treatments for obsessive compulsive disorder. In G. Steketee (Ed.), *The Oxford handbook of obsessive compulsive and spectrum disorders* (pp. 291–306). New York, NY: Oxford University Press.

Douglas, K. S., & Koch, W. J. (2001). Civil commitment and civil competence: Psychological issues. In R. A. Schuller & J. R. P. Ogloff (Eds.), *Introduction to psychology and law: Canadian perspectives* (pp. 353–374). Toronto, ON: University of Toronto Press.

Douglas, K. S., & Webster, C. D. (1999). Predicting violence in mentally and personality disordered individuals. In R. Roesch & S. D. Hart (Eds.), *Psychology and law: The state of the discipline* (pp. 175–239). Dordrecht, The Netherlands: Kluwer.

Douglas, K. S., Nikolova, N. L., Kelley, S. E., Edens, J. F., Cutler, B. L., & Zapf, P. A. (Eds.). (2015). *APA handbook of forensic psychology, Vol. 1: Individual and situational influences in criminal and civil contexts.* APA handbooks in psychology (pp. 257–323). Washington, DC: American Psychological Association, xxii, 594 pp. https://doi.org/10.1037/14461–009

Douglas, V. I. (1972). Stop, look and listen: The problem of sustained attention and impulse control in hyperactive and normal children. *Canadian Journal of Behavioural Science, 4*, 259–282.

Douglas, V. L., Barr, R. G., Desilets, J., & Sherman, E. (1995). Do high doses of stimulants impair flexible thinking in attention-deficit hyperactivity disorder? *Journal of the American Academy of Child & Adolescent Psychiatry, 34*, 877–885.

Douzgou, S., Breen, C., Crow, Y. J., Chandler, K., Metcalfe, K., Jones, E., & Clayton-Smith, J. (2012). Diagnosing fetal alcohol syndrome: New insights from newer genetic technologies. *Archives of Disease in Childhood, 97*(9), 812–817.

Dowling, N., Smith, D., & Thomas, T. (2007). A comparison of individual and group cognitive-behavioural treatment for female pathological gambling. *Behaviour Research and Therapy, 45*(9), 2192–2202.

Dozois, D. J. A., & Dobson, K. S. (2001). Information processing and cognitive organization in unipolar depression: Specificity and comorbidity issues. *Journal of Abnormal Psychology, 110*, 236–246.

Dozois, D. J. A., & Dobson, K. S. (2003). The structure of the self-schema in clinical depression: Differences related to episode recurrence. *Cognition & Emotion, 17*, 933–941.

Dozois, D. J. A., Frewen, P. A., & Covin, R. (2006). Cognitive theories. In J. C. Thomas, D. L. Segal, & M. Hersen (Eds.), *Comprehensive handbook of personality and psychopathology: Personality and everyday functioning* (Vol. 1, pp. 173–191). Hoboken, NJ: John Wiley & Sons.

Dozois, D. J. A., Mikail, S. F., Alden, L. E., Bieling, P. J., Bourgon, G., Clark, D. A., … Johnston, C. (2014). The CPA presidential task force on evidence-based practice of psychological treatments. *Canadian Psychology, 55*, 153–160. https://doi.org/10.1037/a0035767

Dragioti, E., Dimoliatis, I., Fountoulakis, K. N., & Evangelou, E. (2015). A systematic appraisal of allegiance effect in randomized controlled trials of psychotherapy. *Annals of General Psychiatry, 14*, 25–33. https://doi.org/10.1186/s12991-015-0063-1

Drake, R. E., McHugo, G. J., Becker, D. R., Anthony, W. A., & Clark, R. E. (1996). The New Hampshire study of supported employment for people with severe mental illness. *Journal of Consulting and Clinical Psychology, 64*, 391–399.

Drake, R., Bond, G., & Becker, D. (2012). *Individual placement and support: An evidence-based approach to supported employment.* New York, NY: Oxford.

Drogin, E. Y., Commons, M. L., Gutheil, T. G., Meyer, D. J., & Norris, D. M. (2012). "Certainty" and expert mental health opinions in legal proceedings. *International Journal of Law and Psychiatry, 35*(5–6), 348–353.

Drummond, K. D., Bradley, S. J., Peterson-Badali, M., & Zucker, K. J. (2008). A follow-up study of girls with gender identity disorder. *Developmental Psychology, 44*, 34–45.

Drury, V., Birchwood, M., Cochrane, R., & MacMillan, F. (1996). Cognitive therapy and recovery from acute psychosis: A controlled trial. I. Impact on psychotic symptoms. *British Journal of Psychiatry, 169*(5), 593–601.

Dubovsky, S. L. (1983). Psychiatry in Saudi Arabia. *American Journal of Psychiatry, 140*, 1455–1459.

Ducios, J., Vibert, S., Mattar, L., & Godart, N. (2012). Expressed emotion in families of patients with eating disorders: A review of the literature. *Current Psychiatry Reviews, 8*(3), 183–202.

Dugas, M. J. (2018). Le traitement de l'anxiété généralisée: Plus on en sait, moins on en fait [The treatment of generalized anxiety: The more we know, the less we do]. *Canadian Psychology/Psychologie canadienne, 59*(2), 126–131. http://dx.doi.org/10.1037/cap0000144

Dugas, M. J., Anderson, K. G., Deschenes, S. S., & Donegan, E. (2010). Generalized anxiety disorder publications: where do we stand a decade later? *Journal of Anxiety Disorders, 24*(7), 780–784

Dugas, M. J., Freeston, M. H., & Ladouceur, R. (1997). Intolerance of uncertainty and problem orientation in worry. *Cognitive Therapy & Research, 21*, 593–606.

Dugas, M. J., Gagnon, F., Ladouceur, R., & Freeston, M. H. (1998). Generalized anxiety disorder: A preliminary test of a conceptual model. *Behaviour Research and Therapy, 36*, 215–226.

Dugas, M. J., & Koerner, N. (2005). Cognitive-behavioral treatment for generalized anxiety disorder: Current status and future directions. *Journal of Cognitive Psychotherapy, 19*, 61–81.

Dugas, M. J., Ladouceur, R., Leger, E., Freeston, M. H., Langlois, F., Provencher, M., & Boisvert, J. M. (2003). Group cognitive-behavioral therapy for generalized anxiety disorder: Treatment outcome and long-term follow-up. *Journal of Consulting and Clinical Psychology, 71*, 821–825.

Dugas, M. J., Marchand, A., & Ladouceur, R. (2005). Further validation of a cognitive-behavioral model of generalized anxiety dis order: Diagnostic and symptom specificity. *Journal of Anxiety Disorders, 19*, 329–343.

Dulit, R. A., Marin, D. B., & Frances, A. J. (1993). Cluster B personality disorders. In D. L. Dunner (Ed.), *Current psychiatric therapy* (pp. 405–411). Philadelphia, PA: W. B. Saunders.

Dumas, J., & Wahler, R. G. (1983). Predictors of treatment outcome in parent training: Mother insularity and socioeconomic disadvantage. *Behavioral Assessment, 5*, 301–313.

Dummit, E. S., 3rd, Klein, R. G, Tancer, N. K., Asche, B., Martin, J., & Fairbanks, J. A. (1997). Systematic assessment of 50 children with selective mutism. *Journal of the American Academy of Child and Adolescent Psychiatry, 36*(5), 653–660.

Dunkley, D. M., & Grillo, C. M. (2007). Self-criticism, low self-esteem, depressive symptoms, and over-evaluation of shape and weight in binge eating disorder patients. *Behaviour Research and Therapy, 45*, 139–149.

Dunlop, B. W., & Nemeroff, C. B. (2007). The role of dopamine in the pathophysiology of depression. *Archives of General Psychiatry, 64*(3), 327–337.

Dunlop, B. W., Rakofsky, J. J., & Rapaport, M. H. (2013). A simple question answered: Adding moderate-dosage lithium does not help patients with bipolar disorder. *American Journal of Psychiatry, 170*(1), 9–11.

Dunn, E. C., Neighbors, C., & Larimer, M. E. (2006). Motivational enhancement therapy and self-help treatment for binge eaters. *Psychology of Addictive Behaviors, 20*, 44–52.

DuPaul, G. J., Gormley, M. J., & Laracy, S. D. (2013). Comorbidity of LD and ADHD: Implications of DSM-5 for assessment and treatment. *Journal of Learning Disabilities, 46*(1), 43–51.

Durand, V. M. (1990). *Severe behavior problems: A functional communication training approach*. New York, NY: Guilford Press.

Durand, V. M. (1998). *Sleep better: A guide to improving the sleep of children with special needs*. Baltimore, MD: Paul H. Brookes.

Durand, V. M. (1999a). Functional communication training using assistive devices: Recruiting natural communities of reinforcement. *Journal of Applied Behavior Analysis, 32*, 247–267.

Durand, V. M. (1999b). New directions in educational programming for students with autism. In D. Zager (Ed.), *Autism: Identification, education, and treatment* (2nd ed., pp. 323–343). Hillsdale, NJ: Erlbaum.

Durand, V. M. (2001). Future directions for children and adolescents with mental retardation. *Behavior Therapy, 32*(4), 633–650.

Durand, V. M. (2004). Past, present and emerging directions in education. In D. Zager (Ed.), *Autism: Identification, education, and treatment* (3rd ed.). Hillsdale, NJ: Erlbaum.

Durand, V. M. (2008). *When children don't sleep well: Interventions for pediatric sleep disorders, therapist guide*. New York, NY: Oxford University Press.

Durand, V. M. (2011). Disorders of development. In D. H. Barlow (Ed.), *Oxford handbook of clinical psychology* (pp. 551–573). New York, NY: Oxford University Press.

Durand, V. M. (2012). Functional communication training: Treating challenging behavior. In P. Prelock & R. McCauley (Eds.), *Treatment of autism spectrum disorders: Evidence-based intervention strategies for communication & social interaction* (pp. 107–138). Baltimore, MD: Paul H. Brookes.

Durand, V. M., (2014). Disorders of development. In D. H. Barlow (Ed.), *Oxford handbook of clinical psychology: Updated edition*. New York, NY: Oxford University.

Durand, V. M., Blanchard, E. B., & Mindell, J. A. (1988). Training in projective testing: Survey of clinical training directors and internship directors. *Professional Psychology: Research and Practice, 19*, 236–238s.

Durand, V. M., & Carr, E. G. (1988). Autism. In V. B. Van Hasselt, P. S. Strain, & M. Hersen (Eds.), *Handbook of developmental and physical disabilities* (pp. 195–214). New York, NY: Pergamon Press.

Durand, V. M., & Carr, E. G. (1992). An analysis of maintenance following functional communication training. *Journal of Applied Behavior Analysis, 25*, 777–794.

Durand, V. M., & Hieneman, M. (2008). *Helping parents with challenging children: Positive family intervention, Facilitator's guide*. New York, NY: Oxford University Press.

Durand, V. M., Hieneman, M., Clarke, S., Wang, M., & Rinaldi, M. (2013). Positive family intervention for severe challenging behavior I: A multisite randomized clinical trial. *Journal of Positive Behavior Interventions, 15*(3), 133–143.

Durand, V. M., & Mindell, J. A. (1999). Behavioral intervention for childhood sleep terrors. *Behavior Therapy, 30*, 705–715.

Durand, V. M., & Wang, M. (2011). Clinical trials. In J. C. Thomas & M. Hersen (Eds.), *Understanding research in clinical and counseling psychology* (2nd ed.). New York, NY: Routledge.

Durant, C., Christmas, D., & Nutt, D. (2010). The pharmacology of anxiety. *Current Topics in Behavioral Neurosciences, 2*, 303–330.

Durbin, J., Goering, P., Streiner, D. L., & Pink, G. (2006). Does systems integration affect continuity of mental health care? *Administration and Policy in Mental Health and Mental Health Services Research, 33*, 705–711.

Durham v. United States. (1954). 214 F. 2d, 862, 874–875 (D. C. Cir.).

Durkheim, E. (1951). *Suicide: A study in sociology* (J. A. Spaulding & G. Simpson, Trans.). New York, NY: Free Press.

Durkin, M. S., Maenner, M. J., Newschaffer, C. J., Lee, L. C., Cunniff, C. M., Daniels, J. L., ... Zahorodny, W. (2008). Advanced parental age and the risk of autism spectrum disorder. *American Journal of Epidemiology, 168*(11), 1268–1276.

Dusseldorp, E., van Elderen, T., Maes, S., Meulman, J., & Kraaij, V. (1999). A meta-analysis of psychoeducational programs for coronary heart disease patients. *Health Psychology, 18*, 506–519.

Dutton, D. G. (1995). Male abusiveness in intimate relationships. *Clinical Psychology Review, 15*, 567–581.

Dutton, D. G. (2002). Personality dynamics of intimate abusiveness. *Journal of Psychiatric Practice, 8*, 216–228.

Dutton, D. G. (2007). *The abusive personality: Violence and control in intimate relationships* (2nd ed.). New York, NY: Guilford Press.

Dvorak-Bertscha, J., Curtin, J., Rubinstein, T., & Newman, J. (2009). Psychopathic traits moderate the interaction between cognitive and affective processing. *Psychophysiology, 46*(5), 913.

Dwyer, J. T., Feldman, J. J., Seltzer, C. C., & Mayer, J. (1969). Body image in adolescents: Attitudes toward weight and perception of appearance. *American Journal of Clinical Nutrition, 20*, 1045–1056.

Dyck, R. J., & White, J. (1998). Suicide prevention in Canada: Work in progress. In A. A. Leenars, S. Wenckstern, I. Sakinofsky, R. J. Dyck et al. (Eds.), *Suicide in Canada* (pp. 256–274). Toronto, ON: University of Toronto Press.

Dyshniku, F., Murray, M. E., Fazio, R. L., Lykins, A. D., & Cantor, J. M. (1015). Minor physical anomalies as a window into the prenatal origins of pedophilia. *Archives of Sexual Behavior, 44*,

2151–2159. https://doi.org/10.1007/s10508-015-0564-7

Dysken, M. W., Sano, M., Asthana, S., Vertrees, J. E., Pallaki, M., Llorente, M., ... Prieto, S. (2014). Effect of vitamin E and memantine on functional decline in Alzheimer disease: The TEAM-AD VA cooperative randomized trial. *JAMA, 311*(1), 33–44.

Eagles, J. M., Johnston, M. I., Hunter, D., Lobban, M., & Millar, H. R. (1995). Increasing incidence of anorexia nervosa in the female population of northeast Scotland. *American Journal of Psychiatry, 152*, 1266–1271.

Eaker, E. D., Pinsky, J., & Castelli, W. P. (1992). Myocardial infarction and coronary death among women: Psychosocial predictors from a 20-year follow-up of women in the Framingham study. *American Journal of Epidemiology, 135*, 854–864.

Earls, C. M., & Lalumière, M. L. (2002). A case study of preferential bestiality (zoophilia). *Sexual Abuse: A Journal of Research and Treatment, 14*, 83–88.

Earls, C. M., & Lalumière, M. L. (2009). A case study of preferential bestiality. *Archives of Sexual Behavior, 38*, 605–609.

Eaton, W. W., Anthony, J. C., Gallo, J., Cai, G., Tien, A., Romanoski, A., ... Chen, L. S. (1997). Natural history of diagnostic interview schedule/DSM-IV major depression: The Baltimore Epidemiologic Catchment Area follow-up. *Archives of General Psychiatry, 54*, 993–999.

Eaton, W. W., Kessler, R. C., Wittchen, H. U., & Magee, W. J. (1994). Panic and panic disorder in the United States. *American Journal of Psychiatry, 151*, 413–420.

Eaton, W. W., Shao, H., Nestadt, G., Lee, H. B., Bienvenu, O. J., & Zandi, P. (2008). Population-based study of first onset and chronicity in major depressive disorder. *Archives of General Psychiatry, 65*(5), 513–520.

Ebigno, P. (1982). Development of a culture-specific screening scale of somatic complaints indicating psychiatric disturbance. *Culture, Medicine, and Psychiatry, 6*, 29–43.

Ebringer, A. (2015). Creutzfeldt-Jakob Disease and its variants. In *Multiple sclerosis, mad cow disease and acinetobacter* (pp. 141–152). London, UK: Springer International Publishing.

Eckman, T. A., Wirshing, W. C., Marder, S. R., Liberman, R. P., Johnston-Cronk, K., Zimmermann, K., & Mintz, J. (1992). Techniques for training schizophrenic patients in illness self-management: A controlled trial. *American Journal of Psychiatry, 149*, 1549–1555.

Eddy, K. T., Dorer, D. J., Franko, D. L., Tahilani, K., Thompson-Brenner, H., & Herzog, D. B. (2008). Diagnostic crossover in anorexia nervosa and bulimia nervosa: Implications for DSM-V. *American Journal of Psychiatry, 165*(2), 245–250.

Eddy, K. T., Keel, P. K., Dorer, D. J., Delinsky, S. S., Franko, D. L., & Herzog, D. B. (2002). Longitudinal comparison of anorexia nervosa subtypes. *International Journal of Eating Disorders, 31*, 191–201.

Eder, H., Fischer, G., Gombas, W., Jagsch, R., Stuhlinger, G., & Kasper, S. (1998). Comparison of buprenorphine and methadone maintenance in opiate

addicts. *European Addiction Research, 4*(Suppl. 1), 3–7.

Edjoc, R., & Gal, J. (2018). Sleep apnea in Canada, 2016 and 2017. *Health Fact Sheets* (Catalogue No. 82-625-X201800154979). https://www150.statcan.gc.ca/n1/en/catalogue/82-625-X201800154979

Edwards, A. C., & Kendler, K. S. (2012). A twin study of depression and nicotine dependence: Shared liability or causal relationship? *Journal of Affective Disorders, 142*(1–3), 90–97.

Edwards, A. J. (1994). *When memory fails: Helping the Alzheimer's and dementia patient*. New York, NY: Plenum Press.

Edwards, G. (2012). "The evil genius of the habit": DSM-5 seen in historical context. *Journal of Studies on Alcohol and Drugs, 73*(4), 699.

Edwards, R. R., Campbell, C., Jamison, R. N., & Wiech, K. (2009). The neurobiological underpinnings of coping with pain. *Current Directions in Psychological Science, 18*, 237–241.

Eftekhari, A., Ruzek, J. L., Crowley, J. J., Rosen, C. S., Greenbaum, M. A., & Karlin, B. E. (2013). Effectiveness of national implementation of prolonged exposure therapy in veterans affairs care. *JAMA Psychiatry, 70*, 949–955.

Egale Canada. (2003, September 26). *De-listing of sex reassignment surgery (SRS) an injury to public health: Access to SRS by transsexuals is crucial to ensuring full dignity and participation*. Retrieved May 16, 2004, from http://egale.ca/index.asp?langE&menu39&item427

Egeland, J. A., Gerhard, D. S., Pauls, D. L., Sussex, J. N., Kidd, K. K., Allen, C. R., ... Housman, D. E. (1987). Bipolar affective disorders linked to DNA markers on chromosome 11. *Nature, 325*(6107), 783–787.

Ehlers, A., & Clark, D. M. (2003). Early psychological interventions for adult survivors of trauma: A review. *Biological Psychiatry, 53*, 817–826.

Ehlers, A., Clark, D. M., Hackmann, A., McManus, F., Fennell, M., Herbert, C., & Mayou, R. (2003). A randomized controlled trial of cognitive therapy, a self-help booklet, and repeated assessments as early interventions for post-traumatic stress disorder. *Archives of General Psychiatry, 60*, 1024–1032.

Ehlers, C., Gizer, I., Vieten, C., Gilder, D., Stouffer, G., Lau, P., & Wilhelmsen, K. C. (2010). Cannabis dependence in the San Francisco Family Study: Age of onset of use, DSM-IV symptoms, withdrawal, and heritability. *Addictive Behaviors, 35*(2), 102–110.

Ehlers, A., Hofmann, S. G., Herda, C. A., & Roth, W. T. (1994). Clinical characteristics of driving phobia. *Journal of Anxiety Disorders, 8*, 323–339.

Ehrenreich, J. T., Goldstein, C. R., Wright, L. R., & Barlow, D. H. (2009). Development of a unified protocol for the treatment of emotional disorders in youth. *Child & Family Behavior Therapy, 31*(1), 20–37.

Ehrhardt, A. A., & Meyer-Bahlburg, H. F. L. (1981). Effects of prenatal sex hormones on gender-related behavior. *Science, 211*, 1312–1318.

Eich, E., Macaulay, D., Loewenstein, R. J., & Dihle, P. H. (1997a). Implicit memory, interpersonality amnesia, and dissociative identity disorder: Comparing patients with simulators. In D. Read & S. Lindsay (Eds.),

Recollections of trauma (pp. 469–474). New York, NY: Plenum Press.

Eich, E., Macaulay, D., Loewenstein, R. J., & Pihle, P. H. (1997b). Memory, amnesia, and dissociative identity disorder. *Psychological Science, 8,* 417–422.

Eikenaes, I., Egeland, J., Hummelen, B., & Wilberg, T. (2015). Avoidant personality disorder versus social phobia: The significance of childhood neglect. *PloS One, 10*(3), e0122846.

Eikenaes, I., Pedersen, G., and Wilberg, T. (2015). Attachment styles in patients with avoidant personality disorder compared with social phobia. *Psychology and Psychotherapy, 89*(3), 245–260. https://doi.org/10.1111/papt.12075

Eisenberger, N. I. (2012). The neural bases of social pain: Evidence for shared representations with physical pain. *Psychosomatic Medicine, 74*(2), 126–135.

Eisler, I., Dare, C., Hodes, M., Russell, G. F. M., Dodge, E., & Le Grange, D. (2000). Family therapy for adolescent anorexia nervosa: The results of a controlled comparison of two family interventions. *Journal of Child Psychology and Psychiatry, 41,* 727–736.

Elbogen, E. B., Dennis, P. A., & Johnson, S. C. (2016). Beyond mental illness targeting stronger and more direct pathways to violence. *Clinical Psychological Science.* Advance online publication. https://doi.org/10.1177/2167702615619363

Elbogen, E., & Johnson, S. (2009). The intricate link between violence and mental disorder: Results from the National Epidemiologic Survey on Alcohol and Related Conditions. *Archives of General Psychiatry, 66*(2), 152.

Eldevik, S., Jahr, E., Eikeseth, S., Hastings, R. P., & Hughes, C. J. (2010). Cognitive and adaptive behavior outcomes of behavioral intervention for young children with intellectual disability. *Behavior Modification, 34*(1), 16–34.

Eley, T. C. (2011). The interplay between genes and environment in the development of anxiety and depression. In K. S. Kendler, S. Jaffee, & D. Romer (Eds.), *The dynamic genome and mental health: The role of genes and environments in youth development* (pp. 229–254). New York, NY: Oxford University Press.

El-Gabalawy, R., Mackenzie, C. S., Thibodeau, M. A., Asmundson, G. J. G., & Sareen, J. (2013). Health anxiety disorders in older adults: Conceptualizing complex conditions in late life. *Clinical Psychology Review, 33,* 1096–1105.

Elia, J., Gai, X., Xie, H. M., Perin, J. C., Geiger, E., Glessner, J. T., & D'arcy, M. (2009). Rare structural variants found in attention deficit hyperactivity disorder are preferentially associated with neurodevelopmental genes. *Molecular Psychiatry, 15*(6), 637–646.

Elie, M., Rousseau, F., Cole, M., Primeau, F., McCusker, J., & Bellavance, F. (2000). Prevalence and detection of delirium in elderly emergency department patients. *Canadian Medical Association Journal, 163,* 977–981.

Elkin, I., Gibbons, R. D., Shea, M. T., Sotsky, S. M., Watkins, J. T., Pilkonis, P. A., & Hedeker, D. (1995). Initial severity and differential treatment outcome in the National Institute of Mental Health Treatment of Depression Collaborative Research Program. *Journal of Consulting and Clinical Psychology, 63,* 841–847.

Elkin, I., Shea, M. T., Watkins, J. T., Imber, S. D., Sotsky, S. M., Collins, J. F., . . . Parloff, M. B. (1989). National Institute of Mental Health Treatment of Depression Collaborative Research Program: General effectiveness of treatments. *Archives of General Psychiatry, 46*(11), 971–982.

Ellard, K. K. (2013). *An examination of the neural correlates of emotion acceptance versus worry in generalized anxiety disorder.* (Unpublished doctoral dissertation).

Ellason, J. W., & Ross, C. A. (1997). Two-year follow up of inpatients with dissociative identity disorder. *American Journal of Psychiatry, 154,* 832–839.

Ellery, M., Stewart, S. H., & Loba, P. (2005). Alcohol's effects on risk-taking during video lottery terminal (VLT) play among probable pathological and non-pathological gamblers. *Journal of Gambling Studies, 21*(3), 299–324.

Elliot, D. M. (1997). Traumatic events: Prevalence and delayed recall in the general population. *Journal of Consulting and Clinical Psychology, 65,* 811–820.

Elliott, S., Latini, D. M., Walker, L. M., Wassersug, R., Robinson, J. W., & The ADT Survivorship Working Group ASWG. (2010). Androgen deprivation therapy for prostate cancer: Recommendations to improve patient and partner quality of life. *Journal of Sex Medicine, 7,* 2996–3010.

Elliott, R., Malkin, I., & Gold, J. (2002). *Establishing safe injection sites in Canada: Legal and ethical issues.* Montreal, QC: Canadian HIV/AIDS Legal Network.

Ellis, A. (1962). *Reason and emotion in psychotherapy.* Secaucus, NJ: Prentice-Hall.

Ellis, P. M., & Dronsfield, A. T. (2013). Antabuse's diamond anniversary: Still sparkling on? *Drug and Alcohol Review, 32*(4), 342–344.

Elovainio, M., Kivimaki, M., Viikari, J., Ekelund, J., & Keltikangas-Jarvinen, L. (2005). The mediating role of novelty seeking in the association between the type 4 dopamine receptor gene polymorphism and cigarette-smoking behavior. *Personality and Individual Differences, 38,* 639–645.

Emens, J., Lewy, A., Kinzie, J. M., Arntz, D., & Rough, J. (2009). Circadian misalignment in major depressive disorder. *Psychiatry Research, 168,* 259–261.

Emery, C. F., Anderson, D. R., & Andersen, B. L. (2011). Psychological interventions in health care settings. In D. H. Barlow (Ed.), *Oxford handbook of clinical psychology* (pp. 701–716). New York, NY: Oxford University Press.

Emmelkamp, P. M. G., Benner, A., Kuipers, A., Feiertag, G. A., Koster, H. C., & van Apeldoorn, F. J. (2006). Comparison of brief dynamic and cognitive-behavioural therapies in avoidant personality disorder. *British Journal of Psychiatry, 189*(1), 60–64.

Emrick, C. D., Tonigan, J. S., Montgomery, H., & Little, L. (1993). Alcoholics Anonymous: What is currently known? In B. S. McCrady & W. R. Miler (Eds.), *Research on Alcoholics Anonymous: Opportunities and alternatives* (pp. 41–76). New Brunswick, NJ: Rutgers Center of Alcohol Studies.

Emsley, R., Chiliza, B., Asmal, L., & Harvey, B. H. (2013). The nature of relapse in schizophrenia. *BMC Psychiatry, 13*(1), 50.

Emslie, G. J., Rush, A. J., Weinberg, W. A., Rintelmann, J. W., & Roffwarg, H. P. (1994). Sleep EEG features of adolescents with major depression. *Biological Psychiatry, 36,* 573–581.

Endler, N. S. (1990). *Holiday of darkness.* Toronto, ON: Wall & Emerson.

Engelberg, M. J., Gauvin, L., & Steiger, H. (2005). A naturalistic evaluation of the relation between dietary restraint, the urge to binge, and actual binge eating: A clarification. *International Journal of Eating Disorders, 38,* 355–360.

England, P., & Bearak, J. (2014). The sexual double standard and gender differences in attitudes toward casual sex among US university students. *Demographic Research, 30,* 1327.

Enns, M. W., Inayatulla, M., Cox, B., & Cheyne, L. (1997). Prediction of suicide intent in Aboriginal and non-Aboriginal adolescent inpatients: A research note. *Suicide & Life-Threatening Behavior, 27,* 218–224.

Epling, W. F., & Pierce, W. D. (1992). *Solving the anorexia puzzle.* Toronto, ON: Hogrefe & Huber.

Epperson, C. N., Steiner, M., Hartlage, S. A., Eriksson, E., Schmidt, P. J., Jones, I., & Yonkers, K. A. (2012). Premenstrual dysphoric disorder: Evidence for a new category for DSM-5. *American Journal of Psychiatry, 169*(5), 465–475.

Eranti, S., Mogg, A., Pluck, G., Landau, S., Purvis, R., Brown, R. G., . . . McLoughlin, D. M. (2007). A randomized, controlled trial with 6-month follow-up of repetitive transcranial magnetic stimulation and electroconvulsive therapy for severe depression. *American Journal of Psychiatry, 164*(1), 73–81.

Erhardt, D., & Hinshaw, S. P. (1994). Initial sociometric impressions of attention-deficit hyperactivity disorder and comparison boys: Predictions from social behaviors and from nonbehavioral variables. *Journal of Consulting and Clinical Psychology, 62,* 833–842.

Erickson, D. H., Beiser, M., & Iacono, W. G. (1998). Social support predict 5-year outcome in 1st episode schizophrenia. *Journal of Abnormal Psychology, 107,* 681–685.

Erickson, E. (1950). *Childhood and society.* New York, NY: Norton.

Erikson, E. (1982). *The life cycle completed.* New York, NY: Norton.

Erkinjuntti, T. (2012). Vascular dementia. In M. G. Gelder, N. C. Andreasen, J. J., Lopez-Ibor, & J. R. Geddes (Eds.), *New Oxford textbook of psychiatry* (2nd ed., Vol. 1, pp. 375–384). New York, NY: Oxford University Press.

Erkinjuntti, T., Ostbye, T., Steenhuis, R., & Hachinski, V. (1997). The effect of different diagnostic criteria on the prevalence of dementia. *New England Journal of Medicine, 337,* 1667–1674.

Erlich, M. D., Smith, T. E., Horwath, E., & Cournos, F. (2014). Schizophrenia and other psychotic disorders. In J. L. Cutler (Ed.), *Psychiatry* (pp. 97–128). New York, NY: Oxford University Press.

Ersche, K. D., Jones, P. S., Williams, G. B., Robbins, T. W., & Bullmore, E. T. (2012). Cocaine dependence: A fast-track for brain ageing? *Molecular Psychiatry, 18*(2), 134–135. https://doi.org/10.1038/mp.2012.31

Ertekin, C., Colakoglu, Z., & Altay, B. (1995). Hand and genital sympathetic skin potentials in flaccid and erectile penile states in normal potent men and patients with premature ejaculation. *Journal of Urology, 153,* 76–79.

Escobar, J. I., Gara, M. A., Diaz-Martinez, A. M., Interian, A., Warman, M., Allen, L. A., & Rodgers, D. (2007). Effectiveness of a time-limited cognitive behavior therapy type intervention among primary care patients with medically unexplained symptoms. *Annals of Family Medicine, 5*(4), 328–335.

Eser, D., Schule, C., Baghai, T. C., Romeo, E., & Rupprecht, R. (2006). Neuroactive steroids in depression and anxiety disorders: Clinical studies. *Neuroendocrinology, 84*(4), 244–254.

Eslinger, P. J., & Damasio, A. R. (1985). Severe disturbance of higher cognition after bilateral frontal lobe ablation: Patient EVR. *Neurology, 35,* 1731–1741.

Essex, M. J., Klein, M. H., Slattery, M. J., Goldsmith, H. H., & Kalin, N. H. (2010). Early risk factors and developmental pathways to chronic high inhibition and social anxiety disorder in adolescence. *American Journal of Psychiatry, 167*(1), 40–46.

Eth, S. (1990). Posttraumatic stress disorder in childhood. In M. Hersen & C. G. Last (Ed.), *Handbook of child and adult psychopathology: A longitudinal perspective.* Elmsford, NY: Pergamon Press.

Etter, J. (2009). Dependence on the nicotine gum in former smokers. *Addictive Behaviors, 34*(3), 246–251.

Evans, D. A., Funkenstein, H. H., Albert, M. S., Scherr, P. A., Cook, N. R., Chown, M. J., . . . Taylor, J. O. (1989). Prevalence of Alzheimer's disease in a community population of older persons. *JAMA, 262,* 2551–2556.

Evans, J. A., & Hammerton, J. L. (1985). Chromosomal anomalies. In A. M. Clarke, A. D. B. Clarke, & J. M. Berg (Eds.), *Mental deficiency: The changing outlook* (4th ed., pp. 213–266). New York, NY: Free Press.

Evans, M. D., Hollon, S. D., DeRubeis, R. J., Pinsecki, J. M., Grove, W. M., Garvey, M. J., & Tuason, V. B. (1992). Differential relapse following cognitive therapy and pharmacotherapy for depression. *Archives of General Psychiatry, 49*(10), 802–808.

Evans, R. M., Emsley, C. L., Gao, S., Sahota, A., Hall, K. S., Farlow, M. R., Hendrie, H. (2000). Serum cholesterol, APOE genotype, and the risk of Alzheimer's disease: A population-based study of African Americans. *Neurology, 54,* 240–242.

Evenson, B. (2001, April 3). Scientology leads backlash. *National Post.* Retrieved May 20, 2004, from http://www.rickross.com/reference/scien-tology/scien300.html

Everaerd, W., Laan, E. T. M., Roth, S., & van der Velde, J. (2000). Female sexuality. In L. T. Szuchman & F. Muscarella (Eds.), *Psychological perspectives on human sexuality* (pp. 101–146). New York, NY: Wiley.

Everett, J., Lavoie, K., Gagnon, J.-F., & Gosselin, N. (2001). Performance of patients with schizophrenia on the

Wisconsin Card Sorting Test (WCST). *Journal of Psychiatry & Neuroscience*, *26*, 123–130.

Exner, J. E. (2003). The Rorschach: A comprehensive system. *Basic foundations and principles of interpretation* (4th ed.). New York, NY: Wiley.

Eysenck, H. J. (Ed.). (1967). *The biological basis of personality*. Springfield, IL: Charles C. Thomas.

Eysenck, H. J., & Eysenck, S. B. G. (1978). Psychopathy, personality, and genetics. In R. D. Hare & D. Schalling (Eds.), *Psychopathic behaviour: Approaches to research* (pp. 197–223). Chichester, UK: John Wiley & Sons.

Eysenck, M. W. (1992). *Anxiety: The cognitive perspective*. Hove, UK: Erlbaum.

Ezrati-Vinacour, R., & Levin, I. (2004). The relationship between anxiety and stuttering: A multidimensional approach. *Journal of Fluency Disorders*, *29*(2), 135–148.

Ezzati, M., & Riboli, E. (2012). Can noncommunicable diseases be prevented? Lessons from studies of populations and individuals. *Science*, *337*(6101), 1482–1487.

Ezzel, C. (1993). On borrowed time: Long-term survivors of HIV-1 infection. *Journal of NIH Research*, *5*, 77–82.

Faden, R. R. (1987). Health psychology and public health. In G. L. Stone, S. M. Weiss, J. D. Matarazzo, N. E. Miller, J. Rodin, C. D. Belar, et al. (Eds.), *Health psychology: A discipline and a profession*. Chicago: University of Chicago Press.

Fagan, P. J., Wise, T. N., Schmidt, C. W., & Berlin, M. D. (2002). Pedophilia. *JAMA*, *288*, 2458–2465.

Fagundes, C. P., Glaser, R., Johnson, S. L., Andridge, R. R., Yang, E. V., Di Gregorio, M. P., & Kiecolt-Glaser, J. K. (2012). Basal cell carcinoma: Stressful life events and the tumor environment. *Archives of General Psychiatry*, *69*(6), 618–626.

Fahrner, E. M. (1987). Sexual dysfunction in male alcohol addicts: Prevalence and treatment. *Archives of Sexual Behavior*, *16*(3), 247–257.

Fairburn, C. G. (2008). *Cognitive behavior therapy and eating disorders*. New York, NY: Guilford Press.

Fairburn, C. G. (2013). *Overcoming binge eating* (2nd ed.). New York, NY: Guilford Press.

Fairburn, C. G., Bailey-Straebler, S., Basden, S., Doll, H. A., Jones, R., Murphy, R., . . . Cooper, Z. (2015). A transdiagnostic comparison of enhanced cognitive behaviour therapy (CBT-E) and interpersonal psychotherapy in the treatment of eating disorders. *Behaviour Research and Therapy*, *70*, 64–71.

Fairburn, C. G., & Beglin, S. J. (1990). Studies of the epidemiology of bulimia nervosa. *American Journal of Psychiatry*, *147*(4), 401–409.

Fairburn, C. G., & Bohn, K. (2005). Eating disorder NOS (EDNOS): An example of the troublesome "not otherwise specified" (NOS) category in DSM-IV. *Behaviour Research and Therapy*, *43*(6), 691–701.

Fairburn, C. G., & Brownell, K. D. (2002). *Eating disorders and obesity: A comprehensive handbook* (2nd ed.). New York, NY: Guilford Press.

Fairburn, C. G., & Cooper, Z. (2014). Eating disorders: A transdiagnostic protocol. In D. H. Barlow (Ed.), *Clinical handbook of psychological disorders: A step-by-step treatment manual* (5th ed.). New York, NY: Guilford Press.

Fairburn, C. G., Cooper, Z., Bohn, K., O'Connor, M. E., Doll, H. A., & Palmer, R. L. (2007). The severity and status of eating disorder NOS: Implications for DSM-V. *Behavior Research and Therapy*, *45*, 1705–1715.

Fairburn, C. G., Cooper, Z., Doll, H. A., Norman, P., & O'Connor, M. (2000). The natural course of bulimia nervosa and binge eating disorder in young women. *Archives of General Psychiatry*, *57*, 659–665.

Fairburn, C. G., Cooper, Z., Doll, H. A., O'Connor, M. E., Bohn, K., Hawker, D. M., & Palmer, R. L. (2009). Transdiagnostic cognitive-behavioral therapy for patients 60-week follow-up. *American Journal of Psychiatry*, *166*, 311–319.

Fairburn, C. G., Cooper, Z., Doll, H. A., Palmer, R. L., & Dalle Grave, R. (2013). Enhanced cognitive behaviour therapy for adults with anorexia nervosa: A UK-Italy study. *Behaviour Research and Therapy*, *51*(1), R2–R8.

Fairburn, C. G., Cooper, Z., Doll, H. A., & Welch, S. L. (1999). Risk factors for anorexia nervosa. Three integrated case–control comparisons. *Archives of General Psychiatry*, *56*, 468–476.

Fairburn, C. G., Cowen, P. J., & Harrison, P. J. (1999). Twin studies and the etiology of eating disorders. *International Journal of Eating Disorders*, *26*(4), 349–358.

Fairburn, C. G., Doll, H. A., Welch, S. L., Hay, P. J., Davies, B. A., & O'Connor, M. E. (1998). Risk factors for binge eating disorder. *Archives of General Psychiatry*, *55*, 425–432.

Fairburn, C. G., Hay, P. J., & Welch, S. L. (1993). Binge eating and bulimia nervosa: Distribution and determinants. In C. G. Fairburn & G. T. Wilson (Eds.), *Binge eating: Nature, assessment, and treatment*. New York, NY: Guilford Press.

Fairburn, C. G., Jones, R., Peveler, R. C., Hope, R. A., & O'Connor, M. (1993). Psychotherapy and bulimia nervosa: The longer-term effects of interpersonal psychotherapy, behaviour therapy and cognitive behaviour therapy. *Archives of General Psychiatry*, *50*, 419–428.

Fairburn, C. G., Marcus, M. D., & Wilson, G. T. (1993). Cognitive behaviour therapy for binge eating and bulimia nervosa: A comprehensive treatment manual. In C. G. Fairburn & G. T. Wilson (Eds.), *Binge eating: Nature, assessment, and treatment*. New York, NY: Guilford Press.

Fairburn, C. G., Norman, P. A., Welch, S. L., O'Connor, M. E., Doll, H., & Peveler, R. C. (1995). A prospective study of outcome in bulimia nervosa and the long-term effects of three psychological treatments. *Archives of General Psychiatry*, *52*, 304–312.

Fairburn, C. G., Shafran, R., & Cooper, Z. (1999). A cognitive behavioural theory of anorexia nervosa. *Behaviour Research and Therapy*, *37*, 1–13.

Fairburn, C. G., Stice, E., Cooper, Z., Doll, H. A., Norman, P. A., & O'Connor, M. E. (2003). Understanding persistence in bulimia nervosa: A 5-year naturalistic study. *Journal of Consulting and Clinical Psychology*, *71*, 103–109.

Fairburn, C. G., Welch, S. L., Doll, S. A., Davies, B. A., & O'Connor, M. E. (1997). Risk factors for bulimia nervosa: A community-based case–control study. *Archives of General Psychiatry*, *54*, 509–517.

Fairholme, C. P., Boisseau, C. L., Ellard, K. K., Ehrenreich, J. T., & Barlow, D. H. (2010). Emotions, emotion regulation, and psychological treatment: A unified perspective. In A. M. Kring & D. M. Sloan (Eds.), *Emotion regulation and psychopathology: A transdiagnostic approach to etiology and treatment* (pp. 283–309). New York, NY: Guilford Press.

Fallon, A. E., & Rozin, P. (1985). Sex differences in perceptions of desirable body shape. *Journal of Abnormal Psychology*, *94*, 102–105.

Falloon, I. R. (Ed.). (2015). *Handbook of behavioural family therapy*. London, UK: Routledge.

Falloon, I. R. H., Boyd, J. L., McGill, C. W., Williamson, M., Razani, J., Moss, H. B., . . . Simpson, G. M. (1985). Family management in the prevention of morbidity of schizophrenia. *Archives of General Psychiatry*, *42*, 887–896.

Falloon, I. R. H., Brooker, C., & Graham-Hole, V. (1992). Psychosocial interventions for schizophrenia. *Behaviour Change*, *9*, 238–245.

Fang, A., & Hofmann, S. G. (2010). Relationship between social anxiety disorder and body dysmorphic disorder. *Clinical Psychology Review*, *30*, 1040–1048.

Fang, A., & Wilhelm, S. (2015). Clinical features, cognitive biases, and treatment of body dysmorphic disorder. *Annual Review of Clinical Psychology*, *11*, 187–212.

Faraone, S. V. (2000). Attention deficit hyperactivity disorder in adults: Implications for theories of diagnosis. *Current Directions in Psychological Science*, *9*, 33–36.

Faraone, S. V., Biederman, J., Woznaik, J., Mundy, E., Mennin, D., & O'Donnell, D. (1997). Comorbidity w/ADHD a marker for juvenile onset mania? *Journal of the American Academy of Child and Adolescent Psychiatry*, *36*(8), 1046–1055.

Faraone, S. V., Tsuang, M. T., & Tsuang, D. W. (1999). *Genetics of mental disorders: A guide for students, clinicians, and researchers*. Baltimore, MD: Guilford Press.

Farde, L., Gustavsson, J. P., & Jonsson, E. (1997). D2 dopamine receptors and personality traits. *Nature*, *385*, 590.

Farias, S. T., Chand, V., Bonnici, L., Baynes, K., Harvey, D., Mungas, D., & Reed, B. (2012). Idea density measured in late life predicts subsequent cognitive trajectories: Implications for the measurement of cognitive reserve. *Journals of Gerontology Series B: Psychological Sciences and Social Sciences*, *67*(6), 677–686.

Farnam, F., Janghorbani, M., Merghati-Khoei, E., & Raisi, F. (2014). Vaginismus and its correlates in an Iranian clinical sample. *International Journal of Impotence Research*, *26*(6), 230–234.

Fauci, A. S., & Folkers, G. K. (2012). Toward an AIDS-free generation. *JAMA*, *308*(4), 343–344.

Fausto-Sterling, A. (2000a). The five sexes, revisited. *The Sciences*, *40*(4), 19–23.

Fausto-Sterling, A. (2000b). *Sexing the body*. New York, NY: Basic Books.

Fava, C., Sjogren, M., Montagnana, M., Danese, E., Almgren, P., Engstrom, G., & Melander, O. (2013). Prediction of blood pressure changes over time and incidence of hypertension by a genetic risk score in Swedes. *Hypertension*, *61*(2), 319–326.

Fava, G. A., Grandi, S., Rafanelli, C., Fabbri, S., & Cazzaro, M. (2000). Explanatory therapy in hypochondriasis. *Journal of Clinical Psychiatry*, *61*(4), 317–322.

Fava, G. A., Grandi, S., Zielezny, M., Rafanelli, C., & Canestrari, R. (1996). Four-year outcome for cognitive behavioral treatment of residual symptoms in major depression. *American Journal of Psychiatry*, *153*, 945–947.

Fava, G. A., Rafanelli, C., Grandi, S., Conti, S., & Belluardo, P. (1998). Prevention of recurrent depression with cognitive behavioral therapy: Preliminary finding. *Archives of General Psychiatry*, *55*(9), 816–820.

Fava, G. A., Ruini, C., Rafanelli, C., Finos, L., Conti, S., & Grandi, S. (2004). Six-year outcome of cognitive behavior therapy for prevention of recurrent depression. *American Journal of Psychiatry*, *161*, 1872–1876.

Fava, M., & Rosenbaum, J. F. (1991). Suicidality and fluoxetine: Is there a relationship? *Journal of Clinical Psychiatry*, *52*(3), 108–111.

Fazel, S., Wolf, A., Chang, Z., Larsson, H., Goodwin, G. M., & Lichtenstein, P. (2015). Depression and violence: A Swedish population study. *The Lancet*, *2*(3), 224–232. https://doi.org/10.1016/S2215-0366(14)00128-X

Fearing, M. A., & Inouye, S. K. (2009). Delirium. In D. G. Blazer & D. C. Steffens (Eds.), *The American Psychiatric Publishing textbook of geriatric psychiatry* (4th ed., pp. 229–242). Arlington, VA: American Psychiatric Publishing.

Fears, S. C., Mathews, C. A., & Freimer, N. B. (2009). Genetic linkage analysis of psychiatric disorders. In B. J. Sadock, V. A. Sadock, & P. Ruiz (Eds.), *Kaplan & Sadock's comprehensive textbook of psychiatry* (9th ed., Vol. 1, pp. 320–333). Philadelphia, PA: Lippincott Williams & Wilkins.

Fedoroff, I. C., Taylor, S., Asmundson, G. J. G., & Koch, W. J. (2000). Cognitive factors in traumatic stress reactions: Predicting PTSD symptoms from anxiety sensitivity and beliefs about harmful events. *Behavioural and Cognitive Psychotherapy*, *28*, 5–15.

Fedoroff, J. P., Fishell, A., & Fedoroff, B. (1999). A case series of women evaluated for paraphilic sexual disorders. *Canadian Journal of Human Sexuality*, *8*(2), 127–140.

Fein, D. A. (2011). *The neuropsychology of autism*. New York, NY: Oxford University Press.

Feinberg, M., & Carroll, B. J. (1984). Biological "markers" for endogenous depression: Effect of age, severity of illness, weight loss and polarity. *Archives of General Psychiatry*, *41*, 1080–1085.

Feingold, B. F. (1975). *Why your child is hyperactive*. New York, NY: Random House.

Feinstein, A., & Holloway, F. (2002). Evaluating the use of a psychiatric intensive care unit: Is ethnicity a risk factor for admission? *International*

Journal of Social Psychiatry, 48(1), 38-S46.

Feinstein, A., Stergiopoulos, V., Fine, J., & Lang, A. E. (2001). Psychiatric outcome in patients with a psychogenic movement disorder. *Neuropsychiatry, Neuropsychology, and Behavioral Neurology, 14*, 169–176.

Feinstein, C., & Phillips, J. M. (2006). Developmental disorders of communication, motor skills, and learning. In M. K. Dulcan & J. M. Wiener (Eds.), *Essentials of child and adolescent psychiatry* (pp. 203–231). Washington, DC: American Psychiatric Publishing.

Feldman, H. A., Goldstein, I., Hatzichristou, D. G., Krane, R. J., & McKunlay, J. B. (1994). Impotence and its medical and psychosocial correlates: Results of the Massachusetts male aging study. *Journal of Urology, 151*, 54–61.

Feldman, M. B., & Meyer, I. H. (2007). Childhood abuse and eating disorders in gay and bisexual men. *International Journal of Eating Disorders, 40*(5), 418–423.

Feldman, M. D., & Christensen, J. F. (Eds.). (2014). *Behavioral medicine: A guide for clinical practice* (4th ed.). McGraw-Hill Medical.

Feldner, M. T., Smith, R. C., Babson, K. A., Sachs-Ericsson, N., Schmidt, N. B., & Zvolensky, M. J. (2009). Test of the role of nicotine dependence in the relation between posttraumatic stress disorder and panic spectrum problems. *Journal of Traumatic Stress, 22*, 36–44.

Felmingham, K. L., & Bryant, R. A. (2012). Gender differences in the maintenance of response to cognitive behavior therapy for posttraumatic stress disorder. *Journal of Consulting and Clinical Psychology, 80*(2), 196–200.

Fergus, T. A., & Valentiner, D. P. (2010). Disease phobia and disease conviction are separate dimensions underlying hypochondriasis. *Journal of Behavior Therapy and Experimental Psychiatry, 41*, 438–444.

Ferguson, C. (2010a). A meta-analysis of normal and disordered personality across the life span. *Journal of Personality and Social Psychology, 98*(4), 659–667.

Ferguson, C. J., & Negy, C. (2014). Development of a brief screening questionnaire for histrionic personality symptoms. *Personality and Individual Differences, 66*, 124–127.

Ferguson, K. L., & Rodway, M. R. (1994). Cognitive behavioral treatment of perfectionism: Initial evaluation studies. *Research on Social Work Practice, 4*, 283–308.

Ferrazzoli, D., Sica, F., & Sancesario, G. (2013). Sundowning Syndrome: A possible marker of frailty in Alzheimer's disease? *CNS & Neurological Disorders-Drug Targets, 12*(4), 525–528.

Ferreira, C. (2000). Serial killers: Victims of compulsion or masters of control? In D. H. Fishbein (Ed.), *The science, treatment, and prevention of antisocial behaviors: Application to the criminal justice system* (pp. 15-1–15-18). Kingston, NJ: Civic Research Institute.

Ferreira, S. E., De Mello, M. T., Pompéia, S., & De Souza-Formigoni, M. L. O. (2006). Effects of energy drink ingestion on alcohol intoxication. *Alcoholism: Clinical and Experimental Research, 30*(4), 598–605.

Ferster, C. B. (1961). Positive reinforcement and behavioral deficits of autistic children. *Child Development, 32*, 437–456.

Ferster, C. B., & Skinner, B. F. (1957). *Schedules of reinforcement.* New York, NY: Appleton-Century-Crofts.

Feusner, J., Phillips, K., & Stein, D. (2010). Olfactory reference syndrome: Issues for DSM-V. *Depression and Anxiety, 27*(6), 592–599.

Ficks, C., & Waldman, I. (2009). Gene-environment interactions in attention-deficit/hyperactivity disorder. *Current Psychiatry Reports, 11*(5), 387–392.

Ficks, C. A., & Waldman, I. D. (2014). Candidate genes for aggression and antisocial behavior: A meta-analysis of association studies of the 5HTTLPR and MAOA-uVNTR. *Behavior Genetics, 44*(5), 427–444.

Field, A. E., Cheung, L., Wolf, A. M., Herzog, D. B., Gortmaker, S. L., & Colditz, G. A. (1999). Exposure to the mass media and weight concerns among girls. *Pediatrics, 103*, e36.

Field, A. E., Sonneville K. R., Micali N., Crosby R. D., Swanson, S. A., Laird, N. M., & Horton, N. J. (2012). Prospective association of common eating disorders and adverse outcomes. *Pediatrics, 130*(2), e289–e295.

Field, A. E., Sonneville, K. R., Crosby, R. D., Swanson, S. A., Eddy, K. T., Camargo, C. A., . . . Micali, N. (2014). Prospective associations of concerns about physique and the development of obesity, binge drinking, and drug use among adolescent boys and young adult men. *JAMA Pediatrics, 168*(1), 34–39.

Fielder, R. L., Carey, K. B., & Carey, M. P. (2013). Are hookups replacing romantic relationships? A longitudinal study of first-year female college students. *Journal of Adolescent Health, 52*(3), 657–659.

Fields, B. W., & Fristad, M. A. (2009). Assessment of childhood bipolar disorder. *Clinical Psychology: Science and Practice, 16*(2), 166–181.

Figueroa, E., & Silk, K. R. (1997). Biological implications of childhood sexual abuse in borderline personality disorder. *Journal of Personality Disorders, 11*, 71–92.

Fileborn, B., Thorpe, R., Hawkes, G., Minichiello, V., Pitts, M., & Dune, T. (2015). Sex, desire and pleasure: Considering the experiences of older Australian women. *Sexual and Relationship Therapy, 30*(1), 117–130.

Filippi, M. (Ed.). (2015). *Oxford textbook of neuroimaging.* Oxford, UK: Oxford University Press.

Fils-Aime, M. L. (1993). Sedative-hypnotic abuse. In D. L. Dunner (Ed.), *Current psychiatric therapy* (pp. 124–131). Philadelphia, PA: W. B. Saunders.

Fincham, F. D., Beach, S. R. H., Harold, G. T., & Osborne, L. N. (1997). Marital satisfaction and depression: Different causal relationships for men and women? *Psychological Science, 8*(5), 351–357.

Fineberg, N. A., Potenza, M. N., Chamberlain, S. R., Berlin, H. A., Menzies, L., Bechara, A., . . . Hollander, E. (2010). Probing compulsive and impulsive behaviors, from animal models to endophenotypes: A narrative review. *Neuropsychopharmacology, 35*(3), 591–604.

Fink, M., & Sackeim, H. A. (1996). Convulsive therapy in schizophrenia? *Schizophrenia Bulletin, 22*, 27–39.

Finkel, M. (2017). *The stranger in the woods: The extraordinary story of the last true hermit.* Penguin Random House.

Finn, P. R., Sharkansky, E. J., Brandt, K. M., & Turcotte, N. (2000). The effects of family risk, personality, and expectancies on alcohol use and abuse. *Journal of Abnormal Psychology, 109*, 122–133.

Fiore, T. A., Becker, E. A., & Nero, R. C. (1993). Educational interventions for students with attention deficit disorder. *Exceptional Children, 60*, 163–173.

Fiorino, A. S. (1996). Sleep, genes and death: Fatal familial insomnia. *Brain Research Reviews, 22*, 258–264.

First look at conjoined twins. (2006, October 26). *Canada.com.* Retrieved November 1, 2006, from http://www.canada.com/cityguides/toronto/story.html?id0e49832c-7a4f-4ab7-a804-e7cc03c9978f&k13358

First, M. B. (2009). Harmonization of ICD-11 and DSM-V: Opportunities and challenges. *British Journal of Psychiatry, 195*, 382–390.

First, M. B., Bell, C. C., Cuthbert, B., Krystal, J. H., Malison, R., Offord, D. R., . . . Wisner, K. L. (2002). Personality disorders and relational disorders: A research agenda for addressing crucial gaps in DSM. In D. J. Kupfer, M. B. First, & D. A. Regier (Eds.), *A research agenda for DSM-V* (pp. 123–199). Washington, DC: American Psychiatric Association.

First, M. B., & Pincus, H. A. (2002). The DSM-IV text revision: Rationale and potential impact on clinical practice. *Psychiatric Services, 53*, 288–292.

First, M. B., Reed, G. M., Hyman, S. E., & Saxena, S. (2015). The development of the ICD-11 Clinical Descriptions and Diagnostic Guidelines for Mental and Behavioral Disorders. *World Psychiatry, 14*, 82–90.

First, M. B., Williams, J. B. W., Karg, R. S., & Spitzer, R. L. (2015). *User's Guide to Structured Clinical Interview for DSM-5 Disorders (SCID-5-CV), Clinician Version.* American Psychiatric Publishing: Arlington, VA.

First Nations Information Governance Centre. (2018a). *National report of the First Nations Regional Health Survey Phase 3* (Vol. 1). https://fnigc.ca/first-nations-regional-health-survey.html

First Nations Information Governance Centre. (2018b). *National report of the First Nations Regional Health Survey Phase 3* (Vol. 2). https://fnigc.ca/first-nations-regional-health-survey.html

Fischer, C. E., Marchie, A., & Norris, M. (2004). Musical and auditory hallucinations: A spectrum. *Psychiatry and Clinical Neurosciences, 58*(1), 96–98.

Fischer, M. (1971). Psychoses in the offspring of schizophrenic monozygotic twins and their normal co-twins. *British Journal of Psychiatry, 118*, 43–52.

Fish, B. (1987). Infant predictors of the longitudinal course of schizophrenic development. *Schizophrenia Bulletin, 13*, 395–410.

Fishbain, D. A. (1987). Kleptomania as risk-taking behavior in response to depression. *American Journal of Psychotherapy, 41*, 598–603.

Fisher, C. B., & Vacanti-Shova, K. (2012). The responsible conduct of psychological research: An overview of ethical principles, APA Ethics Code standards, and federal regulations. In S. J. Knapp, M. C., Gottlieb, M. M. Handelsman, & L. D. VandeCreek (Eds.), *APA handbook of ethics in psychology, Vol 2: Practice, teaching, and research* (pp. 335–369). Washington, DC: American Psychological Association.

Fisher, J. D., Fisher, W. A., Bryan, A. D., & Misovich, S. J. (2002). Information-motivation-behavioral skills model-based HIV risk behavior change intervention for inner-city high school youth. *Health Psychology, 21*, 177–186.

Fisher, L. (1996). Bizarre right from Day 1. *Maclean's, 109*(28), 14.

Fiske, A., Wetherell, J. L., & Gatz, M. (2009). Depression in older adults. *Annual Review of Clinical Psychology, 5*, 363–389.

Fitts, S. N., Gibson, P., Redding, C. A., & Deiter, P. J. (1989). Body dysmorphic disorder: Implications for its validity as a DSM-III-R clinical syndrome. *Psychological Reports, 64*, 655–658.

Fitzgerald, J. (2000). *Sarah McLachlan: Building a mystery.* Kingston, ON: Quarry Press.

Fitzgerald, P. B., Benitez, J., Daskalakis, J. Z., Brown, T. L., Marston, N. A. U., de Castella, A., & Kulkarni, J. (2005). A double-blind sham-controlled trial of repetitive transcranial magnetic stimulation in the treatment of refractory auditory hallucinations. *Journal of Clinical Psychopharmacology, 25*(4), 358–362.

Fitzgerald, P., Benitez, J., de Castella, A., Daskalakis, Z., Brown, T., & Kulkarni, J. (2006). A randomized controlled trial of sequential bilateral repetitive transcranial magnetic stimulation for treatment-resistant depression. *American Journal of Psychiatry, 163*, 88–94.

Fitzgerald, P. B., Brown, T. L., Marston, N. A., Daskalakis, J., De Castella, A., & Kulkarni, J. (2003). Transcranial magnetic stimulation in the treatment of depression: A double-blind, placebo-controlled trial. *Archives of General Psychiatry, 60*, 1002–1008.

Flaherty, J. H. (2011). The evaluation and management of delirium among older persons. *Medical Clinics of North America, 95*(3), 555–577.

Flament, M. F., Furino, C., & Godart, N. (2005). Evidence-based pharmacotherapy of eating disorders. In D. J. Stein, B. Lerer, & S. Stahl (Eds.), *Evidence-based psychopharmacology* (pp. 204–254). New York, NY: Cambridge University Press.

Fleischman, M. J. (1981). A replication of Patterson's "Intervention for boys with conduct problems." *Journal of Consulting and Clinical Psychology, 49*, 342–351.

Fleming, J. E., Boyle, M. H., & Offord, D. R. (1993). The outcome of adolescent depression in the Ontario child health study follow-up. *Journal of the American Academy of Child and Adolescent Psychiatry, 32*(1), 28–33.

Fleminger, S. (2012). The neuropsychiatry of head injury. In M. G. Gelder, N. C. Andreasen, J. J. Lopez-Ibor, & J. R. Geddes (Eds.), *New Oxford textbook of psychiatry* (2nd ed., Vol. 1, pp. 387–399). New York, NY: Oxford University Press.

Flemming, K. (2010). The use of morphine to treat cancer-related pain: A synthesis of quantitative and qualitative research. *Journal of Pain and Symptom Management, 39*(1), 139–154.

Fliers, E., Vermeulen, S., Rijsdijk, F., Altink, M., Buschgens, C., Rommelse, N., . . . Franke, B. (2009). ADHD and poor motor performance from a family genetic perspective. *Journal of the American Academy of Child & Adolescent Psychiatry, 48*(1), 25–34.

Flight, J. I., & Forth, A. E. (2007). Instrumentally violent youths: The roles of psychopathic traits, empathy, and attachment. *Criminal Justice and Behavior, 34*, 739–751.

Flint, A., Schaffer, A., Meyers, B., Rothschild, A., & Mulsant, B. (2006). Research assessment of patients with psychotic depression: The STOP-PD approach. *Psychiatric Annals, 36*, 48–56.

Flint, J. J. (2009). Molecular genetics. In M. G. Gelder, N. C. Andreasen, J. J. Lopez-Ibor, & J. R. Geddes (Eds.), *New Oxford textbook of psychiatry* (2nd ed., Vol. 1, pp. 222–233). Oxford, UK: Oxford University Press.

Flor, H., Elbert, T., Knecht, S., Weinbruch, C., Pantev, C., Birbaumer, N., . . . Taub, E. (1995). Phantom limb pain as a perceptual correlate of cortical reorganization following arm amputation. *Nature, 375*, 482–484.

Flor, H., & Turk, D. C. (2011). *Chronic pain: An integrated biobehavioral approach.* Seattle: International Association for the Study of Pain Press.

Flores, B., & Schatzberg, A. (2006). Psychotic depression. In D. J. Stein, D. J. Kupfer, & A. F. Schatzberg (Eds.), *The American Psychiatric Publishing textbook of mood disorders* (pp. 561–571). Arlington, VA: American Psychiatric Publishing.

Foa, E. B., Gillihan, S. J., & Bryant, R. A. (2013). Challenge and successes in dissemination of evidence-based treatment for posttraumatic stress: Lessons learned from prolonged exposure therapy for PTSD. *Psychological Science in the Public Interest (Supplement), 14*, 65–11.

Foa, E. B., Jenike, M., Kozak, M. J., Joffe, R., Baer, L., Pauls, D., . . . Turner, S. M. (1996). Obsessive–compulsive disorder. In T. A. Widiger, A. J. Frances, H. A. Pincus, M. R. Ross, M. B. First, & W. W. Davis (Eds.), *DSM-IV sourcebook* (Vol. 2, pp. 549–576). Washington, DC: American Psychiatric Association.

Foa, E. B., Liebowitz, M. R., Kozak, M. J., Davies, S., Campeas, R., Franklin, M. E., . . . Tu, X. (2005). Randomized, placebo-controlled trial of exposure and ritual prevention, clomipramine, and their combination in the treatment of obsessive–compulsive disorder. *American Journal of Psychiatry, 162*, 151–161.

Foa, E. B., McLean, C. P., Capaldi, S., & Rosenfield, D. (2013). Prolonged exposure vs. supportive counseling for sexual abuse-related PTSD in adolescent girls: A randomized controlled trial. *JAMA, 310*, 2650–2657.

Foley, K. R., Dyke, P., Girdler, S., Bourke, J., & Leonard, H. (2012). Young adults with intellectual disability transitioning from school to post-school: A literature review framed within the ICF. *Disability and Rehabilitation, 34*(20), 1747–1764.

Follman, M. (2003, September 8). Canada's safe haven for *junkies. Salon.com.* Retrieved October 27, 2003, from http://www.salon.com/news/feature/2003/09/08/vancouver/index_np.html

Folstein, M. F., Folstein, S. E., & McHugh, P. R. (1975). Mini-mental state: A practical method for grading the cognitive state of patients for the clinician. *Journal of Psychiatric Research, 12*, 189–198.

Fong, T. G., Davis, D., Growdon, M. E., Albuquerque, A., & Inouye, S. K. (2015). The interface between delirium and dementia in elderly adults. *The Lancet Neurology, 14*(8), 823–832.

Foot, M., & Koszyčki, D. (2004). Gender differences in anxiety-related traits in patients with panic disorder. *Depression and Anxiety, 20*, 123–130.

Forand, N. R., & Derubeis, R. J. (2013). Pretreatment anxiety predicts patterns of change in cognitive behavioral therapy and medications for depression. *Journal of Consulting and Clinical Psychology, 81*(5), 774–782. https://doi.org/10.1037/a0032985

Ford, D. E., & Kamerow, D. B. (1989). Epidemiologic study of sleep disturbances and psychiatric disorder: An opportunity for prevention? *JAMA, 262,* 1479–1484.

Ford, E. S., Croft, J. B., Posner, S. F., Goodman, R. A., & Giles, W. H. (2013). Co-occurrence of leading lifestyle-related chronic conditions among adults in the United States, 2002–2009. *Preventing Chronic Disease, 10,* E6. https://doi.org/10.5888/pcd10.120316

Ford, J. B., Sutter, M. E., Owen, K. P., & Albertson, T. E. (2014). Volatile substance misuse: An updated review of toxicity and treatment. *Clinical Reviews in Allergy & Immunology, 46*(1), 19–33. https://doi.org/10.1007/s12016-013-8371-1

Ford, M. R., & Widiger, T. A. (1989). Sex bias in the diagnosis of histrionic and antisocial personality disorders. *Journal of Consulting and Clinical Psychology, 57*, 301–305.

Fordyce, W. E. (1976). *Behavioral methods in chronic pain and illness.* St. Louis, MO: Mosby.

Fordyce, W. E. (1988). Pain and suffering: A reappraisal. *American Psychologist, 43*(4), 276–283.

Forestell, C. A., Humphrey, T. M., & Stewart, S. H. (2004). Involvement of body weight and shape factors in ratings of attractiveness by women: A replication and extension of Tassinary and Hansen (1998). *Personality & Individual Differences, 36*, 295–305.

Forti, G., Corona, G., Vignozzi, L., & Maggi, M. (2012). Testosterone and other hormonal therapies (antiestrogen, DHEA, thyroid hormones) for erectile dysfunction. *Hormonal Therapy for Male Sexual Dysfunction*, 42–54.

Fortier, P., Mottard, J.-P., & Trudel, G. (2003). Study of sexuality-related characteristics in young adults with schizophrenia treated with novel neuroleptics and in a comparison group of young adults. *Schizophrenia Bulletin, 29*, 559–572.

Fossey, M., Libman, E., Bailes, S., Baltzan, M., Schondorf, R., Amsel, R., & Fichten, C. S. (2004). Sleep quality and psychological adjustment in chronic fatigue syndrome. *Journal of Behavioral Medicine, 27*(6), 581–605.

Foster, J. D. (2004, April 6). *Corson getting one more shot at the title.* Retrieved July 15, 2004, from http://www.dallasstars.com/news/news-Detail.jsp?id2121

Fortes, I. S., Paula, C. S., Oliveira, M. C., Bordin, I. A., de Jesus Mari, J., & Rohde, L. A. (2015). A cross-sectional study to assess the prevalence of DSM-5 specific learning disorders in representative school samples from the second to sixth grade in Brazil. *European Child & Adolescent Psychiatry*, 1–13.

Fournier, J. C., DeRubeis, R. J., Hollon, S. D., Dimidjian, S., Amsterdam, J. D., Shelton, R. C., & Fawcett, J. (2010). Antidepressant drug effects and depression severity: A patient-level cap meta-analysis. *JAMA, 303*(1), 47–53.

Fouts, G., & Burggraf, K. (2000). Television situation comedies: Female weight, male negative comments, and audience reactions. *Sex Roles, 42*, 925–932.

Fowler, J. C. (2012). Suicide risk assessment in clinical practice: Pragmatic guidelines for imperfect assessments. *Psychotherapy, 49*(1), 81–90.

Fowles, D. C. (1988). Psychophysiology and psychopathy: A motivational approach. *Psychophysiology, 25*, 373–391.

Fox, E., & Damjanovic, L. (2006). The eyes are sufficient to produce a threat superiority effect. *Emotion, 6*, 534–539.

Fox, J., & Jones, K. D. (2013). DSM-5 and bereavement: The loss of normal grief? Counseling & *Development, 91*(1), 113–119.

Fox, M. J. (2002). *Lucky man: A memoir.* New York, NY: Hyperion Books.

Fox, P. T., Ingham, R. J., Ingham, J. C., Hirsch, T. B., Downs, J. H., Martin, C., . . . Lancaster, J. L. (1996). A PET study of the neural systems of stuttering. *Nature, 382*, 158–161.

Foy, D. W., Resnick, H. S., Sipprelle, R. C., & Carroll, E. M. (1987). Premilitary, military and postmilitary factors in the development of combat related posttraumatic stress disorder. *The Behavior Therapist, 10*, 3–9.

Frances, A. (2009). Whither DSM-V? *British Journal of Psychiatry, 195,* 391–392.

Frances, A. (2010, February 11). Opening Pandora's box: The 19 worst suggestions for DSM-5. *Psychiatric Times.*

Frances, A. J. (2012). *DSM 5 is guide not bible—Ignore its ten worst changes. Psychology Today.* Retrieved from http://www.com/blog/dsm5-in-distress/201212/DSM-5-is-guide-not-bible-ignore-its-ten-worst-changes/comments

Frances, A., & Blumenthal, S. J. (1989). Personality disorders and characteristics in youth suicide. In *Alcohol, drug abuse and mental health administration. Report of the secretary's task force on youth suicide: Vol. 12, risk factors for youth suicide* (DHHS Publication No. ADM89-1622, pp. 172–185). Washington, DC: U.S. Government Printing Office.

Frances, A. J., & Widiger, T. (2012). Psychiatric diagnosis: Lessons from the DSM-IV past and cautions for the DSM-5 future. In S. Nolen-Hoeksema, T. D. Cannon, & T. Widiger (Eds.), *Annual review of clinical psychology* (Vol. 8, pp. 109–130). Palo Alto, CA: Annual Reviews.

Frances, R., Franklin, J., & Flavin, D. (1986). Suicide and alcoholism. *Annals of the New York Academy of Science, 287,* 316–326.

Francis, D. D., Diorio, J., Plotsky, P. M., & Meaney, M. J. (2002). Environmental enrichment reverses the effects of maternal separation on stress reactivity. *Journal of Neuroscience, 22,* 7840–7843.

Francis, D., Diorio, J., Liu, D., & Meaney, M. J. (1999). Nongenomic transmission across generations of maternal behavior and stress responses in the rat. *Science, 286,* 1155–1158.

Francis, J. A., Stewart, S. H., & Hounsell, S. (1997). Dietary restraint and the selective processing of forbidden and nonforbidden food words. *Cognitive Therapy & Research, 21,* 633–646.

Frank, E., Anderson, C., & Rubinstein, D. (1978). Frequency of sexual dysfunction in "normal" couples. *New England Journal of Medicine, 299,* 111–115.

Frank, E., Hlastala, S., Ritenour, A., Houck, P., Tu, X. M., Monk, T. H., Mallinger, A. G., & Kupfer, D. J. (1997). Inducing lifestyle regularity in recovering bipolar disorder patients: Results from the maintenance therapies in bipolar disorder protocol. *Biological Psychiatry, 41,* 1165–1173.

Frank, E., Kupfer, D. J., Perel, J. M., Cornes, C., Jarrett, D. B., Mallinger, A. G., . . . Grochocinski, V. J. (1990). Three-year outcomes for maintenance therapies in recurrent depression. *Archives of General Psychiatry, 47*(12), 1093–1099.

Frank, E., Kupfer, D. J., Thase, M. E., Mallinger, A. G., Swartz, H. A., Fagiolini, A. M., . . . Monk, T. (2005). Two-year outcomes for interpersonal and social rhythm therapy in individuals with bipolar I disorder. *Archives of General Psychiatry, 62,* 996–100.

Frank, E., Swartz, H. A., Mallinger, A. G., Thase, M. E., Weaver, E. V., & Kupfer, D. J. (1999). Adjunctive psychotherapy for bipolar disorder: Effects of changing treatment modality. *Journal of Abnormal Psychology, 108*(4), 579–587.

Frank, E.., Nimgaonkar, V. L., Philips, M. L., & Kupfer, D. J. (2015). All the world's a (clinical) sage: Rethinking bipolar disorder from a longitudinal perspective. *Molecular Psychiatry, 20,* 23–31.

Franklin, J. E., & Frances, R. J. (1999). Alcohol and other psychoactive substance use disorders. In R. E. Hales, S. C. Yudofsky, & J. A. Talbott (Eds.), *Textbook of psychiatry* (3rd ed., pp. 363–423). Washington, DC: American Psychiatric Press.

Franklin, K. A., & Lindberg, E. (2015). Obstructive sleep apnea is a common disorder in the population—A review on the epidemiology of sleep apnea. *Journal of Thoracic Disease, 7*(8), 1311.

Franklin, M. E., & Foa, E. B. (2014). Obsessive–compulsive disorder. In D. H. Barlow (Ed.), *Clinical handbook of psychological disorders: A step-by-step treatment manual* (5th ed.). New York, NY: Guilford Press.

Franko, D. L., Keshaviah, A., Eddy, K. T., Krishna, M., Davis, M. C., Keel, P. K., & Herzog, D. B. (2013). A longitudinal investigation of mortality in anorexia nervosa and bulimia nervosa. *American Journal of Psychiatry, 170*(8), 917–925.

Franko, D. L., Thompson-Brenner, H., Thompson, D. R., Boisseau, C. L., Davis, A., Forbush, K. T., & Wilson, G. T. (2012). Racial/ethnic differences in adult participants in randomized clinical trials of binge eating disorder. *Journal of Consulting and Clinical Psychology, 80*, 186–195.

Franko, D. L., Wonderlich, S. A., Little, D., & Herzog, D. B. (2004). Diagnosis and classification of eating disorders. In J. K. Thompson (Ed.), *Handbook of eating disorders and obesity* (pp. 58–80). New York, NY: John Wiley & Sons.

Fraser, C., & Desjardins, N. (2009). *National justice survey 2009: Mental health disorders in the criminal justice system*. Ottawa, ON: Department of Justice Canada. Retrieved from http://epe.lac-bac.gc.ca/100/200/301/pwgsc-tpsgc/por-ef/justice_canada/2010/043-09-e/summary.htm

Fraser, G. A. (1994). Dissociative phenomena and disorders: Clinical presentations. In R. M. Klei & B. K. Doane (Eds.), *Psychological concepts and dissociative disorders* (pp. 131–151). Hillside, NJ: Erlbaum.

Frasure-Smith, N., & Lesperance, F. (2005). Depression and coronary heart disease: Complex synergism of mind, body, and environment. *Current Directions in Psychological Science, 14*, 39–43.

Frasure-Smith, N., Lesperance, F., Juneau, M., Talajic, M., & Bourassa, M. G. (1999). Gender, depression, and one-year prognosis after myocardial infarction. *Psychosomatic Medicine, 61*, 26–37.

Fratiglioni, L., & Qiu, C. (2009). Prevention of common neurodegenerative disorders in the elderly. *Experimental Gerontology, 44*(1), 46–50.

Fratiglioni, L., Grut, M., Forsell, Y., Viitanen, M., Grafstrom, M., & Holmen, K., . . . Winblad, B. (1991). Prevalence of Alzheimer's disease and other dementias in an elderly urban population: Relationship with age, sex and education. *Neurology, 41*, 1886–1892.

Fratiglioni, L., Winblad, B., & von Strauss, E. (2007). Prevention of Alzheimer's disease and dementia: Major findings from the Kungsholmen Project. *Physiology & Behavior, 92*(1–2), 98–104.

Frazier, T. W., Youngstrom, E. A., Speer, L., Embacher, R., Law, P., Constantino, J. N., & Eng, C. (2012). Validation of proposed DSM-5 criteria for autism spectrum disorder. *Journal of the American Academy of Child & Adolescent Psychiatry, 51*(1), 28–40.

Fredrikson, M., & Matthews, K. A. (1990). Cardiovascular responses to behavioral stress and hypertension: A meta-analytic review. *Annals of Behavioral Medicine, 12*(1), 30–39.

Fredrikson, M., Annas, P., & Wik, G. (1997). Parental history, aversive exposure and the development of snake and spider phobia in women. *Behavior Research and Therapy, 35*, 23–28.

Freed, D. A. (2007, May 13). From jokester to jailbird. *The Toronto Star*. Retrieved June 9, 2007, from http://www.thestar.com/article/213298

Freedman, M., Leach, L., Kaplan, E., Winocur, G., Shulman, K. I., & Delis, D. C. (1994). *Clock drawing: A neuropsychological analysis*. New York, NY: Oxford University Press.

Freeman, A., Pretzer, J., Fleming, B., & Simon, K. M. (1990). *Clinical applications of cognitive therapy*. New York, NY: Plenum Press.

Freeman, E. W., Rickels, K., Sammel, M. D., Lin, H., & Sondheimer, S. J. (2009). Time to relapse after short- or long-term treatment of severe premenstrual syndrome with sertraline. *Archives of General Psychiatry, 66*(5), 537–544.

French-Belgian Collaborative Group. (1982). Ischemic heart disease and psychological patterns: Prevalence and incidence studies in Belgium and France. *Advances in Cardiology, 29*, 25–31.

Frenda, S. J., Nichols, R. M., & Loftus, E. F. (2011). Current issues and advances in misinformation research. *Current Directions in Psychological Science, 20*(1), 20–23.

Freud, A. (1946). *Ego and the mechanisms of defense*. New York, NY: International Universities Press.

Freud, S. (1957). Mourning and melancholia. In J. Strachey (Ed. and Trans.), *The standard edition of the complete psychological works of Sigmund Freud* (Vol. 14). London: Hogarth Press. (Original work published 1917).

Freud, S. (1962). The neuropsychoses of defence. In J. Strachey (Ed.), *The complete psychological works* (Vol. 3, pp. 45–62). London: Hogarth Press. (Original work published 1894).

Freund, K., Seto, M. C., & Kuban, M. (1996). Two types of fetishism. *Behaviour Research and Therapy, 34*, 687–694.

Frick, P. J., Strauss, C. C., Lahey, B. B., & Christ, M. A. G. (1993). Behavior disorders of children. In P. B. Sutker & H. E. Adams (Eds.), *Comprehensive handbook of psychopathology* (pp. 765–789). New York, NY: Plenum.

Friedl, M. C., & Draijer, N. (2000). Dissociative disorders in Dutch psychiatric inpatients. *American Journal of Psychiatry, 157*(6), 1012–1013.

Friedman, A. F., Bonlinskey, P. K., Levak, R. W., & Nichols, D. S. (2014). *Psychological Assessment with the MMPI-2/MMPI-2-RF*. London: Routledge.

Friedman, J. M. (2009). Obesity: Causes and control of excess body fat. *Nature, 459*(7245), 340–342.

Friedman, M. J., Resick, P. A., Bryant, R. A., Strain, J., Horowitz, M., & Spiegel, D. (2011). Classification of trauma and stressor-related disorders in DSM-5. *Depression and Anxiety, 28*(9), 737–749.

Friedman, M., & Rosenman, R. H. (1959). Association of specific overt behavior pattern with blood and cardiovascular findings. *Journal of the American Medical Association, 169*, 1286.

Friedman, M., & Rosenman, R. H. (1974). *Type A behavior and your heart*. New York, NY: Knopf.

Fried-Oken, M., Rowland, C., Daniels, D., Dixon, M., Fuller, B., Mills, C., & Oken, B. (2012). AAC to support conversation in persons with moderate Alzheimer's disease. *Augmentative and Alternative Communication, 28*(4), 219–231.

Fritz, C. O., Morris, P. E., & Richler, J. J. (2012). Effect size estimates: Current use, calculations, and interpretation. *Journal of Experimental Psychology: General, 141*(1), 2–18.

Frodl, T., & Skokauskas, N. (2012). Meta-analysis of structural MRI studies in children and adults with attention deficit hyperactivity disorder indicates

treatment effects. *Acta Psychiatrica Scandinavica, 125*(2), 114–126.

Frombonne, E., Quirke, S., & Hagen, A. (2011). Epidemiology of pervasive developmental disorders. In D. G. Amaral, G. Dawson, & D. Geschwind (Eds.), *Autism spectrum disorders* (pp. 90–111). New York, NY: Oxford University Press.

Fromm-Reichmann, F. (1948). Notes on the development of treatment of schizophrenics by psychoanalytic psychotherapy. *Psychiatry, 11*, 263–273.

Frost, R. O., & Rasmussen, J. L. (2012). Phenomenology and characteristics of compulsive hoarding. In G. Steketee (Ed.), *The Oxford handbook of obsessive compulsive and spectrum disorders* (pp. 70–88). New York, NY: Oxford University Press.

Frost, R. O., Patronek, G., & Rosenfield, E. (2011). Comparison of object and animal hoarding. *Depression and Anxiety, 28*(10), 885–891.

Frost, R. O., Sher, K. J., & Geen, T. (1986). Psychotherapy and personality characteristics of non-clinical compulsive checkers. *Behaviour Research and Therapy, 24*, 133–143.

Frost, R. O., Steketee, G., & Tolin, D. F. (2012). Diagnosis and assessment of hoarding disorder. *Annual Review of Clinical Psychology, 8*, 219–242.

Fruhauf, S., Gerger, H., Schmidt, H. M., Munder, T., & Barth, J. (2013). Efficacy of psychological interventions for sexual dysfunction: A systematic review and meta-analysis. *Archives of Sexual Behavior, 42*(6), 915–933.

Fryar, C., Hirsch, R., Porter, K., Kottiri, B., Brody, D., & Louis, T. (2007). *Drug use and sexual behaviors reported by adults: United States, 1999–2002* (Advance data from Vital and Health Statistics, No. 384). Hyattsville, MD: National Center for Health Statistics.

Fugl-Meyer, A. R., & Sjogren Fugl-Meyer, K. (1999). Sexual disabilities, problems, and satisfaction in 18–74 year old Swedes. *Scandinavian Journal of Sexology, 3*, 79–105.

Fuji, D. E., Tsushima, V., Murakami-Brundage, J., & Kamath, V. (2014). Assessing for schizophrenia in Asian Americans. In *Guide to psychological assessment with Asians* (pp. 305–326). Springer New York.

Fukuda, K., Straus, S. E., Hickie, I., Sharpe, M. B., Dobbins, J. G., & Komaroff, A. L. (1994). Chronic fatigue syndrome: A comprehensive approach to its diagnosis and management. *Annals of Internal Medicine, 121*, 953–959.

Fullana, M. A., Mataix-Cols, D., Caspi, A., Harrington, H., Grisham, J. R., Moffitt, T. E., & Poulton, R. (2009). Obsessions and compulsions in the community: Prevalence, interference, help-seeking, developmental stability, and co-occurring psychiatric conditions. *American Journal of Psychiatry, 166*(3), 329–336.

Fulton, H. G., Krank, M. D., & Stewart, S. H. (2012). Outcome expectancy liking: A self-generated, self-coded measure predicts adolescent substance use trajectories. *Psychology of Addictive Behaviors, 26*, 870–879.

Fulton, J. J., Kiel, E. J., Tull, M. T., & Gratz, K. L. (2014). Associations between perceived parental overprotection, experiential avoidance, and anxiety. *Journal of Experimental*

Psychopathology, 5, 200–211. https://doi.org/10.5127/jep.034813

Fung, J. (2016). *The obesity code: Unlocking the secrets of weight loss*. Greystone.

Furman, W., & Colibee, C. (2014). Sexual activity with romantic and nonromantic partners and psychosocial adjustment in young adults. *Archives of Sexual Behavior, 43*(7), 1327–1341.

Furnham, A., & Crump, J. (2014). A bright side, facet analysis of Schizotypal Personality Disorder: The relationship between the HDS Imaginative Factor, the NEO-PI-R personality trait facets in a large adult sample. *Thinking Skills and Creativity, 11*, 42–47.

Furnham, A., & Wong, L. (2007). A cross-cultural comparison of British and Chinese beliefs about the causes, behaviour manifestations and treatment of schizophrenia. *Psychiatry Research, 151*, 123–138.

Furr, J. M., Comer, J. S., Sacks, H., Chan, P. T., Kerns, C. E., Feinberg, L., & Kurtz, S. M. S. (2012, November). *The Boston University Brave Buddies Program: A replication of the Brave Buddies Intensive, Outpatient Treatment Program for children with selective mutism*. Paper presented at the 46th annual meeting of the Association for Behavioral and Cognitive Therapies, National Harbor, MD.

Furr, J. M., Tiwari, S., Suveg, C., & Kendall, P. C. (2009). Anxiety disorders in children and adolescents. In M. M. Antony & M. B. Stein (Eds.), *Oxford handbook of anxiety and related disorders* (pp. 636–656). New York, NY: Oxford University Press.

Fusar-Poli, P., & Yung, A. R. (2012). Should attenuated psychosis syndrome be included in DSM-5? *The Lancet, 379*(9816), 591–592.

Fusar-Poli, P., Carpenter, W. T., Woods, S. W., & McGlashan, T. H. (2014). Attenuated psychosis syndrome: Ready for DSM-5.1? *Annual Review of Clinical Psychology, 10*, 155–192.

Fyer, A. J., Mannuzza, S., Chapman, T. F., Liebowitz, M. R., & Klein, D. F. (1993). A direct interview family study of social phobia. *Archives of General Psychiatry, 50*, 286–293.

Fyer, A., Liebowitz, M., Gorman, J., Compeas, R., Levin, A., Davies, S., . . . Klein, D. F. (1987). Discontinuation of alprazolam treatment in panic patients. *American Journal of Psychiatry, 144*, 303–308.

Gacono, C. B. (Ed.). (2000). *The clinical and forensic assessment of psychopathy: A practitioner's guide*. Mahwah, NJ: Erlbaum.

Gadsby, J. (2001, October 9). *Benzodiazepines: Responsible prescribing & informed use*. Retrieved August 17, 2004, from http://www.benzo.org.uk/jegres.htm

Gaetz, S., Gulliver, T., & Richter, T. (2014). *The state of homelessness in Canada, 2014*. The Homeless Hub Press. https://www.homelesshub.ca/sites/default/files/attachments/SOHC2014.pdf

Gagnon, J. H. (1990). The explicit and implicit use of the scripting perspective in sex research. *Annual Review of Sex Research, 1*, 1–43.

Gagnon, M., & Ladouceur, R. (1992). Behavioral treatment of child stutterers: Replication and extension. *Behavior Therapy, 23*, 113–129.

Galambos, N. L., & Leadbeater, B. J. (2002). Transitions in adolescent research. In W. W. Hartup & R. K. Silbereisen (Eds.), *Growing points in developmental science: An introduction* (pp. 287–306). Philadelphia, PA: Psychology Press.

Galambos, N. L., Barker, E. T., & Almeida, D. M. (2003). Parents do matter: Trajectories of change in externalizing and internalizing problems in early adolescence. *Child Development, 74*, 578–594.

Galea, S., Ahern, J., Resnick, H., Kilpatrick, D., Bucuvalas, M., Gold, J., and Vlahov, D. (2002). Psychological sequelae of the September 11 terrorist attacks in New York City. *New England Journal of Medicine, 346*, 982–987.

Gallagher, M. W., Bentley, K. H., & Barlow, D. H. (2014). Perceived control and vulnerability to anxiety disorders: A meta-analytic review. *Cognitive Therapy and Research, 38*, 571–584.

Gallagher-Thompson, D., & Osgood, N. J. (1997). Suicide later in life. *Behavior Therapy, 28*, 23–41.

Gallagher-Thompson, D., Rabinowitz, Y., Tang, P., Tse, C., Kwo, E., Hsu, S., … Thompson, L. W. (2006). Recruiting Chinese Americans for dementia caregiver intervention research: Suggestions for success. *American Journal of Geriatric Psychiatry, 14*(8), 676.

Gandaglia, G., Briganti, A., Jackson, G., Kloner, R. A., Montorsi, F., Montorsi, P., & Vlachopoulos, C. (2014). A systematic review of the association between erectile dysfunction and cardiovascular disease. *European Urology, 65*(5), 968–978.

Ganguli, M., Blacker, D., Blazer, D. G., Grant, I., Jeste, D. V., Paulsen, J. S., & Sachdev, P. S. (2011). Classification of neurocognitive disorders in DSM-5: A work in progress. *American Journal of Geriatric Psychiatry, 19*(3), 205–210.

Gansler, D. A., McLaughlin, N. C., Iguchi, L., Jerram, M., Moore, D. W., Bhadelia, R., & Fulwiler, C. (2009). A multivariate approach to aggression and the orbital frontal cortex in psychiatric patients. *Psychiatry Research: Neuroimaging, 171*(3), 145–154.

Garber, J., Clarke, G. N., Weersing, V. R., Beardslee, W. R., Brent, D. A., Gladstone, T. R., & Iyengar, S. (2009). Prevention of depression in at-risk adolescents: A randomized controlled trial. *JAMA, 301*(21), 2215–2224.

Garber, J., Gallerani, C. M., & Frankel, S. A. (2009). Depression in children. In I. H. Gotlib & C. L. Hammen (Eds.), *Handbook of depression* (2nd ed., pp. 405–443). New York, NY: Guilford Press.

Garber, S. W., Garber, M. D., & Spizman, R. F. (1996). *Beyond Ritalin: Facts about medication and other strategies for helping children, adolescents, and adults with attention deficit disorders.* New York, NY: Villard.

Garcia, J., McGowan, B. K., & Green, K. F. (1972). Biological constraints on conditioning. In A. H. Black & W. F. Prokasy (Eds.), *Classical conditioning II: Current research and theory.* New York, NY: Appleton-Century-Crofts.

Garcia-Lopez, L. J., Olivares, J., Beidel, D., Albano, A., Turner, S., & Rosa, A. (2006). Efficacy of three treatment protocols for adolescents with social anxiety disorder: A 5-year follow-up assessment. *Journal of Anxiety Disorders, 20*(2), 175–191.

Garety, P. A., Kuipers, L., Fowler, D., Chamberlain, F., & Dunn, G. (1994). Cognitive behavioural therapy for drug-resistant psychosis. *British Journal of Medical Psychology, 67*, 259–271.

Garfield, A. F., & Zigler, E. (1993). Adolescent suicide prevention: Current research and social policy implications. *American Psychologist, 48*(2), 169–182.

Garfinkel, P. E. (1992). Evidence in support of attitudes to shape and weight as a diagnostic criterion of bulimia nervosa. *International Journal of Eating Disorders, 11*(4), 321–325.

Garfinkel, P. E. (2002). Guest editorial: Eating disorders. *Canadian Journal of Psychiatry, 47*, 225–226.

Garfinkel, P. E., & Dorian, B. J. (2001). Improving understanding and care for the eating disorders. In R. H. Striegel-Moore & L. Smolak (Eds.), *Eating disorders: Innovative directions in research and practice* (pp. 9–26). Washington, DC: American Psychological Association.

Garfinkel, P. E., & Garner, D. M. (1982). *Anorexia nervosa: A multidimensional perspective.* New York, NY: Brunner/Mazel.

Garfinkel, P. E., Kennedy, S. H., & Kaplan, A. S. (1995). Views on classification and diagnosis of eating disorders. *Canadian Journal of Psychiatry, 40*, 445–456.

Garfinkel, P. E., Lin, E., Goering P., Spegg, C., Goldbloom, D. S., Kennedy, S., … Woodside, D. B. (1995). Bulimia nervosa in a Canadian community sample: Prevalence in comparison of subgroups. *American Journal of Psychiatry, 152*, 1052–1058.

Garfinkel, P. E., Lin, E., Goering, P., Spegg, C., Goldbloom, D. S., Kennedy, S., … Woodside, D. B. (1996). Purging and nonpurging forms of bulimia nervosa in a community sample. *International Journal of Eating Disorders, 20*, 231–238.

Garfinkel, P. E., Moldofsky, H., & Garner, D. M. (1979). The heterogeneity of anorexia nervosa: Bulimia as a distinct subgroup. *Archives of General Psychiatry, 37*, 1036–1040.

Garland, E. L., Howard, M. O., Vaughn, M. G., & Perron, B. E. (2011). Volatile substance misuse in the United States. *Substance Use & Misuse, 46*(Supplement 1), 8–20.

Garlow, S., & Nemeroff, C. B. (2003). Neurobiology of depressive disorders. In R. J. Davidson, K. R. Scherer, & H. H. Goldsmith (Eds.), *Handbook of affective sciences* (pp. 1021–1043). New York, NY: Oxford University Press.

Garmezy, N., & Rutter, M. (Eds.). (1983). *Stress, coping and development in children.* New York, NY: McGraw-Hill.

Garner, D. M., & Fairburn, C. G. (1988). Relationship between anorexia nervosa and bulimia nervosa: Diagnostic implications. In D. M. Garner & P. E. Garfinkel (Eds.), *Diagnostic issues in anorexia nervosa and bulimia nervosa.* New York, NY: Brunner/Mazel.

Garner, D. M., & Garfinkel, P. E. (Eds.). (1985). *Handbook of psychotherapy for anorexia nervosa and bulimia.* New York, NY: Guilford Press.

Garner, D. M., & Needleman, L. D. (1996). Step care and the decision-tree models for treating eating disorders. In J. K. Thompson (Ed.), *Body image, eating disorders and obesity* (pp. 225–252). Washington, DC: American Psychological Association.

Garner, D. M., Garfinkel, P. E., Rockert, W., & Olmsted, M. P. (1987). A prospective study of eating disturbances in the ballet. Ninth World Congress of the International College of Psychosomatic Medicine, Sydney, Australia. *Psychotherapy and Psychosomatics, 48*, 170–175.

Garner, D. M., Garfinkel, P. E., Schwartz, D., & Thompson, M. (1980). Cultural expectation of thinness in women. *Psychological Reports, 47*, 483–491.

Garner, D. M., Olmstead, M. P., & Polivy, J. (1983). Development and validation of a multidimensional eating disorder inventory for anorexia nervosa and bulimia. *International Journal of Eating Disorders, 2*(2), 15–34.

Garrabe, J., & Cousin, F. R. (2012). Acute and transient psychotic disorders. In M. G. Gelder, N. C. Andreasen, J. J. Lopez-Ibor, & J. R. Geddes (Eds.), *New Oxford textbook of psychiatry* (2nd ed., Vol. 1, pp. 602–608). New York, NY: Oxford University Press.

Garry, M., & Wade, K. A. (2005). Actually, a picture is worth less than 45 words: Narratives produce more false memories than photographs do. *Psychonomic Bulletin and Review, 12*, 359–366.

Gatchel, R. (2005). *Clinical essentials of pain management.* Washington, DC: American Psychological Association.

Gatchel, R. J., & Turk, D. C. (Eds.). (1996). *Psychological approaches to pain management: A practitioner's handbook.* New York, NY: Guilford Press.

Gatchel, R. J., Peng, Y. B., Peters, M. L., Fuchs, P. N., & Turk, D. C. (2007). The biopsychosocial approach to chronic pain: Scientific advances and future directions. *Psychological Bulletin, 133*, 581–624.

Gatz, M., & Smyer, M. A. (1992). The mental health system and older adults in the 1990s. *American Psychologist, 47*(6), 741–751.

Gaudreau, J.-D. (2012). Insights into the neural mechanisms underlying delirium. *American Journal of Psychiatry, 169*(5), 450–451.

Gavin, N. I., Gaynes, B. N., Lohr, K. N., Meltzer-Brody, S., Gartlehner, G., & Swinson, T. (2005). Perinatal depression—A systematic review of prevalence and incidence. *Obstetrics and Gynecology, 106*(5), 1071–1083.

Gaw, A. C. (2008). Cultural issues. In R. E. Hales, S. C. Yudofsky, & G. O. Gabbard (Eds.), *The American Psychiatric Publishing textbook of psychiatry* (5th ed., pp. 1529–1547). Arlington, VA: American Psychiatric Publishing, Inc.

Gawin, F. H., Kleber, H. D., Byck, R., Rounsaville, B. J., Kosten, T. R., Jatlow, P. I., & Morgan, C. (1989). Desipramine facilitation of initial cocaine abstinence. *Archives of General Psychiatry, 46*, 117–121.

Gearhart, J. P. (1989). Total ablation of the penis after circumcision electrocautery: A method of management and long term follow-up. *Journal of Urology, 42*, 789–801.

Geer, J. H., Morokoff, P., & Greenwood, P. (1974). Sexual arousal in women: The development of a measurement device for vaginal blood volume. *Archives of Sexual Behavior, 3*, 559–564.

Geist, R., Heinmaa, M., Stephens, D., Davis, R., & Katzman, D. K. (2000). Comparison of family therapy and family group psycho-education in adolescents with anorexia nervosa. *Canadian Journal of Psychiatry, 45*, 173–178.

Gelinas, L. (1994). The new rights of persons held in psychiatric institutions following the commission of a criminal offence: The Criminal Code revised and corrected. *Canada's Mental Health, 42*(1), 10–16.

Geller, B., Cooper, T. B., Graham, D. L., Fetaer, H. M., Marsteller, F. A., & Wells, J. M. (1992). Pharmacokinetically designed double blind placebo controlled study of nortriptyline in 6–12 year olds with major depressive disorder: Outcome: Nortriptyline and hydroxy-nortriptyline plasma levels; EKG, BP and side effect measurements. *Journal of the American Academy of Child and Adolescent Psychiatry, 31*, 33–44.

Geller, J. (2002). Estimating readiness for change in anorexia nervosa: Comparing clients, clinicians and research assessors. *International Journal of Eating Disorders, 31*, 251–260.

Gendron, M., & Barrett, L. F. (2009). Reconstructing the past: A century of ideas about emotion in psychology. *Emotion Review, 1*(4), 316–339.

Generations United. (2006). Meth and child welfare: Promising solutions for children, their parents and grandparents. Washington, DC: Author.

George, L. K. (1984). *The burden of caregiving: Center reports of advances in research* (Vol. 8). Durham, NC: Duke University Center for the Study of Aging and Human Development.

George, M. S., Taylor, J. J., & Short, E. B. (2013). The expanding evidence base for rTMS of depression. *Current Opinions in Psychiatry, 26*, 13–18.

Georgiades, K., Lewinsohn, P. M., Monroe, S. M., & Seeley, J. R. (2006). Major depressive disorder in adolescence: The role of subthreshold symptoms. *Journal of the American Academy of Child & Adolescent Psychiatry, 45*, 936–944.

Geraerts, E., & McNally, R. (2008). Forgetting unwanted memories: Directed forgetting and thought suppression methods. *Acta psychologica, 127*(3), 614–622.

Geraerts, E., Lindsay, D. S., Merckelbach, H., Jelicic, M., Raymaekers, L., Arnold, M. M., & Schooler, J. W. (2009). Cognitive mechanisms underlying recovered memory experiences of childhood sexual abuse. *Psychological Science, 20*, 92–98.

Gerin, W., Pickering, T. G., Glynn, L., Christenfeld, N., Schwartz, A., Carroll, D., & Davidson, K. (2000). An historical context for behavioral models of hypertension. *Journal of Psychosomatic Research, 48*, 369–377.

Germain, A., & Kupfer, D. J. (2008). Circadian rhythm disturbances in depression. *Human Psychopharmacology: Clinical and Experimental, 23*(7), 571–585.

Gershon, E. S., Kelsoe, J. R., Kendler, K. S., & Watson, J. D. (2001). It's time to search for susceptibility genes for major mental illnesses. *Science, 294*, 5.

Gerstein, D. R., Volberg, R. A., Toce, M. T., Harwood, H., Johnson, R. A., & Bule, T., & Tucker, J. (1999). *Gambling impact and behavior study: Report to the national gambling impact study commission*. Chicago, IL: University of Chicago.

Geschwind, D. H., & Flint, J. (2015). Genetics and genomics of psychiatric disease. *Science, 349*, 1489–1494.

Gesquiere, L. R., Learn, N. H., Simao, M. C. M., Onyango, P. O., Alberts, S. C., & Altmann J. (2011). Life at the top: Rank and stress in wild male baboons. *Science, 333*(6040), 357–360.

Getsios, D., Caro, J. J., Caro, G., & Ishak, K. (2001). Assessment of health economics in Alzheimer's disease (AHEAD). Galantamine treatment in Canada. *Neurology, 57*, 972–978.

Ghadirian, A.-M., Gregoire, P., & Kosmidis, H. (2001). Creativity and the evolution of psychopathologies. *Creativity Research Journal, 13*, 145–148.

Giacomuzzi, S. M., Riemer, Y., Ertl, M., Kemmler, G., Rossler, H., Hinterhuber, H., & Kurz, M. (2003). Buprenorphine versus methadone maintenance treatment in an ambulant setting: A health-related quality of life assessment. *Addiction, 98*, 693–702.

Giannotti, F., & Cortesi, F. (2009). Family and cultural influences on sleep development. *Child and Adolescent Psychiatric Clinics of North America, 18*(4), 849–861.

Gianoulakis, C. (2001). Influence of the endogenous opioid system on high alcohol consumption and genetic predisposition to alcoholism. *Journal of Psychiatry & Neuroscience, 26*, 304–318.

Gibb, W. R. G. (1989). Dementia and Parkinson's disease. *British Journal of Psychiatry, 154*, 596–614.

Gidron, Y., Davidson, K., & Bata, I. (1999). The short-term effects of a hostility-reduction intervention on male coronary heart disease patients. *Health Psychology, 18*, 416–420.

Giedke, H., & Schwarzler, F. (2002). Therapeutic use of sleep deprivation in depression. *Sleep Medicine Reviews, 6*, 361–377.

Gielen, A. C., McDonald, E. M., & Shields, W. (2015). Unintentional home injuries across the life span: Problems and solutions. *Annual Review of Public Health, 36*, 231–253.

Gielen, A. C., Sleet, D., & DiClemente, R. (Eds.). (2006.) *Injury and violence prevention: Behavioral science theories, methods, and applications.* San Francisco, CA: Jossey-Bass.

Giesbrecht, T., Lynn, S. J., Lilienfeld, S. O., & Merckelbach, H. (2008). Cognitive processes in dissociation: An analysis of core theoretical assumptions. *Psychological Bulletin, 134*(5), 617–647.

Giesbrecht, T., Smeets, T., Leppink, J., Jelicic, M., & Merckelbach, H. (2007). Acute dissociation after 1 night of sleep loss. *Journal of Abnormal Psychology, 116*(3), 599–606.

Giese-Davis, J., Collie, K., Rancourt, K. M., Neri, E., Kraemer, H. C., & Spiegel, D. (2011). Decrease in depression symptoms is associated with longer survival in patients with metastatic breast cancer: A secondary analysis. *Journal of Clinical Oncology, 29*(4), 413–420.

Gieser, L., & Stein, M. I. (Eds.). (1999). *Evocative images: The Thematic Apperception Test and the art of projection.* Washington, DC: American Psychological Association.

Gil, K., Williams, D., Keefe, F., & Beckham, J. (1990). The relationship of negative thoughts to pain and psychological distress. *Behavior Therapy, 21*, 349–362.

Gilham, J. E., Reivich, K. J., Jaycox, L. H., & Seligman, M. E. P. (1995). Prevention of depressive symptoms in schoolchildren: Two-year follow-up. *Psychological Science, 6*(6), 343–351.

Gillberg, C. (1984). Infantile autism and other childhood psychoses in a Swedish urban region: Epidemiological aspects. *Journal of Child Psychology and Psychiatry, 25*, 35–43.

Gillespie, C. F., & Nemeroff, C. B. (2007). Corticotropin-releasing factor and the psychobiology of early-life stress. *Current Directions in Psychological Science, 16*(2), 85–89.

Gillespie-Lynch, K., Sepeta, L., Wang, Y., Marshall, S., Gomez, L., Sigman, M., & Hutman, T. (2012). Early childhood predictors of the social competence of adults with autism. *Journal of Autism and Developmental Disorders, 42*(2), 161–174.

Gillies, L. A. (2001). Interpersonal psychotherapy for depression and other disorders. In D. H. Barlow (Ed.), *Clinical handbook of psychological disorders* (3rd ed., pp. 309–331). New York, NY: Guilford Press.

Gilman, S. E., Breslau, J., Trinh, N.-H., Fava, M., Murphy, J. M., & Smoller, J. W. (2012). Evidence concerning the bereavement exclusion in major depression. *Archives of General Psychiatry, 69*(11), 1179–1180.

Gilmour, H. (2016). Threshold and subthreshold generalized anxiety disorder (GAD) and suicide ideation. *Health Reports, 27*(11), 13–21. https://www150.statcan.gc.ca/n1/pub/82-003-x/2016011/article/14672-eng.htm

Gilmour, H., Ramage-Morin, P. L., & Wong, S. L. (2019). Infant bed sharing in Canada. *Health Reports, 30*(7), 13–19. https://www150.statcan.gc.ca/n1/en/catalogue/82-003-X201900700002

Gilmore, J. H. (2010). Understanding what causes schizophrenia: A developmental perspective. *American Journal of Psychiatry, 167*(1), 8–10.

Ginsburg, G. S., Becker, E. M., Keeton, C. P., Sakolsky, D., Piacentini, J., Albano, A. M., ... Kendall, P. C. (2014). Naturalistic follow-up of youths treated for pediatric anxiety disorders. *JAMA Psychiatry, 71*, 310.

Ginsburg, G. S., Drake, K. L., Tein, J. Y., Teetsel, R., & Riddle, M. A. (2015). Preventing onset of anxiety disorders in offspring of anxious parents: A randomized controlled trial of a family-based intervention. *American Journal of Psychiatry, 172*(12), 1207–1214. https://doi.org/10.1176/appi.ajp.2015.14091178

Girault, J. A., & Greengard, P. (2004). The neurobiology of dopamine signaling. *Archives of Neurology, 61*(5), 641–644.

Gislason, I. L. (1988). Eating disorders in childhood (ages 4 through 11 years). In B. J. Blinder, B. F. Chaitin, & R. S. Goldstein (Eds.), *The eating disorders: Medical and psychological bases of diagnosis and treatment* (pp. 285–293). New York, NY: PMA.

Gitlin, M. J. (2009). Pharmacotherapy and other somatic treatments for depression. In I. H. Gotlib & C. L. Hammen (Eds.), *Handbook of depression* (2nd ed., pp. 554–585). New York, NY: Guilford Press.

Gjerde, L. C., Czajkowski, N., Røysamb, E., Ørstavik, R. E., Knudsen, G. P., Østby, K., & Reichborn-Kjennerud, T. (2012). The heritability of avoidant and dependent personality disorder assessed by personal interview and questionnaire. *Acta Psychiatrica Scandinavica, 126*(6), 448–457.

Gjerde, L. C., Czajkowski, N., Røysamb, E., Ystrom, E., Tambs, K., Aggen, S. H. ... Knudsen, G. P. (2015). A longitudinal, population-based twin study of avoidant and obsessive–compulsive personality disorder traits from early to middle adulthood. *Psychological Medicine, 45*(16), 3539–3548. https://doi.org/10.1017/S0033291715001440

Glaser, R., & Kiecolt-Glaser, J. K. (2005). Stress-induced immune dysfunction: Implications for health. *Nature Reviews Immunology, 5*(3), 243–251.

Glaser, R., Kennedy, S., Lafuse, W. P., Bonneau, R. H., Speicher, C. E., Hillhouse, J., & Kiecolt-Glaser, J. K. (1990). Psychological stress-induced modulation of IL-2 receptor gene expression and IL-2 production in peripheral blood leukocytes. *Archives of General Psychiatry, 47*, 707–712.

Glaser, R., Rice, J., Sheridan, J., Fertel, R., Stout, J., Speicher, C., ... Beck, M. (1987). Stress-related immune suppression: Health implications. *Brain, Behavior, and Immunity, 1*, 7–20.

Glaus, J., Vandeleur, C., Gholam-Rezaee, M., Castelao, E., Perrin, M., Rothen, S., & Preisig, M. (2012). Atypical depression and alcohol misuse are related to the cardiovascular risk in the general population. *Acta Psychiatrica Scandinavica, 1–12*.

Gleason, M. M., Fox, N. A., Drury, S., Smyke, A., Egger, H. L., Nelson, C. A., 3rd, & Zeanah, C. H. (2011). Validity of evidence-derived criteria for reactive attachment disorder: Indiscriminately social/disinhibited and emotionally withdrawn/inhibited types. *Journal of the American Academy of Child and Adolescent Psychiatry, 50*(3), 216–231.

Gleaves, D. H. (1996). The sociocognitive model of dissociative identity disorder: A re-examination of the evidence. *Psychological Bulletin, 120*, 42–59.

Gleaves, D. H., Smith, S. M., Butler, L. D., & Spiegel, D. (2004). False and recovered memories in the laboratory and clinic: A review of experimental and clinical evidence. *Clinical Psychology: Science and Practice, 11*(1), 3–28.

Goater, N., King, M., Cole, E., Leavey, G., Johnson-Sabine, E., Blizard, R., & Hoar, A. (1999). Ethnicity and outcomes of psychosis. *British Journal of Psychiatry, 175*, 34–42.

Goel, A. K., Talwar, D., & Jain, S. K. (2015). Evaluation of short-term use of nocturnal nasal continuous positive airway pressure for a clinical profile and exercise capacity in adult patients with obstructive sleep apnea–hypopnea syndrome. *Lung India, 32*(3), 225.

Goeree, R., Farahati, F., Burke, N., Blackhouse, G., O'Reilly, D., Pyne, J., & Tarride J.-E. (2005). The economic burden of schizophrenia in Canada in 2004. *Current Medical Research and Opinion, 21*, 2017–2028.

Goff, D. C., & Coyle, J. T. (2001). The emerging role of glutamate in the pathophysiology and treatment of schizophrenia. *American Journal of Psychiatry, 158*, 1367–1377.

Gold, J. H. (1997a). Premenstrual dysphoric disorder: What's that? *JAMA, 278*, 1024–1025.

Gold, J. H. (1999). Premenstrual dysphoric disorder: An update. *Journal of Practical Psychiatry and Behavioral Health, 5*, 209–215.

Gold, J. H., Endicott, J., Parry, B. L., Severino, S. K., Stotland, N., & Frank, E. (1996). Late luteal phase dysphoric disorder. In T. A. Widiger, A. J. Frances, H. A. Pincus, R. Ross, et al. (Eds.), *DSM-IV sourcebook* (Vol. 2, pp. 317–394). Washington, DC: American Psychiatric Association.

Gold, M. S. (1997b). Cocaine (and crack): Clinical aspects. In J. H. Lowinson, P. Ruiz, R. B. Millman, & J. G. Langrod (Eds.), *Substance abuse: A comprehensive textbook* (pp. 181–199). Baltimore, MD: Williams & Wilkins.

Gold, S. N., & Seibel, S. L. (2009). Treating dissociation: A contextual approach. In P. F. Dell & J. A. O'Neil (Eds.), *Dissociation and the dissociative disorders: DSM-V and beyond* (pp. 625–636). New York, NY: Routledge/Taylor & Francis Group.

Goldberg, D., & Fawcett, J. (2012). The importance of anxiety in both major depression and bipolar disorder. *Depression and Anxiety, 29*(6), 471–478.

Goldberg, J. F., Harrow, M., & Grossman, L. S. (1995). Course and outcome in bipolar affective disorder: A longitudinal follow-up study. *American Journal of Psychiatry, 152*, 379–384.

Goldberg, J. F., Perlis, R. H., Bowden, C. L., Thase, M. E., Miklowitz, D. J., Marangell, L. B., ... Sachs, G. S. (2009). Manic symptoms during depressive episodes in 1,380 patients with bipolar disorder: Findings from the STEP-BD. *American Journal of Psychiatry, 166*(2), 173–181.

Goldberg, J. O., & Schmidt, L. A. (2001). Shyness, sociability, and social dysfunction in schizophrenia. *Schizophrenia Research, 48*, 343–349.

Golden, C. J., Hammeke, T. A., & Purisch, A. D. (1980). *The Luria-Nebraska battery manual.* Palo Alto, CA: Western Psychological Services.

Goldfarb, W. (1963). Self-awareness in schizophrenic children. *Archives of General Psychiatry, 8*, 63–76.

Goldin, P. R., Manber, T., Hakimi, S., Canli, T., & Gross, J. J. (2009). Neural bases of social anxiety disorder: Emotional reactivity and cognitive regulation during social and physical threat. *Archives of General Psychiatry, 66*(2), 170–180.

Goldin, P. R., Ziv, M., Jazaleri, H., Hahn, K., Heimberg, R., & Gross, J. J. (2013). Impact of cognitive behavioral therapy for social anxiety disorder on the neural dynamics of cognitive reappraisal of negative self-beliefs: Randomized clinical trial. *JAMA Psychiatry, 70*(10), 1048–1056.

Goldman, N., Glei, D. A., Lin, Y., & Weinstein, M. (2010). The serotonin transporter polymorphism (5-HTTLPR): Allelic variation and links with depressive symptoms. *Depression and Anxiety, 27*(3), 260–269.

Goldman, R., Greenberg, L., & Angus, L. (2006) The effects of adding emotion-focused interventions to the therapeutic relationship in the treatment of depression. *Psychotherapy Research, 16*, 537–549.

Goldman, S. J., D'Angelo, E. J., DeMaso, D. R., & Mezzacappa, E. (1992).

Physical and sexual abuse histories among children with borderline personality disorder. *American Journal of Psychiatry, 149*, 1723–1726.

Goldner, E. (1989). Treatment refusal in anorexia nervosa. *International Journal of Eating Disorders, 8*, 297–306.

Goldner, E. M., Cockell, S. J., & Srikameswaran, S. (2002). Perfectionism and eating disorders. In G. L. Flett & P. L. Hewitt (Eds.), *Perfectionism: Theory, research, and treatment* (pp. 319–340). Washington, DC: American Psychological Association.

Goldner, E. M., Geller, J., Birmingham, C. L., & Remick, R. A. (2000). Comparison of shoplifting behaviours in patients with eating disorders, psychiatric control subjects, and undergraduate control subjects. *Canadian Journal of Psychiatry, 45*, 471–475.

Goldner, E. M., Jones, W., & Waraich, P. (2003). Using administrative data to analyze the prevalence and distribution of schizophrenic disorders. *Psychiatric Services, 54*, 1017–1021.

Goldner, E. M., Srikameswaran, S., Schroeder, M. L., Livesley, W. J., & Birmingham, C. L. (1999). Dimensional assessment of personality pathology in patients with eating disorders. *Psychiatry Research, 85*, 151–159.

Goldner, V. (2003). Ironic gender/authentic sex. *Studies in Gender & Sexuality, 4*, 113–139.

Goldschmidt, A. B., Hilbert, A., Manwaring, J. L., Wilfley, D. E., Pike, K. M., Fairburn, C. G., … Striegel-Moore, R. H. (2010). The significance of overvaluation of shape and weight in binge eating disorder. *Behaviour Research and Therapy, 48*(3), 187–193.

Goldstein, A. (1994). *Addiction: From biology to drug policy.* New York, NY: W. H. Freeman.

Goldstein, B. I. (2006). Why do women get depressed and men get drunk? An examination of attributional style and coping style in response to negative life events among Canadian young adults. *Sex Roles, 54*(1/2), 27–37.

Goldstein, G. (2000). Comprehensive neuropsychological assessment batteries. In G. Goldstein & M. Hersen (Eds.), *Handbook of psychological assessment* (pp. 231–261). New York, NY: Pergamon Press.

Goldstein, H. (2002). Communication intervention for children with autism: A review of treatment efficacy. *Journal of Autism and Developmental Disorders, 32*(5), 373–396.

Goldstein, I., Lue, T. F., Padma-Nathan, H., Rosen, R. C., Steers, W. D., & Wicker, P. A., for the Sildenafil Study Group. (1998). Oral sildenafil in the treatment of erectile dysfunction. *New England Journal of Medicine, 338*, 1397–1404.

Goldstein, J. M., & Lewine, R. R. (2000). Overview of sex differences in schizophrenia: Where have we been and where do we go from here? In D. J. Castle, J. J. McGrath, & J. Kulkarni (Eds.), *Women and Schizophrenia* (pp. 111–153). Cambridge, UK: Cambridge University Press.

Goldstein, S., & Brooks, R. B. (Eds.). (2013). *Handbook of resilience in children* (2nd ed.). New York, NY: Springer.

Golembo-Smith, S., Schiffman, J., Kline, E., Sørensen, H. J., Mortensen, E. L., Stapleton, L., … Mednick, S. (2012).

Premorbid multivariate markers of neurodevelopmental instability in the prediction of adult schizophrenia-spectrum disorder: A high-risk prospective investigation. *Schizophrenia Research, 139*(1), 129–135.

Golier, J., Yehuda, R., Lupien, S., Harvey, P., Grossman, R., & Elkin, A. (2002). Memory performance in Holocaust survivors with posttraumatic stress disorder. *American Journal of Psychiatry, 159*, 1682–1688.

Gomez-Caminero, A., Blumentals, W. A., Russo, L., Brown, R. R., & Castilla-Puentes, R. (2005). Does panic disorder increase the risk of coronary heart disease? A cohort study of a national managed care database. *Psychosomatic Medicine, 67*, 688–691.

Gomez-Gil, E., Steva, I., Almaraz, M. C., Pasara, E., Segovia, S., & Guillamon, A. (2010). Familiality of gender identity disorder in non-twin siblings. *Archives of Sexual Behavior, 39*, 546–552.

Gonzalez, J. S., Batchelder, A. W., Psaros, C. P., & Safren, S. A. (2011). Depression and HIV/AIDS treatment nonadherence: A review and meta-analysis. *Journal of Acquired Immune Deficiency Syndromes, 58*(2), 181–187.

Gonzalez, J. S., Hendriksen, E. S., Collins, E. M., Duran, R. E., & Safren, S. A. (2009). Latinos and HIV/AIDS: Examining factors related to disparity and identifying opportunities for psychosocial intervention research. *AIDS and Behavior, 13*(3), 582–602.

Gonzalez-Lavin, A., & Smolak, L. (1995, March). *Relationships between television and eating problems in middle school girls.* Paper presented at the meeting of the Society for Research in Child Development, Indianapolis, IN.

Good, B. J., & Kleinman, A. M. (1985). Culture and anxiety: Cross-cultural evidence for the patterning of anxiety disorders. In A. H. Tuma & J. D. Maser (Eds.), *Anxiety and the anxiety disorders.* Hillsdale, NJ: Erlbaum.

Good, K. P., Kiss, I., Buiteman, C., Woodley, H., Rui, Q., Whitehorn, D., & Kopala, L. (2002). Improvement in cognitive functioning in patients with first-episode psychosis during treatment with quetiapine: An interim analysis. *British Journal of Psychiatry, 181*(Suppl. 43), 45–49.

Goodman, G. S., Quas, J. A., & Ogle, C. M. (2010). Child maltreatment and memory. *Annual Reviews of Psychology, 61*, 325–351.

Goodman, J. T. (2000). Three decades of professional psychology: Reflections and future challenges. *Canadian Psychology, 41*, 25–33.

Goodman, L. A. (2003, December 11). Canadian psychologist stripped of licence faces misconduct charges in Ohio. *CNEWS Canada.* Retrieved May 21, 2004, from http://cnews.canoe.ca/CNEWS/Canada/2003/12/11/284357-cp.html

Goodman, R., & Scott, S. (2012). Sleep disorders. In R. Goodman & S. Scott (Eds.), *Child and adolescent psychiatry* (3rd ed., pp. 163–170). Wiley-Blackwell. http://www.youthinmind.info/GoodmanScott3rdEdition2012.pdf

Goodman, S. H., & Gotlib, I. H. (1999). Risk for psychopathology in the children of depressed mothers: A developmental model for understanding mechanisms of transmission.

Psychological Review, 106(3), 458–490.

Goodnough, A. (2002). Post-9/11 pain found to linger in young minds. Available at http://www.nytimes.com/2002/05/02/health/02SCHO.html?todaysheadlines

Goodrick, S. (2014). Defining narcolepsy. *The Lancet Neurology, 13*(6), 542.

Goodwin, D. W., & Guze, S. B. (1984). *Psychiatric diagnosis* (3rd ed.). New York, NY: Oxford University Press.

Goodwin, F. K., Fireman, B., Simon, G. E., Hunkeler, E. M., Lee, J., & Revicki, D. (2003). Suicide risk in bipolar disorder during treatment with lithium and divalproex. *JAMA, 290*, 1467–1473.

Goodwin, F. K., & Ghaemi, S. N. (1998). Understanding manic-depressive illness. *Archives of General Psychiatry, 55*(1), 23–25.

Goodwin, F. K., & Jamison, K. R. (1990). *Manic depressive illness.* New York, NY: Oxford University Press.

Goodwin, F. K., & Jamison, K. R. (Eds.). (2007). *Manic depressive illness: Bipolar disorders and recurrent depression* (2nd ed.). New York, NY: Oxford University Press.

Goodwin, G. M. (2009). Neurobiological aetiology of mood disorders. In M. G. Gelder, N. C. Andreasen, J. J. Lopez-Ibor, Jr., & J. R. Geddes (Eds.), *New Oxford textbook of psychiatry* (2nd ed., Vol. 1, pp. 658–664). Oxford, UK: Oxford University Press.

Goos, L. M., Crosbie, J., Payne, S., & Schachar, R. (2009). Validation and extension of the endophenotype model in ADHD patterns of inheritance in a family study of inhibitory control. *American Journal of Psychiatry, 166*(6), 711–717.

Goossens, I., Nicholls, T. L., Charette, Y., Wilson, C. M., Seto, M. C., & Crocker, A. G. (2019). Examining the high-risk accused designation for individuals found not criminally responsible on account of mental disorder. *Canadian Psychology/Psychologie canadienne, 60*(2), 102–114.

Gordis, E. (2000a). Alcohol, the brain, and behavior: Mechanisms of addiction. *Alcohol Research & Health, 24*(1), 12–15.

Gordis, E. (2000b). Why do some people drink too much? The role of genetic and psychosocial influences. *Alcohol Research & Health, 24*(1), 17–26.

Gordis, E. (2000c). Latest approaches to preventing alcohol abuse and alcoholism. *Alcohol Research & Health, 24*(1), 42–51.

Gordis, E. (2000d). Research refines alcohol treatment options. *Alcohol Research & Health, 24*(1), 53–61.

Gordon, J. A. (2002). Anxiolytic drug targets: Beyond the usual suspects. *Journal of Clinical Investigation, 110*(7), 915–917.

Gore-Felton, C., & Koopman, C. (2008). Behavioral mediation of the relationship between psychosocial factors and HIV disease progression. *Psychosomatic Medicine, 70*, 569–574.

Gorenstein, E. E. (1984). Debating mental illness: Implications for science, medicine, and social policy. *American Psychologist, 39*, 50–56.

Gorenstein, E. E., & Newman, J. P. (1980). Disinhibitory psychopathology: A new perspective and a model for research. *Psychological Review, 87*, 301–315.

Gosselin, P., Ladouceur, R., Morin, C. M., Dugas, M. J., & Baillargeon, L. (2006). Benzodiazepine discontinuation among adults with GAD: A randomized trial of cognitive-behavioral therapy. *Journal of Consulting and Clinical Psychology, 74*, 908–919.

Gosselin, P., Langlois, F., Freeston, M. H., Ladouceur, R., Laberge, M., & Lemay, D. (2007). Cognitive variables related to worry among adolescents: Avoidance strategies and faulty beliefs about worry. 2007 *Behaviour Research and Therapy, 45*(2), 225–233.

Gotlib, I. H., & Abramson, L. Y. (1999). Attributional theories of emotion. In T. Dagleish & M. J. Power (Eds.), *Handbook of cognition and emotion.* Chichester, UK: John Wiley & Sons.

Gotlib, I. H., & Beach, S. R. H. (1995). A marital/family discord model of depression: Implications for therapeutic intervention. In N. S. Jacobson & A. S. Gurman (Eds.), *Clinical handbook of couple therapy* (pp. 411–436). New York, NY: Guilford Press.

Gotlib, I. H., & Joormann, J. (2010). Cognition and depression: Current status and future directions. *Annual Review of Clinical Psychology, 6*, 285–312.

Gotlib, I. H., & Nolan, S. A. (2000). Depression. In A. S. Bellack & M. Hersen (Eds.), *Psychopathology in adulthood* (2nd ed., pp. 252–277). Boston, MA: Allyn & Bacon.

Gotlib, I. H., Joormann, J., & Foland-Ross, L. C. (2014). Understanding familial risk for depression: A 25-year perspective. *Perspectivers on Psychological Science, 9*, 94–108

Gotlib, I. H., Ranganath, C., & Rosenfeld, J. P. (1998). Frontal EEG alpha asymmetry, depression, and cognitive functioning. *Cognition and Emotion, 12*, 449–478.

Gotlib, I. H., Roberts, J. E., & Gilboa, E. (1996). Cognitive interference in depression. In I. G. Sarason, G. R. Pierce, & B. R. Sarason (Eds.), *Cognitive interference: Theories, methods, and findings* (pp. 347–377). Mahwah, NJ: Erlbaum.

Gotowiec, A., & Beiser, M. (1993–1994). Aboriginal children's mental health: Unique challenges. *Canada's Mental Health, 41*(4), 7–11.

Gottesman, I. I. (1991). *Schizophrenia genesis: The origins of madness.* New York, NY: W. H. Freeman.

Gottesman, I. I., & Bertelsen, A. (1989). Dual mating studies in psychiatry—Offspring of inpatients with examples from reactive (psychogenic) psychoses. *International Review of Psychiatry, 1*, 287–296.

Gould, M. S. (1990). Suicide clusters and media exposure. In S. J. Blumenthal & D. J. Kupfer (Eds.), *Suicide over the life cycle: Risk factors, assessment and treatment of suicidal patients.* Washington, DC: American Psychiatric Press.

Gould, M. S., Greenberg, T., Velting, D. M., & Shaffer, D. (2003). Youth suicide risk and preventive interventions: A review of the past 10 years. *Journal of the American Academy of Child and Adolescent Psychiatry, 42*(4), 386–405.

Gould, M., Marrocco, F., Kleinman, M., Thomas, J., Mostkoff, K., Cote, J., & Davies, M. (2005). Evaluating iatrogenic risk of youth suicide screening programs. *JAMA, 293*, 1635–1643.

Government of Canada. (2014). *Tri-council policy statement: Ethical conduct for research involving humans*. Ottawa, ON: Author.

Government of Canada. (2019). *Cannabis record suspensions*. https://www.canada.ca/en/parole-board/services/cannabis-record-suspensions.html

Goyal, M., Singh, S., Sibinga, E. M., Gould, N. F., Rowland-Seymour, A., Sharma, R., ... Haythornthwaite, J. A. (2014). Meditation programs for psychological stress and well-being: A systematic review and meta-analysis. *JAMA Internal Medicine, 174*(3), 357–368.

Grabe, S., Ward, L. M., & Hyde, J. S. (2008). The role of the media in body image concerns among women: A meta-analysis of experimental and correlational studies. *Psychological Bulletin, 134*(3), 460–476.

Grados, M. A., Riddle, M. A., Samuels, J. F., Liang, K.-Y., Hoehn-Saric, R., Bienvenu, O. J., ... Nestadt, G. (2001). The familial phenotype of obsessive-compulsive disorder in relation to tic disorders: The Hopkins OCD family study. *Biological Psychiatry, 50*, 559–565.

Grady-Weliky, T. (2003). Premenstrual dysphoric disorder. *New England Journal of Medicine, 345*, 433–438.

Graeff, F. G. (1993). Role of 5-ht in defensive behavior and anxiety. *Review in the Neurosciences, 4*, 181–211.

Graeff, F. G. (2004). Serotonin, the periaqueductal gray and panic. *Neuroscience and Biobehavioral Reviews, 28*, 239–259.

Graf, P., Squire, L. R., & Mandler, G. (1984). The information that amnesic patients do not forget. *Journal of Experimental Psychology: Learning, Memory, and Cognition, 10*, 164–178.

Graff, F. S., McClure, M. M., & Siever, L. J. (2014). Remediation and cognitive enhancers in schizotypal personality disorder. *Current Treatment Options in Psychiatry, 1*(4), 369–375.

Graham, C. A. (2010). The DSM criteria for female orgasmic disorder. *Archives of Sexual Behavior, 39*, 256–270.

Grandy, T. (1995). *New occupational hazards of career addicts: Main line intravenous needs assessment (MINA)*. Document prepared by Main Line Needle Exchange with funding from Health Canada.

Granic, I., & Patterson, G. R. (2006). Toward a comprehensive model of antisocial development: A dynamic systems approach. *Psychological Review, 113*, 101–131.

Grant, A. (1996). *No end of grief: Indian residential schools in Canada*. Winnipeg, MB: Pemmican.

Grant, B. F., & Dawson, D. A. (1999). Alcohol and drug use, abuse, and dependence: Classification, prevalence, and comorbidity. In B. S. McCrady & E. E. Epstein (Eds.), *Addictions: A comprehensive guidebook* (pp. 9–29). New York, NY: Oxford University Press.

Grant, B. F., Hasin, D. S., Stinson, F. S., et al. (2005). Prevalence, correlates, comorbidity, and comparative disability of DSM-IV generalized anxiety disorder in the USA: Results from the National Epidemiological Survey of Alcohol and Related Conditions. *Psychological Medicine, 35*, 747–759.

Grant, B., Chou, S., Goldstein, R., Huang, B., Stinson, F., Saha, T., ... Ruan, W. J.

(2008). Prevalence, correlates, disability, and comorbidity of DSM-IV borderline personality disorder: Results from the Wave 2 National Epidemiologic Survey on Alcohol and Related Conditions. *Journal of Clinical Psychiatry, 69*(4), 533.

Grant, I., Patterson, T. L., & Yager, J. (1988). Social supports in relation to physical health and symptoms of depression in the elderly. *American Journal of Psychiatry, 145*, 1254–1258.

Grant, J. E. (2003). Family history and psychiatric comorbidity in persons with kleptomania. *Comprehensive Psychiatry, 44*(6), 437–441.

Grant, J. E., Correia, S., & Brennan-Krohn, T. (2006). White matter integrity in kleptomania: A pilot study. *Psychiatry Research: Neuroimaging, 147*, 233–237.

Grant, J. E., & Kim, S. W. (2002). Temperament and early environmental influences in kleptomania. *Comprehensive Psychiatry, 43*, 223–229.

Grant, J. E., Kim, S. W., & Odlaug, B. L. (2009). A double-blind, placebo-controlled study of the opiate antagonist, naltrexone, in the treatment of kleptomania. *Biological Psychiatry, 65*(7), 600–606.

Grant, J. E., Odlaug, B. L., & Kim, S. W. (2010). Kleptomania: Clinical characteristics and relationship to substance use disorders. *The American Journal of Drug and Alcohol Abuse, 36*(5), 291–295.

Grant, J. E., Odlaug, B. L., & Schreiber, L. R. N. (2015). Pathologic gambling: Clinical characteristics and treatment. In R. K. Ries, D. A. Fiellin, S. C. Miller, & R. Saitz (Eds.), *The ASAM principles of addiction medicine* (5th ed., pp. 575–587). New York, NY: Wolters Kluwer.

Grant, J. E., Stein, D. J., Woods, D. W., & Keuthen, N. J. (Eds.). (2012). *Trichotillomania, skin picking, and other body-focused repetitive behaviors*. Arlington, VA: American Psychiatric Publishing.

Grant, K. E., Compas, B. E., Thurm, A. E., McMahon, S. D., & Gipson, P. Y. (2004). Stressors and child and adolescent psychopathology: Measurement issues and prospective effects. *Journal of Clinical Child and Adolescent Psychology, 33*(2), 412–425.

Grassick, P. (1990). The fear behind the fear: A case study of apparent simple injection phobia. *Journal of Behavior Therapy and Experimental Psychiatry, 21*, 281–287.

Gratten, J., Wray, N. R., Keller, M. C., & Visscher, P. M. (2014). Large-scale genomics unveils the genetic architecture of psychiatric disorders. *Nature Neuroscience, 17*, 782–790.

Gratzer, T. G., & Matas, M. (1994). The right to refuse treatment: Recent Canadian developments. *Bulletin of the American Academy of Psychiatry & the Law, 22*, 249–256.

Gray, J. A. (1982). *The neuropsychology of anxiety*. New York, NY: Oxford University Press.

Gray, J. A. (1985). Issues in the neuropsychology of anxiety. In A. H. Tuma & J. D. Maser (Eds.), *Anxiety and the anxiety disorders* (pp. 5–25). Hillsdale, NJ: Erlbaum.

Gray, J. A. (1987). *The psychology of fear and stress* (2nd ed.). New York, NY: Cambridge University Press.

Gray, J. A., & Buffery, A. W. H. (1971). Sex differences in emotional and cognitive behavior in mammals including man: Adaptive and neural bases. *Acta Psychologica, 35*, 89–111.

Gray, J. A., & McNaughton, N. (1996). The neuropsychology of anxiety: Reprise. In D. A. Hope (Ed.), *Perspectives on anxiety, panic and fear* (the 43rd Annual Nebraska Symposium on Motivation, pp. 61–134). Lincoln, NE: Nebraska University Press.

Gray, J. A., & McNaughton, N. (2003). *The neuropsychology of anxiety: An enquiry into the function of the septo-hippocampal system*. Oxford, UK: Oxford University Press.

Gray, J. E., & O'Reilly, R. L. (2001). Clinically significant differences among Canadian mental health acts. *Canadian Journal of Psychiatry, 46*, 315–321.

Gray, J. E., & O'Reilly, R. L. (2005). Canadian compulsory community treatment laws: Recent reforms. *International Journal of Law and Psychiatry, 28*, 13–22.

Grcevich, S., Rowane, W. A., Marcellino, B., & Sullivan-Hurst, S. (2001). Retrospective comparison of Adderall and methylphenidate in the treatment of attention deficit hyperactivity disorder. *Journal of Child and Adolescent Pscyhopharmacology, 11*, 35–41.

Grebb, J. A., & Carlsson, A. (2009). Introduction and considerations for a brain-based diagnostic system in psychiatry. In B. J. Sadock, V. A. Sadock, & P. Ruiz (Eds.), *Kaplan & Sadock's comprehensive textbook of psychiatry* (9th ed., Vol. 1, pp. 1–5). Philadelphia, PA: Lippincott Williams & Wilkins.

Green, A. I., Mooney, J. J., Posener, J. A., & Schildkraut, J. J. (1995). Mood disorders: Biochemical aspects. In H. I. Kaplan & B. J. Sadock (Eds.), *Comprehensive textbook of psychiatry* (6th ed., pp. 1089–1101). Baltimore, MD: Williams & Wilkins.

Green, B. L., Grace, M. C., Lindy, J. D., Titchener, J. L., & Lindy, J. G. (1983). Levels of functional impairment following a civilian disaster: The Beverly Hills Supper Club fire. *Journal of Consulting and Clinical Psychology, 51*, 573–580.

Green, R. (1987). *The "sissy boy syndrome" and the development of homosexuality*. New Haven, CT: Yale University Press.

Green, R., & Money, J. (1969). *Transsexualism and sex reassignment*. Baltimore, MD: Johns Hopkins University Press.

Greenberg, A. H. (1994). The origins of the NK cell, or a Canadian in King Ivan's court. *Clinical and Investigative Medicine, 17*, 626–631.

Greenberg, B. D., Rauch, S. L., & Haber, S. N. (2010). Invasive circuitry-based neurotherapeutics: Stereotactic ablation and deep brain stimulation for OCD. *Neuropsychopharmacology, 35*(1), 317–336.

Greenberg, H. R. (2005). Impulse-control disorders not elsewhere classified. In B. J. Sadock & V. A. Sadock (Eds.), *Kaplan & Sadock's comprehensive textbook of psychiatry* (8th ed., pp. 2035–2054). Philadelphia, PA: Lippincott Williams & Wilkins.

Greenberg, L. (2004). Introduction to emotion-focused therapy [Special

issue]. *Clinical Psychology and Psychotherapy, 11*, 1–2.

Greenberg, L. S. (2010). Emotion-focused therapy: A clinical synthesis. *Psychotherapy, 8*, 32–42. https://doi.org/10.1176/foc.8.1.foc32

Greenberg, L., & Watson, J. (2005). *Emotion-focused therapy of depression*. Washington, DC: APA Press.

Greenberg, L., Elliott, R., & Lietaer, G. (2003). Humanistic-experiential psychotherapy. In G. Stricker & T. Widiger (Eds.), *Handbook of psychology: Clinical psychology* (Vol. 8, pp. 301–326) Hoboken, NJ: John Wiley & Sons.

Greene, R. W., & Ollendick, T. H. (2000). Behavioral assessment of children. In G. Goldstein & M. Hersen (Eds.), *Handbook of psychological assessment* (pp. 453–470). New York, NY: Pergamon Press.

Greenough, W. T., Withers, G. S., & Wallace, C. S. (1990). Morphological changes in the nervous system arising from behavioral experience: What is the evidence that they are involved in learning and memory? In L. R. Squire & E. Lindenlaub (Eds.), *The biology of memory, Symposia Medica Hoescht 23* (pp. 159–183). Stuttgart/New York, NY: Schattauer Verlag.

Greenwood, T. A., Lazzeroni, L. C., Murray, S. S., Cadenhead, K. S., Calkins, M. E., Dobie, D. J., ... Braff, D. L. (2014). Analysis of 94 candidate genes and 12 endophenotypes for schizophrenia from the Consortium on the Genetics of Schizophrenia. *American Journal of Psychiatry, 168*(9), 930–946. https://doi.org/10.1176/appi.ajp.2011.10050723

Greer, S. (1999). Mind-body research in psychoncology. *Advances in Mind-Body-Medicine, 15*, 236–244.

Gregg, N. (2013). Adults with learning disabilities: Factors contributing to persistence. In H. L. Swanson, K. R. Harris, & S. Graham (Eds.), *Handbook of learning disabilities* (2nd ed., pp. 85–103). New York, NY: Guilford, Press.

Gregoire, A. (1992). New treatments for erectile impotence. *British Journal of Psychiatry, 160*, 315–326.

Grenier, G., & Byers, E. S. (2001). Operationalizing premature or rapid ejaculation. *Journal of Sex Research, 38*, 369–378.

Grenon, R., Carlucci, S., Brugnera, A., Schwartze, D., Hammond, N., Ivanova, I., Mcquaid, N., Proulx, G., & Tasca, G. A. (2018). Psychotherapy for eating disorders: A meta-analysis of direct comparisons. *Psychotherapy Research, 29*(7), 833–845. https://doi.org/10.1080/10503307.2018.1489162

Grenon, R., Schwartze, D., Hammond, N., Ivanova, I., Mcquaid, N., Proulx, G., & Tasca, G. A. (2017). Group psychotherapy for eating disorders: A meta-analysis. *International Journal of Eating Disorders, 50*(9), 997–1013. https://doi.org/10.1002/eat.22744

Greydanus, D. E., Kaplan, G., & Patel, D. R. (2015). Pharmacology of autism spectrum disorder. In S. H. Fatemi (Ed.), *Molecular basis of autism* (pp. 173–194). New York, NY: Springer.

Griebel, G., Holmes A. (2013). 50 years of hurdles and hope in anxiolytics drug discovery. *Nature Reviews Drug Discovery, 12*, 667–687.

Griffin, J. (1989). *In search of sanity: A chronicle of the Canadian Mental Health Association*, 1918–1988. London, ON: Third Eye Publications.

Griffith, E. E. H., English, T., & Mayfield, U. (1980). Possession, prayer and testimony: Therapeutic aspects of the Wednesday night meeting in a black church. *Psychiatry, 43*(5), 120–128.

Grilo, C. M., Crosby, R. D., Wilson, G. T., & Masheb, R. M. (2012). 12-Month follow-up of fluoxetine and cognitive behavioral therapy for binge eating disorder. *Journal of Consulting and Clinical Psychology, 80*(6), 1108–1113.

Grilo, C. M., Masheb, R. M., & White, M. A. (2010). Significance of overvaluation of shape/weight in binge-eating disorder: Comparative study with overweight and bulimia nervosa. *Obesity, 18*, 499–504.

Grilo, C. M., Masheb, R. M., & Wilson, G. T. (2001). Subtyping binge eating disorder. *Journal of Consulting and Clinical Psychology, 69*, 1066–1072.

Grilo, C. M., Masheb, R. M., Wilson, G. T., Gueorguieva, R., & White, M. A. (2011). Cognitive-behavioral therapy, behavioral weight loss, and sequential treatment for obese patients with binge-eating disorder: A randomized controlled trial. *Journal of Consulting and Clinical Psychology, 79*(5), 675–685.

Grinspoon, L., & Bakalar, J. B. (1980). Drug dependence: Non-narcotic agents. In H. I. Kaplan, A. M. Freedman, & B. J. Sadock (Eds.), *Comprehensive textbook of psychiatry* (3rd ed., pp. 1614–1629). Baltimore, MD: Williams & Wilkins.

Grinspoon, L., & Bakalar, J. B. (1997). Marihuana. In J. H. Lowinson, P. Ruiz, R. B. Millman, & J. G. Langrod (Eds.), *Substance abuse: A comprehensive textbook* (pp. 199–206). Baltimore, MD: Williams & Wilkins.

Grisham, J. R., & Barlow, D. H. (2005). Compulsive hoarding: Current research and theory. *Journal of Psychopathology and Behavioral Assessment, 27*, 45–52.

Grisham, J. R., Norberg, M. M., & Certoma, S. P. (2012). *Treatment of compulsive hoarding*. In G. Steketee (Ed.), *The Oxford handbook of obsessive compulsive and spectrum disorders* (pp. 422–435). New York, NY: Oxford University Press.

Grisham, J., Frost, R. O., Steketee, G., Kim, H. J., & Hood, S. (2006). Age of onset of compulsive hoarding. *Journal of Anxiety Disorders, 20*, 675–686.

Grizenko, N., Fortier, M.-E., Zadorozny, C., Thakur, G., Schmitz, N., Duval, R., & Joober, R. (2012). Maternal stress during pregnancy, ADHD symptomatology in children and genotype: Gene–environment interaction. *Journal of the Canadian Academy of Child and Adolescent Psychiatry, 21*(1), 9.

Gross, J. J. (Ed.). (2007). *Handbook of emotion regulation*. New York, NY: Guilford Press.

Gross, J. J. (Ed.). (2015). *Handbook of emotion regulation* (2nd ed.). New York, NY: Guilford Press.

Gross, J., & Rosen, J. C. (1988). Bulimia in adolescents: Prevalence and psychosocial correlates. *International Journal of Eating Disorders, 7*, 51–61.

Gross, S. R., Barrett, S. P., Shestowsky, J. S., & Pihl, R. O. (2002). Ecstasy and drug consumption patterns: A Canadian rave population study. *The Canadian Journal of Psychiatry/La Revue canadienne de psychiatrie, 47*(6), 546–551.

Grossardt, B. R., Bower, J. H., Geda, Y. E., Colligan, R. C., & Rocca, W. A. (2009). Pessimistic, anxious, and depressive personality traits predict all-cause mortality: The Mayo Clinic Cohort Study of Personality and Aging. *Psychosomatic Medicine, 71*, 491–500.

Grossman, C. I., Purcell, D. W., Rotheram-Borus, M. J., & Veniegas, R. (2013). Opportunities for HIV combination prevention to reduce racial and ethnic health disparities. *American Psychologist, 68*(4), 237–246.

Gross-Tsur, V., Manor, O., & Shalev, R. S. (1996). Developmental dyscalcula: Prevalence and demographic features. *Developmental Medicine and Child Neurology, 38*, 25–33.

Grosz, H. J., & Zimmerman, J. (1965). Experimental analysis of hysterical blindness: A follow-up report and new experimental data. *Archives of General Psychiatry, 13*, 255–260.

Grosz, H. J., & Zimmerman, J. (1970). A second detailed case study of functional blindness: Further demonstration of the contribution of objective psychological laboratory data. *Behavior Therapy, 1*, 115–123.

Grove, W. M., & Tellegen, A. (1991). Problems in the classification of personality disorders. *Journal of Personality Disorders, 5*, 31–42.

Gruder, C. L., Mermelstein, R. J., Kirkendol, S., Hedeker, D., Wong, S. C., Schreckengost, J., ... Miller, T. Q. (1993). Effects of social support and relapse prevention training as adjuncts to a televised smoking-cessation intervention. *Journal of Consulting and Clinical Psychology, 61*, 113–120.

Guastella, A. J., Einfeld, S. L., Gray, K. M., Rinehart, N. J., Tonge, B. J., Lambert, T. J., & Hickie, I. B. (2010). Intranasal oxytocin improves emotion recognition for youth with autism spectrum disorders. *Biological Psychiatry, 67*(7), 692–694.

Guedeney, N. (2007). Withdrawal behavior and depression in infancy. *Infant Mental Health Journal, 28*, 393–408.

Guerrero, M. D., Barnes, J. D., Walsh, J. J., Chaput, J.-P., & Tremblay, M. S., & Goldfield, G. S. (2019). 24-hour movement behaviors and impulsivity. *Pediatrics, 144*(3), e20190187. https://doi.org/10.1542/peds.2019-0187

Guilleminault, C. (1989). Clinical features and evaluation of obstructive sleep apnea. In M. H. Kryger, T. Roth, & W. C. Dement (Eds.), *Principles and practice of sleep medicine* (pp. 552–558). Philadelphia, PA: W. B. Saunders.

Guilleminault, C., & Dement, W. C. (1988). Sleep apnea syndromes and related sleep disorders. In R. L. Williams, I. Karacan, & C. A. Moore (Eds.), *Sleep disorders: Diagnosis and treatment* (pp. 47–71). New York, NY: John Wiley & Sons.

Gulliksson, M., Burell, G., Vessby, B., Lundin, L., Toss, H., & Svärdsudd, K. (2011). Randomized controlled ttrial of cognitive behavioral therapy vs standard treatment to prevent recurrent cardiovascular events in patients with coronary heart disease: Secondary Prevention in Uppsala Primary Health Care project (SUPRIM). *Archives of Internal Medicine, 171*(2), 134–140.

Gunderson, J. G. (1992). Diagnostic controversies. In A. Tasman & M. B. Riba (Eds.), *Review of psychiatry* (Vol. 11, pp. 9–24). Washington, DC: American Psychiatric Press.

Gunderson, J. G., & Sabo, A. N. (1993). The phenomenological and conceptual interface between borderline personality disorder and PTSD. *American Journal of Psychiatry, 150*, 19–27.

Gunderson, J. G., Ronningstam, E., & Smith, L. E. (1991). Narcissistic personality disorder: A review of data on DSM-III-R descriptions. *Journal of Personality Disorders, 5*, 167–177.

Gunnar, M. R., & Fisher, P. A. (2006). Bringing basic research on early experience and stress neurobiology to bear on preventive interventions for neglected and maltreated children. *Development and Psychopathology, 18*(3), 651–677.

Gunnar, M. R., Hostinar, C. E., Sanches, M. M., Tottenam, N., & Sullivan, R. M. (2015). Oarental buffering of fear and stress neurobiology: Reviewing parallels across rodent, monkey, and human models. *Social Neuroscience, 10*(5), 474–478. https://doi.org/10.1080/17470919.2015.1070198

Gupta, M. A., Chaturvedi, S. K., Chandarana, P. C., & Johnson, A. M. (2001). Weight-related body image concerns among 18–24-year-old women in Canada and India: An empirical comparative study. *Journal of Psychosomatic Research, 50*, 193–198.

Gupta, S., & Bonanno, G. A. (2011). Complicated grief and deficits in emotional expressive flexibility. *Journal of Abnormal Psychology, 120*(3), 635–643.

Gur, R. E., & Pearlson, G. D. (1993). Neuroimaging in Schizophrenia Research. *Schizophrenia Bulletin, 19*, 337–353.

Guralnick, O., Schmeidler, J., & Simeon, D. (2000). Feeling unreal: Cognitive processes in depersonalization. *American Journal of Psychiatry, 157*(1), 103–109.

Gureje, O., Simon, G. E., Ustun, T. B., & Goldberg, D. P. (1997). Somatization in cross-cultural perspective: A World Health Organization study in primary care. *American Journal of Psychiatry, 154*, 989–995.

Gurvits, T. V., Shenton, M. E., Hokama, H., Ohta, H., Lasko, N. B., Gilbertson, M. W., ... Pitman, R. K. (1996). Magnetic resonance imaging study of hippocampal volume in chronic, combat related posttraumatic stress disorder. *Biological Psychiatry, 40*, 1091–1099.

Gusella, J. F., Wexler, N. S., Conneally, P. M., Naylor, S. L., Anderson, M. A., Tanzi, R. E., ... Martin, J. B. (1983). A polymorphic DNA marker genetically linked to Huntington's disease. *Nature, 306*, 234–239.

Gusella, J., Butler, G., Nichols, L., & Bird, D. (2003). A brief questionnaire to assess readiness to change in adolescents with eating disorders: Its application to group therapy. *European Eating Disorders Review, 11*, 58–71.

Gustad, J., & Phillips, K. A. (2003). Axis I comorbidity in body dysmorphic disorder. *Comprehensive Psychiatry, 44*, 270–276.

Gustafson, L., & Brun, A. (2012). Frontotemporal dementias. In M. G. Gelder, N. C. Andreasen, J. J. Lopez-Ibor, & J. R. Geddes (Eds.), *New Oxford textbook of psychiatry* (2nd ed., Vol. 1, pp. 344–350). New York, NY: Oxford University Press.

Guttmacher, M. S., & Weihofen, H. (1952). *Psychiatry and the law*. New York, NY: Norton.

Guttmannova, K., Bailey, J. A., Hill, K. G., Lee, J. O., Hawkins, J. D., Woods, M. L., & Catalano, R. F. (2011). Sensitive periods for adolescent alcohol use initiation: Predicting the lifetime occurrence and chronicity of alcohol problems in adulthood. *Journal of Studies on Alcohol and Drugs, 72*(2), 221–231.

Guyton, A. (1981). *Textbook of medical physiology*. Philadelphia, PA: W. B. Saunders.

Guze, S. B., Cloninger, C. R., Martin, R. L., & Clayton, P. J. (1986). A follow-up and family study of Briquet's syndrome. *British Journal of Psychiatry, 149*, 17–23.

Haas, A. P., & Hendin, H. (1987). The meaning of chronic marijuana use among adults: A psychosocial perspective. *Journal of Drug Issues, 17*, 333–348.

Hackett, T. P., & Cassem, N. H. (1973). Psychological adaptation to convalescence in myocardial infarction patients. In J. P. Naughton, H. K. Hellerstein, & I. C. Mohler (Eds.), *Exercise testing and exercise training in coronary heart disease*. New York, NY: Academic Press.

Haddad, P. M., Brain, C., & Scott, J. (2014). Nonadherence with antipsychotic medication in schizophrenia: Challenges and management strategies. *Patient-Related Outcome Measures, 5*, 43–62.

Hadley, S., Kim, S., Priday, L., & Hollander, E. (2006). Pharmacologic treatment of body dysmorphic disorder. *Primary Psychiatry, 13*, 61–69.

Haeffel, G. J., & Hames, J. L. (2014). Cognitive vulnerability to depression can be contagious. *Clinical Psychological Science, 2*, 75–85.

Haenen, M. A., de Jong, P. J., Schmidt, A. J. M., Stevens, S., & Visser, L. (2000). Hypochondriacs' estimation of negative outcomes: Domain-specificity and responsiveness to reassuring and alarming information. *Behaviour Research and Therapy, 38*, 819–833.

Haggarty, J. M., Cernovsky, Z., Kermeen, P., & Merskey, H. (2000). Psychiatric disorders in an Arctic community. *Canadian Journal of Psychiatry, 45*, 357–362.

Hagnell, O., Franck, A., Grasbeck, A., Ohman, R., Ojesjo, L., Otterbeck, L., & Rorsman, B. (1992). Vascular dementia in the Lundby study: I. A prospective, epidemiological study of incidence and risk from 1957 to 1972. *Neuropsychobiology, 26*, 43–49.

Haig-Brown, C. (1988). *Resistance and renewal: Surviving the Indian residential school*. Vancouver, BC: Tillacum Library.

Hakim-Larson, J., Kamoo, R., Nassar-McMillan, S. C., & Porcerelli, J. H. (2007). Counseling Arab and Chaldean American families. *Journal of Mental Health Counseling, 29*(4), 301–321.

Hall, A. C., Butterworth, J., Winsor, J., Gilmore, D., & Metzel, D. (2007). Pushing the employment agenda: Case study research of high performing states in integrated employment. *Intellectual* and Developmental Disabilities, 45, 182–198.

Hall, D. E., Eubanks, L., Meyyazhagan, S., Kenney, R. D., & Johnson, S. (2000). Evaluation of covert video surveillance in the diagnosis of Munchausen syndrome by proxy: Lessons from 41 cases. Pediatrics, 6, 1305–1312.

Hall, J. (2007, June 1). Retailers juggle restrictions with curtains, separate entrances. Edmonton Journal, p. A.2.

Halliburton, A. E., & Bray, B. C. (2016). Long-term prevalence and demographic trends in U.S. adolescent inhalant use: Implications for clinicians and prevention Scientists. Substance Use and Misuse, 51(3), 343–356. https://doi.org/10.3109/1082 6084.2015.1110169

Hallmayer, J., Cleveland, S., Torres, A., Phillips, J., Cohen, B., Torigoe, T., & Smith, K. (2011). Genetic heritability and shared environmental factors among twin pairs with autism. Archives of General Psychiatry, 68(11), 1095–1102.

Halmi, K. A., Bellace, D., Berthod, S., Ghosh, S., Berrettini, W., Brandt, H. A., ... Strober, M. (2012). An examination of early childhood perfectionism across anorexia nervosa subtypes. International Journal of Eating Disorders, 45(6), 800–807.

Halmi, K. A., Tozzi, F., Thornton, L. M., Crow, S., Fichter, M. M., Kaplan, A. S., ... Bulik, C. M. (2005). The relation among perfectionism, obsessive–compulsive personality disorder and obsessive–compulsive disorder in individuals with eating disorders. International Journal of Eating Disorders, 38, 371–374.

Hamilton, D. A., Kodituwakku, P., Sutherland, R. J., & Savage, D. D. (2003). Children with fetal alcohol syndrome are impaired at place learning but not cued-navigation in a virtual Morris water task. Behavioural Brain Research, 143(1), 85–94.

Hammen, C. (2005). Stress and depression. Annual Review of Clinical Psychology, 1, 293–319.

Hammen, C., & Keenan-Miller, D. (2013). In G. Stricker, T. A. Widiger & I. B. Weiner (Eds.), Handbook of psychology, Volume 8: Clinical Psychology (pp. 121–146). Hoboken, NJ: Wiley.

Hammen, C., Burge, D., Burney, E., & Adrian, C. (1990). Longitudinal study of diagnoses in children of women with unipolar and bipolar affective disorder. Archives of General Psychiatry, 47(12), 1112–1117.

Hammen, C., Marks, T., Mayol, A., & DeMayo, R. (1985). Depressive self-schemas, life stress, and vulnerability to depression. Journal of Abnormal Psychology, 94, 308–319.

Hammer, S., Saag, M., Scheechter, M., Montaner, J., Schooley, R., Jacobsen, D., ... Volberding, P. A. (2006). Treatment for adult HIV infection: 2006 recommendations of the International AIDS Society-USA Panel. JAMA, 296, 827–843.

Hammill, D. D. (1993). A brief look at the learning disability movement in the United States. Journal of Learning Disabilities, 26, 295–310.

Han, L., McCusker, J., Cole, M., Abrahamowicz, M., Primeau, F., & Élie, M. (2001). Use of medications with anticholinergic effect predicts clinical severity of delirium symptoms in older medical inpatients. Archives of Internal Medicine, 161, 1099–1105.

Hancock, T. B., & Kaiser, A. P. (2012). Implementing enhanced milieu teaching with children who have autism spectrum disorders. In P. A. Prelock & R. J. McCauley (Eds.), Treatment of autism spectrum disorders: Evidence based-intervention strategies for communication and social interactions (pp. 163–187). Baltimore, MD: Paul H. Brookes.

Hankin, B. L., Wetter, E., & Cheely, C. (2007). Sex differences in adolescent depression: A developmental psycho-pathological approach. In J. R. Z. Abela & B. L. Hankin (Eds.), Handbook of depression in children and adolescents (pp. 377–414). New York, NY: Guilford Press.

Hanlon, E. C., & K. L. Kristen. (2014). In M. T. Bianchi (Ed.), Sleep deprivation and disease: Effects on the body, brain and behavior (pp. 111–129). New York, NY: Springer.

Hanlon, E. C., & Van Cauter, E. (2011). Quantification of sleep behavior and of its impact on the cross-talk between the brain and peripheral metabolism. Proceedings of the National Academy of Sciences, 108(Supplement 3), 15609–15616.

Hanna, G. L. (1995). Demographic and clinical features of obsessive–compulsive disorder in children and adolescents. Journal of the American Academy of Child and Adolescent Psychiatry, 34, 19–27.

Hanna, L. (2001). Deinstitutionalization in Canada of the chronically mentally ill: Women as primary family caregivers and the governance of madness. Retrieved November 6, 2003, from International Academy of Law and Mental Health Website: http://www .ialmh.org/Montreal2001/sessions/ governance_of_madness.htm

Hannema, S., Schagen, S., Hoekzema, E., Kreukels, B., Veltman, D., Cohen-Kettenis, P., & Bakker, J. (2014). Brain structure and function in gender dysphoric adolescents. Hormone Research in Paediatrics, 82(Suppl. 1).

Hans, V. P. (1986). An analysis of public attitudes toward the insanity defense. Criminology, 4, 393–415.

Hanson, R. K., Bourgon, G., Helmus, L., & Hodgson, S. (2009). The principles of effective correctional treatment also apply to sexual offenders: A meta-analysis. Criminal Justice and Behavior, 36, 865–891.

Hantouche, E., Akiskal, H., Azorin, J., Chatenet-Duchene, L., & Lancrenon, S. (2006). Clinical and psychometric characterization of depression in mixed mania: A report from the French National Cohort of 1090 manic patients. Journal of Affective Disorders, 96, 225–232.

Hantouche, E., Angst, J., & Azorin, J. M. (2010). Explained factors of suicide attempts in major depression. Journal of Affective Disorders, 127(1), 305–308.

Hara, K., Adachi, N., Akanuma, N., Ito, M., Okazaki, M., Matsubara, R., Adachi, T., Ishii, R., Kanemoto, K., Matsuura, M., Hara, J., Kato, M., & Onuma, T. (2015). Dissociative experiences in epilepsy: Effects of epilepsy-related factors on pathological dissociation. Epilepsy and Behavior, 44, 185–191.

Hardie, T. L., Moss, H. B., & Lynch, K. G. (2006). Genetic correlations between smoking initiation and smoking behaviors in a twin sample. Addictive Behaviors, 31(11), 2030–2037.

Hare, R. D. (1970). Psychopathy: Theory and research. New York, NY: John Wiley & Sons.

Hare, R. D. (1991). Manual for the revised psychopathy checklist. Toronto, ON: Multi-Health Systems.

Hare, R. D. (1993). Without conscience: The disturbing world of the psychopaths among us. New York, NY: Pocket Books.

Hare, R. D. (2003). Manual for the revised psychopathy checklist (2nd ed.). Toronto, ON: Multi-Health Systems.

Hare, R. D., & Neumann, C. S. (2006). The PCL-R Assessment of psychopathy: Development, structural properties, and new directions. In C. J. Patrick (Ed.), Handbook of the psychopathy (pp. 58–88). New York, NY: Guilford Press.

Hare, R. D., McPherson, L. M., & Forth, A. E. (1988). Male psychopaths and their criminal careers. Journal of Consulting and Clinical Psychology, 56, 710–714.

Hare, R. D., Neumann, C. S., & Widiger, T. A. (2012). Psychopathy. In T. A. Widiger (Ed.), The Oxford handbook of personality disorders (pp. 478–504). New York, NY: Oxford University Press.

Hargrave, C. (1999). Homelessness in Canada: From housing to shelters to blankets. Share International. Retrieved February 14, 2004, from http://www .shareintl.org/archives/homelessness/ hl-ch_Canada.htm

Hariri, A. R., Mattay, V. S., Tessitore, A., Kolachana, B., Fera, F., Goldman, D., ... Weinberger, D. R. (2002). Serotonin transporter genetic variation and the response of the human amygdala. Science, 297, 400–402.

Harmer, C. J. (2008). Serotonin and emotional processing: Does it help explain antidepressant drug action? Neuropharmacology, 55(6), 1023–1028.

Harmer, C. J., O'Sullivan, U., Favaron, E., Massey-Chase, R., Ayres, R., Reinecke, A., ... Cowen, P. J. (2009). Effect of acute antidepressant administration on negative affective bias in depressed patients. American Journal of Psychiatry, 166(10), 1178–1184.

Harper, L. V. (2005). Epigenetic inheritance and the intergenerational transfer of experience. Psychological Bulletin, 131, 340–360.

Harpur, T. J., Hare, R. D., & Hakstian, A. R. (1989). Two-factor conceptualization of psychopathy: Construct validity and assessment implications. Psychological Assessment: A Journal of Consulting and Clinical Psychology, 1, 6–17.

Harpur, T. J., Hart, S. D., & Hare, R. D. (2002). Personality of the psychopath. In P. T. Costa & T. A. Widiger (Eds.), Personality disorders and the five-factor model of personality (2nd ed., pp. 299–324). Washington, DC: American Psychological Association.

Harrington, C. (2003). Great Falls residents caught up in Heatherington story. C News. Retrieved May 8, 2003, from at http://cnews.canoe.ca/CNEWS/ Canada/2003/05/08/82654–cp.html

Harris, B. (1979). Whatever happened to little Albert? American Psychologist, 34, 151–160.

Harris, E. C., & Barraclough, B. (1998). Excess mortality of mental disorder. British Journal of Psychiatry, 173, 11–53.

Harris, G. T., & Rice, M. E. (2010). Assessment of risk and dangerousness in adults. In J. Brown & E. A. Campbell (Eds.) Cambridge handbook of forensic psychology (pp. 299–306). New York, NY: Cambridge University Press.

Harris, G. T., Rice, M. E., Quinsey, V. L., & Cormier, C. (2015). Violent offenders: Appraising and managing risk (3rd ed.). Washington, DC: American Psychological Association.

Harris, G. T., Rice, M. E., Quinsey, V. L., Chaplin, T. C., & Earls, C. (1992). Maximizing the discriminant validity of phallometric assessment data. Psychological Assessment, 4, 502–511.

Harrison, B. J., Pujol, J., Cardoner, N., Deus, J., Alonso, P., Lopez-Sola, M., & Soriano-Mas, C. (2013). Brain corticostriatal systems and the major clinical symptom dimensions of obsessive–compulsive disorder. Biological Psychiatry, 73(4), 321–328.

Harrison, P. J. (2012). The neurobiology of mood disorders. In Andreasen, J.J. Lopez-Ibor, & J. R. Geddes (Eds.), New Oxford textbook of psychiatry (2nd ed., Vol. 1, pp. 561–568). New York, NY: Oxford University Press.

Harrow, M., Sands, J. R., Silverstein, M. L., & Goldberg, J. F. (1997). Course and outcome for schizophrenia versus other psychotic patients: A longitudinal study. Schizophrenia Bulletin, 23, 287–303.

Hart, E. L., Lahey, B. B., Loeber, R., Applegate, B., & Frick, P. J. (1995). Developmental change in attention-deficit hyperactivity disorder in boys: A four-year longitudinal study. Journal of Abnormal Child Psychology, 23, 729–749.

Harte, C. B., & Meston, C. M. (2008a). Acute effects of nicotine on physiological and subjective sexual arousal in nonsmoking men: A randomized, double-blind, placebo-controlled trial. Journal of Sexual Medicine, 5(1), 110–121.

Harte, C. B., & Meston, C. M. (2008b). The inhibitory effects of nicotine on physiological sexual arousal in nonsmoking women: Results from a randomized, double-blind, placebo-controlled, cross-over trial. Journal of Sexual Medicine, 5(5), 1184–1197.

Hartenbaum, N., Collop, N., Rosen, I. M., Phillips, B., George, C. F. P., Rowley, J. A., ... Moffitt, G. L. (2006). Sleep apnea and commercial motor vehicle operators: Statement from the Joint Task Force of the American College of Occupational and Environmental Medicine and the National Sleep Foundation. Chest, 130, 902–905.

Hartlage, S. A., Freels, S., Gotman, N., & Yonkers, K. (2012). Criteria for premenstrual dysphoric disorder: Secondary analyses of relevant data sets. Archives of General Psychiatry, 69(3), 300–305.

Harvey, A. G. (2008). Sleep and circadian rhythms in bipolar disorder: Seeking synchrony, harmony, and regulation. American Journal of Psychiatry, 165(7), 820–829.

Harvey, A. G., Soehner, A. M., Kaplan, K. A., Hein, K., Lee, J., Kanady, J., Li, D., Rabe-Hesketh, S., Ketter, T. A., Nylan, T. C., & Buysse, D. J. (2015). Treating insomnia improves mood state, sleep, and functioning in bipolar disorder: A pilot randomized controlled trial. *Journal of Consulting and Clinical Psychology, 83,* 564–577.

Harvey, A. G., Talbot, L. S., & Gershon, A. (2009). Sleep disturbance in bipolar disorder across the lifespan. *Clinical Psychology: Science and Practice, 16*(2), 256–277.

Harvey, L., Inglis, S. J., & Espie, C. (2002). Insomniacs' reported use of CBT components and relationship to long-term clinical outcome. *Behaviour Research and Therapy, 40,* 75–83.

Harvey, P. D., & Bowie, C. R. (2013). Schizophrenia spectrum conditions. In I. B. Weiner (Series Ed.), G. Stricker & T. A. Widiger (Vol. Eds.), *Handbook of psychology: Vol. 8 Clinical psychology* (pp. 240–261). Hoboken, NJ: John Wiley & Sons.

Hasin, D. S. (2012). Combining abuse and dependence in DSM-5. *Journal of Studies on Alcohol and Drugs, 73*(4), 702–704.

Hasin, D. S., Goodwin, R. D., Stinson, F. S., & Grant, B. F. (2005). Epidemiology of major depressive disorder: Results from the National Epidemiologic Survey on alcoholism and related conditions. *Archives of General Psychiatry, 62* (10), 1097–1106.

Hasin, D. S., & Grant, B. F. (2015). The national epidemiologic survey on alcohol and related conditions (NESARC), waves 1 and 2: Review and summary of findings. *Social Psychiatry and Psychiatric Epidemiology, 50,* 1609–1640.

Hasler, B. P., Buysse, D. J., Kupfer, D. J., & Germain, A. (2010). Phase relationships between core body temperature, melatonin, and sleep are associated with depression severity. *Psychiatry Research, 178,* 205–207.

Hathaway, S. R., & McKinley, J. C. (1943). *Manual for the Minnesota Multiphasic Personality Inventory.* New York, NY: Psychological Corporation.

Haukkala, A., Konttinen, H., Laatikainen, T., Kawachi, I., & Uutela, A. (2010). Hostility, anger control, and anger expression as predictors of cardiovascular disease. *Psychosomatic Medicine, 72*(6), 556–562.

Hauner, K. K., Mineka, S., Voss, J. L., & Paller, K. A. (2012). Exposure therapy triggers lasting reorganization of neural fear processing. *Proceedings of the National Academy of Sciences of the United States, 109*(23), 9203–9208.

Hauri, P. (1982). *The sleep disorders* (2nd ed.). Kalamazoo, MI: Upjohn Company.

Hawkley, L. C., & Cacioppo, J. T. (2007). Aging and loneliness: Downhill quickly? *Current Directions in Psychological Science, 16,* 187–191.

Hawkley, L. C., Thisted, R. A., Masi, C. M., & Cacioppo, J. T. (2010). Loneliness predicts increased blood pressure: 5-year cross-lagged analyses in middle-aged and older adults. *Psychology and Aging, 25*(1), 132–141.

Hawton, K. (1995). Treatment of sexual dysfunctions of sex therapy and other approaches. *British Journal of Psychiatry, 167,* 307–314.

Hawton, K., Houston, K., Haw, C., Townsend, E., & Harriss, L. (2003). Comorbidity of axis I and axis II disorders in patients who attempted suicide. *American Journal of Psychiatry, 160,* 1494–1500.

Hay, P. J., & Hall, A. (1991). The prevalence of eating disorders in recently admitted psychiatric in-patients. *British Journal of Psychiatry, 159,* 562–565.

Hay, P., & Fairburn, C. (1998). The validity of the DSM-IV scheme for classifying bulimic eating disorders. *International Journal of Eating Disorders, 23,* 7–15.

Hayes, S. C., Barlow, D. H., & Nelson-Gray, R. O. (1999). *The scientist practitioner: Research and accountability in the age of managed care* (2nd ed.). Needham Heights, MA: Allyn & Bacon.

Hayes-Skelton, S. A., Roemer, L., & Orsillo, S. M. (2013). A randomized clinical trial comparing an acceptance-based behavior therapy to applied relaxation for generalized anxiety disorder. *Journal of Consulting and Clinical Psychology, 81,* 761–773.

Hayes-Skelton, S. A., Roemer, L., & Orsillo, S. M. (2013). An acceptance-based behavior therapy for individuals with generalized anxiety disorder. *Practice, 20*(3), 264–281.

Hayley, A. C., Williams, L. J., Kennedy, G. A., Holloway, K. L., Berk, M., Brennan-Olsen, S. L., & Pasco, J. A. (2015). Excessive daytime sleepiness and falls among older men and women: Cross-sectional examination of a population-based sample. *BMC Geriatrics, 15*(1), 74.

Hayman-Abello, B. A., Hayman-Abello, S. E., & Rourke, B. P. (2003). Human neuropsychology in Canada: The 1990s (a review of research by Canadian neuropsychologists conducted over the past decade). *Canadian Psychology, 44,* 100–138.

Haynes, S. G., & Matthews, K. A. (1988). Area review: Coronary-prone behavior: Continuing evolution of the concept: Review and methodologic critique of recent studies on type A behavior and cardiovascular disease. *Annals of Behavioral Medicine, 10*(2), 47–59.

Haynes, S. G., Feinleib, M., & Kannel, W. B. (1980). The relationship of psychosocial factors to coronary heart disease in the Framingham study: III. Eight-year incidence of coronary heart disease. *American Journal of Epidemiology, 111,* 37–58.

Haynes, S. N., O'Brien, W., & Kaholukula, J. (2011). *Behavioral assessment and case formulation.* New York, NY: Wiley.

Haynos, A. F., & Fruzzetti, A. E. (2011). Anorexia nervosa as a disorder of emotion dysregulation: Evidence and treatment implications. *Clinical Psychology: Science and Practice, 18*(3), 183–202.

Hayward, G., Killen, J. D., Hammer, L. D., Litt, I. F., Wilson, D. M., Simmonds, B., & Taylor, C. B. (1992). Pubertal stage and panic attack history in sixth- and seventh-grade girls. *American Journal of Psychiatry, 149,* 1239–1243.

Hazell, P., O'Connell, D., Heathcote, D., Robertson, J., & Henry, D. (1995). Efficacy of tricyclic drugs in treating child and adolescent depression: A meta-analysis. *BMJ, 310,* 897–901.

Hazlett-Stevens, H., & Bernstein, D. A. (2012). Relaxation. In W. T. O' Donohue & J. E. Fisher (Eds.), *Cognitive behavior therapy: Core principles for practice* (pp. 105–132). Hoboken, NJ: Wiley.

Healey, G., Noah, J., & Mearns, C. (2016). The eigh ujarait (rocks) model: Supporting Inuit adolescent mental health with an intervention model based on Inuit knowledge and ways of knowing. *International Journal of Indigenous Health, 11,* 92–110.

Health Canada. (1999). *New report highlights HIV prevention for youth.* News release #1999–94. Retrieved May 14, 2004, from http://.hc-sc.gc.ca/english/media/releases/1999/99_94e.htm

Health Canada. (2000a). *Risk of important drug interactions between St. John's Wort and other prescription drugs.* Retrieved July 13, 2003, from http://.hc-sc.gc.ca/hpfb-dgpsa/tpd-dpt/st_johns_wort_e.html

Health Canada. (2000b). *Leading causes of death and hospitalization in Canada.* Ottawa, ON: Population and Public Health Branch.

Health Canada. (2002a). *A report on mental illnesses in Canada.* Ottawa, ON: Author.

Health Canada. (2002b). *HIV and AIDS in Canada: Surveillance report to June 30, 2002.* Ottawa, ON: Population and Public Health Branch: Division of HIV/AIDS Epidemiology and Surveillance, Centre for Infectious Disease Prevention and Control.

Health Canada. (2015). Canadian Tobacco, Alcohol and Drugs Survey (CTADS): Summary of results for 2013. Retrieved from http://healthycanadians.gc.ca/science-research-sciences-recherches/data-donnees/ctads-ectad/summary-sommaire-2013-eng.php

Health Canada. (2019). *Canadian tobacco, alcohol and drugs survey (CTADS): Summary of results for 2017.* https://www.canada.ca/en/health-canada/services/canadian-tobacco-alcohol-drugs-survey.html

Heath, A. K., Ganz, J. B., Parker, R., Burke, M., & Ninci, J. (2015). A meta-analytic review of functional communication training across mode of communication, age, and disability. *Review Journal of Autism and Developmental Disorders, 2*(2), 155–166.

Heath, C. A., Cooper, S. A., Murray, K., Lowman, A., Henry, C., MacLeod, M. A., ... Will, R. G. (2010). Validation of diagnostic criteria for variant Creutzfeldt-Jakob disease. *Annals of Neurology, 67*(6), 761–770.

Heatherton, T. F., & Baumeister, R. F. (1991). Binge eating as escape from self-awareness. *Psychological Bulletin, 110,* 86–108.

Heatherton, T. F., Herman, C. P., & Polivy, J. (1991). Effects of physical threat and ego threat on eating behavior. *Journal of Personality and Social Psychology, 60*(1), 138–143.

Heaton, R. K., Velin, R. A., McCutchan, A., Gulevich, S. J., Atkinson, J. H., Wallace, M. R., ... Grant, I. (1994). Neuropsychological impairment in human immunodeficiency virus-infection: Implications for employment. *Psychosomatic Medicine, 56,* 8–17.

Hecht, K. F., Cicchetti, D., Rogosch, F. A., & Crick, N. R. (2014). Borderline personality features in childhood: The role of subtype, developmental timing, and chronicity of child maltreatment. *Development and Psychopathology, 26*(3), 805–815.

Heckers, S., Barch, D. M., Bustillo, J., Gaebel, W., Gur, R., Malaspina, D., ... Van Os, J. (2013). Structure of the psychotic disorders classification in DSM-5. *Schizophrenia Research, 150*(1), 11–14.

Hedegaard, E. (2019, January 18). The anxious comedy of Howie Mandel. Rolling Stone. https://www.rollingstone.com/tv/tv-features/howie-mandel-showtime-comedy-special-interview-780578/

Heier, M. S., Skinningsrud, A., Paus, E., & Gautvik, K. M. (2014). Increased cerebrospinal fluid levels of nerve cell biomarkers in narcolepsy with cataplexy. *Sleep Medicine, 15,* 614–618. https://doi.org/10.1016/j.sleep.2014.02.005

Heim, C., & Nemeroff, C. B. (1999). The impact on early adverse experiences on brain systems involved in the pathophysiology of anxiety and affective disorders. *Biological Psychiatry, 46*(11), 1509–1522.

Heiman, J. R. (2000). Orgasmic disorders in women. In S. R. Leiblum & R. C. Rosen (Eds.), *Principles and practice of sex therapy* (3rd ed., pp. 118–153). New York, NY: Guilford Press.

Heiman, J. R. (2007). Orgasmic disorders in women. In S. R. Leiblum (Ed.), *Principles and practice of sex therapy* (4th ed., pp. 84–123). New York, NY: Guilford Press.

Heiman, J. R., & LoPiccolo, J. (1983a). Clinical outcome of sex therapy: Effects of daily versus weekly treatment. *Archives of General Psychiatry, 40,* 443–449.

Heiman, J. R., & LoPiccolo, J. (1983b). Effectiveness of daily versus weekly therapy in the treatment of sexual dysfunction. Unpublished manuscript, State University of New York at Stony Brook.

Heiman, J. R., & LoPiccolo, J. (1988). *Becoming orgasmic: A sexual and personal growth program for women* (rev. ed.). New York, NY: Prentice-Hall.

Heiman, J. R., & Meston, C. M. (1997). Empirically validated treatment for sexual dysfunction. *Annual Review of Sex Research, 8,* 148–195.

Heimberg, R. G., Dodge, C. S., Hope, D. A., Kennedy, C. R., Zollo, L., & Becker, R. E. (1990). Cognitive behavioral group treatment for social phobia: Comparison to a credible placebo control. *Cognitive Therapy and Research, 14,* 1–23.

Heimberg, R. G., Klosko, J. S., Dodge, C. S., & Shadick, R. (1989). Anxiety disorders, depression and attributional style: A further test of the specificity of depressive attributions. *Cognitive Therapy and Research, 13*(1), 21–36.

Heimberg, R. G., & Magee, L. (2014). Social anxiety disorder. In D. H. Barlow (Ed.), *Clinical handbook of psychological disorders: A step-by-step treatment manual* (5th ed.). New York, NY: Guilford Press.

Heimberg, R. G., Salzman, D. G., Holt, C. S., & Blendell, K. A. (1993). Cognitive-behavioral group treatment for social phobia: Effectiveness at five-year follow-up. *Cognitive Therapy and Research, 17,* 325–339.

Heinrichs, N., Rapee, R. M., & Alden, L. A. (2006). Cultural differences in perceived social norms and social anxiety. *Behaviour Research and Therapy, 44,* 1187–1197.

Heinrichs, N., Rapee, R. M., Alden, L. A., Bogels, S., Hofmann, S. G., Oh, K. J., & Sakano, Y. (2006). Cultural differences in perceived social norms and social anxiety. *Behaviour Research and Therapy, 44*(8), 1187–1197.

Heinrichs, R. W. (2003). Historical origins of schizophrenia: Two early madmen and their illness. *Journal of the*

History of the Behavioral Sciences, 39, 349–363.

Heinrichs, R. W., & Awad, A. G. (1993). Neurocognitive subtypes of chronic schizophrenia. *Schizophrenia Research, 9,* 49–58.

Heinrichs, R. W., Ruttan, L., Zakzanis, K. K., & Case, D. (1997). Parsing schizophrenia in neurocognitive tests: Evidence of stability and validity. *Brain & Cognition, 35,* 207–224.

Heintzelman, S. J., & King, L. A. (2014). (The Feeling of) Meaning-as-Information. *Personality and Social Psychology Review, 18*(2), 153–167.

Helenius, P., Salmelin, R., Service, E., & Connolly, J. F. (1999). Semantic cortical activation in dyslexic readers. *Journal of Cognitive Neuroscience, 11,* 535–550.

Helenius, P., Salmelin, R., Service, E., Connolly, J., Leinonen, S., & Lyytinen, H. (2002). Cortical activation during spoken-words segmentation in non-reading-impaired and dyslexic adults. *Journal of Neuroscience, 22,* 2936–2944.

Heller, W., & Nitschke, J. B. (1997). Regional brain activity in emotion: A framework for understanding cognition in depression. *Cognition and Emotion, 11*(5–6), 737–661.

Heller, W., Nitschke, J. B., & Miller, G. A. (1998). Lateralization in emotion and emotional disorders. *Current Directions in Psychological Science, 7,* 26–27.

Helmes, E., & Ostbye, T. (2002). Beyond memory impairment: Cognitive changes in Alzheimer's disease. *Archives of Clinical Neuropsychology, 17,* 179–193.

Helweg-Larsen, M., & Collins, B. E. (1997). A social psychological perspective on the role of knowledge about AIDS in AIDS prevention. *Current Directions in Psychological Science, 6,* 23–26.

Helzer, J. E., Kraemer, H. C., Krueger, R. F., Wittchen, H. U., Sirovatka, P. J., & Regier, D. A. (2008). *Dimensional approaches in diagnostic classification: Refining the research agenda for DSM-V.* Washington, DC: American Psychiatric Association.

Hendriks, G. J., Kampman, M., Keijers, G. P., Hoogduin, C. A., & Voshaar, R. C. O. (2014). Cognitive-behavioral therapy for panic disorder with agoraphobia in older people: A comparison with younger patients. *Depression and Anxiety, 31,* 669–677.

Herbert, T. B., & Cohen, S. (1993). Depression and immunity: A meta-analytic review. *Psychological Bulletin, 113*(3), 472–486.

Herdt, G. H. (1987). *The Sambia: Ritual and gender in New Guinea.* New York, NY: Holt, Rinehart and Winston.

Herdt, G. H., & Stoller, R. J. (1989). Commentary to "The socialization of homosexuality and heterosexuality in a non-Western society." *Archives of Sexual Behavior, 18,* 31–34.

Herlitz, C. A., & Forsberg, M. (2010). Sexual behavior and risk assessment in different age cohorts in the general population of Sweden (1989–2007). *Scandinavian Journal of Public Health, 38,* 32–39.

Herman, J. L., Perry, C., & van der Kolk, B. A. (1989). Childhood trauma in borderline personality disorder. *American Journal of Psychiatry, 146,* 490–495.

Hermann, N., Lanctôt, K. L., Sambrook, R., Lesnikova, N., Hébert, R., McCracken, P., … Nguyen, E. (2006). The contribution of neuropsychiatric symptoms to the cost of dementia care. *International Journal of Geriatric Psychiatry, 21,* 972–976.

Hermans, E. J., Henckens, M. J. A. G., Joels, M., & Fernandez, G. (2014). Dynamic adaptation of large-scale brain networks in response to acute stressors. *Trends in Neurosciences, 37,* 304–314.

Hermans, E. J., van Marle, H. J., Ossewaarde, L., Henckens, M. J., Qin, S., van Kesteren, M. T., & Fernández, G. (2011). Stress-related noradrenergic activity prompts large-scale neural network reconfiguration. *Science, 334*(6059), 1151–1153.

Heron, J., Barker, E. D., Joinson, C., Lewis, G., Hickman, M., Munafò, M., & Macleod, J. (2013). Childhood conduct disorder trajectories, prior risk factors and cannabis use at age 16: Birth cohort study. *Addiction, 108*(12), 2129–2138.

Herrero, M. E., Hechtman, L., & Weiss, G. (1994). Antisocial disorders in hyperactive subjects from childhood to adulthood: Predictive factors and characterization of subgroups. *American Journal of Orthopsychiatry, 64,* 510–521.

Herrick, J., Shecterle, L. M., & St. Cyr, J. A. (2009). D-ribose—An additive with caffeine. *Medical Hypotheses, 72*(5), 499–500.

Hervé, H. (2007). Psychopathy across the ages: A history of the Hare psychopath. In H. Hervé & J. C. Yuille (Eds.), *The psychopath: Theory, research, and practice* (pp. 31–55). Mahwah, NJ: Lawrence Erlbaum Associates Publishers.

Herz, M. I. (1985). Prodromal symptoms and prevention of relapse in schizophrenia. *Journal of Clinical Psychiatry, 46*(11), 22–25.

Herzog, D. B. (1988). Eating disorders. In A. M. Nicoli, Jr. (Ed.), *The new Harvard guide to psychiatry* (pp. 434–445). Boston, MA: Harvard University Press.

Herzog, D. B., Dorer, D. J., Keel, P. K., Selwyn, S. E., Ekeblad, E. R., Flores, A. T., … Keller, M. B. (1999). Recovery and relapse in anorexia and bulimia nervosa: A 75-year follow-up study. *Journal of the American Academy of Child and Adolescent Psychiatry, 38*(7), 829–837.

Hetherington, E. M., Stanley-Hagan, M., & Anderson, E. R. (1989). Marital transitions: A child's perspective. *American Psychologist, 44,* 303–312.

Hettema, J. M., Neale, M. C., Kendler, K. S. (2001). A review and meta-analysis of the genetic epidemiology of anxiety disorders. *American Journal of Psychiatry, 158,* 1568–1578.

Hettema, J. M., Prescott, C. A., Myers, J. M., Neale, M. C., & Kendler, K. S. (2005). The structure of genetic and environmental risk factors for anxiety disorders in men and women. *Archives of General Psychiatry, 62,* 182–189.

Hewitt, P. L., Flett, G. L., & Ediger, E. (1995). Perfectionism traits and perfectionistic self-presentation in eating disorder attitudes, characteristics, and symptoms. *International Journal of Eating Disorders, 18,* 317–326.

Heylens, G., De Cuypere, G., Zucker, K. J., Schelfaut, C., Elaut, E., Vanden Bossche, H., … T'Sjoen, G. (2012).

Gender identity disorder in twins: A review of the case report literature. *Journal of Sexual Medicine, 9*(3), 751–757.

Hickie, I. B., Naismith, S. L., Robillard, R., Scott, E. M., & Hermens, D. F. (2013). Manipulating the sleep-wake cycle and circadian rhythms to improve clinical management of major depression. *BMC medicine, 11*(1), 79.

Higgins, S. T., Heil, S. H., Dantona, R., Donham, R., Matthews, M., & Badger, G. J. (2006). Effects of varying the monetary value of voucher-based incentives on abstinence achieved during and following treatment among cocaine-dependent outpatients. *Addiction, 102,* 271–281.

Higgins, S. T., Sigmon, S. C., & Heil, S. H. (2014). Drug use disorders. In D. H. Barlow (Ed.), *Clinical handbook of psychological disorders: A step-by-step treatment manual.* New York, NY: Guilford Press.

Hilbert, A., Hildebrandt, T., Agras, W. S., Wilfley, D. E., & Wilson, G. T. (2015). Rapid response in psychological treatments for binge eating disorder. *Journal of Consulting and Clinical Psychology, 83*(3), 649.

Hilgard, E. R. (1992). Divided consciousness and dissociation. *Consciousness & Cognition, 1,* 16–31.

Hill, A. E., & Rosenbloom, L. (1986). Disintegrative psychosis of childhood: Teenage follow-up. *Developmental Medicine and Child Neurology, 28,* 34–40.

Hill, C. (2011). Practitioner Review: Effective treatment of behavioural insomnia in children. *Journal of Child Psychology and Psychiatry, 52*(7), 731–740.

Hill, D. E., Yeo, R. A., Campbell, R. A., Hart, B., Vigil, J., & Brooks, W. (2003). Magnetic resonance imaging correlates of attention-deficit/hyperactivity disorder in children. *Neuropsychology, 17,* 496–506.

Hill, K. G., Bailey, J. A., Hawkins, J. D., Catalano, R. F., Kosterman, R., Oesterle, S., & Abbott, R. D. (2014). The onset of STI diagnosis through age 30: Results from the Seattle Social Development Project intervention. *Prevention Science, 15*(1), 19–32.

Hiller, W., Leibbrand, R., Rief, W., & Fichter, M. (2005). Differentiating hypochondriasis from panic disorder. *Journal of Anxiety Disorders, 19,* 29–49.

Hillman, E., Kripke, D. F., & Gillin, J. C. (1990). Sleep restriction, exercise, and bright lights: Alternate therapies for depression. In A. Tasman, C. Kaufman, & S. Goldfinger (Eds.), *American Psychiatric Press review of psychiatry: Section I: Treatment of refractory affective disorder* (R. Post, section ed., Vol. 9, pp. 132–144). Washington, DC: American Psychiatric Press.

Hinchley, J., & Levy, B. A. (1988). Developmental and individual differences in reading comprehension. *Cognition & Instruction, 5,* 3–47.

Hindmarch, I. (1990). Cognitive impairment with anti-anxiety agents: A solvable problem? In D. Wheatley (Ed.), *The anxiolytic jungle: Where, next?* (pp. 49–61). Chichester, UK: John Wiley & Sons.

Hinshaw, S. P., & Stier, A. (2008). Stigma as related to mental disorders. *Annual*

Review of Clinical Psychology, 4, 367–393.

Hinshelwood, J. A. (1896). A case of dyslexia: A peculiar form of word-blindness. *Lancet, 2,* 1451–1454.

Hinton, L., Guo, Z., Hillygus, J., & Levkoff, S. (2000). Working with culture: A qualitative analysis of barriers to the recruitment of Chinese-American family caregivers for dementia research. *Journal of Cross-Cultural Gerontology, 15*(2), 119–137.

Hirsch, S., Cramer, P., & Bowen, J. (1992). The triggering hypothesis of the role of life events in schizophrenia. *British Journal of Psychiatry, 161,* 84–87.

Hirschfeld, D. R., Rosenbaum, J. F., Biederman, J., Bolduc, E. A., Farone, S. V., Snidman, N., … Kagan, J. (1992). Stable behavioral inhibition and its association with anxiety disorder. *Journal of the American Academy of Child and Adolescent Psychiatry, 31,* 103–111.

Hirschfeld, R. M., Keller, M., Panico, S., Arons, B. S., Barlow, D., Davidoff, F., … Wyatt, R. J. (1997). The national depressive and manic-depressive association consensus statement on the undertreatment of depression. *JAMA, 277,* 333–340.

Hirshkowitz, M., Seplowitz, R. G., & Sharafkhaneh, A. (2009). Sleep disorders. In B. J. Sadock, V. A. Sadock, & P. Ruiz (Eds.), *Kaplan & Sadock's comprehensive textbook of psychiatry* (9th ed., Vol. 1, pp. 2150–2177). Philadelphia, PA: Lippincott Williams & Wilkins.

Hiscock, H., Sciberras, E., Mensah, F., Gerner, B., Efron, D., Khano, S., & Oberklaid, F. (2015). *BMJ: British Medical Journal, 350,* h68. https://doi.org/10.1136/bmj.h68

Hishkowitz, M., Whiton, K., Albert, S. M., Alessi, C., Bruni, O., DonCarlos, L., Hazen, N., Herman, J., Adams Hillard, P. J., Katz, E. S., Kheirandish-Gozal, L., Neubauer, D., O'Donnell, A. E., Ohayon, M., Peever, J., Rawding, R., Sachdeva, R. C., Setters, B., Vitiello, M. V., & Ware, J. C. (2015). National Sleep Foundation's updated sleep duration recommendations: Final report. *Sleep Health, 1,* 233–243. https://doi.org/10.1016/j.sleh.2015.10.004

Hitchcock, P. B., & Mathews, A. (1992). Interpretation of bodily symptoms in hypochondriasis. *Behaviour Research and Therapy, 30*(3), 223–234.

Hlastala, S. A., Kotler, J. S., McClellan, J. M., & McCauley, E. A. (2010). Interpersonal and social rhythm therapy for adolescents with bipolar disorder: Treatment development and results from an open trial. *Depression and Anxiety, 27*(5), 457–464.

Ho, B. C., Black, D. W., & Andreasen, N. C. (2003). Schizophrenia and other psychotic disorders. In R. E. Hales & S. C. Yudofsky (Eds.), *Textbook of clinical psychiatry* (4th ed., pp. 379–438). Washington, DC: American Psychiatric Press.

Hoaken, P. N. S., & Stewart, S. H. (2003). Drugs of abuse and the elicitation of human aggressive behavior. *Addictive Behaviors, 28,* 1533–1554.

Hoaken, P. N. S., Shaughnessy, V. K., & Pihl, R. O. (2003). Executive cognitive functioning and aggression: Is it an issue of impulsivity? *Aggressive Behavior, 29*(1), 15–30.

Hockey Hall of Fame and Museum. (2001). Shayne Corson. Retrieved July 15, 2004, from http://www.legendsofhockey.net:8080/LegendsOf-Hockey/jsp/SearchPlayer.jsp?player10297

Hodgins, D. C., Currie, S., & el-Guebaly, N. (2001). Motivational enhancement and self-help treatments for problem gambling. *Journal of Consulting and Clinical Psychology, 69*(1), 50–57.

Hodgins, D. C., Currie, S., el-Guebaly, N., & Peden, N. (2004). Brief motivational treatment for problem gambling: A 24-month follow-up. *Psychology of Addictive Behaviors, 18*(3), 293–296.

Hodgson, K., & McGuffin, P. (2013). The genetic basis of depression. *Current Topics in Behavioral Neurosciences, 14*, 81–99.

Hoek, H. W. (2002). The distribution of eating disorders. In K. D. Brownell & C. G. Fairburn (Eds.), *Eating disorders and obesity: A comprehensive handbook* (2nd ed., pp. 207–211).

Hoek, H. W., Bartelds, A. I. M., Bosveld, J. J. F., van der Graaf, Y., Limpens, V. E. L., Maiwald, M., & Spaaij, C. J. (1995). Impact of urbanization on detection rates of eating disorders. *American Journal of Psychiatry, 152*, 1272–1278.

Hoffman, B., Papas, R., Chatkoff, D., & Kerns, R. (2007). Meta-analysis of psychological interventions for chronic low back pain. *Health Psychology, 26*, 1–9.

Hoffman, R. E., Boutros, N. N., Hu, S., Berman, R. M., Krystal, J. H., & Charney, D. S. (2000). Transcranial magnetic stimulation and auditory hallucinations in schizophrenia. *Lancet, 355*, 1073–1075.

Hofmann S. G., & Otto, M. W. (2008). *Cognitive-behavior therapy of social anxiety disorder: Evidence-based and disorder specific treatment techniques.* New York, NY: Routledge.

Hofmann, S. G. (2007a). Enhancing exposure-based therapy from a translational research perspective. *Behavior Research and Therapy, 45*(9), 1987–2001.

Hofmann, S. G. (2007b). Cognitive factors that maintain social anxiety disorder: A comprehensive model and its treatment implications. *Cognitive Behavior Therapy, 36*(4), 195–209.

Hofmann, S. G. (2015). *Emotion in therapy: From science to practice.* New York, NY: Guilford Press.

Hofmann, S. G., Alpers, G. W., & Pauli, P. (2009). Phenomenology of panic and phobic disorders. In M. M. Antony & M. B. Stein (Eds.), *Oxford handbook of anxiety and related disorders* (pp. 34–46). New York, NY: Oxford University Press.

Hofmann, S. G., Asnaani, A., & Hinton, D. E. (2010). Cultural aspects in social anxiety and social anxiety disorder. *Depression and Anxiety, 27*(12), 1117–1127.

Hofmann, S. G., Asnaani, A., Vonk, J. J., Sawyer, A. T., & Fang, A. (2012). The efficacy of cognitive behavioral therapy: A review of meta-analyses. *Cognitive Therapy and Research, 36*, 427–440.

Hofmann, S. G., & Barlow, D. H. (1996). Ambulatory psychophysiological monitoring: A potentially useful tool when treating panic relapse. *Cognitive and Behavioral Practice, 3*, 53–61.

Hofmann, S., & Barlow, D. H. (2002). Social phobia (social anxiety disorder). In D. H. Barlow (Ed.), *Anxiety and its disorders: The nature and treatment of anxiety and panic* (2nd ed.). New York, NY: Guilford Press.

Hofmann, S. G., & Hinton, D. E. (2014). Cross-cultural aspects of anxiety disorders. *Current Psychiatry Reports, 16*:450.

Hofmann, S. G., Lehman, C. L., & Barlow, D. H. (1997). How specific are specific phobias? *Journal of Behavior Therapy and Experimental Psychiatry, 28*, 233–240.

Hofmann, S. G., Meuret, A. E., Smitts, J. A. J., Simon, N. M., Pollack, M. H., Eisenmenger, K., & Otto, M. W. (2006). Augmentation of exposure therapy with D-cycloserine for social anxiety disorder. *Archives of General Psychiatry, 63*(3), 298–304.

Hofmann, S. G., Sawyer, A. T., & Asnaani, A. (2012). D-cycloserine as an augmentation strategy for cognitive behavioral therapy of anxiety disorders: An update. *Current Pharmaceutical Design, 18*(35), 5659–5662.

Hofmann, S. G., Sawyer, A. T., Witt, A., & Oh, D. (2010). The effect of mindfulness-based therapy on anxiety and depression: A meta-analytic review. *Journal of Consulting and Clinical Psychology, 78*, 169–183.

Hofmann, S. G., & Smits, J. A. (2008). Cognitive-behavioral therapy for adult anxiety disorders: A meta-analysis of randomized placebo-controlled trials. *Journal of Clinical Psychiatry, 69*(4), 621–632.

Hofmann, S. G., Smits, J. A., Rosenfield, D., Simon, N., Otto, M. W., Meuret, A. E., & Pollack, M. H. (2013). D-cycloserine as an augmentation strategy with cognitive-behavioral therapy for social anxiety disorder. *American Journal of Psychiatry, 170*(7), 751–758.

Hogarty, G. E., Anderson, C. M., Reiss, D. J., Kornblith, S. J., Greenwald, D. P., Javna, C. D., & Madonia, M. J. (1986). Family psychoeducation, social skills training, and maintenance chemotherapy in the aftercare treatment of schizophrenia: I. One year effects of a controlled study on relapse and expressed emotion. *Archives of General Psychiatry, 43*, 633–642.

Hogarty, G. E., Anderson, C. M., Reiss, D. J., Kornblith, S. J., Greenwald, D. P., Ulrich, R. F., Carter, M., & The Environmental-Personal Indicators in the Course of Schizophrenia (EPICS) Research Group. (1991). Family psychoeducation, social skills training, and maintenance chemotherapy in the aftercare treatment of schizophrenia. *Archives of General Psychiatry, 48*, 340–347.

Hogarty, G. E., Reis, D., Kornblith, S. J., Greenwald, D., Ulrich, R., & Carter, M. (1992). In reply. *Archives of General Psychiatry, 49*, 76–77.

Hoge, S. K., Appelbaum, P. S., Lawler, T., Beck, J. C., Litman, R., Greer, A., … Kaplan, E. (1990). A prospective, multicenter study of patients' refusal of antipsychotic medication. *Archives of General Psychiatry, 47*, 949–956.

Holahan, A.-L. V., & O'Driscoll, G. A. (2005). Anti-saccade and smooth pursuit performance in positive- and negative-symptom schizotype. *Schizophrenia Research, 76*(1), 43–54.

Holder, H. D., Gruenewald, P. J., Ponicki, W. R., Treno, A. J., Grube, J. W., Saltz, R. F., … Roeper, P. (2000). Effect of community-based interventions on high-risk drinking and alcohol-related injuries. *JAMA, 284*, 2341–2347.

Holland, A. J. (2012). Classification, diagnosis, psychiatric assessment, and needs assessment. In M. G. Gelder, N. C. Andreasen, J. J. Lopez-Ibor, & J. R. Geddes (Eds.), *New Oxford textbook of psychiatry* (2nd ed., Vol. 2, pp. 1819–1824). New York, NY: Oxford University Press.

Holland, J. M., & Gallagher-Thompson, D. (2011). Interventions for mental health problems in later life. In D. H. Barlow (Ed.), *Oxford handbook of clinical psychology* (pp. 810–836). New York, NY: Oxford University Press.

Hollander, E., Allen, A., Kwon, J., Aronwoitz, B., Schmeidler, J., Wong, C., & Simeon, D. (1999). Clomipramine vs desipramine crossover trial in body dysmorphic disorder: Selective efficacy of a serotonin reuptake inhibitor in imagined ugliness. *Archives of General Psychiatry, 56*(11), 1033–1039.

Hollander, E., Berlin, H. A., & Stein, D. J. (2009). Impulse-control disorders not elsewhere classified. In J. A. Bourgeois, R. E. Hales, J. S. Young, & S. C. Yudofsky (Eds.), *The American psychiatric publishing board review guide for psychiatry* (pp. 469–482). Arlington, VA: American Psychiatric Publishing.

Hollander, J. A., & Kenny, P. J. (2012). Compulsive drug use and brain reward systems. In J. C. Verster, K. Brady, M. Galanter, & P. Conrod (Eds.), *Drug abuse and addiction in medical illness* (pp. 63–72). New York, NY: Springer.

Holley, H., Arboleda-Florez, J., & Crisanti, A. (1998). Do forensic offenders receive harsher sentences? An examination of legal outcomes. *International Journal of Law & Psychiatry, 21*, 43–57.

Hollingshead, A. B., & Redlich, F. C. (1958). *Social class and mental illness.* Oxford, UK: Wiley.

Hollis, J. F., Connett, J. E., Stevens, V. J., & Greenlick, M. R. (1990). Stressful life events, type A behavior, and the prediction of cardiovascular and total mortality over six years. *Journal of Behavioral Medicine, 13*(3), 263–280.

Hollon, S. D. (1993). Review of psychosocial treatments for mood disorders. In D. L. Dunner (Ed.), *Current psychiatric therapy.* Philadelphia, PA: W. B. Saunders.

Hollon, S. D. (2011). Cognitive and behavior therapy in the treatment and prevention of depression. *Depression and Anxiety, 28*(4), 263–266.

Hollon, S. D., DeRubeis, R. J., Evans, M. D., Wiener, M. J., Garvey, M. J., Grove, W. M., & Tuason, V. B. (1992). Cognitive therapy and pharmacotherapy for depression: Singly and in combination. *Archives of General Psychiatry, 49*(10), 772–781.

Hollon, S. D., DeRubeis, R. J., Shelton, R. C., Amsterdam, J. D., Salomon, R. M., O'Reardon, J. P., & Gallop, R. (2005). Prevention of relapse following cognitive therapy vs. medications in moderate to severe depression. *Archives of General Psychiatry, 62*, 417–422.

Hollon, S. D., Stewart, M. O., & Strunk, D. (2006). Cognitive behavior therapy has enduring effects in the treatment of depression and anxiety. *Annual Review of Psychology, 57*, 285–315.

Holly Jones timeline. (2003b, June 20). *CBC News Online.* Retrieved August 5, 2004, from http://www.cbc.ca/news/indepth/background/jones_holly_timeline.html

Hollon, S. D., & Dimidjian, S. (2009). Cognitive and behavioral treatment of depression. In I. H. Gotlib & C. L. Hammen (Eds.), *Handbook of depression* (2nd ed., pp. 586–603). New York, NY: Guilford Press.

Holm, V. A., & Varley, C. K. (1989). Pharmacological treatment of autistic children. In G. Dawson (Ed.), *Autism: Nature, diagnosis, and treatment* (pp. 386–404). New York, NY: Guilford Press.

Holroyd, K. A., & Penzien, D. B. (1986). Client variables in the behavioral treatment of current tension headache: A meta-analytic review. *Journal of Behavioral Medicine, 9*, 515–536.

Holroyd, K. A., Andrasik, F., & Noble, J. (1980). A comparison of EMG biofeedback and a credible pseudotherapy in treating tension headache. *Journal of Behavioral Medicine, 3*, 29–39.

Holroyd, K. A., Nash, J. M., Pingel, J. D., Cordingley, G. E., & Jerome, A. (1991). A comparison of pharmacological (amitriptyline HCL) and non-pharmacological (cognitive-behavioral) therapies for chronic tension headaches. *Journal of Consulting and Clinical Psychology, 59*(3), 387–393.

Holroyd, K. A., Penzien, D. B., Hursey, K. G., Tobin, D. L., Rogers, L., Holm, J. E., … Chila, A. G. (1984). Change mechanisms in EMG biofeedback training. Cognitive changes underlying improvements in tension headache. *Journal of Consulting and Clinical Psychology, 52*, 1039–1053.

Holt-Lunstad, J., Birmingham, W. A., & Light, K. C. (2008). Influence of a "warm touch" support enhancement intervention among married couples on ambulatory blood pressure, oxytocin, alpha amylase, & cortisol. *Psychosomatic Medicine, 70*, 976–985.

Holt-Lunstad, J., Smith, T. B., & Layton, J. B. (2010). Social relationships and mortality risk: A meta-analytic review. *PLoS Med, 7*(7), e1000316.

Hook, E. B. (1982). Epidemiology of Down syndrome. In S. M. Pueschel & J. E. Rynders (Eds.), *Down syndrome: Advances in biomedicine and the behavioral sciences* (pp. 11–88). Cambridge, MA: Ware Press.

Hooley, J. M. (1985). Expressed emotion: A review of the critical literature. *Clinical Psychology Review, 5*, 119–139.

Hooley, J. M., Cole, S. H., & Gironde, S. (2012). Borderline personality disorder. In T. A. Widiger (Ed.), *The Oxford handbook of personality disorders* (pp. 409–436). New York, NY: Oxford University Press.

Hoppenbrouwers, S. S., Neumann, C. S., Lewis, J., Johansson, P. (2015). A latent variable analysis of the Psychopathy Checklist–Revised and behavioral inhibition system/behavioral activation system factors in North American and Swedish offenders. *Personality Disorders: Theory, Research, and Treatment, 6*(3), 251–260. https://doi.org/10.1037/per0000115

Hopwood, C. J., & Thomas, K. M. (2012). Paranoid and schizoid personality disorders. In T. A. Widiger (Ed.), *The Oxford handbook of personality disorders* (pp. 582–602). New York, NY: Oxford University Press.

Horen, S. A., Leichner, P. P., & Lawson, J. S. (1995). Prevalence of dissociative symptoms and disorders in an adult psychiatric inpatient population in Canada. *Canadian Journal of Psychiatry, 40,* 185–191.

Horgan, M. M., Sparrow, M. D., & Brazeau, R. (1986). *Alcoholic beverage taxation and control policies* (6th ed.). Ottawa, ON: Brewers Association of Canada.

Hornby, L. (2001, October 21). Panic hit Corson on leaf 's bench. *Toronto Sun.* Retrieved June 21, 2004, from http://www.canoe.ca/Health0110/18_corson-sun.html

Horney, K. (1967). *Feminine psychology.* New York, NY: W. W. Norton.

Horowitz, M. J., Siegel, B., Holen, A., Bonanno, G. A., Milbrath, C., & Stinson, C. H. (1997). Diagnostic criteria for complicated grief disorder. *American Journal of Psychiatry, 154,* 904–910.

Horwath, E., & Weissman, M. (1997). Epidemiology of anxiety disorders across cultural groups. In S. Friedman (Ed.), *Cultural issues in the treatment of anxiety* (pp. 21–39). New York, NY: Guilford Press.

Horwath, E., & Weissman, M. M. (2000). The epidemiology and cross-national presentation of obsessive–compulsive disorder. *Psychiatric Clinics of North America, 23*(3), 493–507.

Horwitz, A. V. (2002). *Creating mental illness.* Chicago, IL: University of Chicago Press.

House, J. S., Landis, K. R., & Umberson, D. (1988). Social relationships and health. *Science, 241,* 540–545.

House, J. S., Robbins, C., & Metzner, H. M. (1982). The association of social relationships and activities with mortality: Prospective evidence from the Tecumseh community health study. *American Journal of Epidemiology, 116,* 123.

Houston, B. K., Chesney, M. A., Black, G. W., Cates, D. S., & Hecker, M. H. L. (1992). Behavioral clusters and coronary heart disease risk. *Psychosomatic Medicine, 54*(4), 447–461.

Howard, G., Lackland, D. T., Kleindorfer, D. O., Kissela, B. M., Moy, C. S., Judd, S. E., … Howard, V. J. (2013). Racial differences in the impact of elevated systolic blood pressure on stroke risk. *JAMA Internal Medicine, 173*(1), 46–51.

Howard, M. O., Bowen, S. E., Garland, E. L., Perron, B. E., & Vaughn, M. G. (2011). Inhalant use and inhalant use disorders in the United States. *Addiction Science & Clinical Practice, 6*(1), 18–31.

Howard, R., Castle, D., Wessely, S., & Murray, R. (1993). A comparative study of 470 cases of early-onset and late-onset schizophrenia. *British Journal of Psychiatry, 163,* 352–357.

Howell, M. (2012). Parasomnias: An updated review. *Neurotherapeutics, 9*(4), 753–775. https://doi.org/10.1007/s13311-012-0143-8

Howes, J. L., & Vallis, T. M. (1996). Cognitive therapy with nontraditional populations: Application to post-traumatic stress disorder and personality disorders. In K. S. Dobson & K. D. Craig (Eds.), *Advances in cognitive-behavioral therapy* (Vol. 2, pp. 237–271). Thousand Oaks, CA: Sage Publications.

Howland, R. H., Rush, A. J., Wisniewski, S. R., Trivedi, M. H., Warden, D., Fava, M., & Gallop, R. (2009). Concurrent anxiety and substance use disorders among outpatients with major depression: Clinical features and effect on treatment outcome. *Drug and Alcohol Dependence, 99*(1–3), 248–260.

Howlin, P., Goode, S., Hutton, J., & Rutter, M. (2010). Savant skills in autism: Psychometric approaches and parental reports. In F. Happé & U. Frith (Eds.), *Autism and talent* (pp. 13–24). New York, NY: Oxford University Press.

Hser, Y., Anglin, M. D., & Powers, K. (1993). A 24-year follow-up of California narcotics addicts. *Archives of General Psychiatry, 50,* 577–584.

Hser, Y., Evans, E., Grella, C., Ling, W., & Anglin, D. (2015). Long-term course of opioid addiction. *Harvard Review of Psychiatry, 23*(2), 76–89. https://doi.org/10.1097/HRP.0000000000000052

Hsu, L. K. G. (1988). The outcome of anorexia nervosa: A reappraisal. *Psychological Medicine, 18,* 807–812.

Hsu, L. K. G. (1990). *Eating disorders.* New York, NY: Guilford Press.

Huang, Y. C., Lin, C. C., Hung, Y. Y., & Huang, T. L. (2013). Rapid relief of catatonia in mood disorder by lorazepam and diazepam. *Biomedical Journal, 36*(1), 35–39.

Huang, Y., Kotov, R., de Girolamo, G., Preti, A., Angermeyer, M., Benjet, C., & Kessler, R. C. (2009). DSM-IV personality disorders in the WHO World Mental Health Surveys. *British Journal of Psychiatry, 195*(1), 46–53.

Hubert, N. C., Jay, S. M., Saltoun, M., & Hayes, M. (1988). Approach-avoidance and distress in children undergoing preparation for painful medical procedures. *Journal of Clinical Child Psychology, 17,* 194–202.

Hublin, C., Kaprio, J., Partinen, M., & Koskenvuo, M. (1999). Nightmares: Familial aggregation and association with psychiatric disorders in a nationwide twin cohort. *American Journal of Medical Genetics, 88*(4), 329–336.

Hucker, S. J. (2011). Hypoxyphilia. *Archives of Sexual Behavior, 40*(6), 1323–1326.

Hudson, J. I., Hiripi, E., Pope, H. G., Jr., & Kessler, R. C. (2007). The prevalence and correlates of eating disorders in the national comorbidity survey replication. *Biological Psychiatry, 61,* 348–358.

Hudson, J. I., Lalonde, J. K., Berry, J. M., Pindych, L. J., Bulik, C. M., Crow, S. J., & Pope, H. G. (2006). Binge-eating disorder as a distinct familial phenotype in obese individuals. *Archives of General Psychiatry, 63,* 313–319.

Huerta, M., Bishop, S. L., Duncan, A., Hus, V., & Lord, C. (2012). Application of DSM-5 criteria for autism spectrum disorder to three samples of children with DSM-IV diagnoses of pervasive developmental disorders. *American Journal of Psychiatry, 169*(10), 1056–1064.

Huey, S. J., Henggeler, S. W., Brondino, M. J., & Pickrel, S. G. (2000). Mechanisms of change in multisystem therapy: Reducing delinquent behavior through therapist adherence and improved family and peer functioning. *Journal of Consulting and Clinical Psychology, 68,* 451–467.

Hufford, D. J. (1982). *The terror that comes in the night: An experience centered study of supernatural assault traditions.* Philadelphia, PA: University of Pennsylvania Press.

Hughes, J. R. (2009). Nicotine-related disorders. In B. J. Sadock, V. A. Sadock, & P. Ruiz (Eds.), *Kaplan & Sadock's comprehensive textbook of psychiatry* (9th ed., Vol. 1, pp. 1353–1360). Philadelphia, PA: Lippincott Williams & Wilkins.

Huinck, W. J., Langevin, M., Kully, D., Graamans, K., Peters, H. F. M., & Hulstijn, W. (2006). The relationship between pre-treatment clinical profile and treatment outcome in an integrated stuttering program. *Journal of Fluency Disorders, 31,* 43–63.

Human Resources and Skills Development Canada. (2011). *Disability in Canada: A 2006 profile* (Catalogue No. HS64-11/2010E-PDF). Retrieved from: http://www.esdc.gc.ca/eng/disability/arc/disability_2006.pdf

Hummelen, B., Pedersen, G., Wilberg, T., & Karterud, S. (2014). Poor validity of the DSM-IV schizoid personality disorder construct as a diagnostic category. *Journal of Personality Disorders, 29*(3), 334–346.

Humphrey, L. L. (1986). Structural analysis of parent–child relationships in eating disorders. *Journal of Abnormal Psychology, 95,* 395–402.

Humphrey, L. L. (1989). Observed family interactions among subtypes of eating disorders using structural analysis of social behavior. *Journal of Consulting and Clinical Psychology, 57,* 206–214.

Hunicutt, C. P., & Newman, I. A. (1993). Adolescent dieting practices and nutrition knowledge. *Health Values: Journal of Health Behavior, Education and Promotion, 17*(4), 35–40.

Hunsley, J. (2007). Addressing key challenges in evidence-based practice in psychology. *Professional Psychology: Research and Practice, 38,* 113–121.

Hunsley, J., & Johnston, C. (2000). The role of empirically supported treatments in evidence-based psychological practice: A Canadian perspective. *Clinical Psychology: Science & Practice, 7,* 269–272.

Hunsley, J., & Lee C. M. (2007). Research-informed benchmarks for psychological treatments: Efficacy studies, effectiveness studies, and beyond. *Professional Psychology: Research and Practice, 38,* 21–33.

Hunsley, J., & Mash, E. J. (2011). Evidence based assessment. In D. H. Barlow (Ed.), *Oxford handbook of clinical psychology* (pp. 76–97). New York, NY: Oxford University Press.

Hunt, M. (2007). Borderline personality disorder across the life span. *Journal of Women & Aging, 19*(1), 173–191.

Hunt, W. A. (1980). History and classification. In A. E. Kazdin, A. S. Bellack, & M. Hersen (Eds.), *New perspectives in abnormal psychology.* New York, NY: Oxford University Press.

Huntington's Disease Collaborative Research Group. (1993). A novel gene containing a trinucleotide repeat that is expanded and unstable on Huntington's disease chromosomes. *Cell, 72,* 971–983.

Huot, I., Paradis, G., & Ledoux, M. (2004). Effects of the Quebec Heart Health Demonstration Project on adult dietary behaviours. Quebec Heart Health Demonstration Project Research Group. *Preventive Medicine: An International Journal Devoted to Practice and Theory, 38*(2), 137–148.

Huppert, J. D. (2009). Anxiety disorders and depression comorbidity. In M. M. Antony & M. B. Stein (Eds.), *Oxford handbook of anxiety and related disorders* (pp. 576–586). New York, NY: Oxford University Press.

Hurd, H. M., Drewry, W. F., Dewey, R., Pilgrim, C. W., Blumer, G. A., & Burgess, T. J. W. (1916). *The institutional care of the insane in the United States and Canada.* Oxford, UK: Johns Hopkins Press.

Hurt, S. W., Schnurr, P. P., Severino, S. K., Freeman, E. W., Gise, L. H., Rivera-Tovar, A., & Steege, J. F. (1992). Late luteal phase dysphoric disorder in 670 women evaluated for premenstrual complaints. *American Journal of Psychiatry, 149,* 525–530.

Husband of "missing" alderwoman disputes media claims. (2003). *CNEWS Canada.* Retrieved May 12, 2003, from http://cnews.canoe.ca/CNEWS/Canada/2003/05/09/83590–cp.html

Hutchinson, D. M., & Rapee, R. M. (2007). Do friends share similar body image and eating problems? The role of social networks and peer influences in early adolescence. *Behaviour Research and Therapy, 45*(7), 1557–1577.

Hyman, S. E. (2009). How adversity gets under the skin. *Nature Neuroscience, 12*(3), 241–243.

Hyman, S. E. (2010). The diagnosis of mental disorders: The problem of reification. *Annual Review of Clinical Psychology, 6,* 155–179.

Hymowitz, P., Frances, A., Jacobsberg, L., Sickles, M., & Hoyt, R. (1986). Neuroleptic treatment of schizotypal personality disorder. *Comprehensive Psychiatry, 27,* 267–271.

Hynd, G. W., & Semrud-Clikeman, M. (1989). Dyslexia and brain morphology. *Psychological Bulletin, 106,* 447–482.

Hypericum Depression Trial Study Group. (2002). Effect of Hypericum performatum (St. John's Wort) in major depressive disorder: A randomized controlled trial. *JAMA, 287,* 1807–1814.

Iacovino, J. M., Jackson, J. J., & Oltmanns, T. F. (2014). The relative impact of socioeconomic status and childhood trauma on Black-White differences in paranoid personality disorder symptoms. *Journal of Abnormal Psychology, 123*(1), 225–230. https://doi.org/10.1037/a0035258

Iguchi, M. Y., Griffiths, R. R., Bickel, W. K., Handelsman, L., Childress, A. R., & McLellan, A. T. (1990). *Relative abuse liability of benzodiazepines in methadone maintenance populations in three cities.* Problems of drug dependence (pp. 364–365, NIDA Publication No. ADM 90–1663). Washington, DC: U.S. Government Printing Office.

Ihara, H., Berrios, G. E., & McKenna, P. J. (2003). The association between negative and dysexecutive syndromes in schizophrenia: A cross-cultural study. *Behavioral Neurology, 14,* 63–74.

IMS Health Canada. (2004a). *A health information update from IMS health.* Retrieved August 5, 2004, from http://www.imshealthcanada.com/htmen/3_1_39.htm

IMS Health Canada. (2004b). *Early figures show Viagra expanding erectile dysfunction market.* Retrieved August 5, 2004, from http://www.imshealth-canada.com/htmen/4_2_1_13.htm

In-Albon, T., & Schneider, S. (2007). Psychotherapy of childhood anxiety disorders: A meta-analysis. *Psychother Psychosom, 76*, 15–24.

Ingoldsby, E. M., Shelleby, E., Lane, T., & Shaw, D. S. (2012). Extrafamilial contexts and children's conduct problems. In V. Maholmes & R. B. King (Eds.), *The Oxford Handbook of poverty and child development* (pp. 404–422). New York, NY: Oxford University Press.

Ingram, R., Miranda, J., & Segal, Z. (2006). Cognitive vulnerability to depression. In L. B. Alloy & J. H. Riskind (Eds.), *Cognitive vulnerability to emotional disorders* (pp. 63–91). Mahwah, NJ: Erlbaum.

Inouye, S. K., Westendorp, R. G., & Saczynski, J. S. (2014). Delirium in elderly people. *The Lancet, 383*(9920), 911–922.

Insel, T., Cuthbert, B., Garvey, M., Heinssen, R., Pine, D. S., Quinn, K., … Wang, P. (2010). Research domain criteria (RDoC): Toward a new classification framework for research on mental disorders. *American Journal of Psychiatry, 167*(7), 748–751. https://doi.org/10.1176/appi.ajp.2010.09091379

Insel, T. R. (1992). Toward a neuroanatomy of obsessive–compulsive disorder. *Archives of General Psychiatry, 49*, 739–744.

Insel, T. R. (2009). Translating scientific opportunity into public health impact: A strategic plan for research on mental illness. *Archives of General Psychiatry, 66*(2), 128–133.

Insel, T. R. (2014). The NIMH research domain criteria (RDoC) project: Precision medicine for psychiatry. *American Journal of Psychiatry, 171*(4), 395–397.

Insel, T. R., Scanlan, J., Champoux, M., & Suomi, S. J. (1988). Rearing paradigm in a nonhuman primate affects response to B-CCE challenge. *Psychopharmacology, 96*, 81–86.

Institut de la statistique du Québec. (2001). *Enquête sociale et de santé 1998.* Québec, QC: Institut de la statistique du Québec.

Institute of Medicine. (2002). *Reducing suicide: A national imperative.* Washington, DC: National Academic Press.

International Interdisciplinary Conference on Hypertension in Blacks. (1999, July 9). *Linking race and genetics to cardiovascular disease for improved health among ethnic populations.* Retrieved July 15, 2004, from http://www.ishib.org/main/newsrel_lead_i99.htm

Iribarren, C., Sidney, S., Bild, D. E., Liu, K., Markovitz, J. H., Roseman, J. M., & Matthews, K. (2000). Association of hostility with coronary artery calcification in young adults. *JAMA, 283*(19), 2546–2551.

Ironson, G., Friedman, A., Klimas, N., Antoni, M., Fletcher, M. A., Laperriere, A., … Schneiderman, N. (1994). Distress, denial, and low adherence to behavioral interventions predict faster disease progression in gay men infected with human immunodeficiency virus. *International Journal of Behavioral Medicine, 1*, 90–105.

Ironson, G., Taylor, C. B., Boltwood, M., Bartzokis, T., Dennis, C., Chesney, M., … Segall, G. M. (1992). Effects of anger on left ventricular ejection fraction in coronary artery disease. *American Journal of Cardiology, 70*, 281–285.

Irwin, M., Mascovich, A., Gillin, J. C., Willoughby, R., Pike, J., & Smith, T. L. (1994). Partial sleep deprivation reduces natural killer cell activity in humans. *Psychosomatic Medicine, 56*, 493–498.

Isaacowitz, D. M., Smith, T. B., & Carstensen, L. L. (2003). Socioemotional selectivity and mental health among trauma survivors in old age. *Ageing International, 28*, 181–199.

Isenberg-Grzeda, E., Kutner, H. E., & Nicolson, S. E. (2012). Wernicke-Korsakoff syndrome: Under-recognized and under-treated. *Psychosomatics, 53*(6), 507–516.

Iskedjian, M., Hux, M., & Remington, G. J. (1998). The Canadian experience with risperidone for the treatment of schizophrenia: An overview. *Journal of Psychiatry & Neuroscience, 23*, 229–239.

Israeli, A. L., & Stewart, S. H. (2001). Memory bias for forbidden food cues in restrained eaters. *Cognitive Therapy & Research, 25*, 37–47.

Ito, K., Corrigan, B., Zhao, Q., French, J., Miller, R., Soares, H., … Fullerton, T. (2011). Disease progression model for cognitive deterioration from Alzheimer's Disease Neuroimaging Initiative database. *Alzheimer's & Dementia, 7*(2), 151–160.

Ivanov, I. (2009). Disulfiram and acamprosate. In B. J. Sadock, V. A. Sadock, & P. Ruiz (Eds.), *Kaplan & Sadock's comprehensive textbook of psychiatry* (9th ed., Vol. 2, pp. 3099–3105). Philadelphia, PA: Lippincott Williams & Wilkins.

Iversen, L. L. (2000). *The science of marijuana.* New York, NY: Oxford University Press.

Iversen, S. D., & Iversen, L. L. (2007). Dopamine: 50 years in perspective. *Trends in Neuroscience, 30*(5), 188–193. https://doi.org/10.1016/j.tins.2007.03.002

Iverson, L. (2006). Neurotransmitter transporters and their impact on the development of psychopharmacology. *British Journal of Pharmacology, 147* (Suppl. 1), S82–S88.

Izard, C. E. (1992). Basic emotions, relations among emotions, and emotion-cognition relations. *Psychological Review, 99*(3), 561–565.

Jääskeläinen, E., Juola, P., Hirvonen, N., McGrath, J. J., Saha, S., Isohanni, M., … Miettunen, J. (2013). A systematic review and meta-analysis of recovery in schizophrenia. *Schizophrenia Bulletin, 39*(6), 1296–1306.

Jablensky, A. (2012). Epidemiology of schizophrenia. In M. G. Gelder, N. C. Andreasen, J. J. Lopez-Ibor, & J. R. Geddes (Eds.), *New Oxford textbook of psychiatry* (2nd ed., Vol. 1, pp. 540–553). New York, NY: Oxford University Press.

Jack, L., Nicholls, T., & Ogloff, J. R. P. (1998, March). *An investigation of inpatient self-injurious behavior among involuntarily hospitalized patients.* Poster presented at the Biennial Meeting of the American Psychology Law Society, Redondo Beach, CA.

Jackson, C., Brown, J. D., & L'Engle, K. L. (2007). R-rated movies, bedroom televisions, and initiation of smoking by white and black adolescents. *Archives of Pediatrics & Adolescent Medicine, 161*, 260–268.

Jackson, G., Rosen, R., Kloner, R., & Kostis, J. (2006). The second Princeton consensus on sexual dysfunction and cardiac risk: New guidelines for sexual medicine. *Journal of Sexual Medicine, 3*, 28–36.

Jackson, T., & Chen, H. (2011). Risk factors for disordered eating during early and middle adolescence: Prospective evidence from mainland Chinese boys and girls. *Journal of Abnormal Psychology, 120*(2), 454–464.

Jacobi, W., & Winkler, H. (1927). Encephalographsche Studien an chronischen Schizophrenen. *Archiv für Psychiatrie und Nervenkrankheiten, 81*, 299–332.

Jacobson, N. S., & Hollon, S. D. (1996a). Cognitive behavior therapy vs. pharmacotherapy: Now that the jury's returned its verdict, it's time to present the rest of the evidence. *Journal of Consulting and Clinical Psychology, 64*, 74–80.

Jacobson, N. S., & Hollon, S. D. (1996b). Prospects for future comparisons between drugs and psychotherapy: Lessons from the CBT vs. pharmacotherapy exchange. *Journal of Consulting and Clinical Psychology, 64*, 104–108.

Jacobson, N. S., Martell, C. R., & Dimidjian, S. (2001). Behavioral activation treatment for depression: Returning to contextual roots. *Clinical Psychology: Science and Practice, 8*(3), 255–270.

Jaffe, A. J., Rounsaville, B., Chang, G., Schottenfeld, R. S., Meyer, R. E., & O'Malley, S. O. (1996). Naltrexone, relapse prevention, and supportive therapy with alcoholics: An analysis of patient treatment matching. *Journal of Consulting and Clinical Psychology, 64*, 1044–1053.

Jaffe, J. H., Knapp, C. M., & Ciraulo, D. A. (1997). Opiates: Clinical aspects. In J. H. Lowinson, P. Ruiz, R. B. Millman, & J. G. Langrod (Eds.), *Substance abuse: A comprehensive textbook* (pp. 158–166). Baltimore, MD: Williams & Wilkins.

Jaffe, J. H., Rawson, R. A., & Ling, W. (2005). Cocaine-related disorders. In B. J. Sadock & V. A. Sadock (Eds.), *Kaplan & Sadock's comprehensive textbook of psychiatry* (8th ed., pp. 1220–1238). Philadelphia, PA: Lippincott, Williams & Wilkins.

Jaffe, S. E. (2000). Sleep and infectious disease. In M. H. Kryger, T. Roth, & W. C. Dement (Eds.), *Principles and practice of sleep medicine* (3rd ed., pp. 1093–1102). Philadelphia, PA: W. B. Saunders.

Jaffe, S. (2011). Genotype-environment correlations: Definitions, methods of measurement, and implications for research on adolescent psychopathology. In K. S. Kendler, S. Jaffe, & D. Romer (Eds.), *The dynamic genome and mental health: The role of genes and environments in youth development* (pp. 79–102). New York, NY: Oxford University Press.

Jager, G. (2012). Cannabis. In J. C. Verster, K. Brady, M. Galanter, & P. Conrod (Eds.), *Drug abuse and addiction in medical illness* (pp. 151–162). New York, NY: Springer.

James, B. O., Jenkins, R., & Lawani, A. O. (2012). Depression in primary care: The knowledge, attitudes and practice of general practitioners in Benin City, Nigeria. *South African Family Practice, 54*(1), 55–60.

Jamison, K. R. (1989). Mood disorders and patterns of creativity in British writers and artists. *Psychiatry, 52*(2), 125–134.

Jamison, R. N., & Virts, K. L. (1990). The influence of family support on chronic pain. *Behaviour Research and Therapy, 28*(4), 283–287.

Jane, J. S., Oltmanns, T. F., South, S. C., & Turkheimer, E. (2007). Gender bias in diagnostic criteria for personality disorders: An item response theory analysis. *Journal of Abnormal Psychology, 116*, 166–175.

Jang, K. L. (2005). *The behavioral genetics of psychopathology: A clinical guide.* Mahwah, NJ: Lawrence Erlbaum Associates.

Jang, K. L., Paris, J., Zweig-Frank, H., & Livesley, W. J. (1998). Twin study of dissociative experience. *Journal of Nervous and Mental Disease, 186*, 345–351.

Jang, K. L., Vernon, P. A., & Livesley, W. J. (2001). Behavioural genetic perspectives on personality function. *Canadian Journal of Psychiatry, 46*, 234–244.

Jang, S. H., Kim, D. I., & Choi, M. S. (2014). Effects and treatment methods of acupuncture and herbal medicine for premenstrual syndrome/premenstrual dysphoric disorder: Systematic review. *BMC Complementary and Alternative Medicine, 14*(1), 11.

Jarrett, R. B., Kraft, D., Doyle, J., Foster, B. M., Eaves, G. G., & Silver, P. C. (2001). Preventing recurrent depression using cognitive therapy with and without a continuation phase. *Archives of General Psychiatry, 58*, 381–388.

Jarrett, R. B., Minhajuddin, A., Gershenfeld, H., Friedman, E. S., & Thase, M. E. (2013). Preventing depressive relapse and recurrence in higher-risk cognitive therapy responders: A randomized trial of continuation phase cognitive therapy, fluoxetine, or matched pill placebo. *JAMA Psychiatry, 70*, 1152–1160.

Jarvis, E. (1998). Schizophrenia in British immigrants: Recent findings, issues and implications. *Transcultural Psychiatry, 35*(1), 39–74.

Jason, L. A., Fennell, P. A., & Taylor, R. R. (2003). *Handbook of chronic fatigue syndrome.* Hoboken, NJ: John Wiley & Sons.

Jaspers, K. (1963). *General psychopathology* (J. Hoenig & M. W. Hamilton, Trans.). Manchester, UK: Manchester University Press.

Jaussent, I., Dauvilliers, Y., Ancelin, M. L., Dartigues, J. F., Tavernier, B., Touchon, J., & Besset, A. (2011). Insomnia symptoms in older adults: Associated factors and gender differences. *The American Journal of Geriatric Psychiatry, 19*(1), 88.

Javitt, D. C., & Laruelle, M. (2006). Neurochemical theories. In J. A. Lieberman, T. S. Stroup, & D. O. Perkins (Eds.), *The American Psychiatric Publishing textbook of schizophrenia* (pp. 85–116). Washington, DC: American Psychiatric Publishing.

Jeffrey, S. (1995, July 4). Toronto team uncovers Alzheimer's gene. *The Medical Post.* Retrieved May 21, 2004, from http://www.mentalhealth.com/mag1/p5m-alz1.html

Jellinek, E. M. (1946). Phases in the drinking histories of alcoholics. *Quarterly Journal of Studies on Alcohol, 7*, 1–88.

Jellinek, E. M. (1952). Phases of alcohol addiction. *Quarterly Journal of Studies on Alcohol, 13*, 673–684.

Jellinek, E. M. (1960). *The disease concept of alcohol.* New Brunswick, NJ: Hillhouse Press.

Jenike, M. A., Baer, L., Ballantine, H. T., Martuza, R. L., Tynes, S., Giriunas, I., … Cassem, N. H. (1991). Cingulotomy for refractory obsessive-compulsive disorder: A long-term follow-up of 33 patients. *Archives of General Psychiatry, 48*, 548–555.

Jenkins, J. H., & Karno, M. (1992). The meaning of expressed emotion: Theoretical issues raised by cross-cultural research. *American Journal of Psychiatry, 149*, 9–21.

Jenkins, J. H., Kleinman, A., & Good, B. J. (1990). Cross-cultural studies of depression. In J. Becker & A. Kleinman (Eds.), *Psychosocial aspects of depression.* Hillsdale, NJ: Erlbaum.

Jenness, J. L., Hankin, B. L., Abela, J. R., Young, J. F., & Smollen, A. (2011). Chronic family stress interacts with 5-HTTLPR to predict prospective depressive symptoms among youth. *Depression and Anxiety, 28*(12), 1074–1080.

Jennum, P., & Riha, R. L. (2009). Epidemiology of sleep apnoea/hypopnoea syndrome and sleep-disordered breathing. *The European Respiratory Journal–The Official Journal of the European Respiratory Society, 33*(4), 907–914.

Jensen, E. J., Schmidt, E., Pedersen, B., & Dahl, R. (1991). Effect on smoking cessation of silver acetate, nicotine and ordinary chewing gum. *Psychopharmacology, 104*, 470–474.

Jensen, H. M., Gron, R., Lidegaard, O., Pedersen, L. H., Andersen, P. K., & Kessing, L. V. (2013). Maternal depression, antidepressant use in pregnancy and Apgar scores in infants. *British Journal of Psychiatry, 202*(5), 347–351.

Jensen, P. S., Hinshaw, S. P., Swanson, J. M., Greenhill, L. L., Conners, C. K., Arnold, L. E., … Wigal, T. (2001). Findings from the NIMH Multimodal Treatment Study of ADHD (MTA): Implications and applications for primary care providers. *Journal of Developmental & Behavioral Pediatrics, 22*, 60–73.

Jespersen, A. F., Lalumière, M. L., & Seto, M. C. (2009). Sexual abuse history among adult sex offenders and non-sex offenders: A meta-analysis. *Child Abuse and Neglect, 33*, 179–192.

Jiang, W., Samad, Z., Boyle, S., Becker, R. C., Williams, R., Kuhn, C., & Velazquez, E. J. (2013). Prevalence and clinical characteristics of mental stress-induced myocardial ischemia in patients with coronary heart disease. *Journal of the American College of Cardiology, 61*(7), 714–722.

Jiann, B. P., Su, C. C., Yu, C. C., Wu, T. T., & Huang, J. K. (2009). Risk factors for individual domains of female sexual function. *Journal of Sexual Medicine, 6*(12), 3364–3375.

Jilek, W. G. (1982). Altered states of consciousness in North American Indian ceremonials. *Ethos, 10*(4), 326–343.

Jindal, R. D., Thase, M. E., Fasiczka, A. L., Friedman, E. S., Buysse, D. J., Frank, E., & Kupfer, D. J. (2002). Electroencephalographic sleep profiles in single-episode and recurrent unipolar forms of major depression: II. Comparison during remission. *Biological Psychiatry, 1*, 230–236.

Jockin, V., McGue, M., & Lykken, D. T. (1996). Personality and divorce: A genetic analysis. *Journal of Personality and Social Psychology, 71*, 288–299.

Joffe, R., Segal, Z., & Singer, W. (1996). Change in thyroid hormone levels following response to cognitive therapy for major depression. *American Journal of Psychiatry, 153*, 411–413.

Johansson, A., Sundbom, E., Höjerback, T., & Bodlund, O. (2010). A five-year follow-up study of Swedish adults with gender identity disorder. *Archives of Sexual Behavior, 39*(6), 1429–1437.

Johnson stripped of Olympic gold. (2004). *BBC*. Retrieved August 17, 2004, from http://news.bbc.co.uk/onthisday/hi/dates/stories/september/27/newsid_2539000/2539525.stm

Johnson, B. A. (1991). Cannabis. In I. B. Glass (Ed.), *International handbook of addiction behaviour* (pp. 69–76). London, UK: Tavistock/Routledge.

Johnson, B. A., Roache, J. D., Javors, M. A., DiClemente, C. C., Cloninger, C. R., Prihoda, T. J., … Hensler, J. (2000a). Ondansetron for reduction of drinking among biologically predisposed alcoholic patients. *JAMA, 284*(8), 963–971.

Johnson, C. J., & Beitchman, J. H. (2005). Expressive language disorder. In B. J. Sadock & V. A. Sadock (Eds.), *Kaplan & Sadock's comprehensive textbook of psychiatry* (pp. 3136–3142). Philadelphia, PA: Lippincott, Williams & Wilkins.

Johnson, J. G., Bromley, E., & McGeoch, P. G. (2005). Role of childhood experiences in the development of maladaptive and adaptive traits. In J. M. Oldham, A. E. Skodol, & D. S. Bender (Eds.), *Textbook of personality disorders* (pp. 209–221). Washington, DC: American Psychiatric Publishing.

Johnson, J. G., Cohen, P., Kasen, S., & Brook, J. S. (2002). Eating disorders during adolescence and the risk for physical and mental disorders during early adulthood. *Archives of General Psychiatry, 59*, 545–552.

Johnson, J. G., Cohen, P., Pine, D. S., Klein, D. F., Kasen, S., & Brook, J. S. (2000). Association between cigarette smoking and anxiety disorders during adolescence and early adulthood. *JAMA, 284*, 2348–2351.

Johnson, J. M., Baumgart, D., Helmstetter, E., & Curry, C. (1996). *Augmenting basic communication in natural contexts.* Baltimore, MD: Paul H. Brookes.

Johnson, J., Weissman, M. M., & Klerman, G. L. (1990). Panic disorder, comorbidity and suicide attempts. *Archives of General Psychiatry, 47*, 805–808.

Johnson, S. L., & Miller, I. (1997). Negative life events and time to recovery from episodes of bipolar disorder. *Journal of Abnormal Psychology, 106*(3), 449–457.

Johnson, S. L., & Roberts, J. E. (1995). Life events and bipolar disorder: Implications from biological theories. *Psychological Bulletin, 117*(3), 434–449.

Johnson, S. L., Cuellar, A. K., & Miller, C. (2009). Bipolar and unipolar depression: A comparison of clinical phenomenology, biological vulnerability, and psychosocial predictors. In I. H. Gotlib & C. L. Hammen (Eds.), *Handbook of depression* (2nd ed., pp. 142–162). New York, NY: Guilford Press.

Johnson, S. L., Cuellar, A. K., Ruggero, C., Winett-Perlman, C., Goodnick, P., White, R., & Miller, I. (2008). Life events as predictors of mania and depression in bipolar I disorder. *Journal of Abnormal Psychology, 117*(2), 268–277.

Johnson, S. L., Winett, C. A., Meyer, B., Greenhouse, W. J., & Miller, I. (1999). Social support and the course of bipolar disorder. *American Psychological Association, 180*(4), 558–566.

Johnson, W., Turkheimer, E., Gottesman, I. I., & Bouchard, T. J., Jr. (2009). Beyond heritability: Twin studies in behavioral research. *Current Directions in Psychological Science, 18*(4), 217–220.

Johnston, C., Pelham, W. E., & Murphy, H. A. (1985). Peer relationships in ADHD and normal children: A developmental analysis of peer and teacher ratings. *Journal of Abnormal Child Psychology, 13*, 89–100.

Joiner, T. E., & Rudd, D. M. (1996). Toward a categorization of depression-related psychological constructs. *Cognitive Therapy and Research, 20*, 51–68.

Joiner, T. E., Jr. (1997). Shyness and low social support as interactive diatheses, with loneliness as mediator: Testing an interpersonal–personality view of vulnerability to depressive symptoms. *Journal of Abnormal Psychology, 106*(3), 386–394.

Joiner, T. E., Jr. (1999). A test of interpersonal theory of depression in youth psychiatric inpatients. *Journal of Abnormal Child Psychology, 27*(1), 77–85.

Joiner, T. E., Jr., & Rudd, M. D. (2000). Intensity and duration of suicidal crises vary as a function of previous suicide attempts and negative life events. *Journal of Consulting and Clinical Psychology, 68*(5), 909–916.

Joiner, T. E., Jr., & Timmons, K. A. (2009). Depression in its interpersonal context. In I. H. Gotlib & C. L. Hammen (Eds.), *Handbook of depression* (2nd ed., pp. 322–339). New York, NY: Guilford, Press.

Joiner, T. E., Jr., Heatherton, T. F., & Keel, P. K. (1997). Ten year stability and predictive validity of five bulimia-related indicators. *American Journal of Psychiatry, 154*, 1133–1138.

Joiner, T., Kalafat, J., Draper, J., Stokes, H., Knudson, M., Berman, A. L., & McKeon, R. (2007). Establishing standards for the assessment of suicide risk among callers to the national suicide prevention lifeline. *Suicide and Life-Threatening Behavior, 37*(3), 353–365.

Joling, K. J., van Marwijk, H. W., Veldhuijzen, A. E., van der Horst, H. E., Scheltens, P., Smit, F., & van Hout, H. P. (2015). The two-year incidence of depression and anxiety disorders in spousal caregivers of persons with dementia: Who is at the greatest risk? *American Journal of Geriatric Psychiatry, 23*(3), 293–303.

Jones, A. (2007, October 3). Ont. Closing facilities for intellectually disabled in wrong way: Opposition. *The Daily News*. Retrieved January 3, 2008, from http://www.hfxnews.ca/index.cfm?pid1305&cpcatelection&stry62017026

Jones, J. C., & Barlow, D. H. (1990). The etiology of posttraumatic stress disorder. *Clinical Psychology Review, 10*, 299–328.

Jones, K. L., & Smith, D. W. (1973). Recognition of the fetal alcohol syndrome in early infancy. *Lancet, 2*, 999–1001.

Jones, M. C. (1924a). The elimination of children's fears. *Journal of Experimental Psychology, 7*, 383–390.

Jones, M. C. (1924b). A laboratory study of fear. The case of Peter. *Pedagogical Seminary, 31*, 308–315.

Jones, R. T. (2009). Hallucinogen-related disorders. In B. J. Sadock, V. A. Sadock, & P. Ruiz (Eds.), *Kaplan & Sadock's comprehensive textbook of psychiatry* (9th ed., Vol. 1, pp. 1331–1340). Philadelphia, PA: Lippincott Williams & Wilkins.

Jones, R. T., & Haney, J. I. (1984). A primary preventive approach to the acquisition and maintenance of fire emergency responding: Comparison of external and self-instruction strategies. *Journal of Community Psychology, 12*(2), 180–191.

Jones, R. T., & Kazdin, A. E. (1980). Teaching children how and when to make emergency telephone calls. *Behavior Therapy, 11*(4), 509–521.

Jordan, B. D., Relkin, N. R., Ravdin, L. D., Jacobs, A. R., Bennett, A., & Gandy, S. (1997). Apolipoprotein E Epsilon 4 associated with chronic traumatic brain injury in boxing. *JAMA, 278*, 136–140.

Joslyn, G., Ravindranathan, A., Brush, G., Schuckit, M., & White, R. L. (2010). Human variation in alcohol response is influenced by variation in neuronal signaling genes. *Alcoholism, Clinical and Experimental Research, 34*(5), 800–812.

Joyner, M. J., Charkoudian, N., & Wallin, B. G. (2010). Sympathetic nervous system and blood pressure in humans: Individualized patterns of regulation and their implications. *Hypertension, 56*(1), 10–16.

Judd, L. (2000). Course and chronicity of unipolar major depressive disorder: Commentary on Joiner. *Child Psychology Science and Practice, 7*(2), 219–223.

Judd, L. L. (1997). The clinical course of unipolar major depressive disorders. *Archives of General Psychiatry, 54*, 989–991.

Judd, L. L. (2012). Dimensional paradigm of the long-term course of unipolar major depressive disorder. *Depression and Anxiety, 29*(3), 167–171.

Judd, L. L., Akiskal, H. S., Maser, J. D., Zeller, P. J., Endicott, J., Coryell, W., … Keller, M. B. (1998a). A prospective 12-year study of subsyndromal and syndromal depressive symptomatology in 431 patients with unipolar major depressive disorder. *Archives of General Psychiatry, 55*, 694–700.

Judd, L. L., Akiskal, H., Schettler, P., Coryell, W., Endicott, J., Maser, J., & Keller, M. B. (2003). A prospective investigation of the natural history of the long-term weekly symptomatic status of bipolar II disorder. *Archives of General Psychiatry, 60*, 261–269.

Judge, C., O'Donovan, C., Callaghan, G., Gaoatswe, G., & O'Shea, D. (2014). Gender dysphoria–prevalence and comorbidities in an Irish adult population. *Frontiers in Endocrinology, 5*, 87.

Juliano, L. M., & Griffiths, R. R. (2009). Caffeine-related disorders. In B. J. Sadock, V. A. Sadock, & P. Ruiz (Eds.),

Kaplan & Sadock's comprehensive textbook of psychiatry (9th ed., Vol. 1, pp. 1296–1309). Philadelphia, PA: Lippincott Williams & Wilkins.

Juliano, L. M., Ferré, S., & Griffiths, R. R. (2015). The pharmacology of caffeine. In R. K. Ries, D. A. Fiellin, S. C. Miller, & R. Saitz (Eds.), *Principles of addiction medicine* (pp. 180–200). Philadelphia, PA: Lippincott Williams & Wilkins.

Jummani, R., & Coffey, B. J. (2009). Tic disorders. In B. J. Sadock, V. A. Sadock, & P. Ruiz (Eds.), *Kaplan & Sadock's comprehensive textbook of psychiatry* (9th ed., Vol. 2, pp. 3609–3623). Philadelphia, PA: Lippincott Williams & Wilkins.

Junginger, J. (1997). Fetishism: Assessment and treatment. In D. R. Laws & W. O'Donohue (Eds.), *Sexual deviance: Theory, assessment and treatment* (pp. 92–110). New York, NY: Guilford Press.

Kagan, J. (1994). *Galen's prophesy*. New York, NY: Basic Books.

Kagan, J. (1997). Temperament and the reactions to unfamiliarity. *Child Development, 68*, 139–143.

Kagan, J. (2014a). Temperamental contributions to the development of psychological profiles: I. Basic issues. In S. G. Hofmann and P. D. DiBartolo (Eds.), *Social anxiety: Clinical, developmental, and social perspectives* (third edition) (pp. 377–418). Amsterdam, The Netherlands: Elsevier/Academic Press.

Kagan, J. (2014b). Temperamental contributions to the development of psychological profiles: II. Two candidates. In S. G. Hofmann and P. D. DiBartolo (Eds.), *Social anxiety: Clinical, developmental, and social perspectives* (third edition) (pp. 419–450). Amsterdam, The Netherlands: Elsevier/Academic Press.

Kagan, J., & Snidman, N. (1999). Early childhood predictors of adult anxiety disorders. *Biological Psychiatry, 46*, 1536–1541.

Kahn, R. S., Khoury, J., Nichols, W. C., & Lanphear, B. P. (2003). Role of dopamine transporter genotype and maternal prenatal smoking in childhood hyperactive-impulsive, inattentive, and oppositional behaviors. *Journal of Pediatrics, 143*(1), 104–110.

Kaiser Family Foundation, Kates, J., Carbaugh, A., Rousseau, D., & Jankiewicz, A. (2012). HIV/AIDS: The state of the epidemic after 3 decades. *JAMA, 308*(4), 330. https://doi.org/10.1001/jama.2012.8700

Kaiser, J. (2006). Differences in immune cell "brakes" may explain chimp–human split on AIDS. *Science Magazine, 312*, 672–673.

Kalat, J. W. (2013). *Biological psychology* (11th ed.). Belmont, CA: Wadsworth, Cengage Learning.

Kales, A., Soldatos, C. R., Caldwell, A., Kales, J., Humphrey, F., Charney, D., & Schweitzer, P. K. (1980). Somnambulism: Clinical characteristics and personality patterns. *Archives of General Psychiatry, 37*, 1406–1410.

Kalivas, P. W. (2005). New directions pharmacotherapy for addiction or can we forget to be addicted? *Clinical Neuroscience Research, 5*, 147–150.

Kallmann, F. J. (1938). *The genetics of schizophrenia*. New York, NY: Augustin.

Kalra, G., Christodoulou, G., Jenkins, R., Tsipas, V., Christodoulou, N., Lecic-Tosevski, D., … Bhugra, D. (2012). Mental health promotion: Guidance and strategies. *European Psychiatry, 27*(2), 81–86. https://doi.org/10.1016/j.eurpsy.2011.10.001

Kalus, O., Bernstein, D. P., & Siever, L. J. (1993). Schizoid personality disorder: A review of current status and implications for DSM-IV. *Journal of Personality Disorders, 7*, 43–52.

Kamen, C., Tejani, M. A., Chandwani, K., Janelsins, M., Peoples, A. R., Roscoe, J. A., & Morrow, G. R. (2014). Anticipatory nausea and vomiting due to chemotherapy. *European Journal of Pharmacology, 722*, 172–179.

Kaminen, N., Hannula-Jouppi, K., Kestila, M., Lahermo, P., Muller, K., Kaaranen, M., … Kere, J. (2003). A genome scan for developmental dyslexia confirms linkage to chromosome 2p11 and suggests a new locus on 7q32. *Journal of Medical Genetics, 40*, 340–345.

Kaminski, J. W., Valle, L., Filene, J., & Boyle, C. (2008). A meta-analytic review of components associated with parent training program effectiveness. *Journal of Abnormal Child Psychology, 36*(4), 567–589.

Kandel, E. R., Schwartz, J. H., & Jessell, T. M. (Eds.). (2000). *Principles of neural science* (4th ed.). New York, NY: McGraw-Hill.

Kane, J. M. (2006). Tardive dyskinesia circa 2006. *American Journal of Psychiatry, 163*, 1316–1318.

Kane, J. M., Stroup, S., & Marder, S. R. (2009). Schizophrenia: Pharmacological treatment. In B. J. Sadock, V. A. Sadock, & P. Ruiz (Eds.), *Kaplan & Sadock's comprehensive textbook of psychiatry* (9th ed., Vol. 1, pp. 1547–1556). Philadelphia, PA: Lippincott Williams & Wilkins.

Kanigel, R. (1988, October/November). Nicotine becomes addictive. *Science Illustrated*, pp. 12–14, 19–21.

Kanner, L. (1943). Autistic disturbances of affective contact. *Nervous Child, 2*, 217–250.

Kanner, L. (1949). Problems of nosology and psychodynamics of early infantile autism. *American Journal of Orthopsychiatry, 19*, 416–426.

Kanner, L., & Eisenberg, L. (1955). Notes on the follow-up studies of autistic children. In P. Hoch & J. Zubin (Eds.), *Psychopathology of childhood* (pp. 227–239). New York, NY: Grune & Stratton.

Kaplan, A. S., & Garfinkel, P. E. (1999). Difficulties in treating patients with eating disorders: A review of patient and clinician variables. *Canadian Journal of Psychiatry, 44*, 665–670.

Kaplan, M. (1983). A woman's view of DSM-III. *American Psychologist, 38*, 786–792.

Kaplan, R. M. (2010). Behavioral pidemiology. In J. M. Suls, K. W. Davidson, & R. M. Kaplan (Eds.), *Handbook of Health Psychology and Behavioral Medicine*. New York, NY: Guilford Press.

Kaplan, S. A., Reis, R. B., Kohn, I. J., Ikeguchi, E. F., Laor, E., Te, A. E., & Martins, A. C. (1999). Safety and efficacy of sildenafil in postmenopausal women with sexual dysfunction. *Urology, 53*, 481–486.

Kaptchuk, T. J., Kelley, J. M., Conboy, L. A., Davis, R. B., Kerr, C. E., &

Lembo, A. J. (2008). Components of placebo effect: Randomised controlled trial in patients with irritable bowel syndrome. *British Medical Journal, 336*(7651), 999–1003.

Kapur, S., Zipursky, R. B., & Remington, G. (1999). Clinical and theoretical implications of 5-HT2 and D2 receptor occupancy of clozapine, risperidone, and olanzapine in schizophrenia. *American Journal of Psychiatry, 156*, 286–293.

Karg, K., Burmeister, M., Shedden, K., & Sen, S. (2011). The serotonin transporter promoter variant (5-HTTLPR), stress, and depression meta-analysis revisited: Evidence of genetic moderation. *Archives of General Psychiatry*.

Kariuki-Nyuthe, C., & Stein, D. J. (2015). Anxiety and related disorders and physical illness. *Key Issues in Mental Health, 179*, 81–97.

Karkhaneh, M., Clark, B., Ospina, M. B., Seida, J. C., Smith, V., & Hartling, L. (2010). Social Stories(tm) to improve social skills in children with autism spectrum disorder. *Autism, 14*(6), 641–662.

Kasari, C., Gulsrud, A., Freeman, S., Paparella, T., & Hellemann, G. (2012). Longitudinal follow-up of children with autism receiving targeted interventions on joint attention and play. *Journal of the American Academy of Child & Adolescent Psychiatry, 51*(5), 487–495.

Kasen, S., Cohen, P., Skodol, A. E., Johnson, J. G., & Brook, J. S. (1999). Influence of child and adolescent psychiatric disorders on young adult personality disorder. *American Journal of Psychiatry, 156*(10), 1529–1535.

Kashani, J. H., Hoeper, E. W., Beck, N. C., & Corcoran, C. M. (1987). Personality, psychiatric disorders, and parental attitude among a community sample of adolescents. *Journal of the American Academy of Child and Adolescent Psychiatry, 26*(6), 879–885.

Kashani, J. H., McGee, R. O., Clarkson, S. E. A., Walton, L. A., Williams, S., Silva, P. A., … McKnew, D. H. (1983). Depression in a sample of 9-year-old children: Prevalence and associated characteristics. *Archives of General Psychiatry, 40*, 1217–1223.

Kaski, M. (2012). Aetiology of intellectual disability: General issues and prevention. In M. G. Gelder, N. C. Andreasen, J. J. Lopez-Ibor, & J. R. Geddes (Eds.), *New Oxford textbook of psychiatry* (2nd ed., Vol. 2, pp. 1830–1837). New York, NY: Oxford University Press.

Kass, D. J., Silvers, F. M., & Abrams, G. M. (1972). Behavioral group treatment of hysteria. *Archives of General Psychiatry, 26*, 42–50.

Kates, J., Carbaugh, A., Rousseau, D., & Jankiewicz, A. (2012). HIV/AIDS: The state of the epidemic after 3 decades. *JAMA, 308*(4), 330.

Katon, W. (1993). Somatization disorder, hypochondriasis, and conversion disorder. In D. L. Dunner (Ed.), *Current psychiatric therapy* (pp. 314–320). Philadelphia, PA: W. B. Saunders.

Katon, W. J. (2003). Clinical and health services relationships between major depression, depressive symptoms, and general medical illness. *Biological Psychiatry, 54*, 216–226.

Katschnig, H. (1999). Anxiety neurosis, panic disorder or what? In D. J. Nutt, C. Ballenger, & J. P., Lépine (Eds.), *Panic disorder: Clinical diagnosis,*

management and mechanisms (pp. 1–8). London, UK: Dunitz.

Katschnig, H., & Amering, M. (1990). Panic attacks and panic disorder in cross-cultural perspective. In J. C. Ballenger (Ed.), *Clinical aspects of panic disorder* (pp. 67–80). New York, NY: Wiley.

Katz, I. R. (1993). Delirium. In D. L. Dunner (Ed.), *Current psychiatric therapy* (pp. 65–73). Philadelphia, PA: W. B. Saunders.

Katz, I. R., Leshen, E., Kleban, M., & Jethanandani, V. (1989). Clinical features of depression in the nursing home. *International Psychogeriatrics, 1*, 5–15.

Katz, J., & Gagliese, L. (1999). Phantom limb pain: A continuing puzzle. In R. J. Gatchel & D. C. Turk (Eds.), *Psychosocial factors in pain: Critical perspectives* (pp. 284–300). New York, NY: Guilford Press.

Katz, M. J., Lipton, R. B., Hall, C. B., Zimmerman, M. E., Sanders, A. E., Verghese, J., & Derby, C. A. (2012). Age-specific and sex-specific prevalence and incidence of mild cognitive impairment, dementia, and Alzheimer dementia in blacks and whites: A report from the Einstein Aging Study. *Alzheimer Disease & Associated Disorders, 26*(4), 335–343.

Katz, R., & McGuffin P. (1993). The genetics of affective disorders. *Progress in Experimental Personality and Psychopathology Research, 16*, 200–221.

Katzman, D., Mawjee, K., & Norris, M. L. (2016). *Avoidant/restrictive food intake disorder: Introducing a new DSM-5 eating disorder*. Canadian Paediatric Society. https://www.cpsp.cps.ca/uploads/publications/RA-avoidant-restrictive-food-intake-disorder.pdf

Katzman, D. K., & Norris, M. L. (2018). Avoidant/restrictive food intake disorder: January 2016 to December 2017—Final report. *In Canadian Paediatric Surveillance Program, 2017 Results* (pp. 15–17). Canadian Paediatric Society. https://www.cpsp.cps.ca/uploads/publications/CPSP-2017-Results_1.pdf

Kaufman, A. S., & Kaufman, N. L. (Eds.). (2001). *Specific learning disabilities and difficulties in children and adolescents: Psychological assessment and evaluation*. New York, NY: Cambridge University Press.

Kavanagh, D. J. (1992). Recent developments in expressed emotion and schizophrenia. *British Journal of Psychiatry, 160*, 601–620.

Kawamura, K. Y. (2002). Asian American body images. In T. F. Cash & T. Pruzinsky (Eds.), *Body image: A handbook of theory, research and clinical practice* (pp. 243–249). New York, NY: Guilford Press.

Kay, C., & Green, J. (2013). Reactive attachment disorder following early maltreatment: Systematic evidence beyond the institution. *Journal of Abnormal Child Psychology, 41*(4), 571–586.

Kaye, W. (2008). Neurobiology of anorexia and bulimia nervosa. *Physiology and Behavior, 94*(1), 121–135.

Kaye, W. H., Bulik, C. M., Thornton, L., Barbarich, N., Masters, K., & Price Foundation Collaborative Group. (2014). Comorbidity of anxiety disorders with anorexia and bulimia nervosa. *American Journal of Psychiatry, 161*(12), 2215–2221.

Kaye, W. H., Weltzin, T. E., Hsu, L. K. G., McConaha, C. W., & Bolton, B. (1993). Amount of calories retained after binge eating and vomiting. *American Journal of Psychiatry, 150*(6), 969–971.

Kaye, W., Strober, M., Stein, D., & Gendall, K. (1999). New directions in treatment research of anorexia and bulimia nervosa. *Biological Psychiatry, 45*, 1285–1292.

Kazarian, S. S., & Evans, D. R. (Eds.). (2001). Health psychology and culture: Embracing the 21st century. *In Handbook of cultural health psychology* (pp. 3–43). San Diego, CA: Academic Press.

Kazarian, S. S., Malla, A. K., Cole, J. D., & Baker, B. (1990). Comparisons of two expressed emotion scales with the Camberwell Family Interview. *Journal of Clinical Psychology, 46*, 306–309.

Kazdin, A. E. (1983). Hopelessness, depression, and suicidal intent among psychiatrically disturbed inpatient children. *Journal of Consulting and Clinical Psychology, 51*(4), 504–510.

Kazdin, A. E. (2011). *Single-case research designs: Methods for clinical and applied settings.* New York, NY: Oxford University Press.

Kazdin, A. E., & Mazurick, J. L. (1994). Dropping out of child psychotherapy: Distinguishing early and late dropouts over the course of treatment. *Journal of Consulting and Clinical Psychology, 62*, 1069–1074.

Kazdin, A. E., Mazurick, J. L., & Bass, D. (1993). Risk for attrition in treatment of antisocial children and families. *Journal of Child Clinical Psychology, 22*, 2–16.

Kean, S. (2010). An indefatigable debate over chronic fatigue syndrome. *Science, 327*, 254–255.

Keane, T. M., & Barlow, D. H. (2002). Post traumatic stress disorder. In D. H. Barlow (Ed.), *Anxiety and its disorders: The nature and treatment of anxiety and panic* (2nd ed.). New York, NY: Guilford Press.

Keane, T. M., & Miller, M. W. (2012). Future of classification in posttraumatic stress disorder. In J. G. Beck & D. M. Sloan (Eds.), *The Oxford handbook of traumatic stress disorders* (pp. 54–66). New York, NY: Oxford University Press.

Keane, T. M., Marx, B. P., Sloan, D. M., & De Prince, A. (2011). Trauma, dissociation, and post-traumatic stress disorder. In D. H. Barlow (Ed.), *The Oxford handbook of clinical psychology* (pp. 359–386). New York, NY: Oxford University Press.

Kearney, A. J. (2006). A primer of covert sensitization. *Cognitive and Behavioral Practice 2006, 13*(2), 167–175.

Kearns, M. C., Ressler, K. J., Zatzick, D., & Rothbaum, B. O. (2012). Early interventions for PTSD: A review. *Depression and Anxiety, 29*, 833–842.

Keck, P. E., & McElroy, S. L. (2002). Pharmacological treatments for bipolar disorder. In P. E. Nathan & J. M. Gorman (Eds.), *A guide to treatments that work* (2nd ed., pp. 277–299). New York, NY: Oxford University Press.

Keefe, D. L. (2002). Sex hormones and neural mechanisms. *Archives of Sexual Behavior, 31*(5), 401–403.

Keefe, F. J., & France, C. R. (1999). Pain: Biopsychosocial mechanisms and management. *Current Directions in Psychological Science, 8*, 137–141.

Keefe, F. J., Dunsmore, J., & Burnett, R. (1992). Behavioral and cognitive-behavioral approaches to chronic pain: Recent advances and future directions. Special issue: Behavioral medicine: An update for the 1990s. *Journal of Consulting and Clinical Psychology, 60*(4), 528–536.

Keel, P. K., Fichter, M., Quadfleig, N., Bulik, C. M., Baxter, M. G., Thornton, L., & Kaye, W. H. (2004). Application of a latent class analysis to empirically define eating disorder phenotypes. *Archives of General Psychiatry, 61*, 192–200.

Keel, P. K., & Forney, K. J. (2013). Psychosocial risk factors for eating disorders. *International Journal of Eating Disorders, 46*(5), 433–439.

Keel, P. K., Brown, T. A., Holland, L. A., & Bodell, L. P. (2012). Empirical classification of eating disorders. *Annual Review of Clinical Psychology, 8*, 381–404.

Keel, P. K., Dorer, D. J., Eddy, K. T., Franko, D., Charatan, D. L., & Herzog, D. B. (2003). Predictors of mortality in eating disorders. *Archives of General Psychiatry, 60*, 179–183.

Keel, P. K., Mitchell, J. E., Miller, K. B., Davis, T. L., & Crow, S. J. (2000). Predictive validity of bulimia nervosa as a diagnostic strategy. *American Journal of Psychiatry, 157*(1), 136–138.

Keitner, G. I., Ryan, C. E., Miller, I. W., Kohn, R., Bishop, D. S., & Epstein, N. B. (1995). Role of the family in recovery and major depression. *American Journal of Psychiatry, 152*, 1002–1008.

Keller, M. B., & Wunder, J. (1990). Bipolar disorder in childhood. In M. Hersen & C. G. Last (Eds.), *Handbook of child and adult psychopathology: A longitudinal perspective.* Elmsford, NY: Pergamon Press.

Keller, M. B., Klein, D. N., Hirschfeld, R. M. A., Kocsis, J. H., McCullough, J. P., ... Miller, I., Marin, D. B. (1995). Results of the DSM-IV mood disorders field trial. *American Journal of Psychiatry, 152*, 843–849.

Keller, M. B., Lavori, P. W., Endicott, J., Coryell, W., & Klerman, G. L. (1983). Double depression: Two year follow-up. *American Journal of Psychiatry, 140*(6), 689–694.

Keller, M. B., McCollough, J. P., Klein, D. N., Arnow, B., Dunner, D. L., Gelenberg, A. J., ... Zajecka, J. (2000). A comparison of nefazodone, the cognitive behavioral-analysis system of psychotherapy, and their combination for the treatment of chronic depression. *New England Journal of Medicine, 342*(20), 1462–1470.

Kellner, C. H., Greenberg, R. M., Murrough, J. W., Bryson, E. O., Briggs, M. C., & Pasculli, R. M. (2012). ECT in treatment-resistant depression. *American Journal of Psychiatry, 169*(12), 1238–1244.

Kellner, D. (2008). Media spectacle and the "massacre at Virginia Tech." In B. Agger & T. W. Luke (Eds.), *There is a gunman on campus: Tragedy and terror at Virginia Tech* (pp. 29–54). Lanham, MD: Rowman & Littlefield.

Kellner, R. (1985). Functional somatic symptoms and hypochondriasis: A survey of empirical studies. *Archives of General Psychiatry, 42*, 821–833.

Kellner, R. (1986). *Somatization and hypochondriasis.* New York, NY: Praeger-Greenwood.

Kellner, R. (1992). Diagnosis and treatments of hypochondriacal syndromes. *Psychosomatics, 33*(3), 278–279.

Kelly, B. D., Casey, P., Dunn, G., Ayuso-Mateos, J. L., & Dowrick, C. (2007). The role of personality disorder in "difficult to reach" patients with depression: Findings from the ODIN study. *European Psychiatry, 22*, 153–159.

Kelly, J. F. (2013). Alcoholics Anonymous science update: Introduction to the special issue. *Substance Abuse, 34*(1), 1–3.

Kelly, M. P., Strassberg, D. S., & Kircher, J. R. (1990). Attitudinal and experiential correlates of anorgasmia. *Archives of Sexual Behavior, 19*(2), 165–177.

Kelly, P., & Frosch, E. (2012). Recognition of delirium on pediatric hospital services. *Psychosomatics, 53*(5), 446–451.

Kemeny, M. E. (2003). The psychobiology of stress. *Current Directions in Psychological Science, 12*(4), 124–129.

Kemp, S. (1990). *Medieval psychology.* New York, NY: Greenwood Press.

Kendall, P. C., & Peterman, J. S. (2015). CBT for adolescents with anxiety: Mature yet still developing. *American Journal of Psychiatry, 172*, 519–530.

Kendall, P. C., Flannery-Schroeder, E., Panichelli-Mindell, M., Southam-Gerow, M., Henin, A., & Warman, M. (1997). Therapy for youths with anxiety disorder: A second randomized clinical trial. *Journal of Consulting and Clinical Psychology, 65*, 366–380.

Kendall, P. C., Hudson, J. L., Gosch, E., Flannery-Schroeder, E., & Suveg, C. (2008). Cognitive behavioral therapy for anxiety disordered youth: A randomized clinical trial evaluating child and family modalities. *Journal of Consulting and Clinical Psychology, 76*(2), 282–297.

Kendler, K. S. (2001). Twin studies of psychiatric illness. *Achieves of General Psychiatry, 58*, 1005–1013.

Kendler, K. S. (2006). Reflections on the relationship between psychiatric genetics and psychiatric nosology. *American Journal of Psychiatry, 163*, 1138–1146.

Kendler, K. S. (2011). A conceptual overview of gene–environment interaction and correlation in a developmental context. In K. S. Kendler, S. Jaffee & D. Romer (Eds.), *The dynamic genome and mental health: Development* (pp. 5–28). New York, NY: Oxford University Press.

Kendler, K. S. (2013). What psychiatric genetics has taught us about the nature of psychiatric illness and what is left to learn. *Molecular Psychiatry, 18*(10), 1058–1066. https://doi.org/10.1038/mp.1013.50

Kendler, K. S., & Diehl, S. R. (1993). The genetics of schizophrenia: A current, genetic-epidemiologic perspective. *Schizophrenia Bulletin, 19*, 261–285.

Kendler, K. S., Aggen, S. H., & Patrick, C. J. (2013). Familial influences on conduct disorder reflect 2 genetic factors and 1 shared environmental factor. *JAMA Psychiatry, 70*(1), 78–86.

Kendler, K. S., Aggen, S. H., Neale, M. C., Knudsen, G. P., Krueger, R. F., Tambs, K., ... Reichborn-Kjennerud, T. (2015). A longitudinal twin study of cluster A personality disorders. *Psychological Medicine, 45*(7), 1531–1538.

Kendler, K. S., Czajkowski, N., Tambs, K., Torgersen, S., Aggen, S. H., Neale, M. C., & Reichborn-Kjennerud, T. (2006). Dimensional representations of DSM-IV cluster A personality disorders in a population-based sample of Norwegian twins: A multivariate study. *Psychological Medicine, 36*, 1583–1591.

Kendler, K. S., & Gardner, C. O. (2010). Dependent stressful life events and prior depressive episodes in the prediction of major depression: The problem of causal inference in psychiatric epidemiology. *Archives of General Psychiatry, 67*(11), 1120–1127.

Kendler, K. S., & Gardner, C. O. (2014). Sex differences in the pathways to major depression: A study of opposite-sex twin Pairs. *American Journal of Psychiatry, 171*, 426–435.

Kendler, K. S., Gatz, M., Gardner, C. O., & Pedersen, N. L. (2007). Clinical indices of familial depression in the Swedish Twin Registry. *Acta Psychiatrica Scandinavica, 115*(3), 214–220.

Kendler, K. S., Heath, A. C., Martin, N. G., & Eaves, L. J. (1987). Symptoms of anxiety and symptoms of depression: Same genes, different environments? *Archives of General Psychiatry, 44*(5), 451–457.

Kendler, K. S., Hettema, J. M., Butera, F., Gardner, C. O., & Prescott, C. A. (2003). Life event dimensions of loss, humiliation, entrapment, and danger in the prediction of onsets of major depression and generalized anxiety. *Archives of General Psychiatry, 60*, 789–796.

Kendler, K. S., Jaffee, S., & Romer, D. (2011). *The dynamic genome and mental health: The role of genes and environments in youth development.* New York, NY: Oxford University Press.

Kendler, K. S., Karkowski, L. M., & Prescott, C. A. (1999a). The assessment of dependence in the study of stressful life events: Validation using a twin design. *Psychological Medicine, 29*(6), 1455–1460.

Kendler, K. S., Kessler, R. C., Neale, M. C., Heath, A. C., & Eaves, L. J. (1993). The prediction of major depression in women: Toward an integrated etiologic model. *American Journal of Psychiatry, 150*, 1139–1148.

Kendler, K. S., Kessler, R. C., Walters, E. E., MacLean, C., Neale, M. C., Heath, A. C., & Eaves, L. J. (1995). Stressful life events, genetic liability, and onset of an episode of major depression in women. *American Journal of Psychiatry, 152*, 833–842.

Kendler, K. S., Larsson Lönn, S., Morris, N. A., Sundquist, J., Långström, N., & Sundquist, K. (2014). A Swedish national adoption study of criminality. *Psychological Medicine, 44*(9), 1913–1925.

Kendler, K. S., MacLean, C., Neale, M., Kessler, R., Heath, A., & Eaves, L. (1991). The genetic epidemiology of bulimia nervosa. *American Journal of Psychiatry, 148*(12), 1627–1637.

Kendler, K. S., McGuire, M., Gruenberg, A. M., O'Hare, A., Spellman, M., & Walsh, D. (1993). The Roscommon Family Study: I. Methods, diagnosis of probands, and risk of schizophrenia in relatives. *Archives of General Psychiatry, 50*, 527–540.

Kendler, K. S., Myers, J., & Prescott, C. A. (2005). Sex differences in the relationship between social support and risk for major depression: A longitudinal study of opposite-sex twin pairs. *American Journal of Psychiatry, 162*, 250–256.

Kendler, K. S., Myers, J., & Zisook, S. (2008). Does bereavement-related major depression differ from major depression associated with other stressful life events? *American Journal of Psychiatry, 165*(11), 1449–1455.

Kendler, K. S., Neale, M. C., Kessler, R. C., Heath, A. C., & Eaves, L. J. (1992a). Generalized anxiety disorder in women: A population-based twin study. *Archives of General Psychiatry, 49*, 267–272.

Kendler, K. S., Neale, M. C., Kessler, R. C., Heath, A. C., & Eaves, L. J. (1992b). Major depression and generalized anxiety disorder: Same genes, (partly) different environments? *Archives of General Psychiatry, 49*, 716–722.

Kendler, K. S., Neale, M. C., Kessler, R. C., Heath, A. C., & Eaves, L. J. (1993). A longitudinal twin study of 1-year prevalence of major depression in women. *Archives of General Psychiatry, 50*, 843–852.

Kendler, K. S., & Prescott, C. A. (2006). *Genes, environment, and psychopathology: Understanding the causes of psychiatric and substance use disorders*. New York, NY: Guilford, Press.

Kendler, K., & Walsh, D. (2007). Schizophreniform disorder, delusional disorder and psychotic disorder not otherwise specified: Clinical features, outcome and familial psychopathology. *Acta Psychiatrica Scandinavica, 91*(6), 370–378.

Kendrick, D., Young, B., Mason-Jones, A. J., Ilyas, N., Achana, F.A., Cooper, N. J., … Coupland, C. (2012). Home safety education and provision of safety equipment for injury prevention. *Cochrane Database Syst. Rev. 9*:CD005014.

Kennedy, K. (2001, October 22). Brotherly love. *Sports Illustrated*. Retrieved June 21, 2004, from http://www.macanxiety.com/corson.htm

Kennedy, S. (2000). Psychological factors and immunity in HIV infection: Stress, coping, social support, and intervention outcomes. In D. I. Mostofsky & D. H. Barlow (Eds.), *The management of stress and anxiety in medical disorders* (pp. 194–205). Needham Heights, MA: Allyn & Bacon.

Kennedy, S. H., Giacobbe, P., Rizvi, S. J., Placenza, F. M., Nishikawa, Y., Mayberg, H. S., & Lozano, A. M. (2011). Deep brain stimulation for treatment-resistant depression: Follow-up after 3 to 6 years. *American Journal of Psychiatry, 168*(5), 502–510.

Kennedy, S. H., & Goldbloom, D. S. (1996). Eating disorders. In Q. Rae-Grant (Ed.), *Images in psychiatry: Canada* (pp. 229–234). Washington, DC: American Psychiatric Press.

Kennedy, S. H., Katz, R., Neitzert, C. S., Ralevski, E., & Mendlowitz, S. (1995). Exposure with response prevention treatment of anorexia nervosa-bulimic subtype and bulimia nervosa. *Behaviour Research & Therapy, 33*, 685–689.

Kennedy, S. H., Konarski, J. Z., Segal, Z. V., Lau, M. A., Bieling, P. J., McIntyre, R. S., & Mayberg, H. S. (2007). *Differences in brain glucose metabolism between responders to CBT and Venlafaxine in a 16-week randomized controlled trial*. http://www.cme

.psychiatryonline.org/article.aspx?articleID=98367&atab=7

Kennedy, S. H., McVey, G., & Katz, R. (1990). Personality disorders in anorexia nervosa and bulimia nervosa. *Journal of Psychiatric Research, 24*, 259–269.

Kerns, J. G., & Berenbaum, H. (2002). Cognitive impairments associated with formal thought disorder in people with schizophrenia. *Journal of Abnormal Psychology, 111*(2), 211–224.

Kerns, K., Don, A., Mateer, C. A., & Streissguth, A. P. (1997). Cognitive deficits in nonretarded adults with fetal alcohol syndrome. *Journal of Learning Disabilities, 30*(6), 685–693.

Kerns, R. D., Sellinger, J., & Goodin, B. R. (2011). Psychological treatment of chronic pain. *Annual Review of Clinical Psychology, 7*, 411–434.

Kerns, R., Southwick, S., Giller, E., Haythornwaite, J., Jacob, M., & Rosenberg, R. (1991). The relationship between reports of pain-related social interactions and expressions of pain and affective distress. *Behavior Therapy, 22*, 101–111.

Kerr, G., Berman, E., & de Souza, M. J. (2006). Disordered eating in women's gymnastics: Perspectives of athletes, coaches, parents, and judges. *Journal of Applied Sport Psychology, 18*, 28–43.

Kerr, M., Stattin, H., & Burk, W. J. (2010). A reinterpretation of parental monitoring in longitudinal perspective. *Journal of Research on Adolescence, 20*(1), 39–64.

Kersting, A., Brahler, E., Glaesmer, H., & Wagner, B. (2011). Prevalence of complicated grief in a representative population-based sample. *Journal of Affective Disorders, 131*(1–3), 339–343.

Kessler, R. C. (2006). The epidemiology of depression among women. In C. Keye & S. Goodman (Eds.), *A handbook for the social, behavioral, and biomedical sciences: Women and depression* (pp. 22–37). New York, NY: Cambridge University Press.

Kessler, R. C., Avenevoli, S., Costello, H., Georgiades, K., Green, J. G., Gruber, M. J., & Merikangas, K. R. (2012). Prevalence, persistence, and sociodemographic correlates of DSM-IV disorders in the National Comorbidity Survey Replication Adolescent Supplement. *Archives of General Psychiatry, 69*(4), 372–380.

Kessler, R. C., Berglund, P., Borges, G., Nock, M., & Wang, P. (2005). Trends in suicide ideation, plans, gestures, and attempts in the United States, 1990–1992 to 2001–2003. *JAMA: Journal of the American Medical Associatioin, 293*, 2487–2495.

Kessler, R. C., Berglund, P., Demler, O., Jin, R., & Walters, E. E. (2005). Lifetime prevalence and age-of-onset distributions of DSM-IV disorders in the National Comorbidity Survey replication. *Archives of General Psychiatry, 62*, 593–602.

Kessler, R. C., Berglund, P., Demler, O., Jin, R., Koretz, D., Merikangas, K. R., … Wang, P. S. (2003). The epidemiology of major depressive disorder: Results from the National Comorbidity Survey Replication (NCS-R). *Journal of the American Medical Association, 289*, 3095–3105.

Kessler, R. C., & Bromet, E. J. (2013). The epidemiology of depression across cultures. *Annual Review of Public Health, 34*, 119–138.

Kessler, R. C., Chiu, W. T., Demler, O., & Walters, E. E. (2005). Prevalence, severity, and comorbidity of 12-month DSM-IV disorders in the National Comorbidity Survey replication. *Archives of General Psychiatry, 62*, 617–627.

Kessler, R. C., Chiu, W. T., Jin, R., Ruscio, A. M., Shear, K., & Walters, E. E. (2006). The epidemiology of panic attacks, panic disorder, and agoraphobia in the National Comorbidity Survey Replication. *Archives of General Psychiatry, 63*(4), 415–424.

Kessler, R. C., Galea, S., Jones, R. T., & Parker, H. A. (2006). *Mental illness and suicidality after Hurricane Katrina*. Bulletin of the World Health Organization (WHO Publication No. 06-033019).

Kessler, R. C., McGonagle, K. A., Zhao, S., Nelson, C. B., Hughes, M., Eshleman, S., … Kendler, K. S. (1994). Lifetime and 12-month prevalence of DSM-III-R psychiatric disorders among persons aged 15–54 in the United States: Results from the national comorbidity survey. *Archives of General Psychiatry, 51*(1), 8–19.

Kessler, R. C., Petukhova, M., Sampson, N. A., Zaslavsky, A. M., & Wittchen, H. U. (2012). Twelve-month and lifetime prevalence and lifetime morbid risk of anxiety and mood disorders in the United States. *International Journal of Methods in Psychiatric Research, 21*, 169.

Kessler, R. C., Sonnega, A., Bromet, E., Hughes, M., & Nelson, C. B. (1995). Posttraumatic stress disorder in the national comorbidity survey. *Archives of General Psychiatry, 52*, 1048–1060.

Kessler, R. C., & Wang, P. S. (2009). Epidemiology of depression. In I. H. Gotlib & C. L. Hammen (Eds.), *Handbook of depression* (2nd ed., pp. 5–22). New York, NY: Guilford Press.

Kety, S. S. (1990). Genetic factors in suicide: Family, twin, and adoption studies. In S. J. Blumenthal & D. J. Kupfer (Eds.), *Suicide over the life cycle: Risk factors, assessment and treatment of suicidal patients* (pp. 127–133). Washington, DC: American Psychiatric Press.

Keys, A., Brozek, J., Henschel, A., Michelson, O., & Taylor, H. L. (1950). *The biology of human starvation* (Vol. 1). Minneapolis, MN: University of Minnesota Press.

Khachaturian, Z. S. (2007). Alzheimer's 101. *Alzheimer's and Dementia, 3*, 1–2.

Khan, S. (2017). Concurrent mental and substance use disorders in Canada. *Health Reports, 28*(8), 3–8. https://www150.statcan.gc.ca/n1/en/catalogue/82-003-X201700854853

Khan, S., King, A. P., Abelson, J. L., & Liberzon, I. (2009). *Neuroendocrinology of anxiety disorders*. In M. M. Antony & M. B. Stein (Eds.), *Oxford handbook of anxiety and related disorders*. Oxford, UK: Oxford University Press.

Khoury, B., Lecomte, T., Fortin, G., Masse, M., Therien, P., Bouchard, V., Chapleau, M.-A., Paquin, K., & Hofmann, S. G. (2013). Mindfulness-based therapy: A comprehensive meta-analysis. *Clinical Psychology Review, 33*, 763–771.

Kiang, M., Christensen, B. K., Remington, G., & Kapur, S. (2003). Apathy in schizophrenia: Clinical correlates and association with functional

outcome. *Schizophrenia Research, 63*, 79–88.

Kiecolt-Glaser, J. K., & Glaser, R. (1987). Chronic stress and immunity in family caregivers of Alzheimer's disease victims. *Psychosomatic Medicine, 49*(5), 523–535.

Kiecolt-Glaser, J. K., & Glaser, R. (1992). Psychoneuroimmunology: Can psychological interventions modulate immunity? [Special issue: Behavioral medicine: An update for the 1990s]. *Journal of Consulting and Clinical Psychology, 60*(4), 569–575.

Kiecolt-Glaser, J. K., & Newton, T. L. (2001). Marriage and health: His and hers. *Psychological Bulletin, 127*, 475–503.

Kiecolt-Glaser, J. K., Loving, T., Stowell, J., Malarkey, W., Lemeshow, S., & Dickinson, S., & Glaser, R. (2005). Hostile marital interactions, proinflammatory cytokine production, and wound healing. *Archives of General Psychiatry, 62*, 1377–1384.

Kiehl, K. A., Smith, A. M., Hare, R. D., Mendrek, A., Forster, B. B., Brink, J., & Liddle, P. F. (2001). Limbic abnormalities in affective processing by criminal psychopaths as revealed by functional magnetic resonance imaging. *Biological Psychiatry, 50*, 677–684.

Kiesler, D. J. (1966). Some myths of psychotherapy research and the search for a paradigm. *Psychological Bulletin, 65*, 110–136.

Kihlstrom, J. F. (1992). Dissociation and dissociations: A commentary on consciousness and cognition. *Consciousness & Cognition, 1*, 47–53.

Kihlstrom, J. F. (1994). One hundred years of hysteria. In S. J. Lynn & J. W. Rhue (Eds.), *Dissociation: Theoretical, clinical, and research perspectives* (pp. 365–394). New York, NY: Guilford, Press.

Kihlstrom, J. F. (1997). Memory, abuse, and science. *American Psychologist, 52*, 994–995.

Kihlstrom, J. F. (2005a). Dissociative disorders. In S. Nolen-Hoeksema, T. D. Cannon, & T. Widiger (Eds.), *Annual review of clinical psychology* (Vol. 1). Palo Alto, CA: Annual Reviews.

Kihlstrom, J. F. (2005b). Dissociative disorders. *Annual Review of Clinical Psychology, 1*, 227–253.

Kihlstrom, J. F., Barnhardt, T. M., & Tataryn, D. J. (1992). The psychological unconscious: Found, lost, and regained. *American Psychologist, 47*(6), 788–791.

Kihlstrom, J. F., Glisky, M. L., & Anguilo, M. J. (1994). Dissociative tendencies and dissociative disorders. *Journal of Abnormal Psychology, 103*, 117–124.

Killen, J. D. (1996). Development and evaluation of a school-based eating disorder symptoms prevention program. In L. Smolak, M. P. Levine, & R. Striegel-Moore (Eds.), *The developmental psychopathology of eating disorders: Implications for research, prevention, and treatment* (pp. 313–339). Mahwah, NJ: Erlbaum.

Killer of Holly Jones pleads guilty. (2004a, June 17). *CBC News Online*. Retrieved August 5, 2004, from http://www.cbc.ca/stories/2004/06/17/canada/holly040617

Kilpatrick, D. G., Best, C. L., Veronen, L. J., Amick, A. E., VillePonteaux, L. A., & Ruff, G. A. (1985). Mental health correlates of criminal victimization: A random community survey. *Journal of Consulting and Clinical Psychology, 53*, 866–873.

Kilpatrick, D. G., Koenen, K. C., Ruggiero, K. J., Acierno, R., Galea, S., Resnick, H. S., & Gelernter, J. (2007). The serotonin transporter genotype and social support and moderation of post-traumatic stress disorder and depression in hurricane-exposed adults. *American Journal of Psychiatry, 164*(11), 1693–1699.

Kilpatrick, D. G., Resnick, H. S., & Friedman, M. J. (2010). National Stressful Events Survey PTSD Short Scale (NSESSS-PTSD).

Kilzieh, N., & Akiskal, H. S. (1999). Rapid-cycling bipolar disorder: An overview of research and clinical experience. *Psychiatric Clinics of North America, 22*(3), 585–607.

Kim, E. D., & Lipshultz, L. I. (1997, April 15). Advances in the treatment of organic erectile dysfunction. *Hospital Practice*, 101–120.

Kim, H. F., Schulz, P. E., Wilde, E. A., & Yudofsky, S. C. (2008). Laboratory testing and imaging studies in psychiatry. In R. E. Hales, S. C. Yudofsky, & G. O. Gabbard (Eds.), *The American Psychiatric Publishing textbook of psychiatry* (5th ed., pp. 19–72). Arlington, VA: American Psychiatric Publishing.

Kim, J. M., & Lopez, S. R. (2014). The expression of depression in Asian Americans and European Americans. *Journal of Abnormal Psychology, 123*, 745–763.

Kimchi, E. Z., & Lyketos, C. G. (2015). Dementia and milder cognitive symptoms. In D. C. Steffens, D. G. Blazer, & M. E. Thakur (Eds.), *The American Psychiatric Publishing textbook of geriatric psychiatry* (5th ed., pp. 177–242). Washington, DC: American Psychiatric Publishing.

King, D. E., Mainous III, A. G., & Geesey, M. E. (2007). Turning back the clock: Adopting a healthy lifestyle in middle age. *American Journal of Medicine, 120*(7), 598–603.

King, D. W., King, L. A., Foy, D. W., & Gudanowski, D. M. (1996). Prewar factors in combat related posttraumatic stress disorder: Structural equation modeling with a national sample of female and male Vietnam veterans. *Journal of Consulting and Clinical Psychology, 64*, 520–531.

King, G. R., & Ellinwood, E. H. (1997). Amphetamines and other stimulants. In J. H. Lowinson, P. Ruiz, R. B. Millman, & J. G. Langrod (Eds.), *Substance abuse: A comprehensive textbook* (pp. 207–223). Baltimore, MD: Williams & Wilkins.

King, L. A., Pless, A. P., Schuster, J. L., Potter, C. M., Park, C. L., Spiro, A., & King, D. W. (2012). Risk and protective factors for traumatic stress disorder. In J. G. Beck & D. M. Sloan (Eds.), *The Oxford handbook of traumatic stress disorders* (pp. 333–346). New York, NY: Oxford University Press.

King, N. J. (1993). Simple and social phobias. In T. H. Ollendick & R. J. Prinz (Eds.), *Advances in clinical child psychology* (Vol. 15, pp. 305–341). New York, NY: Plenum Press.

King, P., Devichand, P., & Rockwood, K. (2005). Dementia of acute onset in the Canadian study of health and aging. *International Psychogeriatrics, 17*, 451–459.

King, P., Song, X., & Rockwood, K. (2006). Cognitive impairment of acute onset in the consortium to investigate vascular impairment of cognition (CIVIC) study: Occurrences, correlates, and outcomes. *American Journal of Geriatric Psychiatry, 14*, 893–896.

King, S. (2000). Is expressed emotion cause or effect in the mothers of schizophrenic young adults? *Schizophrenia Research, 45*, 65–78.

Kingdon, D. G., & Turkington, D. (1994). *Cognitive-behavioral therapy of schizophrenia*. New York, NY: Guilford Press.

Kingsley, J. (1998, February 12). Snowboarder Rebagliati wins appeal. *Canadian Press NewsWire*. Retrieved December 1, 2007, from http://Proquest.umi.com/pqdweb?did3919301 31&sid11&Fmt3&clientId15814&RQT 309&VNamePQD

Kinne, P., & Bhanot, V. (2008). I've been abducted by aliens. *Current Psychiatry, 7*(7), 82.

Kinsey, A. C., Pomeroy, W. B., & Martin, C. E. (1948). *Sexual behavior in the human male*. Philadelphia, PA: W. B. Saunders.

Kinsey, A. C., Pomeroy, W. B., Martin, C. E., & Gebhard, P. H. (1953). *Sexual behavior in the human female*. Philadelphia, PA: W. B. Saunders.

Kinzie, J. D., Leung, P. K., Boehnlein, J., & Matsunaga, D. (1992). Psychiatric epidemiology of an Indian village: A 19-year replication study. *Journal of Nervous and Mental Disease, 180*(1), 33–39.

Kirch, D. G. (1993). Infection and autoimmunity as etiologic factors in schizophrenia: A review and reappraisal. *Schizophrenia Bulletin, 19*, 355–370.

Kirmayer, L. J. (2001). Cultural variations in the clinical presentation of depression and anxiety: Implications for diagnosis and treatment. *Journal of Clinical Psychiatry, 62*(Suppl. 13), 22–28.

Kirmayer, L. J., & Groleau, D. (2001). Affective disorders in cultural context. *Psychiatric Clinics of North America, 24*, 465–478.

Kirmayer, L. J., & Jarvis, G. E. (2006). Depression across cultures. In D. J. Stein, D. J. Kupfer, & A. F. Schatzberg (Eds.), *The American Psychiatric Publishing textbook of mood disorders* (pp. 699–715). Washington, DC: American Psychiatric Publishing, Inc.

Kirmayer, L. J., & Robbins, J. M. (1991). Three forms of somatization in primary care: Prevalence, co-occurrence, and sociodemographic characteristics. *Journal of Nervous and Mental Disease, 179*, 647–655.

Kirmayer, L. J., Boothroyd, L. J., Tanner, A., Adelson, N., & Robinson, E. (2000). Psychological distress among the Cree of James Bay. *Transcultural Psychiatry, 37*, 35–56.

Kirmayer, L. J., Looper, K. J., & Taillefer, S. (2003). Somatoform disorders. In M. Hersen & S. M. Turner (Eds.), *Adult psychopathology and diagnosis* (4th ed., pp. 420–475). New York, NY: John Wiley & Sons.

Kirmayer, L. J., Malus, M., & Boothroyd, L. J. (1996). Suicide attempts among Inuit youth: A community survey of prevalence and risk factors. *Acta Psychiatrica Scandinavia, 94*, 8–17.

Kirmayer, L. J., Simpson, C., & Cargo, M (2003). Healing traditions: Culture, community and mental health promotion with Canadian Aboriginal peoples.

Australasian Psychiatry, 11(Suppl. 1), S15–S23.

Kirov, G., & Owen, M. J. (2009). Genetics of schizophrenia. In B. J. Sadock, V. A. Sadock, & P. Ruiz (Eds.), *Kaplan & Sadock's comprehensive textbook of psychiatry* (9th ed., Vol. 1, pp. 1462–1475). Philadelphia, PA: Lippincott Williams & Wilkins.

Kistner, J. A. (2009). Sex differences in child and adolescent psychopathology: An introduction to the special section. *Journal of Clinical Child and Adolescent Psychology, 38*(4), 453–459.

Kivimaki, M., Nyberg, S. T., Batty, G. D., Fransson, E. I., Heikkila, K., Alfredsson, L., & Consortium, I. P. W. (2012). Job strain as a risk factor for coronary heart disease: A collaborative meta-analysis of individual participant data. *Lancet, 380*(9852), 1491–1497.

Kleber, H. D. (1999). Opioid: Detoxification. In M. Galanter & H. D. Kleber (Eds.), *Textbook of substance abuse treatment* (2nd ed., pp. 251–279). Washington, DC: American Psychiatric Press.

Klein, D. F. (1989). The pharmacological validation of psychiatric diagnosis. In L. Robins & J. Barrett (Eds.), *Validity of psychiatric diagnosis*. New York, NY: Raven Press.

Klein, D. F. (1999). Harmful dysfunction, disorder, disease, illness, and evolution. *Journal of Abnormal Psychology, 108*, 421–429.

Klein, D. N. (2008). Classification of depressive disorders in the DSM-V: Proposal for a two-dimension system. *Journal of Abnormal Psychology, 117*(3), 552–560.

Klein, D. N. (2010). Chronic depression: Diagnosis and classification. *Current Directions in Psychological Science, 19*(2), 96–100.

Klein, D. N., Lewinsohn, P., Rohde, P., Seeley, J., & Durbin, C. E. (2002). Clinical features of major depressive disorder in adolescents and their relatives: Impact on familial aggregation, implications for phenotype definition, and specificity of transmission. *Journal of Abnormal Psychology, 111*, 98–106.

Klein, D. N., Lewinsohn, P. M., & Seeley, J. R. (1997). Psychosocial characteristics of adolescents with a past history of dysthymic disorder: Comparison with adolescents with past histories of major depressive and non-affective disorders, and never mentally ill controls. *Journal of Affective Disorders, 42*, 127–135.

Klein, D. N., Schwartz, J. E., Rose, S., & Leader, J. B. (2000). Five-year course and outcome of dysthymic disorder: A prospective, naturalistic follow-up study. *American Journal of Psychiatry, 157*(6), 931–939.

Klein, D. N., Shankman, S., & Rose, S. (2006). Ten-year prospective follow-up study of the naturalistic course of dysthymic disorder and double depression. *American Journal of Psychiatry, 163*, 872–880.

Klein, D. N., Taylor, E. B., Dickstein, S., & Harding, K. (1988). The early-late onset distinction in DSM-III-R dysthymia. *Journal of Affective Disorders, 14*(1), 25–33.

Klein, R. G., Mannuzza, S., Ramos Olazagasti, M. A., Roizen, E., Jesse A. Hutchison, J. A., Lashua, E. C., & Castellanos, F. X. (2012). Clinical and functional outcome of childhood attention-deficit/hyperactivity disorder

33 years later. *Archives of General Psychiatry, 69*(12), 1295–1303.

Kleinknecht, R. A., Dinnel, D. L., Kleinknecht, E. E., Hiruma, N., & Hirada, N. (1997). Cultural factors in social anxiety: A comparison of social phobia symptoms and taijin kyofusho. *Journal of Anxiety Disorders, 11*, 157–177.

Kleinman, A. (1986). *Social origins of distress and disease: Depression neurasthenia, and pain in modern China*. New Haven, CT: Yale University Press.

Kleinman, A. (2004). Culture and depression. *New England Journal of Medicine, 351*, 951–953.

Kleinplatz, F. J., Moser, C., & Lev, A. I. (2013). Sex and gender identity disorders. In I. B. Weiner, G. Stricker, & T. A. Widiger (Eds.), *Handbook of psychology, Clinical psychology* (2nd ed., Vol. 8, pp. 171–192). Hoboken, NJ: Wiley.

Kleinstäuber, M., Witthöft, M., & Hiller, W. (2011). Efficacy of short-term psychotherapy for multiple medically unexplained physical symptoms: A meta-analysis. *Clinical Psychology Review, 31*, 146–160.

Klerman, G. L., & Weissman, M. M. (1989). Increasing rates of depression. *JAMA, 261*, 2229–2235.

Klerman, G. L., Weissman, M. M., Rounsaville, B. J., & Chevron, E. S. (1984). *Interpersonal psychotherapy of depression*. New York, NY: Basic Books.

Klimas, N., Koneru, A. O., & Fletcher, M. A. (2008). Overview of HIV. *Psychosomatic Medicine, 70*, 523–530.

Klin, A., Jones, W., Schultz, R., Volkmar, F., & Cohen, D. (2002). Defining and quantifying the social phenotype in autism. *American Journal of Psychiatry, 159*, 895–908.

Kluft, R. (1995). Current controversies surrounding dissociative identity disorder. In L. Cohen, J. Berzoff, & M. Elin (Eds.), *Dissociative identity disorder* (p. 351). Northvale, NJ: Jason Aronson, Inc.

Kluft, R. P. (1984). Treatment of multiple personality disorder. *Psychiatric Clinics of North America, 7*, 9–29.

Kluft, R. P. (1991). Multiple personality disorder. In A. Tasman & S. W. Goldinger (Eds.), *Review of psychiatry* (Vol. 10). Washington, DC: American Psychiatric Press.

Kluft, R. P. (1996). Treating the traumatic memories of patients with dissociative identity disorder. *American Journal of Psychiatry, 153*, 103–110.

Kluft, R. P. (1999). Current issues in dissociative identity disorder. *Journal of Practical Psychology and Behavioral Health, 5*, 3–19.

Kluft, R. P. (2009). A clinician's understanding of dissociation: Fragments of an acquaintance. In P. F. Dell & J. A. O'Neil (Eds.), *Dissociation and the dissociative disorders*. New York, NY: Routledge.

Klump, K. L., Kaye, W. H., & Strober, M. (2001). The evolving genetic foundations of eating disorders. *The Psychiatric Clinics of North America, 24*, 215–225.

Klump, K. L., Racine, S. E., Hildebrandt, B., Burt, S. A., Neale, M., Sisk, C. L., ... & Keel, P. K. (2014). Influences of ovarian hormones on dysregulated eating a comparison of associations in women with versus women without binge episodes. *Clinical Psychological Science, 2*(5), 545–559.

Klumpp, H., Fitzgerald, D. A., & Phan, K. L. (2013). Neural predictors and mechanisms of cognitive behavioral therapy on threat processing in social anxiety disorder. *Progress in Neuro-Psychopharmacology & Biological Psychiatry, 45*, 83–91.

Knight, L. J., & Boland, F. J. (1989). Restrained eating: An experimental disentanglement of the disturbing variables of perceived calories and food type. *Journal of Abnormal Psychology, 98*, 412–420.

Knopik, V. S., Bidwell, L. C., Flessner, C., Nugent, N., Swenson, L., Bucholz, K. K. ... Heath, A. C. (2014). DSM-IV defined conduct disorder and oppositional defiant disorder: An investigation of shared liability infemale twins. *Psychological Medicine, 44*(5), 1053–1064.

Knowles, J. (2010). Cognitive stimulation therapy: Why it deserves better awareness and availability. *Journal of Care Services Management, 4*(2), 188–194.

Knowles, R., McCarthy-Jones, S., & Rowse, G. (2011). Grandiose delusions: A review and theoretical integration of cognitive and affective perspectives. *Clinical Psychology Review, 31*(4), 684–696.

Ko, H. C., Lee, L. R., Chang, F. M., Lu, R. B., & Huang, K. E. (1996). Comorbidity of premenstrual depression and postpartum blues among Chinese women. *Biological Psychiatry, 39*, 648.

Koban, L., & Wager, T. D. (2015). Beyond conformity: Social influences on pain reports and physiology. *Emotion, 16*, 24–32.

Kobau, R., DiIorio, C., Chapman, D., & Delvecchio, P. (2010). Attitudes about mental illness and its treatment: Validation of a generic scale for public health surveillance of mental illness associated stigma. *Community Mental Health Journal, 46*(2), 164–176.

Kochman, F. J., Hantouche, E. G., Ferrari, P., Lancrenon, S., Bayart, D., & Akiskal, H. S. (2005). Cyclothymic temperament as a prospective predictor of bipolarity and suicidality in children and adolescents with major depressive disorder. *Journal of Affective Disorders, 85*, 181–189.

Koegel, L. K. (1995). Communication and language intervention. In R. L. Koegel & L. K. Koegel (Eds.), *Teaching children with autism: Strategies for initiating positive interactions and improving learning opportunities* (pp. 17–32). Baltimore, MD: Paul H. Brookes.

Koegel, R. L., & Koegel, L. K. (2012). *The PRT pocket guide: Pivotal response treatment for autism spectrum disorders*. Baltimore, MD: Paul H. Brookes.

Koegel, R. L., Schreibman, L., O'Neill, R. E., & Burke, J. C. (1983). The personality and family interaction characteristics of parents of autistic children. *Journal of Consulting and Clinical Psychology, 51*, 683–692.

Koen, L., Niehaus, D., Muller, J., & Laurent, C. (2008). Use of traditional treatment methods in a Xhosa schizophrenia population. *South African Medical Journal, 93*(6), 443.

Kogan, C. S., & Paterniti. S. (2017). The true north strong and free? Opportunities for improving Canadian mental health care and education by adopting the WHO's ICD-11 classification. *Canadian Journal of Psychiatry, 62*, 690–696.

Koh, P. O., Bergson, C., Undie, A. S., Goldman-Rakic, P. S., & Lidow, M. S. (2003). Up-regulation of the D1 dopamine receptor-interacting protein, calcyon, in patients with schizophrenia. *Archives of General Psychiatry, 60*, 311–319.

Kohn, M. L. (1968). Social class and schizophrenia: A critical review. In D. Rosenthal & S. S. Kety (Eds.), *The transmission of schizophrenia*. Elmsford, NY: Pergamon Press.

Kohn, R., Wintrob, R. M., & Alarcon, R. D. (2009). Transcultural psychiatry. In B. J. Sadock, V. A. Sadock, & P. Ruiz (Eds.), *Kaplan & Sadock's comprehensive textbook of psychiatry* (9th ed., Vol. 1, pp. 734–753). Philadelphia, PA: Lippincott Williams & Wilkins.

Kohut, H. (1971). *The analysis of self*. New York, NY: International Universities Press.

Kohut, H. (1977). *The restoration of the self*. New York, NY: International Universities Press.

Kokko, K., Tremblay, R. E., Lacourse, E., Nagin, D. S., & Vitaro, F. (2006). Trajectories of prosocial behavior and physical aggression in middle childhood: Links to adolescent school dropout and physical violence. *Journal of Research on Adolescence, 16*(3), 403–428.

Kolb, B., & Whishaw, I. Q. (1998). Brain plasticity and behavior. *Annual Review of Psychology, 49*, 43–64.

Kolb, B., & Whishaw, I. Q. (2003). *Fundamentals of human neuropsychology* (5th ed.). New York, NY: Worth/Freeman.

Kolb, B., Gibb, R., & Gorny, G. (2003). Experience-dependent changes in dendritic arbor and spine density in neocortex vary qualitatively with age and sex. *Neurobiology of Learning & Memory, 79*, 1–10.

Kolb, B., Gibb, R., & Robinson, T. E. (2003). Brain plasticity and behavior. *Current Directions in Psychological Science, 12*, 1–5.

Kolla, B. P., Auger, R., & Morgenthaler, T. (2012). Circadian rhythm sleep disorders. *ChronoPhysiology and Therapy, 2*, 19–34.

Kollei, I., Schieber, K., de Zwaan, M., Svitak, M., & Martin, A. (2013). Body dysmorphic disorder and non-weight-related body image concerns in individuals with eating disorders. *International Journal of Eating Disorders, 46*(1), 52–59.

Koning, C., Magill-Evans, J., Volden, J., & Dick, B. (2011 September 15). Efficacy of cognitive behavior therapy-based social skills intervention for school-aged boys with autism spectrum disorders. *Research in Autism Spectrum Disorders, 7*(10), 1282–1290. https://doi.org/10.1016/j.rasd.2011.07.011

Koocher, G. P. (1996). Pediatric oncology: Medical crisis intervention. In R. J. Resnick & R. H. Rozensky (Eds.), *Health psychology through the lifespan: Practice and research opportunities* (pp. 213–225). Washington, DC: American Psychological Association.

Kopala, L. C., Good, K. P., Milliken, H., Buiteman, C., Woodley, H., Rui, Q., ... Honer, W. G. (2006). Treatment of a first episode of psychotic illness with quetiapine: An analysis of 2 year outcomes. *Schizophrenia Research, 81*(1), 29–39.

Kopala, L., Smith, G., Malla, A., Williams, R., Love, L., Talling, D., & Balshaw, R. (2006). Resource utilization in a Canadian national study of people with schizophrenia and related psychotic disorders. *Acta Psychiatrica Scandinavica, 113*(430), 29–39.

Koran, L. M., Abujaoude, E., Large, M. D., & Serpe, R. T. (2008). The prevalence of body dysmorphic disorder in the United States adult population. *CNS Spectrums, 13*(4), 316–322.

Korczyn, A. D., Kahana, E., & Galper, Y. (1991). Epidemiology of dementia in Ashkelon, Israel. *Neuroepidemiology, 10*, 100.

Korenman, S. G., & Barchas, J. D. (1993). *Biological basis of substance abuse*. New York, NY: Oxford University Press.

Korfine, L., & Hooley, J. M. (2000). Directed forgetting of emotional stimuli in borderline personality disorder. *Journal of Abnormal Psychology, 109*, 214–221.

Korol, C. T., & Craig, K. D. (2001). Pain from the perspectives of health psychology and culture. In S. S. Kazarian & D. R. Evans (Eds.), *Handbook of cultural health psychology* (pp. 241–265). San Diego, CA: Academic Press.

Kosberg, J. I., Kaufman, A. V., Burgio, L. D., Leeper, J. D., & Sun, F. (2007). Family caregiving to those with dementia in rural Alabama: Racial similarities and differences. *Journal of Aging and Health, 19*, 3–21.

Kosson, D. S., Neumann, C. S., Forth, A. E., Salekin, R. T., Hare, R. D., Krischer, M. K., & Sevecke, K. (2013). Revised psychopathy checklist. *Psychological Assessment, 25*(1), 71–83.

Kotsaftis, A., & Neale, J. M. (1993). Schizotypal personality disorder I: The clinical syndrome. *Clinical Psychology Review, 13*, 451–472.

Kovacs, M., Akiskal, H. S., Gatsonis, C., & Parrone, P. L. (1994). Childhood-onset dysthymic disorder. *Archives of General Psychiatry, 51*, 365–374.

Kovacs, M., Gatsonis, C., Paulauskas, S. L., & Richards, C. (1989). Depressive disorders in childhood: IV. A longitudinal study of comorbidity with and risk for anxiety disorders. *Archives of General Psychiatry, 46*(9), 776–782.

Kovacs, M., Goldston, D., & Gatsonis, C. (1993). Suicidal behaviors and childhood-onset depressive disorders: A longitudinal investigation. *Journal of the American Academy of Child and Adolescent Psychiatry, 32*, 8–20.

Kraemer, H. C. (2014). The reliability of clinical diagnoses: State of the art. *Annual Review of Clinical Psychology, 10*, 111–130. https://doi.org/10.1146/annurev-clinpsy-032813–153739

Kraepelin, E. (1898). *The diagnosis and prognosis of dementia praecox*. Paper presented at the 29th Congress of Southwestern German Psychiatry, Heidelberg.

Kraepelin, E. (1899). *Kompendium der Psychiatrie* (6th ed.). Leipzig: Abel.

Kraepelin, E. (1913). *Psychiatry: A textbook*. Leipzig: Barth.

Krambeer, L. L., von McKnelly, W., Jr., Gabrielli, W. F., Jr., & Penick, E. C. (2001). Methadone therapy for opioid dependence. *American Family Physician, 15*, 2404–2410.

Krank, M., Stewart, S. H., O'Connor, R., Woicik, P. B., Wall, A.-M., & Conrod, P. J. (2011). Structural, concurrent and predictive validity of the Substance Use Risk Profile Scale in early adolescence. *Addictive Behaviors, 36*, 37–46.

Krank, M., & Wall, A. M. (2006). Context and retrieval effects on implicit cognition for substance use. In R. W. Wiers & A. W. Stacy (Eds.), *Handbook on implicit cognition and addiction* (pp. 281–292). Thousand Oaks, CA: Sage Publications.

Krank, M., Wall, A. M., Stewart, S. H., Wiers, R., & Goldman, M. S. (2005). Context effects on alcohol cognitions. *Alcoholism: Clinical and Experimental Research, 29*, 196–206.

Krantz, D. S., & Deckel, A. W. (1983). Coping with coronary heart disease and stroke. In T. G. Burish & L. A. Bradley (Eds.), *Coping with chronic disease: Research and applications*. New York, NY: Academic Press.

Kranzler, H. R. (2000). Medications for alcohol dependence: New vistas. *JAMA, 284*(8), 1016–1017.

Krasnianski, A., Juan, P. S., Ponto, C., Bartl, M., Heinemann, U., Varges, D., ... Zerr, I. (2014). A proposal of new diagnostic pathway for fatal familial insomnia. *Journal of Neurology, Neurosurgery & Psychiatry, 85*(6), 654–659.

Krenek, M., & Maisto, S. A. (2013). Life events and treatment outcomes among individuals with substance use disorders: A narrative review. *Clinical Psychology Review, 33*(3), 470–483. https://doi.org/10.1016/j

Kreutzmann, J., Havekes, R., Abel, T., & Meerlo, P. (2015). Sleep deprivation and hippocampal vulnerability: Changes in neuronal plasticity, neurogenesis and cognitive function. *Neuroscience, 19*(309), 173–190.

Kring, A. M., & Sloan, D. M. (2010). *Emotion regulation and psychopathology: A transdiagnostic approach to etiology and treatment*. New York, NY: Guilford Press.

Kristiansen, C. M., Gareau, C., Mittlehold, J., DeCourville, N. H., & Hovdestad, W. E. (1999). The sociopolitical context of the delayed memory debate. In L. M. Williams & V. L. Banyard (Eds.), *Trauma and recovery* (pp. 331–347). Thousand Oaks, CA: Sage Publications.

Kroenke, K. (2007). Efficacy of treatment for somatoform disorders: A review of randomized controlled trials. *Psychosomatic Medicine, 69*(9), 881–888.

Kroll, R., & Beitchman, J. H. (2005). Stuttering. In V. A. S. B. J. Sadock (Ed.), *Kaplan & Sadock's comprehensive textbook of psychiatry* (pp. 3154–3159). Philadelphia, PA: Lippincott, Williams & Wilkins.

Krueger, D. D., & Bear, M. F. (2011). Toward fulfilling the promise of molecular medicine in fragile X syndrome. *Annual Review of Medicine, 62*, 411.

Krueger, R. B. (2010a). The DSM diagnostic criteria for sexual sadism. *Archives of Sexual Behavior, 39*, 325–345.

Krueger, R. B. (2010b). The DSM diagnostic criteria for sexual sadism (part 2). *Archives of Sexual Behavior, 39*, 346–356.

Krueger, R. F., Caspi, A., Moffitt, T. E., Silva, P. A., & McGee, R. (1996). Personality traits are differentially linked to mental disorders: A multitrait-multidiagnosis study of an adolescent birth cohort. *Journal of Abnormal Psychology, 105*, 299–312.

Krueger, R. F., Hopwood, C. J., Wright, A. G., & Markon, K. E. (2014). DSM-5 and the path toward empirically based and clinically useful conceptualization of personality and psychopathology. *Clinical Psychology: Science and Practice, 21*(3), 245–261.

Krueger, R. F., & Markon, K. E. (2014). The role of the DSM-5 personality trait model in moving toward a quantitative and empirically based approach to classifying personality and psychopathology. *Annual Review of Clinical Psychology, 10*, 477–501.

Krueger, R. F., Markon, K. E., Patrick, C. J., & Iacono, W. G. (2005). Externalizing psychopathology in adulthood: A dimensional-spectrum conceptualization and its implications for DSM-V. *Journal of Abnormal Psychology, 114*(4), 537–550.

Krueger, R. F., Watson, D., & Barlow, D. H. (2005). Introduction to the special section: Toward a dimensionally based taxonomy of psychopathology [Special issue]. *Journal of Abnormal Psychology, 114*, 491–493.

Krug, E. G., Kresnow, M. J., Peddicord, J. P., Dahlberg, L. L., Powell, K. E., Crosby, A. E., & Annest, J. L. (1998). Suicide after natural disasters. *New England Journal of Medicine, 338*(6), 373–378.

Kruger, S., & Kennedy, S. H. (2000). Psychopharmacotherapy of anorexia nervosa, bulimia nervosa and binge-eating disorder. *Journal of Psychiatry and Neuroscience, 25*, 497–508.

Kryger, M. H. (2000). Management of obstructive sleep apnea–hypoapnea syndrome: Overview. In M. H. Kryger, T. Roth, & W. C. Dement (Eds.), *Principles and practice of sleep medicine* (3rd ed., pp. 940–954). Philadelphia, PA: W. B. Saunders.

Kumpulainen, K. (2002). Phenomenology and treatment of selective mutism. *CNS Drugs, 16*(3), 175–180.

Kuo, J. R., Khoury, J. E., Metcalfe, R., Fitzpatrick, S., & Goodwill, A. (2015). An examination of the relationship between childhood emotional abuse and borderline personality disorder features: The role of difficulties with emotion regulation. *Child Abuse & Neglect, 39*, 147–155.

Kuo, M., Adlaf, E. M., Lee, H., Gliksman, L., Demers, A., & Wechsler, H. (2003). More Canadian students drink but American students drink more: Comparing college alcohol use in two countries: Corrigendum. *Addiction, 98*, 373.

Kuo, M., Adlaf, E. M., Lee, H., Gliksman, L., Demers, A., & Wechsler, H. (2002). More Canadian students drink but American students drink more: Comparing college alcohol use in two countries. *Addiction, 97*, 1583–1592.

Kuo, W. H., Gallo, J. J., & Tien, A. Y. (2001). Incidence of suicide ideation and attempts in adults: The 13-year follow-up of a community sample in Baltimore, Maryland. *Psychological Medicine, 31*, 1181–1191.

Kupfer, D. J. (1995). Sleep research in depressive illness: Clinical implications—A tasting menu. *Biological Psychiatry, 38*, 391–403.

Kupfer, D. J., First, M. B., & Regier, D. A. (Eds.). (2002). *A research agenda for DSM-V*. Washington, DC: American Psychiatric Association.

Kupfer, D. J., Frank, E., & Ritchey, F. C. (2015). Staging bipolar disorder: What data and what models are needed? *Lancet Psychiatry, 6*, 564–570.

Kupka, R., Luckenbaugh, D., Post, R., Suppes, T., Altshuler, L., Keck, P., & Nolen, W. A. (2005). Comparison of rapid-cycling and non-rapid-cycling bipolar disorder based on prospective mood ratings in 539 outpatients. *American Journal of Psychiatry, 162*, 1273–1280.

Kurihara, T., Kato, M., Reverger, R., & Gusti Rai Tirta, I. (2006). Beliefs about causes of schizophrenia among family members: A community-based survey in Bali. *Psychiatric Services, 57*, 1795–1799.

Kurtz, T. W. (2010). Genome-wide association studies will unlock the genetic basis of hypertension: Con side of the argument. *Hypertension, 56*(6), 1021–1025.

Kushner, M. G., Abrams, K., & Borchardt, C. (2000). The relationship between anxiety disorders and alcohol use disorders: A review of major perspectives and findings. *Clinical Psychology Review, 20*, 149–171.

Kushner, M. G., Sher, K. J., & Beitman, B. D. (1990). The relation between alcohol problems and the anxiety disorders. *American Journal of Psychiatry, 147*, 685–695.

Kuyken, W., Hayes, R., Barrett, B., Byng, R., Dalgleish, T., Kessler, D., … Byford, S. (2015). Effectiveness and cost-effectiveness of mindfulness-based cognitive therapy compared with maintenance antidepressant treatment in the prevention of depressive relapse or recurrence (PREVENT): A randomised controlled trial. *Lancet, 386*, 63–73.

Kwapil, T. R., & Barrantes-Vidal, N. (2012). Schizotypal personality disorder: An integrative review. In T. A. Widiger (Ed.), *The Oxford handbook of personality disorders* (pp. 437–477). New York, NY: Oxford University Press.

Kwok, T., Lee, J., Lam, L., & Woo, J. (2008). Vitamin B12 supplementation did not improve cognition but reduced delirium in demented patients with vitamin B12 deficiency. *Archives of Gerontology and Geriatrics, 46*(3), 273–282.

Kwon, J. S., Shenton, M. E., Hirayasu, Y., Salisbury, D. F., Fischer, I. A., Dickey, C. C., … McCarley, R. W. (1998). MRI study of cavum septi pellucidi in schizophrenia, affective disorder, and schizotypal personality disorder. *American Journal of Psychiatry, 155*(4), 509–515.

La Greca, A. M., Silverman, W. K., Lai, B., & Jaccard, J. (2010). Hurricane-related exposure experiences and stressors, other life events, and social support: Concurrent and prospective impact on children's persistent posttraumatic stress symptoms. *Journal of Consulting and Clinical Psychology, 78*, 794–805.

La Rue, A. (1992). *Aging and neuropsychological assessment*. New York, NY: Plenum Press.

Lacey, J. H. (1992). The treatment demand for bulimia: A catchment area report of referral rates and demography. *Psychiatric Bulletin, 16*, 203–205.

Lack, L. C., Gradisar, M., Van Someren, E. J. W., Wright, H. R., & Lushington, K. (2008). The relationship between insomnia and body temperatures. *Sleep Medicine Reviews, 12*(4), 307–317.

Lacks, P., & Morin, C. M. (1992). Recent advances in the assessment and treatment of insomnia. *Journal of Consulting and Clinical Psychology, 60*, 586–594.

Ladd, C. O., Owens, M. J., & Nemeroff, C. B. (1996). Persistent changes in corticotropin-releasing factor neuronal systems induced by maternal deprivation. *Endocrinology, 137*(4), 1212–1218.

Lader, M. H. (1975). *The psychophysiology of mental illness*. London, UK: Routledge & Kegan Paul.

Lader, M., & Sartorius, N. (1968). Anxiety in patients with hysterical conversion symptoms. *Journal of Neurology, Neurosurgery, and Psychiatry, 31*, 490–495.

Ladouceur, R. (1982). In vivo cognitive desensitization of flight phobia: A case study. *Psychological Reports, 50*, 459–462.

Ladouceur, R., Dugas, M. J., Freeston, M. H., Rheaume, J., Blais, F., Gagnon, F., & Thibodeau, N. (1999). Specificity of generalized anxiety disorder symptoms and processes. *Behavior Therapy, 30*, 191–207.

Ladouceur, R., Gosselin, P., & Dugas, M. J. (2000). Experimental manipulation of intolerance of uncertainty: A study of a theoretical model of worry. *Behaviour Research and Therapy, 38*, 933–941.

Laing, R. D. (1967). *The politics of experience*. New York, NY: Pantheon.

Lakes, K., Vaughan, E., Jones, M., Burke, W., Baker, D., & Swanson, J. (2012). Diverse perceptions of the informed consent process: Implications for the recruitment and participation of diverse communities in the National Children's Study. *American Journal of Community Psychology, 49*(1), 215–232.

Lakin, M. M., Montague, D. K., Vanderbrug Medendorp, S., Tesar, L., & Schover, L. R. (1990). Intracavernous injection therapy: Analysis of results and complications. *Journal of Urology, 143*, 1138–1141.

Lalonde, J. K., Hudson, J. I., Gigante, R. A., & Pope, H. G. (2001). Canadian and American psychiatrists' attitudes toward dissociative disorders diagnoses. *Canadian Journal of Psychiatry, 46*, 407–412.

Lalumière, M. L., & Harris, G. T. (1998). Common questions regarding the use of phallometric testing with sexual offenders. *Sexual Abuse: A Journal of Research and Treatment, 10*, 227–237.

Lalumière, M. L., & Quinsey, V. L. (1998). Pavlovian conditioning of sexual interests in human males. *Archives of Sexual Behavior, 27*, 241–252.

Lalumière, M. L., Sawatsky, M. L., Dawson, S. J., & Suschinsky, K. D. (2019). The empirical status of the preparation hypothesis: Explicating women's genital responses to sexual stimuli in the laboratory. Manuscript submitted for publication.

Lam, D. H., Watkins, E. R., Hayward, P., Bright, J., Wright, K., Kerr, N., … Sham, P. (2003). A randomized controlled study of cognitive therapy for relapse prevention for bipolar affective disorder: Outcome of the first year. *Archives of General Psychiatry, 60*, 145–152.

Lam, R. W., & Lavitan, R. D. (2000). Pathophysiology of seasonal affective disorder: A review. *Journal of Psychiatry and Neuroscience, 25*, 469–480.

Lam, R., Levitt, A., Levitan, R., Enns, M., Morehouse, R., Michalak, E., & Tam, S. E. (2006). The Can-Sad study: A randomized controlled trial of the effectiveness of light therapy and fluoxetine in patients with winter seasonal affective disorder. *American Journal of Psychiatry, 163*, 805–812.

Lambert, M. C., Weisz, J. R., Knight, F., Desrosiers, M., Overly, K., & Thesiger, C. (1992). Jamaican and American adult perspectives on child psychopathology: Further explorations of the threshold model. *Journal of Consulting and Clinical Psychology, 60*, 146–149.

Lamis, D. A., Malone, P. S., Langhinrichsen-Rohling, J., & Ellis, T. E. (2010). Body investment, depression, and alcohol use as risk factors for suicide proneness in college students. *Crisis: Journal of Crisis Intervention and Suicide Prevention, 31*(3), 118–127.

Landis, S. E., Earp, J. L., & Koch, G. G. (1992). Impact of HIV testing and counseling on subsequent sexual behavior. *AIDS Education and Prevention, 4*(1), 61–70.

Landis, S., & Insel, T. R. (2008, November 7). The "neuro" in neurogenetics. *Science, 322*, 821.

Lang, P. J. (1985). The cognitive psychophysiology of emotion: Fear and anxiety. In A. H. Tuma & J. D. Maser (Eds.), *Anxiety and the anxiety disorders*. Hillsdale, NJ: Erlbaum.

Lang, P. J. (1995). The emotion probe: Studies of motivation and attention. *American Psychologist, 50*, 372–385.

Lang, P. J., Bradley, M. M., & Cuthbert, B. N. (1998). Emotion, motivation, and anxiety: Brain mechanisms and psychophysiology. *Biological Psychiatry, 44*, 1248–1263.

Langille, D. (2000). *Adolescent sexual health services and education: Options for Nova Scotia*. [Policy discussion series paper #8]. Halifax, NS: Maritime Centre of Excellence for Women's Health.

Langosch, W., Budde, H. G., & Linden, W. (2007). Psychological interventions for coronary heart disease: Stress management, relaxation, and Ornish groups. In J. Jordan, B. Bardé, & A. M. Andreas (Eds.), *Contributions toward evidence-based psychocardiology: A systematic review of the literature*. American Psychological Association. https://doi.org/10.1037/11531-000

Långström, N., & Seto, M. C. (2006). Exhibitionistic and voyeuristic behavior in a Swedish national population survey. *Archives of Sexual Behavior, 35*, 427–435.

Långström, N., & Zucker, K. (2005). Transvestic fetishism in the general population: Prevalence and correlates. *Journal of Sex & Marital Therapy, 31*, 87–95.

Langton, C. M., Barbaree, H. E., Harkins, L., & Peacock, E. J. (2006). Sex offenders' response to treatment and its association with recidivism as a function of psychopathy. *Sexual Abuse: Journal of Research and Treatment, 18*, 99–120.

Lanius, R. A., Bluhm, R., Lanius, U., & Pain, C. (2006). A review of neuroimaging studies in PTSD: Heterogeneity of response to symptom provocation. *Journal of Psychiatric Research, 40*(8), 709–729.

Lanius, R. A., Brand, B., Vermetten, E., Frewen, P. A., & Spiegel, D. (2012). The dissociative subtype of posttraumatic stress disorder: Rationale, clinical and neurobiological evidence, and implications. *Depression and Anxiety, 29*, 701–708. https://doi.org/10.1002/da.21889

Lapierre, S., Erlangsen, A., Waern, M., De Leo, D., Oyama, H., Scocco, P., & Quinnett, P. (2011). A systematic review of elderly suicide prevention programs. *Crisis: The Journal of Crisis Intervention and Suicide Prevention, 32*(2), 88–98.

LaPierre, Y. D. (1994). Pharmacological therapy of dysthymia. *Acta Psychiatrica Scandinavica Supplemental, 89*(383), 42–48.

LaPorte, L., & Guttman, H. (2001). Abusive relationships in families of women with borderline personality disorder, anorexia nervosa and a control group. *Journal of Nervous and Mental Disease, 189*, 522–531.

Larsson, H., Viding, E., Rijsdijk, F. V., & Plomin, R. (2008). Relationships between parental negativity and childhood antisocial behavior over time: A bidirectional effects model in a longitudinal genetically informative design. *Journal of Abnormal Child Psychology, 36*(5), 633–645.

Lasch, C. (1978). *The culture of narcissism: American life in an age of diminishing expectations*. New York, NY: W. W. Norton.

Latimer, J., & Lawrence, A. (2006). *The Review Board systems in Canada: An overview of results from the Mentally Disordered Accused Data Collection Study* (Report No. rr06-1e). Ottawa, ON: Department of Justice Canada. Retrieved from http://www.justice.gc.ca/eng/rp-pr/csj-sjc/jsp-sjp/rr06_1/rr06_1.pdf

Lau, J. Y. F., & Eley, T. C. (2010). The genetics of mood disorders. *Annual Review of Clinical Psychology, 6*, 313–337.

Lau, M. A., & McMain, S. F. (2005). Integrating mindfulness meditation with cognitive and behavioural therapies: The challenge of combining acceptance- and change-based strategies. *The Canadian Journal of Psychiatry, 50*, 863–869.

Laub, J. H., & Vaillant, G. E. (2000). Delinquency and mortality: A 50-year follow-up study of 1,000 delinquent and nondelinquent boys. *American Journal of Psychiatry, 157*, 96–102.

Laumann, E. O., Paik, A., & Rosen, R. C. (1999). Sexual dysfunction in the United States: Prevalence and predictors. *JAMA, 281*, 537–544.

Laumann, E., Gagnon, J., Michael, R., & Michaels, S. (1994). *The social organization of sexuality: Sexual practices in the United States*. Chicago: University of Chicago Press.

Lavallee, C., Robinson, E., & Laverdure, J. (1991). Description de la clientèle et des services de santé mentale au sein de la Population crie du nord québécois. *Santé Culture Health, 8*(3), 265–284.

Lavoie, K. L., Fleet, R. P., Laurin, C., Arsenault, A., Miller, S. R., & Bacon, S. L. (2004). Heart rate variability in coronary artery disease patients with and without panic disorder. *Psychiatry Research, 128*(3), 289–299.

Lawrence, A. (2005). Sexuality before and after male-to-female sex reassignment surgery. *Archives of Sexual Behavior, 34*, 147–166.

Lawrence, A. A. (2013). Debating the meaning of autogynephilia. In *Men trapped in men's bodies* (pp. 161–178). Springer New York.

Laws, D. R., & O'Donohue, W. (Eds.). (1997). *Sexual deviance: Theory, assessment and treatment*. New York, NY: Guilford Press.

Laws, D. R., & O'Donohue, W. T. (2008). Introduction. In D. R. Laws & W. T. O'Donohue (Eds.), *Sexual deviance: Theory, assessment, and treatment* (2nd ed., pp. 1–20). New York, NY: Guilford Press.

Lawton, K., & Kasari, C. (2012). Teacher-implemented joint attention intervention: Pilot randomized controlled study for preschoolers with autism. *Journal of Consulting and Clinical Psychology, 80*(4), 687.

Laxenaire, M., Ganne-Vevonec, M. O., & Streiff, O. (1982). Les Problèmes d'identité chez les enfants des migrants. *Annales Medico-Psychologiques, 140*, 602–605.

Laxova, R., Ridler, M. A. C., & Bowen-Bravery, M. (1977). An etiological survey of the severely retarded Hertfordshire children who were born between January 1, 1965, and December 31, 1967. *American Journal of Medical Genetics, 1*, 75–86.

Lazarus, R. S. (1968). Emotions and adaptation: Conceptual and empirical relations. In W. J. Arnold (Ed.), *Nebraska Symposium on Motivation* (Vol. 16). Lincoln, NE: University of Nebraska Press.

Lazarus, R. S. (1991). Progress on a cognitive-motivational relational theory of emotion. *American Psychologist, 46*(8), 819–834.

Lazarus, R. S. (1995). Psychological stress in the workplace. In R. Crandall & P. L. Perrewe (Eds.), *Occupational stress: A handbook* (pp. 3–14). Philadelphia, PA: Taylor & Francis.

Lazzeroni, L. C., Lu, Y., Belitskaya-Levy, I. (2014). P-values in genomics: Apparent precision masks high uncertainty. *Molecular Psychiatry, 19*, 1336–1340.

LeFoll, B., Gallo, A., Le Strat, Y., Lu, L., & Gorwood, P. (2009). Genetics of dopamine receptors and drug addiction: A comprehensive review. *Behavioural Pharmacology, 20*(1), 1–17.

Le Grange, D., Crosby, R. D., Rathouz, P. J., & Leventhal, B. L. (2007). A randomized controlled comparison of family-based treatment and supportive psychotherapy for adolescent bulimia nervosa. *Archives of General Psychiatry, 64*(9), 1049–1056.

Le Grange, D., Lock, J., Agras, W. S., Bryson, S. W., & Jo, B. (2015). Randomized clinical trial of family-based treatment and cognitive-behavioral therapy for adolescent bulimia nervosa. *Journal of the American Academy of Child & Adolescent Psychiatry, 54*(11), 886–894.

Leahy, R. L., & McGinn, L. K. (2012). Cognitive therapy for personality disorders. In T. A. Widiger (Ed.), *The Oxford handbook of personality disorders* (pp. 727–750). New York, NY: Oxford University Press.

Leamon, M. H., Wright, T. M., & Myrick, H. (2008). Substance-related disorders. In R. E. Hales, S. C. Yudofsky, & G. O. Gabbard (Eds.), *The American Psychiatric Publishing textbook of psychiatry* (5th ed., pp. 365–406). Arlington, VA: American Psychiatric Publishing.

LeBeau, R., Bogels, S., Moller, E., & Craske, M. (2015). Integrating dimensional assessment and categorical diagnosis in DSM-5: The benefits and challenges of the paradigm shift for the anxiety disorders. *Psychopathology Review, 2*(1), 83–99.

LeBeau, R. T., Glenn, D., Liao, B., Wittchen, H.-U., Beesdo-Baum, K., Ollendick, T., & Craske, M. G. (2010). Specific phobia: A review of DSM-IV specific phobia and preliminary recommendations for DSM-V. *Depression and Anxiety, 27*(2), 148–167.

LeBeau, R., Mischel, E., Resnick, H., Kilpatrick, D., Friedman, M., & Craske, M. (2014). Dimensional assessment of posttraumatic stress disorder in DSM-5. *Psychiatry Research, 218*, 143–147.

Lebedinskaya, K. S., & Nikolskaya, O. S. (1993). Brief report: Analysis of autism and its treatment in modern Russian defectology. *Journal of Autism and Developmental Disorders, 23*, 675–697.

Leccese, A. P. (1991). *Drugs and society: Behavioral medicines and abusable drugs*. Englewood Cliffs, NJ: Prentice-Hall.

Leckman, J. F., Denys, D., Simpson, H. B., Mataix-Cols, D., Hollander, E., Saxena, S., ... Stein, D. J. (2010). Obsessive–compulsive disorder: A review of the diagnostic criteria and possible subtypes and dimensional specifiers for DSM-V. *Depression and Anxiety, 27*(6), 507–527.

Leckman, J. F., Grice, D. E., Boardman, J., Zhang, H., Vitali, A., Bondi, C., ... Pauls, D. L. (1997a). Symptoms of obsessive–compulsive disorder. *American Journal of Psychiatry, 154*, 911–917.

Leckman, J. F., Weissman, M. M., Merikangas, K. R., Pauls, D. L., & Prusoff, B. A. (1983). Panic disorder and major depression. *Archives of General Psychiatry, 40*, 1055–1060.

Leclerc, J., Rahn, M., & Linden, W. (2006). Does personality predict blood pressure over a 10-year period? *Personality and Individual Differences, 40*(6), 1313–1321.

Lecrubier, Y., & Judge, R. (1997). Long term evaluation of paroxetine, clomipramine and placebo in panic disorder. *Acta Psychiatrica Scandinavica, 95*, 153–160.

Lecrubier, Y., Judge, R., & the Collaborative Paroxetine Panic Study Investigators. (1997). Long-term evaluation of paroxetine, clomipramine and placebo in panic disorder. *Acta Psychiatrica Scandinavica, 95*(2), 153–160.

Lecrubier, Y., Bakker, A., Dunbar, G., & Judge, R. (1997). A comparison of paroxetine, clomipramine and placebo in the treatment of panic disorder. *Acta Psychiatrica Scandinavica, 95*, 145–152.

Ledford, H. (2015). First cancer-fighting virus approved. *Nature, 526*, 622–623.

LeDoux, J. (2015). *Anxious: Using the brain to understand and treat fear and anxiety*. New York, NY: Viking.

LeDoux, J. E. (1996). *The emotional brain: The mysterious underpinnings of emotional life*. New York, NY: Simon & Schuster.

LeDoux, J. E. (2002). *Synaptic self: How our brains become who we are*. New York, NY: Penguin Books.

Lee, C. C., Czaja, S. J., & Schulz, R. (2010). The moderating influence of demographic characteristics, social support, and religious coping on the effectiveness of a multicomponent psychosocial caregiver intervention in three racial ethnic groups. *Journals of Gerontology Series B: Psychological Sciences and Social Sciences, 65*B(2), 185–194.

Lee, C. K. (1992). *Alcoholism in Korea*. In J. Helzer & G. Canino (Eds.), *Alcoholism—North America, Europe and Asia: A coordinated analysis of population data from ten regions* (pp. 247–262). London, UK: Oxford University Press.

Lee, K. K. (2000). *Urban poverty in Canada: A statistical profile*. Ottawa, ON: Canadian Council on Social Development.

Lee, S. H., Han, D. H., Oh, S., Lyoo, I. K., Lee, Y. S., Renshaw, P. F., & Lukas, S. (2009). Quantitative electroencephalographic (qEEG) correlates of craving during virtual reality therapy in alcohol-dependent patients. *Pharmacology Biochemistry and Behavior, 91*(3), 393–397.

Lee, S., Hsu, L. K. G., & Wing, Y. K. (1992). Bulimia nervosa in Hong Kong Chinese patients. *British Journal of Psychiatry, 161*, 545–551.

Lee, S., Leung, C. M., Wing, Y. K., Chiu, H. F., & Chen, C. N. (1991). Acne as a risk factor for anorexia nervosa in Chinese. *Australian and New Zealand Journal of Psychiatry, 25*(1), 134–137.

Lee-Baggley, D., DeLongis, A., Voorhoeave, P., & Greenglass, E. (2004). Coping with the threat of severe acute respiratory syndrome: Role of threat appraisals and coping responses in health behaviors. *Asian Journal of Social Psychology, 7*, 9–23.

Leenaars, A. A., & Lester, D. (1996). Gender and the impact of gun control on suicide and homicide. *Archives of Suicide Research, 2*, 223–234.

Leff, J., Sartorius, N., Jablensky, A., Korten, A., & Ernberg, G. (1992). The International Pilot Study of Schizophrenia: Five-year follow-up findings. *Psychological Medicine, 22*, 131–145.

Lefley, H. (2009). *Family psychoeducation in serious mental illness: Models, outcomes, applications*. New York, NY: Oxford University Press.

Lefrancois, G. R. (1990). The lifespan (3rd ed.). Belmont, CA: Wadsworth, Cengage Learning.

Lehman, A. F. (1995). Vocational rehabilitation in schizophrenia. *Schizophrenia Bulletin, 21*, 645–656.

Lehman, B. J., Taylor, S. E., Kiefe, C. I., & Seeman, T. E. (2009). Relationship of early life stress and psychological functioning to blood pressure in the CARDIA study. *Health Psychology, 28*(3), 338–346.

Lehmann, H. E., & Ban, T. A. (1997). The history of the psychopharmacology of schizophrenia. *Canadian Journal of Psychiatry, 42*, 152–162.

Lehmann, H. E., & Hanrahan, G. E. (1954). Chlorpromazine: New inhibiting agent for psychomotor excitement and manic states. *AMA Archives of Neurology and Psychiatry, 71*, 227–237.

Leibbrand, R., Hiller, W., & Fichter, M. M. (2000). Hypochondriasis and somatization: Two distinct aspects of somatoform disorders? *Journal of Clinical Psychology, 56*, 63–72.

Leibenluft, E. (2011). Severe mood dysregulation, irritability, and the diagnostic boundaries of bipolar disorder in youths. *American Journal of Psychiatry, 168*(2), 129–142.

Leibenluft, E., & Rich, B. A. (2008). Pediatric bipolar disorder. *Annual Review of Clinical Psychology, 4*, 163–187.

Leiblum, S. R. (2000). Vaginismus: A most perplexing problem. In S. R. Leiblum & R. C. Rosen (Eds.), *Principles and practice of sex therapy* (3rd ed., pp. 181–202). New York, NY: Guilford Press.

Leiblum, S. R. (2010). *Treating sexual desire disorders: A clinical casebook.* New York, NY: Guilford.

Leiblum, S. R., & Rosen, R. C. (Eds.). (2000). *Principles and practice of sex therapy* (3rd ed.). New York, NY: Guilford Press.

Leichsenring, F., Rabung, S., & Lebing, E. (2004). The efficacy of short-term psychodynamic psychotherapy in specific psychiatric disorders: A meta-analysis. *Archives of General Psychiatry, 61*, 1208–1216.

Lejeune, J., Gauthier, M., & Turpin, R. (1959). Étude des chromosomes somatiques de neuf enfants mongoliens. *Comptes Rendus Hebdomadaires des Séances de l'Académie des Sciences. D: Sciences Naturelles (Paris), 248*, 1721–1722.

Lemay, M., & Landreville, P. (2010). Verbal agitation in dementia: The role of discomfort. *American Journal of Alzheimer's Disease and Other Dementias, 25*(3), 193–201.

Lemoine, P., Harousseau, H., Borteyru, J. P., & Menuet, J. C. (1968). Les enfants de Parents alcooliques: Anomalies observées. À Propos de 127 cas [Children of alcoholic Parents: Anomalies observed in 127 cases]. *Quest Medicine, 21*, 476–482.

Lener, M. S., Wong, E., Tang, C. Y., Byne, W., Goldstein, K. E., Blair, N. J., ... Hazlett, E. A. (2015). White matter abnormalities in schizophrenia and schizotypal personality disorder. *Schizophrenia Bulletin, 41*(1), 300–310. https://doi.org/10.1093/schbul/sbu093

Lengacher, C., Johnson-Mallard, V., Post-White, J., Moscoso, M., Jacobsen, P., Klein, T., ... Kip, K. E. (2009). Randomized controlled trial of mindfulness-based stress reduction (MBSR) for survivors of breast cancer. *Psycho-Oncology, 18*(12), 1261–1272.

Lenke, R. R., & Levy, H. (1980). Maternal phenylketonuria and hyperphenylalanemia: An international survey of the outcome of untreated and treated pregnancies. *New England Journal of Medicine, 303*, 1202–1208.

Lenze, E. J., Mulsant, B. H., Shear, K. M., Schulberg, H. C., Dew, M. A., Begley, A. E., ... Reynolds, C. F. (2000). Comorbid anxiety disorders in depressed elderly patients. *American Journal of Psychiatry, 157*(5), 722–728.

Lenzenweger, M. F. A., & Dworkin, R. H. (1996). The dimensions of schizophrenia phenomenology. Note

one or two, at least three, perhaps four. *British Journal of Psychiatry, 168*, 432–440.

Lenzenweger, M. F., Lane, M. C., Loranger, A. W., & Kessler, R. (2007). DSM-IV personality disorders in the national comorbidity survey replication. *Biological Psychiatry, 62*, 553–564.

Lerman, C., Caporaso, N. E., Audrain, J., Main, D., Bowman, E. D., Lockshin, B., ... Shields, P. G. (1999). Evidence suggesting the role of specific genetic factors in cigarette smoking. *Health Psychology, 18*(1), 14–20.

Lerner, R., Kibler, J. L., & Zeichner, S. B. (2013). Relationship between mindfulness-based stress reduction and immune function in cancer and HIV/AIDS. *Cancer and Clinical Oncology, 2*(1), 62–72.

Lesage, A. D., Morissette, R., Fortier, L., Rienharz, D., & Contandriopoulos, A. P. (2000). Downsizing psychiatric hospitals: Needs for care and services of current and discharged long-stay inpatients. *Canadian Journal of Psychiatry, 45*, 526–531.

Lesch, K. P., Bengel, D., Heils, A., Sabol, S. Z., Greenberg, B. D., Petri, S., ... Murphy, D. L. (1996, November 29). Association of anxiety-related traits with a polymorphism in the serotonin transporter gene regulatory region. *Science, 274*, 1527–1531.

Lesch, K. P., Selch, S., Renner, T. J., Jacob, C., Nguyen, T. T., Hahn, T., & Dempfle, A. (2010). Genome-wide copy number variation analysis in attention-deficit/hyperactivity disorder: Association with neuropeptide Y gene dosage in an extended pedigree. *Molecular Psychiatry, 16*(5), 491–503.

Leserman, J. (2008). Role of depression, stress, and trauma in HIV disease progression. *Psychosomatic Medicine, 70*, 539–545.

Leserman, J., Petitto, J. M., Golden, R. N., Gaynes, B. N., Gu, H., Perkins, D. O., ... Evans, D. L. (2000). Impact of stressful life events, depression, social support, coping, and cortisol on progression to AIDS. *American Journal of Psychiatry, 157*, 1221–1228.

Lester, D. (1991). Do suicide prevention centres prevent suicide? *Homeostasis in Health and Disease, 33*, 190–194.

Leth-Steensen, C., Elbaz, Z. K., & Douglas, V. I. (2000). Mena response times, variability, and skew in the responding of ADHD children: A response time distributional approach. *Acta Psychologica, 104*, 167–190.

Leuchter, A. F., Cook, I. A., Witte, E. A., Morgan, M., & Abrams, M. (2002). Changes in brain function of depressed subjects during treatment with placebo. *American Journal of Psychiatry, 159*, 122–129.

Leung, F., Lam, S., & Sze, S. (2001). Cultural expectations of thinness in Chinese women. *Journal of Treatment and Prevention, 9*, 339–350.

Leung, F., Schwartzman, A., & Steiger, H. (1996). Testing a dual-process family model in understanding the development of eating pathology: A structural equation modeling analysis. *International Journal of Eating Disorders, 20*, 367–375.

Leung, G. M., Yeung, R. Y., Chi, I., & Chu L. W. (2003). The economics of Alzheimer disease. *Dementia & Geriatric Cognitive Disorders, 15*, 34–43.

Levenston, G. K., Patrick, C. J., Bradley, M. M., & Lang, P. J. (2000). The psychopath as observer: Emotion and attention in picture processing. *Journal of Abnormal Psychology, 109*, 373–385.

Leventhal, A. M., & Zvolensky, M. J. (2015). Anxiety, depression, and cigarette smoking: A transdiagnostic vulnerability framework to understand emotion-smoking comorbidity. *Psychological Bulletin, 141*, 176–212.

Levin, F. R., Evans, S. M., Brooks, D. J., & Garawi, F. (2007). Treatment of cocaine dependent treatment seekers with adult ADHD: Double-blind comparison of methylphenidate and placebo. *Drug and Alcohol Dependence, 87*, 20–29.

Levine, M. P., & Smolak, L. (1996). Media as a context for the development of disordered eating. In L. Smolak, M. P. Levine, & R. Striegel-Moore (Eds.), *The developmental psychopathology of eating disorders: Implications for research, prevention, and treatment* (pp. 235–257). Mahwah, NJ: Erlbaum.

Levinson, D. F. (2009). Genetics of major depression. In I. H. Gotlib & C. L. Hammen (Eds.), *Handbook of depression* (2nd ed., pp. 165–186). New York, NY: Guilford Press.

Levinson, D. F., Mahtami, M. M., Nancarrow, D. J., Brown, D., Kruglyak, L., Kirby, A., ... Mowry, B. J. (1998). Genome scan of schizophrenia. *American Journal of Psychiatry, 155*(6), 741–750.

Levitan, R. D., Parikh, S. V., Lesage, A. D., Hegadoren, K. M., Adams, M., Kennedy, S. H., & Goering, P. N. (1998). Major depression in individuals with a history of childhood physical or sexual abuse: Relationship to neurovegetative features, mania, and gender. *American Journal of Psychiatry, 155*, 1746–1752.

Levitan, R. D., Rector, N. A., Sheldon, T., & Goering, P. (2003). Childhood adversities associated with major depression and/or anxiety disorders in a community sample of Ontario: Issues of comorbidity and specificity. *Depression and Anxiety, 17*, 34–42.

Levitsky, A., & Perls, F. S. (1970). The rules and games of Gestalt therapy. In J. Fagan & I. L. Shepherd (Eds.), *Gestalt therapy now: Theory, techniques, applications.* Palo Alto, CA: Science & Behavior Books.

Levitt, A., & Boyle, M. (2002). The impact of latitude on the prevalence of seasonal depression. *Canadian Journal of Psychiatry, 46*, 650–654.

Levitt, J. J., McCarley, R. W., Dickey, C. C., Voglmaier, M. M., Niznikiewicz, M. A., Seidman, L. J., ... Shenton, M. E. (2002). MRI study of caudate nucleus volume and its cognitive correlates in neuroleptic-naive patients with schizotypal personality disorder. *American Journal of Psychiatry, 159*(7), 1190–1197.

Levy, B. R., Slade, M. D., Kunkel, S. R., & Kasl, S. V. (2002). Longevity increased by positive self-perceptions of aging. *Journal of Personality & Social Psychology, 83*, 261–270.

Levy, E., Margolese, H. C., Annable, L., Chouinard, G. (2004). Diabetes, tardive dyskinesia, Parkinsonism, and akathisia in schizophrenia: A retrospective study applying 1998 diabetes health care guidelines to antipsychotic use. *The Canadian Journal of Psychiatry, 49*(6), 398–402.

Lewinsohn, P. M., Allen, N. B., Seeley, J. R., Gotlib, I. H. (1999). First onset versus recurrence of depression: Differential processes of psychosocial risk. *Journal of Abnormal Psychology, 108*(3), 483–489.

Lewinsohn, P. M., Gotlib, I. H., & Seeley, J. R. (1997). Depression-related psychosocial variables: Are they specific to depression in adolescents? *Journal of Abnormal Psychology, 106*(3), 365–375.

Lewinsohn, P. M., Hops, H., Roberts, R. E., Seeley, J. R., & Andrews, J. A. (1993). Adolescent psychopathology: I. Prevalence and incidence of depression and other DSM-III-R disorders in high school students. *Journal of Abnormal Psychology, 102*(1), 133–144.

Lewinsohn, P. M., Rohde, P., & Seeley, J. R. (1993). Psychosocial characteristics of adolescents with a history of suicide attempt. *Journal of the American Academy of Child and Adolescent Psychiatry, 32*(1), 60–68.

Lewinsohn, P. M., Rohde, P., Seeley, J. R., Klein, D. N., & Gotlib, I. H. (2000). Natural course of adolescent major depressive disorder on community sample: Predictors of recurrence in young adults. *American Journal of Psychiatry, 157*(10), 1584–1591.

Lewinsohn, P. M., Rohde, P., Seeley, J. R., Klein, D. N., & Gotlib, I. H. (2003). Psychosocial functioning of young adults who have experienced and recovered from major depressive disorder during adolescence. *Journal of Abnormal Psychology, 112*, 353–363.

Lewinsohn, P. M., Rohde, P., Seeley, J. R., Klein, D. N., & Gotlib, I. H. (2006). The consequences of adolescent major depressive disorder on young adults. In T. E. Joiner, J. S. Brown, & J. Kistner (Eds.), *The interpersonal, cognitive, and social nature of depression* (pp. 43–68). Mahwah, NJ: Lawrence Erlbaum Associates Publishers.

Lewis, D. O., Yeager, C. A., Swica, Y., Pincus, J. H., & Lewis, M. (1997). Objective documentation of child abuse and dissociation in 12 murderers with dissociative identity disorder. *American Journal of Psychiatry, 154*, 1703–1710.

Lewis, G., Croft-Jeffreys, C., & Anthony, D. (1990). Are British psychiatrists racist? *British Journal of Psychiatry, 157*, 410–415.

Lewis, G., David, A., Andreasson, S., & Allsbeck, P. (1992). Schizophrenia and city life. *Lancet, 340*, 137–140.

Lewis, G., Hawton, K., & Jones, P. (1997). Strategies for preventing suicide. *British Journal of Psychiatry, 171*, 351–354.

Lewis, J., & Christopher, J. (1989). Childhood trauma in borderline personality disorder. *American Journal of Psychiatry, 1*, 46.

Lewis, S., Escalona, R., & Keith, S. J. (2009). Phenomenology of schizophrenia. In B. J. Sadock, V. A. Sadock, & P. Ruiz (Eds.), *Kaplan & Sadock's comprehensive textbook of psychiatry* (9th ed., Vol. 1, pp. 1433–1451). Philadelphia, PA: Lippincott Williams & Wilkins.

Lewis-Fernandez, R., Hinton, D. E., Laria, A. J., Patterson, E. H., Hofmann, S. G., Craske, M. G., & Liao, B. (2010). Culture and the anxiety disorders: Recommendations for DSM-V. *Depression and Anxiety, 27*(2), 212–229.

Leyfer, O., & Brown, T. A. (2011). The anxiety-depression spectrum. In D. H. Barlow (Ed.), *Oxford handbook of clinical psychology* (pp. 279–293). New York, NY: Oxford University Press.

Leykin, Y., & DeRubeis, R. J. (2009). Allegiance in psychotherapy outcome research: Separating association from bias. *Clinical Psychology: Science and Practice, 16*(1), 54–65.

Li, H. Z., & Browne, A. J. (2000). Defining mental illness and accessing mental health services: Perspectives of Asian Canadians. *Canadian Journal of Community Mental Health, 19*, 143–159.

Li, X., Zou, H., & Brown, W. T. (2012). Genes associated with autism spectrum disorder. *Brain Research Bulletin, 88*(6), 543–552.

Lidbeck, J. (1997). Group therapy for somatization disorders in general practice: Effectiveness of a short cognitive-behavioral treatment model. *Acta Psychiatrica Scandinavica, 96*, 14–24.

Liddle, P. F. (2000). Schizophrenic syndromes. In M. S. Lidow (Ed.), *Neurotransmitter receptors in actions of antipsychotic medications* (pp. 1–15). Boca Raton, FL: CRC Press.

Liddle, P. F. (2012). Descriptive clinical features of schizophrenia. In M. G. Gelder, N. C. Andreasen, J. J. Lopez-Ibor, & J. R. Geddes (Eds.), *New Oxford textbook of psychiatry* (2nd ed., Vol. 1, pp. 526–531). New York, NY: Oxford University Press.

Lieb, R., Zimmermann, P., Friis, R. H., Hofler, M., Tholen, S., & Wittchen, H. U. (2002). The natural course of DSM-IV somatoform disorders and syndromes among adolescents and young adults: A prospective-longitudinal community study. *European Psychiatry, 17*, 321–331.

Lieberman, J. A., Jody, D., Alvir, J. M. J., Ashtari, M., Levy, D. L., Bogerts, B., ... Cooper, T. (1993). Brain morphology, dopamine, and eye-tracking abnormalities in first-episode schizophrenia. *Archives of General Psychiatry, 50*, 357–368.

Liebeskind, J. (1991). Pain can kill. *Pain, 44*, 3–4.

Liebowitz, M. R., Salman, E., Jusino, C. M., Garfinkel, R., Street, L., Cardenas, D. L., ... Davies, S. (1994). Ataque de nervios and panic disorder. *American Journal of Psychiatry, 151*, 871–875.

Liebowitz, M. R., Schneier, F., Campeas, R., Hollander, E., Hatterer, J., Fyer, A., ... Gully, R. (1992). Phenelzine vs. atenolol in social phobia: A placebo controlled comparison. *Archives of General Psychiatry, 49*, 290–300.

Lilienfeld, S. O. (1992). The association between antisocial personality and somatization disorders: A review and integration of theoretical models. *Clinical Psychology Review, 12*, 641–662.

Lilienfeld, S. O., & Hess, T. H. (2001). Psychopathic personality traits and somatization: Sex differences and the mediating role of negative emotionality. *Journal of Psychopathology and Behavioral Assessment, 23*, 11–24.

Lilienfeld, S. O., Kirsch, I., Sarbin, T. R., Lynn, S. J., Chaves, J. F., & Ganaway, G. K. (1999). Dissociative identity disorder and the sociocognitive

model: Recalling the lessons of the past. *Psychological Bulletin, 125*(5), 507–523.

Lilienfeld, S. O., & Lynn, S. J. (2003). Dissociative identity disorder: Multiple personalities, multiple controversies. In S. O. Lilienfeld, S. J. Lynn, & J. M. Lohr (Eds.), *Science and pseudoscience in clinical psychology* (pp. 109–142). New York, NY: Guilford Press.

Lilienfeld, S. O., & Marino, L. (1995). Mental disorder as a Roschian concept: A critique of Wakefield's "harmful dysfunction" analysis. *Journal of Abnormal Psychology, 104*, 411–420.

Lilienfeld, S. O., & Marino, L. (1999). Essentialism revisited: Evolutionary theory and the concept of mental disorder. *Journal of Abnormal Psychology, 108*, 400–411.

Lilienfeld, S. O., VanValkenburg, C., Larntz, K., & Akiskal, H. S. (1986). The relationship of histrionic personality to antisocial personality and somatization disorders. *American Journal of Psychiatry, 143*, 718–722.

Lillienfield, S. O. (2014). DSM-5: Centripetal scientific and centrifugal antiscientific forces. *Clinical Psychology: Science and Practice, 21*(3), 269–279.

Lima, E. N., Stanley, S., Kaboski, B., Reitzel, L. R., Richey, A., Castro, Y., & Jakobsons, L. J. (2005). The incremental validity of the MMPI-2: When does therapist access not enhance treatment outcome? *Psychological Assessment, 17*(4), 462–468.

Lin, K. M., Hwu, H. G., & Tsuang, M. T. (2012). Schizophrenia and other psychosis in Asians and Asian Americans. In E. C. Chang (Ed.), *Handbook of adult psychopathology in Asians: Theory, diagnosis, and treatment* (p. 83). New York, NY: Oxford University Press.

Lind, M. J., Aggen, S. H., Kirkpatrick, R. M., Kendler, K. S., & Amstadter, A. B. (2015). A longitudinal twin study of insomnia symptoms in adults. *Sleep, 38*(9), 1423–1430.

Lindberg, N., Holi, M. M., Tani, P., & Virkkunen, M. (2005). Looking for pyromania: Characteristics of a consecutive sample of Finnish male criminals with histories of recidivist fire-setting between 1973 and 1993. *BMC Psychiatry, 5*(1), 47–52.

Lindblad, F., & Hjern, A. (2010). ADHD after fetal exposure to maternal smoking. *Nicotine & Tobacco Research, 12*(4), 408–415.

Linden, W., & Moseley, J. V. (2006). The efficacy of behavioral treatments for hypertension. *Applied Psychophysiology and Biofeedback, 31*(1), 51–63.

Linden, W., Gerin, W., & Davidson, K. (2003). Cardiovascular reactivity: Status quo and a research agenda for the new millennium. *Psychosomatic Medicine, 65*, 5–8.

Lindenmayer, J. P., & Khan, A. (2006). Psychopathology. In J. A. Lieberman, T. S. Stroup, & D. O. Perkins (Eds.), *The American Psychiatric Publishing textbook of schizophrenia* (pp. 187–221). Washington, DC: American Psychiatric Publishing.

Lindsay, J., Sykes, E., McDowell, I., Verreault, R., & Laurin, D. (2004). More than the epidemiology of Alzheimer's disease: Contributions of

the Canadian study of health and aging. *Canadian Journal of Psychiatry, 49*, 83–91.

Lindsay, P. S. (1977). Fitness to stand trial in Canada: An overview in light of the recommendations of the law reform commission of Canada. *Criminal Law Quarterly, 19*, 303–348.

Lindsey, S. (2007, July 20). Oxycontin maker and executives fined $634.5M for misleading public. *The Cape Breton Post.* Retrieved December 1, 2007, from http://www.capebretonpost.com/index.cfm?pid1875&cpcatbusiness&stry31849023

Linehan, M. M. (1987). Dialectical behavior therapy for borderline personality disorder: Theory and method. *Bulletin of the Menninger Clinic, 51*, 261–276.

Linehan, M. M. (1993). *Cognitive behavioral treatment of borderline personality disorder.* New York, NY: Guilford Press.

Linehan, M. M. (2015). *DBT skills training manual.* New York, NY: Guilford Press.

Linehan, M. M., & Dexter-Mazza, E. T. (2008). Dialectical behavior therapy for borderline personality disorder. In D. H. Barlow (Ed.), *Clinical handbook of psychological disorders* (4th ed., pp. 365–420). New York, NY: Guilford Press.

Linehan, M. M., & Kehrer, C. A. (1993). Borderline personality disorder. In D. H. Barlow (Ed.), *Clinical handbook of psychological disorders: A step by step treatment manual.* New York, NY: Guilford Press.

Linehan, M. M., Armstrong, H. E., Suarez, A., Allmon, D., & Heard, H. L. (1991). Cognitive-behavioral treatment of chronically parasuicidal borderline patients. *Archives of General Psychiatry, 48*, 1060–1064.

Linehan, M. M., Heard, H. L., & Armstrong, H. E. (1992). *Naturalistic follow-up of a behavioral treatment for chronically parasuicidal borderline patients.* Unpublished manuscript, University of Washington, Seattle.

Lines, E. (2001). *Early psychosis intervention.* Retrieved January 7, 2008, from http://www.cmha.ca/english/intrvenLinks

Links, P. S., & Stockwell, M. (2001). Is couple therapy indicated for borderline personality disorder? *American Journal of Psychotherapy, 55*, 491–506.

Links, P. S., & van Reekum, R. (1993). Childhood sexual abuse, parental impairment and the development of borderline personality disorder. *Canadian Journal of Psychiatry, 38*, 472–474.

Links, P. S., Heslegrave, R., & van Reekum, R. (1999). Impulsivity: Core aspect of borderline personality disorder. *Journal of Personality Disorders, 13*, 1–9.

Links, P. S., Steiner, M., Boiago, I., & Irwin, D. (1990). Lithium therapy for borderline patients: Preliminary findings. *Journal of Personality Disorders, 4*, 173–181.

Links, P., Steiner, M., & Huxley, G. (1988). The occurrence of borderline personality disorder in families of borderline patients. *Journal of Personality Disorders, 2*, 14–20.

Linton, S. J., Kecklund, G., Franklin, K. A., Leissner, L. C., Sivertsen, B., Lindberg, E., ... Björkelund, C. (2015). The effect of the work environment on future sleep disturbances: A systematic review. *Sleep Medicine Reviews, 23*, 10–19.

Lipchik, G. L., Holroyd, K. A., & Nash, J. M. (2002). Cognitive-behavioral management of recurrent headache disorders: A minimal-therapist-contact approach. In D. C. Turk & R. J. Gatchel (Eds.), *Psychological approaches to pain management: A practitioner's handbook* (2nd ed., pp. 365–389). New York, NY: Guilford Press.

Lipowski, Z. J. (1990). *Delirium: Acute confusional states.* New York, NY: Oxford University Press.

Lipton, A. M., & Weiner, M. F. (2003). Differential diagnosis. In M. F. Weiner & A. M. Lipton (Eds.), *The dementias: Diagnosis, treatment and research* (3rd ed., pp. 137–180). Washington, DC: American Psychiatric Press.

Lissek, S., & Grillon, C. (2012). Learning models of PTSD. In J. G. Beck & D. M. Sloan (Eds.), *The Oxford handbook of traumatic stress disorders* (pp. 175–190). New York, NY: Oxford University Press.

Lissek, S., Kaczkurkin, A. N., Rabin, S., Geraci, M., Pine, D. S., & Grillon, C. (2014). Generalized anxiety disorder is associated with overgeneralization of classically conditioned fear. *Biological psychiatry, 75*(11), 909–915.

Lisspers, J., & Öst, L. (1990). Long-term followup of migraine treatment: Do the effects remain up to six years? *Behaviour Research and Therapy, 28*, 313–322.

Litvin, E. B., Ditre, J. W., Heckman, B. W., & Brandon, T. H. (2012). Nicotine. In J. C. Verster, K. Brady, M. Galanter, & P. Conrod (Eds.), *Drug abuse and addiction in medical illness* (pp. 137–150). New York, NY: Springer.

Liu, K., & Bearman, P. S. (2012). Focal points, endogenous processes, and exogenous shocks in the autism epidemic. *Sociological Methods & Research.* Advance online publication. https://doi.org/10.1177/0049124112460369

Livesley, W. J. (2006). The dimensional assessment of personality pathology (DAPP) approach to personality disorder. In Strack, S. (Ed.), *Differentiating normal and abnormal personality* (2nd ed., pp. 401–429). New York, NY: Springer Publishing Co.

Livesley, W. J. (2007). A framework for integrating dimensional and categorical classifications of personality disorder. *Journal of Personality Disorders, 21*, 199–224.

Livesley, W. J., & Jang, K. L. (2000). Toward an empirically based classification of personality disorder. *Journal of Personality Disorders, 14*, 137–151.

Livesley, W. J., & Jang, K. L. (2008). The behavioral genetics of personality disorder. *Annual Review of Clinical Psychology, 4*, 247–274.

Livesley, W. J., Jang, K. L., & Thordarson, D. S. (2005). Etiological relationships between eating disorder symptoms and dimensions of personality disorder [Special issue: Personality Disorders & Eating Disorders]. *Eating Disorders: Journal of Treatment & Prevention, 13*(1), 23–35.

Livesley, W. J., Jang, K. L., & Vernon, P. A. (1998). Phenotypic and genotypic structure of traits delineating personality disorder. *Archives of General Psychiatry, 55*, 941–948.

Livesley, W. J., Schroeder, M. L., Jackson, D. N., & Jang, K. L. (1994).

Categorical distinctions in the study of personality disorder: Implications for classification. *Journal of Abnormal Psychology, 103,* 6–17.

Livingston, G., Kelly, L., Lewis-Holmes, E., Baio, G., Morris, S., Patel, N., ... Cooper, C. (2014). Non-pharmacological interventions for agitation in dementia: Systematic review of randomised controlled trials. *British Journal of Psychiatry, 205*(6), 436–442.

Livingston, J. D., Wilson, D., Tien, G., & Bond, L. (2003). A follow-up study of persons found not criminally responsible on account of mental disorder in British Columbia. *Canadian Journal of Psychiatry, 48,* 408–415.

Lloyd, C. D., Clark, H. J., & Forth, A. E. (2010). Psychopathy, expert testimony, and indeterminate sentences: Exploring the relationship between psychopathy checklist-revised testimony and trial outcome in Canada. *Legal and Criminological Psychology, 15,* 323–339. https://doi.org/10.1348/13553 2509X468432

Lo, S. C., Pripuzova, N., Li, B., Komaroff, A. L., Hung, G. C., Wang, R., & Alter, H. J. (2010). Detection of MLV-related virus gene sequences in blood of patients with chronic fatigue syndrome and healthy blood donors. *Proceedings of the National Academy of Sciences, 107*(36), 15874–15879.

Lobbestael, J., & Arntz, A. (2012). Cognitive contributions to personality disorders. In T. A. Widiger (Ed.), *The Oxford handbook of personality disorders* (pp. 325–344). New York, NY: Oxford University Press.

Lobbestael, J., Arntz, A., & Bernstein, D. P. (2010). Disentangling the relationship between different types of childhood maltreatment and personality disorders. *Journal of Personality Disorders, 24,* 285–295.

Lobo, R. A. (2013). Where are we 10 years after the Women's Health Initiative? *Journal of Clinical Endocrinology & Metabolism, 98*(5), 1771–1780.

Lochner, C., Grant, J. E., Odlaug, B. L., Woods, D. W., Keuthen, N. J., & Stein, D. J. (2012). DSM-5 field survey: Hair-pulling disorder (trichotillomania). *Depression and Anxiety, 29,* 1025–1031.

Lock, J., Le Grange, D., Agras, S., Moye, A., Byrson, S. W., & Jo, B. (2010). Randomized clinical trial comparing family-based treatment with adolescent-focused individual therapy for adolescents with anorexia nervosa. *Archives of General Psychiatry, 67*(10), 1025–1032.

Lock, J., Le Grange, D., Agras, W. S., Fitzpatrick, K. K., Jo, B., Accurso, E., ... Stainer, M. (2015). Can adaptive treatment improve outcomes in family-based therapy for adolescents with anorexia nervosa? Feasibility and treatment effects of a multi-site treatment study. *Behaviour Research and Therapy, 73,* 90–95.

Loeb, K. L., Wilson, G. T., Gilbert, J. S., & Labouvie, E. (2000). Guided and unguided self-help for binge eating. *Behaviour Research and Therapy, 38*(3), 259–272.

Loehlin, J. C. (1992). *Genes and environment in personality development.* Newbury Park, CA: Sage Publications.

Loftus, E., & Davis, D. (2006). Recovered memories. *Annual Review of Clinical Psychology, 2,* 469–498.

Loftus, E. F., Coan, J. A., & Pickrell, J. E. (1996). Manufacturing false memories using bits of reality. In L. Reder (Ed.), *Implicit memory and metacognition* (pp. 195–220). Mahwah, NJ: Erlbaum.

Logan, C. (2009). Sexual deviance in females: Psychopathology and theory. In D. R. Laws & W. T. O'Donohue (Eds.), *Sexual deviance: Theory, assessment, and treatment* (2nd ed., pp. 486–507). New York, NY: Guilford Press.

Logsdon, R., McCurry, S., Pike, K., & Teri, L. (2009). Making physical activity accessible to older adults with memory loss: A feasibility study. *The Gerontologist, 49*(S1), S94.

Lombardi, V. C., Ruscetti, F. W., Gupta, J. D., Pfost, M. A., Hagen, K. S., Peterson, D. L., Ruscetti, S. K., Bagni, R. K., Petrow-Sadowski, C., Gold, B., Dean, M. Silverman, R. H., & Mikovits, J. A. (2009). Detection of an infectious retrovirus, XMRV, in blood cells of patients with chronic fatigue syndrome. *Science, 326*(5952), 585–589.

Lombardo, M. V., Chakrabarti, B., & Baron-Cohen, S. (2009). The amygdala in autism: Not adapting to faces? *American Journal of Psychiatry, 166*(4), 395–397.

Lonczak, H. S. P., Abbott, R. D. P., Hawkins, J. D. P., Kosterman, R. P., & Catalano, R. F. P. (2002). Effects of the Seattle Social Development Project on sexual behavior, pregnancy, birth, and sexually transmitted disease outcomes by age 21 years. *Archives of Pediatrics & Adolescent Medicine, 156*(5), 438–447.

Long, J. C., Knowler, W. C., Hanson, R. L., Robin, R. W., Urbanek, M., Moore, E., ... Goldman, D. (1998). Evidence for genetic linkage to alcohol dependence on chromosomes 4 and 11 from an autosome-wide scan in an American Indian population. *American Journal of Medicine and Genetics, 81,* 216–221.

Loomans, E. M., Hofland, L., van der Stelt, O., van der Wal, M. F., Koot, H. M., Van den Bergh, B. R. H., & Vrijkotte, T. G. M. (2012). Caffeine intake during pregnancy and risk of problem behavior in 5- to 6-year-old children. *Pediatrics, 130*(2), e305–e313.

Looper, K. J., & Kirmayer L. J. (2002). Behavioral medicine approaches to somatoform disorders. *Journal of Consulting and Clinical Psychology, 70,* 810–827.

Looper, K. J., & Paris, J. (2000). What dimensions underlie Cluster B personality disorders? *Comprehensive Psychiatry, 41,* 432–437.

López, S. R., & Guarnaccia, P. J. (2012). Cultural dimensions of psychopathology: The social world's impact on mental disorders. In J. E. Maddux & B. A. Winstead (Eds.), *Psychopathology: Foundations for a contemporary understanding* (pp. 45–68). New York, NY: Routledge.

LoPiccolo, J., & Stock, W. E. (1987). Sexual function, dysfunction and counseling in gynecological practice. In Z. Rosenwaks, F. Benjamin, & M. L. Stone (Eds.), *Gynecology.* New York, NY: Macmillan.

LoPiccolo, J., Heiman, J. R., Hogan, D. R., & Roberts, C. W. (1985). Effectiveness of single therapists versus cotherapy teams in sex therapy. *Journal of Consulting and Clinical Psychology, 53*(3), 287–294.

Lord, C., & Bishop, S. L. (2010). Autism spectrum disorders. *Social Policy Report, 24*(2), 3–21.

losses: Evidence from the national comorbidity survey. *Archives of General Psychiatry, 64,* 433–440.

Loukine, L., O'Donnell, S., Goldner, E. M., McRae, L., & Allen, H. (2016). Health status, activity limitations, work-related restrictions and level of disability among Canadians with mood and/or anxiety disorders. *Health Promotion and Chronic Disease Prevention in Canada, 36*(12), 289–301.

Lovaas, O. I. (1977). *The autistic child: Language development through behavior modification.* New York, NY: Irvington.

Lovaas, O. I. (1987). Behavioral treatment and normal educational and intellectual functioning in young autistic children. *Journal of Consulting and Clinical Psychology, 55,* 3–9.

Lovaas, O. I., Berberich, J. P., Perloff, B. F., & Schaeffer, B. (1966). Acquisition of imitative speech by schizophrenic children. *Science, 151,* 705–707.

Lovallo, W. R. (2010). Cardiovascular responses to stress and disease outcomes: A test of the reactivity hypothesis. *Hypertension, 55*(4), 842–843.

Lovestone, S. (2012). Dementia: Alzheimer's disease. In M. G. Gelder, N. C. Andreasen, J. J. Lopez-Ibor, & J. R. Geddes (Eds.), *New Oxford textbook of psychiatry* (2nd ed., Vol. 1, pp. 333–343). New York, NY: Oxford University Press.

Lovett, M. W., Lacerenza, L., Borden, S. L., Frijters, J. C., Steinbach, K. A., & De Palma, M. (2000). Components of effective remediation for developmental reading disabilities: Combining phonological and strategy-based instruction to improve outcomes. *Journal of Educational Psychology, 92,* 263–283.

Lovibond, P. (2006). Fear and avoidance: An integrated expectancy model. In M. G. Craske, D. Hermans, & D. Vansteenwegen (Eds.), *Fear and learning: From basic processes to clinical implications* (pp. 117–132). Washington, DC: American Psychological Association.

Loza, W., & Hanna, S. (2006). Is schizoid personality a forerunner of homicidal or suicidal behavior? A case study. *International Journal of Offender Therapy and Comparative Criminology, 50,* 338–343.

Lozano, A. M., Giacobbe, P., Hamani, C., Rizvi, S. J., Kennedy, S. H., Kolivakis, T. T., ... Mayberg, H. S. (2012). A multicenter pilot study of subcallosal cingulate area deep brain stimulation for treatment-resistant depression. *Journal of Neurosurgery, 116,* 15–22.

Lu, B., Nagappan, G., Guan, X., Nathan, P. J., & Wren, D. (2013). BDNF-based synaptic repair as a disease-modifying strategy for neurodegenerative diseases. *Nature Reviews Neuroscience, 14*(6), 401–416.

Lubinski, D. (2004). Introduction to the special section of cognitive abilities: 100 years after Spearman's (1904) "General intelligence." *Journal of Personality and Social Psychology, 86,* 96–111.

Lubit, R. H. (2009). Ethics in psychiatry. In B. J. Sadock, V. A. Sadock, & P. Ruiz (Eds.), *Kaplan & Sadock's comprehensive textbook of psychiatry* (9th ed., Vol. 2, pp. 4439–4448). Philadelphia, PA: Lippincott Williams & Wilkins.

Lubs, H. A., Stevenson, R. E., & Schwartz, C. E. (2012). Fragile X and X-linked intellectual disability: Four decades of discovery. *The American Journal of Human Genetics, 90*(4), 579–590.

Lucas, A. R., Beard, C. M., O'Fallon, W. M., & Kurlan, L. T. (1991). 50-year trends in the incidence of anorexia nervosa in Rochester, Minn.: A population-based study. *American Journal of Psychiatry, 148,* 917–922.

Luckasson, R., Coulter, D. L., Polloway, E. A., Reiss, S., Schalock, R. L., Snell, M. E., ... Stark, J. (1992). *Mental retardation: Definition, classification, and systems of supports* (9th ed.). Washington, DC: American Association on Mental Retardation.

Ludescher, B., Leitlein, G., Schaefer, J. E., Vanhoeffen, S., Baar, S., Machann, J., ... Eschweiler, G. W. (2009). Changes of body composition in bulimia nervosa: Increased visceral fat and adrenal gland size. *Psychosomatic Medicine, 71*(1), 93–97.

Ludwig, A. M. (1985). Cognitive processes associated with "spontaneous" recovery from alcoholism. *Journal of Studies on Alcohol, 46,* 53–58.

Ludwig, A., Brandsma, J., Wilbur, C., Bendfeldt, F., & Jameson, D. (1972). The objective study of a multiple personality. *Archives of General Psychiatry, 26,* 298–310.

Lugnegård, T., Hallerbäck, M. U., & Gillberg, C. (2012). Personality disorders and autism spectrum disorders: What are the connections? *Comprehensive Psychiatry, 53*(4), 333–340.

Lukiw, W. J. (2012). Amyloid beta (Ab) peptide modulators and other current treatment strategies for Alzheimer's disease (AD). *Expert Opinion on Emerging Drugs, 17*(1), 43–60.

Lundh, L. G., & Öst, L. G. (1996). Recognition bias for critical faces in social phobics. *Behaviour Research and Therapy, 34,* 787–794.

Lundstrom, B., Pauly, I., & Walinder, J. (1984). Outcome of sex reassignment surgery. *Acta Psychiatrica Scandinavica, 70,* 289–294.

Lurigio, A., & Harris, A. (2009). Mental illness, violence, and risk assessment: An evidence-based review. *Victims & Offenders, 4*(4), 341–347

Lussier, P., & Piché, L. (2008). Frotteurism: Psychopathology and theory. In D. R. Laws & W. T. O'Donohue (Eds.), *Sexual deviance: Theory, assessment, and treatment* (2nd ed., pp. 131–149). New York, NY: Guilford Press.

Lutgendorf, S. K., Antoni, M. H., Ironson, G., Klimas, N., Kumar, M., Starr, K., ... Schneiderman, N. (1997). Cognitive-behavioral stress management decreases dysphoric mood and herpes simplex virus-type 2 antibody titers in symptomatic HIV-seropositive gay men. *Journal of Consulting and Clinical Psychology, 65,* 31–43.

Luxton, D. D., McCann, R. A., Bush, N. E., Mishkind, M. C., & Reger, G. M. (2011). mHealth for mental health: Integrating smartphone technology in behavioral healthcare. *Professional Psychology: Research and Practice, 42*(6), 505–512.

Lydiard, R. B., Brawman-Mintzer, O., & Ballenger, J. C. (1996). Recent developments in the psychopharmacology of anxiety disorders. *Journal of*

Consulting & Clinical Psychology, 64, 660–668.

Lyketos, C. G. (2009). Dementia and milder cognitive syndromes. In D. G. Blazer & D. C. Steffens (Eds.), *The American Psychiatric Publishing textbook of geriatric psychiatry* (4th ed., pp. 243–260). Arlington, VA: American Psychiatric Publishing.

Lykken, D. T. (1957). A study of anxiety in the sociopathic personality. *Journal of Abnormal and Social Psychology, 55,* 6–10.

Lykken, D. T. (1982). Fearlessness: Its carefree charms and deadly risks. *Psychology Today, 16,* 20–28.

Lynam, D. R. (1996). Early identification of chronic offenders: Who is a fledgling psychopath? *Psychological Bulletin, 120,* 209–234.

Lynam, D. R., & Vachon, D. D. (2012). Antisocial personality disorder in DSM-5: Missteps and missed opportunities. *Personality Disorders: Theory, Research, and Treatment, 3*(4), 483–495.

Lynch, S. K., Turkheimer, E., D'Onofrio, B. M., Mendle, J., Emery, R. E., Slutske, W. S., & Martin, N. G. (2006). A genetically informed study of the association between harsh punishment and offspring behavioral problems. *Journal of Family Psychology, 20,* 190–198.

Lynch, T. R., & Cuper, P. F. (2012). Dialectical personality disorders. In T. A. Widiger (Ed.), *The Oxford handbook of personality disorders* (pp. 785–793). New York, NY: Oxford University Press.

Lynn, D. J., Newton, H. B., & Rae-Grant, A. (Eds.). (2012). *The 5-minute neurology consult* (2nd ed.). Philadelphia, PA: Wolters Kluwer Health/Lippincott Williams & Wilkins.

Lynn, S. J., Lilienfeld, S. O., Merckelbach, H., Giesbach T., McNally, R. J., Loftus, E. F., Bruck, M., Garry, M., & Malaktaris, A. (2014). The trauma model of dissociation: Inconvenient truths and stubborn fictions. Comment on Dahlberg et al. (2012). *Psychological Bulletin, 140,* 896–910.

Lyon, D. R., Hart, S. D., & Webster, C. D. (2001). Violence and risk assessment. In R. A. Schuller & J. R. P. Ogloff (Eds.), *Introduction to psychology and law: Canadian perspectives* (pp. 314–350). Toronto, ON: University of Toronto Press.

Lyons, M. J., Eisen, S. A., Goldberg, J., True, W., Lin, N., Meyer, J. M., . . . Tsuang, M. T. (1998). A registry-based twin study of depression in men. *Archives of General Psychiatry, 55,* 468–472.

Lyons, M. J., York, T. P., Franz, C. E., Grant, M. D., Eaves, L. J., Jacobson, K. C., . . . Kremen, W. S. (2009). Genes determine stability and the environment determines change in cognitive ability during 35 years of adulthood. *Psychological Science, 20*(9), 1146–1152.

Lyubomirsky, S. (2001). Why are some people happier than others? The role of cognitive and motivational processes in well-being. *American Psychologist, 56,* 239–249.

Ma, S., Hoang, M. A., Samet, J. M., Wang, J., Mei, C., Xu., X., & Stillman, F. A. (2008). Myths and attitudes that sustain smoking in China. *Journal of Health Communication, 13,* 654–666.

Maccallum, F., & Bryant, R. A. (2011). Imagining the future in complicated grief. *Depression and Anxiety, 28*(8), 658–665.

MacDonald, A. B., Baker, J. M., Stewart, S. H., & Skinner, M. (2000). Effects of alcohol on the response to hyperventilation of participants high and low in anxiety sensitivity. *Alcoholism: Clinical and Experimental research, 24,* 1656–1665.

MacDonald, N. (2019, August 21). Police were called to investigate disturbing videos of Carson Crimeni two hours before he died. *The Globe and Mail.* https://www.theglobeandmail.com/canada/british-columbia/article-police-were-called-to-investigate-disturbing-videos-of-carson-crimeni

Macdonald, P. T., Waldorf, D., Reinarman, C., & Murphy, S. (1988). Heavy cocaine use and sexual behavior. *Journal of Drug Issues, 18,* 437–455.

MacDonald, T. K., Fong, G. T., Zanna, M. P., & Martineau, A. M. (2000). Alcohol myopia and condom use: Can alcohol intoxication be associated with more prudent behavior? *Journal of Personality & Social Psychology, 78,* 605–619.

MacDonald, T. K., MacDonald, G., Zanna, M. P., & Fong, G. (2000). Alcohol, sexual arousal, and intentions to use condoms in young men: Applying alcohol myopia theory to risky sexual behavior. *Health Psychology, 19,* 290–298.

MacDonald, T. K., Zanna, M. P., & Fong, G. T. (1996). Why common sense goes out the window: Effects of alcohol on intentions to use condoms. *Personality & Social Psychology Bulletin, 22,* 763–775.

MacDonald, T. K., Zanna, M. P., & Fong, G. T. (1998). Alcohol and intentions to engage in risky health-related behaviors: Experimental evidence for a causal relationship. In J. G. Adair & D. Belanger (Eds.), *Advances in psychological science* (Vol. 1, pp. 407–428). Hove, UK: Psychology Press/Erlbaum.

Mace, C. J. (1992). Hysterical conversion II: A critique. *British Journal of Psychiatry, 161,* 378–389.

MacFarlane, B. A. (1997). *People who stalk people.* Retrieved November 5, 2003, from http://canadiancriminallaw.com/PDF/PEOPLE%20WHO%20STALK%20PEOPLE.pdf

MacGregor, M. W., Davidson, K. W., Rowan, P., Barksdale, C., & MacLean, D. (2003). The use of defenses and physician health care costs: Are physician health care costs lower in persons with more adaptive defense profiles? *Psychotherapy & Psychosomatics, 72,* 315–323.

Maciejewski, P., Zhang, B., Block, S., & Prigerson, H. (2007). An empirical examination of the stage theory of grief. *JAMA, 297*(7), 716–723.

Mack, A. H., Franklin, J. E., & Frances, R. J. (2003). Substance use disorders. In R. E. Hales & S. C. Yudofsky (Eds.), *Textbook of clinical psychiatry* (4th ed., pp. 309–377). Washington, DC: American Psychiatric Publishing.

MacKinnon, D. F., Zandi, P. P., Gershon, E. S., Nurnberger, J. I., & DePaulo, J. R. (2003). Association of rapid mood switching with panic disorder and familial panic risk in familial bipolar disorder. *American Journal of Psychiatry, 160,* 1696–1698.

MacLeod, C., & Mathews, A. M. (1991). Cognitive-experimental approaches to the emotional disorders. In P. R. Martin (Ed.), *Handbook of behavior therapy and psychological science: An integrative approach* (pp. 116–150). Elmsford, NY: Pergamon Press.

MacLeod, C., Mathews, A., & Tata, P. (1986). Attentional bias in emotional disorders. *Journal of Abnormal Psychology, 95,* 15–20.

Macleod, J., Oakes, R., Copello, A., Crome, I., Egger, M., & Hickman, M., & Davey Smith, G. (2004). Psychological and social sequelae of cannabis and other illicit drug use by young people: A systematic review of longitudinal, general population studies. *Lancet, 363,* 1579–1588.

MacMartin, C., & Yarmey, A. D. (1999). Rhetoric and the recovered memory debate. *Canadian Psychology, 40,* 343–358.

MacMillan, H. L., Fleming, J. E., Streiner, D. L., Lin, E., Boyle, M. H., Jamieson, E., . . . Beardslee, W. R. (2001). Childhood abuse and lifetime psychopathology in a community sample. *American Journal of Psychiatry, 158,* 1878–1883.

Madsen, K. M., Hviid, A., Vestergaard, M., Schendel, D., Wohlfahrt, J., Thorsen, P., . . . Melbye, M. (2002). A population-based study of measles, mumps, and rubella vaccination and autism. *New England Journal of Medicine, 347,* 1477–1482.

Maeng, L. Y., & Milad, M. R. (2015). Sex differences in anxiety disorders: Interactions between fear, stress, and gonadal hormones. *Hormones and Behavior, 76,* 106–107. https://doi.org/10.1016/j.yhbeh.2015.04.002

Magee, W. J., Eaton, W. W., Wittchen, H. U., McGonagle, K. A., & Kessler, R. C. (1996). Agoraphobia, simple phobia, and social phobia in the National Comorbidity Survey. *Archives of General Psychiatry, 53,* 159–168.

Magne-Ingvar, U., Ojehagen, A., & Traskman-Bendz, L. (1992). The social network of people who attempt suicide. *Acta Psychiatrica Scandinavica, 86,* 153–158.

Maguire, G. A., Yeh, C. Y., & Ito, B. S. (2012). Overview of the diagnosis and treatment of stuttering. *Journal of Experimental & Clinical Medicine, 4*(2), 92–97.

Maher, B. A., & Maher, W. B. (1985a). Psychopathology: I. From ancient times to the eighteenth century. In G. A. Kimble & K. Schlesinger (Eds.), *Topics in the history of psychology* (pp. 251–294). Hillsdale, NJ: Erlbaum.

Maher, B. A., & Maher, W. B. (1985b). Psychopathology: II. From the eighteenth century to modern times. In G. A. Kimble & K. Schlesinger (Eds.), *Topics in the history of psychology* (pp. 295–329). Hillsdale, NJ: Erlbaum.

Maher, J. J. (1997). Exploring alcohol's effects on liver function. *Alcohol Health & Research World, 21,* 5–12.

Mahler, M. S. (1952). On childhood psychosis and schizophrenia: Autistic and symbiotic infantile psychosis. *Psychoanalytic Study of the Child, 7,* 286–305.

Mahoney, D. F., Purtilo, R. B., Webbe, F. M., Alwan, M., Bharucha, A. J., Adlam, T. D., . . . Becker, S. A. (2007). In-home monitoring of persons with dementia: Ethical guidelines for technology research and development. *Alzheimer's & Dementia, 3*(3), 217–226.

Mahr, J. (2003, December 13). *Trouble revisits local psychologist as counselor admits affair; state cities ethics breaches.* Retrieved May 21, 2004, from http://www.talkaboutsupport.com/group/alt.support.eatingdisord/messages/237228.html

Maier, S. F. (1997, September). *Stressor controllability, anxiety, and serotonin. Paper presented at the National Institute of Mental Health Workshop on Cognition and Anxiety,* Rockville, MD.

Mainz, V., Schulte-Rüther, M., Fink, G. R., Herpertz-Dahlmann, B., & Konrad, K. (2012). Structural brain abnormalities in adolescent anorexia nervosa before and after weight recovery and associated hormonal changes. *Psychosomatic Medicine, 74,* 574–582.

Maj, M. (2008). Depression, bereavement and "understandable" intense sadness: Should the DSM-IV approach be revised? *American Journal of Psychiatry, 165*(11), 1373–1375.

Maj, M. (2012). Dementia due to HIV disease. In M. G. Gelder, N. C. Andreasen, J. J. Lopez-Ibor, & J. R. Geddes (Eds.), *New Oxford textbook of psychiatry* (2nd ed., Vol. 1, pp. 384–386). New York, NY: Oxford University Press.

Maj, M., Pirozzi, R., Magliano, L., & Bartoli, L. (2002). The prognostic significance of "switching" in patients with bipolar disorder: A 10-year prospective follow-up study. *American Journal of Psychiatry, 159,* 1711–1717.

Maki, P. M., & Henderson, V. W. (2012). Hormone therapy, dementia, and cognition: The Women's Health Initiative 10 years on. *Climacteric, 15*(3), 256–262.

Malatesta, V. J., & Adams, H. E. (1984). The sexual dysfunctions. In H. E. Adams & P. B. Sutker (Eds.), *Comprehensive handbook of psychopathology* (pp. 725–775). New York, NY: Plenum Press.

Malavige, L. S., & Jayawickrema, S. (2015). Premature ejaculation and its management. *Sri Lanka Journal of Diabetes Endocrinology and Metabolism, 5*(1), 13–19.

Malchy, B., Enns, M. W., Young, T. K., & Cox, B. J. (1997). Suicide among Manitoba's Aboriginal people, 1988 to 1994. *Canadian Medical Association Journal, 156*(8), 1133–1138.

Maldonado, J. R., Butler, L. D., & Spiegel, D. (1998). Treatments for dissociative disorders. In P. E. Nathan & J. M. Gorman (Eds.), *A guide to treatments that work.* New York, NY: Oxford University Press.

Maletzky, B. M. (1998). The paraphilias: Research and treatment. In P. E. Nathan & J. M. Gorman (Eds.), *A guide to treatments that work* (pp. 472–500). New York, NY: Oxford University Press.

Malla, A. K., Norman, R. M. G., Scholten, D. J., Zirul, S., & Kotteda, V. (2001). A comparison of long-term outcome in first-episode schizophrenia following treatment with risperidone or a typical antipsychotic. *Journal of Clinical Psychiatry, 62,* 179–184.

Malla, A. K., Takhar, J. J., Norman, R. M. G., Manchanda, R., Cortese, L., Haricharan, R., . . . Ahmed, R. (2002). Negative symptoms in first episode non-affective psychosis. *Acta Psychiatrica Scandinavica, 105*(6), 431–439.

Mallan, K. M., Lipp, O. V., & Cochrane, B. (2013). Slithering snakes, angry men, and out-group members: What and whom are we evolved to fear. *Cognition and Emotion, 27*, 1168–1180.

Manber, R., Edinger, J. D., Gress, J. L., San Pedro-Salcedo, M. G., Kuo, T. F., & Kalista, T. (2008). Cognitive behavioral therapy for insomnia enhances depression outcome in patients with comorbid major depressive disorder and insomnia. *Sleep, 31*(4), 489–495.

Mancuso, S., Knoesen, N., & Castle, D. J. (2010). Delusional vs. nondelusional body dysmorphic disorder. *Comprehensive Psychiatry, 51*(2), 177–182.

Mandalos, G. E., & Szarek, B. L. (1990). Dose-related paranoid reaction associated with fluoxetine. *Journal of Nervous and Mental Disease, 178*(1), 57–58.

Mandel, M. (2007, October 21). A man who killed his 11-year-old son because of a mental disorder shares his pain—and his insight. *The Toronto Sun.* Retrieved October 22, 2007, from http://www.torontosun.com/News/Columnists/Mandel_Michele/2007/10/21/4593856-sun.php

Mandell, A. J., & Knapp, S. (1979). Asymmetry and mood, emergent properties of seratonin regulation: A proposed mechanism of action of lithium. *Archives of General Psychiatry, 36*(8), 909–916.

Manicavasagar, V., Marnane, C., Pini, S., Abelli, M., Rees, S., Eapen, V., & Silove, D. (2010). Adult separation anxiety disorder: A disorder comes of age. *Current Psychiatry Reports, 12*(4), 290–297.

Mann, J. J., Brent, D. A., & Arango, V. (2001). The neurobiology and genetics of suicide and attempted suicide: A focus on the serotonergic system. *Neuropsychopharmacology, 24*(5), 467–477.

Mann, J. J., Malone, K. M., Diehl, D. J., Perel, J., Cooper, T. B., & Mintun, M. A. (1996). Demonstration in vivo of reduced serotonin responsivity in the brain of untreated depressed patients. *American Journal of Psychiatry, 153*, 174–182.

Mann, J. J., Waternaux, C., Haas, G. L., & Malone, K. M. (1999). Toward a clinical model of suicidal behavior in psychiatric patients. *American Journal of Psychiatry, 156*(2), 181–189.

Mann, J., Apter, A., Bertolote, J., Beautrais, A., Currier, D., Haas, A., ... Hendin, H. (2005). Suicide prevention strategies: A systematic review. *JAMA, 294*, 2064–2074.

Mann, K., Klingler, T., Noe, S., Röschke, J., Müller, S., & Benkert, O. (1996). Effects of yohimbine on sexual experiences and rigidity in erectile dysfunction. *Archives of Sexual Behavior, 25*, 1–16.

Manni, R., Ratti, M. T., & Tartara, A. (1997). Nocturnal eating: Prevalence and features in 120 insomniac referrals. *Sleep, 20*, 734–738.

Mannino, D. M., Klevens, R. M., & Flanders, W. D. (1994). Cigarette smoking: An independent risk factor for impotence? *American Journal of Epidemiology, 140*, 1003–1008.

Manson, S. M., & Good, B. J. (1993, January). Cultural considerations in the diagnosis of DSM-IV mood disorders. *Cultural proposals and supporting papers for DSM-IV.* Submitted to the DSM-IV Task Force by the Steering Committee, NIMH-Sponsored Group on Culture and Diagnosis.

Månsson, K. N. T., Carlbring, P., Frick, A., Engman, J., Olsson, C. J., Bodlund, O., Furmark, T., & Andersson, G. (2013). Altered neural correlates of affective processing after internet-delivered cognitive behavior therapy for social anxiety disorder. *Psychiatry Research, 214*(3), 229–237.

Mantovani, A., Pavlicova, M., Avery, D., Nahas, Z., McDonald, W. M., Wajdik, C. D., & Lisanby, S. H. (2012). Long-term efficacy of transcranial magnetic stimulation (TMS) in treatment-resistant depression. *Depression and Anxiety, 29*(10), 883–890.

Marangell, L., Rush, A., George, M., Sackheim, H., Johnson, C, Husain, M., ... Lisanby, S. H. (2002). Vagus nerve stimulation (VNS) for major depressive episodes: One year outcomes. *Biological Psychiatry, 51*, 280–287.

Marcopulos, B. A., & Graves, R. E. (1990). Antidepressant effect on memory in depressed older persons. *Journal of Clinical and Experimental Neuropsychology, 12*(5), 655–663.

Marcus, M. D., Wing, R. R., Ewing, L., Keern, E., Gooding, W., & McDermott, M. (1990). Psychiatric disorders among obese binge eaters. *International Journal of Eating Disorders, 9*, 69–77.

Margo, A., Hemsley, D. R., & Slade, P. D. (1981). The effects of varying auditory input on schizophrenic hallucinations. *British Journal of Psychiatry, 139*, 122–127.

Margolese, H. C., Chouinard, G., Kolivakis, T. T., Beauclair, L., Miller, R., & Annable, L. (2005). Tardive dyskinesia in the era of typical and atypical antipsychotics. Part 2: Incidence and management strategies in patients with schizophrenia. *The Canadian Journal of Psychiatry/La Revue canadienne de psychiatrie, 50*(11), 703–713.

Mariani, M. A., & Barkley, R. A. (1997). Neuropsychological and academic functioning in preschool boys with attention deficit hyperactivity disorder. *Developmental Neuropsychology, 13*, 111–129.

Marinelli, M., & McCutcheon, J. E. (2014). Heterogeneity of dopamine neuron activity across traits and states. *Neuroscience, 282*, 176–197.

Markon, K. E. (2013). Epistemological pluralism and scientific development: An argument against authoritative nosologies. *Journal of Personality Disorders, 27*(5), 554–579.

Marks, I. M. (1969). *Fears and phobias.* New York, NY: Academic.

Marks, I. M. (1985). Behavioural treatment of social phobia. *Psychopharmacology Bulletin, 21*, 615–618.

Marlatt, G. A. (1985). Relapse prevention: Theoretical rationale and overview of the model. In G. A. Marlatt & J. R. Gordon (Eds.), *Relapse prevention: Maintenance strategies in the treatment of addictive behaviors* (pp. 3–70). New York, NY: Guilford Press.

Marlatt, G. A. (Ed.). (1998). *Harm reduction: Pragmatic strategies for managing high-risk behaviors.* New York, NY: Guilford Press.

Marlatt, G. A., & Donovan, D. M. (2005). *Relapse prevention: Maintenance strategies in the treatment of addictive behaviors.* New York, NY: Guilford, Press.

Marlatt, G. A., & Gordon, J. R. (1985). *Relapse prevention: Maintenance strategies in the treatment of addictive behaviors.* New York, NY: Guilford Press.

Marlatt, G. A., Larimer, M. E., Baer, J. S., & Quigley, L. A. (1993). Harm reduction for alcohol problems: Moving beyond the controlled drinking controversy. *Behavior Therapy, 24*, 461–504.

Marmar, C. R., Schlenger, W., Henn-Haase, C., Qian, M., Purchia, E., Li, M., Corry, N., Williams, C. S., Ho, C. L., Horesh, D., Karstoft, K.-I., Shalev, A., & Kulka, R. A. (2015). Course of posttraumatic stress disorder 40 years after the Vietnam war. Findings from the National Vietnam Veterans Longitudinal Study. *JAMA Psychiatry, 72*, 875–881.

Marmot, M. G., & Syme, S. L. (1976). Acculturation and coronary heart disease in Japanese Americans. *American Journal of Epidemiology, 104*, 225–247.

Marques, L., Alegria, M., Becker, A. E., Chen, C. N., Fang, A., Chosak, A., & Diniz, J. B. (2011). Comparative prevalence, correlates of impairment, and service utilization for eating disorders across US ethnic groups: Implications for reducing ethnic disparities in health care access for eating disorders. *International Journal of Eating Disorders, 44*(5), 412–420.

Marsh, L., & Margolis, R. L. (2009). Neuropsychiatric aspects of movement disorders. In B. J. Sadock, V. A. Sadock, & P. Ruiz (Eds.), *Kaplan & Sadock's comprehensive textbook of psychiatry* (9th ed., Vol. 1, pp. 481–503). Philadelphia, PA: Lippincott Williams & Wilkins.

Marsh, R., Horga, G., Wang, Z., Wang, P., Klahr, K. W., Berner, L. A., & Peterson, B. S. (2011). An fMRI study of self-regulatory control and conflict resolution in adolescents with bulimia nervosa. *American Journal of Psychiatry, 168*, 1210–1220.

Marshall, B. D. L., Milloy, M.-J., Wood, E., Montaner, J. S. G., & Kerr, T. (2011). Reduction in overdose mortality after the opening of North America's first medically supervised safer injecting facility: A retrospective population-based study. *The Lancet.* Advance online publication. https://doi.org/10.1016/S0140-6736(10)62353-7

Marshall, W. L. (1997). *Pedophilia: Psychopathology and theory.* In D. R. Laws & W. O'; Donohue (Eds.), *Sexual deviance: Theory, assessment and treatment* (pp. 152–174). New York, NY: Guilford Press.

Marshall, W. L., & Barbaree, H. E. (1990). An integrated theory of the etiology of sexual offending. In W. L. Marshall, D. R. Laws, & H. E. Barbaree (Eds.), *Handbook of sexual assault: Issues, theories, and treatment of the offender* (pp. 257–725). New York, NY: Plenum Press.

Marten, P. A., Brown, T. A., Barlow, D. H., Borkovec, T. D., Shear, M. K., & Lydiard, M. B. (1993). Evaluation of the ratings comprising the associated symptom criterion of DSM-III-R generalized anxiety disorder. *Journal of Nervous and Mental Disease, 181*, 676–682.

Martin, I. (1983). Human classical conditioning. In A. Gale & J. A. Edward (Eds.), *Physiological correlates of human behavior: Vol. 2. Attention and performance.* London, UK: Academic Press.

Martin, J., O'Donovan, M. C., Thapar, A., Langley, K., & Williams, N. (2015). The relative contribution of common and rare genetic variants to ADHD. *Transl Psychiatry, 5*, e506.

Martin, S. D., Martin, E., Rai, S. S., Richardson, M. A., & Royall, R. (2001). Brain blood flow changes in depressed patients treated with interpersonal psychotherapy or venlafaxine hydrochloride. *Archives of General Psychiatry, 58*, 641–648.

Martin, S. L., Ramey, C. T., & Ramey, S. L. (1990). The prevention of intellectual impairment in children of impoverished families: Findings of a randomized trial of educational daycare. *American Journal of Public Health, 80*, 844–847.

Martinez, M. A., & Craighead, L. W. (2015). Toward person(ality)-centered treatment: How consideration of personality and individual differences in anorexia nervosa may improve treatment outcome. *Clinical Psychology: Science and Practice, 22*(3), 296–314.

Martinez, A. G., Piff, P. K., Mendoza-Denton, R., & Hinshaw, S. P. (2011). The power of a label: Mental illness diagnoses, ascribed humanity, and social rejection. *Journal of Social and Clinical Psychology, 30*(1), 1–23.

Martin-Pichora, A. L., & Antony, M. M. (2011). Successful treatment of olfactory reference syndrome with cognitive behavioral therapy: A case study. *Cognitive and Behavioral Practice, 18*, 545–554.

Marx, J. (1998). New gene tied to common form of Alzheimer's. *Science, 281*, 507–509.

Maser, J. D. (1985). List of phobias. In A. H. Tuma & J. D. Maser (Eds.), *Anxiety and the anxiety disorders.* Hillsdale, NJ: Erlbaum.

Maser, J. D., Kaelber, C., & Weise, R. E. (1991). International use and attitudes toward DSM-III and DSM-III-R: Growing consensus in psychiatric classification. *Journal of Abnormal Psychology, 100*(3), 271–279.

Mash, E. J., & Wolfe, D. A. (2003). Disorders of childhood and adolescence. In G. Stricker & T. A. Widiger (Eds.), *Handbook of psychology: Clinical psychology* (Vol. 8, pp. 27–63). New York, NY: John Wiley & Sons.

Masia-Warner, C., Klein, R. G., Dent, H. C., Fisher, P. H., Alvir, J., Albano, A., & Guardino, M. (2005). School-based intervention for adolescents with social anxiety disorder: Results of a controlled study. *Journal of Abnormal Child Psychology, 33*(6), 707–722.

Mason, F. L. (1997). *Fetishism: Psychopathology and theory.* In D. R. Laws & W. O'; Donohue (Eds.), *Sexual deviance: Theory, assessment and treatment* (pp. 75–91). New York, NY: Guilford Press.

Massie, H. N., Miranda, G., Snowdon, D. A., Greiner, L. H., Wekstein, D. R., Danner, D., ... Mortimer, J. A. (1996). Linguistic ability in early life and Alzheimer disease in late life. *JAMA, 275*, 1879.

Master, S. L., Eisenberger, N. I., Taylor, S. E., Naliboff, B. D., Shirinyan, D., & Lieberman, M. D. (2009). A picture's worth: Partner photographs reduce experimentally induced pain. *Psychological Science, 20*, 1316–1318.

Masters, W. H., & Johnson, V. E. (1966). *Human sexual response.* Boston, MA: Little, Brown.

Masters, W. H., & Johnson, V. E. (1970). *Human sexual inadequacy.* Boston, MA: Little, Brown.

Mataix-Cols, D., Boman, M., Monzani, B., Rück, C., Serlachius, E., Långström, N., & Lichtenstein, P. (2013). Population-based, multigenerational family clustering study of obsessive–compulsive disorder. *JAMA Psychiatry, 70*, 709–717.

Mataix-Cols, D., Frost, R. O., Pertusa, A., Clark, L. A., Saxena, S., Leckman, J. F., & Wilhelm, S. (2010). Hoarding disorder: A new diagnosis for DSM-V? *Depression and Anxiety, 27*(6), 556–572.

Matheson, K., Bombay, A., & Anisman, H. (2018). Culture as an ingredient of personalized medicine. *Journal of Psychiatry and Neuroscience, 43*, 3–6.

Matheson, S. L., Vijayan, H., Dickson, H., Shepherd, A. M., Carr, V. J., & Laurens, K. R. (2013). Systematic meta-analysis of childhood social withdrawal in schizophrenia, and comparison with data from at-risk children aged 9–14 years. *Journal of Psychiatric Research, 47*(8), 1061–1068.

Mathew, K. L., Whitford, H. S., Kenny, M. A., & Denson, L. A. (2010). The long-term effects of mindfulness-based cognitive therapy as a relapse prevention treatment for major depressive disorder. *Behavioral and Cognitive Psychotherapy, 38*(5), 561–576.

Mathew, S. J., & Hoffman, E. J. (2009). Pharmacotherapy for generalized anxiety disorder. In M. M. Antony & M. B. Stein (Eds.), *Oxford handbook of anxiety and related disorders* (pp. 350–363). New York, NY: Oxford University Press.

Mathews, A. (1997). Information processing biases in emotional disorders. In D. M. Clark & C. G. Fairburn (Eds.), *Science and practice of cognitive-behavior therapy* (pp. 47–66). Oxford, UK: Oxford University Press.

Mathews, A., & MacLeod, C. (1994). Cognitive approaches to emotion and emotional disorders. *Annual Review of Psychology, 45*, 25–50.

Mathews, A., Mogg, K., Kentish, J., & Eysenck, M. (1995). Effective psychological treatment on cognitive bias and generalized anxiety disorder. *Behavior Research and Therapy, 33*, 293–303.

Mathews, C. A. (2009). Phenomenology of obsessive–compulsive disorder. In M. M. Antony & M. B. Stein (Eds.), *Oxford handbook of anxiety and related disorders.* Oxford, UK: Oxford University Press.

Mathews, K. A. (1988). Coronary heart disease and Type A behaviors: Update on and alternative to the Booth-Kewley and Friedman (1987) quantitative review. *Psychological Bulletin, 104*(3), 373–380.

Matthews, K. A. (2013). Matters of the heart: Advancing psychological perspectives on cardiovascular diseases. *Perspectives on Psychological Science, 8*, 676–678.

Maticka-Tyndale, E. (2001). Sexual Health and Canadian youth: How do we measure up? *Canadian Journal of Human Sexuality, 10*, 1–17.

Maticka-Tyndale, E., McKay, A., & Barrett, F. M. (2001). *Teenage sexual and reproductive behavior in developed countries: Country report for Canada.* Occasional Report No. 4, November, 2001, Alan Guttmacher Institute, New York, NY, p. 52.

Matsubayashi, T., Sawada, Y., & Ueda, M. (2012). Natural disasters and suicide: Evidence from Japan. *Social Science & Medicine, 82*, 126–133.

Matsumoto, D. (1996). *Culture and psychology.* Pacific Grove, CA: Brooks/Cole.

Matthews, K. A. (2013). Matters of the heart: Advancing psychological perspectives on cardiovascular diseases. *Perspectives on Psychological Science, 8*, 676–678.

Matthews, K. (2005). Psychological perspectives on the development of coronary heart disease. *American Psychologist, 60*, 780–796.

Matthews-Ewald, M. R., Zullig, K. J., & Ward, R. M. (2014). Sexual orientation and disordered eating behaviors among self-identified male and female college students. *Eating Behaviors, 15*(3), 441–444.

Mattis, S. G., & Ollendick, T. H. (2002). Nonclinical panic attacks in late adolescence prevalence and associated psychopathology. *Journal of Anxiety Disorders, 16*, 351–367.

Mauler, B. I., Hamm, A. O., Weike, A. I., & Tuschen-Caffier, B. (2006). Affect regula tion and food intake in bulimia nervosa: Emotional responding to food cues after deprivation and subsequent eating. *Journal of Abnormal Psychology, 115*, 567–579.

Maust, D., Cristancho, M., Gray, L., Rushing, S., Tjoa, C., & Thase, M. E. (2012). Psychiatric rating scales. In T. E. Schlaepfer & C. B. Nemeroff (Eds.). *Handbook of clinical neurology* (pp. 227–237). Amsterdam: Elsevier.

Matza, L. S., Revicki, D. A., Davidson, J. R., & Stewart, J. W. (2003). Depression with atypical features in the National Comorbidity Survey: Classification, description, and consequences. *Archives of General Psychiatry, 60*, 817–826.

Mayberg, H., Lozano, A., Voon, V., McNeely, H., Seminowicz, D., Hanani, C., . . . Kennedy, S. H. (2005). Deep brain stimulation for treatment resistant depression. *Neuron, 45*, 651–660.

Mayou, R., Phil, M., Kirmayer, L., Simon, G., Kroenke, G., & Sharpe, M. (2005). Somato-form disorders: Time for a new approach in DSM-V. *American Journal of Psychiatry, 162*, 847–855.

Mayville, S., Katz, R. C., Gipson, M. T., & Cabral, K. (1999). Assessing the prevalence of body dysmorphic disorder in an ethically diverse group of adolescents. *Journal of Child and Family Studies, 8*(3), 357–362.

Mazure, C. M. (1998). Life stressors as risk factors in depression. *Clinical Psychology: Science and Practice, 5*(3), 291–313.

Mazure, C. M., Bruce, M. L., Maciejewski, P. K., & Jacobs, S. C. (2000). Adverse life events and cognitive-personality characteristics in the prediction of major depression and antidepressant response. *American Journal of Psychiatry, 157*(6), 896–903.

Mbata, G., & Chukwuka, J. (2012). Obstructive sleep apnea hypopnea syndrome. *Annals of Medical and Health Sciences Research, 2*(1), 74–77.

McAdoo, W. G., & DeMyer, M. K. (1978). Research related to family factors in autism. *Journal of Pediatric Psychology, 2*, 162–166.

McCabe, R. E. (2003). *SARS and illness phobia.* Presented at a symposium on Clinical issues in the assessment and treatment of health anxiety: A case-based panel discussion (Chair: R. E. McCabe) at the Annual Meeting of the Anxiety Disorders Association of America, Toronto, Ontario, March.

McCabe, R. E., & Antony, M. M. (2002). Specific and social phobia. In M. M. Antony & D. H. Barlow (Eds.), *Handbook of assessment and treatment planning for psychological disorders* (pp. 113–146). New York, NY: Guilford Press.

McCabe, R. E., Antony, M. M., Summerfeldt, L. J., Liss, A., & Swinson, R. P. (2003). A preliminary examination of the relationship between anxiety disorders in adults and self-reported history of teasing or bullying experiences. *Cognitive Behaviour Therapy, 32*(4), 187–193.

McCabe, R. E., McFarlane, T., Polivy, J., & Olmsted, M. P. (2001). Eating disorders, dieting, and the accuracy of self-reported weight. *International Journal of Eating Disorders, 29*, 59–64.

McCaffery, J. M., Papandonatos, G. D., Stanton, C., Lloyd-Richardson, E. E., & Niaura, R. (2008). Depressive symptoms and cigarette smoking in twins from the national longitudinal study of adolescent health. *Health Psychology, 27* (3, Supplement 1), S207–S215.

McCaffrey, R. J., & Bellamy-Campbell, R. (1989). Psychometric detection of fabricated symptoms of combat-related posttraumatic stress disorder: A systematic replication. *Journal of Clinical Psychology, 45*, 76–79.

McCaffrey, R. J., Lynch, J. K., & Westervelt, H. J. (2011). Clinical neuropsychology. In D. H. Barlow (Ed.), *Oxford handbook of clinical psychology* (pp. 680–700). New York, NY: Oxford University.

McCann, D., Barrett, A., Cooper, A., Crumpler, D., Dalen, L., Grimshaw, K., . . . Stevenson, J. (2007). Food additives and hyperactive behaviour in 3-year-old and 8/9-year-old children in the community: A randomised, double-blinded, placebo-controlled trial. *The Lancet, 370*(9598), 1560–1567.

McCann, U. D., & Ricaurte, G. A. (2009). Amphetamine (or amphetamine-like)-related disorders. In B. J. Sadock, V. A. Sadock, & P. Ruiz (Eds.), *Kaplan & Sadock's comprehensive textbook of psychiatry* (9th ed., Vol. 1, pp. 1288–1296). Philadelphia, PA: Lippincott Williams & Wilkins.

McCann, U. D., Sgambati, F. P., Schwartz, A. R., & Ricaurte, G. A. (2009). Sleep apnea in young abstinent recreational MDMA ("ecstasy") consumers. *Neurology, 73*(23), 2011–2017.

McClam, T. D., Marano, C. M., Rosenberg, P. B., & Lyketsos, C. G. (2015). Interventions for neuropsychiatric symptoms in neurocognitive impairment due to Alzheimer's disease: A review of the literature. *Harvard Review of Psychiatry, 23*(5), 377–393.

McClearn, G. E., Johansson, B., Berg, S., Pedersen, N. L., Ahern, F., Petrill, S. A., & Plomin, R. (1997). Substantial genetic influence on cognitive abilities in twins 80 or more years old. *Science, 276*, 1560–1563.

McCloskey, M. S., Noblett, K. L., Deffenbacher, J. L., Gollan, J. K., & Coccaro, E. F. (2008). Cognitive-behavioral therapy for intermittent explosive disorder: A pilot randomized clinical trial. *Journal of Consulting and Clinical Psychology, 76*(5), 876–886.

McClure, M., Harvey, P., Goodman, M., Triebwasser, J., New, A., Koenigsberg, H., & Siever, L. J. (2010). Pergolide treatment of cognitive deficits associated with schizotypal personality disorder: Continued evidence of the importance of the dopamine system in the schizophrenia spectrum. *Neuropsychopharmacology, 35*, 1356–1362.

McCrady, B. S. (2014). Alcohol use disorders. In D. H. Barlow (Ed.), *Clinical handbook of psychological disorders: A step-by-step treatment manual* (5th ed., pp. 533–587). New York, NY: Guilford Press.

McCrady, B. S., & Tonigan, J. S. (2015). Recent research into the twelve-step programs. In R. K. Ries, D. A. Fiellin, S. C. Miller, & R. Saitz (Eds.), *The ASAM principles of addiction medicine* (5th ed., pp. 1043–1059). New York, NY: Wolters Kluwer.

McCrae, R. R., & Costa, P. T. (1997). Personality trait structure as a human universal. *American Psychologist, 52*, 509–516.

McCrae, R., & Costa, P., Jr. (2008). The five-factor theory of personality. In O. P. John, R. W. Robins, & L. A. Pervin (Eds.), *Handbook of personality: Theory and research* (3rd ed., pp. 159–181). New York, NY: Guilford Press.

McCreery, J. M., & Walker, R. D. (1993). Alcohol problems. In D. L. Dunner (Ed.), *Current psychiatric therapy* (pp. 92–98). Philadelphia, PA: W. B. Saunders.

McCullough, J. P., Jr., Klein, D. N., Keller, M. B., Holzer, C. E., III, Davis, S. M., Kornstein, S. G., . . . Harrison, W. M. (2000). Comparison of DSM-II-R chronic major depression and major depression superimposed on dysthymia (double depression): Validity of the distinction. *Journal of Abnormal Psychology, 109*, 419–427.

McCusker, J., Cole, M., Abrahamowicz, M., Han, L., Podoba, J. E., & Ramman-Haddad, L. (2001). Environmental risk factors for delirium in hospitalized older people. *Journal of the American Geriatrics Society, 49*, 1327–1334.

McDermott, S., Harding, A., & Randle, J. (2019). The characteristics of shelter residents. *Income Research Paper Series* (Catalogue No. 75F0002M2019004). https://www150.statcan.gc.ca/n1/en/catalogue/75F0002M2019004

McDiarmid, C. (2019). Heavy drinking, 2018. *Health Fact Sheets* (Catalogue No. 82-625-X201900100007). https://www150.statcan.gc.ca/n1/en/catalogue/82-625-X201900100007

McDonough, J. (2002). *Shakey: Neil Young's biography.* Toronto, ON: Random House.

McDowell, D. M. (1999). MDMA, ketamine, GHB, and the "club drug" scene. In M. Galanter & H. D. Kleber (Eds.), *Textbook of substance abuse treatment* (2nd ed., pp. 295–305). Washington, DC: American Psychiatric Press.

Mcdowell, I., Kristjanson, B., Hill, G. B., & Hebert, R. (1997). Community screening for dementia: The Mini Mental State Exam (MMSE) and Modified Mini Mental State Exam (3MS) compared. *Journal of Clinical Epidemiology, 50,* 377–383.

McEachin, J. J., Smith, T., & Lovaas, O. I. (1993). Long-term outcome for children with autism who received early intensive behavioral treatment. *American Journal on Mental Retardation, 97,* 359–372.

McEwen, B. S., & Karatsoreos, I. N. (2015). Sleep Deprivation and Circadian Disruption: Stress, Allostasis, and Allostatic Load. *Sleep Medicine Clinics, 10*(1), 1–10.

McEwen, B. S., & Magarinos, A. M. (2004). Does stress damage the brain? In J. M. Gorman, *Fear and anxiety: The benefits of translational research* (pp. 23–45). Washington, DC: American Psychiatric Publishing.

McGee, B. J., Hewitt, P. L., Sherry, S. B., Parkin, M., & Flett, G. L. (2005). Perfectionistic self-presentation, body image, and eating disorder symptoms. *Body Image, 2,* 29–40.

McGee, G. G., Morrier, M. J., & Daly, T. (1999). An incidental teaching approach to early intervention for toddlers with autism. *Research and Practice for Persons with Severe Disabilities, 24*(3), 133–146.

McGehee, D. S., Heath, M. J. S., Gelber, S., Devay, P., & Role, L. W. (1995). Nicotine enhancement of fast excitatory synaptic transmission in CNS by presynaptic receptors. *Science, 269,* 1692–1696.

McGinnis, J. M., & Foege, W. H. (1993). Actual causes of death in the United States. *JAMA, 270*(18), 2207–2212.

McGirr, A., Paris, J., Lesage, A., Renaud, J., & Turecki, G. (2009). An examination of DSM-IV borderline personality disorder symptoms and risk for death by suicide: A psychological autopsy study. *Canadian Journal of Psychiatry, 54*(2), 87.

McGoldrick, M., Loonan, R., & Wohlsifer, D. (2007). Sexuality and culture. In S. R. Leiblum (Ed.), *Principles and practice of sex therapy* (4th ed., pp. 416–441). New York, NY: Guilford Press.

McGovern, M. P., Xie, H., Segal, S. R., Siembab, L., & Drake, R. E. (2006). Addiction treatment services and co-occurring disorders: Prevalence estimates, treatment practices, and barriers. *Journal of Substance Abuse Treatment, 31,* 267–275.

McGovern, P. E. (2007). *Ancient wine: The search for the origins of viniculture.* Princeton, NJ: Princeton University Press.

McGrath P. J., Finley G. A., & Turner C. J. (1992). *Making cancer less painful: A handbook for parents.* Halifax, NS: IWK Children's Hospital.

McGrath, P. A., & DeVeber, L. L. (1986). The management of acute pain evoked by medical procedures in children with cancer. *Journal of Pain and Symptom Management, 1,* 145–150.

McGrath, P., Marshall, P. G., & Prior, K. (1979). A comprehensive treatment program for a fire setting child. *Journal of Behavior Therapy and Experimental Psychiatry, 10*(1), 69–72.

McGrath, R. E., & Carroll, E. J. (2012). Current status of "projective" "tests." In H. Cooper, P. M. Camic, D. L. Long, A. T. Panter, D. Rindskopf, & K. Sher (Eds.), *APA methods in psychology, Vol. 1: Handbook of research foundations, planning, measures, and psychometrics.* (pp. 329–348). Washington, DC: American Psychological Association.

McGregor, I., Zanna, M. P., Holmes, J. G., & Spencer, S. J. (2001). Compensatory conviction in the face of personal uncertainty: Going to extremes and being oneself. *Journal of Personality & Social Psychology, 80,* 472–488.

McGue, M. (1999). The behavioral genetics of alcoholism. *Current Directions in Psychological Science, 8*(4), 109–115.

McGue, M., & Lykken, D. T. (1992). Genetic influence on risk of divorce. *Psychological Science, 3*(6), 368–373.

McGue, M., Pickens, R. W., & Svikis, D. S. (1992). Sex and age effects on the inheritance of alcohol problems: A twin study. *Journal of Abnormal Psychology, 101,* 3–17.

McGuffin, P., & Katz, R. (1989). The genetics of depression and manic-depressive disorder. *British Journal of Psychiatry, 155,* 294–304.

McGuffin, P., & Katz, R. (1993). Genes, adversity and depression. In R. Plomin & G. E. McClearn (Eds.), *Nature, nurture & psychology* (pp. 217–230). Washington, DC: American Psychological Association.

McGuffin, P., Rijsdijk, F., Andrew, M., Sham, P., Katz, R., & Cardno, A. (2003). The heritability of bipolar affective disorder and the genetic relationship to unipolar depression. *Archives of General Psychiatry, 60,* 497–502.

McGuire, J. F., Piacentini, J., Scahill, L., Woods, D. W., Villarreal, R., Wilhelm, S., Walkup, J. T., & Peterson, A. L. (2015). Bothersome tics in patients with chronic tic disorders: Characteristics and individualized treatment response to behavior therapy. *Behaviour Research and Therapy, 70,* 56–62.

McHugh, R. K. (2015). Treatment of co-occurring anxiety disorders and substance use disorders. *Harvard Review of Psychiatry, 23,* 99–111.

McHugh, R. K., & Barlow, D. H. (2010). The dissemination and implementation of evidence-based psychological treatments: A review of current efforts. *American Psychologist, 65,* 73–84.

McIntosh, J. L., Santos, J. F., Hubbard, R. W., & Overholser, J. C. (1994). *Elder suicide: Research, theory and treatment.* Washington, DC: American Psychological Association.

McIsaac, H. K., Thordarson, D. S., Shafran, R., Rachman, S., & Poole, G. (1998). Claustrophobia and the magnetic resonance imaging procedure. *Journal of Behavioral Medicine, 21,* 255–268.

McKay, A. (2005). Sexuality and substance use: The impact of tobacco, alcohol, and selected recreational drugs on sexual function. *Canadian Journal of Human Sexuality, 14,* 47–56.

McKay, A. (2006). Trends in teen pregnancy in Canada with comparisons to U.S.A. and England/Wales. *Canadian Journal of Human Sexuality, 15,* 157–161.

McKay, D., Todaro, J., Neziroglu, F., Campisi, T., Moritz, E. K., & Yaryura-Tobias, J. A. (1997). Body dysmorphic disorder: A preliminary evaluation of treatment and maintenance using exposure with response prevention. *Behaviour Research and Therapy, 35,* 67–70.

McKeith, I. G., Dickson, D. W., Lowe, J., Emre, M., O'Brien, J. T., Feldman, H., & Perry, E. K. (2005). Diagnosis and management of dementia with Lewy bodies: Third report of the DLB consortium. *Neurology, 65*(12), 1863–1872.

McKenna, B. S., & Eyler, L. T. (2012). Overlapping prefrontal systems involved in cognitive and emotional processing in euthymic bipolar disorder and following sleep deprivation: A review of functional neuroimaging studies. *Clinical Psychology Review, 32*(7), 650–663.

McKenzie, S. J., Williamson, D. A., & Cubic, B. A. (1993). Stable and reactive body image disturbances in bulimia nervosa. *Behavior Therapy, 24,* 195–207.

McKetin, R., Coen, A., & Kaye, S. (2015). A comprehensive review of the effects of mixing caffeinated energy drinks with alcohol. *Drug and Alcohol Dependence, 151,* 15–30. https://doi.org/10.1016/j.drugalcdep.2015.01.047

McKim, W. A. (1991). *Drugs and behavior: An introduction to behavioral pharmacology* (2nd ed.). Englewood Cliffs, NJ: Prentice-Hall.

McKinnon, W., Weisse, C. S., Reynolds, C. P., Bowles, C. A., & Baum, A. (1989). Chronic stress, leukocyte subpopulations, and hormonal response to latent viruses. *Health Psychology, 8,* 399–402.

McKnight, D. L., Nelson-Gray, R. O., & Barnhill, J. (1992). Dexamethasone suppression test and response to cognitive therapy and antidepressant medication. *Behavior Therapy, 23,* 99–111.

McLaren, A. (1990). *Our own master race: Eugenics in Canada 1885–1945.* Toronto, ON: McClelland & Stewart.

Mclaughlin, K. A., Green, J. G., Hwang, I., Sampson, N. A., Zaslavsky, A. M., & Kessler, R. C. (2012). Intermittent explosive disorder in the national comorbidity survey replication adolescent supplement. *Archives of General Psychiatry, 60,* 1131–1139.

McLaughlin, N. C. R., & Greenberg, B. D. (2012). In G. Steketee (Ed.), *The Oxford handbook of obsessive compulsive and spectrum disorders* (pp. 307–321). New York, NY: Oxford University Press.

McLean, L. M., & Gallop, R. (2003). Implications of childhood sexual abuse for adult borderline personality disorder and complex posttraumatic stress disorder. *American Journal of Psychiatry, 160,* 369–371.

McLean, P. D., Whittal, M. L., Thordarson, D. S., Taylor, S., Socting, I., Koch, W. J., . . . Anderson, K. W. (2001). Cognitive versus behavior therapy in the group treatment of obsessive–compulsive disorder. *Journal of Consulting and Clinical Psychology, 69,* 205–214.

McLean, P., & Taylor, S. (1992). Severity of unipolar depression and choice of treatment. *Behaviour Research and Therapy, 30,* 443–451.

McLewin, L. A., & Muller, R. T. (2006). Childhood trauma, imaginary companions, and the development of pathological dissociation. *Aggression and Violent Behavior, 11,* 531–545.

McLintock, B. (2002, July 22). Montreux clinic under fire. *The Province,* A14. Retrieved June 24, 2004, from http://www.anorexiasfallenangel.com/news/22072002.htm

McMain, S. F., Guimond, T., Streiner, D. L., Cardish, R. J., & Links, P. S. (2012). Dialectical behavior therapy compared with general psychiatric management for borderline personality disorder: Clinical outcomes and functioning over a 2-year follow-up. *American Journal of Psychiatry, 169*(6), 650–661. https://doi.org/10.1176/appi.ajp.2012.11091416

McMain, S. F., Guimond, T., Streiner, D. L., Cardish, R. J., & Links, P. S. (2014). Dialectical behavior therapy compared with general psychiatric management for borderline personality disorder: Clinical outcomes and functioning over a 2-year follow-up. *American Journal of Psychiatry, 169*(6), 650–661.

McMain, S., Korman, L. M., & Dimeff, L. (2001). Dialectical behavior therapy and the treatment of emotion dysregulation. *Journal of Clinical Psychology, 57,* 183–196.

McNab, C., Haslam, N., & Burnett, P. (2007). Expressed emotion, attributions, utility beliefs, and distress in parents of young people with first episode psychosis. *Psychiatry Research, 151,* 97–106.

McNally, R. (2003). *Remembering trauma.* Cambridge, MA: Belknap Press.

McNally, R. J. (1996). Cognitive bias in the anxiety disorders. In D. A. Hope (Ed.), *Perspectives on anxiety, panic and fear* (the 43rd Annual Nebraska Symposium on Motivation, pp. 211–250). Lincoln, NE: Nebraska University Press.

McNally, R. J. (1999). EMDR and mesmerism: A comparative historical analysis. *Journal of Anxiety Disorders, 13,* 225–236.

McNally, R. J. (2011). *What is mental illness?* Cambridge, MA: Harvard University Press.

McNally, R. J. (2012). Are we winning the war against posttraumatic stress disorder? *Science, 336*(6083), 872–874.

McNaughton, N., & Gray, J. H. (2000). Anxiolytic action on the behavioral inhibition system implies multiple types of arousal contribute to anxiety. *Journal of Affective Disorders, 61*(3), 161–176.

McNeil, T. F. (1987). Perinatal influences in the development of schizophrenia. In H. Helmchen & F. A. Henn (Eds.), *Biological perspectives of schizophrenia* (pp. 125–138). New York, NY: John Wiley & Sons.

McNeil, T. F., Cantor-Graae, E., & Weinberger, D. R. (2001). Relationship of obstetric complications and differences in brain structures in monozygotic twin pairs discordant for schizophrenia. *American Journal of Psychiatry, 157*(2), 203–212.

McPartland, J. C., Reichow, B., & Volkmar, F. R. (2012). Sensitivity and specificity of proposed DSM-5 diagnostic criteria for autism spectrum disorder. *Journal of the American Academy of Child & Adolescent Psychiatry, 51*(4), 368–383.

McQuade, J. D., & Hoza, B. (2015). Peer relationships of children with ADHD. In R. A. Barkley (Ed.), *Attention-deficit hyperactivity disorder: A handbook for diagnosis & treatment* (4th ed., pp. 210–222). New Yok, NY: Guilford Press.

McQueen, A. M. (2005, June 29). Alanis battled anorexia, bulimia. *Ottawa Sun*. Retrieved June 30, 2007, from http://jam.canoe.ca/Music/2005/06/29/1109259.html

McVey, G. L., Davis, R., Tweed, S., & Shaw, B. (2004). An evaluation of a school-based program designed to improve body image satisfaction, global self-esteem, and eating attitudes and behaviours: A replication study. *International Journal of Eating Disorders, 36*, 1–11.

McVey, G. L., Pepler, D., Davis, R., Flett, G. L., & Abdolell, M. (2002). Risk and protective factors associated with disordered eating during early adolescence. *Journal of Early Adolescence, 22*, 75–95.

McWilliams, J. M., Meara, E., Zaslavsky, A. M., & Ayanian, J. Z. (2009). Differences in control of cardiovascular disease and diabetes by race, ethnicity, and education: U.S. trends from 1999 to 2006 and effects of medicare coverage. *Annals of Internal Medicine, 150*(8), 505–515.

McWilliams, L. A., & Asmundson, G. J. G. (2001). Is there a negative association between anxiety sensitivity and arousal-increasing substances and activities? *Journal of Anxiety Disorders, 15*, 161–170.

Meagher, D., & Trzapacz, P. (2012). Delirium. In M. G. Gelder, N. C. Andreasen, J. J. Lopez-Ibor, & J. R. Geddes (Eds.), *New Oxford textbook of psychiatry* (2nd ed., Vol. 1, pp. 325–333). New York, NY: Oxford University Press.

Meagher, D., Adamis, D., Trzepacz, P., & Leonard, M. (2012). Features of subsyndromal and persistent delirium. *British Journal of Psychiatry, 200*(1), 37–44.

Meana, M., & Nunnink, S. E. (2005). Gender differences in the content of cognitive distraction during sex [Special issue: Scientific Abstracts, World Congress of Sexology]. *Journal of Sex Research, 43*, 59–67.

Meaney, M. J., & Szyf, M. (2005). Maternal care as a model for experience-dependent chromatin plasticity? *Trends in Neurosciences, 28*(9), 456–463.

Mednick, S. A., & Schulsinger, F. (1965). A longitudinal study of children with a high risk for schizophrenia: A preliminary report. In S. Vandenberg (Ed.), *Methods and goals in human behavior genetics* (pp. 255–296). New York, NY: Academic Press.

Mednick, S. A., & Schulsinger, F. (1968). Some premorbid characteristics related to breakdown in children with schizophrenic mothers. *Journal of Psychiatric Research, 6*, 267–291.

Meehl, P. E. (1962). Schizotaxia, schizotypy, schizophrenia. *American Psychologist, 17*, 827–838.

Meehl, P. E. (1989). *Schizotaxia revisited*. Archives of General Psychiatry, 46, 935–944.

Mehler, P. S., Birmingham, L. C., Crow, S. J., & Jahraus, J. P. (2010). Medical complications of eating disorders. In C. M. Grilo & J. E. Mitchell (Eds.), *The treatment of eating disorders: A clinical handbook* (pp. 66–80). New York, NY: Guilford Press.

Meichenbaum, D. (1977). Dr. Ellis, please stand up. *Counseling Psychologist, 7*, 43–44.

Meichenbaum, D. (2006). Resilience and posttraumatic growth: A constructive

narrative perspective. In L. G. Calhoun & R. G. Tedeschi (Eds.), *Handbook of posttraumatic growth: Research & practice* (pp. 355–367). Mahwah, NJ: Erlbaum.

Meichenbaum, D. H. (1971). Nature and modification of impulsive children: Training impulsive children to talk to themselves. *Catalog of Selected Documents in Psychology, 1*, 15–16.

Meichenbaum, D. H. (1994). *A clinical handbook/ practical therapist manual for assessing and treating adults with posttraumatic stress disorder*. Waterloo, ON: Institute Press.

Meichenbaum, D. H. (1995). Cognitive-behavioral therapy in historical perspective. In B. M. Bongar & L. E. Beutler (Eds.), *Comprehensive textbook of psychotherapy: Theory and practice* (pp. 140–158). London, UK: Oxford University Press.

Meichenbaum, D., & Cameron, R. (1973). Training schizophrenics to talk to themselves: A means of developing attentional controls. *Behavior Therapy, 4*, 515–534.

Meichenbaum, D., & Cameron, R. (1974). The clinical potential of modifying what clients say to themselves. *Psychotherapy: Theory, Research & Practice, 11*, 103–117.

Meichenbaum, D. H., & Goodman, J. (1971). Training impulsive children to talk to themselves: A means of developing self-control. *Journal of Abnormal Psychology, 77*, 115–126.

Melca, I. A., Yucel, M., Mendlowicz, M. V., de Oliveira-Souza, R., & Fontenelle, L. F. (2015). The correlates of obsessive–compulsive, schizotypal, and borderline personality disorders in obsessive–compulsive disorder. *Journal of Anxiety Disorders, 33*, 15–24.

Meleshko, K. A., & Alden, L. E. (1993). Anxiety and self-disclosure: Toward a motivational model. *Journal of Personality and Social Psychology, 64*, 1000–1009.

Mellinger, G. D., Balter, M. B., & Uhlenhuth, E. H. (1985). Insomnia and its treatment: Prevalence and correlates. *Archives of General Psychiatry, 42*, 225–232.

Melton, G. B., Petrila, J., Poythress, N. G., & Slobogin, C. (1987). Psychological evaluations for the courts. New York, NY: Guilford Press.

Meltzer-Brody, S., Stuebe, A., Dole, N., Savitz, D., Rubinow, D., & Thorp, J. (2011). Elevated corticotropin releasing hormone (CRH) during pregnancy and risk of postpartum depression (PPD). *Journal of Clinical Endocrinology & Metabolism, 96*(1), E40–E47.

Melzack, R. (1999). From the gate to the neuromatrix. *Pain* (Suppl. 6), S121–S126.

Melzack, R. (2005). Evolution of the neuromatrix theory of pain. *Pain Practice, 5*, 85–94.

Melzack, R., & Katz, J. (2004). The gate control theory: Reaching for the brain. In T. Hadjistavropoulos & K. D. Craig (Eds.), *Pain: Psychological perspectives* (pp. 13–34). Mahwah, NJ: Lawrence Erlbaum Associates Publishers.

Melzack, R., & Wall, P. D. (1965). Pain mechanisms: A new theory. *Science, 150*, 971–979.

Melzack, R., & Wall, P. D. (1982). *The challenge of pain*. New York, NY: Basic Books.

Mendelson, W. (2005). Sleep disorders. In B. J. Sadock & V. A. Sadock (Eds.), *Kaplan & Sadock's comprehensive textbook of psychiatry* (pp. 2022–2034). Philadelphia, PA: Lippincott Williams & Wilkins.

Mendlewicz, J., & Rainer, J. D. (1977). Adoption study supporting genetic transmission in manic depressive illness. *Nature, 268*(5618), 327–329.

Meng, X., & D'Arcy, C. (2015). Comorbidity between lifetime eating problems and mood and anxiety disorders: Results from the Canadian community health survey of mental health and well-being. *European Eating Disorders Review, 23*, 156–162. https://onlinelibrary.wiley.com/doi/abs/10.1002/erv.2347

Mennes, C. E., Ben Abdallah, A., & Cottler, L. B. (2009). The reliability of self-reported cannabis abuse, dependence and withdrawal symptoms: Multisite study of differences between general population and treatment groups. *Addictive Behaviors, 34*(2), 223–226.

Mercer, K. B., Orcutt, H. K., Quinn, J. F., Fitzgerald, C. A., Conneely, K. N., Barfield, R. T., & Ressler, K. J. (2012). Acute and posttraumatic stress symptoms in a prospective gene x environment study of a university campus shooting. *Archives of General Psychiatry, 69*(1), 89–97.

Meredith, S. E., Juliano, L. M., Hughes, J. R., & Griffiths, R. R. (2013). Caffeine use disorder: A comprehensive review and research agenda. *Journal of Caffeine Research, 3*(3), 114–130.

Merens, W., Willem Van der Does, A. J., & Spinhoven, P. (2007). The effects of serotonin manipulations on emotional information processing and mood. *Journal of Affective Disorders, 103*(1–3), 43–62.

Merikangas, K. R., Akiskal, H. S., Angst, J., Greenberg, P. E., Hirschfeld, R. M., Petukhova, M., & Kessler, R. C. (2007). Lifetime and 12-month prevalence of bipolar spectrum disorder in the National Comorbidity Survey Replication. *Archives of General Psychiatry, 64*(5), 543–552.

Merikangas, K. R., & Pato, M. (2009). Recent developments in the epidemiology of bipolar disorder in adults and children: Magnitude, correlates, and future directions. *Clinical Psychology: Science and Practice, 16*(2), 121–133.

Merikangas, K. R., & Risch, N. (2014). Will the genomics revolution revolutionize psychiatry? *American Journal of Psychiatry, 160*(4), 625–635. https://doi.org/10.1176/appi.ajp.160.4.625

Merikangas, K. R., Cui, L., Kattan, G., Carlson, G. A., Youngstrom, E. A., & Angst, J. (2012). Mania with and without depression in a community sample of US adolescents. *Archives of General Psychiatry, 69*(9), 943–951.

Merikangas, K. R., Jin, R., He, J. P., Kessler, R. C., Lee, S., Sampson, N. A., & Zarkov, Z. (2011). Prevalence and correlates of bipolar spectrum disorder in the World Mental Health Survey Initiative. *Archives of General Psychiatry, 68*(3), 241–251.

Merikangas, K. R., Mehta, R. L., Molnar, B. E., Walters, E. E., Swendsen, J. D., Auilar-Gaziola, S., . . . Kessler, R. C. (1998). Comorbidity of substance use disorders with mood and anxiety disorders: Results of the international consortium in psychiatric

epidemiology. *Addictive Behaviors, 23*, 893–908.

Mermin, J., & Fenton, K. A. (2012). The future of HIV prevention in the United States. *JAMA, 308*(4), 347–348.

Merzenich, M. M., Jenkins, W. M., Johnston, P., Schreiner, C., Miller, S. L., & Tallal, P. (1996). Temporal processing deficits of language-learning impaired children ameliorated by training. *Science, 271*, 77–81.

Meston, C. M. (2000). The psycho physiological assessment of female sexual function. *Journal of Sex Education & Therapy, 25*, 6–16.

Meston, C. M., & Gorzalka, B. B. (1996). The effects of immediate, delayed, and residual sympathetic activation on sexual arousal in women. *Behaviour Research & Therapy, 34*, 143–148.

Meston, C. M., & Heiman, J. R. (2000). Sexual abuse and sexual function: An examination of sexually relevant cognitive processes. *Journal of Consulting & Clinical Psychology, 68*, 399–406.

Meston, C. M., & Worcel, M. (2002). The effects of yohimbine plus L-arginine glutamate on sexual arousal in post-menopausal women with sexual arousal disorder. *Archives of Sexual Behavior, 31*, 323–332.

Meston, C. M., Trapnell, P. D., & Gorzalka, B. B. (1996). Ethnic and gender differences in sexuality: Variations in sexual behavior between Asian and non-Asian university students. *Archives of Sexual Behavior, 25*, 33–72.

Meston, C. M., Trapnell, P. D., & Gorzalka, B. B. (1998). Ethnic, gender, and length-of-residency influences on sexual knowledge and attitudes. *Journal of Sex Research, 35*, 176–188.

Meuret, A. E., Rosenfield, D., Wilhelm, F. H., Zhou, E., Conrad, A., Ritz, T., & Roth, W. T (2011). Do unexpected panic attacks occur spontaneously? *Biological Psychiatry, 70*, 985–991.

Meyer, A. J., Nash, J. D., McAlister, A. L., Maccoby, M., & Farquhar, J. W. (1980). Skills training in a cardiovascular health education campaign. *Journal of Consulting and Clinical Psychology, 2*, 129–142.

Meyer, B., & Carver, C. S. (2000). Negative childhood accounts, sensitivity and pessimism: A study of avoidant personality disorder features in college students. *Journal of Personality Disorders, 14*, 233–248.

Meyer-Bahlberg, H. F. (2010). From mental disorder to iatrogenic hypogonadism: Dilemmas in conceptualizing gender identity variants as psychiatric conditions. *Archives of Sexual Behavior, 39*(2), 461–476.

Meyer-Bahlburg, H., Dolezal, C., Baker, S., Carlson, A., Obeid, J., & New, M. (2004). Prenatal androgenization affects gender-related behavior but not gender identity in 5–12-year-old girls with congenital adrenal hyperplasia. *Archives of Sexual Behavior, 33*, 97–104.

Meyerowitz, B. E. (1983). Postmastectomy coping strategies and quality of life. *Health Psychology, 2*, 117–132.

Meyers, A. (1991). Biobehavioral interactions in behavioral medicine. *Behavior Therapy, 22*, 129–131.

Meyers, K. M., & Davis, M. (2002). Behavioral and neural analysis of extinction learning. *Neuron, 36*(4), 567–584. https://doi.org/10.1016/S0896-6273(02)01064-4

Mezick, E. J., Matthews, K. A., Hall, M., Kamarck, T. W., Strollo, P. J., Buysse, D. J., & Reis, S. E. (2010). Low life purpose and high hostility are related to an attenuated decline in nocturnal blood pressure. *Health Psychology, 29*(2), 196–204.

Mezzich, J. E., Good, B. J., Lewis-Fernandez, R., Guarnaccia, P., Lin, K. M., Parron, D., . . . Hughes, C. (1993, September). *Cultural formulation guidelines.* Revised cultural proposals for DSM-IV. Submitted to the DSM-IV Task Force by the Steering Committee, NIMH-Sponsored Group on Culture and Diagnosis.

Mezzich, J. E., Kirmayer, L. J., Kleinman, A., Fabrega, H., Jr., Parron, D. L., Good, B. J., . . . Manson, S. M. (1999). The place of culture in DSM-IV. *Journal of Nervous and Mental Disease, 187,* 457–464.

Mezzich, J. E., Kleinman, A., Fabrega, H., Jr., Good, B., Johnson-Powell, G., Lin, K. M., . . . Parron, D. (1992). *Cultural proposals for* DSM-IV. Submitted to the DSM-IV Task Force by the Steering Committee, NIMH-Sponsored Group on Culture and Diagnosis.

Michaud, I., & Chaput, J.-P. (2016). Are Canadian children and adolescents sleep deprived? *Public Health, 141,* 126–129.

Michultka, D. M., Blanchard, E. B., Appelbaum, K. A., Jaccard, J., & Dentinger, M. P. (1989). The refractory headache patient: II. High medication consumption (analgesic rebound) headache. *Behaviour Research and Therapy, 27,* 411–420.

Mihura, J. L., Meyer, G. J., Dumitrascu, N., & Bombel, G. (2013). The validity of individual Rorschach variables: Systematic reviews and meta-analyses of the comprehensive system. *Psychological Bulletin, 139,* 548–605.

Miklowitz, D. J. (2014). Bipolar disorder. In D. H. Barlow (Ed.), *Clinical handbook of psychological disorders: A step-by-step treatment manual* (5th ed.). New York, NY: Guilford Press.

Miklowitz, D. J., George, E. L., Richards, J. A., Simoneau, T. L., & Suddath, R. L. (2003). A randomized study of family-focused psychoeducation and pharmacotherapy in the outpatient management of bipolar disorder. *Archives of General Psychiatry, 60,* 904–912.

Miklowitz, D. J., & Goldstein, M. J. (1997). *Bipolar disorder: A family focused treatment approach.* New York, NY: Guilford Press.

Miklowitz, D. J., Goldstein, M. J., Doane, J. A., Nuechterlein, K. H., Strachan, A. M., Snyder, K. S., & Magaña-Amato, A. (1989). Is expressed emotion an index of a transactional process? I. Parents' affective style. *Family Process, 28,* 153–167.

Miklowitz, D. J., & Johnson, S. (2006). The psychopathology and treatment of bipolar disorder. In S. Nolen-Hoeksema, T. D. Cannon, & T. Widiger (Eds.), *Annual review of clinical psychology* (pp. 199–235). Palo Alto, CA: Annual Reviews.

Miklowitz, D. J., Otto, M. W., Frank, E., Reilly-Harrington, N. A., Wisniewski, S. R., Kogan, J. N., . . . Sachs, G. S. (2007). Psychosocial treatments for bipolar depression: A 1-year randomized trial from the Systematic Treatment Enhancement Program. *Archives of General Psychiatry, 64*(4), 419–426.

Miklowitz, D. J., Schneck, C. D., Singh, M. K., Taylor, D. O., George, E. L., Cosgrove, M. E., Howe, M. E., Dickinson, L. M., Garber, J., & Chang, K. D. (2013). Early intervention for symptomatic youth for bipolar disorder: A randomized trial of family-focused therapy. *Journal of the American Academy of Child and Adolescent Psychiatry, 52,* 121–131.

Miklowitz, D. J., Simoneau, T. L., George, E. L., Richards, J. A., Kalbag, A., Sachs-Ericsson, N., & Suddath, R. (2000). Family-focused treatment of bipolar disorder: 1-year effects of a psychoeducational program in conjunction with pharmacotherapy. *Biological Psychiatry, 48,* 582–592.

Miklowitz, D. J., Simoneau, T. L., Sachs-Ericsson, N., Warner, R., & Suddath, R. (1996). Family risk indicators in the course of bipolar affective disorder. In C. Mundt, M. J. Goldstein, K. Hahlweg, P. Fiedler, et al. (Eds.), *Interpersonal factors in the origin and course of affective disorders* (pp. 204–217). London, UK: Gaskell Press.

Milby, J. B., Williams, V., Hall, J. N., Khuder, S., McGill, T., & Wooten, V. (1993). Effectiveness of combined triazolam-behavior therapy for primary insomnia. *American Journal of Psychiatry, 150,* 1259–1260.

Mill, J. (2011). Epigenetic effects on gene function and their role in mediating gene–environment interactions. In K. S. Kendler, S. Jaffee, & D. Romer (Eds.), *The dynamic genome and mental health: The role of genes and environments in youth development* (pp. 145–171). New York, NY: Oxford University Press.

Millan, M. J., Fone, K., Steckler, T., & Horan, W. P. (2014). Negative symptoms of schizophrenia: Clinical characteristics, pathophysiological substrates, experimental models and prospects for improved treatment. *European Neuropsychopharmacology, 24*(5), 645–692.

Millar, H. R., Qrdell, F., Vyvyan, J. P., Naji, S. A., Prescott, G. J., & Eagles, J. M. (2005). Anorexia nervosa mortality in northeast Scotland 1965–1999. *American Journal of Psychiatry, 162,* 753–757.

Millar, W. J. (1998). Multiple medication use among seniors. *Health Reports, 9*(4), 11–17.

Miller, G. (2011). Social neuroscience. Why loneliness is hazardous to your health. *Science, 331*(6014), 138–140.

Miller, G., & Blackwell, E. (2006). Turning up the heat: Inflammation as a mechanism linking chronic stress, depression, and heart disease. *Current Directions in Psychological Science, 15,* 269–277.

Miller, I. W., & Norman, W. H. (1979). Learned helplessness in humans: A review and attribution-theory model. *Psychological Bulletin, 86*(1), 93–118.

Miller, I. W., Keitner, G. I., Epstein, N. B., Bishop, D. S., & Ryan, C. E. (1991). Families of bipolar patients: Dysfunction, course of illness, and pilot treatment study. Paper presented at the annual meeting of the Association for the Advancement of Behavior Therapy, New York.

Miller, I. W., Norman, W. H., & Keitner, G. I. (1989). Cognitive-behavioral treatment of depressed inpatients: Six- and twelve-month follow-up. *American Journal of Psychiatry, 146,* 1274–1279.

Miller, I. W., Norman, W. H., Keitner, G. I., Bishop, S. B., & Down, M. G. (1989). Cognitive-behavioral treatment of depressed inpatients. *Behavior Therapy, 20*(1), 25–47.

Miller, J., Bilder, D., Farley, M., Coon, H., Pinborough-Zimmerman, J., Jenson, W., & McMahon, W. (2013). Autism spectrum disorder reclassified: A second look at the 1980s Utah/UCLA Autism Epidemiologic Study. *Journal of Autism and Developmental Disorders 43*(1), 200–210.

Miller, M. W., Wolf, E. J., Keane, T. M. (2015). Posttraumatic stress disorder in *DSM-5*: New criteria and controversies. *Clinical Psychology: Science and Practice, 21,* 208–220.

Miller, N. E. (1969). Learning of visceral and glandular responses. *Science, 163,* 434–445.

Miller, N. S., Gold, M. S., & Pottash, A. C. (1989). A 12-step treatment approach for marijuana (Cannabis) dependence. *Journal of Substance Abuse Treatment, 6,* 241–250.

Miller, P. M., Smith, G. T., & Goldman, M. S. (1990). Emergence of alcohol expectancies in childhood: A possible critical period. *Journal of Studies on Alcohol, 51,* 343–349.

Miller, S. D. (1989). Optical differences in cases of multiple personality disorder. *Journal of Nervous and Mental Disease, 177*(8), 480–486.

Miller, T. J., McGlashan, T. H., Rosen, J. L., Somjee, L., Markovich, P. J., Stein, K., & Woods, S. W. (2002). Prospective diagnosis of the initial prodrome for schizophrenia based on the Structured Interview for Prodromal Syndromes: Preliminary evidence of interrater reliability and predictive validity. *American Journal of Psychiatry, 159,* 863–865.

Miller, T. Q., Smith, T. W., Turner, C. W., Guijarro, M. L., & Hallet, A. J. (1996). A meta-analytic review of research on hostility and physical health. *Psychology Bulletin, 119*(2), 322–348.

Miller, W. R., & Hester, R. K. (1986). Inpatient alcoholism treatment: Who benefits? *American Psychologist, 41,* 794–805.

Miller, W. R., & McCrady, B. S. (1993). The importance of research on Alcoholics Anonymous. In B. S. McCrady & W. R. Miller (Eds.), *Research on Alcoholics Anonymous: Opportunities and alternatives* (pp. 3–11). New Brunswick, NJ: Rutgers Center of Alcohol Studies.

Miller, W. R., & Rollnick, S. (2002). *Motivational interviewing: Preparing people for change* (2nd ed.). New York, NY: Guilford Press.

Miller, W. R., & Rollnick, S. (2012). *Motivational interviewing: Helping people change* (3rd ed.). New York, NY: Guilford Press.

Millon, T. (1981). *Disorders of personality: DSM-III, Axis II.* New York, NY: John Wiley & Sons.

Millon, T. (1986). Schizoid and avoidant personality disorders in DSM-III. *American Journal of Psychiatry, 143,* 1321–1322.

Millon, T. (1991). Classification in psychopathology: Rationale, alternatives, and standards. *Journal of Abnormal Psychology, 100*(3), 245–261.

Millon, T. (2004). *Masters of the mind.* Hoboken, NJ: John Wiley & Sons.

Millon, T., & Martinez, A. (1995). Avoidant personality disorder. In W. J. Livesley (Ed.), *The DSM-IV personality disorders* (pp. 218–233). New York, NY: Guilford Press.

Mills, P. J., Adler, K. A., Dimsdale, J. E., Perez, C. J., Ziegler, M. G., Ancoli-Israel, S., . . . Grant, I. (2004). Vulnerable caregivers of Alzheimer disease patients have a deficit in beta 2-adrenergic receptor sensitivity and density. *American Journal of Geriatric Psychiatry, 12,* 281–286.

Millson, P., Challacombe, L., Villeneuve, P. J., Strike, C. J., Fischer, B., Myers, T., . . . Hopkins, S. (2007). Reduction in the injection-related HIV risk after 6 months in a low-threshold methadone treatment program. *AIDS Education and Prevention, 19*(2), 124–136.

Milner, C., Fogel, S., & Cote, K. (2006). Experience with napping moderates motor performance improvements following a short daytime nap. *Biological Psychology, 73,* 141–156.

Mindell, J. A. (1993). Sleep disorders in children. *Health Psychology, 12,* 152–163.

Mindell, J. A., & Owens, J. A. (2009). *A clinical guide to pediatric sleep: Diagnosis and management of sleep problems* (2nd ed.). Philadelphia, PA: Lippincott Williams & Wilkins.

Mindell, J. A., & Owens, J. A. (2015). *A clinical guide to pediatric sleep: Diagnosis and management of sleep problems* (3rd ed.). Philadelphia, PA: Lippincott Williams & Wilkins.

Mindham, R. H. S., & Hughes, T. A. (2012). Dementia in Parkinson's disease. In M. G. Gelder, N. C. Andreasen, J. J. Lopez-Ibor, & J. R. Geddes (Eds.), *New Oxford textbook of psychiatry* (2nd ed., Vol. 1, pp. 368–371). New York, NY: Oxford University Press.

Mineka, S. (1985). The frightful complexity of the origins of fears. In F. R. Bruch & J. B. Overmier (Eds.), *Affect, conditioning, and cognition: Essays on the determinants of behavior.* Hillsdale, NJ: Erlbaum.

Mineka, S., & Kelly, K. A. (1989). The relationship between anxiety, lack of control and loss of control. In A. Steptoe & A. Appels (Eds.), *Stress, personal control and worker health.* New York, NY: John Wiley & Sons.

Mineka, S., & Zinbarg, R. (1998). Experimental approaches to understanding the mood and anxiety disorders. In J. Adair (Ed.), *Advances in psychological research: Social, personal, and cultural aspects* (Vol. 2, pp. 429–454). Hove, UK: Psychology Press/Erlbaum.

Mineka, S., & Zinbarg, R. (2006). A contemporary learning theory perspective on the etiology of anxiety disorders. *American Psychologist, 61,* 10–26.

Mineka, S., & Zinbarg, R. E. (1996). Conditioning and ethological models of anxiety disorders: Stress-in-dynamic-context anxiety models. In D. A. Hope (Ed.), *Perspectives on anxiety, panic and fear* (the 43rd Annual Nebraska Symposium on Motivation, pp. 135–210). Lincoln, NE: Nebraska University Press.

Mineka, S., & Zinbarg, R. (2006). A contemporary and physical health. *Psychological Bulletin, 119*(2), 322–348.

Mineka, S., Watson, D., & Clark, L. A. (1998). Comorbidity of anxiety and unipolar mood disorders. *Annual Review of Psychology, 49,* 377–412.

Mingdao, Z., & Zhenyi, X. (1990). Delivery systems and research for schizophrenia in China. In A. Kales, C. N. Stefanis, & J. A. Talbott (Eds.), *Recent advances in schizophrenia* (pp. 373–395). New York, NY: Springer-Verlag.

Minuchin, S., Rosman, B. L., & Baker, L. (1978). *Psychosomatic families.* Cambridge, MA: Harvard University Press.

Mirsky, A. F. (1995). Israeli High-Risk Study: Editor's introduction. *Schizophrenia Bulletin, 21,* 179–182.

Mirsky, A. F., Bieliauskas, L. A., Duncan, C. C., & French, L. M. (2013). The Genain quadruplets: A 55-year follow-up of two of four monozygous sisters with schizophrenia. *Schizophrenia Research, 148,* 186–187.

Mirsky, A. F., Bieliauskas, L. A., French, L. M., Van Kammen, D. P., Joensson, E., & Sedvall, G. (2000). A 39-year followup on the Genain quadruplets. *Schizophrenia Bulletin, 26,* 699–708.

Mishara, B. L. (1999). Suicide in the Montreal subway system. Characteristics of the victims, antecedents, and implications for prevention. *Canadian Journal of Psychiatry, 44,* 690–696.

Mishra, S., & Lalumière, M. L. (2009). Is the crime drop of the 1990s in Canada and the USA associated with a general decline in risky and health-related behavior? *Social Science and Medicine, 68,* 39–48.

Mishra, S., Lalumière, M. L., & Williams, R. J. (2017). Gambling, risk-taking, and antisocial behavior: A replication study supporting the generality of deviance. *Journal of Gambling Studies, 33,* 15–36. https://doi.org/10.1007/s10899-016-9608-8

Miskovic, V., Moscovitch, D. A., Santesso, D. L., McCabe, R. E., Antony, M. M., & Schmidt, L. A. (2011). Changes in EEG cross-frequency coupling during cognitive behavioral therapy for social anxiety disorder. *Psychological Science, 22*(4), 507–516.

Misri, S., Kostaras, X., Fox, D., & Kostaras, D. (2000). The impact of partner support in the treatment of postpartum depression. *Canadian Journal of Psychiatry, 45,* 554–558.

Mistlberger, R. E., & Rusak, B. (2005). Circadian rhythms in mammals: Formal properties and environmental influences. In M. H. Kryger, T. Roth, & W. C. Dement (Eds.), *Principles and practice of sleep medicine* (4th ed.). Philadelphia, PA: W. B. Saunders.

Mistry, H., Bhugra, D., Chaleby, K., Khan, F., & Sauer, J. (2009). Veiled communication: Is uncovering necessary for psychiatric assessment? *Transcultural Psychiatry, 46*(4), 642–650. https://doi.org/10.1177/1363461509351366

Mitchell, D. C., Knight, C. A., Hockenberry, J., Teplansky, R., & Hartman, T. J. (2014). Beverage caffeine intakes in the U.S. *Food and Chemical Toxicology, 63,* 136–142. https://doi.org/10.1016/j.fct.2013.10.042

Mitchell, J. E., & Pyle, R. L. (1988). The diagnosis and clinical characteristics of bulimia. In B. J. Blinder, B. F. Chaitin, & R. S. Goldstein (Eds.), *The eating disorders: Medical and psychological bases of diagnosis and treatment* (pp. 267–273). New York, NY: PMA.

Mitchell, T. L., Walters, W., & Stewart, S. H. (2006). Swissair Flight 111 disaster response impacts: Lessons learned from the voices of disaster

volunteers. *Brief Treatment and Crisis Intervention, 6,* 154–170.

Mitchell, T., Stewart, S. H., Griffin, K., & Loba, P. (2004). "We Will Never Ever Forget…": The Swissair Flight 111 disaster and its impact on volunteers and communities. *Journal of Health Psychology, 9,* 245–262.

Mitton, M. J. E., Links, P. S., & Durocher, G. (1997). A history of childhood sexual abuse and the course of borderline personality disorder. In M. C. Zanarini (Ed.), *Role of sexual abuse in the etiology of borderline personality disorder* (pp. 181–202). Washington, DC: American Psychiatric Association.

Moak, D. H., & Anton, R. F. (1999). Alcohol. In B. S. McCrady & E. E. Epstein (Eds.), *Addictions: A comprehensive guidebook* (pp. 75–94). New York, NY: Oxford University Press.

Modahl, C., Green, L., Fein, D., Morris, M., Waterhouse, L., Feinstein, C., & Levin, H. (1998). Plasma oxytocin levels in autistic children. *Biological Psychiatry, 43,* 270–277.

Modinos, G., Mechelli, A., Ormel, J., Groenewold, N., Aleman, A., & McGuire, P. (2009). Schizotypy and brain structure: A voxel-based morphometry study. *Psychological Medicine, 40,* 1423–1431.

Moeller, F. G. (2009). Impulse-control disorders not elsewhere classified. In B. J. Sadock, V. A. Sadock, & P. Ruiz (Eds.), *Kaplan & Sadock's comprehensive textbook of psychiatry* (9th ed., Vol. 1, pp. 2178–2186). Philadelphia, PA: Lippincott Williams & Wilkins.

Moene, F. C., Landberg, E. H., Hoogduin, K. A., Spinhoven, P., Hertzberger, L. I., Kleyweg, R. P., & Weeda, J. (2000). Organic syndromes diagnosed as conversion disorder: Identification and frequency in a study of 85 patients. *Journal of Psychosomatic Research, 49,* 7–12.

Moene, F. C., Spinhoven, P., Hoogduin, K. A., & van Dyck, R. (2002). A randomised controlled clinical trial on the additional effect of hypnosis in a comprehensive treatment programme for in-patients with conversion disorder of the motor type. *Psychotherapy and Psychosomatics, 71,* 66–76.

Moene, F. C., Spinhoven, P., Hoogduin, K. A., & van Dyck, R. (2003). A randomized controlled clinical trial of a hypnosis-based treatment for patients with conversion disorder, motor type. *International Journal of Clinical and Experimental Hypnosis, 51*(1), 29–50.

Mogg, K., Bradley, B. P., Millar, N., & White, J. (1995). A follow-up study of cognitive bias in generalized anxiety disorder. *Behaviour Research & Therapy, 33,* 927–935.

Mogg, K., Mathews, A., & Weinman, J. (1989). Selective processing of threat cues in anxiety states: A replication. *Behaviour Research and Therapy, 27,* 317–323.

Mogg, K., Philippot, P., & Bradley, B. P. (2004). Selective attention to angry faces in clinical social phobia. *Journal of Abnormal Psychology, 113,* 160–165.

Mogil, J. S., Sternberg, W. F., Kest, B., Marek, P., & Liebeskind, J. C. (1993). Sex differences in the antagonism of non-opioid swim stress-induced analgesia: Effects of gonadectomy and estrogen replacement. *Pain, 53,* 17–25.

Mohr, C., Graves, R. E., Gianotti, L. R. R., Pizzagalli, D., & Brugger, P. (2001).

Loose but normal: A semantic association study. *Journal of Psycholinguistic Research, 30,* 475–483.

Mohr, D. C., & Beutler, L. E. (1990). Erectile dysfunction: A review of diagnostic and treatment procedures. *Clinical Psychology Review, 10*(1), 123–150.

Molina, B. S., & Pelham, W. E. (2003). Childhood predictors of adolescent substance use in a longitudinal study of children with ADHD. *Journal of Abnormal Psychology, 112,* 497–507.

Moll, K., Kunze, S., Neuhoff, N., Bruder, J., & Schulte-Körne, G. (2014). Specific learning disorder: Prevalence and gender differences. *PLoS ONE 9*(7), e103537.

Moller-Madsen, S., & Nystrup, J. (1992). Incidence of anorexia nervosa in Denmark. *Acta Psychiatrica Scandinavica, 86,* 197–200.

Money, J., & Ehrhardt, A. (1972). *Man and woman, boy and girl.* Baltimore, MD: Johns Hopkins University Press.

Monk, T. H., Buysse, D. J., & Rose, L. R. (1999). Wrist actigraphic measures of sleep in space. *Sleep, 22,* 948–954.

Monroe, S. M., & Reid, M. W. (2009). Life stress and major depression. *Current Directions in Psychological Science, 18*(2), 68–72.

Monroe, S. M., & Roberts, J. E. (1990). Conceptualizing and measuring life stress: Problems, principles, procedures, progress. [Special issue: II–IV. Advances in measuring life stress]. *Stress Medicine, 6*(3), 209–216.

Monroe, S. M., Bromet, E. J., Connell, M. M., & Steiner, S. C. (1986). Social support, life events, and depressive symptoms: A 1-year prospective study. *Journal of Consulting and Clinical Psychology, 54*(4), 424–431.

Monroe, S. M., Kupfer, D. J., & Frank, E. (1992). Life stress and treatment course of recurrent depression: I. Response during index episode. *Journal of Consulting and Clinical Psychology, 60*(5), 718–724.

Monroe, S. M., Roberts, J. E., Kupfer, D. J., & Frank, E. (1996). Life stress and treatment course of recurrent depression: II. Postrecovery associations with attrition, symptom course, and recurrence over 3 years. *Journal of Abnormal Psychology, 105*(3), 313–328.

Monroe, S. M., Rohde, P., Seeley, J. R., & Lewinsohn, P. M. (1999). Life events and depression in adolescence: For first onset of major depressive disorder. *Journal of Abnormal Psychology, 108*(4), 606–614.

Monroe, S. M., Slavich, G. M., & Georgiades, K. (2009). The social environment and life stress in depression. In I. H. Gotlib & C. L. Hammen (Eds.), *Handbook of depression* (2nd ed., pp. 340–360). New York, NY: Guilford Press.

Monson, C. M., Resick, P. A., & Rizvi, S. L. (2014). Posttraumatic stress disorder. In D. H. Barlow (Ed.), *Clinical handbook of psychological disorders: A step-by-step treatment manual* (5th ed.). New York, NY: Guilford Press.

Montejo-Gonzalez, A. L., Liorca, G., Izquierdo, J. A., Ledesma, A., Bousono, M., Calcedo, A., . . . Vicens, E. (1997). SSRI-Induced sexual dysfunction: Fluoxetine, paroxetine, sertraline, and fluvoxamine in a prospective, multi-center, and descriptive

clinical study of 344 patients. *Journal of Sex and Marital Therapy, 23,* 176–194.

Monti, J. M., Möhler, H., & Pandi-Perumal, S. R. (2010). *GABA and sleep: Molecular, functional, and clinical aspects.* Basel, Switzerland: Springer.

Montiel-Nava, C., Pena, J. A., & Montiel-Barbero, I. (2003). Epidemiological data about attention deficit hyperactivity disorder in a sample of Marabino children. *Revista de Neurologia, 37,* 815–819.

Moore, D. S. (2001). *The dependent gene: The fallacy of "nature vs. nurture."* New York, NY: Henry Holt & Company, LLC.

Moore, M. (2012). Behavioral sleep problems in children and adolescents. *Journal of Clinical Psychology in Medical Settings, 19*(1), 77–83.

Moore, R. Y. (1999). Circadian rhythms: A clock for the ages. *Science, 284,* 2102–2103.

Moreno, A., Azar, M., Warren, N., Dickerson, T., Koob, G., & Janda, K. (2010). A critical evaluation of a nicotine vaccine within a self-administration behavioral model. *Molecular Pharmaceutics, 7*(2), 431–441.

Moreno, C., Laje, G., Blanco, C., Jiang, H., Schmidt, A. B., & Olfson, M. (2007). National trends in the outpatient diagnosis and treatment of bipolar disorder in youth. *Archives of General Psychiatry, 64*(9), 1032–1039.

Moretti, M. M., Charlton, S., & Taylor, S. The effects of hemispheric asymmetries and depression on the perception of emotion. *Brain and Cognition, 32*(1), 67–82.

Morey, L. C. (1988). Personality disorders in DSM-III and DSM-III-R: Convergence, coverage, and internal consistency. *American Journal of Psychiatry, 145,* 573–577.

Morey, L. C., & Kurtz, J. E. (1989). *The place of neurasthenia in the DSM-IV.* Unpublished report to the DSM-IV subgroup on generalized anxiety disorder and mixed anxiety depression.

Morey, L. C., & Ochoa, E. S. (1989). An investigation of adherence to diagnostic criteria: Clinical diagnosis of the DSM-III personality disorders. *Journal of Personality Disorders, 3*(3), 180–192.

Morey, L. C., Hopwood, C. J., & Klein, D. (2007). Depressive, passive-aggressive, and sadistic personality disorders. In W. O'; Donohue, K. A. Fowler, & S. O. Lilienfeld (Eds.), *Personality disorders: Toward the DSM-V* (pp. 353–374). Thousand Oaks, CA: Sage Publications.

Morgan, D. (2007). The rationale for an immunological approach to Alzheimer's therapeutics. In A. C. Cuello (Ed.), *Pharmacological mechanisms in Alzheimer's therapeutics* (pp. 141–148). New York, NY: Springer.

Morgan, H. W. (1981). *Drugs in America: A social history, 1800–1980.* Syracuse, NY: Syracuse University Press.

Morgan, J. P. (1997). Designer drugs. In J. H. Lowinson, P. Ruiz, R. B. Millman, & J. G. Langrod (Eds.), *Substance abuse: A comprehensive textbook* (pp. 264–269). Baltimore, MD: Williams & Wilkins.

Morgenthaler, T. I., & Silber, M. H. (2002). Amnestic sleep-related eating disorder associated with zolpidem. *Sleep Medicine, 3,* 323–327.

Morgenthaler, T. I., Kapur, V. K., Brown, T., Swick, T. J., Alessi, C., Aurora, R. N., & Standards of Practice Committee of the American Academy of Sleep Medicine. (2007). Practice parameters for the treatment of narcolepsy and other hypersomnias of central origin. *Sleep, 30*(12), 1705–1711.

Morin, C. M. (1993). *Insomnia: Psychological assessment and management.* New York, NY: Guilford Press.

Morin, C. M., & Azrin, N. H. (1988). Behavioral and cognitive treatments of geriatric insomnia. *Journal of Consulting and Clinical Psychology, 56*, 748–753.

Morin, C. M., & Benca, R. (2012). Chronic insomnia. *The Lancet, 379*(9821), 1129–1141.

Morin, C. M., Colecchi, C., Stone, J., Sood, R., & Brink, D. (1999). Behavioral and pharmacological therapies for late-life insomnia: A randomized controlled trial. *JAMA, 281*, 991–999.

Morin, C. M., Kowatch, R. A., Barry, T., & Walton, E. (1993). Cognitive-behavior therapy for late-life insomnia. *Journal of Consulting and Clinical Psychology, 61*, 137–146.

Morin, C. M., Leblanc, M., Bélanger, L., Ivers, H., Mérette, C., & Savard, J. (2011). Prevalence of insomnia and its treatment in Canada. *Canadian Journal of Psychiatry, 56*, 540–548.

Morin, C. M., Rodrigue, S., & Ivers, H. (2003). Role of stress, arousal, and coping skills in primary insomnia. *Psychosomatic Medicine, 65*, 259–267.

Morin, C. M., Savard, J., & Ouellet, M. C. (2012). Nature and treatment of insomnia. In I. B. Weiner, A. M. Nezu, C. M. Nezu, & P. A. Geller (Eds.), *Handbook of psychology: Health psychology* (Vol. 9, pp. 318–339).

Morin, C. M., Savard, J., Ouellet, M. C., & Daley, M. (2003). Insomnia: Nature, epidemiology and treatment. In. A. M. Nezu, C. M. Nezu, & P. A. Geller (Eds.), *Handbook of psychology: Health psychology* (Vol. 9, pp. 317–337). New York, NY: John Wiley & Sons.

Morin, C. M., Stone, J., Trinkle, D., Mercer, J., & Remsberg, S. (1993). Dysfunctional beliefs and attitudes about sleep among older adults with and without insomnia complaints. *Psychology and Aging, 8*, 463–467.

Morin, C. M., & Wooten, V. (1996). Psychological and pharmacological approaches to treating insomnia: Critical issues in assessing their separate and combined effects. *Clinical Psychology Review, 16*, 521–542.

Morris, J. K., Cook, D. G., & Shaper, A. G. (1994). Loss of employment and mortality. *BMJ, 308*, 1135–1139.

Morris, J. S., Öhman, A., & Dolan, R. J. (1998). Conscious and unconscious emotion learning in the human amygdala. *Nature, 393*, 467–470.

Morris, M., Lack, L., & Dawson, D. (1990). Sleep-onset insomniacs have delayed temperature rhythms. *Sleep, 13*, 1–14.

Morris, S., Fawcett, G., Brisebois, L., & Hughes, J. (2018). A demographic, employment and income profile of Canadians with disabilities aged 15 years and over, 2017. *Canadian Survey on Disability Reports* (Catalogue No. 89-654-X2018002). https://www150.statcan.gc.ca/n1/en/catalogue/89-654-X2018002

Morrison, A. S., & Heimberg, R. G. (2013). Social anxiety and social anxiety disorder. *Annual Review of Clinical Psychology, 9*, 249–274.

Morrow, G. R., & Dobkin, P. L. (1988). Anticipatory nausea and vomiting in cancer patients undergoing chemotherapy treatment: Prevalence, etiology, and behavioral interventions. *Clinical Psychology Review, 8*, 517–556.

Mörtberg, E., Clark, D. M., & Bejerot, S. (2011). Intensive group cognitive therapy and individual cognitive therapy for social phobia: Sustained improvement at 5-year follow-up. *Journal of Anxiety Disorders, 25*, 994–1000.

Morton, A. (1992). *Diana: Her true story.* New York, NY: Pocket Books.

Mosher, D. L., & Sirkin, M. (1984). Measuring a macho personality constellation. *Journal of Research in Personality, 18*, 150–163.

Mosher, W. D., Chandra, A., & Jones, J. (2005). Sexual behavior and selected health measures: Men and women 15–44 years of age, United States, 2002. *Advance data from vital and health statistics, 362*, 1–55. Hyattsville, MD: National Center for Health Statistics.

Moskowitz, A. (2004). "Scared stiff": Catatonia as an evolutionary based fear response. *Psychological Review, 111*, 984–1002.

Mostofsky, D. I., & Barlow, D. H. (Eds.). (2000). *The management of stress and anxiety in medical disorders.* Needham Heights, MA: Allyn & Bacon.

Moulton, D. (2004, April 27). N.S.'s concern over oxycontin use rises: Government and college step in to stem narcotic abuse. *Medical Post, 40*(17). Retrieved May 17, 2004, from http://www.medicalpost.com/mpcontent/article.jsp?content20040425_093635_5176

Mucha, T. F., & Reinhardt, R. F. (1970). Conversion reactions in student aviators. *American Journal of Psychiatry, 127*, 493–497.

Mueller, T., Keller, M. B., Leon, A. C., Solomon, D. A., Shea, M. T., Coryell, W., & Endicott, J. (1996). Recovery after 5 years of unremitting major depressive disorder. *Archives of General Psychiatry, 53*, 794–799.

Mueser, K. T., & Berenbaum, H. (1990). Psychodynamic treatment of schizophrenia: Is there a future? *Psychological Medicine, 20*, 253–262.

Mueser, K. T., Liberman, R. P., & Glynn, S. M. (1990). Psychosocial interventions in schizophrenia. In A. Kales, C. N. Stefanis, & J. A. Talbott (Eds.), *Recent advances in schizophrenia* (pp. 213–235). New York, NY: Springer-Verlag.

Mueser, K. T., & Marcello, S. (2010). Schizophrenia. In D. H. Barlow (Ed.), *Oxford handbook of clinical psychology.* New York, NY: Oxford University Press.

Mulder, R., Frampton, C., Luty, S., & Joyce, P. (2009). Eighteen months of drug treatment for depression: Predicting relapse and recovery. *Journal of Affective Disorders, 114*(1–3), 263–270.

Mullane, J., & Corkum, P. (2006). Case series: Evaluation of a behavioral sleep intervention for three children with attention-deficit/hyperactivity disorder and dyssomnia. *Journal of Attention Disorders, 10*, 217–227.

Mullen, P. (2010). The psychiatric expert witness in the criminal justice system. *Criminal Behaviour and Mental Health, 20*(3), 165–176.

Mumford, D. B., Whitehouse, A. M., & Platts, M. (1991). Sociocultural correlates of eating disorders among Asian schoolgirls in Bradford. *British Journal of Psychiatry, 158*, 222–228.

Munder, T., Flückiger, C., Gerger, H., Wampold, B. E., & Barth, J. (2012). Is the allegiance effect an epiphenomenon of true efficacy differences between treatments? A meta-analysis. *Journal of Counseling Psychology, 59*(4), 631–637.

Munjack, D. J. (1984). The onset of driving phobias. *Journal of Behavior Therapy and Experimental Psychiatry, 15*, 305–308.

Muñoz, R. F., Beardslee, W. R., Leykin, Y. (2012). Major depression can be prevented. *American Psychologist, 67*(4), 285–295.

Muñoz, R. F., Cuijpers, P., Smit, F., Barrera, A. Z., & Leykin, Y. (2010). Prevention of major depression. *Annual Review of Clinical Psychology, 6*, 181–212.

Munro, A. (2012). Persistent delusional symptoms and disorders. In M. G. Gelder, N. C. Andreasen, J. J. Lopez-Ibor, & J. R. Geddes (Eds.), *New Oxford textbook of psychiatry* (2nd ed., Vol. 1, pp. 609–628). New York, NY: Oxford University Press.

Muresanu, D. F., Stan, A., & Buzoianu, A. (2012). Neuroplasticity and impulse control disorders. *Journal of the Neurological Sciences, 316*(1–2), 15–20.

Muris, P., & Field, A. P. (2010). The role of verbal threat information in the development of childhood fear. "Beware the Jabberwock." *Clinical Child and Family Psychology Review, 13*, 129–150.

Murphy, J. A., & Byrne, G. J. (2012). Prevalence and correlates of the proposed DSM-5 diagnosis of chronic depressive disorder. *Journal of Affective Disorders, 139*, 172–180.

Murphy, K. R. (2015). Psychological counseling of adults with ADHD. In R. A. Barkley (Ed.), *Attention-deficit hyperactivity disorder: A handbook for diagnosis and treatment* (4th ed., pp. 741–756). New York, NY: Guilford Press.

Murphy, T. K., Storch, E. A., Lewin, A. B., Edge, P. J., & Goodman, W. K. (2012). Clinical factors associated with pediatric autoimmune neuropsychiatric disorders associated with streptococcal infections. *Journal of Pediatrics, 160*, 314–319.

Murphy, W. D., & Page, I. J. (2008). Exhibitionism: Psychopathology and theory. In D. R. Laws & W. T. O Donohue (Eds.), *Sexual deviance: Theory, assessment, and treatment* (2nd ed., pp. 61–75). New York, NY: Guilford Press.

Murray, B. L., & Wright, K. (2006). Integration of a suicide risk assessment and intervention approach: The perspective of youth. *Journal of Psychiatric and Mental Health Nursing, 13*, 157–164.

Murray, J. B. (1998). Effectiveness of methadone maintenance for heroin addiction. *Psychological Reports, 83*, 295–302.

Murray, R. M., & Castle, D. J. (2012). Genetic and environmental risk factors for schizophrenia. In M. G. Gelder, N. C. Andreasen, J. J. Lopez-Ibor, Jr., & J. R. Geddes (Eds.), *New Oxford textbook of psychiatry* (2nd ed., Vol. 1, pp. 553–561). New York, NY: Oxford University Press.

Mushquash, C., & Bova, D. (2007). Cross-cultural measurement and assessment issues. *Journal on Developmental Disabilities, 12*, 53–66.

Mustafa, G. (1990). Delivery systems for the care of schizophrenic patients in Africa—Sub-Sahara. In A. Kales, C. N. Stefanis, & J. A. Talbot (Eds.), *Recent advances in schizophrenia* (pp. 353–371). New York, NY: Springer-Verlag.

Myers, J. K., Weissman, M. M., Tischler, C. E., Holzer, C. E., III, Orvaschel, H., Anthony, J. C., . . . Stoltzman, R. (1984). Six-month prevalence of psychiatric disorders in three communities: 1980 to 1982. *Archives of General Psychiatry, 41*, 959–967.

Myers, K., & Collett, B. (2006). Rating scales. In M. K. Dulcan & J. M. Wiener (Eds.), *Essentials of child and adolescent psychiatry* (pp. 81–97). Washington, DC: American Psychiatric Publishing.

Nachmias, M., Gunnar, M., Mangelsdorf, S., Parritz, R. H., & Buss, K. (1996). Behavioral inhibition and stress reactivity: The moderating role of attachment security. *Child Development, 67*(2), 508–522.

Nagel, D. B. (1991). Psychotherapy of schizophrenia: 1900–1920. In J. G. Howells (Ed.), *The concept of schizophrenia: Historical perspectives* (pp. 191–201). Washington, DC: American Psychiatric Press.

Nagin, D. S., & Tremblay, R. E. (2001). Parental and early childhood predictors of persistent physical aggression in boys from kindergarten to high school. *Archives of General Psychiatry, 58*, 389–394.

Nagin, D., & Tremblay, R. E. (1999). Trajectories of boys' physical aggression, opposition, and hyperactivity on the path to physically violent and nonviolent juvenile delinquency. *Child Development, 70*, 1181–1196.

Nair, N. P., Hariharasubramanian, N., & Pilapil, C. (1984). Circadian rhythm of plasma melatonin in endogenous depression. *Progress in Neuro-Psychopharmacology and Biological Psychiatry, 8*, 715–718.

Najavits, L. M. (2007). Psychosocial treatments for posttraumatic stress disorder. In P. E. Nathan & J. M. Gorman (Eds.), *A guide to treatments that work* (3rd ed.). New York, NY: Oxford University Press.

Narrow, W. E., Clarke, D. E., Kuramoto, S. J., Kraemer, H. C., Kupfer, D. J., Greiner, L., & Regier, D. A. (2014). DSM-5 field trials in the United States and Canada, Part III: Development and reliability testing of a cross-cutting symptom assessment for DSM-5. *American Journal of Psychiatry, 170*(1), 71–82.

Nash, W. P., Boasso, A. M., Steenkamp, M. M., Larson, J. L., Lubin, R. E., & Litz, B. T. (2014). Posttraumatic stress In deployed marines: Prospective trajectories of early adaptation. *Journal of Abnormal Psychology, 124*, 155–171.

Nasser, M. (1988). Eating disorders: The cultural dimension. *Social Psychiatry and Psychiatric Epidemiology, 23*, 184–187.

Nathan, P. E. (1993). Alcoholism: Psychopathology, etiology, and treatment. In P. B. Sutker & H. E. Adams (Eds.), *Comprehensive handbook of psychopathology* (pp. 451–476). New York, NY: Plenum Press.

National Center for Health Statistics. (1993). *Advance report of final mortality statistics, 1990* (Monthly Vital Statistics Report, Vol. 41, No. 7, Suppl.). Hyattsville, MD: Public Health Service.

National Collaborating Centre for Mental Health. (2009). *Borderline personality disorder: The NICE GUIDELINE on treatment and management, clinical practice guideline No. 78*. London, UK: British Psychological Society & Royal College of Psychiatrists.

National Initiative for Eating Disorders. (2019). *About eating disorders in Canada*. https://nied.ca/about-eating-disorders-in-canada/

National Institute of Mental Health. (2003). *Breaking ground, breaking through: The strategic plan for mood disorders research* (NIH Publication No. 03-5121). Washington, DC: U.S. Government Printing Office.

National Institute on Drug Abuse. (2009). *Principles of addiction treatment: A research-based guide* (2nd ed.). NIH Publication No. 09-4180. Rockville, MD: National Institute on Drug Abuse.

Natoli, J. L., Ackerman, D. L., McDermott, S., & Edwards, J. G. (2012). Prenatal diagnosis of Down syndrome: A systematic review of termination rates (1995–2011). *Prenatal diagnosis, 32*(2), 142–153.

Natsuaki, M., Cicchetti, D., & Rogosch, F. (2009). Examining the developmental history of child maltreatment, peer relations, and externalizing problems among adolescents with symptoms of paranoid personality disorder. *Development and Psychopathology, 21*(4), 1181–1193.

Navaneelan, T. (2012). Suicide rates: An overview (Catalogue No. 82-624-X). Ottawa, ON: Statistics Canada. Retrieved from http://www.statcan.gc.ca/pub/82-624-x/2012001/article/11696-eng.pdf

Navarrete, C. D., Olsson, A., Ho, A. K., Mendes, W. B., Thomsen, L., & Sidanius, J. (2009). Fear extinction to an out-group face: The role of target gender. *Psychological Science, 20*(2), 155–158.

Navia, B. A. (1990). The AIDS dementia complex. In J. L. Cummings (Ed.), *Subcortical dementia* (pp. 181–198). New York, NY: Oxford University Press.

Nealis, L. J., Thompson, K. D., Krank, M. D., & Stewart, S. H. (2016). Shifting patterns of variance in adolescent alcohol use: Testing consumption as a developing trait-state. *Addictive Behaviors, 55*, 25–31.

Neighbors, H. W., Jackson, J. S., Campbell, L., & Williams, D. (1989). The influence of racial factors on psychiatric diagnosis: A review and suggestions for research. *Community Mental Health Journal, 25*(4), 301–311.

Neill, M., & Sider, D. (1992, April 27). On the rebound. *People*, 97. Retrieved June 24, 2004, from http://www.eatingdisorderresources.com/peoplemag/042792carlingbassett.htm

Neimeyer, R. A., & Currier, J. M. (2009). Grief therapy: Evidence of efficacy and emerging directions. *Current Directions in Psychological Science, 18*(6), 352–356.

Nelles, W. B. N., & Barlow, D. H. (1988). Do children panic? *Clinical Psychology Review, 8*(4), 359–372.

Nelson, B., Yuen, H. P., Wood, S. J., Lin, A., Spiliotacopoulos, D., Bruxner, A., … Francey, S. M. (2013). Long-term follow-up of a group at ultra high risk ("prodromal") for psychosis: The PACE 400 study. *JAMA Psychiatry, 70*(8), 793–802.

Nelson, R. O., & Barlow, D. H. (1981). Behavioral assessment: Basic strategies and initial procedures. In D. H. Barlow (Ed.), *Behavioral assessment of adult disorders*. New York, NY: Guilford Press.

Nelson, S. E., & Wilson, K. (2017). The mental health of Indigenous peoples in Canada: A critical review of research. *Social Science and Medicine, 176*, 93–112.

Nemeroff, C. (2006). The burden of severe depression: A review of diagnostic challenges and treatment alternatives. *Journal of Psychiatric Research, 41*(3–4), 189–206.

Nepon, J., Belik, S. L., Bolton, J., & Sareen, J. (2010). The relationship between anxiety disorders and suicide attempts: Findings from the national epidemiologic survey on alcohol and related conditions. *Depression and Anxiety, 27*, 791–798.

Nestadt, G., Romanoski, A. J., Chahal, R., Merchant, A., Folstein, M. F., Gruenberg, E. M., & McHugh, P. R. (1990). An epidemiological study of histrionic personality disorder. *Psychological Medicine, 20*, 413–422.

Nestadt, G., Romanoski, A., Chahal, R., Merchant, A., Folstein, M., Gruenberg, E., & McHugh, P. R. (2009). An epidemiological study of histrionic personality disorder. *Psychological Medicine, 20*(2), 413–422.

Nestler, E. J., Hyman, S. E., & Malenka, R. C. (2008). *Molecular neuropharmacology* (2nd ed.). New York, NY: McGraw-Hill.

Nestor, P. G. (2002). Mental disorder and violence: Personality dimensions and clinical features. *American Journal of Psychiatry, 159*, 1973–1978.

Neubauer, D. (2009). New directions in the pharmacologic treatment of sleep disorders. *Primary Psychiatry, 16*(2), 52–58.

Neugroschi, J. A., Kolevzon, A., Samuels, S. C., & Marin, D. B. (2005). Dementia. In B. J. Sadock & V. A. Sadock (Eds.), *Kaplan & Sadock's comprehensive textbook of psychiatry* (pp. 1068–1093). Philadelphia, PA: Lippincott, Williams & Wilkins.

Neumark-Sztainer, D., Wall, M., Larson, N. I., Eisenberg, M. E., & Loth, K. (2011). Dieting and disordered eating behaviors from adolescence to young adulthood: Findings from a 10-year longitudinal study. *Journal of the American Dietetic Association, 111*(7), 1004–1011.

Neutel, C. I. (2005). The epidemiology of long-term benzodiazepine use. *International Review of Psychiatry, 17*(3), 189–197.

Nevsimalova, S. (2009). Narcolepsy in childhood. *Sleep Medicine Reviews, 13*(2), 169–180.

Newlin, D. B. (1989). The skin-flushing response: Autonomic, self-report, and conditioned responses to repeated administrations of alcohol in Asian men. *Journal of Abnormal Psychology, 98*, 421–425.

Newman, J. P., & Wallace, J. F. (1993). Psychopathy and cognition. In K. S. Dobson & P. C. Kendall (Eds.), *Psychopathology and cognition* (pp. 293–349). New York, NY: Academic Press.

Newman, J. P., Patterson, C. M., & Kosson, D. S. (1987). Response perseveration in psychopaths. *Journal of Abnormal Psychology, 96*, 145–148.

Newman, J. P., Widom, C. S., & Nathan, S. (1985). Passive-avoidance in syndromes of disinhibition: Psychopathy and extraversion. *Journal of Personality and Social Psychology, 50*, 624–630.

Newman, M. G., Castonguay, L. G., Borkovec, T. D., Fisher, A. J., Boswell, J. F., Szkodny, L. E., & Nordberg, S. S. (2011). A randomized controlled trial of cognitive-behavioral therapy for generalized anxiety disorder with integrated techniques from emotion-focused and interpersonal therapies. *Journal of Consulting and Clinical Psychology, 79*(2), 171–181.

Newman, S. C., & Bland, R. C. (1994). Life events and the 1-year prevalence of major depressive episode, generalized anxiety disorder, and panic disorder in a community sample. *Comprehensive Psychiatry, 35*, 76–82.

Neylan, T. C., Reynolds, C. F., III, & Kupfer, D. J. (2003). Sleep disorders. In R. E. Hales & S. C. Yudofsky (Eds.), *Textbook of clinical psychiatry* (4th ed., pp. 975–1000). Washington, DC: American Psychiatric Publishing.

Nezami, E., & Butcher, J. N. (2000). Objective personality assessment. In G. Goldstein & M. Hersen (Eds.), *Handbook of psychological assessment* (pp. 413–435). New York, NY: Pergamon Press.

Nezu, C. M., Nezu, A. M., Friedman, S. H., Houts, P. S., DelliCarpini, L., Bildner, C., & Faddis, S. (1999). Cancer and psychological distress: Two investigations regarding the role of social problem-solving. *Journal of Psychosocial Oncology, 16*(3–4), 27–40.

Nicassio, P. M., Greenberg, M. A., & Motivala, S. J. (2010). Clinical psychology and health psychology: Toward an integrated perspective on health. In J. M. Suls, K. W. Davidson, & R. M. Kaplan (Eds.), *Handbook of health psychology and behavioral medicine*. New York, NY: Guilford Press.

Nicol, J. J., Yarema, M. C., Jones, G. R., Martz, W., Purssell, R. A., MacDonald, J. C., Wishart, I., Durigon, M., Tzemis, D., & Buxton, J. A. (2015). Deaths from exposure to paramethoxymethamphetamine in Alberta and British Columbia, Canada: A case series. *CMAJ Open, 3*(1), E83–90. https://doi.org/10.9778/cmajo.20140070

Nicholls, T. L., Ogloff, J. R. P., & Douglas, K. S. (2004). Assessing risk for violence among male and female civil psychiatric patients: The HCR-20, PCL:SV, and VSC. *Behavioral Sciences & the Law, 22*, 127–158.

Nicholls, T. L., Ogloff, J. R. P., Brink, J., & Spidel, A. (2005). Psychopathology in women: A review of its clinical usefulness for assessing risk for aggression and criminality. *Behavioral Sciences and the Law, 23*, 779–802.

Nicholls, T., Jack, L., & Ogloff, J. R. P. (1998, March). *Comorbidity of violence against self and violence against others in a civil psychiatric population*. Poster presented at the Biennial Meeting of the American Psychology Law Society, Redondo Beach, CA.

Nichols, D. S. (2011). *Essentials of MMPI-2 assessment* (2nd ed.). Hoboken, NJ: Wiley.

Nichols, M. (with S. Dolye Driedger & D. Ballon). (1995, January 30). Schizophrenia: Hidden torment. *Maclean's*. Retrieved December 11, 2006, from http://www.mentalhealth.com/mag1/p51-sc01.html

Nicolosi, A., Laumann, E. O., Glasser, D. B., Brock, G., King, R., & Gingell, C. (2006). Sexual activity, sexual disorders and associated help-seeking behavior among mature adults in five anglophone countries from the global survey of sexual attitudes and behaviors (GSSAB). *Journal of Sex & Marital Therapy, 32*, 331–342.

Nielsen, T. A., Stenstrom, P., & Levin, R. (2006). Nightmare frequency as a function of age, gender, and September 11, 2001: Findings from an internet questionnaire. *Dreaming, 16*, 145–158.

Nierenberg, A. A., Akiskal, H. S., Angst, J., Hirschfeld, R. M., Merikangas, K. R., Petukhova, M., & Kessler, R. C. (2010). Bipolar disorder with frequent mood episodes in the national comorbidity survey replication (NCS-R). *Molecular Psychiatry, 15*(11), 1075–1087.

Nierenberg, A. A., Friedman, E. S., Bowden, C. L., Sylvia, L. G., Thase, M. E., Ketter, T., & Calabrese, J. R. (2013). Lithium treatment moderate-dose use study (LiTMUS) for bipolar disorder: A randomized comparative effectiveness trial of optimized personalized treatment with and without lithium. *American Journal of Psychiatry, 170*(1), 102–110.

Nigg, J. T. (2015). Editorial: The shape of the nosology to come in developmental psychopathology. *Journal of Child Psychology and Psychiatry, 56*(4), 397–399.

Nigg, J. T., Nikolas, M., & Burt, S. A. (2010). Measured gene-by-environment interaction in relation to attention-deficit/hyperactivity disorder. *Journal of the American Academy of Child & Adolescent Psychiatry, 49*(9), 863–873.

Nikolas, M., & Burt, S. (2010). Genetic and environmental influences on ADHD symptom dimensions of inattention and hyperactivity: A meta-analysis. *Journal of Abnormal Psychology, 119*(1), 1.

Nikolas, M. A., & Nigg, J. T. (2015). Moderators of neuropsychological mechanism in Attention-Deficit Hyperactivity Disorder. *Journal of Abnormal Child Psychology, 43*(2), 271–281.

Nisbett, R. E., & Ross, L. (1980). *Human inference: Strategies and shortcomings in social judgement*. New York, NY: Century.

Nock, M. K., Borges, G., Bromet, E. J., Cha, C. B., Kessler, R. C., & Lee, S. (2008). Suicide and suicidal behavior. *Epidemiologic Reviews, 30*, 133–154.

Nock, M. K., Cha, C. B., & Dour, H. J. (2011). Disorders of impulse-control and self-harm. In D. H. Barlow (Ed.), *Oxford handbook of clinical psychology* (pp. 504–529). New York, NY: Oxford University.

Nock, M. K., Hwang, I., Sampson, N. A., & Kessler, R. C. (2010). Mental disorders, comorbidity and suicidal behavior: Results from the National Comorbidity Survey Replication. *Molecular Psychiatry, 15*, 868–876.

Nofzinger, E. A., Schwartz, C. F., Reynolds, C. F., Thase, M. E., Jennings, J. R., Frank, E., … Kupfer, D. J. (1994). Affect intensity and phasic REM sleep in depressed men before and after treatment with cognitive-behavior therapy. *Journal of Consulting and Clinical Psychology, 62*, 83–91.

Nolen-Hoeksema, S. (1987). Sex differences in unipolar depression: Evidence and theory. *Psychological Bulletin, 101*(2), 259–282.

Nolen-Hoeksema, S. (1990). *Sex differences in depression.* Stanford, CA: Stanford University Press.

Nolen-Hoeksema, S. (2000a). Further evidence for the role of psychosocial factors in depression chronicity. *Clinical Psychology: Science and Practice, 7*(2), 224–227.

Nolen-Hoeksema, S. (2000b). The role of rumination in depressive disorders and mixed anxiety/depressive symptoms. *Journal of Abnormal Psychology, 109*, 504–511.

Nolen-Hoeksema, S., & Hilt, L. M. (2009). Gender differences in depression. In I. H. Gotlib & C. L. Hammen (Eds.), *Handbook of depression* (2nd ed., pp. 386–404). New York, NY: Guilford, Press.

Nolen-Hoeksema, S., Girgus, J. S., & Seligman, M. E. P. (1992). Predictors and consequences of childhood depressive symptoms: A 5-year longitudinal study. *Journal of Abnormal Psychology, 101*(3), 405–422.

Nolen-Hoeksema, S., Wisco, B. E., & Lyubomirsky, S. (2008). Rethinking rumination. *Perspectives on Psychological Science, 3*(5), 400–424.

Noonan, D. (2003). Exposing the myth of violence. *Schizophrenia Digest.* Retrieved November 10, 2003, from http://www.schizophreniadigest.com/images/archive/phpVQLG8H.pdf

Nordentoft, M., Melau, M., Iversen, T., Petersen, L., Jeppesen, P., Thorup, A., … Jørgensen, P. (2015). From research to practice: How OPUS treatment was accepted and implemented throughout Denmark. *Early Intervention in Psychiatry, 9*(2), 156–162.

Norman, R. M. G., & Townsend, L. A. (1999). Cognitive-behavioural therapy for psychosis: A status report. *Canadian Journal of Psychiatry, 44*, 245–252.

Norman, R. M. G., Malla, A. K., McLean, T. S., McIntosh, E. M., Neufeld, R. W. J., Voruganti, L. P., & Cortese, L. (2002). An evaluation of a stress management program for individuals with schizophrenia. *Schizophrenia Research, 58*(2–3), 293–303.

Normile, D. (2009). Asia grapples with unexpected wave of HIV infections. *Science, 27*, 1174.

Norrholm, S. D., & Ressler, K. J. (2009). Genetics of anxiety and trauma-related disorders. *Neuroscience, 164*(1), 272–287.

Norton, G. R., Harrison, B., Hauch, J., & Rhodes, L. (1985). Characteristics of people with infrequent panic attacks. *Journal of Abnormal Psychology, 94*, 216–221.

Norton, G. R., Norton, P. J., Cox, B. J., & Belik, S. (2008). Panic spectrum disorders and substance use. In S. H. Stewart & P. J. Conrod (Eds.), *Anxiety*

and substance abuse disorders: The vicious cycle of comorbidity. New York, NY: Springer.

Noyes, R., & Kletti, R. (1977). Depersonalization in response to life-threatening danger. *Comprehensive Psychiatry, 18*, 375–384.

Noyes, R., Clarkson, C., Crowe, R. R., Yates, W. R., & McChesney, C. M. (1987). A family study of generalized anxiety disorder. *American Journal of Psychiatry, 144*, 1019–1024.

Noyes, R., Garvey, M. J., Cook, B., & Suelzer, M. (1991). Controlled discontinuation of benzodiazepine treatment for patients with panic disorder. *American Journal of Psychiatry, 148*, 517–523.

Noyes, R., Jr., Stuart, S. P., & Watson, D. B. (2008). A reconceptualization of the somatoform disorders. *Psychosomatics, 49*(1), 14–22.

Noyes, R., Stuart, S. P., Langbehn, D. R., Happel, R. L., Longley, S. L., Muller, B. A., & Yagla, S. J. (2003). Test of an interpersonal model of hypochondriasis. *Psychosomatic Medicine, 65*, 292–300.

Noyes, R., Watson, D., Carney, C., Letuchy, E., Peloso, P., Black, D., & Doebbeling, B. N. (2004). Risk factors for hypochondriacal concerns in a sample of military veterans. *Journal of Psychosomatic Research, 57*, 529–539.

Noyes, R., Woodman, C., Garvey, M. J., Cook, B. L., Suelzer, M., Clancy, J., & Anderson, D. J. (1992). Generalized anxiety disorder vs. panic disorder: Distinguishing characteristics and patterns of comorbidity. *Journal of Nervous and Mental Disease, 180*, 369–379.

Nugent, S. A. (2000). Perfectionism: Its manifestations and classroom-based interventions. *Journal of Secondary Gifted Education, 11*, 215–221.

Nurnberg, H. G., Raskin, M., Levine, P. E., Pollack, S., Siegel, O., & Prince, R. (1991). The comorbidity of borderline personality and other DSM-III-R axis II personality disorders. *American Journal of Psychiatry, 148*, 1371–1377.

Nurnberger, J. I. (2012). Genetics of bipolar disorder: Where we are and where we are going. *Depression and Anxiety, 29*, 991–993.

Nurnberger, J. I., & Gershon, E. S. (1992). Genetics. In E. S. Paykel (Ed.), *Handbook of affective disorders* (pp. 126–145). New York, NY: Guilford Press.

Nusslock, R., Harmon-Jones, E., Alloy, L. B., Urosevic, S., Goldstein, K., & Abramson, L. Y. (2012). Elevated left mid-frontal cortical activity prospectively predicts conversion to bipolar I disorder. *Journal of Abnormal Psychology, 121*(3), 592–601.

Nyhan, W. L. (1978). The Lesch-Nyhan syndrome. *Developmental Medicine and Child Neurology, 20*, 376–387.

Nzwalo, H., Ferreira, L., Peralta, R., & Bentes, C. (2013). Sleep-related eating disorder secondary to zolpidem. *BMJ Case Reports*, bcr2012008003.

O'Brien, C. (2011). Addiction and dependence in DSM-V. *Addiction, 106*(5), 866–867.

O'Brien, C. P. (1996). Recent developments in the pharmacotherapy of substance abuse. *Journal of Consulting and Clinical Psychology, 64*, 677–686.

O'Brien, C. P., & Cornish, J. W. (1999). Opioids: Antagonists and partial

agonists. In M. Galanter & H. D. Kleber (Eds.), *Textbook of substance abuse treatment* (2nd ed., pp. 281–294). Washington, DC: American Psychiatric Press.

O'Brien, K. M., & Vincent, N. K. (2003). Psychiatric comorbidity in anorexia and bulimia nervosa: Nature, prevalence and causal relationships. *Clinical Psychology Review, 23*, 57–74.

O'Brien, M. E., Clark, R. A., Besch, C. L., Myers, L., & Kissinger, P. (2003). Patterns and correlates of discontinuation of the initial HAART regimen in an urban outpatient cohort. *Journal of Acquired Immune Deficiency Syndrome, 34*(4), 407–414.

O'Brien, M. M., Trestman, R. L., & Siever, L. J. (1993). Cluster A personality disorders. In D. L. Dunner (Ed.), *Current psychiatric therapy* (pp. 399–404). Philadelphia, PA: W. B. Saunders.

O'Brien, P. M., Backstrom, T., Brown, C., Dennerstein, L., Endicott, J., Epperson, C. N., & Yonkers, K. (2011). Towards a consensus on diagnostic criteria, measurement and trial design of the premenstrual disorders: The ISPMD Montreal consensus. *Archives of Women's Mental Health, 14*(1), 13–21.

O'Callaghan, E., Sham, P., Takei, N., Glover, G., & Murray, R. M. (1991). Schizophrenia after prenatal exposure to 1957 A2 influenza epidemic. *Lancet, 337*, 1248–1250.

O'Connor, S., Grywacheski, V., & Louie, K. (2018). Hospitalizations and emergency department visits due to opioid poisoning in Canada. *Health Promotion and Chronic Disease Prevention in Canada, 38*(6), 244–247.

O'Carroll, P. W. (1990). Community strategies for suicide prevention and intervention. In S. J. Blumenthal & D. J. Kupfer (Eds.), *Suicide over the life cycle: Risk factors, assessment and treatment of suicidal patients.* Washington, DC: American Psychiatric Press.

O'Donnell, M. L., Varker, T., Creamer, M., Fletcher, S., McFarlane, A. C., Silove, D., & Forbes, D. (2013). Exploration of delayed-onset posttraumatic stress disorder after severe injury. *Psychosomatic Medicine, 75*, 68–75.

O'Donnell, S., Cheung, R., Bennett K., & Lagacé, C. (2016). The 2014 survey on living with chronic diseases in Canada on mood and anxiety disorders: A methodological overview. *Health Promotion and Chronic Disease Prevention in Canada, 36*(12), 275–288. https://www.canada.ca/content/dam/phac-aspc/migration/phac-aspc/publicat/hpcdp-pspmc/36-12/assets/pdf/ar-02-eng.pdf

O'Driscoll, G. A., Benkelfat, C., Florencio, P. S., Wolff, A. L. V. G., Joober, R., Lal, S., & Evans, A. C. (1999). Neural correlates of eye tracking deficits in first-degree relatives of schizophrenic patients: A positron emission tomography study. *Archives of General Psychiatry, 56*, 1127–1134.

O'Driscoll, G. A., Departié, L., Holahan, A. L. V., Savion-Lemieux, T., Barr, R. G., Jolicoeur, C., & Douglas, V. I. (2005). Executive functions and methylphenidate response in subtypes of attentiondeficit/hyperactivity disorder. *Biological Psychiatry, 57*, 1452–1460.

O'Driscoll, G. A., Lenzenweger, M. F., & Holzman, P. S. (1998). Antisaccades and smooth pursuit eye tracking

and schizotypy. *Archives of General Psychiatry, 55*, 837–843.

O'Hagan, S. (1992, February 22). Raving madness. *The Times Saturday Review*, pp. 10–12.

O'Hara, A. (2004). *Missing/murdered First Nations (Native) women.* Retrieved July 4, 2004, from http://www.missingnativewomen.ca/index.html

O'Hara, M. W. (1986). Social support, life events and depression during pregnancy and the puerperium. *Archives of General Psychiatry, 43*(6), 569–575.

O'Hara, M. W., & McCabe, J. E. (2013). Postpartum depression: Current status and future directions. *Annual Review of Clinical Psychology, 9*, 379–407.

O'Hara, M. W., Stuart, S., Gorman, L. L., & Wenzel, A. (2000). Efficacy of interpersonal psychotherapy for postpartum depression. *Archives of General Psychiatry, 57*, 1039–1045.

O'Hara, M. W., Zekoski, E. M., Philipps, L. H., & Wright, E. J. (1990). Controlled prospective study of postpartum mood disorders: Comparison of child bearing and nonbearing women. *Journal of Abnormal Psychology, 99*(1), 3–15.

O'Leary, A. (1990). Stress, emotion, and human immune function. *Psychological Bulletin, 108*(3), 363–382.

O'Malley, M., & Missio, E. (2003, January 13). Gordon Campbell's predicament. *CBC News Online.* Retrieved June 24, 2004, from http://www.cbc.ca/news/features/campbell_gordon.html

O'Malley, S. S. (1996). Opioid antagonists in the treatment of alcohol dependence. Clinical efficacy and prevention of relapse. *Alcohol and Alcoholism, 31*(Suppl. 1), 77–81.

O'Malley, S. S., Jaffe, A. J., Chang, G., Schottenfeld, R. S., Meyer, R. E., & Rounsaville, B. (1992). Naltrexone and coping skills therapy for alcohol dependence: A controlled study. *Archives of General Psychiatry, 49*, 881–887.

O'Neill, P. (1998a). Communities, collectivities, and the ethics of research. *Canadian Journal of Community Mental Health, 17*, 67–78.

O'Rourke, N., & Cappeliez, P. (2002). Perceived control, coping, and expressed burden among spouses of suspected dementia patients: Analysis of the goodness-of-fit hypothesis. *Canadian Journal on Aging, 21*, 385–392.

O'Rourke, N., Cappeliez, P., & Guindon, S. (2003). Depressive symptoms and physical health of caregivers of persons with cognitive impairment: Analysis of reciprocal effects over time. *Journal of Aging and Health, 15*, 688–712.

O'Rourke, N., Tuokko, H., Hayden, S., & Beattie, B. L. (1997). Early identification of dementia: Predictive validity of the clock test. *Archives of Clinical Neuropsychology, 12*, 257–267.

O'Sullivan, K. (1979). Observations on vaginismus in Irish women. *Archives of General Psychiatry, 36*, 824–826.

Oades, R. D. (1985). The role of noradrenaline in tuning and dopamine in switching between signals in the CNS. *Neuroscience and Biobehavioral Reviews, 9*, 261–282.

Oar, E. L., Farrell, L. J., Waters, A. M., Conlon, E. G., & Ollendick, T. H. (2015). One session treatment for pediatric blood-injection-injury phobia: A controlled multiple baseline trial. *Behaviour Research and Therapy, 73*, 131–142.

Ochsner, K. N., Ray, R. R., Hughes, B., McRae, K., Cooper, J. C., Weber, J., ... Gross, J. J. (2009). Bottom-up and top-down processes in emotion generation: Common and distinct neural mechanisms. *Psychological Science, 20*(11), 1322–1331.

Odlaug, B. L., & Grant, J. E.(2012). Pathological skin picking. In J. E. Grant, D. J. Stein, D. W. Woods, & N. J. Keuthen (Eds.), *Trichotillomania, skin picking, and other body-focused repetitive behaviors* (pp. 21–41). Arlington, VA: American Psychiatric Publishing.

Offman, A., & Kleinplatz, P. J. (2004). Does PMDD belong in the DSM? Challenging the medicalization of women's bodies. *Canadian Journal of Human Sexuality, 13*(1), 17–27.

Offord, D. R. (1989). *Ontario Child Health Study: Children at risk.* Toronto, ON: Ontario Ministry of Community and Social Services.

Offord, D. R., Boyle, M. H., Campbell, D., Goering, P., Lin, E., Wong, M., & Racine, Y. A. (1996). One-year prevalence of psychiatric disorder in Ontarians 15 to 64 years of age. *Canadian Journal of Psychiatry, 41*, 559–563.

Offord, D. R., Boyle, M. H., Szatmari, P., Rae-Grant, N. I., Links, P. S., Cadman, D. T., ... Woodward, C. A. (1987). Ontario Child Health Study: II. Six-month prevalence of disorder and rates of service utilization. *Archives of General Psychiatry, 44*, 832–836.

Ogata, S. N., Silk, K. R., Goodrich, S., Lohr, N. E., Westen, D., & Hill, E. M. (1990). Childhood sexual and physical abuse in adult patients with borderline personality disorder. *American Journal of Psychiatry, 147*, 1008–1013.

Ogloff, J. R. P. (2006). Psychopathy/antisocial personality disorder conundrum. *Australian and New Zealand Journal of Psychiatry, 40*, 519–528.

Ogloff, J. R. P., & Daffern, M. (2006). The dynamic appraisal of situational aggression: An instrument to assess risk for imminent aggression in psychiatric patients. *Behavioral Sciences and the Law, 4*, 799–813.

Ogloff, J. R. P., & Olley, M. C. (1998). The interaction between ethics and law: The ongoing refinement of ethical standards for psychologists in Canada. *Canadian Psychology, 39*, 221–230.

Ogloff, J. R. P., & Whittemore, K. E. (2001). Fitness to stand trial and criminal responsibility in Canada. In R. A. Schuller & J. R. P. Ogloff (Eds.), *Introduction to psychology and law: Canadian perspectives* (pp. 283–313). Toronto, ON: University of Toronto Press.

Ogloff, J. R. P., Wong, S., & Greenwood, A. (1990). Treating criminal psychopaths in a therapeutic community program. *Sciences and the Law, 8*, 81–90.

Ogrodniczuk, J. S., & Piper, W. E. (2001). Day treatment for personality disorders: A review of research findings. *Harvard Review of Psychiatry, 9*, 105–117.

Ogrodniczuk, J. S., Piper, W. E., & Joyce, A. S. (2003). Differentiating symptoms of complicated grief and depression among psychiatric outpatients. *The Canadian Journal of Psychiatry, 48*, 87–93.

Ohan, J. L., & Johnston, C. (2007). What is the social impact of ADHD in girls? A multi-method assessment. *Journal of Abnormal Child Psychology, 35*, 239–250.

Ohayon, M. M., & Schatzberg, A. F. (2002). Prevalence of depressive episodes with psychotic features in the general population. *American Journal of Psychiatry, 159*, 1855–1861.

Ohayon, M. M., & Schatzberg, A. F. (2003). Using chronic pain to predict depressive morbidity in the general population. *Archives of General Psychiatry, 60*, 39–47.

Öhman, A. (1996). Preferential pre-attentive processing of threat in anxiety: Preparedness and attentional biases. In R. Rapee (Ed.), *Current controversies in the anxiety disorders* (pp. 253–290). New York, NY: Guilford Press.

Öhman, A., & Dimberg, U. (1978). Facial expressions as conditioned stimuli for electrodermal responses: A case of preparedness? *Journal of Personality and Social Psychology, 36*(11), 1251–1258.

Öhman, A., & Mineka, S. (2001). Fears, phobias, and preparedness: Toward an evolved model of fear and fear learning. *Psychological Review, 108*(3), 483–522.

Öhman, A., Flykt, A., & Lundquist, D. (2000). Unconscious emotion: Evolutionary perspective, psychophysiological data, and neuropsychological mechanisms. In R. Lane & L. Nadel (Eds.), *The cognitive neuroscience of emotion* (pp. 296–327). New York, NY: Oxford University Press.

O'Kearney, R., & Pech, M. (2014). General and sleep-specific worry in insomnia. *Sleep and Biological Rhythms, 12*(3), 212–215.

olde Hartman, T. C., Borghuis, M. S., Lucassen, P. L., van de Laar, F. A., Speckens, A. E., & van Weel, C. (2009). Medically unexplained symptoms, somatisation disorder and hypochondriasis: Course and prognosis. A systematic review. *Journal of Psychosomatic Research, 66*(5), 363–377.

Oldenburg, B., de Courten, M., & Frean, E. (2010). The contribution of health psychology to the advancement of global health. In J. M. Suls, K. W. Davidson, & R. M. Kaplan (Eds.), *Handbook of health psychology and behavioral medicine.* New York, NY: Guilford Press.

Olds, J. (1956). Pleasure centers in the brain. *Scientific American, 195*, 105–116.

Olds, J., & Milner, P. M. (1954). Positive reinforcement produced by electrical stimulation of septal area and other regions of rat brain. *Journal of Comparative and Physiological Psychology, 47*, 419–427.

Olfson, M., King, M., & Schoenbaum, M. (2015). Benzodiazepine use in the United States. *JAMA Psychiatry, 72*, 136–142.

Olin, S. S., Raine, A., Cannon, T. D., Parnas, J., Schulsinger, F., & Mednick, S. A. (1997). Childhood behavior precursors of schizotypal personality disorder. *Schizophrenia Bulletin, 23*, 93–103.

Oliver, M. B., & Hyde, J. S. (1993). Gender differences in sexuality: A meta-analysis. *Psychological Bulletin, 114*(1), 29–51.

Olivier, B. (2015). Serotonin: A never-ending story. *European Journal of Pharmacology, 753*, 2–18.

Olivier, P., Bertrand, L., Tubery, M., Lauque, D., Montastruc, J.-L., & Lapeyre-Mestre, M. (2009). Hospitalizations because of adverse drug reactions in elderly patients admitted through the emergency department: A prospective survey. *Drugs & Aging, 26*(6), 475–482.

Olives, C., Myerson, R., Mokdad, A. H., Murray, C. J., & Lim, S. S. (2013). Prevalence, awareness, treatment, and control of hypertension in United States counties, 2001–2009. *PLoS One, 8*(4), e60308.

Ollendick, T. H., & Huntzinger, R. M. (1990). Separation anxiety disorder in childhood. In M. Hersen & C. G. Last (Eds.), *Handbook of child and adult psychopathology: A longitudinal perspective.* Elmsford, NY: Pergamon Press.

Ollendick, T. H., & Muris, P. (2015). The scientific legacy of little Hans and Little Albert: Future directions for research on specific phobias in youth. *Journal of Clinical Child and Adolescent Psychology, 44*, 689–706.

Ollendick, T. H., & Shirk, S. R. (2010). Clinical interventions with children and adolescents: Current status, future directions. In D. H. Barlow (Ed.), *Oxford handbook of clinical psychology* (pp. 762–788). New York, NY: Oxford University Press.

Olley, M. C., & Ogloff, J. R. P. (1995). Patients' rights advocacy: Implications for program design and implementation. *Journal of Mental Health Administration, 22*, 368–376.

Olmstead, S. B., Pasley, K., & Fincham, F. D. (2013). Hooking up and penetrative hookups: Correlates that differentiate college men. *Archives of Sexual Behavior, 42*(4), 573–583.

Olsen, S., Smith, S. S., Oei, T. P. S., & Douglas, J. (2012). Motivational interviewing (MINT) improves continuous positive airway pressure (CPAP) acceptance and adherence: A randomized controlled trial. *Journal of Consulting and Clinical Psychology, 80*(1), 151.

Oltmanns, T. F., & Powers, A. D. (2012). Gender and personality disorders. In T. A. Widiger (Ed.), *The Oxford handbook of personality disorders* (pp. 206–218). New York, NY: Oxford University Press.

Olver, M. E., Sowden, J. N., Kingston, D. A., Nicholaichuk, T. P., Gordon, A., Beggs Christofferson, S. M., & Wong, S. C. P. (2018). Predictive accuracy of violence risk scale-sexual offender version risk and change scores in treated Canadian Aboriginal and non-Aboriginal sexual offenders. *Sexual Abuse, 30*, 254–275. https://doi.org/10.1177/1079063216649594

Olver, M. E., Lewis, K., & Wong, S. C. P. (2013). Risk reduction treatment of high-risk psychopathic offenders: The relationship of psychopathy and treatment change to violent recidivism. *Personality Disorders: Theory, Research, and Treatment, 4*(2), 160–167.

Olver, M. E., & Wong, S. C. P. (2006). Psychopathy, sexual deviance, and recidivism among sex offenders. *Sexual Abuse: Journal of Research and Treatment, 18*, 65–82.

Onslow, M., Jones, M., O'Brian, S., Packman, A., & Menzies, R. (2012). Stuttering. In P. Sturmey & M. Hersen (Eds.), *Handbook of evidence-based practice in clinical psychology* (Vol. 1, pp. 185–208). New York, NY: John Wiley & Sons, Inc.

Open Science Collaboration. (2015). Estimating the reproducibility of psychological science. *Science, 349*(6251), aac4716. https://doi.org/10.1126/science.aac4716

Opjordsmoen, S. (1989). Delusional disorders: I. Comparative long-term outcome. *Acta Psychiatrica Scandinavica, 80*, 603–612.

Orbach, I. (1997). A taxonomy of factors related to suicidal behavior. *Clinical Psychology: Science and Practice, 4*, 205–224.

Orford, J., & Keddie, A. (2006). Abstinence or controlled drinking in clinical practice: A test of the dependence and persuasion hypotheses. *Addiction, 81*(4), 495–504.

Orne, M. T., Dinges, D. F., & Orne, E. C. (1984). On the differential diagnosis of multiple personality in the forensic context. *International Journal of Clinical and Experimental Hypnosis, 32*, 118–169.

Orsillo, S. M., & Roemer, L. (2011). *The mindful way through anxiety: Break free from chronic worry and reclaim your life.* New York, NY: Guilford Press.

Orth, U., Robins, R. W., Trzesniewski, K. H., Maes, J., & Schmitt, M. (2009). Low self-esteem is a risk factor for depressive symptoms from young adulthood to old age. *Journal of Abnormal Psychology, 118*(3), 472–478.

Orth-Gomer, K., Schneiderman, N., Wang, H. X., Walldin, C., Blom, M., & Jernberg, T. (2009). Stress reduction prolongs life in women with coronary disease: The Stockholm Women's Intervention Trial for Coronary Heart Disease (SWITCHD). *Circulation Cardiovascular Quality and Outcomes, 2*(1), 25–32.

Ortin, A., Lake, A. M., Kleinman, M., & Gould, M. S. (2012). Sensation seeking as risk factor for suicidal ideation and suicide attempts in adolescence. *Journal of Affective Disorders, 143*, 214–222.

Ortiz, A., & Medicna-Mora, M. E. (1988). *Research on drugs in Mexico: Epidemiology of drug abuse and issues among Native American populations.* In Community Epidemiology Work Group Proceedings, December 1987. (Contract No. 271-87-8321). Washington, DC: U.S. Government Printing Office.

Oscar-Berman, M., Shagrin, B., Evert, D. L., & Epstein, C. (1997). Impairments of brain and behavior: The neurological effects of alcohol. *Alcohol Health & Research World, 21*, 65–75.

Oslin, D. W., & Cary, M. S. (2003). Alcohol-related dementia: Validation of diagnostic criteria. *American Journal of Geriatric Psychiatry, 11*, 441–447.

Öst, L. G. (1985). Mode of acquisition of phobias. *Acta Universitatis Uppsaliensis* (Abstracts of Uppsala Dissertations from the Faculty of Medicine) *529*, 1–45.

Öst, L. G. (1987). Age at onset in different phobias. *Journal of Abnormal Psychology, 96*, 223–229.

Öst, L. G. (1992). Blood and injection phobia: Background and cognitive, physiological, and behavioral variables. *Journal of Abnormal Psychology, 101*(1), 68–74.

Öst, L. G., Ferebee, I., & Furmark, T. (1997). One session group therapy of spiderphobia: Direct vs. indirect treatments. *Behaviour Research and Therapy, 35*, 721–732.

Öst, L. G., & Sterner, U. (1987). Applied tension: A specific behavioural method for treatment of blood phobia. *Behaviour Research and Therapy, 25,* 25–30.

Öst, L. G., Svensson, L., Hellström, K., & Lindwall, R. (2001). One-session treatment of specific phobia in youths: A randomized clinical trial. *Journal of Consulting and Clinical Psychology, 69,* 814–824.

Otis, J. D., & Pincus, D. B. (2007). Chronic pain. In B. A. Boyer & I. Paharia (Eds.), *Comprehensive handbook of clinical health psychology* (pp. 349–370). Hoboken, NJ: Wiley.

Otis, J. D., & Pincus, D. B. (2008). Chronic pain. In B. A. Boyer & I. Paharia (Eds.), *Comprehensive handbook of clinical health psychology* (pp. 349–370). Hoboken, NJ: John Wiley & Sons.

Otto, M. W., & Applebaum, A. J. (2011). The nature and treatment of bipolar disorder and the bipolar spectrum. In D. H. Barlow (Ed.), *Handbook of clinical psychology.* New York, NY: Oxford University Press.

Otto, M. W., Behar, E., Smits, J. A. J., & Hofmann, S. G. (2009). Combining pharmacological and cognitive behavioral therapy in the treatment of anxiety disorders. In M. M. Antony & M. B. Stein (Eds.), *Oxford handbook of anxiety and related disorders* (pp. 429–440). New York, NY: Oxford University Press.

Otto, M. W., Reilly-Harrington, N. A., Knauz, R. O., Henin, A., Kogan, J. N., & Sachs, G. S. (2008a). *Managing bipolar disorder: A cognitive-behavioral approach.* (Therapist Guide). New York, NY: Oxford University Press.

Otto, M. W., Reilly-Harrington, N. A., Knauz, R. O., Henin, A., Kogan, J. N., & Sachs, G. S. (2008b). *Managing bipolar disorder: A cognitive-behavioral approach. (Workbook).* New York, NY: Oxford University Press.

Otto, M. W., Tolin, D. F., Simon, N. M., Pearlson, G. D., Basden, S., Meunier, S. A., & Pollack, M. H. (2010). Efficacy of D-cycloserine for enhancing response to cognitive-behavior therapy for panic disorder. *Biological Psychiatry, 67*(4), 365–370.

Ouellet-Morin, I., Boivin, M., Dionne, G., Lupien, S. J., Arsenault, L., Barr, R. G., ... Tremblay, R. E. (2008). Variations in heritability of cortisol reactivity to stress as a function of early familial adversity among 19-month-old twins. *Archives of General Psychiatry, 65*(2), 211–218.

Ouimette, P. C., Finney, J. W., & Moos, R. H. (1997). Twelve-step and cognitive-behavioral treatment for substance abuse: A comparison of treatment effectiveness. *Journal of Consulting and Clinical Psychology, 65,* 230–240.

Overeem, S., & Reading, P. (Eds.). (2010). *Sleep disorders in neurology: A practical approach.* New York, NY: Wiley-Blackwell.

Owen, J. J., Rhoades, G. K., Stanley, S. M., & Fincham, F. D. (2010). "Hooking up" among college students: Demographic and psychosocial correlates. *Archives of Sexual Behavior, 39,* 653–663.

Owen, J., & Fincham, F. D. (2011). Effects of gender and psychosocial factors on "friends with benefits" relationships among young adults. *Archives of Sexual Behavior, 40*(2), 311–320.

Owens, K. M. B., Asmundson, G. J. G., Hadjistavropoulos, T., & Owens, T. J. (2004). Attentional bias toward illness threat in individuals with elevated health anxiety. *Cognitive Therapy and Research, 28*(1), 57–66.

Owens, M. J., Mulchahey, J. J., Stout, S. C., & Plotsky, P. M. (1997). Molecular and neurobiological mechanisms in the treatment of psychiatric disorders. In A. Tasman, J. Kay, & J. A. Lieberman (Eds.), *Psychiatry* (Vol. 1, pp. 210–257). Philadelphia, PA: W. B. Saunders.

Ozonoff, S., Young, G. S., Carter, A., Messinger, D., Yirmiya, N., Zwaigenbaum, L., & Stone, W. L. (2011). Recurrence risk for autism spectrum disorders: A baby siblings research consortium study. *Pediatrics, 128*(3), e488–e495.

Pace-Schott, E. F., Germain, A. Milad, M. R. (2015). Effects of sleep on memory for conditioned fear and fear extinction. *Psychological Bulletin, 141,* 835.

Padmanabhan, S., Caulfield, M., & Dominiczak, A. F. (2015, March 13). Genetic and molecular aspects of hypertension. *Circulation Research.* https://doi.org/10.1161/CIRCRESAHA.116.303647

Page, A. C. (1996). Blood-injury-injection fears in medical practice. *Medical Journal of Australia, 164,* 189.

Page, G. G., Ben-Eliyahu, S., Yirmiya, R., & Liebeskind, J. C. (1993). Morphine attenuates surgery-induced enhancement of metastatic colonization in rats. *Pain, 54*(1), 21–28.

Pagsberg, A. K. (2013). Schizophrenia spectrum and other psychotic disorders. *European Child & Adolescent Psychiatry, 22*(1), 3–9.

Pahlajani, G., Raina, R., Jones, S., Ali, M., & Zippe, C. (2012). Vacuum erection devices revisited: Its emerging role in the treatment of erectile dysfunction and early penile rehabilitation following prostate cancer therapy. *Journal of Sexual Medicine, 9*(4), 1182–1189.

Paillard, T., Rolland, Y., & de Souto Barreto, P. (2015). Protective effects of physical exercise in Alzheimer's disease and Parkinson's disease: A narrative review. *Journal of Clinical Neurology, 11*(3), 212–219.

Palagini, L., Mauri, M., Banfi, T., Mazzei, I., Gronchi, A., Bonanni, E., Maestri, M., Riemann, D., Carney, C. E., & Dell'Osso, L. (2015). Daytime rumination as a feature of Insomnia Disorder: Sleep related cognition is not merely a problem of the night. *Archives Italiennes de Biologie, 153*(2–3), 239–247. http://www.architalbiol.org/index.php/aib/article/download/153239/26742678

Palamar, J. J., & Barratt, M. J. (2016). Synthetic cannabinoids: Undesirable alternatives to natural marijuana. *American Journal of Drug and Alcohol Abuse, 42,* 371–373. https://doi.org/10.3109/00952990.2016.1139584

Pandina, R., & Hendren, R. (1999). Other drugs of abuse: Inhalants, designer drugs, and steroids. In B. S. McCrady & E. E. Epstein (Eds.), *Addictions: A comprehensive guidebook* (pp. 171–184). New York, NY: Oxford University Press.

Pandya, N. H., Mevada, A., Patel, V., & Suthar, M. (2013). Study of effects of advanced maternal agre related risks for Down syndrome & other trisomies. *International Journal of Biomedical and Advance Research, 4*(2), 123–127.

Paniagua, F. A., & Yamada, A. M. (Eds.). (2013). *Handbook of multicultural mental health: Assessment and treatment of diverse populations* (2nd ed.). New York, NY: Academic Press.

Pantaleo, G., Graziosi, C., & Fauci, A. S. (1993). The immunopathogenesis of human immunodeficiency virus infection. *New England Journal of Medicine, 328,* 327–335.

Pantony, K. L., & Caplan, P. J. (1991). Delusional dominating personality disorder: A modest proposal for identifying some consequences of rigid masculine socialization. *Canadian Psychology, 32,* 120–135.

Panza, F., Frisardi, V., Seripa, D., Logroscino, G., Santamato, A., Imbimbo, B. P., & Solfrizzi, V. (2012). Alcohol consumption in mild cognitive impairment and dementia: Harmful or neuroprotective? *International Journal of Geriatric Psychiatry, 27*(12), 1218–1238.

Papadopoulos, F. C., Ekbom, A., Brandt, L., & Ekselius, L. (2009). Excess mortality, causes of death and prognostic factors in anorexia nervosa. *British Journal of Psychiatry, 194*(1), 10–17.

Papazoglou, A., Jacobson, L. A., McCabe, M., Kaufmann, W., & Zabel, T. A. (2014). To ID or not to ID? Changes in classification rates of intellectual disability using DSM-5. *Mental Retardation, 52*(3), 165–174.

Papillo, J. F., & Shapiro, D. (1990). The cardiovascular system. In J. T. Cacioppo & L. G. Tassinaryo (Eds.), *Principles of psychophysiology: Physical, social, and inferential elements.* New York, NY: Cambridge University Press.

Papsdorf, M. P., & Alden, L. E. (1998). Mediators of social rejection in socially anxious individuals. *Journal of Research in Personality, 32,* 351–369.

Paquette, V., Lévesque, J., Mensour, B., Leroux, J. M., Beudoin, G., Bourgouin, P., & Beauregard, M. (2003). "Change the mind and you change the brain": Effects of cognitive-behavioral therapy on the neural correlates of spider phobia. *Neuroimage, 18,* 401–409.

Parcesepe, A. M., & Cabassa, L. J. (2013). Public stigma of mental illness in the United States: A systematic literature review. *Administration and Policy in Mental Health and Mental Health Services Research, 40*(5), 384–399.

Parchi, P., Capellari, S., & Gambetti, P. (2012). Fatal familial and sporadic insomnia. In W. Dickson & R. O. Weller (Eds.), *Neurodegeneration: The molecular pathology of dementia and movement disorders* (2nd ed., pp. 346–349). Oxford, UK: Wiley-Blackwell.

Paris, J. (2002). Chronic suicidality among patients with borderline personality disorder. *Psychiatric Services, 53*(6), 738–742. https://dx.doi.org/10.1176/appi.ps.53.6.738

Paris, J. (2014). The relevance of social capital for the treatment of personality disorders. *Personal Mental Health, 8*(1), 24–29.

Park, D. C. (2007). Eating disorders: A call to arms. *American Psychologist, 62,* 158.

Parker, G., & Hadzi-Pavlovic, D. (1990). Expressed emotion as a predictor of schizophrenic relapse: An analysis of aggregated data. *Psychological Medicine, 20,* 961–965.

Parker, G., McCraw, S., & Fletcher, K. (2012). Cyclothymia. *Depression and Anxiety, 29*(6), 487–494.

Parker, G., McCraw, S., Blanch, B., Hadzi-Pavlovic, D., Synnot, H., & Rees, A. (2013). Discriminating melancholic and non-melancholic depression by prototypic clinical features. *Journal of Affective Disorders, 144,* 199–207.

Parker, S., Schwartz, B., Todd, J., & Pickering, L. (2004). Thimerosal-containing vaccines and autistic spectrum disorder: A critical review of published original data. *Pediatrics, 114*(3), 793.

Parkinson Society of Canada. (2002). *Parkinson's disease: Frequently asked questions.* Retrieved November 24, 2003, from http://www.parkinson.ca/pd/faq.html

Parkinson, L., & Rachman, S. (1981a). Intrusive thoughts: The effects of an uncontrived stress. *Advances in Behaviour Research and Therapy, 3,* 111–118.

Parkinson, L., & Rachman, S. (1981b). Speed of recovery from an uncontrived stress. *Advances in Behaviour Research and Therapy, 3,* 119–123.

Parnas, J., Cannon, T. D., Jacobsen, B., Schulsinger, H., Schulsinger, F., Mednick, S. A. (1993). Lifetime DSM-III-R diagnostic outcomes in the offspring of schizophrenic mothers. *Archives of General Psychiatry, 50,* 707–714.

Parner, E. T., Baron-Cohen, S., Lauritsen, M. B., Jørgensen, M., Schieve, L. A., Yeargin-Allsopp, M., & Obel, C. (2012). Parental age and autism spectrum disorders. *Annals of Epidemiology, 22*(3), 143–150.

Parrott, A. C. (2012). MDMA and LSD. In J. C. Verster, K. Brady, M. Galanter, & P. Conrod (Eds.), *Drug abuse and addiction in medical illness* (pp. 175–188). New York, NY: Springer.

Parrott, A. C. (2013). MDMA, serotonergic neurotoxicity, and the diverse functional deficits of recreational "Ecstasy" users. *Neuroscience & Biobehavioral Reviews, 37*(8), 1466–1484.

Parrott, D. J., Tharp, A. T., Swartout, K. M., Miller, C. A., Hall, G. C. N., & George, W. H. (2012). Validity for an integrated laboratory analogue of sexual aggression and bystander intervention. *Aggressive Behavior, 38*(4), 309–321.

Parry-Jones, B., & Parry-Jones, W. L. (2002). History of bulimia and bulimia nervosa. In K. D. Brownell & C. G. Fairburn (Eds.), *Eating disorders and obesity: A comprehensive handbook* (2nd ed., pp. 145–150). New York, NY: Guilford Press.

Parry-Jones, W. L., & Parry-Jones, B. (1994). Implications of historical evidence for the classification of eating disorders. *British Journal of Psychiatry, 165,* 287–292.

Parsons, O. A., & Nixon, S. J. (1993). Behavioral disorders associated with central nervous system dysfunction. In P. B. Sutker & H. E. Adams (Eds.), *Comprehensive handbook of psychopathology* (pp. 689–733). New York, NY: Plenum Press.

Pasewark, R. A., & Seidenzahl, D. (1979). Opinions concerning the insanity plea and criminality among mental patients.

Bulletin of the American Academy of Psychiatry and Law, 7, 199–202.

Passie, T., & Halpern, J. H. (2015). The pharmacology of hallucinogens. In R. K. Ries, D. A. Fiellin, S. C. Miller, & R. Saitz (Eds.), *The ASAM principles of addiction medicine* (5th ed., pp. 235–255). New York, NY: Wolters Kluwer.

Patel, S. R., White, D. P., Malhotra, A., Stanchina, M. L., & Ayas, N. T. (2003). Continuous positive airway pressure therapy for treating sleepiness in a diverse population with obstructive sleep apnea: Results of a meta-analysis. *Archives of Internal Medicine, 163*(5), 565–571.

Patel, V., & Andrade, C. (2003). Pharmacological treatment of severe psychiatric disorders in the developing world: Lessons from India. *CNS Drugs, 17,* 1071–1080.

Patten, S. B. (2000). Major depression prevalence in Calgary. *Canadian Journal of Psychiatry, 45,* 923–926.

Patten, S. B. (2002). Progress against major depression in Canada. *Canadian Journal of Psychiatry, 47,* 775–780.

Patten, S. B., & Charney, D. A. (1998). Alcohol consumption and major depression in the Canadian population. *Canadian Journal of Psychiatry, 43,* 502–506.

Patten, S. B., Wang, J. L., Williams, J. V. A., Currie, S., Beck, C. A., Maxwell, C. J., & El-Guebaly, N. (2006). Descriptive epidemiology of major depression in Canada. *Canadian Journal of Psychiatry, 51,* 84–90.

Patten, S. B., Williams, J. V. A., Lavorato, D. H., Wang, J. L., McDonald, K., & Bulloch, A. G. M. (2015). Descriptive epidemiology of major depressive disorder in Canada in 2012. *Canadian Journal of Psychiatry, 60*(1), 23–30.

Patten, S. B., Williams, J. V. A., Lavorato, D. H., Wang, J. L., McDonald, K., & Bulloch, A. G. M. (2016). Major depression in Canada: What has changed over the past 10 years? *Canadian Journal of Psychiatry, 61*(2), 80–85.

Patterson, G. R. (1982). *Coercive family process.* Eugene, OR: Castalia.

Patterson, G. R. (1986). Performance models for antisocial boys. *American Psychologist, 41,* 432–444.

Patterson, G. R., Chamberlain, P., & Reid, J. B. (1982). A comparative evaluation of a parent training program. *Behavior Therapy, 13,* 638–650.

Patterson, G. R., DeBaryshe, B. D., & Ramsey, E. (1989). A developmental perspective on antisocial behavior. *American Psychologist, 44,* 329–335.

Patton, G. C. (1988). Mortality in eating disorders. *Psychological Medicine, 18*(4), 947–951.

Patton, G. C., Johnson-Sabine, E., Wood, K., Mann, A. H., & Wakeling, A. (1990). Abnormal eating attitudes in London school girls—A prospective epidemiological study: Outcome at twelve month follow up. *Psychological Medicine, 20,* 383–394.

Paul, G. L., & Lentz, R. J. (1977). *Psychosocial treatment of chronic mental patients: Milieu versus social learning programs.* Cambridge, MA: Harvard University Press.

Paul, T., Schroeter, K., Dahme, B., & Nutzinger, D. O. (2002). Self-injurious behavior in women with eating disorders. *American Journal of Psychiatry, 159,* 408–411.

Paul, R., Augustyn, A., Klin, A., & Volkmar, F. R. (2005). Perception and production of prosody by speakers with autism spectrum disorders. *Journal of Autism and Developmental Disorders, 35*(2), 205–220.

Paulhus, D. L., & Morgan, K. L. (1997). Perceptions of intelligence in leaderless groups: The dynamic effects of shyness and acquaintance. *Journal of Personality and Social Psychology, 71,* 581–591.

Paulhus, D. L., & Williams, K. M. (2002). The Dark Triad of personality: Narcissism, Machiavellianism and psychopathy. *Journal of Research in Personality, 36,* 556–563.

Pauli, P., & Alpers, G. W. (2002). Memory bias in patients with hypochondriasis and somatoform pain disorder. *Journal of Psychosomatic Research, 52,* 45–53.

Paulson, J. F., & Bazemore, S. D. (2010). Prenatal and postpartum depression in fathers and its association with maternal depression: A meta-analysis. *JAMA, 303*(19), 1961–1969.

Pavalko, E. K., Elder, G. H., Jr., & Clipp, E. C. (1993). Work lives and longevity: Insights from a life course perspective. *Journal of Health and Social Behavior, 34,* 363–380.

Paxton, S. J., Schutz, H. K., Wertheim, E. H., & Muir, S. L. (1999). Friendship clique and peer influences on body image concerns, dietary restraint, extreme weight-loss behaviors, and binge eating in adolescent girls. *Journal of Abnormal Psychology, 108*(2), 255–266.

Paykel, E. S., & Scott, J. (2009). Treatment of mood disorders. In M. G. Gelder, N. C. Andreasen, J. J. López-Ibor, & J. R. Geddes (Eds.), *New Oxford textbook of psychiatry* (2nd ed., Vol. 1, pp. 669–680). Oxford, UK: Oxford University Press.

Paykel, E. S., Brayne, C., Huppert, F. A., Gill, C., Barkley, C., Gehlhaar, E., . . . O'Connor, D. (1994). Incidence of dementia in a population older than 75 years in the United Kingdom. *Archives of General Psychiatry, 51,* 325–332.

Payne, K. A., Reissing, E. D., Lahaie, M. A., Yitzchak M. B., Rhonda A., & Samirs K. (2005). What is sexual pain? A critique of DSM's classification of dyspareunia and vaginismus. *Journal of Psychology & Human Sexuality, 17,* 141–154.

Payne, L. A., White, K. S., Gallagher, M. W., Woods, S. W., Shear, M. K., Gorman, J. M., Farchione, T. J., & Barlow, D. H. (2016). Second-stage treatments for relative non-responders to cognitive-behavioral therapy (CBT) for panic disorder with or without agoraphobia: Continued CBT versus SSRI: A randomized controlled trial. *Depression and Anxiety, 33,* 392–399.

Peall, K. J., & Robertson, N. P. (2014). Narcolepsy: Environment, genes and treatment. *Journal of Neurology, 261*(8), 1644–1646.

Pearlstein, T. (2010). Premenstrual dysphoric disorder: Out of the appendix. *Archives of Women's Mental Health, 13*(1), 21–23.

Pearlstein, T., & Steiner, M. (2008). Premenstrual dysphoric disorder: Burden of illness and treatment update. *Journal of Psychiatry & Neuroscience, 33*(4), 291–301.

Pearlstein, T., Yonkers, K. A., Fayyad, R., & Gillespie, J. A. (2005). Pretreatment pattern of symptom expression in premenstrual dysphoric disorder. *Journal of Affective Disorder, 85,* 275–282.

Pearson, C. (2002, October 31). MDs refuse to prescribe medicinal pot. *Windsor Star.* Retrieved October 26, 2003, from http://www.medicalmarihuana.ca/refusal.html

Pearson, C. M., Wonderlich, S. A., & Smith, G. T. (2015). A Risk and Maintenance Model for Bulimia Nervosa: From Impulsive Action to Compulsive Behavior, *Psychological Review, 122*(3), 516–533.

Pearson, C., Janz, T., & Ali, J. (2012). Mental and substance use disorders in Canada. Health at a Glance (Catalogue No. 82-624-X). https://www150.statcan.gc.ca/n1/pub/82-624-x/2013001/article/11855-eng.htm

Pearson, C., Janz, T., & Ali, J. (2013). *Mental and substance use disorders in Canada: Health at a glance.* Ottawa, ON: Statistics Canada. Retrieved from http://www.statcan.gc.ca/pub/82-624-x/2013001/article/11855-eng.htm

Pearson, C., Zamorski, M., & Janz, T. (2014). *Mental health of the Canadian armed forces.* (Catalogue No. 82-624-X). Ottawa, ON: Statistics Canada. Retrieved from http://www.statcan.gc.ca/pub/82-624-x/2014001/article/14121-eng.htm

Peat, C. M., Peyeri, N. L., & Muehlenkamp, J. J. (2008). Body image and eating disorders in older adults: A review. *Journal of General Psychology, 135*(4), 343–358.

Peat, C., Mitchell, J. E., Hoek, H. W., & Wonderlich, S. A. (2009). Validity and utility of subtyping anorexia nervosa. *International Journal of Eating Disorders, 42*(7), 590–594.

Pedersen, C. B., & Mortensen, P. B. (2006). Are the cause(s) responsible for urban-rural differences in schizophrenia risk rooted in families or in individuals? *American Journal of Epidemiology, 163*(11), 971–978.

Pedersen, N. L. (2010). Reaching the limits of genome-wide significance in Alzheimer disease: Back to the environment. *JAMA, 303*(18), 1864–1865.

Peeters, J., Van Beek, A., Meerveld, J., Spreeuwenberg, P., & Francke, A. (2010). Informal caregivers of persons with dementia, their use of and needs for specific professional support: A survey of the National Dementia Programme. *BMC Nursing, 9*(1), 9.

Pelham, W. E., Jr. (1999). The NIMH Multimodal Treatment Study for attention-deficit hyperactivity disorder: Just say yes to drugs alone? *Canadian Journal of Psychiatry, 44,* 981–990.

Pelham, W. E., Jr., Waschbusch, D. A., Hoza, B., Pillow, D. R., & Gnagy, E. M. (2001). Effects of methylphenidate and expectancy on performance, self-evaluations, persistence, and attributions on a social task in boys with ADHD. *Experimental & Clinical Psychopharmacology, 9,* 425–437.

Pelletier, J., Moisan, J., Roussel, R., & Gilbert, M. (1997). Heart health promotion: A community development experiment in a rural area of Quebec, Canada. *Health Promotion International, 12*(4), 291–298.

Pelletier, L., O'Donnell, S., McRae, L., & Grenier, J. (2017). The burden of generalized anxiety disorder in Canada. *Health Promotion and Chronic Disease Prevention in Canada, 37*(2), 54–62. https://www.canada.ca/content/dam/phac-aspc/migration/phac-aspc/publicat/hpcdp-pspmc/37-2/assets/pdf/ar-04-eng.pdf

Pellicano, E., & Stears, M. (2011). Bridging autism, science and society: Moving toward an ethically informed approach to autism research. *Autism Research, 4*(4), 271–282.

Pen, A. E., & Jensen, U. B. (2016). Current status of treating neurodegenerative disease with induced pluripotent stem cells. *Acta Neurologica Scandinavica.* Advance online publication. https://doi.org/10.1111/ane.12545

Penders, T. M., Gestring, R. E., & Vilensky, D. A. (2012). Intoxication delirium following use of synthetic cathinone derivatives. *American Journal of Drug and Alcohol Abuse, 38*(6), 616–617.

Pendery, M. L., Maltzman, I. M., & West, L. J. (1982). Controlled drinking by alcoholics? New findings and a reevaluation of a major affirmative study. *Science, 217,* 169–175.

Pennington, B., & Bishop, D. (2009). Relations among speech, language, and reading disorders. *Annual Review of Psychology, 60,* 283–306.

Pentz, M. A. (1999). Prevention. In M. Galanter & H. D. Kleber (Eds.), *Textbook of substance abuse treatment* (2nd ed., pp. 535–544). Washington, DC: American Psychiatric Press.

People's Courtney, The. (1995). Retrieved November 1, 2006, from http://www.geocities.com/SunsetStrip/4925/Alanis/Articles/art9.html

Pepper, C. M., Klein, D. N., Anderson, R. L., Riso, L. P., Ouimette, P. C., & Lizardi, H. (1995). DSM-III-R Axis II comorbidity in dysthymia and major depression. *American Journal of Psychiatry, 152,* 239–247.

Perez-Sales, P. (1990). Camptocormia. *British Journal of Psychiatry, 157,* 765–767

Pericak-Vance, M. A., Johnson, C. C., Rimmler, J. B., Saunders, A. M., Robinson, L. C., D'Hondt, E. G., . . . Haines, J. L. (1996). Alzheimer's disease and apolipoprotein E-4 allele in an Amish population. *Annals of Neurology, 39,* 700–704.

Perlin, M. L. (1996). The voluntary delivery of mental health services in the community. In B. D. Sales & D. W. Shuman (Eds.), *Law, mental health, & mental disorder* (pp. 150–177). Pacific Grove, CA: Brooks/Cole.

Perlin, M. L. (2000). *The hidden prejudice: Mental disability on trial.* Washington, DC: American Psychological Association.

Perlis, M. L., Smith, L. J., Lyness, J. M., Matteson, S. R., Pigeon, W. R., Jungquist, C. R., & Tu, X. (2006). Insomnia as a risk factor for onset of depression in the elderly. *Behavioral Sleep Medicine, 4*(2), 104–113.

Perls, F. S. (1969). *Gestalt therapy verbatim.* Moab, UT: Real People Press.

Perrault, R., Carrier, J., Desautels, A., Montplaisir, J., & Zadra, A. (2014). Electroencephalographic slow waves prior to sleepwalking episodes. *Sleep medicine, 15*(12), 1468–1472.

Perry, A., Tarrier, N., Morriss, R., McCarthy, E., & Limb, K. (1999). Randomized controlled trial of efficacy of teaching patients with bipolar disorder to identify early symptoms of relapse and obtain treatment. *BMJ, 318,* 149–153.

Perry, J. C. (1993). Longitudinal studies of personality disorders. *Journal of Personality Disorders, 7,* 63–85.

Perry, J. C., Banon, E., & Ianni, F. (1999). Effectiveness of psychotherapy for personality disorders. *American Journal of Psychiatry, 156,* 1312–1321.

Perry, J. C., & Bond, M. (2012). Change in defense mechanisms during long-term dynamic psychotherapy and five-year outcome. *American Journal of Psychiatry, 169*(9), 916–925.

Perry, J. C., & Bond, M. (2014). Change in defense mechanisms during long-term dynamic psychotherapy and five-year outcome. *American Journal of Psychiatry, 169*(9), 916–925.

Perry, S. (1993). Psychiatric treatment of adults with human immunodeficiency virus infection. In D. L. Dunner (Ed.), *Current psychiatric therapy* (pp. 475–482). Philadelphia, PA: W. B. Saunders.

Person, D. C., & Borkovec, T. D. (1995, August). *Anxiety disorders among the elderly: Patterns and issues.* Paper presented at the 103rd annual meeting of the American Psychological Association. New York, NY.

Peters, C. P. (1991). Concepts of schizophrenia after Kraepelin and Bleuler. In J. G. Howells (Ed.), *The concept of schizophrenia: Historical perspectives* (pp. 93–107). Washington, DC: American Psychiatric Press.

Petersen, A. C., Compas, B. E., Brooks-Gunn, J., Stemmler, M., Ey, S., & Grant, K. E. (1993). Depression in adolescence. *American Psychologist, 48*(2), 155–168.

Petersen, J. L., & Hyde, J. S. (2010). A meta-analytic review of research on gender differences in sexuality, 1993–2007. *Psychological Bulletin, 136,* 21–38.

Petersen, R. C., Smith, G. E., Waring, S. C., Ivnik, R. J., Tangalos, E. G., & Kokmen, E. (1999). Mild cognitive impairment: Clinical characterization and outcome. *Archives of Neurology, 56*(3), 303–308.

Peterson, B. S. (1995). Neuroimaging in child and adolescent neuropsychiatric disorders. *Journal of the American Academy of Child and Adolescent Psychiatry, 34,* 1560–1576.

Peterson, C. B., Mitchell, J. E., Engbloom, S., Nugent, S., Mussell, M. P., & Miller, J. P. (1998). Group cognitive-behavioral treatment of binge eating disorders: A comparison of therapist-led versus self-help formats. *International Journal of Eating Disorders, 24,* 125–136.

Peterson, J. B., Conrod, P., Vassileva, J., Gianoulakis, C., & Pihl, R. O. (2006). Differential effects of naltrexone on cardiac, subjective and behavioural reactions to acute ethanol intoxication. *Journal of Psychiatry & Neuroscience, 31*(6), 386–393.

Peterson, J. B., Pihl, R. O., Gianoulakis, C., Conrod, P., Finn, P. R., Stewart, S. H., . . . Bruce, K. R. (1996). Ethanol-induced change in cardiac and endogenous opiate function and risk for alcoholism. *Alcoholism: Clinical & Experimental Research, 20,* 1542–1552.

Peterson, J. B., Pihl, R. O., Seguin, J. R., Finn, P. R., & Stewart, S. H. (1993). Heart rate reactivity and alcohol consumption among sons of male alcoholics and sons of

non-alcoholics. *Journal of Psychiatry and Neuroscience, 18,* 190–198.

Peterson, L., & Roberts, M. C. (1992). Complacency, misdirection, and effective prevention of children's injuries. *American Psychologist, 47*(8), 1040–1044.

Peterson, L., & Thiele, C. (1988). Home safety at school. *Child and Family Behavior Therapy, 10*(1), 1–8.

Peterson, L., Farmer, J., & Kashani, J. H. (1990). Parental injury prevention endeavors: A function of health beliefs? *Health Psychology, 9*(2), 177–191.

Peterson, R. L., & Pennington, B. F. (2012). Developmental dyslexia. *The Lancet, 379*(9830), 1997–2007. https://doi.org/10.1016/S0140–6736(12)60198–6

Petit, D., Pennestri, M. H., Paquet, J., Desautels, A., Zadra, A., Vitaro, F., . . . Montplaisir, J. (2015). Childhood sleepwalking and sleep terrors: A longitudinal study of prevalence and familial aggregation. *JAMA Pediatrics, 169*(7), 653–658. https://doi.org/10.1001/jamapediatrics.2015.127

Peto, R., Lopez, A. D., Boreham, J., & Thun, T. (2006). *Mortality from Smoking in Developed Countries 1950–2000.* Retrieved January 7, 2008, from http://www.deathsfromsmoking.net/untries.html

Petrasek MacDonald, J., Ward, W., & Halseth, R. (2018). *Alzheimer's disease and related dementias in Indigenous populations in Canada: Prevalence and risk factors.* National Collaborating Centre for Aboriginal Health. https://www.ccnsa-nccah.ca/docs/emerging/RPT-Alzheimer-Dementia-MacDonald-Ward-Halseth-EN.pdf

Petrovic, P., Kalso, E., Petersson, K. M., & Ingvar, M. (2002). Placebo and opioid analgesia: Imaging a shared neuronal network. *Science, 295,* 1737–1740.

Petry, N. M., & O'Brien, C. P. (2013). Internet gaming disorder and the DSM-5. *Addiction, 108*(7), 1186–1187.

Petry, N. M., Martin, B., Cooney, J. L., & Kranzler, H. R. (2000). Give them prizes, and they will come: Contingency management for treatment of alcohol dependence. *Journal of Consulting and Clinical Psychology, 68*(2), 250–257.

Pham, T. H., Vanderstukken, O., Philippot, P., & Vanderlinden, M. (2003). Selective attention and executive functions deficits among criminal psychopaths. *Aggressive Behavior, 29,* 393–405.

Pharmacists.ca. (2003). *Products discontinued from the market.* Retrieved August 6, 2004, from http://www.pharmacists.ca/content/hcp/tools/drugnews/discontinued.htm

Phé, V., & Rouprêt, M. (2012). Erectile dysfunction and diabetes: A review of the current evidence-based medicine and a synthesis of the main available therapies. *Diabetes & Metabolism, 38*(1), 1–13.

Philips, H. C., & Grant, L. (1991). Acute back pain: A psychological analysis. *Behaviour Research and Therapy, 29,* 429–434.

Philip, M. (2003). When women run away from their lives. *The Globe and Mail,* May 9, 2003. Retrieved June 17, 2004, from http://www.globeandmail.com/servlet/ArticleNews/TPPrint/LAC/20030509/UAMNEN

Phillips, K. A. (1991). Body dysmorphic disorder: The distress of imagined

ugliness. *American Journal of Psychiatry, 148,* 1138–1149.

Phillips, K. A. (2005). *The broken mirror: Understanding and treating body dysmorphic disorder* (Rev ed.). New York, NY: Oxford University Press.

Phillips, K. A., & Gunderson, J. G. (2000). Personality disorders. In M. H. Kryger, T. Roth, & W. C. Dement (Eds.), *Principles and practice of sleep medicine* (3rd ed., pp. 795–823). Philadelphia, PA: W. B. Saunders.

Phillips, K. A., & Stout, R. (2006). Association in the longitudinal course of body dysmorphic disorder with major depression, obsessive compulsive disorder, and social phobia. *Journal of Psychiatric Research, 40,* 360–369.

Phillips, K. A., Albertini, R. S., & Rasmussen, S. A. (2002). A randomized placebo-controlled trial of fluoxetine in body dysmorphic disorder. *Archives of General Psychiatry, 59,* 381–388.

Phillips, K. A., Dufresne, R. G., Wilkel, C. S., & Vittorio, C. C. (2000). Rate of body dysmorphic disorder in dermatology patients. *Journal of the American Academy of Dermatology, 42,* 436–441.

Phillips, K. A., Grant, J., Siniscalchi, J., & Albertini, R. S. (2001). Surgical and nonpsychiatric medical treatment of patients with body dysmorphic disorder. *Psychosomatics, 42,* 504–510.

Phillips, K. A., McElroy, S. L., Keck, P. E., Jr., Pope, H. G., Jr., & Hudson, J. I. (1993). Body dysmorphic disorder: 30 cases of imagined ugliness. *American Journal of Psychiatry, 150,* 302–308.

Phillips, K. A., Menard, W., & Fay, C. (2006). Gender similarities and differences in 200 individuals with body dysmorphic disorder. *Comprehensive Psychiatry, 47,* 77–87.

Phillips, K. A., Menard, W., Fay, C., & Pagano, M. E. (2005). Psychosocial functioning and quality of life in body dysmorphic disorder. *Comprehensive Psychiatry, 46*(4), 254–260.

Phillips, K. A., Menard, W., Pagano, M., Fay, C., & Stout, R. (2006). Delusional versus nondelusional body dysmorphic disorder: Clinical features and course of illness. *Journal of Psychiatric Research, 40,* 95–104.

Phillips, K. A., Pagano, M., Menard, W., & Stout, R. (2006). A 12-month follow-up study of the course of body dysmorphic disorder. *American Journal of Psychiatry, 163,* 907–912.

Phillips, K. A., Pinto, A., Hart, A. S., Coles, M. E., Eisen, J. L., Menard, W., & Rasmussen, S. A. (2012). A comparison of insight in body dysmorphic disorder and obsessive–compulsive disorder. *Journal of Psychiatric Research, 46,* 1293–1299.

Phillips, K. A., Wilhelm, S., Koran, L. M., Didie, E., Fallon, B., Feusner, J., & Stein, D. J. (2010). Body dysmorphic disorder: Some key issues for DSM-V. *Depression and Anxiety, 27,* 573–591.

Phillips, K. A., Yen, S., & Gunderson, J. G. (2003). Personality disorders. In R. E. Hales & S. C. Yudofsky (Eds.), *Textbook of clinical psychiatry* (4th ed., pp. 804–832). Washington, DC: American Psychiatric Press.

Phillips, L. J., Francey, S. M., Edwards, J., & McMurray, N. (2007). Stress and psychosis: Towards the development of

new models of investigation. *Clinical Psychology Review, 27,* 307–317.

Physicians for a Smoke-Free Canada. (2002). *Percentage of Canadians who smoke (on either a daily or occasional basis), federal surveys, 1965–2003.* http://www.smoke-free.ca/factsheets/pdf/prevalence.pdf

Physicians for a Smoke-Free Canada. (2012). *Smoking in Canada: Smoking prevalence, 1965–2011.* http://www.smoke-free.ca/factsheets/pdf/prevalence.pdf

Pickens, R. W., Svikis, D. S., McGue, M., Lykken, D. T., Heston, L. L., & Clayton, P. J. (1991). Heterogeneity in the inheritence of alcoholism. *Archives of General Psychiatry, 48,* 19–28.

Pierce, K. (2016). Neurodevelopmental disorders: Specific learning disorder, communication disorders, and motor disorders. In M. K. Dulcan (Ed.), *Dulcan's textbook of child and adolescent psychiatry* (2nd ed., pp. 157–171). Arlington, VA: American Psychiatric Publishing.

Pierce, K. A., & Kirkpatrick, D. R. (1992). Do men lie on fear surveys? *Behaviour Research and Therapy, 30,* 415–418.

Pierce, W. D., & Epling, F. W. (1996). Theoretical developments in activity anorexia. In W. F. Epling & W. D. Pierce (Eds.), *Activity anorexia: Theory research, and treatment* (pp. 23–41). Mahwah, NJ: Erlbaum.

Pihl, R. O., Assad, J. M., & Hoaken, P. N. S. (2003). The alcohol-aggression relationship and differential sensitivity to alcohol. *Aggressive Behavior, 29*(4), 302–315.

Pihl, R. O., Peterson, J. B., & Lau, M. A. (1993). A biosocial model of the alcohol-aggression relationship. *Journal of Studies on Alcohol* (Suppl. 11), 128–139.

Piira, T., Hayes, B., Goodenough, B., & von Bayer, C. L. (2006). Effects of attentional direction, age, and coping style on cold-pressor pain in children. *Behaviour Research and Therapy, 44*(6), 835–848.

Pike, K. M., & Rodin, J. (1991). Mothers, daughters, and disordered eating. *Journal of Abnormal Psychology, 100*(2), 198–204.

Pike, K. M., Hoek, H. W., & Dunne, P. E. (2014). Cultural trends and eating disorders. *Current Opinion in Psychiatry, 27*(6), 436–442.

Pike, K. M., Walsh, B. T., Vitousek, K., Wilson, G. T., & Bauer, J. (2003). Cognitive behavior therapy in the post-hospitalization treatment of anorexia nervosa. *American Journal of Psychiatry, 160,* 2046–2048.

Pincus, D. B., Santucci, L. C., Ehrenreich, J. T., & Ryberg, S. M. (2008). The implementation of modified parent-child interaction therapy for youth with separation anxiety disorder. *Cognitive and Behavioral Practice, 15*(2), 118–125.

Pinel, J. P. J., Assanand, S., & Lehman, D. R. (2000). Hunger, eating, and ill health. *American Psychologist, 55,* 1105–1116.

Pinel, P. (1962). *A treatise on insanity.* New York, NY: Hafner. (Original work published in 1801).

Pinhas, L., Morris, A., Crosby, R. D., & Katzman, D. K. (2011). Incidence and age-specific presentation of restrictive eating disorders in children: A Canadian Paediatric Surveillance

Program study. *Archives of Pediatrics and Adolescent Medicine, 165*(10), 895–899.

Pinto, A. (2015). Treatment of obsessive–compulsive personality disorder. In *Clinical handbook of obsessive-compulsive and related disorders* (pp. 415–429). Springer International Publishing.

Piotrowski, C. (2015). On the decline of projective techniques in professional psychology training. *North American Journal of Psychology, 17*, 259–265.

Piper, A., & Merskey, H. (2004). The persistence of folly: Critical examination of dissociative identity disorder. Part I. The excesses of an improbable concept. *Canadian Journal of Psychiatry, 49*, 678–683.

Piran, N. (1997). Prevention of eating disorders: Directions for future research. *Psychopharmacology Bulletin, 33*, 419–423.

Piran, N. (1998). A participatory approach to the prevention of eating disorders in a school. In W. Vandereycken & G. Noordenbos (Eds.), *Prevention of eating disorders* (pp. 173–186). New York, NY: University Press.

Piran, N. (1999). Eating disorders: A trial of prevention in a high risk school setting. *Journal of Primary Prevention, 20*, 75–90.

Piran, N. (2004). Teachers: On "being" (rather than "doing") prevention. *Eating Disorders: Journal of Treatment & Prevention, 12*, 1–9.

Piran, N. V. (2001). Reinhabiting the body. *Feminism & Psychology, 11*, 172–176

Pires, G. N., Tufik, S., & Andersen, M. L. (2015). Sleep Deprivation and Anxiety in Humans and Rodents—Translational Considerations and Hypotheses. *Behavioral Neuroscience.*

Pisetsky, E. M., Thornton, L. M., Lichtenstein, P., Pedersen, N. L., & Bulik, C. M. (2013). Suicide attempts in women with eating disorders. *Journal of Abnormal Psychology, 122*(4), 1042.

Pletcher, M. J., Vittinghoff, E., Kalhan, R., Richman, J., Safford, M., Sidney, S., & Kertesz, S. (2012). Association between marijuana exposure and pulmonary function over 20 years. *JAMA, 307*(2), 173–181.

Pliner, P., & Haddock, G. (1996). Perfectionism in weight-concerned and unconcerned women: An experimental approach. *International Journal of Eating Disorders, 19*, 381–389.

Plomin, R. (1990). The role of inheritance in behavior. *Science, 248*, 183–188.

Plomin, R., & Davis, O. S. P. (2009). The future of genetics in psychology and psychiatry: Microarrays, genome-wide association, and non-coding RNA. *Journal of Child Psychology and Psychiatry, 50*(1–2), 63–71.

Plomin, R., DeFries, J. C., McClearn, G. E., & Rutter, M. (1997). *Behavioral genetics: A primer* (3rd ed.). New York, NY: Freeman.

Plomin, R., McClearn, G. E., Smith, D. L., Skuder, P., Vignetti, S., Chorney, M. J., . . . McGuffin, P. (1995). Allelic association between 100 DNA markers and high versus low IQ. *Intelligence, 21*, 31–48.

Plomin, R., Owen, M. J., & McGuffin, P. (1994). The genetic basis of complex human behaviors. *Science, 264*, 1733–1739.

Pocock, S. J. (2013). *Clinical trials: A practical approach.* Hoboken, NJ: John Wiley & Sons.

Podewils, L. J., Guallar, E., Kuller, L. H., Fried, L. P., Lopez, O. L., Carlson, M., & Lyketsos, C. G. (2005). Physical activity, APOE genotype, and dementia risk: Findings from the Cardiovascular Health Cognition Study. *American Journal of Epidemiology, 161*, 639–651.

Poirier, M. F., Laqueille, X., Jalfre, V., Willard, D., Bourdel, M. C., Fermanian, J., & Olié, J. P. (2004). Clinical profile of responders to buprenorphine as a substitution treatment in heroin addicts: Results of a multicenter study of 73 patients. *Progress in Neuro-Psychopharmacology & Biological Psychiatry, 28*, 267–272.

Polanczyk, G. V., Salum, G. A., Sugaya, L. S., Caye, A., & Rohde, L. A. (2015). Annual research review: A meta-analysis of the worldwide prevalence of mental disorders in children and adolescents. *Journal of Child Psychology and Psychiatry, 56*(3), 345–365.

Polanczyk, G., Zeni, C., Genro, J. P., Guimaraes, A. P., Roman, T., Hutz, M. H., & Rohde, L. A. (2007). Association of the adrenergic 2A receptor gene with methylphenidate improvement of inattentive symptoms in children and adolescents with attention-deficit/hyperactivity disorder. *Archives of General Psychiatry, 64*, 218–224.

Police lay murder charge in Holly Jones case. (2003a, June 21). *CBC News Online.* Retrieved August 5, 2004, from http://www.cbc.ca/stories/2003/06/20/holly030620

Polivy, J. (2001). The false hope syndrome: Unrealistic expectations of self-change. *International Journal of Obesity and Related Metabolic Disorders, 25*(Suppl. 1), 80–84.

Polivy, J., & Heatherton, T. (2015). Spiral model of dieting and disordered eating. In T. Wade (Ed.), *Encyclopedia of feeding and eating disorders.* Springer. https://doi.org/10.1007/978-981-287-087-2_94-1

Polivy, J. M., & Herman, C. P. (1985). Dieting and binging: A causal analysis. *American Psychologist, 40*, 193–201.

Polivy, J. M., & Herman, C. P. (1993). Etiology of binge eating: Psychological mechanisms. In C. G. Fairburn & G. T. Wilson (Eds.), *Binge eating: Nature, assessment, and treatment.* New York, NY: Guilford Press.

Polivy, J., & Herman, C. P. (2002). If at first you don't succeed. False hopes of self-change. *American Psychologist, 57*, 677–689.

Polivy, J., Herman, C. P., Mills, J., & Brock, H. (2003). Eating disorders in adolescence. In G. R. Adams & M. D. Berzonsky (Eds.), *Blackwell handbook of adolescence* (pp. 523–549). Malden, MA: Blackwell.

Pollack, C., & Andrews, G. (1989). Defense styles associated with specific anxiety disorders. *American Journal of Psychiatry, 146*, 1500–1502.

Pollack, M. H. (2005). The pharmacotherapy of panic disorder. *Journal of Clinical Psychiatry, 66*, 23–27.

Pollack, M. H., & Simon, N. M. (2009). Pharmacotherapy for panic disorder and agoraphobia. In M. M. Antony & M. B. Stein (Eds.), *Oxford handbook of anxiety and related disorders*

(pp. 295–307). New York, NY: Oxford University Press.

Polley, S. (Director/Writer). (2006). *Away from her* [Motion picture]. Canada: Capri Films.

Polloway, E. A., Schewel, R., & Patton, J. R. (1992). Learning disabilities in adulthood: Personal perspectives. *Journal of Learning Disabilities, 25*, 520–522.

Polonsky, D. C. (2000). Premature ejaculation. In S. R. Leiblum & R. C. Rosen (Eds.), *Principles and practice of sex therapy* (3rd ed., pp. 305–332). New York, NY: Guilford Press.

Pompili, M., Serafini, G., Innamorati, M., Biondi, M., Siracusano, A., Di Giannantonio, M., & Möller-Leimkühler, A. M. (2012). Substance abuse and suicide risk among adolescents. *European Archives of Psychiatry and Clinical Neuroscience, 262*(6), 469–485.

Pompili, M., Serafini, G., Innamorati, M., Möller-Leimkühler, A. M., Giupponi, G., Girardi, P., & Lester, D. (2010). The hypothalamic–pituitary–adrenal axis and serotonin abnormalities: A selective overview for the implications of suicide prevention. *European Archives of Psychiatry and Clinical Neuroscience, 260*(8), 583–600.

Ponseti, J., Granert, O., Jansen, O., Wolff, S., Beier, K., Neutze, J., & Bosinski, H. (2012). Assessment of pedophilia using hemodynamic brain response to sexual stimuli. *Archives of General Psychiatry, 69*(2), 187.

Poon, K., Watson, L., Baranek, G., & Poe, M. D. (2012). To what extent do joint attention, imitation, and object play behaviors in infancy predict later communication and intellectual functioning in ASD? *Journal of Autism and Developmental Disorders, 42*(6), 1064–1074.

Poorsattar, S., & Hornung, R. (2010). Tanning addiction: Current trends and future treatment. *Expert Review of Dermatology, 5*(2), 123–125.

Pope, C., Pope, H., Menard, W., Fay, C., Olivardia, R., & Phillips, K. (2005). Clinical features of muscle dysmorphia among males with body dysmorphic disorder. *Body Image, 4*, 395–400.

Pope, H. D., Jr., Oliva, P. S., Hudson, J. I., Bodkin, J. A., & Gruber, A. J. (1999). Attitudes toward DSM-IV dissociative disorders diagnoses among board-certified American psychiatrists. *American Journal of Psychiatry, 156*(2), 321–323.

Pope, H. G., Jr., & Kanayama, G. (2012). Anabolic–androgenic steroids. In J. C. Verster, K. Brady, M. Galanter, & P. Conrod (Eds.), *Drug abuse and addiction in medical illness* (pp. 251–264). New York, NY: Springer.

Pope, H. G., Jr., Gruber, A. J., Mangweth, B., Bureau, B., deCol, C., Jouvent, R., & Hudson, J. I. (2000). Body image perception among men in three countries. *American Journal of Psychiatry, 157*, 1297–1301.

Pope, K. S. (1996). Memory, abuse and science: Questioning claims about the false memory syndrome epidemic. *American Psychologist, 51*, 957–974.

Pope, K. S. (1997). Science as careful questioning: Are claims of a false memory syndrome epidemic based on empirical evidence? *American Psychologist, 52*, 997–1006.

Popper, C. W., Gammon, G. D., West, S. A., & Bailey, C. E. (2003). Disorders

usually first diagnosed in infancy, childhood, or adolescence. In: R. E. Hales & S. C. Yudofsky, *Textbook of psychiatry* (4th ed., pp. 833–974). Washington, DC: American Psychiatric Press.

Portenoy, R., & Mathur, G. (2009). Cancer pain. In S. C. J. Yeung, C. P. Escalante, & R. F. Gagel (Eds.), *Medical care of the cancer patient* (pp. 60–71). Shelton, CT: PMPH USA Ltd.

Porter, S. (1996). Without conscience or without active conscience? The etiology of psychopathy revisited. *Aggression and Violent Behavior, 1*, 179–189.

Porter, S., Campbell, M. A., Birt, A. R., & Woodworth, M. T. (2003). "He said, she said": A psychological perspective on historical memory evidence in the courtroom. *Canadian Psychology, 44*, 190–206.

Porter, S., Hervé, H., Fairweather, D., & Birt, A. R. (November, 1999). *Patterns of psychopathy in sexually violent offenders: Is the sexual psychopath a valid entity?* Paper presented at the Conference on Risk Assessment and Management, BC Institute of Family Violence, Vancouver, BC.

Porter, S., Spencer, L., & Birt, A. R. (2003). Blinded by emotion? Effect of the emotionality of a scene on susceptibility to false memories. *Canadian Journal of Behavioural Science, 35*, 165–175.

Porter, S., Woodworth, M., Earle, J., Drugge, J., & Boer, D. (2003). Characteristics of sexual homicides committed by psychopathic and nonpsychopathic offenders. *Law and Human Behavior, 27*, 459–470.

Porter, S., Yuille, J. C., & Lehman, D. R. (1999). The nature of real, implanted, and fabricated memories for emotional childhood events: Implications for the recovered memory debate. *Law and Human Behavior, 23*, 517–537.

Possible Mackay forgets burning body: Expert. (2003). *CBC Saskatchewan.* Retrieved June 8, 2003, from http://sask.cbc.ca/regional/servlet/View?filenamemackay020608

Post, L., Page, C., Conner, T., & Prokhorov, A. (2010). Elder abuse in long-term care: Types, patterns, and risk factors. *Research on Aging, 32*(3), 323.

Post, R. M. (1992). Transduction of psychosocial stress into the neurobiology of recurrent affective disorder. *American Journal of Psychiatry, 149*(8), 999–1010.

Post, R. M., Rubinow, D. R., Uhde, T. W., Roy-Byrne, P. P., Linnoila, M., Rosoff, A., & Cowdry, R. (1989). Dysphoric mania: Clinical and biological correlates. *Archives of General Psychiatry, 46*, 353–358.

Potenza, M. N. (2001). The neurobiology of pathological gambling. *Seminars in Clinical Neuropsychiatry, 6*, 217–226.

Potenza, M. N., Steinberg, M. A., Skudlarski, P., Fulbright, R. K., Lacadie, C. M., Wilber, M. K., & Wexler, B. E. (2003). Gambling urges in pathological gambling: A functional magnetic resonance imaging study. *Archives of General Psychiatry, 60*, 828–836.

Potkin, S. G., Albers, L. J., & Richmond, G. (1993). Schizophrenia: An overview of pharmacological treatment. In D. L. Dunner (Ed.), *Current psychiatric therapy* (pp. 142–154). Philadelphia, PA: W. B. Saunders.

Potter, R., Ellard, D., Rees, K., & Thorogood, M. (2011). A systematic review of the effects of physical activity on physical functioning, quality of life and depression in older people with dementia. *International Journal of Geriatric Psychiatry, 26*(10), 1000–1011.

Potter, S. M., Zelazo, P. R., Stack, D. M., & Papageorgiou, A. N. (2000). Adverse effects of fetal cocaine exposure on neonatal auditory information processing. *Pediatrics, 105*(3), E40.

Potter, W. Z., & Manji, H. K. (1993). Are monoamine metabolites in cerebral spinal fluid worth measuring? *Archives of General Psychiatry, 50*, 653–656.

Poulsen, S., Lunn, S., Daniel, S. I. F., Folke, S., Mathiesen, B. B., Katznelson, H., & Fairburn, C. G. (2014). A randomized controlled trial of psychoanalytic psychotherapy versus cognitive behavior therapy for bulimia nervosa. *American Journal of Psychiatry, 171*, 109–116.

Powell, R. A., & Howell, A. J. (1998). Effectiveness of treatment for dissociative identity disorder. *Psychological Reports, 83*, 483–490.

Powers, A. D., Gleason, M. E., & Oltmanns, T. F. (2013). Symptoms of borderline personality disorder predict interpersonal (but not independent) stressful life events in a community sample of older adults. *Journal of Abnormal Psychology, 122*(2), 469.

Poznanski, E. O., Israel, M. C., & Grossman, J. A. (1984). Hypomania in a four year old. *Journal of the American Academy of Child Psychiatry, 23*(1), 105–110.

Prapavessis, H., Cameron, L., Baldi, J. C., Robinson, S., Borrie, K., Harper, T., & Grove, R. J. (2007). The effects of exercise and nicotine replacement therapy on smoking rates in women. *Addictive Behaviors, 32*(7), 1416–1432.

Pratt, S. I., Mueser, K. T., Driscoll, M., Wolfe, R., & Bartels, S. J. (2006). Medication nonadherence in older people with serious mental illness: Prevalence and correlates. *Psychiatric Rehabilitation Journal, 29*, 299–310.

Prause, N., & Janssen, E. (2006). Blood flow: Vaginal photoplethysmography. In Goldstein, I., Meston, C. M., Davis, S. R., & Traish, A. M. (Eds.), *Women's sexual function and dysfunction: Study, diagnostic and treatment* (pp. 359–367). New York, NY: Taylor & Francis.

Prelior, E. F., Yutzy, S. H., Dean, J. T., & Wetzel, R. D. (1993). Briquet's syndrome, dissociation and abuse. *American Journal of Psychiatry, 150*, 1507–1511.

Prenoveau, J. M., Craske, M. G., Liao, B., & Ornitz, E. M. (2013). Human fear conditioning and extinction: Timing is everything . . . or is it?. *Biological Psychology, 92*(1), 59–68.

Prescott, C. A., & Kendler, K. S. (1999). Genetic and environmental contributions to alcohol abuse and dependence in a population-based sample of male twins. *American Journal of Psychiatry, 156*, 34–40.

Preskorn, S. H. (1995). Comparison of the tolerability of bupropion, fluoxetine, imipramine, nefazodone, paroxetine, sertraline, and venlafaxine. *Journal of Clinical Psychiatry, 56*(Suppl. 6), 12–21.

Presnall, N., Webster-Stratton, C. H., & Constantino, J. N. (2014). Parent Training: Equivalent Improvement in Externalizing Behavior for Children With and Without Familial Risk. *Journal of the American Academy of Child & Adolescent Psychiatry, 53*(8), 879–887.

Price, A. M. H., Wake, M., Ukoumunne, O. C., & Hiscock, H. (2012). Outcomes at six years of age for children with infant sleep problems: Longitudinal community-based study. *Sleep Medicine, 13*(8), 991–998.

Price, R., & Brew, B. (1988). The AIDS dementia complex. *Journal of Infectious Diseases, 158*, 1079–1083.

Price, S. R., Hilchey, C. A., Darredeau, C., Fulton, H. G., & Barrett, S. P. (2010). Energy drink co-administration is associated with increased reported alcohol ingestion. *Drug and Alcohol Review, 29*(3), 331–333.

Pridal, C. G., & LoPiccolo, J. (2000). Multielement treatment of desire disorders: Integration of cognitive, behavioral and systemic therapy. In S. R. Leiblum & R. C. Rosen (Eds.), *Principles and practice of sex therapy* (3rd ed., pp. 57–81). New York, NY: Guilford Press.

Prien, R. F., & Kupfer, D. J. (1986). Continuation drug therapy for major depressive episodes: How long should it be maintained? *American Journal of Psychiatry, 143*(1), 18–23.

Prien, R. F., Kupfer, D. J., Mansky, P. A., Small, J. G., Tuason, V. B., Voss, C. B., & Johnson, W. E. (1984). Drug therapy in the prevention of recurrences in unipolar and bipolar affective disorders: Report of the NIMH collaborative study group comparing lithium carbonate, imipramine and a lithium carbonate-imipramine combination. *Archives of General Psychiatry, 41*, 1096–1104.

Priest, L. (2003). Children's Aid closes suspected case of Munchausen's syndrome. June 25, 2003, *The Globe*. Retrieved June 21, 2004, from http://www.msbp.com/DeSousa.htm

Prince, M. (1906–1907). Hysteria from the point of view of dissociated personality. *Journal of Abnormal Psychology, 1*, 170–187.

Pringsheim, T., Wiltshire, K., Day, L., Dykeman, J., Steeves, T., & Jette, N. (2012). The incidence and prevalence of Huntington's disease: A systematic review and meta-analysis. *Movement Disorders, 27*(9), 1083–1091.

Prins, J., van der Meer, J., & Bleijenberg, G. (2006). Chronic fatigue syndrome. *Lancet, 367*, 346–355.

Prizant, B. M., & Wetherby, A. M. (1989). Enhancing language and communication in autism: From theory to practice. In G. Dawson (Ed.), *Autism: Nature, diagnosis, and treatment* (pp. 282–309). New York, NY: Guilford Press.

Prochaska, J. O., DiClemente, C. C., & Norcross, J. C. (1997). In search of how people change: Applications to addictive behaviors. In G. A. Marlatt & G. R. VandenBos (Eds.), *Addictive behaviors: Readings on etiology, prevention, and treatment* (pp. 671–696). Washington, DC: American Psychological Association.

Project MATCH Research Group. (1993). Project MATCH: Rationale and methods for a multisite clinical trial matching patients to alcoholism treatment. *Alcoholism: Clinical and Experimental Research, 17*, 1130–1145.

Project MATCH Research Group. (1997). Matching alcoholism treatments to client heterogeneity: Project MATCH: Posttreatment drinking outcomes. *Journal of Studies on Alcohol, 58*, 7–29.

Project MATCH Research Group. (1998). Matching alcoholism treatments to client heterogeneity: Treatment main effects and matching effects on drinking during treatment. *Journal of Studies on Alcohol, 59*, 631–639.

Proulx, E. A. (2001). *The shipping news*. New York, NY: Simon & Schuster.

Proulx, T., & Heine, S. J. (2009). Connections from Kafka: Exposure to meaning threats improves implicit learning of an artificial grammar. *Psychological Science, 20*(9), 1125–1131.

Prout, P. I., & Dobson, K. S. (1998). Recovered memories of childhood sexual abuse: Searching for the middle ground in clinical practice. *Canadian Psychology, 39*, 257–265.

Provencher, H. L., & Fincham, F. D. (2000). Attributions of causality, responsibility and blame for positive and negative symptom behaviours in caregivers of persons with schizophrenia. *Psychological Medicine, 30*, 899–910.

Province-wide smoking ban adopted. (2005, July/August). *Human Resources Advisor Newsletter*, p. 3. Retrieved September 15, 2007, from http://proquest.umi.com/pqdweb?index1&did8 70499591&SrchMode1&sid5&Fmt3 &VInstPROD&VTypePQD&RQT30 9&VNamePQD&TS1186253921&cli entId6993

Pruzinsky, T. (1988). Collaboration of plastic surgeon and medical psychotherapist: Elective cosmetic surgery. *Medical Psychotherapy, 1*, 1–13.

Public Health Agency of Canada. (2013). *Congenital anomalies in Canada 2013: A perinatal health surveillance report*. Catalogue No. HP35-40/2013E-PDF. Retrieved from http://www.aphp.ca/pdf/CAC%20report%202013%20EN.pdf

Public Health Agency of Canada. (2014). *HIV and AIDS in Canada: Surveillance report to December 31, 2013*. Ottawa, ON: Minister of Public Works and Government Services Canada.

Public Health Agency of Canada. (2017a). *Down syndrome surveillance in Canada, 2005–2013*. https://www.canada.ca/content/dam/phac-aspc/documents/services/publications/healthy-living/down-syndrome-surveillance-2005-2013/pub1-eng.pdf

Public Health Agency of Canada. (2017b). *Dementia in Canada, including Alzheimer's disease: Highlights from the Canadian chronic disease surveillance system*. https://www.canada.ca/en/public-health/services/publications/diseases-conditions/dementia-highlights-canadian-chronic-disease-surveillance.html

Public Health Agency of Canada. (2018a). *Key health inequalities in Canada: A national portrait*. https://www.canada.ca/en/public-health/services/publications/science-research-data/key-health-inequalities-canada-national-portrait-executive-summary.html

Public Health Agency of Canada. (2018b). *Autism spectrum disorder among children and youth in Canada 2018: A report of the national autism spectrum disorder surveillance system*. https://www.canada.ca/en/public-health/services/publications/diseases-conditions/autism-spectrum-disorder-children-youth-canada-2018.html

Public Health Agency of Canada. (2018c). *Parkinsonism in Canada, including Parkinson's disease: Highlights from the Canadian chronic disease surveillance system*. https://www.canada.ca/en/public-health/services/publications/diseases-conditions/parkinsonism.html

Public Health Agency of Canada. (2019). *A dementia strategy for Canada: Together we aspire*. https://www.canada.ca/en/public-health/services/publications/diseases-conditions/dementia-strategy.html#s3.2

Public Health Agency of Canada & Neurological Health Charities Canada. (2014). *Mapping Connections: An understanding of neurological conditions in Canada* (Catalogue no. HP35-45/2014E-PDF). http://www.phac-aspc.gc.ca/publicat/cd-mc/mc-ec/index-eng.php

Public Works and Government Services Canada. (2003). *Tri-council policy statement: Ethical conduct for research involving humans*. Ottawa, ON: Medical Research Council of Canada.

Pueschel, S. M., & Goldstein, A. (1991). Genetic counseling. In J. L. Matson & J. A. Mulick (Eds.), *Handbook of mental retardation* (2nd ed., pp. 279–291). Elmsford, NY: Pergamon Press.

Puhan, M. A., Suarez, A., Cascio, C. L., Zahn, A., Heitz, M., & Braendli, O. (2006). Didgeridoo playing as alternative treatment for obstructive sleep apnoea syndrome: Randomised controlled trial. *BMJ, 332*(7536), 266–270.

Puig-Antich, J., & Rabinovich, H. (1986). Relationship between affective and anxiety disorders in childhood. In R. G. Helman (Ed.), *Anxiety disorders of childhood* (pp. 136–156). New York, NY: John Wiley & Sons.

Pulay, A. J., Stinson, F. S., Dawson, D. A., Goldstein, R. B., Chou, S. P., Huang, B., & Ruan, W. J. (2009). Prevalence, correlates, disability, and comorbidity of DSM-IV schizotypal personality disorder: Results from the Wave 2 National Epidemiologic Survey on Alcohol and Related Conditions. *Primary Care Companion Journal of Clinical Psychiatry, 11*(2), 53.

Pulkki-Raback, L., Kivimäki, M., Ahola, K., Joutsenniemi, K., Elovainio, M., & Virtanen, M. (2012). Living alone and antidepressant medication use: A prospective study in a working-age population. *BMC Public Health, 12*(1), 236.

Pull, C. B. (2013). Too few or too many? Reactions to removing versus retaining specific personality disorders in DSM-5. *Current Opinion in Psychiatry, 26*(1), 73–78.

Purdon, C. (1999). Thought suppression and psychopathology. *Behaviour Research and Therapy, 37*, 1029–1054.

Purdon, C. (2004). Empirical investigations of thought suppression in OCD. *Journal of Behavior Therapy and Experimental Psychiatry, 35*, 121–136.

Purdon, C. (2009). Psychological approaches to understanding obsessive-compulsive disorder. In M. M. Antony & M. B. Stein (Eds.), *Oxford handbook of anxiety and related disorders* (pp. 238–249). New York, NY: Oxford University Press.

Purdon, C., Antony, M., Monteiro, S., & Swinson, R. P. (2001). Social anxiety in college students. *Journal of Anxiety Disorders, 15*, 203–215.

Purdon, C., & Clark, D. A. (2000). White bears and other elusive intrusions: Assessing the relevance of thought suppression for obsessional phenomena. *Behavior Modification, 24*, 425–453.

Purdy, D., & Frank, E. (1993). Should post-partum mood disorders be given a more prominent or distinct place in DSM-IV? *Depression, 1*, 59–70.

Pury, C. L. S., & Mineka, S. (1997). Covariation bias for blood-injury stimuli and aversion outcomes. *Behavior Research and Therapy, 35*, 35–47.

Putnam, F. W. (1991). Dissociative phenomena. In A. Tasman & S. M. Goldinger (Eds.), *American Psychiatric Press review of psychiatry* (Vol. 10). Washington, DC: American Psychiatric Press.

Putnam, F. W. (1992). Altered states: Peeling away the layers of a multiple personality. *Sciences, 32*(6), 30–36.

Putnam, F. W. (1994). The switch process in multiple personality disorder and other state-change disorders. In R. M. Klein & B. K. Doane (Eds.), *Psychological concepts and dissociative disorders* (pp. 283–304). Hillsdale, NJ: Erlbaum.

Putnam, F. W. (1997). *Dissociation in children and adolescents: A developmental perspective*. New York, NY: Guilford Press.

Putnam, F. W., & Loewenstein, R. J. (1993). Treatment of multiple personality disorder: A survey of current practices. *American Journal of Psychiatry, 150*, 1048–1052.

Putnam, F. W., Guroff, J. J., Silberman, E. K., Barban, L., & Post, R. M. (1986). The clinical phenomenology of multiple personality disorder: Review of 100 recent cases. *Journal of Clinical Psychiatry, 47*, 285–293.

Pyke, J. (Writer & Director). (2014). Twin life: Sharing mind and body [Television series episode]. In L. Mawhinney & M. O'Brian (Executive producers), *Doc Zone with Ann-Marie MacDonald*. Ottawa, ON: Canadian Broadcasting Corporation. http://www.cbc.ca/doczone/episodes/twin-life-sharing-mind-and-body

Pyke, J. (Writer & Director). (2017). Inseparable: Ten years joined at the head [Television series episode]. In C. Engel (Executive producer), *CBC Docs POV*. Canadian Broadcasting Corporation.

Quality Assurance Project. (1990). Treatment outlines for paranoid, schizotypal and schizoid personality disorders. *Australian and New Zealand Journal of Psychiatry, 24*, 339–350.

Quay, H. C. (1993). The psychobiology of undersocialized aggressive conduct disorder: A theoretical perspective. *Development and Psychopathology, 5*, 165–180.

Quebec measles outbreak grows to 119 confirmed cases including student. (2015, March 11). *CBC News Online*. Retrieved July 30, 2015, from http://www.cbc.ca/news/canada/montreal/quebec-measles-outbreak-grows-to-119-confirmed-cases-including-student-1.2990192

Quinsey, V. L., Harris, G. T., Rice, M. E., & Cormier, C. A. (2006). *Violent offenders: Appraising and managing risk*. Washington, DC: American Psychological Association.

Quirk, S. E., Berk, M., Chanen, A. M., Koivumaa-Honkanen, H., Brennan-Olsen, S. L., Pasco, J. A., & Williams, L. J. (2016). Population prevalence of personality disorder and associations with physical health comorbidities and health care service utilization: A review. *Personality Disorders: Theory, Research, and Treatment, 7*(2), 136–146. https://doi.org/10.1037/per0000148

Quoidbach, J., Gilbert, D. T., & Wilson, T. D. (2013). The end of history illusion. *Science, 339*(6115), 96–98.

Rabe, S., Zoellner, T., Beauducel, A., Maercker, A., & Karl, A. (2008). Changes in brain electrical activity after cognitive behavioral therapy for posttraumatic stress disorder in patients injured in motor vehicle accidents. *Psychosomatic Medicine, 70*(1), 13–19.

Rabins, P. V. (2006). Guideline watch: Practice guidelines for the treatment of patients with *Alzheimer's disease and other dementias of late life*. Washington, DC: American Psychiatric Association.

Rabins, P. V., & Lyketsos, C. G. (2011). A commentary on the proposed DSM revision regarding the classification of cognitive disorders. *American Journal of Geriatric Psychiatry, 19*(3), 201–204.

Rachman, S. (1978). *Fear and courage*. San Francisco, CA: W. H. Freeman.

Rachman, S. (1991). Neo-conditioning and the classical theory of fear acquisition. *Clinical Psychology Review, 11*, 155–173.

Rachman, S. (1998). *A cognitive theory of obsessions*. In E. Sanavio (Ed.), *Behavior and cognitive therapy today: Essays in honor of Hans J. Eysenck* (pp. 209–222). Oxford, UK: Elsevier Science Ltd.

Rachman, S. (2003). *The treatment of obsessions*. New York, NY: Oxford University Press.

Rachman, S. (2006). *Fear of contamination*. New York, NY: Oxford University Press.

Rachman, S. J. (1977). The conditioning theory of fear-acquisition: A critical examination. *Behaviour Research and Therapy, 15*, 375–387.

Rachman, S. J. (1984). Agoraphobia: A safety-signal perspective. *Behaviour Research and Therapy, 22*, 59–70.

Rachman, S. J. (1988). Panics and their consequences: A review and prospect. In S. J. Rachman & J. D. Maser (Eds.), *Panic: Psychological perspectives* (pp. 259–304). Hillsdale, NJ: Erlbaum.

Rachman, S. J., & deSilva, P. (2004). *Obsessive compulsive disorder: The facts* (3rd ed.). New York, NY: Oxford University Press.

Rachman, S., & de Silva, P. (1978). Abnormal and normal obsessions. *Behaviour Research & Therapy, 16*, 233–248.

Rachman, S., & Hodgson, R. (1968). Experimentally induced "sexual fetishism": Replication and development. *Psychological Record, 18*(1), 25–27.

Rachman, S., & Philips, C. (1980). *Psychology and behavioral medicine*. Cambridge, NY: Cambridge University Press.

Rachman, S., & Shafran, R. (1998). Cognitive and behavioral features of obsessive–compulsive disorder. In R. P. Swinson & M. M. Antony (Eds.), *Obsessive–compulsive disorder: Theory, research, and treatment* (pp. 51–78). New York, NY: Guilford Press.

Radnitz, C. L., Appelbaum, K. A., Blanchard, E. B., Elliott, L., & Andrasik, F. (1988). The effect of self-regulatory treatment on pain behavior in chronic headache. *Behaviour Research and Therapy, 26*, 253–260.

Rado, S. (1962). Theory and therapy: The theory of schizotypal organization and its application to the treatment of decompensated schizotypal behavior. In S. Rado (Ed.), *Psychoanalysis of behavior* (Vol. 2, pp. 127–140). New York, NY: Grune & Stratton.

Radomsky, A. S., & Taylor, S. (2005). Subtyping OCD: Prospects and problems. *Behavior Therapy, 36*, 371–379.

Radomsky, A. S., Rachman, S. J., Thordarson, D. S., McIsaac, H. K., & Teachman, B. A. (2001). The Claustrophobia Questionnaire. *Journal of Anxiety Disorders, 15*, 287–297.

Rafferty, S., & Mann, R. (2004): *Smoking and culture: The archaeology of tobacco pipes in eastern North America*. University of Tennessee Press.

Rahkonen, T., Eloniemi-Sulkava, U., Paanila, S., Halonen, P., Sivenius, J., & Sulkava, R. (2001). Systematic intervention for supporting community care of elderly people after a delirium episode. *International Psychogeriatrics, 13*, 37–49.

Rahkonen, T., Makela, H., Paanila, S., Halonen, P., Sivenius, J., & Sulkava, R. (2000). Delirium in elderly people without severe predisposing disorders: Etiology and 1-year prognosis after discharge. *International Psychogeriatrics, 12*, 473–481.

Raich, R. M., Rosen, J. C., Deus, J., Perez, O., Requiena, A., & Gross, J. (1992). Eating disorder symptoms among adolescents in the United States and Spain: A comparative study. *International Journal of Eating Disorders, 11*, 63–72.

Raine, A., Mellingen, K., Liu, J., Venables, P., & Mednick, S. A. (2003). Effects of environmental enrichment at ages 3–5 years on schizotypal personality and antisocial behavior at ages 17 and 23 years. *American Journal of Psychiatry, 160*, 1627–1635.

Ramacciotti, C. E., Dell'Osso, L., Paoli, R. A., Ciapparelli, A., Coli, E., Kaplan, A. S., & Garfinkel, P. E. (2002). Characteristics of eating disorder patients without a drive for thinness. *International Journal of Eating Disorders, 32*, 206–212.

Ramachandran, V. S. (1993). Filling in the gaps in perception II: Scotomas and phantom limbs. *Current Directions in Psychological Science, 2*, 56–65.

Ramage-Morin, P. L. (2004). Panic disorder and coping. *Supplement to Health Reports, 15*, 33–63.

Ramchandani, P., Stein, A., Evans, J., O'Connor, T., & the ALSPAC Study Team. (2005). Paternal depression in the postnatal period and child development: A prospective population study. *Lancet, 365*, 2201–2205.

Ramos Olazagasti, M. A., Klein, R. G., Mannuzza, S., Belsky, E. R., Hutchison, J. A., Lashua-Shriftman, E. C., & Xavier Castellanos, F. (2013). Does childhood attention-deficit/hyperactivity disorder predict risk-taking and medical illnesses in adulthood? *Journal of the American Academy of Child & Adolescent Psychiatry, 52*(2), 153–162.

Ramrakha, S., Paul, C., Bell, M. L., Dickson, N., Moffitt, T. E., & Caspi, A. (2013). The relationship between multiple sex partners and anxiety, depression, and substance dependence disorders: A cohort study. *Archives of Sexual Behavior, 42*(5), 863–872.

Ramsawh, H. J., Morgentaler, A., Covino, N., Barlow, D. H., & DeWolf, W. C. (2005). Quality of life following simultaneous placement of penile prosthesis with radical prostatectomy. *Journal of Urology, 174*(4, Part 1 of 2), 1395–1398.

Ramsey, M. (2003, July 28). Bar goers wary of rape drug. *The Vancouver Sun*, p. B.1.

Rangmar, J., Hjern, A., Vinnerljung, B., Strömland, K., Aronson, M., & Fahlke, C. (2015). Psychosocial outcomes of fetal alcohol syndrome in adulthood. *Pediatrics, 135*(1), e52–e58.

Ranson, M. B., Nichols, D. S., Rouse, S. V., & Harrington, J. L. (2009). Changing or replacing an established psychological assessment standard: Issues, goals, and problems with special reference to recent developments in the MMPI-2. In J. N. Butcher (Ed.), *Oxford handbook of personality assessment* (pp. 112–139). New York, NY: Oxford University Press.

Rapee, R. M., & Melville, L. F. (1997). Recall of family factors in social phobia and panic disorder: Comparison of mother and offspring reports. *Depression and Anxiety, 5*, 7–11.

Rapkin, A. J., Chang, L. C., & Reading, A. E. (1989). Mood and cognitive style in premenstrual syndrome. *Obstetrics and Gynecology, 74*, 644–649.

Rapp, S. R., Parisi, S. A., & Wallace, C. E. (1991). Comorbid psychiatric disorders in elderly medical patients: A l-year prospective study. *Journal of the American Geriatrics Society, 39*(2), 124–131.

Rapport, M. D. (2001). Bridging theory and practice: Conceptual understanding of treatments for children with attention deficit hyperactivity disorder (ADHD), obsessive–compulsive disorder (OCD), autism, and depression. *Journal of Clinical Child Psychology, 30*(1), 3–7.

Rasmussen, S. A., & Eisen, J. L. (1990). Epidemiology of obsessive–compulsive disorder. *Journal of Clinical Psychiatry, 51*, 10–14.

Rasmusson, A. M., Anderson, G. M., Krishnan-Sarin, S., Wu, R., & Paliwal, P. (2006). A decrease in plasma DHEA to cortisol ratio during smoking abstinence may predict relapse: A preliminary study. *Psychopharmacology, 186*, 473–480.

Rathod, N. H., Addenbrooke, W. M., & Rosenbach, A. F. (2005). Heroin dependence in an English town: 33-year follow-up. *British Journal of Psychiatry, 187*(5), 421–425. https://doi.org/10.1192/bjp.187.5.421

Rauch, A., Wieczorek, D., Graf, E. R., Wieland, T., Endele, S., Schwarzmayr, T., & Strom, T. M. (2012). Range of genetic mutations associated with severe non-syndromic sporadic intellectual disability: An exome sequencing study. *The Lancet, 380*(9854), 1674–1682.

Rauch, S. A. M., King, A. P., Abelson, J., Tuerk, P. W., Smith, E.,

Rothbaum, B. O., Clifton, E.., Defever, A., & Liberzon, I. (2014). Biological and symptom changes in posttraumatic disorder treatment: A randomized clinical trial. *Depression and Anxiety, 32*, 204–212.

Rauch, S. L., Phillips, K. A., Segal, E., Markis, N., Shin, L. M., Whalen, P. J., . . . Kennedy, D. N. (2003). A preliminary morphometric magnetic resonance imaging study of regional brain volumes in body dysmorphic disorder. *Psychiatry Research, 122*, 13–19.

Ray, L. A. (2012). Clinical neuroscience of addiction: Applications to psychological science and practice. *Clinical Psychology: Science and Practice, 19*(2), 154–166.

Ray, W. A., Gurwitz, J., Decker, M. D., & Kennedy, D. L. (1992). Medications and the safety of the older driver: Is there a basis for concern? [Special issue: Safety and mobility of elderly drivers: ll]. *Human Factors, 34*(1), 33–47.

Ray, W. A., Thapa, P. B., & Gideon, P. (2000). Benzodiazepines and the risk of falls in nursing home residents. *Journal of the American Geriatrics Society, 48*, 682–685.

Raymond, N. C., Coleman, E., Ohlerking, F., Christenson, G. A., & Miner, M. (1999). Psychiatric comorbidity in pedophilic sex offenders. *American Journal of Psychiatry, 156*, 786–788.

Rayner, K. E., Schniering, C. A., Rapee, R. M., Taylor, A., & Hutchinson, D. M. (2012). Adolescent girls' friendship networks, body dissatisfaction, and disordered eating: Examining selection and socialization processes. *Journal of Abnormal Psychology, 122*(1), 93–104.

Raza, G. T., DeMarce, J. M., Lash, S. J., & Parker, J. D. (2014). Paranoid personality disorder in the United States: The role of race, illicit drug use, and income. *Journal of Ethnicity in Substance Abuse, 13*(3), 247–257.

Razran, G. (1961). The observable unconscious and the inferable conscious in current Soviet psychophysiology: Interoceptive conditioning, semantic conditioning, and the orienting reflex. *Psychological Review, 68*, 81–150.

Reas, D. L., & Grilo, C. M. (2014). Current and emerging drug treatments for binge eating disorder. *Expert Opinion on Emerging Drugs, 19*(1), 99–142.

Record, N. B., Onion, D. K., Prior, R. E., Dixon, D. C., Record, S. S., Fowler, F. L., Cayer, G. R., Amos, C. I., & Pearson, T. A. (2015). Community-wide cardiovascular disease prevention programs and health outcomes in a rural county, 1970–2010. *JAMA, 313*(2), 147–155.

Rector, N. A., & Beck, A. T. (2001). Cognitive behavioral therapy for schizophrenia: An empirical review. *Journal of Nervous & Mental Disease, 189*, 278–287.

Rector, N. A., & Beck, A. T. (2002). Cognitive therapy for schizophrenia: From conceptualization to intervention. *Canadian Journal of Psychiatry, 47*, 41–50.

Rector, N. A., Seeman, M. V., & Segal, Z. V. (2003). Cognitive therapy for schizophrenia: A preliminary randomized controlled trial. *Schizophrenia Research, 63*, 1–11.

Rector, N. A., Segal, Z. V., & Gemar, M. (1998). Schema research in depression: A Canadian perspective. *Canadian*

Journal of Behavioural Science, 30, 213–224.

Redd, W. H., & Andrykowski, M. A. (1982). Behavioral intervention in cancer treatment: Controlling aversion reactions to chemotherapy. *Journal of Consulting and Clinical Psychology, 50*, 1018–1029.

Reddy, L. F., Horan, W. P., & Green, M. F. (2016). Motivational deficits and negative symptoms in schizophrenia: Concepts and assessments. *Current Topics in Behavioral Neuroscience, 27*, 357–373.

Reeve, R. E., & Kauffman, J. M. (1988). Learning disabilities. In V. B. Van Hasselt, P. S. Strain, & M. Hersen (Eds.), *Handbook of developmental and physical disabilities* (pp. 316–335). Elmsford, NY: Pergamon Press.

Rea, M., Tompson, M. C., & Miklowitz, D. J. (2003). Family-focused treatment versus individual treatment for bipolar disorder: Results of a randomized clinical trial. *Journal of Consulting and Clinical Psychology, 71*, 482–492.

Regehr, C., & Glancy, G. (1995). Battered woman syndrome defense in Canadian courts. *Canadian Journal of Psychiatry, 40*, 130–135.

Regier, D. A., Narrow, W. E., Clarke, D. E., Kraemer, H. C., Kuramoto, S. J., Kuhl, E. A., & Kupfer, D. J. (2013). DSM-5 field trials in the United States and Canada, part II: Test–retest reliability of selected categorical diagnoses. *American Journal of Psychiatry, 170*(1), 59–70.

Regier, D. A., Narrow, W. E., Kuhl, E. A., & Kupfer, D. J. (2009). The conceptual development of DSM-V. *American Journal of Psychiatry, 166*(6), 645–650

Regina v. Lavallee (1988), 65 C. R. 3d 387.

Regina v. Prichard (1836), 7 Car., and P. 304.

Regina v. Swain (1991), 63 C. C. C. (3d) 481 (S. C. C.).

Rehm, J., Marmet, S., Anderson, P., Gual, A., Kraus, L., Nutt, D. J., . . . Wiers, R. W. (2013). Defining substance use disorders: Do we really need more than heavy use? *Alcohol and Alcoholism, 48*(6), 633–640.

Reich, J. (1987). Sex distribution of DSM-III personality disorders in psychiatric outpatients. *American Journal of Psychiatry, 144*, 485–488.

Reich, J., Yates, W., & Nduaguba, M. (1989). Prevalence of DSM-III personality disorders in the community. *Social Psychiatry and Psychiatric Epidemiology, 24*, 12–16.

Reich, T., Edenberg, H. J., Goate, A., Williams, J. T., Rice, J. P., Van Eerdewegh, P., . . . Begleiter, H. (1998). Genome-wide search for genes affecting the risk of alcohol dependence. *American Journal of Medicine and genetics, 81*, 207–215.

Reichborn-Kjennerud, T., Czajkowski, N., Yström, E., Ørstavik, R., Aggen, S. H., Tambs, K., . . . Kendler, K. S. (2015). A longitudinal twin study of borderline and antisocial personality disorder traits in early to middle adulthood. *Psychological Medicine, 45*(14), 3121–3131.

Reichenberg, A., Gross, R., Weiser, M., Bresnahan, M., Silverman, J., Harlap, S., . . . Lubin, G. (2006). Advancing paternal age and autism. *Archives of General Psychiatry, 63*(9), 1026.

Reid, D. H., Wilson, P. G., & Faw, G. D. (1991). Teaching self-help skills.

In J. L. Matson & J. A. Mulick (Eds.), *Handbook of mental retardation* (2nd ed., pp. 436–450). Elmsford, NY: Pergamon Press.

Reid, G. J., Chambers, C. T., McGrath, P. J., & Finley, G. A. (1997). Coping with pain and surgery: Children's and parents' perspectives. *International Journal of Behavioral Medicine, 4*, 339–363.

Reilly-Harrington, N. A., Alloy, L. B., Fresco, D. M., & Whitehouse, W. G. (1999). Cognitive styles and life events interact to predict bipolar and unipolar symptomatology. *Journal of Abnormal Psychology, 108*(4), 567–578.

Reilly-Harrington, N. A., Deckersbach, T., Knauz, R., Wu, Y., Tran, T., Eidelman, P., & Nierenberg, A. A. (2007). Cognitive behavioral therapy for rapid-cycling bipolar disorder: A pilot study. *Journal of Psychiatric Practice, 13*(5), 291–297.

Reiman, E. M., Webster, J. A., Myers, A. J., Hardy, J., Dunckley, T., Zismann, V. L., . . . Stephan, D. A. (2007). GAB2 alleles modify Alzheimer's risk in APOE e4 Carriers. *Neuron, 54*(5), 713–720.

Reiss, S. (1991). Expectancy model of fear, anxiety and panic. *Clinical Psychology Review, 11*, 141–153.

Reissig, C. J., Strain, E. C., & Griffiths, R. R. (2009). Caffeinated energy drinks—A growing problem. *Drug and Alcohol Dependence, 99*(1–3), 1–10.

Reissing, E. D., Binik, Y. M., & Khalife, S. (1999). Does vaginismus exist? A critical review of the literature. *Journal of Nervous & Mental Disease, 187*, 261–274.

Reitan, R. M., & Davison, I. A. (1974). *Clinical neuropsychology: Current status and applications.* Washington, DC: V.H. Winston.

Rekers, G. A., Kilgus, M., & Rosen, A. C. (1990). Long-term effects of treatment for gender identity disorder of childhood. *Journal of Psychology & Human Sexuality, 3*(2), 121–153.

Renaud, C. A., & Byers, E. S. (2001). Positive and negative sexual cognitions: Subjective experience and relationships to sexual adjustment. *Journal of Sex Research, 38*, 252–262.

Renaud, M. (2019). *An examination of the relationship between the paraphilias and anxiety* (Doctoral dissertation, University of Ottawa, Canada). https://doi.org/10.20381/ruor-24154

Renneberg, B., Goldstein, A. J., Phillips, D., & Chambless, D. L. (1990). Intensive behavioral group treatment of avoidant personality disorder. *Behavior Therapy, 21*, 363–377.

Rentz, D. M., Parra Rodriguez, M. A., Amariglio, R., Stern, Y., Sperling, R., & Ferris, S. (2013). Promising developments in neuropsychological approaches for the detection of pre-clinical Alzheimer's disease: A selective review. *Alzheimers Research & Therapy, 5*(6), 58.

Report of the Advisory Panel on Alzheimer's Disease. (1995). Alzheimer's disease and related dementias: Biomedical update. *Department of Health and Human Services.*

Repp, A. C., & Singh, N. N. (1990). *Perspectives on the use of nonaversive and aversive interventions for persons with developmental disabilities.* Sycamore, IL: Sycamore Publishing.

Rescorla, R. A. (1988). Pavlovian conditioning: It's not what you think it is. *American Psychologist, 43*(3), 151–160.

Resnick, H. S., Kilpatrick, D. G., Dansky, B. S., Saunders, B. E., & Best, C. L. (1993). Prevalence of civilian trauma in posttraumatic stress disorder in a representative national sample of women. *Journal of Consulting and Clinical Psychology, 61*, 984–991.

Ressler, K. J., & Rothbaum, B. O. (2013). Augmenting obsessive–compulsive disorder treatment from brain to mind. *JAMA Psychiatry, 70*, 1129–1131.

Rhebergen, D., & Graham, R. (2014). The re-labelling of dysthymic disorder to persistent depressive disorder in DSM-5: Old wine in new bottler? *Current Opinions in Psychiatry, 27*, 27–31.

Rice, D. P., & MacKenzie, E. J. (1989). *Cost of injury in the United States: A report to Congress.* San Francisco, CA: University of California and Injury Prevention Center, Institute for Health and Aging, and the Johns Hopkins University.

Rice, M. E. (1997). Violent offender research and implications for the criminal justice system. *American Psychologist, 52*, 414–423.

Richards, R., Kinney, D. K., Lunde, I., Benet, M., & Merzel, A. P. C. (1988). Creativity in manic depressives, cyclothymes, their normal relatives, and control subjects. *Journal of Abnormal Psychology, 97*(3), 281–288.

Richards, S. S., & Sweet, R. A. (2009). Dementia. In B. J. Sadock, V. A. Sadock, & P. Ruiz (Eds.), *Kaplan & Sadock's comprehensive textbook of psychiatry* (9th ed., Vol. 1, pp. 1167–1198). Philadelphia, PA: Lippincott Williams & Wilkins.

Richardson, G. S. (2006). Shift work sleep disorder. In T. Lee-Chiong (Ed.), *Sleep: A comprehensive handbook* (pp. 395–399). Hoboken, NJ: John Wiley & Sons.

Richardson, S. A., Katz, M., & Koller, H. (1986). Sex differences in number of children administratively classified as mildly mentally retarded: An epidemiological review. *American Journal of Mental Deficiency, 91*, 250–256.

Richer, K., Cheng, J., & Haag, A. (2018). Historical recidivism rates of Alberta's not criminally responsible population. *Journal of Community Safety and Well-Being, 3*(2), 59–64. https://doi.org/10.35502/jcswb.50

Richman, A., & Harris, P. (1982–1983). Mental hospital deinstitutionalization in Canada: A national perspective with some regional examples. *International Journal of Mental Health, 11*(4), 64–83.

Richters, J. E. (1993). Community violence and children's development: Toward a research agenda for the 1990's. *Psychiatry, 56*, 3–6.

Rickels, K., Rynn, M., Ivengar, M., & Duff, D. (2006). Remission of generalized anxiety disorder: A review of the paroxetine clinical trials database. *Journal of Clinical Psychiatry, 67*, 41–47.

Rickels, K., Schweizer, E., Case, W. G., & Greenblatt, D. J. (1990). Long-term therapeutic use of benzodiazepines: I. Effects of abrupt discontinuation. *Archives of General Psychiatry, 47*, 899–907.

Ridenour, T. A., & Howard, M. O. (2012). Inhalants abuse: Status of etiology and intervention. In J. C. Verster, K. Brady, M. Galanter, & P. Conrod (Eds.), *Drug abuse and addiction in medical illness* (pp. 189–199). New York, NY: Springer.

Riding, A. (1992, November 17). New catechism for Catholics defines sins of modern world. *New York Times*, p. A14.

Ridley, N. J., Draper, B., & Withall, A. (2013). Alcohol-related dementia: An update of the evidence. *Alzheimers Research & Therapy, 5*(3), 1–8.

Rief, W., & Martin, A. (2014). How to use the new DSM-5 somatic symptom disorder diagnosis in research and practice: A critical evaluation and a proposal for modifications. *Annual Review of Clinical Psychology, 10*, 339–367.

Rief, W., Hiller, W., & Margraf, J. (1998). Cognitive aspects of hypochondriasis and the somatization syndrome. *Journal of Abnormal Psychology, 107*, 587–595.

Riemann, D., Berger, M., & Voderholzer, U. (2001). Sleep and depression—Results from psychobiological studies: An overview. *Biological Psychology, 57*, 67–103.

Riggs, J. E. (1993). Smoking and Alzheimer's disease: Protective effect or differential survival bias? *Lancet, 342*, 793–794.

Riihimaki, K., Vuorilehto, M., Melartin, T., Haukka, J., & Isometsä, E. (2013). Incidence and predictors of suicide attempts among primary-care patients with depressive disorders: A 5-year prospective study. *Psychological Medicine*, 1–12.

Ripke, S., Neale, B. M., Corvin, A., Walters, J. T., Farh, K. H., Holmans, P. A., . . . Pers, T. H. (2014). Biological insights from 108 schizophrenia-associated genetic loci. *Nature, 511*(7510), 421.

Risch, N., Herrell, R., Lehner, T., Liang, K. Y., Eaves, L., Hoh, J., & Merikangas, K. R. (2009). Interaction between the serotonin transporter gene (5-HTTLPR), stressful life events, and risk of depression: A meta-analysis. *JAMA, 301*(23), 2462–2471.

Ritenbaugh, C., Shisstak, C., Teufel, N., Leonard-Green, T. K., Prince, R. (1993) Eating disorders: A cross-cultural review in regard to DSM-IV. In J. E. Mezzich, A. Kleinman, H. Fabrega, B. Good, G. Yonson-Powell, K. M. Lin, S. Manson, & D. Parron (Eds.), *Cultural proposals and supporting papers for DSM-IV*. Washington, DC: American Psychiatric Association.

Ritsner, M. S., & Gottesman, I. I. (2011). The schizophrenia construct after 100 years of challenges. In M. S. Ritsner (Ed.), *Handbook of schizophrenia spectrum disorders* (Vol. 1, pp. 1–44). Heidelberg, Germany: Springer.

Ritz, T., Meuret, A. E., & Ayala, E. S. (2010). He psychophysiology of blood-injection-injury phobia: Looking beyond the diphasic response. *International Journal of Psychophysiology, 78*, 50–67.

Riva, P., Lauro, L. J., Dewall, C. N., & Bushman, B. J. (2012). Buffer the pain away: Stimulating the right ventrolateral prefrontal cortex reduces pain following social exclusion. *Psychological Science, 23*(12), 1473–1475.

Rivera-Tovar, A. D., & Frank, E. (1990). Late luteal phase dysphoric disorder in young women. *American Journal of Psychiatry, 147*, 1634–1636.

Rivera-Tovar, A. D., Pilkonis, P., & Frank, E. (1992). Symptom patterns in late luteal-phase dysphoric disorder. *Journal of Psychopathology and Behavioral Assessment, 14*, 189–199.

Rizzuto, D., Orsini, N., Qiu, C., Wang, H. X., & Fratiglioni, L. (2012). Lifestyle, social factors, and survival after age 75: Population based study. *BMJ, 345*, e5568.

Robbins, T. W., & Cools, R. (2014). Cognitive deficits in Parkinson's disease: A cognitive neuroscience perspective. *Movement Disorders, 29*(5), 597–607.

Roberts, A., Cash, T., Feingold, A., & Johnson, B. (2006). Are black–white differences in females' body dissatisfaction decreasing? A meta-analytic review. *Journal of Consulting and Clinical Psychology, 74*, 1121–1131.

Roberts, G. A. (1991). Delusional belief and meaning in life: A preferred reality? British *Journal of Psychiatry, 159*, 20–29.

Roberts, J. M. (2014). Echolalia and language development in children with autism. In J. Arciuli & J. Brock (Eds.), *Communication in autism* (Vol. 11, pp. 55–74). Philadelphia: John Benjamins.

Roberts, L. J., & Marlatt, G. A. (1999). Harm reduction. In P. J. Ott & R. F. Tarter (Eds.), *Sourcebook on substance abuse: Etiology, epidemiology, assessment, and treatment* (pp. 389–398). Needham Heights, MA: Allyn & Bacon.

Roberts, R. F., Kaplan, G. A., Shema, S. J., & Strawbridge, W. J. (1997). Does growing old increase the risk for depression? *American Journal of Psychiatry, 154*, 1384–1390.

Robertson, G. B. (1994). *Mental disability in the law in Canada* (2nd ed.). Scarborough, ON: Carswell.

Robertson, N. (1988). *Getting better: Inside Alcoholics Anonymous*. New York, NY: William Morrow.

Robillard, G., Bouchard, S., Fournier, T., & Renaud, P. (2003). Anxiety and presence during VR immersion: A comparative study of the reactions of phobic and non-phobic participants in therapeutic virtual environments derived from computer games. *CyberPsychology and Behavior, 6*, 467–476.

Robillard, R., Carpenter, J., Feilds, K. L., Hermens, D. F., White, D., Naismith, S. L., Bartlett, D., Whitwell, B., Southan, J., Scott, E. M., & Hickie, I. B. (2018). Parallel changes in mood and melatonin rhythm following an adjunctive multimodal chronobiological intervention with agomelatine in people with depression: A proof of concept open label study. *Frontiers in Psychiatry, 9*, 624. https://doi .org/10.3389/fpsyt.2018.00624

Robillard, R., Carpenter, J. S., Rogers, N. L., Fares, S., Grierson, A. B., Hermens, D. F., Naismith, S. L., Mullin, S. J., Feilds, K.-L., Glozier, N., Scott, E. M., & Hickie, I. B. (2018). Circadian rhythms and psychiatric profiles in young adults with unipolar depressive disorders. *Translational Psychiatry, 8*(1), 213. https://doi .org/10.1038/s41398-018-0255-y

Robillard, R., Hermens, D. F., Naismith, S. L., White, D., Rogers, N. L., Ip, T. K. C., Mullin, S. J., Alvares, G. A., Guastella, A. J., Smith, K. L., Rong, Y., Whitwell, B., Southan, J., Glozier, N., Scott, E. M., & Hickie, I. B. (2015). Ambulatory sleep-wake patterns and variability in young people with emerging mental disorders. *Journal of Psychiatry and Neuroscience, 40*(1), 28. https://doi.org/10.1503/jpn.130247

Robillard, R., Naismith, S. L., Rogers, N. L., Scott, E. M., Ip, T. K., Hermens, D. F., & Hickie, I. B. (2013). Sleep-wake cycle and melatonin rhythms in adolescents and young adults with mood disorders: Comparison of unipolar and bipolar phenotypes. *European Psychiatry, 28*(7), 412–416. https://doi .org/10.1016/j.eurpsy.2013.04.001

Robillard, R., Naismith, S. L., Smith, K. L., Rogers, N. L., White, D., Terpening, Z., Ip, T. K., Hermens, D. F., Whitwell, B., Scott, E. M., & Hickie, I. B. (2014). Sleep-wake cycle in young and older persons with a lifetime history of mood disorders. *PLoS One, 9*(2), e87763. https://doi.org/10.1371/journal .pone.0087763

Robinaugh, D. J., & McNally, R. J. (2013). Remembering the past and envisioning the future in bereaved adults with and without complicated grief. *Clinical Psychological Science, 1*(3), 290–300.

Robins, L. N. (1966). *Deviant children grown up: A sociological and psychiatric study of sociopathic personality*. Baltimore, MD: Williams & Wilkins.

Robins, L. N. (1978). Sturdy childhood predictors of adult antisocial behavior: Replications from longitudinal studies. *Psychological Medicine, 8*, 611–622.

Robins, L. N., Helzer, J. F., & Davis, D. H. (1975). Narcotic use in Southeast Asia and afterwards. *Archives of General Psychiatry, 32*, 955–961.

Robins, R. W., Gosling, S. D., & Craik, K. H. (1999). An empirical analysis of trends in psychology. *American Psychologist, 54*, 117–128.

Robins, S., & Novaco, R. W. (2000). Anger control as a health promotion mechanism. In D. I. Mostofsky & D. H. Barlow (Eds.), *The management of stress and anxiety in medical disorders* (pp. 361–377). Needham Heights, MA: Allyn & Bacon.

Robinson, G. E., Fernald, R. D., & Clayton, D. F. (2008, November 7). Genes and social behavior. *Science, 322*, 896–899.

Robles, T., Glaser, R., & Kiecolt-Glaser, J. (2005). Out of balance: A new look at chronic stress, depression, and immunity. *Current Directions in Psychological Science, 14*, 111–115.

Rockwood, K., & Lindesay, J. (2002). Delirium and dying. *International Psychogeriatrics, 14*, 235–238.

Rockwood, K., & Middleton, L. (2007). Physical activity and the maintenance of cognitive function. *Alzheimer's & Dementia: Journal of the Alzheimer's Association, 3*(2), S38-S44.

Rockwood, K., Stolee, P., & Brahim, A. A. (1991). Outcomes of admission to a psychogeriatric service. *Canadian Journal of Psychiatry, 36*(4), 275–279.

Rockwood, K., Wolfson, C., & McDowell, l. (2001). The Canadian Study of Health and Aging: Organizational lessons from a national, multicenter, epidemiologic study. *International Psychogeriatrics, 13*(Suppl. 1), 233–237.

Rodin, J., & Langer, E. J. (1977). Long-term effects of a controlled relevant intervention with the institutionalized aged. *Journal of Personality and Social Psychology, 35*(12), 897–902.

Rodin, J., & Salovey, P. (1989). Health psychology. *Annual Review of Psychology, 40*, 533–579.

Rodrigue, K. M., Rieck, J. R., Kennedy, K. M., Devous, M. D., Diaz-Arrastia, R., & Park, D. C. (2013). Risk factors for b-amyloid deposition in healthy aging: Vascular and genetic effects. *JAMA Neurology, 70*(5), 600–606.

Roehrich, L., & Kinder, B. N. (1991). Alcohol expectancies and male sexuality: Review and implications for sex therapy. *Journal of Sex and Marital Therapy, 17*(1), 45–54.

Roehrs, T., & Roth, T. (2000). Hypnotics: Efficacy & adverse effects. In M. H. Kryger, T. Roth, & W. C. Dement (Eds.), *Principles and practice of sleep medicine* (3rd ed., pp. 414–418). Philadelphia, PA: W. B. Saunders.

Roehrs, T., Carskadon, M. A., Dement, W. C., & Roth, T. (2000). Daytime sleepiness & alertness. In M. H. Kryger, T. Roth, & W. C. Dement (Eds.), *Principles and practice of sleep medicine* (3rd ed., pp. 43–52). Philadelphia, PA: W. B. Saunders.

Roelofs, K., Keijsers, G. P., Hoogduin, K. A., Naring, G. W., & Moene, F. C. (2002). Childhood abuse in patients with conversion disorder. *American Journal of Psychiatry, 159*, 1908–1913.

Roemer, L., & Borkovec, T. D. (1993). Worry: Unwanted cognitive activity that controls unwanted somatic experience. In D. M. Wegner & J. W. Pennebaker (Eds.), *Handbook of mental control*. Englewood Cliffs, NJ: Prentice-Hall.

Roemer, L., & Orsillo, S. M. (2007). An open trial of an acceptance-based behavior therapy for generalized anxiety disorder. *Behavior Therapy, 38*(1), 72–85.

Roemer, L., & Orsillo, S. M. (2009). *Mindfulness- and acceptance-based behavioral therapies in practice*. New York, NY: Guilford Press.

Roemer, L., Orsillo, S. M., & Barlow, D. H. (2002). Generalized anxiety disorder. In D. H. Barlow (Ed.), *Anxiety and its disorders: The nature and treatment of anxiety and panic* (2nd ed.). New York, NY: Guilford Press.

Roesch, R., Kayfitz, J. H., Watt, M. C., Cooper, B. S., Guy, L. S., Hill, D., Haag, A. M., Pomichalek, M., & Kolton, D. J. C. (2019). Fitness to stand trial and criminal responsibility assessments: Advocating for changes to the Canadian criminal code. *Canadian Psychology/Psychologie canadienne, 60*(3), 148–154. https://doi.org/10.1037/ cap0000173

Roesch, R., Ogloff, J. R. P., Hart, S. D., Dempster, R. J., Zapf, P. A., & Whittemore, K. F. (1997). The impact of Canadian criminal code changes on remands and assessments of fitness to stand trial and criminal responsibility in British Columbia. *Canadian Journal of Psychiatry, 42*, 509–514.

Roesch, R., Zapf, P., Webster, C. D., & Eaves, D. (1999). *The Fitness Interview Test*. Burnaby, BC: Simon Fraser University, Mental Health Law & Policy Institute.

Roffman, R. A., & Barnhart, R. (1987). Assessing need for marijuana dependence treatment through an anonymous telephone interview. *International Journal of the Addictions, 22*, 639–651.

Rogaeva, F., Tadon, A., & St George-Hyslop, P. (2001). Genetic markers in the diagnosis of Alzheimer's disease. *Journal of Alzheimer's Disease, 3*, 293–304.

Rogers, C. R. (1961). *On becoming a person*. Boston, MA: Houghton Mifflin.

Rogers, S. J. (2009). What are infant siblings teaching us about autism in infancy? *Autism Research, 2*(3), 125–137.

Rogler, L. (2007). Framing research on culture in psychiatric diagnosis. In J. E. Mezzich & G. Caracci (Eds.), *Cultural formulation: A reader for psychiatric diagnosis* (pp. 151–166). Lanham, MD: Jason Aronson Inc.

Rohde, P., Lewinsohn, P. M., Klein, D. N., Seeley, J. R., & Gau, J. M. (2013). Key characteristics of major depressive disorder occurring in childhood, adolescence, emerging adulthood, and adulthood. *Clinical Psychological Science, 1*(1), 41–53.

Roid, G. H., & Pomplun, M. (2005). Interpreting the Stanford-Binet intelligence scales (5th ed.). In D. P. Flanagan & P. L. Harrison (Eds.), *Contemporary intellectual assessment: Theories, tests, and issues* (2nd ed., pp. 325–343). New York, NY: Guilford Press.

Roitt, I. (1988). *Essential immunology* (6th ed.). Oxford, UK: Blackwell.

Rojo, L., Conesa, L., Bermudez, O., & Livianos, L. (2006). Influence of stress in the onset of eating disorders: Data from a two stage epidemiologic controlled study. *Psychosomatic Medicine, 68*, 628–635.

Roland, C. G. (1990). *Clarence Hincks: Mental health crusader*. Toronto, ON: Hannah Institute & Dundurn Press.

Rollman, B. L., Belnap, B. H., Mazumdar, S., Houck, P. R., Zhu, F., Gardner, W., & Shear, M. K. (2005). A randomized trial to improve the quality of treatment for panic and generalized anxiety disorders in primary care. *Archives of General Psychiatry, 62*, 1332–1341.

Roma, P. G., Champoux, M., & Suomi, S. J. (2006). Environmental control, social context, and individual differences in behavioral and cortisol responses to novelty in infant rhesus monkeys. *Child Development, 77*, 118–131.

Romanelli, R. J., Wu, F. M., Gamba, R., Mojtabai, R., & Segal, J. B. (2014). Behavioral therapy and serotonin reuptake inhibitor pharmacotherapy in the treatment of obsessive–compulsive disorder: A systematic review and meta-analysis of head-to-head randomized controlled trials. *Depression and Anxiety, 31*, 641–652.

Romano, F., Baillargeon, R. H., Fortier, I., Wu, H.-X, Robaey, P., Zoccolillo, M., & Tremblay, R. E. (2005). Individual change in methylphenidate use in a national sample of children aged 2 to 11 years. *Canadian Journal of Psychiatry, 50*, 144–152.

Romano, F., Baillargeon, R. H., Wu, H. X., Robaey, P., & Tremblay, R. F. (2002). Prevalence of methylphenidate use and change over a two-year period: A nationwide study of 2- to 11-year-old Canadian children. *Journal of Pediatrics, 141*, 71–75.

Romano, J. M., Jensen, M. P., Turner, J. A., Good, A. B., & Hops, H. (2000). Chronic pain patient-partner interactions: Further support for a behavioral model of chronic pain. *Behavior Therapy, 31*, 415–440.

Romney, D. M., & Candido, C. L. (2001). Anhedonia in depression and schizophrenia: A reexamination. *Journal of Nervous & Mental Disease, 189*, 735–740.

Ronningstam, E. (2012). Narcissistic personality disorder: The diagnostic process. In T. A. Widiger (Ed.), *The Oxford handbook of personality disorders* (pp. 527–548). New York, NY: Oxford University Press.

Ronningstam, E. (2014). Introduction to the special series on "Narcissistic personality disorder—New perspectives on diagnosis and treatment." *Personality Disorders: Theory, Research, and Treatment, 5*(4), 419.

Room, R. (1993). Alcoholics Anonymous as a social movement. In B. S. McCrady & W. R. Miller (Eds.), *Research on Alcoholics Anonymous: Opportunities and alternatives* (pp. 167–187). New Brunswick, NJ: Rutgers Center of Alcohol Studies.

Root, T. L., Pinheiro, A. P., Thornton, L., Strober, M., Fernandez-Aranda, F., Brandt, H., . . . Bulik, C. M. (2010). Substance use disorders in women with anorexia nervosa. *International Journal of Eating Disorders, 43*(1), 14–21.

Rorschach, H. (1951). *Psychodiagnostics*. New York, NY: Grune & Stratton. (Original work published 1921).

Rosa-Neto, P., Diksic, M., Okazawa, H., Leyton, M., Ghadirian, N., Mzengeza, S., . . . Benkelfat, C. (2004). Measurement of brain regional [¹¹C] Methyl-L-Tryptophan trapping as a measure of serotonin synthesis in medication-free patients with major depression. *Archives of General Psychiatry, 61*, 556–563.

Rosell, D. R., Futterman, S. E., McMaster, A., & Siever, L. J. (2014). Schizotypal personality disorder: A current review. *Current Psychiatry Reports, 16*(7), 1–12.

Rosellini, A. J., Boettcher, H., Brown, T. A., & Barlow, D. H. (2015). A transdiagnostic temperament-phenotype profile approach to emotional disorder classification: An update. *Psychopathology Review, 2*(1), 110–128.

Rosen, J. C., & Leitenberg, H. (1985). Exposure plus response prevention treatment of bulimia. In D. M. Garner & P. F. Garfinkel (Eds.), *Handbook of psychotherapy for anorexia nervosa and bulimia* (pp. 193–209). New York, NY: Guilford Press.

Rosen, J. C., Reiter, J., Orosan, P. (1995). Cognitive-behavioral body image therapy for body dysmorphic disorder. *Journal of Consulting Clinical Psychology, 63*, 263–269.

Rosen, R. C. (2000). Medical and psychological interventions for erectile dysfunction: Toward a combined treatment approach. In S. R. Leiblum & R. C. Rosen (Eds.), *Principles and practice of sex therapy* (3rd ed., pp. 276–304). New York, NY: Guilford Press.

Rosen, R. C. (2007). Erectile dysfunction: Integration of medical and psychological approaches. In S. R. Leiblum (Ed.), *Principles and practice of sex therapy* (4th ed., pp. 277–312). New York, NY: Guilford Press.

Rosen, R. C., & Beck, J. G. (1988). *Patterns of sexual arousal: Psychophysiological processes and clinical applications*. New York, NY: Guilford Press.

Rosenberg, H. (1993). Prediction of controlled drinking by alcoholics and problem drinkers. *Psychological Bulletin, 113*, 129–139.

Rosenberg, H., & Melville, J. (2005). Controlled drinking and controlled drug use as outcome goals in British treatment services. *Addiction Research and Theory, 13*(1), 85–92.

Rosenberg, R. N., Richter, R. W., Risser, R. C., Taubman, K., Prado-Farmer, I., Ebalo, F., . . . Schellenberg, G. D. (1996). Genetic factors for the development of Alzheimer's disease in the Cherokee Indian. *Archives of Neurology, 53*, 997–1000.

Rosengren, A., Tibblin, G., & Wilhelmsen, L. (1991). Self-perceived psychological stress and incidence of coronary artery disease in middle-aged men. *American Journal of Cardiology, 68*, 1171–1175.

Rosenman, R. H., Brand, R. J., Jenkins, C. D., Friedman, M., Straus, R., & Wurm, M. (1975). Coronary heart disease in the Western Collaborative Group Study: Final follow-up experience of 8 years. *JAMA, 233*, 872–877.

Rosenthal, D. (Ed.). (1963). *The Genain quadruplets: A case study and theoretical analysis of heredity and environment in schizophrenia*. New York, NY: Basic Books.

Rosenthal, P. A., & Rosenthal, S. (1984). Suicidal behavior by preschool children. *American Journal of Psychiatry, 141*, 520–525.

Rösler, A., & Witztum, F. (1998). Treatment of men with paraphilia with a long-acting analogue of gonadotropin-releasing hormone. *New England Journal of Medicine, 338*, 416–422.

Rösler, A., & Witztum, F. (2000). Pharmacotherapy of paraphilias in the next millennium. *Behavioral Sciences & the Law, 18*, 43–56.

Rosowsky, F., & Gurian, B. (1992). Impact of borderline personality disorder in late life on systems of care. *Hospital and Community Psychiatry, 43*, 386–389.

Ross, A. O., & Pelham, W. F. (1981). Child psychopathology. *Annual Review of Psychology, 32*, 243–278.

Ross, C. A. (1991). Epidemiology of multiple personality disorder and dissociation. *Psychiatric Clinics of North America, 14*, 503–517.

Ross, C. A. (1997). *Dissociative identity disorder*. New York, NY: John Wiley & Sons.

Ross, C. A. (2009). Dissociative amnesia and dissociative fugue. In P. F. Dell & J. A. O'Neil (Eds.), *Dissociation and the dissociative disorders* (pp. 429–434). New York, NY: Routledge.

Ross, C. A., Anderson, G., Fleisher, W. P., & Norton, G. R. (1991). The frequency of multiple personality disorder among psychiatric inpatients. *American Journal of Psychiatry, 148*, 1717–1720.

Ross, C. A., Miller, S. D., Reagor, P., Bjornson, L., Fraser, G. A., & Anderson, G. (1990). Structured interview data on 102 cases of multiple personality disorder from four centers. *American Journal of Psychiatry, 147*, 596–601.

Ross, C. A., Norton, G. R., & Wozney, K. (1989). Multiple personality disorder: An analysis of 236 cases. *Canadian Journal of Psychiatry, 34*, 413–418.

Rossow, I., & Bye, E. K. (2012). The problem of alcohol-related violence: An epidemiological and public health perspective. In M. McMurran (Ed.), *Alcohol-related violence* (pp. 1–18). Chichester, UK: Wiley.

Rost, K., Kashner, T. M., & Smith, G. R. Jr. (1994). Effectiveness of psychiatric intervention with somatization disorder patients: Improved outcomes at reduced costs. *General Hospital Psychiatry, 16*, 381–387.

Rotermann, M. (2019). Analysis of trends in the prevalence of cannabis use and related metrics in Canada. *Health Reports, 30*(6), 3–13. https://www150.statcan.gc.ca/n1/en/catalogue/82-003-X201900600001

Roth, T., Coulouvrat, C., Hajak, G., Lakoma, M. D., Sampson, N. A., Shahly, V., & Kessler, R. C. (2011). Prevalence and perceived health associated with insomnia based on DSM-IV-TR; International Statistical Classification of Diseases and Related Health Problems, Tenth Revision; and Research Diagnostic Criteria/International Classification of Sleep Disorders, Second Edition Criteria: Results from the America Insomnia Survey. *Biological Psychiatry, 69*(6), 592–600.

Rothbaum, B. O., Hodges, L., & Kooper, R. (1997). Virtual reality exposure therapy. *Journal of Psychotherapy Practice & Research, 6*, 219–226.

Rothblum, F. D. (2002). Gay and lesbian body images. In T. F. Cash & T. Pruzinsky (Eds.), *Body image: A handbook of theory, research and clinical practice* (pp. 257–265). New York, NY: Guilford Press.

Rothschild, A. J. (2013). Challenges in the treatment of major depressive disorder with psychotic features. *Schizophrenia Bulletin, 39*(4), 787–796.

Rottenberg, J., & Johnson, S. L. (2007). Emotion and psychopathology: *Bridging affective and clinical science*. Washington, DC: American Psychological Association.

Rouff, L. (2000). Schizoid personality traits among the homeless mentally ill: A quantitative and qualitative report. *Journal of Social Distress and the Homeless, 9*, 127–141.

Rounsaville, B. J., Sholomskas, D., & Prusoff, B. A. (1988). Chronic mood disorders in depressed outpatients: Diagnosis and response to pharmacotherapy. *Journal of Affective Disorders, 2*, 72–88.

Roush, W. (1997). Herbert Benson: Mind-body maverick pushes the envelope. *Science, 276*, 357–359.

Rowa, K., McCabe, R. F., & Antony, M. M. (2006). Specific phobias. In F. Andrasik (Ed.), *Comprehensive handbook of personality and psychopathology: Adult Psychopathology* (Vol. 2, pp. 154–168). Hoboken, NJ: Wiley.

Rowe, J. B. (2010). Conversion disorder: Understanding the pathogenic links between emotion and motor systems in the brain. *Brain, 133*(Pt 5), 1295–1297.

Roy, A. K., Lopes, V., & Klein, R.G (2014). Disruptive mood dysregulation disorder: A new diagnostic approach to chronic irritability in youth. *American Journal of Psychiatry, 171*, 918–924.

Roy, A., Segal, N. L., & Sarchiapone, M. (1995). Attempted suicide among living co-twins of twin suicide victims. *American Journal of Psychiatry, 152*, 1075–1076.

Roy-Byrne, P. P., & Katon, W. (2000). Anxiety management in the medical setting: Rationale, barriers to diagnosis and treatment, and proposed solutions. In D. I. Mostofsky & D. H. Barlow (Eds.), *The management of stress and anxiety in medical disorders* (pp. 1–14). Needham Heights, MA: Allyn & Bacon.

Rubinstein, S., & Caballero, B. (2000). Is Miss America an undernourished role model? *JAMA, 283,* 1569.

Rubia, K., Alegria, A. A., Cubillo, A. I., Smith, A. B., Brammer, M. J., & Radua, J. (2014). Effects of stimulants on brain function in attention-deficit/hyperactivity disorder: A systematic review and meta-analysis. *Biological Psychiatry, 76*(8), 616–628.

Rubio, J. M., Markowitz, J. C., Alegria, A., Perez-Fuentes, G., Liu, S. M., Lin, K. H., & Blanco, C. (2011). Epidemiology of chronic and non-chronic major depressive disorder: Results from the national epidemiology survey on alcohol and related conditions. *Depression and Anxiety, 28,* 622–631.

Rück, C., Karlsson, A., Steele, J. D., Edman, G., Meyerson, B. A., Ericson, K., & Svanborg, P. (2008). Capsulotomy for obsessive–compulsive disorder: Long-term follow-up of 25 patients. *Archives of General Psychiatry, 65*(8), 914–921.

Rudaz, M., Craske, M. G., Becker, E. S., Ledermann, T., & Margraf, J. (2010). Health anxiety and fear of fear in panic disorder and agoraphobia vs. social phobia: A prospective longitudinal study. *Depression and Anxiety, 27,* 404–411.

Rudd, M. D., Joiner, Y., & Rajab, M. H. (2001). *Treating suicidal behavior. An effective, time-limited approach.* New York, NY: Guilford Press.

Rudd, M. D., Rajab, M. H., Orman, D. T., Stulman, D. A., Joiner, T., & Dixon, W. (1996). Effectiveness of an outpatient intervention targeting suicidal young adults: Preliminary results. *Journal of Consulting and Clinical Psychology, 64,* 179–190.

Ruffin, R., Ironson, G., Fletcher, M. A., Balbin, E., & Schneiderman, N. (2012). Health locus of control beliefs and healthy survival with AIDS. *International Journal of Behavioral Medicine, 19*(4), 512–517.

Ruiz, I., Offermanns, J., Lanctot, K. L., & Busto, U. (1993). Comparative study on benzodiazepine use in Canada and Chile. *Journal of Clinical Pharmacology, 33,* 124–129.

Ruiz-Veguilla, M., Luisa Barrigón, M., Diaz, F. J., Ferrin, M., Moreno-Granados, J., Dolores Salcedo, M., & Gurpegui, M. (2012). The duration of untreated psychosis is associated with social support and temperament. *Psychiatry Research, 200*(2–3), 687–692. https://doi.org/ https://doi.org/10.1016/j.psychres.2012.03.024

Rupprecht, R., Rammes, G., Eser, D., Baghai, T. C., Schule, C., Nothdurfter, C., . . . Kucher, K. (2009). Translocator protein (18 kD) as target for anxiolytics without benzodiazepine-like side effects. *Science, 325*(5939), 490–493.

Ruscio, J. (2004). Diagnoses and the behaviors they denote: A critical evaluation of the labeling theory of mental illness. *Scientific Review of Mental Health Practice, 3,* 5–22.

Rush, A. J., Erman, M. K., Giles, D. E., Schlesser, M. A., Carpenter, G., Vasavada, N., & Roffwarg, H. P. (1986). Polysomnographic findings in recently drug-free and clinically remitted depressed patients. *Archives of General Psychiatry, 43,* 878–884.

Rush, A. J., Giles, D. F., Schlesser, M. A., Orsulak, P. J., Weissenburger, J. F.,

Fulton, C. L., . . . Roffwarg, H. P. (1997). Dexamethasone response, thyrotropin-releasing hormone stimulation, rapid eye movement latency, and subtypes of Depression. *Biological Psychiatry, 41,* 915–928.

Russell, G. F. M. (1979). Bulimia nervosa: An ominous variant of anorexia nervosa. *Psychological Medicine, 9,* 429–448.

Russell, G. F. M. (2009). Disorders of Eating: Anorexia Nervosa. In M. G. Gelder, N. C. Andreasen, J. J. López-Ibor, & J. R. Geddes (Eds.), *New Oxford textbook of psychiatry* (2nd ed., pp. 777–800). New York, NY: Oxford University Press.

Russell, G. F. M., Szmukler, G. I., Dare, C., & Eisler, I. (1987). An evaluation of family therapy in anorexia nervosa and bulimia nervosa. *Archives of General Psychiatry, 44,* 1047–1056.

Rutherford, J., McGuffin, P., Katz, R. J., & Murray, R. M. (1993). Genetic influences on eating attitudes in a normal female twin population. *Psychological Medicine, 23,* 425–436.

Rutherford, M. D., & Rogers, S. J. (2003). Cognitive underpinnings of pretend play in autism. *Journal of Autism & Developmental Disorders, 33,* 289–302.

Rutledge, T., Groesz, L., Linke, S., Woods, G., & Herbst, K. (2011). Behavioural weight management for the primary careprovider. *Obesity Reviews, 12*(5), e290-e297.

Rutter, M. (2002). The interplay of nature, nurture, and developmental influences: The challenge ahead for mental health. *Archives of General Psychiatry, 59,* 996–1000.

Rutter, M. (2006). *Genes and behavior: Nature–nurture interplay.* Oxford, UK: Blackwell.

Rutter, M. (2010). Gene–environment interplay. *Depression and Anxiety, 27*(1), 1–4.

Rutter, M. (2011a). Progress in Understanding Autism: 2007–2010. *Journal of Autism and Developmental Disorders, 41*(4), 395–404.

Rutter, M. (2011b). Research Review: Child psychiatric diagnosis and classification: Concepts, findings, challenges and potential. *Journal of Child Psychology and Psychiatry, 52*(6), 647–660.

Rutter, M., & Giller, H. (1984). *Juvenile delinquency: Trends and perspectives.* New York, NY: Guilford Press.

Rutter, M., Moffitt, T. E., & Caspi, A. (2006). Gene–environment interplay and psychopathology: Multiple varieties but real effects. *Journal of Child Psychology and Psychiatry, 47,* 226–261.

Rutter, M., & Pickles, A. (2016). Annual research review: Threats to the validity of child psychiatry and psychology. *Journal of Child Psychology and Psychiatry, 57*(3), 398–416.

Ruzek, J. I. (2012). Community-based early intervention with trauma survivors. In J. G. Beck & D. M. Sloan (Eds.), *The Oxford handbook of traumatic stress disorders* (pp. 347–362). New York, NY: Oxford University Press.

Ryan, J. D., & Cohen, N. J. (2003). Evaluating the neuropsychological dissociation evidence for multiple memory systems. *Cognitive, Affective & Behavioral Neuroscience, 3*(3), 168–185.

Ryan, W. D. (1992). The pharmacologic treatment of child and adolescent

depression. *Psychiatric Clinics of North America, 15,* 29–40.

Ryder, A. G., Sunohara, M., & Kirmayer, L. J. (2015). Culture and personality disorder: From a fragmented literature to a contextually grounded alternative. *Current Opinion in Psychiatry, 28*(1), 40–45.

Ryder, A. G., Yang, J., Zhu, X., Yao, S., Yi, J., Heine, S. J., & Bagby, R. M. (2008). The cultural shaping of depression: Somatic symptoms in China, psychological symptoms in North America? *Journal of Abnormal Psychology, 117*(2), 300–313.

Saab, P. G., Llabre, M. M., Hurwitz, B. F., Frame, C. A., Reineke, I., Fins, A. I., . . . Schneiderman, N. (1992). Myocardial and peripheral vascular responses to behavioral challenges and their stability in black and white Americans. *Psychophysiology, 29*(4), 384–397.

Sachdev, P. S., Blacker, D., Blazer, D. G., Ganguli, M., Jeste, D. V., Paulsen, J. S., & Petersen, R. C. (2014). Classifying neurocognitive disorders: The DSM-5 approach. *Nature Reviews Neurology, 10*(11), 634–642.

Sachs, G. S., & Rush, A. J. (2003). Response, remission, and recovery in bipolar disorders: What are the realistic treatment goals? *Journal of Clinical Psychiatry, 64,* 18–22.

Sachs, G. S., Nierenberg, A. A., Calabrese, J. R., Marangell, L. B., Wisniewski, S. R., Gyulai, L., & Thase, M. E. (2007). Effectiveness of adjunctive antidepressant treatment for bipolar depression. *New England Journal of Medicine, 356*(17), 1711–1722.

Sack, R. L., & Lewy, A. J. (1993). Human circadian rhythms: Lessons from the blind. *Annals of Medicine, 25,* 303–305.

Sack, R. L., Auckley, D., Auger, R. R., Carskadon, M. A., Wright, K. P., Jr., Vitiello, M. V., & American Academy of Sleep Medicine. (2007). Circadian rhythm sleep disorders: Part II, Advanced sleep phase disorder, delayed sleep phase disorder, free-running disorder, and irregular sleep-wake rhythm. *Sleep, 30*(11), 1484–1501.

Sackeim, H. A., & Devanand, D. P. (1991). Dissociative disorders. In M. Hersen & S. M. Turner (Eds.), *Adult psychopathology & diagnosis* (2nd ed., pp. 279–322). New York, NY: John Wiley & Sons.

Sackeim, H. A., Nordlie, J. W., & Gur, R. C. (1979). A model of hysterical and hypnotic blindness: Cognition, motivation and awareness. *Journal of Abnormal Psychology, 88,* 474–489.

Sackeim, H., Haskett, R., Mulsant, B., Thase, M., Mann, J., Pettinati, H., & Prudic, J. (2001). Continuation pharmacotherapy in the prevention of relapse following electroconvulsive therapy: A randomized controlled trial. *JAMA, 285,* 1299–1307.

Sacks, J. A., Comer, J. S., Furr, J. M., Pincus, D. B., & Kurtz, S. M. S. (2011, November). Daily speech changes across an intensive group behavioral treatment program for early childhood selective mutism. *Poster presented at the 45th annual meeting of the Association of Behavioral and Cognitive Therapies, Child and Adolescent Anxiety Special Interest Group Exposition.* Toronto, Ontario.

Sahay, S., Piran, N., & Maddocks, S. (2000). Sexual victimization and clinical challenges in women receiving

hospital treatment for depression. *Canadian Journal of Community Mental Health, 19,* 161–174.

Sakai, J. T., & Crowley, T. J. (2009). Inhalant-related disorders. In B. J. Sadock, V. A. Sadock, & P. Ruiz (Eds.), *Kaplan & Sadock's comprehensive textbook of psychiatry* (9th ed., Vol. 1, pp. 1341–1353). Philadelphia, PA: Lippincott Williams & Wilkins.

Sakel, M. (1958). *Schizophrenia.* New York, NY: Philosophical Library.

Sakheim, D. K., Barlow, D. H., Abrahamson, D. J., & Beck, J. G. (1987). Distinguishing between organogenic and psychogenic erectile dysfunction. *Behaviour Research and Therapy, 25,* 379–390.

Sakinofsky, I. (1998). The epidemiology of suicide in Canada. In A. A. Leenars, S. Wenckstern, I. Sakinofsky, R. J. Dyck, et al. (Eds.), *Suicide in Canada* (pp. 37–66). Toronto, ON: University of Toronto Press.

Saklofske, D. H., Hildebrand, D. K., & Gorsuch, R. L. (2000). Replication of the factor structure of the Wechsler Adult Intelligence Scale—Third edition with a Canadian sample. *Psychological Assessment, 12,* 436–439.

Salekin, R. T. (2006). Psychopathy in children and adolescents: Key issues in conceptualization and assessment. In C. J. Patrick (Ed.), *Handbook of psychopathy* (pp. 389–414). New York, NY: Guilford Press.

Salekin, R. T., Rogers, R., & Sewell, K. W. (1997). Construct validity of psychopathy in a female offender sample: A multitrait–multimethod evaluation. *Journal of Abnormal Psychology, 106*(4), 576–585.

Salkovskis, P. M., & Campbell, P. (1994). Thought suppression induces intrusion in naturally occurring negative intrusive thoughts. *Behaviour Research and Therapy, 32*(1), 1–8.

Salkovskis, P., Warwick, H., & Deale, A. (2003). Cognitive-behavioral treatment for severe and persistent health anxiety. *Brief Treatment and Crisis Intervention, 3,* 353–367.

Salzman, C. (1991). Pharmacologic treatment of the anxious elderly patient. In C. Salzman & B. D. Lebowitz (Eds.), *Anxiety in the elderly: Treatment and research* (pp. 149–173). New York, NY: Springer.

Sampson, R. J., Raudenbush, S. W., & Earls, F. (1997). Neighborhoods and violent crime: A multilevel study of collective efficacy. *Science, 277,* 918–924.

Samson, J. A., Mirin, S. M., Hauser, S. T., Fenton, B. T., & Schildkraut, J. J. (1992). Learned helplessness and urinary MHPG levels in unipolar depression. *American Journal of Psychiatry, 149*(6), 806–809.

Samueli, S., Abraham, K., Dressler, A., Groeppel, G., Jonak, C., Muehlebner, A., . . . Feucht, M. (2015). Tuberous sclerosis complex: New criteria for diagnostic work-up and management. *Wiener klinische Wochenschrift, 127*(15–16), 619–630. https://doi.org/10.1007/s00508-015-0758-y

Samuels, J., & Costa, P. T. (2012). Obsessive–compulsive personality disorder. In T. A. Widiger (Ed.), *The Oxford handbook of personality disorders* (pp. 566–581). New York, NY: Oxford University Press.

Sanders, M. R. (1992). Enhancing the impact of behavioural family intervention with children: Emerging perspectives. *Behaviour Change, 9*, 115–119.

Sanders, M. R., Dadds, M. R., Johnston, B. M., & Cash, R. (1992). Childhood depression and conduct disorder: I. Behavioral, affective and cognitive aspects of family problem solving interactions. *Journal of Abnormal Psychology, 101*(3), 495–504.

Sanderson, C., & Clarkin, J. F. (1994). Use of the NFO-PI personality dimensions in differential treatment planning. In P. T. Costa & T. A. Widiger (Eds.), *Personality disorders and the five-factor model of personality* (pp. 219–235). Washington, DC: American Psychological Association.

Sandi, C., & Haller, J. (2015). Stress and the social brain: Behavioural effects and neurobiological mechanisms. *Nature Reviews Neuroscience, 16*, 290–304.

Sandin, B., Chorot, P., Santed, M., & Valiente, R. (2004). Differences in negative life events between patients with anxiety disorders. *Stress & Coping: An International Journal, 17*, 37–47.

Sandys, J. (2007). Work and employment for people with intellectual and developmental disabilities. In I. Brown & M. Percy (Eds.), *A comprehensive guide to intellectual & developmental disabilities* (pp. 527–543). Baltimore, MD: Paul H. Brookes.

Sanislow, C. A., da Cruz, K., Gianoli, M. O., & Reagan, E. R. (2012). Avoidant personality disorder, traits, and type. In T. A. Widiger (Ed.), *The Oxford handbook for personality disorders* (pp. 549–565). New York: Oxford University Press.

Sanislow, C. A., Quinn, K. J., & Sypher, I. (2015). NIMH Research Domain Criteria (RDoC). *The Encyclopedia of Clinical Psychology.*

Sano, M., Ernesto, C., Thomas, R. G., Klauber, M. R., Schafer, K., Grundman, M., . . . Thal, L. J. (1997). A controlled trial of selegiline, alphatocopherol, or both as treatment for Alzheimer's disease. *New England Journal of Medicine, 336*, 1216–1222.

Sansbury, L. L., & Wahler, R. G. (1992). Pathways to maladaptive parenting with mothers and their conduct disordered children. *Behavior Modification, 16*, 574–592.

Santor, D. A., & Kusumakar, V. (2001). Open trial of interpersonal therapy in adolescents with moderate to severe major depression: Effectiveness of novice IPT therapists. *Journal of the American Academy of Child & Adolescent Psychiatry, 40*, 236–240.

Santoro, M. R., Bray, S. M., & Warren, S. T. (2012). Molecular mechanisms of fragile X syndrome: A twenty-year perspective. *Annual Review of Pathology: Mechanisms of Disease, 7*, 219–245.

Santosh, P. J. (2009). Medication for children and adolescents: Current issues. In M. G. Gelder, N. C. Andreasen, J. J. Lopez-Ibor, & J. R. Geddes (Eds.), *New Oxford textbook of psychiatry* (2nd ed., Vol. 2, pp. 1793–1798). Oxford, UK: Oxford University Press.

Santucci, L. C., Ehrenreich, J. T., Trosper, S. E., Bennett, S. M., & Pincus, D. B. (2009). Development and preliminary evaluation of a one-week summer treatment program for separation anxiety disorder. *Cognitive and Behavioral Practice, 16*, 317–331.

Sapolsky, R. M. (1990, January). Stress in the wild. *Scientific American,* pp. 116–123.

Sapolsky, R. M. (2000a). Genetic hyping. *The Sciences, 40*(2), 12–15.

Sapolsky, R. M. (2000b). Glucocorticoids and hippocampal atrophy in neuropsychiatric disorders. *Archives of General Psychiatry, 57*, 925–935.

Sapolsky, R. M. (2002). *A primate's memoir.* New York, NY: Simon & Schuster.

Sapolsky, R. M. (2007). Stress, stress-related disease, and emotional regulation. In J. J. Gross (Ed.), *Handbook of emotion regulation* (pp. 606–615). New York, NY: Guilford Press.

Sapolsky, R. M., & Meaney, M. J. (1986). Maturation of the adrenal stress response: Neuroendocrine control mechanisms and the stress hyporesponsive period. *Brain Research Review, 11*, 65–76.

Sapolsky, R. M., & Ray, J. C. (1989). Styles of dominance and their endocrine correlates among wild, live baboons. *American Journal of Primatology, 18*(1), 1–13.

Sareen, J. (2011). Anxiety disorders and risk for suicide: Why such controversy? *Depression and Anxiety, 28*, 941–945.

Sareen, J., Chartier, M., Paulus, M. P., & Stein, M. B. (2006). Illicit drug use and anxiety disorders: Findings from two community surveys. *Psychiatry Research, 142*, 11–17.

Sari, Y., Johnson, V. R., & Weedman, J. M. (2011). Role of the serotonergic system in alcohol dependence: From animal models to clinics. *Progress in Molecular Biology and Translational Science, 98*, 401–443.

Sarkar, J., & Adshead, G. (Eds.). (2012). *Clinical topics in personality disorder.* London, UK: RJPsych Publications.

Satel, S. (1992). Craving for and fear of cocaine: A phenomenologic update on cocaine craving and paranoia. In T. R. Kosten & H. D. Kleber (Eds.), *Clinician's guide to cocaine addiction: Theory, research, and treatment* (pp. 172–192). New York, NY: Guilford Press.

Saudino, J. J., Pedersen, N. L., Lichtenstein, P., McClearn, G. F., & Plomin, R. (1997). Can personality explain genetic influence on life events? *Journal of Personality & Social Psychology, 72*(1), 196–206.

Saudino, K. J., & Plomin, R. (1996). Personality and behavioral genetics: Where have we been and where are we going? *Journal of Research in Personality, 30*, 335–347.

Saudino, K. J., Plomin, R., & DeFries, J. C. (1996). Tester-rated temperament at 14, 20, and 24 months: Environmental change and genetic continuity. *British Journal of Developmental Psychology, 14*, 129–144.

Savard, J., Laroche, L., Simard, S., Ivers, H., & Morin, C. M. (2003). Chronic insomnia and immune functioning. *Psychosomatic Medicine, 65*, 211–221.

Savin-Williams, R. (2006). Who's gay? Does it matter? *Current Directions in Psychological Science, 15*, 40–44.

Saxe, G. N., Stoddard, F., Hall, E., Chawla, N., Lopez, C., Sheridan, R., . . . Yehuda, R. (2005). Pathways to PTSD: Part I. Children with burns. *American Journal of Psychiatry, 162*, 1299–1304.

Saxe, G. N., van der Kolk, B. A., Berkowitz, R., Chinman, G., Hall, K., Leiberg, G., & Schwartz, J. (1993). Dissociative disorders in psychiatric inpatients. *American Journal of Psychiatry, 150*, 1037–1042.

Saxena, S., & Prasad, K. (1989). DSM-III subclassifications of dissociative disorders applied to psychiatric outpatients in India. *American Journal of Psychiatry, 146*, 261–262.

Saxena, S., Winograd, A., Dunkin, J. J., Maidment, K., Rosen, R., Vapnik, T., & Bystritsky, A. (2001). A retrospective review of clinical characteristics and treatment response in body dysmorphic disorder versus obsessive–compulsive disorder. *Journal of Clinical Psychiatry, 62*, 67–72.

Sbrocco, T., & Barlow, D. H. (1996). Conceptualizing the cognitive component of sexual arousal: Implications for sexuality research and treatment. In P. M. Salkovskis (Ed.), *Frontiers of cognitive therapy* (pp. 419–449). New York, NY: Guilford Press.

Scanlon, D. (2013). Specific learning disability and its newest definition: Which is comprehensive? and Which is insufficient? *Journal of Learning Disabilities, 46*(1), 26–33.

Schachter, H. M., Pham, B., King, J., Langford, S., & Moher, D. (2001). How efficacious and safe is short-acting methylphenidate for the treatment of attention-deficit disorder in children and adolescents? A metaanalysis. *Canadian Medical Association Journal, 165*, 1475–1488.

Schacter, D. L. (Ed.). (1995). *Memory distortion: How minds, brains, and societies reconstruct the past.* Cambridge, MA: Harvard University Press.

Schacter, D. L., Chiu, P., & Ochsner, K. N. (1993). Implicit memory: A selective review. *Annual Review of Neuroscience, 16*, 159–182.

Schaffer, A., Isometsä, E. T., Tondo, L. H., Moreno, D., Turecki, G., Reis, C., . . . Yatham, L. N. (2015). International Society for Bipolar Disorders Task Force on Suicide: Meta-analyses and meta-regression of correlates of suicide attempts and suicide deaths in bipolar disorder. *Bipolar Disorders, 17*, 1–16.

Scharfstein, L. A., Beidel, D., Finnell, L. R., Distler, A., & Carter, N. T. (2011). Do pharmacological and behavioral interventions differentially affect treatment outcome for children with social phobia? *Behavior Modification, 35*(5), 451–467.

Schatzberg, A. F. (2000). New indications for anti-depressants. *Journal of Clinical Psychiatry, 61*(Suppl. 11), 9–17.

Scheel, K. R. (2000). The empirical basis of dialectical behavior therapy: Summary, critique, and implications. *Clinical Psychology: Science and Practice, 7*, 68–86.

Scheerenberger, R. C. (1983). *A history of mental retardation.* Baltimore, MD: Paul H. Brookes.

Scheier, M. F., Matthews, K. A., Owens, J. F., Magovern, G. J., Sr., Lefebvre, R. C., Abbott, R. A., & Carver, C. S. (1989). Dispositional optimism and recovery from coronary artery bypass surgery: The beneficial effects on physical and psychological well-being. *Journal of Personality and Social Psychology, 57*(6), 1024–1040.

Schenck, C. H., Arnulf, I., & Mahowald, M. W. (2007). Sleep and sex: What can go wrong? A review of the literature on sleep related disorders and abnormal sexual behaviors and experiences. *Sleep, 30*(6), 683.

Schenk, L., & Bear, D. (1981). Multiple personality and related dissociative phenomena in patients with temporal lobe epilepsy. *American Journal of Psychiatry, 138*, 1311–1316.

Schiavi, R. C. (1990). Chronic alcoholism and male sexual dysfunction. *Journal of Sex and Marital Therapy, 16*, 23–33.

Schiavi, R. C., White, D, Mandeli, J., & Levine, A. C. (1997). Effect of testosterone administration on sexual behavior and mood in men with erectile dysfunction. *Archives of Sexual Behavior, 26*, 231–241.

Schietecatte, I., Roeyers, H., & Warreyn, P. (2012). Exploring the nature of joint attention impairments in young children with autism spectrum disorder: Associated social and cognitive skills. *Journal of Autism and Developmental Disorders, 42*(1), 1–12.

Schiffer, B., Peschel, T., Paul, T., Gizewski, E., Forsting, M., Leygraf, N., . . . Krueger, T. H. (2007). Structural brain abnormalities in the frontostriatal system and cerebellum in pedophilia. *Journal of Psychiatric Research, 41*, 753–762.

Schildkraut, J. J. (1965). The catecholamine hypothesis of affective disorders: A review of supporting evidence. *American Journal of Psychiatry, 122*, 509–522.

Schlundt, O. G., & Johnson, W. G. (1990). *Eating disorders: Assessment and treatment.* Boston, MA: Allyn & Bacon.

Schmidt, N. B., & Koselka, M. (2000). Gender differences in patients with panic disorder: Evaluating cognitive mediation of phobic avoidance. *Cognitive Therapy and Research, 24*, 533–550.

Schneck, C. D., Miklowitz, D. J., Miyahara, S., Araga, M., Wisniewski, S., Gyulai, L., & Sachs, G. S. (2008). The prospective course of rapid-cycling bipolar disorder: Findings from the STEP-BD. *American Journal of Psychiatry, 165*(3), 370–377.

Schneck, C., Miklowitz, D., Calabrese, J., Allen, M., Thomas, M., Wisniewski, S., . . . Sachs, G. S. (2004). Phenomenology of rapid-cycling bipolar disorder: Data from the first 500 participants in the systematic treatment enhancement program. *American Journal Psychiatry, 161*, 1902–1908.

Schneider, F. R., Blanco, C., Antia, S. X., & Liebowitz, M. R. (2002). The social anxiety spectrum. *Psychiatric Clinics of North America, 25*, 757–774.

Schneider, S., Blatter-Meunier, J., Herren, C., In-Albon, T., Adornetto, C., Meyer, A., & Lavallee, K. L. (2013). The efficacy of a family-based cognitive-behavioral treatment for separation anxiety disorder in children aged 8–13: A randomized comparison with a general anxiety program. *Journal of Consulting and Clinical Psychology, 81*, 932.

Schneiderman, N., Antoni, M. H., Ironson, G., LaPerriere, A., & Fletcher, M. A. (1992). Applied psychological science and HIV-1 spectrum disease. *Applied and Preventive Psychology, 1*, 67–82.

Schoenbach, V. J., Kaplan, B. H., Fredman, L., & Kleinbaum, D. G. (1986). Social ties and mortality in Evans County, Georgia. *American Journal of Epidemiology, 123*, 577.

Schoenberg, M. R., Marsh, P. J., & Benbadis, S. R. (2012). Where are somatoform disorders going? An update on the DSM-V. *Expert Review of Neurotherapeutics, 12*, 1371–1374.

Schoeneman, T. J. (1977). The role of mental illness in the European witch-hunts of the sixteenth and seventeenth centuries: An assessment. *Journal of the History of the Behavioral Sciences, 13*, 337–351.

Schoenmakers, B., Buntinx, F., & DeLepeleire, J. (2010). Supporting the dementia family caregiver: The effect of home care intervention on general well-being. *Aging & Mental Health, 14*(1), 44–56.

Schomerus, G., Schwahn, C., Holzinger, A., Corrigan, P. W., Grabe, H. J., Carta, M. G., & Angermeyer, M. C. (2012). Evolution of public attitudes about mental illness: A systematic review and meta-analysis. *Acta Psychiatrica Scandinavica, 125*(6), 440–452

Schredl, M. (2010). Nightmare frequency and nightmare topics in a representative German sample. *European Archives of Psychiatry and Clinical Neuroscience, 260*(8), 565–570.

Schreiber, F. R. (1973). *Sybil*. Chicago, IL: Regnery.

Schreiner-Engel, P., & Schiavi, R. C. (1986). Lifetime psychopathology in individuals with low sexual desire. *Journal of Nervous and Mental Disease, 174*, 646–651.

Schroeder, M. L., Wormworth, J. A., & Livesley, W. J. (1993). Dimensions of personality disorder and the five-factor model of personality. In P. T. Costa, Jr., & T. A. Widiger (Eds.), *Personality disorders and the five-factor model of personality* (pp. 117–127). Washington, DC: American Psychological Association.

Schuck, P. F., Malgarin, F., Cararo, J. H., Cardoso, F., Streck, E. L., & Ferreira, G. C. (2015). Phenylketonuria pathophysiology: On the role of metabolic alterations. *Aging and Disease, 6*(5), 390–399.

Schuckit, M. A. (2000). Biological phenotypes associated with individuals at high risk for developing alcohol-related disorders. Part 2. *Addiction Biology, 5*(1), 23–36.

Schuckit, M. A. (2009a). Alcohol-related disorders. In B. J. Sadock, V. A. Sadock, & P. Ruiz (Eds.), *Kaplan & Sadock's comprehensive textbook of psychiatry* (9th ed., Vol. 1, pp. 1268–1288). Philadelphia, PA: Lippincott Williams & Wilkins.

Schuckit, M. A. (2009b). Alcohol-use disorders. *The Lancet, 373*(9662), 492–501.

Schuckit, M. A. (2012). Editor's corner: Editorial in reply to the comments of Griffith Edwards. *Journal of studies on alcohol and drugs, 73*(4), 521.

Schuckit, M. A. (2014). A brief history of research on the genetics of alcohol and other drug use disorders. *Journal of Studies on Alcohol and Drugs: Supplement, 75*(Suppl 17), 59–67.

Schuckit, M. A., Smith, T. L., Anthenelli, R., & Irwin, M. (1993). Clinical course of alcoholism in 636 male inpatients. *American Journal of Psychiatry, 150*, 786–792.

Schulberg, H. C., Block, M. R., Madonia, M. J., Scott, C. P., Rodriguez, F., Imber, S. D., . . . Coulehan, J. L. (1996). Treating major depression in primary care practice: Eight-month clinical outcomes. *Archives of General Psychiatry, 53*, 913–919.

Schuller, R. A., & Ogloff, J. R. P. (2001). An introduction to psychology and law. In R. A. Schuller & J. R. P. Ogloff (Eds.), *Introduction to psychology and law: Canadian perspectives* (pp. 3–28). Toronto, ON: University of Toronto Press.

Schuller, R. A., & Yarmey, M. (2001). The jury: Deciding guilt and innocence. In R. A. Schuller & J. R. P. Ogloff (Eds.), *Introduction to psychology and law: Canadian perspectives* (pp. 157–187). Toronto, ON: University of Toronto Press.

Schuller, R. A., Wells, F., Rzepa, S., & Klippenstine, M. A. (2004). Rethinking battered woman syndrome evidence: The impact of alternative forms of expert testimony on mock jurors' decisions. *Canadian Journal of Behavioural Science, 36*, 127–136.

Schulz, R., Drayer, R. A., & Rollman, B. L. (2002). Depression as a risk factor for non-suicide mortality in the elderly. *Biological Psychiatry, 52*, 204–225.

Schumann, C. M., & Amaral, D. G. (2006). Stereological analysis of amygdala neuron number in autism. *Journal of Neuroscience, 26*, 7674–7679.

Schutter, D. J. (2009). Antidepressant efficacy of high-frequency transcranial magnetic stimulation over the left dorsolateral prefrontal cortex in double-blind sham-controlled designs: A meta-analysis. *Psychological Medicine, 39*(1), 65–75.

Schwalberg, M. D., Barlow, D. H., Alger, S. A., & Howard, L. J. (1992). Comparison of bulimics, obese binge eaters, social phobics, and individuals with panic disorder or comorbidity across DSM-III-R anxiety. *Journal of Abnormal Psychology, 101*, 675–681.

Schwartz, A. J. (2011). Rate, relative risk, and method of suicide by students at 4-year colleges and universities in the United States, 2004–2005 through 2008–2009. *Suicide and Life-Threatening Behavior, 41*(4), 353–371.

Schwartz, G. F., & Weiss, S. M. (1978). Behavioral medicine revisited: An amended definition. *Journal of Behavioral Medicine, 1*, 249–252.

Schwartz, I. M. (1993). Affective reactions of American and Swedish women to the first premarital coitus: A cross-cultural comparison. *Journal of Sex Research, 30*(1), 18–26.

Schwartz, J. M., Stoessel, P. W., Baxter, L. R., Martin, K. M., & Phelps, M. E. (1996). Systematic changes in cerebral glucose metabolic rate after successful behavior modification treatment of obsessive–compulsive disorder. *Archives of General Psychiatry, 53*(2), 109–113.

Schwarz, A. (2007, March 14). Wives united by husband's post-NFL trauma. *New York Times*, p. A1. Retrieved from http://www.nytimes.com

Schwarz, K. A., & Pfister, R. (2016). Scientific psychology in the 18th Century: A historical rediscovery. *Perspectives on Psychological Science, 11*(3), 399–407. https://doi.org/10.1177/1745691616635601

Scott, K. M., Lim, C., Al-Hamzawi, A., Alonso, J., Bruffaerts, R., Caldas-de-Almeida, J. M., . . . Kessler R. C. (in press). Association of mental disorders with subsequent chronic physical conditions: World mental health surveys from 17 countries. *JAMA Psychiatry*.

Scott, C. L., Hilty, D. M., & Brook, M. (2003). Impulse-control disorders not elsewhere classified. In R. E. Hales & S. C. Yudofsky (Eds.), *Textbook of clinical psychiatry* (4th ed., pp. 781–802). Washington, DC: American Psychiatric Publishing.

Scott, J. F., & Dixon, L. B. (1995a). Assertive community treatment and case management for schizophrenia. *Schizophrenia Bulletin, 21*, 657–668.

Scott, J. F., & Dixon, L. B. (1995b). Psychological interventions for schizophrenia. *Schizophrenia Bulletin, 21*, 621–630.

Scott, K. M., Lim, C., Al-Hamzawi, A., Alonso, J., Bruffaerts, R., Caldas-de-Almeida, J. M., . . . Kessler, R. C. (2016). Association of mental disorders with subsequent chronic physical conditions: World mental health surveys from 17 countries. *JAMA Psychiatry, 73*(2), 150–158. https://doi.org/10.1001/jamapsychiatry.2015.2688

Scott, S. (2012). Developmental psychopathology and classification in childhood and adolescence. In M. G. Gelder, N. C. Andreasen, J. J. Lopez-Ibor, & J. R. Geddes (Eds.), *New Oxford textbook of psychiatry* (2nd ed., Vol. 2, pp. 1589–1594). New York, NY: Oxford University Press.

Scott, S., Briskman, J., & O'Connor, T. G. (2014). Early prevention of antisocial personality: Long-term follow-up of two randomized controlled trials comparing indicated and selective approaches. *American Journal of Psychiatry, 171*(6), 649–657.

Sealy, P. S., & Whitehead, P. C. (2004). Forty years of deinstitutionalization of psychiatric services in Canada: An empirical assessment. *Canadian Journal of Psychiatry, 49*, 249–257.

Sedlak, T. W., & Kaplin, A. I. (2009). Novel neurotransmitters. In B. J. Sadock, V. A. Sadock, & P. Ruiz (Eds.), *Kaplan & Sadock's comprehensive textbook of psychiatry* (9th ed., pp. 102–117). Philadelphia, PA: Lippincott Williams & Wilkins.

Seedat, S., Scott, K. M., Angermeyer, M. C., Berglund, P., Bromet, E. J., Brugha, T. S., & Kessler, R. C. (2009). Cross-national associations between gender and mental disorders in the WHO World Mental Health Surveys. *Archives of General Psychiatry, 66*(7), 785.

Seeman, M. V. (2007). An outcome measure in schizophrenia: Mortality. *The Canadian Journal of Psychiatry/La Revue canadienne de psychiatrie, 52*(1), 55–60.

Seeman, P., Lee, T., Chau-Wong, M., & Wong, K. (1976). Antipsychotic drug doses and neuroleptic/ dopamine receptors. *Nature, 261*, 717–719.

Segal, N. (2006). Two monozygotic twin pairs discordant for female to male transsexualism. *Archives of Sexual Behavior, 35*, 347–358.

Segal, Z. V., Hood, J. F., Shaw, B. F., & Higgins, F. (1988). A structural analysis of the self-schema construct in major depression. *Cognitive Therapy and Research, 12*(5), 471–485.

Segal, Z. V., Williams, J. M. G., & Teasdale, J. D. (2002). *Mindfulness-based cognitive therapy for depression: A new approach to preventing relapse.* New York, NY: Guilford Press.

Segal, Z., Vincent, P., & Levitt, A. (2002). Efficacy of combined, sequential and crossover psychotherapy and pharmacotherapy in improving outcomes in depression. *Journal of Psychiatry & Neuroscience, 27*, 281–290.

Seglem, K. B., Waaktaar, T., Ask, H., and Torgersen, S. (2015) Sex differences in genetic and environmental contributions to alcohol consumption from early adolescence to young adulthood. *Addiction, 111*, 1188–1195. https://doi.org/10.1111/add.13321

Segerstrom, S. C., & Sephton, S. E. (2010). Optimistic expectancies and cell-mediated immunity: The role of positive affect. *Psychological Science, 21*, 448–455.

Segraves, R. T., & Althof, S. (1998). Psychotherapy and pharmacotherapy of sexual dysfunctions. In P. F. Nathan & J. M. Gorman (Eds.), *A guide to treatments that work* (pp. 447–471). New York, NY: Oxford University Press.

Segraves, R., & Woodard, T. (2006). Female hypoactive sexual desire disorder: History and current status. *Journal of Sexual Medicine, 3*, 408–418.

Seib, D. R., & Martin-Villalba, A. (2015). Neurogenesis in the normal ageing hippocampus: A mini-review. *Gerontology, 61*(4), 327–335.

Seitz, D. P., Adunuri, N., Gill, S. S., & Rochon, P. A. (2011). Prevalence of dementia and cognitive impairment among older adults with hip fractures. *Journal of the American Medical Directors Association, 12*(8), 556–564.

Seligman, M. F. P. (1971). Phobias and preparedness. *Behavior Therapy, 2*, 307–320.

Seligman, M. F. P. (1975). *Helplessness: On depression, development and death.* San Francisco, CA: W. H. Freeman.

Seligman, M. F. P. (1998). The prediction and prevention of depression. In D. K. Routh & R. J. DeRubeis (Eds.), *Science of clinical psychology: Accomplishments and future directions* (pp. 201–214). Washington, DC: American Psychological Association.

Seligman, M. F. P. (2002). Positive psychology, positive prevention, and positive therapy. In C. R. Snyder & S. J. Lopez (Eds.), *Handbook of positive psychology* (pp. 3–9). London, UK: Oxford University Press.

Seligman, M. F. P., & Binik, Y. (1977). The safety signal hypothesis. In H. Davis & H. Horowitz (Eds.), *Operant-Pavlovian interaction.* Hillsdale, NJ: Erlbaum.

Seligman, M. F. P., Schulman, P., DeRubeis, R. J., & Hollon, S. D. (1999). The prevention of depression and anxiety. *Prevention and Treatment, 2*, 8.

Sellick, S. M., & Zaza, C. (1998). Critical review of 5 nonpharmacologic strategies for managing cancer pain. *Cancer Prevention and Control, 2*, 7–14.

Selten, J. P., Frissen, A., Lensvelt-Mulders, G., & Morgan, V. A. (2010). Schizophrenia and 1957 pandemic of influenza: Meta-analysis. *Schizophrenia Bulletin, 36*(2), 228.

Selye, H. (1936). A syndrome produced by diverse noxious agents. *Nature, 138*, 32.

Selye, H. (1950). *The physiology and pathology of exposure to stress.* Montreal: Acta.

Semans, J. H. (1956). Premature ejaculation: A new approach. *Southern Medical Journal, 49*, 353–358.

Semple, R. J., & Burke, C. A. (2012). Mindfulness based treatment for children and adolescents. In P. C. Kendall (Ed.), *Child and adolescent therapy: Cognitive-behavioral procedures* (4th ed., pp. 411–426). New York, NY: Guilford Press.

Sendt, K. V., Tracy, D. K., & Bhattacharyya, S. (2015). A systematic review of factors influencing adherence to antipsychotic medication in schizophrenia-spectrum disorders. *Psychiatry Research, 225*(1), 14–30.

Seshadri, S., Fitzpatrick, A. L., Ikram, M. A., DeStefano, A. L., Gudnason, V., Boada, M., . . . Breteler, M. M. B. (2010). Genome-wide analysis of genetic loci associated with Alzheimer disease. *JAMA, 303*(18), 1832–1840.

Seto, M. C. (2009). Pedophilia. In S. Nolen-Hoeksema, T. D. Cannon, & T. Widiger, T. (Eds.), *Annual review of clinical psychology* (Vol. 5, pp. 391–408). Palo Alto, CA: Annual Reviews.

Seto, M. C. (2013). *Internet sex offenders.* Washington, DC: American Psychological Association.

Seto, M. C., Cantor, J. M., & Blanchard, R. (2006). Child pornography offenses are a valid diagnostic indicator of pedophilia. *Journal of Abnormal Psychology, 115*, 610–615.

Seto, M. C., & Lalumière, M. L. (2001). A brief screening scale to identify pedophilic interests among child molesters. *Sexual Abuse: A Journal of Research and Treatment, 13*, 15–25.

Seto, M. C., & Lalumière, M. L. (2010). What is so special about male adolescent sexual offending? A review and test of explanations through meta-analysis. *Psychological Bulletin, 136*, 526–575.

Seto, M. C., Lalumière, M. L., Harris, G. T., & Chivers, M. L. (2012). The sexual responses of sexual sadists. *Journal of Abnormal Psychology, 121*, 739–753.

Seto, M. C., Stephens, S., Lalumière, M. L., & Cantor, J. M. (2017). The revised screening scale for pedophilic interests (SSPI-2): Development and criterion-related validation. *Sexual Abuse, 29*, 619–635. https://doi.org/10.1177/1079063215612444

Severino, S. K., & Moline, M. L. (1989). *Premenstrual syndrome: A clinician's guide.* New York, NY: Guilford Press.

Sexton, M. M. (1979). Behavioral epidemiology. In O. F. Pomerleau & J. P. Brady (Eds.), *Behavioral medicine: Theory and practice* (pp. 3–21). Baltimore, MD: Williams & Wilkins.

Seyfort, B., Spreen, O., & Lahmer, V. (1980). A critical look at the WISC-R with Native Indian children. *Alberta Journal of Educational Research, 26*, 14–24.

Shabecoff, P. (1987, October 14). Stress and the lure of harmless remedies. *New York Times*, p. 12.

Shaffer, D. R. (1993). *Developmental psychology: Childhood and adolescence* (3rd ed.). Pacific Grove, CA: Brooks/Cole.

Shaffer, D., Garland, A., Gould, M., Fisher, P., & Trautmen, P. (1988). Preventing teenage suicide: A critical review. *Journal of the American Academy of Child and Adolescent Psychiatry, 27*, 675–687.

Shaffer, D., Garland, A., Vieland, V., Underwood, M., & Busner, C. (1991s). The impact of curriculum based suicide prevention programs for teenagers.

Journal of the American Academy of Child and Adolescent Psychiatry, 30(4), 588–596.

Shafran, R., Thordarson, D. S., & Rachman, S. (1996). Thought-action fusion in obsessive compulsive disorder. *Journal of Anxiety Disorders, 10*, 379–391.

Shakespeare, W. (2002). *Macbeth.* New York, NY: Dover Publications.

Shalev, A. Y., Ankri, Y., Israeli-Shalev, Y., Peleg, T., Adessky, R., & Freedman, S. (2012). Prevention of posttraumatic stress disorder by early treatment: Results from the Jerusalem Trauma Outreach and Prevention study. *Archives of General Psychiatry, 69*, 166–176.

Shamloul, R., & Ghanem, H. (2013). Erectile dysfunction. *The Lancet, 381*(9861), 153–165.

Shapiro, F. (1995). *Eye movement desensitization and reprocessing: Basic principles, protocols, and procedures.* New York, NY: Guilford Press.

Shapiro, F. (1999). Eye movement desensitization and reprocessing (FMDR) and the anxiety disorders: Clinical and research implications of an integrated psychotherapy treatment. *Journal of Anxiety Disorders, 13*, 35–67.

Shapiro, F. S., & Lentz, F. F. (1991). Vocational-technical programs: Follow-up of students with learning disabilities. *Exceptional Children, 58*, 47–59.

Shapiro, J. R., Berkman, N. D., Brownley, K. A., Sedway, J. A., Lohr, K. N., & Bulik, C. M. (2007). Bulimia nervosa treatment: A systematic review of randomized controlled trials. *International Journal of Eating Disorders, 40*(4), 321–336.

Sharma, M. P., & Manjula, M. (2013). Behavioral and psychological management of somatic symptom disorder: An overview. *International Review of Psychiatry, 25*, 116–124.

Sharp, T. (2009). Neurotransmitters and signalling. In M. G. Gelder, N. C. Andreasen, J. J. Lopez-Ibor, Jr., & J. R. Geddes (Eds.), *New Oxford textbook of psychiatry* (2nd ed., Vol. 1, pp. 168–176). Oxford, UK: Oxford University Press.

Sharpe, M. (1992). Fatigue and chronic fatigue syndrome. *Current Opinion in Psychiatry, 5*, 207–212.

Sharpe, M. (1993). Chronic fatigue syndrome (pp. 298–317). Chichester, UK: John Wiley & Sons.

Sharpe, M. (1997). Chronic fatigue. In D. M. Clark & C. G. Fairburn (Eds.), *Science and practice of cognitive behavior therapy* (pp. 381–414). Oxford, UK: Oxford University Press.

Sharpe, M., Clements, A., Hawton, K., Young, A., Sargent, P., & Cowen, P. (1996). Increased prolactin response to buspirone in chronic fatigue syndrome. *Journal of Affective Disorders, 41*, 71–76.

Sharpless, B., & Doghramji, K. (2015). *Sleep paralysis: Historical, psychological, and medical perspectives.* Oxford University Press.

Shatkin, J. P., & Ivanenko, A. (2009). Pediatric sleep disorders. In B. J. Sadock, V. A. Sadock, & P. Ruiz (Eds.), *Kaplan & Sadock's comprehensive textbook of psychiatry* (9th ed., Vol. 1, pp. 3903–3908). Philadelphia, PA: Lippincott Williams & Wilkins.

Shaw, J., & Porter, S. (2015). Constructing rich false memories of committing

crime. *Psychological Science, 26*, 291–301.

Shea, M. T., Elkin, I., Imber, S. D., Sotsky, S. M., Watkins, J. T., Collins, J. F., . . . Dolan, R. T. (1992). Course of depressive symptoms over follow-up: Findings from the National Institute of Mental Health Treatment of Depression Collaborative Research Program. *Archives of General Psychiatry, 49*(10), 782–787.

Shea, M. T., Pilkonis, P. A., Beckham, F., Collins, J. F., Elkin, I., Sotsky, S. M., & Docherty, J. P. (1990). Personality disorders and treatment outcome in the NIMH treatment of depression collaborative research program. *American Journal of Psychiatry, 147*, 711–718.

Sheaffer, R. (1986). *The UFO verdict: Examining the evidence.* Buffalo, NY: Prometheus Books.

Shear, K., Jin, R., Ruscio, A. M., Walters, E. E., & Kessler, R. C. (2006). Prevalence and correlates of estimated DSM-IV child and adult separation anxiety disorder in the National Comorbidity Survey Replication. *American Journal of Psychiatry, 163*(6), 1074–1083.

Shear, M. K. (2010). Complicated grief treatment: The theory, practice and outcomes. *Bereavement Care, 29*(3), 10–14.

Shear, M. K. (2012). Getting straight about grief. *Depression and Anxiety, 29*, 461–464.

Shear, M. K., Brown, T. A., Barlow, D. H., Money, R., Sholomskas, D. F., Woods, S. W., . . . Papp, L. A. (1997). Multicenter collaborative panic disorder severity scale. *American Journal of Psychiatry, 154*, 1571–1575.

Shear, M. K., Simon, N., Wall, M., Zisook, S., Neimeyer, R., Duan, N., & Keshaviah, A. (2011). Complicated grief and related bereavement issues for DSM-5. *Depression and Anxiety, 28*, 103–117.

Shedler, J., & Westen, D. (2004a). Dimensions of personality pathology: An alternative to the Five Factor Model. *American Journal of Psychiatry, 161*, 1743–1754.

Shedler, J., & Westen, D. (2004b). Refining personality disorder diagnosis: Integrating science and practice. *American Journal of Psychiatry, 161*(8), 1350–1365. https://doi.org/10.1176/appi.ajp.161.8.1350

Sheets, E. S., & Craighead, W. E. (2014). Comparing chronic interpersonal and noninterpersonal stress domains as predictors of depression recurrence in emerging adults, *Behaviour Research and Therapy, 63*, 36–42.

Sheikh, J. I. (1992). Anxiety and its disorders in old age. In J. F. Birren, K. Sloan, & G. D. Cohen (Eds.), *Handbook of mental health and aging* (pp. 410–432). New York, NY: Academic Press.

Shenton, M. E., & Kubicki, M. (2009). Structural brain imaging in schizophrenia. In B. J. Sadock, V. A. Sadock, & P. Ruiz (Eds.), *Kaplan & Sadock's comprehensive textbook of psychiatry* (9th ed., Vol. 1, pp. 1494–1507). Philadelphia, PA: Lippincott Williams & Wilkins.

Shepard, B., O'Neill, L., & Guenette, F. (2006). Counselling with First Nations women: Considerations of oppression and renewal. *International Journal for the Advancement of Counselling, 28*(3), 227–240.

Sheperis, C. J., Lionetti, T. M., & Snook, J. (2015). Substance-related disorders. In B. Flamez & C. J. Sheperis (Eds.), *Diagnosing and treating children and adolescents: A guide for mental health professionals* (pp. 413–440). Hoboken, NJ: Wiley & Sons.

Shepherd, M., Watt, D., Falloon, I., & Smeeton, N. (1989). The natural history of schizophrenia: A five-year follow-up study of outcome and prediction in a representative sample of schizophrenics. *Psychological Medicine Monograph, 15*(Suppl.), 1–46.

Sherbourne, C. D., Hays, R. D., & Wells, K. B. (1995). Personal and psychosocial risk factors for physical and mental health outcomes and course of depression among depressed patients. *Journal of Consulting and Clinical Psychology, 63*, 345–355.

Sherman, A. C., Leszcz, M., Mosier, J., Burlingame, G. M., Cleary, T., Ulman, K. H., . . . Hazelton, L. (2004). Group interventions for patients with cancer and HIV disease: Part II. Effects on immune, endocrine, and disease outcomes at different phases of illness. *International Journal of Group Psychotherapy, 54*(2), 203–233.

Sherman, S. L., DeFries, J. C., Gottesman, I. I., Loehlin, J. C., Meyer, J. M., Pelias, M. Z., . . . Waldman, I. (1997). Recent developments in human behavioral genetics: Past accomplishments and future directions. *American Journal of Human Genetics, 60*, 1265–1275.

Sherrington, R., Rogaev, F. I., Liang, Y., Rogaeva, F. A., Levesque, G., Ikeda, M., . . . St. George-Hyslop, P. H. (1995). Cloning of a gene bearing missense mutations in early-onset familial Alzheimer's disease. *Nature, 375*, 754–60.

Shields, M. (2004). *Social anxiety disorder—beyond shyness.* (Catalogue No. 82–003). Ottawa, ON: Statistics Canada.

Shiffman, S., Hickcox, M., Paty, J. A., Gnys, M., Kassel, J. D., & Richards, T. J. (1996). Progression from a smoking lapse to relapse: Prediction from abstinence violation effects, nicotine dependence, and lapse characteristics. *Journal of Consulting and Clinical Psychology, 64*, 993–1002.

Shin, L. M., & Liberzon, I. (2010). The neurocircuitry of fear, stress, and anxiety disorders. *Neuropsychopharmacology, 35*(1), 169–191.

Shin, L. M., Lasko, N. B., Macklin, M. L., Karpf, R. D., Milad, M. R., Orr, S. P., . . . Pitman, R. K. (2009). Resting metabolic activity in the cingulate cortex and vulnerability to posttraumatic stress disorder. *Archives of General Psychiatry, 66*(10), 1099–1107.

Shin, L. M., Shin, P. S., Heckers, S., Krangel, T. S., Macklin, M. L., Orr, S. P., . . . Rauch, S. L. (2004). Hippocampal function in posttraumatic stress disorder. *Hippocampus, 14*, 292–300.

Shingleton, R. M., Thompson-Brenner, H., Thompson, D. R., Pratt, E. M., & Franko, D. L. (2015). Gender differences in clinical trials of binge eating disorder: An analysis of aggregated data. *Journal of Consulting and Clinical Psychology, 83*(2), 382.

Shneidman, F. S. (1989). Approaches and commonalities of suicide. In

R. F. W. Diekstra, R. Mariss, S. Platt, A. Schmidtke, et al. (Eds.), *Suicide and its prevention: The role of attitude and imitation. Advances in Suicidology* (Vol. 1). Leiden, The Netherlands: F. J. Brill.

Shneidman, F. S., Farberow, N. L., & Litman, R. F. (Eds.). (1970). *The psychology of suicide.* New York, NY: Science House.

Shulman, K. I. (2000). Clock-drawing: Is it the ideal cognitive screening test? *International Journal of Geriatric Psychiatry, 15,* 548–561.

Shulman, K. I., Shedletsky, R., & Silver, I. (1986). The challenge of time: Clock drawing and cognitive function in the elderly. *International Journal of Geriatric Psychiatry, 1,* 135–140.

Shumaker, S. A., Legault, C., Kuller, L., Rapp, S. R., Thal, L., Lane, D. S., . . . Coker, L. H., & Women's Health Initiative Memory Study. (2004). Conjugated equine estrogens and incidence of probable dementia and mild cognitive impairment in postmenopausal women: Women's Health Initiative Memory Study. *JAMA, 291,* 3005–3007.

Sibley, D. C., & Blinder, B. J. (1988). Anorexia nervosa. In B. J. Blinder, B. F. Chaitin, & R. S. Goldstein (Eds.), *The eating disorders: Medical and psychological bases of diagnosis and treatment* (pp. 247–258). New York, NY: PMA.

Sibrava, N. J., Beard, C., Bjornsson, A. S., Moitra, E., Weisberg, R. B., & Keller, M. B. (2013). Two-year course of generalized anxiety disorder, social anxiety disorder, and panic disorder in a longitudinal sample of African American adults. *Journal of Consulting and Clinical Psychology, 81,* 1052.

Sico, J. J., Amin, H., Sorokin, A., Volpe, D. C., Hamid, H., Machado, D., . . . Brust, J. C. M. (2014). Neurologic disorders related to alcohol and other drug use. In R. K. Ries, D. A. Fiellin, S. C. Miller, & R. Saitz (Eds.), *The ASAM principles of addiction medicine* (5th ed., pp. 1178–1194). New York, NY: Wolters Kluwer.

Siegel, S. (1982). Opioid expectation modifies opioid effects. *Federation Proceedings, 41,* 2339–2343.

Siegel, S., Hinson, R. F., Krank, M. D., & McCully, J. (1982). Heroin "overdose" death: Contribution of drug-associated environmental cues. *Science, 216,* 436–437.

Sierra, M., & Berrios, G. F. (1998). Depersonalization: Neurobiological perspectives. *Society of Biological Psychiatry, 44,* 898–908.

Sierra, M., Senior, C., Dalton, J., McDonough, M., Bond, A., Phillips, M. L., . . . David, A. S. (2002). Autonomic response in depersonalization disorder. *Archives of General Psychiatry, 59,* 833–838.

Siever, L. J., & Davis, K. L. (2004). The pathophysiology of schizophrenia disorders: Perspectives from the spectrum. *American Journal of Psychiatry, 161,* 398–413.

Siever, L. J., Davis, K. L., & Gorman, L. K. (1991). Pathogenesis of mood disorders. In K. Davis, H. Klar, & J. T. Coyle (Eds.), *Foundations of psychiatry.* Philadelphia, PA: W. B. Saunders.

Siffre, M. (1964). *Beyond time* (H. Briffault, Ed. & Trans.). New York, NY: McGraw-Hill.

Sigafoos, J., Arthur-Kelly, M., & Butterfield, N. (2006). *Enhancing everyday communication for children with disabilities.* Baltimore, MD: Paul H. Brookes.

Sigafoos, J., Green, V. A., Schlosser, R., O'Reilly, M. F., Lancioni, G. E., Rispoli, M., & Lang, R. (2009). Communication intervention in Rett syndrome: A systematic review. *Research in Autism Spectrum Disorders, 3*(2), 304–318.

Sigvardsson, S., Cloninger, C. R., Bohman, M., & von Knorring, A. L. (1982). Predisposition to petty criminality in Swedish adoptees. *Archives of General Psychiatry, 39,* 1248–1253.

Sikorska, B., Knight, R., Ironside, J. W., & Liberski, P. P. (2012). Creutzfeldt-Jakob disease. In S. I. Ahmad (Ed.), *Neurodegenerative diseases* (pp. 76–90). New York, NY: Springer.

Silberg, J. L., Maes, H., & Eaves, L. J. (2012). Unraveling the effect of genes and environment in the transmission of parental antisocial behavior to children's conduct disturbance, depression and hyperactivity. *Journal of Child Psychology and Psychiatry, 53*(6), 668–677.

Silbersweig, D. A., Stern, F., Frith, C., Cahill, C., Holmes, A., Grootoonk, S., . . . Frackowiak, R. S. J. (1995). A functional neuroanatomy of hallucinations in schizophrenia. *Nature, 378,* 176–179.

Silove, D. M., Marnane, C. L., Wagner, R., Manicavasagar, V. L., & Rees, S. (2010). The prevalence and correlates of adult separation anxiety disorder in an anxiety clinic. *BMC Psychiatry, 10,* 21.

Silverman, W. K., & La Greca, A. M. (2002). Children experiencing disasters: Definitions, reactions and predictors of outcomes. In A. N. La Greca, W. K. Silverman, & M. C. Roberts (Eds.), *Helping children cope with disasters and terrorism* (Vol. 1, pp. 11–33). Washington, DC: American Psychological Association.

Silverman, W. K., & Rabian, B. (1993). Simple phobias. *Child and Adolescent Psychiatric Clinics of North America, 2,* 603–622.

Silverstone, T. (1985). Dopamine in manic depressive illness: A pharmacological synthesis. *Journal of Affective Disorders, 8*(3), 225–231.

Simeon, D. (2009). Neurobiology of depersonalization disorder. In P. F. Dell & J. A. O'Neil (Eds.), *Dissociation and the dissociative disorders* (pp. 367–372). New York, NY: Routledge.

Simeon, D., & Abugal, J. (2006). *Feeling unreal: Depersonalization disorder and the loss of the self.* Oxford, UK: Oxford University Press.

Simeon, D., Gross, S., Guralnik, O., Stein, M. B., Schmeidler, J., & Hollander F. (1997). Thirty cases of DSM III-R depersonalization disorder. *American Journal of Psychiatry, 154,* 1107–1113.

Simeon, D., Guralnik, O., Hazlett, E. A., Spiegel-Cohen, J., Hollander, E., & Buchsbaum, M. S. (2000). Feeling unreal: A PET study of depersonalization disorder. *American Journal of Psychiatry, 157,* 1782–1788.

Simeon, D., Guralnik, O., Knutelska, M., Hollander, E., & Schmeidler, J. (2001). Hypothalamic–pituitary–adrenal axis dysregulation in depersonalization disorder. *Neuropsychopharmacology, 25,* 793–795.

Simeon, D., Guralnik, O., Schneider, J., & Knutelska, M. (2004). Fluoxetine therapy in depersonalization disorder: Randomised controlled trial. *British Journal of Psychiatry, 185,* 31–36.

Simeon, J., Nixon, M. K., & Milin, R. (2005). Open-label pilot study of St. John's Wort in adolescent depression. *Journal of Child and Adolescent Psychopharmacology, 15,* 293–301.

Simms, L. J., Prisciandaro, J. J., Krueger, R. F., & Goldberg, D. P. (2012). The structure of depression, anxiety, and somatic symptoms in primary care. *Psychological Medicine, 42,* 15–28.

Simon, F. J. (1997). Opiates: Neurobiology. In J. H. Lowinson, P. Ruiz, R. B. Millman, & J. G. Langrod (Eds.), *Substance abuse: A comprehensive textbook* (pp. 148–158). Baltimore, MD: Williams & Wilkins.

Simon, G. E., Gureje, O., & Fullerton, C. (2001). Course of hypochondriasis in an international primary care study. *General Hospital Psychiatry, 23,* 51–55.

Simon, N M. (2012). Is complicated grief a post-loss stress disorder? *Depression and Anxiety, 29,* 541–544.

Simon, R. I., & Shuman, D. W. (2009). Clinical-legal issues in psychiatry. In B. J. Sadock, V. A. Sadock, & P. Ruiz (Eds.), *Kaplan & Sadock's comprehensive textbook of psychiatry* (9th ed., Vol. 2, pp. 4427–4439). Philadelphia, PA: Lippincott Williams & Wilkins.

Simon, R. I., & Shuman, D. W. (2014). Clinical issues in psychiatry and the law. In R. E. Hales, S. C. Yudofsky, & L. Weiss Roberts (Eds.), *The American Psychiatric Publishing textbook of psychiatry* (6th ed., pp.175–204). Washington, DC: American Psychiatric Publishing.

Simoneau, T. L., Miklowitz, D. J., Richards, J. A., Saleem, R., & George, F. L. (1999). Bipolar disorder and family communication: Effects of a psychoeducational treatment program. *Journal of Abnormal Psychology, 108,* 588–597.

Simons, J. S., Dvorak, R. D., & Lau-Barraco, C. (2009). Behavioral inhibition and activation systems: Differences in substance use expectancy organization and activation in memory. *Psychology of Addictive Behaviors, 23*(2), 315–328. https://doi.org/10.1037/a0015834

Simonsen, E., Evensen, J., Røsberg, J. I., Barder, H., Haahr, U. H., ten Welden Hegelstad, W., . . . Opjordsmoen, S. (2012). Flat affect and social functioning. *Schizophrenia Research, 139*(1–3), 99–104

Simpson, E. B., Pistorello, J., Begin, A., Costello, E., Levinson, J., Mulberry, S., . . . Stevens, M. (1998). Use of dialectical behavior therapy in a partial hospital program for women with borderline personality disorder. *Psychiatric Services, 49*(5), 669–673

Simpson, G. K., Tate, R. L., Whiting, D. L., & Cotter, R. E. (2011). Suicide prevention after traumatic brain injury: A randomized controlled trial of a program for the psychological treatment of hopelessness. *Journal of Head Trauma Rehabilitation, 26*(4), 290–300.

Simpson, H. B., Foa, E. B., Liebowitz, M. R., Huppert, J. D., Cahill, S.,

Maher, M. J., McLean, C. P., Bender, J., Marcus, S. M., Williams, M. T., Weaver, J., Vermes, D., Van Meter, P., Rodriguez, C. I., Powers, M., Pinto, A., Imms, P., Hahn, C. G., & Campeas, R. (2014). Cognitive-behavioral therapy vs. resperidone for augmenting serotonin reuptake inhibitors in obsessive-compulsive disorder: A randomized clinical trial. *JAMA Psychiatry, 70,* 1190–1199.

Singal, J. (2016, February 7). How the fight over transgender kids got a leading sex researcher fired. *New York Magazine.* Retrieved from http://nymag.com/scienceofus/2016/02/fight-over-trans-kids-got-a-researcher-fired.html

Singer, J. (1999). "Why can't you be normal for once in your life?" From a "problem with no name" to the emergence of a new category of difference. In M. Corker & S. French (Eds.), *Disability discourse* (pp. 59–67). Buckingham, UK: Open University Press.

Singh, S. P., Harley, K., & Suhail, K. (2013). Cultural specificity of emotional overinvolvement: A systematic review. *Schizophrenia Bulletin, 39*(2), 449–463. https://doi.org/10.1093/schbul/sbr170

Single, F., Robson, L., Rehm, J., & Xie, X. (1996). *The costs of substance abuse in Canada.* Ottawa, ON: Canadian Centre on Substance Abuse.

Sinha, B. K., & Watson, D. C. (2004). Personality disorder clusters and the defence style questionnaire. *Psychology and Psychotherapy: Theory, Research and Practice, 77,* 55–66.

Sisask, M., & Varnik, A. (2012). Media roles in suicide prevention: A systematic review. *International Journal of Environmental Research and Public Health, 9*(1), 123–138.

Sit, D., Rothschild, A. J., & Wisner, K. L. (2006). A review of postpartum psychosis. *Journal of Womens Health, 15*(4), 352–368.

Skeldon, A., Dirks, G., & Dijk, D. J. (2015). Modelling changes in sleep timing and duration across the lifespan: Changes in circadian rhythmicity or sleep homeostasis? *Sleep Medicine Reviews, 28,* 96–107.

Skhiri, D., Annabi, S., Bi, S., & Allani, D. (1982). Enfants d'immigrés: Facteurs de liens ou de rupture? *Annales Medico-Psychologiques, 140,* 597–602.

Skidmore, W., Linsenmeier, J., & Bailey, J. (2006). Gender nonconformity and psychological distress in lesbians and gay men. *Archives of Sexual Behavior, 35,* 685–697.

Skilling, T. A., Harris, G. T., Rice, M. F., & Quinsey, V. L. (2002). Identifying persistently antisocial offenders using the Hare Psychopathy Checklist and DSM antisocial personality disorder criteria. *Psychological Assessment, 14,* 27–38.

Skinner, B. F. (1938). *The behavior of organisms.* New York, NY: Appleton-Century-Crofts.

Skinner, B. F. (1948). *Walden two.* New York, NY: Macmillan.

Skinner, B. F. (1971). *Beyond freedom and dignity.* New York, NY: Knopf.

Skinner, R., McFaull, S., Draca, J., Frechette, M., Kaur, J., Pearson, M. A., & Thompson, W. (2016). Suicide and self-inflicted injury hospitalizations in Canada (1979 to 2014/15). *Health Promotion and Chronic Disease*

Prevention in Canada: Research, Policy and Practice, 36, 243–251. https://www.canada.ca/en/public-health/services/reports-publications/health-promotion-chronic-disease-prevention-canada-research-policy-practice/vol-36-no-11-2016/suicide-self-inflicted-injury-hospitalizations-canada-1979-2014-15.html

Skodol, A. E. (2012). Personality disorders in DSM-5. *Annual Review of Clinical Psychology, 8*, 317–344.

Skodol, A. E., Bender, D. S., Morey, L. C., Clark, L. A., Oldham, J. M., Alarcon, R. D., & Siever, L. J. (2011). Personality disorder types proposed for DSM-5. *Journal of Personality Disorders, 25*(2), 136–169.

Skodol, A. E., Grilo, C. M., Keyes, K. M., Geier, T., Grant, B. F., & Hasin, D. S. (2011). Relationship of personality disorders to the course of major depressive disorder in a nationally representative sample. *American Journal of Psychiatry, 168*(3), 257–264.

Skodol, A. E., & Gunderson, J. G. (2008). Personality disorders. In R. E. Hales, S. C. Yudofsky, & G. O. Gabbard (Eds.), *The American Psychiatric Publishing textbook of psychiatry* (5th ed., pp. 821–860). Arlington, VA: American Psychiatric Publishing.

Skodol, A. E., Oldham, J. M., Bender, D. S., Dyck, I. R., Stout, R. L., & Morey, L. C., . . . Gunderson, J. G. (2005). Dimensional representations of DSM-IV personality disorders: Relationships to functional impairment. *American Journal of Psychiatry, 162*, 1919–1925.

Skodol, A. E., Oldham, J. M., & Gallaher, P. E. (1999). Axis II comorbidity of substance use disorders among patients referred for treatment of personality disorders. *American Journal of Psychiatry, 156*(5), 733–738.

Skuse, D. H. (2012). DSM-5's conceptualization of autistic disorders. *Journal of the American Academy of Child and Adolescent Psychiatry, 51*(4), 344–346.

Slade, J. (1999). Nicotine. In B. S. McCrady & F. F. Epstein (Eds.), *Addictions: A comprehensive guidebook* (pp. 162–170). New York, NY: Oxford University Press.

Slavich, G. M., & Irwin, M. R. (2014). From stress to inflammation and major depressive disorder: A social signal transduction theory of depression. *Psychological Bulletin, 140*, 774–815.

Sleet, D. A., Hammond, R., Jones, R., Thomas, N., & Whitt, B. (2003). Using psychology for injury and violence prevention in the community. In R. H. Rozensky, N. G. Johnson, C. D. Goodheart, & R. Hammond (Eds.), *Psychology builds a healthy world* (pp. 185–216). Washington, DC: American Psychological Association.

Slooter, A. J. C., & de Groot, J.-C. (2014). Neuroimaging of delirium. In R. A. J. O. Dierckx, A. Otte, E. F. J.de Vries, A.van Waarde (Eds.), *PET and SPECT in psychiatry* (pp. 463–470). Berlin, Germany: Springer Berlin Heidelberg.

Slotema, C. W., Aleman, A., Daskalakis, Z. J., & Sommer, I. E. (2012). Meta-analysis of repetitive transcranial magnetic stimula-tion in the treatment of auditory verbal hallucinations: Update and effects after one month. *Schizophrenia Research, 142*(1–3), 40–45.

Small, G. W. (1991). Recognition and treatment of depression in the elderly.

The clinician's challenge: Strategies for treatment of depression in the 1990's. *Journal of Clinical Psychiatry, 52*, 11–22.

Smart, R. G. (1985). Alcohol and alcohol problems research: IV. Canada. *British Journal of Addiction, 80*, 255–263.

Smeets, G., de Jong, P. J., & Mayer, B. (2000). If you suffer from a headache, then you have a brain tumour: Domain-specific reasoning "bias" and hypochondriasis. *Behaviour Research and Therapy, 38*, 763–776.

Smeets, I., Tan, E., Vossen, H., Leroy, P., Lousberg, R., van Os, J., & Schieveld, J. N. M. (2010). Prolonged stay at the paediatric intensive care unit associated with paediatric delirium. *European Child & Adolescent Psychiatry, 19*(4), 389–393.

Smith, B. H., Barkley, R. A., & Shapiro, C. J. (2006). Combined child therapies. In R. A. Barkley (Ed.), *Attention-deficit hyperactivity disorder: A handbook for diagnosis and treatment* (3rd ed., pp. 678–691). New York, NY: Guilford Press.

Smith, B. H., & Shapiro, C. J. (2015). Combined treatments for ADHD. In R. A. Barkley (Ed.), *Attention-deficit hyperactivity disorder: A handbook for diagnosis & treatment* (4th ed., pp. 686–704). New Yok: Guilford Press.

Smith, D. F., & Wesson, D. R. (1999). Benzodiazepines and other sedative-hypnotics. In M. Galanter & H. D. Kleber (Eds.), *Textbook of substance abuse treatment* (2nd ed., pp. 239–250). Washington, DC: American Psychiatric Press.

Smith, D. F., Marcus, M. D., & Kaye, W. (1992). Cognitive-behavioral treatment of obese binge eaters. *International Journal of Eating Disorders, 12*, 257–262.

Smith, G. R., Monson, R. A., & Ray, D. B. (1986). Psychiatric consultation in somatization disorder. *New England Journal of Medicine, 314*, 1407–1413.

Smith, G. T., & Oltmanns, T. F. (2009). Scientific advances in the diagnosis of psychopathology: Introduction to the special section. *Psychological Assessment, 21*(3), 241–242.

Smith, G., Malla, A., Williams, R., Kopala, L., Love, L., & Balshaw, R. (2006). The Canadian National Outcomes Measurement Study in schizophrenia: Overview of the patient sample and methodology. *Acta Psychiatrica Scandinavica, 113*(430), 4–11.

Smith, J. F., & Krejci, J. (1991). Minorities join the majority: Fating disturbances among Hispanic and Native American youth. *International Journal of Eating Disorders, 10*, 179–186.

Smith, M. D. (1992). Community integration and supported employment. In D. F. Berkell (Ed.), *Autism: Identification, education, and treatment* (pp. 253–271). Hillsdale, NJ: Erlbaum.

Smith, M. L., Klim, P., & Hanley, W. B. (2000). Executive function in school-aged children with phenylketonuria. *Journal of Developmental and Physical Disabilities, 12*, 317–332.

Smith, M., & Pazder, L. (1980). *Michelle remembers*. New York, NY: Pocket Books.

Smith, P. G., & Cousens, S. N. (1996). Is the new variant of Creutzfeldt-Jakob disease from mad cows? *Science, 273*, 748.

Smith, T. F., Bellack, A. S., & Liberman, R. P. (1996). Social skills training for

schizophrenia: Review and future directions. *Clinical Psychology Review, 16*, 599–617.

Smith, T. W. (1992). Hostility and health: Current status of a psychosomatic hypothesis. *Health Psychology, 11*(3), 139–150.

Smith, T., & Iadarola, S. (2015). Evidence base update for autism spectrum disorder. *Journal of Clinical Child & Adolescent Psychology, 44*(6), 897–922. https://doi.org/10.1080/15374416.2015.1077448

Smith, T., Horwath, E., & Cournos, F. (2010). Scizophrenia and other psychotic disorders. In J. L. Cutler & E. R. Marcus (Eds.), *Psychiatry* (2nd ed., pp. 101–131). New York, NY: Oxford University Press.

Smitherman, T. A., Burch, R., Sheikh, H., & Loder, E. (2013). The prevalence, impact, and treatment of migraine and severe headaches in the United States: A review of statistics from national surveillance studies. *Headache, 53*(3), 427–436.

Smoller, J. W., Rosenbaum, J. F., Biederman, J., Kennedy, J., Dai, D., Racette, S. R., . . . Slaugenhaupt, S. A. (2003). Association of a genetic marker at the corticotropin-releasing hormone locus with behavioral inhibition. *Biological Psychiatry, 54*, 1376–1381.

Smoller, J. W., Yamaki, L. H., & Fagerness, J. A. (2005). The corticotropin-releasing hormone gene and behavioral inhibition in children at risk for panic disorder. *Biological Psychiatry, 57*, 1485–1492.

Snyder, L. (2012). American College of Physicians ethics manual. *Annals of Internal Medicine, 156*(1 Part 2), 73–104. https://doi.org/10.7326/0003-4819-156-1-201201031-00001

Snyder, S. H. (1976). The dopamine hypothesis of schizophrenia: Focus on the dopamine receptor. *American Journal of Psychiatry, 133*, 197–202.

Snyder, S. H. (1981). Opiate and benzodiazepine receptors. *Psychosomatics, 22*(11), 986–989.

Snyder, S. H., Burt, D. R., & Creese, I. (1976). Dopamine receptor of mammalian brain: Direct demonstration of binding to agonist and antagonist states. *Neuroscience Symposia, 1*, 28–49.

Sobell, M. B., & Sobell, L. C. (1978). *Behavioral treatment of alcohol problems*. New York, NY: Plenum Press.

Sobell, M. B., & Sobell, L. C. (1993). *Problem drinkers: Guided self-change treatment*. New York, NY: Guilford Press.

Social Development Canada. (2004). *Canada pension plan: Disability benefits [Brochure]*. Gatineau, QC: Author.

Society for Research in Child Development. (2007). *Ethical Standards for Research with Children*. Retrieved from www.srcd.org/ethicalstandards.html

Soeiro-de-Souza, M. G., Dias, V. V., Bio, D. S., Post, R. M., & Moreno, R. A. (2011). Creativity and executive function in bipolar I disorder. *Journal of Affective Disorders, 135*(1–3), 292–297.

Sohn, C. H., & Lam, R. W. (2005). Update on the biology of seasonal affective disorder. *CNS Spectrums, 10*, 635–646.

Sokolov, S., & Kutcher, S. (2001). Adolescent depression: Neuroendocrine aspects. In I. M. Goodyer (Ed.), *Depressed child and adolescent* (2nd ed., pp. 233–266). New York, NY: Cambridge University Press.

Solai, L. K. K. (2009). Delirium. In B. J. Sadock, V. A. Sadock, & P. Ruiz (Eds.), *Kaplan & Sadock's comprehensive textbook of psychiatry* (9th ed., Vol. 1, pp. 1153–1167). Philadelphia, PA: Lippincott Williams & Wilkins.

Soloff, P. H., George, A., Nathan, R. S., Schulz, P. M., Cornelius, J. R., Herring, J., & Perel, J. M. (1989). Amitriptyline versus haloperidol in borderlines: Final outcomes and predictors of response. *Journal of Clinical Psychopharmacology, 9*, 238–246.

Soloff, P. H., Lynch, K. G., Kelly, T. M., Malone, K. M., & Mann, J. J. (2000). Characteristics of suicide attempts of patients with major depressive episode and borderline personality disorder: A comparative study. *American Journal of Psychiatry, 157*(4), 601–608.

Solomon, D. A., Leon, A. C., Coryell, W. H., Endicott, J., Li, C., Fiedorowicz, J. G., . . . Keller, M. B. (2010). Longitudinal course of bipolar I disorder: Duration of mood episodes. *Archives of General Psychiatry, 67*(4), 339–347.

Solomon, R. L. (1980). The opponent-process theory of acquired motivation: The costs of pleasure and the benefits of pain. *American Psychologist, 35*, 691–712.

Solomon, R. L., & Corbit, J. D. (1974). An opponent process theory of motivation: I. Temporal dynamics of affect. *Psychological Review, 81*, 119–145.

Somber news from the AIDS front. (1993). *Science, 260*, 1712–1713.

Somers, J. M., Goldner, F. M., Waraich, P., & Hsu, L. (2004). Prevalence studies of substance-related disorders: A systematic review of the literature. *Canadian Journal of Psychiatry, 49*(6), 373–384.

Somers, J. M., Goldner, F. M., Waraich, P., & Hsu, L. (2006). Prevalence and incidence studies of anxiety disorders: A systematic review of the literature. *Canadian Journal of Psychiatry, 51*, 100–113.

Song, X., & Rusak, B. (2000). Acute effects of light on body temperature and activity in Syrian hamsters: Influence of circadian phase. *American Journal of Physiology: Regulatory, Integrative, and Comparative Physiology, 278*, 1369–1380.

Sonuga-Barke, F. J., Daley, D., Thompson, M., Laver-Bradbury, C., & Weeks, A. (2001). Parent-based therapies for preschool attention-deficit/hyperactivity disorder: A randomized, controlled trial with a community sample. *Journal of the American Academy of Child & Adolescent Psychiatry, 40*(4), 402–408.

Soreca, I., Frank, E., & Kupfer, D. J. (2009). The phenomenology of bipolar disorder: What drives the high rate of medical burden and determines long-term prognosis? *Depression and Anxiety, 26*(1), 73–82.

Sosa-Ortiz, A. L., Acosta-Castillo, I., & Prince, M. J. (2012). Epidemiology of dementias and Alzheimer's disease. *Archives of Medical Research, 43*(8), 600–608

Souery, D., Zaninotto, L., Calati, R., Linotte, S., Mendlewicz, J., Sentissi, O., Serretti, A. (2012). Depression across mood disorders: Review and analysis in a clinical sample. *Comprehensive Psychiatry, 53*, 24–38.

South, S. C., Oltmanns, T. F., & Krueger, R. F. (2011). The spectrum of personality disorders. In D. H. Barlow (Ed.),

Oxford handbook of clinical psychology (pp. 530–550). New York, NY: Oxford University Press.

Spangler, D. L., Simons, A. D., Monroe, S. M., & Thase, M. F. (1996). Gender differences in cognitive diathesis-stress domain match: Implications for differential pathways to depression. *Journal of Abnormal Psychology, 105*, 653–657.

Spangler, D. L., Simons, A. D., Monroe, S. M., & Thase, M. F. (1997). Comparison of cognitive models of depression: Relationships between cognitive constructs and cognitive diathesis-stress match. *Journal of Abnormal Psychology, 106*, 395–403.

Spanos, N. P. (1994). Multiple identity enactments and multiple personality disorder: A sociogenic perspective. *Psychological Bulletin, 116*, 143–165.

Spanos, N. P. (1996). *Multiple identities and false memories: A sociocognitive prospective*. Washington, DC: American Psychological Association.

Spanos, N. P., Cross, P. A., Dickson, K., & DuBreuil, S. C. (1993). Close encounters: An examination of UFO experiences. *Journal of Abnormal Psychology, 102*, 624–632.

Spanos, N. P., Weeks, J. R., & Bertrand, L. D. (1985). Multiple personality: A social psychological perspective. *Journal of Abnormal Psychology, 92*, 362–376.

Special Advisory Committee on the Epidemic of Opioid Overdoses. (2019). *National report: Apparent opioid-related deaths in Canada (January 2016 to December 2018)*. Public Health Agency of Canada. https://health-infobase.canada.ca/datalab/national-surveillance-opioid-mortality.html

Spector, I., Pecknold, J. C., & Libman, F. (2003). Selective attentional bias related to the noticeability aspect of anxiety symptoms in generalized social phobia. *Journal of Anxiety Disorders, 17*, 517–531.

Spence, J. D., Barnett, P. A., Linden, W., Ramsden, V., & Taenzer, P. (1999). Recommendations on stress management. *Canadian Medical Association Journal, 160*, S46–S50.

Spiegel, D. (2013). Tranceformations: Hypnosis in brain and body. *Depression and Anxiety, 30*, 342–352.

Spiegel, D., Bloom, J. R., Kramer, H. C., & Gotheil, F. (1989). Effect of psychosocial treatment on survival of patients with metastatic breast cancer. *Lancet, 14*, 888–891.

Spiegel, D., Lewis-Fernandez, R., Lanius, R., Vermetten, E., Simeon, D., & Friedman, M. (2013). Dissociative disorders in DSM-5. *Annual Review of Clinical Psychology, 9*, 299–326.

Spiegel, D., Loewenstein, R. J., Lewis-Fernandez, R., Sar, V., Simeon, D., Vermetten, E., & Dell, P. F. (2011). Dissociative disorders in DSM-5. *Depression and Anxiety, 28*, 824–852.

Spiegel, D., Morrow, G. R., Classen, C., Riggs, G., Stott, P. B., Mudaliar, N., . . . Heard, L. (1996). Effects of group therapy on women with primary breast cancer. *The Breast Journal, 2*(1), 104–106.

Spielberger, C. D., & Frank, R. G. (1992). Injury control: A promising field for psychologists. *American Psychologist, 47*(8), 1029–1030.

Spielman, A. J., & Glovinsky, P. (1991). The varied nature of insomnia. In P. J. Hauri (Ed.), *Case studies in insomnia*

(pp. 1–15). New York, NY: Plenum Press.

Spiker, D., & Ricks, M. (1984). Visual self-recognition in autistic children: Developmental relationships. *Child Development, 55*, 214–225

Spinella, M. (2005). Mood in relation to subclinical symptoms. *International Journal of Neuroscience, 115*, 433–443.

Spinelli, S., Chefer, S., Suomi, S. J., Higley, J. D., Barr, C. S., & Stein, E. (2009). Early-life stress induces long-term morphologic changes in primate brain. *Archives of General Psychiatry, 66*(6), 658–665.

Spitzer, R. L. (1999). Harmful dysfunction and the DSM definition of mental disorder. *Journal of Abnormal Psychology, 108*, 430–432.

Spitzer, R. L., Yanovski, S. Z., Wadden, T., Wing, R., Marcus, M., Stunkard, A., . . . Horne, R. L. (1993). Binge eating disorder: Its further validation in a multi-site study. *International Journal of Eating Disorders, 13*, 137–153.

Spoont, M. R. (1992). Modulatory role of serotonin in neural information processing: Implications for human psychopathology. *Psychological Bulletin, 112*(2), 330–350.

Sprague, J., Javdani, S., Sadeh, N., Newman, J. P., & Verona, E. (2012). Borderline personality disorder as a female phenotypic expression of psychopathy? *Personality Disorders: Theory, Research, and Treatment, 3*(2), 127.

Spreen, O. (1988). Prognosis of learning disability. *Journal of Consulting and Clinical Psychology, 56*, 836–842.

Sprock, J. (2000). Gender-typed behavioral examples of histrionic personality disorder. *Journal of Psychopathology and Behavioral Assessment, 22*, 107–122.

Spurrell, F. B., Wilfley, D. E., Tanofsky, M. B., & Brownell, K. D. (1997). Age of onset for binge eating: Are there different pathways to binge eating? *International Journal of Eating Disorders, 21*, 55–65.

Srivastava, A., & Kahan, M. (2006). Buprenorphine: A potential new treatment option for opioid dependence. *Canadian Medical Association Journal, 174*(13), 1835–1836.

St. John, J., Krichev, A., & Bauman, F. (1976). Northwestern Ontario Indian children and the WISC. *Psychology in the Schools, 13*, 407–411.

Staal, W. G., Pol, H. F. H., Schnack, H. G., Hoogendoorn, M. L. C., Jellema, K., & Kahn, R. S. (2000). Structural brain abnormalities in patients with schizophrenia and their healthy siblings. *American Journal of Psychiatry, 157*, 416–421.

Stacy, A. W. (1997). Memory activation and expectancy as prospective predictors of alcohol and marihuana use. *Journal of Abnormal Psychology, 106*, 61–73.

Stahl, S. M. (2008). *Stahl's essential psychopharmacology* (3rd ed.). New York, NY: Cambridge University Press.

Stam, H., & Steggles, S. (1987). Predicting the onset or progression of cancer from psychological characteristics: Psychometric and theoretical issues. *Journal of Psychosocial Oncology, 5*(2), 35–46.

Stamm, J. M., Bourlas, A. P., Baugh, C. M., Fritts, N. G., Daneshvar, D. H., Martin, B. M., . . . Stern, R. A. (2015). Age of first exposure to football and later-life

cognitive impairment in former NFL players. *Neurology, 84*(11), 1114–1120.

Stangier, U., Schramm, E., Heidenreich, T., Berger, M., & Clark, D. M. (2011). Cognitive therapy vs. interpersonal therapy in social anxiety disorder: A randomized controlled trial. *Archives of General Psychiatry, 68*, 692–700.

Stanley, M. A., Beck, J. G., & Glassco, J. D. (1997). Generalized anxiety in older adults: Treatment with cognitive-behavioral and supportive approaches. *Behavior Therapy, 27*, 565–581.

Stanley, M. A., Beck, J. G., Novy, D. M., Averill, P. M., Swann, A. C., Diefenbach, G. J., & Hopko, D. R. (2003). Cognitive-behavioral treatment of late-life generalized anxiety disorder. *Journal of Consulting and Clinical Psychology, 71*(2), 309–319.

Stanley, M. A., Wilson, N. L., Novy, D. M., Rhoades, H. M., Wagener, P. D., Greisinger, A. J., & Kunik, M. E. (2009). Cognitive behavior therapy for generalized anxiety disorder among older adults in primary care: A randomized clinical trial. *JAMA: Journal of the American Medical Association 301*(14), 1460–1467.

Starkman, M. N., Giordani, B., Gebarski, S. S., Berent, S., Schork, M. A., & Schteingart, D. E. (1999). Decrease in cortisol reverses human hippocampal atrophy following treatment of Cushing's disease. *Biological Psychiatry, 46*, 1595–1602.

Statistics Canada. (1975). *Mental health statistics, volume III: Institutional facilities, services and finances, 1975*. Ottawa, ON: Minister of Industry, Trade and Commerce.

Statistics Canada. (1995). *Mental health statistics, 1992–93*. Ottawa, ON: Minister Responsible for Statistics Canada.

Statistics Canada. (1996). *National longitudinal survey of children and youth: User's handbook and microdata guide* (Microdata documentation: 89M0015GPF). Ottawa, ON: Statistics Canada.

Statistics Canada. (1997). Initial results from the school component. *Education Quarterly Review* (Catalogue no. 81-003-XPB). Retrieved August 17, 2004, from http://www.ldac-taac.ca/english/indepth/bkground/stats01.htm

Statistics Canada. (2000). *The changing face of heart disease and stroke in Canada*. Ottawa, ON: Statistics Canada.

Statistics Canada. (2001a). *Census of population*. Ottawa, ON: Statistics Canada.

Statistics Canada. (2001b). *A profile of disability in Canada*. Ottawa, ON: Statistics Canada.

Statistics Canada. (2002a). *Canadian community health survey: Mental health and well-being*. Ottawa, ON: Statistics Canada.

Statistics Canada. (2002b). *Historical statistics of Canada, Section B. Vital statistics and health (B35–50)*. Ottawa, ON: Statistics Canada.

Statistics Canada. (2003). *Alcohol consumption, by sex, age group and level of education*. Ottawa, ON: Statistics Canada.

Statistics Canada. (2004). *Family violence in Canada: A statistical profile*. Ottawa, ON: Statistics Canada.

Statistics Canada. (2007, March 6). Seniors as victims of crime. *The Daily*. Retrieved October 3, 2007, from

http://www.statcan.ca/Daily/Fnglish/070306/d070306b.htm

Statistics Canada. (2011). 2011 *Census of Population, Statistics Canada* (Catalogue no. 98–313-XCB2011024). Retrieved from: http://www12.statcan.gc.ca/census-recensement/2011/dp-pd/tbt-tt/Rp-eng.cfm?LANG=E&APATH=3&DETAIL=0&DIM=0&FL=A&FREE=0&GC=0&GID=0&GK=0&GRP=1&PID=102239&PRID=0&PTYPE=101955&S=0&SHOWALL=0&SUB=0&Temporal=2011&THEME=91&VID=0&VNAMEE=&VNAMEF=

Statistics Canada. (2012). *Mental health indicators: Table 13-10-0465-01*. https://www150.statcan.gc.ca/t1/tbl1/en/cv.action?pid=1310046501

Statistics Canada. (2013). *Immigration and Ethnocultural Diversity in Canada* (Catalogue no. 99–010-X2011001). Retrieved from: http://www12.statcan.gc.ca/nhs-enm/2011/as-sa/99–010-x/99–010-x2011001-eng.pdf

Statistics Canada. (2014a). *High blood pressure, 2013*. Retrieved from http://www.statcan.gc.ca/pub/82–625-x/2014001/article/14020-eng.htm

Statistics Canada. (2014b). *The 10 leading causes of death, 2011*. Retrieved from: http://www.statcan.gc.ca/pub/82–625-x/2014001/article/11896-eng.htm

Statistics Canada. (2015a). *Canadian Survey on Disability, 2012—A profile of persons with disabilities among Canadians aged 15 years or older, 2012* (Catalogue no. 89–654-X). Retrieved from: http://www.statcan.gc.ca/pub/89–654-x/89–654-x2015001-eng.pdf

Statistics Canada. (2015b). *Population projections for Canada (2013 to 2063)*, provinces and territories (2013 to 2038) (Catalogue no. 91–520-X). Retrieved from: http://www.statcan.gc.ca/pub/91–520-x/91–520-x2014001-eng.pdf

Statistics Canada. (2016a). *Health indicators, by Aboriginal identity, four-year period estimates: Table 13-10-0457-01*. https://www150.statcan.gc.ca/t1/tbl1/en/tv.action?pid=1310045701

Statistics Canada. (2016b). Lifetime and past-year suicidal thoughts among off-reserve First Nations, Métis and Inuit adults, aged 18 years and over, Canada, 2012. *Aboriginal Peoples Survey* (Catalogue No. 89-653-X2016012). https://www150.statcan.gc.ca/n1/en/catalogue/89-653-X2016012

Statistics Canada. (2017a). *Age and sex, and type of dwelling data: Results from the 2016 census*. Retrieved from https://www150.statcan.gc.ca/n1/daily-quotidien/170503/dq170503a-eng.pdf

Statistics Canada. (2017b). *Immigration and ethnocultural diversity: Key results from the 2016 census*. https://www150.statcan.gc.ca/n1/daily-quotidien/171025/dq171025b-eng.pdf

Statistics Canada. (2017c). *Type of disability for persons with disabilities aged 15 years and over, by age group and sex, Canada, provinces and territories: Table 13-10-0376-01*. https://www150.statcan.gc.ca/t1/tbl1/en/tv.action?pid=1310037601.

Statistics Canada. (2017d). *Mental health disorders and life satisfaction in Canada*. https://www150.statcan.gc.ca/n1/pub/11-627-m/11-627-m2017033-eng.htm

Statistics Canada. (2018). Chronic conditions, 2017. *Health Fact Sheets* (Catalogue no. 82-625-x). https://www150.statcan.gc.ca/n1/pub/82-625-x/2018001/article/54983-eng.htm

Statistics Canada. (2019). *Mental health indicators: Table 13-10-0465-01.* https://www150.statcan.gc.ca/t1/tbl1/en/tv.action?pid=1310046501

Steele, C. M., & Josephs, R. A. (1990). Alcohol myopia: Its prized and dangerous effects. *American Psychologist, 45*(8), 921–933.

Steffy, R. A., Hart, J., Craw M., Torney, D., & Marlett, N. (1969). Operant behaviour modification techniques applied to a ward of severely regressed and aggressive patients. *Canadian Psychiatric Association Journal, 14,* 59–67.

Steiger, H., Bruce, K. R., & Groleau, P. (2011). Neural circuits, neurotransmitters, and behavior: Seratonin and temperament in bulimic syndromes. *Current Topics in Behavioral Neurosciences, 6,* 125–138.

Steiger, H., Bruce, K. R., Israel, M. (2013). Eating disorders: Anorexia nervosa, bulimia nervosa, and binge eating disorder. In I. B. Weiner (Series Ed.), G. Stricker, & T. A. Widiger (Vol. Eds.), *Handbook of psychology: Vol. 8 Clinical psychology* (pp. 147–170). Hoboken, NJ: Wiley.

Steiger, H., Stotland, S., Trottier, J., & Ghadirian, A. M. (1996). Familial eating concerns and psychopathological traits: Casual implications of transgenerational effects. *International Journal of Eating Disorders, 19,* 147–157.

Stein, D. J., Phillips, K. A., Bolton, D., Fulford, K. W. M., Sadler, J. Z., & Kendler, K. S. (2010). What is a mental/psychiatric disorder? From DSM-IV to DSM-V. *Psychological Medicine, 40*(11), 1759–1765.

Stein, M. B., & Kean, Y. M. (2000). Disability and quality of life in social phobia: Epidemiologic findings. *American Journal of Psychiatry, 157,* 1606–1613.

Stein, M. B., Goldin, P. R., Sareen, J., Zorrilla, L. T. F., & Brown, G. G. (2002). Increased amygdala activation to angry and contemptuous faces in generalized social phobia. *Archives of General Psychiatry, 59,* 1027–1034.

Stein, M. B., Jang, K. L., & Livesley, W. J. (2002). Heritability of social anxiety-related concerns and personality characteristics: A twin study. *Journal of Nervous and Mental Disease, 190,* 219–224.

Stein, M. B., Jang, K. L., Taylor, S., Vernon, P. A., & Livesley, W. J. (2002). Genetic and environmental influences on trauma exposure and posttraumatic stress disorder symptoms: A twin study. *American Journal of Psychiatry, 159,* 1675–1681.

Stein, M. B., Liebowitz, M. R., Lydiard, R. B., Pitts, C. D., Bushnell, W., & Gergel, I. (1998). Paroxetine treatment of generalized social phobia (social anxiety disorder). A randomized clinical trial. *JAMA, 280,* 708–713.

Stein, M. B., Schork, N. J., & Gelernter, J. (2007). Gene-by-environment (serotonin transporter and childhood maltreatment) interaction for anxiety sensitivity, an intermediate phenotype for anxiety disorders. *Neuropsychopharmacology, 33*(2), 312–319.

Stein, M. B., Torgrud, L. J., & Walker, J. R. (2000). Social phobia symptoms, subtypes, and severity: Findings from a community survey. *Archives of General Psychiatry, 57,* 1046–1052.

Stein, M. I. (1978). Thematic apperception test and related methods. In B. B. Wolman (Ed.), *Clinical diagnosis of mental disorders: A handbook* (pp. 179–235). New York, NY: Plenum Press.

Stein, R. M., & Ellinwood, F. H. (1993). Stimulant use: Cocaine and amphetamine. In D. L. Dunner (Ed.), *Current psychiatric therapy* (pp. 98–105). Philadelphia, PA: W. B. Saunders.

Steinberg, A. B., & Phares, V. (2001). Family functioning, body image, and eating disturbances. In J. K. Thompson & L. Smolak (Eds.), *Body image, eating disorders, and obesity in youth: Assessment, prevention and treatment* (pp. 127–147). Washington, DC: American Psychological Association.

Steinberg, M. (1991). The spectrum of depersonalization: Assessment and treatment. *Annual Review of Psychiatry, 10,* 223–247.

Steinglass, P., Weisstub, F., & Kaplan De-Nour, A. K. (1988). Perceived personal networks as mediators of stress reactions. *American Journal of Psychiatry, 145,* 1259–1264.

Steketee, G., & Barlow, D. H. (2002). Obsessive–compulsive disorder. In D. H. Barlow (Ed.), *Anxiety and its disorders: The nature and treatment of anxiety and panic* (2nd ed.). New York, NY: Guilford Press.

Steketee, G., & Frost, R. O. (2007a). *Compulsive hoarding and acquiring: Client workbook.* New York, NY: Oxford University Press.

Steketee, G., & Frost, R. O. (2007b). *Compulsive hoarding and acquiring: Therapist guide.* New York, NY: Oxford University Press.

Steketee, G., Gibson, A., Frost, R. O., Alabiso, J., Arluke, A., & Patronek, G. (2011). Characteristics and antecedents of people who hoard animals: An exploratory comparative interview study. *Review of General Psychology, 15*(2), 114–124.

Steketee, G., Quay, S., & White, K. (1991). Religion and guilt in OCD patients. *Journal of Anxiety Disorders, 5,* 359–367.

Stellos, K., Panagiota, V., Sachsenmaier, S., Trunk, T., Straten, G., Leyhe, T., . . . Laske, C. (2010). Increased circulating progenitor cells in Alzheimer's disease patients with moderate to severe dementia: Evidence for vascular repair and tissue regeneration? *Journal of Alzheimer's Disease, 19*(2), 591–600.

Stenvall, M., Olofsson, B., Lundstrom, M., Svensson, O., Nyberg, L., & Gustafson, Y. (2006). Inpatient falls and injuries in older patients treated for femoral neck fracture. *Archives of Gerontology and Geriatrics, 43*(3), 389–399.

Stephens, R. S., Roffman, R. A., & Simpson, F. F. (1994). Treating adult marijuana dependence: A test of the relapse prevention model. *Journal of Consulting and Clinical Psychology, 62,* 92–99.

Steptoe, A., & Wardle, J. (2012). Enjoying life and living longer. *Archives of Internal Medicine, 172*(3), 273–275.

Stern, C. F., Owen, A. M., Look, R. B., Tracey, I., Rosen, B. R., & Petrides, M. (2000). Activity in ventrolateral and middorsolateral prefrontal cortex during non-spatial visual working memory processing: Evidence from functional magnetic resonance imaging. *Neuroimage, 11*(5), 392–399.

Stern, Y. (2009). Cognitive reserve. *Neuropsychologia, 47*(10), 2015–2028.

Stern, Y., Gurland, B., Tatemichi, T. K., Tang, M. X., Wilder, D., & Mayeux, R. (1994). Influence of education and occupation on the incidence of Alzheimer's disease. *JAMA, 271,* 1004–1010.

Sternberg, R. J. (1988). Intellectual development: Psychometric and information-processing approaches. In M. H. Bornstein & M. F. Lamb (Eds.), *Developmental psychology: An advanced textbook* (2nd ed.). Hillsdale, NJ: Erlbaum.

Stevens, J. (1987). *Storming heaven: LSD and the American dream.* New York, NY: Atlantic Monthly Press.

Stevens, R. G., & Zhu, Y. (2015). Electric light, particularly at night, disrupts human circadian rhythmicity: Is that a problem? *Philosophical Transactions of the Royal Society of London B: Biological Sciences, 370*(1667), 20140120.

Stewart, S. E., Jenike, E., & Jenike, M. A. (2009). Biological treatment for obsessive–compulsive disorder. In M. M. Antony & M. B. Stein (Eds.), *Oxford handbook of anxiety and related disorders* (pp. 375–390). New York, NY: Oxford University Press.

Stewart, S. H. (2002). The history, current prevalence and consequences of drinking problems. Transactions of the Royal Society of Canada, Seventh Series, Volume II, ISSN: 1710–2839.

Stewart, S. H., & Asmundson, G. J. G. (2006). Anxiety sensitivity and its impact on pain experiences and conditions: A state of the art. *Cognitive Behaviour Therapy, 35,* 185–188.

Stewart, S. H., & Brown, C. G. (2007). The relationship between disordered eating and substance use problems among women: A critical review. In L. Greaves, N. Poole, & J. Greenbaum (Eds.), *Highs and lows: Canadian perspectives on women and substance use* (pp. 157–163). Toronto, ON: Centre for Addiction and Mental Health.

Stewart, S. H., & Conrod, P. J. (2008). Anxiety disorder and substance use disorder comorbidity: Common themes and future directions. In S. H. Stewart & P. J. Conrod (Eds.), *Anxiety and substance use disorders: The vicious cycle of comorbidity* (pp. 239–257). New York, NY: Springer.

Stewart, S. H., & Kushner, M. G. (2003). Recent research on the comorbidity of alcoholism and pathological gambling. *Alcoholism: Clinical & Experimental Research, 27,* 285–291.

Stewart, S. H., & Samoluk, S. B. (1997). Effects of short-term food deprivation and chronic dietary restraint on the selective processing of appetitive-related cues. *International Journal of Eating Disorders, 21,* 129–135.

Stewart, S. H. (1996). Alcohol abuse in individuals exposed to trauma: A critical review. *Psychological Bulletin, 120,* 85–112.

Stewart, S. H., Brown, C. G., Theakston, J. A., Devoulyte, K., & Larsen, S. (2003). Why do women with alcohol use disorder binge eat? Exploring connections between binge eating and heavy drinking in Nova Scotia women. Poster presented at the Dalhousie University Annual Psychiatry Research Day, Halifax.

Stewart, S. H., Buffett-Jerrott, S. E., Finley, G. A., Wright, K. D., &

Gomez, T. V. (2006). Effects of midazolam on explicit vs. implicit memory in a pediatric surgery setting. *Psychopharmacology, 188,* 489–497.

Stewart, S. H., Collins, P., Blackburn, J. R., Ellery, M., & Klein, R. M. (2005). Heart rate increase to alcohol administration and video lottery terminal (VLT) play. *Psychology of Addictive Behaviors, 19*(1), 94–98.

Stewart, S. H., Conrod, P. J., Gignac, M. L., & Pihl, R. O. (1998). Selective processing biases in anxiety-sensitive men and women. *Cognition & Emotion, 12,* 105–133.

Stewart, S. H., Finn, P. R., & Pihl, R. O. (1992). The effects of alcohol on the cardiovascular stress response in men at high risk for alcoholism: A dose response study. *Journal of Studies on Alcohol, 53,* 499–506.

Stewart, S. H., Morris, F., Mellings, T., & Komar, J. (2006). Relations of social anxiety variables to drinking motives, drinking quantity and frequency, and alcohol-related problems in undergraduates. *Journal of Mental Health, 15*(6), 671–682.

Stewart, S. H., Pihl, R. O., Conrod, P. J., & Dongier, M. (1998). Functional associations among trauma, PTSD and substance-related disorders. *Addictive Behaviors, 23,* 797–812.

Stewart, S. H., Samoluk, S. B., & MacDonald, A. B. (1999). Anxiety sensitivity and substance use and abuse. In S. Taylor (Ed.), *Anxiety sensitivity: Theory, research and treatment of the fear of anxiety* (pp. 287–319). Mahwah, NJ: Lawrence Erlbaum.

Stewart, S. H., Taylor, S., & Baker, J. M. (1997). Gender differences in dimensions of anxiety sensitivity. *Journal of Anxiety Disorders, 11,* 179–200.

Stice, E., Akutagawa, D., Gaggar, A., & Agras, W. S. (2000). Negative affect moderates the relation between dieting and binge eating. *International Journal of Eating Disorders, 27,* 218–229.

Stice, E., Cameron, R. P., Killen, J. D., Hayward, C., & Taylor, C. B. (1999). Naturalistic weight-reduction efforts prospectively predict growth in relative weight and onset of obesity among female adolescents. *Journal of Consulting and Clinical Psychology, 67,* 967–974.

Stice, E., Marti, C. N., & Rohde, P. (2013). Prevalence, incidence, impairment, and course of the proposed DSM-5 eating disorder diagnoses in an 8-year prospective community study of young women. *Journal of Abnormal Psychology, 122*(2), 445.

Stice, E., Marti, C. N., Shaw, H., & Jaconis, M. (2009). An 8-year longitudinal study of the natural history of threshold, subthreshold, and partial eating disorders from a community sample of adolescents. *Journal of Abnormal Psychology, 118*(3), 587–597.

Stice, E., Rohde, P., Durant, S., & Shaw, H. (2012). A preliminary trial of a prototype internet dissonance-based eating disorder prevention program for young women with body image concerns. *Journal of Consulting and Clinical Psychology, 80,* 907–916.

Stice, E., Rohde, P., Shaw, H., & Marti, C. N. (2012). Efficacy trial of a selective prevention program targeting both eating disorder symptoms and unhealthy weight gain among female college students. *Journal of Consulting and Clinical Psychology, 80,* 164–170.

Stice, E., & Shaw, H. (2004). Eating disorder prevention programs: A meta-analytic review. *Psychological Bulletin, 130,* 206–227.

Stice, E., Shaw, H., & Marti, C. N. (2007). A meta-analytic review of eating disorder prevention programs: Encouraging findings. *Annual Review of Clinical Psychology, 3,* 207–231.

Stice, E., Schupak-Neuberg, F., Shaw, H. F., & Stein, R. I. (1994). Relation of media exposure to eating disorder symptomatology: An examination of mediating mechanisms. *Journal of Abnormal Psychology, 103,* 836–840.

Stinson, F. S., Dawson, D. A., Goldstein, R. B., Chou, S. P., Huang, B., Smith, S. M., & Pickering, R. P. (2008). Prevalence, correlates, disability, and comorbidity of DSM-IV narcissistic personality disorder: Results from the Wave 2 National Epidemiologic Survey on Alcohol and Related Conditions. *Journal of Clinical Psychiatry, 69*(7), 1033.

Stip, F., Caron, J., & Lane, C. J. (2001). Schizophrenia: People's perceptions in Quebec. *Canadian Medical Association Journal, 164,* 1299–1300.

Stip, F., Fahim, C., Mancini-Marïe, A., Bentaleb, L. A., Mensour, B., Mendrek, A., & Beauregard, M. (2005). Restoration of frontal activation during a treatment with quetiapine: An fMRI study of blunted affect in schizophrenia. *Progress in Neuro-Psychopharmacology & Biological Psychiatry, 29*(1), 21–26.

Stoller, R. J. (1976). Two feminized male American Indians. *Archives of Sexual Behavior, 5,* 529–538.

Stone, A. B., Pearlstein, T. B., & Brown, W. A. (1991). Fluoxetine in the treatment of late luteal phase dysphoric disorder. *Journal of Clinical Psychiatry, 52*(7), 290–293.

Stone, J., Carson, A., Aditya, H., Prescott, R., Zaubi, M., Warlow, C., & Sharpe, M. (2009a). The role of physical injury in motor and sensory conversion symptoms: A systematic and narrative review. *Journal of Psychosomatic Research, 66*(5), 383–390.

Stone, J., Carson, A., Duncan, R., Coleman, R., Roberts, R., Warlow, C., . . . Sharpe, M. (2009b). Symptoms "unexplained by organic disease" in 1144 new neurology out-patients: How often does the diagnosis change at follow-up? *Brain, 132*(Pt 10), 2878–2888.

Stone, J., LaFrance, W. C., Levenson, J. L., & Sharpe, M. (2010). Issues for DSM-5: Conversion disorder. *American Journal of Psychiatry, 167,* 626–627.

Stone, J., Smyth, R., Carson, A., Lewis, S., Prescott, R., Warlow, C., & Sharpe, M. (2005). Systematic review of misdiagnosis of conversion symptoms and hysteria. *BMJ, 331,* 989.

Stone, M. (1983). Psychotherapy with schizotypal borderline patients. *Journal of the American Academy of Psychoanalysis, 11,* 87–111.

Stone, M. H. (1986). Borderline personality disorder. In A. M. Cooper, A. J. Frances, & M. H. Sacks (Eds.), *The personality disorders and neuroses* (pp. 203–217). New York, NY: Basic Books.

Stone, M. H. (1993). Cluster C personality disorders. In D. L. Dunner (Ed.), *Current psychiatric therapy*

(pp. 411–417). Philadelphia, PA: W. B. Saunders.

Stone, M. H. (2001). Schizoid and schizotypical personality disorders. In G. O. Gabbard (Ed.), *Treatment of psychiatric disorders* (3rd ed., Vol. 2, pp. 2237–2250). Washington, DC: American Psychiatric Press.

Stone, R. (2000). Stress: The invisible hand in eastern Europe's death rates. *Science, 288,* 1732–1733.

Strahl, C., Kleinknecht, R. A., & Dinnel, D. L. (2000). The role of pain anxiety, coping, and pain self-efficacy in rheumatoid arthritis patient functioning. *Behaviour Research and Therapy, 38,* 863–873.

Strain, E. C. (2009). Substance-related disorders. In B. J. Sadock, V. A. Sadock, & P. Ruiz (Eds.), *Kaplan & Sadock's comprehensive textbook of psychiatry* (9th ed., Vol. 1, pp. 1237–1268). Philadelphia, PA: Lippincott Williams & Wilkins.

Strain, J. J., & Friedman, M. J. (2011). Considering adjustment disorders as stress response syndromes for DSM-5. *Depression and Anxiety, 28,* 818–823.

Strassberg, D. S., Kelly, M. P., Carroll, C., & Kircher, J. C. (1987). The psychophysiological nature of premature ejaculation. *Archives of Sexual Behavior, 16,* 327–336.

Strathdee, S. A., Patrick, D. M., Currie, S. L., Cornelisse, P. G. A., Rekart, M. L., Montaner, J. S. G., . . . O'Shaughnessy, M. V. (1997). Needle exchange is not enough: Lessons from the Vancouver injecting drug use study. *AIDS, 11*(8), 59–65.

Stratta, P., Capanna, C., Riccardi, I., Carmassi, C., Piccinni, A., Dell'Osso, L., & Rossi, A. (2012). Suicidal intention and negative spiritual coping one year after the earthquake of L'Aquila (Italy). *Journal of Affective Disorders, 136*(3), 1227–1231.

Straus, S. F., Tosato, G., Armstrong, G., Lawley, T., Preble, O. T., Henle, W., . . . Blaese, R. M. (1985). Persisting illness and fatigue in adults with evidence of Epstein Barr virus infection. *Annals of Internal Medicine, 102,* 7–16.

Stravynski, A., Elie, R., & Franche, R. L. (1989). Perception of early parenting by patients diagnosed avoidant personality disorder: A test of the overprotection hypothesis. *Acta Psychiatrica Scandinavica, 80,* 415–420.

Stravynski, A., Lesage, A., Marcouiller, M., & Elie, R. (1989). A test of the therapeutic mechanism in social skills training with avoidant personality disorder. *Journal of Nervous and Mental Disease, 177,* 739–744.

Striegal-Moore, R. H., Cachelin, F. M., Dohm, F. A., Pike, M., Wifley, D. F., & Fairburn, C. G. (2001). Comparison of binge eating disorder and bulimia nervosa in a community sample. *International Journal of Eating Disorders, 29,* 157–165.

Striegal-Moore, R. H., Silberstein, L. R., & Rodin, J. (1986). Toward an understanding of risk factors for bulimia. *American Psychologist, 3,* 246–263.

Striegal-Moore, R. H., Silberstein, L. R., & Rodin, J. (1993). The social self in bulimia nervosa: Public self-consciousness, social anxiety, and perceived fraudulence. *Journal of Abnormal Psychology, 102*(2), 297–303.

Striegel-Moore, R. H., & Franko, D. L. (2002). Body image issues among

girls and women. In T. F. Cash & T. Pruzinsky (Eds.), *Body image: A handbook of theory, research and clinical practice* (pp. 183–191). New York, NY: Guilford, Press.

Striegel-Moore, R. H., & Franko, D. L. (2008). Should binge eating disorder be included in the DSM-V? A critical review of the state of the evidence. *Annual Review of Clinical Psychology, 4,* 305–324.

Striegel-Moore, R. H., Wilson, G. T., DeBar, L., Perrin, N., Lynch, F., Rosselli, F., & Kraemer, H. C. (2010). Cognitive behavioral guided self-help for the treatment of recurrent binge eating. *Journal of Consulting and Clinical Psychology, 78*(3), 312–321.

Strike, P. C., & Steptoe, A. (2005). Behavioral and emotional triggers of acute coronary syndromes: A systematic review and critique. *Psychosomatic Medicine, 67,* 179–186.

Stringer, R., & Stanovich, K. F. (2000). The connection between reaction time and variation in reading ability: Unravelling covariance relationships with cognitive ability and phonological sensitivity. *Scientific Studies of Reading, 4,* 41–53.

Strobel, M. (2002, February 6). Sheena'd be proud. *Toronto Sun.* Retrieved June 24, 2004, from http://www.canoe.ca/Health0202/06_sheena-sun.html

Strober, M., Freeman, R., Lampert, C., Diamond, J., & Kaye, W. (2000). Controlled family study of anorexia nervosa and bulimia nervosa: Evidence of shared liability and transmission of partial syndromes. *American Journal of Psychiatry, 157,* 393–401.

Stroebe, M., Stroebe, W., & Abakoumkin, G. (2005). The broken heart: Suicidal ideation in bereavement. *American Journal of Psychiatry, 162,* 2178–2180.

Strokoff, J., Owen, J., & Fincham, F. D. (2014). Diverse reactions to hooking up among US university students. *Archives of Sexual Behavior, 44*(4), 935–943.

Stuart, H. L., & Arboleda-Florez, J. (2000). Homeless shelter users in the postdeinstitutionalization era. *Canadian Journal of Psychiatry, 45,* 55–62.

Stuss, D. T., & Cummings, J. L. (1990). Subcortical vascular dementias. In J. L. Cummings (Ed.), *Subcortical dementia* (pp. 145–163). New York, NY: Oxford University Press.

Stuss, D. T., & Levine, B. (2002). Adult clinical neuropsychology: Lessons from studies of the frontal lobes. *Annual Review of Psychology, 53*(1), 401–433.

Suárez, L., Bennett, S., Goldstein, C., & Barlow, D. H. (2009). Understanding anxiety disorders from a "triple vulnerabilities" framework. In M. M. Antony & M. B. Stein (Eds.), *Oxford handbook of anxiety and related disorders* (pp. 153–172). New York, NY: Oxford University Press.

Subcommittee on Attention-Deficit/Hyperactivity Disorder, Steering Committee on Quality Improvement, & Management. (2011). ADHD: Clinical Practice Guidelines for the Diagnosis, Evaluation, and Treatment of Attention-Deficit/Hyperactivity Disorder in Children and Adolescents. *Pediatrics, 128*(5), 1007–1022.

Subramanian, S., Bandopadhyay, D., Mishra, P. K., Mathew, M., & John, M. (2010). Design and development of non-fibrillar amyloid b as a potential Alzheimer vaccine. *Biochemical and*

Biophysical Research Communications, 394(2), 393–397.

Substance Abuse and Mental Health Services Administration. (2003). *Emergency department trends from the Drug Abuse Warning Network, Final estimates 1995–2002.* DAWN Series D-24, DHHS Publication No. (SMA) 03–3780, Rockville, MD.

Sue, S., Yan Cheng, J. K., Saad, C. S., & Chu, J. P. (2012). Asian American mental health: A call to action. *American Psychologist, 67*(7), 532.

Sugiyama, T., & Abe, T. (1989). The prevalence of autism in Nagoya, Japan: A total population study. *Journal of Autism and Developmental Disorders, 19,* 87–96.

Sullivan, G. M., & LeDoux, J. E. (2004). Synaptic self: Conditioned fear, developed adversity, and the anxious individual. In J. M. Gorman (Ed.), *Fear and anxiety: The benefits of translational research* (pp. 1–22). Washington, DC: American Psychiatric Publishing.

Sullivan, G. M., Kent, J. M., & Coplan, J. D. (2000). The neurobiology of stress and anxiety. In D. I. Mostofsky & D. H. Barlow (Eds.), *The management of stress and anxiety in medical disorders* (pp. 15–35). Needham Heights, MA: Allyn & Bacon.

Sullivan, M. J. L., & Stanish, W. D. (2003). Psychologically based occupational rehabilitation: The Pain-Disability Prevention Program. *Clinical Journal of Pain, 19,* 97–104.

Sullivan, M. J. L., Adams, H., & Ellis, T. (2013). A psychosocial risk-targeted intervention to reduce work disability: Development, evolution, and implementation challenges. *Psychological Injury and Law, 6,* 250–257.

Sullivan, M. J. L., Bishop, S. R., & Pivik, J. (1995). The Pain Catastrophizing Scale: Development and validation. *Psychological Assessment, 7,* 524–532.

Sullivan, M. J. L., Lynch, M. F., & Clark, A. J. (2005). Dimensions of catastrophic thinking associated with pain experience and disability in patients with neuropathic pain conditions. *Pain, 113*(3), 310–315.

Sullivan, M. J. L., Thorn, B., Haythornthwaite, J. A., Keefe, F., Martin, M., Bradley, L. A., & Lefebvre, J. C. (2001). Theoretical perspectives on the relation between catastrophizing and pain. *Clinical Journal of Pain, 17,* 52–64.

Sullivan, M. J. L., Tripp, D. A., Rodgers, W. M., & Stanish, W. (2000). Catastrophizing and pain perception in sport participants. *Journal of Applied Sport Psychology, 12,* 151–167.

Sullivan, P. F. (1995). Mortality in anorexia nervosa. *American Journal of Psychiatry, 152,* 1073–1074.

Sullivan, P. F., Neale, M. C., & Kendler, K. S. (2000). Genetic epidemiology of major depression: Review and meta-analysis, *American Journal of Psychiatry, 157,* 1552–1562.

Sullivan, S. (2012). Update on emerging drugs for insomnia. *Expert Opinion on Emerging Drugs, 17*(3), 295–298.

Sullivan, S. S., & Guilleminault, C. (2009). Emerging drugs for insomnia: New frontiers for old and novel targets. *Expert Opinion on Emerging Drugs, 14*(3), 411–422.

Suls, J., & Bunde, J. (2005). Anger, anxiety, and depression as risk factors for cardiovascular disease: The problems and implications of overlapping affective dispositions. *Psychological Bulletin, 131*, 260–300.

Summitt, P. H. (2013). *Sum it up: A thousand and ninety-eight victories, a couple of irrelevant losses, and a life in perspective.* New York, NY: Crown Archetype.

Sun, F., Ong, R., & Burnette, D. (2012). The influence of ethnicity and culture on dementia caregiving a review of empirical studies on Chinese Americans. *American Journal of Alzheimer's Disease and Other Dementias, 27*(1), 13–22.

Sun, J. (2011). Seasonality of suicide in Shandong, China, 991–2009: Associations with gender, age, area and methods of suicide. *Journal of Affective Disorders, 135*(1–3), 258–266.

Sun, N., Li, Y., Cai, Y., Chen, J., Shen, Y., Sun, J., & Zhang, K. (2012). A comparison of melancholic and nonmelancholic recurrent major depression in Han Chinese women. *Depression and Anxiety, 29*, 4–9.

Suomi, S. J. (1999). Attachment in rhesus monkeys. In J. Cassidy & P. Shaver (Eds.), *Handbook of attachment: Theory, research, and clinical applications* (pp. 181–197). New York, NY: Guilford Press.

Supremiss: Components and instruments. Geneva, Switzerland: World Health Organization, Department of Mental Health and Substance Dependence.

Suschinsky, K. D., Lalumière, M. L., & Chivers, M. L. (2009). Sex differences in patterns of genital sexual arousal: Measurement artifacts or true phenomena? *Archives of Sexual Behavior, 38*, 559–573.

Sussman, S. (1998). The first asylums in Canada: A response to neglectful community care and current trends. *Canadian Journal of Psychiatry, 43*, 260–264.

Sutherland, K., & Cistulli, P. A. (2015). Recent advances in obstructive sleep apnea pathophysiology and treatment. *Sleep and Biological Rhythms, 13*(1), 26–40.

Sutker, P. B., Bugg, F., & West, J. A. (1993). Antisocial personality disorder. In P. B. Sutker & H. F. Adams (Eds.), *Comprehensive handbook of psychopathology* (2nd ed., pp. 337–369). New York, NY: Plenum Press.

Sutton, D. A., Moldofsky, H., & Badley, F. M. (2001). Insomnia and health problems in Canadians. *Sleep & Hypnosis, 24*, 665–670.

Suvisaari, J., Perälä, J., Saarni, S., Juvonen, H., Tuulio-Henriksson, A., & Lönnqvist, J. (2009). The epidemiology and descriptive and predictive validity of DSM-IV delusional disorder and subtypes of schizophrenia. *Clinical Schizophrenia & Related Psychoses, 2*(4), 289–297.

Suvrathan, A., Hoeffer, C. A., Wong, H., Klann, E., & Chattarji, S. (2010). Characterization and reversal of synaptic defects in the amygdala in a mouse model of fragile X syndrome. *Proceedings of the National Academy of Sciences, 107*(25), 11591–11596.

Svartberg, M., Stiles, T. C., & Seltzer, M. H. (2004). Randomized, controlled trial of the effectiveness of short-term dynamic psychotherapy and cognitive therapy for cluster C personality disorders. *American Journal of Psychiatry, 161*, 810–817.

Swann, A. C., Lafer, B., Perugi, G., Frye, M., Bauer, M., Bahk, W. M., & Suppes, T. (2013). Bipolar mixed states: An international society for bipolar disorders task force report on symptom structure, course of illness, and diagnosis. *American Journal of Psychiatry, 170*(1), 31–42.

Swanson, M. C., Bland, R. C., & Newman, S. C. (1994). Antisocial personality disorders. *Acta Psychiatrica Scandinavica, 376*(Suppl.), 63–70.

Swanson, S. A., Crow, S. J., Le Grange, D., Swendsen, J., & Merikangas K. R. (2011). Prevalence and correlates of eating disorders in adolescents. *Archives of General Psychiatry, 68*, 714–723.

Swartz, M. S., Lauriello, J., & Drake, R. E. (2006). Psychosocial therapies. In J. A. Lieberman, T. S. Stroup, & D. O. Perkins (Eds.), *The American Psychiatric Publishing textbook of schizophrenia* (pp. 327–340). Washington, DC: American Psychiatric Publishing.

Swartz, M., Blazer, D., George, L., & Landerman, R. (1986). Somatization disorder in a community population. *American Journal of Psychiatry, 143*, 1403–1408.

Swartz, M., Blazer, D., Woodbury, M., George, L., & Landerman, R. (1986). Somatization disorder in a U.S. southern community: Use of a new procedure for analysis of medical classification. *Psychological Medicine, 16*, 595–609.

Swedo S. E., Leckman J. F., & Rose N. R. (2012). From research subgroup to clinical syndrome: Modifying the PANDAS criteria to describe PANS (pediatric acute-onset neuropsychiatric syndrome). *Pediatrics & Therapeutics, 2*(2), 1–8.

Swenderman, D., Ramanathan, N., Baetscher, L., Medich, M., Scheffler, A., Comulada, W. S., & Estrin, D. (2015). Smartphone self-monitoring to support self-management among people living with HIV: Perceived benefits and theory of change from a mixed-methods randomized pilot study. *JAIDS Journal of Acquired Immune Deficiency Syndromes, 69*, S80–S91.

Sylvers, P., Ryan, S., Alden, S., & Brennan, P. (2009). Biological factors and the development of persistent criminality. In J. Savage (Ed.), *Handbook of persistent criminality* (pp. 141–162). New York, NY: Oxford University Press.

Syngelaki, E. M., Fairchild, G., Moore, S. C., Savage, J. C., & Goozen, S. H. M. (2013). Fearlessness in juvenile offenders is associated with offending rate. *Developmental Science, 16*(1), 84–90.

Sysko, R., & Wilson, G. T. (2011). Eating disorders. In D. H. Barlow (Ed.), *Handbook of clinical psychology* (pp. 387–404). New York, NY: Oxford University Press.

Szasz, T. (1961). *The myth of mental illness: Foundations of a theory of personal conduct.* New York, NY: Hoeber-Harper.

Szasz, T. S. (1960). The myth of mental illness. *American Psychologist, 15*, 113–118.

Szatmari, P. (2003). The causes of autism spectrum disorders. *BMJ, 326*(7382), 173–174.

Szatmari, P., Georgiades, S., Bryson, S., Zwaigenbaum, L., Roberts, W., Mahoney, W., Goldberg, J., & Tuff, L. (2006). Investigating the structure of the restricted, repetitive behaviours and interests domain of autism. *Journal of Child Psychology and Psychiatry, 47*, 582–590. https://doi.org/10.1111/j.1469-7610.2005.01537.x

Szatmari, P., Offord, D. R., Siegel, L. S., Finlayson, M. A. J., & Tuff, L. (1990). The clinical significance of neurocognitive impairments among children with psychiatric disorders: Diagnosis and situational specificity. *Journal of Child Psychology & Psychiatry & Allied Disciplines, 31*, 287–299.

Szmukler, G. I., Eisler, I., Gillis, C., & Haywood, M. F. (1985). The implications of anorexia nervosa in a ballet school. *Journal of Psychiatric Research, 19*, 177–181.

Tafti, M. (2009). Genetic aspects of normal and disturbed sleep. *Sleep Medicine, 10*(Suppl. 1), S17–S21.

Tager-Flusberg, H., Rogers, S., Cooper, J., Landa, R., Lord, C., Paul, R., ... Yoder, P. (2009). Defining spoken language benchmarks and selecting measures of expressive language development for young children with autism spectrum disorders. *Journal of Speech, Language, and Hearing Research, 52*(3), 643–652.

Takahasi, T. (1989). Social phobia syndrome in Japan. *Comprehensive Psychiatry, 30*, 45–52.

Takei, N., Lewis, S., Jones, P., Harvey, I., & Murray, R. M. (1996). Prenatal exposure to influenza and increased cerebrospinal fluid spaces in schizophrenia. *Schizophrenia Bulletin, 22*, 521–534.

Talbot, L. S., Stone, S., Gruber, J., Hairston, I. S., Eidelman, P., & Harvey, A. G. (2012). A test of the bidirectional association between sleep and mood in bipolar disorder and insomnia. *Journal of Abnormal Psychology, 121*(1), 39–50.

Talbott, J. A. (1990). Current perspectives in the United States on the chronically mentally ill. In A. Kales, C. N. Stefanis, & J. A. Talbott (Eds.), *Recent advances in schizophrenia* (pp. 279–295). New York, NY: Springer-Verlag.

Tan, F. S. (1980). Transcultural aspects of anxiety. In G. D. Burrows & B. Davies (Eds.), *Handbook of studies on anxiety.* Amsterdam: Elsevier/North-Holland.

Tandon, R., & Carpenter, W. T. (2012). DSM-5 status of psychotic disorders: 1 year pre-publication. *Schizophrenia Bulletin, 38*(3), 369–370.

Tandon, R., Gaebel, W., Barch, D. M., Bustillo, J., Gur, R. E., Heckers, S., ... Van Os, J. (2013). Definition and description of schizophrenia in the DSM-5. *Schizophrenia Research, 150*(1), 3–10.

Tarasoff v. Regents of University of California ("Tarasoff I"), 529 P. 2d 553 (Cal. Sup. Ct. 1974); ("Tarasoff II"), 551 P. 2d 334 (Cal. Sup. Ct. 1976).

Tarrier, N., Kinney, C., McCarthy, F., Humphreys, L., Wittkowski, A., & Morris, J. (2000). Two-year follow-up of cognitive behavioural therapy and supportive counseling in the treatment of persistent symptoms in chronic schizophrenia. *Journal of Consulting and Clinical Psychology, 68*(5), 912–922.

Tarrier, N., Wittkowski, A., Kinney, C. McCarthy, F., Morris, J., & Humphreys, L. (1999). Durability of the effects of cognitive-behavioural therapy in the treatment of chronic schizophrenia: 12-month follow-up. *British Journal of Psychiatry, 174*, 500–504.

Tarullo, A. R., & Gunnar, M. R. (2006). Child maltreatment and the developing HPA axis. *Hormones and Behavior, 50*, 632–639.

Tattan, T., & Tarrier, N. (2000). The expressed emotion of case managers of the seriously mentally ill: The influence of expressed emotion on clinical outcomes. *Psychological Medicine, 30*, 195–204.

Tau, G. Z., & Peterson, B. S. (2010). Normal development of brain circuits. *Neuropsychopharmacology, 35*(1), 147–168.

Taubes, T. (1998). "Healthy avenues of the mind": Psychological theory building and the influence of religion during the era of moral treatment. *American Journal of Psychiatry, 155*(8), 1001–1007.

Tauscher, J., Hussain, T., Agid, O., Verhoeff, N. P. L. G., Wilson, A. A., Houle, S., ... Kapur, S. (2004). Equivalent occupancy of dopamine D1 and D2 receptors with clozapine: Differentiation from other atypical antipsychotics. *American Journal of Psychiatry, 161*(9), 1620–1625.

Taylor, C. T., & Alden, L. E. (2005). Social interpretation bias and generalized social phobia: The influence of developmental experiences. *Behaviour Research and Therapy, 43*, 759–777.

Taylor, D., Gehrman, P., Dautovich, N. D., Lichstein, K. L., & McCrae, C. S. (2014). Causes of Insomnia. In D. Taylor, P. Gehrman, N. D. Dautovich, K. L. Lichstein, & C. S. McCrae (Eds.), *Handbook of Insomnia* (pp. 11–27). New York, NY: Springer.

Taylor, E. (2012). Attention deficit and hyperkinetic disorders in childhood and adolescence. In M. G. Gelder, N. C. Andreasen, J. J. Lopez-Ibor, & J. R. Geddes (Eds.), *New Oxford textbook of psychiatry* (2nd ed., Vol. 2, pp. 1643–1654). New York, NY: Oxford University Press.

Taylor, G. M., & Ste-Marie, D. M. (2001). Eating disorders symptoms in Canadian female pair and dance figure skaters. *International Journal of Sport Psychology, 32*, 21–28.

Taylor, G. T., Maloney, S., Dearborn, J., & Weiss, J. (2009). Hormones in the mentally disturbed brain: Steroids and peptides in the development and treatment of psychopathology. *Central Nervous System Agents in Medicinal Chemistry, 9*, 331–360.

Taylor, J., & Lang, A. R. (2006). Psychopathy and substance use disorders. In C. J. Patrick (Ed.), *Handbook of psychopathy* (pp. 495–511). New York, NY: Guilford Press.

Taylor, L., & Ingram, R. F. (1999). Cognitive reactivity and depressotypic information processing in children of depressed mothers. *Journal of Abnormal Psychology, 108*, 202–210.

Taylor, M. A., & Abrams, R. (1981). Early and late-onset bipolar illness. *Archives of General Psychiatry, 38*(1), 58–61.

Taylor, S. (2001). Breathing retraining in the treatment of panic disorder: Efficacy, caveats and indications. *Scandinavian Journal of Behaviour Therapy, 30*, 49–56.

Taylor, S. (2003). *Health psychology* (5th ed.). San Francisco, CA: McGraw-Hill.

Taylor, S. (Ed.). (1999). *Anxiety sensitivity: Theory, research, and treatment of the fear of anxiety.* Mahwah, NJ: Lawrence Erlbaum.

Taylor, S. E. (2002). *The tending instinct: How nurturing is essential to who we are and how we live.* New York, NY: Henry Holt and Company.

Taylor, S. E. (2006). Tend and befriend: Biobehavioral bases of affiliation under stress. *Current Directions in Psychological Science, 15*(6), 273–277.

Taylor, S. E. (2009). *Health psychology* (7th ed.). New York, NY: McGraw-Hill.

Taylor, S. F. (1999). *Health psychology* (4th ed.). Boston, MA: McGraw-Hill.

Taylor, S. F., Klein, L. C., Lewis, B. P., Gruenewald, T. L., Gurung, R. A. R., & Updegraff, J. A. (2000). Biobehavioral responses to stress in females: Tend-and-befriend, not fight-or-flight. *Psychological Review, 107,* 411–429.

Taylor, S. F., Repetti, R. L., & Seeman, T. (1997). Health psychology: What is an unhealthy environment and how does it get under the skin? *Annual Review of Psychology, 48,* 411–447.

Taylor, S., & Asmundson, G. J. (2009). Hypochondriasis and health anxiety. In M. M. Antony & M. B. Stein (Eds.), *Oxford handbook of anxiety and related disorders* (pp. 525–540). Oxford: Oxford University Press.

Taylor, S., & Asmundson, G. J. G. (2004). Treating health anxiety: A cognitive-behavioral approach. New York, NY: Guilford Press.

Taylor, S., & Koch, W. J. (1995). Anxiety disorders due to motor vehicle accidents: Nature and treatment. *Clinical Psychology Review, 15,* 721–738.

Taylor, S., Asmundson, G., & Coons, M. (2005). Current directions in the treatment of hypochondriasis. *Journal of Cognitive Psychotherapy: An International Quarterly, 19,* 285–304.

Taylor, S., Thordarson, D. S., Jang, K. L., & Asmundson, G. J. (2006). Genetic and environmental origins of health anxiety: A twin study. *World Psychiatry, 5*(1), 47–50.

Taylor, S., Thordarson, D. S., Maxfield, L., Fedoroff, I. C., Lovell, K., & Ogrodniczuk, J. (2003). Comparative efficacy, speed, and adverse effects of three PTSD treatments: Exposure therapy, FMDR, and relaxation training. *Journal of Consulting and Clinical Psychology, 71,* 330–338.

Tazici, O. (2014). Unipolar mania: A distinct entity. *Journal of Affective Disorders, 152–154,* 52–56.

Teachman, B. A., & Woody, S. R. (2004). Staying tuned to research in implicit cognition: Relevance for clinical practice with anxiety disorders. *Cognition and Behavioral Practice, 11*(2), 149–159.

Teachman, B. A., Joormann, J., Steinman, S. A., & Gotlib, I. H. (2012). Automaticity in anxiety disorders and depressive disorder. *Clinical Psychology Review, 32,* 575–603.

Teasdale, J. D. (1993). Emotion and two kinds of meaning: Cognitive therapy and applied cognitive science. *Behaviour Research and Therapy, 31*(4), 339–354.

Teasdale, J. D., Moore, R. G., Hayhurst, H., Pope, M., Williams, S., & Segal, Z. V. (2002). Metacognitive awareness and the prevention of relapse in depression: Empirical evidence. *Journal of Consulting and Clinical Psychology, 70,* 275–287.

Teasdale, J. D., Scott, J., Moore, R. G., Hayhurst, H., Pope, M., & Paykel, E. S. (2001). How does cognitive therapy prevent relapse in residual depression? Evidence from a controlled trial. *Journal of Consulting and Clinical Psychology, 69,* 347–357.

Teasdale, J. D., Segal, Z. V., Williams, J. M., Ridgeway, V. A., Soulsby, J. M., & Lau, M. A. (2000). Prevention of relapse/recurrence in major depression by mindfulness-based cognitive therapy. *Journal of Consulting and Clinical Psychology, 68,* 615–623.

Teicher, M. H., Glod, C., & Cole, J. O. (1990). Emergence of intense suicidal preoccupation during fluoxetine treatment. *American Journal of Psychiatry, 147*(1), 207–210.

Telch, C. F., & Agras, W. S. (1993). The effects of a very low calorie diet on binge eating. *Behavior Therapy, 24,* 177–193.

Telch, M. J., Lucas, J. A., & Nelson, P. (1989). Non-clinical panic in college students: An investigation of prevalence and symptomatology. *Journal of Abnormal Psychology, 98,* 300–306.

Telch, M. J., Rosenfield, D., Lee, H.-J., & Pai, A. (2012). Emotional reactivity to a single inhalation of 35% carbon dioxide and its association with later symptoms of posttraumtic stress disorders and anxiety n soldiers deployed to Iraq. *Archives of General Psychiatry, 69,* 1161–1168.

Temoshok, L. R., Wald, R. L., Synowski, S., & Garzino-Demo, A. (2008). Coping as a multisystem construct associated with pathways mediating HIV-relevant immune function and disease progression. *Psychosomatic Medicine, 70,* 555–561.

Tenhula, W. N., Bellack, A. S., & Drake, R. E. (2009). Schizophrenia: Psychosocial approaches. In B. J. Sadock, V. A. Sadock, & P. Ruiz (Eds.), *Kaplan & Sadock's comprehensive textbook of psychiatry* (9th ed., Vol. 1, pp. 1557–1572). Philadelphia, PA: Lippincott Williams & Wilkins.

ter Bogt, T., Schmid, H., Gabhainn, S. N., Fotiou, A., & Vollebergh, W. (2006). Economic and cultural correlates of cannabis use among mid-adolescents in 31 countries. *Addiction, 101*(2), 241–251.

ter Kuile, M. M., Melles, R., de Groot, H. E., Tuijnman-Raasveld, C. C., & van Lankveld, J. J. (2013). Therapist-aided exposure for women with lifelong vaginismus: A randomized waiting-list control trial of efficacy. *Journal of Consulting and Clinical Psychology, 81*(6), 1127.

ter Kuile, M., van Lankveld, J., Jacques, J., de Groot, E., Melles, R., Neffs, J., & Zanbergen, M. (2007). Cognitive-behavioral therapy for women with lifelong vaginismus: Process and prognostic factors. *Behaviour Research and Therapy, 45,* 359–373.

Teri, L., Gibbons, L. F., McCurry, S. M., Logsdon, R. G., Buchner, D. M., Barlow, W. E., ... Larson, E. B. (2003). Exercise plus behavioral management in patients with Alzheimer's disease: A randomized controlled trial. *JAMA, 290,* 2015–2022.

Testad, I., Ballard, C., Brønnick, K., & Aarsland, D. (2010). The effect of staff training on agitation and use of restraint in nursing home residents with dementia: A single-blind, randomized controlled trial. *Journal of Clinical Psychiatry, 71*(1), 80.

Teti, D. M., & Crosby, B. (2012). Maternal depressive symptoms, dysfunctional cognitions, and infant night waking: The role of maternal nighttime behavior. *Child Development, 83*(3), 939–953.

Thaker, G. K., & Avila, M. (2003). Schizophrenia, V: Risk marks. *American Journal of Psychiatry, 160,* 1578.

Thapar, A., & McGuffin, P. (2009). Quantitative genetics. In M. G. Gelder, N. C. Andreasen, J. J. Lopez-Ibor, Jr., & J. R. Geddes (Eds.), *New Oxford textbook of psychiatry* (2nd ed., Vol. 1, pp. 212–221). Oxford, UK: Oxford University Press.

Thapar, A., Cooper, M., Jefferies, R., & Stergiakouli, E. (2012). What causes attention deficit hyperactivity disorder? *Archives of Disease in Childhood, 97*(3), 260–265.

Thapar, A., Langley, K., Fowler, T., Rice, F., Turic, D., Whittinger, N., & O'Donovan, M. (2005). Catechol O-methyltransferase gene variant and birth weight predict early-onset antisocial behavior in children with attention-deficit/hyperactivity disorder. *Archives of General Psychiatry, 62*(11), 1275.

Thase, M. E. (1990). Relapse and recurrence in unipolar major depression: Short-term and long-term approaches. *Journal of Clinical Psychiatry, 51*(Suppl. 6), 51–57.

Thase, M. E. (2009). Neurobiological aspects of depression. In I. H. Gotlib & C. L. Hammen (Eds.), *Handbook of depression* (2nd ed., pp. 187–217). New York, NY: Guilford Press.

Thase, M. E., & Denko, T. (2008). Pharmacotherapy of mood disorders. *Annual Review of Clinical Psychology, 4,* 53–91.

Thase, M. E., & Kupfer, D. J. (1996). Recent developments in the pharmacotherapy of mood disorders. *Journal of Consulting and Clinical Psychology, 64,* 646–659.

Thase, M. E., Simons, A. D., & Reynolds, C. F., III. (1996). Abnormal electroencephalographic sleep profiles in major depression. *Archives of General Psychiatry, 53,* 99–108.

Thibodeau, M. A., Welch, P. G., Sareen, J., & Asmundson, G. L. G. (2013). Anxiety disorders are independently associated with suicide ideation and attempts: Propensity score matching in two epidemiological samples. *Depression and Anxiety, 30,* 947–954.

Thirthalli, J., & Rajkumar, R. P. (2009). Statistical versus clinical significance in psychiatric research—An overview for beginners. *Asian Journal of Psychiatry, 2*(2), 74–79.

Thomas, C. R. (2009). Oppositional defiant disorder and conduct disorder. In M. K. Dulcan (Ed.), *Dulcan's textbook of child and adolescent psychiatry* (pp. 223–239). Arlington, VA: American Psychiatric Publishing.

Thompson, J. K., & Kinder, B. (2003). Eating disorders. In M. Hersen & S. Turner (Eds.), *Handbook of adult psychopathology* (4th ed., pp. 555–582). New York, NY: Plenum Press.

Thompson, J. K., & Stice, E. (2001). Thin-idea internalization: Mounting evidence for a new risk factor for body-image disturbance and eating pathology. *Current Directions in Psychological Science, 11,* 181–183.

Thompson, J. R., Bradley, V. J., Buntinx, W. H. E., Schalock, R. L., Shogren, K. A., Snell, M. E., ... Yeager, M. H. (2009). Conceptualizing supports and the support needs of people with intellectual disability. *Intellectual and Developmental Disabilities, 47*(2), 135–146.

Thompson, M. A., Aberg, J. A., Cahn, P., Montaner, J. S. G., Rizzardini, G., Telenti, A., ... Schooley, R. T. (2010). Antiretroviral treatment of adult HIV infection. *JAMA, 304,* 321–333.

Thompson, M. A., Mugavero, M. J., Amico, K. R., Cargill, V. A., Chang, L. W., Gross, R., & Nachega, J. B. (2012). Guidelines for improving entry into and retention in care and antiretroviral adherence for persons with HIV: Evidence-based recommendations from an International Association of Physicians in AIDS Care panel. *Annals of Internal Medicine, 156*(11), 817–833.

Thompson-Brenner, H., Boisseau, C. L., & St. Paul, M. S. (2011). Representations of ideal figure-size in *Ebony* magazine: A content analysis. *Body Image, 8*(4), 373–378.

Thomson, A. B., & Page, L. A. (2007). Psychotherapies for hypochondriasis. *Cochrane Database of Systematic Reviews*(4), CD006520.

Thoresen, C. F., & Powell, L. H. (1992). Type A behavior pattern: New perspectives on theory, assessment and intervention. [Special issue: Behavioral medicine: An update for the 1990s]. *Journal of Consulting and Clinical Psychology, 60*(4), 595–604.

Thorlton, J., Colby, D. A., & Devine, P. (2014). Proposed actions for the US Food and Drug Administration to implement to minimize adverse effects associated with energy drink consumption. *American Journal of Public Health, 104*(7), 1175–1180. https://doi.org/10.2105/AJPH.2014.301967

Thorne, S. (2000, February 17). Military will treat stress as a disability: Post-traumatic stress disorder eligible for compensation. *The Toronto Star,* A7.

Thorpe, G. L., & Burns, L. F. (1983). *The agoraphobic syndrome.* New York, NY: John Wiley & Sons.

Thorpy, M., & Glovinsky, P. (1987). Parasomnias. *Psychiatric Clinics of North America, 10,* 623–639.

Thurston, R. C., & Kubzansky, L. D. (2009). Women, loneliness, and incident coronary heart disease. *Psychosomatic Medicine, 71*(8), 836–842.

Tienari, P. (1991). Interaction between genetic vulnerability and family environment: The Finnish adoptive family study of schizophrenia. *Acta Psychiatrica Scandinavica, 84,* 460–465.

Tienari, P., Wahlberg, K. E., & Wynne, L. C. (2006). Finnish adoption study of schizophrenia: Implications for family interventions. *Families, Systems & Health, 24,* 442–451.

Tienari, P., Wynne, L. C., Laksy, K., Moring, J., Nieminen, P., Sorri, A., ... Wahlberg, K. E. (2003). Genetic boundaries of the schizophrenia spectrum: Evidence from the Finnish adoptive family study of schizophrenia. *American Journal of Psychiatry, 160,* 1587–1594.

Tienari, P., Wynne, L. C., Moring, J., Lahti, I., Naarala, M., Sorri, A., ... Kaleva, M. (1994). The Finnish adoptive family study of schizophrenia: Implications for family research. *British Journal of Psychiatry, 23*(Suppl. 164), 20–26.

Tierney, M. C., Snow, W. G., Szalai, J. P., Fisher, R. H., & Zorzitto, M. L. (1996). A brief neuropsychological battery for the differential diagnosis of probable Alzheimer's disease. *Clinical Neuropsychologist, 10*, 96–103.

Tierney, M. C., Yao, C., Kiss, A., & McDowell, I. (2005). Neuropsychological tests accurately predict incident Alzheimer disease after 5 and 10 years. *Neurology, 64*(11), 1853–1859.

Tiggemann, M. (2002). Media influences on body image development. In T. F. Cash & T. Pruzinsky (Eds.), *Body image: A handbook of theory, research and clinical practice* (pp. 91–98). New York, NY: Guilford Press.

Tiggemann, M., & Lynch, J. E. (2001). Body image across the life span in adult women: The role of self-objectification. *Developmental Psychology, 37*, 243–253.

Tiihonen, J., Isohanni, M., Rasanen, P., Koiranen, M., & Moring, J. (1997). Specific major mental disorders and criminality: A 26-year prospective study of the 1966 northern Finland birth cohort. *American Journal of Psychiatry, 154*(6), 840–845.

Timeline of BSE in Canada and the U.S. (2004, August 5). *CBC News Online.* Retrieved August 11, 2004, from http://www.cbc.ca/news/background/madcow/timeline.html

Tinbergen, F. A., & Tinbergen, N. (1972). *Early childhood autism: An ethological approach.* Berlin: Paul Parey.

Tingelstad, J. B. (1991). The cardiotoxicity of the tricyclics. *Journal of the American Academy of Child and Adolescent Psychiatry, 30*, 845–846.

Tjepkema, M. (2005). Insomnia. *Health Reports, 17*, 9–25.

Tjio, J. H., & Levan, A. (1956). The chromosome number of man. *Hereditas, 42*, 1–6.

Tober, D. M., & Budiani, D. (2014). Introduction: Why Islam health and body?. *Body and Society, 13*(3), 1.

Tolin, D. F. (2011). Challenges and advances in treating hoarding. *Journal of Clinical Psychology, 67*, 451–455.

Tolin, D. F., Frost, R. O., Steketee, G., & Muroff, J. (2015). Cognitive behavioral therapy for hoarding disorder: A meta-analysis. *Depression and Anxiety, 32*, 158–166.

Tolin, D. F., Stevens, M. C., Villavicencio, A. L., Norberg, M. M., Calhoun, V. D., Frost, R. O., & Pearlson, G. D. (2012). Neural mechanisms of decision making in hoarding disorder. *Archives of General Psychiatry, 69*, 832–841.

Tollefson, G. D. (1993). Major depression. In D. L. Dunner (Ed.), *Current psychiatric therapy.* Philadelphia, PA: W. B. Saunders.

Tomarken, A., & Keener, A. (1998). Frontal brain asymmetry and depression: A self-regulatory perspective. *Cognition and Emotion, 12*, 387–420.

Tomarken, A., Dichter, G., Garber, J., & Simien, C. (2004). Relative left frontal hypo-activation in adolescents at risk for depression. *Biological Psychology, 67*, 77–102.

Tomenson, B., McBeth, J., Chew-Graham, C. A., MacFarlane, G., Davies, I., Jackson, J., & Creed, F. H. (2012). Somatization and health anxiety as predictors of health care use. *Psychosomatic Medicine, 74*(6), 656–664.

Tondo, L., Jamison, K. R., & Baldessarini, R. J. (1997). Effect of lithium maintenance on suicidal behavior in major mood disorders. In D. M. Stoff & J. J. Mann (Eds.), *The neurobiology of suicide: From the bench to the clinic* (Vol. 836, pp. 339–351). New York, NY: Academy of Sciences.

Toomey, R., Faraone, S. V., Simpson, J. C., & Tsuang, M. T. (1998). Negative, positive, and disorganized symptom dimensions in schizophrenia, major depression, and bipolar disorder. *Journal of Nervous and Mental Disorders, 186*, 470–476.

Torgersen, S. (2012). Epidemiology. In T. A. Widiger (Ed.), *The Oxford handbook of personality disorders* (pp. 186–205). New York, NY: Oxford University Press.

Torgersen, S., Onstad, S., Skre, I., Edvardsen, J., & Kringlen, F. (1993). "True" schizotypal personality disorder: A study of co-twins and relatives of schizophrenic probands. *American Journal of Psychiatry, 150*, 1661–1667.

Torrey, E. F., Bartko, J. J., Lun, Z. R., & Yolken, R. H. (2007). Antibodies to Toxoplasma gondii in patients with schizophrenia: A meta-analysis. *Schizophrenia Bulletin, 33*, 729–736.

Torrey, F. F. (1988a). *Nowhere to go: The tragic odyssey of the homeless mentally ill.* New York, NY: Harper & Row.

Torrey, F. F. (1988b). Stalking the schizovirus. *Schizophrenia Bulletin, 14*, 223–229.

Torrey, F. F., Bowler, A. F., Taylor, F. H., & Gottesman, I. I. (1994). *Schizophrenia and manic-depressive disorder: The biological roots of mental illness as revealed by the landmark study of identical twins.* New York, NY: Basic Books.

Torrey, F. F., Rawlings, R., & Waldman, I. (1988). Schizophrenic births and viral diseases in two states. *Schizophrenia Research, 1*, 73–77.

Tortorella, A., Fabrazzo, M., Monteleone, A. M., Steardo, L., & Monteleone, P. (2014). The role of drug therapies in the treatment of anorexia and bulimia nervosa: A review of the literature. *Journal of Psychopathology, 20*, 50–65.

Toth, K., & King, B. H. (2010). Intellectual disability (mental retardation). In M. K. Dulcan (Ed.), *Dulcan's textbook of child and adolescent psychiatry* (5th ed., pp. 151–172). Arlington, VA: American Psychiatric Publishing.

Toth, K., de Lacy, N., & King, B. H. (2016). Intelectual disability. In M. K. Dulcan (Ed.), *Dulcan's textbook of child and adolescent psychiatry* (2nd ed., pp. 105–133). Arlington, VA: American Psychiatric Publishing.

Toth, S. L., Harris, L. S., Goodman, G. S., & Cicchetti, D. (2011). Influence of violence and aggression on children's psychological development: Trauma, attachment, and memory. In P. R. Shaver & M. Mikulincer (Eds.), *Human aggression and violence: Causes, manifestations, and consequences* (pp. 351–365). Washington, DC: American Psychological Association.

Tovote, P., Fadok, J. P., & Lüthi, A. (2015). Neuronal circuits of fear and anxiety. *Nature Reviews Neuroscience, 16*, 317–331.

Townsend, J. M., & Wasserman, T. H. (2011). Sexual hookups among college students: Sex differences in emotional reactions. *Archives of Sexual Behavior, 40*(6), 1173–1181.

Trace, S. E., Baker, J. H., Penas-Lledo, E., & Bulik, C. M. (2013). The genetics of eating disorders. *Annual Review of Clinical Psychology, 9*, 589–620.

Tracey, S. A., Chorpita, B. F., Douban, J., & Barlow, D. H. (1997). Empirical evaluation of DSM-IV generalized anxiety disorder criteria in children and adolescents. *Journal of Clinical Child Psychology, 26*, 404–414.

Trebbe, A. (1979, September 15). Ideal is body beautiful and clean cut. *USA Today*, 1–2.

Tremont, G., Davis, J. D., Papandonatos, G. D., Ott, B. R., Fortinsky, R. H., Gozalo, P., … Bishop, D. S. (2015). Psychosocial telephone intervention for dementia caregivers: A randomized, controlled trial. *Alzheimer's & Dementia, 11*(5), 541–548.

Triebwasser, J., Chemerinski, E., Roussos, P., & Siever, L. J. (2012). Paranoid personality disorder. *Journal of Personality Disorders*, 1–11.

Triebwasser, J., Chemerinski, E., Roussos, P., & Siever, L. J. (2013). Paranoid personality disorder. *Journal of Personality Disorders, 27*(6), 795–805.

Trinh, N., Hoblyn, J., Mohanty, S., & Yaffe, K. (2003). Efficacy of cholinesterase inhibitors in the treatment of neuropsychiatric symptoms and functional impairment in Alzheimer disease: A meta-analysis. *JAMA, 289*(2), 210–216.

Trottier, K., Polivy, J., & Herman, C. P. (2005). Effects of exposure to unrealistic promises about dieting: Are unrealistic expectations about dieting inspirational? *International Journal of Eating Disorders, 37*, 142–149.

Trudel, G., Marchand, A., Ravart, M., Aubin, S., Turgeon, L., & Fortier, P. (2001). The effect of a cognitive-behavioral group treatment program on hypoactive sexual desire in women. *Sexual & Relationship Therapy, 16*, 145–164.

True, W. R., Rice, J., Fisen, S. A., Heath, A. C., Goldberg, J., Lyons, M. J., & Nowak, J. (1993). A twin study of genetic and environmental contributions to liability for posttraumatic stress symptoms. *Archives of General Psychiatry, 50*, 257–264.

Trull, T. J., Carpenter, R. W., Widiger, T. A. (2013). Personality disorders. In I. B. Weiner (Series Ed.), G. Stricker & T. A. Widiger (Vol. Eds.), *Handbook of psychology: Vol. 8 Clinical psychology* (pp. 94–120). Hoboken, NJ: John Wiley & Sons.

Trull, T. J., Jahng, S., Tomko, R. L., Wood, P. K., & Sher, K. J. (2010). Revised NESARC personality disorder diagnoses: Gender, prevalence, and comorbidity with substance dependence disorders. *Journal of Personality Disorders, 24*(3), 412–426.

Trull, T. J., Scheiderer, E. M., & Tomko, R. L. (2012). Axis II comorbidity. In T. A. Widiger (Ed.), *The Oxford handbook of personality disorders* (pp. 566–581). New York, NY: Oxford University Press.

Truong, T., Liquet, B., Menegaux, F., Plancoulaine, S., Laurent-Puig, P., Mulot, C., … Guénel, P. (2014). Breast cancer risk, nightwork, and circadian clock gene polymorphisms. *Endocrine-Related Cancer, 21*(4), 629–638.

Truscott, D., & Crook, K. H. (2004). *Ethics for the practice of psychology in Canada.* Edmonton, AB: University of Alberta Press.

Truth and Reconciliation Commission of Canada. (2015). *Honouring the truth, reconciling for the future: Summary of the final report of the Truth and Reconciliation Commission of Canada* (Catalogue No. IR4-7/2015E-PDF).

Tsai, G. F., Condie, D., Wu, M. T., & Chang, I. W. (1999). Functional magnetic resonance imaging of personality switches in a woman with dissociative identity disorder. *Harvard Review of Psychiatry, 7*(2), 119–122.

Tsai, L. Y., & Ghaziuddin, M. (1992). Biomedical research in autism. In D. F. Berkell (Ed.), *Autism: Identification, education, and treatment* (pp. 53–74). Hillsdale, NJ: Erlbaum.

Tsao, J. C. I., Mystkowski, J. L., Zucker, B. G., & Craske, M. G. (2002). Effects of cognitive-behavioral therapy for panic disorder on comorbid conditions: Replication and extension. *Behavior Therapy, 33*, 493–509.

Tsuang, M. T., Stone, W. S., & Faraone, S. V. (2012). Schizoaffective and schizotypal disorders. In M. G. Gelder, N. C. Andreasen, J. J. Lopez-Ibor, & J. R. Geddes (Eds.), *New Oxford textbook of psychiatry* (2nd ed., Vol. 1, pp. 595–602s). New York, NY: Oxford University Press.

Tuchman, B. (1978). *A distant mirror.* New York, NY: Ballantine Books.

Tucker, G. J., Ferrell, R. B., & Price, T. R. P. (1984). The hospital treatment of schizophrenia. In A. S. Bellack (Ed.), *Schizophrenia: Treatment, management, and rehabilitation* (pp. 175–191). New York, NY: Grune & Stratton.

Tucker, J. A., Murphy, J. G., & Kertesz, S. G. (2011). Substance use disorders. In M. Antony & D. H. Barlow (Eds.), *Handbook of assessment and treatment planning for psychological disorders* (2nd ed.). New York, NY: Guilford, Press.

Tuokko, H., Hadjistavropoulos, T., Miller, J. A., & Beattie, B. L. (1992). The Clock Test: A sensitive measure to differentiate normal elderly from those with Alzheimer Disease. *Journal of the American Geriatrics Society, 40*, 579–584.

Tuokko, H., Hadjistavropoulos, T., Rae, S., & O'Rourke, N. (2000). A comparison of alternative approaches to the scoring of clock drawing. *Archives of Clinical Neuropsychology, 15*, 137–148.

Tuokko, H., Kristjansson, F., & Miller, J. (1995). Neuropsychological detection of dementia: An overview of the neuropsychological component of the Canadian Study of Health and Aging. *Journal of Clinical & Experimental Neuropsychology, 17*, 352–373.

Turgeon, L., Marchand, A., & Dupuis, G. (1998). Clinical features in panic disorder with agoraphobia: A comparison of men and women. *Journal of Anxiety Disorders, 12*, 539–553.

Turk, C. L., Heimberg, R. G., & Magee, L. (2008). Social anxiety disorder. In D. H. Barlow (Ed.), *Clinical handbook of psychological disorders: A step-by-step treatment manual* (4th ed., pp. 123–163). New York, NY: Guilford Press.

Turk, D. C. (1996). Biopsychosocial perspective on chronic pain. In R. J. Gatchel & D. C. Turk (Eds.), *Psychological approaches to pain management: A practitioner's handbook* (pp. 3–32). New York, NY: Guilford Press.

Turk, D. C., & Gatchel, R. J. (2002). *Psychological approaches to pain management: A practitioner's handbook* (2nd ed.). New York, NY: Guilford Press.

Turk, D. C., & Monarch, F. S. (2002). Biopsychosocial perspective on chronic pain. In D. C. Turk & R. J. Gatchel (Eds.), *Psychological approaches to pain management: A practitioner's handbook* (2nd ed.). New York, NY: Guilford Press.

Turk, D. C., Meichenbaum, D., & Genest, M. (1983). *Pain and behavioral medicine: A cognitive-behavioral perspective*. New York, NY: Guilford Press.

Turkat, I. D., & Maisto, S. A. (1985). Personality disorders: Applications of the experimental method to the formulation and modification of personality disorders. In D. H. Barlow (Ed.), *Clinical handbook of psychological disorders*. New York, NY: Guilford Press.

Turkheimer, E., Haley, A., Waldron, M., D'Onofrio, B., & Gottesman, I. I. (2003). Socioeconomic status modifies heritability of IQ in young children. *Psychological Science, 14*, 623–628.

Turkheimer, F. (1998). Heritability and biological explanation. *Psychological Review, 105*, 782–791.

Turkheimer, F., & Parry, C. D. H. (1992). Why the gap? Practice and policy in civil commitment hearings. *American Psychologist, 47*, 646–655.

Turner, B. J., Yiu, A., Layden, B. K., Claes, L., Zaitsoff, S., & Chapman, A. L. (2015). Temporal associations between disordered eating and nonsuicidal self-injury: Examining symptom overlap over 1 year. *Behavior Therapy, 46*(1), 125–138.

Turner, C., Spinks, A., McClure, R., Nixon, J. (2004). Community-based interventions for the prevention of burns and scalds in children. *Cochrane Database Syst. Rev. 3*, CD004335.

Turner, J., Mancl, L., & Aaron, L. (2006). Short- and long-term efficacy of brief cognitive behavioral therapy for patients with chronic temporomandibular disorder pain: A randomized, controlled trial. *Pain, 121*, 181–194.

Turner, S. M., Beidel, D. C., & Jacob, R. G. (1994). Social phobia: A comparison of behavior therapy and atenolol. *Journal of Consulting Psychology, 62*, 350–358.

Turovsky, J., & Barlow, D. H. (1996). Generalized anxiety disorder. In J. Margraf (Ed.), *Textbook of behavior therapy* (pp. 87–106). Berlin: Springer-Verlag.

Tweed, R. G., & Dutton, D. G. (1998). A comparison of impulsive and instrumental subgroups of batterers. *Violence & Victims, 13*, 217–230.

Tyas, S. L., Salazar, J. C., Snowdon, D. A., Desrosiers, M. F., Riley, K. P., Mendiondo, M. S., & Kryscio, R. J. (2007). Transitions to mild cognitive impairments, dementia, and death: Findings from the nun study. *American Journal of Epidemiology, 165*(11), 1231–1238.

Tynes, L. L., White, K., & Steketee, G. S. (1990). Toward a new nosology of obsessive–compulsive disorder. *Comprehensive Psychiatry, 31*, 465–480.

Tyrer, P., Reed, G. M., & Crawford, M. J. (2015). Personality Disorder 1: Classification, assessment, prevalence and effect of personality disorder. *Lancet, 385*, 717–726.

Uchino, B. N. (2009). Understanding the link between social support and physical health: A life-span perspective with emphasis on the separability of perceived and received support. *Perspectives on Psychological Science, 4*, 236–255.

Uchino, B. N., Cacioppo, J. T., & Kiecolt-Glaser, J. K. (1996). The relationship between social support and physiological processes: A review with emphasis on underlying mechanisms and implications for health. *Psychological Bulletin, 119*(3), 488–531.

Uddin, M., Amstadter, A. B., Nugent, N. R., & Koenen, K. C. (2012). Genetics and genomics of posttraumatic stress disorder. In J. G. Beck & D. M. Sloan (Eds.), *The Oxford handbook of traumatic stress disorders* (pp. 143–158). New York, NY: Oxford University Press.

Uddo, M., Malow, R., & Sutker, P. B. (1993). Opioid and cocaine abuse and dependence disorders. In P. B. Sutker & H. F. Adams (Eds.), *Comprehensive handbook of psychopathology* (pp. 477–503). New York, NY: Plenum Press.

Uditsky, B. (1994). Family, friends and community: Together a project to support deinstitutionalization. *Developmental Disabilities Bulletin* [Online]. Retrieved from http://.ualberta.ca/jpdasddc/bulletin/articles/aacl-deinstitutionalize.html

Uebelacker, L., & Whisman, M. (2006). Moderators of the association between relationship discord and major depression in a national population-based sample. *Journal of Family Psychology, 20*, 40–46.

Uhde, T. (1994). The anxiety disorder: Phenomenology and treatment of core symptoms and associated sleep disturbance. In M. Kryger, T. Roth, & W. Dement (Eds.), *Principles and practice of sleep medicine* (pp. 871–898). Philadelphia, PA: W. B. Saunders.

Uhde, T., Cortese, B., & Vedeniapin, A. (2009). Anxiety and sleep problems: Emerging concepts and theoretical treatment implications. *Current Psychiatry Reports, 11*(4), 269–276.

Uher, R. (2011s). Gene–environment interaction. In K. S. Kendler, S. Jaffee, & D. Romer (Eds.), *The dynamic genome and mental health: The role of genes and environments in youth development* (pp. 29–58). New York, NY: Oxford University Press.

Umbricht, D., & Kane, J. M. (1996). Medical complications of new antipsychotic drugs. *Schizophrenia Bulletin, 22*, 475–483.

UNAIDS. (2009). *AIDS epidemic update 2009*. Geneva: Joint United Nations Programme on HIV/AIDS (UNAIDS). Retrieved from http://www.who.int/hiv/pub/epidemiology/epidemic/en/index.html

Urbina, S. (2014). *Essentials of psychological testing*. Hoboken, NJ: John Wiley & Sons.

Urbszat, C., Herman, C. P., & Polivy, J. (2002). Eat, drink, and be merry, for tomorrow we diet: Effects of anticipated deprivation on food intake in restrained and unrestrained eaters. *Journal of Abnormal Psychology, 11*, 396–401.

U.S. Department of Education, National Center for Education Statistics. (2012). *Digest of education statistics, 2011* (NCES 2012-001).

U.S. Department of Health and Human Services. (1990). *Seventh annual report to the U.S. Congress on alcohol and health from the secretary of health and human services*. Rockville, MD: National Institute on Alcohol Abuse and Alcoholism.

Ussher, J. M. (2013). Diagnosing difficult women and pathologising femininity: Gender bias in psychiatric nosology. *Feminism & Psychology, 23*(1), 63–69.

U.S. to allow import of older Canadian cows as of November. (2007, September 14). *CBC News Online*. Retrieved September 28, 2007, from http://www.cbc.ca/canada/story/2007/09/14/usda-ruling.html

Vachon, D. D., Lynam, D. R., Widiger, T. A., Miller, J. D., McCrae, R. R., & Costa, P. T. (2013). Basic Traits Predict the Prevalence of Personality Disorder Across the Life Span The Example of Psychopathy. *Psychological Science, 24*(5), 698–705.

Vaerum, V. N., & McCabe, S. B. (2001). Rejection of dysphoric actors and implications of depressive symptom display. *Journal of Social & Clinical Psychology, 20*, 431–451.

Vahia, I. V., & Cohen, C. I. (2009). Schizophrenia and delusional disorders. In B. J. Sadock, V. A. Sadock, & P. Ruiz (Eds.), *Kaplan & Sadock's comprehensive textbook of psychiatry* (9th ed., Vol. 2, pp. 4073–4081). Philadelphia, PA: Lippincott Williams & Wilkins.

Vaillant, G. E. (1976). Natural history of male psychological health, V: The relation of choice of ego mechanisms of defense to adult adjustment. *Archives of General Psychiatry, 33*, 535–545.

Vaillant, G. E. (1979). Natural history of male psychological health. *New England Journal of Medicine, 301*, 1249–1254.

Vaillant, G. E. (1983). *The natural history of alcoholism*. Cambridge, MA: Harvard University Press.

Vaillant, G. E. (1992). *Ego mechanisms of defense: A guide for clinicians and researchers*. Washington, DC: American Psychiatric Press.

Vaillant, G. E. (2012). Lifting the field's "repression" of defenses. *American Journal of Psychiatry, 169*(9), 885–887.

Vaillant, G. E., Bond, M., & Vaillant, C. D. (1986). An empirically validated hierarchy of defense mechanisms. *Archives of General Psychiatry, 43*, 786–794.

Valchev, V. H., Nel, J. A., Van de Vijver, F. J., Meiring, D., De Bruin, G. P., & Rothmann, S. (2013). Similarities and differences in implicit personality concepts across Ethnocultural groups in South Africa. *Journal of Cross-Cultural Psychology, 44*(3), 365–388.

Valera, E. M., Faraone, S. V., Murray, K. E, and Seidman, L. J. (2007). Meta-analysis of structural imaging findings in attention-deficit/hyperactivity disorder. *Biological Psychiatry, 61*, 1361–1369.

Vallee, B. (1986). *Life with Billy*. Toronto, ON: McClelland and Stewart.

Valliant, P. M., Gristey, C., Pottier, D., & Kosmyna, R. (1999). Risk factors in violent and nonviolent offenders. *Psychological Reports, 85*, 675–680.

Vallières, A., & Morin, C. M. (2003). Actigraphy in the assessment of insomnia. *Sleep, 26*, 902–906.

Vallis, M., Ruggiero, L., Greene, G., Jones, H., Zinman, B., Rossi, S., . . . Prochaska, J. O. (2003). Stages of change for healthy eating in diabetes: Relation to demographic, eating-related, health care utilization, and psychosocial factors. *Diabetes Care, 26*, 1468–1474.

Vallis, T. M., Howes, J. L., & Standage, K. (2000). Is cognitive therapy suitable for treating individuals with personality dysfunction? *Cognitive Therapy & Research, 24*, 595–606.

Valtonen, H. M., Suominen, K., Mantere, O., Leppämäki, S., Arvilommi, P., & Isometsä, E. (2007). Suicidal behaviour during different phases of bipolar disorder. *Journal of Affective Disorders, 97*, 101–107.

Van Ameringen, M., Mancini, C., Patterson, B., & Simpson, W. (2009). Pharmacotherapy for social anxiety disorder: An update. *The Israel Journal of Psychiatry and Related Sciences, 46*(1), 53–61.

van Amsterdam, J., & van den Brink, W. (2013). Reduced-risk drinking as a viable treatment goal in problematic alcohol use and alcohol dependence. *Journal of Psychopharmacology, 27*(11), 987–997.

Van Anders, S. M., Chernick, A. B., Chernick, B. A., Hampson, F., & Fischer, W. A. (2005). Preliminary clinical experience with androgen administration for pre- and postmenopausal women with hypoactive sexual desire. *Journal of Sex and Marital Therapy, 31*, 173–185.

van Beijsterveldt, C., Hudziak, J., & Boomsma, D. (2006). Genetic and environmental influences on cross-gender behavior and relation to behavior problems: A study of Dutch twins at ages 7 and 10 years. *Archives of Sexual Behavior, 35*, 647–658.

van der Kloet, D., Giesbrecht, T., Lynn, S. J., Merckelbach, H., & de Zutter, A. (2012). Sleep normalization and decrease in dissociative experiences: Evaluation in an inpatient sample. *Journal of Abnormal Psychology, 121*, 140–150.

van der Meer, L., Sutherland, D., O'Reilly, M. F., Lancioni, G. E., & Sigafoos, J. (2012). A further comparison of manual signing, picture exchange, and speech-generating devices as communication modes for children with autism spectrum disorders. *Research in Autism Spectrum Disorders, 6*(4), 1247–1257.

Van Dycke, K. C., Rodenburg, W., van Oostrom, C. T., van Kerkhof, L. W., Pennings, J. L., Roenneberg, T., . . . van der Horst, G. T. (2015). Chronically Alternating Light Cycles Increase Breast Cancer Risk in Mice. *Current Biology, 25*(14), 1932–1937.

van Kammen, D. P., Docherty, J. P., & Bunney, W. F. (1982). Prediction of early relapse after pimozide discontinuation by response to d-amphetamine during pimozide treatment. *Biological Psychiatry, 17*, 223–242.

van Laar, M., Volkerts, E., & Verbaten, M. (2001). Subchronic effects of the GABA-agonist lorazepam and the 5-HT2A/2C antagonist ritanserin on driving performance, slow wave sleep and daytime sleepiness in healthy volunteers. *Psychopharmacology* (Berlin), *154*, 189–197.

van Munster, B. C., & de Rooij, S. E. (2014). Delirium: A synthesis of current knowledge. *Clinical Medicine, i*(2), 192–195.

van Os, J. (2011). Should attenuated psychosis syndrome be a DSM-5 diagnosis? *American Journal of Psychiatry, 168*(5), 460–463.

van Os, J., Kenis, G., & Rutten, B. P. (2010). The environment and schizophrenia. *Nature, 468*(7321), 203–212.

van Overveld, M., de Jong, P. J., & Peters, M. L. (2011). The Multi-Dimensional Blood/Injury Phobia Inventory: Its psychometric properties and relationship with disgust propensity and disgust sensitivity. *Journal of Anxiety Disorders, 25*(3), 319–325.

Van Praag, H. M., & Korf, J. (1975). Central monamine deficiency in depressions: Causative of secondary phenomenon? *Pharmakopsychiatr Neuropsychopharmakol, 8*, 322–326.

Van Rooij, A. J., Schoenmakers, T. M., Vermulst, A. A., Van Den Eijnden, R. J. J. M., & Van De Mheen, D. (2011). Online video game addiction: Identification of addicted adolescent gamers. *Addiction, 106*(1), 205–212.

Van Ryzin, M. J., Fosco, G. M., & Dishion, T. J. (2012). Family and peer predictors of substance use from early adolescence to early adulthood: An 11-year prospective analysis. *Addictive Behaviors, 37*(12), 1314–1324.

Vasey, P. L., & Bartlett, N. H. (2007). What can the Samoan Fa'afafine teach us about the Western concept of gender identity disorder in childhood? *Perspectives in Biology and Medicine, 50*, 481–490.

Vandenberg, S. G., Singer, S. M., & Pauls, D. L. (1986). *The heredity of behavior disorders in adults and children.* New York, NY: Plenum Press.

Vander Plate, C., Aral, S. O., & Magder, L. (1988). The relationship among genital herpes simplex virus, stress, and social support. *Health Psychology, 7*, 159–168.

Vannucchi, G., Masi, G., Toni, C., Dell'Osso, L., Marazziti, D., & Perugi, G. (2014). Clinical features, developmental course, and psychiatric comorbidity of adult autism spectrum disorders. *CNS Spectrums, 19*(2), 157–164.

Vassos, E., Pedersen, C. B., Murray, R. M., Collier, D. A., & Lewis, C. M. (2012). Meta-analysis of the association of urbanicity with schizophrenia. *Schizophrenia Bulletin, 38*, 1118–1123.

Vasterling, J. J., Brailey, K., Constans, J. I., & Sotker, P. B. (1998). Attention and memory dysfunction in posttraumatic stress disorders. *Neuropsychology, 12*(1), 125–133.

Vazques, G. H., Holtzman, J. N., Tondo, L., & Baldessarini, R. J. (2015). Efficacy and tolerability of treatment for bipolar depression. *Journal of Affective Disorders, 183*, 258–262.

Vazsonyi, A. T., Ksinan, A., Mikuska, J., & Jiskrova, G. (2015). The Big Five and adolescent adjustment: An empirical test across six cultures. *Personality and Individual Differences, 83*, 234–244.

Veale, D. (2000). Outcome of cosmetic surgery and "DIY" surgery inpatients with body dysmorphic disorder. *Psychiatric Bulletin, 24*(6), 218–221.

Veale, D., & Riley, S. (2001). Mirror, mirror on the wall, who is the ugliest of them all? The psychopathology of mirror gazing in body dysmorphic disorder. *Behaviour Research and Therapy, 39*, 1381–1393.

Veale, D., Boocock, A., Gournay, K., Dryden, W., Shah, F., Willson, R., & Walburn, J. (1996). Body dysmorphic disorder: A survey of 50 cases. *British Journal of Psychiatry, 169*, 196–201.

Veale, D., Ennis, M., & Lambrou, C. (2002). Possible association of body dysmorphic disorder with an occupation or education in art and design. *American Journal of Psychiatry, 159*, 1788–1790.

Veale, D., Gournay, K., Dryden, W., Boocock, A., Shah, F., Willson, R., & Walburn, J. (1996). Body dysmorphic disorder: A cognitive behavioral model and pilot randomized control trial. *Behaviour Research and Therapy, 34*, 717–729.

Vellas, B., Coley, N., Ousset, P. J., Berrut, G., Dartigues, J. F., Dubois, B., . . . Touchon, J. (2012). Long-term use of standardised Ginkgo biloba extract for the prevention of Alzheimer's disease (GuidAge): A randomised placebo-controlled trial. *The Lancet Neurology, 11*(10), 851–859.

Venables, N. C., Hall, J. R., & Patrick, C. J. (2014). Differentiating psychopathy from antisocial personality disorder: A triarchic model perspective. *Psychological Medicine, 44*(5), 1005–1013.

Venables, P. H. (1996). Schizotypy and maternal exposure to influenza and to cold temperature: The Mauritius study. *Journal of Abnormal Psychology, 105*, 53–60.

Ventura, J., Nuechterlein, K. H., Hardesty, J. P., & Gitlin, M. (1992). Life events and schizophrenic relapse after withdrawal of medication: A prospective study. *British Journal of Psychiatry, 161*, 615–620.

Ventura, J., Nuechterlein, K. H., Lukoff, D., & Hardesty, J. P. (1989). A prospective study of stressful life events and schizophrenia relapse. *Journal of Abnormal Psychology, 98*, 407–411.

Ventura, J., Nuechterlein, K. H., Subotnik, K. L., Hardesty, J. P., & Mintz, J. (2000). Life events can trigger depressive exacerbation in the early course of schizophrenia. *Journal of Abnormal Psychology, 109*(1), 139–144.

Verma, K. K., Khaitan, B. K., & Singh, O. P. (1998). The frequency of sexual dysfunction in patients attending a sex therapy clinic in North India. *Archives of Sexual Behavior, 27*, 309–314.

Vermani, M., Milosevic, I., Smith, F., & Katzman, M. A. (2005). Herbs for mental illness: Effectiveness and interaction with conventional medicines. *Journal of Family Practice, 54*, 789–800.

Vermund, S. H., Sheldon, E. K., & Sidat, M. (2015). Southern Africa: The highest priority region for HIV prevention and care interventions. *Current HIV/AIDS Report, 12*, 191–195.

Vernberg, F. M., LaGreca, A. M., Silverman, W. K., & Prinstein, M. J. (1996). Prediction of posttraumatic stress symptoms in children after Hurricane Andrew. *Journal of Abnormal Psychology, 105*, 237–248.

Verrier, R. L., Harper, R. M., & Hobson, J. A. (2000). Cardiovascular physiology: Central and autonomic regulation. In M. H. Kryger, T. Roth, & W. C. Dement (Eds.), *Principles and practice of sleep medicine* (3rd ed., pp. 179–191). Philadelphia, PA: W. B. Saunders.

Viana, A. G., Beidal, D. C., & Rabian, B. (2009). Selective mutism: A review and integration of the last 15 years. *Clinical Psychology Review, 29*(1), 57–67.

Vida, S., Monks, R. C., & Des Rosiers, P. (2002). Prevalence and correlates of elder abuse and neglect in a geriatric psychiatry service. *Canadian Journal of Psychiatry, 47*, 459–467.

Viens, M., De Koninck, J., Mercier, P., St-Onge, M., & Lorrain, D. (2003). Trait anxiety and sleep-onset insomnia: Evaluation of treatment using anxiety management training. *Journal of Psychosomatic Research, 54*, 31–37.

Viguera, A. C., Tondo, L., Koukopoulos, A. E., Reginaldi, D., Lepri, B., & Baldessarini, R. (2011). Episodes of mood disorders in 2,252 pregnancies and postpartum periods. *American Journal of Psychiatry, 168*(11), 1179–1185.

Viljoen, J. L., Roesch, R., & Zapf, P. A. (2002). Interrater reliability of the fitness interview test across 4 professional groups. *Canadian Journal of Psychiatry, 47*, 945–952.

Villeneuve, F., & Lemelin, S. (2005). Open-label study of atypical neuroleptic quetiapine for treatment of borderline personality disorder: Impulsivity as main target. *Journal of Clinical Psychiatry, 66*, 1298–1303.

Virag, R. (1999). Indications and early results of sildenafil (Viagra) in erectile dysfunction. *Urology, 54*, 1073–1077.

Vitacco, M. J., Neumann, C. S., & Caldwell, M. F. (2010). Predicting antisocial behavior in high-risk male adolescents: Contributions of psychopathy and instrumental violence. *Criminal Justice and Behavior, 37*(8), 833–846.

Vitacco, M. J., Neumann, C. S., & Pardini, D. A. (2014). Predicting future criminal offending in a community-based sample of males using self-reported psychopathy. *Criminal Justice and Behavior, 41*(3), 345–363.

Vitiello, B., & Lederhendler, I. (2000). Research on eating disorders: Current status and future prospects. *Biological Psychiatry, 47*, 777–786.

Voderholzer, U., Hohagen, F., Klein, T., Jungnickel, J., Kirschbaum, C., Berger, M., & Riemann, D. (2004). Impact of sleep deprivation and subsequent recovery sleep on cortisol in unmedicated depressed patients. *American Journal of Psychiatry, 161*(8), 1404–1410.

Voderholzer, U., Schwartz, C., Thiel, N., Kuelz, A. K., Hartmann, A., Scheidt, C. E., Schlegl, S., & Zeeck, A. (2014). A comparison of schemas, schema modes and childhood traumas in obsessive–compulsive disorder, chronic pain disorder and eating disorders. *Psychopathology, 47*(1), 24–31.

Vogel, S. A., & Reder, S. (1998). Educational attainment of adults with learning disabilities. In S. A. Vogel & S. Reder (Eds.), *Learning disabilities, literacy, and adult education* (pp. 5–28). Baltimore, MD: Paul H. Brookes.

Voglmaier, M. M., Seidman, L. J., Niznikiewicz, M. A., Dickey, C. C., Shenton, M. F., & McCarley, R. W. (2000). Verbal and nonverbal neuropsychological test performance in subjects with schizotypal personality disorder. *American Journal of Psychiatry, 157*, 787–793.

Vohs, K. D., Bardone, A. M., Joiner, T. F., Jr., Abramson, L. Y., & Heatherton, T. F. (1999). Perfectionism, perceived weight status, and self-esteem interact to predict bulimic symptoms: A model of bulimic symptom development. *Journal of Abnormal Psychology, 108*, 695–700.

Vohs, K. D., Voelz, Z. R., Pettit, J. W., Bardone, A. M., Katz, J., Abramson, L. Y., . . . Joiner, T. E., Jr. (2001). Perfectionism, body dissatisfaction, and self-esteem: An interactive model of bulimic symptom development. *Journal of Social and Clinical Psychology, 20*, 476–497.

Voigt, K., Nagel, A., Meyer, B., Langs, G., Braukhaus, C., & Lowe, B. (2010). Towards positive diagnostic criteria: A systematic review of somatoform disorder diagnoses and suggestions for future classification. *Journal of Psychosomatic Research, 68*(5), 403–414.

Voigt, K., Wollburg, E., Weinmann, N., Herzog, A., Meyer, B., Langs, G., & Lowe, B. (2012). Predictive validity and clinical utility of DSM-5 somatic symptom disorder—Comparison with DSM-IV somatoform disorders and additional criteria for consideration. *Journal of Psychosomatic Research, 73*(5), 345–350.

Volkmar, F. R., Klin, A., & Schultz, R. T. (2005). Pervasive developmental disorders. In B. J. Sadock & V. A. Sadock (Eds.), *Kaplan & Sadock's comprehensive textbook of psychiatry* (pp. 3164–3182). Philadelphia, PA: Lippincott Williams & Wilkins.

Volkmar, F. R., Klin, A., Schultz, R. T., & State, M. W. (2009). Pervasive developmental disorders. In B. J. Sadock, V. A. Sadock, & P. Ruiz (Eds.), *Kaplan & Sadock's comprehensive textbook of psychiatry* (9th ed., Vol. 2, pp. 3540–3559). Philadelphia, PA: Lippincott Williams & Wilkins.

Volkow, N. D., & Swanson, J. M. (2003). Variables that affect the clinical use and abuse of methylphenidate in the treatment of ADHD. *American Journal of Psychiatry, 160*, 1909–1918.

Volkow, N. D., & Warren, K. R. (2015). Drug addiction: The neurobiology of behavior gone awry. In R. K. Ries, D. A. Fiellin, S. C. Miller, & R. Saitz (Eds.), *The ASAM principles of addiction medicine* (5th ed., pp. 3–18). New York, NY: Wolters Kluwer.

Volkow, N. D., Baler, R. D., Compton, W. M., & Weiss, S. R. B. (2014). Adverse health effects of marijuana use. *New England Journal of Medicine, 370*, 2219–2227. https://doi.org/10.1056/NEJMra1402309

Volkow, N. D., Wang, G. J., Kollins, S. H., Wigal, T. L., Newcorn, J. H., Telang, F., . . . Swanson, J. M. (2009). Evaluating dopamine reward pathway in ADHD: Clinical implications. *JAMA, 302*(10), 1084–1091.

Von Knorring, A. L., Cloninger, C. R., Bohman, M., & Sigvardsson, S. (1983). An adoption study of depressive disorders and substance abuse. *Archives of General Psychiatry, 40*, 943–950.

von Ranson, K. M., Iacono, W. G., & McGue, M. (2002). Disordered eating and substance use in an epidemiological sample: I. Associations within individuals. *International Journal of Eating Disorders, 31*, 389–403.

Voon, V., Gallea, C., Hattori, N., Bruno, M., Ekanayake, V., & Hallett, M. (2010). The involuntary nature of conversion disorder. *Neurology, 74*(3), 223–228.

Voos, A., Pelphrey, K., Tirrell, J., Bolling, D., Wyk, B., Kaiser, M., & Ventola, P. (2013). Neural mechanisms of improvements in social motivation after pivotal response treatment: Two case studies. *Journal of Autism and Developmental Disorders, 43*(1), 1–10.

Voyer P., Verreault R., Mengue P., & Morin, M. C. (2006). Prevalence of insomnia and its associated factors in older long-term care residents. *Archives in Gerontology and Geriatrics, 42*, 1–20.

Voyer, P., McCusker, J., Cole, M. G., St-Jacques, S., & Khomenko, L. (2007). Factors associated with delirium severity among older patients. *Journal of Clinical Nursing, 16*, 819–831.

Vriends, N., Pfatz, M. C., Novianti, P., & Hadiyono, J. (2013). Taijin kyofusho and social anxiety and their clinical relevance in Indonesia and Switzerland. *Frontiers in Psychology, 4*, 3.

Vrshek-Schallhorn, S., Stroud, C. B., Mineka, S., Hammen, C., Zinbarg, R. E., Wolitzky-Taylor, K., & Craske, M. G. (2015). Chronic and episodic interpersonal stress as statistically unique predictors of depression in two samples of emerging adults. *Journal of Abnormal Psychology, 124*(4), 918–932. https://doi.org/10.1037/abn0000088

Vuchinich, S., Bank, L., & Patterson, G. R. (1992). Parenting, peers, and the stability of antisocial behavior in preadolescent boys. *Developmental Psychology, 28*, 510–521.

Waddell, J., Morris, R. W., & Bouton, M. E. (2006). Effects of bed nucleus of the stria terminalis lesions on conditioned anxiety: Aversive conditioning with long-duration conditional stimuli and reinstatement of extinguished fear. *Behavioral Neuroscience, 120*, 324–336.

Wadsworth, S. J., DeFries, J. C., Stevenson, J., Gilger, J. W., & Pennington, B. F. (1992). Gender ratios among reading-disabled children and their siblings as a function of parent impairment. *Journal of Child Psychology and Psychiatry, 33*, 1229–1239.

Wager, T. (2005). The neural bases of placebo effects in pain. *Current Directions in Psychological Science, 14*, 175–179.

Wagner, A. W., & Linehan, M. M. (1994). Relationship between childhood sexual abuse and topography of parasuicide among women with borderline personality disorder. *Journal of Personality Disorders, 8*, 1–9.

Wagner, B. M. (1997). Family risk factors for child and adolescent suicidal behavior. *Psychological Bulletin, 121*, 246–298.

Wagner, D., Becker, B., Koester, P., Gouzoulis-Mayfrank, E., & Daumann, J. (2013). A prospective study of learning, memory, and executive function in new MDMA users. *Addiction, 108*(1), 136–145.

Wagner, G., Penelo, E., Wanner, C., Gwinner, P., Trofaier, M. L., Imgart, H., ... Karwautz, A. F. (2013). Internet-delivered cognitive–behavioural therapy v. conventional guided self-help for bulimia nervosa: Long-term evaluation of a randomised controlled trial. *British Journal of Psychiatry, 202*(2), 135–141.

Wagner, M. (1990, April). The school programs and school performance of secondary students classified as learning disabled: Findings from the National Longitudinal Transition Study of special education students. Paper presented at Division G, American Educational Research Association Annual Meeting, Boston, MA.

Wahlbeck, K., Cheine, M., Essali, A., & Adams, C. (1999). Evidence of clozapine's effectiveness in schizophrenia: A systematic review and metaanalysis of randomized trials. *American Journal of Psychiatry, 156*, 990–999.

Wakefield, J. C. (1992). The concept of mental disorder: On the boundary between biological facts and social values. *American Psychologist, 47*, 373–388.

Wakefield, J. C. (1999). Evolutionary versus prototype analyses of the concept of disorder. *Journal of Abnormal Psychology, 108*, 3, 374–399.

Wakefield, J. C. (2003). Dysfunction as a factual component of disorder. *Behavior Research and Therapy, 41*, 969–990.

Wakefield, J. C. (2009). Mental disorder and moral responsibility: Disorders of personhood as harmful dysfunctions, with special reference to alcoholism. *Philosophy, Psychiatry, & Psychology, 16*(1), 91–99.

Wakefield, J. C., Schmitz, M. F., First, M. B., & Horwitz, A. V. (2007). Extending the bereavement exclusion for major depression to other losses: Evidence from the national comorbidity survey. *Archives of General Psychiatry, 64*, 433–440.

Wald, J. (2002). *The efficacy of virtual reality exposure therapy to treat driving phobia.* Unpublished doctoral dissertation, Department of Counseling Psychology, University of British Columbia.

Wald, J., & Taylor, S. (2000). Efficacy of virtual reality exposure therapy to treat driving phobia: A case report. *Journal of Behavior Therapy & Experimental Psychiatry, 31*, 249–257.

Waliszewski, B., & Smithouser, B. (1997). *Plugged in music review—Sarah McLachlan* [Review of the album Surfacing]. Retrieved June 25, 2004, from http://www.pluggedinonline.com/music/music/a0001196.cfm

Walker, D. L., Ressler, K. J., Lu, K.-T., & Davis, M. (2002). Facilitation of conditioned fear extinction by systemic administration or intra-amygdala infusions of D-cycloserine assessed with fear-potentiated startle. *Journal of Neuroscience, 22*, 2343–2351.

Walker, F. (1991). Research on life-span development in schizophrenia. In F. F. Walker (Ed.), *Schizophrenia: A life-course developmental perspective* (pp. 1–6). New York, NY: Academic Press.

Walker, F. F., Grimes, K. F., Davis, D. M., & Smith, A. J. (1993). Childhood precursors of schizophrenia: Facial expressions of emotion. *American Journal of Psychiatry, 150*, 1654–1660.

Walker, L. (1979). *The battered woman.* New York, NY: Harper & Row.

Wall, T. D., Wygant, D. B., & Sellbom, M. (2015). Boldness explains a key difference between psychopathy and antisocial personality disorder. *Psychiatry, Psychology and Law, 22*(1), 94–105.

Wallace, C. S., Kilman, V. L., Withers, G. S., & Greenough, W. T. (1992). Increases in dendritic length in occipital cortex after 4 days of differential housing in weanling rats. *Behavioral and Neural Biology, 58*, 64–68.

Wallace, J., & O'Hara, M. W. (1992). Increases in depressive symptomatology in the rural elderly: Results from a cross-sectional and longitudinal study. *Journal of Abnormal Psychology, 101*, 398–404.

Waller, N. G., & Ross, C. A. (1997). The prevalence and biometric structure of pathological dissociation in the general population: Taxometric and behavior genetic findings. *Journal of Abnormal Psychology, 106*, 499–510.

Waller, N. G., Putnam, F. W., & Carlson, F. B. (1996). Types of dissociation and dissociative types: A taxometric analysis of dissociative experiences. *Psychological Methods, 1*, 300–321.

Waller, R., Gardner, F., Shaw, D. S., Dishion, T. J., Wilson, M. N., & Hyde, L. W. (2014). Callous-unemotional behavior and early-childhood onset of behavior problems: The role of parental harshness and warmth. *Journal of Clinical Child & Adolescent Psychology, 44*(4), 655–667.

Waln, O., & Jankovic, J. (2013). An update on tardive dyskinesia: From phenomenology to treatment. *Tremor and Other Hyperkinetic Movements, 12*(3), 103–161.

Walsh, B. T. (1991). Fluoxetine treatment of bulimia nervosa. *Journal of Psychosomatic Research, 35*, 471–475.

Walsh, B. T. (1995). Pharmacotherapy of eating disorders. In K. D. Brownell & C. G. Fairburn (Eds.), *Eating disorders and obesity: A comprehensive handbook* (pp. 313–317). New York, NY: Guilford Press.

Walsh, B. T. (2010). Eating disorders in DSM-V: Review of existing literature (Part 3). *International Journal of Eating Disorders, 43*(2), 97.

Walsh, B. T., Agras, W. S., Devlin, M. J., Fairburn, C. G., Wilson, G. T., Kahn, C., & Chally, M. K. (2000). Fluoxetine for bulimia nervosa following poor response to psychotherapy. *American Journal of Psychiatry, 157*, 1332–1334.

Walsh, B. T., Hadigan, C. M., Devlin, M. J., Gladis, M., & Roose, S. P. (1991). Long-term outcome of antidepressant treatment of bulimia nervosa. *Archives of General Psychiatry, 148*, 1206–1212.

Walsh, B. T., Kaplan, A. S., Attia, E., Olmsted, M., Parides, M., Carter, J. C., & Rockert, W. (2006). Fluoxetine after weight restoration in anorexia nervosa. *JAMA: Journal of the American Medical Association, 295*, 2605–2612.

Walsh, B. T., Wilson G. T., Loeb, K. L., Devlin, M. J., Pike, K. M., Roose, S. P., . . . Waternaux, C. (1997). Medication and psychotherapy in the treatment of bulimia nervosa. *American Journal of Psychiatry, 154*, 523–531.

Walsh, J. K., & Ustun, T. B. (1999). Prevalence and health consequences of insomnia. *Sleep, 22*(Suppl. 3), S427–S436.

Walsh, J. K., Mayleben, D., Guico-Pabia, C., Vandormael, K., Martinez, R., & Deacon, S. (2008). Efficacy of the selective extrasynaptic GABA A agonist, gaboxadol, in a model of transient insomnia: A randomized, controlled clinical trial. *Sleep Medicine, 9*(4), 393–402.

Walsh, N. P. (2001, October 14). I never discuss my mistresses or my tailors. *The Observer.* Retrieved October 25, 2003, from http://observer.guardian.co.uk/life/story/0,6903,573496,00.html

Walsh, T. M., Stewart, S. H., McLaughlin, F., & Comeau, N. (2004). Gender differences in Childhood Anxiety Sensitivity Index (CASI) dimensions. *Journal of Anxiety Disorders, 18*, 695–706.

Walters, F. F., & Kendler, K. S. (1995). Anorexia nervosa and anorexia-like syndromes in a population based female twin sample. *American Journal of Psychiatry, 152*, 64–71.

Wampold, B. E., Minami, T., Tierney, S. C., Baskin, T. W., & Bhati, K. S. (2005). The placebo is powerful: Estimating placebo effects in medicine and psychotherapy from randomized clinical trials. *Journal of Clinical Psychology, 61*(7), 835–854.

Wan, M., Abel, K., & Green, J. (2008). The transmission of risk to children from mothers with schizophrenia: A developmental psychopathology model. *Clinical Psychology Review, 28*(4), 613–637.

Wang, J., & Patten, S. B. (2001). Perceived work stress and major depression in the Canadian employed population, 20–49 years old. *Journal of Occupational Health Psychology, 6*, 283–289.

Wang, J., & Patten, S. B. (2002). Prospective study of frequent heavy alcohol use and the risk of major depression in the Canadian general population. *Depression & Anxiety, 15*, 42–45.

Wang, J. L., Lesage, A., Schmitz, N., & Drapeau, A. (2008). The relationship between work stress and mental disorders in men and women: Findings from a population-based study. *Journal of Epidemiology and Community Health, 62*, 42–47.

Wang P. S., Bohn, R. L., Glynn, R. J., Mogun, H., & Avorn, J. (2001). Hazardous benzodiazepine regimens in the elderly: Effects of half-life, dosage, and duration on risk of hip fracture. *American Journal of Psychiatry, 158*, 892–898.

Wang, T., Collet, J. P., Shapiro, S., & Ware, M. A. (2008). Adverse effects of medical cannabinoids: A systematic review. *CMAJ, 178*(13), 1669–1678.

Wang, Z., Baker, D. G., Harrer, J., Hamner, M., Price, M., & Amstadter, A. (2011). The relationship between combat-related posttraumatic stress disorder and the 5-HTTLPR/ rs25531 polymorphism. *Depression and Anxiety, 28*, 1067–1073.

Wang, Z., Neylan, T. C., Mueller, S. G., Lenoci, M., Truran, D., Marmar, C. R., ... Schuff, N. (2010). Magnetic resonance imaging of hippocampal subfields in posttraumatic stress disorder. *Archives of General Psychiatry, 67*(3), 296–303.

Wanklin, J. (1998). *Let me make it good: A chronicle of my life with borderline personality disorder* (chap. 15). Retrieved November 1, 2007, from http://www.geocities.com/anorexiannie/chapterfifteen.html

Ward, M. M., Swan, G. F., & Chesney, M. A. (1987). Arousal-reduction treatments for mild hypertension: A meta-analysis of recent studies. *Handbook of Hypertension, 9*, 285–302.

Ward, T., & Beech, A. R. (2008). An integrated theory of sexual offending. In D. R. Laws & W. T. O'Donohue (Eds.), *Sexual deviance: Theory, assessment, and treatment* (2nd ed., pp. 21–36). New York, NY: Guilford Press.

Warneke, L. B. (1991). Benzodiazepines: Abuse and new use. *Canadian Journal of Psychiatry*, 36, 194–205.

Warren, L. A., Shi, Q., Young, K., Borenstein, A., & Martiniuk, A. (2015). Prevalence and incidence of dementia among indigenous populations: A systematic review. *International Psychogeriatrics*, 27(12), 1959–1970.

Warren, S. F., & Reichle, J. (1992). *Causes and effects in communication and language intervention*. Baltimore, MD: Paul H. Brookes.

Warshaw, M. G., Dolan, R. T., & Keller, M. B. (2000). Suicidal behavior in patients with current or past panic disorder: Five years of prospective data from the Harvard/Brown Anxiety Research Program. *American Journal of Psychiatry*, 157, 1876–1878

Warwick, H. M., & Salkovskis, P. M. P. M. (1990). *Hypochondriasis. Behaviour Research & Therapy*, 28, 105–117.

Waschbusch, D. A. (2002). A meta-analytic examination of comorbid hyperactive-impulsive-attention problems and conduct problems. *Psychological Bulletin*, 128, 118–150.

Waschbusch, D. A., Kipp, H. L.; & Pelham, W. F. Jr. (1998). Generalization of behavioral and psychostimulant treatment of attention-deficit/hyperactivity disorder (ADHD): Discussion and examples. *Behaviour Research & Therapy*, 36, 675–694.

Waschbusch, D. A., Pelham, W. F., Jr., & Massetti, G. (2005). The behavior education support and treatment (BFST) school intervention program: Pilot project data examining school wide, targeted-school, and targeted-home approaches. *Journal of Attention Disorders*, 9, 313–322.

Waters, F., Allen, P., Aleman, A., Fernyhough, C., Woodward, T. S., Badcock, J. C., ... Vercammen, A. (2012). Auditory hallucinations in schizophrenia and nonschizophrenia populations: A review and integrated model of cognitive mechanisms. *Schizophrenia Bulletin*, 38(4), 683–693.

Watson, D. (2005). Rethinking the mood and anxiety disorders: A quantitative hierarchical model for DSM-V. *Journal of Abnormal Psychology*, 114[Special issue], 522–536.

Watson, J. B. (1913). Psychology as a behaviorist views it. *Psychology Review*, 20, 158–177.

Watson, J. C., & Greenberg, L. S. (2017). *Emotion-focused therapy for generalized anxiety*. American Psychological Association.

Watt, M. C., Stewart, S. H., Birch, C. D., & Bernier, D. (2006). Brief CBT for high anxiety sensitivity decreases drinking problems, relief alcohol outcome expectancies, and conformity drinking motives: Evidence from a randomized controlled trial. *Journal of Mental Health*, 15, 683–695.

Way, B. M., & Taylor, S. E. (2010). Social influences on health: Is serotonin a critical mediator? *Psychosomatic Medicine*, 72, 107–112.

Weaver, I. C. G., Cervoni, N., Champagne, F. A., D'Alessio, A. C., Sharma, S., Seckl, J. R., ... Meaney, M. J. (2004). Epigenetic programming by maternal behavior. *Nature Neuroscience*, 7(8), 847–854.

Webster, C. D., Douglas, K. S., Faves, D., & Hart, S. D. (1997a). *HCR-20: Assessing risk for violence* (version 2). Vancouver, BC: Simon Fraser University.

Webster, C. D., Douglas, K. S., Faves, D., & Hart, S. D. (1997b). Assessing risk of violence to others. In C. D. Webster & M. A. Jackson (Eds.), *Impulsivity: Theory, assessment, and treatment* (pp. 251–277). New York, NY: Guilford Press.

Webster-Stratton, C., & Hammond, M. (1997). Treating children with early-onset conduct problems: A comparison of child and parent training interventions. *Journal of Consulting and Clinical Psychology*, 65, 93–109.

Wechsler, D. (1997). Wechsler Adult Intelligence Scale—Third Edition: Technical manual. San Antonio, TX: The Psychological Corporation.

Weck, F., Neng, J. M. B., Richtberg, S., Jakob, M., & Stangier, U. (2015). Cognitive therapy versus exposure therapy for hypochondriasis (hleath anxiety): A randomized controlled trial. *Journal of Consulting and Clinical Psychology*, 83, 665–676.

Weems, C. F., Silverman, W. K., & La Greca, A. M. (2000). What do youths referred for anxiety problems worry about? Worry and its relation to anxiety and anxiety disorders in children and adolescents. *Journal of Abnormal Child Psychology*, 28, 63–72.

Weerasinghe, S., Stewart, S. H., & Mitchell, T. L. (2016). Longitudinal follow up of health outcomes of the 1998 Swissair 111 crash. *Journal of Epidemiology and Public Health Review*, 1(6). https://doi.org/10.16966/2471-8211.131

Wegner, D. M. (1989). *White bear and other unwanted thoughts: Suppression, obsession, and the psychology of mental control*. New York, NY: Guilford Press.

Weiden, P. J., Dixon, L., Frances, A., Appelbaum, P., Haas, G., & Rapkin, B. (1991). In C. A. Tamminga & S. C. Schulz (Eds.), *Advances in neuropsychiatry and psychopharmacology. 1: Schizophrenia Research* (pp. 285–296). New York, NY: Raven Press.

Weinberg, M. S., Lottes, I. L., & Shaver, F. M. (1995). Swedish or American youth: Who is more permissive? *Archives of Sexual Behavior*, 24, 409–437.

Weinberg, R. A. (1989). Intelligence and IQ: Landmark issues and great debates. *American Psychologist*, 44, 98–104.

Weinberger, D. R. (1995). Schizophrenia as a neurodevelopmental disorder. In S. R. Hirsch & D. R. Weinberger (Eds.), *Schizophrenia* (pp. 293–323). Oxford, UK: Blackwell.

Weiner, D. B. (1979). The apprenticeship of Philippe Pinel: A new document, "Observations of Citizen Pussin on the insane." *American Journal of Psychiatry*, 136, 1128–1134.

Weiner, D. N. (1996). *Premature ejaculation: An evaluation of sensitivity to erotica*. Unpublished doctoral dissertation, State University of New York, Albany.

Weiner, L., & Avery-Clark, C. (2014). Sensate Focus: Clarifying the Masters and Johnson's model. *Sexual and Relationship Therapy*, 29(3), 307–319.

Weiner, M. F., Hynan, L. S., Beekly, D., Koepsell, T. D., & Kukull, W. A. (2007). Comparison of Alzheimer's disease in American Indians, whites, and African Americans. *Alzheimer's & Dementia*, 3(3), 211–216.

Weiner, M. W., Aisen, P. S., Jack Jr, C. R., Jagust, W. J., Trojanowski, J. Q., Shaw, L., & Schmidt, M. (2010). The Alzheimer's Disease Neuroimaging Initiative: Progress report and future plans. *Alzheimer's and Dementia*, 6(3), 202–211, e207.

Weiner, M. W., Veitch, D. P., Aisen, P. S., Beckett, L. A., Cairns, N. J., Green, R. C., & Trojanowski, J. Q. (2012a). The Alzheimer's Disease Neuroimaging Initiative: A review of papers published since its inception. *Alzheimer's & Dementia*, 8(1, Supplement), S1–S68.

Weinshilboum, R. (2003). Inheritance and drug response. *New England Journal of Medicine*, 348, 529–537.

Weinstock, H., Berman, S., & Cates, W. (2004). Sexually transmitted diseases in American youth: Incidence and prevalence estimates. *Perspectives on Sexual and Reproductive Health*, 36, 6–10.

Weisberg, R. B., Maki, K. M., Culpepper, L., & Keller, M. B. (2005). Is anyone really M.A.D.? The occurrence and course of mixed anxiety-depressive disorder in a sample of primary care patients. *Journal of Nervous and Mental Disease*, 193(4), 223–230.

Weisburg, R. B., Brown, T. A., Wincze, J. P., & Barlow, D. H. (2001). Causal attributions and male sexual arousal: The impact of attributions for a bogus erectile difficulty on sexual arousal, cognitions, and affect. *Journal of Abnormal Psychology*, 110, 324–334.

Weiser, M. (2011). Early intervention for schizophrenia: The risk-benefit ratio of antipsychotic treatment in the prodromal phase. *American Journal of Psychiatry*, 168(8), 761–763.

Weiskrantz, L. (1980). Varieties of residual experience. *Quarterly Journal of Experimental Psychology*, 32, 365–386.

Weiskrantz, L. (1992, September/October). Unconscious vision: The strange phenomenon of blindsight. *The Sciences*, pp. 23–28.

Weiss, B., & Garber, J. (2003). Developmental differences in the phenomenology of depression. *Development and Psychopathology*, 15, 403–430.

Weiss, M. D., Wasdell, M. B., Bomben, M. M., Rea, K. J., & Freeman, R. D. (2006). Sleep hygiene and melatonin treatment for children and adolescents with ADHD and initial insomnia. *Journal of the American Academy of Child and Adolescent Psychiatry*, 45, 512–519.

Weiss, R. D., & Iannucci, R. A. (2009). Cocaine-related disorders. In B. J. Sadock, V. A. Sadock, & P. Ruiz (Eds.), *Kaplan & Sadock's comprehensive textbook of psychiatry* (9th ed., Vol. 1, pp. 1318–1331). Philadelphia, PA: Lippincott Williams & Wilkins.

Weisse, C. S., Pato, C. W., McAllister, C. G., Littman, R., & Breier, A. (1990). Differential effects of controllable and uncontrollable acute stress on lymphocyte proliferation and leukocyte percentages in humans. *Brain, Behavior, and Immunity*, 4, 339–351.

Weissman, M. (1985). The epidemiology of anxiety disorders: Rates, risks, and familial patterns. In A. H. Tuma & J. D. Maser (Eds.), *Anxiety and the anxiety disorders*. Hillsdale, NJ: Erlbaum.

Weissman, M. (1995). *Mastering depression: A patient's guide to interpersonal psychotherapy*. Albany, NY: Graywind.

Weissman, M. M. (1993). The epidemiology of personality disorders: A 1990 update. *Journal of Personality Disorders, Supplement, Spring*, 44–62.

Weissman, M. M., & Klerman, G. L. (1977). Sex differences and the epidemiology of depression. *Archives of General Psychiatry*, 34, 98–111.

Weissman, M. M., & Olfson, M. (1995). Depression in women: Implications for health care research. *Science*, 269, 799–801.

Weissman, M. M., Bland, R. C., Canino, G. J., Faravelli, C., Greenwald, S., Hwu, H. G., ... Yeh, E. K. (1994). The cross national epidemiology of obsessive compulsive disorder. *Journal of Clinical Psychiatry*, 55, 5–10.

Weissman, M. M., Bland, R. C., Canino, G. J., Faravelli, C., Greenwald, S., Hwu, H. G. K., ... Yeh, E. (1996). Cross-national epidemiology of major depression and bipolar disorder. *Journal of the American Medical Association*, 276, 293–299.

Weissman, M. M., Bland, R. C., Canino, G. J., Faravelli, C., Greenwald, S., Hwu, H. G., ... Yeh, E. K. (1997). The cross-national epidemiology of panic disorder. *Archives of General Psychiatry*, 54, 305–312.

Weissman, M. M., Bland, R. C., Canino, G. J., Greenwald, S., Lee, C. K., Newman, S. C., ... Wickramaratne, P. J. (1996). The cross-national epidemiology of social phobia: A preliminary report. *International Clinical Psychopharmacology*, 11, 9–14.

Weissman, M. M., Bruce, M. L., Leaf, P. J., Florio, L. P., & Holzer, C. (1991). Affective disorders. In L. N. Robins & D. A. Regier (Eds.), *Psychiatric disorders of America: The epidemiologic catchment area study* (pp. 53–80). New York, NY: Free Press.

Weissman, M. M., Klerman, G. L., Markowitz, J. S., & Ouellette, R. (1989). Suicidal ideation and suicide attempts in panic disorder and attacks. *New England Journal of Medicine*, 321, 1209–1214.

Weissman, M., Wickramaratne, P., Nomura, Y., Verdeli, H., Pilowsky, D., Grillon, C., & Bruder, G. (2005). Families at high and low risk for depression: A 3-generation study. *Archives of General Psychiatry*, 62, 29–36.

Weitze, C., & Osburg, S. (1996). Transsexualism in Germany: Empirical data on epidemiology and application of the German transsexuals' act during its first ten years. *Archives of Sexual Behavior*, 25, 409–465.

Wekerle, C., & Wall, A. M. (Eds.). (2002). *The violence and addiction equation: Theoretical and clinical issues in substance abuse and relationship violence*. New York, NY: Brunner-Routledge.

Welham, J., Scott, J., Williams, G., Najman, J., Bor, W., O'Callaghan, M., McGrath, J. (2008). Emotional and behavioural antecedents of young adults who screen positive for non-affective psychosis: A 21-year birth cohort study. *Psychological Medicine*, 39(4), 625–634.

Wells, B., & Twenge, J. (2005). Changes in young people's sexual behavior and attitudes, 1943–1999: A cross-temporal metaanalysis. *Review of General Psychology*, 9, 249–261.

Wells, D. L., & Ott, C. A. (2011). The "new" marijuana. *The Annals of Pharmacotherapy*, 45(3), 414–417.

Wells, K. B., Stewart, A., Hays, R. D., Burnam, M. A., Rogers, W., Daniels, M., ... Ware, J. (1989). The functioning and well-being of depressed patients: Results from the medical outcomes study. *JAMA, 262*(7), 914–919.

Wenden v. Trikha (1991), 116 A. R. 81 (Q. B.).

Wender, P. H., Kety, S. S., Rosenthal, D., Schlusinger, F., Ortmann, J., & Lunde, I. (1986). Psychiatric disorders in the biological and adoptive families of adopted individuals with affective disorders. *Archives of General Psychiatry, 43*, 923–929.

Wermter, A. K., Kamp-Becker, I., Hesse, P., Schulte-Körne, G., Strauch, K., & Remschmidt, H. (2010). Evidence for the involvement of genetic variation in the oxytocin receptor gene (OXTR) in the etiology of autistic disorders on high-functioning level. *American Journal of Medical Genetics Part B: Neuropsychiatric Genetics, 153*B(2), 629–639.

Werner, K. B., Few, L. R., & Bucholtz, K. K. (2015). Epidemiology, comorbidity, and behavioral genetics of antisocial personality disorder and psychopathy. *Psychiatric Annals, 45*(4), 195.

Westen, D. (2000). The efficacy of dialectical behavior therapy for borderline personality disorder. *Clinical Psychology: Science and Practice, 7*, 92–94.

Westra, H. A., & Stewart, S. H. (1998). Cognitive behavioural therapy and pharmacotherapy: Complementary or contradictory approaches to the treatment of anxiety? *Clinical Psychology Review, 18*, 307–340.

Westra, H. A., & Stewart, S. H. (2002). As-needed use of benzodiazepines in managing clinical anxiety: Incidence and implications. *Current Pharmaceutical Design, 8*, 59–74.

Westra, H. A., Stewart, S. H., Teehan, M., Johl K., Dozois D. J. A., & Hill, T. (2004). Benzodiazepine use associated with decreased memory for psychoeducation material in cognitive behavioral therapy for panic disorder. *Cognitive Therapy and Research, 28*, 193–208.

Wetherell, J. L., Ayers, C. R., Nuevo, R., Stein, M. B., Ramsdell, J., & Patterson, T. L. (2010). Medical conditions and depressive, anxiety, and somatic symptoms in older adults with and without generalized anxiety disorder. *Aging and Mental Health, 14*, 764–768.

Wetherell, J. L., Lenze, E. J., & Stanley, M. (2005). Evidence-based treatment of geriatric anxiety disorders. *Psychiatric Clinics of North America, 28*, 871–896.

Wetzler, S., & Jose, A. (2012). Passive-aggressive personality disorder: The demise of a syndrome. In T. A. Widiger (Ed.), *The Oxford handbook of personality disorders* (pp. 674–693). New York, NY: Oxford University Press.

Wexler, N. S. (2012). Huntington's disease: Advocacy driving science. *Annual Review of Medicine, 63*, 1–22.

Whiffen, V. F., & Clark, S. F. (1997). Does victimization account for sex differences in depressive symptoms? *British Journal of Clinical Psychology, 36*, 185–193.

Whiffen, V. F., & Demidenko, N. (2006). Mood disturbance across the life span. In J. Worell & C. D. Goodheart (Eds.), *Handbook of girls' and women's psychological health: Gender and well-being across the lifespan* (pp. 51–59). New York, NY: Oxford University Press, 2006.

Whisman, M. A., Johnson, D. P., & Smolen, A. (2011). Dysfunctional attitudes

and the serotonin transporter promoter polymorphism (5-HTTLPR). *Behavior Therapy, 42*(2), 300–305.

Whisman, M., Weinstock, L., & Tolejko, N. (2006). Marriage and depression. In L. M. Corey & S. Goodman (Eds.), *A handbook for the social, behavioral, and biomedical sciences* (pp. 219–240). Boulder, CO: Cambridge University Press.

Whitaker, R. (2010). *Anatomy of an epidemic*. New York, NY: Random House.

Whitbourne, S. K., & Skultety, K. M. (2002). Body image development: Adulthood and aging. In T. M. Cash & T. Pruzinsky (Eds.), *Body image: A handbook of theory, research, and clinical practice* (pp. 83–90). New York, NY: Guilford, Press.

White, J. L., Moffitt, T. F., & Silva, P. A. (1989). A prospective replication of the protective effects of IQ in subjects at high risk for juvenile delinquency. *Journal of Consulting and Clinical Psychology, 57*, 719–724.

White, K. S., Brown, T. A., Somers, T. J., & Barlow, D. H. (2006). Avoidance behavior in panic disorder: The moderating influence of perceived control. *Behaviour Research and Therapy, 44*, 147–157.

White, K. S., Payne, L. A., Gorman, J. M., Shear, M. K., Woods, S. W., Saksa, J. R., & Barlow, D. H. (2013). Does maintenance CBT contribute to long-term treatment response of panic disorder with or without agoraphobia? A randomized controlled clinical trial. *Journal of Consulting and Clinical Psychology, 81*, 47–57.

White, K., Lehman, D. R., Hemphill, K. J., Mandel, D. R., & Lehman, A. M. (2006). Causal attributions, perceived control, and psychological adjustment: A study of chronic fatigue syndrome. *Journal of Applied Social Psychology, 36*(1), 75–99.

White, W., & Kurtz, E. (2008). Twelve defining moments in the history of Alcoholics Anonymous. In M. Galanter & L. A. Kaskutas (Eds.), *Research on Alcoholics Anonymous and spirituality in addiction recovery: The twelve-step program model, spiritually oriented recovery, twelve-step membership, effectiveness and outcome research* (pp. 37–57). New York, NY: Springer-Verlag.

Whitehurst, G. J., Fischel, J. F., Lonigan, C. J., Valdez-Menchaca, M. C., DeBaryshe, B. D., & Caulfield, M. B. (1988). Verbal interaction in families of normal and expressive-language-delayed children. *Developmental Psychology, 24*, 690–699.

Whitfield-Gabrieli, S., Ghosh, S. S., Nieto-Castanon, A., Saygin, Z., Doehrmann, O., Chai, X. J., Reynold, G. O., Hofmann, S. G., Pollack, M. H., & Gabrieli, J. D. E. (2016). Brain connectomics predict response to treatment in social anxiety disorder. *Molecular Psychiatry, 21*(5), 680–685. https://doi .org/10.1038/mp.2015.109

Whitley, R., Kirmayer, L., & Groleau, D. (2006). Understanding immigrants' reluctance to use mental health services: A qualitative study from Montreal. *Canadian Journal of Psychiatry, 51*(4), 205–209.

Whitney, C. W., Enright, P. L., Newman, A. B., Bonekat, W., Foley, D., & Quan, S. F. (1998). Correlates of daytime sleepiness in 4578 elderly persons:

The cardiovascular health study. *Sleep, 21*, 27–36.

Whittal, M. L., Agras, W. S., & Gould, R. A. (1999). *Behavior Therapy, 30*, 117–135.

Whittal, M. L., & Robichaud, M. (2012). Cognitive treatment for OCD. In G. Steketee (Ed.), *The Oxford handbook of obsessive compulsive and spectrum disorders* (pp. 345–364). New York, NY: Oxford University Press.

Whittal, M. L., Thordarson, D. S., & McLean, P. D. (2005). Treatment of obsessive–compulsive disorder: Cognitive behavior therapy vs. exposure and response prevention. *Behaviour Research and Therapy, 43*, 1559–1576.

Wichmann, C., Serin, R., & Motiuk, L. (2000). *Predicting suicide attempts among male offenders in federal penitentiaries*. Ottawa, ON: Correctional Service of Canada.

Wickramaratne, P. J., Weissman, M. M., Leaf, D. J., & Holford, T. R. (1989). Age, period and cohort effects on the risk of major depression: Results from five United States communities. *Journal of Clinical Epidemiology, 42*, 333–343.

Widaman, K. F. (2009). Phenylketonuria in children and mothers: Genes, environments, behavior. *Current Directions in Psychological Science, 18*(1), 48c52.

Widiger, T. A. (1991). Personality disorder dimensional models proposed for the DSM-IV. *Journal of Personality Disorders, 5*, 386–398.

Widiger, T. A. (1993). The DSM-III-R categorical personality disorder diagnoses: A critique and an alternative. *Psychological Inquiry, 4*, 75–90.

Widiger, T. A. (1997). Mental disorders as discrete clinical conditions: Dimensional versus categorical classification. In S. M. Turner & M. Hersen (Eds.), *Adult psychopathology and diagnosis* (3rd ed., pp. 3–23). New York, NY: John Wiley & Sons.

Widiger, T. A. (2011). The DSM-5 dimensional model of personality disorder: Rationale and empirical support. *Journal of Personality Disorders, 25*(2), 222–234.

Widiger, T. A. (2012). Historical developments and current issues. In T. A. Widiger (Ed.), *The Oxford handbook of personality disorders* (pp. 13–34). New York, NY: Oxford University Press.

Widiger, T. A., & Coker, L. A. L. A. (2003). Mental disorders as discrete clinical conditions: Dimensional versus categorical classification. In M. Hersen & S. M. Turner (Eds.), *Adult psychopathology and diagnosis* (4th ed., pp. 3–35). New York, NY: John Wiley & Sons.

Widiger, T. A., & Corbitt, F. M. (1995). Antisocial personality disorder. In W. J. Livesley (Ed.), *The DSM-IV personality disorders* (pp. 103–126). New York, NY: Guilford Press.

Widiger, T. A., & Cregor, C. (2013). Diagnosis and classification. In I. B. Weiner (Series Ed.), G. Stricker & T. A. Widiger (Vol. Eds.), *Handbook of psychology: Vol. 8, Clinical psychology* (pp. 3–18). Hoboken, NJ: John Wiley & Sons.

Widiger, T. A., & Edmundson, M. (2011). Diagnoses, dimensions, and DSM V. In D. H. Barlow (Ed.), *Handbook of clinical psychology*. New York, NY: Oxford University Press.

Widiger, T. A., & Rogers, J. H. (1989). Prevalence and comorbidity of personality disorders. *Psychiatry Annual, 19*, 132.

Widiger, T. A., & Samuel, D. B. (2005). Diagnostic categories or dimensions? A question for the *Diagnostic and statistical manual of mental disorders* (5th ed.). *Journal of Abnormal Psychology, 114*, 494–504.

Widiger, T. A., & Sankis, L. M. (2000). Adult psychopathology: Issues and controversies. *Annual Review of Psychology, 51*, 377–404.

Widiger, T. A., & Simonsen, E. (2005). Alternative dimensional models of personality disorder: Finding a common ground. *Journal of Personality Disorders, 19*(2), 110–130.

Widiger, T. A., & Spitzer, R. L. (1991). Sex bias in the diagnosis of personality disorders: Conceptual and methodological issues. *Clinical Psychology Review, 11*, 1–22.

Widiger, T. A., & Trull, T. J. (1993). Borderline and narcissistic personality disorders. In P. B. Sutker & H. F. Adams (Eds.), *Comprehensive handbook of psychopathology* (2nd ed., pp. 371–394). New York, NY: Plenum Press.

Widiger, T. A., & Trull, T. J. (2007). Plate tectonics in the classification of personality disorder: Shifting to a dimensional model. *American Psychologist, 62*(2), 71.

Widiger, T. A., & Weissman, M. M. (1991). Epidemiology of borderline personality disorder. *Hospital and Community Psychiatry, 42*, 1015–1021.

Widiger, T. A., Frances, A. J., Pincus, H. A., Ross, R., First, M. B., & Davis, W. W. (Eds.). (1996). *DSM-IV sourcebook* (Vol. 2). Washington, DC: American Psychiatric Association.

Widiger, T. A., Frances, A. J., Pincus, H. A., Ross, R., First, M. B., Davis, W. W., et al. (Eds.). (1998). *DSM-IV sourcebook* (Vol. 4). Washington, DC: American Psychiatric Association.

Widiger, T. A., Livesley, W. J., & Clark, L. A. (2009). An integrative dimensional classification of personality disorder. *Psychological Assessment, 21*(3), 243–255.

Widiger, T. A., Trull, T. J., Clarkin, J. F., Sanderson, C., & Costa, P. T., Jr. (1994). A description of the DSM-III-R and DSM-IV personality disorders with the five-factor model of personality. In P. T. Costa, Jr., & T. A. Widiger (Eds.), *Personality disorders and the five-factor model of personality* (pp. 41–56). Washington, DC: American Psychological Association.

Widom, C. S. (1977). A methodology for studying noninstitutionalized psychopaths. *Journal of Consulting and Clinical Psychology, 45*, 674–683.

Widom, C. S. (Ed.). (1984). Sex roles, criminality, and psychopathology. In *Sex roles and psychopathology* (pp. 183–217). New York, NY: Plenum Press.

Wiebe, R. F., & McCabe, S. B. (2002). Relationship perfectionism, dysphoria, and hostile interpersonal behaviors. *Journal of Social & Clinical Psychology, 21*, 67–91.

Wiegel, M. (2008). *Women who sexually abuse minors: Description and instrument validation.* (Unpublished doctoral dissertation). Boston University, Boston, MA.

Wiegel, M., Scepkowski, L., & Barlow, D. (2006). Cognitive and affective processes in female sexual dysfunctions. In I. Goldstein, C. Meston, S. Davis, & A. Traish (Eds.), *Women's sexual function and dysfunction: Study, diagnosis and treatment* (pp. 85–92). London, UK: Taylor & Francis.

Wiegel, M., Wincze, J. P., & Barlow, D. H. (2001). Assessment, treatment planning, and outcome evaluation for sexual dysfunction. In M. M. Anthony & D. H. Barlow (Eds.), *Handbook of assessment, treatment planning, and outcome evaluation: Empirically supported strategies for psychological disorders*. New York, NY: Guilford Press.

Wiegel, M., Wincze, J. P., & Barlow, D. H. (2002). Sexual dysfunction. In M. M. Antony & D. H. Barlow (Eds.), *Handbook of assessment and treatment planning for psychological disorders* (pp. 481–522). New York, NY: Guilford Press.

Wilcox, H. C., Arria, A. M., Caldeira, K. M., Vincent, K. B., Pinchevsky, G. M., & O'Grady, K. E. (2010). Prevalence and predictors of persistent suicide ideation, plans, and attempts during college. *Journal of Affective Disorders, 127*(1), 287–294.

Wilcox, H. C., Storr, C. L., & Breslau, N. (2009). Posttraumatic stress disorder and suicide attempts in a community sample of urban American young adults. *Archives of General Psychiatry, 66*(3), 305–311.

Wilfley, D. F., & Rodin, J. (1995). Cultural influences on eating disorders. In K. D. Brownell & C. G. Fairburn (Eds.), *Eating disorders and obesity: A comprehensive handbook* (pp. 78–82). New York, NY: Guilford Press.

Wilgosh, L., Mulcahy, R., & Watters, B. (1986). Assessing intellectual performance of culturally different, Inuit children with the WISC-R. *Canadian Journal of Behavioural Science, 18*, 270–277.

Wilhelm, S., Buhlmann, U., Tolin, D. F., Meunier, S. A., Pearlson, G. D., Reese, H. E., Cannistraro, P., Jenike, M. A., & Rauch, S. L. (2008). Augmentation of behavior therapy with D-cycloserine for obsessive–compulsive disorder. *American Journal of Psychiatry, 165*, 335–341.

Wilhelm, S., Otto, M. W., Lohr, B., & Deckersbach, T. (1999). Cognitive behavior group therapy for body dysmorphic disorder: A case series. *Behaviour Research and Therapy, 37*, 71–75.

Wilk, K., & Hegerl, U. (2010). Time of mood switches in ultra-rapid cycling disorder: A brief review. *Psychiatry Research, 180*, 1–4.

Wilkie, C., Macdonald, S., & Hildahl, K. (1998). Community case study: Suicide cluster in a small Manitoba community. *Canadian Journal of Psychiatry, 43*, 823–828.

Wilkins, K. L., McGrath, P. J., Finley, G. A., & Katz, J. (2004). Prospective diary study of nonpainful and painful phantom sensations in a preselected sample of child and adolescent amputees reporting phantom limbs. *Clinical Journal of Pain, 20*(5), 293–301.

Wilkinson-Ryan, T., & Westen, D. (2000). Identity disturbance in borderline personality disorder: An empirical investigation. *American Journal of Psychiatry, 157*, 528–541.

Willi, J., & Grossman, S. (1983). Epidemiology of anorexia nervosa in a defined region of Switzerland. *American Journal of Psychiatry, 140*, 564–567.

Williams, J., Hadjistavropoulos, T., & Sharpe, D. (2006). A meta-analysis of psychological and pharmacological treatments for body dysmorphic disorder. *Behaviour Research and Therapy, 44*, 99–111.

Williams, L. (1994). Recall of childhood trauma: A prospective study of women's memories of child sexual abuse. *Journal of Consulting and Clinical Psychology, 62*, 1167–1176.

Williams, M. R., Chaudhry, R., Perera, S., Pearce, R. K. B., Hirsch, S. R., Ansorge, O., ... Maier, M. (2013). Changes in cortical thickness in the frontal lobes in schizophrenia are a result of thinning of pyramidal cell layers. *European Archives of Psychiatry and Clinical Neuroscience, 263*(1), 25–39.

Williams, R. B., & Schneiderman, N. (2002). Resolved: Psychosocial interventions can improve clinical outcomes in organic disease (Pro). *Psychosomatic Medicine, 64*, 552–557.

Williams, R. B., Barefoot, J. C., & Schneiderman, N. (2003). Psychosocial risk factors for cardiovascular disease; More than one culprit at work. *JAMA, 290*, 2190–2192.

Williams, R. B., Marchuk, D. A., Gadde, K. M., Barefoot, J. C., Grichnik, K., Helms, M. J., ... Siegler, I. C. (2001). Central nervous system serotonin function and cardiovascular responses to stress. *Psychosomatic Medicine, 63*, 300–305.

Williams, R. J., Volberg, R. A., & Stevens, R. M. G. (2012). *The population prevalence of problem gambling: Methodological influences, standardized rates, jurisdictional differences, and worldwide trends*. Ontario Problem Gambling Research Centre and the Ontario Ministry of Health and Long Term Care. https://opus.uleth.ca/bitstream/handle/10133/3068/2012-PREVALENCE-OPGRC%20(2).pdf

Williams, S., Connolly, J., & Segal, Z. V. (2001). Intimacy in relationships and cognitive vulnerability to depression in adolescent girls. *Cognitive Therapy & Research, 25*, 477–496.

Wills, T. A., Vaccaro, D., McNamara, G., & Hirky, A. F. (1996). Escalated substance use: A longitudinal grouping analysis from early to middle adolescence. *Journal of Abnormal Psychology, 105*, 166–180.

Wilson, B. M., Mickes, L., Stolarz-Fantino, S., & Evrard, M., & Fantino, E. (2015). Increased false-memory susceptibility after mindfulness meditation. *Psychological Science, 26*, 1567–1573.

Wilson, G. T. (1977). Alcohol and human sexual behavior. *Behaviour Research and Therapy, 15*, 239–252.

Wilson, G. T., & Fairburn, C. G. (2002). Treatments for eating disorders. In P. F. Nathan & J. M. Gorma (Eds.), *A guide to treatments that work* (2nd ed., pp. 559–592). New York, NY: Oxford University Press.

Wilson, G. T., & Fairburn, C. G. (2007). Treatments for eating disorders. In P. E. Nathan & J. M. Gorman (Eds.), *A guide to treatments that work* (3rd ed., pp. 579–610). New York, NY: Oxford University Press.

Wilson, G. T., & Pike, K. M. (2001). Eating disorders. In D. H. Barlow (Ed.), *Clinical handbook of psychological disorders* (3rd ed.). New York, NY: Guilford Press.

Wilson, G. T., & Zandberg, L. (2012). Cognitive-behavioral guided self-help for eating disorders: Effectiveness and scalability. *Clinical Psychology Review, 32*, 343–357.

Wilson, G. T., Loeb, K. L., Walsh, B. T., Labouvie, F., Petkova, F., Liu, S., & Waternaux, C. (1999). Psychological versus pharmacological treatments of bulimia nervosa: Predictors and processes of change. *Journal of Consulting and Clinical Psychology, 67*, 451–459.

Wilson, G. T., Wilfley, D. E., Agras, W. S., & Bryson, S. W. (2010). Psychological treatments of binge eating disorder. *Archives of General Psychiatry, 67*(1), 94–101.

Wilson, R. S., Aggarwal, N. T., Barnes, L. L., Mendes de Leon, C. F., Hebert, L. E., & Evans, D. A. (2010). Cognitive decline in incident Alzheimer disease in a community population. *Neurology, 74*(12), 951–955.

Winchel, R. M., Stanley, B., & Stanley, M. (1990). Biochemical aspects of suicide. In S. J. Blumenthal & D. J. Kupfer (Eds.), *Suicide over the life cycle: Risk factors, assessment and treatment of suicidal patterns* (pp. 97–126). Washington, DC American Psychiatric Press.

Wincze, J. P. (2009). Enhancing sexuality: A problem-solving approach to treating dysfunction: Therapist guide (2nd ed.). New York, NY: Oxford University Press.

Wincze, J. P., & Carey, M. P. (2001). *Sexual dysfunction: A guide for assessment and treatment*. New York, NY: Guilford Press.

Wincze, J. P., & Weisburg, R. B. (2015). *Sexual dysfunction: A guide for assessment and treatment*. Guilford Publications.

Wincze, J. P., Bach, A., & Barlow, D. H. (2008). Sexual dysfunction. In D. H. Barlow (Ed.), *Clinical handbook of psychological disorders: A step-by-step treatment manual* (4th ed., pp. 615–661). New York, NY: Guilford Press.

Windgassen, K. (1992). Treatment with neuroleptics: The patient's perspective. *Acta Psychiatrica Scandinavica, 86*, 405–410.

Winkelman, J. W. (2006). Efficacy and tolerability of open-label topiramate in the treatment of sleep-related eating disorder: A retrospective case series. *Journal of Clinical Psychiatry, 67*, 1729–1734.

Winokur, G., Pfohl, B., & Tsuang, M. (1987). A 40-year follow-up of hebephrenic-catatonic schizophrenia. In N. Miller & G. Cohen (Eds.), *Schizophrenia and aging* (pp. 52–60). New York, NY: Guilford Press.

Winsper, C., Bilgin, A., Thompson, A., Marwaha, S., Chanen, A. M., Singh, S. P., Wang, A., & Furtado, V. (2019). The prevalence of personality disorders in the community: A global systematic review and meta-analysis. *The British Journal of Psychiatry*, 1–10. https://doi.org/10.1192/bjp.2019.166

Winter, A. (1998). *Mesmerized powers of mind in Victorian Britain*. Chicago, IL: University of Chicago Press.

Winter, D., Elzinga, B., & Schmahl, C. (2014). Emotions and memory in borderline personality disorder. *Psychopathology, 47*(2), 71–85. https://doi.org/10.1159/000356360

Winters, R. W., & Schneiderman, N. (2000). Anxiety and coronary heart disease. In D. I. Mostofsky & D. H. Barlow (Eds.), *The management of stress and anxiety in medical disorders* (pp. 206–219). Needham Heights, MA: Allyn & Bacon.

Wise, M. G., Gray, K. F., & Seltzer, B. (1999). Delirium, dementia, and amnestic disorders. In R. F. Hales, S. C. Judofsky, & J. A. Talbott (Eds.), *Textbook of psychiatry* (3rd ed., pp. 317–362). Washington, DC: American Psychiatric Press.

Wise, M. G., Hilty, D. M., & Cerda, G. M. (2001). Delirium due to a general medical condition, delirium due to multiple etiologies, and delirium not otherwise specified. In G. O. Gabbard (Ed.), *Treatment of psychiatric disorders* (3rd ed., Vol. 1, pp. 387–412). Washington, DC: American Psychiatric Press.

Wise, R. A. (1988). The neurobiology of craving: Implications for the understanding and treatment of addiction. *Journal of Abnormal Psychology, 97*, 118–132.

Wiseman, C. V., Gray, J. J., Mosimann, J. F., & Ahrens, A. H. (1992). Cultural expectations of thinness in women: An update. *International Journal of Eating Disorders, 11*, 85–89.

Wiseman, F. K., Alford, K. A., Tybulewicz, V. L. J., & Fisher, E. M. C. (2009). Down syndrome—Recent progress and future prospects. *Human Molecular Genetics, 18*(R1), R75-R83.

Wiseman, F. K., Al-Janabi, T., Hardy, J., Karmiloff-Smith, A., Nizetic, D., Tybulewicz, V. L., ... Ztrydom, A. (2015). A genetic cause of Alzheimer disease: Mechanistic insights from Down syndrome. *Nature Reviews Neuroscience, 16*, 564–574.

Wisner, K. L., Moses-Kolko, E. L., & Sit, D. K. (2010). Postpartum depression: A disorder in search of a definition. *Archives of Women's Mental Health, 13*(1), 37–40.

Wisner, K. L., Parry, B. L., & Piontek, C. M. (2002). Postpartum depression. *New England Journal of Medicine, 347*, 194–199.

Wisner, K. L., Sit, D. K. Y., McShea, M. C., Rizzo, D., Zoretich, R. A., Hughes, C. L., Hanusa, B. H. (2013). Onset timing, thought of self-harm, and diagnoses in postpartum women with screen-positive depression findings. *JAMA Psychiatry, 70*(5), 490–498.

Witherington, R. (1988). Suction device therapy in the management of erectile impotence. *Urologic Clinics of North America, 15*, 123–128.

Wittchen, H. U. (2002). Generalized anxiety disorder: Prevalence, burden, and cost to society. *Depression and Anxiety, 16*, 162–171.

Wittchen, H. U. (2012). The burden of mood disorders. *Science, 338*, 15.

Wittchen, H. U., Gloster, A. T., Beesdo-Baum, K., Fava, G. A., & Craske, M. G. (2010). Agoraphobia: A review of the diagnostic classificatory position and criteria. *Depression and Anxiety, 27*, 113–133.

Wittchen, H. U., Knauper, B., & Kessler, R. C. (1994). Lifetime risk of depression. *British Journal of Psychiatry, 165*(Suppl. 26), 116–122.

Wittchen, H. U., Zhao, S., Kessler, R. C., & Eaton, W. W. (1994). DSM-III-R generalized anxiety disorder in the national comorbidity survey. *Archives of General Psychiatry, 51,* 355–364.

Witthoft, M., & Hiller, W. (2010). Psychological approaches to origins and treatments of somatoform disorders. *Annual Review of Clinical Psychology, 6,* 257–283.

Wolf, E. J., Lunney, C. A., Miller, M. W., Resick, P. A., Friedman, M. J., & Schnurr, P. P. (2012). The dissociative subtype of PTSD: A replication and extension. *Depression and Anxiety, 29,* 679–688.

Wolf, E. J., Miller, M. W., Reardon, A. F., Ryabchenko, K. A., Castillo, D., & Freund, R. (2012). A latent class analysis of dissociation and posttraumatic stress disorder: Evidence for a dissociative subtype. *Archives of General Psychiatry, 69,* 698–705.

Wolf, M. M. (1978). Social validity: The case for subjective measurement or how applied behavior analysis is finding its heart. *Journal of Applied Behavior Analysis, 11,* 203–214.

Wolfe, D. A. (1991). *Preventing physical and emotional abuse of children.* New York, NY: Guilford Press.

Wolff, K. (2012). Ketamine. In J. C. Verster, K. Brady, M. Galanter, & P. Conrod (Eds.), *Drug abuse and addiction in medical illness* (pp. 201–211). New York, NY: Springer.

Wolff, S., Townshed, R., McGuire, R. J., & Weeks, D. J. (1991). "Schizoid" personality in childhood and adult life. II: Adult adjustment and continuity with schizotypal personality disorder. *British Journal of Psychiatry, 159,* 615–620.

Wolf-Maier, K., Cooper, R. S., Banegas, J. R., Giampaoli, S., Hense, H., Joffres, M., ... Vescio, F. (2003). Hypertension prevalence and blood pressure levels in 6 European countries, Canada, and the United States. *JAMA, 289,* 2362–2369.

Wolfson, C., Wolfson, D. B., Asgharian, M., M'Lan, C. F., Ostbye, T., Rockwood, K., & Hogan, D. B. (2001). Clinical Progression of Dementia Study Group. A reevaluation of the duration of survival after the onset of dementia. *New England Journal of Medicine, 344,* 1111–1116.

Wolitzky-Taylor, K. B., Castriotta, N., Lenze, E. J., Stanley, M. A., & Craske, M. G. (2010). Anxiety disorders in older adults: A comprehensive review. *Depression and Anxiety, 27*(2), 190–211.

Wollburg, E., Voigt, K., Braukhaus, C., Herzog, A., & Lowe, B. (2013). Construct validity and descriptive validity of somatoform disorders in light of proposed changes for the DSM-5. *Journal of Psychosomatic Research, 74*(1), 18–24.

Wolpe, J. (1958). *Psychotherapy by reciprocal inhibition.* Stanford, CA: Stanford University Press.

Wonderlich, S. A., Gordon, K. H., Mitchell, J. E., Crosby, R. D., & Engel, S. G. (2009). The validity and clinical utility of binge eating disorder. *International Journal of Eating Disorders, 42*(8), 687–705.

Wong, C., & Kasari, C. (2012). Play and joint attention of children with autism in the preschool special education classroom. *Journal of Autism and Developmental Disorders, 42*(10), 2152–2161.

Wong, S. L., Gilmour, H., & Ramage-Morin, P. L. (2014). Parkinson's disease: Prevalence, diagnosis and impact. *Health Reports, 25*(11), 10–14. Retrieved from http://www.statcan .gc.ca/access_acces/alternative_ alternatif.action?l=eng&loc=14112- eng.pdf

Wong, S. L., Gilmour, H., & Ramage-Morin, P. L. (2016). Alzheimer's disease and other dementias in Canada. *Health Reports, 27*(5), 11–16. https://www150.statcan.gc.ca/n1/en/ catalogue/82-003-X201600514613

Wood, F., & Kerr, T. (2006). What do you do when you hit rock bottom? Responding to drugs in the city of Vancouver. *International Journal of Drug Policy, 17*(2), 55–60.

Wood, F., Kerr, T., Small, W., Li, K., Marsh, D. C., Montaner, J. S. G., & Tyndall, M. W. (2004). Changes in public order after the opening of a medically supervised safer-injecting facility for illicit injection drug users. *Canadian Medical Association Journal, 171*(7), 731–734.

Wood, F., Tyndall, M. W., Qui, Z., Zhang, R., Montaner, J. S. G., & Kerr, T. (2006). Service uptake and characteristics of injection drug users utilizing North America's first medically supervised safer injecting facility. *American Journal of Public Health, 96*(5), 770–773.

Wood, J. M., Garb, H. N., Nezworski, M. T., Lilienfeld, S. O., & Duke, M. C. (2015). A second look at the validity of widely used Rorschach indices: Comment on Mihura, Meyer, Dumitrascu, and Bombel (2013). *Psychology Bulletin, 141*(1), 236–249.

Woodin, E., Caldeira, V., Sotskova, A., Galaugher, T., & Lu, M. (2014). Harmful alcohol use as a predictor of intimate partner violence during the transition to parenthood: Interdependent and interactive effects. *Addictive Behaviors, 39,* 1890–1897. https://doi .org/10.1016/j.addbeh.2014.07.033

Woodman, C. L., Noyes, R., Black, D. W., Schlosser, S., & Yagla, S. J. (1999). A 5-year follow-up study of generalized anxiety disorder and panic disorder. *Journal of Nervous and Mental Disease, 187,* 3–9.

Woods, B., Aguirre, E., Spector, A. E., & Orrell, M. (2012). Cognitive stimulation to improve cognitive functioning in people with dementia. *Cochrane Database Systematic Review, 2,* CD005562.

Woods, F. R., Lin, Y. G., Middleman, A., Beckford, P., Chase, L., & DuRant, R. H. (1997). The associations of suicide attempts in adolescents. *Pediatrics, 99,* 791–796.

Woods, S. W., Walsh, B. C., Saksa, J. R., & McGlashan, T. H. (2010). The case for including attenuated psychotic symptoms Syndrome in DSM-5 as a psychosis risk syndrome. *Schizophrenia Research, 123*(2–3), 199.

Woodside, D. B., Bulik, C. M., Halmi, K. A., Fichter, M. M., Kaplan, A., Berrettini, W. H., ... Kaye, W. H. (2002). Personality, perfectionism, and attitudes towards eating in parents of individuals with eating disorders. *International Journal of Eating Disorders, 31,* 290–299.

Woodside, D. B., Bulik, C. M., Thornton, L., Klump, K. L., Tozzi, F., Fichter, M. M., ... Kaye, W. H. (2004). Personality in men with eating disorders. *Journal of Psychosomatic Research, 57,* 273–278.

Woodside, D. B., Garfinkel, P. F., Lin, F., Goering, P., & Kaplan, A. S. (2001). Comparisons of men with full or partial eating disorders, men without eating disorders, and women with eating disorders in the community. *American Journal of Psychiatry, 158,* 570–574.

Woodworth, M., & Porter, S. (2002). In cold blood: Characteristics of criminal homicides as a function of psychopathy. *Journal of Abnormal Psychology, 111,* 436–445.

Woodworth, M., Peace, K. A., O'Donnell, C., & Porter, S. (2003). Forensic community programs: Recommendations for the management of NCRMD patients in the community. *Journal of Forensic Psychology Practice, 3,* 1–22.

Wooley, M. A., & Wong, J. M. (2013). Depression and cardiovascular disorders. *Annual Review of Clinical Psychology, 9,* 327–354.

Woolfolk, R. L., & Allen, L. A. (2011). Somatoform and physical disorders. In D. H. Barlow (Ed.), *Handbook of clinical psychology.* New York, NY: Oxford University Press.

Wootton, J. M., Frick, P. J., Shelton, K. K., & Silverthorn, P. (1997). Ineffective parenting and childhood conduct problems: The moderating role of callous-unemotional traits. *Journal of Consulting and Clinical Psychology, 65,* 301–308.

Worell, J., & Remer, P. (1992). *Feminist perspectives in therapy: An empowerment model for women.* New York, NY: John Wiley & Sons.

Workman, J. L., Barha, C. K., & Galea, L. A. M. (2012). Endocrinne substrates of cognitive and affective changes during pregnancy and postpartum. *Behavioral Neuroscience, 126*(1), 54–72.

World Health Organization. (1992). *The ICD-10 classification of mental and behavioural disorders: Clinical descriptions and diagnostic guidelines.*

World Health Organization. (2000). *Multisite intervention study on suicidal behaviours—(SUPRE-MISS).*

World Health Organization. (2004). *Global status report on alcohol 2004* (2nd ed.).

World Health Organization. (2014). *Preventing suicide: A global imperative.* https://www.who.int/ mental_health/suicide-prevention/ world_report_2014/en/

World Health Organization. (2018). *Global status report on alcohol and health 2018.* https://apps.who.int/iris/ handle/10665/274603

World Health Organization. (2019). *Global Health Observatory data repository: Suicide rates (per 100 000 population).* https://www.who.int/gho/ mental_health/suicide_rates/en/

Wright, J. W., Kawas, L. H., & Harding, J. W. (2015). The development of small molecule angiotensin IV analogs to treat Alzheimer's and Parkinson's diseases. *Progress in Neurobiology, 125,* 26–46.

Wu, F. (2009). *Suicide and justice: A Chinese perspective.* New York, NY: Routledge.

Wu, L. T., Blazer, D. G., Li, T. K., & Woody, G. E. (2011). Treatment use and barriers among adolescents with prescription opioid use disorders. *Addictive Behaviors, 36*(12), 1233–1239.

Wulfert, E., Franco, C., Williams, K., Roland, B., & Maxson, J. H. (2008). The role of money in the excitement of gambling. *Psychology of Addictive Behaviors, 22*(3), 380–390.

Wulfert, E., Maxson, J., & Jardin, B. (2009). Cue-specific reactivity in experienced gamblers. *Psychology of Addictive Behaviors, 23*(4), 731–735.

Wyatt v. Stickney, 344 F. Supp. 373 (Ala. 1972).

Wyllie, F., Glazer, J. P., Benbaids, S., Kotagal, P., & Wolgamuth, B. (1999). Psychiatric features of children and adolescents with pseudoseizures. *Archives of Pediatric and Adolescent Medicine, 153*(3), 244–248.

Wynne, L. C., Tienari, P., Nieminen, P., Sorri, A., Lahti, I. O., Moring, J., ... Miettunen, J. (2006). I. Genotype-environment interaction in the schizophrenia spectrum: Genetic liability and global family ratings in the Finnish Adoption Study. *Family Process, 45*(4), 419–434.

Xing, G., Zhang, L., Russell, S., & Post, R. (2006). Reduction of dopamine-related transcription factors Nurr1 and NGFI-B in the prefrontal cortex in schizophrenia and bipolar disorders. *Schizophrenia Research, 84,* 36–56.

Yairi, F., & Ambrose, N. (1992). Onset of stuttering in preschool children: Selected factors. *Journal of Speech and Hearing Research, 35,* 782–788.

Yamada, K. (2015). Unremembered nocturnal eating syndrome: 8 case reports. *Reactions, 1541,* 148–7.

Yamada, K., Watanabe, K., Nemoto, N., Fujita, H., Chikaraishi, C., Yamauchi, K., & Kanba, S. (2006). Prediction of medication noncompliance in outpatients with schizophrenia: 2-year follow-up study. *Psychiatry Research, 141,* 61–69.

Yan, L. L., Liu, K., Matthews, K. A., Daviglus, M. L., Ferguson, T. F., & Kiefe, C. I. (2003). Psychosocial risk factors and risk of hypertension: The coronary artery risk development in young adults (CARDIA) study. *JAMA, 290,* 2138–2148.

Yang, J., Bagby, M., Costa, P. T. Jr., Ryder, A. G., & Herbst, J. H. (2002). Assessing the DSM-IV structure of personality disorder with a sample of Chinese psychiatric patients. *Journal of Personality Disorders, 16,* 317–331.

Yanicki, G. M. (2014). *Old man's playing ground: Gaming and trade on the Plains/Plateau Frontier.* Canadian Museum of History/University of Ottawa Press.

Yanicki, G. M. (2017). Reinventing the wheel game: Prestige gambling on the Plains/Plateau frontier. In B. Voorhies (Ed.), *Prehistoric games of North American Indians Subarctic to Mesoamerica* (pp. 104–118). University of Utah Press.

Yatham, L. N., Kennedy, S. H., O'Donovan, C., Parikh, S. V., MacQueen, G., McIntyre, R. S., ... Beaulieu, S., CANMAT guidelines group. (2006). Canadian Network for Mood and Anxiety Treatments (CANMAT) guidelines for the management of patients with bipolar disorder: Update 2007. *Bipolar Disorders, 8,* 721–739.

Yatham, L. N., Kennedy, S. H., Parikh, S. V., Schaffer, A., Beaulieu, S., Alda, M., ... Berk, M. (2013). Canadian Network for Mood and Anxiety Treatments (CANMAT) and International Society for Bipolar Disorders (ISBD) collaborative update of CANMAT guidelines for the management of patients with bipolar disorder: Update 2013. *Biploar Disorders, 15*, 1–44.

Yatham, L. N., Liddle, P. F., Sossi, V., Erez, J., Vafai, N., Lam, R. W., & Blinder, S. (2012). Positron emission tomography study of the effects of tryptophan depletion on brain serotonin receptors in subjects recently remitted from major depression. *Archives of General Psychiatry, 69*(6), 601–609.

Yatham, L., Liddle, P. F., Shiah, I.-S., Lam, R. W., Ngan, F., Scarrow, G., ... Ruth, T. J. (2002). PET study of [18F]6-fluoro-L-dopa uptake in neuroleptic- and mood-stabilizer-naive first-episode nonpsychotic mania: Effects of treatment with divalproex sodium. *American Journal of Psychiatry, 159*, 768–774.

Yau, Y. H. C., Yip, S. W., & Potenza, M. N. (2015). Understanding "behavioral addictions": Insights from research. In R. K. Ries, D. A. Fiellin, S. C. Miller, & R. Saitz (Eds.), *The ASAM principles of addiction medicine* (5th ed., pp. 55–81). New York, NY: Wolters Kluwer.

Ye, X., Mitchell, M., Newman, K., & Batshaw, M. L. (2001). Prospects for prenatal gene therapy in disorders causing mental retardation. *Mental Retardation and Developmental Disabilities Research Review, 7*, 65–72.

Yeaton, W. H., & Bailey, J. S. (1978). Teaching pedestrian safety skills to young children: An analysis and one-year follow-up. *Journal of Applied Behavior Analysis, 11*, 315–329.

Yehuda, R., Pratchett, L., & Pelcovitz, M. (2012). Biological contributions to PTSD: Differentiating normative from pathological response. In J. G. Beck & D. M. Sloan (Eds.), *The Oxford handbook of traumatic stress disorders* (pp. 159–174). New York, NY: Oxford University Press.

Yerkes, R. M., & Dodson, J. D. (1908). The relation of strength of stimulus to rapidity of habit-formation. *Journal of Comprehensive Neurologic and Psychology, 18*, 459–482.

Yeung, A., Yong X., & Chang, D. F. (2005). Prevalence and illness beliefs of sleep paralysis among Chinese psychiatric patients in China and the United States. *Transcultural Psychiatry, 42*, 135–145.

Yiend, J. (2010). The effects of emotion on attention: A review of attentional processing of emotional information *Cognition and Emotion, 24*, 2–47.

Yim, I. S., Glynn, L. M., Dunkel-Schetter, C., Hobel, C. J., Chicz-DeMet, A., & Sandman, C. A. (2009). Risk of postpartum depressive symptoms with elevated corticotropin-releasing hormone in human pregnancy. *Archives of General Psychiatry, 66*(2), 162–169.

Yin, R. K. (2012). *Applications of case study research* (3rd ed.). Thousand Oaks, CA: Sage Publications.

Yonkers, K. A., Kornstein, S. G., Gueorguieva, R., Merry, B., Van Steenburgh, K., & Altemus, M. (2015). Symptom-onset dosing of sertraline for the treatment of premenstrual dysphoric disorder: A randomized clinical trial. *JAMA Psychiatry, 72*(10), 1037–1044.

Yonkers, K. A., Warshaw, M., Massion, A. O., & Keller, M. B. (1996). Phenomenology and course of generalized anxiety disorder. *British Journal of Psychiatry, 168*, 308–313.

Yoo, J. A., & Huang, C. C. (2012). The effects of domestic violence on children's behavior problems: Assessing the moderating roles of poverty and marital status. *Children and Youth Services Review, 34*(12), 2462–2473.

Young, A. M., & Herling, S. (1986). Drugs as reinforcers: Studies in laboratory animals. In S. R. Goldberg & I. P. Stolerman (Eds.), *Behavioral analysis of drug dependence* (pp. 9–67). Orlando, FL: Academic Press.

Young, A. R., Beitchman, J. H., Johnson, C., Douglas, L., Atkinson, L., Escobar, M., & Wilson, B. (2002). Young adult academic outcomes in a longitudinal sample of early identified language impaired and control children. *Journal of Child Psychology and Psychiatry, 43*, 635–645.

Young, J. E., Rygh, J. L., Weinberger, A. D., & Beck, A. T. (2014). Cognitive therapy for depression. In D. H. Barlow (Ed.), *Clinical handbook of psychological disorders: A step-by-step treatment manual* (5th ed.). New York, NY: Guilford Press.

Young, J., Rygh, J., Weinberger, A., & Beck, A. T. (2008). Cognitive therapy for depression. In Barlow, D. H. (Ed.), *Clinical handbook of psychological disorders* (4th ed., pp. 250–305). New York, NY: Guilford Press.

Young, R. (2007, August 8). Store owners to fight tobacco power-wall ban. Transcontinental Media. Retrieved September 1, 2007, from http:// novascotiabusinessjournal.com/index .cfm?sid50720&sc107

Young, R. M. (2013). Cravings and expectancies. In P. M. Miller, A. W. Blume, D. J. Kavanagh, K. M. Kampman, M. E. Bates, M. E. Larimer, N. M. Petry, P.De Witte, & S. A. Ball (Eds.), *Principles of addiction: Comprehensive addictive behaviors and disorders* (Vol. 1, pp. 425–434). Waltham, MA: Elsevier Academic Press.

Youngstrom, E. A. (2009). Definitional issues in bipolar disorder across the life cycle. *Clinical Psychology: Science and Practice, 16*(2), 140–160.

Yu, X., Tam, W. W., Wong, P. T., Lam, T. H., & Stewart, S. M. (2012). The Patient Health Questionnaire-9 for measuring depressive symptoms among the general population in Hong Kong. *Comprehensive Psychiatry, 53*(1), 95–102. https://doi.org/10.1016/j. comppsych.2010.11.002

Zabalegui, A., Hamers, J. P., Karlsson, S., Leino-Kilpi, H., Renom-Guiteras, A., Saks, K., . . . Cabrera, E. (2014). Best practices interventions to improve quality of care of people with dementia living at home. *Patient Education and Counseling, 95*(2), 175–184.

Zachar, P., & Kendler, K. S. (2014). A Diagnostic and statistical manual of mental disorders history of premenstrual dysphoric disorder. *Journal of Nervous and Mental Disease, 202*(4), 346–352. https://doi.org/10.1097/ NMD.0000000000000128

Zacharias, C. A., Goldberg, J., & Chapman, R. (1997, April). Inspirational effects of a consumer-delivered cognitive therapy lecture. Poster presented at McMaster University Department of Psychiatry, Annual Research Day, Hamilton, ON.

Zack, M., Toneatto, T., & MacLeod, C. M. (1999). Implicit activation of alcohol concepts by negative affective cues distinguishes between problem drinkers with high and low psychiatric distress.

Journal of Abnormal Psychology, 108, 518–531.

Zadra, A., & Donderi, D. C. (2000). Nightmares and bad dreams: Their prevalence and relationship to well-being. *Journal of Abnormal Psychology, 109*, 273–281.

Zaheer, J., Jacob, B., de Oliveira, C., Rudoler, D., Juda, A., & Kurdyak, P. (2018). Service utilization and suicide among people with schizophrenia spectrum disorders. *Schizophrenia Research, 202*, 347–353.

Zajonc, R. B. (1984). On the primacy of affect. *American Psychologist, 39*(2), 117–123.

Zajonc, R. B. (1998). Emotions. In D. Gilbert, S. T. Fiske, & G. Lindzey (Eds.), *Handbook of social psychology* (4th ed., Vol. 1, pp. 591–632). New York, NY: McGraw-Hill.

Zaki, N. F., Spence, D. W., BaHammam, A. S., Pandi-Perumal, S. R., Cardinali, D. P., & Brown, G. M. (2018). Chronobiological theories of mood disorder. *European Archives of Psychiatry and Clinical Neuroscience, 268*(2), 107–118.

Zakowski, S. G., McAllister, C. G., Deal, M., & Baum, A. (1992). Stress, reactivity, and immune function in healthy men. *Health Psychology, 11*, 223–232.

Zakzanis, K. K., Troyer, A. K., Rich, J. B., & Heinrichs, W. (2000). Component analysis of verbal fluency in patients with schizophrenia. *Neuropsychiatry, Neuropsychology, & Behavioral Neurology, 13*, 239–245.

Zanarini, M. C., & Frankenberg, F. R. (1997). Pathways to the development of borderline personality disorder. *Journal of Personality Disorders, 11*, 93–104.

Zanarini, M. C., & Wedig, M. M. (2014). Childhood adversity and the development of borderline personality disorder. In *Handbook of borderline personality disorder in children and adolescents* (pp. 265–276). Springer New York.

Zanarini, M. C., Frankenburg, F. R., & Fitzmaurice, G. M. (2014). Severity of anxiety symptoms reported by borderline patients and Axis II comparison subjects: Description and prediction over 16 years of prospective follow-up. *Journal of Personality Disorders, 28*(6), 767–777.

Zanarini, M. C., Frankenburg, F. R., Dubo, F. F., Sickel, A. F., Trikha, A., Levin, A., & Reynolds, V. (1998). Axis I comorbidity of borderline personality disorder. *American Journal of Psychiatry, 155*, 1733–1739.

Zanarini, M. C., Frankenburg, F. R., Hennen, J., Reich, D. B., & Silk, K. R. (2006). Prediction of the 10-year course of borderline personality disorder. *American Journal of Psychiatry, 163*, 827–832.

Zanarini, M. C., Gunderson, J., Marino, M., Schwartz, F., & Frankenburg, F. (1988). DSM-III disorders in the families of borderline outpatients. *Journal of Personality Disorders, 2*, 292–302.

Zanarini, M. C., Reichman, C. A., Frankenburg, F. R., Reich, D. B., & Fitzmaurice, G. (2010). The course of eating disorders in patients with borderline personality disorder: A 10-year follow-up study. *International Journal of Eating Disorders, 43*(3), 226–232.

Zanarini, M. C., Williams, A. A., Lewis, R. F., Reich, R. B., Vera, S. C., Marino, M. F., . . . Frankenburg, F. R. (1997). Reported pathological childhood

experiences associated with the development of borderline personality disorder. *American Journal of Psychiatry, 154*, 1101–1106.

Zapf, P. A. (2001). Assessing fitness to stand trial: The utility of the fitness interview test (revised edition). *Canadian Journal of Psychiatry, 26*, 426–432.

Zapf, P. A., & Roesch, R. (1997). Assessing fitness to stand trial: A comparison of institution-based evaluations and a brief screening interview. *Canadian Journal of Community Mental Health, 16*, 53–66.

Zautra, A., Johnson, L., & Davis, M. (2005). Positive affect as a source of resilience for women in chronic pain. *Journal of Consulting and Clinical Psychology, 73*, 212–220.

Zaza, C., Sellick, S. M., Willan, A., Reyno, L., & Browman, G. P. (1999). Health care professionals' familiarity with non-pharmacological strategies for managing cancer pain. *Psycho-oncology, 8*, 99–111.

Zeanah, C. H., & Gleason, M. M. (2010). *Reactive attachment disorders: A review for DSM-V.* Retrieved December 29, 2010, from http://stage.dsm5. org/Proposed%20Revision%20 Attachments/APA%20DSM-5%20 Reactive%20Attachment%20 Disorder%20Review.pdf

Zelazo, P. D., Burack, J. A., Boseovski, J. J., Jacques, S., & Frye, D. (2001). A cognitive complexity and control framework for the study of autism. In J. A. Burack & T. Charman (Eds.), *Development of autism: Perspectives from theory and research* (pp. 195–217). Mahwah, NJ: Lawrence Erlbaum.

Zelazo, P. D., Jacques, S., Burack, J. A., & Frye, D. (2002). The relation between theory of mind and rule use: Evidence from persons with autism-spectrum disorders. *Infant & Child Development, 11*, 171–195.

Zemore, S. E., Subbaraman, M., & Tonigan, J. S. (2013). Involvement in 12-step activities and treatment outcomes. *Substance Abuse, 34*(1), 60–69.

Zervas, I. M., Theleritis, C., & Soldatos, C. R. (2012). Using ECT in schizophrenia: A review from a clinical perspective. *World Journal of Biological Psychiatry, 13*(2).

Zhai, L., Zhang, H., & Zhang, D. (2015). Sleep duration and depression among adults: A meta-analysis of prospective studies. *Depression and Anxiety, 32*, 644–670.

Zheng, G., Yang, Y., Zhu, X., & Elston, R. C. (2012). *Analysis of genetic association studies.* New York, NY: Springer.

Zhou, J. N., Hofman, M. A., Gooren, L. J., & Swaab, D. F. (1995). A sex difference in the human brain and its relation to transsexuality. *Nature, 378*, 68–70.

Zigler, F., Taussig, C., & Black, K. (1992). Early childhood intervention: A promising preventative for juvenile delinquency. *American Psychologist, 47*, 997–1006.

Zilbergeld, B. (1992). *The new male sexuality.* New York, NY: Bantam Books.

Zilboorg, G., & Henry, G. (1941). *A history of medical psychology.* New York, NY: W. W. Norton.

Zimmerman, M., & Coryell, W. (1989). DSM-III personality disorder diagnoses in a nonpatient sample. *Archives of General Psychiatry, 46*, 682–689.

Zimmerman, M., & Coryell, W. (1990). Diagnosing personality disorders in the community: A comparison of self-report and interview measures. *Archives of General Psychiatry, 47*, 527–531.

Zimmerman, M., & Mattia, J. I. (1998). Body Dysmorphic disorder in psychiatric outpatients: Recognition, prevalence, comorbidity, demographic, and clinical correlates. *Comprehensive Psychiatry, 39*(5), 265–270.

Zinbarg, R. F., & Barlow, D. H. (1996). Structure of anxiety and the anxiety disorders: A hierarchical model. *Journal of Abnormal Psychology, 105*, 181–193.

Zinbarg, R. F., Barlow, D. H., Liebowitz, M. R., Street, L., Broadhead, F., Katon, W., ... Kraemer, H. (1998). The DSM-IV field trial for mixed anxiety-depression. In T. A. Widiger, A. J. Frances, H. A. Pincus, R. Ross, M. B. First, W. Davis, et al. (Eds.), *DSM-IV sourcebook* (Vol. 4, pp. 735–799). Washington, DC: American Psychiatric Association.

Zinbarg, R. F., Barlow, D. H., Liebowitz, M., Street, L., Broadhead, F., Katon, W., ... Kraemer, H. (1994). The DSM-IV field trial for mixed anxiety depression. *American Journal of Psychiatry, 151*, 1153–1162.

Zisook, S., Corruble, E., Duan, N., Inglewicz, A., Karam, E., Lanouette, N., & Young, I. T. (2012). The bereavement exclusion and DSM-5. *Depression and Anxiety, 29*, 425–443.

Zou, L., Chen, W., Shao, S., Sun, Z., Zhong, R., Shi, J., & Song, R. (2012). Genetic variant in KIAA0319, but not in DYX1C1, is associated with risk of dyslexia: An integrated meta-analysis. *American Journal of Medical Genetics Part B: Neuropsychiatric Genetics, 159B*(8), 970–976.

Zubieta, J., Bueller, J., Jackson, L., Scott, D., Xu, Y., & Koeppe, R., & Stohler, C. S. (2005). Placebo effects mediated by endogenous opioid activity on u-opioid receptors. *Journal of Neuroscience, 25*, 7754–7762.

Zuccato, C., & Cattaneo, E. (2009). Brain-derived neurotrophic factor in neurodegenerative diseases. *Nature Reviews Neurology, 5*(6), 311–322.

Zuchner, S., Cuccaro, M. L., Tran-Viet, K. N., Cope, H., Krishnan, R. R., Pericak-Vance, M. A., ... Ashley-Koch, A. (2006). SLITRK1 mutations in trichotillomania. *Molecular Psychiatry, 11*, 887–889.

Zucker, K. J. (2005a). Gender identity disorder in children and adolescents. *Annual Review of Clinical Psychology, 1*, 467–492.

Zucker, K. J. (2005b). Gender identity disorder in girls. In D. J. Bell, S. L. Foster, & F. J. Mash (Eds.), *Handbook of behavioral and emotional problems in girls*. New York, NY: Kluwer Academic/Plenum Publishers.

Zucker, K. J. (2005c). Measurement of psychosexual differentiation. *Archives of Sexual Behavior, 34*, 375–388.

Zucker, K. J. (2010). The DSM diagnostic criteria for gender identity disorder in children. *Archives of Sexual Behavior, 39*, 477–498.

Zuroff, D. C., Blatt, S. J., Sanislow, C. A., III, Bondi, C. M., & Pilkonis, P. A. (1999). Vulnerability to depression: Reexamining state dependence and relative stability. *Journal of Abnormal Psychology, 108*, 76–89.

Zvolensky, M. J., & Bernstein, A. (2005). Cigarette smoking and panic psychopathology. *Current Directions in Psychological Science, 14*, 301–305.

Zwahlen, M., & Egger, M. (2006). *Progression and mortality of untreated HIV-positive individuals living in resource-limited settings: Update of literature review and evidence synthesis* (UNAIDS Obligation HQ/05/42204). http://data.unaids.org/pub/periodical/2006/zwahlen_unaids_hq_05_422204_2007_en.pdf

Zwaigenbaum, L., Bryson, S., & Garon, N. (2013). Early identification of autism spectrum disorders. *Behavioural Brain Research, 251*, 133–146. https://doi.org/10.1016/j.bbr.2013.04.004

Zwaigenbaum, L., Szatmari, P., Jones, M., Bryson, S., MacLean, J. F., Mahoney, W., . . . Tuff, L. (2002). Pregnancy and birth complications in autism and liability to the broader autism phenotype. *Journal of the American Academy of Child and Adolescent Psychiatry, 41*, 572–579.

NAME INDEX

Bonlinskey, P. K., 78
Bonnano, G. A., 193
Boocock, A., 180
Boon, S., 199, 204
Boone, L., 279
Boot, W. R., 116
Boothroyd, L. J., 230, 253, 254
Bor, W., 435
Borden, S. L., 469
Border, R., 38
Bordin, I. A., 465
Borenstein, A., 498
Borg, L., 360, 367
Borgelt, L. M., 364
Borges, G., 251
Borghuis, M. S., 165
Borkovec, T. D., 130–132, OLC-27
Bornath, L. M., 267
Bornstein, R. F., 414
Borodinsky, L. N., 46
Borrie, K., 374
Borteyru, J. P., 351
Boseovski, J. J., 470
Bosinski, H., 332
Boskind-Lodahl, M., 270
Bosmans, J. E., 506
Bosveld, J. J. F., 270
Boswell, J. F., 132
Botteron, K., 47, 48, 94
Bouchard, M. F., 462
Bouchard, S., 147, 394
Bouchard, T. J., Jr., 36
Bouchard, V., 133
Bougie, E., 345, 434
Bouman, T. K., 167
Bourdel, M. C., 373
Bourgeois, J. A., 490, 496
Bourgeois, M. S., 507
Bourgon, G., 334
Bourgouin, P., 147
Bourke, J., 482
Bourlas, A. P., 504
Bouton, M. E., 53, 121, 122, 138
Boutros, N. N., 446
Bova, D., 80
Bowden, C. L., 216, 245, 312, 395
Bowen-Bravery, M., 479
Bowen, J., 443, 444
Bowen, J. D., 502
Bowers, J. S., 55
Bowie, C. R., 94
Bowler, D., 457
Bowman, E. D., 366
Bowman, E. S., 204, 206
Boyce, N., 255
Boyce, W., 255
Boyd, J. L., 448
Boydell, J., 61, 443
Boyer, P., 175
Boyer, R., 129, 145
Boyle, C., 404, OLC-31
Boyle, M., 220
Boyle, M. H., 144, 220, 229, 404, 406
Boyle, W., 220
Boysen, G., 410
Bozigar, J., 256
Bracha, H. S., 442
Bradford, A., 312, 315, 317, 319, 322
Bradley, B. P., 131, 150, 238
Bradley, E. A., 479
Bradley, M. M., 58

Bradley, R. G., 38, 234
Bradley, S. J., 337–339
Bradley, V. J., 478
Bradley, W., 463
Brady, J. P., 171, 467
Braet, C., 279
Braff, D., 437
Brahim, A. A., 229
Brahler, E., 221
Brailey, K., 195
Brain, C., 446
Brammer, M. J., 462
Brand, B., 189, 208
Brand, B. L., 207
Brandon, K. O., 359
Brandsma, J., 203
Brandt, H., 147, 263, 268
Brandt, H. A., 279
Brandt, K. M., 369
Brandt, L., 263
Brannick, M., 274
Brannon, L., OLC-4
Bratulic, A., 516
Braukhaus, C., 164
Brawman-Mintzer, O., 132, 177
Bray, B. C., 365
Bray, S. M., 481
Brean, J., 426
Breitbart, W., 492
Breitborde, N. J., 444
Brekke, J. S., 448
Bremner, J. D., 195
Brenes, G. A., 129
Brennan, P., 401
Brennan-Krohn, T., 381
Brennan-Olsen, S. L., 294, 389
Brenner, D. E., 502
Brenner, I., 200
Brent, D., 228, 234
Brent, D. A., 228, 229, 254, 256
Breslau, J., 194
Breslau, N., 192, 194
Bresnahan, M., 472
Breteler, M. M. B., 503
Breuer, J., 18, 55
Brew, B., 500
Brewer, H., 265
Brewerton, T. D., 269
Bricker, J., 409
Bridges, F. S., 62
Briganti, A., 318
Briggs, M. C., 245
Brink, D., 302
Brink, J., 83, 518
Brinker, J. K., 239
Brisebois, L., 489
Briskman, J., 403
Britton, A., 125
Britton, J. C., 124, 125
Brix, R. J., 382
Broadhead, F., 92
Broadstock, M., 499
Brock, G., 309, 311, 313
Brock, G. B., 324
Brock, H., 272
Brocke, B., 48
Brodeur, D. A., 463
Brodman, D. M., 75, 152
Brody, D., 322
Brody, H., 51, 219
Brody, M. J., 269

Broft, A., 280
Bromet, E., 192
Bromet, E. J., 230, 240, 251, 254
Brondino, M. J., 404
Brondolo, E., OLC-18
Bronen, R. A., 195
Bronnick, K., 508
Brook, J. S., 285, 374, 389
Brook, M., 183
Brooks, D. J., 369
Brooks-Gunn, J., 228, 272, 278
Brotto, L., 309
Brotto, L. A., 318
Brown, C. G., 266
Brown, D., 439
Brown, G. G., 150
Brown, G. K., 414
Brown, G. M., 235
Brown, G. W., 129, 130, 236, 443, 444
Brown, J., 112
Brown, J. D., 370
Brown, P. L., 277
Brown, R. E., 129, 130
Brown, R. G., 246
Brown, R. J., 170, 171
Brown, R. R., 127
Brown, S., 404
Brown, S. L., 401
Brown, T. A., 73, 85, 89, 90, 94, 125,
    127, 129–131, 136, 140, 282
Brown, T. E., 85
Brown, T. G., 372
Brown, T. L., 447
Brown, W. A., 93
Browne, A. J., 61
Browne, H. A., 175
Browne, S., 395
Brownell, K. D., 269, 274, 277, 333
Brownlee, K., 301
Brownley, K. A., 280
Brownridge, D. A., 62
Bruce, K. R., 279, 351, 413
Bruce, M. L., 130, 220, 238
Bruce, S. E., 127
Bruch, H., 267, 278, 279
Bruch, M. A., 152
Bruck, M., 465, 468
Bruder, G., 233
Bruder, J., 465
Brugger, P., 397
Brugha, T. S., 240
Brugnera, A., 285
Brun, A., 499
Brunet, A., 192
Bruno, M., 172
Brunner, H. G., 402
Brunoni, A. R., 246
Brunt, T., 358, 359
Brush, G., 350
Brust, J. C. M., 502
Bruxner, A., 435
Bryant, R. A., 60, 191, 193, 196, 221
Bryson, E. O., 245
Bryson, S., 112, 471, 472, 474
Bryson, S. E., 479
Bryson, S. W., 283, 285
Buchanan, R. W., 442
Buchner, D. M., 508
Bucholtz, K. K., 398
Bucholz, K. K., 233, 400
Buchsbaum, M. S., 199

Buchwald, A. M., 215
Buchy, L., 435
Buckley, P. F., 94
Bucuvalas, M., 193
Buda, M., 251
Budenz, D., 410, 412
Budiani, D., 115
Budnitz, D. S., 491
Buffett-Jerrott, S., 130
Buffett-Jerrott, S. E., 55
Buffum, J., 318
Bufka, L. F., 147
Buhle, J. T., OLC-24
Buhlmann, U., 181
Buiteman, C., 446
Buka, S. L., 441
Bule, T., 379
Bulik, C. M., 147, 263, 268–270,
    278–280, 416
Bullis, J. R., 125, 319
Bulloch, A. G., 240
Bulloch, A. G. M., 227, 254
Bumpass, E. R., 382
Bunde, J., OLC-20
Buntinx, F., 508
Buntinx, W. H. E., 478
Buonora, M., 360, 367
Burack, J. A., 457, 470
Bureau, B., 277
Burge, D., 233
Burgess, T. J. W., 16
Burgin, R., 472
Burgio, L. D., 508
Burk, W. J., 370
Burke, C. A., 133
Burke, J. C., 473
Burke, J. D., Jr., 220
Burke, K. C., 220
Burke, M., 277, 482, 502
Burke, N., 423
Burkhalter, H., 301
Burmeister, M., 46
Burnam, M. A., 92
Burnett, P., 448
Burnette, D., 505
Burney, E., 233
Burnham, M. M., 296
Burns, A., OLC-23
Burri, A., 320
Burris, J. L., 374
Burt, D. R., 43, 439
Burt, S., 461
Burt, S. A., 279
Burton, R., 12
Bury, A. S., 244, 524
Busatto, G. F., 219
Buscher, A. L., OLC-11
Buschgens, C., 460
Bushman, B. J., 354
Bushnell, J. A., 270
Bushnell, W., 153
Busner, C., 256
Bustillo, J., 432, 448
Butcher, J. N., 77, 78
Butelman, E. R., 360, 367
Butera, F., 247
Butler, G., 284
Butler, L. D., 204–207
Butterworth, J., 370
Buxbaum, J. D., 175
Buxton, J. A., 358

Buysse, D. J., 234, 235, 293, 297
Buzoianu, A., 380
Buzzella, B. A., 153
Byck, R., 374
Bye, E. K., 354
Byers, A. L., 130
Byers, E. S., 314, 315, 319
Byne, W., 337–339, 397
Byrne, D., 319
Byrne, E. M., 360
Byrne, G. J., 217
Byrne, S. M., 269
Bystritsky, A., 137, 141, 181

C

Caballero, B., 273
Caballo, V. E., 136
Cabassa, L. J., 90
Cabeza, R., 83
Cabral, K., 180
Cabrera, E., 509
Cachelin, F. M., 265
Cacioppo, J. T., OLC-4
Cacioppo, J. T., 52, 61
Cacioppo, S., 61
Cadenhead, K. S., 435
Cadman, D. T., 220
Cadoret, R. J., 400
Caesar-Chavannes, C. R., 495
Cafri, G., 274
Cahill, C., 428
Cahill, S., 178
Cain, A. S., 270
Caine, E. D., 254
Cairney, J., 240
Cairns, N. J., 503
Calabrese, J., 226, 245
Calabrese, J. R., 245
Calamari, J. E., 174–176
Calati, R., 216, 405
Caldeira, K. M., 252
Caldeira, V., 354
Caldwell, A., 304
Calhoun, S. L., 294
Calhoun, V. D., 183
Caligor, E., 411
Callaghan, G., 335
Callanan, V. J., 251
Calugi, S., 285
Camargo, C. A., 270, 277
Camargo, C. A., Jr., 277
Cameron, J. L., 52
Cameron, L., 374
Cameron, N. M., 39, 40
Cameron, R., 56
Cameron, R. P., 276
Campbell, A. N., 377
Campbell, D., 144, 207
Campbell, H., 153
Campbell, J. M., 129
Campbell, L., 230
Campbell, M. A., 207, 403
Campbell, P., 177
Campbell, W. K., 412
Campbell-Sills, L., 58, 59, 129
Campeas, R., 178
Campisi, T., 181
Campo, J. A., 338
Campo, J. V., 171
Candido, C. L., 429

Canino, G. J., 149, 176
Canli, T., 124, 150
Cannon, M., 438
Cannon, T., 451
Cannon, T. D., 396, 435, 442, 451
Cannon, W. B., 57, 59
Canter, A., 80
Cantor, J. M., 330, 338
Capaldi, S., 196
Capela, J., 356–358
Capela, J. P., 356–358
Capellari, S., 293
Caplan, P. J., 391
Caporaso, N. E., 366
Cappeliez, P., 506
Caprara, D. L., 351
Capreol, M. J., 151
Cararo, J. H., 480
Caraveo-Anduaga, J. J., 60, 230, 231, 240
Cardena, E., 191, 207
Cardena, E. A., 199
Cardenas, D. L., 137
Cardinali, D. P., 235
Cardish, R. J., 408
Cardno, A., 233
Cardoner, N., 49
Cardoso, F., 480
Carey, G., 111
Carey, M. P., 313
Cargo, M., 171, 253
Carl, J. R., 125
Carlat, D. J., 277
Carlbring, P., 152
Carleton, R. N., 143, 162, 165
Carlo, G., 388
Carlson, A., 336
Carlson, E., 191
Carlson, F. B., 205
Carlson, G. A., 229
Carlson, L. E., OLC-14
Carlson, M., 504
Carlucci, S., 285
Carmin, C., 174
Carmo, H., 356–358
Carney, C., 166
Carney, C. E., 295, 303
Caro, G., 495
Caro, J. J., 495
Caron, C., 391
Caron, J., 62, 425
Carpenter, A. L., 153
Carpenter, D., 249
Carpenter, G., 234
Carpenter, J., 235
Carpenter, J. S., 235
Carpenter, M. J., 374
Carpenter, R. W., 94
Carpenter, W. T., 433, 442
Carr, A., 395
Carr, E. G., 116
Carr, V. J., 435
Carrasco, M., 400
Carrico, A. W., OLC-12, OLC-13
Carrier, J., 304
Carrier, S., 324
Carriere, G., 345, 434
Carroll, B. J., 216, 234
Carroll, C., 315
Carroll, E. M., 193
Carroll, R. A., 337, 338

Carskadon, M. A., 293, 301
Carson, A., 169
Carson, R. C., 90, 358
Carson, W. E., 171
Carstairs, G. M., 444
Carstensen, L. L., 62, 63
Carta, M. G., 517
Carter, A., 472
Carter, C. S., 52
Carter, J., 461
Carter, J. C., 280, 283, 284
Carter, J. S., 236
Carter, J. W., 451
Carter, M., 448
Carter, N. T., 152
Cartwright, R. D., 305
Carvalho, M., 356–358
Carver, C. S., 234, 413
Case, D., 423
Caseras, X., 411
Casey, K. R., 304
Casey, P., 394
Cash, R., 248
Cash, T., 180
Cash, T. F., 273
Casner, R., 410
Caspi, A., 36, 38–40, 42, 47, 52, 94, 175, 194, 402, 403, 438
Cassem, N. H., 178, OLC-30
Cassidy, F., 216
Cassin, S. E., 266
Castellanos, F. X., 460
Castilla-Puentes, R., 127
Castillo, D., 189
Castle, D. J., 179, 435, 436, 439, 442
Castonguay, L. G., 132
Castriotta, N., 136
Castro, Y., 78
Catalano, R. F., 112, 353
Cates, W., OLC-32
Caulfield, M. B., 467
Cautela, J. R., 333, 377
Caye, A., 460
Cayer, G. R., OLC-33
Cayton, G. A., 222
Cazzaro, M., 167
Cechnicki, A., 444
Ceci, S. J., 207
Cederlof, M., 268
Celio, A. A., 271
Cernovsky, Z., 230
Cerpolini, S., 338
Certoma, S. P., 182, 183
Cervoni, N., 39
Cha, C. B., 183, 251
Chachamovich, E., 253
Chahal, R., 410
Chai, X. J., 50
Chalder, T., OLC-26
Chaleby, K., 115
Challacombe, L., 361, 373
Chally, M. K., 282
Chamberlain, F., 450
Chamberlain, P., 404
Chamberlain, S. R., 46, 49, 183
Chambless, D. L., 413
Champagne, F. A., 39, 40
Chan, B. W. Y., 447
Chan, P. T., 154
Chandarana, P., 207
Chandarana, P. C., 271

Chandler, M. J., 253
Chandler, S., 467
Chandwani, K., 23
Chanen, A. M., 389
Chang, D. F., 137
Chang, F. M., 93
Chang, G., 368
Chang, I. W., 203
Chang, K. D., 250
Chang, L. C., 93
Chang, V. C., 462
Chang, Z., 517
Chant, D., 403
Chaouloff, F., OLC-5
Chapleau, M.-A., 133
Chaplin, T. C., 382
Chapman, A. L., 266
Chapman, D., 517
Chapman, R., 431
Chapman, T. F., 152
Chaput, J.-P., 291, 294, 462
Charach, A., 463
Charatan, D. L., 268
Charbonneau, J., 199
Charette, Y., 522
Charland, L. C., 398
Charlebois, P., 400
Charles, G., 336
Charles, S. T., 62, 63
Charman, T., 467
Charney, D., 304
Charney, D. S., 47, 48, 63, 94, 446
Chartier, M., 127
Chartrand, H., 127
Chartrand, T. L., 55
Chase, L., 254
Chassin, L., 368
Chatenet-Duchene, L., 216
Chattarji, S., 483
Chaturvedi, S. K., 271
Chaudhry, R., 442
Chau-Wong, M., 439
Chavez, M., 263
Chawla, N., 193
Check, J. R., 168
Checknita, D., 400
Chefer, S., 52
Cheine, M., 440
Chemerenski, E., 395
Chemerinski, E., 393, 394
Chen, C. N., 272
Chen, H., 264
Chen, S., 463
Chen, S. W., 414
Chen, W., 468
Chen, Y., 414
Chenevix-Trench, G., 360
Cheng, C., 144
Cheng, J., 521
Chernick, A. B., 324
Chernick, B. A., 324
Cherry, C. R., 235
Cheung, F. M., 61
Cheung, L., 272
Cheung, R., 126
Chevron, E. S., 247
Chew-Graham, C. A., 162
Chi, I., 495
Chiappe, P., 468
Chicz-DeMet, A., 219
Chida, Y., OLC-18, OLC-19, OLC-20

Kapur, S., 428, 440
Karam, E., 257
Karatsoreos, I. N., 292
Karg, K., 46
Karg, R. S., 73
Karippot, A., 304
Kariuki-Nyuthe, C., 127
Karkhaneh, M., 476
Karkowski, L. M., 236
Karlawish, J. H., 502
Karlberg, A. M., 390
Karlsson, A., 178
Karlsson, S., 509
Karmiloff-Smith, A., 480
Karno, M., 444
Karpf, R. D., 195
Karstoft, K.-I., 193
Karterud, S., 395
Karwautz, A. F., 283
Kasari, C., 475, 476
Kasen, S., 285, 374, 389
Kashani, J. H., 228, OLC-31
Kaski, M., 481
Kasl, S. V., 220
Kass, D. J., 410
Katon, W., 92, 130, 166
Katon, W. J., OLC-7, OLC-8
Katschnig, H., 137
Katz, I. R., 229, 492, OLC-22
Katz, J., 280, 492, OLC-23
Katz, M., 479
Katz, R., 233
Katz, R. C., 180
Katz, R. J., 277
Katzman, D., 272
Katzman, D. K., 265, 272, 284
Katzman, M. A., 244
Katznelson, H., 282
Kauffman, J. M., 469
Kaufman, A. V., 508
Kaufmann, W., 214
Kaur, J., 251
Kavanagh, D. J., 444
Kawamura, K. Y., 271
Kawas, L. H., 505
Kay, C., 197
Kaye, S., 353
Kaye, W., 279, 283
Kaye, W. H., 263, 265, 268, 270,
    278, 279
Kayfitz, J. H., 523
Kazarian, S. S., 444
Kazdin, A. E., 106, 254, 403, 404
Kean, Y. M., 149
Keane, T. M., 189, 190, 192
Kearney, A. J., 377, 465
Kearns, M. C., 196
Keck, P. E., 245
Keck, P. E., Jr., 180
Kecklund, G., 300
Keddie, A., 376
Keefe, D. L., 336
Keefe, F. J., OLC-22, OLC-26,
    OLC-29
Keefe, R. S. E., 440
Keel, P. K., 263, 268, 270, 271, 274,
    279, 282, 284
Keeley, J. W., 6, 84, 85, 93
Keenan-Miller, D., 236, 238, 244, 245
Keener, A., 235
Keenleyside, M., 395

Keern, E., 283
Keeton, C. P., 152
Kehrer, C. A., 256
Keijers, P., 140
Keijsers, G. P., 171
Keith, S., 448
Keitner, G. I., 241, 248
Keller, M., 38, 226, 243
Keller, M. B., 92, 127, 130, 137, 216,
    218, 220, 226, 229, 284
Keller, M. C., 123
Kelley, J. M., 51
Kellner, C. H., 245
Kellner, D., 103
Kellner, R., 166, 167
Kelly, B. D., 394
Kelly, J. F., 376
Kelly, M. P., 315, 320
Kelly, P., 491
Kelly, T. M., 254
Kelsoe, J. R., 36, 37
Kemeny, M. E., OLC-5, OLC-6
Kemmler, G., 373
Kendall, . C., 152
Kendall, P. C., 75, 129, 133, 152
Kendler, K., 433
Kendler, K. S., 6, 36, 37, 39, 129, 130,
    220, 233, 236, 247, 263, 269,
    271, 279, 280, 294, 367, 393,
    400, 436
Kendrick, D., OLC-31
Kenis, G., 437
Kennedy, D. N., 179
Kennedy, G. A., 294
Kennedy, J., 413
Kennedy, J. L., 36, 461
Kennedy, K., 135
Kennedy, K. M., 504
Kennedy, Q., 63
Kennedy, S., 265, 270, 280, 283
Kennedy, S. H., 51, 240, 245, 246,
    263, 266, 280
Kenney, R. D., 170
Kenny, M. A., 409
Kenny, P. J., 369
Kent, J. M., 233
Kentish, J., 133
Kere, J., 468
Kermeen, P., 230
Kerns, C. E., 154
Kerns, J. G., 429
Kerns, K., 351
Kerns, R., OLC-23, OLC-26
Kerr, C. E., 51
Kerr, G., 361
Kerr, M., 370
Kerr, M. M., 256
Kerr, T., 361, 378
Kersting, A., 221
Kertesz, S., 365
Kertesz, S. G., 376
Keshaviah, A., 221, 263
Kessing, L. V., 244
Kessler, R., 279, 389
Kessler, R. C., 129, 130, 148, 149,
    175, 192, 193, 215, 216, 220,
    226–228, 230, 240, 251, 254,
    271, 279, 280, 348, 380,
    412, 436
Kestila, M., 468
Ketter, T., 245

Ketter, T. A., 235
Keyes, K. M., 397
Khaitan, B. K., 320
Khalife, S., 323
Khan, A., 425
Khan, F., 115
Khan, S., 124, 345
Khano, S., 462
Khomenko, L., 490
Khoury, B., 133, OLC-28
Khoury, J., 462
Khoury, J. E., 406
Khuder, S., 302
Kiang, M., 428
Kiecolt-Glaser, J. K., OLC-8
Kiehl, K. A., 83
Kiel, E. J., 125
Kiesler, D. J., 101
Kihlstrom, J. F., 55, 198, 206, 208
Killen, J. D., 276, 285
Kilman, V. L., 52
Kilpatrick, D., 193
Kilpatrick, D. G., 38, 88, 192, 269
Kilzieh, N., 226
Kim, E. D., 313, 324
Kim, H. J., 182
Kim, J. M., 230
Kim, J.-J., 491
Kim, S., 181
Kim, S. I., 491
Kim, S. W., 381
Kimchi, E. Z., 506
Kinder, B., 263
Kinder, B. N., 318
King, A. P., 124, 195
King, B. H., 281, 476, 479, 480
King, D. E., 505
King, D. W., 192, 194, 195
King, G. R., 356
King, J., 463
King, L. A., 100, 192, 194, 195
King, M., 130, 255, 436
King, N. J., 145
King, P., 499
King, R., 309, 311, 313
Kingston, D. A., 518
Kinney, C., 447
Kip, K. E., 409
Kipp, H., 403
Kirby, A., 439
Kircanski, K., 121
Kircher, J. C., 315
Kircher, J. R., 320
Kirchner, P., 442
Kirkley, B. G., 273, 274
Kirkpatrick, D. R., 146
Kirkpatrick, R. M., 294
Kirmayer, L., 61
Kirmayer, L. J., 89, 171, 230, 253,
    254, 394
Kirov, G., 439
Kirsch, I., 207, 208
Kirschbaum, C., 48
Kirsh, C., 265, 338
Kiss, A., 81
Kiss, I., 446
Kistner, J. A., 59
Kivimaki, M., 61, OLC-18
Klann, E., 483
Klauber, M. R., 507
Kleban, M., 229

Kleber, H. D., 373, 374
Klein, D., 417
Klein, D. F., 139, 152, 374
Klein, D. N., 215, 218, 220, 233
Klein, L. C., 60
Klein, M. H., 124
Klein, R. G., 152, 460
Klein, R. G., 222
Klein, T., 409
Kleinbaum, D. G., 60
Kleinman, A., 89, 201
Kleinman, A. M., OLC-24
Kleinman, M., 254, 255
Kleinplatz, F. J., 311, 315, 318
Kleinplatz, P. J., 93
Kleinstauber, M., 167
Klerman, G. L., 127, 220, 240, 247
Kletti, R., 205
Klevens, R. M., 318
Kleyweg, R. P., 169
Klimas, N., OLC-10, OLC-11
Klin, A., 470–472
Kline, E., 435
Kloner, R., 318
Kloner, R. A., 318
Klosko, J. S., 237
Kluft, R. P., 205
Kluft, R. P., 203–205, 207, 208
Klump, K. L., 147, 263, 270, 279
Klumpp, H., 152
Knapp, C. M., 127
Knapp, S., 233
Knauper, B., 130
Knauz, R., 249
Knickmeyer, R., 337
Knight, C. A., 190
Knight, G. P., 388
Knight, R., 502
Knoesen, N., 179
Knopik, V. S., 400
Knowler, W. C., 367
Knowles, J., 426
Knowles, R., 426
Knudsen, G. P., 393, 400, 414, 416
Knudson, M., 129, 255
Knutelska, M., 199
Ko, H. C., 93
Koban, L., OLC-23
Kobau, R., 517
Koch, G. G., 37, 40
Koch, W. J., 177, 192, 194
Kochman, F. J., 227
Kocsis, J. H., 215, 217
Kodituwakku, P., 351
Koegel, L. K., 474, 475
Koegel, R. L., 473, 475
Koen, L., 451
Koenen, K. C., 38, 194
Koenigsberg, H., 397
Koepsell, T. D., 498
Koerner, N. M., 413
Koester, P., 358
Kogan, C. S., 88
Kogan, J. N., 249
Koh, P. O., 441
Kohen, D., 345, 434
Kohn, I. J., 284
Kohn, M. L., 443
Kohn, R., 241, 371
Kohut, H., 411
Koiranen, M., 517

Lawler, T., 446
Lawlor, M., 254
Lawrence, A., 521
Lawrence, A. A., 328
Lawton, K., 475
Laxenaire, M., 406
Laxova, R., 479
Layden, B. K., 266
Layton, J. B., 61
Lazarus, R. S., 58, 59
Lazerson, A., 46
Le Goff, M., 497, 505
Le Grange, D., 268, 283, 285
Le Strat, Y., 48
Leach, L., 497
Leadbeater, B. J., 62
Leader, J. B., 220
Leaf, D. J., 220
Leaf, P. J., 220
Leahy, R. L., 413, 415
Leavey, G., 436
LeBeau, R. T., 142, 143
Lebedinskaya, K. S., 472
Lebing, E., 22
LeBlanc, M., 400
Leblanc, M., 301
Leccese, A. P., 374
Lecic-Tosevski, D., 112
Leckman, J. F., 174, 175, 182
Leclerc, J., OLC-18
Lecomte, T., 133
Lecrubier, Y., 139
Lecruibier, Y., 254
Lederhendler, I., 271
Ledermann, T., 139
Ledford, H., OLC-9
LeDoux, J. E., 46–48, 124
Ledoux, M., 500
Lee, C. K., 149, 371
Lee, C. M., 528
Lee, H., 352, 491
Lee, H.-J., 194
Lee, J., 235, 245
Lee, J. O., 353
Lee, K. K., 62
Lee, L. R., 93
Lee, P. W. H., 472
Lee, S., 227, 251, 371
Lee, S. H., 369
Lee, T., 439
Lee, V., 36
Lee, Y. S., 369
Lee-Baggley, D., 144
Leeper, J. D., 508
Leff, J., 436
Leff, L. P., 101
Lefley, H., 448
LeFoll, B., 48
Lefrancois, G. R., 100
Legault, C., 497
Legault, L., 372
Lehman, A. F., 448
Lehman, B. J., OLC-18
Lehman, C. L., 460
Lehman, D. R., 191, 221, 279
Lehmann, H. E., 445
Lehner, T., 38
Leibbrand, R., 163, 164
Leibenluft, E., 222
Leiberg, G., 204
Leiblum, S. R., 311, 322

Leichsenring, F., 22
Leino-Kilpi, H., 509
Leinonen, S., 468
Leissner, L. C., 300
Leitlein, G., 266
Lejeune, J., 480
Lemay, D., 131
Lemay, M., 496
Lembo, A. J., 51
Lemelin, S., 408
Lemoine, P., 351
Lener, M. S., 397
Lengacher, C., 409
L'Engle, K. L., 370
Lenke, R. R., 480
Lenoci, M., 195
Lentz, F. F., 465
Lentz, R. J., 447
Lenze, E. J., 133, 136, 229
Lenzenweger, M. F., 389, 393, 439
Leon, A. C., 216, 220, 226
Leonard, A., 401
Leonard, H., 482
Leonard, M., 490
Leonard-Green, T. K., 271
Leong, F. T., 61
Leppamaki, S., 226
Leppink, J., 198
Lepri, B., 219
Lerman, C., 366, 502
Leroux, J. M., 147
Leroy, P., 491
Lesage, A., 413
Lesage, A. D., 240, 519
Lesch, K. P., 48
Lesch, K.-P., 124
Leserman, J., 61, OLC-12, OLC-13
Leshen, E., 229
Lesperance, F., OLC-20
Lester, D., 254, 256
Leth-Steensen, C., 460
Letuchy, E., 166
Leuchter, A. F., 51
Leung, F., 271, 278
Leung, G. M., 495
Lev, A. I., 311, 315, 318
Levak, R. W., 78
Levan, A., 480
Levenson, J. L., 169
Levenson, S., 296
Leventhal, A. M., 125
Leventhal, B. L., 283
Levesque, G., 503
Levesque, J., 147
Levin, A., 139, 406
Levin, F. R., 369
Levin, H., 473
Levin, I., 467
Levin, M. J., 105
Levin, R., 303
Levine, A. C., 324
Levine, M. P., 273
Levine, P. E., 391
Levinson, D. F., 232, 439
Levinson, J., 408
Levitan, R. D., 240, 461
Levitt, A., 220, 248
Levitt, J. J., 248
Levitt, J. T., 147
Levkoff, S., 150
Levy, B. A., 465, 469

Levy, B. R., 220
Levy, D. L., 439
Levy, E., 445, 446
Levy, H., 480
Levy, K. N., 411
Lewin, A. B., 175
Lewine, R. R., 80
Lewinsohn, P., 233
Lewinsohn, P. M., 218, 220
Lewis, B. P., 60
Lewis, C. M., 61
Lewis-Fernandez, R., 89, 139
Lewis, G., 205, 208, 364, 436, 442
Lewis, J., 406
Lewis, J. A., 143
Lewis, K., 399, 403
Lewis, R. F., 406
Lewis, S., 169, 442, 443
Lewis-Fernandez, R., 89, 121, 137, 170, 171, 199, 201, 202, 205–207
Lewy, A. J., 300
Leygraf, N., 416
Leyhe, T., 189
Leykin, Y., 248
Leyton, M., 233, 360, 367
Li, C., 216
Li, D., 235
Li, H. Z., 61
Li, K., 378
Li, M., 193
Li, S., 40
Li, X., 472
Liang, K. Y., 38
Liang, K.-Y., 175
Liang, Y., 503
Liao, B., 23, 137, 142, 143
Liao, D., 294
Liberman, R. P., 448
Liberski, P. P., 502
Liberzon, I., 124, 125, 195
Lichstein, K. L., 295
Lichtenstein, P., 175, 263, 268, 517
Lichtenstin, P., 279
Liddle, P., 428
Liddle, P. F., 82, 83, 234, 427, 429
Lidegaard, O., 244
Lidow, M. S., 441
Lieb, R., 130, 164
Lieberman, J. A., 439
Liebeskind, J., OLC-21
Liebowitz, M., 92, 139
Liebowitz, M. R., 92, 130, 137, 139, 143, 152, 153, 178, 413
Lieff, S., 490
Lienard, P., 175
Lietaer, G., 23
Light, K. C., 61
Lilienfeld, S. O., 6, 76, 198, 203, 204, 207, 208, 410
Lima, E. N., 78
Limpens, V. E. L., 270
Lin, A., 435, 499
Lin, E., 144, 265, 270, 406
Lin, F., 270
Lin, H., 93
Lin, K. H., 218
Lin, K. M., 89, 201
Lin, Y., 38
Lin, Y. G., 254
Lind, D. L., 171

Lind, M. J., 294
Lindberg, E., 216, 300
Lindberg, N., 382
Linden, W., OLC-17, OLC-18, OLC-26
Lindenmayer, J. P., 425
Lindsay, D. S., 207
Lindsay, P. S., 522
Lindwall, R., 147
Lindy, J. D., 192
Lindy, J. G., 192
Linehan, M., 405, 408
Linehan, M. M., 256, 406, 408
Lines, E., 449
Ling, W., 358, 361
Links, P. S., 220, 405, 406, 408
Linnoila, M., 237
Linotte, S., 216
Linsenmeier, J., 337
Linton, S. J., 300
Lionetti, T. M., 348
Lipchik, G. L., OLC-29
Lipman, E. L., 404
Lipowski, Z. J., 490
Lipp, O. V., 55
Lipshultz, L. I., 313, 324
Liquet, B., 300
Lisanby, S. H., 246
Liss, A., 150, 151
Lissek, S., 23, 195
Lisspers, J., OLC-27
Litman, R., 446
Litman, R. F., 254
Litt, I. F., 276
Little, D., 265, 268
Litvin, E. B., 359, 360, 374
Litwin, S. E., 467
Litz, B. T., 193
Liu, A., 62
Liu, D., 39
Liu, J., 409
Liu, K., 472
Liu, L., 435
Liu, R. T., 237, 239
Liu, S., 281
Liu, S. M., 127, 218
Liu, W., 38, 234
Liu, W. M., 115
Livesley, W. J., 94, 152, 193, 277, 280
Livianos, L., 280
Livingston, G., 508
Livingston, J. D., 521
Lloyd, C. D., 524
Lo, S. C., OLC-25
Loa, P., 403
Loba, P., 190
Lobbestael, J., 393, 395
Lobo, R. A., 497
Lochner, C., 183
Lock, J., 284, 285
Lockshin, B., 366
Loeb, K. L., 281
Loeber, R., 460
Loehlin, J. C., 36
Loewenstein, R., 208
Loewenstein, R. J., 201, 207, 208
Lofchy, J. S., 518
Loftus, E., 207
Loftus, E. F., 207, 208
Logroscino, G., 351
Logsdon, R. G., 508

Martin, J., 403, 461
Martin, J. B., 501
Martin, K. M., 50
Martin, N. G., 103, 233, 467
Martin, R. L., 166
Martin, S. L., 483
Martineau, A. M., 370
Martinez, A., 412
Martinez, A. G., 90
Martinez, M. A., 279
Martinez, R., 47
Martin-Guehl, C., 50
Martiniuk, A., 498
Martin-Pichora, A. L., 150
Martins, A. C., 284
Martin-Villalba, A., 489
Martuza, R. L., 178
Martz, W., 358
Marwaha, S., 389
Marx, B. P., 189
Marx, J., 503
Maser, J., 226
Maser, J. D., 88, 220, 226
Masheb, R. M., 269, 279, 283
Masi, G., 395
Masia-Warner, C., 152
Mason, F. L., 325
Masse, M., 133
Massetti, G., 463
Massion, A. O., 130
Master, S. L., OLC-23
Masters, W. H., 102
Mataix-Cols, D., 175, 182, 268
Matas, M., 525
Mateer, C. A., 351
Matheson, K., 40, 62
Matheson, S. L., 435
Mathew, A. R., 374
Mathew, K. L., 409
Mathew, S. J., 131
Mathews, A., 131, 133, 165, 238
Mathews, C. A., 111, 174
Mathews, K. A., 238
Mathiesen, B. B., 282
Mathur, G., 348
Matsubara, R., 206
Matsubayashi, T., 255
Matsuura, M., 206
Mattay, V. S., 36
Matteson, S. R., 234
Matthews, K. A., 55, OLC-17
Matthews, M., 377
Matthews-Ewald, M. R., 270
Mattia, J. I., 180
Mattis, S. G., 139
Maughan, B., 398
Mauler, B. I., 280
Mauri, M., 295
Maussion, G., 400
Maust, D., 75
Mawjee, K., 272
Maxwell, C. J., 229
May, J. S., 400
Mayberg, H., 246
Mayberg, H. S., 51, 246
Mayer, B., 165
Mayeux, R., 497
Mayfield, U., 170, 201
Mayleben, D., 47
Mayville, S., 180
Maziade, M., 394

Mazumdar, S., 132
Mazure, C. M., 236, 238
Mazurick, J. L., 403, 404
Mazzei, I., 295
Mazzeo, S. E., 263
Mazziotta, J. C., 50
Mbata, G., 299
McAdoo, W. G., 473
McAlister, A. L., OLC-32
McAndrews, M. P., 55
McBeth, J., 162
McCabe, J. E., 219, 220
McCabe, M., 214
McCabe, R. E., 140, 144, 150, 151, 236
McCabe, R. F., 144
McCabe, S. B., 236
McCaffrey, R. J., 81, 524
McCall, W. V., 129
McCann, D., 462
McCann, U. D., 299, 357
McCarley, R. W., 248, 397
McCarthy, F., 447
McCarthy-Jones, S., 426
McCauley, E. A., 249
McChesney, C. M., 130
McClam, T. D., 506
McClay, J., 403, 438
McClearn, G. E., 36, 233
McClellan, J. M., 249
McCloskey, M., 380
McCloskey, M. S., 48, 381
McClough, J., 75
McClure, M., 397
McConaha, C. W., 265
McCormick, R., 39, 40
McCormick, W. C., 502
McCracken, P., 495
McCrady, B. S., 353, 376
McCrae, C. S., 295
McCrae, R. R., 388, 390
McCraw, S., 225, 227
McCreery, J. M., 374
McCrimmon, S., 377
McCullough, J. P., 215
McCully, J., 369
McCurry, S. M., 508
McCusker, J., 490, 491
McCutchan, A., 500
McCutcheon, J. E., 52
McDermott, B., 152
McDermott, M., 283
McDermott, S., 481, 491
McDiarmid, C., 352
McDonald, F. J., 54
McDonald, K., 227, 254
McDonald, W. M., 246
McDonough, J., 345
McDonough, M., 199
McDowell, D. M., 366
McDowell, I., 81, 496
McElroy, S. L., 180, 245
McEwen, B. S., 195, 292
McFarlane, A., 193
McFarlane, A. C., 191
McFarlane, T., 236
McFarlane, T. L., 284
McFaull, S., 251
McGee, B. J., 280
McGee, G. G., 475
McGee, R. O., 228

McGehee, D. S., 360
McGill, C. W., 448
McGill, T., 302
McGinn, L. K., 413, 415
McGinnis, J. M., OLC-4
McGlashan, T. H., 391, 433
McGoldrick, M., 320
McGonagle, K. A., 129, 149
McGovern, M. P., 348
McGovern, P. E., 349
McGowan, B. K., 55
McGrath, J., 435
McGrath, P., 382
McGrath, P. A., OLC-16
McGrath P. J., OLC-16
McGue, M., 36, 39, 266, 366, 367
McGuffin, P., 36, 233, 277, 439
McGuire, J. F., 175
McGuire, M., 436
McGuire, R. J., 396
McHugh, P. R., 410, 496
McHugh, R. K., 317
McIntosh, E. M., 448
McIntyre, R. S., 51
McIsaac, H. K., 82, 143
McKay, A., 318
McKay, D., 161, 181
McKeith, I. G., 499
McKenna, B. S., 292
McKenzie, S. J., 280
McKeon, R., 255
McKetin, R., 353
McKim, W. A., 354
McKinley, J. C., 78
McKinnon, W., OLC-8
McKintosh, E., 501, 505
McKnew, D. H., 228
McKunlay, J. B., 313, 318
McLaren, A., 482
McLaughlin, F., 136
Mclaughlin, K. A., 380
McLaughlin, N. C., 50
McLaughlin, N. C. R., 178
McLean, C. P., 178, 196
McLean, L. M., 406
McLean, P. D., 177, 178
McLean, T. S., 448
McLellan, A. T., 373
McLewin, L. A., 206
McLintock, B., 285
McLoughlin, D. M., 246
McMahon, S. D., 236
McMahon, W., 471
McMain, S., 408
McMain, S. F., 408
McManus, F., 152, 153
McMaster, A., 395
McNab, C., 448
McNally, R., 207
McNally, R. J., 6, 17, 207, 221
McNamara, G., 372
McNary, S., 208
McNaughton, N., 48, 123
McNeely, H., 246
McNeil, T. F., 442
McPartland, J. C., 483
McPherson, L. M., 390
McQuade, J. D., 458
Mcquaid, N., 285
McQueen, A. M., 264
McRae, A. F., 360

McRae, K., 125
McRae, L., 127, 129
McShea, M. C., 219
McVey, G., 283
McVey, G. L., 272, 285
McWilliams, J. M., OLC-17
McWilliams, L. A., 136
Mead, S., 501, 505
Meagher, D., 490
Meana, M., 319
Meaney, M. J., 36, 39, 40, 124, OLC-5
Mearns, C., 256
Mechelli, A., 50
Medich, M., 75
Medicna-Mora, M. E., 371
Medland, S. E., 360
Mednick, S., 435
Mednick, S. A., 396, 442, 451
Meehl, P. E., 90, 396
Meerlo, P., 292
Meerveld, J., 509
Mehler, P. S., 268
Mehta, R. L., 348
Meichenbaum, D., 56, 196
Meichenbaum, D. H., 23, 56, 196
Meillon, C., 497, 505
Meiring, D., 388
Melartin, T., 253
Melau, M., 397
Melbye, M., 473
Melca, I. A., 416
Meldrum, D., 467
Meleshko, K. A., 151
Meleshko, K. G., 151
Melhem, N., 228, 234
Melles, R., 323
Mellinger, G. D., 294
Mellings, T., 348
Melton, G. B., 524
Meltzer-Brody, S., 219
Melville, J., 376
Melville, L. F., 152
Melzack, R., OLC-23
Menaker, M., 300
Menard, W., 179, 180
Mendes de Leon, C. F., 283
Mendes, W. B., 61
Mendle, J., 103
Mendlewicz, J., 216
Mendlowicz, M. V., 416
Mendoza-Denton, R., 90
Mendrek, A., 83, 445
Menegaux, F., 300
Meng, H., 468
Meng, X., 266
Mengue P., 301
Mennes, C. E., 364
Mensah, F., 462
Mensour, B., 147, 445
Menuet, J. C., 351
Menvielle, E. J., 337–339
Menzies, L., 46, 49, 183
Menzies, R., 467
Merali, Z., 40
Mercer, J., 295
Mercer, K. B., 38
Merchant, A., 410
Mercier, P., 302
Merckelbach, H., 198, 207, 338
Meredith, S. E., 360
Merens, W., 47

Merette, C., 301
Merghati-Khoei, E., 320
Meriggiola, M. C., 338
Merikangas, K. R., 38, 111, 220, 226–228, 348
Mermin, J., OLC-11, OLC-13
Merikangas, K. R., 226
Merikangas K. R., 268
Merskey, H., 205, 207, 230
Merzenich, M. M., 469
Mescarello, R., 207
Messinger, D., 472
Meston, C. M., 312, 315, 317–319, 322–324
Mestre, L. T., 507
Metalsky, G. I., 238
Metcalfe, R., 406
Metzel, D., 370
Metzner, H. M., 60
Meuret, A. E., 34, 123, 147, 152
Mevada, A., 481
Meyer, A., 152
Meyer, A. J., OLC-32, OLC-33
Meyer, B., 162, 413
Meyer, G. J., 76
Meyer, I. H., 227
Meyer-Bahlberg, H. F., 337
Meyer-Bahlburg, H., 336
Meyerowitz, B. E., OLC-30
Meyers, B., 36, 219
Meyers, K. M., 53
Meyerson, B. A., 178
Meyyazhagan, S., 170
Mezzich, J. E., 89, 201
Micali, N., 270, 285
Michael, J., 26
Michael, R., 320
Michaels, S., 320
Michaud, I., 291
Michultka, D., 338
Michultka, D. M., OLC-30
Mick, E., 222, 228
Mickes, L., 207
Middleman, A., 254
Middleton, H., 140
Midwinter, J., 208
Miele, G. M., 377
Miettunen, J., 438
Mihura, J. L., 76
Miklowitz, D., 226
Miklowitz, D. J., 216, 226, 249, 250, 312, 444
Mikovits, J. A., OLC-25
Mikuska, J., 388
Milad, M. R., 59, 195, 196
Milby, J. B., 302
Miles, S. R., 6, 84, 85, 93
Milin, R., 244
Mill, J., 40, 403
Millan, M. J., 428
Millar, H. R., 263
Millar, N., 131
Millar, W. J., 491
Miller, C., 241
Miller, F. G., 51, 219
Miller, G., 60, OLC-8
Miller, G. A., 84
Miller, I., 215, 235, 237, 241
Miller, I. W., 237, 241, 248
Miller, J., 471, 496
Miller, J. A., 496

Miller, J. D., 390, 412
Miller, K. B., 271
Miller, M. E., 129
Miller, M. W., 189, 190
Miller, N. E., OLC-27
Miller, N. S., 318, 375
Miller, R., 445
Miller, S. D., 203, 205
Miller, S. L., 469, OLC-18, OLC-20
Miller, W. R., 272, 293, 375
Milliken, H., 446
Millon, T., 84, 85, 90, 412
Mills, C., 507
Mills, J., 272
Mills, P. J., OLC-8
Millson, P., 373
Milner, C., 293
Milner, P. M., 367
Milosevic, I., 244
Miloslavsky, M., 301
Milstein, V., 204
Mindell, J. A., 293, 304
Mindham, R. H. S., 499
Mineka, S., 50, 53, 55, 131, 138, 147, 239
Mingdao, Z., 450–451
Minichiello, V., 311
Mintun, M. A., 324
Mintz, J., 443
Minuchin, S., 278
Miranda, J., 238
Mirin, S. M., 241
Mirsky, A. F., 437
Mishara, B. L., 252
Mishra, S., 379
Misri, S., 241
Missio, E., 345
Mistlberger, R. E., 300
Mistry, H., 115
Mitchell, A. J., 263
Mitchell, D. C., 190
Mitchell, D. G. V., 401
Mitchell, J. E., 267–269, 271, 280, 365
Mitchell, M., 483
Mitchell, T., 190
Mitchell, T. L., 190
Mittlehold, J., 207
Mitton, M. J. E., 406
Miyahara, S., 226
M'Lan, C. F., 497
Moak, D. H., 350
Modahl, C., 473
Moene, F. C., 169, 171
Moffitt, G. L., 299
Moffitt, T., 403
Moffitt, T. E., 36, 38–40, 42, 47, 52, 94, 175, 194, 402, 438
Mogg, A., 246
Mogg, K., 131, 133, 150
Mogil, J. S., OLC-24
Mogun, H., 132
Mohanty, S., 506
Moher, D., 463
Mohler, H., 47
Mohr, C., 397
Mohs, R. C., 440
Molnar, B. E., 348
Moitra, E., 137
Mojtabai, R., 139, 178
Mokri, H., 497, 505

Moldofsky, H., 267, 292
Molina, B. S., 463
Molina, B. S. G., 368
Moline, M. L., 93
Moll, K., 465
Moller-Leimkuhler, A. M., 254
Moller-Leimkuhler, A. M., 254
Moller-Madsen, S., 263
Monaghan, P., 395
Monarch, F. S., OLC-21
Monck, E. M., 444
Money, J., 336
Monk, T., 249
Monk, T. H., 249, 293
Monroe, S. M., 220, 236, 389
Monson, C. M., 195
Monson, E., 192
Montague, D. K., 324
Montaner, J. S. G., 361, 378
Montastruc, J.-L., 491
Monteiro, S., 148
Monteleone, A. M., 281
Monteleone, P., 281
Montgomery, A., 367
Monti, J. M., 47
Montiel-Barbero, I., 460
Montiel-Nava, C., 460
Montorsi, F., 318
Montorsi, P., 318
Montplaisir, J., 304
Monzani, B., 175
Moore, D. S., 40
Moore, D. W., 50
Moore, M., 296
Moore, R. G., 248, 249
Moore, R. Y., 235
Moore, S.C., 401
Morehouse, R., 301
Morel, C., 52
Moreno, A., 380
Moreno, C., 222
Moreno, D., 227
Moreno-Granados, J., 435
Moreno, R. A., 231
Morey, L. C., 87, 391, 397, 417, OLC-24
Morey, S., OLC-29
Morgan, C., 374
Morgan, D., 507
Morgan, H. W., 375
Morgan, J., 145
Morgan, K. L., 151
Morgan, M., 51
Morgentaler, A., 324
Morgenthaler, T., 300
Morin, C. M., 291–295, 301, 302
Morin, C. M., 302
Morin, M. C., 301
Moring, J., 40, 437, 438, 517
Morissette, R., 519
Morissette, S. B., 127
Moritz, E. K., 181
Morrier, M. J., 475
Morrill, B., 338
Morris, A., 272
Morris, F., 348
Morris, J., 447
Morris, J. K., OLC-4
Morris, J. S., 55
Morris, M., 295, 473
Morris, P. E., 23

Morris, R. W., 122
Morris, S., 489
Morrison, A. S., 148
Morrison, M., 248
Morris-Yates, A., 467
Morrow, G. R., 23
Morselli, P. G., 338
Mortberg, E., 153
Mortensen, E. L., 435
Mortensen, P. B., 61
Morton, A., 264
Morton, J., 401
Moscovitch, A., 301
Moseley, J. V., OLC-18, OLC-26
Moser, C., 311, 315, 318
Moser, D. A., 48
Moses-Kolko, E. L., 219
Mosher, D. L., 391
Mosimann, J. F., 273
Moss, H. B., 366, 448
Mostkoff, K., 255
Mostofsky, D. I., OLC-5
Motiuk, L., 518
Mottron, L., 457
Moulds, M. L., 196
Moulton, D., 361
Mowry, B., 403
Mowry, B. J., 439
Mucha, T. F., 170
Muehlebner, A., 480
Muehlenkamp, J. J., 272
Mueller, A., 48
Mueller, S. G., 195
Mueller, T., 220, 226
Mueser, K. T., 447, 448
Muir, S. L., 275
Mulberry, S., 408
Mulcahy, R., 80
Mulder, R., 394, 397
Mullan, J. T., 508
Mullane, J., 292
Muller, B. A., 167
Muller, J., 451
Muller, K., 468
Muller, R. T., 206
Mullin, S. J., 235
Mulot, C., 300
Mulsant, B., 36, 219, 245
Mulsant, B. H., 229
Mumford, D. B., 271
Munafo, M., 364
Munder, T., 322, 323
Munoz, R. F., 248
Munro, A., 431
Murakami-Brundage, J., 115
Muresanu, D. F., 380
Muris, P., 145, 147
Muroff, J., 183
Murphy, D. G. M., 497
Murphy, J. A., 217
Murphy, J. G., 376
Murphy, J. M., 194
Murphy, R., 282
Murphy, S., 318
Murphy, T. K., 175
Murray, B. L., 518
Murray, J., 398
Murray, J. B., 373
Murray, K., 502
Murray, K. E., 462
Murray, R., 438, 443

Wechsler, H., 352
Weck, F., 167
Wedig, M. M., 406
Weed, N. C., 78
Weeda, J., 169
Weedman, . M., 351
Weeks, A., 463
Weeks, D. J., 396
Weeks, J. R., 202
Weems, C. F., 129
Weerasinghe, S., 190
Weersing, V. R., 228, 229, 254
Wegner, D. M., 177
Weiden, P. J., 446
Weihofen, H., 520
Weike, A. I., 280
Weinberg, R. A., 80
Weinberg, W. A., 292
Weinberger, A. D., 246
Weinberger, D. R., 36, 442
Weiner, L., 322
Weiner, M. F., 498
Weiner, M. W., 503
Weinmann, N., 162
Weinshilboum, R., 464
Weinstein, M., 38
Weinstock, H., OLC-32
Weinstock, L., 239
Weisberg, R. B., 92, 127, 137
Weisburg, R. B., 314
Weise, R. E., 88
Weiser, M., 397, 472
Weiskrantz, L., 55, 170
Weiss, B., 228
Weiss, G., 460
Weiss, M. D., 292
Weiss, R. D., 359
Weiss, S. R. B., 365
Weisse, C. S., OLC-8
Weissenburger, J. F., 234
Weisskopf, M. G., 462
Weissman, M., 176, 233, 247
Weissman, M. M., 127, 142, 149, 176, 220, 240, 247
Weisstub, F., 61
Weitze, C., 335
Wekerle, C., 354
Welch, P. G., 127
Welch, S. L., 228, 265, 270, 271, 282
Welham, J., 435
Wells, D. L., 364
Wells, J. E., 270
Wells, K. B., 92, 241
Wells, K. C., 460
Weltzin, T. E., 265
Wendt, D. C., 114
Wermter, A. K., 472
Werner, K. B., 398
Wertheim, E. H., 275
Wessely, S., OLC-26
Wesson, D. R., 355
West, L. J., 376
West, S. A., 458
Westen, D., 405, 406
Westendorp, R. G., 491
Westervelt, H. J., 81
Westra, H. A., 354, 369
Wetherby, A. M., 474
Wetherell, J. L., 129, 133, 145, 182, 234
Wetter, E., 63

Wetzler, S., 417
Wever, R., 299
Wexler, B. E., 379
Wexler, N. S., 501
Whalen, P. J., 179
Whishaw, I. Q., 52, 55
Whisman, M., 239
Whisman, M. A., 234
Whitaker, L. A., 182
Whitbourne, S. K., 272
White, D., 234, 235, 324
White, D. P., 436
White, J., 131
White, K., 177
White, K. S., 89, 90, 125, 127, 140, 141, OLC-25, OLC-26
White, M. A., 269, 283
White, R., 235, 241
White, R. L., 350
White, W., 375, 395
Whitehead, P. C., 447
Whitehorn, D., 446
Whitehouse, A. M., 271
Whitehouse, W. G., 237, 239, 241
Whitehurst, G. J., 467
Whitfield, J., 501, 505
Whitfield-Gabrieli, S., 50
Whitford, H. S., 409
Whiting, D. L., 254
Whitlatch, C. J., 508
Whitley, R., 61
Whittaker, S., 324
Whittal, M. L., 177, 178, 281
Whittemore, K. E., 521
Whittemore, K. F., 521
Whitwell, B., 234, 235
Wichmann, C., 518
Wicker, P. A., 324
Wickramaratne, P., 233
Wickramaratne, P. J., 149, 220
Widaman, K. F., 480
Widiger, T., 286
Widiger, T. A., 6, 85, 88, 94, 294, 387–390, 397, 439, 441
Wiebe, R. F., 236
Wieczorek, D., 480
Wiegartz, P. S., 174
Wiegel, M., 316–318, 321, 330
Wieland, T., 480
Wiener, M. J., 248
Wierman, M., 309
Wiers, R., 113, 114
Wiers, R. W., 347
Wifley, D. F., 265
Wigal, T., 464
Wigal, T. L., 48
Wik, G., 55
Wilber, M. K., 379
Wilberg, T., 395
Wilbur, C., 203
Wilcox, H. C., 192, 252
Wild, J., 152
Wilde, E. A., 230
Wilder, D., 497
Wilens, T., 463
Wilens, T. E., 222, 228
Wileyto, E. P., 502
Wilfley, D. E., 269, 271, 283
Wilfley, D. F., 269, 271
Wilgosh, L., 80
Wilhelm, F. H., 123

Wilhelm, S., 175, 178, 180–182
Wilk, K., 226
Wilkel, C. S., 180
Wilkins, K. L., OLC-22
Wilkins, S., 443
Wilkinson-Ryan, T., 405
Will, R. G., 502
Willard, D., 373
Willem Van der Does, A. J., 47
Willi, J., 263
Williams, A. A., 406
Williams, C. L., 78
Williams, C. S., 193
Williams, D., 230
Williams, G., 435
Williams, J., 181
Williams, J. B. W., 73
Williams, J. M., 249
Williams, J. M. G., 248
Williams, J. T., 367
Williams, J. V., 240
Williams, J. V. A., 227, 229, 254
Williams, K. M., 412
Williams, L., 207
Williams, L. J., 294, 389
Williams, M. R., 442
Williams, M. T., 178
Williams, N., 461
Williams, R., 423, 446
Williams, R. B., OLC-13, OLC-15, OLC-18, OLC-20
Williams, R. J., 379
Williams, S., 228, 236, 249
Williams, S. H., 403
Williams, V., 302
Williamson, D. A., 280
Williamson, J. D., 129
Williamson, J. W., OLC-31
Williamson, M., 448
Wills, T. A., 372
Willson, R., 180
Wilner, P., 249
Wilson, A. A., 440
Wilson, B., 465, 468
Wilson, B. M., 207
Wilson, C. M., 522
Wilson, D. M., 276
Wilson, G. T., 265, 269, 270, 279–284, 318
Wilson, K., xxi
Wilson, M. N., 403
Wilson, N. L., 133
Wilson, P. G., 482
Wilson, R. S., 283, 504
Wilson, T. D., 62
Wiltshire, K., 501
Winblad, B., 497, 509
Winchel, R. M., 254
Wincze, J. P., 309, 313, 315–318, 321, 322, 327
Wincze, J. P., 314
Windgassen, K., 446
Winett-Perlman, C., 235, 241
Wing, J. K., 444
Wing, R., 269
Wing, R. R., 283
Wing, Y. K., 371
Winkelman, J. W., 297, 305
Winkleby, M. A., 226
Winkler, H., 441
Winocur, G., 497

Winograd, A., 181
Winsor, J., 370
Winsper, C., 389
Winter, D., 406
Winters, R. W., OLC-18, OLC-20
Wintrob, R. M., 371
Wirz-Justice, A., 301
Wise, M. G., 497
Wiseman, C. V., 273
Wiseman, F. K., 480
Wishart, I., 358
Wisner, K. L., 94, 219
Wisniewski, S., 226
Wisniewski, S. R., 89, 245, 249
Withall, A., 351
Witherington, R., 324
Withers, G. S., 52
Witt, A. A., 268
Wittchen, H. U., 60, 121, 130, 134, 142, 143, 149, 164, 228–231, 240
Witte, E. A., 51
Witthoft, M., 165, 167
Wittkowski, A., 447
Wittrock, D., 104
Witztum, F., 334
Wohlfahrt, J., 473
Wohlsifer, D., 320
Woicik, P. B., 113
Wolf, A., 517
Wolf, A. M., 272
Wolf, E. J., 189
Wolf, M. M., 101
Wolfe, D. A., 74
Wolff, A. L. V. G., 442
Wolff, K., 366
Wolff, S., 332, 396
Wolfson, C., 497
Wolfson, D. B., 497
Wolgamuth, B., 171
Wolitzky-Taylor, K., 239
Wolitzky-Taylor, K. B., 136
Wollburg, E., 162, 164
Wolpe, J., 25
Wolters, E. C., 402
Wonderlich, S. A., 265, 268, 269, 279
Wong, C., 181, 475
Wong, E., 397
Wong, H., 483
Wong, K., 439
Wong, L., 451
Wong, M., 144
Wong, P. T., 115
Wong, S., 399
Wong, S. C. P., 399, 403, 518
Wong, S. L., 291, 296, 495, 499
Wood, F., 361, 378
Wood, J. M., 76
Wood, K., 276
Wood, P. K., 389
Wood, S. J., 435
Woodard, T., 309
Woodin, E., 354
Woodley, H., 446
Woodman, C., 130
Woodman, C. L., 130
Woods, B., 507
Woods, D. W., 175
Woods, F. R., 254
Woods, M. L., 353

SUBJECT INDEX

exhibitionistic disorder, 326–327, 327t
exorcism, 10, 11
expectancy effect, 369
expected (cued) panic attack, 122
experiment, 105
experimental designs, 105–106
    control groups in, 105–106
    single-case, 106–108
expert witnesses, 523–524
explicit memory, 55
exposure and response prevention, 50
exposure and ritual prevention
    (ERP), 177
expressed emotion (EE), 444
external validity, 99–101, 100t
extinction, 24
extrapyramidal symptoms, 446
extraversion, 388
eye-movement desensitization and
    reprocessing (EMDR), 196
eye tracking, 439
Eysenck, Hans, 25

F

Fa'afafine, 337
Faces of Meth™, 380
facial agnosia, 494
factitious disorder, 169
    defined, 169
    diagnostic criteria, 169t
    imposed on another, 169, 169t
faking, in DID, 202–203
falling out, 201
False Memory Syndrome Foundation,
    207
false negatives, 81
false positives, 81
family-based treatment (FBT), 284
family influences
    eating disorders, 278
    mood disorders, 232–233
    schizophrenia, 443–444
    substance-related and addictive
        disorders, 366–367
    suicide, 248
family studies
    genetics, 109–110
    schizophrenia, 436–437
fatal familial insomnia, 293
fatalistic suicide, 253
fear, 121–123
    in anxiety disorders, 121–123, 123f
    classically conditioning, 25
    physiology and purpose, 57–58
    prevalence of, 144, 144t
    systematic desensitization, 25
fearlessness hypothesis, 401
fear of negative evaluation, 111
female orgasmic disorder, 313–315
female sexual interest/arousal
    disorder, 309–311, 311t
fetal alcohol syndrome (FAS), 351, 479
fetishistic disorder, 326, 326t
fight/flight system (FFS), 124
fight-or-flight responses, 402

First Episode Psychosis Clinic/Early
    Psychosis Unit, 449
fitness to stand trial, 522–523
five-factor (Big Five) model, 388, 389t
fixation, 20
flashback, 189
flat affect, 429
Fleming, Russell, 525–526
flight of ideas, 215
flight-or-fight response, 57, 121
fluoxetine, 243
folie à deux, 433
Ford, Rob, 345
forebrain, 43
formal observation, 75
Fox, Michael J., 500–501
fragile X syndrome, 481, 483
Framingham Heart Study, OLC-19
Franklin, Benjamin, 17
fraternal (dizygotic) twins, 110–111, 233
free association, 21
Freedman, Morris, 497
frenzy witchcraft, 201
frequency, of compulsions, 73
Freud, Anna, 21
Freud, Sigmund, 17, 18, 23
    narcissistic and, 410
    psychoanalytic model conversion
        disorder, 170–171
    structure of the mind, 17, 19, 19f
    unconscious processes, 18
fright disorders, 59
frigidity, 312
frigo phobia, 145
Fromm, Erich, 21
frontal lobe, 45
frontotemporal neurocognitive
    disorder, 499
frotteuristic disorder, 325
frustro effect, 105
Fumbling Toward Ecstasy (McLachlan
    album), 432
functional communication training,
    108, 116
functional genomics, 367
functional magnetic resonance
    imaging (fMRI), 83, 172, 428
functional neurological symptom
    disorder, 168

G

GABA-benzodiazepine system, 124
galantamine, 506
Galen, 12–13
galvanic skin response (GSR), 83, 401
gambling disorder, 378–379
gamma aminobutyric acid (GABA),
    43, 47
    activity, drugs enhancing, 368
    ADHD, 461
    alcohol effects, 350, 368
    anxiety disorders, 124
    sedative, hypnotic, anxiolytic drug
        effects, 350
gamma hydroxybutyrate (GHB), 366

Garner, David, 524
gate control theory, OLC-23
gender differences
    alcohol abuse, 351–352,
        353f, 354f
    personality disorders, 390–391, 391f
gender dysphoria, 309, 334–339
    case studies, 335, 337
    causes, 336–337
    in children, 338–339
    diagnostic criteria, 335t
    disorders of sex development,
        335, 339
    exploring, 343
    gender reassignment surgery, 338
    overview of, 334–339
    treatment, 337–339
gender nonconformity
    in children, 338
    defined, 336
gender reassignment surgery, 338
gender roles, 59–60
gene-environment correlation model,
    39, 39f, 236
gene-environment interactions, in
    schizophrenia, 438
general adaptation syndrome (GAS),
    OLC-5
generalizability, 101
generalized amnesia, 199
generalized anxiety disorder (GAD),
    128–133, 159
    case study, 128–129
    causes, 130–131
    clinical description, 129
    defined, 128
    diagnostic criteria, 129t
    integrative model of, 132f
    statistics, 129–130
    treatment, 131–133
generalized biological vulnerability
    described, 125, 126f
    obsessive-compulsive disorder,
        177, 177f
    panic disorder, 138, 138f
    PTSD, 193, 195f
    social anxiety disorder, 150, 151f
    specific phobias, 146f
generalized psychological
    vulnerability
    described, 126, 126f
    obsessive-compulsive disorder,
        177, 177f
    panic disorder, 138, 138f
    PTSD, 195f
    social anxiety disorder, 150, 151f
    specific phobias, 146f
general paresis, 13–14
genes
    behaviour and, study of, 36–37
    defined, 35
    dominant, 36
    nature of, 35–36
    recessive, 36
    schizophrenia, evidence of
        multiple, 439

genetic contributions to
    psychopathology, 35–40
    diathesis-stress model, 37–38, 37f
    epigenetics and nongenomic
        inheritance of behaviour, 39–40
    gene-environment correlation
        model, 39, 39f
    genetic and environmental effects
        interaction of, 37–39
genetic influences
    antisocial personality disorder, 400
    autism spectrum disorder, 472–473
    mood disorders, 232–233
    schizophrenia, 436–439
    substance-related and addictive
        disorders, 366–367
genetic linkage analysis, 111
genetic markers, 111
genetics, studying, 108–111
    adoption studies, 110
    association studies, 111
    family studies, 109–110
    genetic linkage analysis, 111
    twin studies, 110–111
genital stage, 20
genito-pelvic pain/penetration
    disorder, 315, 315t
genome, 36, 109
genotypes, 108, 396
Gestalt therapy, 23
Ginkgo biloba, 506
glial cell-derived neurotrophic factor
    (GDNF), 506
*Global Study of Sexual Attitudes and
    Behaviors,* 309
globus hystericus, 169
glutamate, 47, 48
glutamate system, 351
Goldberger, Joseph, 104
gonadal glands, 45
graduated extinction, 302
grandeur, delusion of, 426
grandiose type of delusion, 432
Gray, Jeffrey, 124
Greenough, William, 52
Green, Richard, 336
Grey, John P., 14
grief
    bereavement exclusion, 257
    complicated, 221
    to depression, 220–221
    integrated, 221
    major depressive disorder and, 257
    pangs of, 257
Guilhem, Arnaut, 11
gynecomastia, 338

H

HAART. *See* highly active
    antiretroviral therapy (HAART)
hallucinations, 71, 219, 427–428
hallucinogens, 349, 362–365, 384
Handel, George Frideric, 230
hara-kiri, 253
Hare, Robert, 401